THE MATT SCUDDER MYSTERIES 2

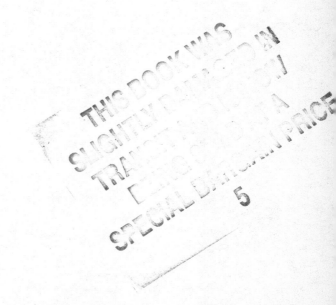

ALSO BY LAWRENCE BLOCK

THE MATT SCUDDER MYSTERIES 2

A STAB IN THE DARK
EIGHT MILLION WAYS TO DIE
WHEN THE SACRED GINMILL CLOSES

Lawrence Block

ORION

Copyright
A Stab in the Dark © 1981 by Lawrence Block
Eight Million Ways to Die © 1982 by Lawrence Block
When the Sacred Ginmill Closes © 1986 by Lawrence Block

The right of Lawrence Block to be identified as the author of
this work has been asserted by him in accordance with the
Copyright, Designs and Patents Act 1988.

This edition first published in Great Britain in 1997 by
Orion
An imprint of Orion Books Ltd
Orion House, 5 Upper St Martin's Lane
London WC2H 9EA

A CIP catalogue record for this book is available
from the British Library

ISBN: (Csd) 0 75280 540 1
(Ppr) 0 75280 539 8

Printed and bound in Great Britain by
Clays Ltd, St Ives plc.

CONTENTS

A Stab in the Dark   vii

Eight Million Ways to Die   143

When the Sacred Ginmill Closes   421

A STAB IN THE DARK

FOR PATRICK TRESE

ONE

I didn't see him coming. I was in Armstrong's at my usual table in the rear. The lunch crowd had thinned out and the noise level had dropped. There was classical music on the radio and you could hear it now without straining. It was a gray day out, a mean wind blowing, the air holding a promise of rain. A good day to be stuck in a Ninth Avenue saloon, drinking bourbon-spiked coffee and reading the *Post*'s story about some madman slashing passersby on First Avenue.

'Mr Scudder?'

Sixty or thereabouts. High forehead, rimless eye-glasses over pale blue eyes. Graying blond hair combed to lie flat on the scalp. Say five-nine or -ten. Say a hundred seventy pounds. Light complexion. Cleanshaven. Narrow nose. Small thin-lipped mouth. Gray suit, white shirt, tie striped in red and black and gold. Briefcase in one hand, umbrella in the other.

'May I sit down?'

I nodded at the chair opposite mine. He took it, drew a wallet from his breast pocket and handed me a card. His hands were small and he was wearing a Masonic ring.

I glanced at the card, handed it back. 'Sorry,' I said.

'But—'

'I don't want any insurance,' I said. 'And you wouldn't want to sell me any. I'm a bad risk.'

He made a sound that might have been nervous laughter. 'God,' he said. 'Of course you'd think that, wouldn't you? I didn't come to sell you anything. I can't remember the last time I wrote an individual policy. My area's group policies for corporations.' He placed the card on the blue-checked cloth between us. 'Please,' he said.

The card identified him as Charles F. London, a general agent with Mutual Life of New Hampshire. The address shown was 42 Pine Street, downtown in the financial district. There were two

telephone numbers, one local, the other with a 914 area code. The northern suburbs, that would be. Westchester County, probably.

I was still holding his card when Trina came over to take our order. He asked for Dewar's and soda. I had half a cup of coffee left. When she was out of earshot he said, 'Francis Fitzroy recommended you.'

'Francis Fitzroy.'

'Detective Fitzroy. Eighteenth Precinct.'

'Oh, Frank,' I said. 'I haven't seen him in a while. I didn't even know he was at the Eighteenth now.'

'I saw him yesterday afternoon.' He took off his glasses, polished their lenses with his napkin. 'He recommended you, as I said, and I decided I wanted to sleep on it. I didn't sleep much. I had appointments this morning, and then I went to your hotel, and they said I might find you here.'

I waited.

'Do you know who I am, Mr Scudder?'

'No.'

'I'm Barbara Ettinger's father.'

'Barbara Ettinger. I don't – wait a minute.'

Trina brought his drink, set it down, slipped wordlessly away. His fingers curled around the glass but he didn't lift it from the table.

I said, 'The Icepick Prowler. Is that how I know the name?'

'That's right.'

'Must have been ten years ago.'

'Nine.'

'She was one of the victims. I was working over in Brooklyn at the time. The Seventy-eighth Precinct, Bergen and Flatbush. Barbara Ettinger. That was our case, wasn't it?'

'Yes.'

I closed my eyes, letting the memory come back. 'She was one of the last victims. The fifth or sixth, she must have been.'

'The sixth.'

'And there were two more after her, and then he went out of business. Barbara Ettinger. She was a schoolteacher. No, but it was something like that. A day-care center. She worked at a day-care center.'

'You have a good memory.'

'It could be better. I just had the case long enough to determine it was the Icepick Prowler again. At that point we turned it over to whoever had been working that case all along.

Midtown North, I think it was. In fact I think Frank Fitzroy was at Midtown North at the time.'

'That's correct.'

I had a sudden rush of sense memory. I remembered a kitchen in Brooklyn, cooking smells overladen with the reek of recent death. A young woman lay on the linoleum, her clothing disarrayed, innumerable wounds in her flesh. I had no memory of what she looked like, only that she was dead.

I finished my coffee, wishing it were straight bourbon. Across the table from me, Charles London was taking a small tentative sip of his scotch. I looked at the Masonic symbols on his gold ring and wondered what they were supposed to mean, and what they meant to him.

I said, 'He killed eight women within a period of a couple months. Used the same MO throughout, attacked them in their own homes during daylight hours. Multiple stab wounds with an icepick. Struck eight times and then went out of business.'

He didn't say anything.

'Then nine years later they catch him. When was it? Two weeks ago?'

'Almost three weeks.'

I hadn't paid too much attention to the newspaper coverage. A couple of patrolmen on the Upper West Side had stopped a suspicious character on the streets, and a frisk turned up an icepick. They took him into the station house and ran a check on him, and it turned out he was back on the streets after an extended confinement in Manhattan State Hospital. Somebody took the trouble to ask him why he was toting an icepick, and they got lucky the way you sometimes do. Before anybody knew what was happening he'd confessed to a whole list of unsolved homicides.

'They ran his picture,' I said. 'A little guy, wasn't he? I don't remember the name.'

'Louis Pinell.'

I glanced at him. His hands rested on the table, fingertips just touching, and he was looking down at his hands. I said that he must have been greatly relieved that the man was in custody after all these years.

'No,' he said.

The music stopped. The radio announcer hawked subscriptions to a magazine published by the Audobon Society. I sat and waited.

'I almost wish they hadn't caught him,' Charles London said.

3

'Why?'

'Because he didn't kill Barbara.'

Later I went back and read all three papers, and there'd been something to the effect that Pinell had confessed to seven Icepick Prowler slayings while maintaining he was innocent of the eighth. If I'd even noted that information first time around, I hadn't paid it any mind. Who knows what a psychotic killer's going to remember nine years after the fact?

According to London, Pinell had more of an alibi than his own memory. The night before Barbara Ettinger was murdered, Pinell had been picked up on the complaint of a counterman at a coffee shop in the east twenties. He was taken to Bellevue for observation, held two days and released. Police and hospital records made it quite clear that he was in a locked ward when Barbara Ettinger was killed.

'I kept trying to tell myself there was a mistake,' London said. 'A clerk can make a mistake recording an admission or release date. But there was no mistake. And Pinell was very adamant on the subject. He was perfectly willing to admit the other murders. I gather he was proud of them in some way or other. But he was genuinely angry at the idea that a murder he hadn't committed was being attributed to him.'

He picked up his glass but put it down without drinking from it. 'I gave up years ago,' he said. 'I took it for granted that Barbara's murderer would never be apprehended. When the series of killings stopped so abruptly, I assumed the killer had either died or moved away. My fantasy was that he'd had a moment of awful clarity, realized what he'd done, and killed himself. It made it easier for me if I was able to believe that, and from what a police officer told me, I gathered that that sort of thing occasionally happens. I came to think of Barbara as having been the victim of a force of nature, as if she'd died in an earthquake or a flood. Her killing was impersonal and her killer unknown and unknowable. Do you see what I mean?'

'I think so.'

'Now everything's changed. Barbara wasn't killed by this force of nature. She was murdered by someone who tried to make it look as though her death was the work of the Icepick Prowler. Hers was a very cold and calculating murder.' He closed his eyes for a moment and a muscle worked in the side of his face. 'For years I thought she'd been killed for no reason at all,' he said, 'and that was horrible, and now I can see that she was killed for a reason, and that's worse.'

4

'Yes.'

'I went to Detective Fitzroy to find out what the police were going to do now. Actually I didn't go to him directly. I went to one place and they sent me to another place. They passed me around, you see, no doubt hoping I'd get discouraged somewhere along the way and leave them alone. I finally wound up with Detective Fitzroy, and he told me that they're not going to do anything about finding Barbara's killer.'

'What were you expecting them to do?'

'Reopen the case. Launch an investigation. Fitzroy made me see my expectations were unrealistic. I got angry at first, but he talked me through my anger. He said the case was nine years old. There weren't any leads or suspects then and there certainly aren't any now. Years ago they gave up on all eight of those killings, and the fact that they can close their files on seven of them is simply a gift. It didn't seem to bother him, or any of the officers I talked to, that there's a killer walking around free. I gather that there are a great many murderers walking around free.'

'I'm afraid there are.'

'But I have a particular interest in this particular murderer.' His little hands had tightened up into fists. 'She must have been killed by someone who knew her. Someone who came to the funeral, someone who pretended to mourn her. God, I can't stand that!'

I didn't say anything for a few minutes. I caught Trina's eye and ordered a drink. The straight goods this time. I'd had enough coffee for a while. When she brought it I drank off half of it and felt its warmth spread through me, taking some of the chill out of the day.

I said, 'What do you want from me?'

'I want you to find out who killed my daughter.'

No surprise there. 'That's probably impossible,' I said.

'I know.'

'If there was ever a trail, it's had nine years to go cold. What can I do that the cops can't?'

'You can make an effort. That's something they can't do, or at least it's something they *won't* do, and that amounts to the same thing. I'm not saying they're wrong not to reopen the case. But the thing is that I want them to do it, and I can't do anything about it, but in your case, well, I can hire you.'

'Not exactly.'

'I beg your pardon?'

5

'You can't hire me,' I explained. 'I'm not a private investigator.'

'Fitzroy said—'

'They have licenses,' I went on. 'I don't. They fill out forms, they write reports in triplicate, they submit vouchers for their expenses, they file tax returns, they do all those things and I don't.'

'What do you do, Mr Scudder?'

I shrugged. 'Sometimes I'll do a favor for a person,' I said, 'and sometimes the person will give me some money. As a favor in return.'

'I think I understand.'

'Do you?' I drank the rest of my drink. I remembered the corpse in that Brooklyn kitchen. White skin, little beads of black blood around the puncture wounds. 'You want a killer brought to justice,' I said. 'You'd better realize in front that that's impossible. Even if there's a killer out there, even if there's a way to find out who he is, there's not going to be any evidence lying around after all these years. No bloodstained icepick in somebody's hardware drawer. I could get lucky and come up with a thread, but it won't turn into the kind of thing you can spread out in front of a jury. Somebody killed your daughter and got away with it and it galls you. Won't it be more frustrating if you know who it is and there's nothing you can do about it?'

'I still want to know.'

'You might learn things you won't like. You said it yourself – somebody probably killed her for a reason. You might be happier not knowing the reason.'

'It's possible.'

'But you'll run that risk.'

'Yes.'

'Well, I guess I can try talking with some people.' I got my pen and notebook from my pocket, opened the notebook to a fresh page, uncapped the pen. 'I might as well start with you,' I said.

We talked for close to an hour and I made a lot of notes. I had another double bourbon and made it last. He had Trina take away his drink and bring him a cup of coffee. She refilled it twice for him before we were finished.

He lived in Hastings-on-Hudson in Westchester County. They'd moved there from the city when Barbara was five and her younger sister Lynn was three. Three years ago, some six years after Barbara's death, London's wife Helen had died of cancer.

He lived there alone now, and every once in a while he thought about selling the house, but so far he hadn't gotten around to listing it with a realtor. He supposed it was something he'd do sooner or later, whereupon he'd either move into the city or take a garden apartment somewhere in Westchester.

Barbara had been twenty-six. She'd be thirty-five now if she had lived. No children. She had been a couple of months' pregnant when she died, and London hadn't even known that until after her death. Telling me this, his voice broke.

Douglas Ettinger had remarried a couple of years after Barbara's death. He'd been a caseworker for the Welfare Department during their marriage, but he'd quit that job shortly after the murder and gone into sales. His second wife's father owned a sporting goods store on Long Island and after the marriage he'd taken in Ettinger as a partner. Ettinger lived in Mineola with his wife and two or three children – London wasn't sure of the number. He had come alone to Helen London's funeral and London hadn't had any contact with him since then, nor had he ever met the new wife.

Lynn London would be thirty-three in a month. She lived in Chelsea and taught fourth-graders at a progressive private school in the Village. She'd been married shortly after Barbara was killed, and she and her husband had separated after a little over two years of marriage and divorced not long after that. No children.

He mentioned other people. Neighbors, friends. The operator of the day-care center where Barbara had worked. A coworker there. Her closest friend from college. Sometimes he remembered names, sometimes not, but he gave me bits and pieces and I could take it from there. Not that any of it would necessarily lead anywhere.

He went off on tangents a lot. I didn't attempt to rein him in. I thought I might get a better picture of the dead woman by letting him wander, but even so I didn't develop any real sense of her. I learned she was attractive, that she'd been popular as a teenager, that she'd done well in school. She was interested in helping people, she liked working with children, and she'd been eager to have a family of her own. The image that came through was of a woman of no vices and the blandest virtues, wavering in age from childhood to an age she hadn't lived to attain. I had the feeling that he hadn't known her terribly well, that he'd been insulated by his work and by his role as her father from any reliable perception of her as a person.

7

Not uncommon, that. Most people don't really know their children until the children have become parents themselves. And Barbara hadn't lived that long.

When he ran out of things to tell me I flipped through my notes, then closed the book. I told him I'd see what I could do.

'I'll need some money,' I said.

'How much?'

I never know how to set a fee. What's too little and what's too much? I knew I needed money – a chronic condition, that – and that he probably had it in fair supply. Insurance agents can earn a lot or a little, but it seemed to me that selling group coverage to corporations was probably quite lucrative. I flipped a mental coin and came up with a figure of fifteen hundred dollars.

'And what will that buy, Mr Scudder?'

I told him I really didn't know. 'It'll buy my efforts,' I said. 'I'll work on this until I come up with something or until it's clear to me that there's nothing to come up with. If that happens before I figure I've earned your money you'll get some back. If I feel I have more coming I'll let you know, and you can decide then whether or not you want to pay me.'

'It's very irregular, isn't it?'

'You might not be comfortable with it.'

He considered that but didn't say anything. Instead he got out a checkbook and asked how he should make the check payable. To Matthew Scudder, I told him, and he wrote it out and tore it out of the book and set it on the table between us.

I didn't pick it up. I said, 'You know, I'm not the only alternative to the police. There are big, well-staffed agencies who operate in a much more conventional manner. They'll report in detail, they'll account for every cent of fees and expenses. On top of that, they've got more resources than I do.'

'Detective Fitzroy said as much. He said there were a couple of major agencies he could recommend.'

'But he recommended me?'

'Yes.'

'Why?' I knew one reason, of course, but it wasn't one he'd have given London.

London smiled for the first time. 'He said you're a crazy son of a bitch,' he said. 'Those were his words, not mine.'

'And?'

'He said you might get caught up in this in a way a large agency wouldn't. That when you get your teeth in something

8

you don't let go. He said the odds were against it, but you just might find out who killed Barbara.'

'He said that, did he?' I picked up his check, studied it, folded it in half. I said, 'Well, he's right. I might.'

TWO

It was too late to get to the bank. After London left I settled my tab and cashed a marker at the bar. My first stop would be the Eighteenth Precinct, and it's considered bad manners to show up empty-handed.

I called first to make sure he'd be there, then took a bus east and another one downtown. Armstrong's is on Ninth Avenue, around the corner from my Fifty-seventh Street hotel. The Eighteenth is housed on the ground floor of the Police Academy, a modern eight-story building with classes for recruits and prep courses for the sergeants' and lieutenants' exams. They've got a pool there, and a gym equipped with weight machines and a running track. You can take martial arts courses, or deafen yourself practicing on the pistol range.

I felt the way I always do when I walk into a station house. Like an impostor, I suppose, and an unsuccessful one at that. I stopped at the desk, said I had business with Detective Fitzroy. The uniformed sergeant waved me on. He probably assumed I was a member in good standing. I must still look like a cop, or walk like one, or something. People read me that way. Even cops.

I walked on through to the squad room and found Fitzroy typing a report at a corner desk. There were half a dozen Styrofoam coffee cups grouped on the desk, each holding about an inch of light coffee. Fitzroy motioned me to a chair and I sat down while he finished what he was typing. A couple of desks away, two cops were hassling a skinny black kid with eyes like a frog. I gather he'd been picked up for dealing three-card monte. They weren't giving him all that hard of a time, but then it wasn't the crime of the century, either.

Fitzroy looked as I remembered him, maybe a little older and a little heavier. I don't suppose he put in many hours on the running track. He had a beefy Irish face and gray hair cropped

close to his skull, and not too many people would have taken him for an accountant or an orchestra conductor or a cabbie. Or a stenographer – he made pretty good time on his typewriter, but he only used two fingers to do it.

He finished finally and pushed the machine to one side. 'I swear the whole thing's paperwork,' he said. 'That and court appearances. Who's got time left to detect anything? Hey, Matt.' We shook hands. 'Been a while. You don't look so bad.'

'Was I supposed to?'

'No, course not. How about some coffee? Milk and sugar?'

'Black is fine.'

He crossed the room to the coffee machine and came back with another pair of Styrofoam cups. The two detectives went on ragging the three-card dealer, telling him they figured he had to be the First Avenue Slasher. The kid kept up his end of the banter reasonably well.

Fitzroy sat down, blew on his coffee, took a sip, made a face. He lit a cigarette and leaned back in his swivel chair. 'This London,' he said. 'You saw him?'

'Just a little while ago.'

'What did you think? You gonna help him out?'

'I don't know if that's the word for it. I told him I'd give it a shot.'

'Yeah, I figured there might be something in it for you, Matt. Here's a guy looking to spend a few dollars. You know what it's like, it's like his daughter up and died all over again and he's got to think he's doing something about it. Now there's nothing he *can* do, but if he spends a few dollars he'll maybe feel better, and why shouldn't it go to a good man who can use it? He's got a couple bucks, you know. It's not like you're taking it from a crippled newsie.'

'That's what I gathered.'

'So you'll give it a shot,' he said. 'That's good. He wanted me to recommend somebody to him and right off I thought of you. Why not give the business to a friend, right? People take care of each other and that makes the world go on spinning. Isn't that what they say?'

I had palmed five twenties while he was getting the coffee. Now I leaned forward and tucked them into his hand. 'Well, I can use a couple days work,' I said. 'I appreciate it.'

'Listen, a friend's a friend, right?' He made the money disappear. A friend's a friend, all right, but a favor's a favor and there are no free lunches, not in or out of the department. And

why should there be? 'So you'll chase around and ask a few questions,' he went on, 'and you can string him for as long as he wants to play, and you don't have to bust your hump over it. Nine years, for Christ's sake. Wrap this one up and we'll fly you down to Dallas, let you figure out who killed J.F.K.'

'It must be a pretty cold trail.'

'Colder'n Kelsey's legendary nuts. If there was any reason at the time to think she wasn't just one more entry in the Icepick Prowler's datebook, then maybe somebody would of done a little digging at the time. But you know how those things work.'

'Sure.'

'We got this guy now over here on First Avenue taking whacks at people on the street, swinging at 'em with a butcher knife. We got to figure they're random attacks, right? You don't run up to the victim's husband and ask him was she fucking the mailman. Same with what's-her-name, Ettinger. Maybe she *was* fucking the mailman and maybe that's why she got killed, but there didn't look to be any reason to check it out at the time and it's gonna be a neat trick to do it now.'

'Well, I can go through the motions.'

'Sure, why not?' He tapped an accordion-pleated manila file. 'I had them pull this for you. Why don't you do a little light reading for a few minutes? There's a guy I gotta see.'

He was gone a little better than half an hour. I spent the time reading my way through the Icepick Prowler file. Early on, the two detectives popped the three-card dealer into a holding cell and rushed out, evidently to run down a tip on the First Avenue Slasher. The Slasher had done his little number right there in the Eighteenth, just a couple of blocks from the station house, and they were evidently pretty anxious to put him away.

I was done with the file when Frank Fitzroy got back. He said, 'Well? Get anything?'

'Not a whole lot. I made a few notes. Mostly names and addresses.'

'They may not match up after nine years. People move. Their whole fucking lives change.'

God knows mine did. Nine years ago I was a detective on the NYPD. I lived on Long Island in a house with a lawn and a backyard and a barbecue grill and a wife and two sons. I had moved, all right, though it was sometimes difficult to determine the direction. Surely my life had changed.

I tapped the file folder. 'Pinell,' I said. 'How sure is it he didn't kill Barbara Ettinger?'

'Gilt-edged, Matt. Bottled in bond. He was in Bellevue at the time.'

'People have been known to slip in and out.'

'Granted, but he was in a straitjacket. That hampers your movement a little. Besides, there's things that set the Ettinger killing apart from the others. You only notice them if you look for them, but they're there.'

'Like what?'

'Number of wounds. Ettinger had the lowest number of wounds of all eight victims. The difference isn't major but maybe it's enough to be significant. Plus all the other victims had wounds in the thighs. Ettinger had nothing in the thighs or legs, no punctures. Thing is, there was a certain amount of variation among the other victims. He didn't stamp out these murders with a cookie cutter. So the discrepancies with Ettinger didn't stand out at the time. The fewer wounds and the no wounds in the thighs, you can look at it that he was rushed, he heard somebody or thought he heard somebody and he didn't have time to give her the full treatment.'

'Sure.'

'The thing that made it so obvious that it was the Icepick guy who cooled her, well, you know what that was.'

'The eyes.'

'Right.' He nodded approval. 'All of the victims were stabbed through the eyes. One shot through each eyeball. That never made the papers. We held it back the way you always try and hold one or two things back to keep the psychos from fooling you with false confessions. You wouldn't believe how many clowns already turned themselves in for the slashings down the street.'

'I can imagine.'

'And you have to check 'em all out, and then you have to write up each interrogation, and that's the real pain in the ass. Anyway, getting back to Ettinger. The Icepick guy always went for the eyes. We kept the wraps on that detail, and Ettinger got it in the eye, so what are you going to figure? Who's gonna give a shit if she got it in the thighs or not when you've got an eyeball puncture to run with?'

'But it was only one eye.'

'Right. Okay, that's a discrepancy, but it lines up with the

fewer punctures and the no wounds in the thighs. He's in a hurry. No time to do it right. Wouldn't you figure it that way?'

'Anybody would.'

'Of course. You want some more coffee?'

'No thanks.'

'I guess I'll pass myself. I've had too much already today.'

'How do you figure it now, Frank?'

'Ettinger? What do I figure happened?'

'Uh-huh.'

He scratched his head. Vertical frown lines creased his forehead on either side of his nose. 'I don't think it was anything complicated,' he said. 'I think somebody read the papers and watched television and got turned on by the stories about the Icepick guy. You get these imitators every now and then. They're psychos without the imagination to think up their own numbers so they hitch a ride on somebody else's craziness. Some loony watched the six o'clock news and went out and bought an icepick.'

'And happened to get her in the eye by chance?'

'Possible. Could be. Or it could be it just struck him as a good idea, same as it did Pinell. Or something leaked.'

'That's what I was thinking.'

'Far as I can remember, there was nothing in the papers or on the news. Nothing about the eye wounds, I mean. But maybe there was and then we squelched it but not before this psycho read it or heard it and it made an impression. Or maybe it never got into the media but the word was around. You got a few hundred cops who know something, plus everybody who's around for the postmortems, plus everybody who sees the records, all the clerks and all, and each of them tells three people and those people all talk, and how long does it take before a lot of people know about it?'

'I see what you mean.'

'If anything, the business with the eyes makes it look like it was just a psycho. A guy who tried it once for a thrill and then let it go.'

'How do you figure that, Frank?'

He leaned back, interlaced his fingers behind his head. 'Well, say it's the husband,' he said. 'Say he wants to kill her because she's fucking the mailman, and he wants to make it look like the Icepick Prowler so he won't carry the can for it himself. If he knows about the eyes, he's gonna do both of them, right? He's not taking any chances. A nut, he's something else again. He

14

does one eye because it's something to do, and then maybe he's bored with it so he doesn't do the other one. Who knows what goes through their fucking heads?'

'If it's a psycho, then there's no way to tag him.'

'Of course there isn't. Nine years later and you're looking for a killer without a motive? That's a needle in a haystack when the needle's not even there. But that's all right. You take this and play with it, and after you've run the string you just tell London it must have been a psycho. Believe me, he'll be happy to hear it.'

'Why?'

'Because that's what he thought nine years ago, and he got used to the idea. He accepted it. Now he's afraid it's somebody he knows and that's driving him crazy, so you'll investigate it all for him and tell him everything's okay, the sun still comes up in the east every morning and his daughter was still killed by a fucking Act of God. He can relax again and go back to his life. He'll get his money's worth.'

'You're probably right.'

'Course I'm right. You could even save yourself running around and just sit on your ass for a week and then tell him what you'll wind up telling him anyway. But I don't suppose you'll do that, will you?'

'No, I'll give it my best shot.'

'I figured you'd at least go through the motions. What it is, you're still a cop, aren't you, Matt?'

'I suppose so. In a way. Whatever that means.'

'You don't have anything steady, huh? You just catch a piece of work like this when it comes along?'

'Right.'

'You ever think about coming back?'

'To the department? Not very often. And never very seriously.'

He hesitated. There were questions he wanted to ask, things he wanted to say to me, but he decided to leave them unsaid. I was grateful for that. He got to his feet and so did I. I thanked him for the time and the information and he said an old friend was an old friend and it was a pleasure to be able to help a pal out. Neither of us mentioned the hundred dollars that had changed hands. Why should we? He'd been glad to get it and I was glad to give it. A favor's no good unless you pay for it. One way or the other, you always do.

15

THREE

It had rained a little while I was with Fitzroy. It wasn't raining when I got back outside, but it didn't feel as though it was through for the day. I had a drink around the corner on Third Avenue and watched part of the newscast. They showed the police artist's sketch of the Slasher, the same drawing that was on the front page of the *Post*. It showed a round-faced black man with a trimmed beard and a cap on his head. Mad zeal glinted in his large almond-shaped eyes.

'Imagine that comin' up the street at you,' the bartender said. 'I'll tell you, there's a lot of guys gettin' pistol permits on the strength of this one. I'm thinkin' about fillin' out an application myself.'

I remember the day I stopped carrying a gun. It was the same day I turned in my shield. I'd had a stretch of feeling terribly vulnerable without that iron on my hip, and now I could hardly recall how it had felt to walk around armed in the first place.

I finished my drink and left. Would the bartender get a gun? Probably not. More people talked about it than did it. But whenever there's the right kind of nut making headlines, a Slasher or an Icepick Prowler, a certain number of people get pistol permits and a certain number of others buy illegal guns. Then some of them get drunk and shoot their wives. None of them ever seems to wind up nailing the Slasher.

I walked uptown, stopped at an Italian place along the way for dinner, then spent a couple of hours at the main library on Forty-second Street, dividing my time between old newspapers on microfilm and new and old Polk city directories. I made some notes, but not many. I was mostly trying to let myself sink into the case, to take a few steps backward in time.

By the time I got out of there it was raining. I took a cab to Armstrong's, got a stool at the bar and settled in. There were people to talk to and bourbon to drink, with enough coffee to

keep fatigue at bay. I didn't hit it very hard, just coasted along, getting by, getting through. You'd be surprised what a person can get through.

The next day was Friday. I read a paper with breakfast. There'd been no slashings the previous night, but neither had there been any progress in the case. In Ecuador, a few hundred people had died in an earthquake. There seemed to be more of those lately, or I was more aware of them.

I went to my bank, put Charles London's check in my savings account, drew out some cash and a money order for five hundred dollars. They gave me an envelope to go with the money order and I addressed it to Ms Anita Scudder in Syosset. I stood at the counter for a few minutes with the bank's pen in my hand, trying to think of a note to include, and wound up sending the money order all by itself. After I'd mailed it I thought about calling to tell her it was in the mail, but that seemed like even more of a chore than thinking of something to put in a note.

It wasn't a bad day. Clouds obscured the sun, but there were patches of blue overhead and the air had a tang to it. I stopped at Armstrong's to cover my marker and left without having anything. It was a little early for the day's first drink. I left, walked east a long block to Columbus Circle, and caught a train.

I rode the D to Smith and Bergen and came out into sunshine. For a while I walked around, trying to get my bearings. The Seventy-eighth Precinct, where I'd served a brief hitch, was only six or seven blocks to the east, but that had been a long time ago and I'd spent little time in Brooklyn since. Nothing looked even faintly familiar. I was in a part of the borough that hadn't had a name until fairly recently. Now a part of it was called Cobble Hill and another chunk was called Boerum Hill and both of them were participating wholeheartedly in the brownstone renaissance. Neighborhoods don't seem to stand still in New York. They either improve or deteriorate. Most of the city seemed to be crumbling. The whole South Bronx was block after block of burned-out buildings, and in Brooklyn the same process was eroding Bushwick and Brownsville.

These blocks were going in the other direction. I walked up one street and down another and found myself becoming aware of changes. There were trees on every block, most of them planted within the past few years. While some of the brown-stones and brickfronts were in disrepair, more sported freshly painted trim. The shops reflected the changes that had been

17

going on. A health food store on Smith Street, a boutique at the corner of Warren and Bond, little up-scale restaurants tucked in all over the place.

The building where Barbara Ettinger had lived and died was on Wyckoff Street between Nevins and Bond. It was a brick tenement, five stories tall with four small apartments on each floor, and it had thus escaped the conversion that had already turned many of the brownstones back into the one-family houses they had originally been. Still, the building had been spruced up some. I stood in the vestibule and checked the names on the mailboxes, comparing them to those I'd copied from an old city directory. Of the twenty apartments, only six held tenants who'd been there at the time of the murder.

Except you can't go by names on mailboxes. People get married or unmarried and their names change. An apartment gets sublet to keep the landlord from raising the rent, and the name of a long-dead tenant stays on the lease and on the mailbox for ages. A roommate moves in, then stays on when the original leaseholder moves out. There are no shortcuts. You have to knock on all the doors.

I rang a bell, got buzzed in, went to the top floor and worked my way down. It's a little easier when you have a badge to flash but the manner's more important than the ID, and I couldn't lose the manner if I tried. I didn't tell anyone I was a cop, but neither did I try to keep anyone from making the assumption.

The first person I talked to was a young mother in one of the rear apartments on the top floor. Her baby cried in the next room while we talked. She'd moved in within the past year, she told me, and she didn't know anything about a murder nine years previously. She asked anxiously if it had taken place in that very apartment, and seemed at once relieved and disappointed to learn it had not.

A Slavic woman, her hands liver-spotted and twisted with arthritis, gave me a cup of coffee in her fourth-floor front apartment. She put me on the couch and turned her own chair to face me. It had been positioned so she could watch the street.

She'd been in that apartment for almost forty years, she told me. Up until four years ago her husband had been there, but now he was gone and she was alone. The neighborhood, she said, was getting better. 'But the old people are going. Places I shopped for years are gone. And the price of everything! I don't believe the prices.'

She remembered the icepick murder, though she was surprised it had been nine years. It didn't seem that long to her. The woman who was killed was a nice woman, she said. 'Only nice people get killed.'

She didn't seem to remember much about Barbara Ettinger beyond her niceness. She didn't know if she had been especially friendly or unfriendly with any of the other neighbors, if she'd gotten on well or poorly with her husband. I wondered if she even remembered what the woman had looked like, and wished I had a picture to show her. I might have asked London for one if I'd thought of it.

Another woman on the fourth floor, a Miss Wicker, was the only person to ask for identification. I told her I wasn't a policeman, and she left the chain lock on the door and spoke to me through a two-inch opening, which didn't strike me as unreasonable. She'd only been in the building a few years, did know about the murder and that the Icepick Prowler had been recently apprehended, but that was the extent of her information.

'People let anyone in,' she said. 'We have an intercom here but people just buzz you in without determining who you are. People talk about crime but they never believe it can happen to them, and then it does.' I thought of telling her how easy it would be to snap her chain lock with a bolt cutter, but I decided her anxiety level was high enough already.

A lot of the tenants were out for the day. On the third floor, Barbara Ettinger's floor, I got no response from one of the rear apartments, then paused in front of the adjoining door. The pulse of disco music came through it. I knocked, and after a moment the door was opened by a man in his late twenties. He had short hair and a mustache, and he was wearing nothing but a pair of blue-striped white gym shorts. His body was well-muscled, and his tanned skin glistened with a light coating of sweat.

I told him my name and that I'd like to ask him a few questions. He led me inside, closed the door, then moved past me and crossed the room to the radio. He lowered the volume about halfway, paused, turned it off altogether.

There was a large mat in the center of the uncarpeted parquet floor. A barbell and a pair of dumbells reposed on it, and a jump rope lay curled on the floor alongside. 'I was just working out,' he said. 'Won't you sit down? That chair's the comfortable one. The other's nice to visit but you wouldn't want to live there.'

I took the chair while he sat on the mat and folded his legs

tailor-fashion. His eyes brightened with recognition when I mentioned the murder in 3-A. 'Donald told me,' he said. 'I've only been here a little over a year but Donald's been living here for ages. He's watched the neighborhood become positively chic around him. Fortunately this particular building retains its essential tackiness. You'll probably want to talk to Donald but he won't be home from work until six or six thirty.'

'What's Donald's last name?'

'Gilman.' He spelled it. 'And I'm Rolfe Waggoner. That's Rolfe with an e. I was just reading about the Icepick Prowler. Of course I don't remember the case. I was in high school then. That was back home in Indiana – Muncie, Indiana – and that was a long ways from here.' He thought for a moment. 'In more ways than one,' he said.

'Was Mr Gilman friendly with the Ettingers?'

'He could answer that better than I can. You've caught the man who did it, haven't you? I read that he was in a mental hospital for years and nobody ever knew he killed anybody, and then he was released and they caught him and he confessed or something?'

'Something like that.'

'And now you want to make sure you have a good case against him.' He smiled. He had a nice open face and he seemed quite at ease, sitting on a mat in his gym shorts. Gay men used to be so much more defensive, especially around cops. 'It must be complicated with something that happened so many years ago. Have you talked with Judy? Judy Fairborn, she's in the apartment where the Ettingers used to live. She works nights, she's a waitress, so she'll be home now unless she's at an audition or a dance class or shopping or – well, she'll be home unless she's out, but that's always the case, isn't it?' He smiled again, showing me perfectly even teeth. 'But maybe you've already spoken with her.'

'Not yet.'

'She's new. I think she moved in about six months ago. Would you want to talk to her anyway?'

'Yes.'

He uncoiled, sprang lightly to his feet. 'I'll introduce you,' he said. 'Just let me put some clothes on. I won't be a minute.'

He reappeared wearing jeans and a flannel shirt and running shoes without socks. We crossed the hall and he knocked on the door of Apartment 3-A. There was silence, then footsteps and a woman's voice asking who it was.

'Just Rolfe,' he said. 'In the company of a policeman who'd like to grill you, Ms Fairborn.'

'Huh?' she said, and opened the door. She might have been Rolfe's sister, with the same light brown hair, the same regular features, the same open Midwestern countenance. She wore jeans, too, and a sweater and penny loafers. Rolfe introduced us and she stepped aside and motioned us in. She didn't know anything about the Ettingers, and her knowledge of the murder was limited to the fact that it had taken place there. 'I'm glad I didn't know before I moved in,' she said, 'because I might have let it spook me, and that would have been silly, wouldn't it? Apartments are too hard to find. Who can afford to be superstitious?'

'Nobody,' Rolfe said. 'Not in this market.'

They talked about the First Avenue Slasher, and about a recent wave of local burglaries, including one a week ago on the first floor. I asked if I could have a look at the kitchen. I was on my way there as I asked the question. I think I'd have remembered the layout anyway, but I'd already been in other apartments in the building and they were all the same.

Judy said, 'Is this where it happened? Here in the kitchen?'

'Where did you think?' Rolfe asked her. 'The bedroom?'

'I guess I didn't think about it.'

'You didn't even wonder? Sounds like repression.'

'Maybe.'

I tuned out their conversation. I tried to remember the room, tried to peel off nine years and be there once again, standing over Barbara Ettinger's body. She'd been near the stove then, her legs extending into the center of the small room, her head turned toward the living room. There had been linoleum on the floor and that was gone, the original wood floor restored and glossy with polyurethane. And the stove looked new, and plaster had been removed to expose the brick exterior wall. I couldn't be sure the brick hadn't been exposed previously, nor could I know how much of my mental picture was real. The memory is a cooperative animal, eager to please; what it cannot supply it occasionally invents, sketching carefully to fill in the blanks.

Why the kitchen? The door led into the living room, and she'd let him in either because she knew who he was or in spite of the fact that she didn't, and then what? He drew the icepick and she tried to get away from him? Caught her heel in the linoleum and went sprawling, and then he was on her with the pick?

The kitchen was the middle room, separating the living room

and bedroom. Maybe he was a lover and they were on their way to bed when he surprised her with a few inches of pointed steel. But wouldn't he wait until they got where they were going?

Maybe she had something on the stove. Maybe she was fixing him a cup of coffee. The kitchen was too small to eat in but more than large enough for two people to stand comfortably waiting for water to boil.

Then a hand over her mouth to muffle her cries and a thrust into her heart to kill her. Then enough other thrusts of the icepick to make it look like the Icepick Prowler's work.

Had the first wound killed her? I remembered beads of blood. Dead bodies don't bleed freely, but neither do most puncture wounds. The autopsy had indicated a wound in the heart that had been more or less instantly fatal. It might have been the first wound inflicted or the last, for all I'd seen in the Medical Examiner's report.

Judy Fairborn filled a teakettle, lit the stove with a wooden match, and poured three cups of instant coffee when the water boiled. I'd have liked bourbon in mine, or instead of mine, but nobody suggested it. We carried our cups into the living room and she said, 'You looked as though you saw a ghost. No, I'm wrong. You looked as though you were looking for one.'

'Maybe that's what I was doing.'

'I'm not sure if I believe in them or not. They're supposed to be more common in cases of sudden death when the victim didn't expect what happened. The theory is that the soul doesn't realize it died, so it hangs around because it doesn't know to pass on to the next plane of existence.'

'I thought it walked the floors crying out for vengeance,' Rolfe said. 'You know, dragging chains, making the boards creak.'

'No, it just doesn't know any better. What you do, you get somebody to lay the ghost.'

'I'm not going to touch that line,' Rolfe said.

'I'm proud of you. You get high marks for restraint. That's what it's called, laying the ghost. It's a sort of exorcism. The ghost expert, or whatever you call him, communicates with the ghost and lets him know what happened, and that he's supposed to pass on. And then the spirit can go wherever spirits go.'

'You really believe all this?'

'I'm not sure what I believe,' she said. She uncrossed her legs, then recrossed them. 'If Barbara's haunting this apartment, she's

22

being very restrained about it. No creaking boards, no midnight apparitions.'

'Your basic low-profile ghost,' he said.

'I'll have nightmares tonight,' she said. 'If I sleep at all.'

I knocked on all the doors on the two lower floors without getting much response. The tenants were either out or had nothing useful to tell me. The building's superintendent had a basement apartment in a similar building on the next block, but I didn't see the point in looking him up. He'd only been on the job for a matter of months, and the old woman in the fourth-floor-front apartment had told me there had been four or five supers in the past nine years.

By the time I got out of the building I was glad for the fresh air, glad to be on the street again. I'd felt something in Judy Fairborn's kitchen, though I wouldn't go so far as to call it a ghost. But it had felt as though something from years past was pulling at me, trying to drag me down and under.

Whether it was Barbara Ettinger's past or my own was something I couldn't say.

I stopped at a bar on the corner of Dean and Smith. They had sandwiches and a microwave oven to heat them in but I wasn't hungry. I had a quick drink and sipped a short beer chaser. The bartender sat on a high stool drinking a large glass of what looked like vodka. The other two customers, black men about my age, were at the far end of the bar watching a game show on TV. From time to time one of them was talking back to the set.

I flipped a few pages in my notebook, went to the phone and looked through the Brooklyn book. The day-care center where Barbara Ettinger had worked didn't seem to be in business. I checked the Yellow Pages to see if there was anything listed under another name at the same address. There wasn't.

The address was on Clinton Street, and I'd been away from the neighborhood long enough so that I had to ask directions, but once I'd done so it was only a walk of a few blocks. The boundaries of Brooklyn neighborhoods aren't usually too well defined – the neighborhoods themselves are often largely the invention of realtors – but when I crossed Court Street I was leaving Boerum Hill for Cobble Hill, and the change wasn't difficult to see. Cobble Hill was a shade or two tonier. More trees, a higher percentage of brownstones, a greater proportion of white faces on the street.

23

I found the number I was seeking on Clinton between Pacific and Amity. There was no day-care center there. The ground floor storefront offered supplies for knitting and needlepoint. The proprietor, a plump Earth Mother with a gold incisor, didn't know anything about a day-care center. She'd moved in a year and a half ago after a health food restaurant had gone out of business. 'I ate there once,' she said, 'and they *deserved* to go out of business. Believe me.'

She gave me the landlord's name and number. I tried him from the corner and kept getting a busy signal so I walked over to Court Street and climbed a flight of stairs. There was just one person in the office, a young man with his sleeves rolled up and a large round ashtray full of cigarette butts on the desk in front of him. He chainsmoked while he talked on the phone. The windows were closed and the room was as thick with smoke as a nightclub at four in the morning.

When he got off the phone I caught him before it could ring again. His own memory went back beyond the health food restaurant to a children's clothing store that had also failed in the same location. 'Now we got needlepoint,' he said. 'If I were gonna guess I'd say she'll be out in another year. How much can you make selling yarn? What happens, somebody has a hobby, an interest, so they open up a business. Health food, needle-point, whatever it is, but they don't know shit about business and they're down and out in a year or two. She breaks the lease, we'll rent it in a month for twice what she pays. It's a renter's market in an upscale neighborhood.' He reached for the phone. 'Sorry I can't help you,' he said.

'Check your records,' I said.

He told me he had lots of important things to do, but halfway through the statement changed from an assertion to a whine. I sat in an old oak swivel chair and let him fumble around in his files. He opened and closed half a dozen drawers before he came up with a folder and slapped it down on his desk.

'Here we go,' he said. 'Happy Hours Child Care Center. Some name, huh?'

'What's wrong with it?'

'Happy hour's in a bar when the drinks are half price. Hell of a thing to call a place for the kiddies, don't you think?' He shook his head. 'Then they wonder why they go out of business.'

I didn't see anything the matter with the name.

'Leaseholder was a Mrs Corwin. Janice Corwin. Took the place on a five-year lease, gave it up after four years. Quit the

premises eight years ago in March.' That would have been a year after Barbara Ettinger's death. 'Jesus, you look at the rent and you can't believe it. You know what she was paying?'

I shook my head.

'Well, you saw the place. Name a figure.' I looked at him. He stubbed out a cigarette and lit another. 'One and a quarter. Hundred and twenty-five dollars a month. Goes for six now and it's going up the minute the needlework lady goes out, or when her lease is up. Whichever comes first.'

'You have a forwarding address for Corwin?'

He shook his head. 'I got a residential address. Want it?' He read off a number on Wyckoff Street. It was just a few doors from the Ettingers' building. I wrote down the address. He read off a phone number and I jotted that down, too.

His phone rang. He picked it up, said hello, listened for a few minutes, then talked in monosyllables. 'Listen, I got someone here,' he said after a moment. 'I'll get back to you in a minute, okay?'

He hung up and asked me if that was all. I couldn't think of anything else. He hefted the file. 'Four years she had the place,' he said. 'Most places drop dead in the first year. Make it through a year you got a chance. Get through two years and you got a good chance. You know what's the problem?'

'What?'

'Women,' he said. 'They're amateurs. They got no need to make a go of it. They open a business like they try on a dress. Take it off if they don't like the color. If that does it, I got calls to make.'

I thanked him for his help.

'Listen,' he said, 'I always cooperate. It's my nature.'

I tried the number he gave me and got a woman who spoke Spanish. She didn't know anything about anybody named Janice Corwin and didn't stay on the line long enough for me to ask her much of anything. I dropped another dime and dialed again on the chance that I'd misdialed the first time. When the same woman answered I broke the connection.

When they disconnect a phone it's close to a year before they reassign the number. Of course Mrs Corwin could have changed her number without moving from the Wyckoff Street address. People, especially women, do that frequently enough to shake off obscene callers.

Still, I figured she'd moved. I figured everyone had moved, out

of Brooklyn, out of the five boroughs, out of the state. I started to walk back toward Wyckoff Street, covered half a block, turned, retraced my steps, started to turn again.

I made myself stop. I had an anxious sensation in my chest and stomach. I was blaming myself for wasting time and starting to wonder why I'd taken London's check in the first place. His daughter was nine years in the grave, and whoever killed her had probably long since started a brand-new life in Australia. All I was doing was spinning my goddamned wheels.

I stood there until the intensity of the feeling wound itself down, knowing that I didn't want to go back to Wyckoff Street. I'd go there later, when Donald Gilman got home from work, and I could check Corwin's address then. Until then I couldn't think of anything I felt like doing about the Ettinger murder. But there was something I could do about the anxiety.

One thing about Brooklyn – you never have to walk very far before you encounter a church. They're all over the place throughout the borough.

The one I found was at the corner of Court and Congress. The church itself was closed and the iron gate locked, but a sign directed me to St Elizabeth Seton's Chapel right around the corner. A gateway led to a one-story chapel tucked in between the church and the rectory. I walked through an ivy-planted courtyard which a plaque proclaimed to be the burial site of Cornelius Heeney. I didn't bother reading who he was or why they'd planted him there. I walked between rows of white statues and into the little chapel. The only other person in it was a frail Irishwoman kneeling in a front pew. I took a seat toward the back.

It's hard to remember just when I started hanging out in churches. It happened sometime after I left the force, sometime after I moved out of the house in Syosset and away from Anita and the boys and into a hotel on West Fifty-seventh. I guess I found them to be citadels of peace and quiet, two commodities hard to come by in New York.

I sat in this one for fifteen or twenty minutes. It was peaceful, and just sitting there I lost some of what I'd been feeling earlier.

Before I left I counted out a hundred fifty dollars, and on my way out I slipped the money into a slot marked 'FOR THE POOR.' I started tithing not long after I began spending odd moments in churches, and I don't know why I started or why I've never

26

stopped. The question doesn't plague me much. There are no end of things I do without knowing the reason why.

I don't know what they do with the money. I don't much care. Charles London had given me fifteen hundred dollars, an act which didn't seem to make much more sense than my passing on a tenth of that sum to the unspecified poor.

There was a shelf of votive candles, and I stopped to light a couple of them. One for Barbara London Ettinger, who had been dead a long time, if not so long as old Cornelius Heeney. Another for Estrellita Rivera, a little girl who had been dead almost as long as Barbara Ettinger.

I didn't say any prayers. I never do.

FOUR

Donald Gilman was twelve or fifteen years older than his roommate, and I don't suppose he put in as many hours with the dumbbells and the jump rope. His neatly combed hair was a sandy brown, his eyes a cool blue through heavy horn-rimmed glasses. He was wearing suit pants and a white shirt and tie. His suit jacket was draped over the chair Rolfe had warned me about.

Rolfe had said Gilman was a lawyer, so I wasn't surprised when he asked to see my identification. I explained that I had resigned from the police force some years earlier. He raised an eyebrow at this news and flicked a glance at Rolfe.

'I'm involved in this at the request of Barbara Ettinger's father,' I went on. 'He's asked me to investigate.'

'But why? The killer's been caught, hasn't he?'

'There's some question about that.'

'Oh?'

I told him that Louis Pinell had an unbreakable alibi for the day of Barbara Ettinger's murder.

'Then someone else killed her,' he said at once. 'Unless the alibi turns out to be unfounded. That would explain the father's interest, wouldn't it? He probably suspects – well, he could suspect anyone at all. I hope you won't take it amiss if I call him to confirm that you're here as his emissary?'

'He may be hard to reach.' I had kept London's card and I got it out of my wallet. 'He's probably left the office by now, and I wouldn't think he's arrived home yet. He lives alone, his wife died a couple years ago, so he most likely takes his meals at restaurants.'

Gilman looked at the card for a moment, then handed it back. I watched his face and could see him make up his mind. 'Oh, well,' he said. 'I can't see the harm in talking with you, Mr Scudder. It's not as though I knew anything substantial. It was

28

all a fair amount of years ago, wasn't it? A lot of water under the bridge since then, or over the dam, or wherever it goes.' His blue eyes brightened. 'Speaking of liquid, we generally have a drink about now. Will you join us?'

'Thank you.'

'We generally mix up some martinis. Unless there's something else you'd prefer?'

'Martinis hit me a little hard,' I said. 'I think I'd better stick with whiskey. Bourbon, if you've got it.'

Of course they had it. They had Wild Turkey, which is a cut or two better than what I'm used to, and Rolfe gave me five or six ounces of it in a cut-crystal Old Fashioned glass. He poured Bombay gin into a pitcher, added ice cubes and a spoonful of vermouth, stirred gently and strained the blend into a pair of glasses that were mates to mine. Donald Gilman raised his glass and proposed a toast to Friday, and we drank to that.

I wound up sitting where Rolfe had had me sit earlier. Rolfe sat as before on the rug, his knees drawn up and his arms locked around them. He was still wearing the jeans and shirt he'd put on to introduce me to Judy Fairborn. His weights and jump rope were out of sight. Gilman sat on the edge of the uncomfortable chair and leaned forward, looking down into his glass, then looking up at me.

'I was trying to remember the day she died,' he said. 'It's difficult. I didn't come home from the office that day. I had drinks with someone after work, and then dinner out, and I think I went to a party in the Village. It's not important. The point is that I didn't get home until the following morning. I knew what to expect when I got here because I read the morning paper with my breakfast. No, that's wrong. I remember that I bought the *News* because it's easier to manage on the train, the business of turning the pages and all. The headline was *Icepick Killer Strikes in Brooklyn*, or words to that effect. I believe there had been a previous killing in Brooklyn.'

'The fourth victim. In Sheepshead Bay.'

'Then I turned to page three, I suppose it must have been, and there was the story. No photograph, but the name and address, of course, and that was unmistakable.' He put a hand to his chest. 'I remember how I felt. It was incredibly shocking. You don't expect that sort of thing to happen to someone you know. And it made me feel so vulnerable myself, you know. It happened in this building. I felt that before I felt the sense of loss one feels over the death of a friend.'

29

'How well did you know the Ettingers?'

'Reasonably well. They were a couple, of course, and most of their social interaction was with other couples. But they were right across the hall and I'd have them in for drinks or coffee from time to time, or they'd ask me over. I had one or two parties that they came to, but they didn't stay very long. I think they were comfortable enough with gay people, but not in great quantity. I can understand that. One doesn't like to be over-whelmingly outnumbered, does one? It's only natural to feel self-conscious.'

'Were they happy?'

The question pulled him back to the Ettingers and he frowned, weighing his answer. 'I suppose he's a suspect,' he said. 'The spouse always is. Have you met him?'

'No.'

' "Were they happy?" The question's inevitable, but who can ever answer it? They seemed happy. Most couples do, and most couples ultimately break up, and when they do their friends are invariably surprised because they *seemed* so bloody happy.' He finished his drink. 'I think they were happy enough. She was expecting a child when she was killed.'

'I know.'

'I hadn't known it. I only learned after her death.' He made a little circle with the empty glass, and Rolfe got gracefully to his feet and replenished Gilman's drink. While he was up he poured me another Wild Turkey. I was feeling the first one a little bit so I took it easy on the second.

Gilman said, 'I thought it might have steadied her.'

'The baby?'

'Yes.'

'She needed steadying?'

He sipped his martini. '*De mortuis* and all that. One hesitates to speak candidly of the dead. There was a restlessness in Barbara. She was a bright girl, you know. Very attractive, energetic, quick-witted. I don't recall where she went to school, but it was a good school. Doug went to Hofstra. I don't suppose there's anything the matter with Hofstra, but it's less prestigious than Barbara's alma mater. I don't know why I can't remember it.'

'Wellesley.' London had told me.

'Of course. I'd have remembered. I dated a Wellesley girl during my own college career. Sometimes self-acceptance takes a certain amount of time.'

30

'Did Barbara marry beneath herself?'

'I wouldn't say that. On the surface, she grew up in Westchester and went to Wellesley and married a social worker who grew up in Queens and went to Hofstra. But a lot of that is just a matter of labels.' He took a sip of gin. 'She may have thought she was too good for him, though.'

'Was she seeing anybody else?'

'You do ask direct questions, don't you? It's not hard to believe you were a policeman. What made you leave the force?'

'Personal reasons. Was she having an affair?'

'There's nothing tackier than dishing the dead, is there? I used to hear them sometimes. She would accuse him of having sex with women he met on the job. He was a welfare caseworker and that involved visiting unattached women in their apartments, and if one's in the market for casual sex the opportunity's certainly there. I don't know that he was taking advantage of it, but he struck me as the sort of man who would. And I gather she thought he was.'

'And she was having an affair to get even?'

'Quick of you. Yes, I think so, but don't ask me with whom because I've no idea. I would sometimes be home during the day. Not often, but now and then. There were times when I heard her coming up the stairs with a man, or I might pass her door and hear a man's voice. You have to understand that I'm not a busybody, so I didn't try to catch a peek of the mystery man, whoever he was. In fact I didn't pay the whole business a great deal of attention.'

'She would entertain this man during the day?'

'I can't swear she was entertaining anybody. Maybe it was the plumber come to repair a leaky faucet. Please understand that. I just had the feeling that she might have been seeing someone, and I knew she had accused her husband of infidelity, so I thought she might be getting a bit of sauce for the goose.'

'But it was during the day. Didn't she work days?'

'Oh, at the day-care center. I gather her schedule was quite flexible. She took the job to have something to do. Restlessness, again. She was a psychology major and she'd been in graduate school but gave it up, and now she wasn't doing anything, so she started helping out at the day-care center. I don't think they paid her very much and I don't suppose they objected if she took the odd afternoon off.'

'Who were her friends?'

'God. I met people at their apartment but I can't remember

any of them. I think most of their friends were his friends. There was the woman from the day-care center, but I'm afraid I don't remember her name.'

'Janice Corwin.'

'Is that it? It doesn't even ring a muted bell. She lived nearby. Just across the street, if I'm right.'

'You are. Do you know if she's still there?'

'No idea. I can't remember when I saw her last. I don't know that I'd recognize her anyway. I think I met her once, but I may just recall her because Barbara talked about her. You say the name was Corwin?'

'Janice Corwin.'

'The day-care center's gone. It closed years ago.'

'I know.'

The conversation didn't go much further. They had a dinner date and I'd run out of questions to ask. And I was feeling the drinks. I'd finished the second one without being aware of it and was surprised when I found the glass empty. I didn't feel drunk but I didn't feel sober either, and my mind could have been clearer.

The cold air helped. There was a wind blowing. I hunched my shoulders against it and walked across the street and down the block to the address I had for Janice Corwin. It turned out to be a four-story brick building, and a few years back someone had bought it, turned out the tenants as soon as their leases expired, and converted it for single-family occupancy.

According to the owner, whose name I didn't bother catching, the conversion process was still going on. 'It's endless,' he said. 'Everything's three times as difficult as you figure, takes four times as long, and costs five times as much. And those are conservative figures. Do you know how long it takes to strip old paint off door jambs? Do you know how many doorways there are in a house like this?'

He didn't remember the names of the tenants he'd dispossessed. The name Janice Corwin was not familiar to him. He said he probably had a list of the tenants somewhere but he didn't even know where to start looking for it. Besides, it wouldn't have their forwarding addresses. I told him not to bother looking.

I walked to Atlantic Avenue. Among the antique shops with their Victorian oak furniture and the plant stores and the Middle Eastern restaurants I managed to find an ordinary coffee shop

with a Formica counter and red leatherette stools. I wanted a drink more than I wanted a meal, but I knew I'd be in trouble if I didn't have something to eat. I had Salisbury steak and mashed potatoes and green beans and made myself eat everything. It wasn't bad. I drank two cups of so-so coffee and paused on my way out to look up Corwin in the phone book. There were two dozen Corwins in Brooklyn, including a J. Corwin with an address that looked to be in Bay Ridge or Bensonhurst. I tried the number but nobody answered.

No reason to think she'd be in Brooklyn. No reason to think she'd be listed under her own name, and I didn't know her husband's name.

No point checking the post office. They don't hold address changes longer than a year, and the building on Wyckoff Street had changed hands longer ago than that. But there would be ways to trace the Corwins. There generally are.

I paid the check and left a tip. According to the counterman, the nearest subway was a couple blocks away on Fulton Street. I was on the train heading for Manhattan before I realized that I hadn't even bothered to walk over to Bergen and Flatbush and take a look at the station house of the Seventy-eighth Precinct. Somehow I hadn't thought of it.

FIVE

I stopped at the desk when I got back to my hotel. No mail, no messages. Upstairs in my room I cracked the seal on a bottle of bourbon and poured a few fingers into a glass. I sat there for a while skipping around in a paperback edition of *The Lives of the Saints*. The martyrs held a curious fascination for me. They'd found such a rich variety of ways of dying.

Couple of days earlier there'd been an item in the paper, a back-pages squib about a suspect arrested for the year-old murder of two women in their East Harlem apartment. The victims, a mother and daughter, had been found in their bedroom, each with a bullet behind the ear. The report said the cops had stayed on the case because of the unusual brutality of the murders. Now they'd made an arrest, taking a fourteen-year-old boy into custody. He'd have been thirteen when the women were killed.

According to the story's last paragraph, five other persons had been killed in or around the victims' building in the year since their murder. There'd been no indication whether those five murders were solved, or whether the kid in custody was suspected of them.

I let my mind slip off on tangents. Now and again I'd put the book aside and find myself thinking about Barbara Ettinger. Donald Gilman had started to say that her father probably suspected someone, then caught himself and left the name unsaid.

The husband, probably. The spouse is always the first suspect. If Barbara hadn't apparently been one of a series of victims, Douglas Ettinger would have been grilled six ways and backwards. As it was, he'd been interrogated automatically by detectives from Midtown North. They could hardly have done otherwise. He was not only the husband. He was also the person

34

who had discovered the body, coming upon her corpse in the kitchen upon returning from work.

I'd read a report of the interrogation. The man who conducted it had already taken it for granted that the killing was the work of the Icepick Prowler, so his questions had concentrated on Barbara's schedule, on her possible propensity for opening the door for strangers, on whether she might have mentioned anyone following her or behaving suspiciously. Had she been bothered recently by obscene telephone calls? People hanging up without speaking? Suspicious wrong numbers?

The questioning had essentially assumed the subject's innocence, and the assumption had certainly been logical enough at the time. Evidently there had been nothing in Douglas Ettinger's manner to arouse suspicion.

I tried, not for the first time, to summon up a memory of Ettinger. It seemed to me that I must have met him. We were on the scene before Midtown North came to take the case away from us, and he'd have had to be somewhere around while I was standing in that kitchen eyeing the body sprawled on the linoleum. I might have tried to offer a word of comfort, might have formed some impression, but I couldn't remember him at all.

Perhaps he'd been in the bedroom when I was there, talking with another detective or with one of the patrolmen who'd been first on the scene. Maybe I'd never laid eyes on him, or maybe we'd spoken and I'd forgotten him altogether. I had by that time spent quite a few years seeing any number of recently bereaved. They couldn't all stand out in sharp relief in the cluttered warehouse of memory.

Well, I'd see him soon enough. My client hadn't said whom he suspected, and I hadn't asked, but it stood to reason that Barbara's husband headed the list. London wouldn't be all that upset by the possibility that she'd died at the hands of someone he didn't even know, some friend or lover who meant nothing to him. But for her to have been killed by her own husband, a man London knew, a man who had been present years later at London's wife's funeral –

There's a phone in my room but the calls go through the switchboard, and it's a nuisance placing them that way even when I don't care if the operator listens in. I went down to the lobby and dialed my client's number in Hastings. He answered on the third ring.

'Scudder,' I said. 'I could use a picture of your daughter. Anything as long as it's a good likeness.'

'I took albums full of pictures. But most of them were of Barbara as a child. You would want a late photograph, I suppose?'

'As late as possible. How about a wedding picture?'

'Oh,' he said. 'Of course. There's a very good pictue of the two of them, it's in a silver frame on a table in the living room. I suppose I could have it copied. Do you want me to do that?'

'If it's not too much trouble.'

He asked if he should mail it and I suggested he bring it to his office Monday. I said I'd call and arrange to pick it up. He asked if I'd had a chance to begin the investigation yet and I told him I'd spent the day in Brooklyn. I tried him on a couple of names – Donald Gilman, Janice Corwin. Neither meant anything to him. He asked, tentatively, if I had any leads.

'It's a pretty cold trail,' I said.

I rang off without asking him who he suspected. I felt restless and went around the corner to Armstrong's. On the way I wished I'd taken the time to go back to my room for my coat. It was colder, and the wind had an edge to it.

I sat at the bar with a couple of nurses from Roosevelt. One of them, Terry, was just finishing up her third week in Pediatrics. 'I thought I'd like the duty,' she said, 'but I can't stand it. Little kids, it's so much worse when you lose one. Some of them are so brave it breaks your heart. I can't handle it, I really can't.'

Estrellita Rivera's image flashed in my mind and was gone. I didn't try to hold onto it. The other nurse, glass in hand, was saying that all in all she thought she preferred Sambucca to Amaretto. Or maybe it was the other way around.

I made it an early night.

SIX

Even if I couldn't recall meeting Douglas Ettinger, I had a picture of him in my mind. Tall and raw-boned, dark hair, pallid skin, knobby wrists, Lincolnesque features. A prominent Adam's apple.

I woke up Saturday morning with his image firmly in mind, as if it had been imprinted there during an unremembered dream. After a quick breakfast I went down to Penn Station and caught a Long Island Railroad local to Hicksville. A phone call to his house in Mineola had established that Ettinger was working at the Hicksville store, and it turned out to be a $2.25 cab ride from the station.

In an aisle lined with squash and racquet-ball equipment I asked a clerk if Mr Ettinger was in. 'I'm Doug Ettinger,' he said. 'What can I do for you?'

He was about five-eight, a chunky one-seventy. Tightly curled light brown hair with red highlights. The plump cheeks and alert brown eyes of a squirrel. Large white teeth, with the upper incisors slightly bucked, consistent with the squirrel image. He didn't look remotely familiar, nor did he bear any resemblance whatsoever to the rail-splitter caricature I'd dreamed up to play his part.

'My name's Scudder,' I said. 'I'd like to talk to you privately, if you don't mind. It's about your wife.'

His open face turned guarded. 'Karen?' he said. 'What about her?'

Christ. 'Your first wife.'

'Oh, Barbara,' he said. 'You had me going for a second there. The serious tone and all, and wanting to talk to me about my wife. I don't know what I thought. You're from the NYPD? Right this way, we can talk in the office.'

His was the smaller of the two desks in the office. Invoices and correspondence were arranged in neat piles on it. A Lucite

photo cube held pictures of a woman and several young children. He saw me looking at it and said, 'That's Karen there. And the kids.'

I picked up the cube, looked at a young woman with short blonde hair and a sunny smile. She was posed next to a car, with an expanse of lawn behind her. The whole effect was very suburban.

I replaced the photo cube and took the chair Ettinger indicated. He sat behind the desk, lit a cigarette with a disposable butane lighter. He knew the Icepick Prowler had been apprehended, knew too that the suspect denied any involvement in his first wife's murder. He assumed Pinell was lying, either out of memory failure or for some insane reason. When I explained that Pinells's alibi had been confirmed, he seemed unimpressed.

'It's been years,' he said. 'People can get mixed up on dates and you never know how accurate records are. He probably did it. I wouldn't take his word that he didn't.'

'The alibi looks sound.'

Ettinger shrugged. 'You'd be a better judge of that than I would. Still, I'm surprised that you guys are reopening the case. What can you expect to accomplish after all this time?'

'I'm not with the police, Mr Ettinger.'

'I thought you said –'

'I didn't bother to correct your impression. I used to be in the department. I'm private now.'

'You're working for somebody?'

'For your former father-in-law.'

'Charlie London hired you?' He frowned, taking it all in. 'Well, I guess it's his privilege. It's not going to bring Barbie back but I guess it's his right to feel like he's doing something. I remember he was talking about posting a reward after she was murdered. I don't know if he ever got around to it or not.'

'I don't believe he did.'

'So now he wants to spend a few dollars finding the real killer. Well, why not? He doesn't have much going for him since Helen died. His wife, Barbara's mother.'

'I know.'

'Maybe it'll do him good to have something he can take an interest in. Not that work doesn't keep him busy, but, well –' He flicked ashes from his cigarette. 'I don't know what help I can give you, Mr Scudder, but ask all the questions you want.'

I asked about Barbara's social contacts, her relationships with

38

people in the building. I asked about her job at the day-care center. He remembered Janice Corwin but couldn't supply her husband's name. 'The job wasn't that important,' he said. 'Basically it was something to get her out of the house, give her a focus for her energy. Oh, the money helped. I was dragging a briefcase around for the Welfare Department, which wasn't exactly the road to riches. But Barbie's job was temporary. She was going to give it up and stay home with the baby.'

The door opened. A teenage clerk started to enter the office, then stopped and stood there looking awkward. 'I'll be a few minutes, Sandy,' Ettinger told him. 'I'm busy right now.'

The boy withdrew, shutting the door. 'Saturday's always busy for us,' Ettinger said. 'I don't want to rush you, but I'm needed out there.'

I asked him some more questions. His memory wasn't very good, and I could understand why. He'd had one life torn up and had had to create a new one, and it was easier to do so if he dwelled on the first life as little as possible. There were no children from that first union to tie him into relations with in-laws. He could leave his marriage to Barbara in Brooklyn, along with his caseworker's files and all the trappings of that life. He lived in the suburbs now and drove a car and mowed a lawn and lived with his kids and his blonde wife. Why sit around remembering a tenement apartment in Boerum Hill?

'Funny,' he said. 'I can't begin to think of anyone we knew who might be capable of … doing what was done to Barbie. But one other thing I could never believe was that she'd let a stranger into the apartment.'

'She was careful about that sort of thing?'

'She was always on guard. Wyckoff Street wasn't the kind of neighborhood she grew up in, although she found it comfortable enough. Of course we weren't going to stay there forever.' His glance flicked to the photo cube, as if he was seeing Barbara standing next to a car and in front of a lawn. 'But she got spooked by the other icepick killings.'

'Oh?'

'Not at first. When he killed the woman in Sheepshead Bay, though, that's when it got to her. Because it was the first time he'd struck in Brooklyn, you see. It freaked her a little.'

'Because of the location? Sheepshead Bay's a long ways from Boerum Hill.'

'But it was Brooklyn. And there was something else, I think, because I remember she identified pretty strongly with the

woman who got killed. I must have known why but I can't remember. Anyway, she got nervous. She told me she had the feeling she was being watched.'

'Did you mention that to the police?'

'I don't think so.' He lowered his eyes, lit another cigarette. 'I'm sure I didn't. I thought at the time that it was part of being pregnant. Like craving odd foods, that sort of thing. Pregnant women get fixated on strange things.' His eyes rose to meet mine. 'Besides, I didn't want to think about it. Just a day or two before the murder she was talking about how she wanted me to get a police lock for the door. You know those locks with a steel bar braced against the door so it can't be forced?'

I nodded.

'Well, we didn't get a lock like that. Not that it would have made any difference because the door wasn't forced. I wondered why she would let anyone in, as nervous as she was, but it was daytime, after all, and people aren't as suspicious in the daytime. A man could pretend to be a plumber or from the gas company or something. Isn't that how the Boston Strangler operated?'

'I think it was something like that.'

'But if it was actually someone she knew –'

'There are some questions I have to ask.'

'Sure.'

'Is it possible your wife was involved with anyone?'

'Involved with – you mean having an affair?'

'That sort of thing.'

'She was pregnant,' he said, as if that answered the question. When I didn't say anything he said, 'We were very happy together. I'm sure she wasn't seeing anyone.'

'Did she often have visitors when you were out?'

'She might have had a friend over. I didn't check up on her. We trusted each other.'

'She left her job early that day.'

'She did that sometimes. She had an easygoing relationship with the woman she worked for.'

'You said you trusted each other. Did she trust you?'

'What are you driving at?'

'Did she ever accuse you of having affairs with other women?'

'Jesus, who've you been talking to? Oh, I bet I know where this is coming from. Sure. We had a couple of arguments that somebody must have heard.'

'Oh?'

'I told you women get odd ideas when they're pregnant. Like food cravings. Barbie got it into her head that I was making it with some of my cases. I was dragging my ass through tenements in Harlem and the South Bronx, filling out forms and trying not to gag on the smell and dodging the crap they throw off the roof at you, and she was accusing me of getting it on with all of those damsels in distress. I came to think of it as a pregnancy neurosis. I'm not Mr Irresistible in the first place, and I was so turned off by what I saw in those hovels that I had trouble performing at home some of the time, let alone being turned on while I was on the job. The hell, you were a cop, I don't have to tell you the kind of thing I saw every day.'

'So you weren't having an affair?'

'Didn't I just tell you that?'

'And you weren't romancing anybody else? A woman in the neighborhood, for example?'

'Certainly not. Did somebody say I was?'

I ignored the question. 'You remarried about three years after your wife died, Mr Ettinger. Is that right?'

'A little less than three years.'

'When did you meet your present wife?'

'About a year before I married her. Maybe more than that, maybe fourteen months. It was in the spring, and we had a June wedding.'

'How did you meet?'

'Mutual friends. We were at a party, although we didn't pay any attention to each other at the time, and then a friend of mine had both of us over for dinner, and –' He broke off abruptly. 'She wasn't one of my ADC cases in the South Bronx, if that's what you're getting at. And she never lived in Brooklyn, either. Jesus, I'm stupid!'

'Mr Ettinger –'

'I'm a suspect, aren't I? Jesus, how could I sit here and not have it occur to me? I'm a suspect, for Christ's sake.'

'There's a routine I have to follow in order to pursue an investigation, Mr Ettinger.'

'Does he think I did it? London? Is that what this whole thing is about?'

'Mr London hasn't told me who he does or doesn't suspect. If he's got any specific suspicions, he's keeping them to himself.'

'Well, isn't that decent of him.' He ran a hand over his forehead. 'Are we about through now, Scudder? I told you we're busy on Saturdays. We get a lot of people who work hard all

week and Saturday's when they want to think about sports. So if I've answered all your questions –'

'You arrived home about six thirty the day your wife was murdered.'

'That sounds about right. I'm sure it's in a police report somewhere.'

'Can you account for your time that afternoon?'

He stared at me. 'We're talking about something that happened nine years ago,' he said. 'I can't distinguish one day of knocking on doors from another. Do you remember what *you* did that afternoon?'

'No, but it was a less significant day in my life. You'd remember if you took any time away from your work.'

'I didn't. I spent the whole day working on my cases. And it was whatever time I said it was when I got back to Brooklyn. Six thirty sounds about right.' He wiped his forehead again. 'But you can't ask me to prove any of this, can you? I probably filed a report but they only keep those things for a few years. I forget whether it's three years or five years, but it's certainly not nine years. Those files get cleaned out on a regular basis.'

'I'm not asking for proof.'

'I didn't kill her, for God's sake. Look at me. Do I look like a killer?'

'I don't know what killers look like. I was just reading the other day about a thirteen-year-old boy who shot two women behind the ear. I don't know what he looks like, and I don't imagine he looks like a killer.' I took a blank memo slip from his desk, wrote a number on it. 'This is my hotel,' I said. 'You might think of something. You never know what you might remember.'

'I don't want to remember anything.'

I got to my feet. So did he.

'That's not my life anymore,' he said. 'I live in the suburbs and I sell skis and sweatsuits. I went to Helen's funeral because I couldn't think of a decent way to skip it. I should have skipped it. I –'

I said, 'Take it easy, Ettinger. You're angry and you're scared but you don't have to be either one. Of course you're a suspect. Who would investigate a woman's murder without checking out the husband? When's the last time you heard of an investigation like that?' I put a hand on his shoulder. 'Somebody killed her,' I said, 'and it may have been somebody she knew. I probably

won't be able to find out much of anything but I'm giving it my best shot. If you think of anything, call me. That's all.'

'You're right,' he said. 'I got angry. I –'

I told him to forget it. I found my own way out.

SEVEN

I read a paper on the train ride back to the city. A feature article discussed the upturn in muggings and suggested ways for the reader to make himself a less attractive target. Walk in pairs and groups, the reporter advised. Stick to well-lighted streets. Walk near the curb, not close to buildings. Move quickly and give an impression of alertness. Avoid confrontations. Muggers want to size you up and see if you'll be easy. They ask you the time, ask for directions. Don't let them take advantage of you.

It's wonderful how the quality of urban life keeps getting better. *'Pardon me, sir, but could you tell me how to get to the Empire State Building?'* *'Fuck off, you creep.'* Manners for a modern city.

The train took forever. It always felt a little strange going out to Long Island. Hicksville was nowhere near where Anita and the boys lived but Long Island is Long Island and I got the vaguely uncomfortable feeling I always get when I go there. I was glad to get to Penn Station.

By then it was time for a drink, and I had a quick one in a commuters' bar right there in the station. Saturday might be a busy day for Douglas Ettinger but it was a slow one for the bartender at the Iron Horse. All his weekday customers must have been out in Hicksville buying pup tents and basketball shoes.

The sun was out when I hit the street. I walked across Thirty-fourth, then headed up Fifth to the library. Nobody asked me what time it was, or how to get to the Holland Tunnel.

Before I went into the library I stopped at a pay phone and called Lynn London. Her father had given me her number and I checked my notebook and dialed it. I got an answering machine with a message that began by repeating the last four digits of the number, announced that no one could come to the phone, and

44

invited me to leave my name. The voice was female, very precise, just the slightest bit nasal, and I supposed it belonged to Barbara's sister. I rang off without leaving a message.

In the library I got the same Polk directory for Brooklyn that I'd used earlier. This time I looked up a different building on Wyckoff Street. It had held four apartments then, and one of them had been rented to a Mr and Mrs Edward Corwin.

That gave me a way to spend the afternoon. In a bar on Forty-first and Madison I ordered a cup of coffee and a shot of bourbon to pour into it and changed a dollar into dimes. I started on the Manhattan book, where I found two Edward Corwins, an E. Corwin, an E. J. Corwin and an E. V. Corwin. When none of those panned out I used Directory Assistance, getting the Brooklyn listings first, then moving on to Queens, the Bronx and Staten Island. Some of the numbers I dialed were busy, and I had to try them four or five times before I got through. Others didn't answer.

I wound up getting more dimes and trying all the J. Corwins in the five boroughs. Somewhere in the course of this I had a second cup of coffee with a second shot of bourbon in it. I used up quite a few dimes to no discernible purpose, but most investigatory work is like that. If she just roots around enough, even a blind sow gets an acorn now and then. Or so they tell me.

By the time I left the bar, some two-thirds of my phone numbers had check marks next to them indicating I'd reached the party and he or she was not the Corwin I was looking for. I'd call the rest of them in due course if I had to, but I didn't feel very hopeful about them. Janice Corwin had closed a business and given up an apartment. She might have moved to Seattle while she was at it. Or she and her husband could be somewhere in Westchester or Jersey or Connecticut, or out in Hicksville pricing tennis rackets. There was a limit to how much walking my fingers could do, in the white or yellow pages.

I went back to the library. I knew when she'd closed up shop at the Happy Hours Child Care Center; I'd learned that much from her landlord. Had she and her husband moved out of Boerum Hill at about the same time?

I worked year by year through the Polk directories and found the year the Corwins dropped out of the brick building on Wyckoff Street. The timing was right. She had probably closed the day-care center as a prelude to moving. Maybe they'd gone to the suburbs, or his company transferred him to Atlanta. Or they split up and went separate ways.

45

I put the directory back, then got an intelligent thought for a change and went back to reclaim it. There were three other tenants in the building who'd remained there for a few years after the Corwins moved out. I copied their names in my notebook.

This time I made my calls from a bar on Forty-second Street, and I bypassed the Manhattan book and went straight to Brooklyn information. I got lucky right away with the Gordon Pomerances, who had stayed in Brooklyn when the Wyckoff Street building was sold out from under them. They'd moved a short mile to Carroll Street.

Mrs Pomerance answered the phone. I gave my name and said I was trying to reach the Corwins. She knew at once who I was talking about but had no idea how I could reach them.

'We didn't keep in touch. He was a nice fellow, Eddie, and he used to bring the children over for dinner after she moved out, but then when he moved we lost contact. It's been so many years. I'm sure we had his address at one point but I can't even remember the city he moved to. It was in California, I think Southern California.'

'But she moved out first?'

'You didn't know that? She left him, left him flat with the two kids. She closed the whatchamacallit, the day-care center, and the next thing you know he's got to find a day-care center for his own children. I'm sorry, but I can't imagine a mother walking out on her own children.'

'Do you know where she might have gone?'

'Greenwich Village, I suppose. To pursue her art. Among other things.'

'Her art?'

'She fancied herself a sculptor. I never saw her work so for all I know she may have had some talent. I'd be surprised if she did, though. There was a woman who had everything. A nice apartment, a husband who was an awfully sweet guy, two beautiful children, and she even had a business that wasn't doing too badly. And she walked away from it, turned her back and walkd away.'

I tried a long shot. 'Did you happen to know a friend of hers named Barbara Ettinger?'

'I didn't know her that well. What was that name? Ettinger? Why is that name familiar to me?'

'A Barbara Ettinger was murdered down the block from where you lived.'

46

'Just before we moved in. Of course. I remember now. I never knew her, naturally, because as I said it was just before we moved in. She was a friend of the Corwins?'

'She worked for Mrs Corwin.'

'Were they that way?'

'What way?'

'There was a lot of talk about the murder. It made me nervous about moving in. My husband and I told each other we didn't have to worry about lightning striking twice in the same place, but privately I was still worried. Then those killings just stopped, didn't they?'

'Yes. You never knew the Ettingers?'

'No, I told you.'

An artist in Greenwich Village. A sculptor. Of the J. Corwins I'd been unable to reach, had any lived in the Village? I didn't think so.

I said, 'Would you happen to remember Mrs Corwin's maiden name?'

'Remember it? I don't think I ever knew it in the first place. Why?'

'I was thinking she might have resumed it if she's pursuing an artistic career.'

'I'm sure she did. Artistic career or not, she'd want her own name back. But I couldn't tell you what it was.'

'Of course she could have remarried by now –'

'Oh, I wouldn't count on it.'

'I beg your pardon?'

'I don't think she remarried,' Mrs Pomerance said. There was a sharpness to her tone and I wondered at it. I asked her what made her say that.

'Put it this way,' she said. 'Sculpture or no sculpture, she'd probably live in Greenwich Village.'

'I don't understand.'

'You don't?' She clicked her tongue, impatient with my obtuseness. 'She left her husband – *and* two children – but not to run off with another man. She left him for another woman.'

Janice Corwin's maiden name was Keane. It took a subway ride to Chambers Street and a couple of hours in various offices of the Department of Records and Informations Services to supply this kernel of information. Most of the time was spent getting clearance. I kept needing the permission of someone who didn't come in on Saturdays.

I tried marriage licenses first, and when that failed to pan out I had a shot at birth certificates. Mrs Pomerance had been a little hazy on the names and ages of the Corwin children, but she was pretty sure the youngest's name was Kelly and that she'd been five or six when her mother left. She'd been seven, it turned out; she'd be around fifteen now. Her father was Edward Francis Corwin, her mother the former Janice Elizabeth Keane.

I wrote the name in my notebook with a sense of triumph. Not that there was much likelihood that it would slip my mind, but as a symbol of accomplishment. I couldn't prove that I was an inch closer to Barbara Ettinger's killer than I'd been when Charles London sat down across from me at Armstrong's, but I'd done some detecting and it felt good. It was plodding work, generally pointless work, but it let me use muscles I didn't get to use all that often and they tingled from the exertion.

A couple of blocks from there I found a Blarney Stone with a steam table. I had a hot pastrami sandwich and drank a beer or two with it. There was a big color set mounted over the bar. It was tuned to one of those sports anthology shows they have on Saturday afternoons. A couple of guys were doing something with logs in a fast-moving stream. Riding them, I think. Nobody in the place was paying much attention to their efforts. By the time I was done with my sandwich the log-riders were through and a stock-car race had replaced them. Nobody paid any attention to the stock cars, either.

I called Lynn London again. This time when her machine picked up I waited for the beep and left my name and number. Then I checked the phone book.

No Janice Keanes in Manhattan. Half a dozen Keanes with the initial J. Plenty of other variations of the name – Keene, Keen, Kean. I thought of that old radio show, *Mr Keene, Tracer of Lost Persons*. I couldn't remember how he spelled it.

I tried all the J. Keanes. I got two that failed to answer, one persistent busy signal, and three people who denied knowing a Janice Keane. The busy signal lived on East Seventy-third Street and I decided that was no address for a lesbian sculptor from Boerum Hill. I dialed Directory Assistance, all set to go through my routine again for the other four boroughs, but something stopped me.

She was in Manhattan. Damn it, I knew she was in Manhattan.

I asked for a Janice Keane in Manhattan, spelled the last name, waited a minute, and was told the only listing in Manhattan

48

under that name and with that spelling was unpublished. I hung up, called back again to get a different operator, and went through the little ritual that a cop uses to obtain an unlisted number. I identified myself as Detective Francis Fitzroy, of the Eighteenth Precinct. I called it the One-Eight Precinct because, although cops don't invariably talk that way, civilians invariably think they do.

I got the address while I was at it. She was on Lispenard Street, and that was a perfectly logical place for a sculptor to be living, and not too long a walk from where I was.

I had another dime in my hand. I put it back in my pocket and went back to the bar. The stock cars had given way to the feature of the program, a couple of black junior-middleweights topping a fight card in some unlikely place. Phoenix, I think it was. I don't know what a junior-middleweight is. They've added all these intermediate weight classes so that they can have more championship fights. Some of the patrons who'd passed up the log-rollers and the stock cars were watching these two boys hit each other, which was something they weren't doing very often. I sat through a few rounds and drank some coffee with bourbon in it.

Because I thought it would help if I had some idea how I was going to approach this woman. I'd been tracking her spoor through books and files and phone wires, as if she held the secret to the Ettinger murder, and for all I knew Barbara Ettinger was nothing to her beyond a faceless lump who put the alphabet blocks away when the kids were done playing with them.

Or she was Barbara's best friend. Or her lover – I remembered Mrs Pomerance's questions: 'She was a friend of the Corwins? Were they that way?'

Maybe she had killed Barbara. Could they have both left the day-care center early? Was that even possible, let alone likely?

I was spinning my wheels and I knew it but I let them spin for a while anyway. On the television screen, the kid with the white stripe on his trunks was finally beginning to use his jab to set up right hands to the body. It didn't look as though he was going to take his man out in the handful of rounds remaining, not like that, but he seemed a safe shot for the decision. He was wearing his opponent down, grinding away at him. Jabbing with the left, hooking the right hand to the rib section. The other boy couldn't seem to find a defense that worked.

I knew how both of them felt.

I thought about Douglas Ettinger. I decided he didn't kill his

wife, and I tried to figure out how I knew that, and decided I knew it the same way I'd known Janice Keane was in Manhattan. Chalk it up to divine inspiration.

Ettinger was right, I decided. Louis Pinell killed Barbara Ettinger, just as he'd killed the other seven women. Barbara had thought some nut was stalking her and she was right.

Then why'd she let the nut into her apartment?

In the tenth round, the kid who'd been getting his ribs barbecued summoned up some reserve of strength and put a couple of combinations together. He had the kid with the stripe on his trunks reeling, but the flurry wasn't enough to end it and the kid with the stripe hung on and got the decision. The crowd booed. I don't know what fight they thought they were watching. The crowd in Phoenix, that is. My companions in the Blarney Stone weren't that involved emotionally.

The hell with it. I went and made my phone call.

It rang four or five times before she answered it. I said, 'Janice Keane, please,' and she said she was Janice Keane.

I said, 'My name's Matthew Scudder, Ms Keane. I'd like to ask you some questions.'

'Oh?'

'About a woman named Barbara Ettinger.'

'Jesus.' A pause. 'What about her?'

'I'm investigating her death. I'd like to come over and talk with you.'

'You're investigating her death? That was ages ago. It must have been ten years.'

'Nine years.'

'I thought it was the Mounties who never gave up. I never heard that about New York's Finest. You're a policeman?'

I was about to say yes, but heard myself say, 'I used to be.'

'What are you now?'

'A private citizen. I'm working for Charles London. Mrs Ettinger's father.'

'That's right, her maiden name was London.' She had a good telephone voice, low-pitched and throaty. 'I can't make out why you're starting an investigation now. And what could I possibly contribute to it?'

'Maybe I could explain that in person,' I said. 'I'm just a few minutes away from you now. Would it be all right if I come over?'

'Jesus. What's today, Saturday? And what time is it? I've been

50

working and I tend to lose track of the time. I've got six o'clock. Is that right?'

'That's right.'

'I'd better fix something to eat. And I have to clean up. Give me an hour, okay?'

'I'll be there at seven.'

'You know the address?' I read it off as I'd received it from Information. 'That's it. That's between Church and Broadway, and you ring the bell and then stand at the curb so I can see you and I'll throw the key down. Ring two long and three short, okay?'

'Two long and three short.'

'Then I'll know it's you. Not that you're anything to me but a voice on the phone. How'd you get this number? It's supposed to be unlisted.'

'I used to be a cop.'

'Right, so you said. So much for unlisted numbers, huh? Tell me your name again.'

'Matthew Scudder.'

She repeated it. Then she said, 'Barbara Ettinger. Oh, if you knew how that name takes me back. I have a feeling I'm going to be sorry I answered the phone. Well, Mr Scudder, I'll be seeing you in an hour.'

EIGHT

Lispenard is a block below Canal Street, which puts it in that section known as Tribeca. Tribeca is a geographical acronym for *Triangle Below Canal*, just as SoHo derives from *South of Houston* Street. There was a time when artists began moving into the blocks south of the Village, living in violation of the housing code in spacious and inexpensive lofts. The code had since been modified to permit residential loft dwelling and SoHo had turned chic and expensive, which led loft seekers further south of Tribeca. The rents aren't cheap there either now, but the streets still have the deserted quality of SoHo ten or twelve years ago.

I stuck to a well-lighted street. I walked near the curb, not close to buildings, and I did my best to move quickly and give an impression of alertness. Confrontations were easily avoided in those empty streets.

Janice Keane's address turned out to be a six-story loft building, a narrow structure fitted in between two taller, wider and more modern buildings. It looked cramped, like a little man on a crowded subway. Floor-to-ceiling windows ran the width of the facade on each of its floors. On the ground floor, shuttered for the weekend, was a wholesaler of plumber's supplies.

I went into a claustrophobic hallway, found a bell marked Keane, rang it two long and three short. I went out to the sidewalk, stood at the curb looking up at all those windows.

She called down from one of them, asking my name. I couldn't see anything in that light. I gave my name, and something small whistled down through the air and jangled on the pavement beside me. 'Fifth floor,' she said. 'There's an elevator.'

There was indeed, and it could have accommodated a grand piano. I rode it to the fifth floor and stepped out into a spacious loft. There were a lot of plants, all deep green and thriving, and

relatively little in the way of furniture. The doors were oak, buffed to a high sheen. The walls were exposed brick. Overhead track lighting provided illumination.

She said, 'You're right on time. The place is a mess but I won't apologize. There's coffee.'

'If it's no trouble.'

'None at all. I'm going to have a cup myself. Just let me steer you to a place to sit and I'll be a proper hostess. Milk? Sugar?'

'Just black.'

She left me in an area with a couch and a pair of chairs grouped around a high-pile rug with an abstract design. A couple of eight-foot-tall bookcases reached a little more than halfway to the ceiling and helped screen the space from the rest of the loft. I walked over to the window and looked down at Lispenard Street but there wasn't a whole lot to see.

There was one piece of sculpture in the room and I was standing in front of it when she came back with the coffee. It was the head of a woman. Her hair was a nest of snakes, her face a high-cheekboned, broad-browed mask of unutterable disappointment.

'That's my Medusa,' she said. 'Don't meet her eyes. Her gaze turns men to stone.'

'She's very good.'

'Thank you.'

'She looks so disappointed.'

'That's the quality,' she agreed. 'I didn't know that until I'd finished her, and then I saw it for myself. You've got a pretty good eye.'

'For disappointment, anyway.'

She was an attractive woman. Medium height, a little more well-fleshed than was strictly fashionable. She wore faded Levi's and a slate-blue chamois shirt with the sleeves rolled to the elbows. Her face was heart-shaped, its contours accentuated by a sharply defined widow's peak. Her hair, dark brown salted with gray, hung almost to her shoulders. Her gray eyes were large and well-spaced, and a touch of mascara around them was the only makeup she wore.

We sat in a pair of chairs at right angles to one another and set our coffee mugs on a table made from a section of tree trunk and a slab of slate. She asked if I'd had trouble finding her address and I said I hadn't. Then she said, 'Well, shall we talk about Barb Ettinger? Maybe you can start by telling me why you're interested in her after all these years.'

53

She'd missed the media coverage of Louis Pinell's arrest. It was news to her that the Icepick Prowler was in custody, so it was also news that her former employee had been killed by someone else.

'So for the first time you're looking for a killer with a motive,' she said. 'If you'd looked at the time –'

'It might have been easier. Yes.'

'And it might be easier now just to look the other way. I don't remember her father. I must have met him, after the murder if not before, but I don't have any recollection of him. I remember her sister. Have you met her?'

'Not yet.'

'I don't know what she's like now, but she struck me as a snotty little bitch. But I didn't know her well, and anyway it was nine years ago. That's what I keep coming back to. Everything was nine years ago.'

'How did you meet Barbara Ettinger?'

'We ran into each other in the neighborhood. Shopping at the Grand Union, going to the candy store for a paper. Maybe I mentioned that I was running a day-care center. Maybe she heard it from someone else. Either way, one morning she walked into the Happy Hours and asked if I needed any help.'

'And you hired her right away?'

'I told her I couldn't pay her much. The place was just about making expenses. I started it for a dumb reason – there was no convenient day-care center in the neighborhood, and I needed a place to dump my own kids, so I found a partner and we opened the Happy Hours, and instead of dumping my kids I was watching them and everybody else's, and of course my partner came to her senses about the time the ink was dry on the lease, and she backed out and I was running the whole show myself. I told Barb I needed her but I couldn't afford her, and she said she mostly wanted something to do and she'd work cheap. I forget what I paid her but it wasn't a whole lot.'

'Was she good at her work?'

'It was essentially baby-sitting. There's a limit to how good you can be at it.' She thought for a moment. 'It's hard to remember. Nine years ago, so I was twenty-nine at the time, and she was a few years younger.'

'She was twenty-six when she died.'

'Jesus, that's not very old, is it?' She closed her eyes, wincing at early death. 'She was a big help to me, and I guess she was

good enough at what she did. She seemed to enjoy it most of the time. She'd have enjoyed it more if she'd been a more contented woman generally.'

'She was discontented?'

'I don't know if that's the right word.' She turned to glance at her bust of Medusa. 'Disappointed? You got the feeling that Barb's life wasn't quite what she'd had in mind for herself. Everything was okay, her husband was okay, her apartment was okay, but she'd hoped for something more than just okay, and she didn't have it.'

'Someone described her as restless.'

'Restless.' She tasted the word. 'That fits her well enough. Of course that was a time for women to be restless. Sexual roles were pretty confused and confusing.'

'Aren't they still?'

'Maybe they always will be. But I think things are a little more settled now than they were for a while there. She was restless, though. Definitely restless.'

'Her marriage was a disappointment?'

'Most of them are, aren't they? I don't suppose it would have lasted, but we'll never know, will we? Is he still with the Welfare Department?'

I brought her up to date on Douglas Ettinger.

'I didn't know him too well,' she said. 'Barb seemed to feel he wasn't good enough for her. At least I got that impression. His background was low-rent compared to hers. Not that she grew up with the Vanderbilts, but I gather she had a proper suburban childhood and a fancy education. He worked long hours and he had a dead-end job. And yes, there was one other thing wrong with him.'

'What was that?'

'He fucked around.'

'Did he really or did she just think so?'

'He made a pass at me. Oh, it was no big deal, just a casual, offhand sort of proposition. I was not greatly interested. The man looked like a chipmunk. I wasn't much flattered, either, because one sensed he did this sort of thing a lot and that it didn't mean I was irresistible. Of course I didn't say anything to Barb, but she had evidence of her own. She caught him once at a party, necking in the kitchen with the hostess. And I gather he was dipping into his welfare clients.'

'What about his wife?'

'I gather he was dipping into her, too. I don't –'

'Was she having an affair with anybody?'

She leaned forward, took hold of her coffee mug. Her hands were large for a woman, her nails clipped short. I suppose long nails would be an impossible hindrance for a sculptor.

She said, 'I was paying her a very low salary. You could almost call it a token salary. I mean, high-school kids got a better hourly rate for baby-sitting, and Barb didn't even get to raid the refrigerator. So if she wanted time off, all she did was take it.'

'Did she take a lot of time off?'

'Not all that much, but I had the impression that she was taking an occasional afternoon or part of an afternoon for something more exciting than a visit to the dentist. A woman has a different air about her when she's off to meet a lover.'

'Did she have that air the day she was killed?'

'I wished you'd asked me nine years ago. I'd have had a better chance of remembering. I know she left early that day but I don't have any memory of the details. You think she met a lover and he killed her?'

'I don't think anything special at this stage. Her husband said she was nervous about the Icepick Prowler.'

'I don't think . . . wait a minute. I remember thinking about that afterward, after she'd been killed. That she'd been talking about the danger of living in the city. I don't know if she said anything specific about the Icepick killings, but there was something about feeling as though she was being watched or followed. I interpreted it as a kind of premonition of her own death.'

'Maybe it was.'

'Or maybe she was being watched and followed. What is it they say? "Paranoiacs have enemies, too." Maybe she really sensed something.'

'Would she let a stranger into the apartment?'

'I wondered about that at the time. If she was on guard to begin with –'

She broke off suddenly. I asked her what was the matter.

'Nothing.'

'I'm a stranger and you let me into your apartment.'

'It's a loft. As if it makes a difference. I –'

I took out my wallet and tossed it onto the table between us. 'Look through it,' I said. 'There's an ID in it. It'll match the name I gave you over the phone, and I think there's something with a photograph on it.'

'That's not necessary.'

'Look it over anyway. You're not going to be very useful as a subject of interrogation if you're anxious about getting killed. The ID won't prove I'm not a rapist or a murderer, but rapists and murderers don't usually give you their right names ahead of time. Go ahead, pick it up.'

She went through the wallet quickly, then handed it back to me. I returned it to my pocket. 'That's a lousy picture of you,' she said. 'But I guess it's you, all right. I don't think she'd let a stranger into her apartment. She'd let a lover in, though. Or a husband.'

'You think her husband killed her?'

'Married people always kill one another. Sometimes it takes them fifty years.'

'Any idea who her lover may have been?'

'It may not have been just one person. I'm just guessing, but she could have had an itch to experiment. And she was pregnant so it was safe.'

She laughed. I asked her what was so funny.

'I was trying to think where she would have met someone. A neighbor, maybe, or a male half of some couple she and her husband saw socially. It's not as though she could have met men on the job. We had plenty of males there, but unfortunately none of them were over eight years old.'

'Not very promising.'

'Except that's not altogether true. Sometimes fathers would bring the kids in, or pick them up after work. There are situations more conducive to flirtation, but I had daddies come on to me while they collected their children, and it probably happened to Barbara. She was very attractive, you know. And she didn't wrap herself up in an old Mother Hubbard when she came to work at the Happy Hours. She had a good figure and she dressed to show it off.'

The conversation went on a little longer before I got a handle on the question. Then I said, 'Did you and Barbara ever become lovers?'

I was watching her eyes when I asked the question, and they widened in response. 'Jesus Christ,' she said.

I waited her out.

'I'm just wondering where the question came from,' she said. 'Did somebody say we were lovers? Or am I an obvious dyke or something?'

'I was told you left your husband for another woman.'

'Well, that's close. I left my husband for thirty or forty

57

reasons, I suppose. And the first relationship I had after I left him *was* with a woman. Who told you? Not Doug Ettinger. He'd moved out of the neighborhood before that particular shit hit the fan. Unless he happened to talk to somebody. Maybe he and Eddie got together and cried on each other's shoulder about how women are no good, they either get stabbed or they run off with each other. Was it Doug?'

'No. It was a woman who lived in your building on Wyckoff Street.'

'Someone in the building. Oh, it must have been Maisie! Except that's not her name. Give me a minute. Mitzi! It was Mitzi Pomerance, wasn't it?'

'I didn't get her first name. I just spoke with her on the telephone.'

'Little Mitzi Pomerance. Are they still married? Of course, they'd have to be. Unless he left, but nothing would propel her away from hearth and home. She'd insist her marriage was heaven even if it meant systematically denying every negative emotion that ever threatened to come to the surface. The worst thing about going back to visit the kids was the look on that twit's face when we passed on the stairs.' She sighed and shook her head at the memory. 'I never had anything going with Barbara. Strangely enough, I never had anything going with anybody, male or female, before I split with Eddie. And the woman I got together with afterward was the first woman I ever slept with in my life.'

'But you were attracted to Barbara Ettinger.'

'Was I? I recognized that she was attractive. That's not the same thing. Was I specifically attracted to her?' She weighed the notion. 'Maybe,' she conceded. 'Not on any conscious level, I don't think. And when I did begin to consider the possibility that I might find it, oh, interesting to go to bed with a woman, I don't think I had any particular woman in mind. As a matter of fact, I don't even think I entertained the fantasy while Barbara was alive.'

'I have to ask these personal questions.'

'You don't have to apologize. Jesus, Mitzi Pomerance. I'll bet she's fat, I'll bet she's a plump little piglet by now. But you only spoke to her over the phone.'

'That's right.'

'Is she still living in the same place? She must be. You wouldn't get them out of there with a crowbar.'

'Somebody did. A buyer converted the house to one-family.'

'They must have been sick. Did they stay in the neighborhood?'

'More or less. They moved to Carroll Street.'

'Well, I hope they're happy. Mitzi and Gordon.' She leaned forward, searched my face with her gray eyes. 'You drink,' she said. 'Right?'

'Pardon?'

'You're a drunk, aren't you?'

'I suppose you could call me a drinking man.'

The words sounded stiff, even to me. They hung in the air for a moment and then her laughter cut in, full-bodied and rich. ' "I suppose you could call me a drinking man." Jesus, that's wonderful. Well, I suppose you could call me a drinking woman, Mr Scudder. People have called me a good deal worse, and it's been a long day and a dry one. How about a little something to cut the dust?'

'That's not a bad idea.'

'What'll it be?'

'Do you have bourbon?'

'I don't think so.' The bar was behind a pair of sliding doors in one of the bookcases. 'Scotch or vodka,' she announced.

'Scotch.'

'Rocks? Water? What?'

'Just straight.'

'The way God made it, huh?' She brought back a pair of rocks glasses filled about halfway, one with Scotch, the other with vodka. She gave me mine, looked into her own. She had the air of someone trying to select a toast, but evidently she couldn't think of one. 'Oh, what the hell,' she said, and took a drink.

'Who do you think killed her?'

'Too early to tell. It could have been somebody I haven't heard of yet. Or it could have been Pinell. I'd like ten minutes with him.'

'You think you could refresh his memory?'

I shook my head. 'I think I might get some sense of him. So much detection is intuition. You gather details and soak up impressions, and then the answer pops into your mind out of nowhere. It's not like Sherlock Holmes, at least it never was for me.'

'You make it sound almost as though there's a psychic element to the process.'

'Well, I can't read palms or see the future. But maybe there is.'

59

I sipped Scotch. It had that medicinal taste that Scotch has but I
didn't mind it as much as I usually do. It was one of the heavier
Scotches, dark and peaty. Teacher's, I think it was. 'I want to get
out to Sheepshead Bay next,' I said.

'Now?'

'Tomorrow. That's where the fourth Icepick killing took
place, and that was the one that's supposed to have spooked
Barbara Ettinger.'

'You think the same person –'

'Louis Pinell admits to the Sheepshead Bay murder. Of course
that doesn't prove anything, either. I'm not sure why I want to
go out there. I guess I want to talk to somebody who was on the
scene, someone who saw the body. There were some physical
details about the killings that were held back from the press
coverage, and they were duplicated in Barbara's murder. Imperfectly duplicated, and I want to know if there was any parallel in
the other Brooklyn homicide.'

'And if there was, what would it prove? That there was a
second killer, a maniac who confined himself to Brooklyn?'

'And who conveniently stopped at two killings. It's possible. It
wouldn't even rule out someone with a motive for killing
Barbara. Say her husband decided to kill her, but he realized the
Icepick Prowler hadn't been to Brooklyn yet, so he killed some
stranger in Sheepshead Bay first to establish a pattern.'

'Do people do things like that?'

'There's nothing you can imagine that somebody hasn't done
at one time or another. Maybe somebody had a motive for
killing the woman in Sheepshead Bay. Then he was worried that
the murder would stand out as the only one of its kind in
Brooklyn, so he went after Barbara. Or maybe that was just his
excuse. Maybe he killed a second time because he'd found out
that he enjoyed it.'

'God.' She drank vodka. 'What was the physical detail?'

'You don't want to know about it.'

'You protecting the little woman from the awful truth?'

'The victims were stabbed through the eyes. An icepick, right
through the eyeballs.'

'Jesus. And the ... what did you call it? Imperfect duplication?'

'Barbara Ettinger just got it in one eye.'

'Like a wink.' She sat for a long moment, then looked down at
her glass and noticed that it was empty. She went to the bar and
came back with both bottles. After she'd filled our glasses she
left the bottles on the slate-topped table.

'I wonder why he would do a thing like that,' she said.

'That's another reason I'd like to see Pinell,' I said. 'To ask him.'

The conversation turned this way and that. At one point she asked whether she should call me Matt or Matthew. I told her it didn't matter to me. She said it mattered to her that I call her not Janice but Jan.

'Unless you're uncomfortable calling murder suspects by their first names.'

When I was a cop I learned always to call suspects by their first names. It gave you a certain amount of psychological leverage. I told her she wasn't a suspect.

'I was at the Happy Hours all that afternoon,' she said. 'Of course it would be hard to prove after all these years. At the time it would have been easy. Alibis must be harder to come by for people who live alone.'

'You live alone here?'

'Unless you count the cats. They're hiding somewhere. They steer clear of strangers. Showing them your ID wouldn't impress them much.'

'Real hard-liners.'

'Uh-huh. I've always lived alone. Since I left Eddie, that is. I've been in relationships but I always lived alone.'

'Unless we count the cats.'

'Unless we count the cats. I never thought at the time that I'd be living by myself for the next eight years. I thought a relationship with a woman might be different in some funda-mental way. See, back then was consciousness-raising time. I decided the problem was men.'

'And it wasn't?'

'Well, it may have been one of the problems. Women turned out to be another problem. For a while I decided I was one of those fortunate people who are capable of relationships with both sexes.'

'Just for a while?'

'Uh-huh. Because what I discovered next was that I may be capable of relationships with men and women, but what I mostly am is not very good at relationships.'

'Well, I can relate to that.'

'I figured you probably could. You live alone, don't you, Matthew?'

'For a while now.'

'Your sons are with your wife? I'm not psychic. There's a picture of them in your wallet.'

'Oh, that. It's an old picture.'

'They're handsome boys.'

'They're good kids, too.' I added a little Scotch to my glass. 'They live out in Syosset. They'll take the train in now and then and we catch a ball game together, or maybe a fight in the Garden.'

'They must enjoy that.'

'I know I enjoy it.'

'You must have moved out a while ago.'

I nodded. 'Around the time I left the cops.'

'Same reason?'

I shrugged.

'How come you quit the cops? Was it this stuff?'

'What stuff?'

She waved a hand at the bottles. 'You know. The booze.'

'Oh, hell, no,' I said. 'I wasn't even that heavy a hitter at the time. I just reached a point where I didn't feel like being a cop anymore.'

'What did it? Disillusionment? A lack of faith in the criminal justice system? Disgust with corruption?'

I shook my head. 'I lost my illusions early in the game and I never had much faith in the criminal justice system. It's a terrible system and the cops just do what they can. As far as corruption goes, I was never enough of an idealist to be bothered by it.'

'What then? Mid-life crisis?'

'You could call it that.'

'Well, we won't talk about it if you don't want to.'

We fell silent for a moment. She drank and then I drank, and then I put my glass down and said, 'Well, it's no secret. It's just not something I talk about a lot. I was in a tavern up in Washington Heights one night. It was a place where cops could drink on the arm. The owner liked having us around so you could run a tab and never be asked for payment. I had every right to be there. I was off-duty and I wanted to unwind a little before I drove back out to the island.'

Or maybe I wouldn't have gone home that night anyway. I didn't always. Sometimes I caught a few hours' sleep in a hotel room to save driving back and forth. Sometimes I didn't have to get a hotel room.

'Two punks held up the place,' I went on. 'They got what was

in the register and shot the bartender on the way out, shot him dead just for the hell of it. I ran out into the street after them. I was in plainclothes but of course I was carrying a gun. You always carry it.

'I emptied the gun at them. I got them both. I killed one of them and crippled the other. Left him paralyzed from the waist down. Two things he'll never do again are walk and fuck.'

I'd told this story before but this time I could feel it all happening again. Washington Heights is hilly and they'd taken off up an incline. I remembered bracing myself, holding the gun with both hands, firing uphill at them. Maybe it was the Scotch that was making the recollection so vivid. Maybe it was something I responded to in her big unwavering gray eyes.

'And because you killed one and crippled another –'

I shook my head. 'That wouldn't have bothered me. I'm only sorry I didn't kill them both. They murdered that bartender for no good reason on God's earth. I wouldn't lose a dime's worth of sleep over those two.'

She waited.

'One of the shots went wide,' I said. 'Shooting uphill at a pair of moving targets, hell, it's remarkable I scored as well as I did. I always shot Expert on the police range, but it's different when it's real.' I tried to draw my eyes away from hers but couldn't manage it. 'One shot missed, though, and it ricocheted off the pavement or something. Took a bad hop. And there was a little girl walking around or standing around, whatever the hell she was doing. She was only six years old. I don't know what the hell she was doing out at that hour.'

This time I looked away. 'The bullet went into her eye,' I said. 'The ricochet took off some of its steam so if it had been an inch to the side one way or the other it probably would have glanced off bone, but life's a game of inches, isn't it? There was no bone to get in the way and the bullet wound up in her brain and she died. Instantly.'

'God.'

'I didn't do anything wrong. There was a departmental investigation because that's standard procedure, and it was agreed unanimously that I hadn't done anything wrong. As a matter of fact I received a commendation. The child was Hispanic, Puerto Rican, Estrellita Rivera her name was, and sometimes the press gets on you when there's a minority group casualty like that, or you get static from community groups, but

there was none of that in this case. If I was anything I was a fast-acting hero cop who had a piece of bad luck.'

'And you quit the police force.'

The Scotch bottle was empty. There was maybe half a pint of vodka in the other bottle and I poured a few ounces of it into my glass. 'Not right away,' I said, 'but before too long. And I don't know what made me do it.'

'Guilt.'

'I'm not sure. All I know is that being a cop didn't seem to be fun anymore. Being a husband and a father didn't seem to work, either. I took a leave of absence from both, moved into a hotel a block west of Columbus Circle. Somewhere down the line it became clear that I wasn't going back, not to my wife, not to the department.'

Neither of us said anything for a while. After a moment she leaned over and touched my hand. It was an unexpected and slightly awkward gesture and for some reason it touched me. I felt a thickening in my throat.

Then she had withdrawn her hand and was on her feet. I thought for a moment that she meant for me to leave. Instead she said, 'I'm going to call the liquor store while they're still open. The nearest place is on Canal and they close early. Do you want to stick with Scotch or would you rather switch to bourbon? And what brand of bourbon?'

'I should probably be going soon.'

'Scotch or bourbon?'

'I'll stay with the Scotch.'

While we waited for the liquor delivery she took me around the loft and showed me some of her work. Most of it was realistic, like the Medusa, but a few pieces were abstract. There was a lot of strength in her sculpture. I told her I liked her work.

'I'm pretty good,' she said.

She wouldn't let me pay for the liquor, insisting that I was her guest. We sat in our chairs again, opened our respective bottles, filled our glasses. She asked me if I really liked her work. I assured her that I did.

'I'm supposed to be good,' she said. 'You know how I got into this? Playing with clay with the kids at the day-care center. I wound up taking the clay home, that yellow modeling clay, and working with it by the hour. Then I took a night course at Brooklyn College, an adult-ed class, and the instructor told me I had talent. He didn't have to tell me. I knew it.

'I've had some recognition. I had a show at the Chuck Levitan

Gallery a little over a year ago. You know the gallery? On Grand Street?' I didn't. 'Well, he gave me a one-man show. A one-woman show. A one-person show. Shit, you have to think before you talk nowadays, have you noticed?'

'Uh-huh.'

'And I had an NEA grant last year. National Endowment for the Arts. Plus a smaller grant from the Einhoorn Foundation. Don't pretend you heard of the Einhoorn Foundation. I never heard of it before I got the grant. I've got pieces in some fairly decent collections. One or two in museums. Well, one, and it's not MOMA, but it's a museum. I'm a sculptor.'

'I never said you weren't.'

'And my kids are in California and I never see them. He has full custody. The hell, I moved out, right? I'm some kind of unnatural woman in the first place, some dyke who deserts husband and kids, so of course he gets custody, right? I didn't make an issue of it. Do you want to know something, Matthew?'

'What?'

'I didn't *want* custody. I was done with day care. I had fucking had it with kids, my own included. What do you make of that?'

'It sounds natural enough.'

'The Maisie Pomperances of the world wouldn't agree with you. Excuse me, I mean Mitzi. Gordon and Mitzi Fucking Pomerance. Mr and Mrs High-School Yearbook.'

I was able to hear the vodka in her voice now. She wasn't slurring her words any but there was a timbre to her speech that the alcohol had provided. It didn't surprise me. She had matched me drink for drink and I was hitting it pretty good myself. Of course I'd had a head start on her.

'When he said he was moving to California I threw a fit. Yelled that it wasn't fair, that he had to stay in New York so I could visit them. I had visitation rights, I said, and what good were my visitation rights if they were three thousand miles away? But do you know something?'

'What?'

'I was relieved. Part of me was glad they were going, because you wouldn't believe what it was like, traipsing out there on the subway once a week, sitting in the apartment with them or walking around Boerum Hill and always risking blank stares from Maisie Pomerance. Goddamn it, why can't I even get that goddamned woman's name right? Mitzi!'

'I've got her number written down. You could always call her up and tell her off.'

She laughed. 'Oh, Jesus,' she said. 'I gotta pee. I'll be right back.'

When she came back she sat on the couch. Without preamble she said, 'You know what we are? Me with my sculpture and you with your existential angst, and what we are is a couple of drunks who copped out. That's all.'

'If you say so.'

'Don't patronize me. Let's face it. We're both alcoholics.'

'I'm a heavy drinker. There's a difference.'

'What's the difference?'

'I could stop anytime I want to.'

'Then why don't you?'

'Why should I?'

Instead of answering the question she leaned forward to fill her glass. 'I stopped for a while,' she said. 'I quit cold for two months. More than two months.'

'You just up and quit?'

'I went to AA.'

'Oh.'

'You ever been?'

I shook my head. 'I don't think it would work for me.'

'But you could stop anytime you want.'

'Yeah, if I wanted.'

'And anyway you're not an alcoholic.'

I didn't say anything at first. Then I said, 'I suppose it depends on how you define the word. Anyway, all it is is a label.'

'They say you decide for yourself if you're an alcoholic.'

'Well, I'm deciding that I'm not.'

'I decided I was. And it worked for me. The thing is, they say it works best if you don't drink.'

'I can see where that might make a difference.'

'I don't know why I got on this subject.' She drained her glass, looked at me over its rim. 'I didn't mean to get on this goddamned subject. First my kids and then my drinking, what a fucking down.'

'It's all right.'

'I'm sorry, Matthew.'

'Forget it.'

'Sit next to me and help me forget it.'

I joined her on the couch and ran a hand over her fine hair. The sprinkling of gray hair enhanced its attractiveness. She

looked at me for a moment out of those bottomless gray eyes, then let the lids drop. I kissed her and she clung to me.

We necked some. I touched her breasts, kissed her throat. Her strong hands worked the muscles in my back and shoulders like modeling clay.

'You'll stay over,' she said.

'I'd like that.'

'So would I.'

I freshened both our drinks.

NINE

I awakened with church bells pealing in the distance. My head was clear and I felt good. I swung my legs over the side of the bed and met the eyes of a long-haired cat curled up at the foot of the bed on the other side. He looked me over, then tucked his head in and resumed napping. Sleep with the lady of the house and the cats accept you.

I got dressed and found Jan in the kitchen. She was drinking a glass of pale orange juice. I figured there was something in it to take the edge off her hangover. She'd made coffee in a Chemex filter pot and poured me a cup. I stood by the window and drank it.

We didn't talk. The church bells had taken a break and the Sunday morning silence stretched out. It was a bright day out, the sun burning away in a cloudless sky. I looked down and couldn't see a single sign of life, not a person on the street, not a car moving.

I finished my coffee and added the cup to the dirty dishes in the stainless-steel sink. Jan used a key to bring the elevator to the floor. She asked if I was going out to Sheepshead Bay and I said I guessed I was. We held onto each other for a moment. I felt the warmth of her fine body through the robe she was wearing.

'I'll call you,' I said, and rode the oversized elevator to the ground.

An Officer O'Byrne gave me directions over the phone. I followed them, riding the BMT Brighton Line to Gravesend Neck Road. The train came up above ground level at some point after it crossed into Brooklyn, and we rode through some neighborhoods of detached houses with yards that didn't look like New York at all.

The station house for the Sixty-first Precinct was on Coney Island Avenue and I managed to find it without too much trouble. In the squad room I played do-you-know with a wiry,

long-jawed detective named Antonelli. We knew enough of the same people for him to relax with me. I told him what I was working on and mentioned that Frank Fitzroy had steered it my way. He knew Frank, too, though I didn't get the impression that they were crazy about each other.

'I'll see what our file looks like,' he said. 'But you probably saw copies of our reports in the file Fitzroy showed you.'

'What I mostly want is to talk with somebody who looked at the body.'

'Wouldn't the names of officers on the scene be in the file you saw in Manhattan?'

I'd thought of that myself. Maybe I could have managed all this without coming out to the ass end of Brooklyn. But when you go out and look for something you occasionally find more than you knew you were looking for.

'Well, maybe I can find that file,' he said, and left me at an old wooden desk scarred with cigarette burns along its edges. Two desks over, a black detective with his sleeves rolled up was talking on the phone. It sounded as though he was talking to a woman, and it didn't sound much like police business. At another desk along the far wall a pair of cops, one uniformed and one in a suit, were questioning a teenager with a mop of unruly yellow hair. I couldn't hear what they were saying.

Antonelli came back with a slim file and dropped it on the desk in front of me. I went through it, pausing now and then to make a note in my notebook. The victim, I learned, was a Susan Potowski of 2705 Haring Street. She'd been a twenty-nine-year-old mother of two, separated from her husband, a construction laborer. She lived with her kids in the lower flat of a two-family semi-detached house, and she'd been killed around two o'clock on a Wednesday afternoon.

Her kids found her. They came home from school together around three thirty, a boy of eight and a girl of ten, and they found their mother on the kitchen floor, her clothing partly removed, her body covered with stab wounds. They ran around the street screaming until the beat cop turned up.

'Finding anything?'

'Maybe,' I said. I copied down the names of the first cop on the scene, added those of two detectives from the Six-One who'd gone to the Haring Street house before switching the case to Midtown North. I showed the three names to Antonelli. 'Any of these guys still work out of here?'

'Patrolman Burton Havermeyer, Detective Third-Grade Kenneth Allgood, Detective First-Grade Michael Quinn. Mick Quinn died two, maybe three years ago. Line of duty. He and a partner had a liquor store staked out on Avenue W and there were shots exchanged and he was killed. Terrible thing. Lost a wife to cancer two years before that, so he left four kids all alone in the world, the oldest just starting college. You must have read about it.'

'I think I did.'

'Guys who shot him pulled good long time. But they're alive and he's dead, so go figure. The other two, Allgood and Havermeyer, I don't even know the names, so they've been off the Six-One since before my time, which is what? Five years? Something like that.'

'Can you find out where they went?'

'I can probably find out something. What do you want to ask 'em, anyway?'

'If she was stabbed in both eyes.'

'Wasn't there an ME's report in the file whats-his-name showed you? Fitzroy?'

I nodded. 'Both eyes.'

'So?'

'Remember that case some years ago? They pulled some woman out of the Hudson, called it death by drowning? Then some genius in the Medical Examiner's office took the skull and started using it for a paperweight, and there was a scandal about that, and because of all the heat somebody finally took a good look at the skull for the first time and found a bullet hole in it.'

'I remember. She was some woman from New Jersey, married to a doctor, wasn't she?'

'That's right.'

'I got a rule-of-thumb. When a doctor's wife gets killed, he did it. I don't give a shit about the evidence. The doc always did it. I don't remember whether this one got off or not.'

'Neither do I.'

'I take your point, though. The ME's report isn't something you want to run to the bank with. But how good is a witness to something that happened nine years ago?'

'Not too good. Still –'

'I'll see what I can see.'

He was gone a little longer this time, and he had a funny expression on his face when he returned. 'Bad luck case,' he said.

70

'Allgood's dead, too. And the patrolman, Havermeyer, he left the department.'

'How did Allgood die?'

'Heart attack, about a year ago. He got transferred out a couple of years back. He was working out of Centre Street headquarters. Collapsed at his desk one day and died. One of the guys in the file room knew him from when he worked here and happened to know how he died. Havermeyer could be dead, too, for all I know.'

'What happened to him?'

He shrugged. 'Who knows? He put in his papers just a few months after the Icepick thing. Cited unspecified personal reasons for returning to civilian life. He'd only been in for two, three years. You know what the drop-out rate's like for the new ones. Hell, you're a drop-out yourself. Personal reasons, right?'

'Something like that.'

'I dug up an address and a number. He probably moved six times between then and now. If he didn't leave a trail, you can always try downtown. He wasn't here long enough to have any pension rights but they usually keep track of ex-cops.'

'Maybe he's still in the same place.'

'Could be. My grandmother's still living in three little rooms on Elizabeth Street, same apartment she's been in since she got off the boat from Palermo. Some people stay put. Others change their houses like they change their socks. Maybe you'll get lucky. Anything else I can do for you?'

'Where's Haring Street?'

'The murder scene?' He laughed. 'Jesus, you're a bloodhound,' he said. 'Want to get the scent, huh?'

He told me how to walk there. He'd given me a fair amount of his time but he didn't want any money for it. I sensed that he probably didn't – some do and some don't – but I made the offer. 'You could probably use a new hat,' I said, and he came back with a tight grin and assured me that he had a whole closetful of hats. 'And I hardly ever wear a hat these days,' he said. I'd been offering him twenty-five dollars, cheap enough for the effort he'd expended. 'It's a slow day at a quiet precinct,' he said, 'and how much mileage can you get out of what I just gave you? You got anybody in mind for that Boerum Hill killing?'

'Not really.'

'Like hunting a black cat in a coal mine,' he said. 'Do me one favor? Let me know how it comes out. *If* it comes out.'

I followed his directions to Haring Street. I don't suppose the

neighborhood had changed much in nine years. The houses were well kept up and there were kids all over the place. There were cars parked at the curb, cars in most of the driveways. It occurred to me that there were probably a dozen people on the block who remembered Susan Potowski, and for all I knew her estranged husband had moved back into the house after the murder and lived there now with his children. They'd be older now, seventeen and nineteen.

She must have been young when she had the first one. Nineteen herself. Early marriage and early childbirth wouldn't have been uncommon in that neighborhood.

He probably moved away, I decided. Assuming he came back for the kids, he wouldn't make them go on living in the house where they found their mother dead on the kitchen floor. Would he?

I didn't ring that doorbell, or any other doorbells. I wasn't investigating Susan Potowski's murder and I didn't have to sift her ashes. I took a last look at the house she'd died in, then turned and walked away.

The address I had for Burton Havermeyer was 212 St Marks Place. The East Village wasn't that likely a place for a cop to live, and it didn't seem terribly likely that he'd still be there nine years later, on or off the force. I called the number Antonelli had given me from a drugstore phone booth on Ocean Avenue.

A woman answered. I asked if I could speak to Mr Havermeyer. There was a pause. 'Mr Havermeyer doesn't live here.'

I started to apologize for having the wrong number but she wasn't through. 'I don't know where Mr Havermeyer can be reached,' she said.

'Is this Mrs Havermeyer?'

'Yes.'

I said, 'I'm sorry to disturb you, Mrs Havermeyer. A detective at the Sixty-first Precinct where your husband used to work supplied this number. I'm trying to –'

'My former husband.'

There was a toneless quality to her speech, as if she was deliberately detaching herself from the words she was speaking. I had noted a similar characteristic in the speech of recovered mental patients.

'I'm trying to reach him in connection with a police matter,' I said.

'He hasn't been a policeman in years.'

'I realize that. Do you happen to know how I can get hold of him?'

'No.'

'I gather you don't see him often, Mrs Havermeyer, but would you have any idea –'

'I never see him.'

'I see.'

'Oh, do you? I never see my former husband. I get a check once a month. It's sent directly to my bank and deposited to my account. I don't see my husband and I don't see the check. Do you see? Do you?'

The words might have been delivered with passion. But the voice remained flat and uninvolved.

I didn't say anything.

'He's in Manhattan,' she said. 'Perhaps he has a phone, and perhaps it's in the book. You could look it up. I know you'll excuse me if I don't offer to look it up for you.'

'Certainly.'

'I'm sure it's important,' she said. 'Police business always is, isn't it?'

There was no Manhattan telephone book at the drugstore so I let the Information operator look for me. She found a Burton Havermeyer on West 103rd Street. I dialed the number and no one answered.

The drugstore had a lunch counter. I sat on a stool and ate a grilled cheese sandwich and a too-sweet piece of cherry pie and drank two cups of black coffee. The coffee wasn't bad, but it couldn't compare with the stuff Jan had brewed in her Chemex filter pot.

I thought about her. Then I went to the phone again and almost dialed her number, but tried Havermeyer again instead. This time he answered.

I said, 'Burton Havermeyer? My name's Matthew Scudder. I wondered if I could come around and see you this afternoon.'

'What about?'

'It's a police matter. Some questions I'd like to ask you. I won't take up much of your time.'

'You're a police officer?'

Hell. 'I used to be one.'

'So did I. Could you tell me what you want with me, Mr –?'

'Scudder,' I supplied. 'It's ancient history, actually. I'm a

73

detective now and I'm working on a case you were involved with when you were with the Six-One.'

'That was years ago.'

'I know.'

'Can't we do this over the phone? I can't imagine what information I could possibly have that would be useful to you. I was a beat patrolman, I didn't work on cases. I –'

'I'd like to drop by if it's all right.'

'Well, I –'

'I won't take up much of your time.'

There was a pause. 'It's my day off,' he said, in what was not quite a whine. 'I just figured to sit around, have a couple of beers, watch a ball game.'

'We can talk during the commercials.'

He laughed. 'Okay, you win. You know the address? The name's on the bell. When should I expect you?'

'An hour, hour and a half.'

'Good enough.'

The Upper West Side is another neighborhood on the upswing, but the local renaissance hasn't crossed Ninety-sixth Street yet. Havermeyer lived on 103rd between Columbus and Amsterdam in one of the rundown brownstones that lined both sides of the street. The neighborhood was mostly Spanish. There were a lot of people sitting on the stoops, listening to enormous portable radios and drinking Miller High Life out of brown paper bags. Every third woman was pregnant.

I found the right building and rang the right bell and climbed four flights of stairs. He was waiting for me in the doorway of one of the back apartments. He said, 'Scudder?' and I nodded. 'Burt Havermeyer,' he said. 'Come on in.'

I followed him into a fair-sized studio with a Pullman kitchen. The overhead light fixture was a bare bulb in one of those Japanese paper shades. The walls were due for paint. I took a seat on the couch and accepted the can of beer he handed me. He popped one for himself, then moved to turn off the television set, a black and white portable perched on top of an orange crate that held paperback books on its lower two shelves.

He pulled up a chair for himself, crossed his legs. He looked to be in his early thirties, five-eight or -nine, pale complected, with narrow shoulders and a beer gut. He wore brown gabardine slacks and a brown and beige patterned sportshirt. He had deep-set brown eyes, heavy jowls and slicked-down dark brown hair,

74

and he hadn't shaved that morning. Neither, come to think of it, had I.

'About nine years ago,' I said. 'A woman named Susan Potowski.'

'I knew it.'

'Oh.'

'I hung up and thought, why's anybody want to talk with me about some case nine or ten years old? Then I figured it had to be the icepick thing. I read the papers. They got the guy, right? They made a lap and he fell in it.'

'That's about it.' I explained how Louis Pinell had denied a role in the death of Barbara Ettinger and how the facts appeared to bear him out.

'I don't get it,' he said. 'That still leaves something like eight killings, doesn't it? Isn't that enough to put him away?'

'It's not enough for the Ettinger woman's father. He wants to know who killed his daughter.'

'And that's your job.' He whistled softly. 'Lucky you.'

'That's about it.' I drank a little beer from the can. 'I don't suppose there's any connection between the Potowski killing and the one I'm investigating, but they're both in Brooklyn and maybe Pinell didn't do either of them. You were the first police officer on the scene. You remember that day pretty well?'

'Jesus,' he said. 'I ought to.'

'Oh?'

'I left the force because of it. But I suppose they told you that out in Sheepshead Bay.'

'All they said was unspecified personal reasons.'

'That right?' He held his beer can in both hands and sat with his head bowed, looking down at it. 'I remember how her kids screamed,' he said. 'I remember knowing I was going to walk in on something really bad, and then the next memory I have is I'm in her kitchen looking down at the body. One of the kids is hanging onto my pants leg the way kids do, you know how they do, and I'm looking down at her and I close my eyes and open 'em again and the picture doesn't change. She was in a whatchacallit, a housecoat. It had like Japanese writing on it and a picture of a bird, Japanese-style art. A kimono? I guess you call it a kimono. I remember the color. Orange, with black trim.

He looked up at me, then dropped his eyes again. 'The housecoat was open. The kimono. Partially open. There were these dots all over her body, like punctuation marks. Where he got her with the icepick. Mostly the torso. She had very nice

breasts. That's a terrible thing to remember but how do you quit remembering? Standing there noticing all the wounds in her breasts, and she's dead. And still noticing that she's got a first-rate pair of tits. And hating yourself for thinking it.'

'It happens.'

'I know, I know, but it sticks in your mind like a bone caught in your throat. And the kids wailing, and noises outside. At first I don't hear any of the noise because the sight of her just blocks everything else. Like it deafens you, knocks out the other senses. Do you know what I mean?'

'Yes.'

'Then the sound comes up, and the kid's still hanging on my pants leg, and if he lives to be a hundred that's how he's gonna remember his mother. Myself, I never saw her before in my life, and I couldn't get that picture out of my head. It repeated on me night and day. When I slept it got in my nightmares and during the day it would come into my mind at odd moments. I didn't want to go in anyplace. I didn't want to risk coming up on another dead body. And it dawned on me finally that I didn't want to stay in a line of work where when people get killed it's up to you to deal with it. "Unspecified personal reasons." Well, I just specified. I gave it a little time and it didn't wear off and I quit.'

'What do you do now?'

'Security guard.' He named a midtown store. 'I tried a couple of other things but I've had this job for seven years now. I wear a uniform and I even have a gun on my hip. Job I had before this, you wore a gun but it wasn't loaded. That drove me nuts. I said I'd carry a gun or not carry a gun, it didn't matter to me, but don't give me an unloaded gun because then the bad guys think you're armed but you can't defend yourself. Now I got a loaded gun and it hasn't been out of the holster in seven years and that's the way I like it. I'm a deterrent to robbery and shoplifting. Not as much of a deterrent to shoplifting as we'd like. Boosters can be pretty slick.'

'I can imagine.'

'It's dull work. I like that. I like knowing I don't have to walk into somebody's kitchen and there's death on the floor. I joke with other people on the job, I hook a shoplifter now and then, and the whole thing's nice and steady. I got a simple life, you know what I mean? I like it that way.'

'A question about the murder scene.'

'Sure.'

'The woman's eyes.'

'Oh, Christ,' he said. 'You had to remind me.'

'Tell me.'

'Her eyes were open. He stabbed all the victims in the eyes. I didn't know that. It was kept out of the papers, the way they'll hold something back, you know? But when the detectives got there they saw it right away and that cinched it, you know, that it wasn't our case and we could buck it on up to some other precinct. I forget which one.'

'Midtown North.'

'If you say so.' He closed his eyes for a moment. 'Did I say her eyes were open? Staring up at the ceiling. But they were like ovals of blood.'

'Both eyes?'

'Pardon?'

'Were both of her eyes the same?'

He nodded. 'Why?'

'Barbara Ettinger was only stabbed in one eye.'

'It make a difference?'

'I don't know.'

'If somebody was going to copy the killer, they'd copy him completely, wouldn't they?'

'You'd think so.'

'Unless it *was* him and he was rushed for a change. Who knows with a crazy person, anyway? Maybe this time God told him only stab one eye. Who knows?'

He went for another beer and offered me one but I passed. I didn't want to hang around long enough to drink it. I had really only had one question to ask him and his answer had done nothing but confirm the medical report. I suppose I could have asked it over the phone, but then I wouldn't have had the same chance to probe his memory and get a real sense of what he'd found in that kitchen. No question now that he'd gone back in time and seen Susan Potowski's body all over again. He wasn't guessing that she'd been stabbed in both eyes. He had closed his own eyes and seen the wounds.

He said, 'Sometimes I wonder. Well, when I read about them arresting this Pinell, and now with you coming over here. Suppose I wasn't the one walked in on the Potowski woman? Or suppose it happened three years later when I had that much more experience? I can see how my whole life might have been different.'

'You might have stayed on the force.'

'It's possible, right? I don't know if I really liked being a cop or if I was any good at it. I liked the classes at the Academy. I liked wearing the uniform. I liked walking the beat and saying hello to people and having them say hello back. Actual police work, I don't know how much I liked it. Maybe if I was really cut out for it I wouldn't have been thrown for a loop by what I saw in that kitchen. Or I would have toughed it out and gotten over it eventually. You were a cop yourself and you quit, right?'

'For unspecified personal reasons.'

'Yeah, I guess there's a lot of that going around.'

'There was a death involved,' I said. 'A child. What happened, I lost my taste for the work.'

'Exactly what happened to me, Matt. I lost my taste for it. You know what I think? If it wasn't that one particular thing it would have been something else.'

Could I say the same thing? It was not a thought that had occurred to me previously. If Estrellita Rivera had been home in bed where she belonged, would I still be living in Syosset and carrying a badge? Or would some other incident have given me an inevitable nudge in a direction I had to walk?

I said, 'You and your wife separated.'

'That's right.'

'Same time you put in your papers?'

'Not too long after that.'

'You move here right away?'

'I was in an SRO hotel a couple blocks down on Broadway. I stayed there for maybe ten weeks until I found this place. Been here ever since.'

'Your wife's still in the East Village.'

'Huh?'

'St Marks Place. She's still living there.'

'Oh. Right.'

'Any kids?'

'No.'

'Makes it easier.'

'I guess so.'

'My wife and sons are out on Long Island. I'm in a hotel on Fifty-seventh Street.'

He nodded, understanding. People move and their lives change. He'd wound up guarding cashmere sweaters. I'd wound up doing whatever it is I do. Looking in a coal mine for a black cat, according to Antonelli. Looking for a cat that wasn't even there.

78

TEN

When I got back to my hotel there was a message from Lynn London. I called her from the pay phone in the lobby and explained who I was and what I wanted.

She said, 'My father hired you? It's funny he didn't say anything to me. I thought they had the man who killed my sister. Why would he suddenly – well, let's let it ride for now. I don't know what help I could be.'

I said I'd like to meet with her to talk about her sister.

'Not tonight,' she said briskly. 'I just got back from the mountains a couple of hours ago. I'm exhausted and I've got to do my lesson plans for the week.'

'Tomorrow?'

'I teach during the day. I've got a dinner date and I'm going to a concert after that. Tuesday's my group therapy night. Maybe Wednesday? That's not terribly good for me either. Hell.'

'Maybe we could –'

'Maybe we could handle it over the phone? I don't really know very much, Mr Scudder, and God knows I'm beat at the moment, but perhaps I could deal with, say, ten minutes' worth of questions right now, because otherwise I honestly don't know when we could get together. I don't really know very much, it was a great many years ago and –'

'When do you finish your classes tomorrow afternoon?'

'Tomorrow afternoon? We dismiss the children at three fifteen, but –'

'I'll meet you at your apartment at four.'

'I told you. I have a dinner date tomorrow.'

'And a concert after it. I'll meet you at four. I won't take that much of your time.'

She wasn't thrilled, but that's how we left it. I spent another dime and called Jan Keane. I recapped the day and she told me she was in awe of my industriousness. 'I don't know,' I said.

79

'Sometimes I think I'm just putting in time. I could have accomplished the same thing today with a couple of phone calls.'

'We could have handled our business over the phone last night,' she said. 'As far as that goes.'

'I'm glad we didn't.'

'So am I,' she said. 'I think. On the other hand, I was planning on working today and I couldn't even look at clay. I'm just hoping this hangover wears off by bedtime.'

"I had a clear head this morning.'

'Mine's just beginning to clear now. Maybe my mistake was staying in the house. The sun might have burned off some of the fog. Now I'm just sitting around until it's a reasonable hour to go to sleep.'

There might have been an unspoken invitation in that last sentence. I probably could have invited myself over. But I was already home, and a short and quiet evening had its appeal. I told her I'd wanted to say how I'd enjoyed her company and that I'd call her.

'I'm glad you called,' she said. 'You're a sweet man, Matthew.' A pause, and then she said, 'I've been thinking about it. He probably did it.'

'He?'

'Doug Ettinger. He probably killed her.'

'Why?'

'I don't know why. People always have motives to kill their spouses, don't they? There was never a day when I didn't have a reason to kill Eddie.'

'I meant why do you think he did it.'

'Oh. What I was thinking, I was thinking how devious you would have to be to kill someone and imitate another murder. And I realized what a devious man he was, what a sneak. He could plan something like that.'

'That's interesting.'

'Listen, I don't have any special knowledge. But it's what I was thinking earlier. And now he's doing what? Selling sporting goods? Is that what you said?'

I sat in my room and read for a while, then had dinner around the corner at Armstrong's. I stayed there for a couple of hours but didn't have very much to drink. The crowd was a light one, as it usually is on a Sunday. I talked to a few people but mostly

80

sat alone and let the events of the past two days thread their way in and out of my consciousness.

I made it an early night, walked down to Eighth Avenue for the early edition of Monday's *News*. Went back to my room, read the paper, took a shower. Looked at myself in the mirror. Thought about shaving, decided to wait until morning.

Had a nightcap, a short one. Went to bed.

I was deep in a dream when the phone rang. I was running in the dream, chasing someone or being chased, and I sat up in bed with my heart pounding.

The phone was ringing. I reached out, answered it.

A woman said, 'Why don't you let the dead bury the dead?'

'Who is this?'

'Leave the dead alone. Let the dead stay buried.'

'Who is this?'

A click. I turned on a light and looked at my watch. It was around one thirty. I'd been sleeping an hour, if that.

Who had called me? It was a voice I'd heard before but I couldn't place it. Lynn London? I didn't think so.

I got out of bed, flipped pages in my notebook, picked up the phone again. When the hotel operator came on I read off a number to him. He put the call through and I listened as it rang twice.

A woman answered it. Same woman who'd just told me to leave the dead alone. I'd heard her voice once before that, and remembered it now.

I had nothing to say to her that wouldn't wait a day or two. Without saying anything, I replaced the receiver and went back to bed.

ELEVEN

After breakfast the next day I called Charles London's office. He hadn't come in yet. I gave my name and said I'd call later.

I spent another dime calling Frank Fitzroy at the Eighteenth Precinct. 'Scudder,' I said. 'Where are they holding Pinell?'

'They had him downtown. Then I think they shunted him out to Rikers Island. Why?'

'I'd like to see him. What are my chances?'

'Not good.'

'You could go out there,' I suggested. 'I could just be a fellow officer along for the ride.'

'I don't know, Matt.'

'You'd get something for your time.'

'That's not it. Believe me. Thing is, this fucker fell in our laps and I'd hate to see him walk on a technicality. We ring in an unauthorized visitor and his lawyer gets wind of it and gets a wild hair up his ass and it could screw up the whole case. You follow me?'

'It doesn't seem very likely.'

'Maybe not, but it's a chance I'm in no rush to take. What do you want from him, anyway?'

'I don't know.'

'Maybe I could ask him a question or two for you. Assuming I could get to see him, which I'm not sure I could. His lawyer may have cut off the flow. But if you've got a specific question –'

I was in the phone booth in my hotel lobby and someone was knocking on the door. I told Frank to hang on for a second and opened the door a crack. It was Vinnie, the desk man, to tell me I had a call. I asked who it was and he said it was a woman and she hadn't given her name. I wondered if it was the same one who'd called last night.

I told him to switch it to the house phone and I'd take it in a

minute. I uncovered the mouthpiece of the phone I was holding and told Frank I couldn't think of anything in particular that I wanted to ask Louis Pinell, but that I'd keep his offer in mind. He asked if I was getting anyplace with my investigation.

'I don't know,' I said. 'It's hard to tell. I'm putting in the hours.'

'Giving what's-his-name his money's worth. London.'

'I suppose so. I have a feeling most of it is wasted motion.'

'It's always that way, isn't it? There's days when I figure I must waste ninety percent of my time. But you have to do that to come up with the ten percent that's not a waste.'

'That's a point.'

'Even if you could see Pinell, that'd be part of the wasted ninety percent. Don't you think?'

'Probably.'

I finished up with him, went over to the desk and picked up the house phone. It was Anita.

She said, 'Matt? I just wanted to tell you that the check came.'

'That's good. I'm sorry it's not more.'

'It came at a good time.'

I sent money for her and the boys when I had it to send. She never called just to say it had arrived.

I asked how the boys were.

'They're fine,' she said. 'Of course they're in school now.'

'Of course.'

'I guess it's been a while since you've seen them.'

I felt a little red pinprick of anger. Had she called just to tell me that? Just to push a little guilt button? 'I'm on a case,' I said. 'Soon as it's finished, whenever that is, maybe they can come in and we'll catch a game at the Garden. Or a boxing match.'

'They'd like that.'

'So would I.' I thought of Jan, relieved that her kids were on the other side of the country, relieved she didn't have to visit them anymore, and guilty over her relief. 'I'd like that very much,' I said.

'Matt, the reason I called –'

'Yes?'

'Oh, God,' she said. She sounded sad and tired. 'It's Bandy,' she said.

'Bandy?'

'The dog. You remember Bandy.'

'Of course. What about him?'

'Oh, it's sad,' she said. 'The vet said he ought to be put to

83

sleep. He said there's really nothing to be done for him at this point.'

'Oh,' I said. 'Well, I suppose if that's what has to be done –'

'I already had him put to sleep. On Friday.'

'Oh.'

'I guess I thought you would want to know.'

'Poor Bandy,' I said. 'He must have been twelve years old.'

'He was fourteen.'

'I didn't realize he was that old. That's a long life for a dog.'

'It's supposed to be the equivalent of ninety-eight for a human being.'

'What was the matter with him?'

'The vet said he just wore out. His kidneys were in bad shape. And he was almost blind. You knew that, didn't you?'

'No.'

'For the past year or two his eyesight was failing. It was so sad, Matt. The boys sort of lost interest in him. I think that was the saddest part. They loved him when they were younger but they grew up and he got old and they lost interest.' She started to cry. I stood there and held the phone to my ear and didn't say anything.

She said, 'I'm sorry, Matt.'

'Don't be silly.'

'I called you because I wanted to tell somebody and who else could I tell? Do you remember when we got him?'

'I remember.'

'I wanted to call him Bandit because of his facial markings, his mask. You said something about give-a-dog-a-bad-name, but we were already calling him Bandy. So we decided it was short for Bandersnatch.'

'From *Alice in Wonderland*.'

'The vet said he didn't feel anything. He just went to sleep. He took care of disposing of the body for me.'

'That's good.'

'He had a good life, don't you think? And he was a good dog. He was such a clown. He could always break me up.'

She talked for a few more minutes. The conversation just wore out, like the dog. She thanked me again for the check and I said again that I wished it could have been more. I told her to tell the boys I'd be seeing them as soon as I was finished with my current case. She said she'd be sure to tell them. I hung up the phone and went outside.

The sun was screened by clouds and there was a chill wind

blowing. Two doors down from the hotel is a bar called McGovern's. They open early.

I went in. The place was empty except for two old men, one behind the bar, one in front of it. The bartender's hand trembled slightly as he poured me a double shot of Early Times and backed it up with a glass of water.

I hoisted the glass, wondered at the wisdom of paying an early visit to London's office with bourbon on my breath, then decided it was a pardonable eccentricity in an unofficial private detective. I thought about poor old Bandy, but of course I wasn't really thinking about the dog. For me, and probably for Anita, he was one of the few threads that had still linked us. Rather like the marriage, he'd taken his sweet time dying.

I drank the drink and got out of there.

London's office was on the sixteenth floor of a twenty-eight-story building on Pine Street. I shared the elevator with two men in forest-green work clothing. One carried a clipboard, the other a tool kit. Neither spoke, nor did I.

I felt like a rat in a maze by the time I found London's office. His name was the first of four lettered on the frosted glass door. Inside, a receptionist with a slight British accent invited me to have a seat, then spoke quietly into a telephone. I looked at a copy of *Sports Illustrated* until a door opened and Charles London beckoned me into his private office.

It was a fair-sized room, comfortable without being luxurious. There was a view of the harbor from his window, only partially blocked by surrounding buildings. We stood on either side of his desk, and I sensed something in the air between us. For a moment I regretted that bourbon at McGovern's, then realized it had nothing to do with the screen that seemed to separate us.

'I wish you'd called,' he said. 'You'd have been able to save a trip down here.'

'I called and they told me you hadn't come in yet.'

'I got a message that you would call later.'

'I thought I'd save a call.'

He nodded. His outfit looked the same as he'd worn to Armstrong's, except that the tie was different. I'm sure the suit and shirt were different, too. He probably had six identical suits, and two drawers of white shirts.

He said, 'I'm going to have to ask you to drop the case, Mr Scudder.'

'Oh?'

'You seem unsurprised.'

'I picked up the vibration walking in here. Why?'

'My reasons aren't important.'

'They are to me.'

He shrugged. 'I made a mistake,' he said. 'I sent you on a fool's errand. It was a waste of money.'

'You already wasted the money. You might as well let me give you something for it. I can't give it back because I already spent it.'

'I wasn't expecting a refund.'

'And I didn't come here to ask for any additional money. So what are you saving by telling me to drop the case?'

The pale blue eyes blinked twice behind the rimless glasses. He asked me if I wouldn't sit down. I said I was comfortable standing. He remained standing himself.

He said, 'I behaved foolishly. Seeking vengeance, retribution. Troubling the waters. Either that man killed her or some other maniac did and there's probably no way we'll ever know for sure. I was wrong to set you to work raking up the past and disturbing the present.'

'Is that what I've been doing?'

'I beg your pardon?'

'Raking up the past and disturbing the present? Maybe that's a good definition of my role. When did you decide to call me off?'

'That's not important.'

'Ettinger got to you, didn't he? It must have been yesterday. Saturday's a busy day at the store, they sell a lot of tennis rackets. He probably called you last night, didn't he?' When he hesitated I said, 'Go ahead. Tell me it's not important.'

'It's not. More to the point, it's not your business, Mr Scudder.'

'I got a wake-up call around one thirty last night from the second Mrs Ettinger. Did she give you a call about the same time?'

'I don't know what you're talking about.'

'She's got a distinctive voice. I heard it the day before when I called Ettinger at home and she told me he was at the Hicksville store. She called last night to tell me to let the dead stay buried. That seems to be what you want, too.'

'Yes,' he said. 'That's what I want.'

I picked a paperweight from the top of his desk. An inch-long brass label identified it as a piece of petrified wood from the Arizona desert.

'I can understand what Karen Ettinger's afraid of. Her husband might turn out to be the killer, and that would really turn her world upside down. You'd think a woman in her position would want to know one way or the other. How comfortable could she be from here on in, living with a man she half-suspects of killing his first wife? But people are funny that way. They can push things out of their minds. Whatever happened was years ago and in Brooklyn. And the wench is dead, right? People move and their lives change, so there's nothing for her to worry about, is there?'

He didn't say anything. His paperweight had a piece of black felt on its bottom to keep it from scratching his desk. I replaced it, felt-side down.

I said, 'You wouldn't be worried about Ettinger's world, or his wife's world. What's it to you if they get hassled a little? Unless Ettinger had a way to put pressure on you, but I don't think that's it. I don't think you'd be all that easy to push around.'

'Mr Scudder –'

'It's something else, but what? Not money, not a physical threat. Oh, hell, I know what it is.'

He avoided my eyes.

'Her reputation. You're afraid of what I'll find in the grave with her. Ettinger must have told you she was having an affair. He told me she wasn't, but I don't think he's that deeply committed to the truth. As a matter of fact, it does look as though she was seeing a man. Maybe more than one man. That may go against the grain of your sense of propriety, but it doesn't weigh too much against the fact that she was murdered. She may have been killed by a lover. She may have been killed by her husband. There are all sorts of possibilities but you don't want to look at any of them because in the course of it the world might find out that your daughter wasn't a virgin.'

For a moment I thought he was going to lose his temper. Then something went out of his eyes. 'I'm afraid I'll have to ask you to leave now,' he said. 'I have some calls to make and I have an appointment scheduled in fifteen minutes.'

'I guess Mondays are busy in insurance. Like Saturdays in sporting goods.'

'I'm sorry that you're embittered. Perhaps later you'll appreciate my position, but –'

'Oh, I appreciate your position,' I said. 'Your daughter was killed for no reason by a madman and you adjusted to that reality. Then you had a new reality to adjust to, and that turned

87

out to mean coming to grips with the possibility that someone had a reason to kill her, and that it might be a good reason.' I shook my head, impatient with myself for talking too much. 'I came here to pick up a picture of your daughter,' I said. 'I don't suppose you happened to bring it.'

'Why would you want it?'

'Didn't I tell you the other day?'

'But you're off the case now,' he said. He might have been explaining something to a slow child. 'I don't expect a refund, but I want you to discontinue your investigation.'

'You want to fire me.'

'If you'd prefer to put it that way.'

'But you never hired me in the first place. So how can you fire me?'

'Mr Scudder —'

'When you open up a can of worms you can't just decide to stuff the worms back in the can. There are a lot of things set in motion and I want to see where they lead. I'm not going to stop now.'

He had an odd look on his face, as though he was a little bit afraid of me. Maybe I'd raised my voice, or looked somehow menacing.

'Relax,' I told him. 'I won't be disturbing the dead. The dead are beyond disturbance. You had a right to ask me to drop the case and I've got the right to tell you to go to hell. I'm a private citizen pursuing an unofficial investigation. I could do it more efficiently if I had your help, but I can get along without it.'

'I wish you'd let it go.'

'And I wish you'd back me up. And wishes aren't horses, not for either of us. I'm sorry this isn't turning out the way you wanted it to. I tried to tell you that might be the case. I guess you didn't want to listen.'

On the way down, the elevator stopped at almost every floor. I went out to the street. It was still overcast, and colder than I remembered it. I walked a block and a half until I found a bar. I had a quick double bourbon and left. A few blocks further along I stopped at another bar and had another drink.

I found a subway, headed for the uptown platform, then changed my mind and waited for a train bound for Brooklyn. I got out at Jay Street and walked up one street and down another and wound up in Boerum Hill. I stopped at a Pentecostal church on Schermerhorn. The bulletin board was full of notices in

Spanish. I sat there for a few minutes, hoping things would sort themselves out in my mind, but it didn't work. I found my thoughts bouncing back and forth among dead things – a dead dog, a dead marriage, a dead woman in her kitchen, a dead trail.

A balding man wearing a sleeveless sweater over a maroon shirt asked me something in Spanish. I suppose he wanted to know if he could help me. I got up and left.

I walked around some more. A curious thing, I thought, was that I felt somehow more committed to the pursuit of Barbara Ettinger's killer than I had before her father fired me. It was still as hopeless a quest as it had ever been, doubly hopeless now that I wouldn't even have the cooperation of my client. And yet I seemed to believe what I had said to him about forces having been set in motion. The dead were indeed beyond disturbance, but I had set about disturbing the living and sensed that it would lead somewhere.

I thought of poor old Bandersnatch, always game to chase a stick or go for a walk. He'd bring one of his toys to you to signal his eagerness to play. If you just stood there he'd drop it at your feet, but if you tried to take it away from him he'd set his jaw and hang on grimly.

Maybe I'd learned it from him.

I went to the building on Wyckoff Street. I rang Donald Gilman and Rolfe Waggoner's bell. They weren't in. Neither was Judy Fairborn. I walked on past the building where Jan had lived with – what was his name? Edward. Eddie.

I stopped at a bar and had a drink. Just a straight shot of bourbon, not a double. Just a little something, maintenance drinking against the chill in the air.

I decided I was going to see Louis Pinell. For one thing, I'd ask him if he used a different icepick each time he killed. The autopsies hadn't indicated anything one way or the other. Perhaps forensic medicine isn't that highly developed yet.

I wondered where he got the icepicks. An icepick struck me as a damned old-fashioned instrument. What would you ever use it for outside of murder? People didn't have iceboxes any more, didn't have blocks of ice brought by the iceman. They filled trays with water to make ice cubes or had a gadget in their refrigerator that produced the cubes automatically.

The refrigerator in Syosset had had an automated ice maker.

Where did you get an icepick? How much did they cost? I was suddenly full of icepick questions. I walked around, found a five-

and-ten, asked a clerk in the housewares department where I'd find an icepick. She shunted me to the hardware department, where another clerk told me they didn't carry icepicks.

'I guess they're out of date,' I said.

She didn't bother to answer. I walked around some more, stopped at a storefront that sold hardware and kitchen things. The fellow behind the counter was wearing a camel-hair cardigan and chewing the stub of a cigar. I asked if he carried icepicks and he turned without a word and came back with one stapled to a piece of cardboard.

'Ninety-eight cents,' he said. 'Is one-oh-six with the tax.'

I didn't really want it. I had just wondered at price and availability. I paid for it anyway. Outside I stopped at a wire trash basket and discarded the brown paper bag and the piece of cardboard and examined my purchase. The blade was four or five inches long, the point sharp. The handle was a cylinder of dark wood. I held it alternately in one hand and then the other, dropped it back in my pocket.

I went back into the store. The man who'd sold it to me looked up from his magazine. 'I just bought that icepick from you,' I said.

'Something wrong with it?'

'It's fine. You sell many of them?'

'Some.'

'How many?'

'Don't keep track,' he said. 'Sell one now and then.'

'What do people buy them for?'

He gave me the guarded look you get when people begin to wonder about your identity. 'Whatever they want,' he said. 'I don't guess they pick their teeth with 'em, but anything else they want.'

'You been here long?'

'How's that?'

'You had this store a long time?'

'Long enough.'

I nodded, left. I didn't ask him who'd bought an icepick from him nine years ago. If I had, he wouldn't have been the only one doubting my sanity. But if someone had asked him that question right after Barbara Ettinger was killed, if someone had asked him and every other housewares and hardware dealer in that part of Brooklyn, and if they'd shown around the appropriate photographs and asked a few other appropriate questions, maybe they would have come up with Barbara's killer then and there.

90

No reason to do so. No reason to think it was anything but what it looked like, another score for the Icepick Prowler.

I walked around, my hand gripping the butt end of the icepick in my pocket. Handy little thing. You couldn't slash with it, you could only stab, but it would still do a pretty good job on someone.

Was it legal to carry it? The law classified it not as a deadly weapon but as a dangerous instrument. Deadly weapons are things like loaded guns, switch knives, gravity knives, daggers, billies, blackjacks and brass knuckles, articles with no function but murderous assault. An icepick had other uses, though the man who sold it hadn't managed to tell me any of them.

Still, that didn't mean you could carry it legally. A machete's a dangerous instrument in the eyes of the law, not a deadly weapon, but you're not allowed to carry one through the streets of New York.

I took the thing out of my pocket a couple of times and looked at it. Somewhere along the way I dropped it through a sewer grating.

Had the icepick used on Barbara Ettinger vanished the same way? It was possible. It was even possible that it had been dropped down that very sewer grating. All kinds of things were possible.

The wind was getting worse instead of better. I stopped for another drink.

I lost track of the time. At one point I looked at my watch and it was twenty-five minutes of four. I remembered that I was supposed to meet Lynn London at four o'clock. I didn't see how I could get there on time. Still, she was in Chelsea, it wouldn't take all that long –

Then I caught myself. What was I worrying about? Why break my neck to keep an appointment when she wouldn't be keeping it herself? Because her father would have talked to her, either early that morning or late the night before, and she'd know by now that there'd been a change in the London family policy. Matthew Scudder was no longer representing the best interests of the Londons. He was persisting in his folly for reasons of his own, and perhaps he had the right to do this, but he couldn't count on the cooperation of Charles London or his schoolmarm daughter.

'You say something?'

I looked up, met the warm brown eyes of the bartender. 'Just talking to myself,' I said.

'Nothin' wrong with that.'

I liked his attitude. 'Might as well give me another,' I said. 'And take something for yourself while you're at it.'

I called Jan twice from Brooklyn and her line was busy both times. When I got back to Manhattan I called her again from Armstrong's and got another busy signal. I finished a cup of coffee with a shot in it and tried her again and the line was still busy.

I had the operator check the line. She came back and told me the receiver was off the hook. There's a way they can make the phone ring even if you've taken it off the hook, and I thought about identifying myself as a policeman and getting her to do that, but decided to let it go.

I had no right to interrupt the woman. Maybe she was asleep. Maybe she had company.

Maybe there was a man there, or a woman. It was no business of mine.

Something settled in my stomach and glowed there like a hot coal. I had another cup of bourbon-flavored coffee to drown it.

The evening hurried on by. I didn't really pay it too much attention. My mind tended to drift.

I had things to think about.

At one point I found myself on the phone, dialing Lynn London's number. No answer. Well, she'd told me she had tickets for a concert. And I couldn't remember why I was calling her, anyway. I'd already decided there was no point. That was why I'd missed my appointment with her.

Not that she'd have shown up herself. Would have left me standing there, feeling stupid.

So I called Jan again. Still busy.

I thought about going over there. Wouldn't take too long by cab. But what was the point? When a woman takes her phone off the hook it's not because she's hoping you'll come knock on her door.

Hell with her.

Back at the bar, somebody was talking about the First Avenue Slasher. I gathered he was still at large. One of the surviving victims had described how the man had attempted to start a

conversation with him before showing his weapon and attacking.

I thought about the little article I'd read about muggers asking you the time or directions. Don't talk to strangers, I thought.

'That's the trouble with this place tonight,' I said. 'Too many strangers.'

A couple of people looked at me. From behind the bar, Billie asked me if I was all right.

'I'm fine,' I assured him. 'Just that it's too crowded tonight. No room to breathe.'

'Probably a good night to turn in early.'

'You said it.'

But I didn't feel like turning in, just like getting the hell out of there. I went around the corner to McGovern's and had a quick one. The place was dead so I didn't hang around. I hit Polly's Cage across the street and left when the jukebox started getting on my nerves.

The air outside was bracing. It struck me that I'd been drinking all day and that it added up to a hell of a lot of booze, but I seemed to be handling it fine. It wasn't affecting me at all. I was wide awake, clear-minded, clear-headed. It'd be hours before I'd be able to sleep.

I circled the block, stopped at a hole in the wall on Eighth Avenue, stopped again at Joey Farrell's. I felt restless and combative and got out of there when the bartender said something that irritated me. I don't remember what it was.

Then I was walking. I was on Ninth Avenue across the street from Armstrong's, walking south, and there was something hanging in the air that was putting me on my guard. Even as I was wondering at the feeling, a young man stepped out of a doorway ten yards ahead of me.

He had a cigarette in one hand. As I approached he moved purposefully into my path and asked me for a match.

That's how the bastards do it. One stops you and sizes you up. The other moves in behind you, and you get a forearm across the windpipe, a knife at your throat.

I don't smoke but I generally have a pack of matches in my pocket. I cupped my hands, scratched a match. He tucked the unlit cigarette between his lips and leaned forward, and I flipped the burning match in his face and went in under it, grabbing and shoving hard, sending him reeling into the brick well behind him.

I whirled myself, ready for his partner.

93

There was nobody behind me. Nothing but an empty street.

That made it simpler. I kept turning, and I was facing him when he came off the wall with his eyes wide and his mouth open. He was my height but lighter in build, late teens or early twenties, uncombed dark hair and a face white as paper in the light of the streetlamps.

I moved in quick and hit him in the middle. He swung at me and I sidestepped the punch and hit him again an inch or two above his belt buckle. That brought his hands down and I swung my right forearm in an arc and hit him in the mouth with my elbow. He drew back and clapped both hands to his mouth.

I said, 'Turn around and grab that wall! Come on, you fucker. Get your hands on the wall!'

He said I was crazy, that he hadn't done anything. The words came out muffled through the hands he was holding to his mouth.

But he turned around and grabbed the wall.

I moved in, hooked a foot in front of his, drew his foot back so that he couldn't come off the wall in a hurry.

'I didn't do nothing,' he said. 'What's the matter with you?'

I told him to put his head against the wall.

'All I did was ask you for a match.'

I told him to shut up. I frisked him and he stood still for it. A little blood trickled from the corner of his mouth. Nothing serious. He was wearing one of those leather jackets with a pile collar and two big pockets in front. Bomber jackets, I think they call them. The pocket on the left held a wad of Kleenex and a pack of Winston Lights. The other pocket held a knife. A flick of my wrist and the blade dropped into place.

A gravity knife. One of the seven deadly weapons.

'I just carry it,' he said.

'For what?'

'Protection.'

'From who? Little old ladies:'

I took a wallet off his hip. He had ID that indicated he was Anthony Sforczak and he lived in Woodside, Queens. I said, 'You're a long ways from home, Tony.'

'So?'

He had two tens and some singles in his wallet. In another pants pocket I found a thick roll of bills secured by a rubber band, and in the breast pocket of his shirt, under the leather jacket, I found one of those disposable butane lighters.

'It's out of fluid,' he said.

I flicked it. Flame leaped from it and I showed it to him. The heat rose and he jerked his head to the side. I released the thumbcatch and the flame died.

'It was out before. Wouldn't light.'

'So why keep it? Why not throw it away?'

'It's against the law to litter.'

'Turn around.'

He came off the wall slowly, eyes wary. A little line of blood trailed from the corner of his mouth down over his chin. His mouth was starting to puff up some where my elbow had caught him.

He wouldn't die of it.

I gave him the wallet and the cigarette lighter. I tucked the roll of bills in my own pocket.

'That's my money,' he said.

'You stole it.'

'Like hell I did! What are you gonna do, keep it?'

'What do you think?' I flicked the knife open and held it so that the light glinted off the face of the blade. 'You better not turn up in this part of the city again. Another thing you better not do is carry a blade when half the department's looking for the First Avenue Slasher.'

He stared at me. Something in his eyes said he wished I didn't have that knife in my hand. I met his gaze and closed the knife, dropped it on the ground behind me.

'Go ahead,' I said. 'Be my guest.'

I balanced on the balls of my feet, waiting for him. For a moment he might have been considering it, and I was hoping he'd make a move. I could feel the blood singing in my veins, pulsing in my temples.

He said, 'You're crazy, you know? What you are is crazy,' and he edged off ten or twenty yards, then half-ran to the corner.

I stood watching until he was out of sight.

The street was still empty. I found the gravity knife on the pavement and put it in my pocket. Across the street, Armstrong's door opened and a young man and woman emerged. They walked down the street holding hands.

I felt fine. I wasn't drunk. I'd had a day of maintenance drinking, nothing more. Look how I'd handled the punk. Nothing wrong with my instincts, nothing slow about my reflexes. The booze wasn't getting in the way. Just a matter of taking on fuel, of keeping a full tank. Nothing wrong with that.

TWELVE

I came suddenly awake. There was no warm-up period. It was as abrupt as turning on a transistor radio.

I was on my bed in my hotel room, lying on top of the covers with my head on the pillow. I had piled my clothes on the chair but slept in my underwear. There was a foul taste in my dry mouth and I had a killer headache.

I got up. I felt shaky and awful, and a sense of impending doom hung in the air, as though if I turned around quickly I could look Death in the eye.

I didn't want a drink but knew I needed one to take the edge off the way I felt. I couldn't find the bourbon bottle and then I finally found it in the wastebasket. Evidently I'd finished it before I went to bed. I wondered how much it had contained.

No matter. It was empty now.

I held out a hand, studied it. No visible tremors. I flexed the fingers. Not as steady as Gibraltar, maybe, but not a case of the shakes, either.

Shaky inside, though.

I couldn't remember returning to the hotel. I probed gingerly at my memory and couldn't get any further than the boy scuttling down the street and around the corner. Anthony Sforczak, that was his name.

See? Nothing wrong with my memory.

Except that it ran out at that point. Or perhaps a moment later, when the young couple came out of Armstrong's and walked up the street holding hands. Then it all went blank, coming into focus again with me coming to in my hotel room. What time was it, anyway?

My watch was still on my wrist. Quarter after nine. And it was light outside my window, so that means a.m. Not that I really had to look to be sure. I hadn't lost a day, just the length of time it took me to walk half a block home and get to bed.

Assuming I'd come straight home.

I stripped off my underwear and got into the shower. While I was under the spray I could hear my phone ringing. I let it ring. I spent a long time under the hot spray, then took a blast of cold for as long as I could stand it, which wasn't very long. I toweled dry and shaved. My hand wasn't as steady as it might have been but I took my time and didn't cut myself.

I didn't like what I saw in the mirror. A lot of red in the eyes. I thought of Havermeyer's description of Susan Potowski, her eyes swimming in blood. I didn't like my red eyes, or the mesh of broken blood vessels on my cheekbones and across the bridge of my nose.

I knew what put them there. Drink put them there. Nothing else. I could forget about what it might be doing to my liver because my liver was tucked away where I didn't have to look at it every morning.

And where nobody else could see it.

I got dressed, put on all clean clothes, stuffed everything else in my laundry bag. The shower helped and the shave helped and the clean clothes helped, but in spite of all three I could feel remorse settling over my shoulders like a cape. I didn't want to look at the previous night because I knew I wasn't going to like what I'd see there.

But what choice did I have?

I put the roll of bills in one pocket, the gravity knife in the other. I went downstairs and out, walking past the desk without breaking stride. I knew there'd be messages there but I figured they'd keep.

I decided not to stop at McGovern's but when I got there I turned in. Just one quick drink to still the invisible shaking. I drank it like the medicine it was.

Around the corner I sat in a rear pew at St Paul's. For what seemed like a long time I didn't even think. I just sat there.

Then the thoughts started. No way to stop them, really.

I'd been drunk the night before and hadn't known it. I'd probably been drunk fairly early in the day. There were patches in Brooklyn that I couldn't remember clearly, and I didn't seem to have any recollection of the subway ride back to Manhattan. For that matter, I couldn't be sure I'd ridden the subway. I might have taken a cab.

I remembered talking to myself in a Brooklyn bar. I must have

been drunk then. I didn't tend to talk to myself when I was sober.

Not yet, anyway.

All right, I could live with all that. I drank too goddamn much, and when you do that with consistency there are going to be times when you get drunk without wanting to. This wasn't the first time and I didn't suspect it would be the last. It came with the territory.

But I'd been drunk when I was playing Hero Cop on Ninth Avenue, drunk with the booze for high-octane fuel. My street-smart instincts that warned me about a mugging were less a source of pride the morning after.

Maybe he just wanted a match.

My gorge rose at the thought and I tasted bile at the back of my throat. Maybe he was just another kid from Woodside having himself a night on the town. Maybe he'd been a mugger only in my mind, my drunken mind. Maybe I'd beaten him and robbed him for no good reason at all.

But he'd asked for a match when he had a working lighter.

So? That was an icebreaker as old as tobacco. Ask for a match, strike up a conversation. He could have been a male hustler. He would hardly have been the first gay man to put on a bomber jacket.

He was carrying a gravity knife.

So? Frisk the city and you could stock an arsenal. Half the city was carrying something to protect it from the other half. The knife was a deadly weapon and he was breaking a law carrying it, but it didn't prove anything.

He knew how to grab that wall. It wasn't his first frisk.

And that didn't prove anything either. There are neighborhoods where you can't grow up without getting stopped and tossed once a week by the cops.

And the money? The roll of bills?

He could have come by it honestly. Or he could have earned it in any of innumerable dishonest ways and still not have been a mugger.

And my vaunted cop instincts? Hell, the minute he came out of the doorway I'd known he was going to approach me.

Right. And I'd also known his partner was moving in behind me, knew it as if I'd had eyes in the back of my head. Except there was nobody there. So much for the infallibility of instinct.

I took out the gravity knife, opened it. Suppose I'd been carrying it the night before. More realistically, suppose I'd still

been carrying the icepick I'd bought in Boerum Hill. Would I have limited myself to a couple of body punches and a forearm smash to the face? Or would I have worked with the materials at hand?

I felt shaky, and it was more than the hangover.

I closed the knife and put it away. I took out the roll of bills, removed the rubber band, counted the cash. I made it a hundred and seventy dollars in five and tens.

If he was a mugger, why didn't he have the knife in his hand? How come it was in his jacket pocket with the flap buttoned down?

Or *was* the flap buttoned?

Didn't matter. I sorted the money and added it to my own. On my way out I lit a couple of candles, then slipped seventeen dollars into the poor box.

At the corner of Fifty-seventh I dropped the gravity knife into a sewer.

THIRTEEN

My cab driver was an Israeli immigrant and I don't think he'd ever heard of Rikers Island. I told him to follow the signs for LaGuardia Airport. When we got close I gave him directions. I got out at a luncheonette at the foot of the bridge that spans Bowery Bay and the channel of the East River that separates the island from the rest of Queens.

Lunch hour had come and gone and the place was mostly empty. A few men in work clothes were seated at the counter. About halfway down a man sat in a booth with a cup of coffee and looked up expectantly at my approach. I introduced myself and he said he was Marvin Hiller.

'My car's outside,' he said. 'Or did you want to grab a cup of coffee? The only thing is I'm a little bit rushed. I had a long morning in Queens Criminal Court and I'm supposed to be at my dentist's in forty-five minutes. If I'm late I'm late.'

I told him I didn't care about coffee. He paid his tab and we went outside and rode his car over the bridge. He was a pleasant and rather earnest man a few years younger than I and he looked like what he was, a lawyer with an office on Queens Boulevard in Elmhurst. One of his clients, one who'd be contributing very little toward the rent on that office, was Louis Pinell.

I'd gotten his name from Frank Fitzroy and managed to get his secretary to beep him and call me at the hotel. I'd expected a flat turndown on my request for clearance to see Pinell and got just the reverse. 'Just so it's kosher,' he had said, 'why don't you meet me out there and we'll drive over together. You'll probably get more out of him that way. He's a little more comfortable about talking with his lawyer present.'

Now he said, 'I don't know what you'll be able to get from him. I suppose you mostly want to satisfy yourself that he didn't kill the Ettinger woman.'

'I suppose.'

'I would think he's in the clear on that one. The evidence is pretty clear-cut. If it was just his word I'd say forget it, because who knows what they remember and what they make up when they're as crazy as he is?'

'He's really crazy?'

'Oh, he's a bedbug,' Hiller said. 'No question about it. You'll see for yourself. I'm his attorney, but between ourselves I see my job as a matter of making sure he never gets out without a leash. It's a good thing I drew this case.'

'Why's that?'

'Because anybody crazy enough to want to could get him off without a whole lot of trouble. I'm going to plead him, but if I made a fight the State's case wouldn't stand up. All they've got is his confession and you could knock that out a dozen different ways, including that he was cuckoo at the time he confessed. They've got no evidence, not after nine years. There's lawyers who think the advocate system means they should go to bat for a guy like Lou and put him back on the streets.'

'He'd do it again.'

'Of course he'd do it again. He had a fucking icepick in his pocket when they collared him. Again between ourselves, I think lawyers with that attitude ought to be in jail alongside their clients. But in the meantime here I am, playing God. What do you want to ask Lou?'

'There was another Brooklyn killing. I might ask him a few questions about that.'

'Sheepshead Bay. He copped to that one.'

'That's right. I don't know what else I'll ask him. I'm probably wasting my time. And yours.'

'Don't worry about it.'

Thirty or forty minutes later we were driving back to the mainland and I was apologizing again for wasting his time.

'You did me a favor,' he said. 'I'm going to have to make another dentist's appointment. You ever have periodontal surgery?'

'No.'

'You're a wise man. This guy's my wife's cousin and he's pretty good, but what they do is they carve your gums. They do a section of your mouth at a time. Last time I went I wound up taking codeine every four hours for a week. I walked around in this perpetual fog. I suppose it's worth it in the long run, but don't feel you took me away from something enjoyable.'

'If you say so.'

I told him he could drop me anywhere but he insisted on giving me a lift to the subway stop at Northern Boulevard. On the way we talked a little about Pinell. 'You can see why they picked him up on the street,' he said. 'That craziness is right there in his eyes. One look and you see it.'

'There are a lot of street crazies.'

'But he's dangerous-crazy and it shows. And yet I'm never nervous in his presence. Well, I'm not a woman and he hasn't got an icepick. That might have something to do with it.'

At the subway entrance I got out of the car and hesitated for a moment, and he leaned toward me, one arm over the back of the seat. We both seemed reluctant to take leave of each other. I liked him and sensed that he held me in similar regard.

'You're not licensed,' he said. 'Isn't that what you said?'

'That's right.'

'Couldn't you get a license?'

'I don't want one.'

'Well, maybe I could throw some work your way all the same, if the right sort of thing came along.'

'Why would you want to?'

'I don't know. I liked your manner with Lou. And I get the feeling with you that you think the truth is important.' He chuckled. 'Besides, I owe you. You spared me a half-hour in the dentist's chair.'

'Well, if I ever need a lawyer—'

'Right. You know who to call.'

I just missed a Manhattan-bound train. While I waited for the next one on the elevated platform I managed to find a phone in working order and tried Lynn London's number. I'd checked the hotel desk before I called Hiller, and there'd been a message from her the night before, probably wondering why I hadn't shown up. I wondered if she'd been the one who called during my shower. Whoever it was hadn't elected to leave a message. The desk man said the caller had been a woman, but I'd learned not to count too heavily on his powers of recollection.

Lynn's number didn't answer. No surprise. She was probably still in school, or on her way home. Had she mentioned any afternoon plans? I couldn't remember.

I retrieved my dime, started to put it and my notebook away. Was there anyone else I should call? I flipped pages in my notebook, struck by how many names and numbers and

addresses I'd written down, considering how little I'd managed to accomplish.

Karen Ettinger? I could ask her what she was afraid of. Hiller had just told me he sensed that I thought the truth was important. Evidently she thought it was worth hiding.

It'd be a toll call, though. And I didn't have much change.

Charles London? Frank Fitzroy? An ex-cop on the Upper West Side? His ex-wife on the Lower East Side?

Mitzi Pomerance? Jan Keane?

Probably still had the phone off the hook.

I put the notebook away, and the dime. I could have used a drink. I'd had nothing since that one eye-opener at McGovern's. I'd eaten a late breakfast since then, had drunk several cups of coffee, but that was it.

I looked over the low wall at the rear of the platform. My eye fastened on red neon in a tavern window. I'd just missed a train. I could have a quick one and be back in plenty of time for the next one.

I sat down on a bench and waited for my train.

I changed trains twice and wound up at Columbus Circle. The sky was darkening by the time I hit the street, turning that particular cobalt blue that it gets over New York. There were no messages waiting for me at my hotel. I called Lynn London from the lobby.

This time I reached her. 'The elusive Mr Scudder,' she said. 'You stood me up.'

'I'm sorry.'

'I waited for you yesterday afternoon. Not for long, because I didn't have too much time available. I suppose something came up, but you didn't call, either.'

I remembered how I had considered keeping the appointment and how I'd decided against it. Alcohol had made the decision for me. I'd been in a warm bar and it was cold outside.

'I'd just spoken to your father,' I said. 'He asked me to drop the case. I figured he'd have been in touch with you to tell you not to cooperate with me.'

'So you just decided to write off the Londons, is that it?' There was a trace of amusement in her voice. 'I was here waiting, as I said. Then I went out and kept my date for the evening, and when I got home my father called. To tell me he'd ordered you off the case but that you intended to persist with it all the same.'

So I could have seen her. Alcohol had made the decision, and had made it badly.

'He told me not to offer you any encouragement. He said he'd made a mistake raking up the past to begin with.'

'But you called me. Or was that before you spoke to him?'

'Once before and once after. The first call was because I was angry with you for standing me up. The second call was because I was angry with my father.'

'Why?'

'Because I don't like being told what to do. I'm funny that way. He says you wanted a picture of Barbara. I gather he refused to give it to you. Do you still want one?'

Did I? I couldn't recall now what I'd planned to do with it. Maybe I'd make the rounds of hardware stores, showing it to everyone who sold icepicks.

'Yes,' I said. 'I still want one.'

'Well, I can supply that much. I don't know what else I can give you. But one thing I can't give you at the moment is time. I was on my way out the door when the phone range. I've got my coat on. I'm meeting a friend for dinner, and then I'm going to be busy this evening.'

'With group therapy.'

'How did you know that? Did I mention it the last time we talked? You have a good memory.'

'Sometimes.'

'Just let me think. Tomorrow night's also impossible. I'd say come over tonight after therapy but by then I generally feel as though I've been through the wringer. After school tomorrow there's a faculty meeting, and by the time that's over – look, could you come to the school?'

'Tomorrow?'

'I've got a free period from one to two. Do you know where I teach?'

'A private school in the Village, but I don't know which one.'

'It's the Devonhurst School. Sounds very preppy, doesn't it? Actually it's anything but. And it's in the East Village. Second Avenue between Tenth and Eleventh. The east side of the street closer to Eleventh than Tenth.'

'I'll find it.'

'I'll be in Room Forty-one. And Mr Scudder? I wouldn't want to be stood up a second time.'

I went around the corner to Armstrong's. I had a hamburger and

a small salad, then some bourbon in coffee. They switch bartenders at eight, and when Billie came in a half-hour before his shift started I went over to him.

'I guess I was pretty bad last night,' I said.

'Oh, you were okay,' he said.

'It was a long day and night.'

'You were talking a little loud,' he said. 'Aside from that you were your usual self. And you knew to leave here and make it an early night.'

Except I hadn't made it an early night.

I went back to my table and had another bourbon and coffee. By the time I was finished with it, the last of my hangover was gone. I'd shaken off the headache fairly early on, but the feeling of being a step or two off the pace had persisted throughout the day.

Great system: the poison and the antidote come in the same bottle.

I went to the phone, dropped a dime. I almost dialed Anita's number and sat there wondering why. I didn't want to talk about a dead dog, and that was as close as we'd come to a meaningful conversation in years.

I dialed Jan's number. My notebook was in my pocket but I didn't have to get it out. The number was just right there at hand.

'It's Matthew,' I said. 'I wondered if you felt like company.'

'Oh.'

'Unless you're busy.'

'No, I'm not. As a matter of fact, I'm a little under the weather. I was just settling in for a quiet evening in front of the television set.'

'Well, if you'd rather be alone—'

'I didn't say that.' There was a pause. 'I wouldn't want to make it a late evening.'

'Neither would I.'

'You remember how to get here?'

'I remember.'

On the way there I felt like a kid on a date. I rang her bell according to the code and stood at the curb. She tossed me the key. I went inside and rode up in the big elevator.

She was wearing a skirt and sweater and had doeskin slippers on her feet. We stood looking at each other for a moment and then I handed her the paper bag I was carrying. She took out the

two bottles, one of Teacher's Scotch, the other of the brand of Russian vodka she favored.

'The perfect hostess gift,' she said. 'I thought you were a bourbon drinker.'

'Well, it's a funny thing. I had a clear head the other morning, and it occurred to me that Scotch might be less likely to give me a hangover.'

She put the bottles down. 'I wasn't going to drink tonight,' she said.

'Well, it'll keep. Vodka doesn't go bad.'

'Not if you don't drink it. Let me fix you something. Straight, right?'

'Right.'

It was stilted at first. We'd been close to one another, we'd spent a night in bed together, but we were nevertheless stiff and awkward with each other. I started talking about the case, partly because I wanted to talk to someone about it, partly because it was what we had in common. I told her how my client had tried to take me off the case and how I was staying with it anyway. She didn't seem to find this unusual.

Then I talked about Pinell.

'He definitely didn't kill Barbara Ettinger,' I said, 'and he definitely did commit the icepick murder in Sheepshead Bay. I didn't really have much doubt about either of those points but I wanted to have my own impressions to work with. And I just plain wanted to see him. I wanted some sense of the man.'

'What was he like?'

'Ordinary. They're always ordinary, aren't they? Except I don't know that that's the right word for it. The thing about Pinell is that he looked insignificant.'

'I think I saw a picture of him in the paper.'

'You don't get the full effect from a photograph. Pinell's the kind of person you don't notice. You see guys like him delivering lunches, taking tickets in a movie theater. Slight build, furtive manner, and a face that just won't stay in your memory.'

' "The Banality of Evil." '

'What's that?'

She repeated the phrase. 'It's the title of an essay about Adolf Eichmann.'

'I don't know that Pinell's evil. He's crazy. Maybe evil's a form of insanity. Anyway, you don't need a psychiatrist's report

to know he's crazy. It's right there in his eyes. Speaking of eyes, that's another thing I wanted to ask him.'

'What?'

'If he stabbed them all in both eyes. He said he did. He did that right away, before he went to work turning their bodies into pincushions.'

She shuddered. 'Why?'

'That was the other thing I wanted to ask him. Why the eyes? It turned out he had a perfectly logical reason. He did it to avoid detection.'

'I don't follow you.'

'He thought a dead person's eyes would retain the last image they perceived before death. If that were the case you could obtain a picture of the murderer by scanning the victim's retina. He was just guarding against this possibility by destroying their eyes.'

'Jesus.'

'The funny thing is that he's not the first person to have that theory. During the last century some criminologists believed the same thing Pinell hit on. They just figured it was a matter of time before the necessary technology existed for recovering the image from the retina. And who knows that it won't be possible someday? A doctor could give you all sorts of reasons why it'll never be physiologically possible, but look at all the things that would have seemed at least as farfetched a hundred years ago. Or even twenty years ago.'

'So Pinell's just a little ahead of his time, is that it?' She got up, carried my empty glass to the bar. She filled it and poured a glass of vodka for herself. 'I do believe that calls for a drink. "Here's looking at you, kid." That's as close as I can come to an imitation of Humphrey Bogart. I do better with clay.'

She sat down and said, 'I wasn't going to drink anything today. Well, what the hell.'

'I want to go fairly light myself.'

She nodded, her eyes aimed at the glass in her hand. 'I was glad when you called, Matthew. I didn't think you were going to.'

'I tried to get you last night. I kept getting a busy signal.'

'I had the phone off the hook.'

'I know.'

'You had them check it? I just wanted to keep the world away last night. When I'm in here with the door locked and the phone

off the hook and the shades down, that's when I'm really safe. Do you know what I mean?'

'I think so.'

'See, I didn't wake up with a clear head Sunday morning. I got drunk Sunday night. And then I got drunk again last night.'

'Oh.'

'And then I got up this morning and took a pill to stop the shakes and decided I'd stay away from it for a day or two. Just to get off the roller-coaster, you know?'

'Sure.'

'And here I am with a glass in my hand. Isn't that a surprise?'

'You should have said something, Jan. I wouldn't have brought the vodka.'

'It's no big deal.'

'I wouldn't have brought the Scotch, either. I had too much to drink last night myself. We could be together tonight without drinking.'

'You really think so?'

'Of course.'

Her large gray eyes looked quite bottomless. She stared sadly at me for a long moment, then brightened. 'Well, it's too late to test that hypothesis right now, isn't it? Why don't we just make the best of what we have?'

We didn't do all that much drinking. She had enough vodka to catch up with me and then we both coasted. She played some records and we sat together on the couch and listened to them, not talking much. We started making love on the couch and then went into the bedroom to finish the job.

We were good together, better than we'd been Saturday night. Novelty is a spice, but when the chemistry is good between lovers, familiarity enhances their love-making. I got out of myself some, and felt a little of what she felt.

Afterward we went back to the couch and I started talking about the murder of Barbara Ettinger. 'She's buried so goddamn deep,' I said. 'It's not just the amount of time that's gone by. Nine years is a long time, but there are people who died nine years ago and you could walk through their lives and find everything pretty much as they left it. The same people in the houses next door and everybody leading the same kind of life.

'With Barbara, everybody's gone through a sea-change. You closed the day-care center and left your husband and moved here. Your husband took the kids and beat it to California. I was one of the first cops on the scene, and God knows my life turned

upside down since then. There were three cops who investigated the case in Sheepshead Bay, or started to. Two of them are dead and one left the force and his wife and lives in a furnished room and stands guard in a department store.'

'And Doug Ettinger's remarried and selling sporting goods.'

I nodded. 'And Lynn London's been married and divorced, and half the neighbors on Wyckoff Street have moved somewhere or other. It's as though every wind on earth's been busy blowing sand on top of her grave. I know Americans lead mobile lives. I read somewhere that every year twenty percent of the country changes its place of residence. Even so, it's as though every wind on earth's been busy blowing sand on top of her grave. It's like digging for Troy.'

' "Deep with the first dead." '

'How's that?'

'I don't know if I remember it right. Just a second.' She crossed the room, searched the bookshelves, removed a slim volume and paged through it. 'It's Dylan Thomas,' she said, 'and it's in here somewhere. Where the hell is it? I'm sure it's in here. Here it is.' She read:

'Deep with the first dead lies London's daughter,
Robed in the long friends,
The grains beyond age, the dark veins of her mother,
Secret by the unmourning water
Of the riding Thames.
After the first death, there is no other.'

'London's daughter,' I said.

'As in the city of London. But that must be what made me think of it. Deep with the first dead lies Charles London's daughter.'

'Read it again.'

She did.

'Except there's a door there somewhere if I could just find the handle to it. It wasn't some nut that killed her. It was someone with a reason, someone she knew. Someone who purposely made it look like Pinell's handiwork. And the killer's still around. He didn't die or drop out of sight. He's still around. I don't have any grounds to believe that but it's a feeling I can't shake.'

'You think it's Doug?'

'If I don't, I'm the only one who doesn't. Even his wife thinks

he did it. She may not know that's what she thinks, but why else is she scared of what I'll find?'

'But you think it's somebody else?'

'I think an awful lot of lives changed radically after her death. Maybe her dying had something to do with those changes. With some of them, anyway.'

'Doug's obviously. Whether he killed her or not.'

'Maybe it affected other lives, too.'

'Like a stone in a pond? The ripple effect?'

'Maybe. I don't know just what happened or how. I told you, it's a matter of a hunch, a feeling. Nothing concrete that I can point at.'

'Your cop instincts, is that it?'

I laughed. She asked what was funny. I said, 'It's not so funny. I've had all day to wonder about the validity of my cop instincts.'

'How do you mean?'

And so I wound up telling her more than I'd planned. About everything from Anita's phone call to a kid with a gravity knife. Two nights ago I'd found out what a good listener she was, and she was no worse at it this time around.

When I was done she said, 'I don't know why you're down on yourself. You could have been killed.'

'If it was really a mugging attempt.'

'What were you supposed to do, wait until he stuck a knife into you? And why was he carrying a knife in the first place? I don't know what a gravity knife is, but it doesn't sound like something you carry around in case you need to cut a piece of string.'

'He could have been carrying it for protection.'

'And the roll of money? It sounds to me as though he's one of those closet cases who pick up gay men and rob them, and sometimes beat them up or kill them while they're at it to prove how straight they are. And you're worrying because you gave a kid like that a bloody lip?'

I shook my head. 'I'm worrying because my judgment wasn't sound.'

'Because you were drunk.'

'And didn't even know it.'

'Was your judgment off the night you shot the two holdup men? The night that Puerto Rican girl got killed?'

'You're a pretty sharp lady, aren't you?'

'A fucking genius.'

'That's the question, I guess. And the answer is no, it wasn't. I hadn't had much to drink and I wasn't feeling it. But—'

'But you got echoes just the same.'

'Right.'

'And didn't want to look straight at them, any more than Karen Ettinger wants to look straight at the fact that she thinks her husband might have murdered his first wife.'

'A very sharp lady.'

'They don't come any sharper. Feel better now?'

'Uh-huh.'

'Talking helps. But you kept it so far inside you didn't even know it was there.' She yawned. 'Being a sharp lady is tiring work.'

'I can believe it.'

'Want to go to bed?'

'Sure.'

But I didn't stay the night. I thought I might, but I was still awake when her breathing changed to indicate that she was sleeping. I lay first on one side and then on the other, and it was clear I wasn't ready to sleep. I got out of bed and padded quietly into the other room.

I dressed, then stood at the window and looked out at Lispenard Street. There was plenty of Scotch left but I didn't want to drink any of it.

I let myself out. A block away on Canal Street I managed to flag a cab. I got uptown in time to catch the last half-hour or so at Armstrong's, but I said the hell with it and went straight to my room.

I got to sleep eventually.

FOURTEEN

I had a night of dreams and shallow sleep. The dog, Bandy, turned up in one of the dreams. He wasn't really dead. His death had been faked as part of some elaborate scam. He told me all this, told me too that he'd always been able to talk but had been afraid to disclose this talent. 'If I'd only known,' I marveled, 'what conversations we could have had!'

I awoke refreshed and clearheaded and fiercely hungry. I had bacon and eggs and home fries at the Red Flame and read the *News*. They'd caught the First Avenue Slasher, or at the least had arrested someone they said was the Slasher. A photograph of the suspect bore a startling resemblance to the police artist's sketch that had run earlier. That doesn't happen too often.

I was on my second cup of coffee when Vinnie slid into the booth across from me. 'Woman in the lobby,' he said.

'For me?'

He nodded. 'Young, not bad-looking. Nice clothes, nice hair. Gave me a couple of bucks to point you out when you came in. I don't even know if you're comin' back, so I figured I'd take a chance, look here and there and see if I could find you. I got Eddie coverin' the desk for me. You comin' back to the hotel?'

'I hadn't planned to.'

'What you could do, see, you could look her over and gimme a sign to point you out or not point you out. I'd just as soon earn the couple of bucks, but I'm not gonna go and retire on it, you know what I mean? If you want to duck this dame –'

'You can point me out,' I said. 'Whoever she is.'

He went back to the desk. I finished my coffee and the paper and took my time returning to the hotel. When I walked in Vinnie nodded significantly toward the wing chair over by the cigarette machine, but he needn't have bothered. I'd have spotted her without help. She looked utterly out of place, a well-groomed, well-coiffed, color-coordinated suburban princess

who'd found her way to the wrong part of Fifty-seventh Street. A few blocks east she might have been having an adventure, making the rounds of the art galleries, looking for a print that would go well with the mushroom-toned drapes in the family room.

I let Vinnie earn his money, strolled past her, stood waiting for the elevator. Its doors were just opening when she spoke my name.

I said, 'Hello, Mrs Ettinger.'

'How –'

'Saw your picture on your husband's desk. And I probably would have recognized your voice, although I've only heard it over the phone.' The blonde hair was a little longer than in the picture in Douglas Ettinger's photo cube, and the voice in person was less nasal, but there was no mistaking her. 'I heard your voice a couple of times. Once when I called you, once when you called me, and again when I called you back.'

'I thought that was you,' she said. 'It frightened me when the phone rang and you didn't say anything.'

'I just wanted to make sure I'd recognized the voice.'

'I called you since then. I called twice yesterday.'

'I didn't get any messages.'

'I didn't leave any. I don't know what I'd have said if I reached you. Is there someplace more private where we can talk?'

I took her out for coffee, not to the Red Flame but to another similar place down the block. On the way out Vinnie tipped me a wink and a sly smile. I wonder how much money she'd given him.

Less, I'm sure, than she was prepared to give me. We were no sooner settled with our coffee than she put her purse on the table and gave it a significant tap.

'I have an envelope in here,' she announced. 'There's five thousand dollars in it.'

'That's a lot of cash to be carrying in this town.'

'Maybe you'd like to carry it for me.' She studied my face, and when I failed to react she leaned forward, dropping her voice conspiratorially. 'The money's for you, Mr Scudder. Just do what Mr London already asked you to do. Drop the case.'

'What are you afraid of, Mrs Ettinger?'

'I just don't want you poking around in our lives.'

'What is it you think I might find there?' Her hand clutched her purse, seeking security in the presumptive power of five

113

thousand dollars. Her nail polish was the color of iron rust. Gently I said, 'Do you think your husband killed his first wife?'

'No!'

'Then what have you got to be afraid of?'

'I don't know.'

'When did you meet your husband, Mrs Ettinger?'

She met my eyes, didn't answer.

'Before his wife was killed?' Her fingers kneaded her handbag. 'He went to college on Long Island. You're younger than he is, but you could have known him then.'

'That was before he even knew her,' she said. 'Long before they were married. Then we happened to run into each other again after her death.'

'And you were afraid I'd find that out?'

'I –'

'You were seeing him before she died, weren't you?'

'You can't prove that.'

'Why would I have to prove it? Why would I even want to prove it?'

She opened the purse. Her fingers clumsy with the clasp but she got the bag open and took out a manila bank envelope. 'Five thousand dollars,' she said.

'Put it away.'

'Isn't it enough? It's a lot of money. Isn't five thousand dollars a lot of money for doing nothing?'

'It's too much. You didn't kill her, did you, Mrs Ettinger?'

'Me?' She had trouble getting a grip on the question. 'Me? Of course not.'

'But you were glad when she died.'

'That's horrible,' she said. 'Don't say that.'

'You were having an affair with him. You wanted to marry him, and then she was killed. How could you help being glad?'

Her eyes were pitched over my shoulder, gazing off into the distance. Her voice was as remote as her gaze. She said, 'I didn't know she was pregnant. He said . . . he said he hadn't known that either. He told me they weren't sleeping together. Having sex, I mean. Of course they slept together, they shared a bed, but he said they weren't having sex. I believed him.'

The waitress was approaching to refill our coffee cups. I held up a hand to ward off the interruption. Karen Ettinger said, 'He said she was carrying another man's child. Because it couldn't have been his baby.'

'Is that what you told Charles London?'

'I never spoke to Mr London.'

'Your husband did, though, didn't he? Is that what he told him? Is that what London was afraid would come out if I stayed on the case?'

Her voice was detached, remote. 'He said she was pregnant by another man. A black man. He said the baby would have been black.'

'That's what he told London.'

'Yes.'

'Had he ever told you that?'

'No. I think it was just something he made up to influence Mr London.' She looked at me, and her eyes showed me a little of the person hidden beneath the careful suburban exterior. 'Just like the rest of it was something he made up for my sake. It was probably his baby.'

'You don't think she was having an affair?'

'Maybe. Maybe she was. But she must have been sleeping with him, too. Or else she would have been careful not to get pregnant. Women aren't stupid.' She blinked her eyes several times. 'Except about some things. Men always tell their girlfriends that they've stopped sleeping with their wives. And it's always a lie.'

'Do you think that –'

She rolled right over my question. 'He's probably telling her that he's not sleeping with me anymore,' she said, her tone very matter-of-fact. 'And it's a lie.'

'Telling whom?'

'Whoever he's having an affair with.'

'Your husband is currently having an affair with someone?'

'Yes,' she said, and frowned. 'I didn't know that until just now. I knew it, but I didn't know that I knew it. I wish you had never taken this case. I wish Mr London had never heard of you in the first place.'

'Mrs Ettinger –'

She was standing now, her purse gripped in both hands, her face showing her pain. 'I had a good marriage,' she insisted. 'And what have I got now? Will you tell me that? What have I got now?'

FIFTEEN

I don't suppose she wanted an answer. I certainly didn't have one for her, and she didn't hang around to find out what else I might have to say. She walked stiffly out of the coffee shop. I stayed long enough to finish my own coffee, then left a tip and paid the check. Not only hadn't I taken her five thousand dollars, but I'd wound up buying her coffee.

It was a nice day out and I thought I'd kill a little time by walking part of the way to my appointment with Lynn London. As it turned out I walked all the way downtown and east, stopping once to sit on a park bench and another time for coffee and a roll. When I crossed Fourteenth Street I ducked into Dan Lynch's and had the first drink of the day. I'd thought earlier that I might switch to Scotch, which had once again spared me a hangover, but I'd ordered a shot of bourbon with a short beer for a chaser before I remembered my decision. I drank it down and enjoyed the warmth of it. The saloon had a rich beery smell and I enjoyed that, too, and would have liked to linger awhile. But I'd already stood up the schoolteacher once.

I found the school, walked in. No one questioned my entering it or stopped me in the corridors. I located Room *41* and stood in the doorway for a moment, studying the woman seated at the blond oak desk. She was reading a book and unaware of my presence. I knocked on the open door and she looked up at me.

'I'm Matthew Scudder,' I said.

'And I'm Lynn London. Come in. Close the door.'

She stood up and we shook hands. There was no place for me to sit, just child-sized desks. The children's art work and test papers, some marked with gold or silver stars, were tacked on bulletin boards. There was a problem in long division worked out in yellow chalk on the blackboard. I found myself checking the arithmetic.

'You wanted a picture,' Lynn London was saying. 'I'm afraid

I'm not much on family memorabilia. This was the best I could do. This was Barbara in college.'

I studied the photo, glanced from it to the woman standing beside me. She caught the eye movement. 'If you're looking for a resemblance,' she said, 'don't waste your time. She looked like our mother.'

Lynn favored her father. She had the same chilly blue eyes. Like him she wore glasses, but hers had heavy rims and rectangular lenses. Her brown hair was pulled back and coiled in a tight bun on the back of her head. There was a severity in her face, a sharpness to her features, and although I knew she was only thirty-three she looked several years older. There were lines at the corners of her eyes, deeper ones at the corners of her mouth.

I couldn't get much from Barbara's picture. I'd seen police photos of her after death, high-contrast black and white shot in the kitchen on Wyckoff Street, but I wanted something that would give me a sense of the person and Lynn's photograph didn't supply that, either. I may have been looking for more than a photograph could furnish.

She said, 'My father's afraid you'll drag Barbara's name through the mud. Will you?'

'I hadn't planned on it.'

'Douglas Ettinger told him something and he's afraid you'll tell it to the world. I wish I knew what it was.'

'He told your father that your sister was carrying a black man's child.'

'Holy Jesus. Is that true?'

'What do you think?'

'I think Doug's a worm. I've always thought that. Now I know why my father hates you.'

'Hates *me?*'

'Uh-huh. I wondered why. In fact I wanted to meet you mostly to find out what kind of man would inspire such a strong reaction in my father. You see, if it weren't for you he wouldn't have been given that piece of information about his sainted daughter. If he hadn't hired you, and if you hadn't talked to Doug – you did talk to Doug, I assume?'

'I met him. At the store in Hicksville.'

'If you hadn't, he wouldn't have told my father something my father emphatically did not want to be told. I think he'd prefer to believe that both of his daughters are virgins. Well, he may not care so much about me. I had the temerity to get divorced so

that makes me beyond redemption. He'd be sick if I got into an interracial romance, because after all there's a limit, but I don't think he cares if I have affairs. I'm already damaged goods.' Her voice was flat, less bitter than the words she was speaking. 'But Barbara was a saint. If I got killed he wouldn't hire you in the first place, but if he did he wouldn't care what you found. With Barbara it's a different story altogether.'

'Was she a saint?'

'We weren't that close.' She looked away, picked up a pencil from the desk top. 'She was my big sister. I put her on a pedestal and wound up seeing her feet of clay, and I went through a period of holier-than-thou contempt for her. I might have outgrown that but then she was killed, so I had all that guilt over the way I'd felt about her.' She looked at me. 'This is one of the things I've been working on in the therapy.'

'Was she having an affair while she was married to Ettinger?'

'She wouldn't have told me if she had been. The one thing she did tell me was that he was playing around. She said he made passes at their friends and that he was screwing his welfare clients. I don't know if that was true or not. He never made a pass at me.'

She said that last as if it was one more item on a long list of resentments. I talked with her for another ten minutes and didn't learn anything beyond the fact that Barbara Ettinger's death had had an impact on her sister's life, and that wasn't news. I wondered how different Lynn had been nine years ago, and how different she might have turned out if Barbara had lived. Perhaps it was all there already, all locked in place, the bitterness, the emotional armor. I wondered – although I could probably have guessed – what Lynn's own marriage had been like. Would she have married the same man if Barbara had been alive? Would she have divorced him if she did?

I left there with a useless photograph and a head full of irrelevant – or unanswerable – questions. I left, too, glad to escape from the woman's cramped personality. Dan Lynch's bar was just a couple blocks uptown, and I turned toward it, remembering the dark wood, the warmth, the boozy, beery aroma.

They were all afraid I'd dig her up, I thought, and it was impossible because she was buried impossibly deep. The bit of poetry Jan had read came to mind and I tried to recall just how it went. *Deep with the first dead?* Was that right?

I decided I wanted the exact wording. More than that, I

wanted the whole poem. I had a vague recollection of a branch library somewhere around there on Second Avenue. I walked a block north, didn't find it, turned around and walked downtown. There was indeed a library, right where I'd remembered it, a squarish three-story building with a nicely ornamented marble facade. A sign in the door gave the hours, and they were closed on Wednesdays.

All of the branch libraries have cut back on their hours, added closed days. Part of the financial pinch. The city can't afford anything, and the administration goes around like an old miser closing off unused rooms in a sprawling cold house. The police force is ten thousand men below what it used to be. Everything drops but the rents and the crime rate.

I walked another block and hit St Marks Place and knew there'd be a bookstore around, and one that would most likely have a poetry section. The busiest commercial block of St Marks Place, and as trendy a block as the East Village possesses, runs between Second and Third Avenues. I turned right and walked toward Third, and two-thirds of the way down the block I found a bookstore. They had a paperback edition of the collected poems of Dylan Thomas. I had to go through it a couple of times before I spotted the poem I was looking for, but it was there and I read it all the way through. 'A refusal to Mourn the Death by Fire of a Child in London' was the title. There were parts I didn't think I understood, but I liked the sound of them anyway, the weight and shape of the words.

The poem was long enough to discourage me from trying to copy it into my notebook. Besides, maybe I'd want to look at some of the other poems. I paid for the book and slipped it into my pocket.

Funny how little things nudge you in one direction or another. I had tired myself with all the walking I'd done. I wanted to catch a subway home, but I also wanted a drink and I stood for a moment on the sidewalk in front of the bookstore, trying to decide what to do and where to go. While I was standing there, two patrolmen walked by in uniform. Both of them looked impossibly young, and one was so fresh-faced his uniform looked like a costume.

Across the street, a shop sign read 'Haberman's.' I don't know what they sold there.

I thought of Burton Havermeyer. I might have thought of him without having seen the cop or having my memory jostled by a

name not unlike his. In any event I thought of him, and remembered that he had once lived on this street, that his wife still lived here. I couldn't remember the address, but it was still in my notebook. 212 St Marks Place, along with the telephone number.

There was still no reason to go look at the building she lived in. He wasn't even part of the case I was working on, because my meeting with Louis Pinell had satisfied me that the little psychopath had killed Susan Potowski and had not killed Barbara Ettinger. But Havermeyer's life had been changed, and in a way that interested me, a way not unlike that in which mine had been changed by another death.

St Marks Place starts at Third Avenue and the numbers get higher as you go eastward. The block between Second and First was more residential and less commercial. A couple of the row houses had ornate windows and letterboards near the entrance to indicate that they were churches. There was a Ukrainian church, a Polish Catholic church.

I walked to First Avenue, waited for the light, walked on across. I made my way down a quiet block, its houses less prepossessing and in poorer repair than on the preceding block. One of a group of parked cars I passed was a derelict, stripped of tires and hubcaps, the radio pulled out, the interior gutted. On the other side of the street three bearded and longhaired men in Hell's Angels colors were trying to get a motorcyle started.

The last number on the block was 132. The street deadended at the corner, where Avenue A formed the western boundary of Tompkins Square Park. I stood there looking at the house number, then at the park, first at one and then at the other.

From Avenue A east to the river are the blocks they call Alphabet City. The population runs to junkies and muggers and crazies. Nobody decent lives there on purpose, not if they can afford to live anywhere else.

I dragged out my notebook. The address was still the same, 212 St Marks Place.

I walked through Tompkins Square and across Avenue B. On my way through the park, drug dealers offered to sell me dope and pills and acid. Either I didn't look like a cop to them or they just didn't care.

On the other side of Avenue B, the numbers started at 300. And the street signs didn't call it St Marks Place. It was East Eighth Street there.

I went back through the park again. At 130 St Marks Place

there was a bar called Blanche's Tavern. I went in. The place was a broken-down bucket of blood that smelled of stale beer and stale urine and bodies that needed washing. Perhaps a dozen of the bodies were there, most of them at the bar, a couple at tables. The place went dead silent when I walked into it. I guess I didn't look as though I belonged there, and I hope to God I never do.

I used the phone book first. The precinct in Sheepshead Bay could have made a mistake, or Antonelli could have read the number to me wrong, or I could have copied it incorrectly. I found him listed, Burton Havermeyer on West 103rd, but I didn't find any Havermeyers listed on St Marks Place.

I was out of dimes. The bartender gave me change. His customers seemed more relaxed now that they realized I had no business with them.

I dropped a dime in the slot, dialed the number in my book. No answer.

I went out and walked a few doors to 112 St Marks Place. I checked the mail boxes in the vestibule, not really expecting to find the name Havermeyer, then went back outside. I wanted a drink but Blanche's wasn't where I wanted to have it.

Any port in a storm. I had a straight shot of bourbon at the bar, a stop-shelf brand. To my right, two men were discussing some mutual friends. 'I told her not to go home with him,' one of them was saying. 'I told her he was no good and he'd beat her up and rip her off, and she went anyhow, took him on home, and he beat her up and ripped her off. So where's she get off coming and crying to me?'

I tried the number again. On the fourth ring a boy answered it. I thought I'd misdialed, asked if I had the Havermeyer residence. He told me I did.

I asked if Mrs Havermeyer was there.

'She's next door,' he said. 'Is it important? Because I could get her.'

'Don't bother. I have to check the address for a delivery. What's the house number there?'

'Two twelve.'

'Two twelve what?'

He started to tell me the apartment number. I told him I needed to know the name of the street.

'Two twelve St Marks Place,' he said.

I had a moment of the sort I have now and then had in dreams, where the sleeping mind confronts an impossible inconsistency

and breaks through to the realization that it is dreaming. Here I was talking to some fresh-voiced child who insisted he lived at an address that did not exist.

Or perhaps he and his mother lived in Tompkins Square Park, with the squirrels.

I said, 'What's that between?'

'Huh?'

'What are the cross streets? What block are you on?'

'Oh,' he said. 'Third and Fourth.'

'What?'

'We're between Third and Fourth Avenues.'

'That's impossible,' I said.

'Huh?'

I looked away from the phone, half-expecting to see something entirely different from the interior of Blanche's Tavern. A lunar landscape, perhaps. St Marks Place started at Third Avenue and ran east. There was no St Marks Place between Third and Fourth Avenues.

I said, 'Where?'

'Huh? Look, mister, I don't –'

'Wait a minute.'

'Maybe I should get my mother. I –'

'What borough?'

'Huh?'

'Are you in Manhattan? Brooklyn? The Bronx? Where are you, son?'

'Brooklyn.'

'Are you sure?'

'Yes, I'm sure.' He sounded close to tears. 'We live in Brooklyn. What do you want, anyway? What's the matter, are you crazy or something?'

'It's all right,' I said. 'You've been a big help. Thanks a lot.'

I hung up, feeling like an idiot. Street names repeated through the five boroughs. I'd had no grounds to assume she lived in Manhattan.

I thought back, replayed what I could of my earlier conversation with the woman. If anything, I might have known that she didn't live in Manhattan. 'He's in Manhattan,' she had said of her husband. She wouldn't have put it that way if she'd been in Manhattan herself.

But what about my conversation with Havermeyer? 'You're wife's still in the East Village,' I'd said, and he'd agreed with me.

Well, maybe he'd just wanted the conversation to end. It was

easier to agree with me than to explain that there was another St Marks Place in Brooklyn.

Still ...

I left Blanche's and hurried west to the bookstore where I'd bought the book of poems. They had a Hagstrom pocket atlas of the five boroughs. I looked up St Marks Place in the back, turned to the appropriate map, found what I was looking for.

St Marks Place, in Brooklyn as in Manhattan, extends for only three blocks. To the east, across Flatbush Avenue, the same street continues at an angle as St Marks Avenue, stretching under that name clear to Brownsville.

To the west, St Marks Place stops at Third Avenue – just as it does at an altogether different Third Avenue in Manhattan. On the other side of Third, Brooklyn's St Marks Place has another name.

Wyckoff Street.

SIXTEEN

It must have been around three o'clock when I spoke with the boy. It was between six thirty and seven by the time I mounted the stoop of his building on West 103rd. I'd found things to do during the intervening hours.

I rang a couple of bells but not his, and someone buzzed me in. Whoever it was peered at me from a doorway on the third floor but didn't challenge my right to pass. I stood at Havermeyer's door and listened for a moment. The television was on, tuned to the local news.

I didn't really expect him to shoot through the door but he did wear a gun as a security guard, and although he probably left it in the store each night I couldn't be sure he didn't have another one at home. They teach you to stand at the side of a door when you knock on it, so I did. I heard his footsteps approach the door, then his voice asking who it was.

'Scudder,' I said.

He opened the door. He was in street clothes and probably left not only the gun but the entire uniform at the store each night. He had a can of beer in one hand. I asked if I could come in. His reaction time was slow but at length he nodded and made room for me. I entered and drew the door shut.

He said, 'Still on that case, huh? Something I can do for you?'

'Yes.'

'Well, I'll be glad to help if I can. Meantime, how about a beer?'

I shook my head. He looked at the can of beer he was holding, moved to set it down on a table, went over and turned off the television set. He held the pose for a moment and I studied his face in profile. He didn't need a shave this time. He turned slowly, expectantly, as if waiting for the blow to fall.

I said, 'I know you killed her, Burt.'

I watched his deep brown eyes. He was rehearsing his denial,

124

running it through his mind, and then there was a moment when he decided not to bother. Something went out of him.

'When did you know?'

'A couple of hours ago.'

'When you left here Sunday I couldn't figure whether you knew or not. I thought maybe you were going cat-and-mouse with me. But I didn't get that feeling. I felt close to you, actually. I felt we were a couple of ex-cops, two guys who left the force for personal reasons. I thought maybe you were playing a part, setting a trap, but it didn't feel like it.'

'I wasn't.'

'How did you find out?'

'St Marks Place. You didn't live in the East Village after all. You lived in Brooklyn three blocks away from Barbara Ettinger.'

'Thousands of people lived that close to her.'

'You let me go on thinking you lived in the East Village. I don't know if I'd have had a second thought about it if I'd known from the beginning that you had lived in Brooklyn. Maybe I would have. But most likely I wouldn't. Brooklyn's a big place. I didn't know there was a St Marks Place in it so I certainly didn't know where it was in relation to Wyckoff Street. For all I knew, it could have been out in Sheepshead Bay near your precinct. But you lied about it.'

'Just to avoid getting into a long explanation. It doesn't prove anything.'

'It gave me a reason to take a look at you. And the first thing I took a look at was another lie you told me. You said you and your wife didn't have any kids. But I talked to your boy on the phone this afternoon, and I called back and asked him his father's name and how old he was. He must have wondered what I was doing asking him all those questions. He's twelve. He was three years old when Barbara Ettinger was killed.'

'So?'

'You used to take him to a place on Clinton Street. The Happy Hours Child Care Center.'

'You're guessing.'

'No.'

'They're out of business. They've been out of business for years.'

'They were still in business when you left Brooklyn. Did you keep tabs on the place?'

'My ex-wife must have mentioned it,' he said. Then he

shrugged. 'Maybe I walked past there once. When I was in Brooklyn visiting Danny.'

'The woman who ran the day-care center is living in New York. She'll remember you.'

'After nine years?'

'That's what she says. And she kept records, Burt. The ledgers with the names and addresses of students and their parents, along with the record of payments. She packed all that stuff in a carton when she closed the business and never bothered to go through it and throw out the things she didn't need to keep anymore. She opened the box today. She says she remembers you. You always brought the boy, she said. She never met your wife but she does remember you.'

'She must have a good memory.'

'You were usually in uniform. That's an easy thing to remember.'

He looked at me for a moment, then turned and walked over to the window and stood looking out of it. I don't suppose he was looking at anything in particular.

'Where'd you get the icepick, Burt?'

Without turning he said, 'I don't have to admit to anything. I don't have to answer any questions.'

'Of course you don't.'

'Even if you were a cop I wouldn't have to say anything. And you're not a cop. You've got no authority.'

'You're absolutely right.'

'So why should I answer your questions?'

'You've been sitting on it a long time, Burt.'

'So?'

'Doesn't it get to you a little? Keeping it inside all that time?'

'Oh, God,' he said. He went over to a chair, dropped into it. 'Bring me that beer,' he said. 'Could you do that for me?'

I gave it to him. He asked me if I was sure I didn't want one for myself. No thanks, I said. He drank some beer and I asked him where he got the icepick.

'Some store,' he said. 'I don't remember.'

'In the neighborhood?'

'I think in Sheepshead Bay. I'm not sure.'

'You knew Barbara Ettinger from the day-care center.'

'And from the neighborhood. I used to see her around the neighborhood before I started taking Danny to the center.'

'And you were having an affair with her?'

'Who told you that? No, I wasn't having an affair with her. I wasn't having an affair with anybody.'

'But you wanted to.'

'No.'

I waited but he seemed willing to leave it there. I said, 'Why did you kill her, Burt?'

He looked at me for a moment, then looked down, then looked at me again. 'You can't prove anything,' he said.

I shrugged.

'You can't. And I don't have to tell you anything.' A deep breath, a long sigh. 'Something happened when I saw the Potowski woman,' he said. 'Something happened.'

'What do you mean?'

'Something happened to *me*. Inside of me. Something came into my head and I couldn't get rid of it. I remember standing and hitting myself in the forehead but I couldn't get it out of my mind.'

'You wanted to kill Barbara Ettinger.'

'No. Don't help me out, okay? Let me find the words by myself.'

'I'm sorry.'

'I looked at the dead woman and it wasn't her I saw on the floor, it was my wife. Every time the picture came back to me, the murder scene, the woman on the floor, I saw my wife in the picture. And I couldn't get it out of my head to kill her that way.'

He took a little sip of beer. Over the top of the can he said, 'I used to think about killing her. Plenty of times I thought that it was the only way out. I couldn't stand being married. I was alone, my parents were dead, I never had any brothers or sisters, and I thought I needed somebody. Besides, I knew she needed me. But it was wrong. I hated being married. It was around my neck like a collar that's too small for you, it was choking me and I couldn't get out of it.'

'Why couldn't you just leave her?'

'How could I leave her? How could I do that to her? What kind of a man leaves a woman like that?'

'Men leave women every day.'

'You don't understand, do you?' Another sigh. 'Where was I? Yeah. I used to think about killing her. I would think about it, and I would think, sure, and the first thing they'd do is check you inside and out, and one way or another they'll hang it on you, because they always go to the husband first and ninety

percent of the time that's who did it, and they'll break your story down and break you down and where does that leave you? But then I saw the Potowski woman and it was all there. I could kill her and make it look like the Icepick Prowler had one more on his string. I saw what we did with the Potowski killing. We just bucked it to Midtown North, we didn't hassle the husband or anything like that.'

'So you decided to kill her.'

'Right.'

'Your wife.'

'Right.'

'Then how does Barbara Ettinger come into this?'

'Oh, God,' he said.

I waited him out.

'I was afraid to kill her. My wife, I mean. I was afraid something would go wrong. I thought, suppose I start and I can't go through with it? I had the icepick and I would take it out and look at it and – I remember now, I bought it on Atlantic Avenue. I don't even know if the store's still there.'

'It doesn't matter.'

'I know. I had visions of, you know, starting to stab her and stopping, of not being able to finish the job, and the things that were going through my mind were driving me crazy. I guess I *was* crazy. Of course I was.'

He drank from the beer can. 'I killed her for practice,' he said.

'Barbara Ettinger.'

'Yes. I had to find out if I could do it. And I told myself it would be a precaution. One more icepick killing in Brooklyn, so that when my wife got murdered three blocks away it would be just one more in the string. And it would be the same. Maybe no matter how I did it they'd notice a difference between it and the real icepick killings, but they would never have a reason to suspect me of killing some stranger like the Ettinger woman, and then my wife would be killed the same way, and – but that was just what I was telling myself. I killed her because I was afraid to kill my wife and I had to kill someone.'

'You had to kill someone?'

'I *had* to.' He leaned forward, sat on the edge of his chair. 'I couldn't get it out of my mind. Do you know what it's like when you can't get something out of your mind?'

'Yes.'

'I couldn't think who to pick. And then one day I took Danny to the day-care center and she and I talked the way we always

did, and the idea came to me. I thought of killing her and the thought fit.'

'What do you mean, "the thought fit"?'

'She belonged in the picture. I could see her, you know, on the kitchen floor. So I started watching her. When I wasn't working I would hang around the neighborhood and keep tabs on her.'

She had sensed that someone was following her, watching her. And she'd been afraid, ever since the Potowski murder, that someone was stalking her.

'And I decided it would be all right to kill her. She didn't have any children. Nobody was dependent upon her. And she was immoral. She flirted with me, she flirted with men at the day-care center. She had men to her apartment when her husband was out. I thought, if I screwed it up and they knew it wasn't the Icepick Prowler, there would be plenty of other suspects. They'd never get to me.'

I asked him about the day of the murder.

'My shift ended around noon that day. I went over to Clinton Street and sat in a coffee shop at the counter where I could keep an eye on the place. When she left early I followed her. I was across the street watching her building when a man went into it. I knew him, I'd seen him with her before.'

'Was he black?'

'Black? No. Why?'

'No reason.'

'I don't remember what he looked like. He was with her for a half-hour or so. Then he left. I waited a little while longer, and something told me, I don't know, I just knew this was the right time. I went up and knocked on her door.'

'And she let you in?'

'I showed her my shield. And I reminded her that she knew me from the day-care center, that I was Danny's father. She let me in.'

'And?'

'I don't want to talk about it.'

'Are you sure of that?'

I guess he thought it over. Then he said, 'We were in the kitchen. She was making me a cup of coffee, she had her back to me, and I put one hand over her mouth and jabbed the icepick into her chest. I wanted to get her heart right away, I didn't want her to suffer. I kept stabbing her in the heart and she collapsed in my arms and I let her fall to the floor.' He raised his liquid

brown eyes to mine. 'I think she was dead right then,' he said. 'I think she died right away.'

'And you went on stabbing her.'

'When I thought about it before I did it, I always went crazy and stabbed over and over like a maniac. I had that picture in my mind. But I couldn't do it that way. I had to make myself stab her and I was sick, I thought I was going to throw up, and I had to keep on sticking that icepick into her body and –' He broke off, gasping for breath. His face was drawn and his pale complexion was ghostly.

'It's all right,' I said.

'Oh, God.'

'Take it easy, Burt.'

'God, God.'

'You only stabbed one of her eyes.'

'It was so *hard*,' he said. 'Her eyes were wide open. I knew she was dead, I knew she couldn't see anything, but those eyes were just staring at me. I had the hardest time making myself stab her in the eye. I did it once and then I just couldn't do it again. I tried but I just couldn't do it again.'

'And then?'

'I left. No one saw me leave. I just left the building and walked away. I put the icepick down a sewer. I thought, I did it, I killed her and I got away with it, but I didn't feel as though I got away with anything. I felt sick to my stomach. I thought about what I had done and I couldn't believe I'd really done it. When the story was on television and in the papers I couldn't believe it. I thought that someone else must have done it.'

'And you didn't kill your wife.'

He shook his head. 'I knew I could never do something like that again. You know something? I've thought about all of it, over and over, and I think I was out of my mind. In fact I'm sure of it. Something about seeing Mrs Potowski, those pools of blood in her eyes, those stab wounds all over her body, it did something to me. It made me crazy, and I went on being crazy until Barbara Ettinger was dead. Then I was all right again, but she was dead.

'All of a sudden certain things were clear. I couldn't stay married anymore, and for the first time I realized I didn't have to. I could leave my wife and Danny. I had thought that would be a horrible thing to do, but here I'd been planning on killing her, and now I'd actually killed somebody and I knew how much

more horrible that was than anything else I could possibly do to her, like leaving.'

I led him through it again, went over a few points. He finished his beer but didn't get another. I wanted a drink, but I didn't want beer and I didn't want to drink with him. I didn't hate him. I don't know exactly what I felt for him. But I didn't want to drink with him.

He broke a silence to say, 'Nobody can prove any of this. It doesn't matter what I told you. There are no witnesses and there's no evidence.'

'People could have seen you in the neighborhood.'

'And still remember nine years later? And remember what day it was?'

He was right, of course. I couldn't imagine a District Attorney who'd even try for an indictment. There was nothing to make a case out of.

I said, 'Why don't you put a coat on, Burt.'

'What for?'

'We'll go down to the Eighteenth Precinct and talk to a cop named Fitzroy. You can tell him what you told me.'

'That'd be pretty stupid, wouldn't it?'

'Why?'

'All I have to do is keep on the way I've been. All I have to do is keep my mouth shut. Nobody can prove anything. They couldn't even try to prove anything.'

'That's probably true.'

'And you want me to confess.'

'That's right.'

His expression was childlike. 'Why?'

To tie off the ends, I thought. To make it neat. To show Frank Fitzroy that he was right when he said I just might solve the case.

What I said was, 'You'll feel better.'

'That's a laugh.'

'How do you feel now, Burt?'

'How do I feel?' He considered the question. Then, as if surprised by his answer, 'I feel okay.'

'Better than when I got here?'

'Yeah.'

'Better than you've felt since Sunday?'

'I suppose so.'

'You never told anybody, did you?'

'Of course not.'

'Not a single person in nine years. You probably didn't think about it much, but there were times when you couldn't help thinking about it, and you never told anybody.'

'So?'

'That's a long time to carry it.'

'God.'

'I don't know what they'll do with you, Burt. You may not do any time. Once I talked a murderer into killing himself, and he did it, and I wouldn't do that again. And another time I talked a murderer into confessing because I convinced him he would probably kill himself if he didn't confess first. I don't think you'd do that. I think you've lived with this for nine years and maybe you could go on living with it. But do you really want to? Wouldn't you rather let go of it?'

'God,' he said. He put his head in his hands. 'I'm all mixed up,' he said.

'You'll be all right.'

'They'll put my picture in the papers. It'll be on the news. What's that going to make it like for Danny?'

'You've got to worry about yourself first.'

'I'll lose my job,' he said. 'What'll happen to me?'

I didn't answer that one. I didn't have an answer.

'Okay,' he said suddenly.

'Ready to go?'

'I guess.'

On the way downtown he said, 'I think I knew Sunday. I knew you'd keep poking at it until you found out I did it. I had an urge to tell you right then.'

'I got lucky. A couple of coincidences put me on St Marks Place and I thought of you and had nothing better to do than see the house where you used to live. But the numbers stopped at One-three-two.'

'If it wasn't that concidence there would have been another one. It was all set from the minute you walked into my apartment. Maybe earlier than that. Maybe it was a sure thing from the minute I killed her. Some people get away with murder but I guess I'm not one of them.'

'Nobody gets away with it. Some people just don't get caught.'

'Isn't that the same thing?'

''You didn't get caught for nine years, Burt. What were you getting away with?'

'Oh,' he said. 'I get it.'

*

And just before we got to the One-Eight I said, 'There's something I don't understand. Why did you think it would be easier to kill your wife than to leave her? You said several times that it would be such a terrible thing to leave a woman like her, that it would be a contemptible act, but men and women leave each other all the time. You couldn't have been worried about what your parents would think because you didn't have any family left. What made it such a big deal?'

'Oh,' he said. 'You don't know.'

'Don't know what?'

'You haven't met her. You didn't go out there this afternoon, did you?'

'No.'

('I never see him ... I never see my former husband ... I don't see my husband and I don't see the check. Do you see? Do you?')

'The Potowski woman, with her eyes staring up through the blood. When I saw her like that it just hit me so hard I couldn't deal with it. But you wouldn't understand that because you don't know about her.'

('Perhaps he has a phone and perhaps it's in the book. You could look it up. I know you'll excuse me if I don't offer to look it up for you.')

The answer was floating out there. I could very nearly reach out and touch it. But my mind wouldn't fasten onto it.

He said, 'My wife is blind.'

SEVENTEEN

It turned out to be a long night, although the trip to Twentieth Street was the least of it. I shared a cab down with Burton Havermeyer. We must have talked about something en route but I can't remember what. I paid for the cab, took Havermeyer to the squad room and introduced him to Frank Fitzroy, and that was pretty much the extent of my contribution. I, after all, was not the arresting officer. I had no official connection with the case and had performed no official function. I didn't have to be around while a stenographer took down Havermeyer's statement, nor was I called upon to make a statement of my own.

Fitzroy slipped away long enough to walk me down to the corner and buy me a drink at P. J. Reynolds.

I didn't much want to accept his invitation. I wanted a drink, but I wasn't much more inclined to drink with him than with Havermeyer. I felt closed off from everyone, locked up tight within myself where dead women and blind women couldn't get at me.

The drinks came and we drank them, and he said, 'Nice piece of work, Matt.'

'I got lucky.'

'You don't get that kind of luck. You make it. Something got you onto Havermeyer in the first place.'

'More luck. The other two cops from the Six-One were dead. He was odd man in.'

'You could have talked to him on the phone. Something made you go see him.'

'Lack of anything better to do.'

'And then you asked him enough questions so that he told a couple of lies that could catch him up further down the line.'

'And I was in the right place at the right time, and the right shop sign caught my eye when the right pair of cops walked in front of me.'

'Oh, shit,' he said, and signaled the bartender. 'Put yourself down if you want.'

'I just don't think I did anything to earn a field promotion to Chief of Detectives. That's all.'

The bartender came around. Fitzroy pointed to our glasses and the bartender filled them up again. I let him pay for this round, as he had paid for the first one.

He said, 'You won't get any official recognition out of this, Matt. You know that, don't you?'

'I'd prefer it that way.'

'What we'll tell the press is the reopening of the case with the arrest of Pinell made him conscience-stricken, and he turned himself in. He talked it over with you, another ex-cop like himself, and decided to confess. How does that sound?'

'It sounds like the truth.'

'Just a few things left out is all. What I was saying, you won't get anything official out of it, but people around the department are gonna know better. You follow me?'

'So?'

'So you couldn't ask for a better passport back onto the force is what it sounds like to me. I was talking to Eddie Koehler over at the Sixth. You wouldn't have any trouble getting 'em to take you on again.'

'It's not what I want.'

'That's what he said you'd say. But are you sure it isn't? All right, you're a loner, you got a hard-on for the world, you hit this stuff –' he touched his glass '– a little harder than you maybe should. But you're a cop, Matt, and you didn't stop being one when you gave the badge back.'

I thought for a moment, not to consider his proposal but to weigh the words of my reply. I said, 'You're right, in a way. But in another way you're wrong, and I stopped being a cop *before* I handed in my shield.'

'All because of that kid that died.'

'Not just that.' I shrugged. 'People move and their lives change.'

'Well,' he said, and then he didn't say anything for a few minutes, and then we found something less unsettling to talk about. We discussed the impossibility of keeping three-card monte dealers off the street, given that the fine for the offense is seventy-five dollars and the profit somewhere between five hundred and a thousand dollars a day. 'And there's this one judge,' he said, 'who told a whole string of them he'd let 'em off

without a fine if they'd promise not to do it again. "Oh, Ah promises, yo' honah." To save seventy-five dollars, those assholes'd promise to grow hair on their tongues.'

We had a third round of drinks, and I let him pay for that round, too, and then he went back to the station house and I caught a cab home. I checked the desk for messages, and when there weren't any I went around the corner to Armstrong's, and that's where it got to be a long night.

But it wasn't a bad one. I drank my bourbon in coffee, sipping it, making it last and my mood didn't turn black or ugly. I talked to people intermittently but spent a lot of time replaying the day, listening to Havermeyer's explanation. Somewhere in the course of things I gave Jan a call to tell her how things had turned out. Her line was busy. Either she was talking to someone or she had the phone off the hook, and this time I didn't get the operator to find out which.

I had just the right amount to drink, for a change. Not so much that I blacked out and lost my memory. But enough to bring sleep without dreams.

By the time I got down to Pine Street the next day, Charles London knew what to expect. The morning papers had the story. The line they carried was pretty much what I'd expected from what Fitzroy had said. I was mentioned by name as the fellow ex-cop who'd heard Havermeyer's confession and escorted him in so he could give himself up for the murder of Barbara Ettinger.

Even so, he didn't look thrilled to see me.

'I owe you an apology,' he said. 'I managed to become convinced that your investigation would only have a damaging effect upon a variety of people. I thought –'

'I know what you thought.'

'It turned out that I was wrong. I'm still concerned about what might come out in a trial, but it doesn't look as though there will be a trial.'

'You don't have to worry about what comes out anyway,' I said. 'Your daughter wasn't carrying a black baby.' He looked as though he'd been slapped. 'She was carrying her husband's baby. She may very well have been having an affair, probably in retaliation for her husband's behavior, but there's no evidence that it had an interracial element. That was an invention of your former son-in-law's.'

'I see.' He took his little walk to the window and made sure

that the harbor was still out there. He turned to me and said, 'At least this has turned out well, Mr Scudder.'

'Oh?'

'Barbara's killer has been brought to justice. I no longer have to worry who might have killed her, or why. Yes, I think we can say it's turned out well.'

He could say it if he wanted. I wasn't sure that justice was what Burton Havermeyer had been brought to, or where his life would go from here. I wasn't sure where justice figured in the ordeal that was just beginning for Haverymeyer's son and his blind ex-wife. And if London didn't have to worry that Douglas Ettinger had killed his daughter, what he'd learned about Ettinger's character couldn't have been monumentally reassuring.

I thought, too, of the fault lines I'd already detected in Ettinger's second marriage. I wondered how long the blonde with the sunny suburban face would hold her space in his desktop cube. If they split, would he be able to go on working for his second father-in-law?

Finally, I thought how people could adjust to one reality after another if they put their minds to it. London had begun by believing that his daughter had been killed for no reason at all, and he'd adjusted to that. Then he came to believe that she had indeed been killed for a reason, and by someone who knew her well. And he'd set about adjusting to that. Now he knew that she'd been killed by a near-stranger for a reason that had nothing much to do with her. Her death had come in a dress rehearsal for murder, and in dying she'd preserved the life of the intended victim. You could see all that as part of some great design or you could see it as further proof that the world was mad, but either way it was a new reality to which he would surely adjust.

Before I left he gave me a check for a thousand dollars. A bonus, he said, and he assured me he wanted me to have it. I gave him no argument. When money comes with no strings on it, take it and put it in your pocket. I was still enough of a cop at heart to remember that much.

I tried Jan around lunchtime and there was no answer. I tried her again later in the afternoon and the line was busy three times running. It was around six when I finally reached her.

'You're hard to get hold of,' I said.

'I was out some. And then I was on the phone.'

'I was out some myself.' I told her a lot of what had happened since I'd left her loft the previous afternoon, armed with the

137

knowledge that Havermeyer's boy Danny had attended the Happy Hours Child Care Center. I told her why Barbara Ettinger had been killed, and I told her that Havermeyer's wife was blind.

'Jesus,' she said.

We talked a little more, and I asked her what she was doing about dinner. 'My client gave me a thousand dollars that I didn't do a thing to earn,' I said, 'and I feel a need to spend some of it frivolously before I piss the rest of it away on necessities.'

'I'm afraid tonight's out,' she said. 'I was just making myself a salad.'

'Well, do you want to hit a couple of high spots after you finish your salad? Anyplace but Blanche's Tavern is fine with me.'

There was a pause. Then she said, 'The thing is, Matthew, I have something on tonight.'

'Oh.'

'And it's not another date. I'm going to a meeting.'

'A meeting?'

'An AA meeting.'

'I see.'

'I'm an alcoholic, Matthew. I've got to face the fact and I've got to deal with it.'

'I didn't have the impression that you drank that much.'

'It's not how much you drink. It's what it does to you. I have blackouts. I have personality changes. I tell myself I'm not going to drink and I do. I tell myself I'm going to have one drink and the next morning the bottle's empty. I'm an alcoholic.'

'You were in AA before.'

'That's right.'

'I thought it didn't work for you.'

'Oh, it was working fine. Until I drank. This time I want to give it a chance.'

I thought for a minute. 'Well, I think that's great,' I said.

'You do?'

'Yes, I do,' I said, and meant it. 'I think it's terrific. I know it works for a lot of people and there's no reason why you can't make it work. You're going to a meeting tonight?'

'That's right. I was at one this afternoon.'

'I thought they only had them at night.'

'They have them all the time, and all over the city.'

'How often do you have to go?'

'You don't have to do anything. They recommend ninety

meetings in the first ninety days, but you can go to more. I have plenty of time. I can go to a lot of them.'

'That's great.'

'After the meeting this afternoon I was on the phone with somebody I knew when I was in the program last time. And I'm going to a meeting tonight, and that'll get me through today, and I'll have one day of sobriety.'

'Uh-huh.'

'That's how it's done, you see. You take it one day at a time.'

'That's great.' I wiped my forehead. It gets warm in a phone booth with the door closed. 'When do those meetings end? Ten or ten thirty something like that?'

'Ten o'clock.'

'Well, suppose –'

'But people generally go out for coffee afterward.'

'Uh-huh. Well, suppose I came by around eleven? Or later, if you figure you'll want to spend more than an hour over coffee.'

'I don't think that's a very good idea, Matthew.'

'Oh.'

'I want to give this a fair shot. I don't want to start sabotaging myself before I even get started.'

I said, 'Jan? I wasn't planning to come over and drink with you.'

'I know that.'

'Or in front of you, as far as that goes. I won't drink when I'm with you. That's no problem.'

'Because you can stop anytime you want to.'

'I can certainly not drink when we're together.'

Another pause, and when she spoke I could hear the strain in her voice. 'God,' she said. 'Matthew, darling, it's not quite that simple.'

'Oh?'

'One of the things they tell us is that we're powerless over people, places and things.'

'I don't know what that means.'

'It means to avoid those elements that can increase our desire to drink.'

'And I'm one of those elements?'

'I'm afraid so.'

I cracked the phone booth door, let a little air in. I said, 'Well, what does that mean, exactly? That we never see each other again?'

'Oh, God.'

'Just tell me the rules so I'll understand.'

'Jesus, God. I can't think in terms of never again. I can't even think in terms of never having a drink again. I'm supposed to take it a day at a time, so let's do this in terms of today.'

'You don't want to see me today.'

'Of *course* I want to see you today! Oh, Jesus. Look, if you want to come over around eleven –'

'No,' I said.

'What?'

'I said no. You were right the first time and I shouldn't be doing a number on you. I'm like my client, that's all. I've just got to adjust to a new reality. I think you're doing the right thing.'

'Do you really?'

'Yes. And if I'm somebody you ought to stay away from, I think that's what you'd better do for the time being. And if we're supposed to get together later on, well, it'll happen.'

A pause. Then, 'Thank you, Matthew.'

For what? I got out of the booth and went back upstairs to my room. I put on a clean shirt and tie and treated myself to a good steak dinner at the Slate. It's a hangout for cops from John Jay College and Midtown North, but I was lucky enough not to see anyone that I knew. I had a big meal all by myself, with a martini in front and a brandy afterward.

I walked back to Ninth Avenue and passed St Paul's. The church itself was closed now. I descended a narrow flight of steps to the basement. Not the big room in front where they have Bingo a couple nights a week, but a smaller room on the side where they have the meetings.

When you live in a neighborhood you know where different things are. Whether you have any interest in them or not.

I stood in front of the door for a minute or two. I felt a little lightheaded, a little congested in the chest. I decided that was probably from the brandy. It's a powerful stimulant. I'm not used to it, don't drink it often.

I opened the door and looked in. A couple dozen people sitting in folding chairs. A table holding a big coffee urn and a few stacks of Styrofoam cups. Some slogans taped to the wall – *Easy Does It, Keep It Simple*. The fucking wisdom of the ages.

She was probably in a room like this downtown. Some church basement in SoHo, say.

Best of luck, lady.

I stepped back, let the door shut, walked up the stairs. I had

visions of the door opening behind me, people chasing after me and dragging me back. Nothing like that happened.

The tight feeling was still there in my chest.

The brandy, I told myself. Probably be a good idea to stay away from it. Stick to what you're used to. Stick to bourbon.

I went on over to Armstrong's. A little bourbon would take the edge off the brandy rush. A little bourbon would take the edge off almost anything.

EIGHT MILLION WAYS
TO DIE

*The death of a beautiful woman is,
unquestionably, the most poetical topic in
the world.*

EDGAR ALLAN POE

ONE

I saw her entrance. It would have been hard to miss. She had blonde hair that was close to white, the sort that's called towhead when it belongs to a child. Hers was plaited in heavy braids that she'd wrapped around her head and secured with pins. She had a high smooth forehead and prominent cheekbones and a mouth that was just a little too wide. In her western-style boots she must have run to six feet, most of her length in her legs. She was wearing designer jeans the color of burgundy and a short fur jacket the color of champagne. It had been raining on and off all day, and she wasn't carrying an umbrella or wearing anything on her head. Beads of water glinted like diamonds on her plaited hair.

She stood for a moment in the doorway getting her bearings. It was around three-thirty on a Wednesday afternoon, which is about as slow as it gets at Armstrong's. The lunch crowd was long gone and it was too early for the after-work people. In another fifteen minutes a couple of schoolteachers would stop in for a quick one, and then some nurses from Roosevelt Hospital whose shift ended at four, but for the moment there were three or four people at the bar and one couple finishing a carafe of wine at a front table and that was it. Except for me, of course, at my usual table in the rear.

She made me right away, and I caught the blue of her eyes all the way across the room. But she stopped at the bar to make sure before making her way between the tables to where I was sitting.

She said, 'Mr Scudder? I'm Kim Dakkinen. I'm a friend of Elaine Mardell's.'

'She called me. Have a seat.'

'Thank you.'

She sat down opposite me, placed her handbag on the table between us, took out a pack of cigarettes and a disposable

lighter, then paused with the cigarette unlit to ask if it was all right if she smoked. I assured her that it was.

Her voice wasn't what I'd expected. It was quite soft, and the only accent it held was Midwestern. After the boots and the fur and the severe facial planes and the exotic name, I'd been anticipating something more out of a masochist's fantasy: harsh and stern and European. She was younger, too, than I'd have guessed at first glance. No more than twenty-five.

She lit her cigarette and positioned the lighter on top of the cigarette pack. The waitress, Evelyn, had been working days for the past two weeks because she'd landed a small part in an off-Broadway showcase. She always looked on the verge of a yawn. She came to the table while Kim Dakkinen was playing with her lighter. Kim ordered a glass of white wine. Evelyn asked me if I wanted more coffee, and when I said yes Kim said, 'Oh, are you having coffee? I think I'd like that instead of wine. Would that be all right?'

When the coffee arrived she added cream and sugar, stirred, sipped, and told me she wasn't much of a drinker, especially early in the day. But she couldn't drink it black the way I did, she'd never been able to drink black coffee, she had to have it sweet and rich, almost like dessert, and she supposed she was just lucky but she'd never had a weight problem, she could eat anything and never gain an ounce, and wasn't that lucky?

I agreed that it was.

Had I known Elaine long? For years, I said. Well, she hadn't really known her that long herself, in fact she hadn't even been in New York too terribly long, and she didn't know her that well either, but she thought Elaine was awfully nice. Didn't I agree? I agreed. Elaine was very levelheaded, too, very sensible, and that was something, wasn't it? I agreed it was something.

I let her take her time. She had acres of small talk, she smiled and held your eyes with hers when she talked, and she could probably have walked off with the Miss Congeniality award in any beauty contest she didn't win outright, and if it took her awhile to get to the point that was fine with me. I had no place else to go and nothing better to do.

She said, 'You used to be a policeman.'

'A few years back.'

'And now you're a private detective.'

'Not exactly.' The eyes widened. They were a very vivid blue, an unusual shade, and I wondered if she were wearing contact

lenses. The soft lenses sometimes do curious things to eye color, altering some shades, intensifying others.

'I don't have a license,' I explained. 'When I decided I didn't want to carry a badge anymore I didn't figure I wanted to carry a license, either.' Or fill out forms or keep records or check in with the tax collector. 'Anything I do is very unofficial.'

'But it's what you do? It's how you make your living?'

'That's right.'

'What do you call it? What you do.'

You could call it hustling a buck, except that I don't hustle a whole lot. The work finds me. I turn down more than I handle, and the jobs I accept are ones I can't think of a way to turn down. Right now I was wondering what this woman wanted from me, and what excuse I'd find to say no.

'I don't know what to call it,' I told her. 'You could say that I do favors for friends.'

Her face lit up. She'd been doing a lot of smiling ever since she walked in the door but this was the first smile that got as far as her eyes. 'Well, hell, that's perfect,' she said. 'I could use a favor. As far as that goes, I could use a friend.'

'What's the problem?'

She bought some thinking time by lighting another cigarette, then lowered her eyes to watch her hands as she centered the lighter on top of the pack. Her nails were well manicured, long but not awkward, lacquered the color of tawny port. She wore a gold ring set with a large square-cut green stone on the third finger of her left hand. She said, 'You know what I do. Same as Elaine.'

'So I gathered.'

'I'm a hooker.'

I nodded. She straightened in her seat, squared her shoulders, adjusted the fur jacket, opened the clasp at her throat. I caught a trace of her perfume. I'd smelled that spicy scent before but couldn't recall the occasion. I picked up my cup, finished my coffee.

'I want out.'

'Of the life?'

She nodded. 'I've been doing this for four years. I came here four years ago in July. August, September, October, November. Four years and four months. I'm twenty-three years old. That's young, isn't it?'

'Yes.'

'It doesn't feel so young.' She adjusted the jacket again,

refastened the clasp. Light glinted off her ring. 'When I got off the bus four years ago I had a suitcase in one hand and a denim jacket over my arm. Now I've got this. It's ranch mink.'

'It's very becoming.'

'I'd trade it for the old denim jacket,' she said, 'if I could have the years back. No, I wouldn't. Because if I had them back I'd just do the same thing with them, wouldn't I? Oh to be nineteen again and know what I know now, but the only way that could be is if I started tricking at fifteen, and then I'd be dead by now. I'm just rambling. I'm sorry.'

'No need.'

'I want to get out of the life.'

'And do what? Go back to Minnesota?'

'Wisconsin. No, I won't be going back. There's nothing there for me. Just because I want out doesn't mean I have to go back.'

'Okay.'

'I can make lots of trouble for myself that way. I reduce things to two alternatives, so if A is no good that means I'm stuck with B. But that's not right. There's the whole rest of the alphabet.'

She could always teach philosophy. I said, 'Where do I come in, Kim?'

'Oh. Right.'

I waited.

'I have this pimp.'

'And he won't let you leave?'

'I haven't said anything to him. I think maybe he knows, but I haven't said anything and *he* hasn't said anything and –' Her whole upper body trembled for a moment, and small beads of perspiration glistened on her upper lip.

'You're afraid of him.'

'How'd you guess?'

'Has he threatened you?'

'Not really.'

'What does that mean?'

'He never threatened me. But I *feel* threatened.'

'Have other girls tried to leave?'

'I don't know. I don't know much about his other girls. He's very different from other pimps. At least from the ones I know about.'

They're all different. Just ask their girls. 'How?' I asked her.

'He's more refined. Subdued.'

Sure. 'What's his name?'

'Chance.'

148

'First name or last name?'

'It's all anybody ever calls him. I don't know if it's a first name or a last name. Maybe it's neither, maybe it's a nickname. People in the life, they'll have different names for different occasions.'

'Is Kim your real name?'

She nodded. 'But I had a street name. I had a pimp before Chance, his name was Duffy. Duffy Green, he called himself, but he was also Eugene Duffy and he had another name he used sometimes that I forget.' She smiled at a memory. 'I was so green when he turned me out. He didn't pick me up right off the bus but he might as well.'

'He a black man?'

'Duffy? Sure. So is Chance. Duffy put me on the street. The Lexington Avenue stroll, and sometimes when it was hot there we'd go across the river to Long Island City.' She closed her eyes for a moment. When she opened them she said, 'I just got this rush of memory, what it was like on the street. My street name was Bambi. In Long Island City we did the johns in their cars. They would drive in from all over Long Island. On Lexington we had a hotel we could use. I can't believe I used to do that, I used to live like that. God, I was *green*! I wasn't innocent. I knew what I came to New York for, but I was green all right.'

'How long were you on the street?'

'It must have been five, six months. I wasn't very good. I had the looks and I could, you know, perform, but I didn't have street smarts. And a couple of times I had anxiety attacks and I couldn't function. Duffy gave me stuff but all it ever did was make me sick.'

'Stuff?'

'You know. Drugs.'

'Right.'

'Then he put me in this house, and that was better, but he didn't like it because he had less control that way. There was this big apartment near Columbus Circle and I went to work there like you would go to an office. I was in the house, I don't know, maybe another six months. Just about that. And then I went with Chance.'

'How did that happen?'

'I was with Duffy. We were at this bar. Not a pimp bar, a jazz club, and Chance came and sat at our table. We all three sat and talked, and then they left me at the table and went off and talked some more, and Duffy came back alone and said I was to

go with Chance. I thought he meant I should do him, you know, like a trick, and I was pissed because this was supposed to be our evening together and why should I be working. See, I didn't take Chance for a pimp. Then he explained that I was going to be Chance's girl from now on. I felt like a car he just sold.'

'Is that what he did? Did he sell you to Chance?'

'I don't know what he did. But I went with Chance and it was all right. It was better than with Duffy. He took me out of that house and put me on a phone and it's been, oh, three years now.'

'And you want me to get you off the hook.'

'Can you do it?'

'I don't know. Maybe you can do it yourself. Haven't you said anything to him? Hinted at it, talked about it, something like that?'

'I'm afraid.'

'Of what?'

'That he'd kill me or mark me or something. Or that he'd talk me out of it.' She leaned forward, put her port-tipped fingers on my wrist. The gesture was clearly calculated but nonetheless effective for it. I breathed in her spicy scent and felt her sexual impact. I wasn't aroused and didn't want her but I could not be unaware of her sexual strength. She said, 'Can't you help me, Matt?' And, immediately, 'Do you mind if I call you Matt?'

I had to laugh. 'No,' I said. 'I don't mind.'

'I make money but I don't get to keep it. And I don't really make more money than I did on the street. But I have a little money.'

'Oh?'

'I have a thousand dollars.'

I didn't say anything. She opened her purse, found a plain white envelope, got a finger under the flap and tore it open. She took a sheaf of bills from it and placed them on the table between us.

'You could see him for me,' she said.

I picked up the money, held it in my hand. I was being offered the opportunity to serve as intermediary between a blonde whore and a black pimp. It was not a role I'd ever hungered for.

I wanted to hand the money back. But I was nine or ten days out of Roosevelt Hospital and I owed money there, and on the first of the month my rent would be due, and I hadn't sent anything to Anita and the boys in longer than I cared to remember. I had money in my wallet and more money in the bank but it didn't add up to much, and Kim Dakkinen's money

was as good as anybody else's and easier to come by, and what difference did it make what she'd done to earn it?

I counted the bills. They were used hundreds and there were ten of them. I left five on the table in front of me and handed the other five to her. Her eyes widened a little and I decided she had to be wearing contacts. Nobody had eyes that color.

I said, 'Five now and five later. If I get you off the hook.'

'Deal,' she said, and grinned suddenly. 'You could have had the whole thousand in front.'

'Maybe I'll work better with an incentive. You want some more coffee?'

'If you're having some. And I think I'd like something sweet. Do they have desserts here?'

'The pecan pie's good. So's the cheesecake.'

'I love pecan pie,' she said. 'I have a terrible sweet tooth but I never gain an ounce. Isn't that lucky?'

TWO

There was a problem. In order for me to talk to Chance I had to find him, and she couldn't tell me how to do it.

'I don't know where he lives,' she said. 'Nobody does.'

'Nobody?'

'None of his girls. That's the big guessing game if a couple of us should happen to be together and he's not in the room. Trying to guess where Chance lives. One night I remember this girl Sunny and I were together and we were just goofing, coming up with one outrageous idea after another. Like he lives in this tenement in Harlem with his crippled mother, or he has this mansion in Sugar Hill, or he has a ranch house in the suburbs and commutes. Or he keeps a couple of suitcases in his car and lives out of them, just sleeping a couple hours a night at one of our apartments.' She thought a moment. 'Except he never sleeps when he's with me. If we do go to bed he'll just lie there afterward for a little while and then he's up and dressed and out. He said once he can't sleep if there's another person in the room.'

'Suppose you have to get in touch with him?'

'There's a number to call. But it's an answering service. You can call the number any time, twenty-four hours a day, and there's always an operator that answers. He always checks in with his service. If we're out or something, he'll check in with them every thirty minutes, every hour.'

She gave me the number and I wrote it in my notebook. I asked here where he garaged his car. She didn't know. Did she remember the car's license number?

She shook her head. 'I never notice things like that. His car is a Cadillac.'

'There's a surprise. Where does he hang out?'

'I don't know. If I want to reach him I leave a message. I don't go out looking for him. You mean is there a regular bar he drinks

in? There's lot of places he'll go sometimes, but nothing regular.'

'What kind of things does he do?'

'What do you mean?'

'Does he go to ball games? Does he gamble? What does he do with himself?'

She considered the question. 'He does different things,' she said.

'What do you mean?'

'Depending who he's with. I like to go to jazz clubs so if he's with me that's where we'll go. I'm the one he calls if he's looking for that kind of an evening. There's another girl, I don't even know her, but they go to concerts. You know, classical music. Carnegie Hall and stuff. Another girl, Sunny, digs sports, and he'll take her to ball games.'

'How many girls has he got?'

'I don't know. There's Sunny and Nan and the girl who likes classical music. Maybe there's one or two others. Maybe more. Chance is very private, you know? He keeps things to himself.'

'The only name you've got for him is Chance?'

'That's right.'

'You've been with him, what, three years? And you've got half a name and no address and the number of his answering service.'

She looked down at her hands.

'How does he pick up the money?'

'From me, you mean? Sometimes he'll come by for it.'

'Does he call first?'

'Not necessarily. Sometimes. Or he'll call and tell me to bring it to him. At a coffee shop or a bar or something, or to be on a certain corner and he'll pick me up.'

'You give him everything you make?'

A nod. 'He found me my apartment, he pays the rent, the phone, all the bills. We'll shop for my clothes and he'll pay. He likes picking out my clothes. I give him what I make and he gives me back some, you know, for walking-around money.'

'You don't hold anything out?'

'Sure I do. How do you think I got the thousand dollars? But it's funny, I don't hold out much.'

The place was filling up with office workers by the time she left. By then she'd had enough coffee and switched to white wine. She had one glass of the wine and left half of it. I stayed with black coffee. I had her address and phone in my notebook

along with Chance's answering service, but I didn't have a whole lot more than that.

On the other hand, how much did I need? Sooner or later I would get hold of him, and when I did I would talk to him, and if it broke right I'd throw a bigger scare into him than he'd managed to throw into Kim. And if not, well, I still had five hundred dollars more than I had when I woke up that morning.

After she left I finished my coffee and cracked one of her hundreds to pay my tab. Armstrong's is on Ninth Avenue between Fifty-seventh and Fifty-eighth, and my hotel is around the corner on Fifty-seventh Street. I went to it, checked the desk for mail and messages, then called Chance's service from the pay phone in the lobby. A woman answered on the third ring, repeating the four final digits of the number and asking if she could help me.

'I want to speak to Mr Chance,' I said.

'I expect to speak with him soon,' she said. She sounded middle-aged, with a chain smoker's rasp to her voice. 'May I take a message for him?'

I gave her my name and my phone number at the hotel. She asked what my call was in reference to. I told her it was personal.

When I hung up the phone I felt shaky, maybe from all the coffee I'd been sipping all day. I wanted a drink. I thought about going across the street to Polly's Cage for a quick one, or hitting the liquor store two doors down from Polly's and picking up a pint of bourbon. I could envision the booze, Jim Beam or J. W. Dant, some no-nonsense brown whiskey in a flat pint bottle.

I thought, C'mon, it's raining out there, you don't want to go out in the rain. I left the phone booth and turned toward the elevator instead of the front door and went up to my room. I locked myself in and pulled the chair over to the window and watched the rain. The urge to drink went away after a few minutes. Then it came back and then it went away again. It came and went for the next hour, winking on and off like a neon sign. I stayed where I was and watched the rain.

Around seven I picked up the phone in my room and called Elaine Mardell. Her machine answered, and when the beep sounded I said, 'This is Matt. I saw your friend and I wanted to thank you for the referral. Maybe one of these days I can return

the favor.' I hung up and waited another half hour. Chance didn't return my call.

I wasn't especially hungry but I made myself go downstairs for something to eat. It had quit raining. I went over to the Blue Jay and ordered a hamburger and fries. A guy two tables over was having a beer with his sandwich and I decided to order one when the waiter brought my burger, but by the time that happened I'd changed my mind. I ate most of the hamburger and about half of the fries and drank two cups of coffee, then ordered cherry pie for dessert and ate most of it.

It was almost eight-thirty when I left there. I stopped at my hotel – no messages – and then walked the rest of the way to Ninth Avenue. There used to be a Greek bar on the corner, Antares and Spiro's, but it's a fruit and vegetable market now. I turned uptown and walked past Armstrong's and across Fifty-eighth Street, and when the light changed I crossed the avenue and walked on up past the hospital to St Paul's. I walked around the side and down a narrow flight of stairs to the basement. A cardboard sign hung from the doorknob, but you'd have to be looking for it to see it.

AA, it said.

They were just getting started when I walked in. There were three tables set up in a U, with people seated on either sides of the tables and perhaps a dozen other chairs arranged at the back. Another table off to the side held refreshments. I got a Styrofoam cup and drew coffee from the urn, then took a chair at the rear. A couple of people nodded to me and I nodded back.

The speaker was a fellow about my age. He was wearing a herringbone tweed jacket over a plaid flannel shirt. He told the story of his life from his first drink in his early teens until he came into the program and got sober four years ago. He was married and divorced a few times, cracked up several cars, lost jobs, hit a few hospitals. Then he stopped drinking and started going to meetings and things got better. '*Things* didn't get better,' he said, correcting himself. '*I* got better.'

They say that a lot. They say a lot of things a lot and you get to hear the same phrases over and over. The stories are pretty interesting, though. People sit up there in front of God and everybody and tell you the goddamnedest things.

He spoke for half an hour. Then they took a ten-minute break and passed the basket for expenses. I put in a dollar, then helped myself to another cup of coffee and a couple of oatmeal cookies. A fellow in an old army jacket greeted me by name. I

remembered his name was Jim and returned the greeting. He asked me how things were going and I told him they were going all right.

'You're here and you're sober,' he said. 'That's the important thing.'

'I suppose.'

'Any day I don't take a drink is a good day. You're staying sober a day at a time. The hardest thing in the world is for an alcoholic to not drink and you're doing it.'

Except I wasn't. I'd been out of the hospital for nine or ten days. I would stay sober for two or three days and then I would pick up a drink. Mostly it was a drink or two drinks or three drinks and it stayed under control, but Sunday night I'd been bad drunk, drinking bourbon at a Blarney Stone on Sixth Avenue where I didn't figure to run into anybody I knew. I couldn't remember leaving the bar and didn't know how I got home, and Monday morning I had the shakes and a dry mouth and felt like walking death.

I didn't tell him any of this.

After ten minutes they started the meeting again and went around the room. People would say their names and say they were alcoholics and thank the speaker for his qualification, which is what they call the life story that he told. Then they would go on to talk about how they'd identified with the speaker, or recall some memory from their drinking days, or speak about some difficulty they were dealing with in the course of trying to lead a sober life. A girl not much older than Kim Dakkinen talked about problems with her lover, and a gay man in his thirties described a hassle he'd had that day with a customer at his travel agency. It made a funny story and got a lot of laughs.

One woman said, 'Staying sober is the easiest thing in the world. All you have to do is don't drink, go to meetings, and be willing to change your whole fucking life.'

When it got to me I said, 'My name is Matt. I'll pass.'

The meeting ended at ten. I stopped at Armstrong's on my way home and took a seat at the bar. They tell you to stay out of bars if you're trying not to drink but I'm comfortable there and the coffee's good. If I'm going to drink I'll drink and it doesn't matter where I am.

By the time I left there the early edition of the *News* was on the street. I picked it up and went back to my room. There was

still no message from Kim Dakkinen's pimp. I called his service again, which established that he had received my message. I left another message and said that it was important I hear from him as soon as possible.

I showered and put on a robe and read the paper. I read the national and international stories but I can never really focus on them. Things have to be on a smaller scale and happen closer to home before I can relate to them.

There was plenty to relate to. Two kids in the Bronx threw a young woman in front of the D train. She'd lain flat and, although six cars passed over her before the motorman got the train stopped, she'd escaped without injury.

Down on West Street, near the Hudson docks, a prostitute had been murdered. Stabbed, the story said.

A housing authority cop in Corona was still in critical condition. Two days ago I'd read how he'd been attacked by two men who hit him with lengths of pipe and stole his gun. He had a wife and four children under ten.

The telephone didn't ring. I didn't really expect it to. I couldn't think of any reason for Chance to return my call outside of curiosity, and perhaps he remembered what that had done to the cat. I could have identified myself as a cop – Mr Scudder was easier to ignore than Police Officer Scudder, or Detective Scudder – but I didn't like to run that kind of game if I didn't have to. I was willing to let people jump to conclusions but reluctant to give them a push.

So I'd have to find him. That was just as well. It would give me something to do. In the meantime the messages I left with his service would fix my name in his head.

The elusive Mr Chance. You'd think he'd have a mobile phone unit in his pimpmobile, along with the bar and the fur upholstery and the pink velvet sun visor. All those touches of class.

I read the sports pages and then went back to the hooker stabbing in the Village. The story was very sketchy. They didn't have a name or any description beyond identifying the victim as being about twenty-five years old.

I called the *News* to see if they had a name for the victim and was told they weren't giving out that information. Pending notification of kin, I suppose. I called the Sixth Precinct but Eddie Koehler wasn't on duty and I couldn't think of anyone else at the Sixth who might know me. I got out my notebook and decided it was too late to call her, that half the women in the

city were hookers and there was no reason to suppose she'd been the one to get sliced up underneath the West Side Highway. I put the notebook away, and ten minutes later I dug it out again and dialed her number.

I said, 'It's Matt Scudder, Kim. I just wondered if you happened to speak to your friend since I saw you.'

'No, I haven't. Why?'

'I thought I might reach him through his service. I don't think he's going to get back to me, so tomorrow I'll have to go out and look for him. You haven't said anything to him about wanting out?'

'Not a word.'

'Good. If you see him before I do, just act as though nothing's changed. And if he calls and wants you to meet him somewhere, call me right away.'

'At the number you gave me?'

'Right. If you reach me I'll be able to keep the appointment in your place. If not, just go ahead and play it straight.'

I talked a little while longer, calming her down some after having alarmed her with the call in the first place. At least I knew she hadn't died on West Street. At least I could sleep easy.

Sure. I killed the light and got into bed and just lay there for a long time, and then I gave up and got up and read the paper again. The thought came to me that a couple of drinks would take the edge off and let me sleep. I couldn't banish the thought but I could make myself stay where I was, and when four o'clock came I told myself to forget it because the bars were closed now. There was an after-hours on Eleventh Avenue but I conveniently forgot about it.

I turned off the light and got in bed again and thought about the dead hooker and the housing cop and the woman who'd been run over by the subway train, and I wondered why anyone would think it a good idea to stay sober in this city, and I held onto that thought and fell asleep with it.

THREE

I got up around ten-thirty, surprisingly well rested after six hours of skimming the surface of sleep. I showered and shaved, had coffee and a roll for breakfast, and went over to St Paul's. Not to the basement this time but to the church proper, where I sat in a pew for ten minutes or so before lighting a couple of candles and slipping fifty dollars into the poor box. At the post office on Sixtieth Street I bought a two-hundred-dollar money order and an envelope with the stamp embossed. I mailed the money order to my ex-wife in Syosset. I tried to write a note to enclose but it came out apologetic. The money was too little and too late but she would know that without my having to tell her. I wrapped the money order in a blank sheet of paper and mailed it that way.

It was a gray day, on the cool side, with the threat of more rain. There was a raw wind blowing and it cut around corners like a scatback. In front of the Coliseum a man was chasing his hat and cursing, and I reached up reflexively and gave a tug to the brim of mine.

I walked most of the way to my bank before deciding I didn't have enough of Kim's advance left to necessitate formal financial transactions. I went to my hotel instead and paid half of the coming month's rent on account. By then I had only one of the hundreds intact and I cracked that into tens and twenties while I was at it.

Why hadn't I taken the full thousand in front? I remembered what I'd said about an incentive. Well, I had one.

My mail was routine – a couple of circulars, a letter from my congressman. Nothing I had to read.

No message from Chance. Not that I'd expected one.

I called his service and left another message just for the hell of it.

I got out of there and stayed out all afternoon. I took the

subway a couple of times but mostly walked. It kept threatening to rain but it kept not raining, and the wind got even more of an edge to it but never did get my hat. I hit two police precinct houses and a few coffee shops and half a dozen gin mills. I drank coffee in the coffee shops and Coca-Cola in the bars, and I talked to a few people and made a couple of notes. I called my hotel desk a few times. I wasn't expecting a call from Chance but I wanted to be in touch in case Kim called. But no one had called me. I tried Kim's number twice and both times her machine answered. Everybody's got one of those machines and someday all the machines will start dialing and talk to each other. I didn't leave any messages.

Toward the end of the afternoon I ducked into a Times Square theater. They had two Clint Eastwood movies paired, ones where he's a rogue cop who settles things by shooting the bad guys. The audience looked to be composed almost entirely of the sort of people he was shooting. They cheered wildly every time he blew somebody away.

I had pork fried rice and vegetables at a Cuban Chinese place on Eighth Avenue, checked my hotel desk again, stopped at Armstrong's and had a cup of coffee. I got into a conversation at the bar and thought I'd stay there awhile, but by eight-thirty I'd managed to get out the door and across the street and down the stairs to the meeting.

The speaker was a housewife who used to drink herself into a stupor while her husband was at his office and the kids were at school. She told how her kid would find her passed out on the kitchen floor and she convinced him it was a yoga exercise to help her back. Everybody laughed.

When it was my turn I said, 'My name is Matt. I'll just listen tonight.'

Kelvin Small's is on Lenox Avenue at 127th Street. It's a long narrow room with a bar running the length of it and a row of banquette tables opposite the bar. There's a small bandstand all the way at the back, and on it two dark-skinned blacks with close-cropped hair and horn-rimmed sunglasses and Brooks Brothers suits played quiet jazz, one on a small upright piano, the other using brushes on cymbals. They looked and sounded like half of the old Modern Jazz Quartet.

It was easy for me to hear them because the rest of the room went silent when I cleared the threshold. I was the only white man in the room and everybody stopped for a long look at me.

160

There were a couple of white women, seated with black men at the banquette tables, and there were two black women sharing a table, and there must have been two dozen men in every shade but mine.

I walked the length of the room and went into the men's room. A man almost tall enough for pro basketball was combing his straightened hair. The scent of his pomade vied with the sharp reek of marijuana. I washed my hands and rubbed them together under one of those hot-air dryers. The tall man was still working on his hair when I left.

Conversation died again when I emerged from the men's room. I walked toward the front again, walked slowly and let my shoulders roll. I couldn't be sure about the musicians, but aside from them I figured there wasn't a man in the room who hadn't taken at least one felony bust. Pimps, drug dealers, gamblers, policy men. Nature's noblemen.

A man on the fifth stool from the front caught my eye. It took a second to place him because when I knew him years ago he had straight hair, but now he was wearing it in a modified Afro. His suit was lime green and his shoes were the skin of some reptile, probably an endangered species.

I moved my head toward the door and walked on past him and out. I walked two doors south on Lenox and stood next to a streetlamp. Two or three minutes went by and he came on out, walking loose-limbed and easy. 'Hey, Matthew,' he said, and extended his hand for a slap. 'How's my man?'

I didn't slap his hand. He looked down at it, up at me, rolled his eyes, gave his head an exaggerated shake, clapped his hands together, dusted them against his trouser legs, then placed them on his slim hips. 'Been some time,' he said. 'They run out of your brand downtown? Or do you just come to Harlem to use the little boy's room?'

'You're looking prosperous, Royal.'

He preened a little. His name was Royal Waldron and I once knew a black cop with a bullet head who rang changes through Royal Flush to Flush Toilet and called him The Crapper. He said, 'Well, I buy and sell. You know.'

'I know.'

'Give the folks an honest deal and you will never miss a meal. That's a rhyme my mama taught me. How come you uptown, Matthew?'

'I'm looking for a guy.'

'Maybe you found him. You off the force these days?'

'For some years now.'

'And you lookin' to buy something? What do you want and what can you spend?'

'What are you selling?'

'Most anything.'

'Business still good with all these Colombians?'

'Shit,' he said, and one hand brushed the front of his pants. I suppose he had a gun in the waistband of the lime green pants. There were probably as many handguns as people in Kelvin Small's. 'Them Colombians be all right,' he said. 'You just don't ever want to cheat them is all. You didn't come up here to buy stuff.'

'No.'

'What you want, man?'

'I'm looking for a pimp.'

'Shit, you just walked past twenty of 'em. And six, seven hoes.'

'I'm looking for a pimp named Chance.'

'Chance.'

'You know him?'

'I might know who he is.'

I waited. A man in a long coat was walking along the block, stopping at each storefront. He might have been looking in the windows except that you couldn't; every shop had steel shutters that descended like garage doors at the close of business. The man stopped in front of each closed store and studied the shutters as if they held meaning for him.

'Window shopping,' Royal said.

A blue-and-white police car cruised by, slowed. The two uniformed officers within looked us over. Royal wished them a good evening. I didn't say anything and neither did they. When the car drove off he said, 'Chance don't come here much.'

'Where would I find him?'

'Hard to say. He'll turn up anyplace but it might be the last place you would look. He don't hang out.'

'So they tell me.'

'Where you been lookin'?'

I'd been to a coffee shop on Sixth Avenue and Forty-fifth Street, a piano bar in the Village, a pair of bars in the West Forties. Royal took all this in and nodded thoughtfully.

'He wouldn't be at Muffin-Burger,' he said, 'on account he don't run no girls on the street. That I *know* of. All the same, he

might be there anyway, you dig? Just to *be* there. What I say, he'll turn up anywhere, but he don't hang out.'

'Where should I look for him, Royal?'

He named a couple of places. I'd been to one of them already and had forgotten to mention it. I made a note of the others. I said, 'What's he like, Royal?'

'Well, shit,' he said. 'He a pimp, man.'

'You don't like him.'

'He ain't to like or not like. My friends is business friends, Matthew, and Chance and I got no business with each other. We don't neither of us buy what the other be sellin'. He don't want to buy no stuff and I don't want to buy no pussy.' His teeth showed in a nasty little smile. 'When you the man with all the candy, you don't never have to pay for no pussy.'

One of the places Royal mentioned was in Harlem, on St Nicholas Avenue. I walked over to 125th Street. It was wide and busy and well lit, but I was starting to feel the not entirely irrational paranoia of a white man on a black street.

I turned north at St Nicholas and walked a couple of blocks to the Club Cameroon. It was a low-rent version of Kelvin Small's with a jukebox instead of live music. The men's room was filthy, and in the stall toilet someone was inhaling briskly. Snorting cocaine, I suppose.

I didn't recognize anyone at the bar. I stood there and drank a glass of club soda and looked at fifteen or twenty black faces reflected in the mirrored back bar. It struck me, not for the first time that evening, that I could be looking at Chance and not knowing it. The description I had for him would fit a third of the men present and stretch to cover half of those remaining. I hadn't been able to see a picture of him. My cop contacts didn't recognize the name, and if it was his last name he didn't have a yellow sheet in the files.

The men on either side had turned away from me. I caught sight of myself in the mirror, a pale man in a colorless suit and a gray topcoat. My suit could have stood pressing and my hat would have looked no worse if the wind had taken it, and here I stood, isolated between these two fashion plates with their wide shoulders and exaggerated lapels and fabric-covered buttons. The pimps used to line up at Phil Kronfeld's Broadway store for suits like that, but Kronfeld's was closed and I had no idea where they went these days. Maybe I should find out, maybe Chance had a charge account and I could trace him that way.

163

Except people in the life didn't have charges because they did everything with cash. They'd even buy cars with cash, bop into Potamkin's and count out hundred dollar bills and take home a Cadillac.

The man on my right crooked a finger at the bartender. 'Put it right in the same glass,' he said. 'Let it build up a taste.' The bartender filled his glass with a jigger of Hennessy and four or five ounces of cold milk. They used to call that combination a White Cadillac. Maybe they still do.

Maybe I should have tried Potamkin's.

Or maybe I should have stayed home. My presence was creating tension and I could feel it thickening the air in the little room. Sooner or later someone would come over and ask me what the fuck I thought I was doing there and it was going to be hard to come up with an answer.

I left before it could happen. A gypsy cab was waiting for the light to change. The door on my side was dented and one fender was crumpled, and I wasn't sure what that said about the driver's ability. I got in anyway.

Royal had mentioned another place on West Ninety-sixth and I let the cab drop me there. It was after two by this time and I was starting to tire. I went into yet another bar where yet another black man was playing piano. This particular piano sounded out of tune, but it might have been me. The crowd was a fairly even mix of black and white. There were a lot of interracial couples, but the white women who were paired with black men looked more like girlfriends than hookers. A few of the men were dressed flashily, but nobody sported the full pimp regalia I'd seen a mile and a half to the north. If the room carried an air of fast living and cash transactions, it was nevertheless subtler and more muted than the Harlem clubs, or the ones around Times Square.

I put a dime in the phone and called my hotel. No messages. The desk clerk that night was a mulatto with a cough-syrup habit that never seemed to keep him from functioning. He could still do the *Times* crossword puzzle with a fountain pen. I said, 'Jacob, do me a favor. Call this number and ask to speak to Chance.'

I gave him the number. He read it back and asked if that was Mr Chance. I said just Chance.

'And if he comes to the phone?'

'Just hang up.'

I went to the bar and almost ordered a beer but made it a Coke instead. A minute later the phone rang and a kid answered it. He looked like a college student. He called out, asking if there was anyone there named Chance. Nobody responded. I kept an eye on the bartender. If he recognized the name he didn't show it. I'm not even certain he was paying attention.

I could have played that little game at every bar I'd been to, and maybe it would have been worth the effort. But it had taken me three hours to think of it.

I was some detective. I was drinking all the Coca-Cola in Manhattan and I couldn't find a goddamned pimp. My teeth would rot before I got hold of the son of a bitch.

There was a jukebox, and one record ended and another began, something by Sinatra, and it triggered something, made some mental connection for me. I left my Coke on the bar and caught a cab going downtown on Columbus Avenue. I got off at the corner of Seventy-second Street and walked half a block west to Poogan's Pub. The clientele was a little less Superspade and a little more Young Godfather but I wasn't really looking for Chance anyway. I was looking for Danny Boy Bell.

He wasn't there. The bartender said, 'Danny Boy? He was in earlier. Try the Top Knot, that's just across Columbus. He's there when he's not here.'

And he was there, all right, on a bar stool all the way at the back. I hadn't seen him in years but he was no mean trick to recognize. He hadn't grown and he wasn't any darker.

Danny Boy's parents were both dark-skinned blacks. He had their features but not their color. He was an albino, as unpigmented as a white mouse. He was quite slender and very short. He claimed to be five two but I've always figured he was lying by an inch and a half or so.

He was wearing a three-piece banker's-stripe suit and the first white shirt I'd seen in a long time. His tie showed muted red and black stripes. His black shoes were highly polished. I don't think I've ever seen him without a suit and tie, or with scuffed shoes.

He said, 'Matt Scudder. By God, if you wait long enough everybody turns up.'

'How are you, Danny?'

'Older. It's been years. You're less than a mile away and when's the last time we saw each other? It has been, if you'll excuse the expression, a coon's age.'

'You haven't changed much.'

He studied me for a moment. 'Neither have you,' he said, but

his voice lacked conviction. It was a surprisingly normal voice to issue from such an unusual person, of medium depth, unaccented. You expected him to sound like Johnny in the old Philip Morris commercials.

He said, 'You were just in the neighborhood? Or you came looking for me?'

'I tried Poogan's first. They told me you might be here.'

'I'm flattered. Purely a social visit, of course.'

'Not exactly.'

'Why don't we take a table? We can talk of old times and dead friends. And whatever mission brought you here.'

The bars Danny Boy favored kept a bottle of Russian vodka in the freezer. That was what he drank and he liked it ice-cold but without any ice cubes rattling around in his glass and diluting his drink. We settled in at a booth in the back and a speedy little waitress brought his drink of choice and Coke for me. Danny Boy lowered his eyes to my glass, than raised them to my face.

'I've been cutting back some,' I said.

'Makes good sense.'

'I guess.'

'Moderation,' he said. 'I tell you, Matt, those old Greeks knew it all. Moderation.'

He drank half his drink. He was good for perhaps eight like it in the course of a day. Call it a quart a day, all in a body that couldn't go more than a hundred pounds, and I'd never seen him show the effects. He never staggered, never slurred his words, just kept on keeping on.

So? What did that have to do with me?

I sipped my Coke.

We sat there and told each other stories. Danny Boy's business, if he had one, was information. Everything you told him got filed away in his mind, and by putting bits of data together and moving them around he brought in enough dollars to keep his shoes shined and his glass full. He would bring people together, taking a slice of their action for his troubles. His own hands stayed clean while he held a limited partnership in a lot of short-term enterprises, most of them faintly illicit. When I was on the force he'd been one of my best sources, an unpaid snitch who took his recompense in information.

He said, 'You remember Lou Rudenko? Louie the Hat, they call him.' I said I did. 'You hear about his mother?'

'What about her?'

'Nice old Ukrainian lady, still lived in the old neighborhood on East Ninth or Tenth, wherever it was. Been a widow for years. Must have been seventy, maybe closer to eighty. Lou's got to be what, fifty?'

'Maybe.'

'Doesn't matter. Point is this nice little old lady has a gentleman friend, a widower the same age as she is. He's over there a couple nights a week and she cooks Ukrainian food for him and maybe they go to a movie if they can find one that doesn't have people fucking all over the screen. Anyway, he comes over one afternoon, he's all excited, he found a television set on the street. Somebody put it out for the garbage. He says people are crazy, they throw perfectly good things away, and he's handy at fixing things and her own set's on the fritz and this one's a color set and twice the size of hers and maybe he can fix it for her.'

'And?'

'And he plugs it in and turns it on to see what happens, and what happens is it blows up. He loses an arm and an eye and Mrs Rudenko, she's right in front of it when it goes, she's killed instantly.'

'What was it, a bomb?'

'You got it. You saw the story in the paper?'

'I must have missed it.'

'Well, it was five, six months ago. What they worked out was somebody rigged the set with a bomb and had it delivered to somebody else. Maybe it was a mob thing and maybe it wasn't, because all the old man knew was what block he picked the set up on, and what does that tell you? Thing is, whoever received the set was suspicious enough to put it right out with the garbage, and it wound up killing Mrs Rudenko. I saw Lou and it was a funny thing because he didn't know who to get mad at. "It's this fucking city," he told me. "It's this goddamn fucking city." But what sense does that make? You live in the middle of Kansas and a tornado comes and picks your house up and spreads it over Nebraska. That's an act of God, right?'

'That's what they say.'

'In Kansas God uses tornadoes. In New York he uses gaffed television sets. Whoever you are, God or anybody else, you work with the materials at hand. You want another Coke?'

'Not right now.'

'What can I do for you?'

'I'm looking for a pimp.'

167

'Diogenes was looking for an honest man. You have more of a field to choose from.'

'I'm looking for a particular pimp.'

'They're all particular. Some of them are downright finicky. Has he got a name?'

'Chance.'

'Oh, sure,' Danny Boy said. 'I know Chance.'

'You know how I can get in touch with him?'

He frowned, picked up his empty glass, put it down. 'He doesn't hang out anywhere,' he said.

'That's what I keep hearing.'

'It's the truth. I think a man should have a home base. I'm always here or at Poogan's. You're at Jimmy Armstrong's, or at least you were the last I heard.'

'I still am.'

'See? I keep tabs on you even when I don't see you. Chance. Let me think. What's today, Thursday?'

'Right. Well, Friday morning.'

'Don't get technical. What do you want with him, if you don't mind the question?'

'I want to talk to him.'

'I don't know where he is now but I might know where he'll be eighteen or twenty hours from now. Let me make a call. If that girl shows up, order me another drink, will you? And whatever you're having.'

I managed to catch the waitress's eye and told her to bring Danny Boy another glass of vodka. She said, 'Right. And another Coke for you?'

I'd been getting little drink urges off and on ever since I sat down and now I got a strong one. My gorge rose at the thought of another Coke. I told her to make it ginger ale this time. Danny Boy was still on the phone when she brought the drinks. She put the ginger ale in front of me and the vodka on his side of the table. I sat there and tried not to look at it and my eyes couldn't find anywhere else to go. I wished he would get back to the table and drink the damn thing.

I breathed in and breathed out and sipped my ginger ale and kept my hands off his vodka and eventually he came back to the table. 'I was right,' he said. 'He'll be at the Garden tomorrow night.'

'Are the Knicks back? I thought they were still on the road.'

'Not the main arena. Matter of fact I think there's some rock

concert. Chance'll be at the Felt Forum for the Friday night fights.'

'He always goes?'

'Not always, but there's a welterweight named Kid Bascomb at the top of the prelim card and Chance has an interest in the young man.'

'He owns a piece of him?'

'Could be, or maybe it's just an intellectual interest. What are you smiling at?'

'The idea of a pimp with an intellectual interest in a welterweight.'

'You never met Chance.'

'No.'

'He's not the usual run.'

'That's the impression I'm getting.'

'Point is, Kid Bascomb's definitely fighting, which doesn't mean Chance'll definitely be there, but I'd call it odds on. You want to talk to him, you can do it for the price of a ticket.'

'How will I know him?'

'You never met him? No, you just said you didn't. You wouldn't recognize him if you saw him?'

'Not in a fight crowd. Not when half the house is pimps and players.'

He thought about it. 'This conversation you're going to have with Chance,' he said. 'Is it going to upset him a lot?'

'I hope not.'

'What I'm getting at, is he likely to have a powerful resentment against whoever points him out?'

'I don't see why he should.'

'Then what it's going to cost you, Matt, is the price of not one but two tickets. Be grateful it's an off-night at the Forum and not a title bout at the Main Garden. Ringside shouldn't be more than ten or twelve dollars, say fifteen at the outside. Thirty dollars at the most for our tickets.'

'You're coming with me?'

'Why not? Thirty dollars for tickets and fifty for my time. I trust your budget can carry the weight?'

'It can if it has to.'

'I'm sorry I have to ask you for money. If it were a track meet I wouldn't charge you a cent. But I've never cared for boxing. If it's any consolation, I'd want at least a hundred dollars to attend a hockey game.'

'I guess that's something. You want to meet me there?'

'Out in front. At nine – that should give us plenty of lee-way. How does that sound?'

'Fine.'

'I'll see if I can't wear something distinctive,' he said, 'so that you'll have no trouble recognizing me.'

FOUR

He wasn't hard to recognize. His suit was a dove gray flannel and with it he wore a bright red vest over a black knit tie and another white dress shirt. He had sunglasses on, dark lenses in metal frames. Danny Boy contrived to sleep when the sun was out – neither his eyes nor his skin could take it – and wore dark glasses even at night unless he was in a dimly lit place like Poogan's or the Top Knot. Years ago he'd told me that he wished the world had a dimmer switch and you could just turn the whole thing down a notch or two. I remember thinking at the time that that was what whiskey did. It dimmed the lights and lowered the volume and rounded the corners.

I admired his outfit. He said, 'You like the vest? I haven't worn it in ages. I wanted to be visible.'

I already had our tickets. The ringside price was $15. I'd bought a pair of $4.50 seats that would have put us closer to God than to the ring. They got us through the gate, and I showed them to an usher down front and slipped a folded bill into his hand. He put us in a pair of seats in the third row.

'Now I might have to move you gentlemen,' he said, 'but probably not, and I guarantee you ringside.'

After he'd moved off Danny Boy said, 'There's always a way, isn't there? What did you give him?'

'Five dollars.'

'So the seats set you back fourteen dollars instead of thirty. What do you figure he makes in a night?'

'Not much on a night like this. When the Knicks or Rangers play he might make five times his salary in tips. Of course he might have to pay somebody off.'

'Everybody's got an angle,' he said.

'It looks that way.'

'I mean everybody. Even me.'

That was my cue. I gave him two twenties and a ten. He put

the money away, then took his first real look around the auditorium. 'Well, I don't see him,' he said, 'but he'll probably just show for the Bascomb fight. Let me take a little walk.'

'Sure.'

He left his seat and moved around the room. I did some looking around myself, not trying to spot Chance but getting a sense of the crowd. There were a lot of men who might have been in the Harlem bars the previous night, pimps and dealers and gamblers and other uptown racket types, most of them accompanied by women. There were some white mob types; they were wearing leisure suits and gold jewelry and they hadn't brought dates. In the less expensive seats the crowd was the sort of mixed bag that turns up for any sporting event, black and white and Hispanic, singles and couples and groups, eating hot dogs and drinking beer from paper cups and talking and joking and, occasionally, having a look at the action in the ring. Here and there I saw a face straight out of any OTB horse room, one of those knobby on-the-come Broadway faces that only gamblers get. But there weren't too many of those. Who bets prizefights anymore?

I turned around and looked at the ring. Two Hispanic kids, one light and one dark, were being very careful not to risk serious injury. They looked like lightweights to me, and the fair-skinned kid was rangy with a lot of reach. I started getting interested, and in the final round the darker of the two figured out how to get in under the other kid's jab. He was working the body pretty good when they rang the bell. He got the decision, and most of the booing came from one spot in the audience. The other boy's friends and family, I suppose.

Danny Boy had returned to his seat during the final round. A couple minutes after the decision, Kid Bascomb climbed over the ropes and did a little shadowboxing. Moments later his opponent entered the ring. Bascomb was very dark, very muscular, with sloping shoulders and a powerful chest. His body might have been oiled the way the light glinted on it. The boy he was fighting was an Italian kid from South Brooklyn named Vito Canelli. He was carrying some fat around the waist and he looked soft as bread dough, but I had seen him before and knew him for a smart fighter.

Danny Boy said, 'Here he comes. Center aisle.'

I turned and looked. The same usher who'd taken my five bucks was leading a man and woman to their seats. She was about five five, with shoulder-length auburn hair and skin like

fine porcelain. He was six one or two, maybe 190 pounds. Broad shoulders, narrow waist, trim hips. His hair was natural, short rather than long, and his skin was a rich brown. He was wearing a camel's-hair blazer and brown flannel slacks. He looked like a professional athlete or a hot lawyer or an up-and-coming black businessman.

I said, 'You're sure?'

Danny Boy laughed. 'Not your usual pimp, is he? I'm sure. That's Chance. I hope your friend didn't put us in his seats.'

He hadn't. Chance and his girl were in the first row and a good deal closer to the center. They took their seats and he tipped the usher, acknowledged greetings from some of the other spectators, then approached Kid Bascomb's corner and said something to the fighter and his handlers. They huddled together for a moment. Then Chance returned to his seat.

'I think I'll leave now,' Danny Boy said. 'I don't really want to watch these two fools pummel each other. I hope you don't need me to introduce you?' I shook my head. 'Then I'll slip out before the mayhem commences. In the ring, that is. Will he have to know I fingered him, Matt?'

'He won't hear it from me.'

'Good. If I can be of further service —'

He made his way up the aisle. He probably wanted a drink and the bars in Madison Square Garden don't stock ice-cold Stolichnaya.

The announcer was introducing the fighters, calling out their ages and weights and hometowns. Bascomb was twenty-two and undefeated. Canelli didn't figure to change his status tonight.

There were two seats empty next to Chance. I thought about taking one but stayed where I was. The warning buzzer sounded, then the bell for round one. It was a slow, thoughtful round, with neither fighter anxious to commit himself. Bascomb jabbed nicely but Canelli managed to be out of range most of the time. Nobody landed anything solid.

The pair next to Chance were still empty at the round's end. I walked over there and sat next to him. He was looking very intently at the ring. He must have been aware of my presence but didn't indicate it if he was.

I said, 'Chance? My name is Scudder.'

He turned, looked at me. His eyes were brown flecked with gold. I thought of my client's eyes, that unreal blue. He'd been at her apartment last night while I was barhopping, dropped in unannounced to pick up some money. She'd told me about it

earlier, called me at the hotel around noon. 'I was afraid,' she'd said. 'I thought, suppose he asks about you, asks me some kind of questions. But it was cool.'

Now he said, 'Matthew Scudder. You left some messages with my service.'

'You didn't return my calls.'

'I don't know you. I don't call people I don't know. And you've been asking around town for me.' His voice was deep and resonant. It sounded trained, as if he'd gone to broadcasting school. 'I want to watch this fight,' he said.

'All I want is a few minutes conversation.'

'Not during the fight and not between rounds.' A frown came and went. 'I want to be able to concentrate. I bought that seat you're sitting in, you see, so I'd have some privacy.'

The warning buzzer sounded. Chance turned, focused his eyes on the ring. Kid Bascomb was standing and his seconds were hauling the stool out of the ring. 'Go back to your seat,' Chance said, 'and I'll talk to you after the fight ends.'

'It's a ten-rounder?'

'It won't go ten.'

It didn't. In the third or fourth round Kid Bascomb started getting to Canelli, punishing him with the jab, putting a couple of combinations together. Canelli was smart but the Kid was young and fast and strong, with a way of moving that reminded me a little of Sugar Ray. Robinson, not Leonard. In the fifth round he staggered Canelli with a short right hand to the heart and if I'd had a bet on the Italian I'd have written it off then and there.

Canelli looked strong by the end of the round but I'd seen the expression on his face when the blow landed, and I wasn't surprised a round later when Kid Bascomb dropped him with a looping left hook. He was up at three and took an eight-count, and then the Kid was all over him, hitting him with everything but the ring posts. Canelli went down again and got right up and the ref jumped between the two of them and looked in Canelli's eyes and stopped it.

There was some halfhearted booing from the diehards who never want a fight stopped, and one of Canelli's cornermen was insisting his fighter could have gone on, but Canelli himself seemed just as happy the show was over. Kid Bascomb did a little war dance and took his bows, then climbed nimbly over the ropes and left the ring.

On his way out he stopped to talk to Chance. The girl with the auburn hair sat forward and rested a hand on the fighter's glossy black arm. Chance and the Kid talked for a moment or two, and then the Kid headed for his dressing room.

I left my seat, walked over to Chance and the girl. They were standing by the time I got there. He said, 'We're not staying for the main bout. If you'd planned on watching it –'

The top of the card matched two middleweights, a Panamanian contender and a black boy from South Philadelphia with a reputation as a spoiler. It would probably be a good bout, but that wasn't what I'd come for. I told him I was ready to leave.

'Then why don't you come with us,' he suggested. 'I have a car nearby.' He headed up the aisle with the girl at his side. A few people said hello to him and some of them told him that the Kid had looked good in there. Chance didn't say much in reply. I tagged along, and when we got outside and hit the fresh air I realized for the first time how stale and smoky it had been inside the Garden.

On the street he said, 'Sonya, this is Matthew Scudder. Mr Scudder, Sonya Hendryx.'

'It's nice to meet you,' she said, but I didn't believe her. Her eyes told me she was withholding judgment until Chance cued her in one way or the other. I wondered if she was the Sunny that Kim had mentioned, the sports fan Chance took to ball games. I wondered, too, if I would have pegged her for a hooker if I'd met her in other circumstances. I couldn't see anything unmistakably whorish about her, and yet she didn't look at all out of place hanging on a pimp's arm.

We walked a block south and half a block east to a parking lot where Chance collected his car and tipped the attendant enough to get thanked with more than the usual degree of enthusiasm. The car surprised me, just as the clothes and manner had surprised me earlier. I was expecting a pimpmobile, complete with custom paint and interior and the usual wretched excess, and what showed up was a Seville, the small Cadillac, silver on the outside with a black leather interior. The girl got in back, Chance sat behind the wheel, and I sat in front next to him.

The ride was smooth, silent. The car's interior smelled of wood polish and leather. Chance said, 'There's a victory party for Kid Bascomb. I'll drop Sonya there now and join her after we've concluded our business. What did you think of the fight?'

'I thought it was hard to figure.'

'Oh?'

'It looked fixed but the knockout looked real.'

He glanced at me, and I saw interest in his gold-flecked eyes for the first time. 'What makes you say that?'

'Canelli had an opening twice in the fourth round and he didn't follow it up either time. He's too smart a fighter for that. But he was trying to get through the sixth and he couldn't. At least that's how it looked from my seat.'

'You ever box, Scudder?'

'Two fights at the Y when I was twelve or thirteen years old. Balloon gloves, protective headgear, two-minute rounds. I was too low and clumsy for it, I could never manage to land a punch.'

'You have an eye for the sport.'

'Well, I guess I've seen a lot of fights.'

He was silent for a moment. A cab cut us off and he braked smoothly, avoiding a collision. He didn't swear or hit the horn. He said, 'Canelli was set to go in the eighth. He was supposed to give the Kid his best fight until then, but not to get out in front or the knockout might not look right. That's why he held back in round four.'

'But the Kid didn't know it was set up.'

'Of course not. Most of his fights have been straight until tonight, but a fighter like Canelli could be dangerous to him, and why chance a bad mark on his record at this stage? He gains experience fighting Canelli and he gains confidence by beating him.' We were on Central Park West now, heading uptown. 'The knockout was real. Canelli would have gone in the tank in the eighth, but we hoped the Kid might get us home early, and you saw him do that. What do you think of him?'

'He's a comer.'

'I agree.'

'Sometimes he telegraphs the right. In the fourth round –'

'Yes,' he said. 'They've worked with him on that. The problem is that he generally manages to get away with it.'

'Well, he wouldn't have gotten by with it tonight. Not if Canelli had been looking to win.'

'Yes. Well, perhaps it's as well that he wasn't.'

We talked boxing until we got to 104th Street, where Chance turned the car around in a careful U-turn and pulled up next to a fire hydrant. He killed the motor but left the keys. 'I'll be right down,' he said, 'after I've seen Sonya upstairs.'

She hadn't said a word since she told me it was nice to meet

176

me. He walked around the car and opened the door for her, and they strolled to the entrance of one of the two large apartment buildings that fronted on that block. I wrote the address in my notebook. In no more than five minutes he was back behind the wheel and we were heading downtown again.

Neither of us spoke for half a dozen blocks. Then he said, 'You wanted to talk to me. It doesn't have anything to do with Kid Bascomb, does it?'

'No.'

'I didn't really think so. What does it have to do with?'

'Kim Dakkinen.'

His eyes were on the road and I couldn't see any change in his expression. He said, 'Oh? What about her?'

'She wants out.'

'Out? Out of what?'

'The life,' I said. 'The relationship she has with you. She wants you to agree to … break things off.'

We stopped for a light. He didn't say anything. The light changed and we went another block or two and he said, 'What's she to you?'

'A friend.'

'What does that mean? You're sleeping with her? You want to marry her? Friend's a big word, it covers a lot of ground.'

'This time it's a small word. She's a friend, she asked me to do her a favor.'

'By talking to me.'

'That's right.'

'Why couldn't she talk to me herself? I see her frequently, you know. She wouldn't have had to run around the city asking after me. Why, I saw her just last night.'

'I know.'

'Do you? Why didn't she say anything when she saw me?'

'She's afraid.'

'Afraid of me?'

'Afraid you might not want her to leave.'

'And so I might beat her? Disfigure her? Stub out cigarettes on her breasts?'

'Something like that.'

He fell silent again. The car's ride was hypnotically smooth. He said, 'She can go.'

'Just like that?'

'How else? I'm not a white slaver, you know.' His tone put an ironic stress on the term. 'My women stay with me out of their

own will, such will as they possess. They're under no duress. You know Nietzsche? "Women are like dogs, the more you beat them the more they love you." But I don't beat them, Scudder. It never seems to be necessary. How does Kim come to have you for a friend?'

'We have an acquaintance in common.'

He glanced at me. 'You were a policeman. A detective, I believe. You left the force several years ago. You killed a child and resigned out of guilt.'

That was close enough for me to let it pass. A stray bullet of mine had killed a young girl named Estrellita Rivera, but I don't know that it was guilt over the incident that propelled me out of the police department. What it had done, really, was change the way the world looked to me, so that being a cop was no longer something I wanted to do. Neither was being a husband and a father and living on Long Island, and in due course I was out of work and out of the marriage and living on Fifty-seventh Street and putting in the hours at Armstrong's. The shooting unquestionably set those currents in motion, but I think I was pointed in those directions anyway and would have gotten there sooner or later.

'Now you're a sort of half-assed detective,' he went on. 'She hire you?'

'More or less.'

'What's that mean?' He didn't wait for clarification. 'Nothing against you, but she wasted her money. Or *my* money, according to how you look at it. If she wants to end our arrangement all she has to do is tell me so. She doesn't need anyone to do her talking for her. What's she plan to do? I hope she's not going back home.'

I didn't say anything.

'I suspect she'll stay in New York. But will she stay in the life? I'm afraid it's the only trade she knows. What else will she do? And where will she live? I provide their apartments, you know, and pay their rent and pick out their clothes. Well, I don't suppose anyone asked Ibsen where Nora would find an apartment. I believe this is where you live, if I'm not mistaken.'

I looked out the window. We were in front of my hotel. I hadn't been paying attention.

'I assume you'll be in touch with Kim,' he said. 'If you want, you can tell her you intimidated me and sent me slinking off into the night.'

'Why would I do that?'

178

'So she'll think she got her money's worth from you.'

'She got her money's worth,' I said, 'and I don't care whether she knows it or not. All I'll tell her is what you've told me.'

'Really? While you're at it, you can let her know that I'll be coming to see her. Just to satisfy myself that all of this is really her idea.'

'I'll mention it.'

'And tell her she has no reason to fear me.' He sighed. 'They think they're irreplaceable. If she had any notion how easily she can be replaced she'd most likely hang herself. The buses bring them, Scudder. Every hour of every day they stream into Port Authority ready to sell themselves. And every day a whole slew of others decide there must be a better way than waiting tables or punching a cash register. I could open an office, Scudder, and take applications, and there'd be a line halfway around the block.'

I opened the door. He said, 'I enjoyed this. Especially earlier. You have a good eye for boxing. Please tell that silly blonde whore that nobody's going to kill her.'

'I'll do that.'

'And if you need to talk to me, just call my service. I'll return your calls now that I know you.'

I got out, closed the door. He waited for an opening, made a U-turn, turned again at Eighth Avenue and headed uptown. The U-turn was illegal and he ran the light making his left turn on Eighth, but I don't suppose it worried him much. I couldn't recall the last time I'd seen a cop ticket anyone for a moving violation in the city of New York. Sometimes you'll see five cars go on through after a light turns red. Even the buses do it these days.

After he made his turn I took out my notebook, made an entry. Across the street, near Polly's Cage, a man and woman were having a loud argument. 'You call yourself a man?' she demanded. He slapped her. She cursed him and he slapped her again.

Maybe he'd beat her senseless. Maybe this was a game they played five nights out of seven. Try to break up that sort of thing and as likely as not they'll both turn on you. When I was a rookie cop, my first partner would do anything to avoid interfering in a domestic argument. Once, facing down a drunken husband, he'd been assaulted from behind by the wife. The husband had knocked out four of her teeth but she leaped to his defense, breaking a bottle over her savior's head. He wound

up with fifteen stitches and a concussion, and he used to run his forefinger over the scar when he told me the story. You couldn't see the scar, his hair covered it, but his finger went right to the spot.

'I say let 'em kill each other,' he used to say. 'It don't matter if she phoned in the complaint herself, she'll still turn on you. Let 'em fucking kill each other.'

Across the street, the woman said something I didn't catch and the man hit her low with his closed fist. She cried out in what sounded like real pain. I put my notebook away and went into my hotel.

I called Kim from the lobby. Her machine answered and I had started to leave a message when she picked up the receiver and interrupted me. 'I leave the machine on sometimes when I'm home,' she explained, 'so I can see who it is before I answer. I haven't heard from Chance since I spoke to you earlier.'

'I just left him a few minutes ago.'

'You saw him?'

'We rode around in his car.'

'What did you think?'

'I think he's a good driver.'

'I meant –'

'I know what you meant. He didn't seem terribly upset to hear that you want to leave him. He assured me that you've got nothing to fear from him. According to him, you didn't need me as your champion. All you had to do was tell him.'

'Yes, well, he'd say that.'

'You don't think it's true?'

'Maybe it is.'

'He said he wants to hear it from you, and I gather he also wants to make some arrangements about your leaving the apartment. I don't know if you're afraid to be alone with him or not.'

'I don't know either.'

'You can keep the door locked and talk to him through it.'

'He has keys.'

'Don't you have a chain lock?'

'Yes.'

'You can use that.'

'I suppose.'

'Shall I come over?'

180

'No, you don't have to do that. Oh, I suppose you want the rest of the money, don't you?'

'Not until you've talked to him and everything's settled. But I'll come over there if you want somebody on your side when he turns up.'

'Is he coming tonight?'

'I don't know when he's coming. Maybe he'll handle the whole thing over the phone.'

'He might not come until tomorrow.'

'Well, I could hole up on the couch if you wanted.'

'Do you think it's necessary?'

'Well, it is if you think it is, Kim. If you're uncomfortable –'

'Do you think I have anything to be afraid of?'

I thought for a moment, replayed the scene with Chance, assessed my own reactions after the fact. 'No,' I said. 'I don't think so. But I don't really know the man.'

'Neither do I.'

'If you're nervous –'

'No, it's silly. Anyway it's late. I'm watching a movie on cable, but when it ends I'm going to sleep. I'll put the chain lock on. That's a good idea.'

'You've got my number.'

'Yes.'

'Call me if anything happens, or if you just want to call me. All right?'

'Sure.'

'Just to put your mind at rest, I think you spent some money you didn't have to spend, but it was money you held out so maybe it doesn't matter.'

'Absolutely.'

'The point is I think you're off the hook. He's not going to hurt you.'

'I think you're right. I'll probably call you tomorrow. And Matt? Thanks.'

'Get some sleep,' I said.

I went upstairs and tried to take my own advice but I was wired. I gave up and got dressed and went around the corner to Armstrong's. I would have had something to eat but the kitchen was closed. Trina told me she could get me a piece of pie if I wanted. I didn't want a piece of pie.

I wanted two ounces of bourbon, neat, and another two ounces in my coffee, and I couldn't think of a single goddamned reason not to have it. It wouldn't get me drunk. It wouldn't put

181

me back in the hospital. That had been the result of a bout of uncontrolled round-the-clock drinking, and I'd learned my lesson. I couldn't drink that way anymore, not safely, and I didn't intend to. But there was a fairly substantial difference between a nightcap and going out on a toot, wasn't there?

They tell you not to drink for ninety days. You're supposed to go to ninety meetings in ninety days and stay away from the first drink one day at a time, and after ninety days you can decide what you want to do next.

I'd had my last drink Sunday night. I'd been to four meetings since then, and if I went to bed without a drink I'd have five days.

So?

I had one cup of coffee, and on the way back to the hotel I stopped at the Greek deli and picked up a cheese danish and a half pint of milk. I ate the pastry and drank a little of the milk in my room.

I turned out the light, got into bed. Now I had five days. So?

FIVE

I read the paper while I ate breakfast. The housing cop in Corona was still in critical condition but his doctors now said they expected him to live. They said there might be some paralysis, which in turn might be permanent. It was too early to tell.

In Grand Central Station, someone had mugged a shopping-bag lady and had stolen two of her three bags. And, in the Gravesend section of Brooklyn, a father and son with arrest records for pornography and what the paper described as links to organized crime bolted from a car and sought sanctuary in the first house they could run to. Their pursuers opened up on them with pistols and a shotgun. The father was wounded, the son was shot dead, and the young wife and mother who'd just recently moved into the house was hanging something in a hall closet when enough of the shotgun blast came through the door to take most of her head off.

They have noon meetings six days a week at the YMCA on Sixty-third Street. The speaker said, 'Just let me tell you how I got here. I woke up one morning and I said to myself, "Hey, it's a beautiful day and I never felt better in my life. My health's tiptop, my marriage is in great shape, my career's going beautifully, and my state of mind has never been better. I think I'll go join AA."'

The room rocked with laughter. After his talk they didn't go around the room. You raised your hand and the speaker called on you. One young fellow said shyly that he'd just reached ninety days. He got a lot of applause. I thought about raising my hand and tried to figure out what I might say. All I could think to talk about was the woman in Gravesend, or perhaps Lou Rudenko's mother, slain by a salvaged television set. But what did either of those deaths have to do with me? I was still looking for something to say when time ran out and we all stood up and

183

said the Lord's Prayer. It was just as well. I probably wouldn't have gotten around to raising my hand anyway.

After the meeting I walked for awhile in Central Park. The sun was out for a change and it was the first good day all week. I took a good long walk and watched the kids and the runners and the cyclists and the roller skaters and tried to reconcile all that wholesome innocent energy with the dark face of the city that showed itself every morning in the newspaper.

The two worlds overlap. Some of these riders would be robbed of their bicycles. Some of these strolling lovers would return home to burglarized apartments. Some of these laughing kids would pull holdups, and shoot or stab, and some would be held up or shot or stabbed, and a person could give himself a headache trying to make sense out of it.

On my way out of the park at Columbus Circle a bum with a baseball jacket and one milky eye hustled me for a dime toward a pint of wine. A few yards to the left of us, two colleagues of his shared a bottle of Night Train and watched our transaction with interest. I was going to tell him to piss off, then surprised myself by giving him a buck. Maybe I was reluctant to shame him in front of his friends. He started to thank me more effusively than I could stomach, and then I guess he saw something in my face that stopped him cold. He backed off and I crossed the street and headed home.

There was no mail, just a message to call Kim. The clerk's supposed to note the time of the call on the slip but this place isn't the Waldorf. I asked if he remembered the time of the call and he didn't.

I called her and she said, 'Oh, I was hoping you'd call. Why don't you come over and pick up the money I owe you?'

'You heard from Chance?'

'He was here about an hour ago. Everything worked out perfectly. Can you come over?'

I told her to give me an hour. I went upstairs and showered and shaved. I got dressed, then decided I didn't like what I was wearing and changed. I was fussing with the knot of my tie when I realized what I was doing. I was dressing for a date.

I had to laugh at myself.

I put on my hat and coat and got out of there. She lived in Murray Hill, Thirty-eighth between Third and Lex. I walked over to Fifth, took a bus, then walked the rest of the way east.

Her building was a prewar apartment house, brickfronted, fourteen stories, with a tile floor and potted palms in the lobby. I gave my name to the doorman and he called upstairs on the intercom and established that I was welcome before pointing me to the elevator. There was something deliberately neutral about his manner, and I decided that he knew Kim's profession and assumed I was a john and was being very careful not to smirk.

I got off at the twelfth floor and walked to her door. It opened as I approached it. She stood framed in the doorway, all blonde braids and blue eyes and cheekbones, and for a moment I could picture her carved on the prow of a Viking ship. 'Oh, Matt,' she said, and reached to embrace me. She was just about my height and she gave me a good hard hug and I felt the pressure of firm breasts and thighs and recognized the sharp tang of her scent. 'Matt,' she said, drawing me inside, closing the door. 'God, I'm so grateful to Elaine for suggesting I get in touch with you. You know what you are? You're my hero.'

'All I did was talk to the man.'

'Whatever you did, it worked. That's all I care about. Sit down, relax a moment. Can I get you anything to drink?'

'No thanks.'

'Some coffee?'

'Well, if it's no trouble.'

'Sit down. It's instant, if that's all right. I'm too lazy to make real coffee.'

I told her instant was fine. I sat down on the couch and waited while she made the coffee. The room was a comfortable one, attractively if sparsely furnished. A recording of solo jazz piano played softly on the stereo. An all-black cat peered cautiously around the corner at me, then disappeared from view.

The coffee table held a few current magazines – *People, TV Guide, Cosmopolitan, Natural History*. A framed poster on the wall over the stereo advertised the Hopper show held a couple years back at the Whitney. A pair of African masks decorated another wall. A Scandinavian area rug, its abstract pattern a whirl of blue and green, covered the central portion of the limed oak floor.

When she returned with the coffee I admired the room. She said she wished she could keep the apartment. 'But in a way,' she said, 'it's good I can't, you know? I mean, to go on living here, and then there'd be people showing up. You know. Men.'

'Sure.'

'Plus the fact that none of this is me. I mean, the only thing in

this room that I picked out is the poster. I went to that show and I wanted to take some of it home with me. The way that man painted loneliness. People together but not together, looking off in different directions. It got to me, it really did.'

'Where will you live?'

'Someplace nice,' she said confidently. She perched on the couch beside me, one long leg folded up beneath her, her coffee cup balanced on the other knee. She was wearing the same wine-colored jeans she'd worn at Armstrong's, along with a lemon yellow sweater. She didn't seem to be wearing anything under the sweater. Her feet were bare, the toe nails the same tawny port as her fingernails. She'd been wearing bedroom slippers but kicked them off before sitting down.

I took in the blue of her eyes, the green of her square-cut ring, then found my eyes drawn to the rug. It looked as though someone had taken each of those colors and beaten them with a wire whisk.

She blew on her coffee, sipped it, leaned far forward and set the cup on the coffee table. Her cigarettes were on the table and she lit one. She said, 'I don't know what you said to Chance but you really made an impression on him.'

'I don't see how.'

'He called this morning and said he would be coming over, and when he got here I had the door on the chain lock, and somehow I just knew I didn't have anything to fear from him. You know how sometimes you just know something?'

I knew, all right. The Boston Strangler never had to break a door down. All his victims opened the door and let him in.

She pursed her lips, blew out a column of smoke. 'He was very nice. He said he hadn't realized I was unhappy and that he had no intention of trying to hold me against my will. He seemed hurt that I could have thought that of him. You know something? He had me just about feeling guilty. And he had me feeling I was making a big mistake, that I was throwing something away and I'd be sorry I couldn't ever get it back. He said, "You know, I never take a girl back," and I thought, God, I'm burning my bridges. Can you imagine?'

'I think so.'

'Because he's such a con artist. Like I'm walking away from a great job and forfeiting my stake in the corporate pension plan. I mean, come on!'

'When do you have to be out of the apartment?'

'He said by the end of the month. I'll probably be gone before

then. Packing's no big deal. None of the furniture's mine. Just clothes and records, and the Hopper poster, but do you want to know something? I think that can stay right here. I don't think I need the memories.'

I drank some of my coffee. It was weaker than I preferred it. The record ended and was followed by a piano trio. She told me again how I had impressed Chance. 'He wanted to know how I happened to call you,' she said. 'I was vague, I said you were a friend of a friend. He said I didn't need to hire you, that all I'd had to do was talk to him.'

'That's probably true.'

'Maybe. But I don't think so. I think I would have started talking to him, assuming I could work up the nerve, and we'd get into this conversation and gradually I would turn around and the whole subject would be shunted off to the side. And I'd leave it shunted off to the side, you know, because without ever coming out and saying it he'd manage to give me the impression that leaving him wasn't something I was going to be allowed to do. He might not say, "Look, bitch, you stay where you're at or I'll ruin your face." He might not say it, but that's what I'd hear.'

'Did you hear it today?'

'No. That's the point. I didn't.' Her hand fastened on my arm just above the wrist. 'Oh, before I forget,' she said, and my arm took some of her weight as she got up from the couch. Then she was across the room rummaging in her purse, and then she was back on the couch handing me five hundred-dollar bills, presumably the ones I'd returned to her three days earlier.

She said, 'It seems like there ought to be a bonus.'

'You paid me well enough.'

'But you did such a good job.'

She had one arm draped over the back of the sofa and she was leaning toward me. I looked at her blonde braids coiled around her head and thought of a woman I know, a sculptor with a loft in Tribeca. She did a head of Medusa with snakes for hair and Kim had the same broad brow and high cheekbones as Jan Keane's piece of sculpture.

The expression was different, though. Jan's Medusa had looked profoundly disappointed. Kim's face was harder to read.

I said, 'Are those contacts?'

'What? Oh, my eyes? That's their natural color. It's kind of weird, isn't it?'

'It's unusual.'

Now I could read her face. It was anticipation that I saw there.

'Beautiful eyes,' I said.

The wide mouth softened into the beginning of a smile. I moved a little toward her and she came at once into my arms, fresh and warm and eager. I kissed her mouth, her throat, her lidded eyes.

Her bedroom was large and flooded with sunlight. The floor was thickly carpeted. The king-size platform bed was unmade, and the black kitten napped on a chintz-covered boudoir chair. Kim drew the curtains, glanced shyly at me, then began to undress.

Ours was a curious passage. Her body was splendid, the stuff of fantasy, and she gave herself with evident abandon. I was surprised by the intensity of my own desire, and yet it was almost wholly physical. My mind remained oddly detached from her body and from my own. I might have been viewing our performance from a distance.

The resolution provided relief and release and precious little pleasure. I drew away from her and felt as though I was in the midst of an infinite wasteland of sand and dry brush. There was a moment of astonishing sadness. Pain throbbed at the back of my throat and I felt myself close to tears.

Then the feeling passed. I don't know what brought it on or what took it away.

She said, 'Well now,' and smiled, and rolled on her side to face me and put a hand on my arm. 'That was nice, Matt,' she said.

I got dressed, turned down the offer of another cup of coffee. She took my hand at the doorway, thanked me again, and said she'd let me know her address and phone once she got relocated. I told her to feel free to call anytime for any reason. We didn't kiss.

In the elevator I remembered something she'd said. *It seems like there ought to be a bonus.* Well, that was as good a word for it as any.

I walked all the way back to the hotel. I stopped a few times along the way, once for coffee and a sandwich, once in a church on Madison Avenue where I was going to put fifty dollars into the poor box until I realized I couldn't. Kim had paid me in hundreds and I didn't have enough in smaller bills.

I don't know why I tithe, or how I got in the habit in the first place. It was one of the things I began doing after I left Anita and the boys and moved into Manhattan. I don't know what the churches do with the money and I'm sure their need for it is no greater than my own, and of late I've tried to break myself of the

habit. But whenever some money comes in I find there's a restlessness that comes with it that I cannot shed until I've handed over 10 percent of the sum to one church or another. I suppose it's superstition. I suppose I think that, having started this, I have to keep it up or something terrible will happen.

God knows it doesn't make any sense. Terrible things happen anyway, and will go on happening whether I give all or none of my income to churches.

This particular tithe would have to wait. I sat for a few minutes anyway, grateful for the peace the empty church provided. I let my mind wander for awhile. After I'd been there a few minutes an elderly man seated himself on the other side of the aisle. He closed his eyes and looked to be in deep concentration.

I wondered if he was praying. I wondered what prayer was like, and what people got out of it. Sometimes, in one church or another, it occurs to me to say a prayer, but I wouldn't know how to go about it.

If there'd been candles to light I would have lit one, but the church was Episcopalian and there weren't.

I went to the meeting that night at St Paul's but couldn't keep my mind on the qualification. I kept drifting off. During the discussion the kid from the noon meeting told how he'd reached his ninety days, and once again he got a round of applause. The speaker said, 'You know what comes after your ninetieth day? Your ninety-first day.'

I said, 'My name is Matt. I'll pass.'

I made it an early night. I fell asleep easily but kept waking up out of dreams. They withdrew from the edge of thought as I tried to catch hold of them.

I got up finally, went out for breakfast, bought a paper and brought it back to the room. There's a Sunday noon meeting within walking distance. I'd never been to it but I had seen it listed in the meeting book. By the time I thought of going, it was already half over. I stayed in my room and finished the paper.

Drinking used to fill up the hours. I used to be able to sit in Armstrong's for hours, drinking coffee with bourbon in it, not getting loaded, just sipping one cup after another while the hours went by. You try and do the same thing without the booze and it doesn't work. It just doesn't work.

Around three I thought of Kim. I reached for the phone to call

189

her and had to stop myself. We'd gone to bed because that was the sort of gift she knew how to bestow and one I didn't know how to reject, but that didn't make us lovers. It didn't make us anything to one another, and whatever business we'd had with each other was finished.

I remembered her hair and Jan Keane's Medusa and thought of calling Jan. And what would the conversation be like?

I could tell her I was halfway through my seventh sober day. I hadn't had any contact with her since she started going to meetings herself. They'd told her to stay away from people, places and things associated with drink, and I was in that category as far as she was concerned. I wasn't drinking today and I could tell her that, but so what? It didn't mean she would want to see me. For that matter, it didn't mean I would want to see her.

We'd had a couple evenings when we had a good time drinking together. Maybe we could have the same kind of enjoyment sober. But maybe it would be like sitting in Armstrong's for five hours with no bourbon in the coffee.

I got as far as looking up her number but never made the call.

The speaker at St Paul's told a really low-bottom story. He'd been a heroin addict for several years, kicked that, then drank his way down to the Bowery. He looked as though he'd seen hell and remembered what it looked like.

During the break, Jim cornered me by the coffee urn and asked me how it was going. I told him it was going okay. He asked how long I'd been sober now.

'Today's my seventh day,' I said.

'Jesus, that's great,' he said. 'That's really great, Matt.'

During the discussion I thought maybe I'd speak up when it was my turn. I didn't know that I'd say I was an alcoholic because I didn't know that I was, but I could say something about it being my seventh day, or just that I was glad to be there, or something. But when it got to me I said what I always say.

After the meeting Jim came up to me while I was carrying my folded chair to where they stack them. He said, 'You know, a bunch of us generally stop over to the Cobb's Corner for coffee after the meeting. Just to hang out and shoot the breeze. Why don't you come along?'

'Gee, I'd like to,' I said, 'but I can't tonight.'

'Some other night, then.'

'Sure,' I said. 'Sounds good, Jim.'

I could have gone. I didn't have anything else to do. Instead I

went to Armstrong's and ate a hamburger and a piece of cheesecake and drank a cup of coffee. I could have had the identical meal at Cobb's Corner.

Well, I always like Armstrong's on a Sunday night. You get a light crowd then, just the regulars. After I was done with my meal I carried my coffee cup over to the bar and chatted for awhile with a CBS technician named Manny and a musician named Gordon. I didn't even feel like drinking.

I went home and went to bed. I got up in the morning with a sense of dread and wrote it off as the residue of an unremembered dream. I showered and shaved and it was still there. I got dressed, went downstairs, dropped a bag of dirty clothes at the laundry and left a suit and a pair of pants at the dry cleaners. I ate breakfast and read the *Daily News*. One of their columnists had interviewed the husband of the woman who'd caught the shotgun blast in Gravesend. They'd just moved into that house, it was their dream house, their chance for a decent life in a decent neighborhood. And then these two gangsters, running for their lives, had picked that particular house to run to. 'It was as if the finger of God had pointed to Clair Ryzcek,' the columnist wrote.

In the 'Metro Briefs' section, I learned that two Bowery derelicts had fought over a shirt one of them had found in a trash can in the Astor Place BMT subway station. One had stabbed the other dead with an eight-inch folding knife. The dead man was fifty-two, his killer thirty-three. I wondered if the item would have made the paper if it hadn't taken place below-ground. When they kill each other in Bowery flophouses, it's not news.

I kept thumbing through the paper as if I expected to find something, and the vague feeling of foreboding persisted. I felt faintly hungover and I had to remind myself I'd had nothing to drink the night before. This was my eighth sober day.

I went to the bank, put some of my five-hundred-dollar fee in my account, changed the rest into tens and twenties. I went to St Paul's to get rid of fifty bucks but there was a mass going on. I went to the Sixty-third Street Y instead and listened to the most boring qualification I'd heard yet. I think the speaker mentioned every drink he'd had from the age of eleven on. He droned on in a monotone for forty solid minutes.

I sat in the park afterward, bought a hotdog from a vendor, ate it. I got back to the hotel around three, took a nap, went out again around four-thirty. I picked up a *Post* and took it around

the corner to Armstrong's. I must have looked at the headline when I bought the paper but somehow it didn't register. I sat down and ordered coffee and looked at the front page and there it was.

CALL GIRL SLASHED TO RIBBONS, it said.

I knew the odds and I also knew that the odds didn't matter. I sat for a moment with my eyes closed and the paper clenched in my fists, trying to alter the story by sheer force of will. Color, the very blue of her northern eyes, flashed behind my closed eyelids. My chest was tight and I could feel that pulse of pain again at the back of my throat.

I turned the goddamned page and there it was on page three just the way I knew it would be. She was dead. The bastard had killed her.

SIX

Kim Dakkinen had died in a room on the seventeenth floor
of the Galaxy Downtowner, one of the new high-rise hotels
on Sixth Avenue in the Fifties. The room had been rented to a
Mr Charles Owen Jones of Fort Wayne, Indiana, who had paid
cash in advance for a one-night stay upon checking in at 9:15
p.m. Sunday, after having phoned ahead for a room half an hour
earlier. Since a preliminary check revealed no one of Mr Jones's
name in Fort Wayne, and since the street address he'd entered
on the registration card did not seem to exist, he was presumed
to have given a false name.

Mr Jones had made no calls from his room, nor had he billed
any charges to his hotel account. After an indeterminable
number of hours he had left, and he'd done so without bothering
to drop off his key at the desk. Indeed, he'd hung the DO NOT
DISTURB sign on the door of his room, and the housekeeping
staff had scrupulously honored it until shortly after the 11:00
a.m. checkout time Monday morning. At that time one of the
maids put through a call to the room. When the phone went
unanswered she knocked on the door; when that brought no
response she opened it with her passkey.

She walked in on what the *Post* reporter called 'a scene of
indescribable horror.' A nude woman lay on the carpet at the
foot of the unmade bed. Bed and carpet were soaked with her
blood. The woman had died of multiple wounds, having been
stabbed and slashed innumerable times with what a deputy
medical examiner guessed might have been a bayonet or
machete. Her killer had hacked her face into 'an unrecognizable
mess,' but a photograph retrieved by an enterprising reporter
from Miss Dakkinen's 'luxurious Murray Hill apartment'
showed what he'd had to work with. Kim's blonde hair was
quite different in the photograph, flowing down over her
shoulders with one single braid wrapped around the crown like a

tiara. She was clear-eyed and radiant in the photo, and looked like a grown-up Heidi.

Identification had been made on the basis of the woman's purse, found at the scene. A sum of cash in the purse had enabled police investigators to rule out money as a motive in the slaying.

No kidding.

I put down the paper. I noticed without much surprise that my hands were shaking. I was even shakier on the inside. I caught Evelyn's eye, and when she came over I asked her to bring me a double shot of bourbon.

She said, 'Are you sure, Matt?'

'Why not?'

'Well, you haven't been drinking. Are you sure you want to start?'

I thought, What's it to you, kid? I took a breath and let it out and said, 'Maybe you're right.'

'How about some more coffee?'

'Sure.'

I went back to the story. A preliminary examination fixed the time of death some time around midnight. I tried to think what I'd been doing when he killed her. I'd come to Armstrong's after the meeting, but what time had it been when I'd left? I made it a fairly early night, but even so it had probably been close to midnight by the time I packed it in. Of course the time of death was approximate, so I might have been already asleep when he started to chop her life away.

I sat there and I kept drinking coffee and I read the story over and over and over.

From Armstrong's I went to St Paul's. I sat in a rear pew and tried to think. Images kept bouncing back and forth, flashes of my two meetings with Kim intercut with my conversation with Chance.

I put fifty futile dollars in the poor box. I lit a candle and stared at it as if I expected to see something dancing in its flame.

I went back and sat down again. I was still sitting there when a soft-spoken young priest came over and told me apologetically that they would be closing for the night. I nodded, got to my feet.

'You seem disturbed,' he offered. 'Could I help you in any way?'

'I don't think so.'

'I've seen you come in here from time to time. Sometimes it helps to talk to someone.'

Does it? I said, 'I'm not even Catholic, Father.'

'That's not a requirement. If there's something troubling you –'

'Just some hard news, Father. The unexpected death of a friend.'

'That's always difficult.'

I was afraid he'd hand me something about God's mysterious plan, but he seemed to be waiting for me to say more. I managed to get out of there and stood for a moment on the sidewalk, wondering where to go next.

It was around six-thirty. The meeting wasn't for another two hours. You could get there an hour early and sit around and have coffee and talk to people, but I never did. I had two hours to kill and I didn't know how.

They tell you not to let yourself get too hungry. I hadn't had anything to eat since that hotdog in the park. I thought of food and my stomach turned at the notion.

I walked back to my hotel. It seemed as though every place I passed was a bar or a liquor store. I went up to my room and stayed there.

I got to the meeting a couple of minutes early. Half a dozen people said hello to me by name. I got some coffee and sat down.

The speaker told an abbreviated drinking story and spent most of the time telling of all the things that had happened to him since he got sober four years ago. His marriage had broken up, his youngest son had been killed by a hit-and-run driver, he'd gone through a period of extended unemployment and several bad bouts of clinical depression.

'But I didn't drink,' he said. 'When I first came here you people told me there's nothing so bad that a drink won't make it worse. You told me the way to work this program is not drink even if my ass falls off. I'll tell you, sometimes I think I stay sober on sheer fucking stubbornness. That's okay. I figure whatever works is fine with me.'

I wanted to leave at the break. Instead I got a cup of coffee and took a couple of Fig Newtons. I could hear Kim telling me that she had an awful sweet tooth. *But I never gain an ounce. Aren't I lucky!*

I ate the cookies. It was like chewing straw but I chewed them and washed them down.

During the discussion one woman got into a long riff about

her relationship. She was a pain in the ass, she said the same thing every night. I tuned out.

I thought, My name is Matt and I'm an alcoholic. A woman I know got killed last night. She hired me to keep her from getting killed and I wound up assuring her that she was safe and she believed me. And her killer conned me and I believed him, and she's dead now, and there's nothing I can do about it. And it eats at me and I don't know what to do about that, and there's a bar on every corner and a liquor store on every block, and drinking won't bring her back to life but neither will staying sober, and why the hell do I have to go through this? Why?

I thought, My name is Matt and I'm an alcoholic and we sit around in these goddamned rooms and say the same damned things all the time and meanwhile out there all the animals are killing each other. We say Don't drink and go to meetings and we say The important thing is you're sober and we say Easy does it and we say One day at a time and while we natter on like brainwashed zombies the world is coming to an end.

I thought, My name is Matt and I'm an alcoholic and I need help.

When they got to me I said, 'My name is Matt. Thanks for your qualification. I enjoyed it. I think I'll just listen tonight.'

I left right after the prayer. I didn't go to Cobb's Corner and I didn't go to Armstrong's, either. Instead I walked to my hotel and past it and halfway around the block to Joey Farrell's on Fifty-eighth Street.

They didn't have much of a crowd. There was a Tony Bennett record on the jukebox. The bartender was nobody I knew.

I looked at the back bar. The first bourbon that caught my eye was Early Times. I ordered a straight shot with water back. The bartender poured it and set it on the bar in front of me.

I picked it up and looked at it. I wonder what I expected to see. I drank it down.

SEVEN

It was no big deal. I didn't even feel the drink at first, and then what I experienced was a vague headache and the suggestion of nausea.

Well, my system wasn't used to it. I'd been away from it for a week. When was the last time I'd gone a full week without a drink?

I couldn't remember. Maybe fifteen years, I thought. Maybe twenty, maybe more.

I stood there, a forearm on the bar, one foot on the bottom rung of the bar stool beside me, and I tried to determine just what it was that I felt. I decided that something didn't hurt quite so much as it had a few minutes ago. On the other hand, I felt a curious sense of loss. But of what?

'Another?'

I started to nod, then caught myself and shook my head. 'Not right now,' I said. 'You want to let me have some dimes? I have to make a couple of calls.'

He changed a dollar for me and pointed me toward the pay phone. I closed myself into the booth and took out my notebook and pen and started making calls. I spent a few dimes learning who was in charge of the Dakkinen case and a couple more reaching him, but finally I was plugged into the squad room at Midtown North. I asked to speak to Detective Durkin and a voice said, 'Just a minute,' and 'Joe? For you,' and after a pause another voice said, 'This is Joe Durkin.'

I said, 'Durkin, my name is Scudder. I'd like to know if you've made an arrest in the Dakkinen murder.'

'I didn't get that name,' he said.

'It's Matthew Scudder, and I'm not trying to get information out of you, I'm trying to give it. If you haven't arrested the pimp yet I may be able to give you a lead.'

After a pause he said, 'We haven't made any arrests.'

'She had a pimp.'

'We know that.'

'Do you have his name?'

'Look, Mr Scudder —'

'Her pimp's name is Chance. That may be a first or last name or it may be an alias. There's no yellow sheet on him, not under that name.'

'How would you know about a yellow sheet?'

'I'm an ex-cop. Look, Durkin, I've got a lot of information and all I want to do is give it to you. Suppose I just talk for a few minutes and then you can ask anything you want.'

'All right.'

I told him what I knew about Chance. I gave him a full physical description, added a description of his car and supplied the license number. I said he had a minimum of four girls on his string and that one of them was a Ms Sonya Hendryx, possibly known as Sunny, and I described her. 'Friday night he dropped Hendryx at 444 Central Park West. It's possible she lives there but more likely that she was going to attend a victory party for a prizefighter named Kid Bascomb. Chance has some sort of interest in Bascomb and it's probable that someone in that building was throwing a party for him.'

He started to interrupt but I kept going. I said, 'Friday night Chance learned that the Dakkinen girl wanted to end their relationship. Saturday afternoon he visited her on East Thirty-eighth Street and told her he had no objection. He told her to vacate the apartment by the end of the month. It was his apartment, he rented it and installed her in it.'

'Just a minute,' Durkin said, and I heard papers rustle. 'The tenant of record is a Mr David Goldman. That's also the name Dakkinen's phone's listed in.'

'Have you been able to trace David Goldman?'

'Not yet.'

'My guess is you won't, or else Goldman'll turn out to be a lawyer or accountant Chance uses to front for him. I'll tell you this much, Chance doesn't look like any David Goldman I ever met.'

'You said he was black.'

'That's right.'

'You met him.'

'That's right. Now he doesn't have a particular hangout, but there are several places he frequents.' I ran down the list. 'I

wasn't able to learn where he lives. I gather he keeps that a secret.'

'No problem,' Durkin said. 'We'll use the reverse directory. You gave us his phone number, remember? We'll look it up and get the address that way.'

'I think the number's his answering service.'

'Well, they'll have a number for him.'

'Maybe.'

'You sound doubtful.'

'I think he likes to keep himself hard to find,' I said.

'How'd you happen to find him? What's your connection to all of this, Scudder?'

I felt like hanging up. I'd given them what I had and I didn't feel like answering questions. But I was a lot easier to find than Chance, and if I hung up on Durkin he could have me picked up in no time.

I said, 'I met him Friday night. Miss Dakkinen asked me to intercede for her.'

'Intercede how?'

'By telling him she wanted to get off the hook. She was scared to tell him herself.'

'So you told him for her.'

'That's right.'

'What, are you a pimp yourself, Scudder? She go from his stable to yours?'

My grip tightened on the receiver. I said, 'No, that's not my line, Durkin. Why? Is your mother looking for a new connection?'

'What in –'

'Just watch your fucking mouth, that's all. I'm handing you things on a plate and I never had to call you at all.'

He didn't say anything.

I said, 'Kim Dakkinen was a friend of a friend. If you want to know about me there used to be a cop named Guzik who knew me. Is he still at Midtown North?'

'You're a friend of Guzik's?'

'We never liked each other much but he can tell you I'm straight. I told Chance she wanted out and he said it was fine with him. He saw her the next day and told her the same thing. Then last night somebody killed her. You still have the time of death figured as midnight?'

'Yeah, but that's approximate. It was twelve hours later that

199

they found her. And the condition of the corpse, you know, the ME probably wanted to move on to something else.'

'Bad.'

'The one I feel sorry for is that poor little chambermaid. She's from Ecuador, I think she's an illegal, barely speaks a word of English, and she had to walk in on that.' He snorted. 'You want to look at the body, give us a positive make? You'll see something'll stick in your memory.'

'Don't you have an identification?'

'Oh, yeah,' he said. 'We got fingerprints. She was arrested once a few years back in Long Island City. Loitering with intent, fifteen days suspended. No arrests since then.'

'She worked in a house after that,' I said. 'And then Chance put her in the apartment on Thirty-eighth Street.'

'A real New York odyssey. What else have you got, Scudder? And how do I get hold of you if I need you?'

I didn't have anything else. I gave him my address and phone. We said a few more polite things to each other and I hung up and the phone rang. I owed forty-five cents for going over the three minutes my dime had bought me. I broke another dollar at the bar, put the money in the slot, and returned to the bar to order another drink. Early Times, straight up, water back.

This one tasted better. And after it hit bottom I felt something loosen up inside me.

At the meetings they tell you it's the first drink that gets you drunk. You have one and it triggers an irresistible compulsion and without meaning it you have another and another and you wind up drunk again. Well, maybe I wasn't an alcoholic because that wasn't what was happening. I'd had two drinks and I felt a whole lot better than I did before I'd had them and I certainly didn't feel any need to drink anymore.

I gave myself a chance, though. I stood there for a few minutes and thought about having a third drink.

No. No, I really didn't want it. I was fine the way I was.

I left a buck on the bar, scooped the rest of my change, and headed for home. I walked past Armstrong's and didn't feel like stopping in. I certainly didn't have the urge to stop for a drink.

The early News would be out by now. Did I want to walk down to the corner for it?

No, the hell with it.

I stopped at the desk. No messages. Jacob was on duty, riding a gentle codeine buzz, filling in the squares of a crossword puzzle.

200

I said, 'Say, Jacob, I want to thank you for what you did the other night. Making that phone call.'

'Oh, well,' he said.

'No, that was terrific,' I said. 'I really appreciate it.'

I went upstairs and got ready for bed. I was tired and felt out of breath. For a moment, just before sleep came, I experienced again that odd sensation of having lost something. But what could I have lost?

I thought, Seven days. You had seven sober days and most of an eighth, and you lost them. They're gone.

EIGHT

I bought the *News* the next morning. A new atrocity had already driven Kim Dakkinen off the front page. Up in Washington Heights a young surgeon, a resident at Columbia Presbyterian, had been shot dead in a robbery attempt on Riverside Drive. He hadn't resisted his assailant, who had shot him for no apparent reason. The victim's widow was expecting their first child in early February.

The call-girl slashing was on an inside page. I didn't learn anything I hadn't heard the previous night from Durkin.

I walked around a lot. At noon I dropped over to the Y but got restless and left during the qualification. I had a pastrami sandwich at a Broadway deli and drank a bottle of Prior Dark with it. I had another beer around dinnertime. At eight-thirty I went over to St Paul's, walked once around the block and returned to my hotel without entering the basement meeting room. I made myself stay in my room. I felt like a drink, but I'd had two beers and I decided that two drinks a day would be my ration. As long as I didn't exceed that quota I didn't see how I could get in trouble. It didn't matter whether I had them first thing in the morning or last thing at night, in my room or at a bar, alone or in company.

The following day, Wednesday, I slept late and ate a late breakfast at Armstrong's. I walked to the main library and spent a couple hours there, then sat in Bryant Park until the drug dealers got on my nerves. They've so completely taken over the parks that they assume only a potential customer would bother coming there, so you can't read a paper without being constantly offered uppers and downers and pot and acid and God knows what else.

I went to the eight-thirty meeting that night. Mildred, one of the regulars, got a round of applause when she announced that it

was her anniversary, eleven years since her last drink. She said she didn't have any secret, she just did it a day at a time.

I thought that if I went to bed sober I'd have one day. I decided, what the hell, I'd do that. After the meeting I went over to Polly's Cage instead and had my two drinks. I got into a discussion with a guy and he wanted to buy me a third drink, but I told the bartender to make it Coke instead. I was quietly pleased with myself, knowing my limit and sticking to it.

Thursday I had a beer with dinner, went to the meeting and left on the break. I stopped in at Armstrong's but something kept me from ordering a drink there and I didn't stay long. I was restless, I walked in and out of Farrell's and Polly's without ordering a drink in either place. The liquor store down the block from Polly's was still open. I bought a fifth of J. W. Dant and took it back to my room.

I took a shower first and got ready for bed. Then I broke the seal on the bottle, poured about two ounces of bourbon in a water glass, drank it down and went to sleep.

Friday I had another two ounces first thing when I got out of bed. I really felt the drink and it was a good feeling. I went all day without having another. Then around bedtime I had one more and fell asleep.

Saturday I awoke clearheaded with no desire for a morning drink. I couldn't get over how well I was controlling my drinking. I almost felt like going to a meeting and sharing my secret with them, but I could imagine the reaction I'd get. Knowing looks, knowing laughter. Holier-than-thou sobriety. Besides, just because I could control my drinking didn't mean I was justified in recommending it to other people.

I had two drinks before bed. I barely felt them, but Sunday morning I woke up a little rocky and poured myself a generous eye-opener to start the day. It did the job. I read the paper, then checked the meeting book and found an afternoon meeting in the Village. I went down there on the subway. The crowd was almost entirely gay. I left at the break.

I went back to the hotel and took a nap. After dinner I finished reading the paper and decided to have my second drink. I poured two or three ounces of bourbon into my glass and drank it off. I sat down and read some more but I couldn't concentrate very well on what I was reading. I thought of having another drink but I reminded myself I'd already had two that day.

Then I realized something. I'd had my morning drink more than twelve hours ago. More time had elapsed since then than

had separated it from my last drink the night before. So that drink had long since left my system, and shouldn't properly be counted as part of *today's* drinks.

Which meant I was entitled to another drink before I went to bed.

I was pleased with having figured that out, and decided to reward myself for my insight by making the drink a respectable one. I filled the water glass to within a half inch of the top and took my time drinking it, sitting in my chair with it like a model in one of those Man of Distinction ads. I had the sense to realize that it was the number of drinks that was significant, not their size, and then it struck me that I'd cheated myself. My first drink, if you could call it that, had been a short measure. In a sense, I owed myself about four ounces of bourbon.

I poured what I judged to be four ounces and drained the glass.

I was pleased to note that the drinks hadn't had any discernible effect on me. I certainly wasn't drunk. As a matter of fact, I felt better than I'd felt in a long time. Too good, in fact, to sit around the room. I'd go out, find a congenial spot, have a Coke or a cup of coffee. Not a drink, because in the first place I didn't want any more and, just as important, I'd already had my two drinks for the day.

I had a Coke at Polly's. On Ninth Avenue I had a glass of ginger ale at a gay bar called Kid Gloves. Some of the other drinkers looked faintly familiar, and I wondered if any of them had been at the meeting that afternoon in the Village.

A block further downtown I realized something. I'd been controlling my drinking for days now, and before that I'd been off the sauce entirely for over a week, and that proved something. Hell, if I could limit myself to two drinks a day, that was fairly strong evidence that I didn't *need* to limit myself to two drinks a day. I'd had my problems with alcohol in the past, I couldn't very well deny it, but evidently I had outgrown that stage in my life.

So, although I certainly didn't *need* another drink, I could just as certainly have one if I wanted one. And I did want one, as a matter of fact, so why not have it?

I went into the saloon and ordered a double bourbon with water back. I remember the bartender had a shiny bald head, and I remember him pouring the drink, and I remember picking it up.

That's the last thing I remember.

NINE

I woke up suddenly, consciousness coming on abruptly and at
top volume. I was in a hospital bed.

That was the first shock. The second came a little later when I
found out it was Wednesday. I couldn't remember anything after
I picked up that third drink Sunday night.

I'd had occasional blackouts for years. Sometimes I'd lose the
last half hour of the night. Sometimes I'd lose a few hours.

I'd never lost two whole days before.

They didn't want to let me go. I'd been admitted late the
previous night and they wanted to keep me in detox for a full
five days.

An intern said, 'The booze isn't even out of your system yet.
You'll walk around the corner and pick up a drink five minutes
after you get out of here.'

'No I won't.'

'You just went through detox here a couple of weeks ago. It's
on your chart. We cleaned you up and how long did you last?'

I didn't say anything.

'You know how you got here last night? You had a convulsion, a full-scale grand mal seizure. Ever have one of those
before?'

'No.'

'Well, you'll have them again. If you keep on drinking you can
pretty much count on it. Not every time, but sooner or later.
And sooner or later you'll die of it. If you don't die of something
else first.'

'Stop it.'

He grabbed me by the shoulder. 'No, I won't stop it,' he said.
'Why the hell should I stop it? I can't be polite and considerate of
your feelings and expect to cut through all your bullshit at the

same time. Look at me. *Listen* to me. You're an alcoholic. If you drink you'll die.'

I didn't say anything.

He had it all figured out. I would spend ten days in detox. Then I'd go to Smithers for twenty-eight days of alcoholic rehabilitation. He let up on that part when he found out I didn't have medical insurance or the couple of thousand dollars rehab would cost, but he was still holding out for a five-day stay in the detox ward.

'I don't have to stay,' I said. 'I'm not going to drink.'

'Everybody says that.'

'In my case it's true and you can't keep me here if I don't agree to stay. You have to let me sign out.'

'If you do you'll be signing out AMA. Against Medical Advice.'

'Then that's what I'll do.'

He looked angry for a moment. Then he shrugged. 'Suit yourself,' he said cheerfully. 'Next time maybe you'll listen to advice.'

'There won't be a next time.'

'Oh, there'll be a next time, all right,' he said. 'Unless you fall on your face closer to some other hospital. Or die before you get here.'

The clothes they brought me were a mess, dirty from rolling in the street, the shirt and jacket stained with blood. I'd been bleeding from a scalp wound when they brought me in and they'd stitched it up for me. I had evidently sustained the wound during the seizure, unless I'd acquired it earlier in my adventures.

I had enough cash on me for the hospital bill. A minor miracle, that.

It had rained during the morning and the streets were still wet. I stood on the sidewalk and felt the confidence drain out of me. There was a bar right across the street. I had money in my pocket for a drink and I knew it would make me feel better.

I went back to my hotel instead. I had to get up the nerve to approach the desk and collect my mail and messages, as if I'd done something shameful and owed some profound apology to the desk clerk. The worst of it was not knowing what I might have done during the time I was in blackout.

Nothing showed in the clerk's expression. Maybe I'd spent

most of the lost time in my room, drinking in isolation. Maybe I'd never returned to the hotel since I left it Sunday night.

I went upstairs and ruled out the latter hypothesis. I'd evidently returned sometime either Monday or Tuesday, because I'd finished the bottle of J. W. Dant and there was a half-full quart of Jim Beam on the bureau beside the empty Dant bottle. The dealer's label indicated it was from a store on Eighth Avenue.

I thought, Well, here's the first test. Either you drink or you don't.

I poured the bourbon down the sink, rinsed out both bottles and put them in the trash.

The mail was all junk. I got rid of it and looked at my messages. Anita had called Monday morning. Someone named Jim Faber had called Tuesday night and left a number. And Chance had called once last night and once this morning.

I took a long hot shower and a careful shave and put on clean clothes. I threw out the shirt and socks and underwear I'd worn home from the hospital and put the suit aside. Maybe the dry cleaner would be able to do something with it. I picked up my messages and went through them again.

My ex-wife Anita. Chance, the pimp who'd killed Kim Dakkinen. And somebody named Faber. I didn't know anybody named Faber, unless he was some drunk who'd become a long-lost buddy during my drunken wanderings.

I discarded the slip with his number and weighed a trip downstairs against the hassle of placing a call through the hotel operator. If I hadn't poured out the bourbon I might have had a drink just about then. Instead I went downstairs and called Anita from the lobby booth.

It was a curious conversation. We were carefully polite, as we often are, and after we'd circled one another like first-round prizefighters she asked me why I'd called. 'I'm just returning your call,' I said. 'I'm sorry it took me awhile.'

'Returning my call?'

'There's a message that you called Monday.'

There was a pause. Then she said, 'Matt, we spoke Monday night. You called me back. Don't you remember?'

I felt a chill, as if someone had just scraped a piece of chalk on a blackboard. 'Of course I remember,' I said. 'But how did this slip get back in my box? I thought you'd called a second time.'

'No.'

'I must have dropped the message slip and then some helpful

207

idiot returned it to my box, and it got handed to me just now and I thought it was another call.'

'That's what must have happened.'

'Sure,' I said. 'Anita, I'd had a couple drinks when I spoke to you the other night. My memory's a little vague. You want to remind me what we talked about in case there's anything I forgot?'

We had talked about orthodontia for Mickey. I'd told her to get another opinion. I remembered that part of the conversation, I assured her. Was there anything else? I had said I was hoping to send more money soon, a more substantial contribution than I'd made lately, and paying for the kid's braces shouldn't be any problem. I told her I remembered that part, too, and she said that was about all, except that of course I'd talked to the children. Oh, sure, I told her. I remembered my conversation with the boys. And that was all? Well, then, my memory wasn't so bad after all, was it?

I was shaking when I hung up the phone. I sat there and tried to summon up a memory of the conversation she had just described and it was hopeless. Everything was a blank from the moment just before the third drink Sunday night to the time I'd come out of it in the hospital. Everything, all of it, gone.

I tore up the message slip, tore it in half again, put the scraps in my pocket. I looked at the other message. The number Chance had left was his service number. I called Midtown North instead. Durkin wasn't in but they gave me his home number.

He sounded groggy when he answered. 'Gimme a second, lemme light a cigarette,' he said. When he came back on the line he sounded all right. 'I was watching teevee,' he said, 'and I went and fell asleep in front of the set. What's on your mind, Scudder?'

'That pimp's been trying to reach me. Chance.'

'Trying to reach you how?'

'By phone. He left a number for me to call. His answering service. So he's probably in town, and if you want me to set him up –'

'We're not looking for him.'

For an awful moment I thought I must have spoken to Durkin during my blackout, that one of us had called the other and I didn't remember it. But he went on talking and I realized that hadn't happened.

'We had him over at the station house and we sweated him,' he explained. 'We put out a pickup order but he wound up

coming in on his own accord. He had a slick lawyer with him and he was pretty slick himself.'

'You let him go?'

'We didn't have one damn thing to hold him on. He had an alibi for the whole stretch from several hours before the estimated time of death to six or eight hours after. The alibi looks solid and we haven't got anything to stack up against it. The clerk who checked Charles Jones into the Galaxy can't come up with a description. I mean he can't say for sure if the man he signed in was black or white. He sort of thinks he was white. How'd you like to hand that to the DA?'

'He could have had someone else rent the room. Those big hotels, they don't keep any track of who goes in and out.'

'You're right. He could have had someone rent the room. He also could have had someone kill her.'

'Is that what you figure he did?'

'I don't get paid to figure. I know we haven't got a case against the son of a bitch.'

I thought for a moment. 'Why would he call me?'

'How would I know?'

'Does he know I steered you to him?'

'He didn't hear it from me.'

'Then what does he want with me?'

'Why don't you ask him yourself?'

It was warm in the booth. I cracked the door, let a little air in. 'Maybe I'll do that.'

'Sure. Scudder? Don't meet him in a dark alley, huh? Because if he's got some kind of a hard-on for you, you want to watch your back.'

'Right.'

'And if he does nail you, leave a dying message, will you? That's what they always do on television.'

'I'll see what I can do.'

'Make it clever,' he said. 'but not *too* clever, you know? Keep it simple enough so I can figure it out.'

I dropped a dime and called his service. The woman with the smoker's rasp to her voice said, 'Eight-oh-nine-two. May I help you?'

I said, 'My name's Scudder. Chance called me and I'm returning his call.'

She said she expected to be speaking to him soon and asked

209

for my number. I gave it to her and went upstairs and stretched out on the bed.

A little less than an hour later the phone rang. 'It's Chance,' he said. 'I want to thank you for returning my call.'

'I just got the message an hour or so ago. Both of the messages.'

'I'd like to speak with you,' he said. 'Face to face, that is.'

'All right.'

'I'm downstairs, I'm in your lobby. I thought we could get a drink or a cup of coffee in the neighborhood. Could you come down?'

'All right.'

TEN

He said, 'You still think I killed her, don't you?'

'What does it matter what I think?'

'It matters to me.'

I borrowed Durkin's line. 'Nobody pays me to think.'

We were in the back booth of a coffee shop a few doors from Eighth Avenue. My coffee was black. His was just a shade lighter than his skin tone. I'd ordered a toasted English muffin, figuring that I probably ought to eat something, but I hadn't been able to bring myself to touch it.

He said, 'I didn't do it.'

'All right.'

'I have what you might call an alibi in depth. A whole roomful of people can account for my time that night. I wasn't anywhere near that hotel.'

'That's handy.'

'What's that supposed to mean?'

'Whatever you want it to mean.'

'You're saying I could have hired it done.'

I shrugged. I felt edgy, sitting across the table from him, but more than that I felt tired. I wasn't afraid of him.

'Maybe I could have. But I didn't.'

'If you say so.'

'God *damn*,' he said, and drank some of his coffee. 'She anything more to you than you let on that night?'

'No.'

'Just a friend of a friend?'

'That's right.'

He looked at me, and his gaze was like a too-bright light shining in my eyes. 'You went to bed with her,' he said. Before I could respond he said, 'Sure, that's what you did. How else would she say thank you? The woman only spoke one language.

I hope that wasn't the only compensation you got, Scudder. I hope she didn't pay the whole fee in whore's coin.'

'My fees are my business,' I said. 'Anything that happened between us is my business.'

He nodded. 'I'm just getting a fix on where you're coming from, that's all.'

'I'm not coming from anyplace and I'm not going anywhere. I did a piece of work and I was paid in full. The client's dead and I didn't have anything to do with that and it doesn't have anything to do with me. You say you had nothing to do with her death. Maybe that's true and maybe it isn't. I don't know and I don't have to know and I don't honestly give a damn. That's between you and the police. I'm not the police.'

'You used to be.'

'But I'm not anymore. I'm not the police and I'm not the dead girl's brother and I'm not some avenging angel with a flaming sword. You think it matters to me who killed Kim Dakkinen? You think I give a damn?'

'Yes.'

I looked at him.

He said, 'Yes, I think it matters to you. I think you care who killed her. That's why I'm here.' He smiled gently. 'See,' he said, 'what I want is to hire you, Mr Matthew Scudder. I want you to find out who killed her.'

I took a while before I believed he was serious. Then I did what I could to talk him out of it. If there was any kind of trail leading to Kim's killer, I told him, the police had the best chance of finding and following it. They had the authority and the manpower and the talent and the connections and the skills. I had none of the above.

'You're forgetting something,' he said.

'Oh?'

'They won't be looking. Far as they're concerned, they already *know* who killed her. They got no evidence so they can't do anything with it, but that's their excuse not to kill themselves trying. They'll say, "Well, we know Chance killed her but we can't prove it so let's work on something else." God knows they got plenty other things to work on. And if they did work on it, all they'd be looking for is some way to hang it onto me. They wouldn't even look to see if there's somebody else on earth with a reason for wanting her dead.'

'Like who?'

'That's what you would be looking to find out.'

'Why?'

'For money,' he said, and smiled again. 'I wasn't asking you to work for free. I have a lot of money coming in, all of it cash. I can pay a good fee.'

'That's not what I meant. Why would you want me on the case? Why would you want the killer found, assuming I had any chance of finding him? It's not to get you off the hook because you're not on the hook. The cops haven't got a case against you and they're not likely to come up with one. What's it to you if the case stays on the books as unsolved?'

His gaze was calm, steady. 'Maybe I'm concerned about my reputation,' he suggested.

'How? It looks to me as though your reputation gets a boost. If the word on the street is that you killed her and got away with it, the next girl who wants to quit your string is going to have something else to think about. Even if you didn't have anything to do with her murder, I can see where you'd be just as happy to take the credit for it.'

He flicked his index finger a couple times against his empty coffee cup. He said, 'Somebody killed a woman of mine. Nobody should be able to do that and get away with it.'

'She wasn't yours when she got killed.'

'Who knew that? You knew it and she knew it and I knew it. My other girls, did they know? Did the people in the bars and on the street know? Do they know now? Far as the world knows, one of my girls got killed and the killer's getting away with it.'

'And that hurts your reputation?'

'I don't see it helping it any. There's other things. My girls are afraid. Kim got killed and the guy who did it is still out there. Suppose he repeats?'

'Kills another prostitute?'

'Kills another of mine,' he said levelly. 'Scudder, that killer's a loaded gun and I don't know who he's pointed at. Maybe killing Kim's a way for somebody to get at me. Maybe another girl of mine is next on his list. I know one thing. My business is hurting already. I told my girls not to take any hotel tricks, that's for starters, and not to take any new johns if there's anything funny about them. That's like telling them to leave the phone off the hook.'

The waiter drifted over with a pot of coffee and refilled our cups. I still hadn't touched my English muffin and the melted butter was starting to congeal. I got him to take it away. Chance

213

added milk to his coffee. I remembered sitting with Kim while she drank hers heavily diluted with cream and sugar.

I said, 'Why me, Chance?'

'I told you. The cops aren't going to kill themselves. The only way somebody's going to give this his best shot is if he's earning my money for it.'

'There's other people who work private. You could hire a whole firm, get 'em working around the clock.'

'I never did like team sports. Rather see somebody go one on one. 'Sides, you got an inside track. You knew the woman.'

'I don't know how much of an edge that gives me.'

'And I know you.'

'Because you met me once?'

'And liked your style. That counts some.'

'Does it? The only thing you know about me is I know how to look at a boxing match. That's not a whole lot.'

'It's something. But I know more than that. I know how you handle yourself. And I've asked around, you know. A lot of folks know you and most of 'em said good things about you.'

I was silent for a minute or two. Then I said, 'It could have been a psycho that killed her. That's what he made it look like so maybe that's what it was.'

'Friday I learn she wants out of my string of girls. Saturday I tell her it's cool. Sunday some crazy man flies in from Indiana and chops her up, just by coincidence. You figure?'

'Coincidences happen all the time,' I said, 'but no, I don't think it was coincidence.' God, I felt tired. I said, 'I don't much want the case.'

'Why not?'

I thought, Because I don't want to have to do anything. I want to sit in a dark corner and turn the world off. I want a drink, damn it.

'You could use the money,' he said.

That was true enough. I hadn't gotten all that much mileage out of my last fee. And my son Mickey needed braces on his teeth, and after that there'd be something else.

I said, 'I've got to think it over.'

'All right.'

'I can't concentrate right now. I need a little time to sort out my thoughts.'

'How much time?'

Months, I thought. 'A couple of hours. I'll call you sometime

tonight. Is there a number where I can reach you or do I just call the service?'

'Pick a time,' he said. 'I'll meet you in front of your hotel.'

'You don't have to do that.'

'It's too easy to say no over the phone. I figure the odds are better face to face. Besides, if the answer's yes we'll want to talk some. And you'll want some money from me.'

I shrugged.

'Pick a time.'

'Ten?'

'In front of your hotel.'

'All right,' I said. 'If I had to answer now, it'd be no.'

'Then it's good you got until ten.'

He paid for the coffee. I didn't put up a fight.

I went back to the hotel and up to the room. I tried to think straight and couldn't. I couldn't seem to sit still, either. I kept moving from the bed to the chair and back again, wondering why I hadn't given him a final no right away. Now I had the aggravation of getting through the hours until ten o'clock and then finding the resolve to turn down what he was offering.

Without thinking too much about what I was doing I put on my hat and coat and went around the corner to Armstrong's. I walked in the door not knowing what I was going to order. I went up to the bar and Billie started shaking his head when he saw me coming. He said, 'I can't serve you, Matt. I'm sorry as hell.'

I felt the color mounting in my face. I was embarrassed and I was angry. I said, 'What are you talking about? Do I look drunk to you?'

'No.'

'Then how the hell did I get to be eighty-six around here?'

His eyes avoided mine. 'I don't make the rules,' he said. 'I'm not saying you're not welcome here. Coffee or a Coke or a meal, hell, you're a valued longtime customer. But I'm not allowed to sell you booze.'

'Who says?'

'The boss says. When you were in here the other night –'

Oh, God. I said, 'I'm sorry about that Billie. I'll tell you the truth, I had a couple of bad nights. I didn't even know I came in here.'

'Don't worry about it.'

Christ, I wanted to hide behind something. 'Was I very bad, Billie? Did I make trouble?'

'Aw, shit,' he said. 'You were drunk, you know? It happens, right? I used to have this Irish landlady, I came in bagged one night and apologized the next day, and she would say, 'Jaysus, son, it could happen to a bishop.' You didn't make any trouble, Matt.'

'Then –'

'Look,' he said, and leaned forward. 'I'll just repeat what I was told. He told me, he said, if the guy wants to drink himself to death I can't stop him, and if he wants to come in here he's welcome, but I'm not selling him the booze. This isn't me talking, Matt. I'm just saying what was said.'

'I understand.'

'If it was up to me –'

'I didn't come in for a drink anyway,' I said. 'I came in for coffee.'

'In that case –'

'In that case the hell with it,' I said. 'In that case I think what I want is a drink and it shouldn't be all that hard to find somebody willing to sell it to me.'

'Matt, don't take it that way.'

'Don't tell me how to take it,' I said. 'Don't give me that shit.'

There was something clean and satisfying about the rage I felt. I stalked out of there, my anger burning with a pure flame, and stood on the sidewalk trying to decide where to go for a drink.

Then someone was calling my name.

I turned. A fellow in an army jacket was smiling gently at me. I couldn't place him at first. He said it was good to see me and asked how I was doing, and then of course I knew who it was.

I said, 'Oh, hi, Jim. I'm okay, I guess.'

'Going to the meeting? I'll walk with you.'

'Oh,' I said. 'Gee, I don't think I'm going to be able to make it tonight. I have to see a guy.'

He just smiled. Something clicked, and I asked him if his last name was Faber.

'That's right,' he said.

'You called me at the hotel.'

'Just wanted to say hello. Nothing important.'

'I didn't recognize the name. Otherwise I would have called you back.'

'Sure. You sure you don't want to tag along to the meeting, Matt?'

'I wish I could. Oh, Jesus.'

He waited.

'I've been having a little trouble, Jim.'

'That's not so unusual, you know.'

I couldn't look at him. I said, 'I started drinking again. I went, I don't know, seven or eight days. Then I started again, and I was doing okay, you know, controlling it, and then one night I got into trouble.'

'You got in trouble when you picked up the first one.'

'I don't know. Maybe.'

'That's why I called,' he said gently. 'I figured maybe you could use a little help.'

'You knew?'

'Well, you were in pretty rocky shape at the meeting Monday night.'

'I was at the meeting?'

'You don't remember, do you? I had a feeling you were in a blackout.'

'Oh my God.'

'What's the matter?'

'I went there drunk? I showed up drunk at an AA meeting?'

He laughed. 'You make it sound like a mortal sin. You think you're the first person who ever did that?'

I wanted to die. 'But it's terrible,' I said.

'What's so terrible?'

'I can never go back. I can never walk into that room.'

'You're ashamed of yourself, aren't you?'

'Of course.'

He nodded. 'I was always ashamed of my blackouts. I didn't want to know about them and I was always afraid of what I might have done. Just for the record, you weren't so bad. You didn't make trouble. You didn't talk out of turn. You spilled a cup of coffee –'

'Oh, God.'

'It's not as if you spilled it *on* anybody. You were just drunk, that's all. In case you were wondering, you didn't look to be having a very good time. Matter of fact, you looked pretty miserable.'

I found the courage to say, 'I wound up in the hospital.'

'And you're out already?'

'I signed myself out this afternoon. I had a convulsion, that's how I got there.'

'That'll do it.'

We walked a little ways in silence. I said, 'I wouldn't be able

217

to stay for the whole meeting. I have to meet a guy at ten o'clock.'

'You could stay for most of the meeting.'

'I guess so.'

It seemed to me as though everybody was staring at me. Some people said hello to me and I found myself reading implications into their greetings. Others didn't say anything and I decided they were avoiding me because my drunkenness had offended them. I was so maddeningly self-conscious I wanted to jump out of my own skin.

I couldn't stay in my seat during the qualification. I kept going back to the coffee urn. I was sure my constant visits to the urn were drawing disapproval but I seemed irresistibly drawn to it.

My mind kept going off on tangents of its own. The speaker was a Brooklyn fireman and he had a very lively story but I couldn't keep my mind on it. He told how everyone in his firehouse had been a heavy drinker and how anyone who didn't drink that way got transferred out. 'The captain was an alcoholic and he wanted to surround himself with other alcoholics,' he explained. 'He used to say, "Give me enough drunken firemen and I'll put out any fire there is." And he was right. Man, we would do anything, we would go in anywhere, take any crazy goddamned chances. Because we were too drunk to know better.'

It was such a goddamned puzzle. I'd been controlling my drinking and it had worked fine. Except when it didn't.

On the break I put a buck in the basket and went to the urn for still another cup of coffee. This time I managed to make myself eat an oatmeal cookie. I was back in my seat when the discussion started.

I kept losing the thread but it didn't seem to matter. I listened as well as I could and I stayed there as long as I could. At a quarter of ten I got up and slipped out the door as unobtrusively as possible. I had the feeling every eye in the place was on me and I wanted to assure them all that I wasn't going for a drink, that I had to meet somebody, that it was a business matter.

It struck me later that I could have stayed for the end. St Paul's was only five minutes from my hotel. Chance would have waited.

Maybe I wanted an excuse to leave before it was my turn to talk.

*

I was in the lobby at ten o'clock. I saw his car pull up and I went out the door and crossed the sidewalk to the curb. I opened the door, got in, swung it shut.

He looked at me.

'That job still open?'

He nodded. 'If you want it.'

'I want it.'

He nodded again, put the car in gear, and pulled away from the curb.

ELEVEN

The circular drive in Central Park is almost exactly six miles around. We were on our fourth counterclockwise lap, the Cadillac cruising effortlessly. Chance did most of the talking. I had my notebook out, and now and then I wrote something in it.

At first he talked about Kim. Her parents were Finnish immigrants who had settled on a farm in western Wisconsin. The nearest city of any size was Eau Claire. Kim had been named Kiraa and grew up milking cows and weeding the vegetable garden. When she was nine years old her older brother began abusing her sexually, coming into her room every night, doing things to her, making her do things to him.

'Except one time she told the story and it was her uncle on her mother's side, and another time it was her father, so maybe it never happened at all outside of her mind. Or maybe it did and she changed it to keep it from being so real.'

During her junior year in high school she had an affair with a middle-aged realtor. He told her he was going to leave his wife for her. She packed a suitcase and they drove to Chicago, where they stayed for three days at the Palmer House, ordering all their meals from room service. The realtor got maudlin drunk the second day and kept telling her he was ruining her life. He was in better spirits the third day, but the following morning she awoke to find him gone. A note explained that he had returned to his wife, that the room was paid for four more days, and that he would never forget Kim. Along with the note he left six hundred dollars in a hotel envelope.

She stayed out the week, had a look at Chicago, and slept with several men. Two of them gave her money without being asked. She'd intended to ask the others but couldn't bring herself to do so. She thought about going back to the farm. Then, on her final night at the Palmer House, she picked up a fellow hotel guest, a Nigerian delegate to some sort of trade conference.

'That burned her bridges,' Chance said. 'Sleeping with a black man meant she couldn't go back to the farm. First thing the next morning she went and caught a bus for New York.'

She'd been all wrong for the life until he took her away from Duffy and put her in her own apartment. She had the looks and the bearing for the carriage trade, and that was good because she hadn't had the hustle to make it on the street.

'She was lazy,' he said, and thought for a moment. 'Whores are lazy.'

He'd had six women working for him. Now, with Kim dead, he had five. He talked about them for a few moments in general terms, then got down to cases, supplying names and addresses and phone numbers and personal data. I made a lot of notes. We finished our fourth circuit of the park and he pulled off to the right, exited at West Seventy-second Street, drove two blocks and pulled over to the curb.

'Be a minute,' he said.

I stayed where I was while he made a call from a booth on the corner. He'd left the motor idling. I looked at my notes and tried to see a pattern in the wisps and fragments I'd been given.

Chance returned to the car, checked the mirror, swung us around in a deft if illegal U-turn. 'Just checking with my service,' he said. 'Just keeping in touch.'

'You ought to have a phone in the car.'

'Too complicated.'

He drove downtown and east, pulling up next to a fire hydrant in front of a white brick apartment house on Seventeenth between Second and Third. 'Collection time,' he told me. Once again he left the motor idling, but this time fifteen minutes elapsed before he reappeared, striding jauntily past the liveried doorman, sliding nimbly behind the wheel.

'That's Donna's place,' he said. 'I told you about Donna.'

'The poet.'

'She's all excited. She got two poems accepted by this magazine in San Francisco. She'll get six free copies of the issue the poems appear in. That's as much pay as she'll get, just copies of the magazine.'

A light turned red in front of us. He braked for it, looked left and right, then coasted through the light.

'Couple times,' he said, 'she's had poems in magazines that pay you for them. Once she got twenty-five dollars. That's the best she ever did.'

'It sounds like a hard way to make a living.'

'A poet can't make any money. Whores are lazy but this one's not lazy when it comes to her poems. She'll sit for six or eight hours to get the words right, and she's always got a dozen batches of poems in the mail. They come back from one place and she sends 'em out someplace else. She spends more on postage than they'll ever pay her for the poems.' He fell silent for a moment, then laughed softly. 'You know how much money I just took off of Donna? Eight hundred dollars, and that's just for the past two days. Of course there's days when her phone won't ring once.'

'But it averages out pretty well.'

'Pays better than poems.' He looked at me. 'Want to go for a ride?'

'Isn't that what we've been doing?'

'We been going around in circles,' he said. 'Now I'm gonna take you to a whole nother world.'

We drove down Second Avenue, through the Lower East Side, and over the Williamsburg Bridge into Brooklyn. Coming off the bridge we took enough turns to throw off my sense of direction, and the street signs didn't help much. I didn't recognize the names. But I watched the neighborhood change from Jewish to Italian to Polish and had a fair idea of where we were.

On a dark, silent street of two-family frame houses, Chance slowed in front of a three-story brick structure with a garage door in the middle. He used a remote-control unit to raise the door, then closed it after we had driven in. I followed him up a flight of stairs and into a spacious high-ceilinged room.

He asked if I knew where we were. I guessed Greenpoint. 'Very good,' he said. 'I guess you know Brooklyn.'

'I don't know this part of it very well. The meat market signs advertising kielbasa were a tip-off.'

'I guess. Know whose house we're in? Ever hear of a Dr Casimir Levandowski?'

'No.'

'No reason why you should have. He's an old fellow. Retired, confined to a wheelchair. Eccentric, too. Keeps himself to himself. This place used to be a firehouse.'

'I thought it must have been something like that.'

'Two architects bought it some years ago and converted it. They pretty much gutted the interior and started from scratch. They must have had a few dollars to play with because they didn't cut many corners. Look at the floors. Look at the window

moldings.' He pointed out details, commented on them. 'Then they got tired of the place or each other, I don't know what, and they sold out to old Dr Levandowski.'

'And he lives here?'

'He don't exist,' he said. His speech patterns kept shifting, from ghetto to university and back again. 'The neighbors never see the old doc. They just see his faithful black servant and all they see him do is drive in and drive out. This is my house, Matthew. Can I give you the ten-cent tour?'

It was quite a place. There was a gym on the top floor, fully equipped with weights and exercise machines and furnished with sauna and Jacuzzi. His bedroom was on the same floor, and the bed, covered with a fur spread, was centered beneath a skylight. A library on the second floor contained one whole wall of books and an eight-foot pool table.

There were African masks all over the place, and occasional groups of free-standing African sculpture. Chance pointed out a piece from time to time, naming the tribe that had produced it. I mentioned having seen African masks at Kim's apartment.

'Poro Society masks,' he said. 'From the Dan tribe. I keep one or two African things in all my girls' apartments. Not the most valuable things, of course, but not junk, either. I don't own any junk.'

He took a rather crudely fashioned mask from the wall and presented it for my inspection. The eye openings were square, the features all geometrically precise, the overall effect powerful in its primitiveness. 'This is Dogon,' he said. 'Take hold of it. You can't appreciate sculpture with your eyes alone. The hands have to participate. Go ahead, handle it.'

I took the mask from him. Its weight was greater than I anticipated. The wood that composed it must have been very dense.

He lifted a telephone from a low teakwood table and dialed a number. He said, 'Hey, darlin'. Any messages?' He listened for a moment, then put the phone down. 'Peace and quiet,' he said. 'Shall I make some coffee?'

'Not if it's any trouble.'

He assured me it wasn't. While the coffee brewed he told me about his African sculpture, how the craftsmen who produced it did not think of their work as art. 'Everything they make has a specific function,' he explained. 'It's to guard your house or keep off spirits or to use in a particular tribal rite. If a mask doesn't have the power in it anymore they'll throw it away and

somebody'll carve a new one. The old one's trash, you burn it up or toss it away cause it's no good.'

He laughed. 'Then the Europeans came and discovered African art. Some of those French painters got their inspiration from tribal masks. Now you've got a situation where there are carvers in Africa spending all their time making masks and statues for export to Europe and America. They follow the old forms because that's what their customers want, but it's a funny thing. Their work's no good. It doesn't have any feeling in it. It's not real. You look at it and you take it in your hand, and you do the same with the real thing, and you can tell the difference right away. If you have any feeling at all for the stuff. Funny, isn't it?'

'It's interesting.'

'If I had any of the junk around I'd show you, but I don't own any. I bought some when I was starting out. You have to make mistakes to develop a feel for it. But I got rid of that stuff, burned it in the fireplace there.' He smiled. 'The very first piece I bought, I still have it. It's hanging in the bedroom. A Dan mask. Poro Society. I didn't know shit about African art but I saw it in an antique shop and I responded to the mask's artistic integrity.' He stopped, shook his head. 'Hell I did. What happened was I looked at that piece of smooth black wood and I was looking in a mirror. I saw myself, I saw my father, I was looking back through the damned ages. You know what I'm talking about?'

'I'm not sure.'

'Hell. Maybe I don't know either.' He gave his head a shake. 'What do you figure one of those old carvers'd make of this? He'd say, "Shit, what's this crazy nigger want with all these old masks? Why'd he go and hang 'em all over the damn wall?" That coffee's ready. You take yours black, right?'

He said, 'How's a detective go about detecting, anyway? Where do you start?'

'By going around and talking to people. Unless Kim got killed coincidentally by a maniac, her death grew out of her life.' I tapped my notebook. 'There's a lot you don't know about her life.'

'I guess.'

'I'll talk to people and see what they can tell me. Maybe it'll fit together and point somewhere. Maybe not.'

'My girls'll know it's cool to talk to you.'

'That'll help.'

224

'Not that they necessarily know anything, but if they do.'

'Sometimes people know things without knowing they know them.'

'And sometimes they tell without knowing they told.'

'That's true, too.'

He stood up, put his hands on his hips. 'You know,' he said, 'I didn't figure to bring you here. I didn't figure you needed to know about this house. And I brought you without you even asking.'

'It's quite a house.'

'Thank you.'

'Was Kim impressed with it?'

'She never saw it. None of 'em ever did. There's an old German woman comes here once a week to clean. Makes the whole place shine. She's the only woman's ever been inside of this house. Since I owned it, anyway, and the architects who used to live here didn't have much use for women. Here's the last of the coffee.'

It was awfully good coffee. I'd had too much of it already but it was too good to pass up. When I complimented it earlier he'd told me it was a mixture of Jamaica Blue Mountain and a dark roast Colombian bean. He'd offered me a pound of it, and I'd told him it wouldn't be much use to me in a hotel room.

I sipped the coffee while he made yet another call to his service. When he hung up I said, 'You want to give me the number here? Or is that one secret you want to keep?'

He laughed. 'I'm not here that much. It's easier if you just call the service.'

'All right.'

'And this number wouldn't do you much. I don't know it myself. I'd have to look at an old phone bill to make sure I got it right. And if you dialed it, nothing would happen.'

'Why's that?'

'Because the bells won't ring. The phones are to make calls out. When I set this place up I got telephone service and I put in extensions so I'd never be far from a phone, but I never gave the number to anybody. Not even my service, not anybody.'

'And?'

'And I was here one night, I think I was playing pool, and the damn phone rang. I like to jumped. It was somebody wanted to know did I want a subscription to the *New York Times*. Then two days later I got another call and it was a wrong number, and I realized the only calls I was ever going to get were wrong

225

numbers and somebody selling something, and I took a screwdriver and went around and opened up each of the phones, and
there's this little clapper that rings the bell when a current
passes through a particular wire, and I just took the little clapper
off each of the phones. I dialed the number once from another
phone, and you think it rings because there's no telling the
clapper's gone, but there's no bell going off in this house.'

'Clever.'

'No doorbell, either. There's a thing you ring by the door
outside, but it's not connected to anything. That door's never
been opened since I moved in, and you can't see in the windows,
and there's burglar alarms on everything. Not that you get much
burglary in Greenpoint, a nice settled Polish neighborhood like
this, but old Dr Levandowski, he likes his security and he likes
his privacy.'

'I guess he does.'

'I'm not here much, Matthew, but when that garage door
closes behind me it keeps the whole world out. Nothing touches
me here. Nothing.'

'I'm surprised you brought me here.'

'So am I.'

We saved the money for last. He asked how much I wanted. I
told him I wanted twenty-five hundred dollars.

He asked what that bought.

'I don't know,' I said. 'I don't charge by the hour and I don't
keep track of my expenses. If I wind up laying out a lot of money
or if the thing goes on too long, I might wind up asking you for
more money. But I'm not going to send you a bill and I'm not
going to sue you if you don't pay.'

'You keep it all very informal.'

'That's right.'

'I like that. Cash on the line and no receipts. I don't mind
paying a price. The women bring in a lot of money, but there's a
lot that has to go out, too. Rent. Operating costs. Payoffs. You
got a whore installed in a building, you pay off the building. You
can't give the doorman twenty dollars for Christmas and let it go
at that, same as any other tenant. It's more like twenty a month
and a hundred for Christmas, and it's the same for all the
building employees. It adds up.'

'It must.'

'But there's a lot left. And I don't blow it on coke or waste it
gambling. You said what? Twenty-five hundred? I paid more

than twice that for the Dogon mask I gave you to hold. I paid $6,200, plus the auction galleries charge buyers a 10 percent commission these days. Comes to what? $6,820. And then there's sales tax.'

I didn't say anything. He said, 'Shit, I don't know what I'm proving. That I'm nigger-rich, I guess. Wait here a minute.' He came back with a sheaf of hundreds and counted out twenty-five of them. Used bills, out of sequence. I wondered how much cash he kept around the house, how much he habitually carried on his person. Years ago I'd known a loan shark who made it a rule never to walk out his door with less than ten thousand dollars in his pocket. He didn't keep it a secret, and everybody who knew him knew about the roll he carried.

Nobody ever tried to take it off him, either.

He drove me home. We took a different route back, over the Pulaski Bridge into Queens and through the tunnel to Manhattan. Neither of us talked much, and somewhere along the way I must have dozed off because he had to put a hand on my shoulder to waken me.

I blinked, straightened up in my seat. We were at the curb in front of my hotel.

'Door-to-door delivery service,' he said.

I got out and stood on the curb. He waited for a couple of cabs to pass, then made his U-turn. I watched until the Cadillac was out of sight.

Thoughts struggled in my brain like exhausted swimmers. I was far too tired to think. I went up to bed.

TWELVE

'I didn't know her all that well. I met her a year or so ago at the beauty parlor and we had a cup of coffee together, and reading between the lines of her conversation I figured out she wasn't the Avon lady. We exchanged numbers and we would talk now and then over the phone, but we never got close. Then whenever it was, a couple weeks ago, she called and wanted to get together. I was surprised. We'd been out of touch for months.'

We were in Elaine Mardell's apartment on Fifty-first between First and Second. White shag carpet on the floor, bold abstract oils on the walls, something inoffensive on the stereo. I had a cup of coffee. Elaine was drinking a diet soda.

'What did she want?'

'She told me she was leaving her pimp. She wanted to make the break without getting hurt. Which is where you came in, remember?'

I nodded. 'Why'd she come to you?'

'I don't know. I had the feeling she didn't have too many friends. It wasn't the sort of thing she could talk over with one of Chance's other girls, and she probably wouldn't have wanted to discuss it with someone who was out of the life altogether. And she was young, you know, compared to me. She may have seen me as a sort of wise old aunt.'

'That's you, all right.'

'Isn't it just? What was she, about twenty-five?'

'She said twenty-three. I think it said twenty-four in the papers.'

'Jesus, that's young.'

'I know.'

'More coffee, Matt?'

'I'm fine.'

'You know why I think she picked me to have that little

228

conversation with? I think it's because I don't have a pimp.' She settled herself in her seat, uncrossed and recrossed her legs. I remembered other times in this apartment, one of us on the couch, the other on the Eames chair, the same sort of unobtrusive music softening the room's hard edges.

I said, 'You never had one, did you?'

'No.'

'Do most girls?'

'The ones she knew did. I think you pretty much have to on the street. Somebody's got to defend your right to a particular corner and bail you out when you get arrested. When you work out of an apartment like this, well, that's different. But even so, most of the hookers I know have boyfriends.'

'Is that the same thing as a pimp?'

'Oh, no. A boyfriend isn't running a batch of girls. He just happens to be your boyfriend. And you don't turn your money over to him. But you buy him a lot of things, just because you want to, and you help out with cash when he hits a rough spot in life, or if there's some business opportunity he wants to take advantage of, or because he needs a little loan and, gee, it's not like you were *giving* him the money. That's what a boyfriend is.'

'Sort of a one-woman pimp.'

'Sort of, except every girl swears her boyfriend's different, her relationship's different, and what never changes is who earns the money and who spends it.'

'And you never had a pimp, did you? Or a boyfriend?'

'Never. I had my palm read once and the woman who did it was impressed. "You have a double head line, dear," she told me. "Your head rules your heart."' She came over, showed me her hand. 'It's this line right here. See?'

'Looks good to me.'

'Damn straight.' She went back for her glass of soda, then came and sat on the couch beside me. She said, 'When I learned what happened to Kim, the first thing I did was call you. But you weren't in.'

'I never got the message.'

'I didn't leave one. I hung up and called a travel agent I know. A couple hours later I was on a plane for Barbados.'

'Were you afraid you were on somebody's list?'

'Hardly that. I just figured Chance killed her. I didn't think he'd start knocking off all her friends and relations. No, I just knew it was time for a break. A week at a beachfront hotel. A

little sun in the afternoon, a little roulette at night, and enough steel-drum music and limbo dancing to hold me for a long time.'

'Sounds good.'

'Second night out I met a fellow at the poolside cocktail party. He was staying at the next hotel over. Very nice fellow, tax lawyer, got divorced a year and a half ago and then went through a tough little affair with someone too young for him, and he's over that now, and who does he meet but me.'

'And?'

'And we had a nice little romance for the rest of the week. Long walks on the beach. Snorkeling, tennis. Romantic dinners. Drinks on my terrace. I had a terrace looking out at the sea.'

'Here you've got one looking at the East River.'

'It's not the same. We had a great time, Matt. Good sex, too. I thought I'd have my work cut out for me, you know, acting shy. But I didn't have to act. I *was* shy, and then I got over my shyness.'

'You didn't tell him –'

'Are you kidding? Of course not. I told him I work for art galleries. I restore paintings. I'm a free-lance art restoration expert. He thought that was really fascinating and he had a lot of questions. It would have been easier if I'd had the sense to pick something a little more humdrum, but, see, I *wanted* to be fascinating.'

'Sure.'

She had her hands in her lap and she was looking at them. Her face was unlined but her years were beginning to show themselves on the back of her hands. I wondered how old she was. Thirty-six? Thirty-eight?

'Matt, he wanted to see me in the city. We weren't telling each other it was love, nothing like that, but there was this sense that we might have something that might go somewhere, and he wanted to follow it up and see where it led. He lives in Merrick. You know where that is?'

'Sure, out on the Island. It's not that far from where I used to live.'

'Is it nice out there?'

'Parts of it are very nice.'

'I gave him a phony number. He knows my name but the phone here is unlisted. I haven't heard from him and I don't expect to. I wanted a week in the sun and a nice little romance, and that's what I had, but once in a while I think I could call

him and make up something about the wrong number. I could lie my way out of that one.'

'Probably.'

'But for what? I could even lie my way into being his wife or girlfriend or something. And I could give up this apartment and drop my john book in the incinerator. But for what?' She looked at me. 'I've got a good life. I save my money. I always saved my money.'

'And invested it,' I remembered. 'Real estate, isn't it? Apartment houses in Queens?'

'Not just Queens. I could retire now if I had to and I'd get by all right. But why would I want to retire and what do I need with a boyfriend?'

'Why did Kim Dakkinen want to retire?'

'Is that what she wanted?'

'I don't know. Why did she want to leave Chance?'

She thought it over, shook her head. 'I never asked.'

'Neither did I.'

'I've never been able to understand why a girl would have a pimp in the first place, so I don't need an explanation when somebody tells me she wants to get rid of one.'

'Was she in love with anybody?'

'Kim? Could be. She didn't mention it if she was.'

'Was she planning to leave the city?'

'I didn't get that impression. But she wouldn't tell me if she was, would she?'

'Hell,' I said. I put my empty cup on the end table. 'She was involved someway with someone. I just wish I knew who.'

'Why?'

'Because that's the only way I'm going to find out who killed her.'

'You think that's how it works?'

'That's usually how it works.'

'Suppose I got killed tomorrow. What would you do?'

'I guess I'd send flowers.'

'Seriously.'

'Seriously? I'd check tax lawyers from Merrick.'

'There's probably a few of them, don't you think?'

'Could be. I don't suppose there's too many who spent a week in Barbados this month. You said he stayed at the next hotel down the beach from you? I don't think he'd be hard to find, or that I'd have much trouble tying him to you.'

'Would you actually do all that?'

'Why not?'

'No one would be paying you.'

I laughed. 'Well, you and I, we go back a ways, Elaine.'

And we did. When I was on the force we'd had an arrangement. I helped her out when she needed the kind of hand a cop could provide, whether with the law or with an unruly john. She, in turn, had been available to me when I wanted her. What, I wondered suddenly, had that made me? Neither pimp nor boyfriend, but what?

'Matt? Why did Chance hire you?'

'To find out who killed her.'

'Why?'

I thought of the reasons he'd given. 'I don't know,' I said.

'Why'd you take the job?'

'I can use the money, Elaine.'

'You don't care that much about money.'

'Sure I do. It's time I started providing for my old age. I've got an eye on these apartment houses in Queens.'

'Very funny.'

'I'll bet you're some landlady. I'll bet they love it when you come around to collect the rent.'

'There's a management firm that takes care of all that. I never see my tenants.'

'I wish you hadn't told me that. You just ruined a great fantasy.'

'I'll bet.'

I said, 'Kim took me to bed after I finished the job for her. I went over there and she paid me and then afterward we went to bed.'

'And?'

'It was like a tip, almost. A friendly way of saying thank you.'

'Beats ten dollars at Christmas time.'

'But would she do that? If she was involved with somebody, I mean. Would she just go to bed with me for the hell of it?'

'Matt, you're forgetting something.'

She looked, for just a moment, like somebody's wise old aunt. I asked what I was forgetting.

'Matt, she was a hooker.'

'Were you a hooker in Barbados?'

'I don't know,' she said. 'Maybe I was and maybe I wasn't. But I can tell you this much. I was damn glad when the mating dance was over and we were in bed together because for a

232

change I knew what I was doing. And going to bed with guys is what I do.'

I thought a moment. Then I said, 'When I called earlier you said to give you an hour. Not to come over right away.'

'So?'

'Because you had a john booked?'

'Well, it wasn't the meter reader.'

'Did you need the money?'

'Did I need the money? What kind of question is that? I *took* the money.'

'But you would have made the rent without it.'

'And I wouldn't have missed any meals, or had to wear the panty hose with the runs in it. What's this all about?'

'So you saw the guy today because that's what you do.'

'I suppose.'

'Well, you're the one who asked why I took the job.'

'It's what you do,' she said.

'Something like that.'

She thought of something and laughed. She said, 'When Heinrich Heine was dying – the German poet?'

'Yeah?'

'When he was dying he said, 'God will pardon me. It's His profession.'

'That's not bad.'

'It's probably even better in German. I shtup and you detect and God pardons.' She lowered her eyes. 'I just hope He does,' she said. 'When it's my turn in the barrel, I hope He's not down in Barbados for the weekend.'

THIRTEEN

When I left Elaine's the sky was growing dark and the streets were thick with rush-hour traffic. It was raining again, a nagging drizzle that slowed the commuters to a crawl. I looked at the swollen river of cars and wondered if one of them held Elaine's tax lawyer. I thought about him and tried to guess how he might have reacted when the number she gave him turned out to be a fake.

He could find her if he wanted to. He knew her name. The phone company wouldn't give out her unlisted number, but he wouldn't have to be too well connected to find somebody who could pry it out of them for him. Failing that, he could trace her without too much trouble through her hotel. They could tell him her travel agent and somewhere along the line he could pick up her address. I'd been a cop, I automatically thought of this sort of thing, but couldn't anybody make this sort of connection? It didn't seem terribly complicated to me.

Perhaps he'd been hurt when her number proved phony. Perhaps knowing she didn't want to see him would keep him from wanting to see her. But wouldn't his first thought be that the mistake might have been an accident? Then he'd try Information, and might guess that the unobtainable number differed from what she'd given him by no more than a transposed couple of digits. So why wouldn't he pursue it?

Maybe he never called her in the first place, never even learned that the number was phony. Maybe he'd discarded her number in the airplane washroom on the way home to his wife and kids.

Maybe he had a few guilt-ridden moments now and then, thinking of the art restorer waiting by her telephone for his call. Maybe he would find himself regretting his haste. No need, after all, to have thrown her number away. He might have been able to fit in a date with her from time to time. No reason she had to

learn about the wife and kids. The hell, she'd probably be grateful for someone to take her away from her paint tubes and turpentine.

Halfway home I stopped at a deli and had soup and a sandwich and coffee. There was a bizarre story in the *Post*. Two neighbors in Queens had been arguing for months because of a dog that barked in its owner's absence. The previous night, the owner was walking the dog when the animal relieved itself on a tree in front of the neighbor's house. The neighbor happened to be watching and shot at the dog from an upstairs window with a bow and arrow. The dog's owner ran back into his house and came out with a Walther P-38, a World War II souvenir. The neighbor also ran outside with his bow and arrow, and the dog's owner shot him dead. The neighbor was eighty-one, the dog's owner was sixty-two, and the two men had lived side by side in Little Neck for over twenty years. The dog's age wasn't given, but there was a picture of him in the paper, straining against a leash in the hands of a uniformed police officer.

Midtown North was a few blocks from my hotel. It was still raining in the same halfhearted fashion when I went over there a little after nine that night. I stopped at the front desk and a young fellow with a moustache and blow-dry hair pointed me to the staircase. I went up a flight and found the detective squad room. There were four plainclothes cops sitting at desks, a couple more down at the far end watching something on television. Three young black males in a holding pen paid some attention when I entered, then lost interest when they saw I wasn't their lawyer.

I approached the nearest desk. A balding cop looked up from the report he was typing. I told him I had an appointment with Detective Durkin.

A cop at another desk looked up and caught my eye. 'You must be Scudder,' he said. 'I'm Joe Durkin.'

His handshake was overly firm, almost a test of masculinity. He waved me into a chair and took his own seat, stubbed out a cigarette in an overflowing ashtray, lit a fresh one, leaned back and looked at me. His eyes were that pale shade of gray that doesn't show you a thing.

He said, 'Still raining out there?'

'Off and on.'

'Miserable weather. You want some coffee?'

'No thanks.'

'What can I do for you?'

I told him I'd like to see whatever he could show me on the Kim Dakkinen killing.

'Why?'

'I told somebody I'd look into it.'

'You told somebody you'd look into it? You mean you got a client?'

'You could say that.'

'Who?'

'I can't tell you that.'

A muscle worked along the side of his jaw. He was around thirty-five and a few pounds overweight, enough to make him look a little older than his years. He hadn't lost any hair yet and it was all dark brown, almost black. He wore it combed flat down on his head. He should have borrowed a blow dryer from the guy downstairs.

He said, 'You can't hold that out. You don't have a license and it wouldn't be privileged information even if you did.'

'I didn't know we were in court.'

'We're not. But you come in here asking a favor —'

I shrugged. 'I can't tell you my client's name. He has an interest in seeing her killer caught. That's all.'

'And he thinks that'll happen faster if he hires you.'

'Evidently.'

'You think so too?'

'What I think is I got a living to make.'

'Jesus,' he said. 'Who doesn't?'

I'd said the right thing. I wasn't a threat now. I was just a guy going through the motions and trying to turn a dollar. He sighed, slapped the top of his desk, got up and crossed the room to a bank of filing cabinets. He was a chunkily built, bandy-legged man with his sleeves rolled up and his collar open, and he walked with the rolling gait of a sailor. He brought back a manila accordion file, dropped into his chair, found a photograph in the files and pitched it onto the desk.

'Here,' he said. 'Feast your eyes.'

It was a five-by-seven black and white glossy of Kim, but if I hadn't known that I don't see how I could have recognized her. I looked at the picture, fought off a wave of nausea, and made myself go on looking at it.

'Really did a job on her,' I said.

'He got her sixty-six times with what the doc thinks was

probably a machete or something like it. How'd you like the job of counting? I don't know how they do that work. I swear it's a worse job than the one I got.'

'All that blood.'

'Be grateful you're seeing it in black and white. It was worse in color.'

'I can imagine.'

'He hit arteries. You do that, you get spurting, you get blood all over the room. I never saw so much blood.'

'He must have gotten blood all over himself.'

'No way to avoid it.'

'Then how did he get out of there without anybody noticing?'

'It was cold that night. Say he had a coat, he'd put that on over whatever else he was wearing.' He drew on his cigarette. 'Or maybe he wasn't wearing any clothes when he did the number on her. The hell, she was in her birthday suit, maybe he didn't want to feel overdressed. Then all he'd have to do afterward was take a shower. There was a nice beautiful bathroom there and he had all the time in the world so why not use it?'

'Were the towels used?'

He looked at me. The gray eyes were still unreadable, but I sensed a little more respect in his manner. 'I don't remember any soiled towels,' he said.

'I don't suppose they're something you'd notice, not with a scene like that in the same room.'

'They ought to be inventoried, though.' He thumbed through the file. 'You know what they do, they take pictures of everything, and everything that might turn out to be evidence gets bagged and labeled and inventoried. Then it goes down to the warehouse, and when it's time to prepare a case nobody can find it.' He closed the file for a moment, leaned forward. 'You want to hear something? Two, three weeks ago I get a call from my sister. She and her husband live over in Brooklyn. The Midwood section. You familiar with the area?'

'I used to be.'

'Well, it was probably nicer when you knew it. It's not so bad. I mean, the whole city's a cesspool, so it's not so bad in comparison. Why she called, they came home and found out there'd been a burglary. Somebody broke in, took a portable teevee, a typewriter, some jewelry. She called me to find out how to report it, who to call and everything. First thing I asked her is has she got insurance. No, she says, they didn't figure it

was worth it. I told her to forget it. Don't report it, I told her. You'd just be wasting your time.

'So she says how are they gonna catch the guys if she doesn't report it? So I explain how nobody's got the time to investigate a burglary anymore. You fill out a report and it goes in a file, but you don't run around looking to see who did it. Catching a burglar in the act is one thing, but investigating, hell, it's low priority, nobody's got time for it. She says okay, she can understand that, but suppose they happen to recover the goods? If she never reported the theft in the first place, how will the stuff get returned to her? And then I had to tell her just how fucked up the whole system is. We got warehouses full of stolen goods we recovered, and we got files full of reports people filled out, stuff lost to burglars, and we can't get the shit back to the rightful owners. I went on and on, I won't bore you with it, but I don't think she really wound up believing me. Because you don't want to believe it's that bad.'

He found a sheet in the file, frowned at it. He read, 'One bath towel, white. One hand towel, white. Two wash cloths, white. Doesn't say used or unused.' He drew out a sheaf of glossies and went rapidly through them. I looked over his shoulder at interior shots of the room where Kim Dakkinen had died. She was in some but not all of the pictures; the photographer had documented the murder scene by shooting virtually every inch of the hotel room.

A shot of the bathroom showed a towel rack with unused linen on it.

'No dirty towels,' he said.

'He took them along.'

'Huh?'

'He had to wash up. Even if he just threw a topcoat over his bloody clothes. And there aren't enough towels there. There ought to be at least two of everything. A double room in a class hotel, they give you more than one bath towel and one hand towel.'

'Why would he take 'em along?'

'Maybe to wrap the machete in.'

'He had to have a case for it in the first place, some kind of a bag to get it into the hotel. Why couldn't he take it out the same way?'

I agreed that he could have.

'And why wrap it in the dirty towels? Say you took a shower and dried yourself off and you wanted to wrap a machete before

238

you put it in your suitcase. There's clean towels there. Wouldn't you wrap it in a clean one instead of sticking a wet towel in your bag?'

'You're right.'

'It's a waste of time worrying about it,' he said, tapping the photo against the top of his desk. 'But I shoulda noticed the missing towels. That's something I should have thought of.'

We went through the file together. The medical report held few surprises. Death was attributed to massive hemorrhaging from multiple wounds resulting in excessive loss of blood. I guess you could call it that.

I read through witness interrogation reports, made my way through all the other forms and scraps of paper that wind up in a homicide victim's file. I had trouble paying attention. My head was developing a dull ache and my mind was spinning its wheels. Somewhere along the way Durkin let me go through the rest of the file on my own. He lit a fresh cigarette and went back to what he'd been typing earlier.

When I'd had as much as I could handle I closed the file and gave it back to him. He returned it to the cabinet, detouring on the way back to make a stop at the coffee machine.

'I got 'em both with cream and sugar,' he said, setting mine before me. 'Maybe that's not how you like it.'

'It's fine,' I said.

'Now you know what we know,' he said. I told him I appreciated it. He said, 'Listen, you saved us some time and aggravation with the tip about the pimp. We owed you one. If you can turn a buck for yourself, why not?'

'Where do you go from here?'

He shrugged. 'We proceed in normal fashion with our investigation. We run down leads and assemble evidence until such time as we have something to present to the district attorney's office.'

'That sounds like a recording.'

'Does it?'

'What happens next, Joe?'

'Aw, Jesus,' he said. 'The coffee's terrible, isn't it?'

'It's okay.'

'I used to think it was the cups. Then one day I brought my own cup, you know, so I was drinking it out of china instead of Styrofoam. Not fancy china, just, you know, an ordinary china cup like they give you in a coffee shop. You know what I mean.'

'Sure.'

'It tasted just as bad out of a real cup. And the second day after I brought the cup I was writing out an arrest report on some scumbag and I knocked the fucking cup off the desk and broke it. You got someplace you gotta be?'

'No.'

'Then let's go downstairs,' he said. 'Let's go around the corner.'

FOURTEEN

He took me around the corner and a block and a half south on Tenth Avenue to a tavern that belonged at the end of somebody's qualification. I didn't catch the name and I'm not sure if it had one. They could have called it Last Stop Before Detox. Two old men in thrift-shop suits sat together at the bar, drinking in silence. A Hispanic in his forties stood at the far end of the bar, sipping an eight-ounce glass of red wine and reading the paper. The bartender, a rawboned man in a tee shirt and jeans, was watching something on a small black and white television set. He had the volume turned way down.

Durkin and I took a table and I went to the bar to get our drinks, a double vodka for him, ginger ale for myself. I carried them back to our table. His eyes registered my ginger ale without comment.

It could have been a medium-strength scotch and soda. The color was about right.

He drank some of his vodka and said, 'Aw, Jesus, that helps. It really helps.'

I didn't say anything.

'What you were asking before. Where do we go from here. Can't you answer that yourself?'

'Probably.'

'I told my own sister to buy a new teevee and a new typewriter and hang some more locks on the door. But don't bother calling the cops. Where do we go with Dakkinen? We don't go anywhere.'

'That's what I figured.'

'We know who killed her.'

'Chance?' He nodded. 'I thought his alibi looked pretty good.'

'Oh, it's gilt-edged. It's bottled in bond. So what? He still could have done it. The people he says he was with are people who would lie for him.'

'You think they were lying?'

'No, but I wouldn't swear they weren't. Anyway, he could have hired it. We already talked about that.'

'Right.'

'If he did it he's clear. We're not going to be able to put a dent in that alibi. If he hired it we're not gonna find out who he hired. Unless we get lucky. That happens sometimes, you know. Things fall in your lap. One guy says something in a gin joint and somebody with a grudge passes it on, and all of a sudden we know something we didn't know before. But even if that happens, we'll be a long way from putting a case together. Meanwhile, we don't figure to kill ourselves over it.'

What he was saying was no surprise but there was something deadening about the words. I picked up my ginger ale and looked at it.

He said, 'Half the job is knowing the odds. Working the cases where you got a chance, letting the others flap in the breeze. You know the murder rate in this town?'

'I know it keeps going higher.'

'Tell me about it. It's up every year. All crimes are up every year, except we're starting to get a statistical drop in some of the less serious ones because people aren't bothering to report them. Like my sister's burglary. You got mugged coming home and all that happened was he took your money? Well, shit, why make a federal case out of it, right? Be grateful you're alive. Go home and say a prayer of thanks.'

'With Kim Dakkinen —'

'Screw Kim Dakkinen,' he said. 'Some dumb little bitch comes fifteen hundred miles to peddle her ass and give the money to a nigger pimp, who cares if somebody chopped her up? I mean why didn't she stay in fucking Minnesota?'

'Wisconsin.'

'I meant Wisconsin. Most of 'em come from Minnesota.'

'I know.'

'The murder rate used to be around a thousand a year. Three a day in the five boroughs. That always seemed high.'

'High enough.'

'It's just about double that now.' He leaned forward. 'But that's *nothing*, Matt. Most homicides are husband-wife things, or two friends drinking together and one of 'em shoots the other and doesn't even remember it the next day. That rate never changes. It's the same as it always was. What's changed are stranger murders, where the killer and the victim don't know

242

each other. That's the rate that shows you how dangerous it is to live somewhere. If you just take the stranger murders, if you throw out the other cases and put the stranger murders on a graph, the line goes up like a rocket.'

'There was a guy in Queens yesterday with a bow and arrow,' I said, 'and the guy next door shot him with a .38.'

'I read about that. Something about a dog shitting on the wrong lawn?'

'Something like that.'

'Well, that wouldn't be on the chart. That's two guys who knew each other.'

'Right.'

'But it's all part of the same thing. People keep killing each other. They don't even stop and think, they just go ahead and do it. You been off the force what, a couple years now? I'll tell you this much. It's a lot worse than you remember.'

'I believe you.'

'I mean it. It's a jungle out there and all the animals are armed. Everybody's got a gun. You realize the number of people out there walking around with a piece? Your honest citizen, he's gotta have a gun now for his own protection, so he gets one and somewhere down the line he shoots himself or his wife or the guy next door.'

'The guy with the bow and arrow.'

'Whatever. But who's gonna tell him not to have a gun?' He slapped his abdomen, where his service revolver was tucked under his belt. 'I gotta carry this,' he said. 'It's regulations. But I'll tell you, I wouldn't walk around out there without it. I'd feel naked.'

'I used to think that. You get used to it.'

'You don't carry anything?'

'Nothing.'

'And it doesn't bother you?'

I went to the bar and got fresh drinks, more vodka for him, more ginger ale for me. When I brought them back to the table Durkin drank the whole thing in one long swallow and sighed like a tire going flat. He cupped his hands and lit a cigarette, inhaled deeply, blew out the smoke as if in a hurry to be rid of it.

'This fucking city,' he said.

It was hopeless, he said, and he went on to tell me just how hopeless it was. He rang changes on the whole criminal justice system, from the cops to the courts to the jails, explaining how none of it worked and all of it was getting worse every day. You

couldn't arrest a guy and then you couldn't convict him and finally you couldn't keep the son of a bitch in jail.

'The prisons are overcrowded,' he said, 'so the judges don't want to hand out long sentences and the parole boards release people early. And the DA's let the guys cop to a reduced charge, they plea bargain good cases down to nothing, because the court calendars are so jammed up and the courts are so careful to protect the rights of the accused that you just about need a photo of the guy committing the crime in order to get a conviction, and then you might get a reversal because you were violating his civil rights by taking his photograph without prior permission. And in the meantime there's no cops. The department's got ten thousand men below what it had twelve years ago. Ten thousand fewer cops on the street!'

'I know.'

'Twice as many crooks and a third less cops and you wonder why it's not safe to walk down the street. You know what it is? The city's broke. There's no money for cops, no money to keep the subways running, no money for anything. The whole country's leaking money, it's all winding up in Saudi fucking Arabia. All those assholes are trading in their camels for Cadillacs while this country goes down the fucking tubes.' He stood up. 'My turn to buy.'

'No, I'll get them. I'm on expenses.'

'Right, you got a client.' He sat down. I came back with another round and he said, 'What are you drinking there?'

'Just ginger ale.'

'Yeah, I thought that's what it looked like. Whyntcha have a real drink?'

'I'm sort of cutting back on it these days.'

'Oh yeah?' The gray eyes focused on me as he registered this information. He picked up his glass and drank about half of it, set it down on the worn wooden table with a thunk. 'You got the right idea,' he said, and I thought he meant the ginger ale, but he had shifted gears by then. 'Quitting the job. Getting out. You know what I want? All I want is six more years.'

'Then you got your twenty?'

'Then I got my twenty,' he said, 'and then I got my pension, and then I'm fucking well gone. Out of this job and out of this shithole of a city. Florida, Texas, New Mexico, someplace warm and dry and clean. Forget Florida, I heard things about Florida, all the fucking Cubans, they got crime like you get here. Plus

they got all the dope coming in there. Those crazy Colombians. You know about the Colombians?'

I thought of Royal Waldron. 'A fellow I know says they're all right,' I said. 'He said you just don't want to cheat 'em.'

'You bet your ass you don't want to cheat 'em. You read about those two girls over in Long Island City? Must have been six, eight months ago. Sisters, one's twelve and one's fourteen, and they found 'em in the back room of this out-of-business gas station, hands tied behind their backs, each of 'em shot twice in the head with a small-caliber weapon, I think a .22, but who gives a shit?' He drank the rest of his drink. 'Well, it didn't figure. No sex angle, nothing. It's an execution, but who executes a couple of teenage sisters?

'Well, it clears itself up, because a week later somebody breaks into the house where they lived and shoots their mother. We found her in the kitchen with dinner still cooking on the stove. See, the family's Colombian, and the father's in the cocaine business, which is the chief industry down there outside of smuggling emeralds –'

'I thought they grew a lot of coffee.'

'That's probably a front. Where was I? The point is, the father turns up dead a month later in whatever's the capital of Colombia. He crossed somebody and he ran for it, and they wound up getting him in Colombia, but first they killed his kids and his wife. See, the Colombians, they play by a different set of rules. You fuck with them and they don't just kill you. They wipe out your whole family. Kids, any age, it don't matter. You got a dog and a cat and some tropical fish, they're dead too.'

'Jesus.'

'The Mafia was always considerate about family. They'd even make sure to arrange a hit so your family wouldn't be there to see it happen. Now we got criminals that kill the whole family. Nice?'

'Jesus.'

He put his palms on the table for leverage, hoisted himself to his feet. 'I'm getting this round,' he announced. 'I don't need some pimp payin' for my drinks.'

Back at the table he said, 'He's your client, right? Chance?' When I failed to respond he said, 'Well, shit, you met with him last night. He wanted to see you, and now you got a client that you won't say his name. Two and two's gotta be four, doesn't it?'

245

'I can't tell you how to add it.'

'Let's just say I'm right and he's your client. For the sake of argument. You won't be givin' nothin' away.'

'All right.'

He leaned forward. 'He killed her,' he said. 'So why would he hire you to investigate it?'

'Maybe he didn't kill her.'

'Oh, sure he did.' He dismissed the possibility of Chance's innocence with a wave of his hand. 'She says she's quitting him and he says okay and the next day she's dead. Come on, Matt. What's that if it's not cut and dried?'

'Then we get back to your question. Why'd he hire me?'

'Maybe to take the heat off.'

'How?'

'Maybe he'll figure we'll figure he must be innocent or he wouldn't have hired you.'

'But that's not what you figured at all.'

'No.'

'You think he'd really think that?'

'How do I know what some coked-up spade pimp is gonna think?'

'You figure he's a cokehead?'

'He's got to spend it on something, doesn't he? It's not gonna go for country-club dues and a box at the charity ball. Lemme ask *you* something.'

'Go ahead.'

'You think there's a chance in the world he didn't kill her? Or set her up and hire it done?'

'I think there's a chance.'

'Why?'

'For one thing, he hired me. And it wasn't to take the heat off because what heat are we talking about? You already said there wasn't going to be any heat. You're planning to clear the case and work on something else.'

'He wouldn't necessarily know that.'

I let that pass. 'Take it from another angle,' I suggested. 'Let's say I never called you.'

'Called me when?'

'The first call I made. Let's say you didn't know she was breaking with her pimp.'

'If we didn't get it from you we'd of gotten it somewhere else.'

'Where? Kim was dead and Chance wouldn't volunteer the information. I'm not sure anybody else in the world knew.'

Except for Elaine, but I wasn't going to bring her into it. 'I don't think you'd have gotten it. Not right off the bat, anyway.'

'So?'

'So how would you have figured the killing then?'

He didn't answer right away. He looked down at his near-empty glass, and a couple of vertical frown lines creased his forehead. He said, 'I see what you mean.'

'How would you have pegged it?'

'The way we did before you called. A psycho. You know we're not supposed to call 'em that anymore? There was a departmental directive went out about a year ago. From now on we don't call 'em psychos. From now on it's EDPs.'

'What's an EDP?'

'Emotionally Disturbed Person. That's what some asshole on Centre Street's got nothing better to worry about. The whole city's up to its ass in more nuts than a fruitcake and our first priority is how we refer to them. We don't want to hurt their feelings. No, I'd figure a psycho, some new version of Jack the Ripper. Calls up a hooker, invites her over, chops her up.'

'And if it was a psycho?'

'You know what happens then. You hope you get lucky with a piece of physical evidence. In this case fingerprints were hopeless, it's a transient hotel room, there's a million latents and no place to start with them. Be nice if there was a big bloody fingerprint and you knew it belonged to the killer, but we didn't have that kind of luck.'

'Even if you did –'

'Even if we did, a single print wouldn't lead anywhere. Not until we had a suspect. You can't get a make from Washington on a single print. They keep saying you're gonna be able to eventually, but –'

'They've been saying that for years.'

'It'll never happen. Or it will, but I'll have my six years by then and I'll be in Arizona. Barring physical evidence that leads somewhere, I guess we'd be waiting for the nut to do it again. You get another couple of cases with the same MO and sooner or later he fucks up and you got him, and then you match him to some latents in the room at the Galaxy and you wind up with a case.' He drained his glass. 'Then he plea bargains his way to manslaughter and he's out in three years tops and he does it again, but I don't want to get started on that again. I honest to Christ don't want to get started on that again.'

247

I bought our next round. Any compunctions he had about having a pimp's money pay for his booze seemed to have been dissolved by the same alcohol that had given rise to them. He was visibly drunk now, but only if you knew where to look. The eyes had a glaze on them, and there was a matching glaze on his whole manner. He was holding up his end of a typical alcoholic conversation, wherein two drunks take polite turns talking aloud to their own selves.

I wouldn't have noticed this if I'd been matching him drink for drink. But I was sober, and as the booze got to him I felt the gulf widening between us.

I tried to keep the conversation on the subject of Kim Dakkinen but it wouldn't stay there. He wanted to talk about everything that was wrong with New York.

'You know what it is,' he said, leaning forward, lowering his voice, as if we weren't the only two customers in the bar by now, just us and the bartender. 'I'll tell you what it is. It's niggers.'

I didn't say anything.

'And spics. The blacks and the Hispanics.'

I said something about black and Puerto Rican cops. He rode right over it. 'Listen, don't tell me,' he said. 'I got a guy I been partnered with a lot, Larry Haynes his name is, maybe you know him –' I didn't '– and he's as good as they come. I'd trust the man with my life. Shit, I *have* trusted him with my life. He's black as coal and I never met a better man in or out of the department. But that's got nothing to do with what I'm talking about.' He wiped his mouth with the back of his hand. 'Look,' he said, 'you ever ride the subway?'

'When I have to.'

'Well, shit, nobody rides it by choice. It's the whole city in a nutshell, the equipment breaks down all the time, the cars are filthy with spray paint and they stink of piss and the transit cops can't make a dent in the crime down there, but what I'm talking about, shit, *I* get on a subway and I look around and you know where I am? I'm in a fucking foreign country.'

'What do you mean?'

'I mean everybody's black or Spanish. Or oriental, we got all these new Chinese immigrants coming in, plus there's the Koreans. Now the Koreans are perfect citizens, they open up all these great vegetable markets all over the city, they work twenty hours a day and send their kids to college, but it's all part of something.'

'Part of what?'

'Oh, shit, it sounds ignorant and bigoted but I can't help it. This used to be a white city and now there's days when I feel like I'm the only white man left in it.'

The silence stretched. Then he said, 'They smoke on the subway now. You ever notice?'

'I've noticed.'

'Never used to happen. A guy might murder both his parents with a fire axe but he wouldn't dare light up a cigarette on the subway. Now you got middle-class people lighting their cigarettes, puffing away. Just in the last few months. You know how it started?'

'How?'

'Remember about a year ago? A guy was smoking on the PATH train and a PATH cop asked him to put it out, and the guy drew a gun and shot the cop dead? Remember?'

'I remember.'

'That's what started it. You read about that and whoever you are, a cop or a private citizen, you're not in a rush to tell the guy across the aisle to put out his fucking cigarette. So a few people light up and nobody does anything about it, and more people do it, and who's gonna give a shit about smoking in the subway when it's a waste of time to report a major crime like burglary? Stop enforcing a law and people stop respecting it.' He frowned. 'But think about that PATH cop. You like that for a way to die? Ask a guy to put out a cigarette and bang, you're dead.'

I found myself telling him about Rudenko's mother, dead of a bomb blast because her friend had brought home the wrong television set. And so we traded horror stories. He told of a social worker, lured onto a tenement roof, raped repeatedly and thrown off the building to her death. I recalled something I'd read about a fourteen-year-old shot by another boy the same age, both of them strangers to each other, the killer insisted that his victim had laughed at him. Durkin told me about some child-abuse cases that had ended in death, and about a man who had smothered his girlfriend's infant daughter because he was sick of paying for a baby-sitter everytime the two of them went to the movies. I mentioned the woman in Gravesend, dead of a shotgun blast while she hung clothes in her closet. There was an air of *Can You Top This?* to our dialogue.

He said, 'The mayor thinks he's got the answer. The death penalty. Bring back the big black chair.'

'Think it'll happen?'

'No question the public wants it. And there's one way it works and you can't tell me it doesn't. You fry one of these bastards and at least you know he's not gonna do it again. The hell, I'd vote for it. Bring back the chair and televise the fucking executions, run commercials, make a few dollars and hire a few more cops. You want to know something?'

'What?'

'We *got* the death penalty. Not for murderers. For ordinary citizens. Everybody out there runs a better chance of getting killed than a killer does of getting the chair. We get the death penalty five, six, seven times a day.'

He had raised his voice and the bartender was auditing our conversation now. We'd lured him away from his program.

Durkin said, 'I like the one about the exploding television set. I don't know how I missed that one. You think you heard 'em all but there's always something new, isn't there?'

'I guess.'

'There are eight million stories in the naked city,' he intoned. 'You remember that program? Used to be on television some years back.'

'I remember.'

'They had that line at the end of every show. "There are eight million stories in the naked city. This has been one of them."'

'I remember it.'

'Eight million stories,' he said. 'You know what you got in this city, this fucked-up toilet of a naked fucking city? You know what you got? You got eight million ways to die.'

I got him out of there. Outside in the cool night air he fell silent. We circled a couple of blocks, wound up down the street from the station house. His car was a Mercury a few years old. It had been beaten up a little around the corners. The license plate had a prefix which would indicate to other cops that this was a vehicle used for police business and not to be ticketed. Some of the more knowledgeable crooks could also recognize it as a cop's car.

I asked if he was okay to drive. He didn't much care for the question. He said, 'What are you, a cop?' and then the absurdity of the remark struck him and he started to laugh. He clung to the car's open door for support, helpless with laughter, and swung back and forth on the car door. 'What are you, a cop?' he said, giggling. 'What are you, a cop?'

That mood passed like a fast cut in a film. In an instant he was

serious and apparently sober, eyes narrowed, jaw thrust forward like a bulldog's. 'Listen,' he said, voice low and hard. 'Don't be so goddamn superior, you understand?'

I didn't know what he was talking about.

'You sanctimonious bastard. You're no better than I am, you son of a bitch.'

He pulled out and drove off. He seemed to be driving all right for as far as I was able to track him. I hoped he didn't have too far to go.

FIFTEEN

I walked straight back to my hotel. The liquor stores were closed but the bars were still open. I passed them without much effort, resisted too the call of street whores on Fifty-seventh Street on either side of the Holiday Inn. I gave Jacob a nod, confirmed that I'd had no calls, and went upstairs.

Sanctimonious bastard. No better than I am. He'd been ugly drunk, with that defensive belligerence of the drinker who had exposed too much of himself. His words didn't mean anything. He'd have addressed them to any companion, or to the night itself.

Still, they echoed in my head.

I got into bed but couldn't sleep, got up and put the light on and sat on the edge of the bed with my notebook. I looked over some of the notes I made, then jotted down a point or two from our conversation in the bar on Tenth Avenue. I made a few further notes to myself, playing with ideas like a kitten with a yarn ball. I put the notebook down when the process reached a point of diminishing returns, with the same thoughts turning over and over upon themselves. I picked up a paperback I'd bought earlier but couldn't get into it. I kept reading the same paragraph without getting the sense of it.

For the first time in hours I really wanted a drink. I was anxious and edgy and wanted to change it. There was a deli with a cooler full of beer just three doors from the hotel, and when had beer ever led me into a blackout?

I stayed where I was.

Chance hadn't asked my reason for working for him. Durkin had accepted money as a valid motive. Elaine was willing to believe I was doing it because it was what I did, even as she turned tricks and God pardoned sinners. And it was all true, I could indeed use the money and detecting was what I did insofar as I did anything, it was as much of a profession as I had.

But I had another motive, and perhaps it was a deeper one. Searching for Kim's killer was something I could do instead of drinking.

For awhile, anyway.

When I woke up the sun was shining. By the time I showered and shaved and hit the street it was gone, tucked away behind a bank of clouds. It came and went all day, as if whoever was in charge didn't want to commit himself.

I ate a light breakfast, made some phone calls, then walked over to the Galaxy Downtowner. The clerk who'd checked in Charles Jones wasn't on duty. I'd read his interrogation report in the file and didn't really expect I could get more out of him than the cops could.

An assistant manager let me look at Jones's registration card. He'd printed 'Charles Owen Jones' on the line marked 'Name,' and on the 'Signature' line he'd printed 'C. O. JONES' in block capitals. I pointed this out to the assistant manager, who told me the discrepancy was common. 'People will put their full name on one line and a shorter version on the other,' he said. 'Either way is legal.'

'But this isn't a signature.'

'Why not?'

'He printed it.'

He shrugged. 'Some people print everything,' he said. 'The fellow made a telephone reservation and paid cash in advance. I wouldn't expect my people to question a signature under such circumstances.'

That wasn't my point. What had struck me was that Jones had managed to avoid leaving a specimen of his handwriting, and I found that interesting. I looked at the name where he'd printed it in full. The first three letters of *Charles*, I found myself thinking, were also the first three letters of *Chance*. And what, pray tell, did that signify? And why look for ways to hang my own client?

I asked if there'd been any previous visits by our Mr Jones in the past few months. 'Nothing in the past *year*,' he assured me. 'We carry previous registrations alphabetically in our computer and one of the detectives had that information checked. If that's all –'

'How many other guests signed their names in block caps?'

'I've no idea.'

253

'Suppose you let me look through the registration cards for the past two, three months.'

'To look for what?'

'People who print like this guy.'

'Oh, I really don't think so,' he said. 'Do you realize how many cards are involved? This is a 635-room hotel. Mr –'

'Scudder.'

'Mr Scudder. That's over eighteen thousand cards a month.'

'Only if all your guests leave after one night.'

'The average stay is three nights. Even so, that's over six thousand registration cards a month, twelve thousand cards in two months. Do you realize how long it would take to look at twelve thousand cards?'

'A person could probably do a couple thousand an hour,' I said, 'since all he'd be doing is scanning the signature to see if it's in script or in block caps. We're just talking about a couple of hours. I could do it or you could have some of your people do it.'

He shook his head. 'I couldn't authorize that,' he said. 'I really couldn't. You're a private citizen, not a policeman, and while I did want to cooperate there's a limit to my authority here. If the police should make an official request –'

'I realize I'm asking a favor.'

'If it were the sort of favor I could grant –'

'It's an imposition,' I went on, 'and I'd certainly expect to pay for the time involved, the time and inconvenience.'

It would have worked at a smaller hotel, but here I was wasting my time. I don't think he even realized I was offering him a bribe. He said again that he'd be glad to go along if the police made the request for me, and this time I let it lie. I asked instead if I could borrow the Jones registration card long enough to have a photocopy made.

'Oh, we have a machine right here,' he said, grateful to be able to help. 'Just wait one moment.'

He came back with a copy. I thanked him and he asked if there was anything else, his tone suggesting he was confident there wouldn't be. I said I'd like a look at the room she died in.

'But the police have quite finished there,' he said. 'The room's in a transitional state now. The carpet had to be replaced, you see, and the walls painted.'

'I'd still like to see it.'

'There's really nothing to see. I think there are workmen in there today. The painters are gone, I believe, but I think the carpet installers –'

'I won't get in their way.'

He gave me a key and let me go up myself. I found the room and congratulated myself on my ability as a detective. The door was locked. The carpet installers looked to be on their lunch break. The old carpet had been removed, and new carpet covered about a third of the floor, with more of it rolled up awaiting installation.

I spent a few minutes there. As the man had assured me, there was really nothing to see. The room was as empty of traces of Kim as it was of furniture. The walls were bright with fresh paint and the bathroom fairly sparkled. I walked around like some psychic practitioner, trying to pick up vibrations through the tips of my fingers. If there were any vibrations present, they eluded me.

The window faced downtown, the view chopped up by the facades of other tall buildings. Through a gap between two of them I could catch a glimpse of the World Trade Center all the way downtown.

Had she had time to look out the window? Had Mr Jones looked out the window, before or afterward?

I took the subway downtown. The train was one of the new ones, its interior a pleasing pattern of yellow and orange and tan. The inscribers of graffiti had already scarred it badly, scrawling their indecipherable messages over every available space.

I didn't notice anyone smoking.

I got off at West Fourth and walked south and west to Morton Street, where Fran Schecter had a small apartment on the top floor of a four-story brownstone. I rang her bell, announced myself over the intercom, and was buzzed through the vestibule door.

The stairwell was full of smells – baking smells on the first floor, cat odor halfway up, and the unmistakable scent of marijuana at the top. I thought that you could draw a building's profile from the aromas in its stairwell.

Fran was waiting for me in her doorway. Short curly hair, light brown in color, framed a round baby face. She had a button nose, a pouty mouth, and cheeks a chipmunk would have been proud of.

She said, 'Hi, I'm Fran. And you're Matt. Can I call you Matt?' I assured her that she could, and her hand settled on my arm as she steered me inside.

The marijuana reek was much stronger inside. The apartment

255

was a studio. One fairly large room with a pullman kitchen on one wall. The furniture consisted of a canvas sling chair, a pillow sofa, some plastic milk crates assembled as shelves for books and clothes, and a large waterbed covered with a fake-fur spread. A framed poster on one wall over the waterbed showed a room interior, with a railway locomotive emerging from the fireplace.

I turned down a drink, accepted a can of diet soda. I sat with it on the pillow sofa, which turned out to be more comfortable than it looked. She took the sling chair, which must have been more comfortable than it looked.

'Chance said you're investigating what happened to Kim,' she said. 'He said to tell you whatever you want to know.'

There was a breathless little-girl quality to her voice and I couldn't tell how much of it was deliberate. I asked her what she knew about Kim.

'Not much. I met her a few times. Sometimes Chance'll take two girls at once out to dinner or a show. I guess I met everyone at one time or another. I just met Donna once, she's on her own trip, it's like she's lost in space. Have you met Donna?' I shook my head. 'I like Sunny. I don't know if we're friends exactly, but she's the only one I'd call up to talk to. I'll call her once, twice a week, or she'll call me, you know, and we'll talk.'

'But you never called Kim?'

'Oh, no. I never had her number, even.' She thought for a moment. 'She had beautiful eyes. I can close my eyes and picture the color of them.'

Her own eyes were large, somewhere between brown and green. Her eyelashes were unusually long, and it struck me that they were probably false. She was a short girl of the body type they call a pony in Las Vegas chorus lines. She was wearing faded Levi's with the cuffs turned up and a hot pink sweater that was stretched tight over her full breasts.

She hadn't known that Kim had planned to leave Chance, and she found the information interesting. 'Well, I can understand that,' she said after some thought. 'He didn't really care for her, you know, and you don't want to stay forever with a man who doesn't care for you.'

'What makes you say he didn't care for her?'

'You pick these things up. I suppose he was glad to have her around, like she didn't make trouble and she brought in the bread, but he didn't have a feeling for her.'

'Does he have a feeling for the others?'

256

'He has a feeling for me,' she said.

'And anybody else?'

'He likes Sunny. Everybody likes Sunny, she's fun to be with. I don't know if he *cares* for her. Or Donna, I'm sure he doesn't care for Donna, but I don't think she cares for him either. I think that's strictly business on both sides. Donna, I don't think Donna cares for anybody. I don't think she knows there are people in the world.'

'How about Ruby?'

'Have you met her?' I hadn't. 'Well, she's like, you know, exotic. So he'd like that. And Mary Lou's very intelligent and they go to concerts and shit, like Lincoln Center, classical music, but that doesn't mean he has a feeling for her.'

She started to giggle. I asked her what was so funny. 'Oh, I just flashed that I'm the typical dumb hooker, thinks she's the only one the pimp loves. But you know what it is? I'm the only one he can relax with. He can come up here and take his shoes off and let his mind roll out. Do you know what a karmic tie is?'

'No.'

'Well, it has something to do with reincarnation. I don't know if you believe in that.'

'I never thought about it much.'

'Well, I don't know if I believe in it either, but sometimes I think Chance and I knew each other in another life. Not necessarily as lovers or man and wife or anything like that. Like we could have been brother and sister, or maybe he was my father or I was his mother. Or we could even have both been the same sex because that can change from one lifetime to another. I mean we could have been sisters or something Anything, really.'

The telephone cut into her speculations. She crossed the room to answer it, standing with her back to me, one hand propped against her hip. I couldn't hear her conversation. She talked for a moment or two, then covered the mouthpiece and turned to me.

'Matt,' she said, 'I don't want to hassle you, but do you have any idea how long we're gonna be?'

'Not long.'

'Like could I tell somebody it would be cool to come over in an hour?'

'No problem.'

She turned again, finished the conversation quietly, hung up. 'That was one of my regulars,' she said. 'He's a real nice guy. I told him an hour.'

She sat down again. I asked her if she'd had the apartment

257

before she hooked up with Chance. She said she'd been with Chance for two years and eight months and no, before that she shared a bigger place in Chelsea with three other girls. Chance had had this apartment all ready for her. All she'd had to do was move into it.

'I just moved my furniture in,' she said. 'Except the waterbed. That was already here. I had a single bed that I got rid of. And I bought the Magritte poster, and the masks were here.' I hadn't noticed the masks and had to turn in my seat to see them, a grouping of three solemn ebony carvings on the wall behind me. 'He knows about them,' she said. 'What tribe made them and everything. He knows things like that.'

I said that the apartment was an unlikely one for the use being made of it. She frowned, puzzled.

'Most girls in the game live in doorman buildings,' I said. 'With elevators and all.'

'Oh, right. I didn't know what you meant. Yes, that's true.' She grinned brightly. 'This is something different,' she said. 'The johns who come here, they don't think they're johns.'

'How do you mean?'

'They think they're friends of mine,' she explained. 'They think I'm this spacey Village chick, which I am, and that they're my friends, which they are. I mean, they come here to get laid, let's face it, but they could get laid quicker and easier in a massage parlor, no muss no fuss no bother, dig? But they can come up here and take off their shoes and smoke a joint, and it's a sort of a raunchy Village pad, I mean you have to climb three flights of stairs and then you roll around in a waterbed. I mean, I'm not a hooker. I'm a girlfriend. I don't get paid. They give me money because I got rent to pay and, you know, I'm a poor little Village chick who wants to make it as an actress and she's never going to. Which I'm not, and I don't care much, but I still take dancing lessons a couple mornings a week and I have an acting class with Ed Kovens every Thursday night, and I was in a showcase last May for three weekends in Tribeca. We did Ibsen, *When We Dead Awake*, and do you believe that three of my johns came?'

She chatted about the play, then began telling me how her clients brought her presents in addition to the money they gave her. 'I never have to buy any booze. In fact I have it to give away because I don't drink myself. And I haven't bought any grass in ages. You know who gets the best grass? Wall Street guys. They'll buy an ounce and we'll smoke a little and they'll leave

me the ounce.' She batted her long lashes at me. 'I kind of like to smoke,' she said.

'I guessed that.'

'Why? Do I seem stoned?'

'The smell.'

'Oh, right. I don't smell it because I'm here, but when I go out and then I come back in, whew! It's like a friend of mine has four cats and she swears they don't smell, but the smell could knock you down. It's just that she's used to it.' She shifted in her seat. 'Do you ever smoke, Matt?'

'No.'

'You don't drink and you don't smoke, that's terrific. Can I get you another diet soda?'

'No thanks.'

'Are you sure? Look, would it bother you if I smoked a quick joint? Just to unwind a little.'

'Go ahead.'

'Because I've got this fellow coming over and it'll help me be in the mood.'

I told her it was fine with me. She fetched a plastic baggie of marijuana from a shelf over the stove and hand-rolled a cigarette with evident expertise. 'He'll probably want to smoke,' she said, and manufactured two more cigarettes. She lit one, put everything else away, and returned to the sling chair. She smoked the joint all the way down, chattering about her life between drags, finally stubbing the tiny roach and setting it aside for later. Her manner didn't change visibly for having smoked the thing. Perhaps she'd been smoking throughout the day and had been stoned when I arrived. Perhaps she just didn't show the effects of the drug, as some drinkers don't show their drinks.

I asked if Chance smoked when he came to see her and she laughed at the idea. 'He never drinks, never smokes. Same as you. Hey, is that where you know him from? Do you both hang out in a nonbar together? Or maybe you both have the same undealer.'

I managed to get the conversation back to Kim. If Chance didn't care for Kim, did Fran think she might have been seeing someone else?

'He didn't care for her,' she said. 'You know something? I'm the only one he loves.'

I could taste the grass in her speech now. Her voice was the same, but her mind made different connections, switching along paths of smoke.

'Do you think Kim had a boyfriend?'

'I have boyfriends. Kim had tricks. All of the others have tricks.'

'If Kim had someone special –'

'Sure, I can dig it. Somebody who wasn't a john, and that's why she wanted to split with Chance. That what you mean?'

'It's possible.'

'And then he killed her.'

'Chance?'

'Are you crazy? Chance never cared enough about her to kill her. You know how long it'd take to replace her? Shit.'

'You mean the boyfriend killed her.'

'Sure.'

'Why?'

''Cause he's on the spot. She leaves Chance, there she is, all ready for happily ever after, and what does he want with that? I mean he's got a wife, he's got a job, he's got a family, he's got a house in Scarsdale –'

'How do you know all this?'

She sighed. 'I'm just speedballing, baby. I'm just throwing chalk at the blackboard. Can you dig it? He's a married guy, he digs Kim, it's kicky being in love with a hooker and having her in love with you, and that way you get it for free, but you don't want anybody turning your life around. She says, Hey, I'm free now, time to ditch your wife and we'll run into the sunset, and the sunset's something he watches from the terrace at the country club and he wants to keep it that way. Next thing you know, zip, she's dead and he's back in Larchmont.'

'It was Scarsdale a minute ago.'

'Whatever.'

'Who would he be, Fran?'

'The boyfriend? I don't know. Anybody.'

'A john?'

'You don't fall in love with a john.'

'Where would she meet a guy? And what kind of guy would she meet?'

She struggled with the notion, shrugged and gave up. The conversation never got any further than that. I used her phone, talked for a moment, then wrote my name and number on a pad next to the phone.

'In case you think of anything,' I said.

'I'll call you if I do. You going? You sure you don't want another soda?'

'No thanks.'

'Well,' she said. She came over to me, stifled a lazy yawn with the back of her hand, looked up at me through the long lashes. 'Hey, I'm really glad you could come over,' she said. 'Anytime you feel like company, you know, give me a call, okay? Just to hang out and talk.'

'Sure.'

'I'd like that,' she said softly, coming up onto her toes, planting an astonishing kiss on my cheek. 'I'd really like that, Matt,' she said.

Halfway down the stairs I started laughing. How automatically she'd slipped into her whore's manner, warm and earnest at parting, and how good she was at it. No wonder those stockbrokers didn't mind climbing all those stairs. No wonder they turned out to watch her try to be an actress. The hell, she *was* an actress, and not a bad one, either.

Two blocks away I could still feel the imprint of her kiss on my cheek.

SIXTEEN

Donna Campion's apartment was on the tenth floor of the white brick building on East Seventeenth Street. The living room window faced west, and the sun was making one of its intermittent appearances when I got there. Sunlight flooded the room. There were plants everywhere, all of them vividly green and thriving, plants on the floor and the windowsills, plants hanging in the window, plants on ledges and tables throughout the room. The sunlight streamed through the curtain of plants and cast intricate patterns on the dark parquet flooring.

I sat in a wicker armchair and sipped a cup of black coffee. Donna was perched sideways on a backed oak bench about four feet wide. It had been a church pew, she'd told me, and it was English oak, Jacobite or possibly Elizabethan, dark with the passing years and worn smooth by three or four centuries of pious bottoms. Some vicar in rural Devon had decided to redecorate and in due course she'd bought the little pew at a University Place auction gallery.

She had the face to go with it, a long face that tapered from a high broad forehead to a pointed chin. Her skin was very pale, as if the only sunlight she ever got was what passed through the screen of plants. She was wearing a crisp white blouse with a Peter Pan collar and a short pleated skirt of gray flannel over a pair of black tights. Her slippers were doeskin, with pointed toes.

A long narrow nose, a small thin-lipped mouth. Dark brown hair, shoulder length, combed straight back from a well-defined widow's peak. Circles under her eyes, tobacco stains on two fingers of her right hand. No nail polish, no jewelry, no visible makeup. No prettiness, certainly, but a medieval quality that came quite close to beauty.

She didn't look like any whore I'd ever met. She did look like a poet, though, or what I thought a poet ought to look like.

She said, 'Chance said to give you my complete cooperation. He said you're trying to find out who killed the Dairy Queen.'

'The Dairy Queen?'

'She looked like a beauty queen, and then I learned she was from Wisconsin, and I thought of all that robust milk-fed innocence. She was a sort of regal milkmaid.' She smiled softly. 'That's my imagination talking. I didn't really know her.'

'Did you ever meet her boyfriend?'

'I didn't know she had one.'

Nor had she known that Kim had been planning to leave Chance, and she seemed to find the information interesting. 'I wonder,' she said. 'Was she an emigrant or an immigrant?'

'What do you mean?'

'Was she going from or to? It's a matter of emphasis. When I first came to New York I was coming *to*. I'd also just made a break with my family and the town I grew up in, but that was secondary. Later on, when I split with my husband, I was running from. The act of leaving was more important than the destination.'

'You were married?'

'For three years. Well, together for three years. Lived together for one year, married for two.'

'How long ago was that?'

'Four years?' She worked it out. 'Five years this coming spring. Although I'm still married, technically. I never bothered to get a divorce. Do you think I should?'

'I don't know.'

'I probably ought to. Just to tie off a loose end.'

'How long have you been with Chance?'

'Going on three years. Why?'

'You don't seem the type.'

'Is there a type? I don't suppose I'm much like Kim. Neither regal nor a milkmaid.' She laughed. 'I don't know which is which, but we're like the colonel's lady and Judy O'Grady.'

'Sisters under the skin?'

She looked surprised that I'd recognized the quotation. She said, 'After I left my husband I was living on the Lower East Side. Do you know Norfolk Street? Between Stanton and Rivington?'

'Not specifically.'

'I knew it very specifically. I lived there and I had these little jobs in the neighborhood. I worked in a Laundromat, I waited tables. I clerked in shops. I would quit the jobs or the jobs would

quit me and there was never enough money and I hated where I was living and I was starting to hate my life. I was going to call my husband and ask him to take me back just so he would take care of me. I kept thinking about it. One time I dialed his number but the line was busy.'

And so she'd drifted almost accidentally into selling herself. There was a store owner down the block who kept coming on to her. One day without preplanning it she heard herself say, 'Look, if you really want to ball me, would you give me twenty dollars?' He'd been flustered, blurting that he hadn't known she was a hooker. 'I'm not,' she told him, 'but I need the money. And I'm supposed to be a pretty good fuck.'

She started turning a few tricks a week. She moved from Norfolk Street to a better block in the same neighborhood, then moved again to Ninth Street just east of Tompkins Square. She didn't have to work now but there were other hassles to contend with. She was beaten up once, robbed several times. Again she found herself thinking of calling her ex-husband.

Then she met a girl in the neighborhood who worked in a midtown massage parlor. Donna tried out there and liked the security of it. There was a man in front to deal with anyone who tried to cause trouble, and the work itself was mechanical, almost clinical in its detachment. Virtually all her tricks were manual or oral. Her own flesh was uninvaded, and there was no illusion of intimacy beyond the pure fact of physical intimacy.

At first she welcomed this. She saw herself as a sexual technician, a kind of physiotherapist. Then it turned on her.

'The place had Mafia vibes,' she said, 'and you could smell death in the drapes and carpets. And it got like a job, I worked regular hours, I took the subway back and forth. It sucked – I love that word – it sucked the poetry right out of me.'

And so she'd quit and resumed free-lancing, and somewhere along the way Chance found her and everything fell into place. He'd installed her in this apartment, the first decent place she ever had in New York, and he got her phone number circulating and took all the hassles away. Her bills got paid, her apartment got cleaned, everything got done for her, and all she had to do was work on her poems and mail them off to magazines and be nice and charming whenever the telephone rang.

'Chance takes all the money you earn,' I said. 'Doesn't that bother you?'

'Should it?'

'I don't know.'

'It's not real money anyway,' she said. 'Fast money doesn't last. If it did, all the drug dealers would own the stock exchange. But that kind of money goes out the way it comes in.' She swung her legs around, sat facing forward on the church pew. 'Anyway,' she said, 'I have everything I want. All I ever wanted was to be left alone. I wanted a decent place to live and time to do my work. I'm talking about my poetry.'

'I realize that.'

'You know what most poets go through? They teach, or they work a straight job, or they play the poetry game, giving readings and lectures and writing out proposals for foundation grants and getting to know the right people and kissing the right behinds. I never wanted to do all that shit. I just wanted to make poems.'

'What did Kim want to do?'

'God knows.'

'I think she was involved with somebody. I think that's what got her killed.'

'Then I'm safe,' she said. 'I'm involved with no one. Of course you could argue that I'm involved with mankind. Would that put me in grave danger, do you suppose?'

I didn't know what she meant. With her eyes closed she said, '"Any man's death diminishes me, because I am involved in Mankind," John Donne. Do you know how she was involved, or with whom?'

'No.'

'Does her death diminish me, do you suppose? I wonder if I was involved with her. I didn't know her, not really, and yet I wrote a poem about her.'

'Could I see it?'

'I suppose so, but I don't see how it could tell you anything. I wrote a poem about the Big Dipper but if you want to know anything real about it you'd have to go to an astronomer, not to me. Poems are never about what they're about, you know. They're all about the poet.'

'I'd still like to see it.'

This seemed to please her. She went to her desk, a modern version of the old rolltop, and found what she was looking for almost immediately. The poem was hand-lettered on white bond paper with an italic-nibbed pen.

'I type them up for submission,' she said, 'but I like to see how they look on the page this way. I taught myself to do calligraphy. I learned from a book. It's easier than it looks.'

I read:

Bathe her in milk, let the white stream run
Pure in its bovine baptism,
Heal the least schism
Under the soonest sun. Take her
Hand, tell her it doesn't matter,
Milk's not to cry over. Scatter
Seed from a silver gun. Break her
Bones in a mortar, shatter
Wine bottles at her feet, let green glass
Sparkle upon her hand. Let it be done.
Let the milk run.
Let it flow down, down to the ancient grass.

I asked if I could copy it into my notebook. Her laugh was light, merry. 'Why? Does it tell who killed her?'

'I don't know what it tells me. Maybe if I keep it I'll figure out what it tells me.'

'If you figure out what it means,' she said, 'I hope you'll tell *me*. That's an exaggeration. I sort of know what I'm getting at. But don't bother copying it. You can have that copy.'

'Don't be silly. That's your copy.'

She shook her head. 'It's not finished. It needs more work. I want to get her eyes into it. If you met Kim you must have noticed her eyes.'

'Yes.'

'I originally wanted to contrast the blue eyes with the green glass, that's how that image got there in the first place, but the eyes disappeared when I wrote it. I think they were in an earlier draft but somewhere along the line they dropped out.' She smiled. 'They were gone in a wink. I've got the silver and the green and the white and I left the eyes out.' She stood with her hand on my shoulder, looking down at the poem. 'It's what, twelve lines? I think it should be fourteen anyway. Sonnet length, even if the lines are irregular. I don't know about *schism*, either. Maybe an off-rhyme would be better. Spasm, chasm, something.'

She went on, talking more to herself than to me, discussing possible revisions in the poem. 'By all means keep that,' she concluded. 'It's a long way from final form. It's funny. I haven't even looked at it since she was killed.'

'You wrote it before she was killed?'

'Completely. And I don't think I ever thought of it as finished, even though I copied it in pen and ink. I'll do that with drafts. I

can get a better idea of what does and doesn't work that way. I'd have kept on working on this one if she hadn't been killed.'

'What stopped you? The shock?'

'Was I shocked? I suppose I must have been. "This could happen to me." Except of course I don't believe that. It's like lung cancer, it happens to other people. "Any man's death diminishes me." Did Kim's death diminish me? I don't think so. I don't think I'm as involved in mankind as John Donne was. Or as he said he was.'

'Then why did you put the poem aside?'

'I didn't put it aside. I left it aside. That's nitpicking, isn't it?' She considered this. 'Her death changed how I saw her. I wanted to work on the poem, but I didn't want to get her death into it. I had enough colors. I didn't need blood in there, too.'

SEVENTEEN

I had taken a cab from Morton Street to Donna's place on East Seventeenth. Now I took another to Kim's building on Thirty-seventh. As I paid the driver I realized I hadn't made it to the bank. Tomorrow was Saturday, so I'd have Chance's money on my hands all weekend. Unless some mugger got lucky.

I lightened the load some by slipping five bucks to the doorman for a key to Kim's apartment, along with some story about acting as the tenant's representative. For five dollars he was eager to believe me. I went up to the elevator and let myself in.

The police had been through the place earlier. I didn't know what they were looking for and couldn't say what they found. The sheet in the file Durkin showed me hadn't said much, but nobody writes down everything that comes to his attention.

I couldn't know what the officers on the scene might have noticed. For that matter, I couldn't be sure what might have stuck to their fingers. There are cops who'll rob the dead, doing so as a matter of course, and they are not necessarily men who are especially dishonest in other matters.

Cops see too much of death and squalor, and in order to go on dealing with it they often have the need to dehumanize the dead. I remember the first time I helped remove a corpse from a room in an SRO hotel. The deceased had died vomiting blood and had lain there for several days before his death was discovered. A veteran patrolman and I wrestled the corpse into a body bag and on the way downstairs my companion made sure the bag hit every single step. He'd have been more careful with a sack of potatoes.

I can still recall the way the hotel's other residents looked at us. And I can remember how my partner went through the dead man's belongings, scooping up the little cash he had to his name, counting it deliberately and dividing it with me.

I hadn't wanted to take it. 'Put it in your pocket,' he told me. 'What do you think happens to it otherwise? Somebody else takes it. Or it goes to the state. What's the state of New York gonna do with forty-four dollars? Put it in your pocket, then buy yourself some perfumed soap and try to get this poor fucker's stink off your hands.'

I put it in my pocket. Later on, I was the one who bounced bagged corpses down the stairs, the one who counted and divided their leavings.

Someday, I suppose, it'll come full circle, and I'll be the one in the bag.

I spent over an hour there. I went through drawers and closets without really knowing what I was looking for. I didn't find very much. If she'd had a little black book full of telephone numbers, the call girl's legendary stock in trade, someone else had found it before I did. Not that I had any reason to assume she'd had such a book. Elaine kept one, but Fran and Donna had both told me they didn't.

I didn't find any drugs or drug paraphernalia, which proved little in and of itself. A cop might appropriate drugs just as he'd take money from the dead. Or Chance might have picked up any contraband that he found lying around. He'd said that he visited the apartment once after her death. I noticed, though, that he'd left the African masks. They glared at me from their spot on the wall, guarding the premises on behalf of whatever eager young whore Chance would install in Kim's place.

The Hopper poster was still in place over the stereo. Would that stay behind for the next tenant, too?

Her spoor was all over the place. I breathed it when I went through the clothes in her dresser drawers and in her closet. Her bed was unmade. I lifted the mattress, looked under it. No doubt others had done so before me. I didn't find anything and I let the mattress fall back into place, and her spicy scent rose from the rumpled bedclothing and filled my nostrils.

In the living room, I opened a closet and found her fur jacket, other coats and jackets, and a shelf full of wine and liquor bottles. A fifth of Wild Turkey caught my eye, and I swear I could taste that rich overproof bourbon, could feel the bite of it in my throat, the hot rush flowing down to my stomach, the warmth spreading clear to my toes and fingers. I closed the door, crossed the room and sat down on the couch. I hadn't wanted a drink, hadn't so much as thought of a drink in hours, and the

unexpected glimpse of a bottle of booze had caught me unawares.

I went back to the bedroom. She had a jewelry box on the top of her dressing table and I went through it. A lot of earrings, a couple of necklaces, a string of unconvincing pearls. Several bangle bracelets, including an attractive one made of ivory and trimmed in what looked to be gold. A gaudy class ring from LaFollette High in Eau Claire, Wisconsin. The ring was gold, stamped 14K on the inside, heavy enough by the feel of it to be worth something.

Who would get all of this? There had been some cash in her bag at the Galaxy Downtowner, four hundred bucks and change according to the note in her file, and that would probably wind up going to her parents in Wisconsin. But would they fly in and claim her coats and sweaters? Would they take possession of the fur jacket, the high school ring, the ivory bracelet?

I stayed long enough to make a few notes and managed to get out of there without again opening the front closet. I rode the elevator to the lobby, waved at the doorman and nodded at an entering tenant, an elderly woman with a small short-haired dog on a rhinestone-studded leash. The dog yipped at me, and I wondered for the first time what had become of Kim's little black kitten. I'd seen no traces of the animal, no litter pan in the bathroom. Someone must have taken it.

I caught a cab at the corner. I was paying it off in front of my hotel when I found Kim's key with my pocket change. I hadn't remembered to return it to the doorman, and he hadn't thought to ask me for it.

There was a message for me. Joe Durkin had called and left his number at the precinct. I called and was told he was out but was expected back. I left my name and number.

I went up to my room, feeling winded and tired. I lay down but I couldn't get any rest that way, couldn't turn off the tapes in my head. I went downstairs again, had a cheese sandwich and french fries and coffee. Over a second cup of coffee I took Donna Campion's poem out of my pocket. Something about it was trying to get through to me but I couldn't figure out what. I read it again. I didn't know what the poem meant, assuming that it was intended to have any literal meaning. But it seemed to me that some element of it was winking at me, trying to get my attention, and I was just too brain damaged to catch on.

I went over to St Paul's. The speaker told a horrible story in a

chatty matter-of-fact fashion. Both his parents had died of alcoholism, his father of acute pancreatitis, his mother of suicide committed while drunk. Two brothers and a sister had died of the disease. A third brother was in a state hospital with a wet brain.

'After I was sober a few months,' he said, 'I started hearing how alcohol kills brain cells, and I got worried about how much brain damage I might have. So I went to my sponsor and told him what was on my mind. "Well," he said, "maybe you've had some brain damage. It's possible. But let me ask you this. Are you able to remember where the meetings are from one day to the next? Can you find your way to them without any trouble?" "Yeah," I told him, "I can manage that all right." "Well then," he said, "you got all the brain cells you need for the time being."'

I left on the break.

There was another message from Durkin at the hotel desk. I called right back and he was out again. I left my name and number and went upstairs. I was having another look at Donna's poem when the phone rang.

It was Durkin. He said, 'Hey, Matt. I just wanted to say I hope I didn't give you the wrong impression last night.'

'About what?'

'Oh, things in general,' he said. 'Once in a while the whole business gets to me, you know what I mean? I have the need to break out, drink too much, run off at the mouth. I don't make a habit of it but once in a while I have to do it.'

'Sure.'

'Most of the time I love the job, but there's things that get to you, things you try not to look at, and every now and then I have to get all that shit out of my system. I hope I didn't get out of line there toward the end.'

I assured him that he'd done nothing wrong. I wondered how clearly he recalled the previous evening. He'd been drunk enough to be in a blackout, but not everybody has blackouts. Maybe he was just a little vague, and uncertain how I'd taken his outbursts.

I thought of what Billie's landlady had told him. 'Forget it,' I said. 'It could happen to a bishop.'

'Hey, I got to remember that one. It could happen to a bishop. And probably does.'

'Probably.'

'You getting anywhere with your investigation? Coming up with anything?'

'It's hard to tell.'

'I know what you mean. If there's anything I can do for you –'

'Matter of fact, there is.'

'Oh?'

'I went over to the Galaxy Downtowner,' I said. 'Talked to an assistant manager. He showed me the registration card Mr Jones signed.'

'The famous Mr Jones.'

'There was no signature on it. The name was hand-printed.'

'Figures.'

'I asked if I could go through the cards for the past few months and see if there were any other hand-printed signatures, and how they compared to Jones's printing. He couldn't authorize it.'

'You should have slipped him a few bucks.'

'I tried. He didn't even know what I was getting at. But you could have him pull the printed cards. He wouldn't do it for me because I've got no official standing, but he'd hop to it if a cop made the request.'

He didn't say anything for a moment. Then he asked if I thought it was going to lead anywhere.

'It might,' I said.

'You think whoever did it stayed at the hotel before? Under some other name?'

'It's possible.'

'But not his own name, or he would have signed it in script instead of being cute. So what we'd wind up with, assuming we got very lucky and there was a card to be found and we actually came up with it, what we'd have is another alias for the same son of a bitch, and we wouldn't be any closer'n we are now to knowing who he is.'

'There's another thing you could do, while you were at it.'

'What's that?'

'Have other hotels in the area check their registrations for, oh, the past six months or a year.'

'Check 'em for what? Printed registrations. Come on, Matt. You know the man-hours you're talking about?'

'Not printed registrations. Have them check for guests named Jones. I'm talking about hotels like the Galaxy Downtowner, modern hotels in that price range. Most of them'll be like the Galaxy and have their registrations on computer. They can pull

their Jones registrations in five or ten minutes, but not unless someone with a tin shield asks 'em to.'

'And then what have you got?'

'You pull the appropriate cards, look for a guest named Jones, probably with the first initial *C* or the initials *CO*, and you compare printing and see if you find him anywhere. If you come up with anything you see where it leads. I don't have to tell you what to do with a lead.'

He was silent again. 'I don't know,' he said at length. 'It sounds pretty thin.'

'Maybe it is.'

'I'll tell you what I think it is. I think it's a waste of time.'

'It's not a waste of all that much time. And it's not that thin. Joe, you'd do it if the case wasn't already closed in your mind.'

'I don't know about that.'

'Of course you would. You think it's a hired killer or a lunatic. If it's a hired killer you want to close it out and if it's a lunatic you want to wait until he does it again.'

'I wouldn't go that far.'

'You went that far last night.'

'Last night was last night, for Christ's sake. I already explained about last night.'

'It wasn't a hired killer,' I said. 'And it wasn't a lunatic just picking her out of the blue.'

'You sound like you're sure of it.'

'Reasonably sure.'

'Why?'

'No hired hitman goes crazy that way. What did he hit her, sixty times with a machete?'

'I think it was sixty-six.'

'Sixty-six, then.'

'And it wasn't necessarily a machete. Something *like* a machete.'

'He had her strip. Then he butchered her like that, he got so much blood on the walls that they had to paint the room. When did you ever hear of a professional hit like that?'

'Who knows what kind of animal a pimp hires? Maybe he tells the guy to make it ugly, do a real job on her, make an example out of her. Who knows what goes through his mind?'

'And then he hires me to look into it.'

'I admit it sounds weird, Matt, but –'

'It can't be a crazy, either. It was somebody who *went* crazy, but it's not a psycho getting his kicks.'

'How do you know that?'

'He's too careful. Printing his name when he signed in. Carrying the dirty towels away with him. This is a guy who took the trouble to avoid leaving a shred of physical evidence.'

'I thought he used the towels to wrap the machete.'

'Why would he do that? After he washed the machete he'd put it back in the case the way he brought it. Or, if he wanted to wrap it in towels, he'd use clean towels. He wouldn't carry away the towels he washed up with unless he wanted to keep them from being found. But towels can hold things – a hair, a bloodstain – and he knew he might be a suspect because he knew something linked him to Kim.'

'We don't know for sure the towels were dirty, Matt. We don't know he took a shower.'

'He chopped her up and put blood all over the walls. You think he got out of there without washing up?'

'I guess not.'

'Would you take wet towels home for a souvenir? He had a reason.'

'Okay.' A pause. 'A psycho might not want to leave evidence. You're saying he's someone who knew her, who had a reason to kill her. You can't be sure of that.'

'Why did he have her come to the hotel?'

'Because that's where he was waiting. Him and his little machete.'

'Why didn't he take his little machete to her place on Thirty-seventh Street?'

'Instead of having her make house calls?'

'Right. I spent the day talking to hookers. They aren't nuts about outcalls because of the travel time. They'll do them, but they usually invite the caller to come to their place instead, tell him how much more comfortable it is. She probably would have done that but he wasn't having any.'

'Well, he already paid for the room. Wanted to get his money's worth.'

'Why wouldn't he just as soon go to her place?'

He thought about it. 'She had a doorman,' he said. 'Maybe he didn't want to walk past the doorman.'

'Instead he had to walk through a whole hotel lobby and sign a registration card and speak to a desk clerk. Maybe he didn't want to pass that doorman because the doorman had seen him before. Otherwise a doorman's a lot less of a challenge than an entire hotel.'

'That's pretty iffy, Matt.'

'I can't help it. Somebody did a whole batch of things that don't make sense unless he knew the girl and had a personal reason for wanting her dead. He may be emotionally disturbed. Perfectly levelheaded people don't generally go batshit with a machete. But he's more than a psycho picking women at random.'

'How do you figure it? A boyfriend?'

'Something like that.'

'She splits with the pimp, tells the boyfriend she's free, and he panics?'

'I was thinking along those lines, yes.'

'And goes crazy with a machete? How does that mesh with your profile of a guy who decides he'd rather stay home with his wife?'

'I don't know.'

'Do you know for sure she had a boyfriend?'

'No,' I admitted.

'These registration cards. Charles O. Jones and all his aliases, if he ever had any. You think they're gonna lead anywhere?'

'They could.'

'That's not what I asked you, Matt.'

'Then the answer's no. I don't think they're going to lead to anything.'

'But you still think it's worth doing.'

'I'd have gone through the cards myself at the Galaxy Downtowner,' I reminded him. 'On my own time, if the guy would have let me.'

'I suppose we could run the cards.'

'Thanks, Joe.'

'I suppose we can run the other check, too. First-class commercial hotels in the area, their Jones registrations for the past six months or whatever. That what you wanted?'

'That's right.'

'The autopsy showed semen in her throat and esophagus. You happen to notice that?'

'I saw it in the file last night.'

'First he had her blow him, then he chopped her up with his boy scout hatchet. And you figure it was a boyfriend.'

'The semen could have been from an earlier contact. She was a hooker, she had a lot of contacts.'

'I suppose,' he said. 'You know, they can type semen now. It's not like a fingerprint, more like a blood type. Makes useful

275

circumstantial evidence. But you're right, with her lifestyle it doesn't rule a guy out if the semen type's not a match.'

'And it doesn't rule him in if it does.'

'No, but it'd fucking well give him a headache. I wish she'd scratched him, got some skin under her nails. That always helps.'

'You can't have everything.'

'For sure. If she blew him, you'd think she could have wound up with a hair or two between her teeth. Whole trouble is she's too ladylike.'

'That's the trouble, all right.'

'And my trouble is I'm starting to believe there's a case here, with a killer at the end of a rainbow. I got a desk full of shit I haven't got time for and you've got me pulling my chain with this one.'

'Think how good you'll look if it breaks.'

'I get the glory, huh?'

'Somebody might as well.'

I had three more hookers to call, Sunny and Ruby and Mary Lou. Their numbers were in my notebook. But I'd talked to enough whores for one day. I called Chance's service, left word for him to call me. It was Friday night. Maybe he was at the Garden, watching a couple of boys hit each other. Or did he just go when Kid Bascomb was fighting?

I took out Donna Campion's poem and read it. In my mind's eye all the poem's colors were overlaid with blood, bright arterial blood that faded from scarlet to rust. I reminded myself that Kim had been alive when the poem was written. Why, then, did I sense a note of doom in Donna's lines? Had she picked up on something? Or was I seeing things that weren't really there?

She'd left out the gold of Kim's hair. Unless the sun was supposed to cover that base. I saw those gold braids wrapped around her head and thought of Jan Keane's Medusa. Without giving it too much thought I picked up the phone and placed a call. I hadn't dialed the number in a long time but memory supplied it, pushing it at me as a magician forces a card on one.

It rang four times. I was going to hang up when I heard her voice, low pitched, out of breath.

I said, 'Jan, it's Matt Scudder.'

'Matt! I was just thinking of you not an hour ago. Give me a minute, I just walked in the door, let me get my coat off ... There. How've you been? It's so good to hear from you.'

276

'I've been all right. And you?'

'Oh, things are going well. A day at a time.'

The little catchphrases. 'Still going to those meetings?'

'Uh-huh. I just came from one, as a matter of fact. How are you doing?'

'Not so bad.'

'That's good.'

What was it, Friday? Wednesday, Thursday, Friday. 'I've got three days,' I said.

'Matt, that's wonderful!'

What was so wonderful about it? 'I suppose,' I said.

'Have you been going to meetings?'

'Sort of. I'm not sure I'm ready for all that.'

We talked a little. She said maybe we'd run into each other at a meeting one of these days. I allowed that it was possible. She'd been sober almost six months, she'd qualified a couple of times already. I said it would be interesting sometime to hear her story. She said, 'Hear it? God, you're *in* it.'

She was just getting back to sculpture. She'd put it all on hold when she got sober, and it was hard to make the clay do what she wanted it to do. But she was working at it, trying to keep it all in perspective, putting her sobriety first and letting the rest of her life fall into shape at its own pace.

And what about me? Well, I said, I had a case, I was looking into a matter for an acquaintance. I didn't go into detail and she didn't press. The conversation slowed, and there were a few pauses in it, and I said, 'Well, I just thought I'd call and say hello.'

'I'm glad you did, Matthew.'

'Maybe we'll run into each other one of these days.'

'I'd like that.'

I hung up and remembered drinking in her loft on Lispenard Street, warming and mellowing as the booze worked its magic in our veins. What a fine sweet evening that had been.

At meetings you'll hear people say, 'My worst day sober is better than my best day drunk.' And everybody nods like a plastic dog on a Puerto Rican's dashboard. I thought about that night with Jan and looked around my little cell of a room and tried to figure out why this night was better than the other had been.

I looked at my watch. The liquor stores were closed. The bars, though, would be open for hours yet.

I stayed where I was. Outside, a squad car went by with its

siren open. The sound died down, the minutes slipped by, and my phone rang.

It was Chance. 'You been working,' he said with approval. 'I've been getting reports. The girls cooperate okay?'

'They've been fine.'

'You getting anywhere?'

'It's hard to tell. You pick up a piece here and a piece there and you never know if they're going to fit together. What did you take from Kim's apartment?'

'Just some money. Why?'

'How much?'

'Couple hundred. She kept cash in the top dresser drawer. It was no secret hiding place, just where she kept it. I looked around some to see if she had any holdout money stashed anywhere, but I couldn't find any. Didn't turn up any bank-books, safe-deposit keys. Did you?'

'No.'

'Or any money? S'pose it's finders keepers if you did, but I'm just asking.'

'No money. That's all you took?'

'And a picture a nightclub photographer took of her and me. Couldn't see any rightful reason to leave that for the police. Why?'

'I just wondered. You went there before the police picked you up?'

'They didn't pick me up. I walked in voluntarily. And yes, I went there first, and it was before they got there, far as that goes. Or the couple hundred would have been gone.'

Maybe, maybe not. I said, 'Did you take the cat?'

'The cat?'

'She had a little black kitten.'

'Right, she did. I never thought about the kitten. No, I didn't take it. I would have put out food for it if I thought. Why? Is it gone?'

I said it was, and its litter box too. I asked if the kitten had been around when he went to the apartment but he didn't know. He hadn't noticed a kitten, but then he hadn't been looking for one.

'And I was moving quickly, you know. I was in and out in five minutes. Kitten could have brushed against my ankles and I might not have paid it any mind. What's it matter? Kitten didn't kill her.'

'No.'

'You don't think she took the kitten to the hotel, do you?'
'Why would she do that?'
'*I* don't know, man. I don't know why we're *talking* about the kitten.'
'Somebody must have taken it. Somebody besides you must have gone to her apartment after she died and took the kitten out of there.'
'You sure the kitten wasn't there today? Animals get scared when a stranger comes around. They hide.'
'The kitten wasn't there.'
'Could have walked out when the cops came. Doors open, kitten runs out, goodbye kitty.'
'I never heard of a cat taking its litter pan along.'
'Maybe some neighbor took it. Heard it meowing, like they do, and didn't want it to go hungry.'
'Some neighbor with a key?'
'Some people exchange keys with a neighbor. In case they get locked out. Or the neighbor could have got the key from the doorman.'
'That's probably what happened.'
'Must be.'
'I'll check with the neighbors tomorrow.'
He whistled softly. 'You chase down everything, don't you? Little thing like a kitten, you're at it like a dog at a bone.'
'That's the way it's done. Goyakod.'
'How's that?'
'Goyakod,' I said, and spelled it out. 'It stands for Get Off Your Ass and Knock On Doors.'
'Oh, I like that. Say it again?'
I said it again.
'"Get off your ass and knock on doors." I like that.'

EIGHTEEN

Saturday was a good day for knocking on doors. It usually is because more people are at home than during the week. This Saturday the weather didn't invite them out. A fine rain was falling out of a dark sky and there was a stiff wind blowing, whipping the rain around.

Wind sometimes behaves curiously in New York. The tall buildings seem to break it up and put a spin on it, like english on a billiard ball, so that it takes odd bounces and blows in different directions on different blocks. That morning and afternoon it seemed to be always in my face. I would turn a corner and it would turn with me, always coming at me, always driving the spray of rain at me. There were moments when I found it invigorating, others when I hunched my shoulders and lowered my head and cursed the wind and the rain and myself for being out in them.

My first stop was Kim's building, where I nodded and walked past the doorman, key in hand. I hadn't seen him before and I doubt that I was any more familiar to him than he was to me, but he didn't challenge my right to be there. I rode upstairs and let myself into Kim's apartment.

Maybe I was making sure the cat was still missing. I had no other reason to go in. The apartment was as I had left it, as far as I could tell, and I couldn't find a kitten or a litter pan anywhere. While I thought of it I checked the kitchen. There were no cans or boxes of cat food in the cupboards, no bag of kitty litter, no nonspill bowl for a cat to eat out of. I couldn't detect any cat odor in the apartment, and I was beginning to wonder if my memory of the animal might have been a false one. Then, in the refrigerator, I found a half-full can of Puss 'n Boots topped with a plastic lid.

How about that, I thought. The great detective found a clue. Not long after that the great detective found a cat. I walked up

and down the hallway and knocked on doors. Not everyone was home, rainy Saturday or no, and the first three people who were had no idea that Kim had ever owned a cat, let alone any information on its present whereabouts.

The fourth door that opened to my knock belonged to an Alice Simkins, a small woman in her fifties whose conversation was guarded until I mentioned Kim's cat.

'Oh, Panther,' she said. 'You've come for Panther. You know, I was afraid someone would. Come in, won't you?'

She led me to an upholstered chair, brought me a cup of coffee, and apologized for the excess of furniture in the room. She was a widow, she told me, and had moved to this small apartment from a suburban house, and while she'd rid herself of a great many things she'd made the mistake of keeping too much furniture.

'It's like an obstacle course in here,' she said, 'and it's not as if I just moved in yesterday. I've been here almost two years. But because there's no real urgency I seem to find it all too easy to put it off and put it off.'

She had heard about Kim's death from someone in the building. The following morning she was at her desk at the office when she thought of Kim's cat. Who would feed it? Who would take care of it?

'I made myself wait until lunch hour,' she said, 'because I decided I just wasn't crazy enough to run out of the office lest a kitten go an extra hour without food. I fed the kitten and cleaned out the litter pan and freshened its water, and I checked on it that evening when I came home from the office, and it was evident that no one had been in to care for it. I thought about the poor little thing that night, and the next morning when I went to feed it I decided it might as well live with me for the time being.' She smiled. 'It seems to have adjusted. Do you suppose it misses her?'

'I don't know.'

'I don't suppose it'll miss me, either, but I'll miss it. I never kept a cat before. We had dogs years ago. I don't think I'd want to keep a dog, not in the city, but a cat doesn't seem to be any trouble. Panther was declawed so there's no problem of furniture scratching, although I almost wish he'd scratched some of this furniture, it might move me to get rid of it.' She laughed softly. 'I'm afraid I took all his food from her apartment. I can get all of that together for you. And Panther's hiding somewhere, but I'm sure I can find him.'

281

I assured her I hadn't come for the cat, that she could keep the animal if she wanted. She was surprised, and obviously relieved. But if I hadn't come for the cat, what was I there for? I gave her an abbreviated explanation of my role. While she was digesting that I asked her how she'd gained access to Kim's apartment.

'Oh, I had a key. I'd given her a key to my apartment some months ago. I was going out of town and wanted her to water my plants, and shortly after I came back she gave me her key. I can't remember why. Did she want me to feed Panther? I really can't remember. Do you suppose I can change his name?'

'I beg your pardon?'

'It's just that I don't much care for the cat's name, but I don't know if it's proper to change it. I don't believe he recognizes it. What he recognizes is the whirr of the electric can opener, announcing that dinner is served.' She smiled. 'T. S. Eliot wrote that every cat has a secret name, known only to the cat himself. So I don't suppose it really matters what name *I* call him.'

I turned the conversation to Kim, asked how close a friend she'd been.

'I don't know if we were friends,' she said. 'We were neighbors. We were good neighbors, I kept a key to her apartment, but I'm not sure we were friends.'

'You knew she was a prostitute?'

'I suppose I knew. At first I thought she was a model. She had the looks for it.'

'Yes.'

'But somewhere in the course of things I gathered what her actual profession was. She never mentioned it. I think it may have been her failure to discuss her work that made me guess what it was. And then there was that black man who visited her frequently. Somehow I found myself assuming he was her pimp.'

'Did she have a boyfriend, Mrs Simkins?'

'Besides the black man?' She thought about it, and while she did so a black streak darted across the rug, leaped onto a couch, leaped again and was gone. 'You see?' the woman said. 'He's not at all like a panther. I don't know what he is like, but he's nothing like a panther. You asked if she had a boyfriend.'

'Yes.'

'I just wonder. She must have had some sort of secret plan because she hinted at it the last time we talked – that she'd be moving away, that her life was going to take a turn for the better. I'm afraid I wrote it off as a pipe dream.'

'Why?'

'Because I assumed she meant she and her pimp were going to run off into the sunset and live happily ever after, only she wouldn't say as much to me because she'd never come out and told me that she *had* a pimp, that she was a prostitute. I understand pimps will assure a girl that their other girls are unimportant, that as soon as enough money's saved they'll go off and buy a sheep station in Australia or something equally realistic.'

I thought of Fran Schecter on Morton Street, convinced she and Chance were bound by karmic ties, with innumerable lifetimes ahead of them.

'She was planning on leaving her pimp,' I said.

'For another man?'

'That's what I'm trying to find out.'

She'd never seen Kim with anyone in particular, never paid much attention to the men who visited Kim's apartment. Such visitors were few at night, anyway, she explained, and she herself was at work during the day.

'I thought she'd bought the fur herself,' she said. 'She was so proud of it, as if someone had bought it for her, but I thought she wanted to conceal her shame at having had to buy it for herself. I'll bet she did have a boyfriend. She showed it off with that air, as if it had been a gift from a man, but she didn't come out and say so.'

'Because the relationship was a secret.'

'Yes. She was proud of the fur, proud of the jewelry. You said she was leaving her pimp. Is that why she was killed?'

'I don't know.'

'I try not to think about her having been killed, or how or why it happened. Did you ever read a book called *Watership Down?*' I hadn't. 'There's one colony of rabbits in the book; a sort of semidomesticated colony. The food's in good supply there because human beings leave food for the rabbits. It's sort of rabbit heaven, except that the men who do this do so in order to set snares and provide themselves with a rabbit dinner from time to time. And the surviving rabbits, they never refer to the snare, they never mention any of their fellows who've been killed that way. They have an unspoken agreement to pretend that the snare does not exist, and that their dead companions never existed.' She'd been looking to one side as she spoke. Now her eyes found mine. 'Do you know, I think New Yorkers are like those rabbits. We live here for whatever it is that the city

283

provides – the culture, the job opportunities, whatever it is. And we look the other way when the city kills off our friends and neighbors. Oh, we read about it and we talk about it for a day or two days but then we blink it all away. Because otherwise we'd have to do something about it, and we can't. Or we'd have to move, and we don't want to move. We're like those rabbits, aren't we?'

I left my number, told her to call if she thought of anything. She said she would. I took the elevator to the lobby, but when it got there I stayed in the car and rode it back to twelve again. Just because I'd located the black kitten didn't mean I'd be wasting my time knocking on a few more doors.

Except that's what I did. I talked to half a dozen people and didn't learn a thing, other than that they and Kim did a good job of keeping to themselves. One man had even managed to miss out on the knowledge that a neighbor of his had been murdered. The others knew that much, but not a great deal more.

When I'd run out of doors to knock on I found myself approaching Kim's door, key in hand. Why? Because of the fifth of Wild Turkey in the front closet?

I put her key in my pocket and got out of there.

The meeting book led me to a noon meeting just a few blocks from Kim's. The speaker was just finishing her qualification when I walked in. At first glance I thought she was Jan, but when I took another look I saw there was no real resemblance. I got a cup of coffee and took a seat at the back.

The room was crowded, thick with smoke. The discussion seemed to center itself on the spiritual side of the program, and I wasn't too clear on what that was, nor did anything I hear clarify it for me.

One guy said something good, though, a big fellow with a voice like a load of gravel. 'I came in here to save my ass,' he said, 'and then I found out it was attached to my soul.'

If Saturday was a good day for knocking on doors, it was equally good for visiting hookers. While a Saturday-afternoon trick may not be unheard of, it's the exception.

I ate some lunch, then rode uptown on the Lexington IRT. The car was uncrowded, and directly opposite me a black kid in a pea jacket and heavy-soled boots was smoking a cigarette. I

remembered my conversation with Durkin and wanted to tell the kid to put out the cigarette.

Jesus, I thought, mind your own business. Leave it alone.

I got off at Sixty-eighth Street and walked a block north and two blocks east. Ruby Lee and Mary Lou Barcker lived in apartment buildings diagonally opposite one another. Ruby's was on the southwest corner and I went there first because I came to it first. The doorman announced me over the intercom and I shared the elevator with a florist's delivery boy. He had his arms full of roses and the car was heavy with their scent.

Ruby opened the door to my knock, smiled coolly, led me inside. The apartment was sparsely if tastefully furnished. The furniture was contemporary and neutral, but there were other items to give the place an oriental cast – a Chinese rug, a group of Japanese prints in black lacquered frames, a bamboo screen. They weren't enough to render the apartment exotic, but Ruby managed that all by herself.

She was tall, though not so tall as Kim, and her figure was lithe and willowy. She showed it off in a black sheath dress with a skirt slit to show a flash of thigh when she walked. She put me in a chair and offered me a drink, and I heard myself ask for tea. She smiled and came back with tea for both of us. It was Lipton's, I noted. God knows what I expected.

Her father was half French and half Senegalese, her mother Chinese. She'd been born in Hong Kong, lived for a time in Macao, then came to America via Paris and London. She didn't tell me her age and I didn't ask, nor could I have possibly guessed it. She might have been twenty or forty-five or almost anything in between.

She had met Kim once. She didn't really know anything about her, didn't know much about any of the girls. She herself had been with Chance for a time and found their arrangement comfortable.

She didn't know if Kim had had a boyfriend. Why, she wondered, would a woman want two men in her life? Then she would have to give money to both of them.

I suggested that Kim might have had a different sort of relationship with her boyfriend, that he might have given her gifts. She seemed to find the idea baffling. Did I mean a customer? I said that was possible. But a customer was not a boyfriend, she said. A customer was just another man in a long line of men. How could one feel anything for a customer?

*

285

Across the street, Mary Lou Barcker poured me a Coke and set out a plate of cheese and crackers. 'So you met the Dragon Lady,' she said. 'Striking, isn't she?'

'That's putting it mildly.'

'Three races blended into one absolutely stunning woman. Then the shock comes. You open the door and nobody's home. Come here a minute.'

I joined her at the window, looked where she was pointing.

'That's her window,' she said. 'You can see her apartment from mine. You'd think we'd be great friends, wouldn't you? Dropping in at odd hours to borrow a cup of sugar or complain about premenstrual tension. Figures, doesn't it?'

'And it hasn't worked out that way?'

'She's always polite. But she's just not there. The woman doesn't relate. I've known a lot of johns who've gone over there. I've steered some business her way, as far as that goes. A guy'll say he's had fantasies about oriental girls, for example. Or I might just tell a guy that I know a girl he might like. You know something? It's the safest thing in the world. They're grateful because she *is* beautiful, she *is* exotic, and I gather she knows her way around a mattress, but they almost never go back. They go once and they're glad they went, but they don't go back. They'll pass her number on to their buddies instead of ringing it again themselves. I'm sure she keeps busy but I'll bet she doesn't know what a steady trick is, I'll bet she's never had one.'

She was a slender woman, dark haired, a little taller than average, with precise features and small even teeth. She had her hair pulled back and done in a chignon, I think they call it, and she was wearing aviator glasses, the lenses tinted a pale amber. The hair and the glasses combined to give her a rather severe look, an effect of which she was by no means unaware. 'When I take off the glasses and let my hair down,' she said at one point, 'I look a whole lot softer, a good deal less threatening. Of course some johns want a woman to look threatening.'

Of Kim she said, 'I didn't know her well. I don't know any of them really well. What a crew they are! Sunny's the goodtime party girl, she thinks she's made a huge leap in status by becoming a prostitute. Ruby's a sort of autistic adult, untouched by human minds. I'm sure she's socking away the dollars, and one of these days she'll go back to Macao or Port Said and open up an opium den. Chance probably knows she's holding out and has the good sense to let her.'

She put a slice of cheese on a biscuit, handed it to me, took

286

some for herself, sipped her red wine. 'Fran's a charming kook out of *Wonderful Town*. I call her the Village Idiot. She's raised self-deception to the level of an art form. She must have to smoke a ton of grass to support the structure of illusion she's created. More Coke?'

'No thanks.'

'You sure you wouldn't rather have a glass of wine? Or something stronger?'

I shook my head. A radio played unobtrusively in the background, tuned to one of the classical music stations. Mary Lou took off her glasses, breathed on them, wiped them with a napkin.

'And Donna,' she said. 'Whoredom's answer to Edna St Vincent Millay. I think the poetry does for her what the grass does for Fran. She's a good poet, you know.'

I had Donna's poem with me and showed it to Mary Lou. Vertical frown lines appeared in her forehead as she scanned the lines.

'It's not finished,' I said. 'She still has work to do on it.'

'I don't know how poets know when they're finished. Or painters. How do they know when to stop? It baffles me. This is supposed to be about Kim?'

'Yes.'

'I don't know what it means, but there's something, she's onto something here.' She thought for a moment, her head cocked like a bird's. She said, 'I guess I thought of Kim as the archetypical whore. A spectacular ice blonde from the northern Midwest, the kind that was just plain born to walk through life on a black pimp's arm. I'll tell you something. I wasn't surprised when she was murdered.'

'Why not?'

'I'm not entirely sure. I was shocked but not surprised. I guess I expected her to come to a bad end. An abrupt end. Not necessarily as a murder victim, but as some sort of victim of the life. Suicide, for instance. Or one of those unholy combinations of pills and liquor. Not that she drank much, or took drugs as far as I know. I suppose I expected suicide, but murder would do as well, wouldn't it? To get her out of the life. Because I couldn't see her going on with it forever. Once that corn-fed innocence left her she wouldn't be able to handle it. And I couldn't see her finding her way out, either.'

'She *was* getting out. She told Chance she wanted out.'

'Do you know that for a fact?'

'Yes.'

'And what did he do?'

'He told her it was her decision to make.'

'Just like that?'

'Evidently.'

'And then she got killed. Is there a connection?'

'I think there has to be. I think she had a boyfriend and I think the boyfriend's the connection. I think he's why she wanted to get away from Chance and I think he's also the reason she was killed.'

'But you don't know who he was.'

'No.'

'Does anybody have a clue?'

'Not so far.'

'Well, I'm not going to be able to change that. I can't remember the last time I saw her, but I don't remember her eyes being agleam with true love. It would fit though. A man got her into this. She'd probably need another man to get her out.'

And then she was telling me how she'd gotten into it. I hadn't thought to ask but I got to hear it anyway.

Someone had pointed Chance out to her at an opening in SoHo, one of the West Broadway galleries. He was with Donna, and whoever pointed him out told Mary Lou he was a pimp. Fortified by an extra glass or two of the cheap wine they were pouring, she approached him, introduced herself, told him she'd like to write a story about him.

She wasn't exactly a writer. At the time she'd been living in the West Nineties with a man who did something incomprehensible in Wall Street. The man was divorced and still half in love with his ex-wife, and his bratty kids came over every weekend, and it wasn't working out. Mary Lou did free-lance copy editing and had a part-time proofreading job, and she'd published a couple of articles in a feminist monthly newspaper.

Chance met with her, took her out to dinner, and turned the interview inside out. She realized over cocktails that she wanted to go to bed with him, and that the urge stemmed more from curiosity than sexual desire. Before dinner was over he was suggesting that she forget about some surface article and write something real, a genuine inside view of a prostitute's life. She was obviously fascinated, he told her. Why not use that fascination, why not go with it, why not buy the whole package for a couple of months and see where she went with it?

She made a joke out of the suggestion. He took her home after

dinner, didn't make a pass, and managed to remain oblivious to her sexual invitation. For the next week she couldn't get his proposal out of her mind. Everything about her own life seemed unsatisfactory. Her relationship was exhausted, and she sometimes felt she only stayed with her lover out of reluctance to hunt an apartment of her own. Her career was dead-ended and unsatisfying, and the money she earned wasn't enough to live on.

'And the book,' she said, 'the book was suddenly everything. De Maupassant obtained human flesh from a morgue and ate it so that he could describe its taste accurately. Couldn't I spend a month as a call girl in order to write the best book ever written on the subject?'

Once she accepted Chance's offer, everything was taken care of. Chance moved her out of her place on West Ninety-fourth and installed her where she was now. He took her out, showed her off, took her to bed. In bed he told her precisely what to do, and she found this curiously exhilarating. Other men in her experience had always been reticent that way, expecting you to read their minds. Even johns, she said, had trouble telling you what they wanted.

For the first few months she still thought she was doing research for a book. She took notes every time a john left, writing down her impressions. She kept a diary. She detached herself from what she was doing and from who she was, using her journalistic objectivity as Donna used poetry and as Fran used marijuana.

When it dawned on her that whoring was an end in itself she went through an emotional crisis. She had never considered suicide before, but for a week she hovered on its brink. Then she worked it out. The fact that she was whoring didn't mean she had to label herself a whore. This was something she was doing for a while. The book, just an excuse to get into the life, might someday turn out to be something she really wanted to do. It didn't really matter. Her individual days were pleasant enough, and the only thing that was unsettling was when she pictured herself living this way forever. But that wouldn't happen. When the time was right, she would drift out of the life as effortlessly as she had drifted in.

'So that's how I keep my particular cool, Matt. I'm not a hooker. I'm just "into hooking." You know, there are worse ways to spend a couple of years.'

'I'm sure there are.'

'Plenty of time, plenty of creature comforts. I read a lot, I get to movies and museums and Chance likes to take me to concerts. You know the bit about the blind men and the elephant? One grabs the tail and thinks the elephant is like a snake, another touches the side of the elephant and thinks it's like a wall?'

'So?'

'I think Chance is the elephant and his girls are the blind men. We each see a different person.'

'And you all have some African sculpture on the premises.'

Hers was a statue about thirty inches high, a little man holding a bundle of sticks in one hand. His face and hands were rendered in blue and red beadwork, while all the rest of him was covered with small seashells.

'My household god,' she said. 'That's a Batum ancestor figure from Cameroun. Those are cowry shells. Primitive societies all over the world use the cowry shell as a medium of exchange, it's the Swiss franc of the tribal world. You see how it's shaped?'

I went and had a look.

'Like the female genitalia,' she said. 'So men automatically use it to buy and sell. Can I get you some more of that cheese?'

'No thanks.'

'Another Coke?'

'No.'

'Well,' she said, 'if there's anything you'd like, just let me know what it is.'

NINETEEN

Just as I was leaving her building, a cab pulled up in front to discharge a passenger. I got in and gave the address of my hotel.

The windshield wiper on the driver's side didn't work. The driver was white; the picture on the posted license showed a black man. A sign cautioned, NO SMOKING/DRIVER ALLERGIC. The cab's interior reeked of marijuana.

'Can't see a fucking thing,' the driver said.

I sat back and enjoyed the ride.

I called Chance from the lobby, went up to my room. About fifteen minutes later he got back to me. 'Goyakod,' he said. 'I'll tell you, I like that word. Knock on many doors today?'

'A few.'

'And?'

'She had a boyfriend. He bought her presents and she showed them off.'

'To who? To my girls?'

'No, and that's what makes me sure it was something she wanted to keep secret. It was one of her neighbors who mentioned the gifts.'

'Neighbor turn out to have the kitten?'

'That's right.'

'Goyakod. Damn if it don't work. You start with a missing cat and you wind up with a clue. What presents?'

'A fur and some jewelry.'

'Fur,' he said. 'You mean that rabbit coat?'

'She said it was ranch mink.'

'Dyed rabbit,' he said. 'I bought her that coat, took her shopping and paid cash for it. Last winter, that was. The neighbor said it was mink, shit, I'd like to sell the neighbor a couple of minks just like it. Give her a good price on 'em.'

'Kim said it was mink.'

'Said it to the neighbor?'

'Said it to me.' I closed my eyes, pictured her at my table in Armstrong's. 'Said she came to town in a denim jacket and now she was wearing ranch mink and she'd trade it for the denim jacket if she could have the years back.'

His laughter rang through the phone wire. 'Dyed rabbit,' he said with certainty. 'Worth more than the rag she got off the bus with, maybe, but no king's ransom. And no boyfriend bought it for her 'cause *I* bought it for her.'

'Well –'

'Unless I was the boyfriend she was talking about.'

'I suppose that's possible.'

'You said jewelry. All she had was costume, man. You see the jewelry in her jewelry box? Wasn't nothing valuable there.'

'I know.'

'Fake pearls, a school ring. The one nice thing she had was somethin' else I got her. Maybe you saw it. The bracelet?'

'Was it ivory, something like that?'

'Elephant tusk ivory, *old* ivory, and the fittings are gold. The hinge and the clasp. Not a lot of gold, but gold's gold, you know?'

'You bought it for her?'

'Got it for a hundred dollar bill. Cost you three hundred in a shop, maybe a little more, if you were to find one that nice.'

'It was stolen?'

'Let's just say I didn't get no bill of sale. Fellow who sold it to me, he never said it was stolen. All he said was he'd take a hundred dollars for it. I should have picked that up when I got the photograph. See, I bought it 'cause I liked it, and then I gave it to her because I wasn't about to wear it, see, and I thought it'd look good on her wrist. Which it did. You still think she had a boyfriend?'

'I think so.'

'You don't sound so sure no more. Or maybe you just sound tired. You tired?'

'Yes.'

'Knockin' on too many doors. Wha'd this boyfriend of hers do besides buy her all these presents that don't exist?'

'He was going to take care of her.'

'Well, shit,' he said. 'That's what *I* did, man. What else did I do for that girl but take care of her?'

*

292

I stretched out on the bed and fell asleep with my clothes on. I'd knocked on too many doors and talked to too many people. I was supposed to see Sunny Hendryx, I'd called and told her I would be coming over, but I took a nap instead. I dreamed of blood and a woman screaming, and I woke up bathed in sweat and with a metallic taste in the back of my mouth.

I showered and changed my clothes. I checked Sunny's number in my notebook, dialed it from the lobby. No answer.

I was relieved. I looked at my watch, headed over to St Paul's.

The speaker was a soft-spoken fellow with receding light brown hair and a boyish face. At first I thought he might be a clergyman.

He turned out to be a murderer. He was homosexual, and one night in a blackout he had stabbed his lover thirty or forty times with a kitchen knife. He had, he said quietly, faint memories of the incident, because he'd kept going in and out of blackout, coming to with the knife in his hand, being struck by the horror of it, and then slipping back into the darkness. He'd served seven years at Attica and had been sober three years now on the outside.

It was disturbing, listening to him. I couldn't decide how I felt about him. I didn't know whether to be glad or sorry that he was alive, that he was out of prison.

On the break I got to talking with Jim. Maybe I was reacting to the qualification, maybe I was carrying Kim's death around with me, but I started talking about all the violence, all the crime, all the killings. 'It gets to me,' I said. 'I pick up the paper and I read some damn thing or other and it gets to me.'

'You know that vaudeville routine? "Doctor, it hurts when I do this." "So don't do this!"'

'So?'

'So maybe you should stop picking up the paper.' I gave him a look. 'I'm serious,' he said. 'Those stories bother me, too. So do the stories about the world situation. If the news was good they wouldn't put it in the paper. But one day it struck me, or maybe I got the idea from somebody else, but it came to me that there was no law saying I had to read that crap.'

'Just ignore it.'

'Why not?'

'That's the ostrich approach, isn't it? What I don't look at can't hurt me?'

'Maybe, but I see it a little differently. I figure I don't have to

293

make myself crazy with things I can't do anything about anyway.'

'I can't see myself overlooking that sort of thing.'

'Why not?'

I thought of Donna. 'Maybe I'm involved with mankind.'

'Me too,' he said. 'I come here, I listen, I talk. I stay sober. That's how I'm involved in mankind.'

I got some more coffee and a couple of cookies. During the discussion people kept telling the speaker how much they appreciated his honesty.

I thought, Jesus, I never did anything like that. And my eyes went to the wall. They hang these slogans on the wall, gems of wisdom like Keep It Simple and Easy Does It, and the sign my eyes went to as if magnetized read There But For The Grace Of God.

I thought, no, screw that. I don't turn murderous in blackouts. Don't tell me about the grace of God.

When it was my turn I passed.

TWENTY

Danny Boy held his glass of Russian vodka aloft so that he could look at the light shine through it. 'Purity. Clarity. Precision,' he said, rolling the words, pronouncing them with elaborate care. 'The best vodka is a razor, Matthew. A sharp scalpel in the hand of a skilled surgeon. It leaves no ragged edges.'

He tipped back the glass and swallowed an ounce or so of purity and clarity. We were at Poogan's and he was wearing a navy suit with a red stripe that barely showed in the bar's half-light. I was drinking club soda with lime. At another stop along the way a freckled-faced waitress had informed me that my drink was called a Lime Rickey. I had a feeling I'd never ask for it by that name.

Danny Boy said, 'Just to recapitulate. Her name was Kim Dakkinen. She was a big blonde, early twenties, lived in Murray Hill, got killed two weeks ago in the Galaxy Downtowner.'

'Not quite two weeks ago.'

'Right. She was one of Chance's girls. And she had a boyfriend, and that's what you want. The boyfriend.'

'That's right.'

'And you're paying for whoever can give you the skinny on this. How much?'

I shrugged. 'A couple of dollars.'

'Like a bill? Like a half a K? How many dollars?'

I shrugged again. 'I don't know, Danny. It depends on the information and where it comes from and where it goes. I haven't got a million dollars to play with but I'm not strapped either.'

'You said she was one of Chance's girls.'

'Right.'

'You were looking for Chance a little over two weeks ago,

Matthew. And then you took me to the boxing matches just so I could point him out to you.'

'That's right.'

'And a couple of days after that, your big blonde had her picture in the papers. You were looking for her pimp, and now she's dead, and here you are looking for her boyfriend.'

'So?'

He drank the rest of his vodka. 'Chance know what you're doing?'

'He knows.'

'You talk to him about it?'

'I've talked to him.'

'Interesting.' He raised his empty glass to the light, squinted through it. Checking it, no doubt, for purity and clarity and precision. He said, 'Who's your client?'

'That's confidential.'

'Funny how people looking for information are never looking to furnish it. No problem. I can ask around, put the word out in certain quarters. That's what you want?'

'That's what I want.'

'Do you know anything about this boyfriend?'

'Like what?'

'Like is he old or young, wise or straight, married or single? Does he walk to school or take his lunch?'

'He may have given her presents.'

'That narrows the field.'

'I know.'

'Well,' he said, 'all we can do is try.'

It was certainly all *I* could do. I'd gone back to the hotel after the meeting and found a message waiting for me. *Call Sunny*, it said, and included the number which I'd called earlier. I rang her from the booth in the lobby and got no answer. Didn't she have a machine? Didn't they all have machines nowadays?

I went to my room but I couldn't stay in it. I wasn't tired, the nap had taken the edge off my tiredness, and all the coffee I'd drunk at the meeting had me restless and edgy. I went through my notebook and reread Donna's poem and it struck me that I was very likely looking for an answer someone else already knew.

That's very often the case in police work. The easiest way to find out something is to ask someone who knows. The hard part is figuring out who that person is, the one with the answer.

Who might Kim have confided in? Not the girls I'd talked to so far. Not her neighbor on Thirty-seventh Street. Who, then?

Sunny? Maybe. But Sunny wasn't answering her phone. I tried her again, placing the call through the hotel switchboard.

No answer. Just as well. I didn't much feel like spending the next hour drinking ginger ale with yet another hooker.

What had they done, Kim and her faceless friend? If they'd spent all their time behind closed doors, rolling together on a mattress and swearing eternal love, never saying a word to anyone else, then I might be up against it. But maybe they'd gone out, maybe he'd shown her off in some circle or other. Maybe he talked to somebody who talked to somebody else, maybe –

I wouldn't learn the answers in my hotel room. The hell, it wasn't such a bad night. The rain had quit sometime during the meeting and the wind had died down some. Time to get off my ass, time to take a few taxis and spend a little money. I didn't seem to be putting it in the bank or stuffing it into poor boxes or shipping it home to Syosset. Might as well spread it around.

And so I'd been doing that. Poogan's Pub was perhaps the ninth place I'd hit and Danny Boy Bell perhaps the fifteenth person I'd talked to. Some of the places were ones I'd visited while looking for Chance, but others were not. I tried saloons in the Village, gin joints in Murray Hill and Turtle Bay, singles bars on First Avenue. I kept doing this after I left Poogan's, spending frequent small sums on cabs and drink orders, having the same conversation over and over again.

No one knew anything. You live in hope when you run that sort of fool's errand. There's always the chance that you'll deliver your spiel and the person you're talking to will turn and point and say, 'That's him, that's her boyfriend, that big guy in the corner over there.'

It almost never happens that way. What does happen, if you're lucky, is that the word gets around. There may be eight million people in the goddamned city but it's amazing how they all talk to each other. If I did this right, it wouldn't be long before a fair share of those eight million knew that a dead whore had a boyfriend and a guy named Scudder was looking for him.

Two cabbies in a row refused to go to Harlem. There's a law that says they have to. If an orderly fare requests a destination anywhere in the five boroughs of New York City, the driver has

to take him there. I didn't bother citing the relevant statute. It was easier to walk a block and catch a subway.

The station was a local stop, the platform deserted. The attendant sat in the bulletproof token booth, locked in. I wondered if she felt secure in there. New York taxis have thick plexiglas partitions to protect the drivers, but the cabbies I'd hailed weren't willing to go uptown, partition or no.

Not long ago an attendant had had a heart attack in one of those token booths. The CPR team couldn't get into the locked booth to revive him and so the poor bastard had died in there. Still, I suppose they protect more people than they kill.

Of course they hadn't protected the two women at the Broad Channel stop on the A train. A couple of kids had a grudge against an attendant who'd reported them for turnstile jumping, so they'd filled a fire extinguisher with gasoline, pumped it into the booth, and lit a match. The whole booth exploded, incinerated both women. One more way to die.

That had been in the paper a year ago. Of course there was no law saying I had to read the papers.

I bought tokens. When my train came I rode it uptown. I worked Kelvin Small's and a few other places on Lenox Avenue. I ran into Royal Waldron at a rib joint, had the same conversation with him I'd been having with everybody else. I drank a cup of coffee on 125th Street, walked the rest of the way to St Nicholas, had a glass of ginger ale at the bar of Club Cameroon.

The statue in Mary Lou's apartment was from Cameroun. An ancestor statue, encrusted with cowry shells.

I found no one at the bar I knew well enough to talk to. I looked at my watch. It was getting late. On Saturday night the bars in New York close an hour early, at three instead of four. I've never understood why. Perhaps so that the heavy hitters can sober up in time for church.

I motioned to the bartender, asked about after-hours joints. He just looked at me, his face impassive. I found myself laying my rap on him, telling him I was looking for information about Kim's boyfriend. I knew I wasn't going to get an answer from him, knew I wouldn't get the time of day from him, but I was getting the message across all the same. He'd hear me and so would the men on either side of me, and they'd all talk to people, and that was how it worked.

''Fraid I can't help you,' he said. 'Whatever you lookin' for, you lookin' awful far uptown for it.'

*

I suppose the boy followed me out of the bar. I didn't notice, and I should have. You have to pay attention to that sort of thing.

I was walking along the street, my mind jumping all over the place, from Kim's mysterious boyfriend to the speaker who'd stabbed his lover. By the time I sensed movement alongside of me there was no time left to react. I was just starting to turn when his hand fastened on my shoulder and propelled me into the mouth of the alley.

He came right in after me. He was an inch or so shorter than me but his bushy Afro made up those two inches and more. He was eighteen or twenty or twenty-two, with a drooping moustache and a burn scar on one cheek. He was wearing a flight jacket with zippered pockets and a pair of tight black jeans, and he had a little gun in his hand and it was pointed right at me.

He said, 'Motherfucker, fucking motherfucker. Gimme your money, you motherfucker. Gimme it, gimme all of it, gimme it or you dead, you motherfucker.'

I thought, Why didn't I get to the bank? Why didn't I leave some of it at my hotel? I thought, Jesus, Mickey could forget getting his teeth straightened, St Paul's could forget about their ten percent.

And I could forget about tomorrow.

'Motherfucking honky bastard, dirty motherfucker –'

Because he was going to kill me. I reached in my pocket for my wallet and I looked at his eyes and at his finger on the trigger and I knew it. He was working himself up, he was primed, and whatever money I had wasn't going to be enough for him. He'd be scoring big, better than two grand, but I'd be dead whatever money I had.

We were in an alley about five feet wide, just a gap between two brick tenements. Light from a streetlamp spilled into the alley, illuminating the passage for another ten or fifteen yards beyond where we stood. There was rain-soaked litter on the ground, scraps of paper, beer cans, broken bottles.

Fine place to die. Fine *way* to die, not even a very original one. Shot dead by a mugger, crime in the streets, a terse paragraph on a back page.

I drew the wallet out of my pocket. I said, 'You can have it, everything I've got, you're welcome to it,' knowing it wasn't enough, knowing he'd resolved to shoot me for five dollars or five thousand. I extended the wallet, hand shaking, and I dropped it.

'I'm sorry,' I said, 'very sorry, I'll get it,' and bent to retrieve it, hoping he'd bend forward also, figuring he had to. I bent at the knees and I gathered my feet under me and I thought *Now!* and I straightened up hard and fast, slapping at the gun as I drove my head full force into his chin.

The gun went off, deafening in that enclosed space. I thought I must have been hit but I didn't feel anything. I grabbed and butted him again, then shoved hard and he stumbled back against the wall behind him, eyes glazed, the gun held loose in his hand. I kicked his wrist and the gun went flying.

He came off the wall, his eyes full of murder. I feinted with a left and hit him with my right in the pit of the stomach. He made a retching sound and doubled up, and I grabbed that son of a bitch, one hand gripping the nylon flight jacket, the other tangled up in his mop of hair, and I ran him right into the wall, three quick steps that ended with his face smacking into the bricks. Three, four times I drew him back by the hair and smashed his face into the wall. When I let go of him he dropped like a marionette with the strings cut, sprawling on the floor of the alley.

My heart was pounding as if I'd run at top speed up ten flights of stairs. I couldn't catch my breath. I leaned against the brick wall, panting for breath, waiting for the cops to come.

Nobody came. There had been a noisy scuffle, hell, there had been a gunshot, but nobody came and nobody was going to come. I looked down at the young man who would have killed me if he could. He lay with his mouth open, showing teeth broken off at the gumline. His nose was smashed flat against his face and blood flowed from it in a stream.

I checked, made sure I wasn't shot. Sometimes, I understand, you can take a bullet and not feel it at the time. Shock and adrenalin anesthetize the pain. But he'd missed me. I examined the wall behind where I was standing, found a fresh indentation in the brick where the bullet had dug out a chip before ricocheting. I figured out where I'd been standing and calculated that he hadn't missed me by much.

Now what?

I found my wallet, put it back in my pocket. I rooted around until I located the gun, a .32-caliber revolver with a spent cartridge in one of its chambers and live rounds in the other five. Had he killed anyone else with it? He'd seemed nervous, so maybe I'd been scheduled to be his first. Then again, maybe

some people always get nervous before they pull the trigger, just as some actors always feel anxious before they step on stage.

I knelt down and frisked him. He had a switch knife in one pocket, another knife tucked into his sock. No wallet, no ID, but he had a thick roll of bills on his hip. I slipped off the rubber band and gave the roll a fast count. He had over three hundred dollars, the bastard. He hadn't been looking to make the rent money or score a bag of dope.

And what the hell was I going to do with him?

Call the cops? And hand them what? No evidence, no witnesses, and the guy on the ground was the one who'd sustained the damages. There was nothing good enough for a courtroom, not even anything to hold him on. They'd rush him to the hospital, fix him up, even give him his money back. No way to prove it was stolen. No way to prove it wasn't rightfully his.

They wouldn't give him the gun back. But they couldn't hang a weapons charge on him, either, because I couldn't prove he'd been carrying it.

I put his roll of bills in my own pocket, took out the gun that I'd placed there earlier. I turned the gun over and over in my hand, trying to recall the last time I'd handled one. It had been a while.

He lay there, his breath bubbling through the blood in his nose and throat, and I crouched at his side. After a moment or two I stuck the gun into his ruined mouth and let my finger curl around the trigger.

Why not?

Something stopped me, and it wasn't fear of punishment, not in this world or the next. I'm not sure what it was, but after what seemed like a long time I sighed and withdrew the gun from his mouth. There were traces of blood on the barrel, glowing like brass in the soft light of the alley. I wiped the gun on his jacket front, put it back in my pocket.

I thought, Damn you, goddamn you, what am I going to do with you?

I couldn't kill him and I couldn't hand him to the cops. What could I do? Leave him there?

What else?

I stood up. A wave of dizziness came over me and I stumbled, reached out, caught onto the wall for support. After a moment the dizziness passed and I was all right.

I took a deep breath, let it out. I bent down again and grabbed

him by the feet, dragged him some yards back into the alley to a ledge about a foot high, the top frame of a barred basement window. I stretched him out across the alley on his back with his feet up on the ledge and his head wedged against the opposite wall.

I stamped full force on one of his knees, but that didn't do it. I had to jump into the air and come down with both feet. His left leg snapped like a matchstick on my first attempt, but it took me four times to break the right one. He remained unconscious throughout, moaning a bit, then crying out when the right leg broke.

I stumbled, fell, landed on one knee, got up again. Another wave of dizziness hit me, this one accompanied by nausea, and I clung to the wall and gave myself up to dry heaves. The dizziness passed, and the nausea, but I still couldn't catch my breath and I was shaking like a leaf. I held my hand out in front of me and watched my fingers tremble. I'd never seen anything like that before. I'd faked the shaking when I took out my wallet and dropped it, but this shaking was perfectly real, and I couldn't control it by force of will. My hands had a will of their own and they wanted to shake.

The shakes were even worse on the inside.

I turned, took a last look at him. I turned again and made my way over the littered pavement to the street. I was still shaking and it wasn't getting any better.

Well, there was a way to stop the shakes, the ones on the outside and the inner ones as well. There was a specific remedy for that specific disease.

Red neon winked at me from the other side of the street. BAR, it said.

TWENTY-ONE

I didn't cross the street. The kid with the smashed face and broken legs was not the only mugger in the neighborhood, and it struck me that I wouldn't want to meet another one with drink in me.

No, I had to get to my home ground. I was only going to have one drink, maybe two, but I couldn't guarantee that was all I would have, nor could I say with assurance what one or two drinks would do to me.

The safe thing would be to get back to my neighborhood, have one or at the most two shots in a bar, then take a couple of beers back to my room.

Except that there was no safe way to drink. Not for me, not anymore. Hadn't I proved that? How many times did I have to go on proving it?

So what was I supposed to do? Shake until I fell apart? I wasn't going to be able to sleep without a drink. I wasn't going to be able to sit still without a drink, for Christ's sake.

Well, fuck it. I had to have one. It was medicinal. Any doctor who looked at me would prescribe it.

Any doctor? How about that intern at Roosevelt. I could feel his hand on my shoulder, right where the mugger had grabbed me to shove me into the alley. *'Look at me. Listen to me. You're an alcoholic. If you drink you'll die.'*

I'd die anyway, in one of eight million ways. But if I had the choice, at least I could die closer to home.

I walked over to the curb. A gypsy cab, the only kind that cruises Harlem, slowed as it approached. The driver, a middle-aged Hispanic woman wearing a brimmed cap over kinky red hair, decided I looked all right. I got in the back seat, closed the door, told her to take me to Fifty-eighth and Ninth.

On the way there my mind was all over the place. My hands were still trembling, though not so violently as before, but the

303

internal shakes were as bad as ever. The ride seemed to take forever, and then before I knew it the woman was asking me which corner I wanted. I told her to pull up in front of Armstrong's. When the light changed she nosed the cab across the intersection and stopped where I'd told her. When I made no move she turned around to see what was wrong.

I'd just remembered that I couldn't get a drink at Armstrong's. Of course they might have forgotten by now that Jimmy had eighty-sixed me, but maybe they hadn't, and I felt myself burning with resentment already at the thought of walking in there and being refused service. No, fuck them, I wouldn't walk through their goddamned door.

Where, then? Polly's would be closed, they never ran all the way to closing hour. Farrell's?

That was where I'd had the first drink after Kim's death. I'd had eight sober days before I picked up that drink. I remembered that drink. Early Times, it was.

Funny how I always remember what brand I was drinking. It's all the same crap, but that's the sort of detail that sticks in your mind.

I'd heard someone make that very observation at a meeting a while back.

What did I have now? Four days? I could go up to my room and just make myself stay there and when I woke up I'd be starting my fifth day.

Except that I'd never fall asleep. I wouldn't even stay in the room. I'd try, but I couldn't stay anywhere, not the way I felt right now, not with only my own whirling mind to keep me company. If I didn't drink now I'd drink an hour from now.

'Mister? You okay?'

I blinked at the woman, then dug my wallet out of my pocket and found a twenty. 'I want to make a phone call,' I said. 'From the booth right there on the corner. You take this and wait for me. All right?'

Maybe she'd drive off with the twenty. I didn't really care. I walked to the corner, dropped a dime, stood there listening to the dial tone.

It was too late to call. What time was it? After two, much too late for a social call.

Hell, I could go to my room. All I had to do was stay put for an hour and I'd be in the clear. At three the bars would close.

So? There was a deli that would sell me beer, legally or not. There was an after-hours on Fifty-first, way west between

Eleventh and Twelfth. Unless it had closed by now; I hadn't been there in a long time.

There was a bottle of Wild Turkey in Kim Dakkinen's front closet. And I had her key in my pocket.

That scared me. The booze was right there, accessible to me at any hour, and if I went there I'd never stop after one or two drinks. I'd finish the bottle, and when I did there were a lot of other bottles to keep it company.

I made my call.

She'd been sleeping. I heard that in her voice when she answered the phone.

I said, 'It's Matt. I'm sorry to call you so late.'

'That's all right. What time is it? God, it's after two.'

'I'm sorry.'

'It's all right. Are you okay, Matthew?'

'No.'

'Have you been drinking?'

'No.'

'Then you're okay.'

'I'm falling apart,' I said. 'I called you because it was the only way I could think of to keep from drinking.'

'You did the right thing.'

'Can I come over?'

There was a pause. Never mind, I thought. Forget it. One quick drink at Farrell's before they closed, then back to the hotel. Never should have called her in the first place.

'Matthew, I don't know if it's a good idea. Just take it an hour at a time, a minute at a time if you have to, and call me as much as you want. I don't mind if you wake me, but –'

I said, 'I almost got killed half an hour ago. I beat a kid up and broke his legs for him. I'm shaking like I never shook before in my life. The only thing that's going to make me feel right is a drink and I'm afraid to take one and scared I'll do it anyway. I thought being with someone and talking with someone might get me through it but it probably wouldn't anyway, and I'm sorry, I shouldn't have called. I'm not your responsibility. I'm sorry.'

'Wait!'

'I'm here.'

'There's a clubhouse on St Marks Place where they have meetings all night long on the weekends. It's in the book, I can look it up for you.'

'Sure.'

'You won't go, will you?'

'I can't talk up at meetings. Forget it, Jan. I'll be all right.'

'Where are you?'

'Fifty-eighth and Ninth.'

'How long will it take you to get here?'

I glanced over at Armstrong's. My gypsy cab was still parked there. 'I've got a cab waiting,' I said.

'You remember how to get here?'

'I remember.'

The cab dropped me in front of Jan's six-story loft building on Lispenard. The meter had eaten up most of the original twenty dollars. I gave her another twenty to go with it. It was too much but I was feeling grateful, and could afford to be generous.

I rang Jan's bell, two long and three short, and went out in front so that she could toss the key down to me. I rode the industrial elevator to the fifth floor and stepped out into her loft.

'That was quick,' she said. 'You really did have a cab waiting.'

She'd had time to dress. She was wearing old Lee jeans and a flannel shirt with a red-and-black checkerboard pattern. She's an attractive woman, medium height, well fleshed, built more for comfort than for speed. A heart-shaped face, her hair dark brown salted with gray and hanging to her shoulders. Large well-spaced gray eyes. No makeup.

She said, 'I made coffee. You don't take anything in it, do you?'

'Just bourbon.'

'We're fresh out. Go sit down, I'll get the coffee.'

When she came back with it I was standing by her Medusa, tracing a hair-snake with my fingertip. 'Her hair reminded me of your girl here,' I said. 'She had blonde braids but she wrapped them around her head in a way that made me think of your Medusa.'

'Who?'

'A woman who got killed. I don't know where to start.'

'Anywhere,' she said.

*

I talked for a long time and I skipped all over the place, from the beginning to that night's events and back and forth again. She got up now and then to get us more coffee, and when she came back I'd start in where I left off. Or I'd start somewhere else. It didn't seem to matter.

I said, 'I didn't know what the hell to do with him. After I'd knocked him out, after I'd searched him. I couldn't have him arrested and I couldn't stand the thought of letting him go. I was going to shoot him but I couldn't do it. I don't know why. If I'd just smacked his head against the wall a couple more times it might have killed him, and I'll tell you, I'd have been glad of it. But I couldn't shoot him while he was lying there unconscious.'

'Of course not.'

'But I couldn't leave him there, I didn't want him walking the streets. He'd just get another gun and do it again. So I broke his legs. Eventually the bones'll knit and he'll be able to resume his career, but in the meantime he's off the streets.' I shrugged. 'It doesn't make any sense. But I couldn't think of anything else to do.'

'The important thing is you didn't drink.'

'Is that the important thing?'

'I think so.'

'I almost drank. If I'd been in my own neighborhood, or if I hadn't reached you. God knows I wanted to drink. I *still* want to drink.'

'But you're not going to.'

'No.'

'Do you have a sponsor, Matthew?'

'No.'

'You should. It's a big help.'

'How?'

'Well, a sponsor's someone you can call anytime, someone you can tell anything to.'

'You have one?'

She nodded. 'I called her after I spoke to you.'

'Why?'

'Because I was nervous. Because it calms me down to talk to her. Because I wanted to see what she would say.'

'What did she say?'

'That I shouldn't have told you to come over.' She laughed. 'Fortunately, you were already on your way.'

'What else did she say?'

The big gray eyes avoided mine. 'That I shouldn't sleep with you.'

'Why'd she say that?'

'Because it's not a good idea to have relationships during the first year. And because it's a terrible idea to get involved with anybody who's newly sober.'

'Christ,' I said. 'I came over because I was jumping out of my skin, not because I was horny.'

'I know that.'

'Do you do everything your sponsor says?'

'I try to.'

'Who is this woman that she's the voice of God on earth?'

'Just a woman. She's my age, actually she's a year and a half younger. But she's been sober almost six years.'

'Long time.'

'It seems like a long time to me.' She picked up her cup, saw it was empty, put it down again. 'Isn't there someone you could ask to be your sponsor?'

'Is that how it works? You have to ask somebody?'

'That's right.'

'Suppose I asked you?'

She shook her head. 'In the first place, you should get a male sponsor. In the second place, I haven't been sober long enough. In the third place we're friends.'

'A sponsor shouldn't be a friend?'

'Not that kind of friend. An AA friend. In the fourth place, it ought to be somebody in your home group so you have frequent contact.'

I thought unwillingly of Jim. 'There's a guy I talk to sometimes.'

'It's important to pick someone you can talk to.'

'I don't know if I can talk to him. I suppose I could.'

'Do you respect his sobriety?'

'I don't know what that means.'

'Well, do you –'

'This evening I told him I got upset by the stories in the newspapers. All the crime in the streets, the things people keep doing to each other. It gets to me, Jan.'

'I know it does.'

'He told me to quit reading the papers. Why are you laughing?'

'It's just such a program thing to say.'

'People talk the damnedest crap. "I lost my job and my mother's dying of cancer and I'm going to have to have my nose amputated but I didn't drink today so that makes me a winner."'

'They really sound like that, don't they?'

'Sometimes. What's so funny?'

'"I'm going to have my nose amputated." A *nose* amputated?'

'Don't laugh,' I said. 'It's a serious problem.'

A little later she was telling me about a member of her home

group whose son had been killed by a hit-and-run driver. The man had gone to a meeting and talked about it, drawing strength from the group, and evidently it had been an inspirational experience all around. He'd stayed sober, and his sobriety had enabled him to deal with the situation and bolster the other members of his family while fully experiencing his own grief.

I wondered what was so wonderful about being able to experience your grief. Then I found myself speculating what would have happened some years ago if I'd stayed sober after an errant bullet of mine ricocheted and fatally wounded a six-year-old girl named Estrellita Rivera. I'd dealt with the resultant feelings by pouring bourbon on them. It had certainly seemed like a good idea at the time.

Maybe it hadn't been. Maybe there were no shortcuts, no detours. Maybe you had to go through things.

I said, 'You don't worry about getting hit by a car in New York. But it happens here, the same as anywhere else. Did they ever catch the driver?'

'No.'

'He was probably drunk. They usually are.'

'Maybe he was in a blackout. Maybe he came to the next day and never knew what he'd done.'

'Jesus,' I said, and thought of that night's speaker, the man who stabbed his lover. 'Eight million stories in the Emerald City. And eight million ways to die.'

'The naked city.'

'Isn't that what I said?'

'You said the Emerald City.'

'I did? Where did I get that from?'

'*The Wizard of Oz*. Remember? Dorothy and Toto in Kansas? Judy Garland going over the rainbow?'

'Of course I remember.'

'"Follow the Yellow Brick Road." It led to the Emerald City, where the wonderful wizard lived.'

'I remember. The Scarecrow, the Tin Man, the Cowardly Lion, I remember the whole thing. But where'd I get emeralds from?'

'You're an alcoholic,' she suggested. 'You're missing a couple of brain cells, that's all.'

I nodded. 'Must be it,' I said.

The sky was turning light when we went to sleep. I slept on the couch wrapped up in a couple of spare blankets. At first I thought I wouldn't be able to sleep, but the tiredness came over

309

me like a towering wave. I gave up and let it take me wherever it wanted.

I can't say where it took me because I slept like a dead man. If I dreamed at all I never knew about it. I awoke to the smells of coffee perking and bacon frying, showered, shaved with a disposable razor she'd laid out for me, then got dressed and joined her at a pine plank table in the kitchen. I drank orange juice and coffee and ate scrambled eggs and bacon and whole-wheat muffins with peach preserves, and I couldn't remember when my appetite had been so keen.

There was a group that met Sunday afternoons a few blocks to the east of us, she informed me. She made it one of her regular meetings. Did I feel like joining her?

'I ought to do some work,' I said.

'On a Sunday?'

'What's the difference?'

'Are you really going to be able to accomplish anything on a Sunday afternoon?'

I hadn't really accomplished anything since I'd started. Was there anything I could do today?

I got out my notebook, dialed Sunny's number. No answer. I called my hotel. Nothing from Sunny, nothing from Danny Boy Bell or anyone else I'd seen last night. Well, Danny Boy would still be sleeping at this hour, and so might most of the others.

There was a message to call Chance. I started dialing his number, then stopped myself. If Jan was going to a meeting, I didn't want to sit around her loft waiting for him to call back. Her sponsor might not approve.

The meeting was on the second floor of a synagogue on Forsythe Street. You couldn't smoke there. It was an unusual experience being in an AA meeting that wasn't thick with cigarette smoke.

There were about fifty people there and she seemed to know most of them. She introduced me to several people, all of whose names I promptly forgot. I felt self-conscious, uncomfortable with the attention I was getting. My appearance didn't help, either. While I hadn't slept in my clothes, they looked as though I had, showing the effects of last night's fight in the alley.

And I was feeling the fight's effects, too. It wasn't until we left her loft that I realized how much I ached. My head was sore where I'd butted him and I had a bruise on one forearm and one shoulder was black and blue and ached. Other muscles hurt

when I moved. I hadn't felt anything after the incident but all those aches and pains turn up the next day.

I got some coffee and cookies and sat through the meeting. It was all right. The speaker qualified very briefly, leaving the rest of the meeting for discussion. You had to raise your hand to get called on.

Fifteen minutes from the end, Jan raised her hand and said how grateful she was to be sober and how much of a role her sponsor played in her sobriety, how helpful the woman was when she had something bothering her or didn't know what to do. She didn't get more specific than that. I had a feeling she was sending me a message and I wasn't too crazy about that.

I didn't raise my hand.

Afterward she was going out with some people for coffee and asked me if I'd like to come along. I didn't want any more coffee and I didn't want company, either. I made an excuse.

Outside, before we went separate ways, she asked me how I felt. I said I felt all right.

'Do you still feel like drinking?'

'No,' I said.

'I'm glad you called last night.'

'So am I.'

'Call anytime, Matthew. Even in the middle of the night if you have to.'

'Let's hope I don't have to.'

'But if you do, call. All right?'

'Sure.'

'Matthew? Promise me one thing?'

'What?'

'Don't have a drink without calling me first.'

'I'm not going to drink today.'

'I know. But if you ever decide to, if you're going to, call me first. Promise?'

'Okay.'

On the subway heading uptown I thought about the conversation and felt foolish for having made the promise. Well, it had made her happy. What was the harm in it if it made her happy?

There was another message from Chance. I called from the lobby, told his service I was back at my hotel. I bought a paper and took it upstairs with me to kill the time it took him to call back.

The lead story was a honey. A family in Queens – father,

mother, two kids under five – had gone for a ride in their shiny new Mercedes. Someone pulled up next to them and emptied both barrels of a shotgun into the car, killing all four of them. A police search of their apartment in Jamaica Estates had revealed a large amount of cash and a quantity of uncut cocaine. Police theorized the massacre was drug related.

No kidding.

There was nothing about the kid I'd left in the alley. Well, there wouldn't be. The Sunday papers were already on the street when he and I encountered one another. Not that he'd be much likelier to make tomorrow's paper, or the next day's. If I'd killed him he might have earned a paragraph somewhere, but what was the news of a black youth with a pair of broken legs?

I was pondering that point when someone knocked on my door.

Funny. The maids have Sunday off, and the few visitors I get call from downstairs. I got my coat off the chair, took the .32 from the pocket. I hadn't gotten rid of it yet, or of the two knives I'd taken from my broken-legged friend. I carried the gun over to the door and asked who it was.

'Chance.'

I dropped the gun in a pocket, opened the door. 'Most people call,' I said.

'The fellow down there was reading. I didn't want to disturb him.'

'That was considerate.'

'That's my trademark.' His eyes were taking me in, appraising me. They left me to scan my room. 'Nice place,' he said.

The words were ironic but the tone of voice was not. I closed the door, pointed to a chair. He remained standing. 'It seems to suit me,' I said.

'I can see that. Spartan, uncluttered.'

He was wearing a navy blazer and gray flannel slacks. No topcoat. Well, it was a little warmer today and he had a car to get around in.

He walked over to my window, looked out of it. 'Tried you last night,' he said.

'I know.'

'You didn't call back.'

'I didn't get the message until a little while ago and I wasn't where I could be reached.'

'Didn't sleep here last night?'

'No.'

312

He nodded. He had turned to face me and his expression was guarded and hard to read. I hadn't seen that look on his face before.

He said, 'You speak to all my girls?'

'All but Sunny.'

'Yeah. You didn't see her yet, huh?'

'No. I tried her a few times last night and again around noon today. I didn't get any answer.'

'You didn't.'

'No. I had a message from her last night, but when I called back she wasn't there.'

'She called you last night.'

'That's right.'

'What time?'

I tried to remember. 'I left the hotel around eight and got back a little after ten. The message was waiting for me. I don't know what time it came in. They're supposed to put the time on the message slip but they don't always bother. Anyway, I probably threw away the slip.'

'No reason to hang onto it.'

'No. What difference does it make when she called?'

He looked at me for a long moment. I saw the gold flecks in the deep brown eyes. He said, 'Shit, I don't know what to do. I'm not used to that. Most of the time I at least *think* I know what to do.'

I didn't say anything.

'You're my man, like you're working for me. But I don't know as I'm sure what that means.'

'I don't know what you're getting at, Chance.'

'Shit,' he said. 'Question is, how much can I trust you? What I keep coming back to is whether I can or not. I *do* trust you. I mean, I took you to my *house*, man. I never took anybody else to my house. Why'd I do that?'

'I don't know.'

'I mean, was I showing off? Was I saying something along the lines of, Look at the class this here nigger has got? Or was I inviting you inside for a look at my soul? Either way, shit, I got to believe I trust you. But am I right to do it?'

'I can't decide that for you.'

'No,' he said, 'you can't.' He pinched his chin between thumb and forefinger. 'I called her last night. Sunny. Couple of times, same as you, didn't get no answer. Well, okay, that's cool. No machine, but that's cool, too, 'cause sometimes she'll forget to

put it on. Then I called again, one-thirty, two o'clock maybe, and again no answer, so what I did, I drove over there. Naturally I got a key. It's my apartment. Why shouldn't I have a key?'

By now I knew where this was going. But I let him tell it himself.

'Well, she was there,' he said. 'She's still there. See, what she is, she's dead.'

TWENTY-TWO

She was dead, all right. She lay on her back, nude, one arm flung back over her head and her face turned to that side, the other arm bent at the elbow with the hand resting on her rib cage just below her breast. She was on the floor a few feet from her unmade bed, her auburn hair spread out above and behind her head, and alongside her lipsticked mouth an ellipse of vomit floated on the ivory carpet like scum on a pond. Between her well-muscled white thighs, the carpet was dark with urine.

There were bruises on her face and forehead, another on her shoulder. I touched her wrist automatically, groping for a pulse, but her flesh was far too cold to have any life left in it.

Her eye was open, rolled up into her head. I wanted to coax the eyelid shut with a fingertip. I left it alone.

I said, 'You move her?'

'No way. I didn't touch a thing.'

'Don't lie to me. You tossed Kim's apartment after she was dead. You must have looked around.'

'I opened a couple of drawers. I didn't take anything.'

'What were you looking for?'

'I don't know, man. Just anything I ought to know about. I found some money, couple hundred dollars. I left it there. I found a bankbook. I left it, too.'

'What did she have in the bank?'

'Under a thousand. No big deal. What I found, she had a ton of pills. That's how she did this here.'

He pointed to a mirrored vanity across the room from the corpse. There, among innumerable jars and bottles of makeup and scent, were two empty plastic vials containing prescription labels. The patient's name on both was S. Hendryx, although the prescriptions had been written by different physicians and filled at different pharmacies, both nearby. One prescription had been for Valium, the other for Seconal.

'I always looked in her medicine chest,' he was saying. 'Just automatically, you know? And all she ever had was this antihistamine stuff for her hay fever. Then I open this drawer last night and it's a regular drugstore in there. All prescription stuff.'

'What kind of stuff?'

'I didn't read every label. Didn't want to leave any prints where they shouldn't be. From what I saw, it's mostly downs. A lot of tranks. Valium, Librium, Elavil. Sleeping pills like the Seconal here. A couple things of ups, like whatchacallit, Ritalin. But mostly downs.' He shook his head. 'There's things I never heard of. You'd need a doctor to tell you what everything was.'

'You didn't know she took pills?'

'Had no idea. Come here, look at this.' He opened a dresser drawer carefully so as not to leave prints. 'Look,' he said, pointing. At one side of the drawer, beside a stack of folded sweaters, stood perhaps two dozen pill bottles.

'That's somebody who's into this shit pretty heavy,' he said. 'Somebody who's scared to run out. And I didn't know about it. That gets to me, Matt. You read that note?'

The note was on the vanity, anchored with a bottle of Norell cologne. I nudged the bottle aside with the back of my hand and carried the note over to the window. She'd written it in brown ink on beige notepaper and I wanted to read it in decent light.

I read:

Kim, you were lucky. You found someone to do it for you, I have to do it myself.

If I had the guts I would use the window. I could change my mind halfway down and laugh the rest of the way. But I haven't got the guts and the razor blade didn't work.

I hope I took enough this time.
It's no use. The good times are all used up. Chance, I'm sorry. You showed me good times but they're gone. The crowds went home in the eighth inning. All the cheering stopped. Nobody's even keeping score anymore.

There's no way off the merry-go-round. She grabbed the brass ring and it turned her finger green.

Nobody's going to buy me emeralds. Nobody's going to give me babies. Nobody's going to save my life.

I'm sick of smiling. I'm tired of trying to catch up and catch on. All the good times are gone.

I looked out the window across the Hudson at the Jersey skyline. Sunny had lived and died on the thirty-second floor of a high-rise apartment complex called Lincoln View Gardens, though I hadn't seen any trace of garden beyond the potted palms in the lobby.

'That's Lincoln Center down there,' Chance said.

I nodded.

'I should have put Mary Lou here. She likes concerts, she could just walk over. Thing is, she used to live on the West Side. So I wanted to move her to the East Side. You want to do that, you know. Make a big change in their lives right away.'

I didn't much care about the philosophy of pimping. I said, 'She do this before?'

'Kill herself?'

'Try to. She wrote "I hope I took enough this time." Was there a time she didn't take enough?'

'Not since I've known her. And that's a couple years.'

'What does she mean when she says the razor blade didn't work?'

'I don't know.'

I went to her, examined the wrist of the arm stretched out above her head. There was a clearly perceptible horizontal scar. I found an identical scar on her other wrist. I stood up, read the note again.

'What happens now, man?'

I got out my notebook and copied what she'd written word for word. I used a Kleenex to remove what prints I'd left on it, then put it back where I'd found it and anchored it again with the cologne bottle.

I said, 'Tell me again what you did last night.'

'Just what I already told you. I called her and I got a feeling, I don't know why, and I came here.'

'What time?'

'After two. I didn't notice the exact time.'

'You came right upstairs?'

'That's right.'

'The doorman see you?'

'We sort of nodded at each other. He knows me, thinks I live here.'

'Will he remember you?'

317

'Man, I don't know what he remembers and what he forgets.'

'He just work weekends or was he on Friday as well?'

'I don't know. What's the difference?'

'If he's been on every night he might remember he saw you but not remember when. If he just works Saturdays –'

'I get you.'

In the small kitchen a bottle of Georgi vodka stood on the sink board with an inch's depth of liquor left in it. Beside it was an empty cardboard quart of orange juice. A glass in the sink held a residue of what looked like a mixture of the two, and there'd been a faint trace of orange in the reek of her vomit. You didn't need to be much of a detective to put those pieces together. Pills, washed down with a batch of strong screwdrivers, their sedative effect boosted by the alcohol.

I hope I took enough this time.

I had to fight the impulse to pour the last of the vodka down the drain.

'How long were you here, Chance?'

'I don't know. Didn't pay attention to the time.'

'Talk to the doorman on the way out?'

He shook his head. 'I went down to the basement and out through the garage.'

'So he wouldn't have seen you.'

'Nobody saw me.'

'And while you were here –'

'Like I said. I looked in the drawers and closets. I didn't touch many things and I didn't move anything.'

'You read the note?'

'Yeah. But I didn't pick it up to do it.'

'Make any phone calls?'

'My service, to check in. And I called you. But you weren't there.'

No, I hadn't been there. I'd been breaking a boy's legs in an alley three miles to the north.

I said, 'No long-distance calls.'

'Just those two calls, man. That ain't a long distance. You can just about throw a rock from here to your hotel.'

And I could have walked over last night, after my meeting, when her number failed to answer. Would she still have been alive by then? I imagined her, lying on the bed, waiting for the pills and vodka to do their work, letting the phone ring and ring and ring. Would she have ignored the doorbell the same way?

Maybe. Or maybe she'd have been unconscious by then. But I

might have sensed that something was wrong, might have summoned the super or kicked the door in, might have gotten to her in time –

Oh, sure. And I could have saved Cleopatra from the fucking asp, too, if I hadn't been born too late.

I said, 'You had a key to this place?'

'I have keys to all their places.'

'So you just let yourself in.'

He shook his head. 'She had the chain lock on. That's when I knew something was wrong. I used the key and the door opened two, three inches and stopped on account of the chain, and I knew there was trouble. I busted the chain and came on in and just knew I was gonna find something I didn't want to see.'

'You could have gone right out. Left the chain on, gone home.'

'I thought of that.' He looked full at me and I was seeing his face less armored than I'd seen it before. 'You know something? When that chain was on, the thought came to me right away that she killed herself. First thing I thought of, *only* thing I thought of. Reason I broke that chain, I figured maybe she was still alive, maybe I could save her. But it was too late.'

I went to the door, examined the chain lock. The chain itself had not broken; rather, the assembly had ripped loose from its moorings on the doorjamb and hung from the door itself. I hadn't noticed it when we let ourselves into the apartment.

'You broke this when you came in?'

'Like I said.'

'The chain could have been unfastened when you let yourself in. Then you could have locked it and broken it from inside.'

'Why would I do that?'

'To make it look as though the apartment was locked from the inside when you got here.'

'Well, it was. I didn't have to. I don't get where you're comin' from, man.'

'I'm just making sure she was locked in when you got here.'

'Didn't I say she was?'

'And you checked the apartment? There wasn't anybody else here?'

'Not unless they was hiding in the toaster.'

It was a pretty clear suicide. The only thing problematic was his earlier visit. He'd sat on the knowledge of her death for over twelve hours without reporting it.

I thought for a moment. We were north of Sixtieth Street, so that put us in the Twentieth Precinct and out of Durkin's

bailiwick. They'd close it as a suicide unless the medical evidence didn't match, in which case his earlier visit would come to light later on.

I said, 'There's a few ways we could do it. We could say that you couldn't reach her all night and you got worried. You talked to me this afternoon and we came over here together. You had a key. You opened the door and we found her and called it in.'

'All right.'

'But the chain lock gets in the way. If you weren't here before, how did it get broken? If somebody else broke it, who was he and what was he doing here?'

'What if we say we broke it getting in?'

I shook my head. 'That doesn't work. Suppose they come up with solid evidence that you were here last night. Then I'm caught swearing to a lie. I could lie for you to the extent of treating something you told me as confidential, but I'm not going to get nailed to a lie that cuts across the grain of the facts. No, I have to say the chain lock was broken when we got here.'

'So it's been broken for weeks.'

'Except the break's fresh. You can see where the screws came out of the wood. The one thing you don't want to do is get caught in that kind of a lie, where your story and the evidence wind up pointing in different directions. I'll tell you what I think you have to do.'

'What's that?'

'Tell the truth. You came here, you kicked the door in, she was dead and you split. You drove around, tried to sort things out in your mind. And you wanted to reach me before you did anything, and I was hard to reach. Then you called me and we came here and called it in.'

'That's the best way?'

'It looks like it to me.'

'All because of that chain thing?'

'That's the most obvious loose end. But even without the chain lock you're better off telling the truth. Look, Chance, you didn't kill her. She killed herself.'

'So?'

'If you didn't kill her, the best thing you can do is tell the truth. If you're guilty, the best thing to do is say nothing, not a word. Call a lawyer and keep your mouth shut. But anytime you're innocent, just tell the truth. It's easier, it's simpler, and it saves trying to remember what you said before. Because I'll tell you one thing. Crooks lie all the time and cops know it and they

320

hate it. And once they get hold of a lie they pull on it until something comes loose. You're looking to lie to save yourself a hassle, and it might work, it's an obvious suicide, you might get by with it, but if it doesn't work you're going to get ten times the hassle you're trying to avoid.'

He thought about it, then sighed. 'They're gonna ask why I didn't call right away.'

'Why didn't you?'

''Cause I didn't know what to do, man. I didn't know whether to shit or go blind.'

'Tell them that.'

'Yeah, I guess.'

'What did you do after you got out of here?'

'Last night? Like you said, I drove around some. Drove around the park a few times. Drove over the George Washington Bridge, up the Palisades Parkway. Like a Sunday drive, only a little early.' He shook his head at the memory. 'Came back, drove over to see Mary Lou. Let myself in, didn't have to bust no chain lock. She was sleepin'. I got in bed with her, woke her up, stayed with her a little. Then I went on home.'

'To your house?'

'To my house. I'm not gonna tell 'em about my house.'

'No need to. You got a little sleep at Mary Lou's.'

'I never sleep when someone else is around. I can't. But they don't have to know that.'

'No.'

'I was at my house for awhile. Then I came on into town, lookin' for you.'

'What did you do at your house?'

'Slept some. A couple hours. I don't need a whole lot of sleep, but I got what I needed.'

'Uh-huh.'

'And I was just there, you know?' He walked over to the wall, took a staring mask from the nail where it hung. He started telling me about it, the tribe, their geographical location, the purpose of the mask. I didn't pay much attention. 'Now I got fingerprints on it,' he said. 'Well, that's okay. You can tell 'em while we were waiting for them I took the mask off the wall and told you it's history. I might as well tell the truth. Wouldn't want to get caught in some nasty old little white lie.' He smiled at the last phrase. 'Little black lie,' he said. 'Whyn't you make that call?'

TWENTY-THREE

It wasn't half the hassle it might have been. I didn't know either of the cops who came out from the Twentieth, but it couldn't have gone much smoother if I had. We answered questions on the scene and went back to the station house on West Eighty-second to give our statements. The on-scene medical evidence all seemed to be consistent with what we'd reported. The cops were quick to point out that Chance should have called in as soon as he found the dead girl, but they didn't really jump on him for taking his time. Walking in on an unexpected corpse is a shock, even if you're a pimp and she's a whore, and this, after all, was New York, the city of the uninvolved, and what was remarkable was not that he'd called it in late but that he'd called it in at all.

I was at ease by the time we got to the station house. I'd only been anxious early on when it occurred to me that it might occur to them to frisk us. My coat was a small-time arsenal, still holding the gun and the two knives I'd taken from the kid in the alley. The knives were both illegal weapons. The gun was that and possibly more; God only knew what kind of a provenance it had. But we'd done nothing to rate a frisk, and, happily, we didn't get one.

'Whores'll kill themselves,' Joe Durkin said. 'It's something they do, and this one had a history. You saw the wrist scars? Those were a few years old, according to the report. What you might not know is she tried the pill route a little less than a year ago. A girlfriend took her over to St Clare's to get her stomach pumped.'

'There was something in the note. She hoped she had enough this time, something like that.'

'Well, she got her wish.'

We were at the Slate, a Tenth Avenue steak house that draws

a lot of cops from John Jay College and Midtown North. I'd been back at my hotel, changing my clothes, finding places to stow the weapons and some of the money I'd been carrying, when he called to suggest I buy him a dinner. 'I thought I'd hit you up for a meal now,' he said, 'before all your client's girls are dead and your expense account gets trimmed.'

He had the mixed grill and drank a couple of Carlsbergs with it. I ordered the chopped sirloin and drank black coffee with my meal. We talked a little about Sunny's suicide but it didn't carry us very far. He said, 'If it wasn't for the other one, the blonde, you wouldn't even think to look at it twice. All the medical evidence fits in with suicide. The bruises, that's easy. She was groggy, she didn't know what she was doing, she fell and bumped into things. Same reason she was on the floor instead of the bed. There was nothing special about the bruises. Her prints were where they belonged – the bottle, the glass, the pill bottles. The note matches other samples of her handwriting. If we buy your guy's story, she was even in a locked room when he found her. Locked from inside, the chain on. You figure that for the truth?'

'His whole story sounded true to me.'

'So she killed herself. It even fits with the Dakkinen death two weeks ago. They were friends and she was depressed by what happened to her friend. You see any way it was anything but suicide?'

I shook my head. 'It's the hardest kind of suicide to stage. What do you do, stuff the pills down her throat with a funnel? Make her take them at gunpoint?'

'You can dissolve the contents, let her take them without knowing it. But they found traces of the Seconal capsules in the stomach contents. So forget that. It's suicide.'

I tried to remember the annual suicide rate in the city. I couldn't even come up with an educated guess, and Durkin was no help. I wondered what the rate was, and if it was on the rise like everything else.

Over coffee he said, 'I had a couple of clerks go through the registration cards at the Galaxy Downtowner since the first of the year. Pulling the block-printed ones. Nothing ties into the Jones registration.'

'And the other hotels?'

'Nothing that fits. A batch of people called Jones, it's a common enough name, but they're all signatures and credit cards and they look bona fide. Waste of time.'

'Sorry.'

'Why? Ninety percent of what I do is a waste of time. You were right, it was worth checking. If this had been a big case, front-page stuff, top brass putting pressure on, you can believe I'd have thought of it myself and we'd be checking every hotel in the five boroughs. How about you?'

'What about me?'

'You getting anywhere with Dakkinen?'

I had to think. 'No,' I said, finally.

'It's aggravating. I went over the file again and you know what got stuck in my throat? That desk clerk.'

'The one I talked to?'

'That was a manager, assistant manager, something like that. No, the one who checked the killer in. Now here's a guy comes in, prints his name instead of writing it, and pays cash. Those are two unusual things for a person to do, right? I mean, who pays cash in front for a hotel nowadays? I don't mean in a hot-pillow joint, I mean a decent hotel where you're going to spend sixty or eighty dollars for a room. Everything's plastic nowadays, credit cards, that's the whole business. But this guy paid cash and the desk clerk doesn't remember shit about him.'

'Did you check him out?'

He nodded. 'I went and talked to him last night. Well, he's this South American kid, up from one of those countries. He was in a fog when I talked to him. He was probably in a fog when the killer checked in. He probably lives his life in a fog. I don't know where his fog comes from, whether he smokes it or snorts it or what he does, but I think he probably comes by it honestly. You know the percentage of this city that's stoned all the time?'

'I know what you mean.'

'You see 'em at lunch hour. Office workers, midtown, Wall Street, I don't care what neighborhood you're talking about. They buy the fucking joints in the street and spend their lunch hour smoking 'em in the park. How does anybody get any work done?'

'I don't know.'

'And there's all these pillheads. Like this woman who killed herself. Taking all those pills all the time, and she wasn't even breaking the law. Drugs.' He sighed, shook his head, smoothed his dark hair. 'Well, what I'm gonna have is a brandy,' he said, 'if you think your client can afford it.'

*

324

I got over to St Paul's in time for the last ten minutes of the meeting. I had coffee and a cookie and barely listened to what was being said. I didn't even have to say my name, and I ducked out during the prayer.

I went back to the hotel. There were no messages. I'd had a couple of calls, the desk man told me, but nobody'd left a name. I went upstairs and tried to sort out how I felt about Sunny's suicide, but all I seemed to feel so far was numb. It was tempting to beat myself up with the thought that I might have learned something if I hadn't saved her interrogation for last, might even have said or done something to forestall her suicide, but I couldn't get much mileage out of that one. I'd talked to her on the phone. She could have said something and she hadn't. And suicide, after all, was something she'd tried at least twice in the past, and very likely a time or two of which there'd been no record.

Try something long enough, sooner or later you get it right.

In the morning I had a light breakfast and went over to the bank, where I deposited some cash and bought a money order. I went to the post office and mailed it to Anita. I hadn't given a whole lot of thought to my son's orthodontia and now I could forget it altogether.

I walked on to St Paul's and lit a candle for Sonya Hendryx. I sat in a pew, giving myself a few minutes to remember Sunny. There wasn't much to remember. We'd barely met. I couldn't even recall very clearly what she looked like because her image in death pushed my dim memory of the living Sunny to the side.

It occurred to me that I owed the church money. Ten percent of Chance's fee came to $250, and they were further entitled to a tithe of the three hundred bucks and change I'd taken off the kid who'd tried mugging me. I didn't have an exact count but $350 struck me as a fair estimate, so I could give them $285 and call it even.

But I'd put most of my money in the bank. I had a few hundred dollars in my wallet but if I gave the church $285 I'd be strapped for walk-around money. I weighed the nuisance of another trip to the bank, and then the fundamental insanity of my little game struck me like a kidney punch.

What was I doing anyway? Why did I figure I owed anybody money? And who did I owe it to? Not the church, I didn't belong to any church. I gave my tithes to whatever house of worship came along at the right time.

To whom, then, was I in debt? To God?

Where was the sense in that? And what was the nature of this debt? How did I owe it? Was I repaying borrowed funds? Or had I invented some sort of bribe scheme, some celestial protection racket?

I'd never had trouble rationalizing it before. It was just a custom, a minor eccentricity. I didn't file a tax return so I paid a tithe instead.

I'd never really let myself ask myself why.

I wasn't sure I liked the answer. I remembered, too, a thought that had crossed my mind momentarily in that alley off St Nicholas Avenue – that I was going to get killed by this boy because I hadn't paid my tithe. Not that I'd really believed it, not that I thought the world worked that way, but how remarkable that I'd had such a thought at all.

After awhile I took out my wallet, counted out the $285. I sat there with the money in my hand. Then I put it all back in my wallet, all but a dollar.

At least I could pay for the candle.

That afternoon I walked all the way to Kim's building. The weather wasn't bad and I didn't have anything better to do. I walked past the doorman and let myself into her apartment.

The first thing I did was pour the bottle of Wild Turkey down the sink.

I don't know how much sense that made. There was plenty of other booze there and I didn't feel like doing my Carrie Nation imitation. But the Wild Turkey had taken on the status of a symbol. I pictured the bottle every time I thought of going to that apartment, and the picture was accompanied more often than not by a vivid memory of the taste and smell. When the last of it went down the sink I was able to relax.

Then I went back to the front closet and checked out the fur coat hanging there. A label sewn to the lining identified the garment as consisting of dyed lapin. I used the Yellow Pages, called a furrier at random and learned that *lapin* was the French word for 'rabbit.' 'You could find it in a dictionary,' I was told. 'A regular American dictionary. It's an English word now, it came into the language from the fur business. Plain old rabbit.'

Just as Chance had said.

On the way home something triggered the thought of having a beer. I don't even recall what the stimulus was, but the response

was a picture of myself with a shoulder pressed against a bar and one foot up on the brass rail, bell-shaped glass in hand, sawdust on the floor, my nostrils full of the smell of a musty old tavern.

It wasn't a strong drink urge and I never considered acting on it, but it put me in mind of what I'd promised Jan. Since I wasn't going to have a drink I felt no compulsion to call her but decided to anyway. I spent a dime and dialed her number from a booth around the corner from the main public library.

Our conversation had traffic noises for competition, and so we kept it brief and light. I didn't get around to telling her about Sunny's suicide. I didn't mention the bottle of Wild Turkey, either.

I read the *Post* while I ate dinner. Sunny's suicide had had a couple of paragraphs in the *News* that morning, which is as much as it merited, but the *Post* would hype anything that might sell papers, and their hook was that Sunny had the same pimp as Kim, who'd been chopped to pieces in a hotel just two weeks ago. Nobody had been able to turn up a picture of Sunny so they ran the shot of Kim again.

The story, though, couldn't fulfill the promise of the headlines. All they had was a suicide and some airy speculation that Sunny had killed herself because of what she knew about Kim's murder.

I couldn't find anything about the boy whose legs I'd broken. But there was the usual complement of crime and deaths scattered throughout the paper. I thought about what Jim Faber had said about giving up newspapers. It didn't seem like I'd be giving up all that much.

After dinner I picked up my mail at the desk. The mail was the usual junk, along with a phone message to call Chance. I called his service and he rang back to ask how things were going. I said that they weren't, really. He asked if I was going to keep at it.

'For a while,' I said. 'Just to see if it goes anywhere.'

The cops, he said, had not been hassling him. He'd spent his day arranging funeral services for Sunny. Unlike Kim, whose body had been shipped back to Wisconsin, Sunny didn't have parents or kin to claim her. There was a question about when Sunny's body would be released from the morgue, so he'd made arrangements to have a memorial service at Walter B. Cooke's on West Seventy-second Street. That would take place Thursday, he told me, at two in the afternoon.

'I should have done the same for Kim,' he said, 'but I never thought of it. It's mostly for the girls. They're in a state, you know.'

'I can imagine.'

'They're all thinking the same thing. That business about death comes in threes. They're all worrying about who's next.'

I went to my meeting that night. It struck me during the qualification that a week ago I'd been in a blackout, wandering around doing God knows what.

'My name's Matt,' I said when my turn came. 'I'll just listen tonight. Thanks.'

When the meeting broke up a guy followed me up the stairs to street level, then fell into step with me. He was about thirty, wearing a plaid lumber jacket and a peaked cap. I couldn't recall seeing him before.

He said, 'Your name is Matt, right?' I allowed that it was. 'You like that story tonight?'

'It was interesting,' I said.

'You wanna hear an interesting story? I heard a story about a man uptown with a broken face and two broken legs. That's some story, man.'

I felt a chill. The gun was in my dresser drawer, all rolled up in a pair of socks. The knives were in the same drawer.

He said, 'You got some pair of balls, man. You got *cojones*, you know what I mean?' He cupped his groin with one hand like a baseball player adjusting his jock. 'All the same,' he said, 'you don' wanna look for trouble.'

'What are you talking about?'

He spread his hands. 'What do I know? I'm Western Union, man. I bring the message, tha's all I do. Some chick gets herself iced in a hotel, man, is one thing, but who her friends are is another. Is not important, you know?'

'Who's the message from?'

He just looked at me.

'How'd you know to find me at the meeting?'

'Followed you in, followed you out.' He chuckled. 'That *maricón* with the broken legs, that was too much, man. That was too much.'

328

TWENTY-FOUR

Tuesday was largely devoted to a game of Follow the Fur.

It started in that state that lies somewhere between dreaming and full consciousness. I'd awakened from a dream and dozed off again, and I found myself running a mental videotape of my meeting with Kim at Armstrong's. I began with a false memory, seeing her as she must have been when she arrived on the bus from Chicago, a cheap suitcase in one hand, a denim jacket tight on her shoulders. Then she was sitting at my table, her hand at her throat, light glinting off her ring while she toyed with the clasp at the throat of her fur jacket. She was telling me that it was ranch mink but she'd trade it for the denim jacket she'd come to town in.

The whole sequence played itself off and my mind moved on to something else. I was back in that alley in Harlem, except now my assailant had help. Royal Waldron and the messenger from the night before were flanking him on either side. The conscious part of my mind tried to get them the hell out of there, perhaps to even the odds a little, and then a realization screamed at me and I tossed my legs over the side of my bed and sat up, the dream images all scurrying off into the corners of the mind where they live.

It was a different jacket.

I showered and shaved and got out of there. I cabbed first to Kim's building to check her closet yet again. The lapin coat, the dyed rabbit Chance had bought her, was not the garment I had seen in Armstrong's. It was longer, it was fuller, it didn't fasten with a clasp at the throat. It was not what she'd been wearing, not what she'd described as ranch mink and offered to trade for her old denim jacket.

Nor was the jacket I remembered to be found anywhere else in the apartment.

I took another cab to Midtown North. Durkin wasn't on duty.

329

I got another cop to call him at home and finally got unofficial access to the file, and yes, the inventory of impounded articles found in the room at the Galaxy Downtowner included a fur jacket. I checked the photos in the file and couldn't find the jacket in any of them.

A subway took me downtown to One Police Plaza, where I talked to some more people and waited while my request went through some channels and around others. I got to one office just after the guy I was supposed to see left for lunch. I had my meeting book with me, and it turned out there was a meeting less than a block away at St Andrew's Church, so I killed an hour there. Afterward I got a sandwich at a deli and ate it standing up.

I went back to One Police Plaza and finally got to examine the fur jacket Kim had had with her when she died. I couldn't have sworn it was the one I'd seen in Armstrong's but it seemed to match my memory. I ran my hand over the rich fur and tried to replay the tape that had run in my mind that morning. It all seemed to go together. This fur was the right length, the right color, and there was a clasp at the throat that her port-tipped fingers might have toyed with.

The label sewn to the lining told me it was genuine ranch mink and that a furrier named Arvin Tannenbaum had made it.

The Tannenbaum firm was on the third floor of a loft building on West Twenty-ninth, right in the heart of the fur district. It would have simplified things if I could have taken Kim's fur along, but NYPD cooperation, official or otherwise, only went so far. I described the jacket, which didn't help much, and I described Kim. A check of their sales records revealed the purchase of a mink jacket six weeks previously by Kim Dakkinen, and the sales slip led us to the right salesman and he remembered the sale.

The salesman was round faced and balding, with watery blue eyes behind thick lenses. He said, 'Tall girl, very pretty girl. You know, I read that name in the newspaper and it rang a bell but I couldn't think why. Terrible thing, such a pretty girl.'

She'd been with a gentleman, he recalled, and it was the gentleman who had paid for the coat. Paid cash for it, he remembered. And no, that wasn't so unusual, not in the fur business. They only did a small volume of retail sales and a lot of it was people in the garment trade or people who knew somebody in the trade, although of course anyone could walk in off the street and buy any garment in the place. But mostly it

was cash because the customer didn't usually want to wait for his check to clear, and besides a fur was often a luxury gift for a luxury friend, so to speak, and the customer was happier if no record of the transaction existed. Thus payment in cash, thus the sales slip not in the buyer's name but in Miss Dakkinen's.

The sale had come to just under twenty-five hundred dollars with the tax. A lot of cash to carry, but not unheard of. I'd been carrying almost that myself not too long ago.

Could he describe the gentleman? The salesman sighed. It was much easier, he explained, to describe the lady. He could picture her now, those gold braids wrapped around her head, the piercing blue of her eyes. She'd tried on several jackets, she looked quite elegant in fur, but the man –

Thirty-eight, forty years old, he supposed. Tall rather than short, as he remembered, but not tall as the girl had been tall.

'I'm sorry,' he said. 'I have a sense of him but I can't picture him. If he'd been wearing a fur I could tell you more than you'd want to know about it, but as it was –'

'What was he wearing?'

'A suit, I think, but I don't remember it. He was the type of man who'd wear a suit. I can't recall what he was wearing, though.'

'Would you recognize him if you saw him again?'

'I might pass him on the street and not think twice.'

'Suppose he was pointed out to you.'

'Then I would probably recognize him, yes. You mean like a lineup? Yes, I suppose so.'

I told him he probably remembered more than he thought he did. I asked him the man's profession.

'I don't even know his name. How would I know what he did for a living?'

'Your impression,' I said. 'Was he an auto mechanic? A stockbroker? A rodeo performer?'

'Oh,' he said, and thought it over. 'Maybe an accountant,' he said.

'An accountant?'

'Something like that. A tax lawyer, an accountant. This is a game, I'm just guessing, you understand that –'

'I understand. What nationality?'

'American. What do you mean?'

'English, Irish, Italian –'

'Oh,' he said. 'I see, more of the game. I would say Jewish, I would say Italian, I would say dark, Mediterranean. Because she

331

was so blonde, you know? A contrast. I don't know that he was dark, but there was a contrast. Could be Greek, could be Spanish.'

'Did he go to college?'

'He didn't show me a diploma.'

'No, but he must have talked, to you or to her. Did he sound like college or did he sound like the streets?'

'He didn't sound like the streets. He was a gentleman, an educated man.'

'Married?'

'Not to her.'

'To anybody?'

'Aren't they always? You're not married, you don't have to buy mink for your girlfriend. He probably bought another one for his wife, to keep her happy.'

'Was he wearing a wedding ring?'

'I don't remember a ring.' He touched his own gold band. 'Maybe yes, maybe no. I don't recall a ring.'

He didn't recall much, and the impressions I'd pried out of him were suspect. They might have been valid, might as easily have grown out of an unconscious desire to supply me with the answers he thought I wanted. I could have kept going – '*All right, you don't remember his shoes, but what kind of shoes would a guy like him wear? Chukka boots? Penny loafers? Cordovans? Adidas? What?*' But I'd reached and passed a point of diminishing returns. I thanked him and got out of there.

There was a coffee shop on the building's first floor, just a long counter with stools and a takeout window. I sat over coffee and tried to assess what I had.

She had a boyfriend. No question. Somebody bought her that jacket, counted out hundred dollar bills, kept his own name out of the transaction.

Did the boyfriend have a machete? There was a question I hadn't asked the fur salesman. '*All right, use your imagination. Picture this guy in a hotel room with the blonde. Let's say he wants to chop her. What does he use? An axe? A cavalry saber? A machete? Just give me your impression.*'

Sure. He was an accountant, right? He'd probably use a pen. A Pilot Razor Point, deadly as a sword in the hands of a samurai. Zip zip, take that, you bitch.

The coffee wasn't very good. I ordered a second cup anyway. I interlaced my fingers and looked down at my hands. That was

the trouble, my fingers meshed well enough but nothing else did. What kind of accountant type went batshit with a machete? Granted, anyone could explode that way, but this had been a curiously planned explosion, the hotel room rented under a false name, the murder performed with no traces left of the murderer's identity.

Did that sound like the same man who bought the fur?

I sipped my coffee and decided it didn't. Nor did the picture I got of the boyfriend jibe with the message I'd been given after last night's meeting. The fellow in the lumber jacket had been muscle, pure and simple, even if he hadn't been called upon to do anything more with that muscle than flex it. Would a mild-mannered accountant command that sort of muscle?

Not likely.

Were the boyfriend and Charles Owen Jones one and the same? And why such an elaborate alias, middle name and all? People who used a surname like Smith or Jones for an alias usually picked Joe or John to go with it. Charles Owen Jones?

Maybe his name was Charles Owens. Maybe he'd started to write that, then changed his mind in the nick of time and dropped the last letter of Owens, converting it to a middle name. Did that make sense?

I decided that it didn't.

The goddamned room clerk. It struck me that he hadn't been interrogated properly. Durkin had said he was in a fog, and evidently he was South American, possibly somewhat at a loss in English. But he'd have had to be reasonably fluent to get hired by a decent hotel for a position that put him in contact with the public. No, the problem was that nobody pushed him. If he'd been questioned the way I questioned the fur salesman, say, he'd have let go of something. Witnesses always remember more than they think they remember.

The room clerk who checked in Charles Owen Jones was named Octavio Calderón, and he'd worked last on Saturday when he was on the desk from four to midnight. Sunday afternoon he'd called in sick. There had been another call yesterday and a third call an hour or so before I got to the hotel and braced the assistant manager. Calderón was still sick. He'd be out another day, maybe longer.

I asked what was the matter with him. The assistant manager sighed and shook his head. '*I* don't know,' he said. 'It's hard to get a straight answer out of these people. When they want to

333

turn evasive their grasp of the English language weakens considerably. They slip off into the convenient little world of *No comprendo*.'

'You mean you hire room clerks who can't speak English?'

'No, no. Calderón's fluent. Someone else called in for him.' He shook his head again. 'He's a very diffident young man, 'Tavio is. I suspect he reasoned that if he had a friend make the call, I couldn't intimidate him over the phone. The implication, of course, is that he's not hale and hearty enough to get from his bed to the phone. I gather he lives in some sort of rooming house with the telephone in the hallway. Someone with a much heavier Latin accent than 'Tavio made the call.'

'Did he call yesterday?'

'Someone called for him.'

'The same person who called today?'

'I'm sure I don't know. One Hispanic voice over the phone is rather like another. It was a male voice both times. I think it was the same voice, but I couldn't swear to it. What difference does it make?'

None that I could think of. How about Sunday? Had Calderón done his own telephoning then?

'I wasn't here Sunday.'

'You have a phone number for him?'

'It rings in the hall. I doubt that he'll come to the phone.'

'I'd like the number anyway.'

He gave it to me, along with an address on Barnett Avenue in Queens. I'd never heard of Barnett Avenue and I asked the assistant manager if he knew what part of Queens Calderón lived in.

'I don't know anything about Queens,' he said. 'You're not going out there, are you?' He made it sound as though I'd need a passport, and supplies of food and water. 'Because I'm sure 'Tavio will be back on the job in a day or two.'

'What makes you so sure?'

'It's a good job,' he said. 'He'll lose it if he's not back soon. And he must know that.'

'How's his absenteeism record?'

'Excellent. And I'm sure his sickness is legitimate enough. Probably one of those viruses that runs its course in three days. There's a lot of that going around.'

I called Octavio Calderón's number from a pay phone right there in the Galaxy lobby. It rang for a long time, nine or ten rings,

before a woman answered it in Spanish. I asked for Octavio Calderón.

'*No está aquí,*' she told me.

I tried to form questions in Spanish. *Es enfermo?* Is he sick? I couldn't tell if I was making myself understood. Her replies were delivered in a Spanish that was very different in inflection from the Puerto Rican idiom I was used to hearing around New York, and when she tried to accommodate me in English her accent was heavy and her vocabulary inadequate. *No está aquí,* she kept saying, and it was the one thing she said that I understood with no difficulty. *No está aquí.* He is not here.

I went back to my hotel. I had a pocket atlas for the five boroughs in my room and I looked up Barnett Avenue in the Queens index, turned to the appropriate page and hunted until I found it. It was in Woodside. I studied the map and wondered what a Hispanic rooming house was doing in an Irish neighborhood.

Barnett Avenue extended only ten or twelve blocks, running east from Forty-third Street and ending at Woodside Avenue. I had my choice of trains. I could take either the E or F on the Independent line or the IRT Flushing Line.

Assuming I wanted to go there at all.

I called again from my room. Once again the phone rang for a long time. This time a man answered it. I said, 'Octavio Calderón, *por favor.*'

'*Momento,*' he said. Then there was a thumping sound, as if he let the receiver hang from its cord and it was knocking against the wall. Then there was no sound at all except that of a radio in the background tuned to a Latin broadcast. I was thinking about hanging up by the time he came back on the line.

'*No está aquí,*' he said, and rang off before I could say anything in any language.

I looked in the pocket atlas again and tried to think of a way to avoid a trip to Woodside. It was rush hour already. If I went now I'd have to stand up all the way out there. And what was I going to accomplish? I'd have a long ride jammed into a subway car like a sardine in a can so that someone could tell me *No está aquí* face to face. What was the point? Either he was taking a drug-assisted vacation or he was really sick, and either way I didn't stand much chance of getting anything out of him. If I actually managed to run him down, I'd be rewarded with *No lo*

335

se instead of *No está aquí*. I don't know, he's not here, I don't know, he's not here –

Shit.

Joe Durkin had done a follow-up interrogation of Calderón on Saturday night, around the time that I was passing the word to every snitch and hanger-on I could find. That same night I took a gun away from a mugger and Sunny Hendryx washed down a load of pills with vodka and orange juice.

The very next day, Calderón called in sick. And the day after that a man in a lumber jacket followed me in and out of an AA meeting and warned me off Kim Dakkinen's trail.

The phone rang. It was Chance. There'd been a message that he'd called, but evidently he'd decided not to wait for me to get back to him.

'Just checking,' he said. 'You getting anywhere?'

'I must be. Last night I got a warning.'

'What kind of a warning?'

'A guy told me not to go looking for trouble.'

'You sure it was about Kim?'

'I'm sure.'

'You know the guy?'

'No.'

'What are you fixing to do?'

I laughed. 'I'm going to go looking for trouble,' I said. 'In Woodside.'

'Woodside?'

'That's in Queens.'

'I know where Woodside is, man. What's happening in Woodside?'

I decided I didn't want to get into it. 'Probably nothing,' I said, 'and I wish I could save myself the trip, but I can't. Kim had a boyfriend.'

'In Woodside?'

'No, Woodside's something else. But it's definite she had a boyfriend. He bought her a mink jacket.'

He sighed. 'I *told* you about that. Dyed rabbit.'

'I know about the dyed rabbit. It's in her closet.'

'So?'

'She also had a short jacket, ranch mink. She was wearing it the first time I met her. She was also wearing it when she went to the Galaxy Downtowner and got killed. It's in a lockbox at One Police Plaza.'

'What's it doin' there?'

'It's evidence.'

'Of what?'

'Nobody knows. I got to it and I traced it and I talked to the man who sold it to her. She's the buyer of record, her name's on the sales slip, but there was a man with her and he counted out the money and paid for it.'

'How much?'

'Twenty-five hundred.'

He thought it over. 'Maybe she held out,' he said. 'Be easy to do, couple hundred a week, you know they hold out from time to time. I wouldn'ta missed it.'

'The man paid out the money, Chance.'

'Maybe she gave it to him to pay with. Like a woman'll slip a man money for a restaurant check, so it don't look bad.'

'How come you don't want it to be that she had a boyfriend?'

'Shit,' he said. 'I don't care about that. I want it to be whatever way it was. I just can't believe it, that's all.'

I let it go.

'Could be a trick instead of a boyfriend. Sometimes a john wants to pretend like he's a special friend, he don't have to pay, so he wants to give presents instead of cash. Maybe he was just a john and she was like hustling him for the fur.'

'Maybe.'

'You think he was a boyfriend?'

'That's what I think, yes.'

'And he killed her?'

'I don't know who killed her.'

'And whoever killed her wants you to drop the whole thing.'

'I don't know,' I said. 'Maybe the killing had nothing to do with the boyfriend. Maybe it was a psycho, the way the cops want to figure it, and maybe the boyfriend just doesn't want to get roped into any investigation.'

'He wasn't in it and he wants to stay out of it. That what you mean?'

'Something like that.'

'I don't know, man. Maybe you should let it go.'

'Drop the investigation?'

'Maybe you should. A warning, shit, you don't want to get killed over it.'

'No,' I said. 'I don't.'

'What are you gonna do, then?'

'Right now I'm going to catch a train to Queens.'

'To Woodside.'

'Right.'

'I could bring the car around. Drive you out there.'

'I don't mind the subway.'

'Be faster in the car. I could wear my little chauffeur's cap. You could sit in the back.'

'Some other time.'

'Suit yourself,' he said. 'Call me after, huh?'

'Sure.'

I wound up taking the Flushing line to a stop at Roosevelt Avenue and Fifty-second Street. The train came up out of the ground after it left Manhattan. I almost missed my stop because it was hard to tell where I was. The station signs on the elevated platforms were so disfigured with graffiti that their messages were indecipherable.

A flight of steel steps led me back down to street level. I checked my pocket atlas, got my bearings, and set out for Barnett Avenue. I hadn't walked far before I managed to figure out what a Hispanic rooming house was doing in Woodside. The neighborhood wasn't Irish anymore. There were still a few places with names like the Emerald Tavern and the Shamrock scattered in the shadow of the El, but most of the signs were Spanish and most of the markets were *bodegas* now. Posters in the window of the Tara Travel Agency offered charter flights to Bogotá and Caracas.

Octavio Calderón's rooming house was a dark two-story frame house with a front porch. There were five or six plastic lawn chairs lined up on the porch, and an upended orange crate holding magazines and newspapers. The chairs were unoccupied, which wasn't surprising. It was a little chilly for porch sitting.

I rang the doorbell. Nothing happened. I heard conversation within, and several radios playing. I rang the bell again, and a middle-aged woman, short and very stout, came to the door and opened it. '*Sí?*' she said, expectant.

'Octavio Calderón,' I said.

'*No está aquí.*'

She may have been the woman I spoke to the first time I called. It was hard to tell and I didn't care a whole lot. I stood there talking through the screen door, trying to make myself understood in a mixture of Spanish and English. After awhile she went away and came back with a tall hollow-cheeked man

338

with a severely trimmed moustache. He spoke English, and I told him that I wanted to see Calderón's room.

But Calderón wasn't there, he told me.

'*No me importa*,' I said. I wanted to see his room anyway. But there was nothing to see, he replied, mystified. Calderón was not there. What was I to gain by seeing a room?

They weren't refusing to cooperate. They weren't even particularly reluctant to cooperate. They just couldn't see the point. When it became clear that the only way to get rid of me, or at least the easiest way, was to show me to Calderón's room, that was what they did. I followed the woman down a hallway and past a kitchen to a staircase. We climbed the stairs, walked the length of another hallway. She opened a door without knocking on it, stood aside and gestured for me to enter.

There was a piece of linoleum on the floor, an old iron bedstead with the mattress stripped of linen, a chest of drawers in blonde maple, and a little writing table with a folding chair in front of it. A wing chair slipcovered in a floral print stood on the opposite side of the room near the window. There was a table lamp with a patterned paper shade on the chest of drawers, an overhead light fixture with two bare bulbs in the center of the ceiling.

And that's all there was.

'*Entiende usted ahora? No está acquí.*'

I went through the room mechanically, automatically. It could hardly have been emptier. The small closet held nothing but a couple of wire hangers. The drawers in the blonde chest and the single drawer in the writing table were utterly empty. Their corners had been wiped clean.

With the hollow-cheeked man as interpreter, I managed to question the woman. She wasn't a mine of information in any language. She didn't know when Calderón had left. Sunday or Monday, she believed. Monday she had come into his room to clean it and discovered he had removed all his possessions, leaving nothing behind. Understandably enough, she took this to mean that he was relinquishing the room. Like all of her tenants, he had paid by the week. He'd had a couple of days left before his rent was due, but evidently he had had someplace else to go, and no, it was not remarkable that he had left without telling her. Tenants did that with some frequency, even when they were not behind in their rent. She and her daughter had given the room a good cleaning, and now it was ready to be

rented to someone else. It would not be vacant long. Her rooms never stood vacant long.

Had Calderón been a good tenant. *Sí*, an excellent tenant, but she had never had trouble with her tenants. She rented only to Colombians and Panamanians and Ecuadorians and never had trouble with any of them. Sometimes they had to move suddenly because of the Immigration Service. Perhaps that was why Calderón had left so abruptly. But that was not her business. Her business was cleaning his room and renting it to someone else.

Calderón wouldn't have had trouble with Immigration, I knew. He wasn't an illegal or he wouldn't have been working at the Galaxy Downtowner. A big hotel wouldn't employ an alien without a green card.

He'd had some other reason for leaving in a hurry.

I spent about an hour interviewing other tenants. The picture of Calderón that emerged didn't help a bit. He was a quiet young man who kept to himself. His hours at work were such that he was likely to be out when the other tenants were at home. He did not, to anyone's knowledge, have a girlfriend. In the eight months that he'd lived on Barnett Avenue, he had not had a visitor of either sex, nor had he had frequent phone calls. He'd lived elsewhere in New York before moving to Barnett Avenue, but no one knew his previous address or even if it had been in Queens.

Had he used drugs? Everyone I spoke to seemed quite shocked by the suggestion. I gathered that the fat little landlady ran a tight ship. Her tenants were all regularly employed and they led respectable lives. If Calderón smoked marijuana, one of them assured me, he certainly hadn't done so in his room. Or the landlady would have detected the smell and he would have been asked to leave.

'Maybe he is homesick,' a dark-eyed young man suggested. 'Maybe he is fly back to Cartagena.'

'Is that where he came from?'

'He is Colombian. I think he say Cartagena.'

So that was what I learned in an hour, that Octavio Calderón had come from Cartagena. And nobody was too certain of that either.

TWENTY-FIVE

I called Durkin from a Dunkin' Donuts on Woodside Avenue. There was no booth, just a pay phone mounted on the wall. A few feet from me a couple of kids were playing one of those electronic games. Somebody else was listening to disco music on a satchel-sized portable radio. I cupped the telephone mouthpiece with my hand and told Durkin what I'd found out.

'I can put out a pickup order on him. Octavio Calderón, male Hispanic, early twenties. What is he, about five seven?'

'I never met him.'

'That's right, you didn't. I can check the hotel for a description. You sure he's gone, Scudder? I talked to him just a couple of days ago.'

'Saturday night.'

'I think that's right. Yeah, before the Hendryx suicide. Right.'

'That's still a suicide?'

'Any reason why it shouldn't be?'

'None that I know of. You talked to Calderón Saturday night and that's the last anybody's seen of him.'

'I have that effect on a lot of people.'

'Something spooked him. You think it was you?'

He said something but I couldn't hear it over the din. I asked him to repeat it.

'I said he didn't seem to be paying that much attention. I thought he was stoned.'

'The neighbors describe him as a pretty straight young man.'

'Yeah, a nice quiet boy. The kind that goes batshit and wipes out his family. Where are you calling from, it's noisy as hell there?'

'A donut shop on Woodside Avenue.'

'Couldn't you find a nice quiet bowling alley? What's your guess on Calderón? You figure he's dead?'

341

'He packed everything before he left his room. And some-body's been calling in sick for him. That sounds like a lot of trouble to go through if you're going to kill somebody.'

'The calling in sounds like a way to give him a head start. Let him get a few extra miles before they start the blood-hounds.'

'That's what I was thinking.'

'Maybe he went home,' Durkin said. 'They go home all the time, you know. It's a new world these days. My grandparents came over here, they never saw Ireland again outside of the annual calendar from Treaty Stone Wines & Liquors. These fucking people are on a plane to the islands once a month and they come back carrying two chickens and another fucking relative. Of course, my grandparents worked, maybe that's the difference. They didn't have welfare giving 'em a trip around the world.'

'Calderón worked.'

'Well, good for him, the little prick. Maybe what I'll check is the flights out of Kennedy the past three days. Where's he from?'

'Somebody said Cartagena.'

'What's that, a city? Or is it one of those islands?'

'I think it's a city. And it's in either Panama or Colombia or Ecuador or she wouldn't have rented him a room. I think it's Colombia.'

'The gem of the ocean. The calling in fits if he went home. He had somebody phone for him so the job'd be there when he gets back. He can't call up every afternoon from Cartagena.'

'Why'd he clear out of the room?'

'Maybe he didn't like it there. Maybe the exterminator came and knocked off all his pet cockroaches. Maybe he owed rent and he was skipping.'

'She said no. He was paid up through the week.'

He was silent a moment. Then, reluctantly, he said, 'Some-body spooked him and he ran.'

'It looks that way, doesn't it?'

'I'm afraid it does. I don't think he left the city, either. I think he moved a subway stop away, picked himself a new name, and checked into another furnished room. There's something like half a million illegals in the five boroughs. He doesn't have to be Houdini to hide where we're not gonna find him.'

'You could get lucky.'

'Always a chance. I'll check the morgue first, and then the airlines. We'll stand the best chance if he's dead or out of the country.' He laughed, and I asked what was so funny. 'If he's

dead or out of the country,' he said, 'he's not gonna be a whole lot of good to us, is he?'

The train back to Manhattan was one of the worst, its interior vandalized beyond recognition. I sat in a corner and tried to fight off a wave of despair. My life was an ice floe that had broken up at sea, with the different chunks floating off in different directions. Nothing was ever going to come together, in this case or out of it. Everything was senseless, pointless, and hopeless.

Nobody's going to buy me emeralds. Nobody's going to give me babies. Nobody's going to save my life.

All the good times are gone.

Eight million ways to die, and among them there's a wide variety suitable for the do-it-yourselfer. For all that was wrong with the subways, they still did the job when you threw yourself in front of them. And the city has no end of bridges and high windows, and stores stay open twenty-four hours a day selling razor blades and clothesline and pills.

I had a .32 in my dresser drawer, and my hotel room window was far enough from the pavement to make death a certainty. But I've never tried that sort of thing, and I've somehow always known I never will. I'm either too scared or too stubborn, or perhaps my particular despair is never as unequivocal as I think it is. Something seems to keep me going.

Of course all bets were off if I drank. I'd heard a man at a meeting who told of coming out of a blackout on the Brooklyn Bridge. He was over the railing and he had one foot in space when he came to. He retrieved the foot, climbed back over the railing, and got the hell out of there.

Suppose he'd come to a second later, with both feet in the air.

If I drank I'd feel better.

I couldn't get the thought out of my head. The worst of it was that I knew it was true. I felt horrible, and if I had a drink the feeling would go away. I'd regret it in the long run, I'd feel as bad and worse again in the long run, but so what? In the long run we're all dead.

I remembered something I'd heard at a meeting. Mary, one of the regulars at St Paul's, had said it. She was a birdlike woman with a tiny voice, always well dressed and well groomed and soft-spoken. I'd heard her qualify once, and evidently she'd been the next thing to a shopping-bag lady before she hit bottom.

One night, speaking from the floor, she'd said. 'You know, it was a revelation to me to learn that I don't have to be comfortable. Nowhere is it written that I *must* be comfortable. I always thought if I felt nervous or anxious or unhappy I had to do something about it. But I learned that's not true. Bad feelings won't kill me. Alcohol will kill me, but my feelings won't.'

The train plunged into the tunnel. As it dropped below ground level all the lights went out for a moment. Then they came back on again. I could hear Mary, pronouncing each word very precisely. I could see her, her fine-boned hands resting one on top of the other in her lap as she spoke.

Funny what comes to mind.

When I emerged from the subway station at Columbus Circle I still wanted a drink. I walked past a couple of bars and went to my meeting.

The speaker was a big beefy Irishman from Bay Ridge. He looked like a cop, and it turned out he'd been one, retiring after twenty years and currently supplementing his city pension as a security guard. Alcohol never interfered with his job or his marriage, but after a certain number of years it began to get to him physically. His capacity decreased, his hangovers worsened, and a doctor told him his liver was enlarged.

'He told me the booze was threatening my life,' he said. 'Well, I wasn't some derelict, I wasn't some degenerate drunk, I wasn't some guy who had to drink to get rid of the blues. I was just your normal happy-go-lucky guy who liked a shot an' a beer after work and a six-pack in front of the television set. So if it's gonna kill me, the hell with it, right? I walked out of that doctor's office and resolved to stop drinking. And eight years later that's just what I did.'

A drunk kept interrupting the qualification. He was a well-dressed man and he didn't seem to want to make trouble. He just seemed incapable of listening quietly, and after his fifth or sixth outburst a couple of members escorted him out and the meeting went on.

I thought how I'd come to the meeting myself in blackout. God, had I been like that?

I couldn't keep my mind on what I was hearing. I thought about Octavio Calderón and I thought about Sunny Hendryx and I thought how little I'd accomplished. I'd been just a little bit out of synch from the very beginning. I could have seen Sunny before she killed herself. She might have done it anyway,

I wasn't going to carry the weight for her self-destruction, but I could have learned something from her first.

And I could have talked to Calderón before he did his disappearing act. I'd asked for him on my first visit to the hotel, then forgot about him when he proved temporarily unavailable. Maybe I couldn't have gotten anything out of him, but at least I might have sensed that he was holding something back. But it didn't occur to me to pursue him until he'd already checked out and headed for the woods.

My timing was terrible. I was always a date late and a dollar short, and it struck me that it wasn't just this one case. It was the story of my life.

Poor me, poor me, pour me a drink.

During the discussion, a woman named Grace got a round of applause when she said it was her second anniversary. I clapped for her, and when the applause died down I counted up and realized today was my seventh day. If I went to bed sober, I'd have seven days.

How far did I get before my last drink? Eight days?

Maybe I could break that record. Or maybe I couldn't, maybe I'd drink tomorrow.

Not tonight, though. I was all right for tonight. I didn't feel any better than I'd felt before the meeting. My opinion of myself was certainly no higher. All the numbers on the scorecard were the same, but earlier they'd added up to a drink and now they didn't.

I didn't know why that was. But I knew I was safe.

TWENTY-SIX

There was a message at the desk to call Danny Boy Bell. I dialed the number on the slip and the man who answered said, 'Poogan's Pub.' I asked for Danny Boy and waited until he came on the line.

He said, 'Matt, I think you should come up and let me buy you a ginger ale. That's what I think you should do.'

'Now?'

'What better time?'

I was almost out of the door when I turned, went upstairs, and got the .32 out of my dresser. I didn't really think Danny Boy would set me up but I didn't want to bet my life that he wouldn't. Either way, you never knew who might be drinking in Poogan's.

I'd received a warning last night and I'd spent the intervening hours disregarding it. And the clerk who gave me Danny Boy's message had volunteered that I'd had a couple of other calls from people who'd declined to leave their names. They might have been friends of the chap in the lumber jacket, calling to offer a word to the wise.

I dropped the gun into a pocket, went out and hailed a cab.

Danny Boy insisted on buying the drinks, vodka for himself, ginger ale for me. He looked as natty as ever, and he'd been to the barber since I last saw him. His cap of tight white curls was closer to his scalp, and his manicured nails showed a coating of clear polish.

He said, 'I've got two things for you. A message and an opinion.'

'Oh?'

'The message first. It's a warning.'

'I thought it might be.'

'You should forget about the Dakkinen girl.'

'Or what?'

'Or what? Or else, I suppose. Or you get what she got, something like that. You want a specific warning so you can decide whether it's worth it or not?'

'Who's the warning come from, Danny?'

'I don't know.'

'What spoke to you? A burning bush?'

He drank off some of his vodka. 'Somebody talked to somebody who talked to somebody who talked to me.'

'That's pretty roundabout.'

'Isn't it? I could give you the person who talked to me, but I won't, because I don't do that. And even if I did it wouldn't do you any good, because you probably couldn't find him, and if you did he still wouldn't talk to you, and meanwhile somebody's probably going to whack you out. You want another ginger ale?'

'I've still got most of this one.'

'So you do. I *don't* know who the warning's from, Matt, but from the messenger they used I'd guess it's some very heavy types. And what's interesting is I get absolutely nowhere trying to find anybody who saw Dakkinen on the town with anybody but our friend Chance. Now if she's going with somebody with all this firepower, you'd think he'd show her around, wouldn't you? Why not?'

I nodded. For that matter, why would she need me to ease her out of Chance's string?

'Anyway,' he was saying, 'that's the message. You want the opinion?'

'Sure.'

'The opinion is I think you should heed the message. Either I'm getting old in a hurry or this town's gotten nastier in the past couple of years. People seem to pull the trigger a lot quicker than they used to. They used to need more of a reason to kill. You know what I mean?'

'Yes.'

'Now they'll do it unless they've got a reason not to. They'll sooner kill than not. It's an automatic response. I'll tell you, it scares me.'

'It scares everybody.'

'You had a little scene uptown a few nights back, didn't you? Or was somebody making up stories?'

'What did you hear?'

'Just that a brother jumped you in the alley and wound up with multiple fractures.'

'News travels.'

'It does for a fact. Of course there's more dangerous things in this city than a young punk on angel dust.'

'Is that what he was on?'

'Aren't they all? I don't know. I stick to basics, myself.' He underscored the line with a sip of his vodka. 'About Dakkinen,' he said. 'I could pass a message back up the line.'

'What kind of message?'

'That you're letting it lay.'

'That might not be true, Danny Boy.'

'Matt –'

'You remember Jack Benny?'

'Do I remember Jack Benny? Of course I remember Jack Benny.'

'Remember that bit with the stickup man? The guy says, "Your money or your life," and there's a long pause, a really long pause, and Benny says, "I'm thinking it over."'

'That's the answer? You're thinking it over?'

'That's the answer.'

Outside on Seventy-second Street I stood in the shadows in the doorway of a stationery store, waiting to see if anyone would follow me out of Poogan's. I stood there for a full five minutes and thought about what Danny Boy had said. A couple of people left Poogan's while I was standing there but they didn't look like anything I had to worry about.

I went to the curb to hail a cab, then decided I might as well walk half a block to Columbus and get one going in the right direction. By the time I got to the corner I decided it was a nice night and I was in no hurry, and an easy stroll fifteen blocks down Columbus Avenue would probably do me good, make sleep come that much easier. I crossed the street and headed downtown and before I'd covered a block I noticed that my hand was in my coat pocket and I was holding onto the little gun.

Funny. No one had followed me. What the hell was I afraid of? Just something in the air.

I kept walking, displaying all the street smarts I hadn't shown Saturday night. I stayed at the edge of the sidewalk near the curb, keeping my distance from buildings and doorways. I looked left and right, and now and then I turned to see if anyone

was moving up behind me. And I went on clutching the gun, my finger resting lightly alongside the trigger.

I crossed Broadway, walked on past Lincoln Center and O'Neal's. I was on the dark block between Sixtieth and Sixty-first, across the street from Fordham, when I heard the car behind me and spun around. It was slanting across the wide avenue toward me and had cut off a cab. Maybe it was his brakes I heard, maybe that's what made me turn.

I threw myself down on the pavement, rolled away from the street toward the buildings, came up with the .32 in my hand. The car was even with me now, its wheels straightened out. I'd thought it was going to vault the curb but it wasn't. And the windows were open and someone was leaning out the rear window, looking my way, and he had something in his hand –

I had the gun pointed at him. I was prone, elbows braced in front of me, holding the gun in both hands. I had my finger on the trigger.

The man leaning out the window threw something, tossed it underhand. I thought, *Jesus, a bomb,* and I aimed at him and felt the trigger beneath my finger, felt it tremble like some little live thing, and I froze, I froze, I couldn't pull the fucking trigger.

Time froze, too, like a stop-frame sequence in a film. Eight or ten yards from me a bottle struck the brick wall of a building and smashed. There was no explosion beyond the shattering of the glass. It was just an empty bottle.

And the car was just a car. I watched now as it went on careening south on Ninth Avenue, six kids in it, six drunken kids, and they might well kill somebody, they were drunk enough to do it, but when they did it would be an accident. They weren't professional killers, hitmen dispatched to murder me. They were just a bunch of kids who'd had more to drink than they could handle. Maybe they'd cripple someone, maybe they'd total their car, maybe they'd make it home without bending a fender.

I got up slowly, looked at the gun in my hand. Thank God I hadn't fired it. I could have shot them, I could have killed them.

God knows I'd wanted to. I'd *tried* to, thinking logically enough that they were trying to kill me.

But I'd been unable to do it. And if it *had* been pros, if the object I'd seen had been not a whiskey bottle but the gun or bomb I'd thought it was, I'd have been no more able to pull the trigger. They'd have killed me and I'd have died with an unfired revolver in my hands.

Jesus.

I dropped the useless gun in my pocket. I held out my hand, surprised that it wasn't shaking. I didn't even feel particularly shaky inside, and I was damned if I could figure out why not.

I went over to examine the broken bottle, if only to make sure it was just that and not a Molotov cocktail that had providentially failed to ignite. But there was no puddle, no reek of gasoline. There was a slight whiskey smell, unless I imagined it, and a label attached to one chunk of glass indicated that the bottle had contained J & B Scotch. Other fragments of green glass sparkled like jewels in the light of the streetlamp.

I bent over and picked up a little cube of glass. I placed it in the palm of my hand and stared at it like a gypsy at a crystal. I thought of Donna's poem and Sunny's note and my own slip of the tongue.

I started walking. It was all I could do to keep from running.

TWENTY-SEVEN

'**J**esus, I need a shave,' Durkin said. He'd just dropped what was left of his cigarette into what was left of his coffee, and he was running one hand over his cheek, feeling the stubble. 'I need a shave, I need a shower, I need a drink. Not necessarily in that order. I put out an APB on your little Colombian friend. Octavio Ignacio Calderón y La Barra. Name's longer'n he is. I checked the morgue. They haven't got him down there in a drawer. Not yet, anyway.'

He opened his top desk drawer, withdrew a metal shaving mirror and a cordless electric shaver. He leaned the mirror against his empty coffee cup, positioned his face in front of it and began shaving. Over the whirr of the shaver he said, 'I don't see anything in her file about a ring.'

'Mind if I look?'

'Be my guest.'

I studied the inventory sheet, knowing the ring wouldn't be on it. Then I went over the photographs of the death scene. I tried to look only at her hands. I looked at every picture, and in none of them could I spot anything that suggested she was wearing a ring.

I said as much to Durkin. He switched off the shaver, reached for the photographs, went through them carefully and deliberately. 'It's hard to see her hands in some of these,' he complained. 'All right, there's definitely no ring on that hand. What's that, the left hand? No ring on the left hand. Now in this shot, okay, definitely no ring on that hand. Wait a minute. Shit, that's the left hand again. It's not clear in this one. Okay, here we go. That's definitely her right hand and there's no ring on it.' He gathered the photos together like cards to be shuffled and dealt. 'No ring,' he said. 'What's that prove?'

'She had a ring when I saw her. Both times I saw her.'

'And?'

351

'And it disappeared. It's not at her apartment. There's a ring in her jewelry box, a high school class ring, but that's not what I remember seeing on her hand.'

'Maybe your memory's false.'

I shook my head. 'The class ring doesn't even have a stone. I went over there before I came here, just to check my memory. It's one of those klutzy school rings with too much lettering on it. It's not what she was wearing. She wouldn't have worn it, not with this mink and the wine-colored nails.'

I wasn't the only one who'd said so. After my little epiphany with the bit of broken glass, I'd gone straight to Kim's apartment, then used her phone to call Donna Campion. 'It's Matt Scudder,' I said. 'I know it's late, but I wanted to ask you about a line in your poem.'

She'd said, 'What line? What poem?'

'Your poem about Kim. You gave me a copy.'

'Oh, yes. Just give me a moment, will you? I'm not completely awake.'

'I'm sorry to call so late, but –'

'That's all right. What was the line?'

'Shatter/Wine bottles at her feet, let green glass/Sparkle upon her hand.'

'*Sparkle*'s wrong.'

'I've got the poem right here, it says –'

'Oh, I know that's what I wrote,' she said, 'but it's wrong. I'll have to change it. I *think*. What about the line?'

'Where did you get the green glass from?'

'From the shattered wine bottles.'

'Why green glass on her hand? What's it a reference to?'

'Oh,' she said. 'Oh, I see what you mean. Her ring.'

'She had a ring with a green stone, didn't she?'

'That's right.'

'How long did she have it?'

'I don't know.' She thought it over. 'The first time I saw it was just before I wrote the poem.'

'You're sure of that?'

'At least that's the first time I noticed it. It gave me a handle on the poem, as a matter of fact. The contrast of the blue of her eyes and the green of the ring, but then I lost the blue when I got working on the poem.'

She'd told me something along those lines when she first showed me the poem. I hadn't known then what she was talking about.

352

She wasn't sure when that might have been. How long had she been working on one or another version of the poem? Since a month before Kim's murder? Two months?

'I don't know,' she said. 'I have trouble placing events in time. I don't tend to keep track.'

'But it was a ring with a green stone.'

'Oh, yes. I can picture it now.'

'Do you know where she got it? Who gave it to her?'

'I don't know anything about it,' she said. 'Maybe –'

'Yes?'

'Maybe she shattered a wine bottle.'

To Durkin I said, 'A friend of Kim's wrote a poem and mentioned the ring. And there's Sunny Hendryx's suicide note.' I got out my notebook, flipped it open. I read, '"There's no way off the merry-go-round. She grabbed the brass ring and it turned her finger green. Nobody's going to buy me emeralds."'

He took the book from me. '*She* meaning Dakkinen, I suppose,' he said. 'There's more here. "Nobody's going to give me babies. Nobody's going to save my life." Dakkinen wasn't pregnant and neither was Hendryx, so what's this shit about babies? And neither one of them had her life saved.' He closed the book with a snap, handed it across the desk to me. 'I don't know where you can go with this,' he said. 'It doesn't look to me like something you can take to the bank. Who knows when Hendryx wrote this? Maybe after the booze and the pills started working, and who can say where she was coming from?'

Behind us, two men in plainclothes were putting a young white kid in the holding cage. A desk away, a sullen black woman was answering questions. I picked up the top photo on the stack and looked at Kim Dakkinen's butchered body. Durkin switched on the razor and finished shaving.

'What I don't understand,' he said, 'is what you think you got. You think she had a boyfriend and the boyfriend gave her the ring. Okay. You also figured she had a boyfriend and he gave her the fur jacket, and you traced that and it looks as though you were right, but the jacket won't lead to the boyfriend because he kept his name out of it. If you can't trace him with a jacket that we've got, how can you trace him with a ring that all we know about it is it's missing? You see what I mean?'

'I see what you mean.'

'That Sherlock Holmes thing, the dog that didn't bark, well what you got is a ring that isn't there, and what does it prove?'

353

'It's gone.'

'Right.'

'Where'd it go?'

'Same place a bathtub ring goes. Down the fucking drain. How do I know where it went?'

'It disappeared.'

'So? Either it walked away or someone took it.'

'Who?'

'How do I know who?'

'Let's say she wore it to the hotel where she was killed.'

'You can't know that.'

'Let's just say so, all right?'

'Okay, run with it.'

'Who took it? Some cop yank it off her finger?'

'No,' he said. 'Nobody'd do that. There's people who'll take cash if it's loose, we both know that, but a ring off a murder victim's finger?' He shook his head. 'Besides, nobody was alone with her. It's something nobody'd do with somebody else watching.'

'How about the maid? The one who discovered the body?'

'Jesus, no way. I questioned the poor woman. She took one look at the body and started screaming and she'd still be screaming now if she had the breath left. You couldn'ta got her close enough to Dakkinen to touch her with a mop handle.'

'Who took the ring?'

'Assuming she wore it there –'

'Right.'

'So the killer took it.'

'Why?'

'Maybe he's queer for jewelry. Maybe green's his favorite color.'

'Keep going.'

'Maybe it's valuable. You got a guy who goes around killing people, his morals aren't the best. He might not draw the line at stealing.'

'He left a few hundred dollars in her purse, Joe.'

'Maybe he didn't have time to go through her bag.'

'He had time to take a shower, for Christ's sake. He had time to go through her bag. In fact, we don't know that he didn't go through her bag. We just know he didn't take the money.'

'So?'

'But he took the ring. He had time to take hold of her bloody hand and tug it off her finger.'

'Maybe it came off easy. Maybe it wasn't a snug fit.'

'Why'd he take it?'

'He wanted it for his sister.'

'Got any better reasons?'

'No,' he said. 'No, goddamn it, I don't have any better reasons. What are you getting at? He took it because it could be traced to him?'

'Why not?'

'Then why didn't he take the fur? We fucking *know* a boyfriend bought her the fur. Maybe he didn't use his name, but how can he be sure of what he let slip and what the salesman remembers? He took towels, for Christ's sake, so he wouldn't leave a fucking pubic hair behind, but he left the fur. And now you say he took the ring. Where did this ring come from besides left field? Why have I got to hear about this ring tonight when I never heard of it once in the past two and a half weeks?'

I didn't say anything. He picked up his cigarettes, offered me one. I shook my head. He took one for himself and lit it. He took a drag, blew out a column of smoke, then ran a hand over his head, smoothing down the dark hair that already lay flat upon his scalp.

He said, 'Could be there was some engraving. People do that with rings, engraving on the inside. To Kim from Freddie, some shit like that. You think that's it?'

'I don't know.'

'You got a theory?'

I remembered what Danny Boy Bell had said. If the boyfriend commanded such muscle, was so well connected, how come he hadn't shown her off? And if it was someone else with the muscle and the connections and the insufficient words to the wise, how did that someone else fit in with the boyfriend? Who was this accountant type who paid for her mink, and why wasn't I getting a smell of him from anywhere else?

And why did the killer take the ring?

I reached into my pocket. My fingers touched the gun, felt its cool metal, slipped beneath it to find the little cube of broken green glass that had started all of this. I took it from my pocket and looked at it, and Durkin asked me what it was.

'Green glass,' I said.

'Like the ring.'

I nodded. He took the piece of glass from me, held it to the light, dropped it back in my palm. 'We don't know she wore the

355

ring to the hotel,' he reminded me. 'We just said so for the sake of argument.'

'I know.'

'Maybe she left it at the apartment. Maybe someone took it from there.'

'Who?'

'The boyfriend. Let's say he didn't kill her, let's say it was an EDP like I said from the beginning –'

'You really use that expression?'

'You get so you use the expressions they want you to use, you know how it works. Let's say the psycho killed her and the boyfriend's worried he'll be tied into it. So he goes to the apartment, he's got a key, and he takes the ring. Maybe he bought her other presents and he took them, too. He would've taken the fur, too, but it was in the hotel. Why isn't that theory just as good as the killer yanking the ring off her finger?'

Because it wasn't a psycho, I thought. Because a psycho killer wouldn't be sending men in lumber jackets to warn me off, wouldn't be passing messages to me through Danny Boy Bell. Because a psycho wouldn't have worried about handwriting or fingerprints or towels.

Unless he was some sort of Jack the Ripper type, a psycho who planned and took precautions. But that wasn't it, that couldn't be it, and the ring had to be significant. I dropped the piece of glass back into my pocket. It meant something, it had to mean something.

Durkin's phone rang. He picked it up, said 'Joe Durkin' and 'Yeah, right, right.' He listened, grunting acknowledgment from time to time, darting a pointed look in my direction, making notes on a memo pad.

I went over to the coffee machine and got us both coffee. I couldn't remember what he took in his coffee, then remembered how bad the coffee was out of that machine and added cream and sugar to both cups.

He was still on the phone when I got back to the desk. He took the coffee, nodded his thanks, sipped it, lit a fresh cigarette to go with it. I drank some of my own coffee and made my way through Kim's file, hoping something I saw might bridge a gap for me. I thought of my conversation with Donna. What was wrong with the word *sparkle?* Hadn't the ring sparkled on Kim's finger? I remembered how it had looked with the light striking it. Or was I just fabricating the memory to reinforce my own theory? And did I even have a theory? I had a missing ring and

no hard evidence that the ring had even existed. A poem, a suicide note, and my own remark about eight million stories in the Emerald City. Had the ring triggered that subconsciously? Or was I just identifying with the crew on the Yellow Brick Road, wishing I had a brain and a heart and a dose of courage?

Durkin said, 'Yeah, it's a pisser, all right. Don't go 'way, okay? I'll be right out.'

He hung up, looked at me. His expression was a curious one, self-satisfaction mixed with something that might have been pity.

He said, 'The Powhattan Motel, you know where Queens Boulevard cuts the Long Island Expressway? It's just past the intersection. I don't know just where, Elmhurst or Rego Park. Right about where they run into each other.'

'So?'

'One of those adult motels, waterbeds in some of the rooms, X-rated movies on the teevee. They get cheaters, the hot-sheet trade, take a room for two hours. They'll turn a room five, six times a night if they get the volume, and a lot of it's cash, they can skim it. Very profitable, motels like that.'

'What's the point?'

'Guy drove up, rented a room a couple of hours ago. Well, that business, you make up the room soon as the customer leaves it. Manager noticed the car was gone, went to the room. Do Not Disturb sign hanging on the door. He knocks, no answer, he knocks again, still no answer. He opens the door and guess what he finds?'

I waited.

'Cop named Lennie Garfein responded to the call, first thing that struck him was the similarity to what we had at the Galaxy Downtowner. That was him on the phone. We won't know until we get the medical evidence, direction of thrust, nature of wounds, all that, but it sure as hell sounds identical. Killer even took a shower, took the towels with him when he left.'

'Was it –'

'Was it what?'

It wasn't Donna. I'd just spoken to her. Fran, Ruby, Mary Lou –

'Was it one of Chance's women?'

'Hell,' he said, 'how do I know who Chance's women are? You think all I do is keep tabs on pimps?'

'Who was it?'

'Not one of anybody's women,' he said. He crushed out his

357

cigarette, started to help himself to a fresh one, changed his mind and pushed it back into the pack. 'Not a woman,' he said.

'Not –'

'Not who?'

'Not Calderón. Octavio Calderón, the room clerk.'

He let out a bark of laughter. 'Jesus, what a mind you got,' he said. 'You really want things to make sense. No, not a woman, and not your boy Calderón either. This was a transsexual hooker off the Long Island City stroll. Preoperative, from what Garfein said. Means the tits are there, the silicone implants, but she's still got her male genitals. You hear me? *Her* male genitals. Jesus, what a world. Of course maybe she got the operation tonight. Maybe that was surgery there, with a machete.'

I couldn't react. I sat there, numb. Durkin got to his feet, put a hand on my shoulder. 'I got a car downstairs. I'm gonna run out there, take a look at what they got. You want to tag along?'

TWENTY-EIGHT

The body was still there, sprawled full-length on the king-size bed. It had bled white, leaving the skin with the translucence of old china. Only the genitalia, hacked almost beyond recognition, identified the victim as male. The face was that of a woman. So was the smooth and hairless skin, the slender but full-breasted body.

'She'd fool you,' Garfein said. 'See, she had the preliminary surgery. The breast implants, the Adam's apple, the cheekbones. And of course the hormone shots all along. That keeps down the beard and the body hair, makes the skin nice and feminine. Look at the wound in the left breast there. You can see the silicone sac. See?'

Blood all over, and the smell of fresh death in the air. Not the stale reek of a late-found corpse, not the stench of decomposition, but the horrible odor of a slaughterhouse, the raw throat-catching smell of fresh blood. I felt not so much nauseated as overpowered, oppressed by the warmth and density of the air.

'What was lucky is I recognized her,' Garfein was saying. 'That way I knew right off she was a pross and that made the connection in my mind with that case of yours, Joe. Was the one you caught as bloody as this?'

'Same thing,' Durkin said.

I said, 'You recognized her?'

'Oh, right away. I did a hitch not that long ago with the Pussy Posse over in Long Island City. They still got a stroll there, they've had street prostitution in that same location for forty or fifty years, but now you're getting a lot of middle-class people moving in there, converting lofts for residential use, buying up the old brownstones and converting them back from rooming houses to nice homes. They sign the lease in the daytime and then they move in and they look at what's around them and they aren't happy, and the pressure comes down to clean up the

street.' He pointed at the figure on the bed. 'I must have arrested her, oh, say three times.'

'You know her name?'

'Which name do you want? They've all got more than one. Her street name was Cookie. That was the name that came to me when I saw her. Then I called in to the station house at Fiftieth and Vernon and had somebody pull her file. She was calling herself Sara but back when she made her bar mitzvah the name they wrote down was Mark Blaustein.'

'She had a bar mitzvah?'

'Who knows? I wasn't invited. But she's a nice Jewish girl from Floral Park is the point I'm making. A nice Jewish girl who used to be a nice Jewish boy.'

'Sara Blaustein?'

'Sara Bluestone a/k/a Sara Blue. A/k/a Cookie. Notice the hands and feet? They're on the large side for a girl. That's one way you can tell a transsexual. Of course it's not foolproof, you get girls with big hands and boys with small ones. She'd fool you, wouldn't she?'

I nodded.

'She would have had the rest of the surgery soon. Probably already had herself scheduled for the operation. Law says they have to live as a woman for a year before Medicaid'll pick up the tab. Of course they all got Medicaid, they all got welfare. They'll turn ten or twenty tricks a night, all quickie blow jobs in the john's cars for ten or twenty bucks a pop, they'll bring in a couple of hundred dollars a night seven nights a week, all of it tax free, and they got Medicaid and welfare and the ones with kids get ADC and half the pimps are on SSI.'

He and Durkin batted that ball around a little. Meanwhile the technical people were busy around us, measuring things, taking photographs, dusting for prints. We got out of their way and stood together in the motel parking lot.

Durkin said, 'You know what we got, don't you? We got us Jack the fucking Ripper.'

'I know it,' Garfein said.

'You get anything with the other guests? She musta made some noise.'

'You kidding? Cheaters? "I didn't see nothin', I didn't hear nothin', I gotta go now." Even if she did some screaming, in a job like this everybody'd figure it was a new way to have fun. Assuming they weren't too busy having their own fun to notice.'

'First he checks into a decent midtown hotel and phones up a

fancy call girl. Then he picks up a TV streetwalker and drags her to a cheater's motel. You figure the cock and balls came as a shock to him?'

Garfein shrugged. 'Maybe. You know, half your street prostitutes are guys in drag. Some sections it's more than half.'

'The West Side docks it's a lot more than half.'

'I've heard that,' Garfein said. 'You talk to the johns, some of 'em'll admit they prefer if it's a guy. They say a guy gives better head. Of course there's nothing queer about them, see, because they're just receiving it.'

'Well, go figure a john,' Durkin said.

'Whether he knew or not, I don't think it put him off much. He went and did his number all the same.'

'Figure he had sex with her?'

'Hard to tell unless there's traces on the sheets. He doesn't figure as her first trick of the evening.'

'He took a shower?'

Garfein shrugged, showed his hands palms up. 'Don't know,' he said. 'The manager says there's towels missing. When they make up the room they put out two bath towels and two hand towels, and both of the bath towels are missing.'

'He took towels from the Galaxy.'

'Then he probably took 'em here, but who knows in a dump like this? I mean who knows if they always remember to make up the room right. Same with the shower. I don't figure they gave it a scrub after the last party left.'

'Maybe you'll find something.'

'Maybe.'

'Fingerprints, something. You see any skin under her nails?'

'No. But that's not to say the lab boys won't.' A muscle worked in his jaw. 'I'll say one thing. Thank God I'm not a medical examiner or a technician. It's bad enough being a cop.'

'Amen to that,' Durkin said.

I said, 'If he picked her up on the street, somebody might have seen her get into the car.'

'A couple of guys are out there now trying to take statements. We might get something. If anybody saw anything, and if they remember, and if they feel like talking.'

'Lots of ifs,' Durkin said.

'The manager here must have seen him,' I said. 'What does he remember?'

'Not a whole lot. Let's go talk to him some more.'

*

361

The manager had a night worker's sallow complexion and a pair of red-rimmed eyes. There was alcohol on his breath but he didn't have a drinker's way about him, and I guessed he'd tried to fortify himself with liquor after discovering the body. It only made him vague and ineffectual. 'This is a decent place,' he insisted, and the statement was so palpably absurd no one responded to it. I suppose he meant murder wasn't a daily occurrence.

He never saw Cookie. The man who had presumably killed her had come in alone, filled out the card, paid cash. This was not unusual. It was common practice for the woman to wait in the car while the man checked in. The car had not stopped directly in front of the office, so he hadn't seen it while the man was checking in. In fact he hadn't really seen the car at all.

'You saw it was missing,' Garfein reminded him. 'That's how you knew the room was empty.'

'Except it wasn't. I opened the door and –'

'You thought it was empty because the car was gone. How'd you know it was gone if you never saw it?'

'The parking space was empty. There's a space in front of each unit, the spaces are numbered same as the units. I looked out, that space was empty, that meant his car was gone.'

'They always park in the proper spaces?'

'They're supposed to.'

'Lots of things people are supposed to do. Pay their taxes, don't spit on the sidewalk, cross only at corners. A guy's in a hurry to dip his wick, what does he care about a number on a parking space? You got a look at the car.'

'I –'

'You looked once, maybe twice, and the car was parked in the space. Then you looked later and it wasn't and that's when you decided they were gone. Isn't that what happened?'

'I guess so.'

'Describe the car.'

'I didn't really look at it. I looked to see that it was there, that's all.'

'What color was it?'

'Dark.'

'Terrific. Two door? Four door?'

'I didn't notice.'

'New? Old? What make?'

'It was a late-model car,' he said. 'American. Not a foreign car.

362

As far as the make, when I was a kid they all looked different. Now every car's the same.'

'He's right,' Durkin said.

'Except American Motors,' he said. 'A Gremlin, a Pacer, those you can tell. The rest all look the same.'

'And this wasn't a Gremlin or a Pacer.'

'No.'

'Was it a sedan? A hatchback?'

'I'll tell you the truth,' the man said. 'All I noticed is it was a car. It says on the card, the make and model, the plate number.'

'You're talking about the registration card?'

'Yeah. They have to fill all that in.'

The card was on the desk, a sheet of clear acetate over it to preserve prints until the lab boys had their shot at it. *Name: Martin Albert Ricone. Address:* 211 Gilford Way. City: Fort Smith, Arkansas. Make of Auto: Chevrolet. Year: 1980. *Model: Sedan. Color: Black. License No.: LJK-914. Signature: M. A. RICONE.*

'Looks like the same hand,' I told Durkin. 'But who can tell with printing?'

'The experts can say. Same as they can tell you if he had the same light touch with the machete. Guy likes forts, you notice? Fort Wayne, Indiana and Fort Smith, Arkansas.'

'A subtle pattern begins to emerge,' Garfein said.

'Ricone,' Durkin said. 'Must be Italian.'

'M. A. Ricone sounds like the guy who invented the radio.'

'That's Marconi,' Durkin said.

'Well, that's close. This guy's Macaroni. Stuck a feather in his hat and called it Macaroni.'

'Stuck a feather up his ass,' Durkin said.

'Maybe he stuck it up Cookie's ass and maybe it wasn't a feather. Martin Albert Ricone, that's a fancy alias. What did he use last time?'

'Charles Owen Jones,' I said.

'Oh, he likes middle names. He's a cute fucker, isn't he?'

'Very cute,' Durkin said.

'The cute ones, the really cute ones, usually everything means something. Like *Jones* is slang, it means a habit. You know, like a heroin jones. Like a junkie says he's got a hundred-dollar jones, that's what his habit costs him per day.'

'I'm really glad you explained that for me,' Durkin said.

'Just trying to be helpful.'

"Cause I only got fourteen years in, I never had any contact yet with smack addicts.'

'So be a smart fuck,' Garfein said.

'The license plate go anywhere?'

'It's gonna go the same place as the name and address. I got a call in to Arkansas Motor Vehicles but it's a waste of time. A place like this, even the legitimate guests make up the plate number. They don't park in front of the window when they sign in so our guy here can't check. Not that he would anyway, would you?'

'There's no law says I have to check,' the man said.

'They use false names, too. Funny our boy used Jones at the Galaxy and Ricone here. They must get a lot of Joneses here, along with the usual run of Smiths and Browns. You get a lot of Smiths?'

'There's no law says I'm supposed to check ID,' the man said.

'Or wedding rings, huh?'

'Or wedding rings or marriage licenses or anything. Consenting adults, the hell, it's none of my business.'

'Maybe Ricone means something in Italian,' Garfein suggested.

'Now you're thinking,' Durkin said. He asked the manager if he had an Italian dictionary. The man stared at him, baffled. 'And they call this place a motel,' he said, shaking his head. 'There's probably no Gideon Bibles, either.'

'Most of the rooms have them.'

'Jesus, really? Right next to the television with the X-rated movies, right? Conveniently located near the waterbed.'

'Only two of the units have waterbeds,' the poor bastard said. 'There's an extra charge for a waterbed.'

'Good thing our Mr Ricone's a cheap prick,' Garfein said. 'Cookie'da wound up underwater.'

'Tell me about this guy,' Durkin said. 'Describe him again.'

'I told you –'

'You're gonna get to tell this again and again. How tall was he?'

'Tall.'

'My height? Shorter? Taller?'

'I –'

'What was he wearing? He have a hat on? He wearing a tie?'

'It's hard to remember.'

'He walks in the door, asks you for a room. Now he's filling

364

out the card. Pays you in cash. What do you get for a room like that, incidentally?'

'Twenty-eight dollars.'

'That's not such a bad deal. I suppose the porn movies are extra.'

'It's coin-operated.'

'Handy. Twenty-eight's fair, and it's a good deal for you if you can flip the room a few times a night. How'd he pay you?'

'I told you. Cash.'

'I mean what kind of bills? What'd he give you, a pair of fifteens?'

'A pair of –'

'He give you a twenty and a ten?'

'I think it was two twenties.'

'And you gave him twelve bucks back? Wait, there must have been tax, right?'

'It's twenty-nine forty with the tax.'

'And he gave you forty bucks and you gave him the change.'

Something registered. 'He gave me two twenties and forty cents in change,' the man said. 'And I gave him a ten and a one.'

'See? You remember the transaction.'

'Yeah, I do. Sort of.'

'Now tell me what he looked like. He white?'

'Yeah, sure. White.'

'Heavy? Thin?'

'Thin but not too thin. On the thin side.'

'Beard?'

'No.'

'Moustache?'

'Maybe. I don't know.'

'There was something about him, though, something that stuck in your memory.'

'What?'

'That's what we're trying to get, John. That what they call you? John?'

'Mostly it's Jack.'

'Okay, Jack. You're doin' fine now. What about his hair?'

'I didn't pay attention to his hair.'

'Sure you did. He bent over to sign in and you saw the top of his head, remember?'

'I don't –'

'Full head of hair?'

'I don't –'

'They'll sit him down with one of our artists,' Durkin said, 'and he'll come up with something. And when this fucking psycho ripper steps on his cock one of these days, when we catch him in the act or on his way out the door, he'll look as much like the police artist's sketch as I look like Sara fucking Blaustein. She looked like a woman, didn't she?'

'Mostly she looked dead.'

'I know. Meat in a butcher's window.' We were in his car, driving over the bumpy surface of the Queensboro Bridge. The sky was starting to lighten up already. I was beyond tiredness by now, with the ragged edges of my emotions perilously close to the surface. I could feel my own vulnerability; the smallest thing could nudge me to tears or laughter.

'You gotta wonder what it would be like,' he said.

'What?'

'Picking up somebody who looked like that. On the street or in a bar, whatever. Then you get her someplace and she takes her clothes off and surprise. I mean, how do you react?'

'I don't know.'

''Course if she already had the operation, you could go with her and never know. Her hands didn't look so big to me. There's women with big hands and men with little hands, far as that goes.'

'Uh-huh.'

'She had a couple rings on, speaking of her hands. You happen to notice?'

'I noticed.'

'One on each hand, she had.'

'So?'

'So he didn't take 'em.'

'Why would he take her rings?'

'You were saying he took Dakkinen's.'

I didn't say anything.

Gently he said, 'Matt, you don't still think Dakkinen got killed for a reason?'

I felt rage swelling up within me, bulging like an aneurysm in a blood vessel. I sat there trying to will it away.

'And don't tell me about the towels. He's a ripper, he's a cute fucking psycho who makes plans and plays by his own private rules. He's not the first case like that to come along.'

'I got warned off the case, Joe. I got very professionally warned off the case.'

'So? She got killed by a psycho and there could still be something about her life that some friends of hers don't want to come out in the open. Maybe she had a boyfriend and he's a married guy, just like you figured, and even if what she died of was scarlet fucking fever he wouldn't want you poking around in the ashes.'

I gave myself the Miranda warning. *You have the right to remain silent*, I told myself, and exercised the right.

'Unless you figure Dakkinen and Blaustein are tied together. Long-lost sisters, say. Excuse me, brother and sister. Or maybe they were brothers, maybe Dakkinen had her operation a few years ago. Tall for a girl, wasn't she?'

'Maybe Cookie was a smokescreen,' I said.

'How's that?'

I went on talking in spite of myself. 'Maybe he killed her to take the heat off,' I said. 'Make it look like a train of random murders. To hide his motive for killing Dakkinen.'

'To take the heat off. What heat, for Christ's sake?'

'I don't know.'

'There's been no fucking heat. There will be now. Nothing turns the fucking press on like a series of random killings. The readers eat it up, they pour it on their corn flakes. Anything gives 'em a chance to run a sidebar on the original Jack the Ripper, those editors go crazy for it. You talk about heat, there'll be enough heat now to scorch his ass for him.'

'I suppose.'

'You know what you are, Scudder? You're stubborn.'

'Maybe.'

'Your problem is you work private and you only carry one case at a time. I got so much shit on my desk it's a pleasure when I get to let go of something, but with you it's just the opposite. You want to hang onto it as long as you can.'

'Is that what it is?'

'I don't know. It sounds like it.' He took one hand off the wheel, tapped me on the forearm. 'I don't mean to bust balls,' he said. 'I see something like that, somebody chopped up like that, I try to clamp a lid on it and it comes out in other directions. You did a lot of good work.'

'Did I?'

'No question. There were things we missed. It might give us a little jump on the psycho, some of the stuff you came up with. Who knows?'

Not I. All I knew was how tired I was.

He fell silent as we drove across town. In front of my hotel he braked to a stop and said, 'What Garfein said there. Maybe Ricone means something in Italian.'

'It won't be hard to check.'

'Oh, of course not. Everything should be that easy to run down. No, we'll check, and you know what we'll find? It'll turn out it means Jones.'

I went upstairs and got out of my clothes and into bed. Ten minutes later I got up again. I felt unclean and my scalp itched. I stood under a too-hot shower and scrubbed myself raw. I got out of the shower, told myself it didn't make any sense to shave before going to bed, then lathered up and shaved anyway. When I was done I put a robe on and sat down on the edge of my bed, then moved to the chair.

They tell you not to let yourself get too hungry, too angry, too lonely or too tired. Any of the four can put you off balance and turn you in the direction of a drink. It seemed to me that I'd touched all four bases. I'd boxed that particular compass in the course of the day and night. Oddly enough, I didn't feel the urge for a drink.

I got the gun from my coat pocket, I started to return it to the dresser drawer, then changed my mind and sat in the chair again, turning the gun in my hands.

When was the last time I'd fired a gun?

I didn't really have to think very hard. It had been that night in Washington Heights when I chased two holdup men into the street, shot them down and killed that little girl in the process. In the time I remained on the force after that incident, I never had occasion to draw my service revolver, let alone discharge it. And I certainly hadn't fired a gun since I left the force.

And tonight I'd been unable to do it. Because something clued me that the car I was aiming at held drunken kids instead of assassins? Because some subtle intuitive perception made me wait until I was certain what I was shooting at?

No. I couldn't make myself believe that.

I had frozen. If instead of a kid with a whiskey bottle I'd seen a thug with a tommy gun, I wouldn't have been any more capable of squeezing the trigger. My finger'd been paralyzed.

I broke the gun, shook the bullets out of the cylinder, closed it up again. I pointed the empty weapon at the wastebasket across the room and squeezed the trigger a couple of times. The *click* the hammer made as it fell upon an empty chamber was surprisingly loud and sharp in my little room.

I aimed at the mirror over the dresser. *Click!*

Proved nothing. It was empty, I knew it was empty. I could take the thing to a pistol range, load it and fire at targets, and that wouldn't prove anything either.

It bothered me that I'd been unable to fire the gun. And yet I was grateful it had happened that way, because otherwise I'd have emptied the gun into that car of kids, probably killed a few of them, and what would that have done to my peace of mind? Tired as I was, I went a few hard rounds with that particular conundrum. I was glad I hadn't shot anyone and frightened of the implications of not shooting, and my mind went around and around, chasing its tail.

I took off the robe, got into bed, and couldn't even begin to loosen up. I got dressed again in street clothes, used the back end of a nail file as a screwdriver, and took the revolver apart for cleaning. I put its parts in one pocket, and in another I stowed the four live cartridges along with the two knives I'd taken from the mugger.

It was morning and the sky was bright. I walked over to Ninth Avenue and up to Fifty-eighth Street, where I dropped both knives into a sewer grating. I crossed the street and walked to another grating and stood near it with my hands in my pockets, one holding the four cartridges, the other touching the pieces of the disassembled revolver.

Why carry a gun you're not going to shoot? Why own a gun you can't carry?

I stopped in a deli on the way back to the hotel. The customer ahead of me bought two six-packs of Old English 800 Malt Liquor. I picked out four candy bars and paid for them, ate one as I walked and the other three in my room. Then I took the revolver's parts from my pocket and put them back together again. I loaded four of the six chambers and put the gun in the dresser drawer.

I got into bed, told myself I'd stay there whether I could sleep or not, and smiled at the thought as I felt myself drifting off.

TWENTY-NINE

The telephone woke me. I fought my way out of sleep like an underwater swimmer coming up for air. I sat up, blinking and trying to catch my breath. The phone was still ringing and I couldn't figure out what was making that damned sound. Then I caught on and answered it.

It was Chance. 'Just saw the paper,' he said. 'What do you figure? That the same guy as got Kim?'

'Give me a minute,' I said.

'You asleep?'

'I'm awake now.'

'Then you don't know what I'm talkin' about. There was another killing, this time in Queens, some sex-change street-walker cut to ribbons.'

'I know.'

'How do you know if you been sleeping?'

'I was out there last night.'

'Out there in Queens?'

He sounded impressed. 'Out there on Queens Boulevard,' I told him. 'With a couple of cops. It was the same killer.'

'You sure of that?'

'They didn't have the scientific evidence sorted out when I was there. But yes, I'm sure of it.'

He thought about it. 'Then Kim was just unlucky,' he said. 'Just in the wrong place at the wrong time.'

'Maybe.'

'Just maybe?'

I got my watch from the nightstand. It was almost noon. 'There are elements that don't fit,' I said. 'At least it seems that way to me. A cop last night told me my problem is I'm too stubborn. I've only got the one case and I don't want to let go of it.'

'So?'

370

'He could be right, but there are still some things that don't fit. What happened to Kim's ring?'

'What ring?'

'She had a ring with a green stone.'

'Ring,' he said, and thought about it. 'Was it Kim had that ring? I guess it was.'

'What happened to it?'

'Wasn't it in her jewelry box?'

'That was her class ring. From high school back home.'

'Yeah, right. I recall the ring you mean. Big green stone. Was a birthstone ring, something like that.'

'Where'd she get it?'

'Out of a Crackerjack box, most likely. Think she said she bought it for herself. It was just a piece of junk, man. Chunk of green glass is all.'

Shatter wine bottles at her feet.

'It wasn't an emerald?'

'You shuckin', man? You know what emeralds cost?'

'No.'

'More'n diamonds. Why's the ring important?'

'Maybe it's not.'

'What do you do next?'

'I don't know,' I said. 'If Kim got killed by a psycho striking at random, I don't know what I can do that the cops can't do better. But there's somebody who wants me off the case, and there's a hotel clerk who got scared into leaving town, and there's a missing ring.'

'That maybe doesn't mean anything.'

'Maybe.'

'Wasn't there something in Sunny's note about a ring turning somebody's finger green? Maybe it was a cheap ring, turned Kim's finger green, and she got rid of it.'

'I don't think that's what Sunny meant.'

'What did she mean, then?'

'I don't know that either.' I took a breath. 'I'd like to connect Cookie Blue and Kim Dakkinen,' I said. 'That's what I'd like to do. If I can manage that I can probably find the man who killed them both.'

'Maybe. You be at Sunny's service tomorrow?'

'I'll be there.'

'Then I'll see you. Maybe we can talk a little afterward.'

'Fine.'

'Yeah,' he said. 'Kim and Cookie. What could they have in common?'

'Didn't Kim work the streets for a while? Didn't she take a bust on that Long Island City stroll?'

'Years ago.'

'She had a pimp named Duffy, didn't she? Did Cookie have a pimp?'

'Could be. Some of the TVs do. Most of 'em don't, from what I know. Maybe I could ask around.'

'Maybe you could.'

'I haven't seen Duffy in months. I think I heard he was dead. But I'll ask around. Hard to figure, though, that a girl like Kim had anything in common with a little Jewish queen from the Island.'

A Jewish queen and a Dairy Queen, I thought, and thought of Donna.

'Maybe they were sisters,' I suggested.

'Sisters?'

'Under the skin.'

I wanted breakfast, but when I hit the street I bought a paper before I did anything else, and I could see right away that it wasn't going to make a good accompaniment for my bacon and eggs. *Hotel Ripper Claims Second Victim*, the top teaser headline announced. And then, in big block caps, SEX-CHANGE HOOKER BUTCHERED IN QUEENS.

I folded it, tucked it under my arm. I don't know what I thought I was going to do first, read the paper or eat, but my feet decided for me and picked neither of those choices. I walked two blocks before I realized I was heading for the Y on West Sixty-third, and that I was going to get there just in time for the twelve-thirty meeting.

What the hell, I thought. Their coffee was as good as anybody else's.

I got out of there an hour later and had breakfast in a Greek joint around the corner on Broadway. I read the paper while I ate. It didn't seem to bother me now.

There wasn't much in the story I didn't already know. The victim was described as having lived in the East Village; I'd somehow assumed she lived across the river in Queens. Garfein had mentioned Floral Park, just across the line in Nassau County, and evidently that was where she'd grown up. Her

parents, according to the *Post*, had both died several years earlier in an air crash. Mark/Sara/Cookie's sole surviving relative was a brother, Adrian Blaustein, a wholesale jeweler residing in Forest Hills with offices on West Forty-seventh Street. He was out of the country and had not yet been notified of his brother's death.

His brother's death? Or his sister's? How did a relative relate to someone who'd changed sex? How did a respectable business-man regard a brother-turned-sister who turned quick tricks in strangers' parked cars? What would Cookie Blue's death mean to Adrian Blaustein?

What did it mean to me?

Any man's death diminishes me, because I am involved in mankind. Any man's death, any woman's death, any death in between. But did it diminish me? And was I truly involved?

I could still feel the trigger of the .32 trembling beneath my finger.

I ordered another cup of coffee and turned to a story about a young soldier home on furlough, playing pickup basketball at a sandlot game in the Bronx. A gun had apparently fallen out of some bystander's pocket, discharging on impact, and the bullet had struck this young serviceman and killed him instantly. I read the story through a second time and sat there shaking my head at it.

One more way to die. Jesus, there really were eight million of them, weren't there?

At twenty to nine that evening I slipped into the basement of a church on Prince Street in SoHo. I got myself a cup of coffee, and while I looked for a seat I scanned the room for Jan. She was near the front on the right-hand side. I sat further back near the coffee.

The speaker was a woman in her thirties who drank for ten years and spent the last three of them on the Bowery, panhan-dling and wiping windshields to get money for wine. 'Even on the Bowery,' she said, 'there are some people who know how to take care of themselves. Some of the men down there always carry a razor and a bar of soap. I gravitated straight to the other kind, the ones who don't shave and don't wash and don't change their clothes. A little voice in my head said, "Rita, you're right where you belong."'

During the break I ran into Jan on her way to the coffee urn. She seemed pleased to see me. 'I was in the neighborhood,' I

373

explained, 'and it got to be meeting time. It occurred to me I might see you here.'

'Oh, this is one of my regular meetings,' she said. 'We'll go for coffee after, okay?'

'Sure.'

A dozen of us wound up around a couple of tables in a coffee shop on West Broadway. I didn't take a very active part in the conversation, or pay too much attention to it. Eventually the waiter distributed separate checks. Jan paid hers and I paid mine and the two of us headed downtown toward her place.

I said, 'I didn't just happen to be in the neighborhood.'

'There's a big surprise.'

'I wanted to talk to you. I don't know if you read today's paper –'

'About the killing in Queens? Yes, I did.'

'I was out there. I'm all wound up and I feel the need to talk about it.'

We went up to her loft and she made a pot of coffee. I sat with a cup of coffee in front of me and by the time I stopped talking and took a sip it was cold. I brought her up to date, told her about Kim's fur jacket, about the drunken kids and the broken wine bottle, about the trip to Queens and what we'd found there. And I told her, too, how I'd spent this afternoon, riding the subway across the river and walking around Long Island City, returning to knock on doors in Cookie Blue's East Village tenement, then crossed the island to work the gay bars on Christopher Street and up and down West Street.

By then it had been late enough to get in touch with Joe Durkin and learn what the lab had come up with.

'It was the same killer,' I told Jan. 'And he used the same weapon. He's tall, right handed, and pretty powerful, and he keeps a sharp edge on his machete, or whatever the hell he uses.'

Phone checks with Arkansas yielded nothing. The Fort Smith street address was a phony, predictably enough, and the auto license plate belonged to an orange Volkswagen owned by a nursery school teacher in Fayetteville.

'And she only drove it on Sundays,' Jan said.

'Something like that. He made up the whole Arkansas business the same as he made up Fort Wayne, Indiana. But the license plate was real, or almost real. Somebody thought to check the hot-car sheet, and there was a navy blue Impala stolen off the street in Jackson Heights just a couple hours before Cookie was killed. The plate number's the same as he used

checking in except for a pair of digits reversed, and of course it's a New York plate instead of Arkansas.

'The car fits the motel clerk's description, such as it was. It also fits what they got from some other hookers who were on the stroll when Cookie was picked up. They say there was a car like that cruising around for a while before the dude in it made up his mind and picked up Cookie.

'The car hasn't turned up yet, but that doesn't mean he's still driving it. It can take a long time before an abandoned stolen car turns up. Sometimes the thieves leave 'em in a No Parking zone and the police tow truck hauls them to the pound. That's not supposed to happen, somebody's supposed to check towed cars against the hot sheet, but it doesn't always go the way it's supposed to. It doesn't matter. It'll turn out the killer dumped the car twenty minutes after he finished with Cookie, and that he wiped it clean of prints.'

'Matt, can't you let go of it?'

'Of the whole business?'

She nodded. 'It's police procedure from here on in, isn't it? Sifting evidence, running down all the details.'

'I suppose so.'

'And it's not as though they're likely to put this on the shelf and forget about it, the way you thought they might when it was just Kim who was dead. The papers wouldn't let them shelve it even if they wanted to.'

'That's true.'

'So is there a reason why you have to push yourself on this? You already gave your client his money's worth.'

'Did I?'

'Didn't you? I think you worked harder for the money than he did.'

'I guess you're right.'

'So why stay with it? What can you do that the whole police force can't.'

I wrestled with that one. After a moment I said, 'There's got to be a connection.'

'What kind of connection?'

'Between Kim and Cookie. Because, damnit, otherwise they don't make sense. A psycho killer always has a pattern for what he's doing, even if it only exists in his own mind. Kim and Cookie didn't look alike and didn't have similar lives. For Christ's sake, they weren't even the same sex to start with. Kim worked off a phone in her own apartment and had a pimp.

375

Cookie was a transsexual streetwalker doing the johns in their cars. She was an outlaw. Chance is doing some double-checking to see if she had a pimp nobody knew about, but it doesn't look likely.'

I drank some cold coffee. 'And he *picked* Cookie,' I went on. 'He took his time, he drove up and down those streets, he made sure he got her and not somebody else. Where's the connection? It's not a matter of type. She was a completely different physical type from Kim.'

'Something in her personal life?'

'Maybe. Her personal life's hard to trace. She lived in the East Village and tricked in Long Island City. I couldn't find anybody in the West Side gay bars who knew her. She didn't have a pimp and she didn't have a lover. Her neighbors on East Fifth Street never knew she was a prostitute, and only a few of them suspected she wasn't a woman. Her only family's her brother and he doesn't even know she's dead.'

I talked some more. *Ricone* wasn't an Italian word, and if it was a name it was an uncommon one. I'd checked telephone directories for Manhattan and Queens without finding a single Ricone listed.

When I ran dry she got more coffee for both of us and we sat for a few minutes without speaking. Then I said, 'Thanks.'

'For the coffee?'

'For listening. I feel better now. I had to talk my way through it.'

'Talking always helps.'

'I suppose so.'

'You don't talk at meetings, do you?'

'Jesus, I couldn't talk about this stuff.'

'Not specifically, maybe, but you could talk about what you're going through and the way it makes you feel. That might help more than you think, Matt.'

'I don't think I could do it. Hell, I can't even say I'm an alcoholic. "My name is Matt and I pass." I could phone it in.'

'Maybe that'll change.'

'Maybe.'

'How long have you been sober, Matt?'

I had to think. 'Eight days.'

'Gee, that's terrific. What's so funny?'

'Something I've noticed. One person asks another how long he's been sober, and whatever the answer is, the reply is, "Gee, that's terrific, that's wonderful." If I said eight days or eight

years the reaction'd be the same. "Gee, isn't that great, isn't that terrific."'

'Well, it is.'

'I guess.'

'What's terrific is that you're sober. Eight years is terrific and so is eight days.'

'Uh-huh.'

'What's the matter?'

'Nothing. Sunny's funeral is tomorrow afternoon.'

'Are you going?'

'I said I would.'

'Are you worried about that?'

'Worried?'

'Nervous, anxious.'

'I don't know about that. I'm not looking forward to it.' I looked into her large gray eyes, then looked away. 'Eight days is as long as I've gone,' I said casually. 'I had eight days last time, and then I drank.'

'That doesn't mean you have to drink tomorrow.'

'Oh, shit, I know that. I'm not going to drink tomorrow.'

'Take someone with you.'

'What do you mean?'

'To the funeral. Ask someone from the program to go along with you.'

'I couldn't ask anyone to do that.'

'Of course you could.'

'Who? There's nobody I know well enough to ask.'

'How well do you have to know somebody to sit next to them at a funeral?'

'Well?'

'Well what?'

'Would you go with me? Never mind, I don't want to put you on the spot.'

'I'll go.'

'Really?'

'Why not? Of course I might look pretty dowdy. Next to all those flashy hookers.'

'Oh, I don't think so.'

'No?'

'No, I don't think so at all.'

I tipped up her chin and tasted her mouth with mine. I touched her hair. Dark hair, lightly salted with gray. Gray to match her eyes.

She said, 'I was afraid this would happen. And then I was afraid it wouldn't.'

'And now?'

'Now I'm just afraid.'

'Do you want me to leave?'

'Do I want you to leave? No, I don't want you to leave. I want you to kiss me again.'

I kissed her. She put her arms around me and drew me close and I felt the warmth of her body through our clothing.

'Ah, darling,' she said.

Afterward, lying in her bed and listening to my own heartbeat, I had a moment of utter loneliness and desolation. I felt as though I had taken the cover off a bottomless well. I reached over and laid a hand on her flank, and the physical contact cut the thread of my mood.

'Hello,' I said.

'Hello.'

'What are you thinking?'

She laughed. 'Nothing very romantic. I was trying to guess what my sponsor's going to say.'

'Do you have to tell her?'

'I don't have to do anything, but I will tell her. "Oh, by the way, I hopped into bed with a guy who's eight days sober."'

'That's a mortal sin, huh?'

'Let's just say it's a no-no.'

'What'll she give you? Six Our Fathers?'

She laughed again. She had a good laugh, full and hearty. I'd always liked it.

'She'll say, "Well, at least you didn't drink. That's the important thing." And she'll say, "I hope you enjoyed it."'

'Did you?'

'Enjoy it?'

'Yeah.'

'Hell, no. I was faking orgasm.'

'Both times, huh?'

'You betcha.' She drew close to me, put her hand on my chest. 'You'll stay over, won't you?'

'What would your sponsor say?'

'Probably that I might as well hang for a sheep as a lamb. Oh, shit, I almost forgot.'

'Where are you going?'

'Gotta make a phone call.'

'You're actually calling your sponsor?'

She shook her head. She'd put a robe on and now she was paging through a small address book. She dialed a number and said, 'Hi, this is Jan. You weren't sleeping, were you? Look, this is out of left field, but does the word *Ricone* mean anything to you?' She spelled it. 'I thought it might be a dirty word or something. Uh-huh.' Then she listened for a moment and said, 'No, nothing like that. I'm doing crossword puzzles in Sicilian, that's all. On nights when I can't sleep. Listen, you can only spend so much time reading the Big Book.'

She finished the conversation, hung up and said, 'Well, it was a thought. I figured if it was a dialect or an obscenity it might not be in the dictionary.'

'What obscenity did you think it might be? And when did the thought happen to cross your mind?'

'None of your business, wiseass.'

'You're blushing.'

'I know, I can feel it. That'll teach me to try to help a friend solve a murder.'

'No good deed goes unpunished.'

'That's what they say. Martin Albert Ricone and Charles Otis Jones? Are those the names he used?'

'Owen. Charles Owen Jones.'

'And you think it means something.'

'It has to mean something. Even if he's a lunatic, anything that elaborate would have to mean something.'

'Like Fort Wayne and Fort Smith?'

'Like that, maybe, but I think the names he used are more significant than that. Ricone's such an unusual name.'

'Maybe he started by writing *Rico*.'

'I thought of that. There are plenty of Ricos in the phone book. Or maybe he's from Puerto Rico.'

'Why not? Everybody else is. Maybe he's a Cagney fan.'

'Cagney?'

'In the death scene. "Mother of mercy, is this the end of Rico?" Remember?'

'I thought that was Edward G. Robinson.'

'Maybe it was. I was always drunk when I watched the "Late Show" and all those Warner Brothers gangsters tend to merge in my mind. It was one of those ballsy guys. "Mother of mercy, is this the —"'

'Some pair of balls,' I said.

'Huh?'

379

'Jesus Christ.'

'What's the matter?'

'He's a comedian. A fucking comedian.'

'What are you talking about?'

'The killer. C. O. Jones and M. A. Ricone. I thought they were names.'

'They're not?'

'*Cojones. Maricón.*'

'That's Spanish.'

'Right.'

'*Cojones* means "balls," doesn't it?'

'And *maricón* means "faggot." I don't think there's an e on the end of it, though.'

'Maybe it's especially nasty with an E on the end.'

'Or maybe he's just a lousy speller.'

'Well, hell,' she said. 'Nobody's perfect.'

THIRTY

Around mid-morning I went home to shower and shave and put on my best suit. I caught a noon meeting, ate a Sabrett hotdog on the street, and met Jan as arranged at the papaya stand at Seventy-second and Broadway. She was wearing a knit dress, dove gray with touches of black. I'd never seen her in anything that dressy.

We went around the corner to Cooke's, where a professionally sympathetic young man in black determined which set of bereaved we belonged to and ushered us through a hallway to Suite Three, where a card in a slot on the open door said HENDRYX. Inside, there were perhaps six rows of four chairs each on either side of a center aisle. In the front, to the left of the lectern on a raised platform, an open casket stood amid a glut of floral sprays. I'd sent flowers that morning but I needn't have bothered. Sunny had enough of them to see a Prohibition era mobster on his way to the Promised Land.

Chance had the aisle seat in the front row on the right. Donna Campion was seated beside him, with Fran Schecter and Mary Lou Barcker filling out the row. Chance was wearing a black suit, a white shirt, and a narrow black silk tie. The women were all wearing black, and I wondered if he'd taken them shopping the previous afternoon.

He turned at our entrance, got to his feet. Jan and I walked over there and I managed the introductions. We stood awkwardly for a moment, and then Chance said, 'You'll want to view the body,' and gave a nod toward the casket.

Did anyone ever want to view a body? I walked over there and Jan walked beside me. Sunny was laid out in a brightly colored dress on a casket lining of cream-colored satin. Her hands, clasped upon her breast, held a single red rose. Her face might have been carved from a block of wax, and yet she certainly looked no worse than when I'd seen her last.

Chance was standing beside me. He said, 'Talk to you a moment?'

'Sure.'

Jan gave my hand a quick squeeze and slipped away. Chance and I stood side by side, looking down at Sunny.

I said, 'I thought the body was still at the morgue.'

'They called yesterday, said they were ready to release it. The people here worked late getting her ready. Did a pretty good job.'

'Uh-huh.'

'Doesn't look much like her. Didn't look like her when we found her, either, did it?'

'No.'

'They'll cremate the body after. Simpler that way. The girls look right, don't they? The way they're dressed and all?'

'They look fine.'

'Dignified,' he said. After a pause he said, 'Ruby didn't come.'

'I noticed.'

'She doesn't believe in funerals. Different cultures, different customs, you know? And she always kept to herself, hardly knew Sunny.'

I didn't say anything.

'After this is over,' he said, 'I be taking the girls to their homes, you know. Then we ought to talk.'

'All right.'

'You know Parke Bernet? The auction gallery, the main place on Madison Avenue. There's a sale tomorrow and I wanted to look at a couple of lots I might bid on. You want to meet me there?'

'What time?'

'I don't know. This here won't be long. Be out of here by three. Say four-fifteen, four-thirty?'

'Fine.'

'Say, Matt?' I turned. ''Preciate your coming.'

There were perhaps ten more mourners in attendance by the time the service got underway. A party of four blacks sat in the middle on the left-hand side, and among them I thought I recognized Kid Bascomb, the fighter I'd watched the one time I met Sunny. Two elderly women sat together in the rear, and another elderly man sat by himself near the front. There are lonely people who drop in on the funerals of strangers as a way of passing the time, and I suspected these three were of their number.

Just as the service started, Joe Durkin and another plain-clothes detective slipped into a pair of seats in the last row.

The minister looked like a kid. I don't know how thoroughly he'd been briefed, but he talked about the special tragedy of a life cut short in its prime, and about God's mysterious ways, and about the survivors being the true victims of such apparently senseless tragedy. He read passages from Emerson, Teilhard de Chardin, Martin Buber, and the Book of Ecclesiastes. Then he suggested that any of Sunny's friends who wished to might come forward and say a few words.

Donna Campion read two short poems which I assumed she'd written herself. I learned later that they were by Sylvia Plath and Anne Sexton, two poets who had themselves committed suicide. Fran Schecter followed her and said, 'Sunny, I don't know if you can hear me but I want to tell you this anyway,' and went on to say how she'd valued the dead girl's friendship and cheerfulness and zest for living. She started off light and bubbly herself and wound up breaking down in tears, and the minister had to help her off stage. Mary Lou Barcker spoke just two or three sentences, and those in a low monotone, saying that she wished she'd known Sunny better and hoped she was at peace now.

Nobody else came forward. I had a brief fantasy of Joe Durkin mounting the platform and telling the crowd how the NYPD was going to get it together and win this one for the Gipper, but he stayed right where he was. The minister said a few more words – I wasn't paying attention – and then one of the attendants played a recording, Judy Collins singing 'Amazing Grace.'

Outside, Jan and I walked for a couple of blocks without saying anything. Then I said, 'Thanks for coming.'

'Thanks for asking me. God, that sounds foolish. Like a conversation after the Junior Prom. "Thanks for asking me. I had a lovely time."' She took a handkerchief from her purse, dabbed at her eyes, blew her nose. 'I'm glad you didn't go to that alone,' she said.

'So am I.'

'And I'm glad I went. It was so sad and so beautiful. Who was that man who spoke to you on the way out?'

'That was Durkin.'

'Oh, was it? What was he doing there?'

'Hoping to get lucky, I suppose. You never know who'll show up at a funeral.'

'Not many people showed up at this one.'

'Just a handful.'

'I'm glad we were there.'

'Uh-huh.'

I bought her a cup of coffee, then put her in a cab. She insisted she could take the subway but I got her into a cab and made her take ten bucks for the fare.

A lobby attendant at Parke Bernet directed me to the second-floor gallery where Friday's African and Oceanic art was on display. I found Chance in front of a set of glassed-in shelves housing a collection of eighteen or twenty small gold figurines. Some represented animals while others depicted human beings and various household articles. One I recall showed a man sitting on his haunches and milking a goat. The largest would fit easily in a child's hand, and many of them had a droll quality about them.

'Ashanti gold weights,' Chance explained. 'From the land the British called the Gold Coast. It's Ghana now. You see plated reproductions in the shops. Fakes. These are the real thing.'

'Are you planning to buy them?'

He shook his head. 'They don't speak to me. I try to buy things that do. I'll show you something.'

We crossed the room. A bronze head of a woman stood mounted on a four-foot pedestal. Her nose was broad and flattened, her cheekbones pronounced. Her throat was so thickly ringed by bronze necklaces that the overall appearance of the head was conical.

'A bronze sculpture of the lost Kingdom of Benin,' he announced. 'The head of a queen. You can tell her rank by the number of necklaces she's wearing. Does she speak to you, Matt? She does to me.'

I read strength in the bronze features, cold strength and a merciless will.

'Know what she says? She says, "Nigger, why you be lookin' at me dat way? You know you ain't got de money to take me home."' He laughed. 'The presale estimate is forty to sixty thousand dollars.'

'You won't be bidding?'

'I don't know what I'll be doing. There are a few pieces I wouldn't mind owning. But sometimes I come to auctions the

384

way some people go to the track even when they don't feel like betting. Just to sit in the sun and watch the horses run. I like the way an auction room feels. I like to hear the hammer drop. You seen enough? Let's go.'

His car was parked at a garage on Seventy-eighth Street. We rode over the Fifty-ninth Street Bridge and through Long Island City. Here and there street prostitutes stood along the curb singly or in pairs.

'Not many out last night,' he said. 'I guess they feel safer in daylight.'

'You were here last night?'

'Just driving around. He picked up Cookie around here, then drove out Queens Boulevard. Or did he take the expressway? I don't guess it matters.'

'No.'

We took Queens Boulevard. 'Want to thank you for coming to the funeral,' he said.

'I wanted to come.'

'Fine-looking woman with you.'

'Thank you.'

'Jan, you say her name was?'

'That's right.'

'You go with her or –'

'We're friends.'

'Uh-huh.' He braked for a light. 'Ruby didn't come.'

'I know.'

'What I told you was a bunch of shit. I didn't want to contradict what I told the others. Ruby split, she packed up and went.'

'When did this happen?'

'Sometime yesterday, I guess. Last night I had a message on my service. I was running around all yesterday, trying to get this funeral organized. I thought it went okay, didn't you?'

'It was a nice service.'

'That's what I thought. Anyway, there's a message to call Ruby and a 415 area code. That's San Francisco. I thought, huh? And I called, and she said she had decided to move on. I thought it was some kind of a joke, you know? Then I went over there and checked her apartment, and all her things were gone. Her clothes. She left the furniture. That makes three empty apartments I got, man. Big housing shortage, nobody can find a place to live, and I'm sitting on three empty apartments. Something, huh?'

'You sure it was her you spoke to?'

'Positive.'

'And she was in San Francisco?'

'Had to be. Or Berkeley or Oakland or some such place. I dialed the number, area code and all. She had to be out there to have that kind of number, didn't she?'

'Did she say why she left?'

'Said it was time to move on. Doing her inscrutable oriental number.'

'You think she was afraid of getting killed?'

'Powhattan Motel,' he said, pointing. 'That's the place, isn't it?'

'That's the place.'

'And you were out here to find the body.'

'It had already been found. But I was out here before they moved it.'

'Must have been some sight.'

'It wasn't pretty.'

'That Cookie worked alone. No pimp.'

'That's what the police said.'

'Well, she coulda had a pimp that they didn't know about. But I talked to some people. She worked alone, and if she ever knew Duffy Green, nobody ever heard tell of it.' He turned right at the corner. 'We'll head back to my house, okay?'

'All right.'

'I'll make us some coffee. You liked that coffee I fixed last time, didn't you?'

'It was good.'

'Well, I'll fix us some more.'

His block in Greenpoint was almost as quiet by day as it had been by night. The garage door ascended at the touch of a button. He lowered it with a second touch of the button and we got out of the car and walked on into the house. 'I want to work out some,' he said. 'Do a little lifting. You like to work out with weights?'

'I haven't in years.'

'Want to go through the motions?'

'I think I'll pass.'

My name is Matt and I pass.

'Be a minute,' he said.

He went into a room, came out wearing a pair of scarlet gym shorts and carrying a hooded terry-cloth robe. We went to the

room he'd fitted out as a gym, and for fifteen or twenty minutes he worked out with loose weights and on the Universal machine. His skin became glossy with perspiration as he worked and his heavy muscles rippled beneath it.

'Now I want ten minutes in the sauna,' he said. 'You didn't earn the sauna by pumping the iron, but we could grant a special dispensation in your case.'

'No thanks.'

'Want to wait downstairs then? Be more comfortable.'

I waited while he took a sauna and shower. I studied some of his African sculpture, thumbed through a couple of magazines. He emerged in due course wearing light blue jeans and a navy pullover and rope sandals. He asked if I was ready for coffee. I told him I'd been ready for half an hour.

'Won't be long,' he said. He started it brewing, then came back and perched on a leather hassock. He said, 'You want to know something? I make a lousy pimp.'

'I thought you were a class act. Restraint, dignity, all of that.'

'I had six girls and I got three. And Mary Lou'll be leaving soon.'

'You think so?'

'I know it. She's a tourist, man. You ever hear how I turned her out?'

'She told me.'

'First tricks she did, she got to tell herself she was a reporter, a journalist, this was all research. Then she decided she was really into it. Now she's finding out a couple of things.'

'Like what?'

'Like you can get killed, or kill yourself. Like when you die there's twelve people at your funeral. Not much of a turnout for Sunny, was there?'

'It was on the small side.'

'You could say that. You know something? I could have filled that fucking room three times over.'

'Probably.'

'Not just probably. Definitely.' He stood up, clasped his hands behind his back, paced the floor. 'I thought about that. I could have taken their biggest suite and filled it. Uptown people, pimps and whores, and the ringside crowd. Could have mentioned it to people in her building. Might be she had some neighbors who would have wanted to come. But see, I didn't want too many people.'

'I see.'

'It was really for the girls. The four of them. I didn't know they'd be down to three when I organized the thing. Then I thought, shit, it might be pretty grim, just me and the four girls. So I told a couple of other people. It was nice of Kid Bascomb to come, wasn't it?'

'Yes.'

'I'll get that coffee.'

He came back with two cups. I took a sip, nodded my approval.

'You'll take a couple pounds home with you.'

'I told you last time. It's no good to me in a hotel room.'

'So you give it to your lady friend. Let her make you a cup of the best.'

'Thanks.'

'You just drink coffee, right? You don't drink booze?'

'Not these days.'

'But you used to.'

And probably will again, I thought. But not today.

'Same as me,' he said. 'I don't drink, don't smoke dope, don't do any of that shit. Used to.'

'Why'd you stop?'

'Didn't go with the image.'

'Which image? The pimp image?'

'The connoisseur,' he said. 'The art collector.'

'How'd you learn so much about African art?'

'Self-taught,' he said. 'I read everything I could find, went around to the dealers and talked to them. And I had a feel for it.' He smiled at something. 'Long time ago I went to college.'

'Where was that?'

'Hofstra. I grew up in Hempstead. Born in Bedford-Stuyvesant, but my folks bought a house when I was two, three years old. I don't even remember Bed-Stuy.' He had returned to the hassock and he was leaning back, his hands clasped around his knees for balance. 'Middle-class house, lawn to mow and leaves to rake and a driveway to shovel. I can slip in and out of the ghetto talk, but it's mostly a shuck. We weren't rich but we lived decent. And there was enough money to send me to Hofstra.'

'What did you study.'

'Majored in art history. And didn't learn shit about African art there, incidentally. Just that dudes like Braque and Picasso got a lot of inspiration from African masks, same as the Impressionists got turned on by Japanese prints. But I never took a look at an African carving until I got back from Nam.'

388

'When were you over there?'

'After my third year of college. My father died, see. I could have finished all the same but, I don't know, I was crazy enough to drop out of school and enlist.' His head was back and his eyes were closed. 'Did a ton of drugs over there. We had everything. Reefer, hash, acid. What I liked, I liked heroin. They did it different there. You used to get it in cigarettes, used to smoke it.'

'I never heard of that.'

'Well, it's wasteful,' he said. 'But it was so cheap over there. They grew the opium in those countries and it was cheap. You get a real muzzy high that way, smoking skag in a cigarette. I was stoned that way when I got the news that my mother died. Her pressure was always high, you know, and she had a stroke and died. I wasn't nodding or anything but I was high from a skag joint and I got the news and I didn't feel anything, you know? And when it wore off and I was straight again I still didn't feel anything. First time I felt it was this afternoon, sitting there listening to some hired preacher reading Ralph Waldo Emerson over a dead whore.' He straightened up and looked at me. 'I sat there and wanted to cry for my mama,' he said, 'but I didn't. I don't guess I'll ever cry for her.'

He broke the mood by getting us both more coffee. When he came back he said, 'I don't know why I pick you to tell things to. Like with a shrink, I suppose. You took my money and now you have to listen.'

'All part of the service. How did you decide to be a pimp?'

'How did a nice boy like me get into a business like this?' He chuckled, then stopped and thought for a moment. 'I had this friend,' he said. 'A white boy from Oak Park, Illinois. That's outside of Chicago.'

'I've heard of it.'

'I had this act for him, that I was from the ghetto, that I'd done it all, you know? Then he got killed. It was stupid, we weren't near the line, he got drunk and a jeep ran over him. But he was dead and I wasn't telling those stories anymore, and my mama was dead and I knew when I got home I wasn't going back to college.'

He walked over to the window. 'And I had this girl over there,' he said, his back to me. 'Little bit of a thing, and I'd go over to her place and smoke skag and lay around. I'd give her money, and, you know, I found out she was taking my money and giving it to her boyfriend, and here I was having fantasies of marrying this woman, bringing her back Stateside. I wouldn't have done

it, but I was thinking about it, and then I found out she wasn't but a whore. I don't know why I ever thought she was anything else, but a man'll do that, you know.'

'I thought about killing her, but shit, I didn't want to do that. I wasn't even that angry. What I did, I stopped smoking, I stopped drinking, I stopped all kinds of getting high.'

'Just like that?'

'Just like that. And I asked myself, Okay, what do you want to be? And the picture filled in, you know, a few lines here and a few lines there. I was a good little soldier for the rest of my hitch. Then I came back and went into business.'

'You just taught yourself?'

'Shit, I *invented* myself. Gave myself the name Chance. I started out in life with a first name and a middle name and a last name, and wasn't any of them Chance. I gave myself a name and created a style and the rest just fell into place. Pimping's easy to learn. The whole thing is power. You just act like you already got it and the women come and give it to you. That's all it really is.'

'Don't you have to have a purple hat?'

'It's probably easiest if you look and dress the part. But if you go and play against the stereotype they think you're something special.'

'Were you?'

'I was always fair with them. Never knocked them around, never threatened them. Kim wanted to quit me and what did I do? Told her to go ahead and God bless.'

'The pimp with the heart of gold.'

'You think you're joking. But I cared for them. And I had a heavenly dream for a life, man. I really did.'

'You still do.'

He shook his head. 'No,' he said. 'It's slipping away. Whole thing's slipping away and I can't hold onto it.'

THIRTY-ONE

We left the converted firehouse with me in the back seat and Chance wearing a chauffeur's cap. A few blocks away he pulled over and returned the cap to the glove compartment while I joined him in front. The commuter traffic had pretty much thinned out by then and we made the trip into Manhattan quickly and in relative silence. We were a little aloof with each other, as if we'd already shared more than either of us had anticipated.

No messages at the desk. I went upstairs, changed my clothes, paused on the way out the door and got the .32 from my dresser drawer. Was there any point in carrying a gun I seemed unable to fire? I couldn't see any, but I put it in my pocket anyway.

I went downstairs and bought a paper, and without thinking too much about it I walked around the corner and took a table in Armstrong's. My usual corner table. Trina came over, said it had been a long time, and took my order for a cheeseburger and a small salad and coffee.

After she headed for the kitchen I got a sudden flash of a martini, straight up and bone dry and ice cold in a stemmed glass. I could see it, I could smell the odor of juniper and the tang of a lemon twist. I could feel the bite as it hit bottom.

Jesus, I thought.

The urge for a drink passed as suddenly as it had come on me. I decided it was a reflex, a reaction to the atmosphere of Armstrong's. I'd done so much drinking here for so long, I'd been eighty-sixed here after my last bender, and I hadn't crossed the threshold since. It was only natural that I'd think of a drink. It didn't mean I had to have one.

I ate my meal, drank a second cup of coffee afterward. I read my newspaper, paid my check, left a tip. Then it was time to go over to St Paul's.

391

The qualification was an alcoholic version of the American Dream. The speaker was a poor boy from Worcester, Mass. who worked his way through college, rose to a vice-presidency at one of the television networks, then lost it all drinking. He went all the way down, wound up in Los Angeles drinking Sterno in Pershing Square, then found AA and got it all back.

It would have been inspiring if I could have kept my mind on it. But my attention kept straying. I thought about Sunny's funeral, I thought about what Chance had told me, and I found my thoughts wandering all over the whole case, trying to make sense out of it.

Damnit, it was all there. I just wasn't looking at it right.

I left during the discussion, before it was my turn to speak. I didn't even feel like saying my name tonight. I walked back to my hotel, fighting the urge to stop in at Armstrong's for a minute or two.

I called Durkin. He was out. I hung up without leaving a message and called Jan.

No answer. Well, she was probably still at her meeting. And she'd go out for coffee afterward, probably wouldn't get home until after eleven.

I could have stayed at my own meeting until it ended, then gone to coffee with some of the others. I could join them now, as far as that went. The Cobb's Corner where they hung out wasn't all that far away.

I thought about it. And decided I didn't really want to go there.

I picked up a book but couldn't make sense out of it. I tossed it down, got undressed, went into the bathroom and ran the shower. But I didn't need a shower, for Christ's sake, I just had a shower that morning, and the most strenuous activity I'd had all day was watching Chance working out with weights. What the hell did I need with a shower?

I turned the water off and got dressed again.

Jesus, I felt like a caged lion. I picked up the phone. I might have called Chance but you couldn't just call the son of a bitch, you had to call his service and wait for him to call back, and I didn't feel like doing that. I called Jan, who was still out, and I called Durkin. He wasn't there either, and once again I decided against leaving a message.

Maybe he was at that place on Tenth Avenue, unwinding with a couple of belts. I thought about going over there and looking for him, and it struck me that it wasn't Durkin I'd be

392

looking for, that all I wanted was an excuse to walk through the door of that bucket of blood and put my foot upon the brass rail.

Did they even have a brass rail? I closed my eyes and tried to picture the place, and in an instant I was recalling everything about it, the smells of spilled booze and stale beer and urine, that dank tavern smell that welcomes you home.

I thought, You've got nine days and you went to two meetings today, a noon meeting and an evening meeting, and you've never been closer to a drink. What the hell's the matter with you?

If I went to Durkin's boozer I'd drink. If I went to Farrell's or Polly's or Armstrong's I would drink. If I stayed in my room I'd go crazy, and when I went crazy enough I'd get away from those four walls and what would I do? I'd go out, to one bar or another, and I'd drink.

I made myself stay there. I'd gotten through the eighth day and there was no reason why I couldn't get through the ninth. I sat there and every now and then I looked at my watch and sometimes a whole minute went by between looks. Finally it got to be eleven o'clock and I went downstairs and hailed a taxi.

There's a midnight meeting seven nights a week at the Moravian Church on the corner of Thirtieth and Lexington. The doors open about an hour before meeting time. I got there and took a seat, and when the coffee was ready I got myself a cup.

I didn't pay attention to the qualification or the discussion. I just sat there and let myself feel safe. There were a lot of newly sober people in the room, a lot of people who were having a hard time. Why else would they be there at that hour?

There were some people who hadn't stopped drinking yet, too. They had to put one of them out, but the others didn't make any trouble. Just a roomful of people getting through one more hour.

When the hour was up I helped fold the chairs and empty the ashtrays. Another chair folder introduced himself as Kevin and asked me how long I'd been sober. I told him it was my ninth day.

'That's great,' he said. 'Keep coming back.'

They always say that.

I went outside and signaled a passing cab, but when he cut over and started to brake I changed my mind and waved him off. He gunned his engine as he drove away.

I didn't want to go back to the room.

So instead I walked seven blocks north to Kim's building,

393

bluffed my way past her doorman, let myself into her apartment. I knew there was a closetful of booze there but it didn't bother me. I didn't even feel the need to pour it down the sink, as I'd done with the bottle of Wild Turkey earlier.

In her bedroom, I went through her jewelry. I wasn't really looking for the green ring. I picked up the ivory bracelet, unfastened the clasp, tried it for size on my own wrist. It was too small. I got some paper towels from the kitchen and wrapped the bracelet carefully, put it in my pocket.

Maybe Jan would like it. I'd pictured it on her wrist a few times – at her loft, during the funeral service.

If she didn't like it she didn't have to wear it.

I went over, picked up the phone. The service hadn't been disconnected yet. I supposed it would be sooner or later, just as sooner or later the apartment would be cleaned and Kim's things removed from it. But for now it was still as if she'd just stepped out for a moment.

I hung up the phone without calling anyone. Somewhere around three o'clock I got undressed and went to sleep in her bed. I didn't change the linen, and it seemed to me that her scent, still faintly discernible, constituted a presence in the room.

If so, it didn't keep me awake. I went right off to sleep.

I woke up bathed in perspiration, convinced that I'd solved the case in a dream and then forgot the solution. I showered and dressed and got out of there.

There were several messages at my hotel, all of them from Mary Lou Barcker. She'd called just after I left the night before and a couple of times that morning.

When I called her she said, 'I've been trying to reach you. I would have called you at your girlfriend's but I couldn't remember her last name.'

'Her number's unlisted.' And I wasn't there, I thought, but left it unsaid.

'I'm trying to reach Chance,' she went on. 'I thought you might have talked to him.'

'Not since around seven last night. Why?'

'I can't get hold of him. The only way I know is to call his service –'

'That's the only way I know.'

'Oh. I thought you might have a special number.'

'Only the service.'

'I've called there. He always returns his calls. I've left, God, I don't know how many messages and he hasn't called me back.'

'Has that ever happened before?'

'Not for this length of time. I started trying him late yesterday afternoon. What time is it, eleven o'clock? That's over seventeen hours. He wouldn't go that long without checking with his service.'

I thought back to our conversation at his house. Had he checked with his service in all the time we were together? I didn't think he had.

Other times we'd been together he called in every half hour or so.

'And it's not just me,' she was saying. 'He hasn't called Fran, either. I checked with her and she called him and he never returned her calls.'

'What about Donna?'

'She's here with me. Neither of us wanted to be alone. And Ruby, I don't know where Ruby is. Her number doesn't answer.'

'She's in San Francisco.'

'She's where?'

I gave her a brief explanation, then listened as she relayed the information to Donna. 'Donna's quoting Yeats,' she told me. 'Things fall apart, the center cannot hold.' Even I can recognize that. Apt, though. Things are falling apart all over the place.'

'I'm going to try to get hold of Chance.'

'Call me when you do?'

'I will.'

'Meanwhile Donna's staying here and we're not booking any tricks or answering the door. I already told the doorman not to let anybody come up.'

'Good.'

'I invited Fran to come over here but she said she didn't want to. She sounded very stoned. I'm going to call her again and instead of inviting her to come over I'm going to *tell* her to come over.'

'Good idea.'

'Donna says the three little pigs will all be hiding in the brick house. Waiting for the wolf to come down the chimney. I wish she'd stick to Yeats.'

I couldn't get anywhere with his answering service. They were happy to take my message but wouldn't disclose whether Chance had called in recently. 'I expect to hear from him

shortly,' a woman told me, 'and I will see that he receives your message.'

I called Brooklyn information and got the number for the house in Greenpoint. I dialed it and let it ring for a dozen times. I'd remembered what he'd told me about removing the clappers from the bells of his telephones, but I thought it was worth a check.

I called Parke Bernet. The sale of African and Oceanic art and artifacts was scheduled for two o'clock.

I had a shower and a shave, had a roll and a cup of coffee and read the paper. The *Post* managed to keep the Motel Ripper on the front page, but it took some stretching to do it. A man in the Bedford Park section of the Bronx had stabbed his wife three times with a kitchen knife, then called the police to tell them what he'd done. This normally would have rated two paragraphs on the back page at the most, but the *Post* put it on the front page and topped it with a teaser headline that wondered, DID THE MOTEL RIPPER INSPIRE HIM?

I went to a meeting at twelve-thirty and got to Parke Bernet a few minutes after two. The auction was being held in a different room from the one where the sale lots had been displayed. You had to have a sale catalog to get a seat, and the catalogs cost five dollars. I explained I was just looking for someone and scanned the room. Chance wasn't there.

The attendant didn't want me to hang around unless I bought a catalog, and it was easier to do that than argue with him. I gave him the five dollars and wound up registering and getting a bidder's number while I was at it. I didn't want to register, I didn't want a bidder's number, I didn't want the goddamned catalog.

I sat there for almost two hours while one lot after another went under the hammer. By two-thirty I was fairly certain he wasn't going to show but I stayed in my seat because I couldn't think of anything better to do. I paid minimal attention to the auction and looked around every couple of minutes for Chance. At twenty to four the Benin bronze was offered for bids and sold for $65,000, which was just a little higher than the estimate. It was the star of the sale and quite a few bidders left once it had been sold. I hung on a few minutes longer, knowing he wasn't coming, just trying to grapple with the same thing I'd been grappling with for days.

It seemed to me that I already had all the pieces. It was just a question of fitting them together.

Kim. Kim's ring and Kim's mink jacket. *Cojones. Maricón.* The towels. The warning. Calderón. Cookie Blue.

I got up and left. I was crossing the lobby when a table full of catalogs of past sales caught my eye. I picked up a catalog of a jewelry auction held that spring and leafed through it. It didn't tell me anything. I put it back and asked the lobby attendant if the gallery had a resident expert on gems and jewelry. 'You want Mr Hillquist,' he said, and told me what room to go to and pointed me in the right direction.

Mr Hillquist sat at an uncluttered desk as if he'd been waiting all day for me to consult him. I gave him my name and told him I wanted some vague approximation of the value of an emerald. He asked if he could see the stone, and I explained that I didn't have it with me.

'You would have to bring it in,' he explained. 'The value of a gem depends upon so many variables. Size, cut, color, brilliance –'

I put my hand in my pocket, touched the .32, felt around for the bit of green glass. 'It's about this size,' I said, and he fitted a jeweler's loupe into one eye and took the piece of glass from me. He looked at it, went absolutely rigid for an instant, then fixed his other eye warily upon me.

'This is not an emerald,' he said carefully. He might have been talking to a small child, or to a lunatic.

'I know that. It's a piece of glass.'

'Yes.'

'It's the approximate size of the stone I'm talking about. I'm a detective, I'm trying to get some idea of the value of a ring that has disappeared since I saw it, I –'

'Oh,' he said, and sighed. 'For a moment I thought –'

'I know what you thought.'

He took the loupe from his eye, set it on the desk in front of him. 'When you sit here,' he said, 'you are at the absolute mercy of the public. You wouldn't believe the people who come here, the things they show me, the questions they ask.'

'I can imagine.'

'No, you can't.' He picked up the bit of green glass and shook his head at it. 'I still can't tell you the value. Size is only one of several considerations. There's also color, there's clarity, there's brilliance. Do you even know that the stone is an emerald? Did you test it for hardness?'

'No.'

'So it could even be colored glass. Like the, uh, treasure you've given me here.'

'For all I know it is glass. But I want to know what it could be worth if it did happen to be an emerald.'

'I think I see what you mean.' He frowned at the piece of glass. 'You have to understand that my every inclination is to avoid naming any sort of a figure. You see, even assuming the stone is a genuine emerald, its range in value could be considerable. It could be extremely valuable or very nearly worthless. It could be seriously flawed, for example. Or it could simply be a very low grade stone. There are mail order firms that actually offer emeralds by the carat for some ridiculous sum, forty or fifty dollars the carat, and what they're selling is no bargain, either. Yet they are genuine emeralds, however worthless they may be as gemstones.'

'I see.'

'Even a gem-quality emerald could vary enormously in value. You could buy a stone this size –' he weighed the chunk of glass in his hand '– for a couple thousand dollars. And that would be a good stone, not industrial-grade corundum from western North Carolina. On the other hand, a stone of the highest quality, the best color, perfect brilliance, unflawed, not even Peruvian but the very best Colombian emerald, might bring forty or fifty or sixty thousand dollars. And even that's approximate and imprecise.'

He had more to say but I wasn't paying attention. He hadn't really told me anything, hadn't added a fresh piece to the puzzle, but he'd given the box a good shake. Now I could see where everything went.

I took the cube of green glass with me when I left.

THIRTY-TWO

Around ten-thirty that night I walked in and out of Poogan's Pub on West Seventy-second Street. A light rain had begun falling an hour or so earlier. Most of the people on the street were carrying umbrellas. I wasn't, but I had a hat, and I paused on the sidewalk to straighten it and adjust its brim.

Across the street I saw a Mercury sedan with its motor riding.

I turned to my left and walked to the Top Knot. I spotted Danny Boy at a table in back but went to the bar anyway and asked for him. I must have spoken loudly because people looked at me. The bartender motioned toward the rear and I went back there and joined him.

He already had company. He was sharing his table with a slender fox-faced girl whose hair was as white as his own, but in her case nature couldn't take the credit. Her eyebrows were severely plucked and her forehead had a shine to it. Danny Boy introduced her as Bryna. 'Rhymes with angina,' he said, 'among other things.' She smiled, showing sharp little canine teeth.

I pulled a chair out and sat down heavily. I said, 'Danny Boy, you can pass the word. I know all about Kim Dakkinen's boyfriend. I know who killed her and I know why she was killed.'

'Matt, are you all right?'

'I'm fine,' I said. 'You know why I had so much trouble getting a line on Kim's boyfriend? Because he wasn't an action guy, that's why. Didn't go to clubs, didn't gamble, didn't hang out. Wasn't connected.'

'You been drinking, Matt?'

'What are you, the Spanish Inquisition? What do you care if I've been drinking or not?'

'I just wondered. You're talking loud, that's all.'

'Well, I'm trying to tell you about Kim,' I said. 'About her

399

boyfriend. See, he was in the jewelry business. He didn't get rich, he didn't starve. He made a living.'

'Bryna,' he said, 'suppose you powder your nose for a few minutes.'

'Oh, let her stay,' I told him. 'Her nose doesn't look shiny to me.'

'Matt —'

'What I'm telling you's no secret, Danny Boy.'

'Suit yourself.'

'This jeweler,' I went on. 'The way it looks, he started seeing Kim as a john. But something happened. One way or another, he fell for her.'

'These things happen.'

'They do indeed. Anyway, he fell in love. Meanwhile, some people got in touch with him. They had some precious stones that never went through Customs and that they had no bill of sale for. Emeralds. Colombian emeralds. Real quality stuff.'

'Matt, would you please tell my why in the hell you're telling me all this?'

'It makes an interesting story.'

'You're not just telling me, you're telling the whole room. Do you know what you're doing?'

I looked at him.

'Okay,' he said, after a moment. 'Bryna, pay attention, darling. The crazy man wants to talk about emeralds.'

'Kim's boyfriend was going to be the middleman, handling the sale of the emeralds for the men who'd brought them into the country. He did this sort of thing before, made a few dollars for himself. But now he was in love with an expensive lady and he had a reason to want some real money. So he tried a cross.'

'How?'

'I don't know. Maybe he switched some stones. Maybe he held out. Maybe he decided to grab the whole bundle and run with it. He must have told Kim something because on the strength of it she told Chance she wanted out. She wasn't going to be turning tricks anymore. If I were going to guess, I'd say he did a switch and went out of the country to unload the good stuff. Kim got herself free of Chance while he was gone, and when he got back it was going to be Happily Ever After time. But he never came back.'

'If he never came back, who killed her?'

'The people he crossed. They decoyed her to that room at the Galaxy Downtowner. She probably thought she was going to be

meeting him there. She wasn't hooking any more, she wouldn't have gone to a hotel room to meet a john. In fact she'd never been much on hotel tricks. But suppose she gets a call from somebody who says he's a friend and the boyfriend's afraid to come to her place because he thinks he's being followed, so would she please meet him at the hotel?'

'And she went.'

'Sure she went. She got all dressed up, she wore the presents he gave her, the mink jacket and the emerald ring. The jacket wasn't worth a fortune because the guy wasn't rich, he didn't have money to burn, but he could give her a terrific emerald because the emeralds didn't cost him anything. He was in the business, he could take one of those smuggled stones and have it set in a ring for her.'

'So she went over and got killed.'

'Right.'

Danny Boy drank some vodka. 'Why? You figure they killed her to get the ring back?'

'No. They killed her to kill her.'

'Why?'

'Because they were Colombians,' I said, 'and that's how they do it. When they have a reason to hit somebody they go for the whole family.'

'Jesus.'

'Maybe they figure it's a deterrent,' I said. 'I could see where it might be. The cases make the papers pretty regularly, especially in Miami. A whole family gets waxed because somebody burned somebody else in a coke deal. Colombia's a rich little country. They've got the best coffee, the best marijuana, the best cocaine.'

'And the best emeralds?'

'That's right. Kim's jeweler wasn't a married guy. I figured he was, that's why he was so hard to get a line on, but he never married. Maybe he never fell in love until he fell in love with Kim, and maybe that's why he was ready to kick his life over. Anyway, he was a bachelor. No wife, no kids, no living parents. You want to rub out his family, what do you do? You kill his girlfriend.'

Bryna's face was as white as her hair now. She didn't like stories where they killed the girlfriend.

'The killing was pretty professional,' I went on, 'in that the killer was careful about evidence. He covered his tracks pretty well. But something made him do a butcher job instead of a

couple of quick bullets from a silenced handgun. Maybe he had a thing about prostitutes, or maybe it was women in general. One way or another, he went and did a number on Kim.

'Then he cleaned up, packed the dirty towels along with the machete, and got out of there. He left the fur jacket and he left the money in the purse but he took her ring.'

'Because it was worth so much money?'

'Possibly. There's no hard evidence on the ring, and for all I know it was cut glass and she bought it for herself. But it might have been an emerald, and even if it wasn't the killer might have thought it was. It's one thing to leave a few hundred dollars on a dead body to show you don't rob the dead. It's something else to leave an emerald that might be worth fifty thousand dollars, especially if it's your emerald in the first place.'

'I follow you.'

'The room clerk at the Galaxy Downtowner was a Colombian, a young kid named Octavio Calderón. Maybe that was a coincidence. There are a lot of Colombians in town these days. Maybe the killer picked the Galaxy because he knew somebody who worked there. It doesn't matter. Calderón probably recognized the killer, or at least knew enough about him to keep his mouth shut. When a cop came back to have another talk with him, Calderón disappeared. Either the killer's friends told him to disappear or Calderón decided he'd be safer somewhere else. Back home in Cartagena, say, or another rooming house in another part of Queens.'

Or maybe he got killed, I thought. That was possible, too. But I didn't think so. When these people killed, they liked to leave the corpses in plain sight.

'There was another whore that got killed.'

'Sunny Hendryx,' I said. 'That was a suicide. Maybe Kim's death triggered that, so maybe the man who killed Kim has some moral responsibility for Sunny's death. But she killed herself.'

'I'm talking about the street hustler. The TV.'

'Cookie Blue.'

'That's the one. Why did she get killed? To throw you off the track? Except you weren't on the track to begin with.'

'No.'

'Then why? You think the first killing turned the killer nuts? Triggered something in him that made him want to do it again?'

'I think that's part of it,' I said. 'Nobody would do a second butcher job like that unless he enjoyed the first one. I don't

know if he had sex with either of his victims, but the kick he got out of the killings had to be sexual.'

'So he just picked up Cookie for the hell of it?'

Bryna blanched again. It was bad enough hearing about someone who got killed for being the wrong person's girlfriend. It was even worse hearing about a girl getting killed at random.

'No,' I said, 'Cookie was killed for a specific reason. The killer went looking for her and passed up a batch of other street-walkers until he found her. Cookie was family.'

'Family? Whose family?'

'The boyfriend's.'

'He had two sweeties, this jeweler? A call girl and a transvestite hustler?'

'Cookie wasn't his sweetie. Cookie was his brother.'

'Cookie –'

'Cookie Blue started life as Mark Blaustein. Mark had an older brother named Adrian who went into the jewelry business. Adrian Blaustein had a girlfriend named Kim and some business associates from Colombia.'

'So Cookie and Kim were connected.'

'They had to be connected. I'm sure they never met each other. I don't think Mark and Adrian had any contact in recent years. That may explain why it took the killer so long to find Cookie. But I knew there had to be some kind of link. I told someone earlier that they were sisters under the skin. That wasn't far off. They were almost sisters-in-law.'

He thought about this, then told Bryna to give us a few moments alone. This time I didn't interfere. She left the table and Danny Boy motioned to the waitress. He ordered vodka for himself and asked me what I wanted.

'Nothing right now,' I said.

When she brought back the vodka he took a careful little sip and set the glass down. 'You've been to the cops,' he said.

'No cops.'

'Why not?'

'Just didn't get around to it yet.'

'You had to come here instead.'

'That's right.'

'I can keep my mouth shut, Matt, but Bryna the Vagina wouldn't know how. She thinks unexpressed thoughts build up inside your head and explode your skull, and she's not taking any chances. Anyway, you were talking loud enough for half the room to pick up on what you were saying.'

'I know that.'

'I figured you did. What do you want?'

'I want the killer to know what I know.'

'That shouldn't take long.'

'I want you to pass it on, Danny Boy. I'm leaving here, I'm walking back to my neighborhood. I'll probably spend a couple of hours in Armstrong's. Then I'll walk around the corner to my room.'

'You're gonna get killed, Matt.'

'This fucker only kills girls,' I said.

'Cookie was only half a girl. Maybe he's working his way up to men.'

'Maybe.'

'You want him to make a move on you.'

'Looks that way, doesn't it?'

'Looks to me as though you're crazy, Matt. I tried to head you off the minute you came over here. Tried to cool you down some.'

'I know.'

'It's probably too late now. Whether I pass it on or not.'

'It was too late before then. I was uptown before I came down here. You know a man named Royal Waldron?'

'Sure, I know Royal.'

'He and I talked some. Royal's been known to do a little business with some fellows from Colombia.'

'He would,' Danny Boy said. 'The business he's in.'

'So they probably already know. But you could pass it on anyway, just for insurance.'

'Insurance,' he said. 'What's the opposite of life insurance?'

'I don't know.'

'Death insurance. They may be waiting outside for you right now, Matt.'

'It's possible.'

'Why don't you go pick up the phone and call the cops? They could send a car and you go somewhere and make a statement. Let the bastards earn their money.'

'I want the killer,' I said. 'I want him one-on-one.'

'You're not Latin. Where'd you get this *macho* hangup?'

'Just pass the word, Danny Boy.'

'Sit down a minute.' He leaned forward, dropped his voice. 'You don't want to walk out of here without a piece. Just sit here a minute and I'll get you something.'

'I don't need a gun.'

'No, of course not. Who needs one? You can take his machete away from him and make him eat it. Then break both his legs and leave him in an alley.'

'Something like that.'

'Will you let me get you a gun?' His eyes searched mine. 'You've already got one,' he said. 'On you, right now. Haven't you?'

'I don't need a gun,' I said.

And I didn't. On the way out of the Top Knot I put my hand in my pocket and felt the butt and barrel of the little .32. Who needed it? A little gun like that doesn't have a whole lot of stopping power anyway.

Especially when you can't make yourself squeeze the trigger.

I went outside. It was still raining but no harder than before. I tugged the brim of my hat and took a good look around.

The Mercury sedan was parked on the other side of the street. I recognized it by its crimped fenders. While I was standing there the driver started the engine.

I walked over to Columbus Avenue. While I waited for the light to change I saw that the Mercury had come around in a U-turn and was approaching. The light changed and I walked across the street.

I had the gun in my hand and my hand in my pocket. My index finger was on the trigger. I remembered how the trigger had trembled beneath my finger not too long ago.

I'd been on this same street then.

I walked on downtown. A couple of times I looked over my shoulder. The Mercury stayed a little less than a block behind me all the way.

I never relaxed, but I was especially tense when I got to the block where I'd drawn the gun once before. I couldn't help looking back, expecting to see a car careening toward me. I spun around involuntarily once at the sound of brakes screeching, then realized the sound was a good two blocks away.

Nerves.

I passed the spot where I'd dropped to the pavement and rolled. I checked the place where the bottle had broken. There was still some broken glass there, though I couldn't be sure it was the same broken glass. A lot of bottles get broken every day.

I kept walking all the way to Armstrong's. When I got there I went in and ordered a piece of pecan pie and a cup of coffee. I kept my right hand in my pocket while my eyes scanned the

room, checking everybody out. After I was done with the pie I put my hand back in my pocket and drank my coffee left-handed.

After awhile I ordered more coffee.

The telephone rang. Trina answered it, walked over to the bar. There was a heavyset fellow there with dark blond hair. She said something to him and he went to the phone. He talked for a few minutes, looked around the room, came over to my table. Both of his hands were where I could see them.

He said, 'Scudder? My name's George Lightner, I don't think we met.' He pulled a chair out and sat in it. 'That was Joe just now,' he said. 'There's no activity out there, nothing at all. They're laying doggo in the Mercury plus he's got two sharp-shooters in second-floor windows across the street.'

'Good.'

'I'm in here, and there's the two fellows at the front table. I figured you made us when you walked in.'

'I made them,' I said. 'I figured you were either a cop or the killer.'

'Jesus, what a thought. This is a nice place. You more or less hang out here, huh?'

'Not as much as I used to.'

'It's pleasant here. I'd like to come back sometime when I can drink something instead of coffee. They're selling a lot of coffee tonight, what with you and me and the two guys down front.'

'It's pretty good coffee.'

'Yeah, it's not bad. Better than the shit in the station house.' He lit a cigarette with a Zippo lighter. 'Joe said there's no activity elsewhere either. There's two men staked out down-town with your girlfriend. There's a couple others with the three hookers on the East Side.' He grinned. 'That's the detail I shoulda drawn. Can't win 'em all, huh?'

'I guess not.'

'How long you want to stay here? Joe's guess is that the guy's either set up by now or he's not gonna move tonight. We can cover you every step from here back to the hotel. Of course we can't insure against the possibility of a sniper firing from a rooftop or a high window. We did a rooftop check earlier but there's no guarantee.'

'I don't think he'll do it from a distance.'

'Then we're in pretty good shape. And you're wearing the bulletproof vest.'

'Yes.'

'That's a help. Of course it's mesh, it doesn't always stop a blade, but nobody's about to let him get that close to you. We figure if he's out there he'll make a move between here and the doorway of your hotel.'

'That's what I figure, too.'

'When do you want to run the gauntlet?'

'A few minutes,' I said. 'I might as well finish this coffee.'

'Listen,' he said, rising, 'what the hell. Enjoy it.'

He returned to his spot at the bar. I finished my coffee, got up, went to the lavatory. There I checked my .32 and made sure I had a round under the hammer and three more rounds to back it up. I could have asked Durkin for a couple more cartridges to fill the empty chambers. For that matter, he'd have given me a larger gun with more of a punch to it. But he didn't even know I was carrying the .32 and I hadn't wanted to tell him. The way things were set up, I wasn't going to have to shoot anybody. The killer was supposed to walk right into our arms.

Except it wasn't going to happen that way.

I paid the check, left a tip. It wasn't going to work. I could feel it. The son of a bitch wasn't out there.

I walked out the door. The rain had let up some. I looked at the Mercury and glanced at the buildings across the street, wondering where the police sharpshooters were planted. It didn't matter. They weren't going to have any work to do tonight. Our quarry wasn't taking the bait.

I walked down to Fifty-seventh Street, staying close to the curb just in case he'd managed to find a spot in a dark doorway. I walked slowly and hoped I was right and he wouldn't try to do it from a distance, because a bulletproof vest doesn't always stop a bullet and it doesn't do anything to protect you from a head shot.

But it didn't matter. He wasn't there. Damnit, I knew he wasn't there.

Still, I breathed easier when I walked into my hotel. I may have been disappointed but I was also relieved.

There were three plainclothesmen in the lobby. They identified themselves right away. I stood around with them for a few minutes, and then Durkin came in alone. He went into a huddle with one of them, then came over to me.

'We struck out,' he said.

'Looks that way.'

'Shit,' he said. 'We didn't leave many loopholes. Maybe he smelled something but I don't see how. Or maybe he flew home

407

to fucking Bogotá yesterday and we're setting a trap for somebody who's on another continent.'

'It's possible.'

'You can go get some sleep, anyway. If you're not too wired to unwind. Have a couple of drinks, knock yourself out for eight hours.'

'Good idea.'

'The guys have had the lobby staked out all night. There've been no visitors, no check-ins. I'm gonna keep a guard down here all night.'

'You think it's necessary?'

'I think it can't hurt.'

'Whatever you say.'

'We gave it our best shot, Matt. It's worth it if we can smoke the fucker out because God knows how we could get anyplace combing the city for emerald smugglers. Sometimes you get lucky and sometimes you don't.'

'I know.'

'We'll catch the cocksucker sooner or later. You know that.'

'Sure.'

'Well,' he said, and shifted his weight awkwardly. 'Well, listen. Get some sleep, huh?'

'Sure.'

I rode up on the elevator. He wasn't in South America, I thought. I knew damned well he wasn't in South America. He was here in New York and he was going to kill again because he liked it.

Maybe he'd done it before. Maybe Kim was the first time he found out it felt good to him. But he'd liked it enough to do it again the same way, and the next time he wouldn't need an excuse. Just a victim and a hotel room and his trusty machete.

Have a couple of drinks, Durkin had suggested.

I didn't even feel like a drink.

Ten days, I thought. Just go to bed sober and you've got ten days.

I took the gun out of my pocket and put it on the dresser. I was still carrying the ivory bracelet in another pocket and I took it out and set it down next to the gun, still wrapped in paper towels from Kim's kitchen. I got out of my slacks and jacket, hung them in the closet, and took off my shirt. The bulletproof vest was a tricky thing to get out of and a cumbersome thing to wear, and most of the cops I knew hated wearing them. On the other hand, nobody likes getting shot.

I took the thing off and draped it over the dresser next to the gun and bracelet. Bulletproof vests aren't just bulky, they're also warm, and I'd perspired inside this one and my undershirt had dark circles under the arms. I took off the undershirt and my shorts and my socks, and something clicked, some little alarm went off, and I was turning toward the bathroom door when it flew open.

He sailed through it, a big man, olive skinned, wild-eyed. He was as naked as I was and there was a machete in his hand with a gleaming foot-long blade.

I threw the mesh at him. He swung the machete and knocked it aside. I grabbed the gun off the dresser and dove out of his way. The blade arced down, missing me, and his arm rose again and I shot him four times in the chest.

THIRTY-THREE

The LL train starts at Eighth Avenue, crosses Manhattan along Fourteenth Street, and winds up way the hell out in Canarsie. Its first stop across the river in Brooklyn is at Bedford Avenue and North Seventh Street. I left it there and walked around until I found his house. It took me a while and I took a couple of wrong turns, but it was a good day for walking, the sun out, the sky clear, and a little warmth in the air for a change.

There was a heavy windowless door to the right of the garage. I poked the doorbell but got no response, and I couldn't hear the bell sounding within. Hadn't he said something about disconnecting the bell? I jabbed it again, heard nothing.

There was a brass knocker mounted on the door and I used it. Nothing happened. I cupped my hands and shouted, 'Chance, open up! It's Scudder.' Then I pounded on the door some more, with the knocker and with my hands.

The door looked and felt awfully solid. I gave it a tentative nudge with my shoulder and decided it was unlikely I could kick it in. I could break a window and get in that way, but in Greenpoint some neighbor would call the cops, or pick up a gun and come over himself.

I banged on the door some more. A motor worked, and a winch began lifting the electrically-operated garage door.

'This way,' he said. 'Before you knock my damn door down.'

I went in through the garage and he pushed a button to lower the door again. 'My front door doesn't open,' he said. 'Didn't I show you that before? It's all sealed shut with bars and shit.'

'That's great if you have a fire.'

'Then I go out a window. But when'd you ever hear of the firehouse burning down?'

He was dressed as I'd last seen him, in light blue denim pants and a navy blue pullover. 'You forgot your coffee,' he said. 'Or I

forgot to give it to you. Day before yesterday, remember? You were gonna take a couple pounds home with you.'

'You're right, I forgot.'

'For your girlfriend. Fine-looking woman. I got some coffee made. You'll have a cup, won't you?'

'Thanks.'

I went into the kitchen with him. I said, 'You're a hard man to get hold of.'

'Well, I sort of stopped checking with my service.'

'I know. Have you heard a newscast lately? Or read a paper?'

'Not lately. You drink it black, right?'

'Right. It's all over, Chance.' He looked at me. 'We got the guy.'

'The guy. The killer.'

'That's right. I thought I'd come out and tell you about it.'

'Well,' he said. 'I guess I'd like to hear it.'

I went through the whole thing in a fair amount of detail. I was used to it by now. It was the middle of the afternoon and I'd been telling the story to one person or another ever since I'd put four bullets into Pedro Antonio Marquez a little after two in the morning.

'So you killed him,' Chance said. 'How do you feel about that?'

'It's too early to tell.'

I knew how Durkin felt about it. He couldn't have been happier. 'When they're dead,' he had said, 'you know they're not going to be back on the street in three years, doing it again. And this one was a fucking animal. He had that taste of blood and he liked it.'

'It's the same guy?' Chance wanted to know. 'There's no question?'

'No question. They got confirmation from the manager of the Powhattan Motel. They also matched a couple of latent prints, one from the Powhattan and one from the Galaxy, so that ties him to both killings. And the machete's the weapon used in both killings. They even found minute traces of blood where the hilt meets the handle, and the type matches either Kim or Cookie, I forget which one.'

'How'd he get into your hotel?'

'He walked right through the lobby and rode up in the elevator.'

'I thought they had the place staked out.'

411

'They did. He walked right past them, picked up his key at the desk and went to his room.'

'How could he do that?'

'Easiest thing in the world,' I said. 'He checked in the day before, just in case. He was setting things up. When he got the word that I was looking for him, he went back to my hotel, went up to his room, then went to my room and let himself in. The locks in my hotel aren't much of a challenge. He took off his clothes and sharpened his machete and waited for me to come home.'

'And it almost worked.'

'It should have worked. He could have waited behind the door and killed me before I knew what was happening. Or he could have stayed in the bathroom a few more minutes and given me time to get into bed. But he got too much of a kick out of killing and that's what screwed him up. He wanted us both naked when he took me out, so he waited in the bathroom, and he couldn't wait for me to get into bed because he was too keyed up, too excited. Of course if I hadn't had the gun handy he'd have killed me anyway.'

'He couldn't have been all alone.'

'He was alone as far as the killings were concerned. He probably had partners in the emerald operation. The cops may get somewhere looking for them and they may not. Even if they do, there's no real way to make a case against anybody.'

He nodded. 'What happened to the brother? Kim's boyfriend, the one who started everything.'

'He hasn't turned up. He's probably dead. Or he's still running, and he'll live until his Colombian friends catch up with him.'

'Will they do that?'

'Probably. They're supposed to be relentless.'

'And that room clerk? What's his name, Calderón?'

'That's right. Well, if he's holed up somewhere in Queens, he can read about it in the paper and ask for his old job back.'

He started to say something, then changed his mind and took both our cups back to the kitchen to refill them. He came back with them and gave me mine.

'You were up late,' he said.

'All night.'

'You been to sleep at all?'

'Not yet.'

'Myself, I doze off in a chair now and then. But when I get in

bed I can't sleep, I can't even lie there. I go work out and take a sauna and a shower and drink some more coffee and sit around some more. Over and over.'

'You stopped calling your service.'

'I stopped calling my service. I stopped leaving the house. I guess I been eating. I take something from the refrigerator and eat it without paying attention. Kim's dead and Sunny's dead and this Cookie's dead, and maybe the brother's dead, the boyfriend, and what's-his-name is dead. The one you shot, I disremember his name.'

'Marquez.'

'Marquez is dead, and Calderón disappeared, and Ruby's in San Francisco. And the question is where's Chance, and the answer is I don't know. Where I think I am is out of business.'

'The girls are all right.'

'So you said.'

'Mary Lou isn't going to be turning tricks anymore. She's glad she did it, she learned a lot from it, but she's ready for a new stage in her life.'

'Yeah, well, I called that one. Didn't I tell you after the funeral?'

I nodded. 'And Donna thinks she can get a foundation grant, and she can earn money through readings and workshops. She says she's reached a point where selling herself is starting to undermine her poetry.'

'She's pretty talented, Donna. Be good if she could make it on her poetry. You say she's getting a grant?'

'She thinks she's got a shot at it.'

He grinned. 'Aren't you gonna tell me the rest of it? Little Fran just got a Hollywood contract and she's gonna be the next Goldie Hawn.'

'Maybe tomorrow,' I said. 'For now she just wants to live in the Village and stay stoned and entertain nice men from Wall Street.'

'So I still got Fran.'

'That's right.'

He'd been pacing the floor. Now he dropped onto the hassock again. 'Be a cinch to get five, six more of them,' he said. 'You don't know how easy it is. Easiest thing in the world.'

'You told me that once before.'

'It's the truth, man. So many women just waiting to be told what to do with their damn lives. I could walk out of here and

413

have me a full string in no more than a week's time.' He shook his head ruefully. 'Except for one thing.'

'What's that?'

'I don't think I can do that anymore.' He stood up again. 'Damn, I been a good pimp! And I liked it. I tailored a life for myself and it fit me like my own skin. And you know what I went and did?'

'What?'

'I outgrew it.'

'It happens.'

'Some spic goes crazy with a blade and I'm out of business. You know something? It would have happened anyway, wouldn't it?'

'Sooner or later.' Just as I'd have left the police force even if a bullet of mine hadn't killed Estrellita Rivera. 'Lives change,' I said. 'It doesn't seem to do much good to fight it.'

'What am I gonna do?'

'Whatever you want.'

'Like what?'

'You could go back to school.'

He laughed. 'And study art history? Shit, I don't want to do that. Sit in classrooms again? It was bullshit then, I went into the fuckin' army to get away from it. You know what I thought about the other night?'

'What?'

'I was gonna build a fire. Pile all the masks in the middle of the floor, spill a little gas on 'em, put a match to 'em. Go out like one of those Vikings and take all my treasures with me. I can't say I thought about it for long. What I could do, I could sell all this shit. The house, the art, the car. I guess the money'd last me a time.'

'Probably.'

'But then what'd I do?'

'Suppose you set up as a dealer?'

'Are you crazy, man? Me deal drugs? I can't even pimp no more, and pimping's cleaner'n dealing.'

'Not drugs.'

'What, then?'

'The African stuff. You seem to own a lot of it and I gather the quality's high.'

'I don't own any garbage.'

'So you told me. Could you use that as your stock to get you

414

started? And do you know enough about the field to go into the business?'

He frowned, thinking. 'I was thinking about this earlier,' he said.

'And?'

'There's a lot I don't know. But there's a lot I do know, plus I got a feel for it and that's something you can't get in a classroom or out of a book. But shit, you need more'n that to be a dealer. You need a whole manner, a personality to go with it.'

'You invented Chance, didn't you?'

'So? Oh, I dig. I could invent some nigger art dealer same way I invented myself as a pimp.'

'Couldn't you?'

''Course I could.' He thought once more. 'It might work,' he said. 'I'll have to study it.'

'You got time.'

'Plenty of time.' He looked intently at me, the gold flecks glinting in his brown eyes. 'I don't know what made me hire you,' he said. 'I swear to God I don't. If I wanted to look good or what, the superpimp avenging his dead whore. If I knew where it was going to lead –'

'It probably saved a few lives,' I said. 'If that's any consolation.'

'Didn't save Kim or Sunny or Cookie.'

'Kim was already dead. And Sunny killed herself and that was her choice, and Cookie was going to be killed as soon as Marquez tracked her down. But he'd have gone on killing if I hadn't stopped him. The cops would have landed on him sooner or later but there'd have been more dead women by then. He never would have stopped. It was too much of a turn-on for him. When he came out of the bathroom with the machete, he had an erection.'

'You serious?'

'Absolutely.'

'He came at you with a hard-on?'

'Well, I was more afraid of the machete.'

'Well, yeah,' he said. 'I could see where you would be.'

He wanted to give me a bonus. I told him it wasn't necessary, that I'd been adequately paid for my time, but he insisted, and when people insist on giving me money I don't generally argue. I told him I'd taken the ivory bracelet from Kim's apartment. He laughed and said he'd forgotten all about it, that I was welcome

to it and he hoped my lady would like it. It would be part of my bonus, he said, along with the cash and two pounds of his specially-blended coffee.

'And if you like the coffee,' he said, 'I can tell you where to get more of it.'

He drove me back into the city. I'd have taken the subway but he insisted he had to go to Manhattan anyway to talk to Mary Lou and Donna and Fran and get things smoothed out. 'Might as well enjoy the Seville while I can,' he said. 'Might wind up selling it to raise cash for operating expenses. Might sell the house, too.' He shook his head. 'I swear it suits me, though. Living here.'

'Get the business started with a government loan.'

'You jiving?'

'You're a minority group member. There's agencies just waiting to lend you money.'

'What a notion,' he said.

In front of my hotel he said, 'That Colombian asshole, I still can't remember his name.'

'Pedro Marquez.'

'That's him. When he registered at your hotel, is that the name he used?'

'No, it was on his ID.'

'That's what I thought. Like he was C. O. Jones and M. A. Ricone, and I wondered what dirty word he used for you.'

'He was Mr Starudo,' I said. 'Thomas Edward Starudo.'

'T. E. Starudo? *Testarudo*? That a curse in Spanish?'

'Not a curse. But it's a word.'

'What's it mean?'

'Stubborn,' I said. 'Stubborn or pig-headed.'

'Well,' he said, laughing. 'Well, hell, you can't blame him for that one, can you?'

THIRTY-FOUR

In my room I put the two pounds of coffee on the dresser, then went and made sure nobody was in the bathroom. I felt silly, like an old maid looking under the bed, but I figured it would be a while before I got over it. And I wasn't carrying a gun any more. The .32 had been impounded, of course, and the official story was that Durkin had issued it to me for my protection. He hadn't even asked how I'd really come by it. I don't suppose he cared.

I sat in my chair and looked at the place on the floor where Marquez had fallen. Some of his bloodstains remained in the rug, along with traces of the chalk marks they place around dead bodies.

I wondered if I'd be able to sleep in the room. I could always get them to change it, but I'd been here a few years now and I'd grown accustomed to it. Chance had said it suited me, and I suppose it did.

How did I feel about having killed him?

I thought it over and decided I felt fine. I didn't really know anything about the son of a bitch. To understand all is to forgive all, they say, and maybe if I knew his whole story I'd understand where the blood lust came from. But I didn't have to forgive him. That was God's job not mine.

And I'd been able to squeeze the trigger. And there'd been no ricochets, no bad bounces, no bullets that went wide. Four shots, all in the chest. Good detective work, good decoy work, and good shooting at the end.

Not bad.

I went downstairs and around the corner. I walked to Armstrong's, glanced in the window, but went on walking to Fifty-eighth and around the corner and halfway down the block. I went into Joey Farrell's and stood at the bar.

417

Not much of a crowd. Music on the jukebox, some baritone crooner backed up with a lot of strings.

'Double Early Times,' I said. 'With water back.'

I stood there, not really thinking of anything, while the bearded barman poured the drink and drew the chaser and set them both before me. I had placed a ten dollar bill on the counter. He cracked it, brought my change.

I looked at the drink. Light danced in the rich amber fluid. I reached for it, and a soft inner voice murmured *Welcome home*.

I withdrew my hand. I left the drink on the bar and took a dime from my pile of change. I went to the phone and dropped the dime and dialed Jan's number.

No answer.

Fine, I thought. I'd kept my promise. Of course I might have misdialed, or the phone company might have fucked up. Such things have been known to happen.

I put the dime back in the slot and dialed again. I let it ring a dozen times.

No answer.

Fair enough. I got my dime back and returned to the bar. My change was as I'd left it, and so were the two glasses in front of me, the bourbon and the water.

I thought, *Why?*

The case was finished, solved, wrapped up. The killer would never kill anyone again. I had done a whole lot of things right and felt very good about my role in the proceedings. I wasn't nervous, I wasn't anxious, I wasn't depressed. I was fine, for Christ's sake.

And there was a double shot of bourbon on the bar in front of me. I hadn't wanted a drink, I hadn't even thought of a drink, and here I was with a drink in front of me and I was going to swallow it.

Why? What the hell was the matter with me?

If I drank the fucking drink I would end up dead or in the hospital. It might take a day or a week or a month but that was how it would play. I knew that. And I didn't want to be dead and I didn't want to go to the hospital, but here I was in a gin joint with a drink in front of me.

Because –

Because what?

Because –

I left the drink on the bar. I left my change on the bar. I got out of there.

At half past eight I walked down the flight of basement stairs and into the meeting room at St Paul's. I got a cup of coffee and some cookies and took a seat.

I thought, You almost drank. You're eleven days sober and you went into a bar you had no reason to be in and ordered a drink for no reason at all. You almost picked up the drink, you were that close to it, you almost blew eleven days after the way you sweated to get them. What the hell is the matter with you?

The chairman read the preamble and introduced the speaker. I sat there and tried to listen to his story and I couldn't. My mind kept returning to the flat reality of that glass of bourbon. I hadn't wanted it, I hadn't even thought about it, and yet I'd been drawn to it like iron filings to a magnet.

I thought, My name is Matt and I think I'm going crazy.

The speaker finished what he was saying. I joined in the applause. I went to the bathroom during the break, less out of need than to avoid having to talk to anybody. I came back to the room and got yet another cup of coffee that I neither needed nor wanted. I thought about leaving the coffee and going back to my hotel. The hell, I'd been up two days and a night without a break. Some sleep would do me more good than a meeting I couldn't pay attention to in the first place.

I kept my coffee cup and took it to my seat and sat down.

I sat there during the discussion. The words people spoke rolled over me like waves. I just sat there, unable to hear a thing.

Then it was my turn.

'My name is Matt,' I said, and paused, and started over. 'My name is Matt,' I said, 'and I'm an alcoholic.'

And the goddamnedest thing happened. I started to cry.

WHEN THE SACRED GINMILL CLOSES

FOR KENNETH REICHEL

And so we've had another night
Of poetry and poses
And each man knows he'll be alone
When the sacred ginmill closes

DAVE VAN RONK

ONE

The windows at Morrissey's were painted black. The blast was loud enough and close enough to rattle them. It chopped off conversation in midsyllable, froze a waiter in midstride, making of him a statue with a tray of drinks on his shoulder and one foot in the air. The great round noise died out like dust settling, and for a long moment afterward the room remained hushed, as if with respect.

Someone said, 'Jesus Christ,' and a lot of people let out the breath they'd been holding. At our table, Bobby Ruslander reached for a cigarette and said, 'Sounded like a bomb.'

Skip Devoe said, 'Cherry bomb.'

'Is that all?'

'It's enough,' Skip said. 'Cherry bomb's major ordnance. Same charge had a metal casing instead of a paper wrapper, you'd have a weapon instead of a toy. You light one of those little mothers and forget to let go of it, you're gonna have to learn to do a lot of basic things left-handed.'

'Sounded like more than a firecracker,' Bobby insisted. 'Like dynamite or a grenade or something. Sounded like fucking World War Three, if you want to know.'

'Get the actor,' Skip said affectionately. 'Don't you love this guy? Fighting it out in the trenches, storming the windswept hills, slogging through the mud. Bobby Ruslander, battle-scarred veteran of a thousand campaigns.'

'You mean *bottle*-scarred,' somebody said.

'Fucking actor,' Skip said, reaching to rumple Bobby's hair. '"Hark I hear the cannon's roar." You know that joke?'

'I told *you* the joke.'

'"Hark I hear the cannon's roar." When'd you ever hear a shot fired in anger? Last time they had a war,' he said, 'Bobby brought a note from his shrink. "Dear Uncle Sam, Please excuse Bobby's absence, bullets make him crazy."'

'My old man's idea,' Bobby said.

'But you tried to talk him out of it. "Gimmie a gun," you said. "I wanna serve my country."'

Bobby laughed. He had one arm around his girl and picked up his drink with his free hand. He said, 'All I said was it sounded like dynamite to me.'

Skip shook his head. 'Dynamite's different. They're all different, different kinds of a bang. Dynamite's like one loud note, and a flatter sound than a cherry bomb. They all make a different sound. Grenade's completely different, it's like a chord.'

'The lost chord,' somebody said, and somebody else said, 'Listen to this, it's poetry.'

'I was going to call my joint Horseshoes & Hand Grenades,' Skip said. 'You know what they say, coming close don't count outside of horseshoes and hand grenades.'

'It's a good name,' Billie Keegan said.

'My partner hated it,' Skip said. 'Fucking Kasabian, he said it didn't sound like a saloon, sounded like some kind of candy-ass boutique, some store in SoHo sells toys for private-school kids. I don't know, though. Horseshoes & Hand Grenades, I still like the sound of it.'

'Horseshit and Hand Jobs,' somebody said.

'Maybe Kasabian was right, if that's what everybody woulda wound up calling it.' To Bobby he said, 'You want to talk about the different sounds they make, you should hear a mortar. Someday get Kasabian to tell you about the mortar. It's a hell of a story.'

'I'll do that.'

'Horseshoes & Hand Grenades,' Skip said. 'That's what we shoulda called the joint.'

Instead he and his partner had called their place Miss Kitty's. Most people assumed a reference to 'Gunsmoke,' but their inspiration had been a whorehouse in Saigon. I did most of my own drinking at Jimmy Armstrong's, on Ninth Avenue between Fifty-seventh and Fifty-eighth. Miss Kitty's was on Ninth just below Fifty-sixth, and it was a little larger and more boisterous than I liked. I stayed away from it on the weekends, but late on a weekday night when the crowd thinned down and the noise level dropped, it wasn't a bad place to be.

I'd been in there earlier that night. I had gone first to Armstrong's, and around two-thirty there were only four of us left – Billie Keegan behind the bar and I in front of it and a

424

couple of nurses who were pretty far gone on Black Russians. Billie locked up and the nurses staggered off into the night and the two of us went down to Miss Kitty's, and a little before four Skip closed up, too, and a handful of us went on down to Morrissey's.

Morrissey's wouldn't close until nine or ten in the morning. The legal closing hour for bars in the city of New York is 4:00 a.m., an hour earlier on Saturday nights, but Morrissey's was an illegal establishment and was thus not bound by regulations of that sort. It was one flight up from street level in one of a block of four-story brick houses on Fifty-first Street between Eleventh and Twelfth Avenues. About a third of the houses on the block were abandoned, their windows boarded up or broken, some of their entrances closed off with concrete block.

The Morrissey brothers owned their building. It couldn't have cost them much. They lived in the upper two stories, let out the ground floor to an Irish amateur theater group, and sold beer and whiskey after hours on the second floor. They had removed all of the interior walls on the second floor to create a large open space. They'd stripped one wall to the brick, scraped and sanded and urethaned the wide pine floors, installed some soft lighting and decorated the walls with some framed Aer Lingus posters and a copy of Pearse's 1916 proclamation of the Irish Republic ('Irishmen and Irishwomen, in the name of God and of the dead generations ...'). There was a small service bar along one wall, and there were twenty or thirty square tables with butcher-block tops.

We sat at two tables pushed together. Skip Devoe was there, and Billie Keegan, the night bartender at Armstrong's. And Bobby Ruslander, and Bobby's girl for the evening, a sleepy-eyed redhead named Helen. And a fellow named Eddie Grillo who tended bar at an Italian restaurant in the West Forties, and another fellow named Vince who was a sound technician or something like that at CBS Television.

I was drinking bourbon, and it must have been either Jack Daniel's or Early Times, as those were the only brands the Morrisseys stocked. They also carried three or four scotches, Canadian Club, and one brand each of gin and vodka. Two beers, Bud and Heineken. A Cognac and a couple of odd cordials. Kahlúa, I suppose, because a lot of people were drinking Black Russians that year. Three brands of Irish whiskey, Bushmill's and Jameson and one called Power's, which nobody ever seemed to order but to which the Morrissey brothers were partial. You'd

have thought they'd carry Irish beer, Guinness at least, but Tim Pat Morrissey had told me once that he didn't fancy the bottled Guinness, that it was awful stuff, that he only liked the draft stout and only on the other side of the Atlantic.

They were big men, the Morrisseys, with broad high foreheads and full rust-colored beards. They wore black trousers and highly polished black brogans and white shirts with the sleeves rolled to the elbow, and they wore white butcher's aprons that covered them to their knees. The waiter, a slim, clean-shaven youth, wore the same outfit, but on him it looked like a costume. I think he may have been a cousin. I think he'd have had to have been some sort of blood kin to work there.

They were open seven days a week, from around 2:00 a.m. to nine or ten. They charged three dollars for a drink, which was higher than the bars but reasonable compared to most after-hour joints, and they poured a good drink. Beer was two dollars. They would mix most of the common drinks, but it was no place to order a pousse-café.

I don't think the police ever gave the Morrisseys a hard time. While there was no neon sign out front, the place wasn't the best-kept secret in the neighborhood. The cops knew it was there, and that particular evening I noticed a couple of patrolmen from Midtown North and a detective I'd known years back in Brooklyn. There were two black men in the room and I recognized both of them; one I'd seen at ringside at a lot of fights, while his companion was a state senator. I'm sure the Morrissey brothers paid money to stay open, but they had some strong connections beyond the money they paid, ties to the local political clubhouse.

They didn't water the booze and they poured a good drink. Wasn't that as much of a character reference as any man needed?

Outside, another cherry bomb exploded. It was farther off, a block or two away, and it didn't slam the door shut on any conversations. At our table, the CBS guy complained that they were rushing the season. He said, 'The Fourth isn't until Friday, right? Today's what, the first?'

'It's been the second for the past two hours.'

'So that's still two days. What's the hurry?'

'They get these fucking fireworks and they get the itch,' Bobby Ruslander said. 'You know who's the worst? The fucking chinks. For a while there I was seein' this girl, she lived down

near Chinatown. You'd get Roman candles in the middle of the night, you'd get cherry bombs, anything. Not just July, any time of the year. Comes to firecrackers, they're all little kids down there.'

'My partner wanted to call the joint Little Saigon,' Skip said. 'I told him, John, for Christ's sake, people're gonna think it's a Chinese restaurant, you're gonna get family groups from Rego Park ordering moo goo gai pan and two from Column B. He said what the hell's Chinese about Saigon? I told him, I said, John, you know that and I know that, but when it comes to the people from Rego Park, John, to them a slope is a slope and it all adds up to moo goo gai pan.'

Billie said, 'What about the people in Park Slope?'

'What about the people in Park Slope?' Skip frowned, thinking it over. 'The people in Park Slope,' he said. '*Fuck* the people in Park Slope.'

Bobby Ruslander's girl Helen said, very seriously, that she had an aunt in Park Slope. Skip looked at her. I picked up my glass. It was empty, and I looked around for the beardless waiter or one of the brothers.

So I was looking at the door when it flew open. The brother who kept the door downstairs stumbled through it and careened into a table. Drinks spilled and a chair tipped over.

Two men burst into the room behind him. One was about five-nine, the other a couple inches shorter. Both were thin. Both wore blue jeans and tennis sneakers. The taller one had on a baseball jacket, the shorter one a royal-blue nylon windbreaker. Both had billed baseball caps on their heads and blood-red kerchiefs knotted around their faces, forming triangular wedges that hid their mouths and cheeks.

Each had a gun in his hand. One had a snub-nosed revolver, the other a long-barreled automatic. The one with the automatic raised it and fired two shots into the stamped-tin ceiling. It didn't sound like a cherry bomb or a hand grenade, either.

They got in and out in a hurry. One went behind the bar and emerged with the Garcia y Vega cigar box where Tim Pat kept the night's receipts. There was a glass jar on top of the bar with a hand-lettered sign soliciting contributions for the families of IRA men imprisoned in the North of Ireland, and he scooped the bills out of it, leaving the silver.

While he was doing this, the taller man held a gun on the Morrisseys and had them turn out their pockets. He took the cash from their wallets and a roll of bills from Tim Pat. The

shorter man set down the cigar box for a moment and went to the back of the room, removing a framed Aer Lingus poster of the Cliffs of Moher from the wall to expose a locked cupboard. He shot the lock off and withdrew a metal strongbox, tucked it unopened under his arm, went back to pick up the cigar box again, and ducked out the door and raced down the stairs.

His partner continued to hold the Morrisseys at gunpoint until he'd left the building. He had the gun centered at Tim Pat's chest, and for a moment I thought he was going to shoot. His gun was the long-barreled automatic, he'd been the one who put two bullets in the tin ceiling, and if he shot Tim Pat, he seemed unlikely to miss.

There was nothing I could do about it.

Then the moment passed. The gunman breathed out through his mouth, the red kerchief billowing with his breath. He backed to the door and out, fled down the stairs.

No one moved.

Then Tim Pat held a brief whispered conference with one of his brothers, the one who'd been keeping the door downstairs. After a moment the brother nodded and walked to the gaping cupboard at the back of the room. He closed it and hung the Cliffs of Moher poster where it had been.

Tim Pat spoke to his other brother, then cleared his throat. 'Gentlemen,' he said, and smoothed his beard with his big right hand. 'Gentlemen, if I may take a moment to explain the performance ye just witnessed. Two good friends of ours came in to ask for the loan of a couple of dollars, which we lent them with pleasure. None of us recognized them or took note of their appearance, and I'm sure no one in this room would know them should we by God's grace meet up with them again.' His fingertips dabbed at his broad forehead, moved again to groom his beard. 'Gentlemen,' he said, 'ye'd honor me and my brothers by havin' the next drink with us.'

And the Morrisseys bought a round for the house. Bourbon for me. Jameson for Billie Keegan, scotch for Skip, brandy for Bobby, and a scotch sour for his date. A beer for the guy from CBS, a brandy for Eddie the bartender. Drinks all around – for the cops, for the black politicians, for a roomful of waiters and bartenders and night people. Nobody got up and left, not with the house buying a round, not with a couple of guys out there with masks and guns.

The clean-shaven cousin and two of the brothers served the drinks. Tim Pat stood at the side with his arms folded on his

white apron and his face expressionless. After everyone had been served, one of his brothers whispered something to Tim Pat and showed him the glass jar, empty except for a handful of coins. Tim Pat's face darkened.

'Gentlemen,' he said, and the room quieted down. 'Gentlemen, in the moment of confusion there was money taken as was contributed to Norad, money for the relief of the misfortunate wives and children of political prisoners in the North. Our loss is our own, myself and my brothers, and we'll speak no more of it, but them in the North with no money for food ...' He stopped for breath, continued in a lower voice. 'We'll let the jar pass amongst ye,' he said, 'and if some of ye should care to contribute, the blessings of God on ye.'

I probably stayed another half-hour, not much more than that. I drank the drink Tim Pat bought and one more besides, and that was enough. Billie and Skip left when I did. Bobby and his girl were going to stick around for a while, Vince had already left, and Eddie had joined another table and was trying to make points with a tall girl who waitressed at O'Neal's.

The sky was light, the streets empty still, silent with early dawn. Skip said, 'Well, Norad made a couple of bucks, anyway. There couldn't have been a whole lot Frank and Jesse took out of the jar, and the crowd coughed up a fair amount to fill it up again.'

'Frank and Jesse?'

'Well, those red hankies, for Christ's sake. You know, Frank and Jesse James. But that was ones and fives they took out of the jar, and it was all tens and twenties got put back into it, so the poor wives and wee childer in the North came out all right.'

Billie said, 'What do you figure the Morrisseys lost?'

'Jesus, I don't know. That strongbox could have been full of insurance policies and pictures of their sainted mither, but that would be a surprise all around, wouldn't it? I bet they walked with enough to send a lot of guns to the bold lads in Derry and Belfast.'

'You think the robbers were IRA?'

'The hell,' he said. He threw his cigarette into the gutter. 'I think the Morrisseys are. I think that's where their money goes. I figure—'

'Hey, guys! Wait up, huh?'

We turned. A man named Tommy Tillary was hailing us from the stoop of the Morrisseys' house. He was a heavyset fellow, full in the cheeks and jowls, big in the chest, big in the belly,

too. He was wearing a summer-weight burgundy blazer and a pair of white pants. He was wearing a tie, too. He almost always wore a tie.

The woman with him was short and slender, with light brown hair that showed red highlights. She was wearing tight faded jeans and a pink button-down shirt with the sleeves rolled up. She looked very tired, and a little drunk.

He said, 'You guys know Carolyn? Course you do.' We all said hello to her. He said, 'I got a car parked around the corner, plenty of room for everybody. Drop you guys off.'

'It's a nice morning,' Billie said. 'I think I'd as soon walk, Tommy.'

'Oh, yeah?'

Skip and I said the same. 'Walk off some of the booze,' Skip said. 'Wind down, get ready for bed.'

'You sure? No trouble to run you home.' We were sure. 'Well, you mind walking as far as the car with us? That little demonstration back there, makes a person nervous.'

'Sure thing, Tom.'

'Nice morning, huh? Be a hot one today but it's beautiful right now. I swear I thought he was gonna shoot whatsisname, Tim Pat. You see the look on his face at the end there?'

'There was a moment,' Billie said, 'it could have gone either way.'

'I was thinking, there's gonna be shooting, back and forth, I'm looking to see which table to dive under. Fucking little tables, there's not a lot of cover, you know?'

'Not too much.'

'And I'm a big target, right? What are you smoking, Skip, Camels? Lemme try one of those if you don't mind. I smoke these filters and this time of night they got no taste left to them. Thanks. Was I imagining things or was there a couple of cops in the room?'

'There were a few, anyway.'

'They got to carry their guns on or off duty, isn't that right?'

He'd asked the question of me, and I agreed that there was a regulation to that effect.

'You'd think one of 'em would have tried something.'

'You mean draw down on the holdup men?'

'Something.'

'It's a good way to get people killed,' I said. 'Throwing lead around a crowded room like that.'

'I guess there'd be a danger of ricochets.'

430

'Why'd you say that?'

He looked at me, surprised by the snap in my tone. 'Why, the brick walls, I guess,' he said. 'Even shooting into the tin ceiling the way he did, a bullet could glance off, do some damage. Couldn't it?'

'I guess,' I said. A cab cruised by, its off-duty light lit, a passenger sharing the front seat with the driver. I said. 'On or off duty, a cop wouldn't start anything in a situation like that unless someone else had already started shooting. There were a couple of bulls in the room tonight who probably had their hands on their guns toward the end there. If that fellow'd shot Tim Pat, he'd probably have been dodging bullets on the way out the door. *If* anybody had a clear shot at him.'

'And if they were sober enough to see straight,' Skip put in.

'Makes sense,' Tommy said. 'Matt, didn't you break up a bar holdup a couple of years ago? Somebody was saying something about it.'

'That was a little different,' I said. 'They'd already shot the bartender dead before I made a move. And I didn't spray bullets around inside, I went out into the street after them.' And I thought about that, and missed the next few sentences of the conversation. When I came back into focus Tommy was saying he'd expected to be held up.

'Lot of people in that room tonight,' he said. 'Night workers, people closed up their places and carrying cash on 'em. You'd think they would have passed the hat, wouldn't you?'

'I guess they were in a hurry.'

'I only got a few hundred on me, but I'd rather keep it than give it to a guy with a hanky on his face. You feel relieved not to get robbed, you're real generous when they pass the jug for whatchacallit, Norad? I gave twenty bucks to the widows and orphans, didn't think twice.'

'It's all staged,' Billie Keegan suggested. 'The guys with the handkerchiefs are friends of the family, they put on this little act every couple of weeks to boost the Norad take.'

'Jesus,' Tommy said, laughing at the idea. 'Be something, wouldn't it? There's my car, the Riv. Big boat'll carry everybody easy, you want to change your mind and let me run you on home.'

We all stayed with our decision to walk. His car was a maroon Buick Riviera with a white leather interior. He let Carolyn in, then walked around the car and unlocked his door, making a

face at her failure to lean across the seat and unlock the door for him.

After they drove off, Billie said, 'They were at Armstrong's until one, one-thirty. I didn't expect to see 'em again tonight. I hope he's not driving back to Brooklyn tonight.'

'Is that where they live?'

'Where *he* lives,' he told Skip. 'She's here in the neighborhood. He's a married guy. Doesn't he wear a ring?'

'I never noticed.'

'Caro-lyn from the Caro-line,' Billie said. 'That's how he introduces her. She was sure shitfaced tonight, wasn't she? When he left earlier I thought for sure he was takin' her home – and come to think of it I guess he was. She was wearin' a dress earlier tonight, wasn't she, Matt?'

'I don't remember.'

'I could swear she was. Office clothes, anyway, not jeans and a Brooks shirt like she had on now. Took her home, gave her a bounce, then they got thirsty and by that time the stores were closed, so off we go to the neighborhood after-hours, T. P. Morrissey, Prop. What do you think, Matt? Have I got the makings of a detective?'

'You're doing fine.'

'He put on the same clothes but she changed. Now the question is will he go home to the wife or sleep over at Carolyn's and show up at the office tomorrow in the same outfit. The only problem is, who gives a shit?'

'I was just going to ask that,' Skip said.

'Yeah. One thing *he* asked, I'll ask it myself. Why didn't they stick up the customers tonight? There must have been a lot of guys carryin' a few hundred each and a couple with more than that.'

'Not worth it.'

'That's a few grand we're talking about.'

'I know,' Skip said. 'It's also another twenty minutes if you're gonna do it right, and that's in a room full of drunks with God knows how many of them carrying guns. I bet there were fifteen guns in that room.'

'Are you serious?'

'I'm not only serious, I bet I'm guessing low. For openers you got three or four cops. You got Eddie Grillo, right at our table.'

'Eddie carries a piece?'

'Eddie runs around with some pretty heavy guys, not even talking about who owns the joint where he works. There was a

guy named Chuck, I don't really know him, works at Polly's Cage—'

'I know who you mean. He walks around with a gun on him?'

'Either that or he walks around with a permanent hardon and he's built funny. Believe me, there's a whole lot of guys walk around packing iron. You tell a whole roomful to reach for their wallets, some of them'll reach for their guns instead. Meanwhile they're in and out in what, five minutes tops? I don't think it was five minutes from the door flying open and the bullets in the ceiling until they're out the door and Tim Pat's standing there with his arms crossed and a scowl on his face.'

'That's a point.'

'And whatever they'd of got from people's wallets, that's small change.'

'You figure the box was that heavy? What do you figure it held?'

Skip shrugged. 'Twenty grand.'

'Seriously?'

'Twenty grand, fifty grand, pick a number.'

'IRA money, you were saying earlier.'

'Well, what else do you figure they spend it on, Bill? I don't know what they take in but they do a nice business seven days a week and where's the overhead? They probably got the building for back taxes, and they live in half of it, so they got no rent to pay and no real payroll to come up with. I'm sure they don't report any income or pay any taxes, unless they pretend that playhouse on the ground floor shows a profit and pay a token tax on that. They have to be dragging ten or twenty grand a week out of that place and what do you think they spend it on?'

'They have to pay off to stay open,' I put in.

'Payoffs and political contributions, of course, but not ten or twenty K a week's worth. And they don't drive big cars, and they never go out and spend a dollar in somebody else's joint. I don't see Tim Pat buying emeralds for some sweet young thing, or his brothers putting grams of coke up their Irish noses.'

'Up your Irish nose,' Billie Keegan said.

'I liked Tim Pat's little speech, and then buying a round. Far as I know, that's the first time the Morrisseys ever set 'em up for the house.'

'Fucking Irish,' Billie said.

'Jesus, Keegan, you're drunk again.'

'Praise be to God, you're right.'

'What do you think, Matt? Did Tim Pat recognize Frank and Jesse?'

I thought about it. 'I don't know. What he was saying added up to "Keep out of this and we'll settle it ourselves." Maybe it was political.'

'Fucking-A right,' Billie said. 'The Reform Democrats were behind it.'

'Maybe Protestants,' Skip said.

'Funny,' Billie said. 'They didn't look Protestant.'

'Or some other IRA faction. There's different factions, aren't there?'

'Of course you rarely see Protestants with handkerchiefs over their faces,' Billie said. 'They usually tuck them in the breast pocks, the breast pockets—'

'Jesus, Keegan.'

'Fucking Protestants,' Billie said.

'Fucking Billie Keegan,' Skip said. 'Matt, we better walk this asshole home.'

'Fucking guns,' Billie said, back on that track suddenly. 'Go out for a nightcap and you're surrounded by fucking guns. You carry a gun, Matt?'

'Not me, Billie.'

'Really?' He put a hand on my shoulder for support. 'But you're a cop.'

'Used to be.'

'Private cop now. Even the rent-a-cop, security guard in a bookstore, guy tells you to check your briefcase on the way in, he's got a gun.'

'They're generally just for show.'

'You mean I won't get shot if I walk off with the Modern Library edition of *The Scarlet Letter*? You should of told me before I went and paid for it. You really don't carry a gun?'

'Another illusion shattered,' Skip said.

'What about your buddy the actor?' Billie demanded of him. 'Is little Bobby a gunslinger?'

'Who, Ruslander?'

'He'd shoot you in the back,' Billie said.

'If Ruslander carried a gun,' Skip said, 'it'd be a stage prop. It'd shoot blanks.'

'Shoot you in the back,' Billie insisted. 'Like whatsisname, Bobby the Kid.'

'You mean Billy the Kid.'

'Who are you to tell me what I mean? Does he?'

434

'Does he what?'

'Pack a piece, for Christ's sake. Isn't that what we've been talking about?'

'Jesus, Keegan, don't ask *me* what we've been talking about.'

'You mean you weren't paying attention either? *Jeezus.*'

Billie Keegan lived in a high-rise on Fifty-sixth near Eighth. He straightened up as we approached his building and appeared sober enough when he greeted the doorman. 'Matt, Skip,' he said. 'See you guys.'

'Keegan's all right,' Skip told me.

'He's a good man.'

'Not as drunk as he pretended, either. He was just riding it, enjoying himself.'

'Sure.'

'We keep a gun behind the bar at Miss Kitty's, you know. We got held up, the place I used to work before John and I opened up together. I was behind the stick in this place on Second Avenue in the Eighties, guy walked in, white guy, stuck a gun in my face and got the money from the register. Held up the customers, too. Only have five, six people in the joint at the time, but he took wallets off of them. I think he took their watches too, if I remember it right. Class operation.'

'Sounds it.'

'All the time I was being a hero in Nam, fucking Special Forces, I never had to stand and look at the wrong end of a gun. I didn't feel anything while it was going on, but later I felt angry, you know what I mean? I was in a rage. Went out, bought a gun, ever since then it's been with me when I been working. At that joint, and now in Miss Kitty's. I still think we should have called it Horseshoes & Hand Grenades.'

'You got a permit for it?'

'The gun?' He shook his head. 'It's not registered. You work saloons, you don't have too much trouble knowing where to go to buy a gun. I spent two days asking around and on the third day I was a hundred dollars poorer. We got robbed once since we opened the place. John was working, he left the gun right where it was and handed over whatever was in the till. He didn't rob the customers. John figured he was a junkie, said he didn't even think of the gun until the guy was out the door. Maybe, or maybe he thought of it and decided against it. I probably would have done the same thing, or maybe not. You don't really know until it happens, do you?'

'No.'

'You really haven't had a piece since you quit the cops? They say after a guy gets in the habit he feels naked without it.'

'Not me. I felt like I laid down a burden.'

'Oh, lawdie, I'se gwine lay my burden down. Like you lightened up some, huh?'

'Something like that.'

'Yeah. He didn't mean anything, incidentally. Talking about ricochets.'

'Huh? Oh, Tommy.'

'Tough Tommy Tillary. Something of an asshole, but not a bad guy. Tough Tommy, it's like calling a big guy Tiny. I'm sure he didn't mean anything.'

'I'm sure you're right.'

'Tough Tommy. There's something else they call him.'

'Telephone Tommy.'

'Or Tommy Telephone, right. He sells shit over the phone. I didn't think grown men did that. I thought it was for house-wives and they wind up making thirty-five cents an hour.'

'I gather it can be lucrative.'

'Evidently. You saw the car. We all saw the car. We didn't get to see her open the door for him, but we got to see the car. Matt, you want to come up and have one more before we call it a day? I got scotch and bourbon, I probably got some food in the fridge.'

'I think I'll just get on home, Skip. But thanks.'

'I don't blame you.' He drew on his cigarette. He lived at the Parc Vendome, across the street and a few doors west of my hotel. He threw his cigarette away and we shook hands, and five or six shots sounded a block or so from us.

'Jesus,' he said. 'Was that gunfire or half a dozen little firecrackers? Could you say for sure?'

'No.'

'Neither could I. Probably firecrackers, considering what day it is. Or the Morrisseys caught up with Frank and Jesse, or I don't know what. This is the second, right? July second?'

'I guess so.'

'Gonna be some summer,' he said.

TWO

All of this happened a long time ago.

It was the summer of '75, and in a larger context it seems in memory to have been a season in which nothing very important happened. Nixon's resignation had been a year earlier, and the coming year would bring the convention and the campaigns, the Olympics, the Bicentennial.

Meanwhile Ford was in the White House, his presence oddly comforting if not terribly convincing. A fellow named Abe Beame was in Gracie Mansion, although I never had the feeling he really believed he was mayor of New York, any more than Gerry Ford believed he was president of the United States of America.

Somewhere along the way Ford declined to help the city through a financial crisis, and the *News* headline read, '*Ford to City: Drop Dead!*'

I remember the headline but I don't recall whether it ran before, during or after that summer. I read that headline. I rarely missed the *News*, picking up an early edition on my way back to my hotel at night or scanning a later one over breakfast. I read the *Times* now and then as well, if there was a story I was following, and more often than not I'd pick up a *Post* during the afternoon. I never paid much attention to the international news or the political stuff, or anything much aside from sports and local crime, but I was at least peripherally aware of what was going on in the world, and it's funny how utterly it's all vanished.

What do I remember? Well, three months after the stickup at Morrissey's, Cincinnati would take a seven-game Series from the Red Sox. I remember that, and Fisk's home run in game six, and Pete Rose playing throughout as if all of human destiny rode on every pitch. Neither of the New York teams made the playoffs, but beyond that I couldn't tell you how they did, and I

know I went to half a dozen games. I took my boys to Shea a couple of times, and I went a few times with friends. The Stadium was being renovated that year and both the Mets and Yanks were at Shea. Billie Keegan and I watched the Yankees play somebody, I remember, and they stopped the game because some idiots were throwing garbage onto the field.

Was Reggie Jackson with the Yankees that year? He was still in Oakland playing for Charlie Finley in '73, I remember the Series, the Mets losing badly. But when did Steinbrenner buy him for the Yankees?

What else? Boxing?

Did Ali fight that summer? I watched the second Norton fight on closed circuit, the one where Ali left the ring with a broken jaw and an unearned decision, but that was at least a year earlier, wasn't it? And then I'd seen Ali up close, ringside at the Garden. Earnie Shavers had fought Jimmy Ellis knocking him out early in the first round. For God's sake, I remember the punch that took Ellis out, remember the look on his wife's face two rows away from me, but when was that?

Not in '75, I'm sure of that. I must have gone to the fights that summer. I wonder who I watched.

Does it matter? I don't suppose it does. If it did I could go to the library and check the *Times Index*, or just hunt up a *World Almanac* for the year. But I already remember everything I really need to remember.

Skip Devoe and Tommy Tillary. Theirs are the faces I see when I think of the summer of '75. Between them, they were the season.

Were they friends of mine?

They were, but with a qualification. They were saloon friends. I rarely saw them – or anyone else, in those days – other than in a room where strangers gathered to drink liquor. I was still drinking then, of course, and I was at a point where the booze did (or seemed to do) more for me than it did to me.

A couple of years previously, my world had narrowed as if with a will of its own until it encompassed only a few square blocks south and west of Columbus Circle. I had left my marriage after a dozen years and two children, moving from Syosset, which is on Long Island, to my hotel, which was on West Fifty-seventh Street between Eighth and Ninth Avenues. I had at about the same time left the New York Police Department, where I'd put in about as many years with about as much to show for it. I supported myself, and sent checks irregularly to

438

Syosset, by doing things for people. I was not a private detective – private detectives are licensed and fill out reports and file tax returns. So I did favors for people, and they gave me money, and my rent always got paid and there was always money for booze, and intermittently I was able to put a check in the mail for Anita and the boys.

My world, as I said, had shrunk geographically, and within that area it confined itself largely to the room where I slept and the bars where I spent most of my waking hours. There was Morrissey's, but not all that often. I was off to bed more often than not by one or two, sometimes hung on until the bars closed, and only rarely went to an after-hours and made a full night of it.

There was Miss Kitty's, Skip Devoe's place. On the same block as my hotel, there was Polly's Cage, with its red-flocked bordello wallpaper and its crowd of after-work drinkers who thinned out by ten or ten-thirty; and McGovern's, a drab narrow room with unshielded overhead lights and customers who never said a word. I stopped in sometimes for a quick drink on a hard morning, and the bartender's hand shook when he poured it, as often as not.

On the same block there were two French restaurants, one next to the other. One of them, Mont-St-Michel, was always three-quarters empty. I took women there for dinner a few times over the years, and stopped in alone once in a while for a drink at the bar. The establishment next door had a good reputation and did a better business, but I don't think I ever set foot inside it.

There was a place over on Tenth Avenue called the Slate; they got a lot of cops from Midtown North and John Jay College, and I went there when I was in the mood for that kind of crowd. The steaks were good there, and the surroundings comfortable. There was a Martin's Bar on Broadway and Sixtieth with low-priced drinks and good corned beef and ham on the steam table; they had a big color set over the bar, and it wasn't a bad place to watch a ball game.

There was O'Neal's Baloon across from Lincoln Center – an old law still on the books that year prohibited calling a place a saloon, and they didn't know that when they ordered the sign, so they changed the first letter and said the hell with it. I'd stop in once in a while during the afternoon, but it was too trendy and upbeat at night. There was Antares and Spiro's, a Greek place at the corner of Ninth and Fifty-seventh. Not really my

kind of place, a lot of guys with bushy moustaches drinking ouzo, but I passed it every night on the way home and sometimes I'd stop in for a quick one.

There was the all-night newsstand at the corner of Fifty-seventh and Eighth. I generally bought the paper there, unless I bought it from the shopping-bag lady who hawked them on the sidewalk in front of the 400 Deli. She bought them for a quarter each from the newsstand – I think they were all a quarter that year, or maybe the *News* was twenty cents – and she sold them for the same price, which is a tough way to make a living. Sometimes I'd give her a buck and tell her to keep the change. Her name was Mary Alice Redfield, but I never knew that until a couple of years later, when someone stabbed her to death.

There was a coffee shop called the Red Flame and there was the 400 Deli. There were a couple of okay pizza stands, and there was a place that sold cheese steaks that nobody ever went to twice.

There was a spaghetti joint called Ralph's and a couple of Chinese restaurants. There was a Thai place that Skip Devoe was crazy about. There was Joey Farrell's on Fifty-eighth Street – they'd just opened the past winter. There was, hell, there were a lot of joints.

Mostly there was Armstrong's.

Christ, I lived there. I had my room to sleep in and I had other bars and restaurants to go to, but for a few years there, Jimmy Armstrong's was home to me. People who were looking for me knew to check for me there, and sometimes they called Armstrong's before they called the hotel. The place opened up around eleven, with a Filipino kid named Dennis behind the stick days. Billie Keegan took over around seven and closed at two or three or four, depending on the crowd and how he was feeling. (That was the weekday routine. There were different day and night bartenders on weekends, and the turnover among them was high.)

Waitresses came and went. They got acting jobs or broke up with their boyfriends or got new boyfriends or moved to Los Angeles or went home to Sioux Falls or had a fight with the Dominican kid in the kitchen or got fired for stealing or quit or got pregnant. Jimmy himself wasn't around much that summer. I think that was the year he was looking to buy land in North Carolina.

What can I say about the place? A long bar on the right hand side as you came in, tables on the left. Blue-checkered cloths on

them. Dark wood-paneled walls. Pictures on the walls, and framed advertisements from old magazines. A deer's head was mounted incongruously on the back wall; my favourite table was right under the thing, so I didn't have to look at it.

The crowd was a mixed bag. Doctors and nurses from Roosevelt Hospital across the street. Professors and students from Fordham. People from the television studios – CBS was a block away, and ABC a short walk. And people who lived nearby, or kept shops in the neighborhood. A couple of classical musicians. A writer. Two Lebanese brothers who had just opened a shoe store.

Not many kids. When I first moved into the neighborhood Armstrong's had a jukebox with a nice selection of jazz and country blues, but Jimmy took it out early on and replaced it with a stereo system and classical music on tape. That kept the younger crowd out, to the delight of the waitresses who hated the kids for staying late, ordering little, and tipping hardly at all. It also kept the noise level down and made the room more suitable for long-haul maintenance drinking.

Which was what I was there for. I wanted to keep an edge on but I didn't want to get drunk, except once in a while. I mostly mixed my bourbon with coffee, moving to straight booze toward the end of an evening. I could read a paper there, and have a hamburger or a full meal, and as much or as little conversation as I was in the mood for. I wasn't always there all day and night, but it was a rare day that I didn't get in the door at least once, and some days I got there a few minutes after Dennis opened up and was still there when Billie was ready to close. Everybody's got to be someplace.

Saloon friends.

I got to know Tommy Tillary in Armstrong's. He was a regular, apt to turn up three or four nights out of seven. I don't recall the first time I was aware of him, but it was hard to be in a room with him and not notice him. He was a big fellow and his voice tended to carry. He wasn't raucous, but after a few drinks his voice filled a room.

He ate a lot of beef and drank a lot of Chivas Regal, and they both showed in his face. He must have been close to forty-five. He was getting jowly, and his cheeks were blooming with a tracery of broken capillaries.

I never knew why they called him Tough Tommy. Perhaps Skip was right, perhaps the name's intent was ironic. They

called him Tommy Telephone because of his job. He worked in telephone sales, peddling investments over the phone from a bucket shop in the Wall Street area. I understand people change jobs a lot in that line of work. The ability to coax investment dollars out of strangers over a telephone line is a rather special talent, and its possessors can get work readily, moving from one employer to another at will.

That summer, Tommy was working for an outfit called Tannahill & Company, selling limited partnerships in real estate syndications. There were tax advantages, I gather, and the prospect of capital gains. I picked this up inferentially, because Tommy never pitched anything, to me or anyone else at the bar. I was there one time when an obstetrics resident from Roosevelt tried to ask him about his offerings. Tommy brushed him off with a joke.

'No, I'm serious,' the doctor insisted. 'I'm finally making a buck, I ought to start thinking about things like that.'

Tommy shrugged. 'You got a card?' The doctor didn't. 'Then write your phone on this and a good time to call you. You want a pitch, I'll call you and give you the full treatment. But I got to warn you, I'm irresistible over the phone.'

A couple of weeks later they ran into each other and the resident complained that Tommy hadn't called him.

'Jesus, I been meaning to,' Tommy said. 'First thing, I'll make a note of it now.'

He was acceptable company. He told dialect jokes and he told them reasonably well, and I laughed at my share of them. I suppose some of them were offensive, but they weren't often mean-spirited. If I was in a mood to reminisce about my days on the force, he was a good enough listener, and if the story I told was a funny one his laugh was as loud as anybody's.

He was, on balance, a little too loud and a little too cheery. He talked a little too much and he could get on your nerves. As I said, he'd turn up at Armstrong's three or four nights a week, and about half the time she was with him. Carolyn Cheatham, Carolyn from the Caro-line, with a soft you-all accent that, like certain culinary herbs, became stronger when you steeped it in alcohol. Sometimes she came in on his arm. Other times he'd get there first and she'd join him. She lived in the neighborhood and she and Tommy worked in the same office, and I figured – if I bothered to think about it – that the office romance had served to introduce Tommy to Armstrong's.

He followed sports. He bet with a bookie – mostly ball games,

sometimes horses – and he let you know when he won. He was a little too friendly, a little too indiscriminately friendly, and sometimes there was a chill in his eyes that belied the friendship in his voice. He had cold little eyes, and there was a softening around his mouth, a weakness there, but none of that got into his voice.

You could see how he'd be good over the phone.

Skip Devoe's first name was Arthur, but Bobby Ruslander was the only person I ever heard call him that. Bobby could get away with it. They'd been friends since fourth grade, they grew up on the same block in Jackson Heights. Skip had been christened Arthur Jr, and he'd acquired the nickname early on. 'Because he used to skip school all the time,' Bobby said, but Skip had another explanation.

'I had this uncle was in the navy and never got over it,' he told me once. 'My mother's brother. Bought me sailor suits, toy boats. I had this whole fleet and he called me Skipper, and pretty soon so did everybody else. Coulda been worse. There was a guy in our class everybody called Worm. Don't ask me why. Imagine if they still call him that. He's in bed with his wife: 'Oh, Wormy, put it in deeper.'

He was around thirty-four, thirty-five, about my height but lean and muscular. The veins showed on his forearms and the backs of his hands. There was no spare flesh on his face, and the skin followed the curve of the bone, giving him deeply sculpted cheeks. He had a hawk nose and piercing blue eyes that showed a little green under the right lighting. All of this combined with assurance and an easy manner to make him quite attractive to women, and he rarely had trouble finding a girl to go home with when he wanted one. But he was living alone and not keeping steady company with anyone, and seemed to prefer the regular company of other men. He had either lived with or been married to someone and it had ended a few years ago, and he seemed disinclined to get involved with anyone else.

Tommy Tillary got called Tough Tommy, and had a certain tough-guy quality to his manner. Skip Devoe actually *was* tough, but you had to sense it underneath the surface. It wasn't on display.

He'd been in the service, not the navy you'd have thought his uncle would have preconditioned him for but the army's Special Forces, the Green Berets. He enlisted fresh out of high school and got sent to Southeast Asia during the Kennedy years. He got

out sometime in the late Sixties, tried college and dropped out, then broke in behind the stick at an Upper East Side singles' bar. After a couple of years he and John Kasabian pooled their savings, signed a long lease on an out-of-business hardware store, spent what they had to remodel it, and opened up Miss Kitty's.

I saw him occasionally at his own place, but more often at Armstrong's, where he'd drop in frequently when he wasn't working. He was pleasant company, easy to be with, and not much rattled him.

There was something about him, though, and I think what it may have been was an air of cool competence. You sensed that he'd be able to handle just about anything that came along, and without working up a sweat. He came across as a man who could do things, one too who could make quick decisions in midaction. Maybe he acquired that quality wearing a green hat in Vietnam, or maybe I endowed him with it because I knew he'd been over there.

I'd met that quality most often in criminals. I have known several heavy heist men who had it, guys who took off banks and armored cars. And there was a long-haul driver for a moving company who was like that. I got to know him after he'd come back from the Coast ahead of schedule, found his wife in bed with a lover, and killed them both with his hands.

THREE

There was nothing in the papers about the robbery at Morrissey's, but for the next few days you heard a lot of talk about it around the neighborhood. The rumored loss Tim Pat and his brothers had sustained kept escalating. The numbers I heard ranged from ten thousand to a hundred thousand. Since only the Morrisseys and the gunmen would know, and neither were terribly likely to talk, one number seemed as good as the next.

'I think they got around fifty,' Billie Keegan told me the night of the Fourth. 'That's the number keeps coming up. Of course everybody and his brother was there and saw it.'

'What do you mean?'

'I mean so far there's been at least three guys assured me they were there when it happened, and I *was* there and can swear for a fact that they weren't. And they can supply bits of color that somehow slipped by me. Did you know that one of the gunmen slapped a woman around?'

'Really.'

'So I'm told. Oh, and one of the Morrissey brothers was shot, but it was only a flesh wound. I thought it was exciting enough the way it went down, but I guess it's a lot more dramatic when you're not there. Well, ten years after the 1916 Rising they say it was hard to find a man in Dublin who hadn't been part of it. That glorious Monday morning, when thirty brave men marched into the post office and ten thousand heroes marched out. What do you think, Matt? Fifty grand sound about right to you?'

Tommy Tillary had been there, and I figured he'd dine out on it. Maybe he did. I didn't see him for a couple of days, and when I did he never even mentioned the robbery. He'd discovered the secret of betting baseball, he told everybody around. You just bet

against the Mets and the Yankees and they'd always come through for you.

Early the next week, Skip came by Armstrong's in midafternoon and found me at my table in the back. He'd picked up a dark beer at the bar and brought it with him. He sat down across from me and said he'd been at Morrissey's the night before.

'I haven't been there since I was there with you,' I told him.

'Well, last night was my first time since then. They got the ceiling fixed. Tim Pat was asking for you.'

'Me?'

'Uh-huh.' He lit a cigarette. 'He'd appreciate it if you could drop by.'

'What for?'

'He didn't say. You're a detective, aren't you? Maybe he wants you to find something. What do you figure he might have lost?'

'I don't want to get in the middle of that.'

'Don't tell me.'

'Some Irish war, just what I need to cut myself in on.'

He shrugged. 'You don't have to go. He said to ask you to drop by any time after eight in the evening.'

'I guess they sleep until then.'

'If they sleep at all.'

He drank some beer, wiped his upper lip with the back of his hand. I said, 'You were there last night? What was it like?'

'What it's always like. I told you they patched the ceiling, did a good job of it as far as I could tell. Tim Pat and his brothers were their usual charming selves. I just said I'd pass the word to you next time I ran into you. You can go or not go.'

'I don't think I will,' I said.

But the next night around ten, ten-thirty, I figured what the hell and went over there. On the ground floor, the theater troupe was rehearsing Brendan Behan's *The Quare Fellow*. It was scheduled to open Thursday night. I rang the upstairs bell and waited until one of the brothers came downstairs and cracked the door. He told me they were closed, that they didn't open until two. I told him my name was Matthew Scudder and Tim Pat had said he wanted to see me.

'Oh, sure, an' I didn't now ye in that light,' he said. 'Come inside and I'll tell himself you're here.'

I waited in the big room on the second floor. I was studying the ceiling, looking for patched bullet holes, when Tim Pat

446

came in and switched on some more lights. He was wearing his usual garb, but without the butcher's apron.

You're good to come,' he said. 'Ye'll have a drink with me? And your drink is bourbon, is it not?'

He poured drinks and we sat down at a table. It may have been the one his brother fell into when he came stumbling through the door. Tim Pat held his glass to the light, tipped it back and drained it.

He said, 'Ye were here the night of the incident.'

'Yes.'

'One of those fine young lads left a hat behind, but misfortunately his mother never got around to sewing a name tape in it, so it's impossible to return it to him.'

'I see.'

'If I only knew who he was and where to find him, I could see that he got what was rightfully his.'

I'll bet you could, I thought.

'Ye were a policeman.'

'Not anymore.'

'Ye might hear something. People talk, don't they, and a man who keeps his eyes and ears open might do himself a bit of good.'

I didn't say anything.

He groomed his beard with his fingertips. 'My brothers and I,' he said, his eyes fixed on a point over my shoulder, 'would be greatly pleased to pay ten thousand dollars for the names and whereabouts of the two lads who visited us the other night.'

'Just to return a hat.'

'Why, we've a sense of obligation,' he said. 'Wasn't it your George Washington who walked miles through the snow to return a penny to a customer?'

'I think it was Abraham Lincoln.'

'Of course it was. George Washington was the other, the cherry tree. 'Father, I cannot tell a lie.' This nation's heroes are great ones for honesty.'

'They used to be.'

'And then himself, tellin' us all he's not a crook. Jaysus.' He shook his big head. 'Well, then,' he said. 'Do ye think ye'll be able to help us out?'

'I don't see what help I could be.'

'Ye were here and saw them.'

'They were wearing masks and they had caps on their heads.

In fact I could swear they both had their caps on when they left. You don't suppose you found somebody else's hat, do you?'

'Perhaps the lad dropped it on the stairs. If you hear anything, Matt, ye'll let us know?'

'Why not?'

'Are ye of Irish stock yourself, Matt?'

'No.'

'I'd have thought maybe one of your forebears was from Kerry. The Kerryman is famous for answering a question with a question.'

'I don't know who they were, Tim Pat.'

'If you learn anything ...'

'If I learn anything.'

'Ye've no quarrel with the price? It's a fair price?'

'No quarrel,' I said. 'It's a very fair price.'

It was a good price, the fairness of it notwithstanding. I said as much to Skip the next time I saw him.

'He didn't want to hire me,' I said. 'He wanted to post a reward. Ten K to the man who tells him who they are and where he can lay his hands on them.'

'Would you do it?'

'What, go hunting for them? I told you the other day I wouldn't take the job for a fee. I'm certainly not going to go nosing around on the come.'

He shook his head. 'Suppose you found out without trying. You walked around the corner on the way to buy a paper and there they were.'

'How would I recognize them?'

'How often do you see two guys wearing red kerchiefs for masks? No, seriously, say you recognized them. Or you got hold of the information, the word got out and some contact of yours from the old days put a flea in your ear. You used to have stool pigeons, didn't you?'

'Snitches,' I said. 'Every cop had them, you couldn't get anywhere without them. Still, I –'

'Forget *how* you find out,' he said. 'Just suppose it happened. Would you?'

'Would I –'

'Sell 'em out. Collect the ten grand.'

'I don't know anything about them.'

'Fine, let's say you don't know whether they're assholes or altar boys. What's the difference? Either way it's blood money,

right? The Morrisseys find those kids, they gotta be dead as Kelsey's nuts, right?'

'I don't suppose Tim Pat wants to send them an invitation to a christening.'

'Or ask 'em to join the Holy Name Society. Could you do it?'

I shook my head. 'I can't answer that,' I said. 'It would depend on who they were and how bad I needed the money.'

'I don't think you'd do it.'

'I don't think I would either.'

'I sure as shit wouldn't,' he said. He tapped the ashes from his cigarette. 'There's enough people who would.'

'There's people who would kill for less than that.'

'I was thinking that myself.'

'There were a few cops in the room that night,' I said. 'You want to bet they'll know about the reward?'

'No bet.'

'Say a cop finds out who the holdup men were. He can't make a collar. There's no crime, right? Nothing ever got reported, no witnesses, nothing. But he can turn the two bums over to Tim Pat and walk with half a year's pay.'

'Knowing he's aided and abetted murder.'

'I'm not saying everybody would do it. But you tell yourself the guys are scum, they've probably killed people themselves, they're a cinch to kill someone sooner or later, and it's not like you know for certain the Morrisseys are going to kill them. Maybe they'll just break a few bones, just scare 'em a little. Try to get their money back, something like that. You can tell yourself that.'

'And believe it?'

'Most people believe what they want to believe.'

'Yeah,' he said. 'Can't argue with that.'

You decide something in your mind and then your body goes and decides something else. I wasn't going to have anything to do with Tim Pat's problem, and then I kept finding myself sniffing around it like a dog at a lamppost. The same night I assured Skip I wasn't playing, I wound up on Seventy-second Street at a place called Poogan's Pub, sitting at a rear table and buying iced Stolichnaya for a tiny albino Negro named Danny Boy Bell. Danny Boy was always interesting company, but he was also a prime snitch, an information broker who knew everyone and heard everything.

Of course he'd heard about the robbery at Morrissey's. He'd

heard a wide range of figures quoted for the take, and for his own part guessed that the right number was somewhere between fifty and a hundred thousand dollars.

'Whoever took it,' he said, 'they're not spending it in the bars. My sense of it is that it's an Irish thing, Matthew. Irish Irish, not the local Harps. You know, it went down right in the middle of Westy country, but I can't see the Westies taking off Tim Pat like that.'

The Westies are a loosely organized mob of toughs and killers, most of them Irish, and they've been operating in Hell's Kitchen since the turn of the century. Maybe longer, maybe since the Potato Famine.

'I don't know,' I said. 'With that kind of money involved –'

'If those two were Westies, if they were anybody from the neighborhood, it wouldn't be a secret for more than eight hours. Everybody on Tenth Avenue'd know it.'

'You're right.'

'Some kind of Irish thing, that's my best guess. You were there, you'd know this. The masks were red?'

'Red handkerchiefs.'

'A shame. If they were green or orange they'd be making some sort of political statement. I understand the brothers are offering a generous reward. Is that what brings you here, Matthew?'

'Oh, no,' I said. 'Definitely not.'

'Not doing a bit of exploratory work on speculation?'

'Absolutely not,' I said.

Friday afternoon I was drinking in Armstrong's and fell into conversation with a couple of nurses at the next table. They had tickets for an off-off-Broadway show that night. Dolores couldn't go, and Fran really wanted to but she wasn't sure she felt like going by herself, and besides they had the extra ticket.

And of course the show turned out to be *The Quare Fellow*. It didn't relate in any way to the incident at Morrissey's, it was just coincidentally being performed downstairs of the after-hours joint, and it hadn't been my idea in the first place, but what was I doing there? I sat on a flimsy wooden folding chair and watched Behan's play about imprisoned criminals in Dublin and wondered what the hell I was doing in the audience.

Afterward Fran and I wound up at Miss Kitty's with a group that included two of the members of the cast. One of them, a slim red-haired girl with enormous green eyes, was Fran's friend

450

Mary Margaret, and the reason why Fran had been so anxious to go. That was Fran's reason, but what was mine?

There was talk at the table of the robbery. I didn't raise the subject or contribute much to the discussion, but I couldn't stay out of it altogether because Fran told the group I was a former police detective and asked for my professional opinion of the affair. My reply was as noncommittal as I could make it, and I avoided mentioning that I'd been an eyewitness to the holdup.

Skip was there, so busy behind the bar with the Fridaynight crowd that I didn't bother to do more than wave hello at him. The place was mobbed and noisy, as it always was on weekends, but that was where everyone else had wanted to go, and I'd gone along.

Fran lived on Sixty-eighth between Columbus and Amsterdam. I walked her home, and at her door she said, 'Matt, you were a sweetheart to keep me company. The play was okay, wasn't it?'

'It was fine.'

'I thought Mary Margaret was good, anyway. Matt, would you mind awfully if I don't ask you to come up? I'm beat and I've got an early day tomorrow.'

'That's okay,' I said. 'Now that you mention it, so do I.'

'Being a detective?'

I shook my head. 'Being a father.'

The next morning Anita put the kids on the Long Island Rail Road and I picked them up at the station in Corona and took them to Shea and watched the Mets lose to the Astros. The boys would be going to camp for four weeks in August and they were excited about that. We ate hot dogs and peanuts and popcorn. They had Cokes, I had a couple of beers. There was some sort of special promotion that day, and the boys got free caps or pennants, I forget which.

Afterward I took them back to the city on the subway and to a movie at Loew's 83rd. We had pizza on Broadway after the film let out and took a cab back to my hotel, where I'd rented a twin-bedded room for them a floor below mine. They went to bed and I went up to my own room. After an hour I checked their room. They were sleeping soundly. I locked their door again and went around the corner to Armstrong's. I didn't stay long, maybe an hour. Then I went back to my hotel, checked the boys again, and went upstairs and to bed.

In the morning we went out for a big breakfast, pancakes and

bacon and sausages. I took them up to the Museum of the American Indian in Washington Heights. There are a couple dozen museums in the city of New York, and when you leave your wife you get to discover them all.

It felt strange being in Washington Heights. It was in that neighborhood a few years earlier that I'd been having a few off-duty drinks when a couple of punks held up the bar and shot the bartender dead on their way out.

I went out into the street after them. There are a lot of hills in Washington Heights. They ran down one of them and I had to shoot downhill. I brought them both down, but one shot went wide and ricocheted, and it killed a small child named Estrellita Rivera.

Those things happen. There was a departmental hearing, there always is when you kill someone, and I was found to have acted properly and with justification.

Shortly thereafter I put in my papers and left the police department.

I can't say that one event caused the other. I can only say that the one led to the other. I had been the unwitting instrument of a child's death, and after that something was different for me. The life I had been living without complaint no longer seemed to suit me. I suppose it had ceased to suit me before then. I suppose the child's death precipitated a life change that was long overdue. But I can't say that for certain, either. Just that one thing led to another.

We took a train to Penn Station. I told the boys how good it had been to spend some time with them, and they told me what a good time they'd had. I put them on a train, made a phone call and told their mother what train they'd be on. She assured me she'd meet it, then mentioned hesitantly that it would be good if I sent money soon. Soon, I assured her.

I hung up and thought of the ten thousand dollars Tim Pat was offering. And shook my head, amused at the thought.

But that night I got restless and wound up down in the Village, stopping in a string of bars for one drink each. I took the A train to West Fourth Street and started at McBell's and worked my way west. Jimmy Day's, the 55, the Lion's Head, George Hertz's, the Corner Bistro. I told myself I was just having a couple of drinks, unwinding after the pressure of a weekend with my sons, settling myself down after awakening old memories with a visit to Washington Heights.

But I knew better. I was starting some half-assed purposeless

investigation, trying to turn up a lead to the pair who'd hit Morrissey's.

I wound up in a gay bar called Sinthia's. Kenny, who owned the place, was minding the store, serving drinks to men in Levi's and ribbed tank tops. Kenny was slender, willowy, with dyed blond hair and a face that had been tucked and lifted enough to look no more than twenty-eight, which was about half as many years as Kenny had been on the planet.

'Matthew!' he called out. 'You can all relax now, girls. Law and order has come to Grove Street.'

Of course he didn't know anything about the robbery at Morrissey's. He didn't know Morrissey's to begin with; no gay man had to leave the Village to find a place where he could get a drink after closing. But the holdup men could have been gay as easily as not, and if they weren't spending their take elsewhere they might be spending it in the joints around Christopher Street, and anyhow that was the way you worked it, you nosed around, you worked all your sources, you put the word out and waited to see if anything came back to you.

But why was I doing this? Why was I wasting my time?

I don't know what would have happened – whether I would have kept at it or let go of it, whether I would have gotten someplace or ultimately turned away from a cold trail. I didn't seem to be getting anywhere, but that's often the way it is, and you go through the motions with no indication of progress until you get lucky and something breaks. Maybe something like that would have happened. Maybe not.

Instead, some other things happened to take my mind off Tim Pat Morrissey and his quest for vengeance.

For openers, somebody killed Tommy Tillary's wife.

FOUR

Tuesday night I took Fran to dinner at the Thai restaurant Skip Devoe liked so much. Afterward I walked her home, with a stop for after-dinner drinks at Joey Farrell's. In front of her building she pleaded an early day again, and I left her there and walked back to Armstrong's with a stop or two en route. I was in a sour mood, and a stomachful of unfamiliar food didn't help any. I probably hit the bourbon a little harder than usual, rolling out of there around one or two. I took the long way home, picked up the *Daily News*, and sat on the edge of my bed in my underwear taking a quick look at a couple of stories.

On one of the inside pages I read about a Brooklyn woman who'd been killed in the course of a burglary. I was tired and I'd had a lot to drink and the name didn't register.

But I woke up the next morning with something buzzing in my mind, half dream and half memory. I sat up and reached for the paper and found the story.

Margaret Tillary, forty-seven, had been stabbed to death in the upstairs bedroom of her home on Colonial Road, in the Bay Ridge section of Brooklyn, evidently having awakened in the course of a burglary. Her husband, securities salesman Thomas J. Tillary, had become concerned when his wife failed to answer the telephone Tuesday afternoon. He called a relative living nearby who entered the house, finding the premises ransacked and the woman dead.

'This is a good neighborhood,' a neighbor was quoted as saying. 'Things like this don't happen here.' But a police source cited a marked increase in area burglaries in recent months, and another neighbor referred obliquely to the presence of a 'bad element' in the neighborhood.

It's not a common name. There's a Tillary Street in Brooklyn, not far from the entrance to the Brooklyn Bridge, but I've no idea what war hero or ward heeler they named it after, or if he's a

relative of Tommy's. There are several Tillerys in the Manhattan phone directory, spelled with an *e*. Thomas Tillary, securities salesman, Brooklyn – it seemed as though it had to be Telephone Tommy.

I took a shower and shaved and went out for breakfast. I thought about what I'd read and tried to figure out how I felt about it. It didn't seem real to me. I didn't know him well and I hadn't known her at all, had never known her name, had known only that she existed somewhere in Brooklyn.

I looked at my left hand, the ring finger. No ring, no mark. I had worn a wedding ring for years, and I had taken it off when I moved from Syosset to Manhattan. For months there had been a mark where the ring had been, and then one day I noticed that the mark was gone.

Tommy wore a ring. A yellow gold band, maybe three-eighths of an inch wide. And he wore a pinkie ring on his right hand, a high-school class ring, I think it must have been. I remembered it, sitting there over coffee in the Red Flame. A class ring with a blue stone on his right pinkie, a yellow gold band on his left ring finger.

I couldn't tell how I felt.

That afternoon I went to St. Paul's and lit a candle for Margaret Tillary. I had discovered churches in my retirement, and while I did not pray or attend services, I dropped in now and then and sat in the darkened silence. Sometimes I lit candles for people who had recently died, or for those longer dead who were on my mind. I don't know why I thought this was something I ought to do, nor do I know why I felt compelled to tuck a tenth of any income I received into the poor box of whatever church I next visited.

I sat in a rear pew and thought a bit about sudden death. When I left the church a light rain was falling. I crossed Ninth Avenue and ducked into Armstrong's. Dennis was behind the bar. I ordered bourbon neat, drank it straight down, and motioned for another and said I'd have a cup of coffee with it.

While I poured the bourbon into the coffee, he asked if I'd heard about Tillary. I said I'd read the story in the *News*.

'There's a piece in this afternoon's *Post*, too. Pretty much the same story. It happened the night before last is how they figure it. He evidently didn't make it home and he went straight to the office in the morning, and then after he called a few times to apologize and couldn't get through, he got worried.'

'It said that in the paper?'

'Just about. That would have been the night before last. He didn't come in while I was here. Did you see him?'

I tried to remember. 'I think so. The night before last yeah, I think he was here with Carolyn.'

'The Dixie Belle.'

'That's the one.'

'Wonder how she feels about now.' He used thumb and forefinger to smooth the points of his wispy moustache. 'Probably guilty for having her wish come true.'

'You think she wanted the wife dead?'

'I don't know. Isn't that a girl's fantasy when she's running around with a married guy? Look, I'm not married. What do I know about these things?'

The story faded out of the papers during the next couple of days. There was a death notice in Thursday's *News*. Margaret Wayland Tillary, beloved wife of Thomas, mother of the late James Alan Tillary, aunt of Mrs Richard Paulsen. There would be a wake that evening, a funeral service the following afternoon at Walter B. Cooke's, Fourth and Bay Ridge Avenues, in Brooklyn.

That night Billie Keegan said, 'I haven't seen Tillary since it happened. I'm not sure we're gonna see him again.' He poured himself a glass of JJ&S, the twelve-year-old Jameson that nobody else ever ordered. 'I bet we don't see him with her again.'

'The girlfriend?'

He nodded. 'What's got to be on both their minds is he was with her when his wife was getting knifed to death in Brooklyn. And if he'd only been home where he was supposed to be, di dah di dah di dah. You're fooling around and you want a quick bounce and a couple of laughs, the last thing you need is something to remind you how you got your wife killed by fooling around.'

I thought about it, nodded. 'The wake was tonight,' I said.

'Yeah? You go?' I shook my head. 'I don't know anybody that went.'

I left before closing. I had a drink at Polly's and another at Miss Kitty's. Skip was tense and remote. I sat at the bar and tried to ignore the man standing next to me without being actively hostile. He wanted to tell me how all the city's problems were the fault of the former mayor. I didn't necessarily disagree but I didn't want to hear about it.

I finished my drink and headed for the door. Halfway there Skip called my name. I turned and he motioned to me.

I walked back to the bar. He said, 'This is the wrong time for it, but I'd like to talk to you soon.

'Ask your advice, maybe throw a little work your way. You be around Jimmy's tomorrow afternoon?'

'Probably,' I said. 'If I don't go to the funeral.'

'Who died?'

'Tillary's wife.'

'Oh, the funeral's tomorrow? Are you thinking about going? I didn't know you were that close to the guy.'

'I'm not.'

'Then why would you want to go? Forget it, not my business. I'll look for you at Armstrong's around two, two-thirty. If you're not there I'll catch you some other time.'

I was there when he came in the next day around two-thirty. I had just finished lunch and was sitting over a cup of coffee when Skip came in and scanned the room from the doorway. He saw me and came on over and sat down.

'You didn't go,' he said. 'Well, it's no day for a funeral. I was just over at the gym, I felt silly sitting in the sauna after. The whole city's a sauna. What have you got there, some of that famous Kentucky coffee of yours?'

'Just plain coffee.'

'That'll never do.' He turned, beckoned the waitress. 'Let me have a Prior Dark,' he told her, 'and bring my father here something to put in his coffee.'

She brought a shot for me and a beer for him. He poured it slowly against the side of the glass, examined the half-inch head, took a sip, put the glass down.

He said, 'I might have a problem.'

I didn't say anything.

'This is confidential, okay?'

'Sure.'

'You know much about the bar business?'

'Just from the consumer's point of view.'

'I like that. You know it's all cash.'

'Of course.'

'A lot of places take plastic. We don't. Strictly cash. Oh, if we know you we'll take your check, or if you run a tab, whatever. But it's basically a cash business. I'd say ninety-five percent of

457

our gross is cash. As a matter of fact it's probably higher than that.'

'And?'

He took out a cigarette, tapped the end against his thumbnail. 'I hate talking about all this,' he said.

'Then don't.'

He lit the cigarette. 'Everybody skims,' he said. 'A certain percentage of the take comes right off the top before it gets recorded. It doesn't get listed in the books, it doesn't get deposited, it doesn't exist. The dollar you don't declare is worth two dollars that you do, because you don't pay tax on it. You follow me?'

'It's not all that hard to follow, Skip.'

'Everybody does it, Matt. The candy store, the newsie, everybody who takes in cash. Christ's sake, it's the American way – the president'd cheat on his taxes if he could get by with it.'

'The last one did.'

'Don't remind me. That asshole'd give tax fraud a bad name.' He sucked hard on the cigarette. 'We opened up, couple years ago, John kept the books. I yell at people, do the hiring and firing, he does the buying and keeps the books. Works out about right.'

'And?'

'Get to the point, right? Fuck it. From the beginning we keep two sets of books, one for us and one for Uncle.' His face darkened and he shook his head. 'Never made sense to me. I figured keep one phony set and that's that, but he says you need honest books so you'll know how you're doing. That make sense to you? You count your money and you know how you're doing, you don't need two sets of books to tell you, but he's the guy with the business head, he knows these things, so I say fine, do it.'

He picked up his glass, drank some beer. 'They're gone,' he said.

'The books.'

'John comes in Saturday mornings, does the week's bookkeeping. Everything was fine this past Saturday. Day before yesterday he has to check something, looks for the books, no books.'

'Both sets gone?'

'Only the dark set, the honest set.' He drank some beer, wiped his mouth with the back of his hand. 'He spent a day taking

Valium and going nuts by himself, then told me yesterday. And I been going nuts ever since.'

'How bad is it, Skip?'

'Aw, shit,' he said. 'It's pretty bad. We could go away for it.'

'Really?'

He nodded. 'It's all our records since we opened, and we been making money from the first week. I don't know why, it's just another joint, but we been pulling 'em in. And we've been stealing with both hands. They come up with the books, we're fucking *nailed*, you know? You can't call it a mistake, it's all down there in black and white, one set of figures, and there's another completely different set on each year's tax return. You can't even make up a story, all you can do is ask 'em where they want you, Atlanta or Leavenworth.'

We sat silent for a few moments. I drank some of my coffee. He lit another cigarette and blew smoke at the ceiling. Music played on the tape deck, something contra-puntal with woodwinds.

I said, 'What would you want me to do?'

'Find out who took 'em. Get 'em back.'

'Maybe John got rattled, misplaced them. He could have –'

He was shaking his head. 'I turned the office upside down yesterday afternoon. They're fuckin' gone.'

'They just disappeared? No signs of forced entry? Where did you keep 'em, under lock and key?'

'They're supposed to be locked up. Sometimes he would forget, leave 'em out, stick 'em in a desk drawer. You get careless, you know what I mean? You never have an incident, you take the whole thing for granted, and if you're rushed, you don't take the trouble to put things away where they belong. He tells me he locked up Saturday but in the next breath he admits maybe he didn't, it's a routine thing, he does the same thing every Saturday, so how do you remember one Saturday from the next? What's the difference? The stuff is capital-G Gone.'

'So somebody took it.'

'Right.'

'If they go the IRS with it –'

'Then we're dead. That's all. They can plant us next to whatsisname's wife, Tillary's. You miss the funeral, don't worry about it. I'll understand.'

'Was anything else missing, Skip?'

'Didn't seem to be.'

459

'So it was a very specific theft. Somebody walked in, took the books, and left.'

'Bingo.'

I worked it out in my mind. 'If it was somebody with a grudge against you, somebody you fired, say –'

'Yeah, I thought of that.'

'If they go to the Feds, you'll know about it when a couple of guys in suits come around and show you their ID. They'll take all your records, slap a lien on your bank accounts, and whatever else they do.'

'Keep talking, Matt. You're really making my day.'

'If it's not somebody who's got a hardon for you, then it's somebody looking to turn a dollar.'

'By selling the books.'

'Uh-huh.'

'To us.'

'You're the ideal customers.'

'I thought of that. So did Kasabian. Sit tight, he tells me. Sit tight, and whoever took 'em'll get in touch, and we worry about it then. Just sit tight in the meantime. Tight's no problem, it's the sitting that's getting to me. Can you get bail for cheating on taxes?'

'Of course.'

'Then I suppose I can get it and run out on it. Leave the country. Live the rest of my life in Nepal selling hash to hippies.'

'All that's still a long ways off.'

'I suppose.' He looked thoughtfully at his cigarette, drowned it in the dregs of his beer. 'I hate it when they do that,' he said thoughtfully. 'Send back glasses with butts floating in them. Disgusting.' He looked at me, his eyes probing mine. 'Anything you can do for me on this? I mean for hire.'

'I don't see what. Not at this point.'

'So in the meantime I just wait. That's always the hard part for me, always has been. I ran track in high school, the quarter-mile. I was lighter then. I smoked heavy, I smoked since I was thirteen, but you can do anything at that age and it doesn't touch you. Nothing touches kids, that's why they all think they're gonna live forever.' He drew another cigarette halfway out of the pack, put it back again. 'I loved the races, but waiting for the event to start, I hated that. Some guys would puke. I never puked but I used to feel like it. I would pee and then I'd think I had to pee again five minutes later.' He shook his head at

460

the memory. 'And the same thing overseas, waiting to go into combat. I never minded combat, and there was a lot about it to mind. Things that bother me now, remembering them, but while they were going on it was a different story.'

'I can understand that.'

'Waiting, though, that was murder.' He pushed his chair back. 'What do I owe you, Matt?'

'For what? I didn't do anything.'

'For the advice.'

I waved the thought away. 'You can buy me that drink,' I said, 'and that'll be fine.'

'Done,' he said. He stood up. 'I may need a hand from you somewhere down the line.'

'Sure,' I said.

He stopped to talk to Dennis on the way out. I nursed my coffee. By the time I was done with it a woman two tables away had paid her check and left her newspaper behind. I read it, and had another cup of coffee with it, and a shot of bourbon to sweeten the coffee.

The afternoon crowd was starting to fill the room when I called the waitress over. I palmed her a buck and told her to put the check on my tab.

'No check,' she said. 'The gentleman paid it.'

She was new, she didn't know Skip by name. 'He wasn't supposed to do that,' I said. 'Anyway, I had a drink after he left. Put it on my tab, all right?'

'Talk to Dennis,' she said.

She went to take somebody's order before I could reply. I went to the bar and crooked a finger for Dennis. 'She tells me there's no check for my table,' I said.

'She speaks the truth.' He smiled. He often smiled, as if much of what he saw amused him. 'Devoe paid the check.'

'He wasn't supposed to do that. Anyway, I had a drink after he left and told her to put it on my tab, and she said to see you. Is this something new? Don't I have a tab?'

His smile broadened. 'Anytime you want one, but as a matter of fact you don't have one now. Mr Devoe covered it. Wiped the slate clean.'

'What did it come to?'

'Eighty dollars and change. I could probably come up with the exact figure if it mattered. Does it?'

'No.'

'He gave me a hundred dollars to cover your tab, the check

today, a tip for Lyddie and something to ease my own weariness of the soul. I suppose one could maintain that your most recent drink was not covered, but my inscrutable sense of the rightness of things is that it was.' Another wide smile. 'So you owe us nothing,' he said.

I didn't argue. If there was one thing I learned in the NYPD, it was to take what people gave me.

FIVE

I went back to my hotel, checked for mail and messages. There were none of either. The desk clerk, a loose-limbed black man from Antigua, said that he didn't mind the heat but he missed the ocean breezes.

I went upstairs and took a shower. My room was hot. There was an air-conditioner, but something was wrong with its cooling element. It moved the warm air around and gave it a chemical flavor but didn't do much about the heat or the humidity. I could shut it off and open the window from the top, but the air outside was no better. I stretched out and must have dozed off for an hour or so, and when I woke up I needed another shower.

I took it and then called Fran. Her roommate answered. I gave my name and waited what seemed like a long time for Fran to come to the phone.

I suggested dinner, and maybe a movie afterward if we felt up to it. 'Oh, I'm afraid I can't tonight, Matt,' she said. 'I have other plans. Maybe some other time?'

I hung up regretting that I'd called. I checked the mirror, decided I didn't really need a shave after all, got dressed and got out of there.

It was hot on the street, but it would cool down in a couple of hours. Meanwhile, there were bars all over the place, and their air-conditioners all worked better than mine.

Curiously, I didn't hit it all that hard. I was in a surly mood, gruff and ill-tempered, and that usually led me to take my drinks fast. But I was restless, and as a result I moved around a lot. There were even a few bars that I walked into and out of without ordering anything.

At one point I almost got into a fight. In a joint on Tenth Avenue a rawboned drunk with a couple of teeth missing

463

bumped into me and spilled part of his drink on me, then took exception to the way I accepted his apology. It was all over nothing – he was looking for a fight and I was very nearly ready to oblige him. Then one of his friends grabbed his arms from behind and another stepped between us, and I came to my senses and got out of there.

I walked east on Fifty-seventh. A couple of black hookers were working the pavement in front of the Holiday Inn. I noticed them more than I usually did. One, with a face like an ebony mask, challenged me with her eyes. I felt a rush of anger, and I didn't know who or what I was angry at.

I walked over to Ninth, up half a block to Armstrong's. I wasn't surprised to see Fran there. It was almost as if I had expected her to be there, seated at a table along the north wall. She had her back to me and hadn't noticed me come in.

Hers was a table for two, and her partner was no one I recognized. He had blond hair and eyebrows and an open young face, and he was wearing a slate-blue short-sleeved shirt with epaulets. I think they call it a safari shirt. He was smoking a pipe and drinking a beer. Her drink was something red in an oversize stemmed glass.

Probably a tequila sunrise. That was a big year for tequila sunrises.

I turned to the bar, and there was Carolyn. The tables were crowded but the bar was half empty, lightly attended for that hour on a Friday night. At her right, toward the door, a couple of beer drinkers stood talking baseball. To her left, there were three vacant stools in a row.

I took the middle one and ordered bourbon, a double with water back. Billie served it, saying something about the weather. I took a sip of my drink and shot a quick glance at Carolyn.

She didn't appear to be waiting for Tommy or for anyone else, nor did she look as though she'd just breezed in a few minutes ago. She was wearing yellow pedal pushers and a sleeveless lime-green blouse. Her light brown hair was combed to frame her little fox face. She was drinking something dark from a lowball glass.

At least it wasn't a tequila sunrise.

I drank some bourbon, glanced in spite of myself at Fran and was irritated with my own irritation. I'd had two dates with her, there was no great mutual attraction, no chemical magic, just two nights of leaving her at her door. And tonight I'd called her,

late, and she'd said she had other plans, and here she was, drinking a tequila sunrise with her other plan.

Where did I get off being mad about that?

I thought, I'll bet she doesn't tell him she's got an early day tomorrow. I bet the White Hunter there doesn't have to say goodnight downstairs.

To my right, a voice with a Piedmont softness to it said, 'I forget your name.'

I looked up.

'I believe we were introduced,' she said, 'but I don't recall your name.'

'It's Matthew Scudder,' I said, 'and you're right, Tommy introduced us. You're Carolyn.'

'Carolyn Cheatham. Have you seen him?'

'Tommy? Not since it happened.'

'Neither have I. Were you-all at the funeral?'

'No. I thought about going but I didn't get there.'

'Why would you go? You never met her, did you?'

'No.'

'Neither did I.' She laughed. There wasn't much mirth in it. 'Big surprise, I never met his wife. I would have gone this afternoon. But I didn't.' She took her lower lip between her teeth. 'Matt. Whyn't you buy me a drink? Or I'll buy you one, but come sit next to me so's I don't have to shout. Please?'

She was drinking Amaretto, a sweet almond-flavored liqueur that she took on the rocks. It tastes like dessert but it's almost as strong as whiskey.

'He told me not to come,' she said. 'To the funeral. It was someplace in Brooklyn, that's a whole foreign nation to me, Brooklyn, but a lot of people went from the office. I wouldn't have had to *know* how to get there, I could have had a ride, I could have been part of the office crowd, come to pay my respects along with everybody else. But he said not to, he said it wouldn't look right.'

Her bare arms were lightly dusted with golden hair. She was wearing perfume, a floral scent with an undertaste of musk.

'He said it wouldn't look right,' she said. 'He said it was a matter of respect for the dead.' She picked up her glass and stared into it.

She said, 'Respect. What's the man care about respect? What's he so much as know about respect, for the dead or for the living? I would just have been part of the office crowd. We both work

465

there at Tannahill, far as anyone knows we're just friends. Lord's sake, all we ever were is friends.'

'Whatever you say.'

'Well, *shit*,' she said, drawling it, giving the word an extra syllable or two. 'Ah *don't* mean to say Ah wasn't fucking him. Ah surely don't mean that. But all it ever was was laughs and good times. He was married and went home to mama most every night' – she drank some Amaretto – 'and that was jes fine, believe me, because who in her right mind'd want Tommy Tillary around by the dawn's early light? Christ in the foothills, Matthew, did I spill this or drink it?'

We agreed that she was drinking them a little too fast. Sweet drinks, we assured each other, had a way of sneaking up on a person. It was this fancy New York Amaretto shit, she maintained. It wasn't like the bourbon she'd grown up on. You knew where you stood with bourbon.

I reminded her that I was a bourbon drinker myself, and it pleased her to learn this. Alliances have been forged on more tenuous bonds than that, and she sealed ours with a sip from my glass. I offered it to her, and she put her little hand on mine to steady the glass, sipping daintily at the liquor.

'Bourbon is low-down,' she said. 'You know what I mean?'

'Here I thought it was a gentleman's drink.'

'It's for a gentleman likes to get down in the dirt. Scotch is vests and ties and prep school. Bourbon is an old boy ready to let the animal out, ready to let the nasty show. Bourbon is sitting up on a hot night and not minding if you sweat.'

Nobody was sweating. We were in her apartment, sitting on her couch in a sunken living room set about a foot below the level of the kitchen and foyer. Her building was an Art Deco apartment house on Fifty-seventh just a few doors west of Ninth. A bottle of Maker's Mark from the store around the corner stood on top of her glass-and-wrought-iron coffee table. Her air-conditioner was on, quieter than mine and more effective. We were drinking out of rocks glasses but we weren't bothering with ice.

'You were a cop,' she said. 'Didn't he tell me that?'

'He could have.'

'And now you're a detective?'

'In a way.'

'Just so you're not a robber. Be something if I got myself stabbed by a burglar tonight, wouldn't it? He's with me and she

466

gets killed, and then he's with her and *I* get killed. Except I don't guess he's with her right about now, is he. She's in the ground by now.'

Her apartment was small but comfortable. The furniture had clean lines, the op art prints on the brick wall were framed simply in aluminum frames. From her window you could see the green copper roof of the Parc Vendome on the far corner.

'If a burglar came in here,' she said, 'I'd stand a better chance than she did.'

'Because you've got me to protect you?'

'Mmmm,' she said. 'Mah hero.'

We kissed then. I tipped up her chin and kissed her, and we moved into an easy clinch. I breathed in her perfume, felt her softness. We clung together for a moment or two, then withdrew and reached as if in synchronization for our drinks.

'Even if I was alone,' she said, picking up the conversation as readily as she'd picked up the drink. 'I could protect myself.'

'You're a karate black belt.'

'I'm a beaded belt, honey, to match my purse. No, I could protect myself with this here, just give me a minute and I'll show you.'

A pair of modern matte-black step tables flanked the sofa. She leaned across me to grope for something in the drawer of the one on my side. She was sprawled facedown across my lap. An inch of golden skin showed between the tops of the yellow pedal pushers and the bottom of her green blouse. I put my hand on her behind.

'Now quit that, Matthew! I'll forget what I'm looking for.'

'That's all right.'

'No it's not. Here. See?'

She sat up, a gun in her hand. It was the same matte-black finish as the table. It was a revolver, and looked to be a .32. A small gun, all black, with a one-inch barrel.

'Maybe you should put that away,' I said.

'I know how to behave around guns,' she said. 'I grew up in a house full of guns. Rifles, shotguns, handguns. My pa and both my brothers hunted. Quail, pheasants. Some ducks. I know about guns.'

'Is that one loaded?'

'Wouldn't be much good if it wasn't, would it? Can't point at a burglar and say *bang*. He loaded it 'fore he gave it to me.'

'Tommy gave it to you?'

'Uh-huh.' She held the gun at arm's length, sighted across the

467

room at an imaginary burglar. 'Bang,' she said. 'He didn't leave me any shells, just the loaded gun. So if I was to shoot a burglar I'd have to ask him for more bullets the next day.'

'Why'd he give it to you?'

'Not to go duck hunting.' She laughed. 'For protection,' she said. 'I said how I got nervous sometimes, a girl living alone in this city, and one time he brought me this here. He said he bought it for her, to have it for protection, but she wouldn't have any part of it, wouldn't even take it in her hand.' She broke off and giggled.

'What's so funny?'

'Oh, that's what they all say. 'My wife won't even take it in her hand.' I got a dirty mind, Matthew.'

'Nothing wrong with that.'

'I told you bourbon was low-down. Brings out the beast in a person. You could kiss me.'

'You could put the gun away.'

'You got something against kissing a woman with a gun in her hand?' She rolled to her left, put the gun in the drawer and closed it. 'I keep it in the bedside table,' she explained, 'so it'll be handy if I need it in a hurry. This here makes up into a bed.'

'I don't believe you.'

'You don't huh? Want me to prove it to you?'

'Maybe you'd better.'

And so we did what grownups do when they find themselves alone together. The sofa opened up into an adequate bed and we lay upon it with the lights out and the room lit by a couple of candles in straw-wrapped wine bottles. Music played on an FM station. She had a sweet body, an eager mouth, perfect skin. She made a lot of enthusiastic noises and more than a few skillful moves, and afterward she cried some.

Then we talked and had a little more of the bourbon, and before long she dropped off to sleep. I covered her with the top sheet and a cotton blanket. I could have slept myself, but instead I put on my clothes and sent myself home. Because who in her right mind'd want Matt Scudder around by the dawn's early light?

On my way home I stopped at the little Syrian deli and had the clerk loosen the caps on two bottles of Molson Ale. I went up to my room and sat with my feet up on the windowsill and drank from one of the bottles.

468

I thought about Tillary. Where was he now? In the house where she died? Staying with friends or relatives?

I thought of him in the bars or Carolyn's bed while a burglar was killing his wife, and I wondered what he thought about that. Or if he thought about it.

And my own thoughts turned suddenly to Anita, out there in Syosset with the boys. I had a moment of fear for her, seeing her menaced, drawing back in terror from some unseen danger. I recognized the fear as irrational, and I was able after a moment to know it for what it was, something I'd brought home with me, something that clung to me now along with Carolyn Cheatham's scent. I was carrying around Tommy Tillary's guilt by proxy.

Well, the hell with that. I didn't need his guilt. I had plenty of my own.

SIX

The weekend was quiet. I talked to my sons, but they didn't come in. Saturday afternoon I earned a hundred dollars by accompanying one of the partners in the antique shop down the block from Armstrong's. We cabbed together to East Seventy-fourth Street, where we collected clothing and other possessions from his ex-lover's apartment. The lover was thirty or forty pounds overweight, bitter and bitchy.

'I don't believe this, Gerald,' he said. 'Did you actually bring a bodyguard or is this my summer replacement? Either way I don't know whether to be flattered or insulted.'

'Oh, I'm sure you'll work it out,' Gerald told him.

In the cab back to the West Side Gerald said, 'I really loved that cunt, Matthew, and I will be goddamned if I can figure out why. Thank you for this, Matthew. I could have hired a schlepper for five dollars an hour, but your presence was all the difference in the world. Did you see how ready he was to remember that the Handel lamp was his? The fucking *hell* it was his. When I met him he didn't know from Handel, not the lamps or the composer, either. All he knew was to *hondle*. You know that word, *hondle?* It means to haggle over a price, like if I were to try to pay you fifty dollars now instead of the hundred we agreed on. I'm just joking, dear. I have no problem with paying you the hundred, I think you were worth every penny of it.'

Sunday night Bobby Ruslander found me in Armstrong's. Skip was looking for me, he said. He was at Miss Kitty's, and if I got a minute why didn't I drop over? I had time then, and Bobby walked over there with me.

It was a little cooler; the worst of the heat wave had broken Saturday, and there had been some rain to cool the streets down

a little. A fire truck raced past us as we waited for the light to change. When the siren died down, Bobby said, 'Crazy business.'

'Oh?'

'He'll tell you about it.'

As we crossed the street he said, 'I never see him like this, you know what I mean? He's always supercool, Arthur is.'

'Nobody else calls him Arthur.'

'Nobody ever did. Back when we're kids, nobody calls him Arthur. It was like going against type, you know? Everybody calls him Skip, I'm his best friend, *I* call him by his formal name.'

When we got there Skip tossed Bobby a bar towel and asked him to take over for him. 'He's a lousy bartender,' he announced, 'but he doesn't steal much.'

'That's what you think,' Bobby said.

We went in back and Skip closed the door. There were a couple of old desks, two swivel chairs and a straight-backed chair, a coatrack, a file cabinet, and a big old Mosler safe that was taller than I was. 'That's where the books shoulda been,' he said, pointing at the safe. 'Except we're too smart for that, me and John. There's an audit, that's the first place they're gonna look, right? So all that's in there is a thousand in cash and some papers and shit, the lease on this place, the partnership agreement, his divorce papers, shit like that. Terrific. We saved that crap and let somebody walk off with the store.'

He lit a cigarette. 'Safe was here when we took the place,' he said. 'Left over from when the joint was a hardware store, and it cost more to move than it was worth, so we inherited it. Massive fucker, isn't it? You could put a body in there if you had one around. That way nobody'd steal it. He called, the fucker who stole the books.'

'Oh?'

He nodded. 'It's a ransom pitch. "I got something of yours and you can have it back."'

'He name a price?'

'No. Said he'll be in touch.'

'You recognize the voice?'

'Uh-uh. Sounded phony.'

'How do you mean?'

'Like it wasn't his real voice I was hearing. Anyway, I didn't recognize it.' He clasped his hands, extended his arms to crack his knuckles. 'I'm supposed to sit around until I hear from him.'

'When did you get the call?'

'Couple hours ago. I was working, he called me here. Good start to the evening, I'll tell you.'

'At least he's coming to you instead of sending the stuff straight to the IRS.'

'Yeah, I thought of that. This way we get the chance to do something. If he went and dropped a dime on us, all we could do is bend over and take it.'

'Did you talk to your partner?'

'Not yet. I called his house, he wasn't in.'

'So you sit tight.'

'Yeah. That's a switch. What the hell have I been doing, hanging loose?' There was a water tumbler on his desk, a third full with a brownish liquid. He took a last drag on his cigarette and dropped it into the glass. 'Disgusting,' he said. 'I never want to see you do that, Matt. You don't smoke, do you?'

'Once in a great while.'

'Yeah? You have one now and then and don't get hooked? I know a guy takes heroin that way. You know him, too, for that matter. But these little fuckers' – he tapped the pack – 'I think they're more addictive than smack. You want one now?'

'No thanks.'

He stood up. 'The only things I don't get addicted to,' he said, 'are the ones I didn't like that much in the first place. Hey, thanks for coming by. There's nothing to do but wait, but I figured I wanted to keep you in the picture, let you know what's going on.'

'That's fine,' I said, 'but I want you to know you don't owe me anything for it.'

'What do you mean?'

'I mean don't go paying my bar tab for this.'

'Are you sore?'

'No.'

'It was just something I felt like doing.'

'I appreciate it, but it wasn't necessary.'

'Yeah, I guess.' He shrugged. 'When you're skimming you get to be very free with cash. You spend it on things that don't show. The hell with it. I can stand you a drink, though, can't I? In my own joint?'

'That you can do.'

'C'mon then,' he said, 'before fucking Ruslander gives the whole store away.'

Every time I went into Armstrong's I wondered if I'd run into

Carolyn, and each time I was more relieved than disappointed when I didn't. I could have called her, but I sensed that it was perfectly appropriate not to. Friday night had been just what each of us had evidently wanted, and it looked as though it had been complete in itself for both of us, and I was glad of that. As a fringe benefit, I was over whatever had had me bugged about Fran, and it was beginning to look as though it had been nothing much more complicated than old-fashioned horniness. I suppose a half-hour with one of the streetwalkers would have served me as well, if less pleasurably.

I didn't run into Tommy, either, and that, too, was a relief, and in no sense disappointing.

Then Monday morning I picked up the *News* and read that they'd pulled in a pair of young Hispanics from Sunset Park for the Tillary burglary and homicide. The paper ran the usual photo – two skinny youths, their hair unruly, one of them trying to hide his face from the camera, the other smirking defiantly, and each of them handcuffed to a broad-shouldered grimfaced Irishman in a suit. There was a caption to tell you which ones were the good guys, but you didn't really need it.

I was in Armstrong's that afternoon when the phone rang. Dennis put down the glass he was wiping and answered it. 'He was here a minute ago,' he said. 'I'll see if he stepped out.' He covered the mouthpiece with his hand and looked quizzically at me. 'Are you still here?' he asked. 'Or did you slip away while my attention was somehow diverted?'

'Who wants to know?'

'Tommy Tillary.'

You never know what a woman will decide to tell a man, or how a man will react to it. I didn't much want to find out, but I was better off learning over the phone than face-to-face. I nodded and Dennis passed the phone across the bar.

I said, 'Matt Scudder, Tommy. I was sorry to hear about your wife.'

'Thanks, Matt. Jesus, it feels like it happened a year ago. It was what, a little over a week?'

'At least they got the bastards.'

There was a pause. Then he said, 'Jesus. You haven't seen a paper, huh?'

'Sure I did. Two Spanish kids, had their pictures.'

'I guess you read this morning's *News*.'

'I generally do. Why?'

'But not this afternoon's *Post*.'

'No. Why, what happened? They turn out to be clean?'

'Clean,' he said, and snorted. Then he said, 'I figured you'd know. The cops came by early this morning, before I saw the story in the *News*, so I didn't even know about the arrest. Shit. Be easier if you already knew this.'

'I'm not following you, Tommy.'

'The two Latin lovers. Clean? Shit, the men's room in the Times Square subway station, that's how clean they are. The cops hit their place and found stuff from my house everywhere they looked. Jewelry they had descriptions of, a stereo that I gave them the serial number, everything. Monogrammed shit. I mean that's how clean they were, for Christ's sake.'

'So?'

'So they admitted the burglary but not the murder.'

'Crooks do that all the time, Tommy.'

'Lemme finish, huh? They admitted the burglary, but according to them it wasn't really a burglary. I was giving them all that stuff.'

'And they just came to pick it up in the middle of the night.'

'Yeah, right. No, their story was they were supposed to make it look like a burglary so I could collect from my insurance. I could claim a loss on top of what they were actually taking, and that way everybody's to the good.'

'What did the actual loss amount to?'

'Shit, *I* don't know. There were twice as many things turned up at their place as I ever listed when I made out a report. There's things I missed a few days after I filled out the report and other stuff I didn't know was gone until the cops found them. And they took things weren't covered. There was a fur of Peg's, we were gonna get a floater on it and we never did. And some of her jewelry, same story. I got a standard homeowner's policy, it didn't cover anywheres near everything they took. They got a set of sterling, it came down to us from her aunt, I swear I forgot we owned the stuff. And *it* wasn't covered, either.'

'It hardly sounds like an insurance setup.'

'No, of course not. How the hell could it be? Anyway, the important thing is according to them the house was empty when they hit it. Peg wasn't home.'

'And?'

'And I set them up is their story. They hit the place, they carted everything away, and then I came home with Peg and

stabbed her six, eight times, whatever it was, and left her there so it looked like it happened during a burglary.'

'How could the burglars testify that you stabbed your wife?'

'They couldn't. All they said was they didn't and she wasn't home when they were there and I had it arranged with them to do the burglary. The cops pieced the rest of it together.'

'What did they do, arrest you?'

'No. They came over to the hotel where I'm staying, it was early, I was just out of the shower. Now this was the first I knew that the spics were arrested, let alone that they were trying to do a job on me. They just wanted to talk, the cops, and at first I talked to them, and then I started to get the drift of what they were trying to put on me. So I said I wasn't saying anything more without my lawyer present, and I called him, and he left half his breakfast on the table and came over in a hurry, and he wouldn't let me say a word.'

'And they didn't take you in or book you?'

'No.'

'But they didn't entirely buy your story either?'

'No way. I didn't really tell 'em a story because Kaplan wouldn't let me say anything. They didn't drag me in because they don't have a case yet, but according to Kaplan they're going to be building one if they can. They told me not to leave town. You believe it? My wife's dead, the *Post* headline says "Quiz Husband in Burglary Murder," and what the hell do they think I'm gonna do? Am I going fishing for fucking trout in Montana? "Don't leave town." You see this shit on television, you think nobody in real life talks like that. Maybe television's where they get it from.'

I waited for him to tell me what he wanted from me. I didn't have long to wait.

'Why I called,' he said, 'is Kaplan thinks we ought to hire a detective. He figures maybe these guys talked around the neighborhood, maybe they bragged to their friends, maybe there's a way to prove they did the killing. He says the cops won't concentrate on that end if they're too busy trying to nail the lid shut on me.'

I explained that I didn't have any official standing, that I had no license and filed no reports.

'That's okay,' he insisted. 'I told Kaplan what I want is somebody I can trust, somebody'll do a job for me. I don't think they're gonna have any kind of a case at all, Matt, because I can account for my time and I couldn't ta been where I woulda hadda

475

be to do what they said I did. But the longer this shit drags on the worse it is for me. I want it cleared up, I want it in the papers that these Spanish assholes did it all and I had nothing to do with anything. I want that for me and for the people I do business with and for my relatives and Peg's relatives and all the wonderful people who voted for me. You remember the old "Amateur Hour"? "I want to thank mom and dad and Aunt Edith and my piano teacher Mrs Pelton and all the wonderful people who voted for me." Listen, you'll meet me and Kaplan in his office, hear what the man has to say, do me a hell of a big favor, and pick up a couple of bucks for yourself. What do you say, Matt?'

He wanted somebody he could trust. Had Carolyn from the Caroline told him how trustworthy I was?

What did I say? I said yes.

SEVEN

I took a train one stop into Brooklyn and met Tommy Tillary in Drew Kaplan's office on Court Street a few blocks from Brooklyn's Borough Hall. There was a Lebanese restaurant next door. At the corner a grocery store specializing in Middle Eastern imports stood next to an antique shop overflowing with stripped oak furniture and brass lamps and bedsteads. In front of Kaplan's building, a legless black man reposed on a platform with wheels. An open cigar box on one side of him held a couple of singles and a lot of coins. He was wearing horn-rimmed sunglasses, and a hand-lettered sign on the pavement in front of him said, 'Don't Be Fooled by the Sunglasses. Not Blind Just No Legs.'

Kaplan's office ran to wood paneling and leather chairs and oak file cabinets that might have come from the place on the corner. His name and the names of two partners were painted on the frosted glass of the hall door in old-fashioned gold and black lettering. Framed diplomas on the wall of his personal office showed he'd earned his BA at Adelphi, his LLB at Brooklyn Law. A lucite cube on top of a Victorian oak desk held photographs of his wife and young children. A bronzed railway spike served as a desktop paperweight. On the wall alongside the desk, a pendulum clock ticked away the afternoon.

Kaplan himself looked conservatively up-to-date in a tropical-weight gray pinstripe suit and a yellow pin-dot tie. He looked to be in his early thirties, which would fit the dates on the diplomas. He was shorter than I and of course much shorter than Tommy, trimly built, clean-shaven, with dark hair and eyes and a slightly lopsided smile. His handshake was medium-firm, his gaze direct but measuring, calculating.

Tommy wore his burgundy blazer over gray flannel trousers and white loafers. Strain showed at the corners of his blue eyes

477

and around his mouth. His complexion was off, too, as if anxiety had caused the blood to draw inward, leaving the skin sallow.

'All we want you to do,' Drew Kaplan said, 'is find a key in one of their pants pockets, Herrera's or Cruz's, and trace it to a locker in Penn Station, and in the locker there's a foot-long knife with both their prints and her blood on it.'

'Is that what it's going to take?'

He smiled. 'Let's just say it wouldn't hurt. No, actually we're not in such bad shape. What they've got is some shaky testimony from a pair of Latins who've been in and out of trouble since they got weaned onto Tropicana. And they've got what looks to them like a good motive on Tommy's part.'

'Which is?'

I was looking at Tommy when I asked. His eyes slipped away from mine. Kaplan said, 'A marital triangle, a case of the shorts, and a strong money motive. Margaret Tillary came into some money this past spring upon the death of an aunt. The estate's not through probate yet but the value's somewhere in excess of half a million dollars.'

'Be less than that when they get done hackin' away at it,' Tommy said. 'A whole lot less.'

'Plus there's insurance. Tommy and his wife had a pair of straight-life policies, each naming the other as beneficiary, both with double-indemnity clauses and a face amount of' – he consulted a slip on his desk – 'a hundred and fifty thousand dollars, which doubled for accidental death is three hundred thousand. At this point we've got what begins to look like seven, eight hundred thousand motives for murder.'

'My lawyer talkin',' Tommy said.

'Same time, Tommy here's hurting a little for cash. He's having a bad year gambling, he's into the bookies and maybe they're starting to press him a little.'

'Not so it amounts to anything,' Tommy put in.

'I'm telling it the way the cops would tell it, all right? He owes some money around town, he's a couple of payments behind with the Buick. Meanwhile he's putting away this girl at the office, bouncing around the bars with her, sometimes not making it home altogether –'

'Hardly ever, Drew. I'd almost always make it home, an' if I couldn't grab a few hours in the sack I'd at least shower and change and have breakfast with Peg.'

'What was breakfast? Dexamyl?'

'Sometimes. I had an office to go to, a job to do.'

Kaplan sat on a corner of his desk, crossed his legs at the ankle. 'That'll do for motive,' he said. 'What they don't bother to notice is a couple of things. One, he loved his wife, and how many husbands cheat? What is it they say? Ninety percent admit they cheat and ten percent lie about it? Two, he's got debts but he's not in a crunch. He's a guy makes good money over the year but he runs hot and cold, and for years he's been fat one month and strapped the next.'

'You get used to it,' Tommy said.

'Plus the numbers sound like a fortune, but they're not unusual figures. A half-million is substantial, but as Tommy said it won't net out to that much after taxes, and part of it consists of title to the house he's been occupying for years. A hundred fifty thousand dollars' insurance on a breadwinner isn't high by any means, and having the same coverage on the wife isn't uncommon, a lot of insurance agents try to write policies that way. They make it sound logically balanced, so you overlook the fact that you don't really need that kind of coverage on someone you don't depend upon for income.' He spread his hands. 'Anyway, the policies were taken out over ten years ago. This isn't something he went and set up last week.'

He stood up, talked over to the window. Tommy had picked up the railway spike from the desk and was playing with it, slapping it against the palm of his hand, consciously or unconsciously matching the rhythm of the clock's pendulum.

Kaplan said, 'One of the killers, Angel Herrera, except I suppose he pronounces it Ahn-hell, did some odd jobs at the Tillary house last March or April. Spring cleaning, he hauled stuff out of the basement and attic, did a little donkey work for hourly wages. According to Herrera, that's how Tommy knew to contact him to fake the burglary. According to common sense, that's how Herrera and his buddy Cruz knew the house and what was in it and how to gain access.'

'How'd they do that?'

'Broke a small pane in the side door, reached in and unlocked it. Their story is Tommy left it open for them and must have broken the glass after. It's also their story that they left the place relatively neat.'

'Looked like a cyclone hit it,' Tommy said. 'I had to go there. Made me sick to look at it.'

'Their story is Tommy did that the same time he was murdering his wife. Except none of this works out if you take a good look at it. The times are all wrong. They went in around

479

midnight, and the medical examiner places the time of death at between ten p.m. and four a.m. Now Tommy here never made it home from the office that evening. He worked past five, he met his friend for dinner, and he was with her in a variety of public places over the course of the evening.' He looked over at his client. 'We're lucky he's not much on discretion. His alibi'd be a whole lot thinner if he'd spent every minute in her apartment with the blinds drawn.'

'I was discreet as far as Peg was concerned,' Tommy said. 'In Brooklyn I was a family man. What I did in the city never hurt her.'

'After midnight his time's harder to account for,' Kaplan went on. 'The only substantiation for some of those hours is the girlfriend, because for a while they *were* in her apartment with the blinds drawn.'

You didn't have to draw the blinds, I thought. Nobody could see in.

'Plus there was some time she couldn't account for.'

'She fell asleep and I couldn't,' Tommy said, 'so I got dressed and went out for a couple of pops. But I wasn't gone that long, and she woke up when I got back. I had a helicopter, maybe I coulda got to Bay Ridge'n' back in that amount of time. Never do it in a Buick.'

'The thing is,' Kaplan said, 'even supposing there was time, or discounting the girlfriend's alibi altogether and only accepting the times substantiated by unbiased witnesses, how could he possibly have done it? Say he sneaks home sometime after the Spanish kids have paid their visit and before four a.m., which was the latest the murder could have taken place. Where was she all this time? According to Cruz and Herrera, there was nobody home. Well, where did he find her to kill her? What did he do, haul her around in the trunk all night?'

'Let's say he killed her before they got there,' I suggested.

'And I'm lookin' to *hire* this guy,' Tommy said. 'I got an instinct, you know what I mean?'

'Doesn't work,' Kaplan said. 'In the first place the times simply won't fit. He's alibied solid from before eight until past midnight, out in public with the girl. The ME says she was definitely alive at ten, that's the absolute earliest she could have been killed. Plus even forgetting the times it doesn't work. How could they go in, rob the whole house, and not see a dead woman in the bedroom? They were in that room, they were in possession of stolen articles from that room, I think they even

found prints in there. Well, the police found the corpse of Margaret Tillary in that room, too, and it's the sort of thing they probably would have noticed.'

'Maybe the body was covered up.' I thought of Skip's big Mosler safe. 'Locked in a closet they didn't look in.'

He shook his head. 'The cause of death was stabbing. There was a lot of blood and it was all over the place. The bed was soaked, the bedroom carpet.' We both avoided looking at Tommy. 'So she wasn't killed elsewhere,' he concluded. 'She was killed right there, and if it wasn't Herrera did it it was Cruz, and either way it wasn't Tommy.'

I looked for a hole in it and couldn't find one. 'Then I don't see what you need me for,' I said. 'The case against Tommy sounds pretty thin.'

'So thin there isn't any case.'

'Then –'

'The thing is,' he said, 'you get near a courtroom with something like this and even if you win you still lose. Because for the rest of your life all everybody remembers about you is you once stood trial for murdering your wife. Never mind that you won an acquittal. Everybody just figures some Jew lawyer bought a judge or conned a jury.'

'So I'll get a guinea lawyer,' Tommy said, 'and they'll think he threatened the judge and beat up the jury.'

'Besides,' Kaplan said, 'you never know which way a jury's going to jump. Remember, Tommy's alibi is he was with another woman at the time of the burglary. The woman's a colleague, they could choose to regard it as completely above-board, but did you see the piece in the *Post*? What juries'll go and do, they decide they don't believe the alibi because it's your girlfriend lying for you, and at the same time they label you a scumbag for getting your carrot scraped while your wife's getting killed.'

'You keep it up,' Tommy said, 'I'll find my own self guilty, the way you make it sound.'

'Plus he's hard to get a sympathetic jury for. He's a big handsome guy, a sharp dresser, and you'd love him in a gin joint but how much do you love him in a courtroom? He's a telephone securities salesman, perfectly respectable thing to be, calls you up, advises you how to invest your money. Fine. That means every clown who ever lost a hundred dollars on a stock tip or bought magazine subscriptions over the phone is going to

walk into the courtroom with a hardon for him. I'm telling you, I want to stay the hell *out* of court. I'll *win* in court, I know that, or worse comes to worst I'll win on appeal, but who needs it? This is a case that shouldn't be in the first place, and what I'd love is to clear it up before they even go so far as presenting a bill to the grand jury.'

'So from me you want –'

'Whatever you can find out, Matt. Whatever discredits Cruz and Herrera. I don't know what's there to find. I'd love it if you could find blood, their clothes with stains on it, anything like that. The point is that I don't know what's there to be found, and you were a cop and now you're working private, and you can get down in the streets and the bars and nose around. You familiar with Brooklyn?'

'Parts of it. I worked over here, off and on.'

'So you can find your way around.'

'Well enough. But wouldn't you be better off with a Spanish-speaker? I know enough to buy a beer in a bodega, but I'm a long way from fluent.'

'Tommy says he wants somebody he can trust, and he was very adamant about calling you in. I think he's right. A personal relationship's worth more than a dime's worth of "*Me llamo Matteo y como está usted?*"'

'That's the truth,' Tommy Tillary said. 'Matt, I know I can count on you, and that's worth a lot.'

I wanted to tell him all he could count on were his fingers, but why was I trying to talk myself out of a fee? His money was as good as anybody else's. I wasn't sure I liked him, but I was just as happy not to like the men I worked for. It bothered me less that way if I felt I was giving them less than full value.

And I didn't see how I could give him much. The case against him sounded loose enough to fall apart without my help. I wondered if Kaplan just wanted to create some activity to justify a high fee of his own, in the event that the whole thing blew itself out in a week's time. That was possible, and that wasn't my problem, either.

I said I would be glad to help. I said I hoped I would be able to come up with something useful.

Tommy said he was sure I could.

Drew Kaplan said, 'Now you'll want a retainer. I suppose that'll be an advance against a per diem fee plus expenses, or do you bill at hourly rates? Why are you shaking your head?'

'I'm unlicensed,' I said. 'I have no official standing.'

'That's no problem. We can carry you on the books as a consultant.'

'I don't want to be on the books at all,' I said. 'I don't keep track of my time or expenses. I pay my own expenses out of my own pocket. I get paid in cash.'

'How do you set your fees?'

'I think up a number. If I think I should have more coming when I'm finished, I say so. If you disagree, you don't have to pay me. I'm not going to take anybody to court.'

'It seems a haphazard way to do business,' Kaplan said.

'It's not a business. I do favors for friends.'

'And take money for them.'

'Is there anything wrong with taking money for a favor?'

'I don't suppose there is.' He looked thoughtful. 'How much would you expect for this favor?'

'I don't know what's involved,' I said. 'Suppose you let me have fifteen hundred dollars today. If things drag on and I feel entitled to more, I'll let you know.'

'Fifteen hundred. And of course Tommy doesn't know exactly what he's getting for that.'

'No,' I said. 'Neither do I.'

Kaplan narrowed his eyes. 'That seems high for a retainer,' he said. 'I'd have thought a third of that would be ample for starters.'

I thought of my antique dealer friend. Did I know what it was to *hondle?* Kaplan evidently did.

'It's not that much,' I said. 'It's one percent of the insurance money, and that's part of the reason for hiring an investigator, isn't it? The company won't pay off until Tommy's in the clear.'

Kaplan looked slightly startled. 'That's true,' he admitted, 'but I don't know that it's the reason for hiring you. The company will pay up sooner or later. I don't think your fee is necessarily high, it just seemed a disproportionately large sum to lay out in advance, and –'

'Don't argue price,' Tommy cut in. 'The fee sounds fine to me, Matt. The only thing is, being a little short right now, and coming up with fifteen C in cash –'

'Maybe your lawyer will front it to you,' I suggested.

Kaplan thought that was irregular. I went into the outer office while they talked it over. The receptionist was reading a copy of *Fate* magazine. A pair of hand-tinted etchings in antiqued

frames showed scenes of nineteenth-century downtown Brooklyn. I was looking at them when Kaplan's door opened and he beckoned me back inside.

'Tommy's going to be able to borrow on the basis of his expectations from the insurance monies and his wife's estate,' he said. 'Meanwhile I can let you have the fifteen hundred. I hope you have no objection to signing a receipt?'

'None at all,' I said. I counted the bills, twelve hundreds and six fifties, all circulated bills out of sequence. Everybody seems to have some cash around, even lawyers.

He wrote out a receipt and I signed it. He apologized for what he called a little awkwardness around the subject of my fee. 'Lawyers are schooled to be very conventional human beings,' he said. 'I sometimes have a slow reaction time when it comes to adjusting to irregular procedure. I hope I wasn't offensive.'

'Not at all.'

'I'm glad of that. Now I won't be expecting written reports or a precise account of your movements, but you'll report to me as you go along and let me know what turns up? And please tell me too much rather than too little. It's hard to know what will prove useful.'

'I know that myself.'

'I'm sure you do.' He walked me to the door. 'And incidentally,' he said, 'your fee is only one-half of one percent of the insurance money. I think I mentioned that the policy had a double-indemnity clause, and murder is considered accidental.'

'I know,' I said. 'I've always wondered why.'

EIGHT

The Sixty-eighth Precinct is stationed on Sixty-fifth Street between Third and Fourth Avenues, straddling the approximate boundary of Bay Ridge and Sunset Park. On the south side of the street a housing project loomed; across from it, the station house looked like something from Picasso's cubist period, all blocky with cantilevered cubes and recessed areas. The structure reminded me of the building that houses the Two-three in East Harlem, and I learned later that the same architect designed them both.

The building was six years old then, according to the plaque in the entranceway that mentioned the architect, the police commissioner, the mayor, and a couple of other worthies making a bid for municipal immortality. I stood there and read the whole plaque as if it had a special message for me. Then I went up to the desk and said I was there to see Detective Calvin Neumann. The officer on duty made a phone call, then pointed me to the squad room.

The building's interior was clean and spacious and well lit. It had been open enough years, though, to begin to feel like what it was.

The squad room contained a bank of gray metal file cabinets, a row of green metal lockers, and twin rows of five-foot steel desks set back to back. A television set was on in one corner with nobody watching it. Half of the eight or ten desks were occupied. At the water cooler, a man in a suit talked with a man in his shirt sleeves. In the holding pen, a drunk sang something tuneless in Spanish.

I recognized one of the seated detectives but couldn't recall his name. He didn't look up. Across the room, another man looked familiar. I went up to a man I didn't know and he pointed out Neumann, two desks down on the opposite side.

He was filling in a form, and I stood while he finished what he

was typing. He looked up then and said, 'Scudder?' and pointed to a chair. He swiveled around to face me and waved a hand at the typewriter.

'They don't tell you,' he said, 'the hours you're gonna spend typing crud. Nobody out there realizes how much of this job is clerical.'

'That's the part it's hard to get nostalgic about.'

'I don't think I'd miss it myself.' He yawned elaborately. 'Eddie Koehler gave you high marks,' he said. 'I gave him a call like you suggested. He said you're okay.'

'You know Eddie?'

He shook his head. 'But I know what a lieutenant is,' he said. 'I haven't got a whole lot to give you, but you're welcome to it. You may not get the same cooperation from Brooklyn Homicide.'

'Why's that?'

'They drew the case to start with. It got called in originally to the One-oh-four, which was actually wrong, it should have been ours, but that happens a lot. Then Brooklyn Homicide responded along with the One-oh-four, and they took the case away from the precinct guys.'

'When did you come into it?'

'When a favorite snitch of mine came up with a lot of talk coming out of the bars and bakeries on Third under the expressway. A nice mink coat at a real good price, but you got to keep this quiet because there's a lot of heat. Well, July's a funny time to sell fur coats in Sunset Park. A guy buys a coat for his señora, he wants her to be able to wear it that night. So my guy comes to me with the impression that Miguelito Cruz has a houseful of stuff he's looking to sell and it just might be he hasn't got sales slips for many of the items. With the mink and a couple other items he mentioned, I remembered the Tillary job on Colonial Road, and it was enough to get a judge to issue a search warrant.'

He ran a hand through his hair. It was medium brown, lighter where the sun had bleached it, and it was on the shaggy side. Cops were starting to wear their hair a little longer around about then, and the younger ones were beginning to show up in beards and moustaches. Neumann, though, was clean-shaven, his features regular except for a nose that had been broken and imperfectly reset.

'The stuff was in Cruz's house,' he said. 'He lives over on Fifty-first, the other side of the Gowanus Expressway. I have the

address somewhere if you want it. Those are some pretty blighted blocks over by the Bush Terminal Warehouse, if you know where that is. A lot of empty lots and boarded-up buildings and others nobody bothered boarding up, or somebody opened them up again and there's junkies camped out there. Where Cruz lived wasn't so bad. You'll see it if you go over there.'

'He live alone?'

He shook his head. 'With his *abuela*. His grandmother. Little old lady, doesn't speak English, she probably ought to be in a home. Maybe they'll take her in at the Marien-Heim, it's right in the neighborhood. Old lady comes here from Puerto Rico, before she can learn English she winds up in a home with a German name. That's New York, right?'

'You found Tillary's possessions in the Cruz apartment?'

'Oh, yeah. No question. I mean the serial numbers matched on the record player. He tried to deny it. What else is new, right? 'Oh, I buy dis stuff on de street, it was some guy I met in a bar. I doan know hees name.' We told him, sure, Miguelito, but meanwhile a woman got cut bad in the house this stuff came out of, so it sure looks like you're gonna go away for murder one. The next minute he's copping to the burglary but insisting there was no dead woman when he was there.'

'He must have known a woman got killed there.'

'Of course, no matter who killed her. It was in the papers, right? One minute he says he didn't see the story, the next minute he didn't happen to recognize the address, you know how their stories keep changing.'

'Where does Herrera come in?'

'They're cousins or something. Herrera lives in a furnished room on Forty-eighth between Fifth and Sixth just a couple of blocks from the park. Lived there, anyway. Right now they're both living at the Brooklyn House of Detention and they'll be living there until they move upstate.'

'They both have sheets?'

'Be a surprise if they didn't, wouldn't it?' He grinned. 'They're your typical fuckups. A few juvenile arrests for gang stuff. They both beat a burglary charge a year and a half ago, a judge ruled there wasn't probable cause to justify a frisk.' He shook his head. 'The fucking rules you have to play by. Anyway, they beat that one, and another time they got collared for burglary and plea-bargained it to criminal trespass and got suspended sentences for

it. And another time, another burglary case, the evidence disappeared.'

'It disappeared?'

'It got lost or misfiled or something, I don't know. It's a miracle anybody ever goes to jail in this city. You really need a death wish to wind up in prison.'

'So they did a fair amount of burglary.'

'It looks like. In-and-out stuff, nickel-and-dime crap. Kick the door in, grab a radio, run into the street and sell it on the street for five or ten dollars. Cruz was worse than Herrera. Herrera worked from time to time, pushing a hand truck in the garment center or delivering lunches, minimum-wage stuff. I don't think Miguelito ever held a job.'

'But neither of them ever killed anybody before.'

'Cruz did.'

'Oh?'

He nodded. 'In a tavern fight, him and another asshole fighting over some woman.'

'The papers didn't have that.'

'It never got to court. There were no charges pressed. There were a dozen witnesses reporting that the dead guy went after Cruz first with a broken bottle.'

'What weapon did Cruz use?'

'A knife. He said it wasn't his, and there were witnesses prepared to swear they'd seen somebody toss him the knife. And of course they hadn't happened to notice who it was did the tossing. We didn't have enough to make a case of weapon possession, let alone homicide.'

'But Cruz normally carried a knife?'

'You'd be more likely to catch him leaving the house without underwear.'

That was early afternoon, the day after I'd taken fifteen hundred dollars from Drew Kaplan. That morning I'd bought a money order and mailed it to Syosset. I paid my August rent in advance, settled a bar tab or two, and rode the BMT to Sunset Park.

It's in Brooklyn, of course, on the borough's western edge, above Bay Ridge and south and west of Green-Wood Cemetery. These days there's a fair amount of brownstoning going on in Sunset Park, with young urban professionals fleeing the Manhattan rents and renovating the old row houses, gentrifying the neighborhood. Back then the upwardly mobile young had not yet discovered the place, and the population was a mixture of

Latins and Scandinavians. Most of the former were Puerto Ricans, most of the latter Norwegians, and the balance was gradually shifting from Europe to the islands, from light to dark, but this was a process that had been going on for ages and there was nothing hurried about it.

I'd walked around some before my visit to the Six-eight, keeping mostly within a block or so of Fourth Avenue, the main commercial thoroughfare, and orienting myself intermittently by looking around for Saint Michael's Church. Few of the buildings stood more than three stories, and the egg-shaped church dome, set atop a two-hundred-foot tower, was visible a long ways off.

I walked north on Third Avenue now, on the right-hand side of the street, in the shade of the expressway overhead. As I neared Cruz's street I stopped in a couple of bars, more to immerse myself in the neighborhood than to ask any questions. I had a short shot of bourbon in one place, stuck to beer otherwise.

The block where Miguelito Cruz had lived with his grandmother was as Neumann described it. There were several vast vacant lots, one of them staked out in cyclone fencing, the others open and rubble-strewn. In one, small children played in the burned-out shell of a Volkswagen beetle. Four three-story buildings with scalloped brick fronts stood in a row on the north side of the block, closer to Second Avenue than to Third. The buildings abutting the group on either side had been torn down, and the newly exposed brick side walls looked raw except for the graffiti spray-painted on their lower portions.

Cruz had lived in the building closest to Second Avenue, closest too to the river. The vestibule was a lot of cracked and missing tiles and peeling paint. Six mailboxes were set into one wall, their locks broken and repaired and broken again. There were no bells to ring, nor was there a lock on the front door. I opened it and walked up two flights of stairs. The stairwell held cooking smells, rodent smells, a faint ammoniac reek of urine. All old buildings housing poor people smell like that. Rats die in the walls, kids and drunks piss. Cruz's building was no worse than thousands.

The grandmother lived on the top floor, in a perfectly neat railroad flat filled with holy pictures and little candle-illuminated shrines. If she spoke any English, she didn't let me know it.

No one answered my knock at the apartment across the hall.

489

I worked my way through the building. On the second floor, the apartment directly below the Cruz apartment was occupied by a very dark-skinned Hispanic woman with what looked like five children under six years old. A television set and a radio were playing in the front room, another radio in the kitchen. The children were in constant motion and at least two of them were crying or yelling at all times. The woman was cooperative enough, but she didn't have much English and it was impossible to concentrate on anything in there.

Across the hall, no one responded to my knock. I could hear a television set playing and went on knocking. Finally the door opened. An enormously fat man in his underwear opened the door and walked back inside without a word, evidently assuming I would follow. He led me through several rooms littered with old newspapers and empty Pabst Blue Ribbon cans to the front room, where he sat in a sprung armchair watching a game show. The color on his set was curiously distorted, giving the panelists faces that were red one moment and green the next.

He was white, with lank hair that had been blond once but was mostly gray now. It was hard to estimate his age because of the weight he was carrying, but he was probably somewhere between forty and sixty. He hadn't shaved in several days and may not have bathed or changed his bed linen in months. He stank, and his apartment stank, and I stayed there anyway and asked him questions. He had three beers left from a six-pack when I went in there, and he drank them one after another and padded barefoot through the apartment to return with a fresh six-pack from the refrigerator.

His name was Illing, he said, Paul Illing, and he had heard about Cruz, it was on television, and he thought it was terrible but he wasn't surprised, hell no. He'd lived here all his life, he told me, and this had been a nice neighborhood once, decent people, respected theirselves and respected their neighbors. But now you had the wrong element, and what could you expect?

'They live like animals,' he told me. 'You wouldn't believe it.'

Angel Herrera's rooming house was a four-story red brick building, its ground floor given over to a coin laundry. Two men in their late twenties lounged on the stoop, drinking their beer from cans held in brown paper bags. I asked for Herrera's room. They decided I was a cop; the assumption showed in their faces, and the set of their shoulders. One of them told me to try the fourth floor.

490

There was a reek of marijuana smoke floating on top of the other smells in the hallway. A tiny woman, dark and bright-eyed, stood at the third-floor landing. She was wearing an apron and holding a folded copy of *El Diario*, one of the Spanish-language newspapers. I asked for Herrera's room.

'Twenty-two,' she said, and pointed upstairs. 'But he's not in. 'Her eyes fixed on mine. 'You know where he is?'

'Yes.'

'Then you know he is not here. His door is lock.'

'Do you have the key?'

She looked at me sharply. 'You a cop?'

'I used to be.'

Her laugh was loud, unexpected. 'Wha'd you get, laid off? They got no work for cops, all the crooks in jail? You want to go in Angel's room, come on, I let you in.'

A cheap padlock secured the door of Room 22. She tried three keys before finding the right one, then opened the door and entered the room ahead of me. A cord hung from the bare-bulb ceiling fixture over the narrow iron bedstead. She pulled it, then raised a window shade to illuminate the room a little more.

I looked out the window, walked around the room, examined the contents of the closet and the small bureau. There were several photographs in drugstore frames on top of the bureau, and half a dozen unframed snapshots. Two different women, several children. In one snapshot, a man and woman in bathing suits squinted into the sun, the surf behind them. I showed the photograph to the woman and she identified the man as Herrera. I had seen his photo in the paper, along with Cruz and the two arresting officers, but he looked completely different in the snapshot.

The woman, I learned, was Herrera's girlfriend. The woman who appeared in some of the other photos with the children was Herrera's wife in Puerto Rico. He was a good boy, Herrera was, the woman assured me. He was polite, he kept his room neat, he didn't drink too much or play his radio loud late at night. And he loved his babies, he sent money home to Puerto Rico when he had it to send.

Fourth Avenue had churches on the average of one to a block – Norse Methodist, German Lutheran, Spanish Seventh-Day Adventists, and one called the Salem Tabernacle. They were all closed, and by the time I got to it, so was Saint Michael's. I was ecumenical enough in my tithing, but the Catholics got most of my money simply because they kept longer hours, but by the

time I left Herrera's rooming house and stopped for a quick one at the bar on the corner, Saint Michael's was locked up as tight as its Protestant fellows.

Two blocks away, between a bodega and an OTB parlor, a gaunt Christ writhed on the cross in the window of a storefront *iglesia*. There were a couple of backless benches inside in front of a small altar, and on one of them two shapeless women in black huddled silent and motionless.

I slipped inside and sat on one of the benches myself for a few moments. I had my hundred-fifty-dollar tithe ready and I'd have been as happy giving it to this hole in the wall as to some more imposing and long-established firm, but I couldn't think of an inconspicuous way to manage it. There was no poor box in evidence, no receptacle designed to accommodate donations. I didn't want to call attention to myself by finding someone in charge and handing him the money, nor did I feel comfortable just leaving it on the bench, say, where anybody could pick it up and walk off with it.

I walked out of there no poorer than I'd walked in.

I spent the evening in Sunset Park.

I don't know if it was work, or if I even thought I was doing Tommy Tillary any good. I walked the streets and worked the bars, but I wasn't looking for anyone and I didn't ask a lot of questions.

On Sixtieth Street east of Fourth Avenue I found a dark beery tavern called the Fjord. There were nautical decorations on the walls but they looked to have accumulated haphazardly over the years – a length of fishnet, a life preserver, and, curiously, a Minnesota Vikings football pennant. A black-and-white TV sat at one end of the bar, its volume turned down low. Old men sat with their shots and beers, not talking much, letting the night pass.

When I left there I flagged a gypsy cab and got the driver to take me to Colonial Road in Bay Ridge. I wanted to see the house where Tommy Tillary had lived, the house where his wife had died. But I wasn't sure of the address. That stretch of Colonial Road was mostly brick apartment houses and I was pretty sure that Tommy's place was a private house. There were a few such houses tucked in between the apartment buildings but I didn't have the number written down and wasn't sure of the cross streets. I told the cabdriver I was looking for the house where the woman was stabbed to death and he didn't know

what the hell I was talking about, and seemed generally wary of me, as though I might do something unpredictable at any moment.

I suppose I was a little drunk. I sobered up on the way back to Manhattan. He wasn't that enthusiastic about taking me, but he set a price of ten dollars and I agreed to it and leaned back in my seat. He took the expressway, and en route I saw the tower of Saint Michael's and told the driver that it wasn't right, that churches should be open twenty-four hours a day. He didn't say anything, and I closed my eyes and when I opened them the cab was pulling up in front of my hotel.

There were a couple of messages for me at the desk. Tommy Tillary had called twice and wanted me to call him. Skip Devoe had called once.

It was too late to call Tommy, probably too late for Skip. Late enough, anyway, to call it a night.

NINE

I rode out to Brooklyn again the next day. I stayed on the train past the Sunset Park stations and got off at Bay Ridge Avenue. The subway entrance was right across the street from the funeral parlor Margaret Tillary had been buried from. Burial had been in Green-Wood Cemetery, two miles to the north. I turned and looked up Fourth Avenue, as if following the route of the funeral cortege with my eyes. Then I walked west on Bay Ridge Avenue toward the water.

At Third Avenue I looked to my left and saw the Verrazano Bridge off in the distance, spanning the Narrows between Brooklyn and Staten Island. I walked on, through a better neighborhood than the one I'd spent the previous day in, and at Colonial Road I turned right and walked until I found the Tillary house. I'd looked up the address before leaving my hotel and now found it easily. It may have been one of the houses I'd stared at the night before. The cab ride had since faded some from memory. It was indistinct, as if seen through a veil.

The house was a huge brick-and-frame affair three stories tall, just across the street from the southeast corner of Owl's Head Park. Four-story apartment buildings of red brick flanked the house. It had a broad porch, an aluminum awning, a steeply pitched roof. I mounted the steps to the porch and rang the doorbell. A four-note chime sounded within.

No one answered. I tried the door and it was locked. The lock didn't look terribly challenging, but I had no reason to force it.

A driveway ran past the house on its left-hand side. It led past a side door, also locked, to a padlocked garage. The burglars had broken a pane of glass in the side door, and it had been since replaced with a rectangle of cardboard cut from a corrugated carton and secured with metallic tape.

I crossed the street and sat in the park for a while. Then I moved to where I could observe the Tillary house from the other

494

side of the street. I was trying to visualize the burglary. Cruz and Herrera had had a car, and I wondered where they'd parked it. In the driveway, out of sight and close to the door they'd entered through? Or on the street, making a getaway a simpler matter? The garage could have been open then; maybe they stowed the car in it, so no one would see it in the driveway and wonder about it.

I had a lunch of beans and rice and hot sausage. I got to Saint Michael's by midafternoon. It was open this time, and I sat for a while in a pew off to the side, then lit a couple of candles. My $150 finally made it to the poor box.

I did what you do. Mostly, I walked around and knocked on doors and asked questions. I went back to both their residences, Herrera's and Cruz's. I talked to neighbors of Cruz's who hadn't been around the previous day, and I talked to some of the other tenants in Herrera's rooming house. I walked over to the Six-eight looking for Cal Neumann. He wasn't there, but I talked to a couple of cops in the station house and went out for coffee with one of them.

I made a couple of phone calls, but most of my activity was walking around and talking to people face-to-face, writing down bits and pieces in my notebook, going through the motions and trying not to question the point of my actions. I was amassing a certain amount of data but I had no idea whether or not it added up to anything. I didn't know what exactly I was looking for, or if there was anything there *to* look for. I suppose I was trying to perform enough action and produce enough information to justify, to myself and to Tommy and his lawyer, the fee I had already collected and largely dispersed.

By early evening I'd had enough. I took the train home. There was a message at the desk for me from Tommy Tillary, with his office number. I put it in my pocket and walked around the corner, and Billie Keegan told me Skip was looking for me.

'Everybody's looking for me,' I said.

'It's nice to be wanted,' Billie said. 'I had an uncle was wanted in four states. You had a phone message, too. Where'd I put it?' He handed me a slip. Tommy Tillary again, but a different phone number this time. 'Something to drink, Matt? Or did you just drop by to check your mail and messages?'

I'd been taking it easy in Brooklyn, mostly sticking with cups of coffee in bakeries and bodegas, drinking a little beer in the bars. I let Billie pour me a double bourbon and it went down easy.

'Looked for you today,' Billie said. 'Couple of us went out to the track. Thought you might want to come along.'

'I had work to do,' I said. 'Anyway, I'm not much for horses.'

'It's fun,' he said, 'if you don't take it serious.'

The number Tommy Tillary left turned out to be a hotel switchboard in Murray Hill. He came on the line and asked if I could drop by the Hotel. 'You know where it is? Thirty-seventh and Lex?'

'I ought to be able to find it.'

'They got a bar downstairs, nice quiet little place. It's full of these Jap businessmen in Brooks Brothers suits. Every once in a while they put down their scotches long enough to take snapshots of each other. Then they smile and order more drinks. You'll love it.'

I caught a cab and went over there, and he hadn't been exaggerating much. The cocktail lounge, plush and dimly lit, had a largely Japanese clientele that evening. Tommy was by himself at the bar, and when I walked in he pumped my hand and introduced me to the bartender.

We took our drinks to a table. 'Crazy place,' he said. 'Look at that, will you? You thought I was kidding about the cameras, didn't you? I wonder what they do with all the pictures. You'd need a whole room in your house just to keep them, the way they click 'em off.'

'There's no film in the cameras.'

'Be a kick, wouldn't it?' He laughed. 'No film in the cameras. Shit, they're probably not real Japs, either. Where I mostly been going, there's the Blueprint a block away on Park, and there's another place, a pub-type place, Dirty Dick's or something like that. But I'm staying here and I wanted you to be able to reach me. Is this okay for now or should we go somewhere else?'

'This is fine.'

'You sure? I never had a detective work for me before, I want to make sure I keep him happy.' He grinned, then let his face turn serious. 'I was just wondering,' he said, 'if you were, you know, making any progress. Getting any-place.'

I told him some of what I'd run into. He got very excited when he heard about the barroom stabbing.

'That's great,' he said. 'That ought to wrap it up for our little brown brothers, shouldn't it?'

'How do you figure that?'

'He's a knife artist,' he said, 'and he already killed somebody

496

once and got away with it. Jesus, this is great stuff, Matt. I knew it was the right move to get you in on this. Have you talked to Kaplan yet?'

'No.'

'That's what you want to do. This is the kind of stuff he can use.'

I wondered at that. For openers, it struck me that Drew Kaplan should have been able to inform himself of Miguelito Cruz's no-bill for homicide without hiring a detective. Nor did it seem to me that the information would weigh heavily in a courtroom, or that you could even introduce it in court, for that matter. Anyway, Kaplan had said he was looking for something that would keep him and his client out of court in the first place, and I couldn't see how I'd uncovered anything that qualified.

'You want to fill Drew in on everything you come up with,' Tommy assured me. 'Some little bit you hand him, might not look like anything to you, and it might fit with something he already has and it's just what he needs, you know what I mean? Even if it looks like nothing all by itself.'

'I can see how that would work.'

'Sure. Call him once a day, give him whatever you got. I know you don't file reports, but you don't mind checking in regular by phone, do you?'

'No, of course not.'

'Great,' he said. 'That's great, Matt. Let me get us a couple more of these.' He went to the bar, came back with fresh drinks. 'So you been out in my part of the world, huh? Like it out there?'

'I like your neighborhood better than Cruz and Herrera's.'

'Shit, I hope so. What, were you out by the house? My house?'

I nodded. 'To get a sense of it. You have a key, Tommy?'

'A key? You mean a house key? Sure, I'd have to have a key to my own house, wouldn't I? Why? You want a key to the place, Matt?'

'If you don't mind.'

'Jesus, everybody's been through there, cops, insurance, not to mention the spics.' He took a ring of keys from his pocket, removed one and held it out to me. 'This is for the front door,' he said. 'You want the side door key too? That's how they went in, there's cardboard taped up where they broke a pane to let themselves in.'

'I noticed it this afternoon.'

'So what do you need with the key? Just pull off the cardboard

497

and let yourself in. While you're at it, see if there's anything left worth stealing and carry it outta there in a pillowcase.'

'Is that how they did it?'

'Who knows how they did it? That's how they do it on television, isn't it? Jesus, look at that, will ya? They take each other's pictures, they trade cameras and take 'em all over again. There's a lot of 'em stay at this hotel, that's why they come in here.' He looked down at his hands, clasped loosely on the table in front of him. His pinkie ring had turned to one side and he reached to straighten it. 'The hotel's not bad,' he said, 'but I can't stay here forever. You pay day rates, it adds up.'

'Will you be moving back to Bay Ridge?'

He shook his head. 'What do I need with a place like that? It was too big for the two of us and I'd rattle around there by myself. Forgetting about the feelings connected with it.'

'How did you come to have such a large house for two people, Tommy?'

'Well, it wasn't for two.' He looked off, remembering. 'It was Peg's aunt's house. What happened, she put up the money to buy the place. She had some insurance money left after she buried her husband some years ago, and we needed a place to live because we had the baby coming. You knew we had a kid that died?'

'I think there was something in the paper.'

'In the death notice, yeah, I put it in. We had a boy, Jimmy. He wasn't right, he had congenital heart damage and some mental retardation. He died, it was just before his sixth birthday.'

'That's hard, Tommy.'

'It was harder for her. I think it woulda been worse than it was except he didn't live at home after the first few months. The medical problems, you couldn't really cope in a private home, you know what I mean? Plus the doctor took me aside and said, look, Mr Tillary, the more your wife gets attached to the kid, the rougher it's gonna be on her when the inevitable happens. Because they knew he wasn't gonna live more than a couple of years.'

Without saying anything he got up and brought back fresh drinks. 'So it was the three of us,' he went on, 'me and Peg and the aunt, and she had her room and her own bath an' all on the third floor, an' it was still a big house for three people, but the two women, you know, they kept each other company. And then when the old woman died, well, we talked about moving, but Peg was used to the house and used to the neighborhood.'

He took a breath and let his shoulders drop. 'What do I need, big house, drive back and forth or fight the subway, whole thing's a pain in the ass. Soon as all this clears up I'll sell the place, find myself a little apartment in the city.'

'What part of town?'

'You know, I don't even know. Around Gramercy Park is kind of nice. Or maybe the Upper East Side. Maybe buy a co-op in a decent building. I don't need a whole lot of space.' He snorted. 'I could move in with whatsername. You know. Carolyn.'

'Oh?'

'You know we work at the same place. I see her there every day. "I gave at the office."' He sighed. 'I been sort of stayin' away from the neighborhood until all of this is cleared up.'

'Sure.'

And then we got on the subject of churches, and I don't remember how. Something to the effect that bars kept better hours than churches, that churches closed early. 'Well, they got to,' he said, 'on account of the crime problem. Matt, when we were kids, who ever heard of somebody stealing from a church?'

'I suppose it happened.'

'I suppose it did but when did you ever hear of it? Nowadays you got a different class of people, they don't respect anything. Of course there's that church in Bensonhurst, I guess they keep whatever hours they want to.'

'What do you mean?'

'I think it's Bensonhurst. Big church, I forget the name of it. Saint Something or other.'

'That narrows it down.'

'Don't you remember? Couple of years ago two black kids stole something off the altar. Gold candlesticks, whatever the hell it was. And it turns out Dominic Tutto's mother goes to mass there every morning. The capo, runs half of Brooklyn?'

'Oh, right.'

'And the word went out, and a week later the candlesticks are back on the altar. Or whatever the hell they were. I think it was candlesticks.'

'Whatever.'

'And the punks who took 'em,' he said, 'disappeared. And the story I heard, well, you don't know if it was anything more than a story. I wasn't there, and I forget who I heard it from, but *he* wasn't there either, you know?'

'What did you hear?'

'I heard they hauled the two niggers to Tutto's basement,' he

said, 'and hung 'em on meat hooks.' A flashbulb winked two tables away from us. 'And skinned 'em alive,' he said. 'But who knows? You hear all these stories, you don't know what to believe.'

'You should've been with us this afternoon,' Skip told me. 'Me and Keegan and Ruslander, we took my car and drove out to the Big A.' He drawled in imitation of W. C. Fields: 'Participated in the sport of kings, made our contribution to the improvement of the breed, yes indeed.'

'I was doing some work.'

'I'd have been better off working. Fucking Keegan, he's got a pocket full of miniatures, he's knocking 'em off one a race, he's got his pockets full of these little bottles. And he's betting horses on the basis of their names. There's this plater, Jill the Queen, hasn't won anything since Victoria was the queen, and Keegan remembers this girl named Jill he had this mad passion for in the sixth grade. So of course he bets the horse.'

'And the horse wins.'

'Of *course* the horse wins. The horse wins at something like twelve-to-one, and Keegan's got a ten-dollar win ticket on her, and he's saying he made a mistake. What mistake? "Her name was Rita," he says. "It was her sister's name was Jill. I remembered it wrong."'

'That's Billie.'

'Well, the whole afternoon was like that,' Skip said. 'He bets his old girlfriends and their sisters and he drinks half a quart of whiskey out of these little bottles, and Ruslander and I both lose I don't know, a hundred, hundred and fifty, and fucking Billie Keegan wins six hundred dollars by betting on girls' names.'

'How did you and Ruslander pick horses?'

'Well, you know the actor. He hunches his shoulders and talks out of the side of his mouth like a tout, and he talks to a couple of horsey-looking guys and comes back with a tip. The guys he talks to are probably other actors.'

'And you both followed his tips?'

'Are you crazy? I bet scientific.'

'You read the form?'

'I can't make sense out of it. I watch which ones have the odds drop when the smart money comes in, and also I go down and watch 'em walk around, and I notice which one takes a good crap.'

'Scientific.'

'Absolutely. Who wants to invest serious money in some fucking constipated horse? Some steed wracked with irregularity? My horses' – he lowered his eyes, mockshy – 'are M/O-kay.'

'And Keegan's crazy.'

'You got it. The man trivializes a scientific pursuit.' He leaned forward, ground out his cigarette. 'Ah, Jesus, I love this life,' he said. 'I swear to God I was born for it. I spend half my life running my own saloon and the other half in other people's saloons, with a sunny afternoon away from it now and then to get close to nature and commune with God's handiwork.' His eyes locked on mine. 'I love it,' he said levelly. 'That's why I'm gonna pay those cock-suckers.'

'You heard from them?'

'Before we left for the track. They presented their nonnegotiable demands.'

'How much?'

'Enough to make my bets seem somehow beside the point. Who cares if you win or lose a hundred dollars? And I don't bet heavy, it's not fun once it gets into serious money. *They* want serious money.'

'And you're going to pay it?'

He picked up his drink. 'We're meeting with some people tomorrow. The lawyer, the accountants. That's if Kasabian stops throwing up.'

'And then?'

'And then I suppose we try to negotiate the nonnegotiable, and then we fucking pay. What else are the lawyers and accountants going to tell us? Raise an army? Fight a guerrilla war? That's not the kind of answer you get from lawyers and accountants.' He took another cigarette from the pack, tapped it, held it up, looked at it, tapped it again, then lit it. 'I'm a machine that smokes and drinks,' he said through a cloud of smoke, 'and I'll tell you, I don't know why I fucking bother with any of it.'

'A minute ago you loved this life.'

'Was I the one who said that? You know the story about the guy bought a Volkswagen and his friend asks him how does he like it? "Well, it's like eating pussy,' the guy says. 'I'm crazy about it, but I don't take a whole lot of pride in it."'

TEN

I called Drew Kaplan the next morning before I went out to Brooklyn. His secretary said he was in a meeting, and could he call me back? I said I'd call him back, and I did forty minutes later when I got off the subway in Sunset Park. By then he'd gone for lunch. I told her I'd call back later.

That afternoon I managed to meet a woman who was friendly with Angel Herrera's girlfriend. She had strong Indio features and a face badly pitted by acne. She said it was a pity for Herrera that he had to go to jail, but it was probably good for her friend, because Herrera would never marry her or even live with her because he considered himself still married in Puerto Rico. 'An' his wife divorce him, but he doan accept it,' she said. 'So my fren, she wanna get pregnant, but he doan get her pregnant and he woan marry her. What's she want with him, you know? Better for her if he goes away for a while. Better for everybody.'

I called Kaplan again from a street corner phone booth and reached him this time. I got out my notebook and gave him what I had. None of it added up to anything as far as I could see, except for Cruz's prior arrest for manslaughter, which was something he should have known about, as he was quick enough to point out himself. 'That's not something an investigator should have to come up with,' he said. 'They should have put that on the table. True, you can't introduce it in court, but there's ways to use it. You may have earned your fee with that little bit of information. Not that I want to discourage you from digging for more.'

But when I'd hung up the phone I didn't really feel like digging for more. I went over to the Fjord and had a couple of drinks, but then a lanky kid with a lot of yellow hair and a blond Zapata moustache came in and tried to hustle me into a game on the shuffle-bowling machine. I wasn't interested and neither was

anyone else, so he went and played the thing by himself, feigning noisy drunkenness, I suppose in an attempt to look like easy pickings. The noise drove me out of there, and I wound up walking all the way to Tommy's house on Colonial Road.

His key unlocked the front door. I walked in, half expecting the scene that had greeted the discoverer of Margaret Tillary's body, but of course things had been cleaned up and put right long ago, after the lab crew and the photographer had done their work and gone.

I walked through the rooms on the ground floor, found the side entrance that led to a vestibule off the kitchen, walked back through the kitchen and the dining room, trying to imagine myself into Cruz and Herrera's shoes as they moved through the rooms of the empty house.

Except it wouldn't have been empty. Margaret Tillary had been upstairs in her bedroom. Doing what? Sleeping? Watching television?

I climbed the stairs. A couple of the boards creaked underfoot. Had they done so the night of the burglary? Had Peg Tillary heard, and had she reacted? Maybe she thought it was Tommy's step, got out of bed to greet him. Maybe she knew it was someone else. Footsteps are recognizable to some people, and a stranger's footfall is unfamiliar, enough so sometimes to intrude on sleep.

She'd been killed in the bedroom. Up the stairs, open the door, find a woman cowering in there and stab her? Or maybe she'd come out of the bedroom door, expecting Tommy, or not expecting him but not thinking straight, confronting the burglar, people did that all the time, not thinking, outraged at the invasion of their home, acting as if their righteous indignation would serve them as armor.

Then she'd have seen the knife in his hand, and she'd have gone back inside the room, tried to shut the door, maybe, and he'd come in after her, and maybe she was screaming and he had to get to her to shut her up, and –

I kept seeing Anita backing away from a knife, kept turning the scene into our bedroom in Syosset.

Silly.

I walked over to one of the dressers, opened drawers, closed them. Her dresser, long and low. His was a highboy in the same French Provincial styling, part of a suite with the bed and a nightstand and a mirrored dressing table. I opened and closed

drawers in his dresser. He'd left a lot of clothes behind, but he probably owned a lot of clothes.

I opened the closet door. She could have hidden in the closet, though not comfortably. It was full, the shelf loaded with a couple dozen shoe boxes, the rack packed with clothes on hangers. He must have taken a couple of suits and jackets with him, but the clothes he'd left behind were more than I owned.

There were bottles of perfume on the dressing table. I lifted the stopper of one and held it to my nose. The scent was lily-of-the-valley.

I was in the room for a long time. There are people who are psychically sensitive, they pick up things at a murder scene. Maybe everyone does, maybe the sensitive ones are simply better at figuring out what it is that they're attuned to. I had no illusions about my ability to glean vibrations from the room or the clothing or the furniture. Smell is the sense most directly hooked into the memory, but all her perfume did was remind me that an aunt of mine had smelled of that same floral scent.

I don't know what I thought I was doing there.

There was a television set in the bedroom. I turned it on, turned it off. She might have been watching it, she might not even have heard the burglar until he opened the door. But wouldn't he have heard the set? Why would he come into a room if he knew someone was there, when he could just slip away undetected?

Of course he could have had rape in mind. There hadn't been any rape, none detected in the autopsy, although that hardly proved the absence of intent. He might have achieved sexual release from the murder, might have been turned off by the violence, might have ...

Tommy had slept in this room, had lived with the woman who smelled of lilies-of-the-valley. I knew him from the bars, I knew him with a girl on his arm and a drink in his hand and his laugh echoing off paneled walls. I didn't know him in a room like this, in a house like this.

I went in and out of other rooms on the second floor. In what I suppose was the upstairs sitting room, photos in silver frames were grouped on top of a mahogany radio-phonograph console. There was a formal wedding picture, Tommy in a tuxedo, the bride in white with her bouquet all pink and white. Tommy was lean in the photo, and impossibly young. He was sporting a crew cut, which looked outlandish in 1975, especially in counterpoint to the formal clothes.

Margaret Tillary – she might still have been Margaret Wayland when the photo was taken – had been a tall woman, with strong features even then. I looked at her and tried to imagine her with years added. She'd probably put on a few pounds over the years. Most people did.

Most of the other photos showed people I didn't recognize. Relatives, I suppose. I didn't notice any of the son Tommy'd told me about.

One door led to a linen closet, another to a bathroom. A third opened on a flight of stairs leading to the third floor. There was a bedroom up there, its window affording a good view of the park. I drew up an armchair, its seat and back worked in needlepoint, and watched the traffic on Colonial Road and a baseball game in the park.

I imagined the aunt sitting as I was sitting, watching the world through her window. If I'd heard her name I didn't remember it, and when I thought of her the image that came to mind was some sort of generic aunt, some combination of the various unidentifiable female faces in the photographs downstairs mixed, I suppose, with elements of some aunts of my own. She was gone now, this unnamed composite aunt, and her niece was gone, and before long the house would be sold and other people living in it.

And it would be a piece of work, too, removing the traces of the Tillary occupancy. The aunt's bedroom and bathroom took up the front third of the top floor; the rest was a large open space given over to storage, with trunks and cardboard cartons fitted in under the pitched roof along with pieces of furniture that had been removed from service. Some were covered with cloths. Others were not. Everything was lightly coated with dust, and you could smell the dust in the air.

I went back to the aunt's bedroom. Her clothes were still in the dresser and closet, her toilet articles in the bathroom medicine chest. Easy enough to leave everything, if they didn't need the room.

I wondered what Herrera had hauled away. That was how he'd first come to the house, carting off jetsam after the aunt's death.

I sat in the chair again. I smelled the dust of the storage room, and the scent of the old woman's clothes, but I still held the lily-of-the-valley perfume in my nostrils and it overscored all of the other aromas. It cloyed now, and I wished I could stop smelling it. It seemed to me that I was smelling the memory of the scent more than the scent itself.

505

In the park across the street, two boys were playing a game of keep-away, with a third boy running vainly back and forth between them, trying to get the striped ball they tossed back and forth. I leaned forward, propping my elbows on the radiator to watch them. I tired of the game before they did. I left the chair facing the window and walked through the open area and down both flights of stairs.

I was in the living room, wondering what Tommy had around the house to drink and where he kept it, when someone cleared his throat a couple of yards behind me.

I froze.

ELEVEN

'Yeah,' a voice said. 'I sort of figured it was you. Whyntcha sit down, Matt. You look white as a ghost. You look like you seen one.'

I knew but couldn't place the voice. I turned, my breath still stuck in my chest, and I knew the man. He was sitting in an overstuffed armchair, deep in the room's long shadows. He was wearing a short-sleeved shirt open at the throat. His suit jacket was draped over the chair's arm, and the end of his tie peeped out of a pocket.

'Jack Diebold,' I said.

'The same,' he said. 'How you doin', Matt? I got to tell you you'd make the world's worst cat burglar. You were clompin' around up there like the horse cavalry.'

'You scared the shit out of me, Jack.'

He laughed softly. 'Well, what was I gonna do, Matt? A neighbor called in, lights on in the house, blah blah blah, and since I was handy and it was my case I took the squeal myself and came on over. I figured it was probably you. Guy from the Six-eight called me the other day, mentioned you were doin' something for this Tillary asshole.'

'Neumann called you? You're at Brooklyn Homicide now?'

'Oh, a while now. I made Detective First, shit, it's been almost two years.'

'Congratulations.'

'Thanks. Anyway, I came over, but I don't know it's you and I don't want to charge the stairs and I thought, shit, we'll let Mohammad come to the mountain for a change. I didn't mean to scare you.'

'The hell you didn't.'

'Well, you walked right past me, for God's sake, and you looked so funny goin' about it. What were you lookin' for just now?'

'Just now? I was trying to guess where he keeps his liquor.'

'Well, don't let me stop you. Find a couple of glasses too, while you're at it.'

A pair of cut-glass decanters stood on a sideboard in the dining room. Little silver nameplates around their necks identified them as Scotch and Rye. You needed a key to remove them from their silver caddy. The sideboard itself held linen in its center drawers, glassware on the right-hand side, bottles of whiskey and cordials on the left. I found a fifth of Wild Turkey and a couple of glasses, showed the bottle to Diebold. He nodded and I poured drinks for both of us.

He was a big man a couple of years my senior. He'd lost some hair since I'd seen him last, and he was heavy, but then he'd always been heavy. He looked at his glass for a moment, raised it to me, took a sip.

'Good stuff,' he said.

'Not bad.'

'What were you doin' up there, Matt? Lookin' for clues?' He stretched the last word.

I shook my head. 'Just getting the feel of it.'

'You're working for Tillary.'

I nodded. 'He gave me the key.'

'Shit, I don't care if you came down the chimney like Santy Claus. What's he want you to do for him?'

'Clear him.'

'Clear him? The cocksucker's already clear enough to see through. No way we're gonna tag him for it.'

'But you think he did it.'

He gave me a sour look. 'I don't think he did it,' he said, 'if doin' it means stickin' a knife in her. I'd love thinkin' he did but he's alibied better than a fuckin' Mafia don. He was out in public with this broad, a million people saw him, he's got charge-card receipts from a restaurant, for Christ's sake.' He drank the rest of his whiskey. 'I think he set her up.'

'Hired them to kill her?'

'Something like that.'

'They're not hired killers by trade, are they?'

'Shit, of course they're not. Cruz and Herrera, button men for the Sunset Park syndicate. Rubouts a specialty.'

'But you think he hired them.'

He came over and took the bottle from me, poured his glass half full. 'He set them up,' he said.

'How?'

508

He shook his head, impatient with the question. 'I wish I was the first person to question them,' he said. 'The guys from the Six-eight went over with a burglary warrant, they didn't know when they went in where the stuff was from. So they already talked to the PRs before I got a crack at 'em.'

'And?'

'First time out, they denied everything. 'I bought the stuff on the street.' You know how it goes.'

'Of course.'

'Then they didn't know anything about a woman who got killed. Now that was horseshit. They ran that story and then they changed it, or it died a natural death, because of course they knew, it was in the papers and on the television. Then the story was that there was no woman around when they did the job, and on top of that they were never upstairs of the first floor. Well, that's nice, but their fucking fingerprints were on the bedroom mirror and the dresser top and a couple of other places.'

'You had prints putting them in the bedroom? I didn't know that.'

'Maybe I shouldn't tell you. Except I can't see how it makes a difference. Yeah, we found prints.'

'Whose? Herrera's or Cruz's?'

'Why?'

'Because I was figuring Cruz for the one who knifed her.'

'Why him?'

'His record. And he carried a knife.'

'A flick knife. He didn't use it on the woman.'

'Oh?'

'She was killed with something had a blade six inches long and two or two-and-a-half inches wide. Whatever. A kitchen knife, it sounds like.'

'You didn't recover it, though.'

'No. She had a whole mess of knives in the kitchen, a couple of different sets. You keep house for twenty years, you accumulate knives. Tillary couldn't tell if one was missing. The lab took the ones we found, couldn't find blood on any of them.'

'So you think –'

'That one of 'em picked up a knife in the kitchen and went upstairs with it and killed her and then threw it down a sewer somewhere, or in the river, or who knows where.'

'Picked up a knife in the kitchen.'

'Or brought it along. Cruz carried a flick knife as a regular

thing, but maybe he didn't want to use his own knife to kill the woman.'

'Figuring he came here planning to do it.'

'How else can you figure it?'

'I figure it was a burglary and they didn't know she was here.'

'Yeah, well, you want to figure it that way because you're trying to clear the prick. He goes upstairs and takes a knife along with him. Why the knife?'

'In case someone's up there.'

'Then why go upstairs?'

'He's looking for money. A lot of people keep cash in the bedroom. He opens the door, she's there, she panics, he panics –'

'And he kills her.'

'Why not?'

'Shit, it sounds as good as anything else, Matt.' He put his glass on the coffee table. 'One more session with 'em,' he said, 'and they woulda spilled.'

'They talked a lot as it was.'

'I know. You know what's the most important thing to teach a new recruit? How to read 'em Miranda-Escobedo in such a way that they don't attach any significance to it. 'You have the right to remain silent. Now I want you to tell me what really went down.' One more time and they woulda seen that the way to cop out on Tillary was to say he hired them to kill her.'

'That means admitting they did it.'

'I know, but they were admitting a little more each time. I don't know. I think I could've got more out of them. But once they got legal counsel on the spot, shit, that's the end of our cozy little conversations.'

'Why do you like Tillary for it? Just because he was playing around?'

'Everybody plays around.'

'That's what I mean.'

'The ones who kill their wives are the ones who aren't playing around and want to be. Or the ones who're in love with something sweet and young and want to marry it and keep it around forever. He's not in love with anybody but himself. Or doctors. Doctors are always killing their wives.'

'Then –'

'We got tons of motive, Matt. He owed money that he didn't have. And she was gettin' ready to dump him.'

'The girlfriend?'

'The wife.'

'I never heard that.'

'Who would you hear it from, him? She talked to a neighbor woman, she talked to a lawyer. The aunt dyin' made the difference. She came into the property, for one thing, and she didn't have the old woman around for company. Oh, we got lots of motive, my friend. If motive was enough to hang a man we could go shoppin' for a rope.'

Jack Diebold said, 'He's a friend of yours, huh? That's why you're involved?'

We had left the Tillary house somewhere in the early evening. I remember the sky was still light, but it was July and it stayed light well into the evening hours. I turned off the lights and put the bottle of Wild Turkey away. There wasn't much left in it. Diebold joked that I should wipe my prints off the bottle, and off the glasses we had used.

He was driving his own car, a Ford Fairlane that was showing a lot of rust. He chose the place, a plush steak-and-seafood restaurant near the approach to the Verrazano Bridge. They knew him there, and I sensed that there wouldn't be a check. Most cops have a certain number of restaurants where they can eat a certain number of free meals. This bothers some people, and I have never really understood why.

We ate well – shrimp cocktails, strip sirloins, hot pumpernickel rolls, stuffed baked potatoes. 'When we were growin' up,' Diebold said, 'a man who ate like this was treating himself right. You never heard a goddamned word about cholesterol. Now it's all you hear.'

'I know.'

'I had a partner, I don't know if you ever knew him. Gerry O'Bannon. You know him?'

'I don't think so.'

'Well, he got on this health kick. What started it was he quit smoking. I never smoked so I never had to quit, but he quit and then it was one thing after another. He lost a lot of weight, he changed his diet, he started jogging. He looked terrible, he looked all drawn, you know how guys get? But he was happy, he was really pleased with himself. Wouldn't go drinking, just order one beer and make it last, or he'd have one and then switch to club soda. The French stuff. Perrier?'

'Uh-huh.'

'Very popular all of a sudden, it's plain soda water and it costs

more than beer. Figure it out and explain it to me sometime. He shot himself.'

'O'Bannon?'

'Yeah. I don't mean it's connected, losing the weight and drinking club soda and killing himself. The life you lead and the things you see, I'll tell you, a cop goes and eats his gun, I never figure it requires an explanation. You know what I mean?'

'I know what you mean.'

He looked at me. 'Yeah,' he said. 'Course you do.' And then the conversation took a turn in another direction, and a little while later, with a slab of hot apple pie topped with cheddar in front of Diebold and coffee poured for both of us, he returned to the subject of Tommy Tillary, identifying him as my friend.

'Sort of a friend,' I said. 'I know him around the bars.'

'Right, she lives up in your neighborhood, doesn't she? The girlfriend, I forget her name.'

'Carolyn Cheatham.'

'I wish she was all the alibi he had. But even if he got away from her for a few hours, what was the wife doing during the burglary? Waiting for Tommy to come home and kill her? I mean, take it to extremes, say she hides under the bed while they rifle the bedroom and get their prints on everything. They leave, she calls the cops, right?'

'He couldn't have killed her.'

'I know, and it drives me crazy. How come you like him?'

'He's not a bad guy. And I'm getting paid for this, Jack. I'm doing him a favor, but it's one I'm getting paid for. And it's a waste of my time and his money anyway, because you haven't got a case against him.'

'No.'

'You don't, do you?'

'Not even close.' He ate some pie, drank some coffee. 'I'm glad you're getting paid. Not just because I like to see a guy turn a buck. I'd hate to see you bust your balls for him for free.'

'I'm not busting anything.'

'You know what I mean.'

'Am I missing something, Jack?'

'Huh?'

'What did he do, steal baseballs from the Police Athletic League? How come you've got the red ass for him?'

He thought it over. His jaws worked. He frowned.

'Well, I'll tell you,' he said at length. 'He's a phony.'

'He sells stock and shit over the phone. Of course he's a phony.'

'More than that. I don't know how to explain it so it makes sense, but shit, you were a cop. You know how you get feelings.'

'Of course.'

'Well, I get a feeling with that guy. There's something about him that's wrong, something about her death.'

'I'll tell you what it is,' I said. 'He's glad she's dead and he's pretending he isn't. It gets him out of a jam and he's glad, but he's acting like a sanctimonious son of a bitch and that's what you're responding to.'

'Maybe that's part of it.'

'I think it's the whole thing. You're sensing that he's acting guilty. Well, he is. He feels guilty. He's glad she's dead, but at the same time he lived with the woman for I forget how many years, he had a life with her, part of him was busy being a husband while the other part was running around on her –'

'Yeah, yeah, I follow you.'

'So?'

'It's more than that.'

'Why does it have to be more? Look, maybe he did set up Cruz and whatsisname –'

'Hernandez.'

'No, not Hernandez. What the hell's his name?'

'Angel. Angel eyes.'

'Herrera. Maybe he set them up to go in, rob the place. Maybe he even had it in the back of his mind she might get in the way.'

'Keep going.'

'Except it's too iffy, isn't it? I think he just feels guilty for wishing she'd get killed, or being glad of it after the fact, and you're picking up on the guilt and that's why you like him for the murder.'

'No.'

'You sure?'

'I'm not sure that I'm sure of anything. You know, I'm glad you're gettin' paid. I hope you're costin' him a ton.'

'Not all that much.'

'Well, soak him all you can. Because at least it's costin' him money, even if that's all it's costin' him, and it's money he doesn't have to pay. Because we can't touch him. Even if those two changed their story, admitted the killing and said he put 'em up to it, that's not enough to put him away. And they're *not* gonna change their story, and who would ever hire them to

commit murder anyway, and they wouldn't take a contract like that. I *know* they wouldn't. Cruz is a mean little bastard but Herrera's just a stupid guy, and – aw, shit.'

'What?'

'It just kills me to see him get away with it.'

'But he didn't do it, Jack.'

'He's gettin' away with *something*,' he said, 'and I hate to see it happen. You know what I hope? I hope he runs a red light sometime, in that fucking boat of his. What's it, a Buick he's got?'

'I think so.'

'I hope he runs a light and I tag him for it, that's what I hope.'

'Is that what Brooklyn Homicide does these days? A lot of traffic detail?'

'I just hope it happens,' he said. 'That's all.'

TWELVE

Diebold insisted on driving me home. When I offered to take the subway he told me not to be ridiculous, that it was midnight already and I was in no condition for public transportation.

'You'll pass out,' he said, 'and some bum'll steal the shoes off your feet.'

He was probably right. As it was I nodded off during the ride back to Manhattan, coming awake when he pulled up at the corner of Fifty-seventh and Ninth. I thanked him for the ride, asked him if he had time for a drink before he went back.

'Hey, enough's enough,' he said. 'I can't go all night like I used to.'

'You know, I think I'll call it a night myself,' I said.

But I didn't. I watched him pull away, started walking to my hotel, then turned and went around the corner to Armstrong's. The place was mostly empty. I went in, and Billie gave me a wave.

I went up to the bar. And she was there at the end of the bar, all alone, staring down into the glass on the bar in front of her. Carolyn Cheatham. I hadn't seen her since the night I'd gone home with her.

While I was trying to decide whether or not to say anything, she looked up and her eyes met mine. Her face was frozen with stubborn old pain. It took her a blink or two to recognize me, and when she did a muscle worked in her cheek and tears started to form in the corners of her eyes. She used the back of her hand to wipe them away. She'd been crying earlier; there was a tissue crumpled on the bar, black with mascara.

'My bourbon-drinking friend,' she said. 'Billie,' she said, 'this man is a gentleman. Will you please bring my gentleman friend a drink of good bourbon?'

Billie looked at me. I nodded. He brought a couple of ounces of bourbon and a mug of black coffee.

515

'I called you my gentleman friend,' Carolyn Cheatham said, 'but that has an unintentional connotation.' She pronounced her words with a drunk's deliberate care. 'You are a gentleman *and* a friend, but not a gentleman friend. My gentleman friend, on the other hand, is neither.'

I drank some of the bourbon, poured some of it into the coffee.

'Billie,' she said, 'do you know how you can tell that Mr Scudder is a gentleman?'

'He always removes his lady in the presence of a hat.'

'He is a bourbon drinker,' she said.

'That makes him a gentleman, huh, Carolyn?'

'It makes him a far cry removed from a hypocritical scotch-drinking son of a bitch.'

She didn't speak in a loud voice, but there was enough edge to her words to shut down conversations across the room. There were only three or four tables occupied, and the people sitting at them all picked the same instant to stop talking. For a moment the taped music was startlingly audible. It was one of the few pieces I could identify, one of the Brandenburg concertos. They played it so often there that even I was now able to tell what it was.

Then Billie said, 'Suppose a man drinks Irish whiskey, Carolyn. What does that make him?'

'An Irishman,' she said.

'Makes sense.'

'I'm drinking bourbon,' she said, and shoved her glass forward a significant inch. 'God damn it, I'm a *lady*.'

He looked at her, then looked at me. I nodded, and he shrugged and poured for her.

'On me,' I said.

'Thank you,' she said. 'Thank you, Matthew.' And her eyes started to water, and she dug a fresh tissue from her bag.

She wanted to talk about Tommy. He was being nice to her, she said. Calling up, sending flowers. But it just wouldn't do if she made a scene around the office, and he just might have to testify how he spent the night his wife was killed, and he had to keep on the good side of her for the time being.

But he wouldn't see her because it wouldn't look right. Not for a new widower, not for a man who'd been virtually accused of complicity in his wife's death.

'He sends flowers with no card enclosed,' she said. 'He calls me from pay phones. The son of a bitch.'

'Maybe the florist forgot to enclose a card.'

'Oh, Matt. Don't make excuses for him.'

'And he's in a hotel, of course he would use a pay phone.'

'He could call from his room. He as much as said he didn't want the call to go through the hotel switchboard, in case the operator's listening in. There was no card with the flowers because he doesn't want anything in writing. He came to my apartment the other night, but he won't be seen with me, he won't go out with me, and – oh, the hypocrite. The scotch-drinking son of a bitch.'

Billie called me aside. 'I didn't want to put her out,' he said, 'a nice woman like that, shitfaced as she is. But I thought I was gonna have to. You'll see she gets home?'

'Sure.'

First I had to let her buy us another round. She insisted. Then I got her out of there and walked her around the corner to her building. There was rain coming, you could smell it in the air, and when we went from Armstrong's air conditioning into the sultry humidity that heralds a summer storm it took some of the spirit out of her. She held my arm as we walked, gripped it with something on the edge of desperation. In the elevator she sagged against the back panel and braced her feet.

'Oh, God,' she said.

I took the keys from her and unlocked her door. I got her inside. She half sat, half sprawled on the couch. Her eyes were open but I don't know if she saw much through them. I had to use the bathroom, and when I came back her eyes were closed and she was snoring lightly.

I got her shoes off, moved her to a chair, struggled with the couch until I managed to open it into a bed. I put her on it. I figured I ought to loosen her clothing, and while I was at it I undressed her completely. She remained unconscious throughout the operation, and I remembered what a mortician's assistant had told me once about the difficulty of dressing and undressing the dead. My gorge rose at the image and I thought I was going to be sick, but I sat down and my stomach settled itself.

I covered her with the top sheet, sat back down again. There was something else I'd wanted to do but I couldn't think what it was. I tried to think, and I guess I must have dozed off myself. I don't suppose I was out for more than a few minutes, just time enough to lose myself in a dream that fled from me the minute I opened my eyes and blinked it away.

I let myself out. Her door had a spring lock. There was a dead bolt you could engage with the key for extra security, but all I

had to do was draw the door shut and it was locked, and reasonably secure. I took the elevator down and went outside.

The rain was holding off. At the corner of Ninth Avenue a jogger passed, running doggedly uptown against what little traffic there was. His T-shirt was gray with sweat and he looked ready to drop. I thought of O'Bannon, Jack Diebold's old partner, getting physically fit before blowing his brains out.

And then I remembered what I'd wanted to do at Carolyn's apartment. I'd been planning on taking away the little gun Tommy had given her. If she was going to drink like that and get depressed like that, she didn't need to have a weapon in the bedside table.

But the door was locked. And she was out cold, she wasn't going to wake up and kill herself.

I crossed the street. The steel gate was drawn most of the way across the front of Armstrong's, and the white globe lights over the front were out, but light showed from within. I walked over to the door, saw that the chairs were on top of the tables, ready for the Dominican kid who came in first thing in the morning to sweep the place out. I didn't see Billie at first, and then I saw him at a stool at the far end of the bar. The door was locked, but he spotted me and came over and let me in.

He locked the door again after I was through it, walked me over to the bar and slipped behind it. Without my saying anything he poured me a glass of bourbon. I curled my hand around it but didn't pick it up from the top of the bar.

'The coffee's all gone,' he said.

'That's all right. I didn't want any more.'

'She all right? Carolyn?'

'Well, she might have a hangover tomorrow.'

'Just about everybody I know might have a hangover tomorrow,' he said. '*I* might have a hangover tomorrow. It's gonna pour, I might as well sit in the house and eat aspirin all day.'

Someone banged on the door. Billie shook his head at him, waved him away. The man knocked again. Billie ignored him.

'Can't they see the place is closed?' he complained. 'Put your money away, Matt. We're closed, the register's locked up, it's private-party time.' He held his glass to the light and looked at it. 'Beautiful color,' he said. 'She's a pisser, old Carolyn. A bourbon drinker's a gentleman and a scotch drinker's – what did she say a scotch drinker was?'

'I think a hypocrite.'

'So I gave her the straight line, didn't I? What's it make a man if he drinks Irish whiskey? An Irishman.'

'Well, you asked.'

'What else it makes him is drunk, but in a nice way. I only get drunk in the nicest possible way. Ah, Jesus, Matt, these are the best hours of the day. You can keep your Morrissey's. This is like having your own private after-hours, you know? The joint empty and dark, the music off, the chairs up, one or two people around for company, the rest of the world locked the hell out. Great, huh?'

'It's not bad.'

'No, it's not.'

He was freshening my drink. I didn't remember drinking it. I said, 'You know, my trouble is I can't go home.'

'That's what Thomas Wolfe said, "You Can't Go Home Again." That's everybody's trouble.'

'No, I mean it. My feet keep taking me to a bar instead. I was out in Brooklyn, I got home late, I was tired, I was already half in the bag, I started to walk to my hotel and I turned around and came here instead. And just now I put her to sleep, Carolyn, and I had to drag myself out of there before I fell asleep in her chair, and instead of going home like a sane human being I came back here again like some dim homing pigeon.'

'You're a swallow and this is Capistrano.'

'Is that what I am? I don't know what the hell I am anymore.'

'Oh, bullshit. You're a guy, a human being. Just another poor son of a bitch who doesn't want to be alone when the sacred ginmill closes.'

'The what?' I started to laugh. 'Is that what this place is? The sacred ginmill?'

'Don't you know the song?'

'What song?'

'The Van Ronk song. "And so we've had another night –"' He broke off. 'Hell, I can't sing, I can't even get the tune right. "Last Call," Dave Von Ronk. You don't know it?'

'I don't know what you're talking about.'

'Well, *Christ*,' he said. 'You have got to hear it. You have by Christ got to hear this song. It's what we've been talking about, and on top of that it's the fucking national anthem. Come on.'

'Come on and what?'

'Just come on,' he said. He put a Piedmont Airlines flight bag on top of the bar, rooted around under the back bar and came up with two unopened bottles, one of the twelve-year-old Jameson Irish he favored and one of Jack Daniel's. 'This okay?' he asked me.

'Okay for what?'

'For pouring over your head to kill the cooties. Is it okay to drink is my question. You've been drinking Forester, but I can't find an unopened bottle, and there's a law against carrying an opened bottle on the street.'

'There is?'

'There ought to be. I never steal opened bottles. Will you please answer a simple question? Is Jack Black all right?'

'Of course it's all right, but where the hell are we going?'

'My place,' he said. 'You've got to hear this record.'

'Bartenders drink free,' he said. 'Even at home. It's a fringe benefit. Other people get pension plans and dental care. We get all the booze we can steal. You're gonna love this song, Matt.'

We were in his apartment, an L-shaped studio with a parquet floor and a fireplace. He was on the twenty-second floor and his window looked south. He had a good view of the Empire State Building and, farther down on the right, the World Trade Center.

The place was sparsely furnished. There was a white mica platform bed and dresser in the sleeping alcove, a couch and a sling chair in the middle of the room. Books and records overflowed a bookcase and stood around in stacks on the floor. Stereo components were placed here and there – a turntable on an upended milk crate, speakers resting on the floor.

'Where did I put the thing?' Billie wondered.

I walked over to the window, looked out at the city. I was wearing a watch but I purposely didn't look at it because I didn't want to know what time it was. I suppose it must have been somewhere around four o'clock. It still wasn't raining.

'Here,' he said, holding up an album. 'Dave Van Ronk. You know him?'

'Never heard of him.'

'Got a Dutch name, looks like a mick and I swear on the blues numbers he sounds just like a nigger. He's also one bitchin' guitar player but he doesn't play anything on this cut. "Last Call." He sings it al fresco.'

'Okay.'

'*Not* al fresco. I forget the expression. How do you say it when you sing without accompaniment?'

'What difference does it make?'

'How can I forget something like that? I got a mind like a fucking sieve. You're gonna love this song.'

'That's if I ever get to hear it.'

'A cappella. That's what it is, a cappella. As soon as I stopped actively trying to think of it, it popped right into my head. The Zen of Remembering. Where did I put the Irish?'

'Right behind you.'

'Thanks. You all right with the Daniel's? Oh, you got the bottle right there. Okay, listen to this. Ooops, wrong groove. It's the last one on the album. Naturally, you couldn't have anything come after this one. *Listen.*'

> *And so we've had another night*
> *Of poetry and poses*
> *And each man knows he'll be alone*
> *When the sacred ginmill closes.*

The melody sounded like an Irish folk air. The singer did indeed sing without accompaniment, his voice rough but curiously gentle.

'Now listen to this,' Billie said.

> *And so we'll drink the final glass*
> *Each to his joy and sorrow*
> *And hope the numbing drunk will last*
> *Till opening tomorrow*

'Jesus,' Billie said.

> *And when we stumble back again*
> *Like paralytic dancers*
> *Each knows the question he must ask*
> *And each man knows the answer*

I had a bottle in one hand, a glass in the other. I poured from the bottle into the glass. 'Catch this next part,' Billie was saying.

> *And so we'll drink the final drink*
> *That cuts the brain in sections*
> *Where answers do not signify*
> *And there aren't any questions*

Billie was saying something but the words weren't registering. There was only the song.

> *I broke my heart the other day.*
> *It will mend again tomorrow.*
> *If I'd been drunk when I was born*
> *I'd be ignorant of sorrow*

'Play that again,' I said.

'Wait. There's more.'

And so we'll drink the final toast
That never can be spoken:
Here's to the heart that is wise enough
To know when it's better off broken

He said, 'Well?'

'I'd like to hear it again.'

'"Play it again, Sam. You played it for her, you can play it for me. I can take it if she can." Isn't it great?'

'Play it again, will you?'

We listened to it a couple of times through. Finally he took it off and returned it to its jacket and asked me if I understood why he had to drag me up there and play it for me. I just nodded.

'Listen,' he said, 'you're welcome to crash here if you want. That couch is more comfortable than it looks.'

'I can make it home.'

'I don't know. Is it raining yet?' He looked out the window. 'No, but it could start any minute.'

'I'll chance it. I want to be at my place when I wake up.'

'I got to respect a man who can plan that far in the future. You okay to go out on the street? Sure, you're okay. Here, I'll get you a paper bag, you can take the JD home with you. Or here, take the flight bag, they'll think you're a pilot.'

'No, keep it, Billie.'

'What do I want with it? I don't drink bourbon.'

'Well, I've had enough.'

'You might want a nightcap. You might want something in the morning. It's a doggie bag, for Christ's sake. When'd you get so fancy you can't take a doggie bag home with you?'

'Somebody told me it's illegal to carry an opened bottle on the street.'

'Don't worry. It's a first offense, you're odds-on to get probation. Hey, Matt? Thanks for coming by.'

I walked home with the song's phrases echoing in my mind, coming back at me in fragments. 'If I'd been drunk when I was born I'd be ignorant of sorrow.' Jesus.

I got back to my hotel, went straight upstairs without checking the desk for messages. I got out of my clothes, threw them on the chair, took one short pull straight from the bottle and got into bed.

Just as I was drifting off the rain started.

THIRTEEN

The rain kept up all weekend. It was lashing my window when I opened my eyes around noon Friday, but it must have been the phone that woke me. I sat on the edge of the bed and decided not to answer it, and after a few more rings it quit.

My head ached fiercely and my gut felt like it had taken somebody's best shot. I lay down again, got up quickly when the room started to spin. In the bathroom I washed down a couple of aspirin with a half-glass of water, but they came right back up again.

I remembered the bottle Billie had pressed on me. I looked around for it and finally found it in the flight bag. I couldn't remember putting it back after the last drink of the night, but then there were other things I couldn't recall either, like most of the walk home from his apartment. That sort of miniblackout didn't bother me much. When you drove cross-country you didn't remember every billboard, every mile of highway. Why bother recalling every minute of your life?

The bottle was a third gone, and that surprised me. I could recall having had one drink with Billie while we listened to the record, then a short one before I turned the lights out. I didn't want one now, but there are the ones you want and the ones you need, and this came under the latter heading. I poured a short shot into the water glass and shuddered when I swallowed it. It didn't stay down either, but it fixed things so the next one did. And then I could swallow another couple of aspirins with another half-glass of water, and this time they stayed swallowed.

If I'd been drunk when I was born ...

I stayed right there in my room. The weather gave me every reason to remain where I was, but I didn't really need an excuse. I had the sort of hangover I knew enough to treat with respect. If I'd ever felt that bad without having drunk the night before, I'd have gone straight to a hospital. As it was, I stayed put and

treated myself like a man with an illness, which in retrospect would seem to have been more than metaphor.

The phone rang again later in the afternoon. I could have had the desk stop my calls, but I didn't feel equal to the conversation that would have required. It seemed easier to let it ring itself out.

It rang a third time in the early evening, and this time I picked it up. It was Skip Devoe.

'I was looking for you,' he said. 'You going to bounce around later?'

'I don't want to go out in this.'

'Yeah, it's coming down again. It was slacking off for a while there and now it's teeming. The weather guy says we're gonna get a lot of it. We saw those guys yesterday.'

'Already?'

'Not the guys in the black hats, not the bad guys. The lawyers and the accountants. Our accountant's armed with what he calls a Jewish revolver. You know what that is?'

'A fountain pen.'

'You heard it, huh? Anyway, they all told us what we already knew, which is terrific, considering they'll bill us for the advice. We got to pay.'

'Well, that's what you figured.'

'Yeah, but it doesn't mean I like it. I spoke to the guy again, Mr Voice on the Phone. I told old Telephone Tommy we needed the weekend to find the money.'

'You told Tillary?'

'Tillary? What are you talking about?'

'You said –'

'Oh, right, I didn't even make the connection. No, not Tillary, I just said Telephone Tommy, I could have said Teddy or any name with a T. Which suddenly I can't think of. Name me some names start with T.'

'Do I have to?'

There was a pause. 'You don't feel so hot,' he said.

'Keegan had me up till dawn listening to records,' I said. 'I'm not a hundred percent yet.'

'Fucking Keegan,' he said. 'We all hit it pretty good, but he's gonna kill himself with it.'

'He does keep at it.'

'Yeah. Listen, I won't keep you. What I want to know, can you keep Monday open? The day and the night. Because I think

524

that's when we're gonna move on this, and if we have to do it I'd just as soon get it over with.'

'What do you want me to do?'

'We'll talk about that, iron it out. Okay?'

What did I have to do on Monday? I was still working for Tommy Tillary, but I didn't much care what hours I put in. My conversation with Jack Diebold had confirmed my own opinion that I was wasting my time and Tillary's money, that they didn't have a case against him and weren't likely to make one. Carolyn Cheatham's diatribe had left me not greatly inclined to do much for Tommy anyway, or to feel all that guilty about taking his money and giving him small value for it.

I had a couple of things to tell Drew Kaplan next time I talked to him. And I'd dig up a few more along the way. But I might not have to put in too many long hours in Sunset Park's bars and bodegas.

I told Skip Monday was wide open.

Later that evening I called the liquor store across the street. I ordered up two quarts of Early Times and asked them to have the kid stop at the deli and pick up a six-pack of ale and a couple of sandwiches. They knew me and knew I'd make it worth the delivery boy's while to give me special service, and I did. It was worth it to me.

I took it easy with the hard booze, drank a can of ale, and made myself eat half a sandwich. I took a hot shower, and that helped, and then I ate another half-sandwich and drank another can of ale.

I went to sleep, and when I woke up I put the TV on and watched Bogart and Ida Lupino, I guess it was, in *High Sierra*. I didn't pay a whole lot of attention to the movie but it was company. I went over to the window now and then and watched the rain. I ate part of the remaining sandwich, drank some more ale, and nipped a little from the bourbon bottle. When the movie ended I turned the set off and had a couple of aspirins and went back to bed.

Saturday I was a little more mobile. I needed a drink again on awakening but I made it a short one, and the first one stayed down this time. I had a shower, drank the last can of ale, and went downstairs and had breakfast at the Red Flame. I left half of the eggs but ate the potatoes and a double order of rye toast

and drank a lot of coffee. I read the paper, or tried to. I couldn't make much sense out of what I read.

After breakfast I stopped in McGovern's for a quick one. Then I went around the corner to St Paul's and sat there in the soft stillness for a half-hour or so.

Then back to the hotel.

I watched a baseball game in my room, and a fight on 'Wide World of Sports,' along with the arm-wrestling championship of the world and some women doing some kind of aquatic mono-ski exhibition. What they were doing was evidently very difficult, but not terribly interesting to look at. I turned them off and left. I dropped in at Armstrong's and talked to a couple of people, then went over to Joey Farrell's for a bowl of three-alarm chili and a couple of Carta Blancas.

I had a brandy with my coffee before returning to the hotel for the night. I had enough bourbon in the room to get me through Sunday but I stopped and picked up some beer because I was almost out and the stores can't sell it before noon on Sunday. Nobody knows why. Maybe the churches are behind it, maybe they want the faithful showing up with their hangovers sharp at the edges, maybe repentance is easier to sell to the severely afflicted.

I sipped and watched TV movies. I slept in front of the set, woke up in the middle of a war movie, had a shower and shaved and sat around in my underwear watching the end of that movie and the start of another, sipping bourbon and beer until I could go back to sleep again.

When I woke up again, it was Sunday afternoon and it was still raining.

Around three-thirty the phone rang. I picked it up on the third ring and said hello.

'Matthew?' It was a woman, and for an instant I thought it was Anita. Then she said, 'I tried you day before yesterday, but there was no answer,' and I heard the Tarheel in her voice.

'I want to thank you,' she said.

'Nothing to thank me for, Carolyn.'

'I want to thank you for being a gentleman,' she said, and her laughter came gently. 'A bourbon-drinking gentleman. I seem to remember having a lot to say on that subject.'

'As I recall, you were reasonably eloquent.'

'And on other subjects as well. I apologized to Billie for being less than a lady and he assured me I was fine, but bartenders

526

always tell you that, don't they? I want to thank you-all for seeing me home.' A pause. 'Uh, did we –'

'No.'

A sigh. 'Well, I'm glad of that, but only 'cause I'd hate to not remember it. I hope I wasn't too disgraceful, Matthew.'

'You were perfectly fine.'

'I was *not* perfectly fine. I remember that much. Matthew, I said some hard things about Tommy. I was bad-mouthing him something awful, and I hope you know that was just the drink talking.'

'I never thought otherwise.'

'He treats me fine, you know. He's a good man. He's got his faults. He's strong, but he has his weaknesses.'

At a fellow police officer's wake, I once heard an Irish woman speak thus of the drink. 'Sure, it's a strong man's weakness,' she had said.

'He cares for me,' Carolyn said. 'Don't you pay any mind to what I said before.'

I told her I'd never doubted he cared for her, and that I wasn't all that clear on what she had or hadn't said, that I'd been hitting it pretty hard that night myself.

Sunday night I walked over to Miss Kitty's. A light rain was falling but it didn't amount to much.

I'd stopped at Armstrong's first, briefly, and Miss Kitty's had the same Sunday-night feel to it. A handful of regulars and neighborhood people rode a mood that was the flip side of Thank God It's Friday. On the jukebox, a girl sang about having a brand-new pair of roller skates. Her voice seemed to slip in between the notes and find sounds that weren't on the scale.

I didn't know the bartender. When I asked for Skip he pointed toward the office in back.

Skip was there, and so was his partner. John Kasabian had a round face, and he wore wire-rimmed glasses with circular lenses that magnified his deep-set dark eyes. He was Skip's age or close to it, but he looked younger, an owlish schoolboy. He had tattoos on both forearms, and he didn't look at all to be the sort of person who got tattooed.

One tattoo was a conventional if garish representation of a snake entwined around a dagger. The snake was ready to strike, and the tip of the dagger dripped blood. The other tattoo was simpler, even tasteful: a chain-link bracelet encircling his right

wrist. 'If I'd at least had it on the other wrist,' he had said, 'at least the watch'd cover it.'

I don't know how he really felt about the tattoos. He affected disdain for them, contempt for the young man who'd elected to get himself thus branded, and sometimes he did seem genuinely embarrassed by them. At other times I sensed that he was proud of them.

I didn't really know him all that well. His was a less expansive personality than Skip's. He didn't like to bounce around the bars, worked the early shift and did the marketing before that. And he wasn't the drinker his partner was. He liked his beer, but he didn't hit it the way Skip did.

'Matt,' he said, and pointed to a chair. 'Glad you're going to help us with this.'

'Whatever I can.'

'It's tomorrow night,' Skip said. 'We're supposed to be in this room, eight o'clock sharp, phone's gonna ring.'

'And?'

'We get instructions. I should have a car ready. That's part of the instructions.'

'Have you got a car?'

'I got my car, it's no hassle having it ready.'

'Has John got a car?'

'I'll get it out of the garage,' John said. 'You think we might want to take two cars?'

'I don't know. He told you to have a car and I presume he told you to have the money ready –'

'Yeah, strangely enough he happened to mention it.'

'– but he didn't give any indication of where he's going to want you to drive.'

'None.'

I thought about it. 'What concerns me –'

'Is walking into something.'

'That's right.'

'I got the same concern. It's like walking point, you're out there and they can just bang away at you. It's bad enough paying ransom, but who knows if we're even gonna get what we pay for? It could wind up being a hijack, and they could waste us while they're at it.'

'Why would they do that?'

'I don't know. "Dead men tell no tales." Isn't that what they say?'

'Maybe they do, but murder brings heat.' I was trying to

concentrate, and I wasn't thinking as clearly as I wanted to. I asked if I could have a beer.

'Oh, Jesus, where's my manners? What do you want, bourbon, cup of coffee?'

'I think just a beer.'

Skip went to get it. While he was gone his partner said, 'This is crazy. It's unreal, you know what I mean? Stolen books, extortion, voices over the phone. It has no reality.'

'I guess.'

'The money has no reality. I can't relate to it. The number –'

Skip brought me a bottle of Carlsberg and a bell-shaped glass. I sipped a little beer and frowned in what was supposed to be thought. Skip lit a cigarette, offered the pack to me, then said, 'No, of course you don't want one, you don't smoke,' and put the pack in his pocket.

I said, 'It shouldn't be a hijack. But there's one way it could be.'

'How's that?'

'If they haven't got the books.'

'Of course they got the books. The books are gone and there's this voice on the phone.'

'Suppose someone hasn't got the books, but knows that they're missing. If he doesn't have to prove possession of them, he's got a chance to take a few dollars off you.'

'A few dollars,' John Kasabian said.

Skip said, 'Then who's got the books? The Feds? You mean they could have them all along and be preparing a case and in the meantime we're paying ransom to somebody who hasn't got shit.' He stood up, walked around the desk. 'I fuckin' love it,' he said. 'I love it so much I want to marry it, I want to have babies with it. Jesus.'

'It's just a possibility, but I think we have to guard against it.'

'How? Everything's set for tomorrow.'

'When he calls, you have him read a page from the books.'

He stared at me. 'You just thought of that? Just now? Nobody move.' Kasabian asked him where he was going. 'To get two more of those Carlsbergs,' he said. 'The fucking beer stimulates thought. They should use it in their advertising.'

He brought back two bottles. He sat on the edge of the desk with his feet swinging, sipping his beer straight from the brown bottle. Kasabian stayed in his chair and peeled the label from his bottle. He was in no hurry to drink it. We had our war council,

making what plans we could. John and Skip were both coming along, and so of course was I.

'And I was thinking Bobby'd come,' Skip said.

'Ruslander?'

'He's my best friend, he knows what's happening. I don't know if he could do much if the shit hit the fan, but who could? I'm gonna be armed, but if it's a trap I suppose they'll shoot first, so a lot of fucking good a gun's gonna do me. You got anybody you want to bring in on this?'

Kasabian shook his head. 'I thought of my brother,' he said. 'First person I thought of, but what does Zeke need with this shit, you know?'

'What does anybody need with it? Matt, you got anybody you want to bring?'

'No.'

'I was thinking maybe Billie Keegan,' Skip said. 'What do you think?'

'He's good company.'

'Yeah, right. When you think about it, who the hell needs good company? What we need is heavy artillery and air support. Set up the meet and lay down a mortar barrage on their position. John, tell him about the spades with the mortar.'

'Oh,' Kasabian said.

'Tell him.'

'It was just something I saw.'

'Something he saw. Listen to this.'

'It was whenever it was, a month or so ago. I was at my girl's house, she's on West End in the Eighties, I'm supposed to walk her dog, and I come out of the building and diagonally across the street there are these three black guys.'

'So he turns around and goes back in the building,' Skip offered.

'No, they didn't even look in my direction,' Kasabian said. 'They're wearing fatigue jackets, like, and one's got a cap. They look like soldiers.'

'Tell him what they did.'

'Well, it's hard to believe I really saw this,' he said. He took off his glasses, massaged the bridge of his nose. 'They took a look around, and if they saw me they decided I was nothing to worry about –'

'Shrewd judges of character,' Skip put in.

'– and they set up this mortar, like they've done this drill a thousand times before, and one of them drops a shell in, and

they lob a round into the Hudson, nice easy shot, they're on the corner and they can see clear to the river, and we all like check it out, and they still don't pay any attention to me, and they nod to each other and strip the mortar down and pack it up and walk off together.'

'Jesus,' I said.

'It happened so fast,' he said, 'and with so little fanfare, I wondered if I imagined it. But it happened.'

'Did the round make a lot of noise?'

'No, not a whole lot. There was the sort of *whump!* sound a mortar makes on firing, and if there was an explosion when the round hit the water I didn't hear it.'

'Probably a blank,' Skip said. 'They were probably, you know, testing the firing mechanism, checking out the trajectory.'

'Yeah, but for what?'

'Well, shit,' he said. 'You never know when you're gonna need a mortar in this town.' He tipped up his beer bottle, drank deeply, and drummed his heels against the side of the desk. 'I don't know,' he said, 'I'm drinking this stuff but I'm not thinking any better than before. Matt, let's talk about money.'

I thought he was referring to the ransom. But he meant money for me, and I was at a loss. I didn't know how to set a price, said something about being a friend.

He said, 'So? This is what you do for a living, right? Do favors for friends?'

'Sure, but –'

'You're doing us a favor. Kasabian and I don't know what the hell we're doing. Am I right, John?'

'Absolutely.'

'I'm not gonna give Bobby anything for coming, he wouldn't take it, and if Keegan comes along it won't be for the money. But you're a professional and a professional gets paid. Tillary's paying you, isn't he?'

'There's a difference.'

'What's the difference?'

'You're a friend of mine.'

'And he isn't?'

'Not in the same way. In fact I like him less and less. He's –'

'He's an asshole,' Skip said. 'No argument. Makes no difference.' He opened a drawer in the desk, counted money, folded the bills, handed them to me. 'Here,' he said. 'That's twenty-five there. Tell me if it's not enough.'

'I don't know,' I said slowly. 'Twenty-five dollars doesn't seem like much, but –'

'It's twenty-five hundred, you dumb fuck.' We all started laughing. '"Twenty-five dollars doesn't seem like much." Johnny, why did we have to hire a comedian? Seriously, Matt, is it okay?'

'Seriously, it seems a little high.'

'You know what the ransom comes to?'

I shook my head. 'Everybody's been careful not to mention it.'

'Well, you don't mention rope in the house of the hanged, do you? We're paying those cocksuckers fifty grand.'

'Jesus Christ,' I said.

'His name came up already,' Kasabian said. 'He a friend of yours, by any chance? Bring him along tomorrow, he's got nothing else on for the evening.'

FOURTEEN

I tried to make it an early night. I went home and went to bed, and somewhere around four I knew I wasn't going to be able to sleep. There was enough bourbon on hand to knock myself out, but I didn't want that, either. I didn't want to be hung over when we dealt with the blackmailers.

I got up and tried sitting around, but I couldn't sit still and there was nothing on television I was willing to watch. I got dressed and went out for a walk, and I was halfway there before I realized my feet were taking me to Morrissey's.

One of the brothers was on the downstairs door. He gave me a bright smile and let me in. Upstairs, another brother sat on a stool opposite the door. His right hand was concealed beneath his white butcher's apron, and I had been given to understand that there was a gun in it. I hadn't been to Morrissey's since Tim Pat had told me of the reward he and his brothers were offering, but I'd heard that the brothers took turns at guard duty, and that anyone who walked in the door was facing a loaded weapon. Opinions differed on the sort of weapon; I'd had various reports, ranging from revolver to automatic pistol to sawed-off shotgun. My thought was that you'd have to be crazy to plan on using a shotgun, sawed-off or otherwise, in a roomful of your own customers, but no one had ever established the Morrisseys' sanity.

I walked in and looked around the room, and Tim Pat saw me and motioned to me, and I took a step toward him when Skip Devoe called my name from a table in the front near the blacked-out window. He was sitting with Bobby Ruslander. I held up a hand, indicating I'd be with them in a minute, and Bobby put his hand to his mouth and a police whistle pierced the room, cutting off all conversation as cleanly as a gunshot. Skip and Bobby laughed, and the other drinkers realized the noise had been a joke, not an official raid, and, after a few people

had assured Bobby he was an asshole, conversation resumed. I followed Tim Pat toward the rear of the room, where we stood on opposite sides of an empty table.

'We've not seen you here since we spoke,' he said. 'Do you bring me news?'

I told him I didn't have any news to bring him. 'I just came in for a drink,' I said.

'And you've heard nothing?'

'Not a thing. I went around, I talked to some people. If there were anything in the air I would have had word back by now, I think it must be some kind of Irish thing, Tim Pat.'

'An Irish thing.'

'Political,' I said.

'Then we should have heard tell of it. Some braggart would have let a word slip.' His fingertips caressed his beard. 'They knew right where to go for the money,' he mused. 'And they even took the few dollars from the Norad jar.'

'That's why I thought—'

'If it was Proddies we should have heard tell. Or if it was a faction of our own.' He smiled without humor. 'We have our factional disagreements, don't you know. The Cause has more than one voice speakin' for it.'

'So I've heard.'

'If it were an "Irish thing,"' he said, pronouncing the phrase deliberately, 'there would be other incidents. But there's been only the one.'

'That you know of,' I said.

'Aye,' he said. 'That I know of.'

I went over and joined Skip and Bobby. Bobby was wearing a gray sweat shirt with the sleeves cut off. Around his neck was a blue plastic whistle on one of those lanyards of plastic braid that boys make at summer camp.

'The actor is feeling his way into the role,' Skip said, aiming a thumb at Bobby.

'Oh?'

'I got a call-back on a commercial,' Bobby said. 'I'm a basketball referee, I'm with these kids at a playground. They all tower over me, that's part of the point of it.'

'Everybody towers over you,' Skip said. 'What are they supposed to be selling? Because if it's deodorant, you want to wear a different sweatshirt.'

'It's brotherhood,' Bobby said.

'Brotherhood?'

'Black kids, white kids, Spanish kids, all united in brother-hood as they drive for the fuckin' hoop. It's some public-service thing, show it during slow spots on the Joe Franklin show.'

'You get paid for this?' Skip demanded.

'Oh! shit, yes. I think the agencies donate their time, and the TV stations run it free, but the talent gets paid.'

'The talent,' Skip said.

'*Le talent, c'est moi*,' Bobby said.

I ordered a drink. Skip and Bobby stayed with what they had. Skip lit a cigarette and the smoke hung in the air. My drink came and I sipped it.

'I thought you were going to make it an early night,' Skip said. I said I'd been unable to sleep. 'Because of tomorrow?'

I shook my head. 'Just not tired yet. Restless.'

'I get that way. Hey, actor,' he said. 'What time's your audition?'

'Supposed to be two o'clock.'

'Supposed to be?'

'You can get there and sit around a lot. I'm supposed to be there at two.'

'You be done in time to give us a hand?'

'Oh, no problem,' he said. 'These agency cats, they got to catch the five forty-eight to Scarsdale. Couple of pops in the bar car, then find out how Jason and Tracy did in school today.'

'Jason and Tracy are on summer break, dumbbell.'

'So he's got to see the postcard they sent home from camp. They go to this fancy camp in Maine, the postcards are already written by the staff, all they gotta do is sign them.'

My boys would be going to camp in a couple of weeks. One of them had woven me a lanyard like the one Bobby wore. I had it somewhere, packed away in a drawer or something. Or was it still in Syosset? If I were a proper father, I thought, I'd wear the damned thing, whistle and all.

Skip was telling Bobby that he needed his beauty sleep.

'I'm supposed to look like a jock,' Bobby said.

'We don't get you outta here, you're gonna look more like a truss.' He looked at his cigarette, dropped it in what was left of his drink. 'I never want to see you do that,' he told me. 'I never want to see either of you do that. Disgusting habit.'

The sky was lightening up outside. We walked slowly, not saying much. Bobby bobbed and weaved a ways ahead of us, dribbling an imaginary basketball, faking out an invisible opponent and driving for the hoop. Skip looked at me and

shrugged. 'What can I tell you?' he said. 'The man is my friend. What else is there to say?'

'You're just jealous,' Bobby said. 'You got the height but you haven't got the moves. A good little man can fake you out of your socks.'

'I wept because I had no shoes,' Skip said solemnly, 'and then I met a man who had no socks. What the hell was *that*?'

An explosion echoed half a mile or so to the north of us.

'Kasabian's mortar,' Bobby said.

'Fucking draft-dodger,' Skip said. 'You wouldn't know a mortar from a pessary. I don't mean a pessary. What is it a pharmacist uses?'

'What the fuck are you talking about?'

'A pestle,' Skip said. 'You wouldn't know a mortar from a pestle. That's not what a mortar sounds like.'

'Whatever you say.'

'It sounded like blasting for a foundation,' he said. 'But it's too early, the neighbors would kill anybody started blasting at this hour. I'll tell you, I'm glad it's done raining.'

'Yeah, we had enough of it, didn't we?'

'I suppose we needed it,' he said. 'That's always what they say, isn't it? Every time it rains its ass off, somebody says how we needed it. Because the reservoirs are drying up, or else the farmers need it or something.'

'This is a wonderful conversation,' Bobby said. 'You'd never get a conversation like this in a less sophisticated city.'

'Fuck you,' Skip said. He lit a cigarette and started coughing, got control of the cough and took another puff on the cigarette, this time without a cough. It was like a drink in the morning, I thought. Once you got one to stay down you were all right.

'The air's nice after a storm,' Skip said. 'I think it cleans it.'

'Washes it,' Bobby said.

'Maybe.' He looked around. 'I almost hate to say this,' he said, 'but it ought to be a beautiful day.'

FIFTEEN

At six minutes past eight, the phone on Skip's desk rang. Billie Keegan had been talking about a girl he'd met the previous year on a three-week holiday in the west of Ireland. He stopped his story in midsentence. Skip put his hand on the phone and looked at me, and I reached for the phone that sat on top of the file cabinet. He nodded once, a quick bob of the head, and we lifted the two receivers in unison.

He said, 'Yeah.'

A male voice said, 'Devoe?'

'Yeah.'

'You have the money?'

'All set.'

'Then get a pencil and write this down. You want to get in your car and drive to –'

'Hold on,' Skip said. 'First you got to prove you got what you say you got.'

'What do you mean?'

'Read the entries for the first week of June. That's this June, June of '75.'

There was a pause. Then the voice, taut now, said, 'You don't give us orders, man. We're the ones say frog, you're the ones jump.' Skip straightened up a little in his chair, leaned forward. I held up a hand to stop whatever he was about to say.

I said, 'We want to confirm we're dealing with the right people. We want to buy it as long as we know you've got it to sell. Establish that much and we'll play out the hand.'

'You're not Devoe speaking. Who the hell are you?'

'I'm a friend of Mr Devoe's.'

'You got a name, friend?'

'Scudder.'

'Scudder. You want us to read something?'

Skip told him again what to read.

537

'Get back to you,' the man said, and broke the connection.

Skip looked over at me, the receiver in his hand. I hung up the one I was holding. He passed his own from hand to hand like a hot potato. I had to tell him to hang up.

'Why'd they do that?' he wanted to know.

'Maybe they had to have a conference,' I suggested. 'Or get the books so they can read you what you want to hear.'

'And maybe they never had them in the first place.'

'I don't think so. They'd have tried to stall.'

'Hanging up on somebody's a pretty good way to stall.' He lit a cigarette, shoved the pack back into his shirt pocket. He was wearing a short-sleeved forest-green work shirt with *Alvin's Texaco Service* embroidered in yellow over the breast pocket. 'Why hang up?' he said petulantly.

'Maybe he thought we could trace the call.'

'Could we do that?'

'It's hard even when you've got the cops and the telephone company cooperating on it,' I said. 'It'd be out of the question for us. But they don't necessarily know that.'

'Catch us tracing calls,' John Kasabian put in. 'We had our hands full installing the second phone this afternoon.'

They had done that a few hours earlier, running wires from the terminal on the wall and hooking an extension phone borrowed from Kasabian's girl's apartment into the line so that Skip and I could be on the line at the same time. While Skip and John were doing that, Bobby had been auditioning for the role of referee in the brotherhood commercial and Billie Keegan had been finding someone to fill in for him behind the stick at Armstrong's. I'd used that time to stuff two hundred and fifty dollars into a parish fund box, light a couple of candles, and phone in another meaningless report to Drew Kaplan in Brooklyn. And now we were all five in Miss Kitty's back office, waiting for the phone to ring again.

'Sort of a southern accent,' Skip said. 'You happen to notice?'

'It sounded phony.'

'Think so?'

'When he got angry,' I said. 'Or pretended to get angry, whatever it was. That bit about jump when he says frog.'

'He wasn't the only one got angry just about then.'

'I noticed. But when he first got angry the accent wasn't there, and when he started with the frog shit he was putting it on thicker than before, trying to sound country.'

He frowned, summoning up the memory. 'You're right,' he said shortly.

'Was it the same guy you talked to before?'

'I don't know. His voice sounded phony before, but it wasn't the same as I was hearing tonight. Maybe he's a man of a thousand voices, all of them unconvincing.'

'Guy could do voiceovers,' Bobby suggested, 'in fucking brotherhood commercials.'

The phone rang again.

This time we made less of a thing out of synchronizing our answering, since I'd already made my presence known. When I had the receiver to my ear, Skip said, 'Yeah?' and the voice I'd heard before asked what he was supposed to read. Skip told him and the voice began reading ledger entries. Skip had the fake set of books open on his desk and followed along on the page.

After half a minute the reader stopped and asked if we were satisfied. Skip looked as though he wanted to take exception to the word. Instead he shrugged and nodded, and I spoke up to say we were assured we were dealing with the right people.

'Then here's what you do,' he said, and we both took up pencils and wrote down the directions.

'Two cars,' Skip was saying. 'All they know is me and Matt are coming, so the two of us'll go in my car. John, you take Billie and Bobby. What do you think, Matt, they'll follow us?'

I shook my head. 'Somebody may be watching us leave here,' I said. 'John, why don't you three go ahead now. Your car's handy?'

'I'm parked two blocks from here.'

'The three of you can drive out there now. Bobby, you and Bill walk on ahead and wait at the car. I'd just as soon you all didn't walk out together, just in case somebody's keeping an eye on the front door. You two wait ahead, and John, give them two, three minutes, and then meet them at the car.'

'And then drive out to – where is it, Emmons Avenue?'

'In Sheepshead Bay. You know where that is?'

'Vaguely. I know it's the ass end of Brooklyn. I've gone out on fishing boats there, but somebody else drove and I didn't pay too much attention.'

'You can take the Belt, the Shore Parkway.'

'All right.'

'Get off, let me think, probably the best place is Ocean Avenue. You'll probably see a sign.'

'Hang on,' Skip said. 'I think I got a map someplace, I saw it the other day.'

He found a Hagstrom street map of the borough and the three of us gave it some study. Bobby Ruslander leaned in over Kasabian's shoulder. Billie Keegan picked up a beer somebody had abandoned earlier and took a sip and made a face. We worked out a route, and Skip told John to take the map along with him.

'I can never fold these things right,' Kasabian said.

Skip said, 'Who cares how you fold the fucking thing?' He took the map away from his partner and began tearing it along some of its fold lines, handing a section some eight inches square to Kasabian and dropping the rest to the floor. 'Here's Sheepshead Bay,' he said. 'You want to know where to get off the parkway, right? What do you need with all the rest of fucking Brooklyn?'

'Jesus,' Kasabian said.

'I'm sorry, Johnny. I'm fuckin' twitchy. Johnny, you got a weapon?'

'I don't want anything.'

Skip opened the desk drawer, put a blue-steel automatic pistol on top of the desk. 'We keep it behind the bar,' he told me, 'case we want to blow our brains out when we count up the night's receipts. You don't want it, John?' Kasabian shook his head. 'Matt?'

'I don't think I'll need it.'

'You don't want to carry it?'

'I'd just as soon not.'

He hefted the gun, looked for a place to put it. It was a 45 and it looked like the kind they issue to officers in the army. A big heavy gun, and what they called a forgiving one – its stopping power could compensate for poor aim, bringing a man down with a shoulder wound.

'Weighs a fucking ton,' Skip said. He worked it underneath the waistband of his jeans and frowned at the way it looked. He tugged his shirt free of his belt, let it hang out over the gun. It wasn't the sort of shirt you wear out of your pants and it looked all wrong. 'Jesus,' he complained, 'where am I gonna put the thing?'

'You'll work it out,' Kasabian told him. 'Meanwhile we ought to get going. Don't you think so, Matt?'

I agreed with him. We went over it one more time while Keegan and Ruslander walked on ahead. They would drive to

Sheepshead Bay and park across the street from the restaurant, but not directly across the street. They would wait there, motor off, lights out, and keep an eye on the place and on us when we arrived.

'Don't try and do anything,' I told him. 'If you see anything suspicious, just observe it. Write down license numbers, anything like that.'

'Should I try and follow them?'

'How would you know who you were following?' He shrugged. 'Play it by ear,' I said. 'Mostly just be around, keep an eye open.'

'Got it.'

After he'd left Skip put an attaché case on top of the desk and popped the catches. Banded stacks of used currency filled the case. 'That's what fifty grand looks like,' he said. 'Doesn't look like much, does it?'

'Just paper.'

'It do anything for you, looking at it?'

'Not really.'

'Me either.' He put the .45 on top of the bills, closed the case. It didn't fit right. He rearranged the bills to make a little nest for the gun and closed it again.

'Just until we get in the car,' he said. 'I don't want to walk down the street like Gary Cooper in *High Noon*.' He tucked his shirt back into his pants. On the way to the car he said, 'You'd think people'd be staring at me. I'm dressed like a grease monkey and carrying a case like a banker. Fucking New Yorkers, I could wear a gorilla suit and nobody'd look twice. Remind me, soon as we get in the car, I want to take the gun out of the case.'

'All right.'

'Bad enough if they pull something and shoot us. Be worse if they used my gun to do it.'

His car was garaged on Fifty-fifth Street. He tipped the attendant a buck and drove around the corner, pulled up in front of a hydrant. He opened the attaché case and removed the pistol and checked the clip, then put the gun on the seat between us, thought better of it and wedged it down into the space between the cushion and the seat back.

The car was a Chevy Impala a couple of years old, long and low, loosely sprung. It was white, with a beige and white interior, and it looked as though it hadn't been through a car

wash since it left Detroit. The ashtray overflowed with cigarette butts and the floor was deep in litter.

'Car's like my life,' he said as we caught a light at Tenth Avenue.

'A comfortable mess. What do we do, take the same route we worked out for Kasabian?'

'No.'

'You know a better way?'

'Not better, just different. Take the West Side Drive for now, but instead of the Belt we'll take local streets through Brooklyn.'

'Be slower, won't it?'

'Probably. Let them get there ahead of us.'

'Whatever you say. Any particular reason?'

'Might be easier this way to see if we're being followed.'

'You think we are?'

'I don't see the point offhand, not when they know where we're going. But there's no way to know whether we're dealing with one man or an army.'

'That's a point.'

'Take a right the next corner, pick up the Drive at Fifty-sixth Street.'

'Got it. Matt? You want something?'

'What do you mean?'

'You want a pop? Check the glove box, there ought to be something there.'

There was a pint of Black & White in the glove compartment. Actually it wouldn't have been a pint, it would have been a tenth. I remember the bottle, green glass, curved slightly like a hip flask to fit comfortably in a pocket.

'I don't know about you,' he said, 'but I'm kind of wired. I don't want to get sloppy, but it might not hurt to have something to take the edge off.'

'Just a short one,' I agreed, and opened the bottle.

We took the West Side Drive to Canal Street, crossed into Brooklyn via the Manhattan Bridge, and took Flatbush Avenue until it crossed Ocean Avenue. We kept catching red lights, and several times I noticed his gaze fixing on the glove box. But he didn't say anything, and we left the bottle of Black & White untouched after the one short pull each of us had taken earlier.

He drove with his window rolled down all the way and his left elbow out the window, his fingertips resting on the roof,

occasionally drumming the metal. Sometimes we made conversation and sometimes we rode along in silence.

At one point he said, 'Matt, I want to know who set this up. It's gotta be inside, don't you think? Somebody saw an opportunity and took it, somebody who took a look at the books and knew what he was looking at. Somebody who used to work for me, except how would they get back in? If I fired some asshole, some drunk bartender or spastic waitress, how do they wind up prancing into my office and waltzing out with my books? Can you figure that?'

'Your office isn't that hard to get into, Skip. Anybody familiar with the layout could head for the bathroom and slip into your office without anybody paying any attention.'

'I suppose. I suppose I'm lucky they didn't piss in the top drawer while they were at it.' He drew a cigarette from the pack in his breast pocket, tapped it against the steering wheel. 'I owe Johnny five grand,' he said.

'How's that?'

'The ransom. He came up with thirty and I put up twenty. His safe-deposit box was in better shape than mine. For all I know he's got another fifty tucked away, or maybe the thirty was enough to tap him.' He braked, letting a gypsy cab change lanes in front of us. 'Look at that asshole,' he said, without rancor. 'Do people drive like that everywhere or is it just Brooklyn? I swear everybody starts driving funny the minute you cross the river. What was I talking about?'

'The money Kasabian put up.'

'Yeah. So he'll cut a few bills extra per week until he makes up the five-grand difference. Matt, I had twenty thousand dollars in a bank vault and now it's all packed up and ready for delivery, and in a few minutes I won't have it anymore, and it's got no reality. You know what I mean?'

'I think so.'

'I don't mean it's just paper. It's more than paper, if it was just paper people wouldn't go so nuts over it. But it wasn't real when it was locked up tight in the bank and it won't be real when it's gone. I have to know who's doing this to me, Matt.'

'Maybe we'll find out.'

'I fucking have to know. I trust Kasabian, you know? This kind of business, you're dead if you can't trust your partner. Two guys in the bar business watching each other all the time, they're gonna go flat fucking nuts in six months. Never make it work, the place'll have the kind of vibe a Bowery bum wouldn't

543

tolerate. On top of which you could watch your partner twenty-three hours a day and he could steal you blind in the hour he's got open. Kasabian does the buying, for Christ's sake. You know how deep you can stick it in when you're doing the buying for a joint?'

'What's your point, Skip?'

'My point is there's a voice in my head saying maybe this is a nice neat way for Johnny to take twenty grand off me, and it doesn't make any sense, Matt. He'd have to split it with a partner, he has to put up a lot of his own cash to do it, and why would he pick this way to steal from me? All aside from the fact that I trust him, I got no reason not to trust him, he's always been straight with me and if he wanted to rip me off there's a thousand easier ways that pay better and I'd never even know I was being taken. But I still get this voice, and I fuckin' bet he gets it, too, because I caught him looking at me a little different earlier, and I probably been looking at him the same way, and who *needs* this shit? I mean this is worse than what it's costing us. This is the kind of thing makes a joint close up overnight.'

'I think that's Ocean Avenue coming up.'

'Yeah? And to think we've only been driving for six days and six nights. I hang a left at Ocean?'

'You want to turn right.'

'You sure?'

'Positive.'

'I'm always lost in Brooklyn,' he said. 'I swear this place was settled by the Ten Lost Tribes. They couldn't find their way back, they broke ground and built houses. Put in sewer lines, ran in electricity. All the comforts of home.'

The restaurants on Emmons Avenue specialized in seafood. One of them, Lundy's, was a great barn of a place where serious eaters would tuck themselves in at big tables for enormous shore dinners. The place we were headed for was two blocks away at a corner. Carlo's Clam House was its name, and its red neon sign winked to show a clam opening and closing.

Kasabian was parked on the other side of the street a few doors up from the restaurant. We pulled up alongside him. Bobby was in the front passenger seat. Billie Keegan sat alone in the back. Kasabian, of course, was behind the wheel. Bobby said, 'Took you long enough. If there's anything going on, you can't see it from here.'

Skip nodded. We drove a half-block farther and he parked next to a hydrant. 'They don't tow you out here,' he said. 'Do they?'

'I don't think so.'

'All we need,' he said. He killed the engine and we exchanged glances, and his eyes moved to the glove compartment.

He said, 'You see Keegan? In the back seat there?'

'Uh-huh.'

'You can bet he's had a couple since they left.'

'Probably.'

'We'll wait, right? Celebrate after.'

'Sure.'

He shoved the gun into the waistband of his pants, draped his shirt to conceal it. 'Probably the style here,' he said, opening the door, hefting the attaché case. 'Sheepshead Bay, home of the flapping shirttail. You nervous, Matt?'

'A little.'

'Good. I don't want to be the only one.'

We walked across the wide street and approached the restaurant. The night was balmy and you could smell the salt water. I wondered for a moment if I should have been the one to take the gun. I wondered if he'd even fire the pistol, or if it was just there for comfort. I wondered if he'd be any good with it. He'd been in the service, but that didn't mean he was proficient with a handgun.

I'd been good with handguns. Barring ricochets, anyway.

'Catch the sign,' he said. 'Clam opening and closing, it's a goddamned obscenity. "C'mere, honey, let's see you open your clam." Place looks empty.'

'It's Monday night and it's getting late.'

'Midmorning's probably late out here. Gun weighs a ton, you ever notice? My pants feel like they're gonna get dragged down around my knees.'

'You want to leave it in the car?'

'Are you kidding? "This is your weapon, soldier. It could save your life." I'm all right, Matt. I'm just running on nerves is all.'

'Sure.'

He reached the door first and held it for me. The place wasn't much more than a glorified diner, all formica and stainless steel, with a long lunch counter on our left and booths on the right and more tables in back. Four boys in their midteens sat at a booth near the front, eating french fries with their fingers from a communal platter. Farther back, a gray-haired woman with a lot of rings on both fingers was reading a hardcover book in a lending library's plastic cover.

The man behind the counter was tall and fat and completely bald. I suppose he shaved his head. Sweat was beaded on his forehead and had soaked through his shirt. The place was cool enough, with the air conditioning running full blast. There were two customers at the counter, one a round-shouldered man in a short-sleeved white shirt who looked like a failed accountant, the other a stolid girl with heavy legs and bad skin. At the rear of the counter the waitress was taking a cigarette break.

We took seats at the counter and ordered coffee. Someone had left that afternoon's *Post* on an adjoining stool. Skip picked it up, paged through it.

He lit a cigarette, smoked it, glancing every few seconds at the door. We both drank our coffee. He picked up a menu and ran his eyes over its listings. 'They got a million different things,' he said. 'Name something, it's probably on here. Why am I looking? I couldn't eat.'

He lit another cigarette, put his pack on the counter. I took one from it and put it between my lips. He raised his eyebrows but didn't say anything, just gave me a light. I took two, three puffs and put out the cigarette.

I must have heard the phone ring, but it didn't register until the waitress had already walked back to answer it and come forward to ask the round-shouldered man if he was Arthur Devoe. He looked astonished at the idea. Skip went to take the call and I tagged along.

He took the phone, listened for a moment, then began motioning for paper and pencil. I got my notebook and wrote down what he repeated to me.

A whoop of laughter came at us from the front of the restaurant. The kids were throwing french fries at each other. The counterman was leaning his bulk onto the formica, saying something to them. I turned my eyes from them and concentrated on writing down what Skip was saying.

SIXTEEN

Skip said, 'Eighteenth and Ovington. You know where that is?'

'I think so. I know Ovington, it runs through Bay Ridge, but Eighteenth Avenue is west of there. I think that would put it in Bensonhurst, a little ways south of Washington Cemetery.'

'How can anybody know all this shit? Did you say Eighteenth *Avenue?* They got avenues up to Eighteen?'

'I think they go up to Twenty-eight, but Twenty-eighth Avenue's only two blocks long. It runs from Cropsey to Stillwell.'

'Where's that?'

'Coney Island. Not all that far from where we are now.'

He waved a hand, dismissing the borough and all its unknowable streets. 'You know where we're going,' he said. 'And we'll get the map from Kasabian. Oh, fuck. Is this going to be on the part of the map they're carrying?'

'Probably not.'

'Fuck. What did I have to go and rip the map for? Jesus.'

We were out of the restaurant by now. We stood in front, with the winking neon in back of us. Skip said, 'Matt, I'm out of my element. Why'd they have us come here first, then call us up and send us to the church?'

'So they can get a look at us first, I guess. And interrupt our lines of communication.'

'You think someone's looking at us right now? How'm I gonna tell Johnny to follow us? Is that what they oughta do, follow us?'

'They probably ought to go home.'

'Why's that?'

'Because they'll be spotted following us, and they'll be spotted anyway when we tell them what's going on.'

'You think we're being watched?'

'It's possible. It's one reason for them to set things up this way.'

'Shit,' he said. 'I can't send Johnny home. If I suspect him, he probably suspects me at the same time, and I can't ... Suppose we all go in one car?'

'Two cars would be better.'

'You just said two cars won't work.'

'We'll try it this way,' I said, and took his arm to steer him. We walked not toward the car where Kasabian and the others were parked but to Skip's Impala. At my direction he started the car up, blinked the lights a couple of times, and drove to the corner, took a right, drove a block and pulled to the curb.

A few minutes later Kasabian's car pulled up beside us.

'You were right,' Skip said to me. To the others he said, 'You guys are smarter than I gave you credit. We got a phone call, they're sending us on a treasure hunt only we got the treasure. We're supposed to go to a church on Eighteenth Avenue and something.'

'Ovington,' I said.

No one knew where that was. 'Follow us,' I told them. 'Stay half a block to a block in back of us, and when we park go around the block and park behind us.'

'Suppose we get lost?' Bobby wanted to know.

'Go home.'

'How?'

'Just follow us,' I said. 'You won't get lost.'

We took Coney Island Avenue and Kings Highway into Bay Parkway, and then we got disoriented and it took me a few blocks to get my bearings. We went across one of the numbered streets, caught Eighteenth Avenue, and found the church we were looking for on the corner of Ovington. In Bay Ridge, Ovington Avenue runs parallel to Bay Ridge Avenue a block to the south of it. Somewhere around Fort Hamilton Parkway it winds up still parallel to Bay Ridge Avenue but a block *north* of it, where Sixty-eighth Street used to be. Even when you know the area, this sort of thing can drive you crazy, and Brooklyn is full of it.

There was a No Parking zone directly across from the church, and Skip pulled the Chevy into it. He cut the lights, killed the engine. We sat in silence until Kasabian's car had moved up, passed us, and turned at the corner.

'Did he even see us?' Skip wondered. I said that they had, that was why they'd turned at the corner. 'I guess,' he said.

I turned and watched out the rear window. A couple of minutes later I saw their lights. They found a parking spot half a block back, and their lights went out.

The neighborhood was mostly prewar frame houses, large ones, set on lots with lawns and trees out in front. Skip said, 'It doesn't look like New York out here. You know what I mean? It looks like some normal place in the rest of the country.'

'A lot of Brooklyn is like this.'

'Parts of Queens, too. Not where I grew up, but here and there. You know what this reminds me of? Richmond Hill. You know Richmond Hill?'

'Not well.'

'Track team had a meet out there once. We got the shit kicked out of us. The houses, though, they looked a lot like this.' He dropped his cigarette out the window. 'I guess we might as well do it,' he said. 'Right?'

'I don't like it,' I said.

'*You* don't like it? I haven't liked it since the books disappeared.'

'The other place was public,' I said. I opened my notebook, read what I'd written down. 'There's supposed to be a flight of steps on the left-hand side of the church leading down to the basement. The door's supposed to be open. I don't even see a light on, do you?'

'No.'

'This looks like an awfully easy way to get sandbagged. I think you'd better stay here, Skip.'

'You figure you're safer alone?'

I shook my head. 'I figure we're both safer separated for the moment. The money stays with you. I want to go down there and see what kind of a reception they've got set up for us. If there looks to be a safe way to make the switch, I'll have them blink the lights three times.'

'What lights?'

'Some light that you can see.' I leaned across him, pointed. 'Those are the basement windows down there. There must be lights, and you'll be able to see them.'

'So you wink the lights three times and I bring the money. Suppose you don't like the setup?'

'Then I tell them I have to get you, and I come out and we drive back to Manhattan.'

549

'Assuming we can find it.' He frowned. 'What if – never mind.'

'What?'

'I was gonna say what if you don't come out.'

'You'll find your way home sooner or later.'

'Funny man. What are you doing?'

I'd popped the cover of the dome light and I was unscrewing the bulb. 'In case they're watching,' I said. 'I don't want them to know when I open the door.'

'The man thinks of everything. It's good you're not Polish, we'd need fifteen guys to turn the car while you held onto the bulb. You want the gun, Matt?'

'I don't think so.'

'"Bare-handed, he went up alone against an army." Take the fucking gun, will you?'

'Gimme.'

'And how about a quick one?'

I reached for the glove box.

I got out and stayed low, keeping the car between me and the church basement windows. I walked half a block to the other car and ran down the situation for them. I had Kasabian stay with the car and told him to start the motor when he saw Skip enter the church. I sent the other two around the block on foot. If the other side made their getaway through a rear exit of the church and over a fence and through a yard, Bobby and Billie might be able to spot them. I didn't know that they could do much, but maybe one of them could come up with a license-plate number.

I returned to the Impala and told Skip what I'd done. I put the bulb back in the dome light, and when I opened the door again it went on, lighting up the car's interior. I swung the door shut and crossed the street.

The gun was tucked into the waistband of my slacks, the butt protruding, the whole thing positioned for a draw across the front of my body. I'd have preferred to have it riding in a holster on my hip but I didn't have the choice. It got in the way as I walked, and when I was in the shadows at the side of the church I drew the gun and walked along holding it, but I didn't like that either, and I put it back where I'd had it.

The flight of stairs was steep. Concrete steps with a rusted iron railing that was loosely mounted into the surrounding brick. A bolt or two had evidently worked loose. I walked down the steps and felt myself disappearing into the darkness. There was a door at the bottom. I groped until I found the knob and I

hesitated with my hand on it, listening carefully, trying to hear something within.

Nothing.

I turned the knob, eased the door inward just far enough to be sure that it was unlocked. Then I drew it shut and knocked on it.

Nothing.

I knocked again. This time I heard movement inside, and a voice called out something unintelligible. I turned the knob again and stepped through the doorway.

The time I'd spent in the pitch-dark stairwell had worked to my advantage. A little light filtered into the basement through the windows at the front, and my pupils had dilated enough to make use of it. I was standing in a room that must have measured about thirty by fifty feet. There were chairs and tables scattered around the floor. I pulled the door closed after me and moved into the shadows against one wall.

A voice said, 'Devoe?'

'Scudder,' I said.

'Where's Devoe?'

'In the car.'

'It doesn't matter,' another voice said. I couldn't recognize either of them as the one I'd heard over the phone, but it had been disguised, and for all I knew these voices were disguised, too. They didn't sound like New York but they didn't sound like anyplace else in particular, either.

The first speaker said, 'You bring the money, Scudder?'

'It's in the car.'

'With Devoe.'

'With Devoe,' I agreed.

Still just the two speakers. One was at the far end of the room, the other to his right. I could place them by their voices but the darkness shrouded them, and one of them sounded as if he might be speaking from behind something, some upended table or something of the sort. If they came out where I could see them, I could draw the gun and throw down on them, shoot them if I had to. On the other hand, it was more than possible that they already had guns trained on me and could drop me where I stood before I got the gun out of my pants. And even if I shot first and got them both, there could be another couple of armed men standing in the shadows, and they could shoot me full of holes before I even knew they existed.

Besides, I didn't want to shoot anybody. I just wanted to trade the money for the books and get the hell out of there.

'Tell your friend to bring the money,' one of them said. I decided he might have been the voice on the phone, if he were to let his speech soften into a southern accent. 'Unless he wants the books sent to the IRS.'

'He doesn't want that,' I said. 'But he's not going to walk into a blind alley, either.'

'Keep talking.'

'First of all, put a light on. We don't want to do business in the dark.'

There was a whispered conference, then a fair amount of moving around. One of them flicked a wall switch and a fluorescent fixture in the center of the ceiling came on one tube at a time. There was a flickering quality to its light, the way fluorescents get when they're starting to go.

I blinked, as much at what I saw as at the flickering light. For a moment I thought they were hippies or mountain men, some curious breed. Then I realized they were disguised.

There were two of them, shorter than I, slender in build. Both wore full beards and fright wigs that started low on their foreheads and concealed not only their hair but the whole shapes of their heads. Between the low hairline and the beginning of the beard, each wore an oval mask over the eyes and the top half of the nose. The taller of the two, the one who'd turned on the light, had a chrome-yellow wig and a black face mask. The other, half concealed by a table with chairs stacked on it, sported dark brown hair and a white mask. Both had black beards, and the short one had a gun in his hand.

With the light on, I think we all three felt vulnerable, almost naked. I know I did, and there was a tension in their stance that indicated the same feeling. The one with the gun was not exactly training it on me, but neither was he pointing it in another direction altogether. Darkness had protected all three of us, and now we'd flicked it aside.

'The trouble is we're afraid of each other,' I told him. 'You're afraid we'll try to get the books without paying for them. We're afraid you'll rip us off for the money and give us nothing in return, hold us up again with the books or peddle them to somebody else.'

The tall one shook his head. 'This is a one-time deal.'

'For both of us. We pay once and that's all. If you made a copy of the books, get rid of it.'

'No copies.'

'Good,' I said. 'You have the books here?' The short one with the dark wig shoved a navy-blue laundry bag across the room with his foot. His partner hefted it, put it back on the floor. I said it could be anything, it could be laundry, and would they show me what was in the bag.

'When we see money,' the tall one said, 'you get to see the books.'

'I don't want to examine them. Just take them out of the sack before I tell my friend to bring the money.'

They looked at each other. The one with the gun shrugged. He moved the pistol to cover me while the other one worked the drawstring on the laundry bag and withdrew a hinged-post bound ledger similar to the set of fake books I'd seen on Skip's desk.

'All right,' I said. 'Flick the light on and off three times.'

'Who are you signaling?'

'The Coast Guard.'

They exchanged glances, and the one by the light switch worked it up and down three times. The fluorescent fixture winked on and off in ragged fashion. The three of us stood awkwardly and waited what seemed like a long time. I wondered if Skip had seen the signal, wondered if he'd had enough time alone in the car to lose his nerve.

Then I heard him on the stairs and at the door. I called out to him to come in. The door opened and he entered, the attaché case in his left hand.

He looked at me, then caught sight of the two of them in their beards and wigs and masks.

'Jesus,' he said.

I said, 'Each side will have one man to make the exchange and one to cover him. That way nobody will be able to take anybody off and the books and money will pass at the same time.'

The taller one, the one at the light switch, said, 'You sound like an old hand at this.'

'I had time to think about it. Skip, I'll back you up. Bring the case over here, set it down by me. Good. Now you and one of our friends can set up a table in the middle of the room and clear some of the other furniture out from around it.'

The two of them looked at each other, and predictably the taller one kicked the laundry bag over to his partner and came forward. He asked what I wanted him to do and I put him and Skip to work rearranging the furniture.

553

'I don't know what the union's going to say about this,' he said. The beard hid his mouth, and the mask covered him around the eyes, but I sensed he was smiling.

At my direction, he and Skip positioned a table in the center of the room, almost directly beneath the overhead light fixture. The table was eight feet long and four feet wide, placed to divide their side of the room from ours.

I got down on one knee, crouched behind a nest of chairs. At the far end of the room, the one with the gun was similarly concealing himself. I called Skip back for the case full of money, sent the tall yellow-haired fellow for the books. Moving deliberately, each carried his part of the bargain to one end of the long table. Skip set the case down first, worked the buttons to release the catches. The man in the blond wig slipped the set of books out of the bag and put them down gently, then stepped back, his hands hovering.

I had each of them retreat a few yards, then switch ends of the table. Skip opened the heavy ledger, made sure the books were the ones he'd negotiated for. His opposite number opened the attaché case and took out a banded stack of bills. He riffled through it, put it back, took up another stack.

'Books are okay,' Skip announced. He closed the heavy volume, got it into the laundry bag, hoisted it and started back toward me.

The one with the gun said, 'Hold it.'

'What for?'

'Stay where you are until he counts it.'

'I got to stand here while he counts fifty grand? Be serious.'

'Take a fast count,' the one with the gun told his partner. 'Make sure it's all money. We don't want to go home with a bag full of cut-up newspaper.'

'I'd really do that,' Skip said. 'I'd really walk up into a gun with a case full of fucking Monopoly money. Point that thing somewhere else, will you? It's getting on my nerves.'

There was no answer. Skip held his position, balanced on the balls of his feet. My back was cramping and my knee, the one I was kneeling on, was giving me a little trouble. Time came to a stop while the yellow-haired one flipped through the packets of money, assuring himself that none of it consisted of cut paper or one-dollar bills. He probably did this as quickly as he could but it seemed forever before he was satisfied, closing the case and engaging the clasps.

'All right,' I said. 'Now the two of you –'

Skip said, 'Wait a minute. We get the laundry bag and they get the attaché case, right?'

'So?'

'So it seems uneven. That case was close to a hundred bucks and it's less than two years old, and how much could a laundry bag be worth? A couple of bucks, right?'

'What are you getting at, Devoe?'

'You could throw in something,' he said, his voice tightening. 'You could tell me who set this up.'

They both looked hard at him.

'I don't know you,' he said. 'I don't know either of you. You ripped me off, fine, maybe your kid sister needs an operation or something. I mean everybody's gotta make a living, right?'

No answer.

'But somebody set this up, somebody I know, somebody who knows me. Tell me who. That's all.'

There was a long silence. Then the one with the brown wig said, 'Forget it,' flat, final. Skip's shoulders dropped in resignation.

'We try,' he said.

And he and the man in the yellow wig backed away from the table, one with the attaché case and one with the laundry bag. I called the shots, sending Skip to the door he'd come in, watching the other move not surprisingly through a curtained archway in the rear. Skip had the door open and was backing through it when the one in the dark wig said, 'Hold it.'

His long-barreled pistol had swung around to cover Skip, and for a moment I thought he was going to shoot. I got both hands on the .45 and took a bead on him. Then his gun swung to the side and he raised it and said, 'We leave first. Stay where you are for ten minutes. You got that?'

'All right,' I said.

He pointed the gun at the ceiling, fired twice. The fluorescent tubes exploded overhead, plunging the room into darkness. The gunshots were loud and the exploding tubes were louder, but for some reason neither the noise nor the darkness rattled me. I watched as he moved to the archway, a shadow among shadows, and the .45 stayed centered on him and my finger stayed on the trigger.

We didn't wait ten minutes as instructed. We got out of there in a hurry, Skip lugging the books in the laundry bag, me with the gun still clutched in one hand. Before we could cross the street

to the Chevy, Kasabian had put his car in gear and roared down the block, pulling up next to us with a great screech of brakes. We piled into the back seat and told him to go around the block, but the car was already in motion before we got the words out.

We took a left and then another left. On Seventeenth Avenue, we found Bobby Ruslander hanging on to a tree with one hand, struggling to catch his breath. Across the street, Billie Keegan took a few slow steps toward us, then paused to cup his hands around a match and light a cigarette.

Bobby said, 'Oh, Jesus, am I out of shape. They came tearin' out of that driveway, had to be them, they had the case with the money. I was four houses down, I saw 'em but I didn't want to run up on 'em right away, you know? I think one of 'em was carrying a gun.'

'Didn't you hear the shots?'

He hadn't, nor had either of the others. I wasn't surprised. The dark-haired gunman had used a small-caliber pistol, and while the noise was loud enough in a closed room, it wouldn't have been likely to carry very far.

'They jumped into this car,' Bobby said, pointing to where it had been parked, 'and they got out in a hurry and left rubber. I started moving once they were in the car, figuring I could get a look at the plate number, and I chased 'em and the light was rotten and –' He shrugged. 'Nothing,' he said.

Skip said, 'Least you tried.'

'I'm so out of shape,' Bobby said. He slapped himself across the belly. 'No legs, no wind, and my eyes aren't so good, either. I couldn't referee a real basketball game, running up and down the court. I'd fuckin' die.'

'You could have blown your whistle,' Skip suggested.

'Jesus, if I'd had it with me I might have. You think they would have stopped and surrendered?'

'I think they'd probably have shot you,' I said. 'Forget the plate number.'

'At least I tried,' he said. He looked over at Billie. 'Keegan there, he was closer to them and he didn't budge. Just sat under the tree like Ferdinand the bull, smelling the flowers.'

'Smelling the dogshit,' Keegan said. 'We have to work with the materials at hand.'

'Been working on those minibottles, Billie?'

'Just maintaining,' Keegan said.

I asked Bobby if he got the make of the car. He pursed his lips,

blew out, shook his head. 'Dark late-model sedan,' he said. 'They all look alike these days anyway.'

'That's the truth,' Kasabian said, and Skip agreed with him. I started to form another question when Billie Keegan announced that the car was a Mercury Marquis, three or four years old, black or navy blue.

We all stopped and looked at him. His face carefully expressionless, he took a scrap of paper from his breast pocket, unfolded it. 'LJK914,' he read. 'Does that mean anything to any of you?' And while we went on staring at him, he said, 'That's the license number. New York plates. I wrote down all the makes and plate numbers earlier to keep from dying of boredom. It seemed easier than chasing cars like a fucking cocker spaniel.'

'Fucking Billie Keegan,' Skip said with wonder, and went over and hugged him.

'You gentlemen will rush to judgment of the man who drinks a bit,' Keegan said. He took a miniature bottle from a pocket, twisted the cap until the seal broke, tipped back his head and drank the whiskey down.

'Maintenance,' he said. 'That's all.'

SEVENTEEN

Bobby couldn't get over it. He seemed almost hurt by Billie's ingenuity. 'Why didn't you say something?' he demanded. 'I could have been writing down numbers the same time, we could have covered more of them.'

Keegan shrugged. 'I figured I'd keep it to myself,' he said. 'So that when they ran past all these cars and caught a bus on Jerome Avenue I wouldn't look like an asshole.'

'Jerome Avenue's in the Bronx,' somebody said. Billie said he knew where Jerome Avenue was, that he had an uncle used to live on Jerome Avenue. I asked if the pair had been wearing their disguises when they emerged from the driveway.

'I don't know,' Bobby said. 'What were they supposed to look like? They had little masks on.' He made twin circles of his thumbs and forefingers, held them to his face in imitation of the masks.

'Were they wearing beards?'

'Of course they were wearing beards. What do you think, they stopped to shave?'

'The beards were fake,' Skip said.

'Oh.'

'They have the wigs on, too? One dark and one light?'

'I guess. I didn't know they were wigs. I – there wasn't a hell of a lot of light, Arthur. Streetlamps there and there, but they came out that driveway and ran to their car, and they didn't exactly pause and hold a press conference, pose for the photographers.'

I said, 'We'd better get out of here.'

'Why's that? I like standing around in the middle of Brooklyn, it reminds me of hanging out on the corner when I was a boy. You're thinking cops?'

'Well, there were gunshots. No point being conspicuous.'

'Makes sense.'

We walked over to Kasabian's car, got in, and circled the block

again. We caught a red light, and I gave Kasabian directions back to Manhattan. We had the books in hand, we'd paid the ransom, and we were all alive to tell or not tell the tale. Besides that, we had Keegan's drunken resourcefulness to celebrate. All of this changed our mood for the better, and I was now able to provide clear directions back to the city and Kasabian for his part was able to absorb them.

As we neared the church, we saw a handful of people in front of it, men in undershirts, teenagers, all of them standing around as if waiting for someone. Somewhere in the distance, I heard the undulating siren of a blue-and-white.

I wanted to tell Kasabian to drive us all home, that we could come back tomorrow for Skip's car. But it was parked next to a hydrant, it would stand out. He pulled up – he may not have put the crowd and the siren together – and Skip and I got out. One of the men across the street, balding and beer-gutted, was looking us over.

I called out, asked him what was up. He wanted to know if I was from the precinct. I shook my head.

'Somebody busted into the church,' he said. 'Kids, probably. We got the exits covered, the cops coming.'

'Kids,' I said heavily, and he laughed.

'I think I was more nervous just now than I was in the church basement,' Skip said, after we'd driven a few blocks. 'I'm standing with a laundry bag over my shoulder like I just committed a burglary and you've got a forty-five in your belt. I figured we're in great shape if they see the gun.'

'I forgot it was there.'

'And we just got out of a car full of drunks. Another point in our favor.'

'Keegan was the only one who was drunk.'

'And he was the brilliant one. Figure that out, will you? Speaking of drinking –'

I got the scotch from the glove compartment and uncapped it for him. He took a long pull, handed it to me. We passed it back and forth until it was gone, and Skip said, 'Fuck Brooklyn,' and tossed it out the window. I'd have been just as happy if he hadn't – we had booze on our breath, an unlicensed gun in our possession, and no good way to account for our presence – but I kept it to myself.

'They were pretty professional,' Skip said. 'The disguises, everything. Why did he shoot the light out?'

'To slow us down.'

'I thought he was going to shoot me for a minute there. Matt?'

'What?'

'How come you didn't shoot him?'

'When he was aiming at you? I might have, if I sensed he was about to shoot. I had him covered. As it stood, if I shot him he would shoot you.'

'I mean after that. After he shot the light out. You still had him covered. You were aiming at him when he went out the door.'

I took a moment to answer. I said, 'You decided to pay the ransom to keep the books away from the IRS. What do you think happens if you're tagged to a shooting in a church in Bensonhurst?'

'Jesus, I wasn't thinking.'

'And shooting him wouldn't have recovered the money, anyway. It was already out the back door with the other one.'

'I know. I really wasn't thinking. The thing is, *I* mighta shot him. Not because it was the right thing to do, but in the heat of the moment.'

'Well,' I said. 'You never know what you'll do in the heat of the moment.'

The next light we caught, I got out my notebook and began sketching. Skip asked me what I was drawing.

'Ears,' I said.

'How's that?'

'Something an instructor told us when I was at the Police Academy. The shapes of people's ears are very distinctive and it's something that's rarely disguised or changed by plastic surgery. There wasn't a hell of a lot to see of these two. I want to make sketches of their ears before I forget.'

'You remember what their ears looked like?'

'Well, I made a point of remembering.'

'Oh, that makes a difference.' He drew on his cigarette. 'I couldn't swear they *had* ears. Didn't the wigs cover them? I guess not, or you wouldn't be drawing pictures. You can't check their ears in some file, can you? Like fingerprints?'

'I just want to have a way to recognize them,' I said. 'I think I might know their voices, if they were using their real ones tonight, and I think they probably were. As far as their height, one was around five-nine or -ten and the other was either a little shorter or it looked that way because he was standing farther back.' I shook my head at my notebook. 'I don't know which set

of ears went with which of them. I should have done this right away. That kind of memory fades on you fast.'

'You think it matters, Matt?'

'What their ears look like?' I considered. 'Probably not,' I granted. 'At least ninety percent of what you do in an investigation doesn't lead anywhere. Make that ninety-five percent – the people you talk to, the things you take time to check. But if you do enough things, the one thing that does work is in there.'

'You miss it?'

'Being a cop? Not often.'

'I can see where a person would miss it,' he said. 'Anyway, I didn't mean just ears. I mean is there a point to the whole thing? They did us a dirty and they got away with it. You think the license plate will lead anywhere?'

'No. I think they were smart enough to use a stolen car.'

'That's what I think, too. I didn't want to say anything because I wanted to feel good back there, and I didn't want to piss on Billie's parade, but the trouble they took, disguises, sending us all around the barn before we got to the right place, I don't think they're gonna get tripped up by a license number.'

'Sometimes it happens.'

'I guess. Maybe we're better off if they stole a car.'

'How do you figure that?'

'Maybe they'll get picked up in it, some sharp-eyed patrolman who looked at the hot-car list. Is that what they call it?'

'The hot-car sheet. It takes a while for a car to get on it, though.'

'Maybe they planned in advance. Stole the car a week ago, took it in for a tune-up. What else could they get charged with? Desecrating a church?'

'Oh, Jesus,' I said.

'What's the matter?'

'That church.'

'What about it?'

'Stop the car, Skip.'

'Huh?'

'Stop the car a minute, all right?'

'You serious?' He looked at me. 'You're serious,' he said, and pulled over to the curb.

I closed my eyes, tried to bring things into focus. 'The church,' I said. 'What kind of church was it, did you happen to notice?'

'They all look the same to me. It was, I don't know, brick, stone. What the hell's the difference?'

'I mean was it Protestant or Catholic or what?'

'How would I know which it was?'

'There was one of those signs out in front. A glass case with white letters on a black background, tells you when the services are and what the sermon's going to be about.'

'It's always about the same thing. Figure out all the things you like to do and don't do 'em.'

I could close my eyes and see the damn thing but I couldn't bring the letters into focus. 'You didn't notice?'

'I had things on my mind, Matt. What fucking difference does it make?'

'Was it Catholic?'

'*I* don't know. You got something for or against Catholic? The nuns hit you with a ruler when you were a kid? "Impure thoughts, *wham*, take that, you little bastard." You gonna be a while, Matt?' I had my eyes closed, wrestling with memory, and I didn't answer him. 'Because there's a liquor store across the street, and much as I hate to spend money in Brooklyn, I think I'm gonna. All right?'

'Sure.'

'You can pretend it's altar wine,' he said.

He returned with a pint of Teacher's in a brown bag. He cracked the seal and uncapped the bottle without removing it from the bag, took a drink and gave it to me. I held on to it for a moment, then drank.

'We can go now,' I said.

'Go where?'

'Home. Back to Manhattan.'

'We don't have to go back, make a novena or something?'

'The church was some kind of Lutheran.'

'And that means we can go to Manhattan.'

'Right.'

He started the engine, pulled out from the curb. He reached out a hand and I gave him the bottle and he drank and handed it back to me.

He said, 'I don't mean to pry, Detective Scudder, but –'

'But what was all that about?'

'Yeah.'

'I feel silly mentioning it,' I said. 'It's something Tillary told

me a few days ago. I don't even know if it was true, but it was supposed to be a church in Bensonhurst.'

'A Catholic one.'

'It would have to be,' I said, and I told him the story Tommy had told me, of the two kids who'd burglarized a Mafia capo's mother's church, and what had supposedly been done to them in return.

Skip said, 'Really? It really happened?'

'I don't know. Neither does Tommy. Stories get around.'

'Hung on meat hooks and fucking skinned alive –'

'It might appeal to Tutto. They call him Dom the Butcher. I think he's got interests in the wholesale meat industry.'

'Jesus. If that was his church –'

'His mother's church.'

'Whatever. You gonna hang on to that bottle until the glass melts?'

'Sorry.'

'If that was his church, or his mother's church, or whatever it was –'

'I wouldn't want him to know we were there tonight while it got shot up. Not that it's the same as burglarizing the premises, but he still might take it personally. Who knows how he'd react?'

'Jesus.'

'But it was definitely a Protestant church and his mother would go to a Catholic one. Even if it was Catholic, there's probably four or five Catholic churches in Bensonhurst. Maybe more, I don't know.'

'Someday we'll have to count 'em.' He drew on his cigarette, coughed, tossed it out the window. 'Why would anybody do something like that?'

'You mean –'

'I mean hang two kids up and fucking skin 'em, that's what I mean. Why would somebody do that, two kids that all they did was stole some shit from a church?'

'I don't know,' I said. 'I know why Tutto probably thought he was doing it.'

'Why?'

'To teach them a lesson.'

He thought about this. 'Well, I bet it worked,' he said. 'I bet those little fuckers never rob another church.'

563

EIGHTEEN

By the time we were back home the pint of Teacher's was empty. I hadn't had much of it. Skip had kept chipping away at it, finally flipping it empty into the back seat. I guess he only threw them out the window on the other side of the river.

We hadn't talked much since our conversation about Dom the Butcher. The booze was working in him now, showing up a little in his driving. He ran a couple of lights and took a corner a little wildly, but we didn't hit anything or anybody. Nor did we get flagged down by a traffic cop. You just about had to run down a nun to get cited for a moving violation that year in the city of New York.

When we'd pulled up in front of Miss Kitty's he leaned forward and put his elbows on the steering wheel. 'Well, the joint's still open,' he said. 'I got a guy working the bar tonight, he probably took as much off of us as the boys from Bensonhurst. Come on in, I want to put the books away.'

In his office, I suggested he might want to put the ledger in the safe. He gave me a look and worked the combination dial. 'Just overnight,' he said. 'Tomorrow all this shit goes down a couple different incinerators. No more honest books. All you do is leave yourself wide open.'

He put the books in the safe and started to close the big door. I put a hand on his arm to stop him. 'Maybe this should go in there,' I said, and handed him the .45.

'Forgot about that,' he said. 'It doesn't go in the safe. You gonna tell a holdup man, 'Please excuse me a minute, I wanna get the gun from the safe, blow your head off'? We keep it behind the bar.' He took it from me, then looked around for an inconspicuous way to carry it. There was a white paper bag on the desk, stained from the takeout coffee and sandwiches it had once held, and Skip put the gun in it.

'There,' he said. He closed the safe, spun the dial, tugged the

handle to make sure the lock had engaged. 'Perfect,' he said. 'Now let me buy you a drink.'

We went out front and he slipped behind the bar, pouring out two drinks of the same scotch we'd had in the car. 'Maybe you wanted bourbon,' he said. 'I didn't think, didn't think when I bought the bottle, either.'

'This is fine.'

'You sure?' He moved off, put the gun somewhere behind the bar. The bartender he had on that night came over and wanted a conference with him, and they walked off and spoke for a few minutes. Skip came back and finished his drink and said he wanted to put his car in the parking garage before somebody towed it, but he'd be back in a few minutes. Or I could come along for the ride.

'You go ahead,' I told him. 'I may go on home myself.'

'Make it an early night?'

'Not the worst idea.'

'No. Well, if you're gone when I get back I'll see you tomorrow.'

I didn't go right home. I hit a few joints first. Not Armstrong's. I didn't want any conversation. I didn't want to get drunk, either. I'm not sure what I wanted.

I was leaving Polly's Cage when I saw a car that looked like Tommy's Buick cruising west on Fifty-seventh. I didn't get a good look at the person behind the wheel. I walked along after it, saw it pull into a parking space in the middle of the next block. By the time the driver got out and locked up, I was close enough to see it was Tommy. He was wearing a jacket and tie and carrying two packages. One, fan-shaped, looked to be flowers.

I watched him enter Carolyn's building.

For some reason I went and stood on the sidewalk across the street from her building. I picked out her window, or what I decided was her window. Her light was on. I stood there for quite a while, until the light went out.

I went to a pay phone, called 411. The Information operator reported to me that she did indeed have a listing for Carolyn Cheatham at the address I gave her, but that the number was unpublished. I called again, got a different operator, and went through the procedure a policeman uses to get an unlisted number. I got it and wrote it down in my notebook, on the same page with my witless little sketch of ears. They were, I thought, rather unremarkable ears. They would pass in a crowd.

I put a dime in the phone and dialed the number. It rang four or five times, and then she picked it up and said hello. I don't know what the hell else I expected. I didn't say anything, and she said hello a second time and broke the connection.

I felt tight across my upper back and in my shoulders. I wanted to go to some bucket of blood and get in a fight. I wanted to hit something.

Where had the anger come from? I wanted to go up there and pull him off of her and hit him in the face, but what the hell had he done? A few days ago I'd been angry with him for neglecting her. Now I was enraged because he wasn't.

Was I jealous? But why? I wasn't interested in her.

Crazy.

I went and looked at her window again. The light was still out. An ambulance from Roosevelt sped down Ninth Avenue, its siren wailing. Rock music blared on the radio of a car waiting for the light to change. Then the car sped away and the ambulance siren faded in the distance, and for a moment the city seemed utterly silent. Then the silence, too, was gone, as I became aware again of all the background noises that never completely disappear.

That song Keegan had played for me came into my mind. Not all of it. I couldn't get the tune right and I only remembered snatches of the lyrics. Something about a night of poetry and poses. Well, you could call it that. And knowing you're all alone when the sacred ginmill closes.

I picked up some beer on the way home.

NINETEEN

The Sixth Precinct is housed on West Tenth Street between Bleecker and Hudson, in the Village. Years before, when I did a tour of duty there, it was in an ornate structure farther west on Charles Street. That building has since been converted into co-op apartments, and named the Gendarme.

The new station house is an ugly modern building that no one will ever carve into apartments. I was there a little before noon on Tuesday and I walked past the front desk and straight to Eddie Koehler's office. I didn't have to ask, I knew where it was.

He looked up from a report he'd been reading, blinked at me. 'Thing about that door,' he said, 'anybody could walk through it.'

'You're looking good, Eddie.'

'Well, you know. Clean living. Sit down, Matt.'

I sat, and we talked a little. We went back a long ways, Eddie and I. When the small talk faded, he said, 'You just happened to be in the neighborhood, right?'

'I just thought of you and figured you needed a new hat.'

'In this weather?'

'Maybe a panama. Nice straw, keep the sun off.'

'Maybe a pith helmet. But in thith neighborhood,' he said, 'Thome of the girlth would make dirty crackth.'

I had my notebook out. 'A license number,' I said. 'I thought maybe you could check it for me.'

'You mean call Motor Vehicles?'

'First check the hot-car sheet.'

'What's it, a hit-and-run? Your client wants to know who hit him, maybe take quiet cash instead of press charges?'

'You've got a great imagination.'

'You got a license number and I should check the hot cars before anything else? Shit. What's the number?'

I read it out to him. He jotted it down and pushed away from his desk. 'Be a minute,' he said.

While he was gone I looked at my ear drawings. Ears really do look different. The thing is you have to train yourself to notice them.

He wasn't gone long. He came back and dropped into his swivel chair. 'Not on the sheet,' he said.

'Could you check the registration with Motor Vehicles?'

'I could, but I don't have to. They don't always get on the sheet so quick. So I called in, and it's hot, all right, it'll be listed on the next sheet. It was phoned in last night, stolen late afternoon or early evening.'

'It figured,' I said.

''Seventy-three Mercury, right? Sedan, dark blue?'

'That's right.'

'That what you wanted?'

'Where was it stolen from?'

'Somewhere in Brooklyn. Ocean Parkway, the high numbers, it must be pretty far out.'

'Makes sense.'

'It does?' he said. 'Why?'

I shook my head. 'It's nothing,' I said. 'I thought the car might be important, but if it's stolen it doesn't lead anywhere.' I took out my wallet, drew out a twenty and a five, the traditional price of a hat in police parlance. I put the bills on his desk. He covered them with his hand but did not pick them up.

'Now I got a question,' he said.

'Oh?'

'Why?'

'That's private,' I said. 'I'm working for someone, I can't –'

He was shaking his head. 'Why spend twenty-five dollars on something you coulda got for nothing over the telephone? Jesus Christ, Matt, how many years did you carry a shield that you don't remember how to get a listing out of the DMV? You call up, you identify yourself, you know the drill, don't you?'

'I thought it was hot.'

'So you want to check hot cars first, you call somebody in the Department. You're a police officer on a stakeout, whatever you want to say, you just spotted a car you think might be hot, and could they check it for you? That saves you running down here and saves you the price of a hat on top of it.'

'That's impersonating an officer,' I said.

'Oh, really?' He patted the money. 'This,' he said, 'is *bribing*

an officer, you want to get technical. You pick a funny place to draw the line.'

The conversation was making me uncomfortable. I had impersonated an officer less than twelve hours ago, getting Carolyn Cheatham's unlisted number from Information. I said, 'Maybe I missed the sight of you, Eddie. How's that?'

'Maybe. Maybe your brain's getting rusty.'

'That's possible.'

'Maybe you should lay off the booze and rejoin the human race. Is that possible?'

I stood up. 'Always a pleasure, Eddie.' He had more to say, but I didn't have to stay there and listen to it.

There was a church nearby, Saint Veronica's, a red-brick pile on Christopher Street near the river. A derelict had arranged himself on the steps, an empty bottle of Night Train still clutched in his hand. The thought came to me that Eddie had phoned ahead and had the man placed there, a grim example of what could lie in store for me. I didn't know whether to laugh or to shudder.

I climbed the steps and went inside. The church was cavernous and empty. I found a seat and closed my eyes for a minute. I thought about my two clients, Tommy and Skip, and the ineffectual work I was performing for each of them. Tommy didn't need my help and wasn't getting it. As for Skip, perhaps I'd helped make the exchange go smoothly, but I'd made mistakes. For God's sake, I should have had Billie and Bobby taking down license numbers, I shouldn't have left it for Billie to think of on his own.

I was almost glad the car had turned out to be stolen. So that Keegan's clue wouldn't lead anywhere and my lack of foresight would be less significant.

Stupid. Anyway, I'd posted them there, hadn't I? They wouldn't have seen the car, let alone got the number, if they'd been with Kasabian on the other side of the block.

I went and put a dollar in the slot and lit a candle. A woman was kneeling a few yards to my left. When she rose to her full height I saw she was a transsexual. She stood two inches taller than I. Her features were a mix of Latin and Oriental, her shoulders and upper arms were muscular, and her breasts were the size of cantaloupes, straining the polka-dot sun halter.

'Well, hello,' she said.

'Hello.'

'Have you come to light a candle to Saint Veronica? Do you know anything about her?'

'No.'

'Neither do I. But I prefer to think of her' – She arranged a strand of hair to fall across her forehead – 'as Saint Veronica *Lake*.'

The N train took me to within a few blocks of the church at Ovington and Eighteenth Avenue. A rather scattered woman in paint-spattered jeans and an army shirt pointed me to the pastor's office. There was no one at the desk, just a pudgy young man with an open freckled face. He had one foot on the arm of a chair and was tuning a guitar.

I asked where the pastor was.

'That's me,' he said, straightening up. 'How can I help you?'

I said I understood he'd had some minor vandalism in the basement the previous evening. He grinned at me. 'Is that what it was? Someone seems to have shot up our light fixture. The damage won't amount to much. Would you like to see where it happened?'

We didn't have to use the stairs I'd gone down last night. We walked down an inside staircase and a hallway, entering the room through the curtained archway our wigged and bearded friends had used to make their departure. The room had been straightened since then, the chairs stacked, the tables folded. Daylight filtered in through the windows.

'That's the fixture, of course,' he said, pointing. 'There was glass on the floor but it's been swept up. I suppose you've seen the police report.'

I didn't say anything, just looked around.

'You are with the police, aren't you?'

He wasn't probing. He simply wanted to be reassured. But something stopped me. Maybe the tail end of my conversation with Eddie Koehler.

'No,' I said. 'I'm not.'

'Oh? Then your interest is –'

'I was here last night.'

He looked at me, waiting for me to go on. He was, I thought, a very patient young man. You sensed that he wanted to hear what you had to say, and in your own good time. I suppose that quality would be a useful one for a minister.

I said, 'I used to be a cop. I'm a private detective now.' That was perhaps technically incorrect, but close enough to the truth.

'I was here last night on behalf of a client, seeking to exchange money for some goods of the client's that were being held for ransom.'

'I see.'

'The other parties, the criminals who had stolen my client's goods in the first place, selected this location for the exchange. They were the ones who did the shooting.'

'I see,' he said again. 'Was anyone . . . shot? The police looked for bloodstains. I don't know that all wounds bleed.'

'No one was shot. There were only two shots fired and they both went into the ceiling.'

He sighed. 'That's a relief. Well, Mr. Uh –'

'Scudder. Matthew Scudder.'

'And I'm Nelson Fuhrmann. I guess we missed introducing ourselves earlier.' He ran a hand over a freckled forehead. 'I gather the police don't know about any of this.'

'No, they don't.'

'And you'd rather they didn't.'

'It would certainly be simpler if they didn't.'

He considered, nodded. 'I doubt I'd have occasion to communicate it to them anyway,' he said. 'I don't suppose they'll come around again, do you? It's no major crime.'

'Somebody might follow up. But don't be surprised if you never hear further.'

'They'll file a report,' he said, 'and that will be that.' He sighed again. 'Well, Mr Scudder, you must have had a reason to take the chance that I *would* mention your visit to the police. What is it you're hoping to find out?'

'I'd like to know who they were.'

'The villains?' He laughed. 'I don't know what else to call them. If I were a policeman I suppose I'd call them perpetrators.'

'You could call them sinners.'

'Ah, but we're all that, aren't we?' He smiled at me. 'You don't know their identity?'

'No. And they wore disguises, wigs and false beards, so I don't even know what they looked like.'

'I don't see how I could help you. You don't suppose they're connected with the church, do you?'

'I'm almost certain they're not. But they picked this place, Reverend Fuhrmann, and –'

'Call me Nelson.'

'– and it suggests a familiarity with the church, and with this

room in particular. Did the cops find any evidence of forced entry?'

'I don't believe so, no.'

'Mind if I look at the door?' I examined the lock of the door leading to the outside stairs. If it had been tampered with, I couldn't see it. I asked him what other doors led to the outside, and he took me around and we checked, and none of them bore the scars of illegal entry.

'The police said a door must have been left open,' he said.

'That would be a logical guess if this were just a case of vandalism or malicious mischief. A couple of kids happen to find a door left unlocked, go inside, horse around a little. But this was planned and arranged. I don't think our sinners could count on the door being left open. Or is locking up a hit-or-miss business here?'

He shook his head. 'No, we always lock up. We have to, even in a decent neighborhood like this one. Two doors were open when the police arrived last night, this one and the one in the rear. We certainly wouldn't have left both doors unlocked.'

'If one was open, the other could be unlocked from inside without a key.'

'Oh, of course. Still —'

'There must be a lot of keys in circulation, reverend. I'm sure a lot of community groups use the space.'

'Oh, absolutely,' he said. 'We feel it's part of our function to make our space available when we don't require it for our own purposes. And the rent we collect for it is an important part of our income.'

'So the basement is often in use at night.'

'Oh, it certainly is. Let's see, AA meets in this room every Thursday night, and there's an Al-Anon group that uses the room on Tuesdays, they'll be here tonight, come to think of it. And Fridays, who's here Fridays? This space has been put to no end of uses in the few years I've been here. We had a little theater group doing their rehearsals, we have a monthly cub scout meeting when the whole pack assembles together, we have — well, you can see that there are a lot of different groups with access to the premises.'

'But no one meets here on Monday nights.'

'No. There was a women's consciousness-raising group that met here Mondays up until about three months ago, but I believe they decided to meet in one another's homes instead.' He cocked his head. 'You're suggesting that the, uh, sinners

would have had to be in a position to know the space would be empty last night.'

'I was thinking that.'

'But they could have called and asked. Anyone could have called and posed as someone interested in the space, and checking on its availability.'

'Did you get any calls like that?'

'Oh, we get them all the time,' he said. 'It's not something anyone here would bother to remember.'

'Why are you comin' around here all the time?' the woman wanted to know. 'Askin' everybody about Mickey Mouse.'

'Who?'

She let out a laugh. 'Miguelito Cruz. Miguelito means Little Michael, you know? Like Mickey. People call him Mickey Mouse. *I* do, anyway.'

We were in a Puerto Rican bar on Fourth Avenue, nestled between a shop that sold botanicals and one that rented formal wear. I'd gotten back on the N train after my visit to the Lutheran church in Bensonhurst, intending to ride it back into the city, but instead I found myself rising abruptly at Fifty-third Street in Sunset Park and leaving the train there. I had nothing else to do with the day, no logical direction to take in Skip's behalf, and I thought I might as well put in some time justifying my fee from Tommy Tillary.

Besides, it was lunchtime, and a plate of black beans and rice sounded good to me.

It tasted as good as it sounded. I washed it down with a bottle of cold beer, then ordered flan for dessert and had a couple of cups of espresso. The Italians give you a thimble of the stuff; the Puerto Ricans pour you a full cup of it.

Then I barhopped, staying with beers and making them last, and now I'd met this woman who wanted to know why I was interested in Mickey Mouse. She was around thirty-five, with dark hair and eyes and a hardness to her face that matched the hardness in her voice. Her voice, scarred by cigarettes and booze and hot food, was the sort that would cut glass.

Her eyes were large and soft, and what showed of her body suggested that it would have a softness to match the eyes. She was wearing a lot of bright colors. Her hair was wrapped up in a hot-pink scarf, her blouse was an electric blue, her hip-hugging slacks canary yellow, her high-heeled shoes Day-Glo orange. The blouse was unbuttoned far enough to reveal the swell of her

573

full breasts. Her skin was like copper, but with a blush to it, as if lighted from within.

I said, 'You know Mickey Mouse?'

'Sure I know him. I see him all the time in the cartoons. He is one funny mouse.'

'I mean Miguelito Cruz. You know that Mickey Mouse?'

'You a cop?'

'No.'

'You look like one, you move like one, you ask questions like one.'

'I used to be a cop.'

'They kick you out for stealin'?' She laughed, showing a couple of gold teeth. 'Takin' bribes?'

I shook my head. 'Shooting kids,' I said.

She laughed louder. 'No way,' she said. 'They don't kick you out for that. They give you a promotion, make you the chief.'

There was no island accent in her speech. She was a Brooklyn girl from the jump. I asked her again if she knew Cruz.

'Why?'

'Forget it.'

'Huh?'

'Forget it,' I said, and turned a shoulder to her and went back to my beer. I didn't figure she'd leave it alone. I watched out of the corner of my eye. She was drinking something colorful through a straw, and as I watched she sucked up the last of it.

'Hey,' she said. 'Buy me a drink?'

I looked at her. The dark eyes didn't waver. I motioned to the bartender, a sullen fat man who gazed on the world with a look of universal disapproval. He made her whatever the hell she was drinking. He needed most of the bottles on the back bar to do it. He put it in front of her and looked at me, and I held my glass aloft to show I was all right.

'I know him pretty good,' she said.

'Yeah? Does he ever smile?'

'I don't mean him, I mean Mickey Mouse.'

'Uh-huh.'

'Whattaya mean, "uh-huh"? He's a baby. When he grows up, then he can come see me. *If* he grows up.'

'Tell me about him.'

'What's to tell?' She sipped her drink. 'He gets in trouble showin' everybody how he's so tough and so smart. But he's not so tough, you know, and he's not so smart either.' Her mouth softened. 'He is nice-lookin', though. Always the nice clothes,

574

always the hair combed neat, always a fresh shave.' Her hand reached to stroke my cheek. 'Smooth, you know? And he's little, and he's cute, and you want to reach out and give him a hug, just wrap him up and take him home.'

'But you never did?'

She laughed again. 'Hey, man, I got all the troubles I need.'

'You figure him for trouble?'

'If I ever took him home,' she said, 'he'd be all the time thinkin', "Now how am I gonna get this bitch to let me put her on the street?"'

'He's a pimp? I never heard that.'

'If you're thinkin' about a pimp with the purple hat and the Eldorado, forget it.' She laughed. 'That's what Mickey Rat wishes he was. One time he hits on this new girl, she's fresh up from Santurce, from a village near Santurce, you know? Very green, and she's not Señorita Einstein to start with, you know? And he gets her to turn tricks for him, you know, workin' outta her apartment, seein' one or two guys a day, guys he finds and brings up to her.'

'"Hey, Joe, you wanna fock my seestair?"'

'You do one lousy PR accent, man. But you got the idea. She works about two weeks, you know, and she gets sick of it, and she takes the plane back to the island. And that's the story of Mickey the pimp.'

By then she needed another drink and I was ready for a beer myself. She had the bartender bring us a little bag of plantain chips and split the side seam so the chips spilled out on the bar between us. They tasted like a cross between potato chips and wood shavings.

Mickey Mouse's trouble, she told me, was how hard he worked trying to prove something. In high school he had proved his toughness by going into Manhattan with a couple of buddies, roaming the crooked streets of the West Village in search of homosexuals to beat up.

She said, 'He was the bait, you know? Small and pretty. And then when they got the guy, he was the guy who went crazy, almost wanted to kill him. Guys who went with him, first time they said he had heart, but later they started to say he had no brains.' She shook her head. 'So I never took him home,' she said. 'He's cute, but cute disappears when you turn the lights out, you know? I don't think he woulda done me much good.' She extended a painted nail, touched my chin. 'You don't want a man that's too cute, you know?'

It was an overture, and one I somehow knew I didn't want to follow up on. The realization brought a wave of sadness rolling in on me out of nowhere. I had nothing for this woman and she had nothing for me. I didn't even know her name; if we'd introduced ourselves I couldn't remember it. And I didn't think we had. The only names mentioned had been Miguelito Cruz and Mickey Mouse.

I mentioned another, Angel Herrera's. She didn't want to talk about Herrera. He was nice, she said. He was not so cute and maybe not so smart, but maybe that was better. But she didn't want to talk about Herrera.

I told her I had to go. I put a bill on the bar and instructed the bartender to keep her glass full. She laughed, either mocking me or enjoying the humor of the situation, I don't know which. Her laughter sounded like someone pouring a sack of broken glass down a staircase. It followed me to the door and out.

TWENTY

When I got back to my hotel there was a message from Anita and another from Skip. I called Syosset first, talked with Anita and the boys. I talked with her about money, saying I'd collected a fee and would be sending some soon. I talked with my sons about baseball, and about the camp they'd be going to soon.

I called Skip at Miss Kitty's. Someone else answered the phone and I held while they summoned him.

'I want to get together with you,' he said. 'I'm working tonight. You want to come by afterward?'

'All right.'

'What time is it now? Ten to nine? I've been on less than two hours? Feels like five. Matt, what I'll do, I'll close up around two. Come by then and we'll have a few.'

I watched the Mets. They were out of town. Chicago, I think. I kept my eyes on the screen but I couldn't keep my mind on the game.

There was a beer left over from the night before. I sipped at it during the game, but I couldn't work up much enthusiasm for it, either. After the game ended I watched about half of the newscast, then turned the set off and stretched out on the bed.

I had a paperback edition of *The Lives of the Saints*, and at one point I looked up Saint Veronica. I read that there was no great certainty that she had existed, but that she was supposed to have been a Jerusalem woman who wiped Christ's sweating face with a cloth while he was suffering on his way to Calvary, and that an image of his face remained on the cloth.

I pictured the act that had brought her twenty centuries of fame, and I had to laugh. The woman I was seeing, reaching out to soothe His brow, had the face and hairstyle of Veronica Lake.

*

577

Miss Kitty's was closed when I got there, and for a moment I thought that Skip had said the hell with it and gone home. Then I saw that the iron gates, though drawn, were not secured by a padlock, and that a low-wattage bulb glowed behind the bar. I slid the accordion gates open a foot or so and knocked, and he came and opened up for me, then rearranged the gates and turned the key in the door.

He looked tired. He clapped me on the shoulder, told me it was good to see me, led me to the end of the bar farthest from the door. Without asking he poured me a long drink of Wild Turkey, then topped up his own glass with scotch.

'First of the day,' I said.

'Yeah? I'm impressed. Of course the day's only two hours and ten minutes old.'

I shook my head. 'First since I woke up. I had some beer, but not too much of that, either.' I drank off some of my bourbon. It had a good bite to it.

'Yeah, well, I'm the same way,' he said. 'I have days when I don't drink. I even have days when I don't have so much as a beer. You know what it is? For you and me, drinking's something we choose to do. It's a choice.'

'There's mornings when I don't think it was the most brilliant choice I could have made.'

'Jesus, tell me about it. But even so it's a choice for us. That's the difference between you and me and a guy like Billie Keegan.'

'You think so?'

'Don't you? Matt, the man is always drinking. I mean take last night. All the rest of us, okay, we're pretty heavy drinkers, but we took it easy last night, right? Because it's sometimes appropriate and sometimes not. Am I right?'

'I guess.'

'Afterward, another story. Afterward a man wants to unwind, loosen up. But Keegan was shitfaced before we got there, for God's sake.'

'Then he turned out to be the hero.'

'Yeah, go figure that one. Uh, the plate number, did you –'

'Stolen.'

'Shit. Well, we figured that.'

'Sure.'

He drank some of his drink. 'Keegan,' he said '*has* to drink. For myself, I could stop anytime. I don't, because I happen to like what the stuff does for me. But I could stop anytime, and I figure you're the same.'

'Oh, I would think so.'

'Of course you are. Now Keegan, I don't know. I don't like to call the man an alcoholic –'

'That's a hell of a thing to call a man.'

'I agree with you. I'm not saying that's what he is, and God knows I like the man, but I think he's got a problem.' He straightened up. 'The hell with it. He could be a fucking Bowery bum, I still wish the car hadn't been stolen. C'mon back, we'll spread out and relax a little.'

In the office, with the two whiskey bottles on the desk between us, he leaned back in his chair and put his feet up.

'You checked the license number,' he said. 'So I guess you're already working on it.'

I nodded. 'I went out to Brooklyn, too.'

'Where? Not where we were last night?'

'The church.'

'What did you think you stood to learn there? You figure one of them left his wallet on the floor?'

'You never know what you'll find, Skip. You have to look around.'

'I suppose. I wouldn't know where to start.'

'You start anyplace. And do anything you think of.'

'You learn anything?'

'A few things.'

'Like what? Never mind, I don't want to be sitting on your shoulder while you do all this. You find out anything useful?'

'Maybe. You don't always know until later on what's useful and what isn't. You can look at it that everything you learn is useful. For instance, just knowing that the car was stolen tells me something, even if it doesn't tell me who was driving it.'

'At least you can rule out the owner. Now you know one person out of eight million couldn't have done it. Who was the owner? Some old lady, only drives it to bingo?'

'I don't know, but it was lifted from Ocean Parkway, not far from the clam bar they sent us to first.'

'Means they live out in Brooklyn?'

'Or they drove their own car out there, parked it and stole the one we saw. Or they went out on the subway or took a cab. Or –'

'So we don't know a whole lot.'

'Not yet.'

He leaned back with his hands behind his head. 'Bobby got another call-back on that commercial,' he said. 'The basketball referee in the fight against prejudice? He's got to go in again

579

tomorrow. It's now down to him and four other guys so they want to look at everybody again.'

'That's good, I guess.'

'How can you tell? You believe a profession like that, running your ass off and fighting the competition so you can be on the tube for twenty seconds. You know how many actors it takes to change a light bulb? Nine. One to climb up and replace it and eight others to stand around the ladder and say, 'That should be *me* up there!''

'That's not bad.'

'Well, credit where it's due, it was the actor told me the joke.' He touched up his drink, sat back in his chair. 'Matt, that was strange last night. That was fucking strange last night.'

'In the church basement.'

A nod. 'Those disguises of theirs. What they needed was Groucho noses and moustaches and glasses, you know the kind the kids wear. Because it was like that, the wigs and beards, they didn't even come close to looking real, but they weren't funny. The gun kept it from being funny.'

'Why'd they wear disguises?'

'So we wouldn't recognize them. Why does anybody wear a disguise?'

'Would you have recognized them?'

'I don't know, I didn't get to see them without the disguises. What are we here, Abbott and Costello?'

'I don't think they recognized us,' I said. 'When I went into the basement, one of them called out your name. It was dark, but they'd had time for their eyes to get used to it. You and I don't look alike.'

'I'm the pretty one.' He drew on his cigarette, blew out a great cloud of smoke. 'What are you getting at?'

'I don't know. I'm just wondering why they would bother with disguises if we didn't know them in the first place.'

'To make it harder to find them later, I suppose.'

'I guess. But why should they think we'd bother to look for them? There's not a hell of a lot we can do to them. We made a deal, traded money for your books. What did you wind up doing with the books, incidentally?'

'Burned them, like I said. And what do you mean, there's nothing we could do to them? We could murder them in their beds.'

'Sure.'

'Find the right church, take a shit on the altar, and tell

Dominic Tutto they did it. That has a certain charm, now that I think of it. Fix 'em up, get 'em a date with the Butcher. Maybe they wore disguises for the same reason they stole the car. Because they're pros.'

'They look familiar to you, Skip?'

'You mean looking past the wigs and beards and shit? I don't know that I could *see* past it. I didn't recognize the voices.'

'No.'

'There *was* something familiar about them, but I don't know what it was. The way they moved, maybe. That's it.'

'I think I know what you mean.'

'An economy of motion. You could almost say they were light on their feet.' He laughed. 'Call 'em up, see if they want to go dancing.'

My glass was empty. I poured a little bourbon into it, sat back, and sipped it slowly. Skip drowned his cigarette in a coffee cup and told me, inevitably, that he never wanted to see me do the same. I assured him he wasn't likely to. He lit another cigarette and we sat there in a comfortable silence.

After a while he said, 'You want to explain something to me, forget about disguises. Tell me why they shot the lights out.'

'To cover their exit. Give them a step or two on us.'

'You think they thought we were gonna come stampeding after them? Chase armed men through backyards and driveways?'

'Maybe they wanted it dark, thought they stood a better chance that way.' I frowned. 'All he had to do was take a step and flick the switch. You know the worst thing about the gunshots?'

'Yeah, they scared the shit out of me.'

'They drew heat. One thing a pro knows is you don't do anything that brings the cops. Not if you can help it.'

'Maybe they figured it was worth it. It was a warning: "Don't try to get even."'

'Maybe.'

'A little touch of the dramatic.'

'Maybe.'

'And God knows it was dramatic enough. When the gun was aimed at me I thought I was gonna get shot. I really did. Then when he shot up the ceiling instead I didn't know whether to shit or go blind. What's the matter?'

'Oh, for Christ's sake,' I said.

'What?'

'He pointed the gun at you and then he fired two shots into the ceiling.'

'Is that something we're supposed to have overlooked? What do you think we've been talking about?'

I held up a hand. 'Think a minute,' I said. 'I'd been thinking of him shooting out the lights, that's why I missed it.'

'Missed what? Matt, I don't –'

'Where have you been lately that somebody pointed a gun at someone but didn't shoot him? And fired two bullets into the ceiling?'

'Jesus Christ.'

'Well?'

'Jesus Christ on stilts. Frank and Jesse.'

'What do you think?'

'I don't know what I think. It's such a crazy thought. They didn't sound Irish.'

'How do we know they were Irish at Morrissey's?'

'We don't. I guess I assumed it. Those handkerchief masks, and taking the money for Northern Relief, and the whole sense that it was political. They had that same economy of movement, you know? The way they were so precise, they didn't take extra steps, they moved through that whole robbery like somebody choreographed it.'

'Maybe they're dancers.'

'Right,' he said. '*Ballet Desperadoes of '75*. I'm still trying to wrap my mind around all of this. Two clowns in red hankies take off the Morrissey brothers for fifty grand, and then they jack off me and Kasabian for – hey, it's the same amount. A subtle pattern begins to emerge.'

'We don't know what the Morrisseys lost.'

'No, and they didn't know what was gonna be in the safe, but a pattern's a pattern. I'll take it. What about their ears? You got pictures of their ears from last night. Are those the ears of Frank and Jesse?' He started to laugh. 'I can't believe the lines I'm speaking. "Are those the ears of Frank and Jesse?" Sentence sounds like it was translated from another language. Are they?'

'Skip, I never noticed their ears.'

'I thought you detectives are working all the time.'

'I was trying to figure out how to get out of the line of fire. If I was thinking of anything. They were fair-skinned, Frank and Jesse. And they were fair last night.'

'Fair and warmer. You see their eyes?'

'I didn't see the color.'

'I was close enough to see the eyes of the one who made the trade with me. But if I saw them I wasn't paying attention. Not that it makes any difference. Did either of them speak a word at Morrissey's?'

'I don't think so.'

He closed his eyes. 'I'm trying to remember. I think the whole thing was pantomime. Two gunshots and then silence until they were out the door and down the stairs.'

'That's how I remember it.'

He stood up, paced around the room. 'It's crazy,' he said. 'Hey, maybe we can stop looking for the viper in my bosom. We're not looking at an inside job. We're dealing with a daring gang of two who're specializing in taking off bars in Hell's Kitchen. You don't suppose that local Irish gang, what do they call them –'

'The Westies. No, we'd have heard. Or Morrissey would have heard. That reward of his would have smoked it out in a day if any of them had anything to do with it.' I picked up my glass and drank what was in it. God, it tasted good right now. We had them, I knew we did. I didn't know a single goddamned thing about them I hadn't known an hour ago but now I knew that I was going to bag them.

'That's why they wore disguises,' I said. 'Oh, they might have worn them anyway, but that's why they didn't want us to get a look at them. They made a mistake. We're going to get them.'

'Jesus, look at you, Matt. Like an old firehouse dog when the alarm goes off. How the hell are you going to get them? You still don't know who they are.'

'I know they're Frank and Jesse.'

'So? Morrissey's been trying to find Frank and Jesse for a long time. Fact he tried to get you to go looking for them. What gives you the edge now?'

I poured myself just one more little slug of the Wild Turkey. I said, 'When you plant a bug on a car and then you want to pick it up, you need two cars. One won't do it, but with two you can triangulate on the signal and home in on it.'

'I'm missing something.'

'It's not quite the same thing, but it's close. We've got them at Morrissey's, and we've got them in that church basement in Bensonhurst. That's two points of reference. Now we can home in on them, we can triangulate on their signal. Two bullets in the ceiling – it's their fucking trade-mark. You'd think they wanted to get caught, giving the job a signature like that.'

'Yeah, I feel sorry for 'em,' he said. 'I bet they're really shitting

in their pants. So far they only made a hundred grand this month. What they don't realize is Matt 'Bulldog' Scudder is on their trail, and the poor bastards won't get to spend a dime of it.'

TWENTY-ONE

The telephone woke me. I sat up, blinked at daylight. It went on ringing.

I picked it up. Tommy Tillary said, 'Matt, that cop was here. He came here, can you believe it?'

'Where?'

'The office, I'm at my office. You know him. At least he said he knew you. A detective, a very unpleasant man.'

'I don't know who you're talking about, Tommy.'

'I forget his name. He said –'

'What did he say?'

'He said the two of you were in my house together.'

'Jack Diebold.'

'That's it. He was right then? You were in my house together?'

I rubbed my temples, reached over and looked at my watch. It was a few minutes past ten. I tried to figure out when I'd gone to sleep.

'We didn't go there together,' I said. 'I was there, checking the setting, and he turned up. I used to know him years ago.'

It was no use. I couldn't remember anything after I'd assured Skip that Frank and Jesse were living on borrowed time. Maybe I went home right away, maybe I sat drinking with him until dawn. I had no way of knowing.

'Matt? He's been bothering Carolyn.'

'Bothering her?'

My door was bolted. That was a good sign. I couldn't have been in too bad shape if I'd remembered to bolt the door. On the other hand, my pants were tossed over the chair. It would have been better if they'd been hung in the closet. Then again, they weren't in a tangled heap on the floor, nor was I still wearing them. The great detective, sifting clues, trying to find out how bad he'd been last night.

'Bothering her. Called her a couple of times and went over to

her place once. Insinuating things, you know, like she's covering for me. Matt, all it's doing is upsetting Carolyn, plus it makes things awkward for me around the office.'

'I can see how it would.'

'Matt, I gather you knew him of old. Do you think you could get him to lay off me?'

'Jesus, Tommy, I don't see how. A cop doesn't ease up on a homicide investigation as a favor to an old friend.'

'Oh, I wouldn't suggest anything out of line, Matt. Don't get me wrong. But a homicide investigation is one thing and harassment's another, don't you agree?' He didn't give me a chance to answer. 'The thing is, the guy's got it in for me. He's got it in his head I'm a lowlife, and if you could just, you know, have a word with him. Tell him I'm good people.'

I tried to remember what I'd told Jack about Tommy. I couldn't recall, but I didn't think it amounted to much in the way of a character reference.

'And touch base with Drew, just as a favor to me, okay? He was asking me just yesterday what I'd heard from you, if you'd come up with anything. I know you're working hard for me, Matt, and we might as well let him know, too. Keep him in the picture, you know what I mean?'

'Sure, Tommy.'

After he hung up I chased two aspirins with a glass of water from the tap. I had a shower and was halfway through with my shave before I realized I'd virtually agreed to try to talk Jack Diebold into letting up on Tommy. For the first time I realized how good the son of a bitch must be at getting people to buy his real-estate syndications, or whatever the hell he was peddling. It was just as everybody said. He was very persuasive over the telephone.

Outside the day was clear, the sun brighter than it needed to be. I stopped at McGovern's for one quick one, just a bracer. I bought a paper from the bag lady on the corner, tossed her a buck and walked away wrapped in a fog of blessings. Well, I'd take her blessing. I could use all the help I could get.

I had coffee and an English muffin at the Red Flame and read the paper. It bothered me that I couldn't remember leaving Skip's office. I told myself I couldn't have been too bad because I didn't have all that bad of a hangover, but there wasn't necessarily any correlation there. Sometimes I awoke clear-headed and physically fit after a night of ugly drinking and a

large memory gap. Other times a hangover that kept me in bed all day would follow a night when I hadn't even felt drunk and nothing untoward had taken place, no memory lost.

Never mind. Forget it.

I ordered a refill on the coffee and thought about my discourse on triangulating on the two men we had taken to calling Frank and Jesse. I remembered the confidence I had felt and wondered what had become of it. Maybe I'd had a plan, maybe I'd come up with a brilliant insight and had known just how to track them down. I looked in my notebook on the chance that I'd written down a passing thought that I'd since forgotten. No such luck. There were no entries after I'd left the bar in Sunset Park.

But I did have that entry, notes on Mickey Mouse and his adolescent career as a fag-basher in the Village. So many working-class teenagers take up that sport, sure that they're acting on genuine outrage and confirming their manliness in the process, never realizing they're trying to kill a part of themselves they don't dare acknowledge. Sometimes they over-achieve, maiming or killing a gay man. I'd made a couple of arrests in cases like that, and on every occasion the boys had been astonished to find out that they were in genuine trouble, that we cops were not on their side, that they might actually go away for what they'd done.

I started to put my notebook away, then went over and put a dime in the phone instead. I looked up Drew Kaplan's number and dialed it. I thought of the woman who'd told me about Mickey Mouse, glad I didn't have to see her bright clothing on a morning like this one.

'Scudder,' I said, when the girl rang me through to Kaplan. 'I don't know if it helps, but I've got a little more proof that our friends aren't choirboys.'

Afterward I went for a long walk. I walked down Ninth Avenue, stopping at Miss Kitty's to say a quick hello to John Kasabian, but I didn't stay long. I dropped into a church on Forty-second Street, then continued on downtown, past the rear entrance of the Port Authority bus terminal, down through Hell's Kitchen and Chelsea to the Village. I walked through the meatpacking district and stopped at a butchers' bar on the corner of Washington and Thirteenth and stood among men in bloody aprons drinking shots with short beer chasers. I went outside and watched carcasses of beef and lamb suspended on steel

hooks, with flies buzzing around them in the heat of the midday sun.

I walked some more and got out of the sun to have a drink at the Corner Bistro on Jane and Fourth and another at the Cookie Bar on Hudson. I sat at a table at the White Horse and ate a hamburger and drank a beer.

Through all of this I kept running things through my mind.

I swear to God I don't know how anybody ever figures anything out, myself included. I'll watch a movie in which someone explains how he figured something out, fitting clues together until a solution appeared, and it will make perfect sense to me as I listen along.

But in my own work it is rarely like that. When I was on the force most of my cases moved toward solution (if they moved that way at all) in one of two ways. Either I didn't know the answer at all until a fresh piece of information made itself instantly evident, or I knew all along who had done whatever had been done, and all that was ever needed was sufficient evidence to prove it in court. In the tiny percentage of cases where I actually worked out a solution, I did so by a process I did not understand then and do not understand now. I took what I had and stared at it and stared at it and stared at it, and all of a sudden I saw the same thing in a new light, and the answer was in my hand.

Have you ever worked a jigsaw puzzle? And have you then been stuck for the moment, and kept taking up pieces and holding them this way and that, until finally you take up a piece you must have already held between thumb and forefinger a hundred times, one you've turned this way and that, fitted here and fitted there? And this time the piece drops neatly into place, it fits where you'd swear you tried it a minute ago, fits perfectly, fits in a way that should have been obvious all along.

I was at a table in the White Horse, a table in which someone had carved his initials, a dark brown table with the varnish wearing thin here and there. I had finished my hamburger, I had finished my beer, I was drinking a cup of coffee with a discreet shot of bourbon in it. Shreds and images flitted through my mind. I heard Nelson Fuhrmann talking about all the people with access to the basement of his church. I saw Billie Keegan draw a record from its jacket and place it on a turntable. I watched Bobby Ruslander put the blue whistle between his lips. I saw the yellow-wigged sinner, Frank or Jesse, grudgingly agree

to move furniture. I watched *The Quare Fellow* with Fran the nurse, walked with her and her friends to Miss Kitty's.

There was a moment when I didn't have the answer, and then there was a moment when I did.

I can't say I did anything to make this happen. I didn't work anything out. I kept picking up pieces of the puzzle, I kept turning them this way and that, and all of a sudden I had the whole puzzle, with one piece after another locking effortlessly and infallibly into place.

Had I thought of all this the night before, with all my thoughts unraveled in blackout like Penelope's tapestry? I don't really think so, although such is the nature of blackouts that I shall never be able to say with certainty one way or the other. Yet it almost felt that way. The answers as they came were so obvious – just as with a jigsaw puzzle, once the piece fits you can't believe you didn't see it right away. They were so obvious I felt as though I were discovering something I had known all along.

I called Nelson Fuhrmann. He didn't have the information I wanted, but his secretary gave me a phone number, and I managed to reach a woman who was able to answer some of my questions.

I started to phone Eddie Koehler, then realized I was only a couple of blocks from the Sixth Precinct, I walked over there, found him at his desk, and told him he had a chance to earn the rest of the hat I'd bought him the day before. He made a couple of telephone calls without leaving his desk, and when I left there I had a few more entries in my notebook.

I made phone calls of my own from a booth on the corner, then walked over to Hudson and caught a cab uptown. I got out at the corner of Eleventh Avenue and Fifty-first Street and walked toward the river. I stopped in front of Morissey's, but I didn't bang on the door or ring the bell. Instead I took a moment to read the poster for the theater downstairs. *The Quare Fellow* had finished its brief run. A play by John B. Keane was scheduled to open the following night. *The Man from Clare*, it was called. There was a photograph of the actor who was to play the leading role. He had wiry red hair and a haunted, brooding face.

I tried the door to the theater. It was locked. I knocked on it, and when that brought no response I knocked on it some more. Eventually it opened.

A very short woman in her mid-twenties looked up at me. 'I'm

sorry,' she said. 'The box office will be open tomorrow during the afternoon. We're shorthanded right now and we're in final rehearsals and –'

I told her I hadn't come to buy tickets. 'I just need a couple minutes of your time,' I said.

'That's all anybody ever needs, and there's not enough of my time to go around.' She said the line airily, as if a playwright had written it for her. 'I'm sorry,' she said more matter-of-factly. 'It'll have to be some other time.'

'No, it'll have to be now.'

'My god, what is this? You're not the police, are you? What did we do, forget to pay somebody off?'

'I'm working for the fellow upstairs,' I said, gesturing. 'He'd want you to cooperate with me.'

'Mr Morrisey?'

'Call Tim Pat and ask him, if you want. My name is Scudder.'

From the rear of the theater, someone with a rich brogue called out, 'Mary Jean, what in Christ's fucking name is taking you so long?'

She rolled her eyes, sighed, and held the door open for me.

After I left the Irish theater I called Skip at his apartment and looked for him at his saloon. Kasabian suggested I try the gym.

I tried Armstrong's first. He wasn't there, and hadn't been in, but Dennis said someone else had. 'A fellow was looking for you,' he told me.

'Who?'

'He didn't leave his name.'

'What did he look like?'

He considered the question. 'If you were choosing up sides for a game of cops and robbers,' he said thoughtfully, you would not pick him to be one of the robbers.'

'Did he leave a message?'

'No. Or a tip.'

I went to Skip's gym, a large open second-floor loft on broadway over a delicatessen. A bowling alley had gone broke there a year or two earlier, and the gym had the air of a place that wouldn't outlast the term of its lease. A couple of men were working out with free weights. A black man, glossy with sweat, struggled with bench presses while a white partner spotted him. On the right, a big man stood flat-footed, working the heavy bag with both hands.

I found Skip doing pulldowns on the lat machine. He was

wearing gray sweat pants and no shirt and he was sweating fiercely. The muscles worked in his back and shoulders and upper arms. I stood a few yards off watching while he finished a set. I called his name, and he turned and saw me and smiled in surprise, then did another set of pulldowns before rising and coming over to take my hand.

He said, 'What's up? How'd you find me here?'

'Your partner's suggestion.'

'Well, your timing's good. I can use a break. Let me get my cigarettes.'

There was an area where you could smoke, a couple of armchairs grouped around a water cooler. He lit up and said, 'It helps, working out. I had a head and a half when I woke up. We kicked it around last night, didn't we? You get home all right?'

'Why, was I in bad shape?'

'No worse'n I was. You were feeling pretty good. The way you were talking, Frank and Jesse had their tits in the wringer and you were ready to start cranking.'

'You think I was a little optimistic?'

'Hey, that's okay.' He drew on his Camel. 'Me, I'm starting to feel human again. You get the blood moving, sweat out some of the poison, it makes a difference. You ever work with weights, Matt?'

'Not in years and years.'

'But you used to?'

'Oh, a hundred years ago I thought I might like to box a little.'

'You serious? You used to duke it out?'

'This was in high school. I started hanging out at the Y gym, lifting a little, training. Then I had a couple of PAL fights and I found out I didn't like getting hit in the face. And I was clumsy in the ring, and I *felt* clumsy, and I didn't like that.'

'So you got a job where they let you carry a gun instead.'

'And a badge and a stick.'

He laughed. 'The runner and the boxer,' he said. 'Look at them now. You came up here for a reason.'

'Uh-huh.'

'And?'

'I know who they are.'

'Frank and Jesse? You're kidding.'

'No.'

'Who are they? And how did you manage it? And –'

'I wondered if we could get the crew together tonight. After closing time, say.'

'The crew? Who do you mean?'

'Everybody we had with us chasing around Brooklyn the other night. We need some manpower, and there's no point involving new people.'

'We need manpower? What are we going to do?'

'Nothing tonight, but I'd like to hold a war council. If that's all right with you.'

He jabbed his cigarette into an ashtray. 'All right with me?' he said. 'Of course it's all right with me. Who do you want, the Magnificent Seven? No, there were five of us. The Magnificent Seven Minus Two. You, me, Kasabian, Keegan and Ruslander. What's tonight, Wednesday? Billie'll close around one-thirty if I ask him nice. I'll call Bobby, I'll talk to John. You really know who they are?'

'I really do.'

'I mean do you know specifically or –'

'The whole thing,' I said. 'Names, addresses, the works.'

'The whole shmear. So who are they?'

'I'll come by your office around two.'

'You fuck. Suppose you get hit by a bus between now and then?'

'Then the secret dies with me.'

'You prick. I'm gonna do some bench presses. You want to try a set of bench presses, just sort of warm up your muscles?'

'No,' I said. 'I want to go have a drink.'

I didn't have the drink. I looked into one bar but it was crowded, and when I got back to my hotel Jack Diebold was sitting in a chair in the lobby.

I said, 'I figured it was you.'

'What, the Chinese bartender describe me?'

'He's Filipino. He said a fat old man who didn't leave a tip.'

'Who tips at bars?'

'Everybody.'

'Are you serious? I tip at tables, I don't tip standing up at a bar. I didn't think anybody did.'

'Oh, come on. Where have you been doing your drinking, the Blarney Stone? The White Rose?'

He looked at me. 'You're in a funny mood,' he said. 'Bouncy, peppy.'

'Well, I'm right in the middle of something.'

'Oh?'

'You know how it is when it all falls into place and things break apart for you? I had an afternoon like that.'

'We're not talking about the same case, are we?'

I looked at him. 'You haven't been talking about anything,' I said. 'What case are you – oh, Tommy, Christ. No, I'm not talking about that. There's nothing there to crack.'

'I know.'

I remembered how my day had started. 'He called me this morning,' I said. 'To complain about you.'

'Did he now.'

'You're harassing him, he said.'

'Yeah, and a hot lot of good it's doing me.'

'I'm supposed to give you a character reference, tell you he's really good people.'

'Is that right. Well, is he really good people?'

'No, he's an asshole. But I could be prejudiced.'

'Sure. After all, he's your client.'

'Right.' During all of this he had gotten up from his chair and the two of us had walked to the sidewalk in front of the hotel. At the curb, a cabdriver and the driver of a florist's delivery van were having an argument.

I said, 'Jack, why'd you come looking for me today?'

'Happened to be in the neighborhood and I thought of you.'

'Uh-huh.'

'Oh, hell,' he said. 'I wondered if you had anything.'

'On Tillary? There's not going to be anything on him, and if I found it – he *is* my client.'

'I meant did you find anything on the Spanish kids.' He sighed. 'Because I'm starting to get worried that we're gonna lose that one in court.'

'Seriously? You've got them admitting to the burglary.'

'Yeah, and if they plead to burglary that's the end of it. But the DA's office wants to go for some kind of homicide charge, and if it goes to trial I could see losin' the whole thing.'

'You've got stolen goods ID'd with serial numbers found in their residence, you've got fingerprints, you've –'

'Aw, shit,' he said. 'You know what can happen in a courtroom. All of a sudden the stolen goods isn't evidence anymore because there's some technicality about the search, they found a stolen typewriter when they were only empowered to search for a stolen adding machine, whatever the hell it was. And the fingerprints, well, the one was over there months ago hauling trash for Tillary, that would account for the prints,

593

right? I can see a smart lawyer kicking holes in a solid case. And I just thought, well, if you ran into something good, I'd like to know about it. And it helps your client if it locks up Cruz and Herrera, right?'

'I suppose so. But I haven't got anything.'

'Not a thing?'

'Not as far as I can see.'

I wound up taking him to Armstrong's and buying us both a couple of drinks. I tipped Dennis a pound just for the pleasure of seeing Jack's reaction. Then I went back to my hotel and left a call at the desk for one in the morning, and set my alarm clock for insurance.

I took a shower and sat on the edge of my bed, looking out at the city. The sky was darkening, turning that cobalt blue it shows all too briefly.

I lay down, stretched out, not really expecting to sleep. The next thing I knew the phone was ringing, and I had no sooner answered it and hung it up again than my clock sounded. I put on my clothes, splashed a little cold water on my face, and went out to earn my money.

TWENTY-TWO

When I got there they were still waiting for Keegan. Skip had the top of a file cabinet set up as a bar, with four or five bottles and some mix and a bucket of ice cubes. A Styrofoam ice chest on the floor was full of cold beer. I asked if there was any coffee left. Kasabian said there was probably some in the kitchen, and he came back with an insulated plastic pitcher full of coffee and a mug and some cream and sugar. I poured myself black coffee, and I didn't put any booze in it for the time being.

I took a sip of the coffee and there was a knock on the door out front. Skip answered it and came back with Billie. 'The late Billie Keegan,' Bobby said, and Kasabian fixed him a drink of the same twelve-year-old Irish Billie drank at Armstrong's.

There was a lot of banter, joking back and forth. Then it all died down at once, and before it could start up again I stood up and said, 'Something I wanted to talk to all of you about.'

'Life insurance,' Bobby Ruslander said. 'I mean, have you guys thought about it? I mean, like, really *thought* about it?'

I said, 'Skip and I were talking last night, and we came up with something. The two guys with the wigs and beards, we realized we'd seen them before. A couple of weeks ago, they were the ones who stuck up Morrissey's after-hours.'

'They wore handkerchief masks,' Bobby said. 'And last night they wore wigs and beards *and* masks, so how could you tell?'

'It was them,' Skip said. 'Believe it. Two shots into the ceiling? Remember?'

'I don't know what you're talking about,' Bobby said.

Billie said, 'Bobby and I only saw 'em Monday night from a distance, and you didn't see 'em at all, did you, John? No, of course not, you were around the block. And were you at Morrissey's the night of the holdup? I don't recall seeing you there.'

Kasabian said he never went to Morrissey's.

'So the three of us got no opinion,' Billie went on. 'If you say it was the same two guys, I say fine. Is that it? Because unless I missed something, we still don't know who they are.'

'Yes we do.'

Everybody looked at me.

I said, 'I got very cocky last night, telling Skip here that we had them, that once we knew they pulled both jobs it was only a question of zeroing in on them. I think that was mostly some Wild Turkey talking, but there was a certain amount of truth in it, and today I got lucky. I know who they are. Skip and I were right last night, the same pair did pull both jobs, and I know who they are.'

'So where do we go from here?' Bobby wanted to know. 'What do we do now?'

'That comes later,' I said. 'First I'd like to tell you who they are.'

'Let's hear.'

'Their names are Gary Atwood and Lee David Cutler,' I said. 'Skip calls them Frank and Jesse, as in the James brothers, and he may have been picking up on a family resemblance. Atwood and Cutler are cousins. Atwood lives in the East Village, way over in Alphabet City on Ninth Street between B and C. Cutler lives with his girlfriend. She's a schoolteacher and she lives in Washington Heights. Her name is Rita Donegian.'

'An Armenian,' Keegan said. 'She must be a cousin of yours, John. The plot thickens.'

'How'd you find them?' Kasabian wondered. 'Have they done this before? Have they got records?'

'I don't think they have records,' I said. 'That's something I haven't checked yet because it didn't seem important. They probably have Equity cards.'

'Huh?'

'Membership cards in Actors Equity,' I said. 'They're actors.'

Skip said, 'You're kidding.'

'No.'

'I'll be a son of a bitch. It fits. It fucking fits.'

'You see it?'

'Of course I see it,' he said. 'That's why the accents. That's why they seemed Irish when they hit Morrissey's. They didn't make a sound, they didn't *do* anything Irish, but it felt Irish because they were acting.' He turned and glared at Bobby Ruslander. 'Actors,' he said. 'I been robbed by fucking *actors*.'

'You were robbed by two actors,' Bobby said. 'Not by the entire profession.'

'Actors,' Skip said. 'John, we paid fifty thousand dollars to a couple of actors.'

'They had real bullets in their guns,' Keegan reminded him.

'Actors,' Skip said. 'We shoulda paid off in stage money.'

I poured out more coffee from the insulated pitcher. I said, 'I don't know what made me think of it. The thought was just there. But once I had it, I could see a lot of places it could have come from. One was a general impression, there was something off about them, some sense that we were getting a performance. And there was the very different performance at Morrissey's compared to the one staged for us Monday night. Once we knew it was the same two men both times, the difference in their manner became noteworthy.'

'I don't see how that makes them actors,' Bobby said. 'It just makes them phonies.'

'There were other things,' I said. 'They moved like people who were professionally conscious of movement. Skip, you commented that they could have been dancers, that their movements might have been choreographed. And there was a line one of them said, and it was so out of character it could only be *in* character – in character for the person if not for the role he was playing.'

Skip said, 'Which line was that? Was I there to hear it?'

'In the church basement. When you and the one in the yellow wig moved the extra furniture out of the way.'

'I remember. What did he say?'

'Something about not knowing whether the union would approve.'

'Yeah, I remember him saying it. It was an odd line but I didn't pay attention.'

'Neither did I, but it registered. And his voice was different when he delivered it, too.'

He closed his eyes, thinking back. 'You're right,' he said.

Bobby said, 'How does that make him an actor? All it makes him is a union member.'

'The stagehands have a very strong union,' I said, 'and they make sure actors don't move scenery or do other similar jobs that would properly employ a stagehand. It was very much an actor's line and the delivery fit with that interpretation.'

'How'd you get on to them in particular?' Kasabian asked.

'Once you got that they were actors, you were still a long way from knowing their names and addresses.'

'Ears,' Skip said.

Everybody looked at him.

'He drew their ears,' he said, pointing to me. 'In his notebook. The ears are the hardest part of the body to disguise. Don't look at me, I got it from the horse's mouth. He made drawings of their ears.'

'And did what?' Bobby demanded. 'Advertised an open audition and looked at everybody's ears?'

'You could go through albums,' Skip said. 'Look at actors' publicity pictures, looking for the right pair of ears.'

'When they take your picture for your passport,' Billie Keegan said, 'it has to show both your ears.'

'Or what?'

'Or they won't give you a passport.'

'Poor Van Gogh,' Skip said. 'The Man Without a Country.'

'How did you find them?' Kasabian still wanted to know. 'It couldn't have been ears.'

'No, of course not,' I said.

'The license number,' Billie said. 'Has everyone forgotten the license number?'

'The license number turned up on the hot-car sheet,' I told him. 'Once I got the idea that they were actors, I took another look at the church. I knew they hadn't just picked that particular church basement at random and broken into it. They had access to it, probably with a key. According to the pastor, there were a lot of community groups with access, and probably a great many keys in circulation. One of the groups he mentioned in passing was an amateur theater group that had used the basement room for auditions and rehearsals.'

'Aha,' someone said.

'I called the church, got the name of someone connected with the theater group. I managed to reach that person and explained that I was trying to contact an actor who had worked with the group within the past several months. I gave a physical description that would have fit either of the two men. Remember, aside from a two-inch difference in height, they were very similar in physical type.'

'And did you get a name?'

'I got a couple of names. One of them was Lee David Cutler.'

'And a bell rang,' Skip said.

598

'What bell?' Kasabian said. 'That was the first the name came up, wasn't it? Or am I missing something?'

'No, you're right,' I told him. 'At this point Cutler was just one of several names in my notebook. What I had to do was tie one of those names to the other crime.'

'What other crime? Oh, Morrissey's. How? He's the one saloonkeeper doesn't hire out-of-work actors as waiters and bartenders. He's got his own family to work with.'

I said, 'What's on the ground floor, Skip?'

'Oh,' he said.

Billie Keegan said, 'That Irish theater. The Donkey Repertory Company or whatever they call it.'

'I went there this afternoon,' I said. 'They were in final rehearsals for a new play, but I managed to drop Tim Pat's name and get a few minutes of one young woman's time. They have display posters in the lobby, individual promotional pictures of each cast member. Head shots, I think they're called. She showed me posters for the various casts of the plays they've staged over the past year. They do short runs, you know, so they've put on quite a few shows.'

'And?'

'Lee David Cutler was in *Donnybrook*, a Brian Friel play that ran the last week of May and the first week of June. I recognized his picture before I saw the name under it. And I recognized his cousin's picture, too. The family resemblance is even stronger when they're not wearing disguises. In fact it's unmistakable. Maybe that helped them get the parts, since they're not regular members of the rep company. But they played two brothers, so the resemblance was a definite asset.'

'Lee David Cutler,' Skip said. 'And what was the other one's name? Something Atwood.'

'Gary Atwood.'

'Actors.'

'Right.'

He tapped a cigarette on the back of his hand, put it in his mouth, lit it. 'Actors. They were in the play on the ground floor and decided to move up in the world, is that it? Being there gave them the idea to hit Morrissey's.'

'Probably.' I took a slug of coffee. The Wild Turkey bottle was right there on the file cabinet, and my eyes were drawn to it, but right now I didn't want anything to take the edge off my perceptions. I was glad I wasn't drinking, and just as glad that everyone else was.

I said, 'They must have had a drink upstairs once or twice in the course of the run of the play. Maybe they heard about the locked wall cupboard, maybe they saw Tim Pat but money into it or take some out of it. One way or another, it must have occurred to them that the place would be easy pickings.'

'If you live to spend it.'

'Maybe they didn't know enough to be afraid of the Morrisseys. That's possible. They probably started planning the job as a lark, making a play out of it, casting themselves as members of some other Irish faction, silent gunmen out of some old play about the Troubles. Then they got carried away with the possibilities of it, went out and got some guns and staged their play.'

'Just like that.'

I shrugged. 'Or maybe they've pulled stickups before. There's no reason to assume Morrissey's was their debut.'

'I suppose it beats walking people's dogs and working office temp,' Bobby said. 'The hell, an actor's got to make a living. Maybe I ought to get myself a mask and a gun.'

'You tend bar sometimes,' Skip said. 'It's the same idea and you don't need props for it.'

'How'd they get on to us?' Kasabian asked. 'Did they start hanging out here while they were working at the Irish theater?'

'Maybe.'

'But that wouldn't explain how they knew about the books,' he said. 'Skip, did they ever work for us? Atwood and Cutler? Do we know those names?'

'I don't think so.'

'I don't either,' I said. 'They may have known the place, but it's not important. They almost certainly didn't work here because they didn't know Skip by sight.'

'That could have been part of the act,' Skip suggested.

'Possibly. As I said, it doesn't really matter. They had an inside man who stole the books and arranged for them to ransom them.'

'An inside man?'

I nodded. 'That's what we figured from the beginning, remember? That's why you hired me, Skip. Partly to see that the exchange went off without a hitch and partly to find out after the fact who it was that set you up.'

'Right.'

'Well, that's how they got the books, and that's how they got on to you in the first place. For all I know they never set foot

inside Miss Kitty's. They didn't have to. They had it all set up for them.'

'By an inside man.'

'That's right.'

'And you know who the inside man was?'

'Yes,' I said. 'I know.'

The room got very quiet. I walked around the desk and took the bottle of Wild Turkey from the top of the file cabinet. I poured a couple of ounces into a rocks glass and put the bottle back. I held the glass without tasting the whiskey. I didn't want the drink so much as I wanted to stretch the moment and let the tension build.

I said, 'The inside man had a role to play afterward, too. He had to let Atwood and Cutler know that we got their license number.'

Bobby said, 'I thought the car was stolen.'

'The car was reported stolen. That's how it got on the hot-car sheet. Stolen between five and seven p.m. Monday from an address on Ocean Parkway.'

'So?'

'That was the report, and at the time I let it go at that. This afternoon I did what I probably should have done off the bat, and I got the name of the car's owner. It was Rita Donegian.'

'Atwood's girlfriend,' Skip said.

'Cutler's. Not that it makes a difference.'

'I'm confused,' Kasabian said. 'He stole his girlfriend's car? I don't get it.'

'Everyone picks on the Armenians,' Keegan said.

I said, 'They took her car. Atwood and Cutler took Rita Donegian's car. Afterward they got a call from their accomplice telling them that the plate had been spotted. So they called in then and reported it as having been stolen, and they said it had been taken thus and so many hours earlier, and from an address way out on Ocean Parkway. When I dug a little deeper this afternoon I managed to establish that the report of the theft hadn't been called in until close to midnight.

'I've got things a little out of sequence. The hot-car sheet didn't carry the name of the Mercury's owner as Rita Donegian. It was an Irish name, Flaherty or Farley, I forget, and the address was the one on Ocean Parkway. There was a phone number, but it turned out to be wrong, and I couldn't pick up any listing for the Flaherty or Farley name at that address. So I checked Motor Vehicles, working from the plate number, and the car's

owner turned out to be Rita Donegian with an address on Cabrini Boulevard, which is way up in Washington Heights and a long ways from Ocean Parkway or any other part of Brooklyn.'

I drank some of the Wild Turkey.

'I called Rita Donegian,' I said. 'I represented myself as a cop checking the hot-car sheet automatically, making sure what cars have been recovered and what ones are still missing. Oh, yes, she said, they got the car back right away. She didn't think it was really stolen after all; her husband had a few drinks and forgot where he parked it, then found it a couple blocks away after she'd gone and reported it stolen. I said we must have made a clerical error, we had the car listed as stolen in Brooklyn and here she was in upper Manhattan. No, she said, they were visiting her husband's brother in Brooklyn. I said we had an error in the name, too, that it was Flaherty, whatever the hell it was. No, she said, that was no error, that was the brother's name. Then she got a little rattled and explained it was her husband's brother-in-law, actually, that her husband's sister had married a man named Flaherty.'

'A poor Armenian girl,' Keegan said, 'gone to ruination with the Irish. Think of it, Johnny.'

Skip said, 'Was any of what she said true?'

'I asked her if she was Rita Donegian and if she was the owner of a Mercury Marquis with the license number LJK914. She said yes to both of those questions. That was the last time she told me the truth. She told a whole string of lies, and she knew she was covering for them or she'd never have been so inventive. She hasn't got a husband. She might refer to Cutler as her husband but she was calling him Mr Donegian, and the only Mr Donegian is her father. I didn't want to push too hard because I didn't want her to get the idea that my call was anything beyond simple routine.'

Skip said, 'Somebody called them *after* the payoff. To tell them we had the plate number.'

'That's right.'

'So who knew? The five of us and who else? Keegan, did you get waxed and tell a roomful of people how you were the hero and wrote down the plate number? Is that what happened?'

'I went to confession,' Billie said, 'and I told Father O'Houlihan.'

'I'm serious, goddammit.'

'I never did trust the shifty-eyed bastard,' Billie said.

Gently, John Kasabian said, 'Skip, I don't think anybody told anybody. I think that's what Matt's leading up to. It was one of us, wasn't it, Matt?'

Skip said, 'One of us? One of us *here!*'

'Wasn't it, Matt?'

'That's right,' I said. 'It was Bobby.'

TWENTY-THREE

The silence stretched, with everybody looking at Bobby. Then Skip let out a fierce laugh that caromed wildly around the room.

'Matt, you fuck,' he said. 'You had me going there. You just about had me buying it.'

'It's true, Skip.'

'Because I'm an actor, Matt?' Bobby grinned at me. 'You figure all actors know each other, the way Billie figured Kasabian would have to know the schoolteacher. For Christ's sake, there's probably more actors in this town than there are Armenians.'

'Two much-maligned groups,' Keegan intoned. 'Actors and Armenians, both of them much given to starving.'

'I never heard of these guys,' Bobby said. 'Atwood and Cutler? Are those their names? I never heard of either of them.'

I said, 'It won't wash, Bobby. You were in classes with Gary Atwood at the New York Academy of Dramatic Arts. You were in a showcase at the Galinda Theater on Second Avenue last year, and that was one of Lee David Cutler's credits.'

'You're talking about that Strindberg thing? Six performances to a roomful of empty seats and not even the director knew what the play was supposed to be about? Oh, that was Cutler, the thin guy who played Berndt? Is that who you mean?'

I didn't say anything.

'The Lee threw me. Everybody called him Dave. I suppose I remember him but –'

'*Bobby, you son of a bitch, you're lying!*'

He turned, looked at Skip. He said, 'Am I, Arthur? Is that what you think?'

'It's what I fucking know. I know you, I know you all my life. I know when you're lying.'

'The Human Polygraph.' He sighed. 'Happens you're right.'

'I don't believe it.'

604

'Well, make up your mind, Arthur. You're a hard man to agree with. Either I'm lying or I'm not. Which way do you want it?'

'You robbed me. You stole the books, you sold me down the fucking river. How could you do it? You little fuck, how could you do it?'

Skip was standing up. Bobby was still sitting in his chair, an empty glass in his hand. Keegan and John Kasabian were on either side of Bobby, but they drew a little ways away from him during this exchange, as if to give them room.

I was standing to Skip's right, and I was watching Bobby. He took his time with the question, as if it deserved careful consideration.

'Well, hell,' he said finally. 'Why would anybody do it? I wanted the money.'

'How much did they give you?'

'Not all that much, tell you the truth.'

'How much?'

'I wanted, you know, a third. They laughed. I wanted ten, they said five, we wound up at seven grand.' He spread his hands. 'I'm a lousy negotiator. I'm an actor, I'm not a businessman. What do I know about haggling?'

'You screwed me for seven thousand dollars.'

'Listen, I wish it was more. Believe me.'

'Don't joke with me, you cocksucker.'

'Then don't feed me straight lines, you asshole.'

Skip closed his eyes. The sweat was beading up on his forehead and tendons showed in his neck. His hands knotted into fists, relaxed, knotted up again. He was breathing through his mouth like a fighter between rounds.

He said, 'Why'd you need the money?'

'Well, see, my kid sister needs this operation, and –'

'Bobby, don't clown with me. I'll fucking kill you, I swear it.'

'Yeah? I needed the money, believe it. I was gonna need the operation. I was gonna get my legs broken.'

'What the hell are you talking about?'

'I'm talking about I borrowed five thousand dollars and put it into a cocaine deal and it fell in the shit, and I had to pay back the five because I didn't borrow it from Chase Manhattan. I haven't got that good of a friend there. I borrowed it from a guy out in Woodside who told me my legs were all the collateral I'd need.'

'What the hell were you doing in a coke deal?'

'Trying to make a dollar for a change. Trying to get out from under.'

'You make it sound like the American Dream.'

'It was a fucking nightmare. The deal went in the toilet, I still owed the money, I had to come up with a hundred a week just to keep paying the vig. You know how it works. You pay a hundred a week forever and you still owe the five grand, and I can't cover my expenses to begin with, never mind finding another hundred a week. I was running behind, and there's interest on the interest, and the seven grand I got from Cutler and Atwood, it's fucking *gone*, man. I paid the shy six grand to get him off my back forever. I paid some other debts I owed, I got a couple hundred dollars in my wallet. That's what's left.' He shrugged. 'Easy come, easy go. Right?'

Skip put a cigarette in his mouth and fumbled with his lighter. He dropped it, and when he reached to pick it up he accidentally kicked it under the desk. Kasabian put a hand on his shoulder to steady him, then lit a match and gave him a light. Billie Keegan got down on the floor and looked around until he found the lighter.

Skip said, 'You know what you cost me?'

'I cost you twenty grand. I cost John thirty.'

'You cost us each twenty-five. I owe Johnny five, he knows he'll get it.'

'Whatever you say.'

'You cost us fifty thousand fucking dollars so you could wind up with seven. What am I talking about? You cost us fifty thousand dollars so you could wind up even.'

'I said I got no head for business.'

'You got no head at all, Bobby. You needed money, you could have sold your friends to Tim Pat Morrissey for ten grand. That's the reward he was offering, that's three thousand more than they gave you.'

'I wasn't gonna rat 'em out.'

'No, of course not. But you'd sell me'n John down shit creek, wouldn't you?'

Bobby shrugged.

Skip dropped his cigarette on the floor, stepped on it. 'You needed money,' he said, 'why didn't you come and ask me for it? Will you just tell me that? You coulda come to me before you went to the shy. Or the shy's pushing you, you need money to cover, you could of come to me then.'

'I didn't want to ask you for the money.'

'You didn't want to ask me for it. It's okay to steal it from me, but you didn't want to ask me for it.'

Bobby drew back his head. 'Yeah, that's right, Arrrr-thur. I didn't want to ask you for it.'

'Did I ever refuse you?'

'No.'

'Did I ever make you crawl?'

'Yeah.'

'When?'

'All the time. Let the actor play bartender for a while. Let's put the actor behind the stick, hope he don't give away the whole store. It's a big joke, my acting. I'm your little windup toy, your fucking pet actor.'

'You don't think I take your acting seriously?'

'Of course you don't.'

'I can't believe I'm hearing this. That piece of shit you were in on Second Avenue, fucking Strindberg, how many people did I bring to see that? There was twenty-five people in the house and I brought twenty of them.'

'To see your pet actor. 'That piece of shit you were in.' That's taking my acting seriously, Skippy baby. That's real support.'

'I don't fucking believe this,' Skip said. 'You hate me.' He looked around the room. 'He hates me.'

Bobby just looked at him.

'You did this to screw me. That's all.'

'I did it for the money.'

'*I woulda given you the fucking money!*'

'I didn't want to take it from you.'

'You didn't want to take it from me. Where do you think you did take it from, you cocksucker? You think it came from God? You think it rained outta the sky?'

'I figure I earned it.'

'You what?'

Bobby shrugged. 'Like I said. I figure I earned it. I worked for it. I was with you, I don't know how many times, from the day I took the books. I was along for the ride Monday night, on the scene, everything. And you never had the least suspicion. That's not the worst job of acting anybody ever did.'

'Just an acting job.'

'You could look at it that way.'

'Judas was pretty good, too. He got an Oscar nomination but he couldn't be present at the awards ceremony.'

'You make a funny-looking Jesus, Arthur. You're just not right for the part.'

Skip stared hard at him. 'I don't get it,' he said. 'You're not even ashamed of yourself.'

'Would that make you happy? A little show of shame?'

'You think it's okay, right? Putting your best friend through hell, costing him a lot of money? Stealing from him?'

'You never stole, right, Arthur?'

'What are you talking about?'

'How'd you come up with twenty grand, Arthur? What did you do, save your lunch money?'

'We skimmed it. That's not much of a secret. You mean I stole from the government? Show me anybody with a cash business who doesn't.'

'And how did you get the money to open the joint? How did you and John get started? Did you skim that, too? Tips you didn't declare?'

'So?'

'Bullshit! You worked behind the stick at Jack Balkin's joint and you stole with both hands. You did everything but take the empties to the grocery store for the deposit. You stole so much offa Jack it's a wonder he didn't have to close the place.'

'He made money.'

'Yeah, and so did you. You stole, and Johnny stole where he was working, and lo and behold, the two of you got enough to open a place of your own. Talk about the American Dream, that's the American Dream. Steal from the boss until you can afford to open up in competition with him.'

Skip said something inaudible.

'What's that? I can't hear you, Arthur.'

'I said bartenders steal. It's expected.'

'Makes it honest, right?'

'I didn't screw Balkin. I made money for him. You can twist it all you want, Bobby, you can't make me into what you are.'

'No, you're a fucking saint, Arthur.'

'Jesus,' Skip said. 'I don't know what to do. I don't know what I'm going to do.'

'I do. You're not gonna do anything.'

'I'm not?'

Bobby shook his head. 'What are you gonna do? You gonna get the gun from behind the bar, come back and shoot me with it? You're not gonna do that.'

'I ought to.'

'Yeah, but it's not gonna happen. You want to hit me? You're not even mad anymore, Arthur. You think you oughta be mad but you don't feel it. You don't feel anything.'

'I –'

'Listen, I'm beat,' Bobby said. 'I'm gonna make it an early night if nobody objects. Listen, guys, I'll pay it back one of these days. The whole fifty thousand. When I'm a star, you know? I'm good for it.'

'Bobby –'

'I'll see you,' he said.

After the three of us had walked Skip around the corner and said goodnight to him, after John Kasabian had flagged a cab and headed uptown, I stood on the corner with Billie Keegan and told him I'd made a mistake, that I shouldn't have told Skip what I'd learned.

'No,' he said. 'You had to.'

'Now he knows his best friend hates his guts.' I turned, looked up at the Parc Vendome. 'He lives on a high floor,' I said. 'I hope he doesn't decide to go out a window.'

'He's not the type.'

'I guess not.'

'You had to tell him,' Billie Keegan said. 'What are you gonna do, let him go on thinking Bobby's his friend? That kind of ignorance isn't bliss. What you did, you lanced a boil for him. Right now it hurts like a bastard but it'll heal. You leave it, it just gets worse.'

'I suppose.'

'Count on it. If Bobby got by with this he'd do something else. He'd keep on until Skip knew about it, because it's not enough to screw Skip, Bobby's gotta rub his nose in it while he's at it. You see what I mean?'

'Yeah.'

'Am I right?'

'Probably. Billie? I want to hear that song.'

'Huh?'

'The sacred ginmill, cuts the brain in sections. The one you played for me.'

'"Last Call."'

'You don't mind?'

'Hey, come on up. We'll have a couple.'

We didn't really drink much. I went with him to his apartment and he played the song five, six times for me. We

talked a little, but mostly we just listened to the record. When I left he told me again that I'd done the right thing in exposing Bobby Ruslander. I still wasn't sure he was right.

TWENTY-FOUR

I slept late the next day. That night I went out to Sunnyside Gardens in Queens with Danny Boy Bell and two uptown friends of his. There was a middleweight on the card, a Bedford-Stuyvesant kid Danny Boy's friends had an interest in. He won his fight handily, but I didn't think he showed a whole lot.

The following day was Friday, and I was having a late lunch in Armstrong's when Skip came in and had a beer with me. He'd just come from the gym and he was thirsty.

'Jesus, I was strong today,' he said. 'All the anger goes right into the muscles. I could have lifted the roof off the place. Matt? Did I patronize him?'

'What do you mean?'

'All that shit about I made him my pet actor. Was that true?'

'I think he was just looking for a way to justify what he did.'

'I don't know,' he said. 'Maybe I do what he said. Remember you got a hair up your ass when I paid your bar tab?'

'So?'

'Maybe I did that with him. But on a bigger scale.' He lit a cigarette, coughed hard. Recovering, he said, 'Fuck it, the man's a scumbag. That's all. I'm just gonna forget about it.'

'What else can you do?'

'I wish I knew. He'll pay me back when he's rich and famous, I liked that part. Is there any way we can get the money back from those other two fucks? We know who they are.'

'What can you threaten them with?'

'I don't know. Nothing, I guess. The other night you gathered everybody together for a war council, but that was just setting the stage, wasn't it? To have everybody on hand when you put it all on Bobby.'

'It seemed like a good idea.'

'Yeah. But as far as having a war council, or whatever you

want to call it, and figuring out a way to sandbag those actors and get the money back –'

'I can't see it.'

'No, neither can I. What am I gonna do, stick up the stickup men? Not really my style. And the thing is, it's only money. I mean that's really all it is. I had this money in the bank, where I wasn't really getting anything out of it, and now I haven't got it, and what difference does it make in my life? You know what I mean?'

'I think so.'

'I just wish I could let go of it,' he said, 'because I go around and around and around with it in my mind. I just wish I could leave it alone.'

I had my sons with me that weekend. It was going to be our last weekend together before they went off to camp. I picked them up at the train station Saturday morning and put them back on the train Sunday night. We saw a movie, I remember, and I think we spent Sunday morning exploring down around Wall Street and the Fulton Fish Market, but that may have been a different weekend. It's hard to distinguish them in memory.

I spent Sunday evening in the Village and didn't get back to my hotel until almost dawn. The telephone woke me out of a frustrating dream, an exercise in acrophobic frustration; I kept trying to descend from a perilous catwalk and kept not reaching the ground.

I picked up the phone. A gruff voice said, 'Well, it's not the way I figured it would go, but at least we don't have to worry about losing it in court.'

'Who is this?'

'Jack Diebold. What's the matter with you? You sound like you're half asleep.'

'I'm up now,' I said. 'What were you talking about?'

'You haven't seen a paper?'

'I was sleeping. What did –'

'You know what time it is? It's almost noon. You're keeping pimp's hours, you son of a bitch.'

'Jesus,' I said.

'Go get yourself a newspaper,' he said. 'I'll call you in an hour.'

The *News* gave it the front page. KILL SUSPECT HANGS SELF IN CELL, with the story on page three.

Miguelito Cruz had torn his clothing into strips, knotted the

strips together, stood his iron bedstead on its side, climbed onto it, looped his homemade rope around an overhead pipe, and jumped off the upended bedstead and into the next world.

Jack Diebold never did call me back, but that evening's six o'clock TV news had the rest of the story. Informed of his friend's death, Angel Herrera had recanted his original story and admitted that he and Cruz had conceived and executed the Tillary burglary on their own. It had been Miguelito who heard noises upstairs and picked up a kitchen knife on his way to investigate. He'd stabbed the woman to death while Herrera watched in horror. Miguelito always had a short temper, Herrera said, but they were friends, even cousins, and they had concocted their story to protect Miguelito. But now that Miguelito was dead, Herrera could admit what had really happened.

The funny thing was that I felt like going out to Sunset Park. I was done with the case, everyone was done with the case, but I felt as though I ought to be working my way through the Fourth Avenue bars, buying rum drinks for ladies and eating bags of plantain chips.

Of course I didn't go there. I never really considered it. I just had the feeling that it was something I ought to do.

That night I was in Armstrong's. I wasn't drinking particularly hard or fast, but I was working at it, and then somewhere around ten-thirty or eleven the door opened and I knew who it was before I turned around. Tommy Tillary, all dressed up and freshly barbered, was making his first appearance in Armstrong's since his wife got herself killed.

'Hey, look who's back,' he sang out, and grinned that big grin. People rushed over to shake his hand. Billie was behind the stick, and he'd no sooner set up one on the house for our hero than Tommy insisted on buying a round for the bar. It was an expensive gesture, there must have been thirty or forty people in there, but I don't think he cared if there were three or four hundred.

I stayed where I was, letting the others mob him, but he worked his way over to me and got an arm around my shoulders. 'This is the man,' he announced. 'Best fucking detective ever wore out a pair of shoes. This man's money,' he told Billie, 'is no good at all tonight. He can't buy a drink, he can't buy a cup of coffee, and if you went and put in pay toilets since I was last here, he can't use his own dime.'

'The john's still free,' Billie said, 'but don't go giving Jimmy any ideas.'

'Oh, don't tell me he didn't already think of it,' Tommy said. 'Matt, my boy, I love you. I was in a tight spot, the world was lookin' to fall in on me, and you came through for me.'

What the hell had I done? I hadn't hanged Miguelito Cruz or coaxed a confession out of Angel Herrera. I hadn't even set eyes on either man. But I had taken his money, and now it looked as though I had to let him buy my drinks.

I don't know how long we stayed there. Curiously, my own drinking slowed even as Tommy's picked up speed. I wondered why he hadn't brought Carolyn; I didn't figure he'd care much about appearances now that the case was closed forever. And I wondered if she would walk in. It was, after all, her neighborhood bar, and she'd been known to come to it all by herself.

After a while Tommy was hustling me out of Armstrong's, so maybe I wasn't the only one who realized that Carolyn might turn up. 'This is celebration time,' he told me. 'We don't want to hang around one place until we grow roots. We want to get out and bounce a little.'

He had the Riviera, and I just went along for the ride. We hit a few places. There was a noisy Greek place on the East Side where the waiters all looked like mob hit men. There were a couple of trendy singles joints, including the one Jack Balkin owned, where Skip had reportedly stolen enough money to open Miss Kitty's. There was, finally, a dark beery cave down in the Village; I realized after a while that it reminded me of the Norwegian bar in Sunset Park, the Fjord. I knew the Village bars fairly well in those days, but this place was new to me, and I was never able to find it again. Maybe it wasn't in the Village, maybe it was somewhere in Chelsea. He was doing the driving and I wasn't paying too much attention to the geography.

Wherever the place was, it was quiet for a change and conversation became possible. I found myself asking him what I'd done that deserved such lavish praise. One man had killed himself and another had confessed, and what part had I played in either incident?

'The stuff you came up with,' he said.

'What stuff? I should have brought back fingernail parings, you could have had someone work voodoo on them.'

'About Cruz and the fairies.'

'He was up for murder. He didn't hang himself because he was

afraid they'd nail him for fag-bashing when he was a juvenile offender.'

Tommy took a sip of scotch. He said, 'Couple days ago, black guy comes up to Cruz in the chow line. Huge spade, built like the Seagram's Building. "Wait'll you gets up to Green Haven," he tells him. "Every blood there's gwine have you for a girlfriend. Doctor gwine have to cut you a brand-new asshole, time you gets outta there."'

I didn't say anything.

'Kaplan,' he said. 'Talked to somebody who talked to somebody, and that did it. Cruz took a good look at the idea of playin' Drop the Soap for half the jigs in captivity, and the next thing you know the murderous little bastard was dancing on air. And good riddance to him.'

I couldn't seem to catch my breath. I worked on it while Tommy went to the bar for another round. I hadn't touched the one in front of me but I let him buy for both of us.

When he got back I said, 'Herrera.'

'Changed his story. Made a full confession.'

'And pinned the killing on Cruz.'

'Why not? Cruz wasn't around to complain. Cruz probably did it, but who knows which one it really was, and for that matter who cares? The thing is you gave us the lever.'

'For Cruz,' I said. 'To get him to kill himself.'

'And for Herrera. Those kids of his back in Puerto Rico. Drew spoke to Herrera's lawyer and Herrera's lawyer spoke to Herrera, and the message was, look, you're going up for burglary whatever you do, and probably for murder, but if you tell the right story you'll draw shorter time than if you don't, and on top of that, that nice Mr Tillary's gonna let bygones by bygones and every month there's a nice check for your wife and kiddies back home in Santurce.'

At the bar, a couple of old men were reliving the Louis-Schmeling fight. The second one, the one where Louis deliberately punished the German champion. One of the old boys was throwing roundhouse punches in the air, demonstrating.

I said, 'Who killed your wife?'

'One or the other of them. If I had to bet I'd say Cruz. He had those beady little eyes, you looked at him up close and got that he was a killer.'

'When did you look at him close?'

'When they were over to the house. The first time, when they

615

cleaned the basement and the attic. I told you they hauled stuff
for me?'

'You told me.'

'Not the second time,' he said, 'when they cleaned me out
altogether.'

He smiled broadly, but I kept looking at him until the smile
turned uncertain. 'That was Herrera who helped around the
house,' I said. 'You never met Cruz.'

'Cruz came along, gave him a hand.'

'You never mentioned that before.'

'I must of, Matt. Or I left it out. What difference does it make,
anyway?'

'Cruz wasn't much for manual labor,' I said. 'He wouldn't
come along to haul trash. When did you ever get a look at his
eyes?'

'Jesus Christ. Maybe it was seeing a picture in the paper,
maybe I just have a sense of him as if I saw his eyes. Leave it
alone, will you? Whatever kind of eyes he had, they're not
seeing anything anymore.'

'Who killed her, Tommy?'

'Hey, didn't I say let it alone?'

'Answer the question.'

'I already answered it.'

'You killed her, didn't you?'

'What are you, crazy? And keep your voice down, for Christ's
sake. There's people can hear you.'

'You killed your wife.'

'Cruz killed her and Herrera swore to it. Isn't that enough for
you? And your fucking cop friend's been all over my alibi,
pickin' at it like a monkey hunting lice. There's no way I coulda
killed her.'

'Sure there is.'

'Huh?'

A chair covered in needlepoint, a view of Owl's Head Park.
The smell of dust, and layered over it the smell of a spray of
little white flowers.

'Lily-of-the-valley,' I said.

'Huh?'

'That's how you did it.'

'What are you talking about?'

'The third floor, the room her aunt used to live in. I smelled
her perfume up there. I thought I was just carrying the scent in
my nostrils from being in her bedroom earlier, but that wasn't it.

616

She was up there, and it was traces of her perfume I was smelling. That's why the room held me, I sensed her presence there, the room was trying to tell me something but I couldn't get it.'

'I don't know what you're talking about. You know what you are, Matt? You're a little drunk is all. You'll wake up tomorrow and –'

'You left the office at the end of the day, rushed home to Bay Ridge, and stowed her on the third floor. What did you do, drug her? You probably slipped her a mickey, maybe left her tied up in the room on the third floor. Tied her up, gagged her, left her unconscious. Then you got your ass back to Manhattan and went out to dinner with Carolyn.'

'I'm not listening to this shit.'

'Herrera and Cruz showed up around midnight, just the way you arranged it. They thought they were knocking off an empty house. Your wife was gagged and tucked away on the third floor and they had no reason to go up there. You probably locked the door there anyway just to make sure. They pulled their burglary and went home, figuring it was the safest and easiest illegal buck they ever turned.'

I picked up my glass. Then I remembered he had bought the drink, and I started to put it down. I decided that was ridiculous. Just as money knows no owner, whiskey never remembers who paid for it.

I took a drink.

I said, 'Then a couple hours after that you jumped in your car and raced back to Bay Ridge again. Maybe you slipped something into your girlfriend's drink to keep her out of it. All you had to do was find an hour, hour and a half, and there's room enough in your alibi to find ninety spare minutes. The drive wouldn't take you long, not at that hour. Nobody would see you drive in. You just had to go up to the third floor, carry your wife down a flight, stab her to death, get rid of the knife, and drive back into the city. That's how you did it, Tommy. Isn't it?'

'You're full of shit, you know that?'

'Tell me you didn't kill her.'

'I already told you.'

'Tell me again.'

'I didn't kill her, Matt. I didn't kill anybody.'

'Again.'

'What's the matter with you? I didn't kill her. Jesus, you're the

one helped prove it, and now you're trying to twist and turn it back on me. I swear to Christ I didn't kill her.'

'I don't believe you.'

A man at the bar was talking about Rocky Marciano. There was the best fighter ever lived, he said. He wasn't pretty, he wasn't fancy, but it was a funny thing, he was always on his feet at the end of the fight and the other guy wasn't.

'Oh, Jesus,' Tommy said.

He closed his eyes, put his head in his hands. He sighed and looked up and said, 'You know, it's a funny thing with me. Over the phone I'm as good a salesman as Marciano was a fighter. I'm the best you could ever imagine. I swear I could sell sand to the Arabs, I could sell ice in the winter, but face-to-face I'm just no good at all. Wasn't for phones, I'd have trouble making a living selling. Why do you figure that is?'

'You tell me.'

'I swear I don't know. I used to think it was my face, around the eyes and mouth, *I* don't know. Over the phone's a cinch. I'm talkin' to a stranger, I don't know who he is or what he looks like, and he's not lookin' at me, and there's nothing to it. Face-to-face, somebody I know, whole different story.' He looked at me, his eyes not quite meeting mine. 'If we were doin' this over the phone, you'd buy what I'm telling you.'

'It's possible.'

'It's fucking certain. Word for word, you'd buy the package. Matt, suppose for the sake of argument I said I killed her. It was an accident, it was an impulse, we were both upset over the burglary, I was half in the bag, and –'

'You planned the whole thing, Tommy. It was all set up and worked out.'

'The whole story you told, the way you worked it all out, there's not a thing you can prove.'

I didn't say anything.

'And you helped me, don't forget that part of it.'

'I won't.'

'And I wouldn'ta gone away for it anyway, with or without you, Matt. It wouldn'ta got to court, and if it did I'da beat it in court. All you saved is a hassle. And you know something?'

'What?'

'All we got tonight is the booze talking, your booze and my booze, two bottles of whiskey talkin' to each other. That's all. Morning comes, we can forget everything was said here tonight.

618

I didn't kill anybody, you didn't say I did, everything's cool, we're still buddies. Right? Right?'

I just looked at him.

TWENTY-FIVE

That was Monday night. I don't remember exactly when I talked to Jack Diebold, but it must have been Tuesday or Wednesday. I tried him at the squad room and wound up reaching him at home. We sparred a bit, and then I said, 'You know, I thought of a way he could have done it.'

'Where have you been? We got one dead and one confessed to it, it's history now.'

'I know,' I said, 'but listen to this.' And I explained, just as an exercise in applied logic, how Tommy Tillary could have murdered his wife. I had to go over it a couple of times before he got a handle on it, and even then he wasn't crazy about it.

'I don't know,' he said. 'It sounds pretty complicated. You've got her stuck there in the attic for what, eight, ten hours? That's a long time with no one keeping an eye on her. Suppose she comes to, works herself free? Then he's got his ass in the crack, doesn't he?'

'Not for murder. She can press charges for tying her up, but when's the last time a husband went to jail for that?'

'Yeah, he's not really at risk until he kills her, and by then she's dead. I see what you mean. Even so, Matt, it's pretty farfetched, don't you think?'

'Well, I was just thinking of a way it could have happened.'

'They never happen that way in real life.'

'I guess not.'

'And if they did you couldn't go anywheres with it. Look what you went through explaining it to me, and I'm in the business. You want to try it on a jury, with some prick lawyer interrupting every thirty seconds with an objection? What a jury likes, a jury likes somebody with greasy hair and olive skin and a knife in one hand and blood on his shirt, that's what a jury likes.'

'Yeah.'

620

'And anyhow, the whole thing's history. You know what I got now? I got that family in Borough Park. You read about it?'

'The Orthodox Jews?'

'Three Orthodox Jews, mother father son, the father's got the beard, the kid's got the earlocks, all sitting at the dinner table, all shot in the back of the head. That's what I got. Far as Tommy Tillary, I don't care right now if he killed Cock Robin and both Kennedys.'

'Well, it was just an idea,' I said.

'And it's a cute one, I'll grant you that. But it's not very realistic, and even if it was, who's got time for it? You know?'

I figured it was time for a drink. My two cases were closed, albeit unsatisfactorily. My sons were on their way to camp. My rent was paid, my bar tabs were all settled, and I had a few dollars in the bank. I had, it seemed to me, every reason in the world to check out for a week or so and stay drunk.

But my body seemed to know there was more to come, and while I did not by any means stay sober, neither did I find myself launched upon the bender to which I felt roundly entitled. And, a day or two later, I was nursing a cup of bourbon-flavored coffee at my table in Armstrong's when Skip Devoe came in.

He gave me a nod from the doorway. Then he went to the bar and had a quick drink, knocking it back while he stood there. And then he came back to my table and pulled out a chair and dropped down into it.

'Here,' he said, and put a brown manila envelope on the table between us. A small envelope, the kind they give you in banks.

I said, 'What's this?'

'For you.'

I opened it. It was full of money. I took out a sheaf of bills and fanned them.

'For Christ's sake,' he said, 'don't do that, you want everybody following you home? Put it in your pocket, count it when you get home.'

'What is it?'

'Your share. Put it away, will you?'

'My share of what?'

He sighed, impatient with me. He had a cigarette going and he dragged angrily on it, turning his head to avoid blowing the smoke in my face. 'Your share of ten grand,' he said. 'You get half. Half of ten grand is five grand, and five grand is what's in

the envelope, and whyntcha do us both a favor and put it the hell away?'

'What's this my share of, Skip?'

'The reward.'

'What reward?'

His eyes challenged me. 'Well, I could get something back, couldn't I? No way I owed those cocksuckers anything. Right?'

'I don't know what you're talking about.'

'Atwood and Cutler,' he said. 'I turned 'em in to Tim Pat Morrissey. For the reward.'

I looked at him.

'I couldn't go to them, ask for the money back. I couldn't get a dime from fuckin' Ruslander, he already paid it all out. I went over and sat down with Tim Pat, asked him did he and his brothers still want to pay out that reward. His eyes lit up like fucking stars. I gave him names and addresses and I thought he was gonna kiss me.'

I put the brown envelope on the table between us. I pushed it toward him and he pushed it back. I said, 'This doesn't belong to me, Skip.'

'Yes it does. I already told Tim Pat half of it was yours, that you did all the work. Take it.'

'I don't want it. I already got paid for what I did. The information was yours. You bought it. If you sold it to Tim Pat, you get the reward.'

He drew on his cigarette. 'I already gave half of it to Kasabian. The five grand I owed him. He didn't want to take it either. I told him, listen, you take this and we're, square. He took it. And this here is yours.'

'I don't want it.'

'It's money. What the hell's the matter with it?'

I didn't say anything.

'Look,' he said, 'just take it, will you? You don't want to keep it, don't keep it. Burn it, throw it out, give it away, I don't give a shit what you do with it. Because I cannot keep it. I can't. You understand?'

'Why not?'

'Oh, shit,' he said. 'Oh, fucking shit. I don't know why I did it.'

'What are you talking about?'

'And I'd do it again. That's what's crazy. It's eating me up, but if I had to do it all over again, I'd fucking do it.'

'Do what?'

He looked at me. 'I gave Tim Pat three names,' he said, 'and three addresses.'

He took his cigarette between thumb and forefinger, stared at it. 'I never want to see you do this,' he said, and dropped the butt into my cup of coffee. Then he said, 'Oh, Jesus, what am I doing? You had half a cup of coffee left there. I was thinking it was my cup and I didn't even have a cup. What's the matter with me? I'm sorry, I'll get you another cup of coffee.'

'Forget the coffee.'

'It was just reflex, I wasn't thinking, I –'

'Skip, forget the coffee. Sit down.'

'You sure you don't want –'

'Forget the coffee.'

'Yeah, right,' he said. He took out another cigarette and tapped it against the back of his wrist.

I said, 'You gave Tim Pat three names.'

'Yeah.'

'Atwood and Cutler and –'

'And Bobby,' he said. 'I sold him Bobby Ruslander.'

He put the cigarette in his mouth, took out his lighter and lit it. His eyes half-lidded against the smoke, he said, 'I ratted him out, Matt. My best friend, except it turns out he's not my friend, and now I went and ratted him out. I told Tim Pat how Bobby was the inside man, he set it up.' He looked at me. 'You think I'm a bastard?'

'I don't think anything.'

'It was something I had to do.'

'All right.'

'But you can see I can't keep the money.'

'Yeah, I guess I can see that.'

'He could get out from under, you know. He's pretty good at squirming off the hook. The other night, Christ, he walked outta the office at my joint like he owned the place. The Actor, let's see him act his way outta this, huh?' I didn't say anything.

'It could happen. He could pull it off.'

'Could be.'

He wiped his eyes with the back of his hand. 'I loved the man,' he said. 'I thought, I thought he loved me.' He took a deep breath, let it out. 'From here on in,' he said, 'I don't love nobody.' He stood up. 'I figure he's got a sporting chance, anyway. Maybe he'll get out of it.'

'Maybe.'

*

623

But he didn't. None of them did. By the weekend they had all turned up in the newspapers, Gary Michael Atwood, Lee David Cutler, Robert Joel Ruslander, all three found in different parts of the city, their heads covered with black hoods, their hands secured with wire behind their backs, each shot once in the back of the head with a .25-caliber automatic. Rita Donegian was found with Cutler, similarly hooded and wired and shot. I guess she got in the way.

When I read about it I still had the money in the brown bank envelope. I still hadn't decided what to do with it. I don't know that I ever quite came to a conscious decision, but the following day I tithed five hundred dollars to the poor box at Saint Paul's. I had, after all, a lot of candles to light. And some of the money went to Anita, and some went in the bank, and somewhere along the line it stopped being blood money and became, well, just money.

I figured that was the end of it. But I kept figuring that, and I kept being wrong.

The call came in the middle of the night. I'd been asleep for a couple of hours but the phone woke me and I groped for it. It took me a minute to recognize the voice on the other end.

It was Carolyn Cheatham.

'I had to call you,' she said, 'on account of you're a bourbon drinker and a gentleman. I owed it to you to call you.'

'What's the matter?'

'Our mutual friend ditched me,' she said, 'and he got me fired out of Tannahill & Co. so he won't have to look at me around the office. Once he didn't need me he just went and cut the string, and do you know he did it over the *phone?*'

'Carolyn –'

'It's all in the note,' she said. 'I'm leaving a note.'

'Look, don't do anything yet,' I said. I was out of bed, fumbling for my clothes. 'I'll be right over. We'll sit down and talk about it.'

'You can't stop me, Matthew.'

'I won't try to stop you. We'll talk a little, and then you can do whatever you want to do.'

The phone clicked in my ear.

I threw my clothes on, rushed over there, hoping it would be pills, something that took its time. I broke a small pane of glass in the downstairs door and let myself in, then used an old credit card to slip the bolt of her spring lock. If she had engaged the

dead-bolt lock, I would have had to kick it in, but she hadn't, and that made it easier.

I smelled the cordite before I had the door open. Inside, the room reeked of it. She was sprawled on the couch, her head hanging to one side. The gun was still in her hand, limp at her side, and there was a black-rimmed hole in her temple.

There was a note, too, one page torn from a spiral notebook and anchored to the coffee table with an empty bottle of Maker's Mark bourbon. There was an empty glass next to the empty bottle. The booze showed in her handwriting, and in the sullen phrasing of the suicide note.

I read the note. I stood there for a few minutes, not for very long, and then I got a dish towel from the kitchen and wiped the bottle and the glass. I took another matching glass, rinsed it out and wiped it, and put it in the dish strainer on the counter.

I stuffed the note in my pocket. I took the little gun from her fingers, checked routinely for a pulse, then wrapped a sofa pillow around the gun to muffle its report.

I fired one round into the soft tissue below the rib cage, another into her open mouth.

I dropped the gun into a pocket and got out of there.

They found the gun in Tommy Tillary's house on Colonial Road, stuffed between the cushions of the living-room sofa. The outside of the gun had been wiped clean of prints, but they found an identifiable print inside, on the clip, and it turned out to be Tommy's.

Ballistics got a perfect match. Bullets can shatter when they hit bone, but the shot into her abdomen didn't hit any bones and it was recovered intact.

After the story made the papers, I picked up the phone and called Drew Kaplan. 'I don't understand it,' I said. 'He was free and clear, why the hell did he go and kill the girl?'

'Ask him yourself,' Kaplan said. He did not sound happy. 'You want my opinion, he's a lunatic. I honestly didn't think he was. I figured maybe he killed his wife, maybe he didn't, not my job to try him, right? But I didn't figure the son of a bitch for a homicidal maniac.'

'There's no question he killed the girl?'

'No question that I can see. The gun's pretty strong evidence. Talk about finding somebody with the smoking pistol in his hand, here it was in Tommy's couch. The idiot.'

'Funny he kept it.'

'Maybe he had other people he wanted to shoot. Go figure a crazy man. No, the gun's damning evidence, and there was a phone tip, some man called in the shooting, reported a man running out of the building and gave a description that fitted Tommy better than his clothes. In fact his clothes were in the description. Had him wearing that red blazer of his, tacky thing makes him look like an usher at the old Brooklyn Paramount.'

'It sounds tough to square.'

'Well, somebody else'll have to try to do it,' Kaplan said. 'I told him it wouldn't be appropriate for me to defend him this time. What it amounts to, I wash my hands of him.'

I thought of all this when I read that Angel Herrera got out just the other day. He did all ten years of a five-to-ten because he was at least as good at getting into trouble inside the walls as he had been outside.

Somebody killed Tommy Tillary with a homemade knife after he'd served two years and three months of a manslaughter stretch. I wondered at the time if that was Herrera getting even, and I don't suppose I'll ever know. Maybe the checks stopped going to Santurce and Herrera took it the wrong way. Or maybe Tommy made the wrong remark to some other hard case, and did it face-to-face instead of over the phone.

So many things have changed, so many people are gone.

Antares & Spiro's, the Greek bar on the corner, is gone. It's a Korean fruit store now. Polly's Cage is now Cafe 57, changed from sleazy to chic, with the red flocked wallpaper and the neon parrot long gone. The Red Flame is gone, and the Blue Jay. There's a steak house called Desmond's where McGovern's used to be. Miss Kitty's closed about a year and a half after they bought their books back. John and Skip sold the lease and got out. The new owners opened a gay club called Kid Gloves, and two years later it was out and something else was in.

The gym where I watched Skip do lat-machine pulldowns went out of business within the year. A modern-dance studio took over the premises, and then a couple of years ago the whole building came down and a new one went up. Of the two side-by-side French restaurants, the one where I had dinner with Fran is gone, and the latest tenant is a fancy Indian restaurant. The other French place is still there, and I still haven't eaten there.

So many changes.

Jack Diebold is dead. A heart attack. He was dead six months

626

before I even heard about it, but then we didn't have much contact after the Tillary incident.

John Kasabian left the city after he and Skip sold Miss Kitty's. He opened up a similar joint out in the Hamptons, and I heard he got married.

Morrissey's closed late in '77. Tim Pat skipped bail on a federal gunrunning charge and his brothers disappeared. The ground-floor theater is still running, oddly enough.

Skip is dead. He sort of hung around after Miss Kitty's closed, spending more and more of his time by himself in his apartment. Then one day he got an attack of acute pancreatitis and died on the table at Roosevelt.

Billie Keegan left Armstrong's in early '76, if I remember it right. Left Armstrong's and left New York, too. The last I heard he was off the drink entirely, living north of San Francisco and making candles or silk flowers or something equally unlikely. And I ran into Dennis a month or so ago in a bookstore on lower Fifth Avenue, full of odd volumes on yoga and spiritualism and holistic healing.

Eddie Koehler retired from the NYPD a couple of years back. I got cards from him the first two Christmases, mailed from a little fishing village in the Florida panhandle, I didn't hear from him last year, which probably only means that he's dropped me from his list, which is what happens to people who don't send cards in return.

Jesus, where did ten years go? I've got one son in college now, and another in the service. I couldn't tell you the last time we went to a ball game together, let alone a museum.

Anita's remarried. She still lives in Syosset, but I don't send money there anymore.

So many changes, eating away at the world like water dripping on a rock. For God's sake, last summer the sacred ginmill closed, if you want to call it that. The lease on Armstrong's came up for renewal and Jimmy walked away from it, and now there's yet another goddamned Chinese restaurant where the old joint used to be. He reopened a block farther west, at the corner of Fifty-seventh and Tenth, but that's a little out of my way these days.

In more ways than one. Because I don't drink anymore, one day at a time, and thus have no business in ginmills, be they sacred or profane. I spend less of my time lighting candles and more in church basements, drinking my coffee without bourbon, and out of styrofoam cups.

627

So when I look ten years into the past I can say that I would very likely have handled things differently now, but everything is different now. Everything. All changed, changed utterly. I live in the same hotel, I walk the same streets, I go to a fight or a ball game the same as ever, but ten years ago I was always drinking and now I don't drink at all. I don't regret a single one of the drinks I took, and I hope to God I never take another.

Because that, you see, is the less-traveled road on which I find myself these days, and it has made all the difference. Oh, yes. All the difference.

THE OFFICIAL FOOTB

C000199553

NON-LEAGUE
CLUB
DIRECTORY
2003

(25th Edition)

EDITOR TONY WILLIAMS

Ladbrokes

ISBN 0 9539111 2 8

Published by Tony Williams Publications Ltd. under license from Greenways Media Ltd.

Printed by Westpoint Printing Co. Ltd, Birmingham

Typesetting by Nina Whatmore and George Brown

All distributing queries to Pat Vaughan
Tel: 01823 490080 or 01458 241592

Front Cover Photo: Carl Alford's spectacular goal to give Yeovil Town
the lead in the FA Trophy Final at Villa Park.
Photo: Roger Turner

FOREWORD

Although this edition of our Directory is a very special twenty-fifth it has been extremely difficult to prepare. The Non-League Media Plc had been floated on the Stock Exchange in 2000 and I had sold them the publishing rights for the book for five years.

In the first two years the book sold well, but sadly internal company problems with nothing to do with football took its toll and the company was soon in administration.

Happily a new consortium has bought out 'The Non-League Paper' and this superb publication will continue to give non-League football terrific coverage every Sunday of the year. The Directory will be compiled, published, marketed and sold by Tony Williams Publications under license from Greenways Media Ltd. for the next three issues.

The final dealings of 'the Administrators' continued on into October so sadly this year's Directory had to be printed later than usual, but once again my thanks go to the vast majority of clubs, leagues and county officials who have co-operated to let us know their changes of personnel and statistics.   T.W.

ACKNOWLEDGEMENTS

I have mentioned the problem of the ill fated 'Non-League Media Plc' in the foreword, but thankfully the response from club, league and county officials has been as helpful, warm and positive as ever.

We do appreciate all the congratulations and thanks for the last twenty-four books, but sadly although this is the twenty-fifth non-league annual publication that we have produced, the circumstances may not allow too many celebrations!

Our loyal band of photographers have carried on and as you will see their contributions are a special part of this book. Once again my sincere thanks goes to them all:

Peter Barber, Peter Barnes, Graham Brown, Paul Carter, Andrew Chitty, Keith Clayton, Alan Coomes, Graham Cotterill, Paul Dennis, Tim Edwards, Keith Gillard, Ken Gregory, Tim Lancaster, Garry Letts, Peter Lirettoc, Eric Marsh, Dennis Nicholson, Francis Short, Colin Stevens, Neil Thaler, Darren Thomas, Roger Thomas, Roger Turner, Alan Watson, Bill Wheatcroft, Gordon Whittington and Martin Wray,

Much appreciated contributors supplying information for the specialist section are the Wales F.A., Stewart Davidson (Editor of the Scottish Non-League Review - Contact 0141 5662 5721). Jen O'Neill, Keith Masters, Dave Phillips, Mike Simmonds, Mike Ford, Mike Amos, A.J. Sarnecki, Wally Goss, Mike Brown and Mike Wilson.

Two special helpers in recent years have been John Anderson (F.A. Trophy - F.A. Vase and F.A. Cup Statistics) and Arthur Evans (match reports and photos) and while life had been a little insecure in recent months we especially appreciated the help and loyalty of all the aforementioned contributors.

Two of non-league football's most knowledgable and experienced journalists are James Wright and Steve Whitney and once again their contributions have been invaluable.The typesetting has again been painstakingly undertaken to great effect by George Brown in house and Nina Whatmore and protecting me from the phone and most of the nasty office jobs has been Jenny Gullick.

My thanks go to the whole team!   T.W.

3

Long Service -
some 'real football people' who have been with us all the way

While browsing through the old directories I noted some names consistently featuring in their respective club sections and I wondered just how many had held the same position with the same clubs during our twenty-five year span.

For example Frank Parr has seen Buscough develop into a strong Unibond Premier Division club as chairman and I am sure he must have been pleased with attracting such managers as John Davison and Shaun Teale.

I hadn't realised that C.B. or Ben Robinson had been at the helm of Burton Albion for the whole period so what a thrill for him to see Nigel Clough taking his boys up to the Conference

Derek Nutthall now holds a unique position at Northwich Victoria as Football Secretary/President and he has been associated with the Conference for its whole history as the Vics are one of just two `ever presents' in the competition.

Secretary Chris Gay at Chertsey Town has been with the club through some ups and downs,but certainly enjoyed the period of Isthmian Premier Football when his club were a match for any at the Trophy level. In the same league has been Oxford City's John Shepherd who actually weathered a period of rebuilding when the club lost its Isthmian place. He is back with a lovely new ground and flourishing club.

Another Isthmian club is Staines Town whose Ken Ballard is back after a spell away, as their manager who has been at the helm in European competitions and, of course is now soon to enjoy a new ground.

I once signed on as a sort of player/manager (with no pay) at Harrow Borough in their darkest hour, but carrying all the administration responsibility then (as they have done for much of the period) were Secretary 'Jim' Rogers and his son Peter. In 1978 Peter was chairman and Jim secretary, In this year's book I see that Jim is President and Peter Secretary having served as Chairman!

Up at Spennymoor Mr. & Mrs. Hindmarch have given stirling service in different administrative posts and from the same background, Tow Law Town have Bernard Fairbairn breaking records as a long serving Secretary, but he took over from another stalwart who had held the position for a lifetime (his father) and rumour has it Bernard's son is in the middle of a twenty year apprenticeship, so he will be ready to take over!

Secretaries who have served different clubs in their respective geographical areas are Tony Turpin in the West Midlands and Graeme Auger in the Northern Home Counties.Derek York gave good service to Ilford before moving to Hailsham and Roy Merryweather was the lynch pin at Wokingham Town for years before joining neighbours Slough Town.

When I played my first game for Corinthian-Casuals at Barking in the Isthmian League a long time ago(!) Brian Wakefield was in goal with David Harrison and Geoff Hewitson were the full backs - they are still all vital members of the clubs administration today. It's a special club!

The East End also breeds stamina as Dave Andrews was chairman of Leytonstone after a distinguished playing career and now after much merging of local clubs he is chairman of Dagenham & Redbridge. While Ted Hardy, although not managing a senior club anymore is still actively supporting the Daggers with ex-Walthamstow Avenue secretary Norman Moss also involved.

Finally a mention of a special friend Ron Tarry who has practically carried Hungerford Town along single handed at times. I worked with him as a general manager and have been in touch ever since. He has seen the twenty-five years out and many before that.

Ron was mayor of Hungerford at the time of the shooting in the town and had to handle the world's media. He excelled! And just like so many other unsung heroes of the non-League world, I'm sure he could have been outstanding in any walk of life.

Here's to all those wonderful people with our thanks for all they have given 'our game'!

Note: I am sure there are many more personalities within non-League football who have been with their clubs `or within' the game for the last twenty-five years. So please write to me at the Directory with details of any long serving heroes you may know and next year we will try to give them a mention and who knows we might be able to arrange a special party!

CONTENTS

EDITORIAL 7

Ladbrokes 13

25 in 25 17

Annual Awards 19

League Pecking Order 2001-02 26

AXA F.A. Cup 27

F.A. Umbro Trophy 57

F.A. Carlsberg Vase 85

England Semi-Professionals 113

Only the major leagues are listed in this section. The full list will be found in the index of leagues on page 1072

CONFERENCE 125

NORTHERN PREMIER 271
(Unibond League)

Division One 326

North West Counties 351

Northern Counties East 391

Northern League 425

SOUTHERN LEAGUE 467
(Dr Martens)

Western Division 522

Eastern Division 545

Eastern Counties 569

Hellenic League 589

Kent 613

Sussex 631

United Counties 653

Wessex 675

Western 695

Midland Football Alliance 733

ISTHMIAN LEAGUE 769
(Ryman)

Division One South 827

Division One North 851

Division Two 875

Combined Counties 891

Essex Senior 901

Spartan South Midlands 909

COUNTY F.A. SECTION 935

This county section starts at page 935 and runs through the various county associations in alphabetical order

South West Counties Championship 997

Wirral Programme Survey 1000

Universities 1004

Welsh Football 1005

Scottish Football 1015

Amateur Football Alliance 1034

Services Football 1042

Channel Islands 1044

Isle of Man 1047

Middlesex Wanderers 1049

English Schools F.A. 1051

F.A. Youth Cup 1057

F.A. Sunday Cup 1060

F.A. County Cup 1061

Tribute to Boston United 1062

F.A. Fixture List 1066

Womens Football 1069

Index of Leagues 1072

Index of Clubs 1073

Editorial Team

Tony Williams (Editor)

George Brown (House Editor), Steve Whitney, James Wright, Michael Williams, Jenny Gullick & Nina Whatmore

Editorial Address

Non-League Club Directory, Helland, North Curry, Taunton, Somerset TA3 6DU
Tel: 01823 490080 Fax: 01823 491481 Email: tony.williams@virgin.net

Tony Williams

Educated at Malvern College, one of the country's best football schools in the late sixties, he represented England Under 18 against Scotland at Celtic Park before serving as an administrative officer in the Royal Air Force for five years.

He was on Reading's books from the age of 16-22, but also represented F.A. Amateur XI's and the R.A.F. while playing mainly in the old Isthmian League for Corinthian Casuals, Dulwich Hamlet and Kingstonian joining Hereford United and Grantham during R.A.F. postings.

After taking an F.A. Coaching badge he coached at Harrow Borough, Epsom & Ewell and Hungerford Town and was asked to edit Jimmy Hill's Football Weekly after initial experience with the Amateur Footballer. Monthly Soccer and Sportsweek followed before he had the idea for a football Wisdens and was helped by The Bagnall Harvey Agency to find a suitable sponsor in Rothmans.

After launching the Rothmans Football Yearbook in 1970 as its founder and co-compiler with Roy Peskett, he was asked to join Rothmans (although a non-smoker!) in the company's public relations department and was soon able to persuade the Marketing Director that Rothmans should become the first ever sponsor of a football league.

After a season's trial sponsoring the Hellenic and Isthmian Leagues, it was decided to go national with the Northern and Western Leagues and for four years he looked after the football department at Rothmans, with Jimmy Hill and Doug Insole presenting a brilliant sponsorship package which amongst many other innovations included three points for a win and goal difference.

So Non-League football led the way with sponsorship and two, now well accepted, innovations.

Sportsmanship and goals were also rewarded in a sponsorship that proved a great success for football and for Rothmans.

After the cigarette company pulled out of their sports sponsorship Tony produced the first Non-League Annual and later The Football League Club Directory, launching 'Non-League Football' magazine with The Mail on Sunday and then Team Talk.

After his ten years with Hungerford Town, he moved West and served Yeovil Town as a Director for seven years but was thrilled when David Emery's plans for the exciting Non-League Media emerged and came into reality, thus giving the Non-League game the publicity and promotion that he and his team had been attempting to set up since the Annual (now Directory) was launched in 1978.

Sadly Non-League Media Plc is no more, although the excellent Non-League Paper will continue under new ownership. The magazine has died, but Tony Williams has been given the license to publish The Directory until it reverts to him officially after the 2005 edition.

Editorial

The 2001-2002 season was launched amongst much bitter niggling throughout the higher levels of the pyramid regarding re-structuring. Ever since the Conference had been forced to drop their idea for a second national division, their apparent links with the Northern Premier League (Unibond) and Southern Premier League (Dr Martens) with a view to just two regional feeders north and south had enraged the Isthmian (Ryman) family tree and the Football Association had stepped in to find out just what was wanted by those who really mattered - the Clubs.

Feelings on this subject emerged in the press from time to time throughout the season, but on a more positive note the drive for two up and two down between the Conference and the Football League, although heavily outvoted at the 2001 Football League meeting, looked as though it just had to be accepted, as Conference clubs became stronger, Football League clubs worried more and more about finances and once again The Football Association pledged its support for the cause, by helping to find the much discussed parachute payments for future relegated Football League clubs.

As the season developed, the Conference must have been extremely pleased suddenly to find the Football Association willing to take on such responsibilities, as the Conference dealings with the FA and indeed the Football League in recent seasons had not struck anyone as being conducive to happy co-operation or a harmonious understanding of each other's points of view!

With **Rushden & Diamonds**, a wonderful representative (but certainly not typical) making their way into Division Three as non-League football's latest promotion winners, the favourites to follow them were likely to emerge from **Yeovil Town**, **Doncaster Rovers**, **Morecambe**, **Barnet** or **Dagenham & Redbridge**.

Although the 'Daggers' were always in the hunt and **Yeovil Town** at their best looked the classiest of challengers, it was left to **Boston United** really to match their east end rivals in a race that lasted to the final day and gave their supporters, the non-League world and indeed a thrilled Sky Sports a superb championship chase that veered backwards and forwards as cup ties, injuries, referees' decisions and the quirks of the fixture list all gave the Conference a wonderful chase.

The fact that the **Boston United** manager could be instantly disliked for his attitude and comments by anyone who didn't actually know him added spice to the race. His quotes and actions were perfect for stirring emotions and involving everyone and reminding one of the professional wrestling 'bad guy', who thrives on the jeers from the fans.

Around the regions, pre season favourites **Canvey Island** and **Burton Albion** were proving the tipsters right, but in the Dr Martens League **Kettering Town** were taking time to settle.

New names to throw down a challenge were **Grays Athletic** and **Gravesend & Northfleet** in the Ryman Competition, **Lancaster City**, **Vauxhall Motors** and the famous **Altrincham** in the Unibond, while the outsiders **Havant & Waterlooville** were joined by **Weymouth**, **Crawley Town** and **Tamworth** at the top of the Dr Martens.

The F.A. Cup, of course, sees its earliest rounds completed in August and, by the time the comparative big boys of the Conference came in, the competition already had its heroes.

Last season **Brigg Town**, **Mangotsfield United** and **Lewes** looked like teams determined to continue their progress and, as luck would have it, the latter two were drawn together in the Fourth Qualifying Round with **Lewes** going through after a replay. **Brigg** meanwhile won at **Boston United** in what must have been one of the results of the whole competition.

Glamourous First Round ties saw **Bedford Town** revive memories of glory in an earlier life with two local 'derbies' with Peterborough United and **Newport County** met Blackpool.

Doncaster Rovers took on local rivals Scunthorpe in a thriller and **Gravesend & Northfleet** and **Lewes** enjoyed their close battles at Huddersfield Town and Stoke City respectively.

Forest Green Rovers lost a replay with Macclesfield after a record 11-10 penalty shoot out, while **Whitby Town**, **Tamworth** and **Barrow** forced replays with Plymouth Argyle, Rochdale and Oldham Athletic, but couldn't progress to the Second Round.

The heroes were **Hereford United** against Wrexham and **Canvey Island** at Wigan Athletic, as both won 1-0, but this was a disappointing F.A. Cup honours board. **Canvey** did produce another 1-0 success at home to Northampton Town, while their Essex neighbours **Dagenham & Redbridge** turned on a great performance to beat Exeter City 3-0 in a replay. Both clubs lost 4-1 in Round Three and non-League's F.A. Cup season quietly came to a close.

Cup runs can badly affect championship challenges, but the 'Daggers' didn't lose touch after their F.A. Cup efforts and neither they nor their rivals **Boston United** stayed too long in the F.A. Trophy!

Holders **Canvey** also lost in a quality tie at **Yeovil Town**, who must have realised it was their year when they recovered from 0-3 at **Doncaster Rovers** in a replay, to win 5-4 in added time. What a game!

If eyebrows had been raised when **Burton Albion** chose to try their luck in the Unibond League rather than battle for promotion in the Dr Martens, the quality of Nigel Clough's squad was never in doubt as they outclassed their Northern opposition, and also eliminated **Farnborough Town**, **Woking** and **Chester City** in the Trophy before losing on aggregate to **Yeovil Town** in the Semi-Final, although they did win the home leg 2-1.

Three **Burton** players won England caps and, just as his father Brian had insisted, disciplined and sporting players do become winners. **Burton Albion** finished with the best sportsmanship record in the Unibond League and the whole level of Trophy competing clubs, while becoming the first squad in the club's long history to win a championship.

It was interesting to see how top clubs coped with the pressures. The Conference saw both leaders drop unexpected points, but they were too far ahead of **Yeovil Town** or **Doncaster Rovers** to have any worries from outside their private battle.

Gravesend & Northfleet just coped a fraction better than **Canvey Island**, who were accused of a little over confidence at times, but there was no real challenge to these two.

In the Dr Martens, early challengers **Crawley Town** and particularly **Weymouth** completely lost their way while **Havant & Waterlooville**, who enjoyed the impressive achievement of providing two England caps, had a consistent season without ever looking strong enough to finish at the top.

Kettering Town, in their first season out of the Conference since the competition's inception, timed their run to perfection and, in a thrilling finish to the season, won 2-1 at **Tiverton** on the last day as rivals **Tamworth**, who needed to win at **Folkestone**, could only draw in a 3-3 thriller.

With the Ryman and Conference championships also decided on the last day it was, perhaps, the best finish to a non-League football season for many a year.

Our two national knock-out cups also provided thrills throughout their respective campaigns. The Vase produced a most unlikely fairy story as humble Eastern League strugglers **Tiptree United** kept winning ties as perpetual underdogs and included holders **Taunton Town** (away), Sussex Champions **Burgess Hill Town** (away) and their own League Champions **AFC Sudbury** (2-0 away and 0-0 home) in the semi-final, amongst their victims.

The F.A. Carlsberg Vase never fails to produce wonderful football stories and the spirit and fun along with the excitement and glamour in the later rounds always lights up the season.

This year a strong North Eastern challenge, including **Bedlington Terriers** and **Durham City**, was led by **Whitley Bay**. An ex-F.A. Amateur Cup semi-finalist and recently a member of the Unibond League, **Whitley Bay** are now rebuilding and what a boost they got from a wonderful Vase run culminating in an extra time victory over plucky **Tiptree**.

Our two finals were on consecutive days early in May and this gave the end of season a special touch of glamour as once again everyone at Villa Park gave all those involved in the two games wonderful memories to take home with them.

For many years we had wondered just how many fans would turn up if **Yeovil Town** reached a Wembley Final. Well it was Villa Park, so perhaps it hadn't quite the same appeal, but the atmosphere and support provided by the followers of **Yeovil** and **Stevenage Borough** was a credit to their clubs. The packed Holte End

created a wonderful green wall of noise with amazing fancy dress costumes to the fore, and the attendance of 20,000, although nowhere near the Trophy record, created a terrific atmosphere which was rewarded by an excellent Final.

Yeovil Town's first major cup success despite all their F.A. Cup giant killing history was a well deserved reward for an excellent season under the sound managership of Gary Johnson aided by Steve Thompson. It was especially good to witness the players, who were so pleased to see their previous manager Colin Addison at Villa Park to watch their triumph.

Straight after the F.A. Trophy Final the England team were due to meet as a squad to prepare for the first competitive tournament for fifteen years.

We cover this in the Representative Football Section, but it was sad that all through the season England manager John Owens was struggling to work with his best players through no fault of his own. Hopefully administration will be easier in the future and to be positive we must praise the Football Association for getting the competition off the ground and hopefully it will go from strength to strength, but clubs and supporters must also do what they can to help. A successful England squad creates stars at the top of our 'pyramid', attracting offers from League clubs who bring more money to our level of the game and more prestige as our players move on to more famous clubs.

During the season Non-League Media Plc suffered a terrible blow when it's Chairman and Finance Director both left, as a quarter of a million pounds was misplaced from our accounts.

Following this traumatic turn of events, the general running of the Company became well nigh impossible, but thankfully the tremendously popular 'Non-League Paper' kept going and the upsets didn't affect the Directory too much.

At the time of writing the future is not certain, but obviously after 25 years of battling to promote non-League football I will do all I can to ensure that, as the game improves in so many ways, we too will continue to give it the coverage it deserves.

This editorial is being written as clubs are organising their pre-season training, getting excited about their fixtures and enjoying the annual buzz from seeing the early F.A. Cup, Trophy and Vase draws.

Every club finds reasons to be positive and can see why this could be 'their season'. Sadly for **Boston United** supporters the pre-season was a tragic mixture of excitement as the Division Three fixtures came out amidst a dread of what could happen to them if their club officials are found guilty of irregularities.

The decision by the Football Association to allow **Boston United** to take their place in The Football League despite being found guilty of breaking rules, was reached amidst derision from all angles but the administrative chaos threatened by their possible expulsion from The Football League and The Conference probably proved just too much of a threat to the system.

At the same time **AFC Wimbledon** supporters loyal to the real club, that worked its way through the Isthmian and Southern Leagues before reaching fame and some degree of fortune at Wembley in an F.A. Cup Final and then in The Premier Division, have now banded together to start again in the Combined Counties League.

I have happy memories of Plough Lane where I played some of my best games against the mighty 'Dons' including such stars as Roy Law, Bobby Ardrey, Brian Martin and Eddie Reynolds. I wish the club every success, but if they do attract big crowds I hope they keep their happy sense of fun and the good spirit that their club has stood for so often in their past.

So as usual a new season starts with hopes high. The 'new' re-structuring debate appears to have settled down with the same three feeder leagues expected to carry on serving the Conference, but they will have some geographical 'tweaking' to make league boundaries more sensible. However, the great excitement is at the top where the Conference clubs will go into a season knowing that two of their members can go up to the Third Division.

The champions will be promoted automatically and the winner of a thrilling play-off competition will join them. The fact that the top four clubs will be involved in this end of season pressure will create a wonderful second half to the season when practically every game will be affected by promotion or relegation issues - and this is how it should be.

Last season was one of the most thrilling ever, but now as we celebrate our 25th edition of this Directory, just what have we got ahead of us? It could be the most memorable non-League season ever and I hope you enjoy it.

T.W.

NON-LEAGUE PUBLICATIONS

WEEKLY:

FOOTBALL TRAVELLER
Twenty pages (ALL the Weekly Fixtures) £1.25 reach - (01386 853288) - Bill Berry, Top O' The Bank, Evesham Road, Broadway, Worcs., WR12 7DG.

THE NON-LEAGUE PAPER
Sunday Paper giving all results and news regarding non-League football - All newsagents - Price - £1.00. - David Emery - Editor, The Non-League Paper, 2nd Floor, Hill House, Highgate Hill, London, N19 5NA. (0207 6877678).

BRISTOL SOCCERWORLD
All the results, league tables and fixtures for your league every week - 50p - M. B. Brown - Editor, Bristol Soccerworld, P.O. Box 72, Patchway, Bristol, BS34 8HT - 0117 969 5487 (T) - 0117 969 4544 (F) email www.bristol-soccerworld.com

MONTHLY:

EVERYTHING FOOTBALL
Two smart magazines Sunday Only and Park Life have featured Sunday football and junior Saturday competitions respectively; well as there are over 500 different leagues and F.A. Competitions the hard working publisher, Mark Kettlety has decided to merge the two and bring out a new 96 page magazine called `EVERYTHING FOOTBALL' costing £2.50.
Any queries regarding subscriptions should be sent to Mark at 23 Lancer Way, Billericay, Essex, CM12 0XA.

GRASS ROOTS -
MIdland Newspaper supplement produced by The Sports Argus published by The Birmingham Post & Mail, Colmore Circus, Queensway, Birmingham, B4 6AX. (0121 236 3366)

BUREAU OF NON-LEAGUE FOOTBALL
Monthly update of league tables and non-league cup competitions. Mike Ford, B.N.L.F., 173 Leytonstone Road, London, E15 1LH (0208 534 0423 P/F). Annual Subscription (UK) £21.95 (EC) £22.95 (International) £25.50

WELSH FOOTBALL
Edited by Dave Collins, Welsh Football, 57 Thornhill Road, Cardiff, CF14 6PE - £2.00 each - (029 2075 3179) email welshfootball@lineone.net

EVERY SIX WEEKS:

NORTHERN VENTURES NORTHERN GAINS
The Northern League Magazine - Price - 30p - Subscriptions £3.50 for six issues including postage. Available from Peter Lax, 21 Carlton Avenue, Billingham, Cleveland.

QUARTERLY:

GROUNDTASTIC
The Football Grounds Magazine - Vince Taylor, 21 Tiptree Grove, Wickford, SS12 9AL - (01268 730076) - email vtbrooklands@btinternet.com - Price £4.20 each (including postage) - cheques made payable to Groundtastic.

YEARLY:

THE CHERRY RED NON-LEAGUE NEWSDESK ANNUAL - (Usually available in May)
Compiled by: James Wright, Non-League Newsdesk email james@nlnewsdesk.co.uk - Price £4.00 + £2.00 P&P (Normal Price - £6.95 + P&P) Cheques/PO made payable to Non-League Newsdesk Annual and sent to James Wright, 6 Harp Chase, Shoreditch Road, Taunton, TA1 3RY. (01823 324938)

F.A. NON-LEAGUE CLUB DIRECTORY - (Normally available in September)
Over 1,000 pages of information, statistics, 700 photos, club details and much much more. Cost £19.95 (including postage). Can be purchased from Tony Williams Publishing, Helland, North Curry, Taunton, Somerset, TA3 6DU. 01823 490080(T) 01823 491481(F) Discounts are available for multiple books - email tony.williams12@virgin.net. Or from your local bookshop.

Ladbrokes

Ladbrokes is proud to be the official sponsor of this year's Non-League Club Directory. The sponsorship is an extension of the Ladbrokes Fair Play Awards initiative which began last season. We're pleased to announce that the Fair Play Award scheme will continue this year and will be expanded to include more leagues and more clubs than ever before.

Fair Play is at the heart of everything that Ladbrokes does. A sense of sportsmanship and fun balanced with integrity and trust is what the World's biggest bookmaking business has been built upon.

We handle more than 500 million bets a year and the vast majority of those bets will be decided by the outcome of some kind of sporting event.

Every one of the bets placed with us depends upon the trust between our company and its customers. It's that trust that your bet will be handled fairly and honestly and that has made Ladbrokes the number one bookmaker for Football.

Most of our fourteen thousand staff are sports fans themselves and many of them are active participants at levels ranging from keeping fit and active with their families to representing their country at the Olympic Games.

We see our support of Non League Football in the UK as our chance to put something back into the grass roots of a sport that is becoming an increasingly popular and important part of our business.

More than that though it's a chance to recognise all that is best about our national game. The fun, the drama and the passion that motivate so many people to get involved as players, officials and fans. Have a great season!

Ladbrokes

Whether your are playing or watching the game, there is nothing better in football than a full blooded, fiercely contested game which is also played in a sporting atmosphere on and off the field.

Players, officials and fans all enjoy themselves and usually the quality of play has every chance of reaching high standards.

Well, Ladbrokes are sponsoring a national non-league fair play competition this season which will cover the majority of leagues supplying clubs competing in the F.A. Trophy and F.A. Vase.

Players who are officially cautioned in a league match will lose one point for each yellow card and three points for a red card when dismissed.

Every club's record will be monitored and displayed on the special Ladbrokes website - ladbrokesfairplay.com

Supporters will be able to check on their clubs' record and their average points lost per game will decide who finishes the season as the country's most sporting senior non-league football club.

It will also be interesting to see which clubs lead their respective leagues or conversely which clubs have a terrible record.

At our level it is usually the disciplined clubs who prove the most successful, but one thing is certain, the Ladbrokes Fair Play Champions will be earning their prize of special kit, which will save them a large bill next season.

Back in the seventies non-league referees thoroughly enjoyed the reaction of the clubs in the Isthmian, Northern, Western and Hellenic Leagues as the introduction of good behaviour awards practically eliminated dissent and retaliation over night.

I'll bet we will all benefit from this latest sponsorship innovation and, of course, if I do bet I'll make sure it's with Ladbrokes who certainly deserve the support for their interest in our level of the game.   T.W.

Football Betting past, present and future

There was a time when football betting meant picking your pools numbers every Friday night and hoping for the best.

Pools betting is still a popular pastime of course but the options open to the football flutterer have increased immeasurably in recent years. There are now more ways than ever to back your judgement with a wager and more ways than ever to place your bets.

Placing a cash bet in a betting shop or at the football ground remains the most popular way to place a bet. The thrill of picking up a win in the form of crisp readies obviously still has a particular appeal to many of us!

The latest technological innovations mean that you can now bet via the phone, on the internet, on your WAP phone or even through your TV set using your remote control.

Just as the technology and the channels for betting have expanded so has the range of bets available. Shrewd football followers can now pit their wits against the bookie by betting on who will score the first goal in a game, or the last, what the correct score will be and even a combination of the two in a bet known as a Scorecast.

If you're following a game live on TV we will normally offer 'betting in running'. This means you can continue betting on the outcome of a match even after it has kicked off with the odds on offer fluctuating to reflect the scoreline in the game and patterns of play on the pitch.

Whatever your team and whatever your budget there is sure to be a bet available to suit you. The average bet is for a few pounds but one intrepid Manchester United fan (and yes, he's from Manchester!) placed a one thousand pound bet with us at Old Trafford at the start of the season. If United do the 'quadruple' this season winning the Premiership, the FA Cup, the Champions League and the League Cup he'll win £275,000.

Whatever your view on that punters prospects he has at least put his money where his mouth is. As long as football is played and as long as its talked about in clubhouse and bar, in workplace and pub people will always have an opinion. As long as people have an opinion they will want the chance to back that opinion up and that's where we come in.

Best of luck for the coming season!

25 - 25

For season 1978-79 a little 256 page pocket book was published by Queen Anne Press at a price of 70p.

My idea for an annual dedicated to non-league football was bravely supported by the famous publishing house and in the twenty-five years since I have enjoyed editing or publishing an annual review of football outside The Football League in a publication which is now 1,088 pages of A5 size and a cost of £19.95.

For the last ten years it has topped the sports' books bestsellers list when published in the Autumn and the beginning of each season.

When we considered how to celebrate our twenty-fifth edition of the Directory we realised that details of the progress and development within the leagues and their member clubs should be reported along with all the highlights of the 1976/77-2001/2 era.

However, the Directory is already over 1,000 pages in size, so we could hardly blow it up into obscene proportions by adding many more pages, so we have decided to record all that is important for clubs in senior leagues, national competitions and general non-League football in twenty-five extra publications,

Following the sad problems of The Non-League Media we realised that this season's Directory would have to be published later than usual and we would only be able to produce a maximum of two special books per month throughout the year, so the editions produced at the end of the present 2002-2003 season will probably have to contain a record of twenty-six years not twenty-five! So you will be getting a bonus!

Most books will be 176 pages in size although the major leagues will obviously be much larger and they will contain reviews of club and league progress through the twenty-five years. There will be plenty of photos and statistics with particular highlights for each League during the specific period.

Individual books can be ordered in advance and we will be announcing the availability of each edition in the regional media and in non-league publications as they are published. Those wishing t o order the complete set of twenty-five in advance will obviously be offered a substantial discount and a special presentation.

The books we hope to publish are listed below, but exact dates of availability and price will be subject to change depending on the progress made on compilation and marketing.

One fact is definite and that is they will be fun to work on and hopefully all connected with the clubs and leagues will enjoy having their respective achievements publicised - T.W.

	Proposed Publishing Date	Minimum No. of Pages	Cost (P & P Free)
Western League	Nov-Dec 2002	176	£9.50
United Counties	Nov-Dec 2002	176	£9.50
N.W. Counties	Jan 2003	176	£9.50
Eastern Counties	Jan 2003	176	£9.50
Wessex League	Feb 2003	144	£7.50
Midland Alliance	Feb 2003	176	£9.50
F.A. Vase	March 2003	144	£7.50
Conference	March 2003	640	£15.50
F.A. Trophy	April 2003	144	£7.50
England Representative	April 2003	144	£7.50
Combined Counties	May 2003	144	£7.50
Essex Senior	May 2003	144	£7.50
Hellenic League	June 2003	176	£9.50
South Western League	June 2003	144	£7.50
West Midlands	July 2003	144	£7.50
Midland Combination	July 2003	144	£7.50
Kent	August 2003	176	£9.50
Northern	August 2003	176	£9.50
F.A. Cup	September 2003	176	£9.50
N.Co. East	September 2003	176	£9.50
Isthmian League	October 2003	640	£15.50
Northern Premier Lge	October 2003	640	£15.50
Southern League	November 2003	640	£15.50
Spartan S. Midlands	November 2003	144	£7.50
Sussex League	November 2003	176	£9.50

To book your copies of 25 - 25 please use the form at the back of this Directory

The Non-League Club Directory

2001-2002
AWARDS

• ROLL OF HONOUR •

FOOTBALLER OF THE YEAR
Daryl Clare (Boston United)

MANAGER OF THE YEAR
Nigel Clough (Burton Albion)

ENGLAND PLAYER OF THE YEAR
Jason Goodliffe (Stevenage Borough)

REGIONAL AWARDS	INDIVIDUAL MERIT AWARDS
Alfreton Town	Jon Goddard-Watts
Vauxhall Motors	Frank Harwood
Tiptree United	Bob Lucas
Halesowen Town	Jack Pearce
Dagenham & Redbridge	Steve Portway
Lewes	
Gravesend & Northfleet	Norman Matthews
St Blazey	
Yeovil Town	

FA CUP
Canvey Island

• REGIONAL CLUB AWARDS 2001-02 •

North East
ALFRETON TOWN

What a season! A quite inspired Alfreton Town won their championship and promotion from the Northern Counties East to the Unibond League, plus their League Cup, the President's Cup and The Derbyshire County Senior Cup. Everyone involved should be extremely proud of themselves and will be looking to the future with great confidence, although it will be difficult to keep up with last season's standards!

North West
VAUXHALL MOTORS

This club is obviously enjoying a wonderful spell of successful development as they have won membership of the Unibond League, moved up to the Premier Division and last season proved to be one of the outstanding sides, enjoying a consistent season and finishing as worthy runners-up. With ground improvements planned and attendances increasing the club is moving forward on and off the field. Manager Alan McDonald even has the knack of producing a line of successful strikers with Terry Fearns the latest.

East Midlands
TIPTREE UNITED

The fairy story of the season was provided by Tiptree United in the F.A. Vase. As complete outsiders they took on, and beat, such impressive opposition as holders Taunton Town, Sussex League champions Burgess Hill Town and, of course, their own champions AFC Sudbury.

The 'Jam Makers' success was typical of the wonderful competition which year after year provides the opportunity for real 'minnows' to enjoy some wonderful football experiences. The result of their Villa Park Final was in doubt well into extra time and their superb Vase season will long be remembered.

West Midlands
HALESOWEN TOWN

It didn't take manager Brendan Phillips long to stop the Halesowen slide and after a tough season in which the squad was steadily strengthened and confidence restored, it was good to see 'The Yeltz' competing near the top of their table again. With neighbours Bromsgrove Rovers also recovering and Kidderminster Harriers and Cheltenham Town now in 'the big time' Halesowen are obviously keen to re-establish themselves as one of the West Midlands' top non-League clubs.

Home Counties East
DAGENHAM & REDBRIDGE

The disappointment of just missing out on goal difference added to the political troubles at Boston all made for a sad end to a tremendous season in which their titanic Conference struggle was matched by another good cup run with Exeter City thrashed 3-0 and Ipswich Town entertained with some style. Memories will be mixed for Daggers fans, but it was a great season all the same.

• REGIONAL CLUB AWARDS 2001-02 •

Home Counties South
LEWES

One of the first clubs to benefit from The Football Association's exciting F.A. Cup bonuses was Ryman Division Two club Lewes. They collected a mammoth £46,000 and also had a useful run in the F.A. Vase to the Quarter Finals. Ad promotion to Division One and substantial ground improvements and it can be seen that the club are enjoying the best period of their history.

South East
GRAVESEND & NORTHFLEET

The advantage of playing alongside a red hot favourite - in this case Canvey Island, allowed 'The Fleet' to establish themselves as a very strong threat without too much publicity. But by half way through the season it was clear to see that Andy Ford had built well and his squad were a very real promotion prospect. Their F.A. Cup victory over Burton Albion brought them a trip to Huddersfield and when the pressure was on in the final weeks, the Kent club proved the strongest Ryman candidate and earned their Conference place.

South West
ST BLAZEY

When a club attracts the majority of the region's star players they should do well. And while it is easy to be envious of the situation, it takes years of hard work and dedication to build a club capable of achieving these heights and even more hard work to stay at the top. St Blazey were unbeaten in the Carlsberg South Western League and had a terrific cup season. A near perfect year in fact, but look out for them in this year's F.A. Vase.

West Country and Wales
YEOVIL TOWN

'The Glovers' first cup success was greeted with great joy by massive support at Villa Park as the F.A. Umbro Trophy was deservedly won.

The young side whose foundations were built the previous season developed nicely under the care of Gary Johnson and some of the football played, as the club enjoyed the lack of pressure in third place, was probably the best of the Conference season.

The squad looks happy, well balanced and well led and the Trophy triumph was a just reward for much hard work.

F.A. Cup Team of the Year
CANVEY ISLAND

In a relatively quiet season for F.A. Cup heroics, Canvey Island carried the non-League banner with pride by beating high flying Wigan Athletic away 1-0 and Northampton Town also 1-0, live in front of the Sky TV cameras at Ark Lane. They met their match at Turf Moor when an on form Burnley proved too strong, but Jeff King's squad had once again continued to fill the headlines magnificently for a club from the Ryman Premier Division.

Tony Williams

NON LEAGUE FOOTBALLER OF THE YEAR
DARYL CLARE
(Boston United)

Photo: Garry Letts

The thrilling race between Boston United and Dagenham & Redbridge for the coveted place in the Football League took centre stage in the run in to a very exciting season. On reflection, the ultimate factor that decided the epic struggle was the general form and finishing skills of their star Irish goalscorer Daryl Clare, who hit form just at the right time and finished the season as the Conference top goalscorer.

As an Eire Under 21 international Daryl had set himself the target of proving he was good enough for a return to the Football League and for more international honours. This he did in fine style and the fact that he scored thirteen goals in the last sixteen vital league games underlines his massive contribution to 'The Pilgrims' success. Hopefully he will continue to shine this season and attract the attention of the Irish selectors once again.

PAST WINNERS

2000-01	Ray Warburton (Rushden & Dia)	1991-92	Tommy Killick (Wimborne Town)
1999-00	Gary Abbott (Aldershot Town)	1990-91	Mark West (Wycombe Wndrs)
1998-99	Neil Grayson (Cheltenham Town)	1989-90	Phil Gridelet (Barnet)
1997-98	Phil Everett (Tiverton Town)	1988-89	Steve Butler (Maidstone Utd)
1996-97	Howard Forinton (Yeovil Town)	1987-88	David Howell (Enfield)
1995-96	Barry Hayles (Stevenage Boro)	1986-87	Mark Carter (Runcorn)
1994-95	Kevan Brown (Woking)	1985-86	Jeff Johnson (Altrincham)
1993-94	Chris Brindley (Kidderminster H.)	1984-85	Alan Cordice (Wealdstone)
1992-93	Steve Guppy (Wycombe Wndrs)	1983-84	Brian Thompson (Maidstone Utd)

NON LEAGUE MANAGER OF THE YEAR

NIGEL CLOUGH
(Burton Albion)

Photo: Peter Barnes

To carry around the mantle of the son of a famous football manager must be a huge burden at times, but Nigel Clough appears to have shouldered any worries that his background may have caused him, while using the massive advantages of his father's football philosphies, many of which were so admired.

For example, Burton Albion won their first ever championship by playing simple passing football in an uncomplicated way with a squad of players who were disciplined on and off the field and easily topped their league's sportsmanship table.

Nigel isn't as controversial or outspoken as his famous father but, Burton Albion have enjoyed all the headlines for the right reasons thanks to a spectacular Unibond Championship, an F.A. Trophy semi-final place having beaten three Conference clubs on the way, and three of his players winning England International caps at the end of the season.

The manager could hardly have asked for more!

PAST WINNERS

2000-01	Jeff King (Canvey Island)	1995-96	Paul Fairclough (Stevenage Boro)
1999-00	Jan Molby (Kidderminster Harr.)	1994-95	Sammy McIlroy (Macclesfield T)
1998-99	Brendan Phillips (Nuneaton Boro)	1993-94	Bill Punton (Diss Town)
1997-98	Steve Cotterill (Cheltenham Town)	1992-93	Martin O'Neill (Wycombe Wndrs)
1996-97	Paul Futcher (Southport)		

ENGLAND PLAYER OF THE YEAR

JASON GOODLIFFE
(Stevenage Borough)

Photo: Peter Barnes

Following Gary Butterworth, Gary Patterson and Tim Ryan, John Owens, England chief coach selected Jason Goodliffe as his player of the year for sheer consistency of performance and a driving spirit that was an inspiration to all around him, especially when the team needed a lift. Jason skippered the side at his home ground against USA and helped his lads come from behind to win. He was again a stalwart in the Four Nations Tournament and, of course, he also enjoyed the thrill of leading his club side to the F.A. Trophy Final. Quite a season for a very popular footballer!

• INDIVIDUAL MERIT AWARDS 2001-02 •

JON GODDARD-WATTS

It is not often that a man discovers football in his seventies, but Jon Goddard-Watts really enjoyed his matches as the sponsor when his Screwfix Western League clubs played in the F.A. Cup, especially against Yeovil Town. He was also impressed with the friendly atmosphere created at the club by Yeovil chairman Bryan Moore at the time, and when Screwfix was bought out for millions he offered to help `The Glovers' as they were his local senior club. Last season when he realised the club's finances had been allowed to reach dangerous proportions, his massive contribution saved the club and enabled it to push for honours. Although now the owner he does not wish to have a hands on, day to day involvement with the club and his own nominees George Smith and David Cox are now in charge.

What a unique and wonderful situation - a successful business man saving a club and helping it without any desire for personal publicity or power. In fact the perfect 'Football Fairy God Father'.

FRANK HARWOOD

Frank became chairman of the Central Midlands League in 1979/80 season and since 1993 has also worked as Secretary of the competition. His work for the League has helped it to become a sound, well run, successful competition. Dedicated officials like Frank are the life blood of football throughout the country. They receive very little praise, there is even less glamour, but a lot of hard graft, which enables his club to enjoy their football every weekend.

Backed by an excellent Public Relations Officer, Stan Wilton, Frank Harwood can be proud of the reputation that The Central Midlands now enjoys within the English pyramid of football competitions.

BOB LUCAS

Bob was recently appointed President of Weymouth Football Club after 30 years service as physiotherapist to his beloved `Terras'. He was also goalkeeper when Weymouth played Manchester United in the F.A. Cup Third Round in 1950 but injury curtailed his playing career. Bob served his club loyally and now is a charming and caring host for visitors to the Weymouth boardroom. It is great to see such a dedicated clubman happily still serving, and at the same time being honoured by his club.

JACK PEARCE

Looking through our first little Non-League Annual before season 1978-79 it was no surprise to see Jack Pearce as manager for Bognor Regis Town. He is still holding down that position and has taken responsibility for just about every job at the Sussex club including Chairman. He has always supported non-League functions and his enthusiasm for the game is a wonderful example to the younger generation. Jack is now also an F.A. Councillor and no one could be better qualified to be part of the game's ruling body.

STEVE PORTWAY

One senior player has featured amongst the goalscorers of non-League football for the last seventeen seasons and alongside Gary Abbott has probably scored more goals than anyone at this level. He is Steve Portway whose career started with Walthamstow. Avenue, a famous amateur club. He broke goalscoring records at Gravesend & Northfleet and he is currently featuring in the Tonbridge Angels squad. However, the most amazing fact, concerning Steve, is that he lost an eye when playing with Gloucester City and in the following year lost the sight of the other eye after another one in a million football accident. He was blind for ten days, but recovered and has since scored well over 100 goals playing with one good eye. Steve is obviously a very special player!

NORMAN MATTHEWS

The founder of the Hellenic League was one of the kindest, most appreciative gentlemen one could meet. His contribution to his treasured Hellenic League has been well documented and I appreciated his efforts in this role during my time at Hungerford Town.

However, his comradeship and support during my efforts to run the first ever sponsorship of football leagues for Rothmans in the seventies was quite outstanding. His hard work, enthusiasm and loyalty made the job so much more enjoyable and he was also so appreciative of the work of others.

Norman was a very special football person and indeed a quite wonderful human being from whom so much could be learnt. His recent death from cancer took away someone who will be greatly missed within the game.

PECKING ORDER 2001-2002   by A J Sarnecki

98-9	99-00	00-01	01-02	Code	League	FA Cup ent	FA Cup xmt	FA Cup won	FA Trophy ent	FA Trophy xmt	FA Trophy won	FA Vase ent	FA Vase xmt	FA Vase won	C pts	T pts	V pts	Total pts
1	1	1	1	ap	FOOTBALL CONFERENCE	22	176	14	22	88	42	0	0	0	212	218	0	430
3	2	2	2	npa	NORTHERN PREMIER Premier	23	92	32	23	8	25	0	0	0	147	125	0	272
2	1	3	3	isa	ISTHMIAN Premier	22	88	29	22	8	31	0	0	0	139	127	0	266
4	3	4	4	soa	SOUTHERN Premier	22	88	40	22	8	18	0	0	0	150	114	0	264
7	4	5	5	isb	ISTHMIAN First	22	0	37	22	4	10	0	0	0	59	102	0	161
5	5	6	6	npb	NORTHERN PREMIER First	22	0	38	22	0	12	0	0	0	60	100	0	160
9	9	7	7	sow	SOUTHERN Western	22	0	33	22	2	14	0	0	0	55	104	0	159
8)	6	8	8	soe	SOUTHERN Eastern	22	0	31	22	2	14	0	0	0	53	104	0	157
6)	8	9	9	isc	ISTHMIAN Second	22	0	26	0	0	0	22	40	33	48	0	95	143
11	10	10	10	nora	NORTHERN First	20	0	19	0	0	0	21	32	45	39	0	98	137
11=	11	12	11	nwca	NORTH WEST COUNTIES First	23	0	12	0	0	0	23	34	30	35	0	87	122
12	12	12	12=	ecoa	EASTERN COUNTIES Premier	19	0	21	0	0	0	21	16	37	40	0	74	114
13=	15	15	12=	ncea	NORTHERN COUNTIES EAST Premier	20	0	23	0	0	0	20	28	23	43	0	71	114
13=	13	14	14	wsx	WESSEX	20	0	19	0	0	0	20	12	40	39	0	72	111
15	17	17	15	isd	ISTHMIAN Third	22	0	15	0	0	0	20	12	32	37	0	64	101
16=	16	13	16	mda	MIDLAND ALLIANCE	19	0	11	0	0	0	20	24	23	30	0	67	97
21	13	18	17	ucoa	UNITED COUNTIES Premier	19	0	7	0	0	0	20	18	24	26	0	62	88
17=	19	19	18	ssxa	SUSSEX COUNTY First	18	0	8	0	0	0	19	12	21	26	0	52	78
13=	19	19	19	wesa	WESTERN Premier	15	0	11	0	0	0	19	6	25	26	0	50	76
16	16	16	20	ssma	SPARTAN SOUTH MIDLANDS Premier	16	0	11	0	0	0	19	4	19	27	0	42	69
21	18	21	21	ken	KENT	14	0	9	0	0	0	15	18	9	23	0	42	65
18	23	23	22	coc	COMBINED COUNTIES	14	0	4	0	0	0	17	10	16	18	0	43	61
23	24	24	23	hela	HELLENIC Premier	10	0	5	0	0	0	16	8	13	15	0	37	52
28=	25	26	24	nceb	NORTHERN COUNTIES EAST First	12	0	4	0	0	0	16	6	11	16	0	33	49
22	26	25	25	norb	NORTHERN Second	9	0	7	0	0	0	13	0	10	16	0	23	39
28=	28	28	26	nwcb	NORTH WEST COUNTIES Second	7	0	6	0	0	0	13	0	10	13	0	23	36
25=	29	29	27	wesb	WESTERN First	10	0	3	0	0	0	14	0	11	10	0	25	35
30=	31=	31=	28	esxs	ESSEX Senior	10	0	5	0	0	0	11	0	5	15	0	16	31
28=	31=	31=	29	swe	SOUTH-WESTERN	7	0	0	0	0	0	13	0	9	7	0	22	29
24	24	29	30	wmda	WEST MIDLAND REGIONAL Premier	0	0	0	0	0	0	13	0	10	0	0	23	23
27	25=	30	31	cmda	CENTRAL MIDLANDS Supreme	0	0	0	0	0	0	9	0	14	0	0	23	23
34	33=	33=	32	ecob	EASTERN COUNTIES First	0	0	0	0	0	0	14	0	7	0	0	21	21
32	28	33=	33	lesa	LEICESTERSHIRE SENIOR Premier	0	0	0	0	0	0	10	0	9	0	0	19	19
30=	30	36	34	mdca	MIDLAND COMBINATION Premier	0	0	0	0	0	0	10	0	8	0	0	18	18
26	36	33=	35	ssmb	SPARTAN SOUTH MIDLANDS Senior	0	0	0	0	0	0	9	0	9	0	0	18	18
35	33=	33=	36	ssxb	SUSSEX COUNTY Second	0	0	0	0	0	0	5	0	10	0	0	15	15
36	33=	37	37	ucob	UNITED COUNTIES First	0	0	0	0	0	0	4	0	11	0	0	15	15
33	37	38	38	hama	HAMPSHIRE Premier	0	0	0	0	0	0	3	0	8	0	0	11	11
38=	40=	40=	39=	ntaa	NOTTS ALLIANCE Senior	0	0	0	0	0	0	3	0	2	0	0	5	5
38	40	40	39=	wcha	WEST CHESHIRE First	0	0	0	0	0	0	3	0	2	0	0	5	5
37	40=	37=	41=	nala	NORTHERN ALLIANCE Premier	0	0	0	0	0	0	2	0	1	0	0	3	3
38=	37=	41=	41=	smsa	SOMERSET SENIOR Premier	0	0	0	0	0	0	2	0	1	0	0	3	3
41=	37=	39	43=	dvc	DEVON COUNTY LEAGUE	0	0	0	0	0	0	1	0	0	0	0	1	1
			43=	hebe	HELLENIC First East	0	0	0	0	0	0	1	0	0	0	0	1	1
40=	40=	40=	43=	hebw	HELLENIC First West	0	0	0	0	0	0	1	0	0	0	0	1	1
41=			43=	wea	WEARSIDE	0	0	0	0	0	0	1	0	0	0	0	1	1

(figures in parentheses refer to slightly different leagues: SOUTHERN South and Midland) With apologies to the current year's sponsors.

Points are given for status (acceptance into each of the three competitions), for prestige (exemption from early rounds) and performance (number of wins, however achieved, even by walkover). Entry to the Vase is valued at one point, that to the Trophy at 4. Cup entry gives a further bonus of one point. Points for exemptions are valued at two for each round missed. The entry in the table is of the total points so gained by the given league, not the number of teams given exemptions. Finally, all wins are valued at one point, regardless of opposition; giving extra points for defeating 'stronger' opponents would be too arbitrary. After all, if they lost then they were not stronger on the day!

FA CHALLENGE CUP

sponsored by AXA

2001 - 2002 REVIEW

NON LEAGUE HONOURS BOARD 2001-2002

FIRST ROUND PROPER (32)

NATIONWIDE CONFERENCE (11)	**DR MARTENS (8)**	**RYMAN (cont)**
Barnet	Cambridge City	Canvey Island
Dagenham & Redbridge	Hinckley United	Gravesend & Northfleet
Doncaster Rovers	Kettering Town	Grays Athletic
Farnborough Town	Newport County	Lewes (Div 2)
Forest Green Rovers	Tamworth	
Hayes	Tiverton Town	**UNIBOND (5)**
Hereford United	Welling United	Altrincham
Morecambe	Worcester City	Barrow
Northwich Victoria		Lancaster City
Southport	**RYMAN (7)**	Whitby Town
Stalybridge Celtic	Aldershot	Worksop Town
	Aylesbury United (Div 1)	
	Bedford Town	**NORTHERN COUNTIES EAST**
		Brigg Town

SECOND ROUND (6)

Canvey Island 1 v 0 Northampton Town Swindon Town (Div 2) 3 v 2 **Hereford United**

Exeter City 0 v 0 **Dagenham & Redbridge** **Hinckley United** 0 v 2 Swindon Town

Dagenham & Redbridge 3 v 0 Exeter City (Div 3) **Altrincham** 1 v 2 Darlington (Div 3)

THIRD ROUND (2)

Dagenham & Redbridge 1 v 4 Ipswich Town

Burnley 4 v 1 **Canvey Island**

EXTRA PRELIMINARY ROUND
Saturday 25 August 2001

1	Newcastle Blue Star	v	Hebburn	5-0	105
	Greenhill (3), Potts, Suddes				
2	Prescot Cables	v	Salford City	2-4	96
	Robinson (2)		*Cullen, Evans (2), Vaughan*		
3	Brigg Town	v	Great Harwood Town	2-2	192
	Bartlett, Raspin		*Bartlett, Riley*		
	Great Harwood Town	v	Brigg Town	*0-1	188
			Rowland		
4	Brandon United	v	St Helens Town	3-2	125
	Burton, Cuthbertson, Robson		*Cooper (2)*		
5	Clitheroe	v	Rossington Main	1-3	183
	Whittingham		*Henderson, Walker (2)*		
6	Flixton	v	Maine Road	0-0	57
	Maine Road	v	Flixton	2-0	97
	Mitchell, Russell				
7	Marske United	v	Abbey Hey	8-1	117
	Bell, Booth, Gibbin, Reeve		*Levendis*		
	Ward, Woods (3)				
8	Lymington & New Milton	v	Burgess Hill Town	0-6	160
			Brown (2), Carr, Carter (2), Harper		
9	Slade Green	v	Chipstead	5-1	119
	Bowey (2), Hudson, Oboyle		*Berry*		
	Sillinge				
10	Saltdean United	v	Walton Casuals	3-3	69
	Costello, Macmillan, Rowland		*Barrs-James, Pearson*		
	Walton Casuals	v	Saltdean United	7-0	100
	Barrs-James, Fitzgerald (2)				
	Pearson (2), Reive, Woolger				
11	Ramsgate	v	AFC Newbury	2-1	123
	Brown, Utterson		*Neville*		
12	Street	v	Frome Town	1-2	404
	Morgan		*Miller, Peters*		

STATISTICS OF THE ROUND
Number of Games: 14

Home Wins: 7	Away Wins: 5	Draws: 3
Home Goals: 41	Away Goals: 26	Hat Tricks: 2

Best Home Wins
Walton Casuals v Saltdean United   7-0
Marske United v Abbey Hey   8-1
Best Away Win
Lymington & New Milton v Burgess Hill Tn   0-6
Best Attendance
Street v Frome Town   404
Average Attendance 142

PRELIMINARY ROUND
Saturday 1 September 2001   £1,000 to each winning club

1	Warrington Town	v	Ashington	0-0	112
	Ashington	v	Warrington Town	3-0	237
	Irwin, Peary (2)				
2*	Spennymoor United	v	Mossley	4-2	184
	Elrington, Kasonali, McGinley		*Wosahlo, Missing scorer*		
	Suddick				
3	Hatfield Main	v	Salford City	0-2	66
			Evans, Hughes		
4	Eccleshill United	v	Chester-le-Street T.	3-1	37
	Cochrane, Heppinstall, Ramsden		*Maddison*		
5	Woodley Sports	v	Gretna	1-2	75
	Norton		*Dobie, Flannigan*		
6	Yorkshire Amateur	v	Shildon	3-6	88
	Barnes (2), Dimbylow		*Bolton, Brumpton, Fairhurst,*		
			Outhwaite (2), Walton		
7	Ossett Town	v	Tadcaster Albion	5-1	165
	Aspinall, Jackson (2), Sykes		*Batley*		
8	Curzon Ashton	v	Louth United	3-4	87
	Birch, Brown, Dorma		*Bailey, Grocock, Jones (2)*		
9	Guisborough Town	v	Bacup Borough	1-0	89
	Ritchie				
10	Esh Winning	v	Ashton United	0-3	105
			Cornelly, Garvey, Gomersal		
11	West Auckland Town	v	Harrogate Town	2-2	110
	McGuire, Stanger		*Albery, Atkinson*		
	Harrogate Town	v	West Auckland T.	4-1	220
	Albery, Ball (2), McNaughton		*Anderson*		
12	Horden CW	v	Evenwood Town	2-0	48
	Atkinson, Cowley				
13	Northallerton Town	v	Chorley	0-3	83
			Mason, Schofield (2)		
14	Shotton Comrades	v	Pickering Town	1-5	47
	Stewart		*Chapman (2), Connor (2), Zoll*		
15	Selby Town	v	South Shields	3-2	119
	Tucker (2), Turner		*Croft, Ryan*		
16*	Rossington Main	v	Stocksbridge P.S.	1-5	88
	Missing goalscorer		*Biggins, Fearon (3), Hurlstone*		
17*	Marske United	v	Maine Road	3-3	118
	Booth, Knight, Missing Scorer		*Goodall, Pritchard, Wiltshire*		
	Maine Road	v	Marske United	*0-0	82
	Maine Road won 4-3 after penalties				
18	Chadderton	v	Maltby Main	0-2	80
			Clark, Haythorne		
19	Billingham Synthonia	v	Tow Law Town	4-2	141
	Fawcett, Flanagan, Marron, Walker		*Maughan (2)*		
20	Squires Gate	v	Oldham Town	2-0	62
	Booth, Longworth				
21	Brigg Town	v	Morpeth Town	3-1	199
	Cadman, Drayton, Wilby		*Lawton*		
22	Kendal Town	v	Consett	4-0	109
	Diggle, Foster, Hayton, Rogan				
23	Farsley Celtic	v	Trafford	1-0	113
	Newton				
24*	Radcliffe Borough	v	Atherton LR	3-3	164
	Landon, Walker, Wilson		*Jones, Rhead, Strange*		
	Atherton LR	v	Radcliffe Borough	2-5	134
	Missing goalscorers		*Banim, Bean, Elliot (2), Kissock*		
25	Skelmersdale United	v	Jarrow Roofing Boldon CA	2-0	107
	Cowley, Scott				
26	Willington	v	Durham City	0-8	129
			Dawson, Edgecumbe, Irvine (2),		
			Ludlow (3), Mudd		
27	Sheffield	v	Dunston Fed. Brewery	1-1	221
	Bullivant		*Dalton*		
	Dunston Federation Brewery	v	Sheffield	3-1	173
	Fletcher, Hogg, Scaife		*Owen*		
28	Fleetwood Freeport	v	Pontefract Collieries	4-0	84
	Barnes, Cygal, Flynn, McGinley				
29*	Blackpool Mechanics	v	Ramsbottom United	0-2	60
			Brookes, Missing Scorer		

Top:
*Newcastle Blue Star
(Northern Div 1) v Hebburn
(Northern Div 2) 5-0.
A superb flying save by
Simon Parkin of Hebburn
Photo: Graham Brown*

Centre:
*Slade Green (Kent)
v Chipstead (Combined Co)
5-1
Slade Green's No 3 Steve
O'Boyle holds the ball up
Photo: Neil Thaler*

Bottom:
*Chessington & Hook
(Combined Co) v Didcot
Town (Hellenic) 2-0
Chessington & Hook's Neil
Wick, scorer of both goals in
their only FA Cup win to date
Photo: Neil Thaler*

#	Home		Away	Score	Att
30*	Witton Albion	v	Atherton Collieries	4-0	276
	Moseley, Rendell (2)				
	Missing scorer				
31	Workington	v	Penrith	1-0	273
	Fell				
32	Liversedge	v	Darwen	2-2	84
	Flynn, Smith		*Baker (2)*		
	Darwen	v	Liversedge	0-1	75
			Smith		
33	Garforth Town	v	Rossendale United	0-4	161
			Bird, Denning, Heffernan,		
			Patterson		
34	Parkgate	v	Crook Town	3-3	65
	Cusworth (2), Telling		*Atkinson, Blythe, Sutcliffe*		
	Crook Town	v	Parkgate	1-0	133
	Ball				
35	Cheadle Town	v	North Ferriby United	4-1	97
	*Elwell, **Wardle (3)***		*Featherstone*		
36	Harrogate Railway	v	Bridlington Town	2-0	125
	Ames, Wrigley				
37	Peterlee Newtown	v	Castleton Gabriels	4-0	58
	Fitzgerald, Hall (2), White				
38	Hallam	v	Armthorpe Welfare	1-0	65
	Morris		*(at Armthorpe Welfare FC)*		
39*	Easington Colliery	v	Denaby United	4-3	50
	***Matthews (3)**, Missing scorer*		*Clarke, Gregory, Hammond*		
40	Glasshoughton Welfare	v	Winsford United	0-2	45
			Burns, Worthington		
41	Seaham Red Star	v	Brandon United	0-7	70
			Burton, Cunningham (2)		
			Cuthbertson (2), Huggins, Smith		
42	Thornaby	v	Billingham Town	0-3	133
			Hutchinson, Rowntree (2)		
43	Ossett Albion	v	Bedlington Terriers	0-3	150
			Cockburn, Gibb, Milner		
44	Newcastle Blue Star	v	Whitley Bay	0-8	170
			Chandler, Chivers (2), Cook,		
			Cuggy (2), Milbourne, Smith		
45	Brodsworth	v	Guiseley	1-4	55
	Fox		*Henry, Senior, Stuart, Trevitt*		
46	Thackley	v	Goole	1-0	97
	Cunningham				
47	Buxton	v	Atherstone United	1-3	229
	Martin		*Doughty, Marowe, Middleton*		
48	Borrowash Victoria	v	Boston Town	2-2	102
	Brookes, Murphy		*Graham, Price*		
	(at Boston Town FC)				
	Boston Town	v	Borrowash Victoria	1-0	84
	Harrold				
49	Willenhall Town	v	Solihull Borough	1-6	137
	Goodall		*Amos, Dutton, Hall, Shaw, Smith(2)*		
50	Bourne Town	v	Eastwood Town	1-2	123
	Munton		*Davies, White*		
51	Belper Town	v	Paget Rangers	1-0	148
	Cunningham				
52	Pelsall Villa	v	Knypersley Victoria	1-2	45
	Cartwright		*Burndred, Horton*		
53	Stafford Town	v	Cradley Town	5-0	50
	Anderson (2), Peaks, Sheridan, Wallace				
54	Oadby Town	v	Leek Town	0-3	220
			Hobby, Tucker, Whittaker		
55	Blackstone	v	Bromsgrove Rovers	0-1	107
			Ford		
56	Mickleover Sports	v	Stapenhill	1-0	85
	Hurst				
57	Matlock Town	v	Holbeach United	3-1	187
	Capuano, Clarke, Sucharewycz		*Taylor*		
58	Bloxwich United	v	Gresley Rovers	0-2	164
			Allsop (2)		
59	Halesowen Harriers	v	Redditch United	0-4	105
			***Danks (3)**, Mitchell*		
60	Leek CSOB	v	Nantwich Town	2-3	83
	Banks, Sheldon		*Brooks, Griggs, Walker*		
	(Tie awarded to Leek CSOB –				
	Nantwich Town removed for playing an ineligible player)				
61	Stamford	v	Congleton Town	3-2	174
	Ndekwe, Pritchard, Staff		*Baker (2)*		
62	Arnold Town	v	Kidsgrove Athletic	4-1	177
	Brown, Manners, Mitchell		*Twigg*		
63	Corby Town	v	Alfreton Town	1-2	136
	Warner		*France, Housley*		
64	Bilston Town	v	Gedling Town	4-2	117
	Bennett, Rollason, Smith (2)		*Hollis-Smith (2)*		
65	Halesowen Town	v	Chasetown	2-0	357
	Hall, Smith				
66	Grantham Town	v	Glapwell	3-2	278
	Hawley, Marshall, Simmons		*Booth, Taylor*		
67*	Rocester	v	Boldmere St Michaels	2-1	82
	Bourne, Scorer missing		*Scorer missing*		
68	Oldbury United	v	Bedworth United	0-4	121
			Partridge (2), Webster, White		
69	Newcastle Town	v	Shepshed Dynamo	3-1	155
	Bott, Pesteridge, Richie		*Master*		
70	Glossop North End	v	Stourbridge	0-1	148
			Briscoe		
71	Shifnal Town	v	Rushall Olympic	0-4	66
			Currier (2), Wright (2)		
72	Barwell	v	Racing Club Warwick	2-0	123
	Lucas (2)				
73	Stourport Swifts	v	Rugby United	5-1	136
	Booth, Charlton, Marsh (2)		*Padmore*		
74	Staveley MW	v	Stratford Town	1-0	74
	Chambers				
75	Bridgnorth Town	v	Sutton Coldfield Town	2-3	66
	Blakemore, Reid		*Baker (2), Bellingham*		
76	Lincoln United	v	Spalding United	3-0	135
	Tomlinson (3)				
77	Clacton Town	v	Tiptree United	2-1	185
	Farmer, Springett		*Daly*		
78	Hullbridge Sports	v	Concord Rangers	0-1	59
			Cates		
79	Rothwell Town	v	Hornchurch	2-2	126
	Foreman (2)		*Wolff (2)*		
	Hornchurch	v	Rothwell Town	2-0	80
	Bower, Wolfe		*(at Aveley FC)*		
80*	Burnham	v	Flackwell Heath	4-0	91
	Alleyne, Bartley, Potter				
	Missing Scorer				
81	Northwood	v	Bishop's Stortford	3-3	196
	Gell, Yaku (2)		*John (2), Riches*		
	Bishop's Stortford	v	Northwood	0-1	294
			Yaku		
82	Witham Town	v	Saffron Walden Town	6-0	69
	***Driver (3)**, Inglis, Walton, Window*				
83	AFC Wallingford	v	Mildenhall Town	1-2	92
	Hannigan		*Smith (2)*		
84	Stotfold	v	Harlow Town	0-2	94
			Samuel (2)		
85	AFC Sudbury (receive walkover to First Qualifying Round)				
86	Potters Bar Town	v	Staines Town	0-5	72
			Butler, Harris, Hooper, Talboys,		
			Underwood		
87	Romford	v	Southend Manor	1-2	122
	Read		*Barnett, Rolfe*		
88	Wivenhoe Town	v	Harwich & Parkeston	0-2	156
			Grayson, Head		
89	Leyton	v	Felixstowe & Walton U.	2-1	133
	Curley, Wood		*Deasy*		
90	Wroxham	v	Aveley	2-1	114
	Fox, Howes		*Mas*		
91*	Ford United	v	Royston Town	3-2	112
	Rose (2), Willis		*Dobson, Missing scorer*		
	(at Dagenham & Redbridge FC)				

92* Maldon Town v Buckingham Town 0-0 111
Buckingham Town v Maldon Town 2-4 70
Missing scorers — *Knowles, Warwick, Witney (2)*

93 Leighton Town v Dunstable Town 1-4 176
Perry — *Benham, Blackett, Reed, Sanders*

94 Aylesbury United v Brentwood 10-1 301
Bangura, Clark (5), Marshall — *Cousins*
Silveestri (2), Williams

95 Long Buckby v Berkhamsted Town 0-9 70
— *Dawber, Lowe, Mullins, Pedder (2), Smith (3)*

96 London Colney v Soham Town Rangers 1-2 60
Sippetts — *Docking, Metcalf*

97 Wisbech Town v Bowers United 3-2 227
Nuttall (2), Reeson — *Warner, Williams*

98 Woodbridge Town v Diss Town 1-2 133
Coote — *Miller, Nozedar*

99 Hertford Town v Haringey Borough 3-1 83
Barnaby, Cooper, Jordan — *Fung*

100 Kingsbury Town v Wootton Blue Cross 0-3 43
— *Evason, Joswiak, Lawes*

101 St Neots Town v Northampton Spencer 5-0 141
Bloss, Byrne, Claridge, Kunne — *McCreanor*

102 Wingate & Finchley v Barking & East Ham U. 0-0 80
Barking & East Ham Utd. v Wingate & Finchley 1-2 113
Hunt — *Butterfield, Fitzpatrick*

103 Fakenham Town v Marlow 4-3 134
Belton, Coe, Dickerson, Magee — *Goodall, Pritchard, Wiltshire*

104 Yeading v Ilford 3-1 82
Edwards, Tucker (2) — *Emmanuel*

105 Clapton v Somerset Ambury V&E 0-5 37
— *Gildersleve, Ulatowski (4)*
(at Somersett Ambury V&E FC)

106 Beaconsfield SYCOB v Brackley Town 2-3 45
Hughes, Webb — *Dorian, Holmes, Parrott*

107 Hemel Hempstead Town v Holmer Green 4-0 125
Armstrong, Dockett, Field, Hill

108 Burnham Ramblers v Leyton Pennant 0-2 48
— *Cove, Notley*

109 Bedford United v Newmarket Town 0-1 38
— *Claydon*

110* Southall v Uxbridge 1-11 52
Missing scorer — *Bamford, Goodall, Moore (4), Tunnell (3), Walters*

111 St Margaretsbury v Gorleston 3-1 51
Bates, Howard, Winger — *Wooldridge*

112* Tilbury v Wealdstone 1-1 153
Burbridge — *Greene*
Wealdstone v Tilbury 2-1 212
Somers, Missing scorer — *Jones*

113 Barton Rovers v Cheshunt 1-3 71
Carey — *Boyce, Cox, Walters*

114 Bury Town v Gt. Wakering Rovers 1-2 146
Stringfellow — *Trenkel (2)*

115 Bugbrooke St Michaels v Histon 0-0 85
Histon v Bugbrooke St Michaels 3-1 108
Barker, Harrington, Munns — *Jameson*

116 Tring Town v Cogenhoe United 0-2 50
— *Parsons, Wagstaff*

117 Arlesey Town v Chalfont St Peter 4-0 191
Catt, Dellar (2), Fontenelle

118* Stowmarket Town v Ruislip Manor 4-3 106
Jopling (2), Pannell (2) — *Layzell, Whitby, Missing scorer*

119 Desborough Town v Great Yarmouth Town 1-2 93
Chong — *Humphreys, Pillar*

120 Yaxley v Raunds Town 2-1 85
Acton, Doyle — *Evans*

121 Banbury United v Ware 4-0 274
Gooderick, Milner, Redknapp (2)
(tie awarded to Ware –
Banbury United removed for playing a suspended player)

122 Hoddesdon Town v Wellingborough Town 6-1 45
Ardiles, Connor, Johnson, Mann — *Summerfield*
Pullen, White
(at Ware FC)

123 Brook House v Hanwell Town 2-1 72
McGee (2) — *Elder*

124* Ipswich Wanderers v Kempston Rovers 3-1 56
Glyn, Harewood (2) — *Missing goalscorer*

125 Lowestoft Town v Wembley 3-4 254
Durrant, Roach, Thompson — *Acquah (3), Hewitt*

126 East Thurrock United v Sawbridgeworth Town 3-0 81
Finning, Hall, Mallon

127 Milton Keynes City v Edgware Town 2-0 89
Lancaster (2)

128 Ford Sports Daventry v Stewarts & Lloyds 0-1 40
— *Drain*

129 Brockenhurst v Three Bridges 3-1 95
Bryant, Stone (2) — *Edwards*

130 Fareham Town v Chessington United 2-0 146
Chamberlain, Lacey

131 Horsham v Dulwich Hamlet 2-0 209
Charman, Dennis

132 Banstead Athletic v Carshalton Athletic 0-2 186
— *McKenzie, York*

133 Fisher Athletic v Ashford Town (Middx) 3-0 111
Dolby, Taylor, Missing scorer

134* Tooting & Mitcham United v Burgess Hill Town 0-0 269
Burgess Hill Town v Tooting & Mitcham Utd.* 1-3 271
Missing scorer — *Kane (3)*

135 Walton Casuals v Horsham YMCA 4-4 101
— *Boxall, Dhiman, Sleat, Taylor*

136 Thamesmead Town v Corinthian Casuals 1-1 46
Gallagher — *Horwood*
Corinthian Casuals v Thamesmead Town *3-1 71
Waghorn (2), White — *Smith*

137 Walton & Hersham v Slade Green 4-0 101
Edgar (2), Harkness (2)

138 Lordswood v Hungerford Town 4-2 72
Beckwith, Holbrook (2), Pearson — *Howell, Mildenhall*

139 Hastings Town v Ringmer 3-0 346
Jones, McArthur, Ruddy

140 Whyteleafe v Eastbourne United 2-0 132
Elliott, Lock

141 Greenwich Borough v Cowes Sports 2-2 60
Hayworth, Taylor — *Plenty, Stevens*
Cowes Sports v Greenwich Borough 0-3 36
— *Muldowney, Simpson (2)*

142 Whitehawk v Leatherhead 2-2 99
Allen, Rowland — *Burton, Inglethorpe*
Leatherhead v Whitehawk 2-0 118
Ingelthorpe (2)

143 Chatham Town v Moneyfields 1-1 173
Austin — *Mould*
Moneyfields v Chatham Town 4-0 80
Bedden (2), Hopkins, Stewart

144 Hillingdon Borough v BAT Sports *2-3 47
Dennison, Prydderch — *Doling, Jenvey, Proctor*

145 Egham Town v Cobham 3-0 30
Davies, Mernagh, Nesbeth

146 Molesey v Arundel 2-1 47
Nedip, Reddings — *Scerri*

147 Hassocks v Ashford Town 3-2 81
Budret (2), Low — *Guiver, Smith*

148 Hailsham Town v Peacehaven & Telsc. 0-1 98
— *Gilmour*

149* Tonbridge Angels v AFC Totton 4-1 278
Cass (2), Greatorex, Missing — *Willes*

150 VCD Athletic v Chichester City Utd. 1-3 108
Dimmock — *Chandler, Moore (2)*

151 Dartford v Eastbourne Town 3-1 237
Frost, Godden, Guiver — *Brockwell*

152	Eastbourne Borough v	Whitchurch United	3-1	260	183	Chard Town v	Evesham United	0-4	109

152 Eastbourne Borough v Whitchurch United 3-1 260
Adams, More, Westcott *Caswell*

153 Selsey v Littlehampton Town 0-2 140
Hudson, Sell

154 Thame United v Worthing 3-2 112
Cort (2), West *Tuck, Webber*

155 Cove v Erith & Belvedere 1-3 65
Marshall *Adams, White, Whitehouse*

156 Windsor & Eton v Fleet Town 3-1 97
Agudosi, Jeffries (2) *Taylor*

157 Bracknell Town v Reading Town 5-0 102
*Day, Harte, **Osgood (3)***

158 Ramsgate v Andover 0-4 114
Asker, Blake, Dyke, Forbes

159 Croydon Athletic v Erith Town 6-2 69
***Fowler (3)**, Jackson, Quinton, Wood* *Adeniyi, Putnam*

160 Bedfont v Epsom & Ewell 5-0 72
*Farbiszewski, **Morrow (3)**, Postins*

161 Abingdon United v Lancing 2-1 55
Henry, Maciak *Gurney*

162 Redhill v Oxford City 2-2 140
Allen, Amanuel *Mitchell, Whitehead*

Oxford City v Redhill 4-0 132
***Mitchell (3)**, Wimble*

163 Sandhurst Town v Deal Town 2-3 76
Hutchings, Obe *Bridger, Marriott, Pollard*

164* Lewes v Slough Town 3-0 234
Francis (2), Missing scorer

165 Abingdon Town v Bognor Regis Town 1-3 94
Scanes *Funnell, Russell, Wright*

166 Blackfield & Langley v Chertsey Town 2-5 101
James, Moore *Lewis (2), Pomroy, Taylor (2)*

167 Beckenham Town v Dorking 2-2 78
Smith (2) *Chaasan, Hartigan*

Dorking v Beckenham Town 1-0 154
Lunn

168 Metropolitan Police v Carterton Town 2-1 45
Prins, Wickens *Holder*

169 Wick v Bashley 2-2 131
Green (2) *Gee, Quirke*

Bashley v Wick 3-2 146
Davis, Higgins, Hussey *Bridle, Loversidge*

170 Thatcham Town v North Leigh 3-1 103
Anderson, Cook (2) *Timms*

171 Chessington & Hook United v Didcot Town 2-0 102
Wicks (2)

172 Whitstable Town v Merstham 4-0 151
Constable, Cooper, Toms (2)

173 Wokingham Town v Sittingbourne 0-4 124
Drury, Fisher, King, Russell

174 Eastleigh v Tunbridge Wells 2-2 116
Jones, Platt *Hickmott, Nicklin*

Tunbridge Wells v Eastleigh 2-3 85
Clark, Valli *McAllister (2), Sotoudeh*

175 Ash United v East Preston 3-0 110
Brophy (2), Mitchell

176 Godalming & Guildford v Gosport Borough 0-3 96
Hensman, Mann, Wheatland

177 Herne Bay v St Leonards 0-2 184
Reid (2)

178 Bromley v Pagham 2-0 198
Cain, Myatt

179 Hythe Town v Camberley Town 1-0 102
Light

180 Cray Wanderers v Southwick 3-0 96
Heaslewood (2), Willy

181 Torrington v Elmore 0-1 58
Payne

182 St Blazey v Bishop Sutton 4-2 136
Gosling, Harrington, Hooper, Richardson *Lane, Maggs*

183 Chard Town v Evesham United 0-4 109
Lutz, Payne, Preedy, Roberts

184 Bournemouth v Dorchester Town 3-1 241
Clark, Honeybun, Lucas *Groves*

185 Frome Town v Melksham Town 2-0 285
Fricker, Salter

186 Downton v Falmouth Town 0-3 90
Ashburn, Burchell, Pope

187 Backwell United v Christchurch 0-1 84
Woolner

188* Cinderford Town v Bideford 1-1 162
Harris *Crook*

Bideford v Cinderford Town 3-1 220
Crook, Gough, Southgate *Missing scorer*

189 Swindon Supermarine v Calne Town 1-1 133
Hadgkiss *Wheeler*

Calne Town v Swindon Supermarine 0-1 167
Garbutt

190* Yate Town v Shortwood United 1-3 92
Missing scorer *Ackland, Cole, Groves*

191 Mangotsfield United v Clevedon Town 1-0 248
Seal

192 Weston Super Mare v Taunton Town 0-0 228

Taunton Town v Weston Super Mare 1-3 387
Gammon *Bevan, Cox, King*

193 Cirencester Town v Gloucester City 2-1 207
Harris (2) *Marshall*

194 Clevedon United v Barnstaple Town 3-3 73
Nash, Ward (2) *Amooie, Green, Harris*

Barnstaple Town v Clevedon United 2-1 55
Harris, Murray *Smith*

195 Highworth Town v Welton Rovers 2-0 70
Desando, Moss

196 Devizes Town v Odd Down 0-3 75
Carter (2), Thomas

197 Minehead Town v Bemerton Heath Harl. 4-1 64
Carr, Hodgson, Hopkins, Perkins *Cole*

198 Bridgwater Town v Fairford Town 0-0 121

Fairford Town v Bridgwater Town 1-2 67
Clark *Heywood, Knox*

199 Brislington v Paulton Rovers 3-1 104
Churchill, Mehew, O'Sullivan *Buxton*

200 Tuffley Rovers v Wimborne Town 2-5 70
Medcroft, Nicholas ***Cannie (3)**, Lovell (2)*

201 Westbury United v Bristol Manor Farm 1-4 92
Thorne *Cook (2), Edwards, Jones*

202* Shepton Mallet v Chippenham Town 1-1 271
Burr *Bright*

Chippenham Town v Shepton Mallet 3-0 245
Dicks, Rawlins, Missing scorer

STATISTICS OF THE ROUND

Nos. of Games: 201 + 29 replays
Home Wins: 112 **Away Wins:** 89 **Draws:** 29
Home Goals: 436 **Away Goals:** 396 **Hat Tricks:** 19
Best Home Win
Aylesbury United v Brentwood 10-1
Best Away Wins
Southall v Uxbridge 1-11
Long Buckby v Berkhamsted Town 0-9
Best Attendances:
Taunton Town v Weston Super Mare 387
Halesowen Town v Chasetown 357
Hastings Town v Ringmer 346
Average Attendance: 124

* Where there are missing goalscorers we presume 'own goals' were scored but not listed on match details returns from clubs

Leyton (Essex Senior) v Felixstowe & Walton United (Eastern Premier) 2-1
Slide rule! Leyton keeper Steve Wallduck rules his area as a 'Seasider' slides in. Photo: Dennis Nicholson

Corby Town (Dr Martens Eastern) v Alfreton Town (Northern Counties East) 1-2. Alfreton's Scott Oxley on left
clears the ball before Corby's James Miller can challenge. James Elliott watches closely. Photo: Bill Wheatcroft

Woodley Sports (North West Counties Div 1) v Gretna (Unibond Div 1) 1-2.
Gretna's Mark Dobie (9) is foiled by a last-ditch tackle by Woodley's Matthew Wilson. Photo: Alan Watson

FIRST QUALIFYING ROUND

Saturday 15 September 2001   £7,500 to each winning club

#	Home v Away	Score	Att
1	Spennymoor United v Cheadle Town	2-0	147
	Leonard, Skedd		
2	Horden CW v Witton Albion	1-2	113
	Atkinson / Garritty, Moseley		
3	Stocksbridge Park Steels v Easington Colliery	3-2	100
	Flynn (2), Hurlstone / Dixon, Matthews		
4	Rossendale United v Guisborough Town	3-2	223
	Cunningham, Fitzgerald, West / Clark (2)		
5	Dunston FB v Hallam	3-1	131
	Fletcher, Mason (2) / Worsfield		
6*	Bandon United v Kendal Town	1-3	99
	Missing scorer / **Maddock (3)**		
7	Louth United v Durham City	0-3	105
	Ludlow (2), Moan		
8	Squires Gate v Ossett Town	3-2	120
	Catlow, Noblett, Sugden / Jackson, Shaw		
9	Crook Town v Pickering Town	1-1	171
	Roberts / Zoll		
	Pickering Town v Crook Town	1-0	186
	Sturdy		
10	Farsley Celtic v Radcliffe Borough	3-1	134
	Henderson, Newton, Spence / Bean		
11	Ramsbottom United v Ashington	6-1	209
	Brierley (3), Porter, Thomas Yorke-Robinson / Atkinson		
12	Chorley v Maine Road	1-2	191
	Sutch / Russell, Simms		
13	Whitley Bay v Workington	1-0	249
	Walton		
14	Ashton United v Skelmersdale Ut.d	4-2	132
	Cornelly, Garvey, Miller, Morris / Cavanagh, Cowley		
15	Billingham Synthonia v Liversedge	0-2	89
	Flynn, Sykes		
16	Selby Town v Gretna	0-2	143
	Dobie (2)		
17	Guiseley v Eccleshill United	1-2	256
	Daly / Cochrane, Price		
18	Bedlington Terriers v Peterlee Newtown	2-0	241
	Boon, Gibb		
19	Shildon v Brigg Town	2-8	416
	Langley, Outhwaite / Cadman (2), Carter, **Lytollis (3)**, Roach (2)		
20	Salford City v Harrogate Town	2-3	112
	Margison (2) / Ball, Whellans (2)		
21	Billingham Town v Fleetwood Freeport	7-0	65
	Casey (2), Jackson Osborne (2), Rowntree (2)		
22	Thackley v Maltby Main	2-1	70
	Patterson (2) / Evans		
23	Harrogate Railway v Winsford United	1-1	145
	McLean / Lowe		
	Winsford United v Harrogate Railway	1-4	101
	Lowe / Davey (2), McLean, Watkinson		
24	Alfreton Town v Newcastle Town	0-2	208
	Bott (2)		
25*	Belper Town v Leek Town	1-1	231
	Kennedy / Missing scorer		
	Leek Town v Belper Town	1-2	264
	Ridley / Kennedy, Payne		
26	Matlock Town v Bilston Town	2-2	258
	Simpson, Taylor / Stone, Williams		
	Bilston Town v Matlock Town	4-2	188
	Bennett, Rollason, Smith, Williams / Noteman, Pidcock		
27	Mickleover Sports v Bromsgrove Rovers	1-2	144
	Marsden / Banner, Bowen		
28	Halesowen Town v Staveley MW	2-0	358
	Giddings, May		
29	Arnold Town v Rushall Olympic	2-2	195
	Maddison, Manners / Currier (2)		
	Rushall Olympic v Arnold Town	0-3	149
	Bogan, Coke (2)		
30*	Gresley Rovers v Redditch United	1-1	305
	Wooley / Missing scorer		
	Redditch United v Gresley Rovers	2-1	220
	Colcombe, Danks / Wooley		
31	Stamford v Grantham Town	0-3	516
	Hawley, McDaid (2)		
32	Lincoln United v Stourport Swifts	3-3	130
	Walters (2), Ward / Booth, Nicholls (2)		
	Stourport Swifts v Lincoln United	1-0	131
	Knight		
33	Rocester v Barwell	1-2	102
	Myatt / Davies, Lucas		
34	Atherstone United v Bedworth United	1-1	228
	Emeke / Richardson		
	Bedworth United v Atherstone United	0-1	284
	Doughty		
35	Stourbridge v Knypersley Victoria	3-2	153
	Baker (2), Black / Burndred (2)		
36	Solihull Borough v Sutton Coldfield T.	4-1	278
	Hall (2), Hollis, Smith / Baker		
37	Stafford Town v Boston Town	2-1	59
	Brown, Rawlinson / Graham		
38	Eastwood Town v Leek CSOB	5-0	107
	Davies, Morgan, Smith, Todd (2)		
39	Great Yarmouth Town v Hoddesdon Town	0-1	161
	Redford		
40	Great Wakering Rovers v Northwood	2-3	150
	Ewers, Sibanda / Cook, Yaku (2)		
41	Uxbridge v Wroxham	0-3	94
	Howes, Lewis, Stock		
42	Hertford Town v St Margaretsbury	0-4	140
	Casha, **Howard (3)**		
43	Mildenhall Town v Wingate & Finchley	1-5	141
	Reeder / Donn, Fitzpatrick, Thompson (2), Williams		
44	Fakenham Town v Leyton	1-1	151
	Delicata / Reilly		
	Leyton v Fakenham Town	3-0	114
	Curley, Reilly, Wood		
45	Southend Manor v Diss Town	0-0	104
	Diss Town v Southend Manor	1-2	174
	Miller / Dawson, Nicks		
46	Hornchurch v Wisbech Town	1-2	120
	Wolff / Leggett (2)		
47	Wootton Blue Cross v Harwich & Parkeston	2-0	78
	Stupple (2)		
48	Somersett Ambury V&E v Stewart & Lloyds	3-0	44
	Ulatowski, Wales (2)		
49	Ware v Wealdstone	1-5	162
	Haag / Hammatt, Moore, Pither, Somers, Walker		
50	Clacton Town v Leyton Pennant	3-0	192
	Bailey, Gray, Hepburn		
51	St Neots Town v Ipswich Wanderers	0-2	156
	Burman, Harewood		
52	Burnham v Soham Town R'gers	4-3	72
	Alleyne, Durkin, Potter (2) / Bullet, Davis, Simpson		
53	Aylesbury United v AFC Sudbury	4-3	408
	Bangura, Marshall, Maynard, Stanbridge / Banya, Owen (2)		

Stamford (Dr Martens Eastern) v Grantham Town (Dr Martens Eastern) 0-3.
Grantham's Gary Bull shoots through a packed Stamford defence. Photo: Gavin Tutcher

Eastbourne Borough (Dr Martens Eastern) v Whyteleafe (Ryman Div 1) 3-2
Leion Dillon scores for Whyteleafe against Eastbourne Borough at Priory Lane. Photo: Roger Turner

Whitley Bay (Northern League) v Workington (Unibond Div 1) 1-0
Ian Chandler (stripes) goes close for Whitley Bay during their 1-0 win against Workington. Photo: Graham Brown

54	Brackley Town v	Ford United	1-1	80	
	Holmes	*Aransibia*			
	Ford United v	Brackley Town	*4-2	89	
	Bejeda, Rose (2), Woodards	*Dorrian, King*			
55	Witham Town v	Harlow Town	1-1	133	
	Brown	*Coley*			
	Harlow Town v	Witham Town	7-2	117	
	Coley, Cowley, Hooker(2) Salmon, Young(2)	*Driver (2)*			
56	Concord Rangers v	Stowmarket Town	1-2	57	
	Vallelly	*Aldis, Platt*			
57	Yeading v	Staines Town	1-1	138	
	Tucker	*Selby*			
	Staines Town v	Yeading	1-4	117	
	Newman	*Edwards, Miller (2), Telemaque*			
58	Dunstable Town v	Cogenhoe United	1-1	142	
	Castleman	*Westley*			
	Cogenhoe United v	Dunstable Town	*2-2	99	
	Freeman, Westley	*Carney, King*			
	(Dunstable Town won 4-2 on kicks from the penalty mark)				
59	Berkhamsted Town v	Brook House	3-2	222	
	Brockett, Richardson, Williams	*Gallagher (2)*			
60	Wembley v	Maldon Town	2-1	97	
	Davies (2)	*Huttley*			
61	Arlesey Town v	Cheshunt	2-0	216	
	Broughton, Catt				
62	Histon v	Yaxley	3-0	136	
	Cambridge (2), Jones				
63	Newmarket Town v	Hemel Hempstead T.	3-1	123	
	Rhodes, Shaw (2)	*Duckett*			
64	East Thurrock United v	Milton Keynes City	2-1	89	
	Carter, Double	*Hyde*			
65	Chessington & Hook Utd v	Eastleigh	2-5	119	
	Wicks (2)	*McAllister (3), Roberts (2)*			
66	Chertsey Town v	Fisher Athletic	0-6	138	
		Bowell, Dolby, Kwashi (2)			
67	Oxford City v	Leatherhead	2-0	185	
	Arkins, Mitchell				
68	Dartford v	Deal Town	1-1	283	
	Spriggs	*Pollard*			
	Deal Town v	Dartford	0-3	206	
		Arnold, Morgan, Morrish			
69	Horsham YMCA v	Thame United	0-0	95	
	Thame United v	Horsham YMCA	2-0	143	
	Cort, Simms				
70	Erith & Belvedere v	Greenwich Borough	3-2	146	
	Vercesi, White (2)	*Gibbs, Simpson*			
71	Hastings Town v	Chichester City Utd.	3-0	377	
	Ferguson, Honey, Simmonds				
72	Horsham v	Tonbridge Angels	2-0	382	
	Bird, McGowan				
73	Eastbourne Borough v	Whyteleafe	3-2	346	
	Crabb (2), More	*Dillon*			
74	Bracknell Town v	Cray Wanderers	3-1	132	
	Day, Osgood (2)	*Wood*			
75	Sittingbourne v	Lewes	1-1	215	
	Hales	*Newman*			
	Lewes v	Sittingbourne	6-3	171	
	Brackley (3),Francis,Harris,Shepherd	*Hales, Miller, Spice*			
76	Brockenhurst v	Bedfont	3-3	113	
	Rossi, Stone (2)	*Farbiszewski, Williams (2)*			
	Bedfont v	Brockenhurst	*2-3	91	
	Williams (2)	*Jones, Perkin, Stone*			
77*	Littlehampton Town v	Gosport Borough	3-3	113	
	Chester, Thornton	*Mann, Scammell, Wallsgrove*			
	Missing scorer				
	Gosport Borough v	Littlehampton Town	3-0	153	
	Scammell (2), Wallsgrove				

78	Carshalton Athletic v	Peacehaven & Telsc.	1-0	200	
	McKinzie				
79	Molesey v	Walton & Hersham	0-0	183	
	Walton & Hersham v	Molesey	0-1	188	
		Campard			
80	Andover v	Moneyfields	2-1	161	
	Kennedy, Rusher	*Bedden*			
81	Tooting & Mitcham Utd v	Corinthian Casuals	0-2	242	
		Russell-Smith, Watney			
82	Fareham Town v	Thatcham Town	2-1	144	
	Musselwhite, Woods	*Czastka*			
83	Windsor & Eton v	Lordswood	4-0	94	
	Catlin (2), Walton, Wojtowicz				
84	Egham Town v	Metropolitan Police	0-0	60	
	Metropolitan Police v	Egham Town	*1-1	73	
	Cormack	*McLaughlin*			
	(Egham Town won 5-3 after penalties)				
85	Hassocks v	Ash United	1-1	118	
	Hewitt	*Joyce*			
	Ash United v	Hassocks	0-3	120	
		Laing, Rendall			
86	St Leonards v	BAT Sports	3-0	161	
	Boateng, Chatelier, Ramsden				
87	Bashley v	Bognor Regis Town	3-0	293	
	Quirke, Robson, Tilley				
88	Dorking v	Whitstable Town	1-2	163	
	Coyle	*Toms (2)*			
89	Abingdon United v	Croydon Athletic	0-5	95	
		Fowler, Jones, Liddle (3)			
90	Bromley v	Hythe Town	1-0	246	
	Forbes				
91	Christchurch v	Bristol Manor Farm	2-0	107	
	Gogan, Nicholas				
92	Bideford v	Wimborne Town	1-0	270	
	Duff				
93	Chippenham Town v	Frome Town	3-0	625	
	Bright, Mings, Rawlins				
94	Elmore v	Swindon S'marine	1-2	115	
	Stansfield	*Fearon, Toomey*			
95	Cirencester Town v	Bournemouth	5-0	140	
	Belcher (3), Godley (2)				
96	Evesham United v	Bridgwater Town	1-3	184	
	Taylor	*Knox, Pope, Young*			
97	Weston Super Mare v	Mangotsfield United	3-4	218	
	Bevan (2), Cox	*Campbell (2), Seal (2)*			
98	Falmouth Town v	Odd Down	2-1	120	
	Sweet, Wheeler	*Colbourne*			
99	Highworth Town v	Brislington	2-1	163	
	Moss, Stewart	*Cherry*			
100	St Blazey v	Shortwood United	5-0	177	
	Band, Harrington, Hooper, Richardson				
101	Minehead Town v	Barnstaple Town	0-2	139	
		Murray, Squire			

STATISTICS FOR THE ROUND

Number of Games: 101 + 22 replays

Home Wins: 58	**Away Wins:** 43	**Draws:** 22
Home Goals: 230	**Away Goals:** 195	**Hat tricks:** 7

Best Home Win
Billingham Town v Fleetwood Freeport 7-0

Best Away Wins
Chertsey Town v Fisher Athletic 0-6
Shildon v Brigg Town 2-8

Best Attendance: Chippenham Town v Frome Town 625
Average Attendance: 171

SECOND QUALIFYING ROUND
Saturday 29 September 2001   £7,500 to each winning club

1	Blyth Spartans v Eccleshill United	5-0	555	
Innes, Radigan, Robson (2), Stewart				
2	Barrow v Kendal Town	3-0	1180	
Gaughan, Holt, Peverell				
3	Maine Road v Marine	0-2	228	
	Gautrey, Townsend			
4	Durham City v Lancaster City	0-0	289	
	Lancaster City v Durham City	2-1	215	
Haddow, Welch	*Ludlow*			
5	Spennymoor United v Billingham Town	6-1	145	
Banks (2), Grant, McGinnley				
Pickering, Suddick				
6	Gretna v Brigg Town	3-3	112	
Flannigan, Gordon, Henney	*Blanchard (2), Carter*			
	Brigg Town v Gretna	2-1	349	
Cadman, Drayton	*Dobie*			
7	Witton Albion v Whitley Bay	4-2	278	
Birdsey, Garrity	*Chandler, Walton*			
Prtichard, Rendell				
8	Gainsborough Trinity v Dunston FB	5-1	328	
Ellinston (2), Gore, Stanhope	*Fletcher*			
9	Whitby Town v Ramsbottom United	5-2	256	
Dunning (2), Rennison, Ure (2)	*O'Shaughnessy, Yorke-Robinson*			
10	Emley v Bamber Bridge	1-0	308	
Norbury				
11	Vauxhall Motors v Hyde United	2-1	358	
Fearns, Lynch	*Yeo*			
12	Worksop Town v Bishop Auckland	3-1	441	
Eshelby, Whitehead (2)	*Lee*			
13	Gateshead v Runcorn FC Halton	2-4	242	
Nelson, Preen	*Carragher, Lunt (3)*			
14	Ashton United v Stocksbridge P.S.	1-1	193	
Hamlet	*Hurlstone*			
	Stocksbridge Park Steels v Ashton United	*2-1	239	
Askey (2)	*Jefferson*			
15	Harrogate Town v Burscough	1-1	391	
Ord	*Bowen*			
	Burscough v Harrogate Town	*2-2	187	
Birch (2)	*Dunn, Whellans*			
(Harrogate Town won 5-4 after penalties)				
16	Liversedge v Harrogate Railway	3-3	215	
Flynn, Hatfield, Melvin	*Davey (2), Smith*			
	Harrogate Railway v Liversedge	2-1	191	
Hart, McLean	*Sykes*			
17	Thackley v Rossendale United	0-3	160	
18	Squires Gate v Bedlington Terriers	2-2	202	
Catlow, Longworth	*Gibb, Milner*			
	Bedlington Terriers v Squires Gate	4-0	471	
*Gibb, **Milner (3)***				
19	Pickering Town v Accrington Stanley	1-2	324	
Wood	*Mullin (2)*			
20	Bradford (Park Avenue) v Droylsden	3-2	297	
Calcutt, Hayward	*Brumskill, Kimmey*			
21	Colwyn Bay v Farsley Celtic	2-2	392	
Caton, McIlvogue	*Brooker, Lamb*			
	Farsley Celtic v Colwyn Bay	*3-1	187	
Lamb, Newton, Reagan	*Caton*			

22	Altrincham v Frickley Athletic	4-1	537	
*Hulme, **Thornley (3)***	*Fortheruiki*			
23	Redditch United v Kettering Town	0-0	660	
	Kettering Town v Redditch United	2-0	1044	
Collins, Watkins				
24	Grantham Town v Ilkeston Town	2-1	568	
Hawley, Ranshaw	*Kirkwood*			
25	Moor Green v Halesowen Town	0-2	561	
	Hall, Jones			
26	Newcastle Town v Stafford Rangers	0-1	580	
	O'Connor			
27	Stourport Swifts v Solihull Borough	2-0	207	
Booth (2)				
28	Bromsgrove Rovers v Tamworth	2-2	873	
Moore, Palmer	*Hallam (2)*			
	Tamworth v Bromsgrove Rovers	*1-0	724	
Wilson				
29	Bilston Town v Hinckley United	1-3	310	
Jackson	*Lucas (2), Penny*			
30	Stourbridge v Atherstone United	0-2	266	
	Beazeley, Redgate			
31	Arnold Town v Burton Albion	1-1	1156	
Mitchell	*Blought*			
	Burton Albion v Arnold Town	4-0	1329	
Stride, Wassall, Webster (2)				
32	Eastwood Town v Hucknall Town	0-1	422	
	Ricketts			
33	Belper Town v Barwell	2-1	256	
Cunningham, Payne	*Russell*			
34	Hednesford Town v Stafford Town	4-3	401	
Davis, Francis (2), Pickess				
35	Boreham Wood v Harlow Town	2-2	168	
Eberendu, Wotton	*Samuel*			
	Harlow Town v Boreham Wood	*0-0	216	
(Harlow Town won 4-2 after penalties)				
36	Bedford Town v Leyton	3-0	436	
Miller, Slinn, Tucker				
37	Clacton Town v Heybridge Swifts	3-2	302	
Bailey, Mayes, Springett	*Parker, Streetroy*			
38	Southend Manor v Hendon	1-2	203	
Wright	*Towler, Watson*			
39	Hoddesdon Town v Berkhamsted Town	0-2	134	
	Adebowale (2)			
40	Ford United v Yeading	1-2	97	
Rose	*Lee, Telemaque*			
(at Leyton Pennant FC)				
41	Northwood v Ipswich Wanderers	5-1	217	
Cook, Hale (2), Williams, Yaku	*Howell*			
42	Grays Athletic v Wingate & Finchley	4-1	186	
*Robinson, **Thomas (3)***	*Butterfield*			
43	Purfleet v Wealdstone	3-2	190	
Linger, Martin, Southon	*Hammatt, Tilbury*			
44	Chesham United v East Thurrock Utd.	2-0	238	
Andrews (2)				
45	Kings Lynn v Harrow Borough	1-0	916	
Robinson				

37

Blyth Spartans
(Unibond Premier) 5
Eccleshill United
(Northern Co East) 0

Eccleshill keeper
Stuart Wilkinson fails
to stop this Gary
Innes shot, giving
Blyth a two goal lead.
Photo:
William Broadley

Purfleet
(Ryman Premier) 3
Wealdstone
(Ryman Div 1) 2

Wealdstone's Billy
Amarteifio can only
watch as Purfleet's
Keith Martin fails to
connect with this
cross.
Photo:
Alan Coomes

Aylesbury United
(Ryman Div 1) 2
Arlesey Town
(Ryman Div 2) 0

Arlesey's Dave
Hatchett goes close
against Aylesbury at a
corner.
Photo:
Steve Ayre

Whitby Town
(Unibond Prem) 5
Ramsbottom United
(North West Co) 2

Whitby Town's
Richard Dunning
shoots and scores his
second of Whitby's
four goals at home to
Ramsbottom United.
Photo:
Neil Thaler

46	St Albans City v	Billericay Town	0-1	6	
		Carthy			
47	Hampton & Richmond B v	Hitchin Town	1-1	298	
	Maskell	*Marshall*			
	Hitchin Town v	Hampton & Rich B	2-1	243	
	Alturang, Bone	*Deegan*			
48	Burnham v	Wroxham	1-3	91	
	Dugdale	*Johnson (2), Pauling*			
49	Dunstable Town v	Cambridge City	2-3	294	
	Capehorn (2)	*Taylor (2), Wenlock*			
50	Aylesbury United v	Arlesey Town	2-0	414	
	Bangers, Clark				
51	Wembley v	St Margaretsbury	1-4	87	
	Acquah	***Howard (3)**, Lovett*			
52	Wisbech Town v	Stowmarket Town	0-2	377	
		Whatling, Yeomans			
53	Wootton Blue Cross v	Histon	0-1	134	
		Walker			
54	Braintree Town v	Chelmsford City	0-1	1093	
		Dobinson			
55	Canvey Island v	Somersett Am. V&E	9-1	453	
	*Bennett, **Boylan (3)**, Cobb (2),*				
	Gregory (2), Vaughan				
56	Newmarket Town v	Enfield	1-3	219	
	Stokes	*Cooper, Narty, Peterson*			
57	Lewes v	Gosport Borough	0-0	263	
	Gosport Borough v	Lewes	0-2	216	
		Shepherd (2)			
58	Croydon Athletic v	Dartford	2-2	175	
	Gibson, Liddle	*Godden (2)*			
	Dartford v	Croydon Athletic	4-2	329	
	Godden (2), Guiver, Morrish	*Fowler, Liddle*			
59	Windsor & Eton v	Oxford City	0-4	154	
		Billington, Mitchell, Whitehead			
60	Andover v	Bashley	1-1	305	
	Rusher	*Cooper*			
	Bashley v	Andover	0-2	272	
		Blake, Simpson			
61	Basingstoke Town v	Corinthian Casuals	6-0	369	
	Cook, Eaton(2), Fraser(2), Sills				
62	Bracknell Town v	Horsham	1-3	242	
	Day	*Dennis (2), Kirby*			
63	Maidenhead United v	Aldershot Town	1-1	917	
	Ibe	*Protheroe*			
	Aldershot Town v	Maidenhead United	1-0	1742	
	Forrester				
64	Brockenhurst v	Kingstonian	2-1	485	
	Bailey, Sheppards	*Bolt*			
65	Fareham Town v	Crawley Town	1-1	451	
	Woods	*Restarick*			
	Crawley Town v	Fareham Town	4-0	617	
	Bagnall, Carroll				
	Harlow, Restarick				
66	Hassocks v	Bromley	2-0	273	
	Rendall, Wilkins				
67	Erith & Belvedere v	Whitstable Town	3-0	199	
	Billeness (2), Marwa				
68	Carshalton Athletic v	Croydon	1-2	256	
	Hynes	*McDonnell (2)*			

69	Thame United v	Havant & W'looville	3-4	287	
	Cort, Saulsbury, Swaysland	*Daish, Hambley, O'Rourke*			
70	Welling United v	Egham Town	1-0	373	
	Abbott				
71	Sutton United v	Eastleigh	5-1	402	
	***Akuamoah (3)**, Haworth, Keevill*	*Puckett*			
72	Molesey v	Folkestone Invicta	1-3	316	
	Papa	*Dent, Dryden, Hogg*			
73	Fisher Athletic v	St Leonards	3-1	143	
	Dolby, Mighty, Taylor	*Barclay*			
74	Gravesend & Northfleet v	Eastbourne Borough	1-0	570	
	Wilkins				
75	Hastings Town v	Newport (IW)	0-2	516	
		Gibbons, Rew			
76	Christchurch v	Cirencester Town	1-3	190	
	Nicholas	*Carter, Godley, Minturn*			
77	Salisbury City v	Tiverton Town	3-3	586	
	Emms, Killick, Shepherd	*Nancekevill (2), Ovens*			
	Tiverton Town v	Salisbury City	3-1	779	
	Nancekevill, Pears (2)	*Mathie*			
78	Bath City v	Bideford	1-3	765	
	Powell	*Crook, Southgate*			
79	Merthyr Tydfil v	Bridgwater Town	4-1	385	
		Knox			
80	Barnstaple Town v	Worcester City	0-5	320	
		*Middleton, **Owen (3)**, Stant*			
81	Mangotsfield United v	Falmouth Town	10-1	279	
	Campbell (3), Seal (5)	*Pope*			
	Summers (2)				
82	Highworth Town v	Weymouth	0-3	305	
		Browne, Hutchinson, Rowbotham			
83	St Blazey v	Chippenham Town	3-1	401	
	Daly, Hooper, Richardson	*Rawlins*			
84	Swindon Supermarine v	Newport County	1-1	560	
	Toomey	*Eckhardt*			
	Newport County v	Swindon S'marine	3-1	455	
	Paul (2), Shephard	*Toomey*			

STATISTICS FOR THE ROUND

Number of Games: 84 + 19 replays

Home Wins: 51	**Away Wins:** 33	**Draws:** 19
Home Goals: 210	**Away Goals:** 148	**Hat tricks:** 9

Best Home Wins
Mangotsfield United v Falmouth Town 10-1
Canvey Island v Somersett Ambury V&E 9-1

Best Away Wins
Barnstaple Town v Worcester City 0-5
Windsor & Eton v Oxford City 0-4

Best Attendance
Aldershot Town v Maidenhead United 1742
Average Attendance: 398

Dartford
(Dr Martens East)   0
Gravesend &
Northfleet
(Dr Martens Prem)   2

Dartford's Danny
Evans (3) blocks this
shot from
Gravesend's Robert
Owen.
Photo:
Alan Coomes

Blyth Spartans
(Unibond Premier)   1
Harrogate Railway
(Northern Co East)   2

Andy Martin has
scored for the home
side, Blyth Spartans,
in their shock 2-1
defeat by Harrogate
Railway.
Photo:
Graham Brown

Tamworth
(Dr Martens Prem)   3
Wroxham
(Eastern Counties)   1

Gould slides home a
goal in Tamworth's
home victory over
Wroxham.
Photo: Steve Ayre

St Margaretsbury
(Spartan Sth Mids)   0
Stafford Rangers
(Dr Martens Prem)   3

Stafford goalkeeper
Richard Williams gets
down well to save at
the feet of James
Menage (St
Margaretsbury)
Photo: Francis Short

THIRD QUALIFYING ROUND

Saturday 13 October 2001   £10,000 to each winning club

No	Fixture		Score	Att
1	Farsley Celtic v	Brigg Town	2-2	252
	Newton, Reagan	Blanchard, Nevis		
	Brigg Town v	Farsley Celtic	*4-3	401
	Cadman, Carter, Hope, Lytollis	Newton (2), Spence		
2	Vauxhall Motors v	Harrogate Town	3-1	409
	Fearns (2), Young			
3	Lancaster City v	Stocksbridge P.S.	2-1	339
	Welch, Whittaker	Higgins		
4	Emley v	Accrington Stanley	1-0	433
	Thorpe			
5	Worksop Town v	Gainsborough Trinity	4-0	756
	Cropper, Godarrd, Townsend			
	Whitehead			
6	Altrincham v	Witton Albion	4-1	841
	Hawes, Murphy, Poland	Rendell		
	Thornley			
7	Barrow v	Rossendale United	1-1	1325
	Peverell	Gray		
	Rossendale United v	Barrow	*3-3	1023
	Patterson (2), Sargeson	Holt (2), Hulme		
	(Barrow won 5-3 after penalties)			
8	Whitby Town v	Spennymoor United	3-0	411
	Burt, Ingram, Ure			
9	Runcorn FC Halton v	Bedlington Terriers	2-2	396
	McNally, Watson	Bogie, Moat		
	Bedlington Terriers v	Runcorn FC Halton	4-1	821
	Chapman, Cockburn (2), Moat	Latham		
10	Marine v	Bradford (Park Ave.)	4-2	371
	Douglas, Morgan (2), Randles	Hayward, Maxwell		
11	Blyth Spartans v	Harrogate Railway	1-2	670
	Martin	Davey, Gore		
12	Chesham United v	Cambridge City	0-1	436
		O'Flynn		
13	Kings Lynn v	Clacton Town	3-2	1137
	Clarke, Fluff, Hayes	Hillier, Senk		
14	Halesowen Town v	Canvey Island	0-2	823
		Cobb, Miller		
15	St Margaretsbury v	Stafford Rangers	0-3	340
		Francis, Kiely, Simkin		
16	Belper Town v	Stowmarket Town	2-1	404
	Cunningham, Walsme	Platt		
17	Bedford Town v	Hednesford Town	2-0	736
	Paul, Slinn			
18	Burton Albion v	Berkhamsted Town	2-1	1378
	Moore, Stride	Morgan		
19	Enfield v	Yeading	3-4	81
	Ayres, Georgiou (2)	Edwards, Saroya, Telemaque		
20	Hucknall Town v	Stourport Swifts	2-0	289
	Chambers, Ricketts			
21	Billericay Town v	Grantham Town	2-1	642
	Simba (2)	Bull		
22	Kettering Town v	Northwood	3-0	1204
	Butcher, Collins, Natkins			
23	Hendon v	Hitchin Town	0-0	335
	Hitchin Town v	Hendon	*3-1	338
	Cretton, Marshall, Nolan	Ruggles		
24	Tamworth v	Wroxham	3-1	804
	Gould, Hallam, Rickards	Terrington		
25	Aylesbury United v	Atherstone United	3-1	543
	Bangura, Clarke, Marshall	Ejiofor		
26	Chelmsford City v	Harlow Town	1-1	835
	Lee	Salmon		
	Harlow Town v	Chelmsford City	3-0	636
	Salmon (2), Young			
27	Purfleet v	Grays Athletic	1-1	389
	Marshall	O'Sullivan		
	Grays Athletic v	Purfleet	3-2	487
	Fiddes, Thomas (2)	Marshall, Pashley		
28	Histon v	Hinckley United	3-3	284
	Cambridge, Farrington, Goddard	Gordon, Lenton, Penny		
	Hinckley United v	Histon	2-0	360
	Lucas, Titterton			
29	Aldershot Town v	Sutton United	3-0	1961
	Browne (2), Payne			
30	Basingstoke Town v	Bideford	3-1	523
	Davis, Eaton, Sills	Gough		
31	Merthyr Tydfil v	Mangotsfield United	3-3	476
	Carter, Lima, Staton	Campbell, Edwards, Seal		
	Mangotsfield United v	Merthyr Tydfil	4-1	769
	Edwards, Seal (2), Sims	Savage		
32	Welling United v	Newport (IW)	3-0	424
	Abbott, Flemming, Riviere			
33	Horsham v	Folkestone Invicta	1-2	549
	Warrilow	Dryden (2)		
34	Fisher Athletic v	Erith & Belvedere	4-0	245
	Huggins (3), Mighty			
35	Andover v	Newport County	0-4	642
		Clark, Plant (2), Ryan		
36	Dartford v	Gravesend & N'fleet	0-2	1270
		Martin, Owen		
37	Cirencester Town v	Brockenhurst	2-0	272
	Grange, Miller			
38	Croydon v	Havant & W'looville	0-1	168
		Hambley		
39	Weymouth v	Crawley Town	3-1	851
	Browne, Laws, Phillips	Restarick		
40	Lewes v	Hassocks	3-1	450
	Francis, Shepherd, Venables	Laing		
41	St Blazey v	Worcester City	2-3	596
	Daly, Richardson	Shepherd (2), Stant		
42	Tiverton Town v	Oxford City	3-1	676
	Everett, Lynch, Winter			

STATISTICS FOR THE ROUND

Number of Games: 42 + 8 replays

Home Wins: 31	Away Wins: 11	Draws: 8
Home Goals: 113	Away Goals: 64	Hat tricks: 1

Best Home Wins

Worksop Town v Gainsborough Trinity 4-0

Fisher Athletic v Erith & Belvedere 4-0

Best Away Win

Andover v Newport County 0-4

Best Attendance

Aldershot Town v Sutton United 1961

Average Attendance: 616

*Billericay Town
(Ryman Premier) 1
Tiverton Town
(Dr Martens Prem) 2*

*Tiverton sub Richard Pears heads the winning goal against Billericay in the FA Cup Fourth Qualifying Round.
Photo:
Alan Coomes*

*Tamworth
(Dr Martens Prem) 2
Cirencester Town
(Dr Martens West) 1*

*Tamworth v Cirencester. Gary Horgan (No 8) scores for Cirencester from a free kick.
Photo:
Paul Barber*

*Mangotsfield United
(Dr Martens West) 0
Lewes
(Ryman Div 2) 0*

*Mangotsfield's Darren Edwards gets in a shot as Marc Cable closes in. The 0-0 draw against Lewes was watched by a good crowd of 1151.
Photo:
Ken Gregory*

*Belper Town
(Unibond Div 1) 2
Worcester City
(Dr Martens Prem) 2*

*Worcester keeper Paul Wyatt reaches the ball first with Belper's Carl Cunningham and Karl Payne closing in.
Photo:
Bill Wheatcroft*

FOURTH QUALIFYING ROUND

Saturday 27 October 2001   £20,000 to each winning club

(C) Stalybridge Celtic *Clements 8 Pickford 59*	2 v 1	Bedlington Terriers (NL) *Teasdale 90*	812
(NCE) Harrogate Rlwy *Davey 12 Hart 21*	2 v 3	Morecambe (C) *Drummond 3 Curtis 90 Hardiker 34*	900
(C) Telford United *Smith 31*	1 v 1	Northwich Victoria (C) *Blundell 35*	1,004
Northwich Victoria *Mike 30 Devlin 90*	2 v 1	Telford United *Edwards 68*	1,063
(C) Doncaster Rovers *Paterson11(p),65 Jackson 16*	3 v 2	Emley (U-P) *Hatto 22(p) Day 83*	2,730
(C) Boston United	0 v 1	Brigg Town (NCE) *Roach 44*	1,727
(C) Leigh RMI *Twis 12 Whitehead 90 (o.g.)*	2 v 4	Worksop Town (U-P) *Townsend 2 Cropper 39 Whitehead 32 Smith A 80*	674
(U-P) Barrow *Holt 58*	1 v 0	Chester City (C)	2,833
(U-P) Altrincham *Thornley 45(P),65 Hulme 63*	3 v 0	Nuneaton Borough (C)	1,306
(U-P) Marine *Townsend 21*	1 v 1	Southport (C) *Lane 5*	1,305
Southport *Jones R 24 Jones L 61*	2 v 1	Marine *Hussin 90*	1,145
(U-P) Whitby Town *Williams I 15 Ure 57 Burt 90*	3 v 1	Scarborough (C) *Stamp 8*	1,862
(U-P) Lancaster City *Mayers 10 Welch 52*	2 v 2	Vauxhall Motors (U-P) *Cumiskey 30(P),53*	630s
Vauxhall Motors	0 v 1	Lancaster City *Whittaker 40*	601
Kings Lynn	0 v 4	Farnborough Town (C) *PIPER L. 3(8, 24,65) Vansittart 79*	1,758
(C) Dover Athletic	0 v 1	Hereford United (C) *Williams G 31*	1.221
(R-1) Harlow Town *Tompkins 36*	1 v 2	Bedford Town (R-P) *Paul 13 Slinn 48*	940
(DM-P) Havant &W'ville *Connelly 50*	1 v 1	Barnet (C) *Purser 17*	1,143
Barnet *PURSER 3 (35,37,39)*	3 v 0	Havant &Waterlooville	1,414
(R-P) Grays Athletic *Boardman 10 (O.G.) Fiddes 27*	2 v 0	Margate (C)	832
(U-1) Belper Town *Kennedy 26 Morgan 56*	2 v 2	Worcester City (DM-P) *Heeley 24 Middleton 51*	1,228
Worcester City *Heeley 16 Middleton 80,84*	3 v 1	Belper Town *Cunningham 89*	2,377
(R-1) Yeading	0 v 5	Aylesbury United (R-1) *MARSHALL 3(17,18,48) Maynard 37 Clarke 64*	340
(C) Hayes *HODGES 3 (2,39,89)*	3 v 1	Yeovil Town (C) *Turner 38*	1,182

(U-P) Hucknall Town *Kennerdale 50*	1 v 1	Cambridge City (DM-P) *Holden 14*	593
Cambridge City *Wilkins 3,40 Pope 84*	3 v 1	Hucknall Town *Miller 40*	398
(C) Woking	0 v 0	Newport County (DMP)	2,119
Newport County *Ryan 11,65 Paul79*	3 v 1	Woking *Moore 30*	1,431
(DM-P) Folkestone Inv. *Dryden 10*	1 v 1	Welling United (DM-P) *Abbott 31*	724
Welling United *POWELL 3 (35,47,72) Overton 39 Edwards 53*	5 v 1	Folkestone Invicta *Hogg 28*	1,026
(DM-W) Mangotsfield U	0 v 0	Lewes (R-2)	1,154
Lewes *Stokes 31 Shepherd 77*	2 v 0	Mangotsfield United	1,802
(C) Stevenage Borough	0 v 0	Kettering Town	1,937
Kettering Town *Norman 31 Collins 60*	2 v 0	Stevenage Borough *Warimull 31*	2,079
(U-P) Burton Albion	0 v 2	Gravesend & N (R-P) *Stadhart 27 McKimm 33*	1,647
(DM-E) Fisher Athletic *Powell 20*	1 v 3	Forest Green R (C) *Howey 15 Futcher 37 Odejayl 88*	420
(R-P) Aldershot Town *Parker 32 Browne 64*	2 v 1	Hitchin Town (R-P) *Sarll 72*	2,238
(R-P) Billericay Town *Williams L 57*	1 v 2	Tiverton Town (DM-P) *Rogers 52 Pears 63*	926
(R-P) Basingstoke Town *Davis 30 Sills 38*	2 v 2	Dagenham & Red (C) *Charlery 56 Roberts 90**	1,089
Dagenham & Redbridge *McDougald 3 Bristow 42 (o.g.) Charlery 73*	2 v 1	Basingstoke Town	2,079
(DM-P) Weymouth *Browne S 70 (Pen)*	1 v 2	Hinckley Utd. (DM-P) *Lucas 72 Lenton 90*	1,258
(DM-P) Tamworth *Gould 26 Colley 84*	2 v 1	Cirencester T (DM-W) *Horgan 40*	1,210
(R-P) Canvey Island *TILSON 3(17(p),68,72) Miller 35 Vaughan 36*	5 v 1	Stafford Rangers (DM-P) *Kiely 56*	561

STATISTICS FOR THE ROUND

Number of Games: 32 + 11

Home Wins: 20   **Away Wins:** 12   **Draws:** 11

Home Goals: 73   **Away Goals:** 56   **Hat tricks:** 6

Best Home Wins
Welling United v Folkestone Invicta   5-1
Canvey Island v Stafford Rangers   5-1

Best Away Wins
Yeading v Aylesbury United   0-5
Kings Lynn v Farnborough Town   0-4

Best Attendance
Barrow v Chester City 2833

Average Attendance: 1293

Bedford Town (Ryman Premier) v Peterborough United (Football League Div 3) 0-0. David Farrell heads just over the bar for Peterborough United at Bedford Town in the FA Cup First Round tie. Photo: Peter Barnes

Lewes (Ryman Div 2) v Stoke City (Football League Div 2) 0-2 (played at Stoke). Lewes players enjoy a standing ovation at Stoke City. Photo: Bill Wheatcroft

Grays Athletic (Ryman Premier) v Hinckley United (Dr Martens Premier) 1-2. Grays' goalkeeper Jamie Lunan is beaten by a deflected free kick for Hinckley's winning goal in this First Round tie. Photo: Francis Short

FIRST ROUND PROPER

Hayes 3 v 4 Wycombe W.
Warner K 36, Clark 41(p)   3475   Rammell 26, 74
Warner D 86   Currie 45, 84

HAYES: Bossu, Spencer, Gallen, Grey, Sterling, Charles, Clark, Dyer, Hodge (sub 81 mins Currie), Molesley (sub 79 mins Warner D) Warner K.

Aldershot Town 0 v 0 Bristol Rovers
5059
ALDERSHOT: Howells, Coll, Chewins, Kirby, Adedejl, Bentley, Graham, Harford (sub 72 mins Protheroe), Browne (sub 72 mins Forrester), Watson, Parker A.

Bristol Rovers 1 v 0 **Aldershot Town**
Astafjevs 85   4848
ALDERSHOT: Howells, Coll, Kirby, Adedejl, Chewins, Graham, Protheroe, Harford (sub 88 mins Watson), Bentley, Parker (sub 75 mins Gell), Browne (sub 75 mins Payne)

Altrincham 1 v 1 **Lancaster City**
Thornley 6   2076   Whittaker 12
ALTRINCHAM: Coburn, Scott G, Adams, Maddox, Sertori, Hawes, Hulme, Craney, Murphy, Gallagher (sub 70 mins Swannick) Thornley
LANCASTER: Thornley, Haddow, Lyons, Kilbane, Mayers, Clitheroe, L., Martin, Butler, Botts (sub 75 mins Holiday), Whittaker (sub 90 mins Rigby), Brown.

Lancaster City 1 v 4 **Altrincham**
Mayers 21   1934   **Poland 3 (40, 106, 120)**
                          Thornley 119 (Pen)
LANCASTER: Thornley, Haddow, Lyons, Clitheroe L. (sub 79 mins Holiday), Kilbane, Mayers, Martin, Butler, Whittaker, Brown, Potts.
ALTRINCHAM: Coburn, Scott G, Adams, Maddox, Serton, Hawes, Hulme (sub 98 mins Swannick), Craney, Gallagher (sub 33 mins Poland), Thornley, Murphy (sub 98 mins Hargreaves)*

Barnet 0 v 0 Carlisle
2277
BARNET: Harrison, Gledhill, Flynn, Sawyers, Heald, Arber, Niven, Bell (sub 77 mins Midgley), Gower, Strevens, Purser

Carlisle 1 v 0 **Barnet**
Soley 57   1470
BARNET: Harrison, Sawyers, Heald, Arber, Flynn, Bell (sub 59 mins Toms), Niven (sub 70 mins Midgley), Gledhill, Gower, Purser, Strevens.

Bedford Town 0 v 0 Peterborough
2581
BEDFORD TOWN: Heeps, Haley, Harvey, Convington (sub 50 mins Wilson), Jackman, Turner, Dyer, Adams, Slinn, Paul, Miller

Peterborough 2 v 1 **Bedford Town**
Clarke 19, Fenn 59   5751   Slinn 54
BEDFORD TOWN: Heeps, Haley (sub 81 mins Lawley), Harvey, Wilson, Jackman, Turner, Dyer, Adams, Slinn, Paul, Miller.

Blackpool 2 v 2 **Newport County**
Jaszczun 35   5005   Hughes 18 (og), Clark 36
MacKenzie 76 (Pen)
NEWPORT: Mountain, Robinson, Benton, Clark, Eckhardt, Davies, Perry, Ryan, Rose, Shepherd (sub 72 mins Cowe), James (sub 83 mins Walker)

Newport 1 v 4 Blackpool
Rose 24   3721   Ormerod 65, 115,
                       Murphy J 91
                       Benton 114 (OG)
NEWPORT: Mountain, Robinson, Benton, Clark, Eckhardt, Davies, Perry (sub 48 mins Cowe), Ryan, Rose, Shepherd (sub 110 mins Paul), James.

Bournemouth 3 v 0 **Worksop Town**
Hughes 14, Hayter (26)   4414
Fletcher, S (77)
WORKSOP: Holmshaw, Kotylo, Davis, Bradshaw, Bennett (sub 68 mins Ludlam), Gray (sub 74 mins Waddle), Smith G, Smith C, (sub 70 mins Smith A,) Whitehead, Townsend, Cropper.

Brentford 1 v 0 **Morecambe**
Gibbs 77   4026
MORECAMBE: Mawson, Fensome, Colkin (sub 43 mins Murphy), McGuire, Hardiker, Drummond, Thompson, Rigoglioso, Talbot, Arnold (sub 82 mins Curtis), Perkins

---

Dagenham& Redbridge 1 v 0 **Southport**
Stein 25 (pen)   1736
DAGENHAM & REDBRIDGE: Roberts, McDlougald, Vickers, Goodwin, Heffer, Janney, Terry, Shipp, Stein (sub 80 mins Charlery), Hazelden, Smith
SOUTHPORT: Dickinson, Macauley, Grayston, Teale, Robertson (sub 46 mins Whittaker), Clark, Bauress (sub 81 mins Sullivan), Jones, S, Parke, Whitehall (sub 85 mins Leadbetter), Elam

---

Doncaster Rovers 2 v 3 Scunthorpe
Tierney 20 Watson 40   6222   Hodges 42,
                                      Carruthers 45
                                      Calvo-Garcia 62
DONCASTER: Richardson, Marples, Barrick, Kelly, Miller, Hawkins, Tierney, Owen, Barnes (sub 76 mins Sale), Jackson, Watson (sub 76 mins Whitman)

Exeter 3 v 0 **Cambridge City**
Curran 43, Tomlinson 62   2849
Roscoe 90
CAMBRIDGE CITY: Nurse, Nacca (sub 83 mins Taylor), Fox, Holden, Wignall, Challinor (sub 70 mins Pope), Nightingale, Wenlock, Wilde, Wilkin, Hann

---

Gray's Athletic 1 v 2 **Hinckley United**
Locke 52   1133   Hunter 48, Lenton 67
GRAY'S ATH: Lunan, Robinson, Halle, O'Sullivan (sub 85 mins Abraham), Sussex, Siddes (sub 74 mins Morgan), McCloud, Rainford, Thomas, Edwards, Lock
HINCKLEY: Beattie, Cartwright, Lenton, Hadland, Penny, Eustace, Storer, Coates, Hunter, Lucas (sub 67 mins Gordon), Wilkes

Halifax 2 v 1 Farnborough Town
Middleton 35, Wood 52 1914 *Piper 50*
FARNBOROUGH: Bonfield, Warner, Bunce (sub 70 mins Dublin), Patterson, Laker (sub 90 mins Harper), Annon, Piper, C, Watson, Taggert, Piper, L, Baptiste

Huddersfield 2 v 1 Gravesend & Northfleet
Moses 63, Knight 90 6112 *Clarke 2 (og)*
GRAVESEND: Turner, Lee, Lye (sub 86 mins McKinn), Barnett, Martin, Duku, Smith, Owen, Jackson, Wilkins (sub 75 mins Hatch), Stadhart (sub 66 mins Booth)

Kettering Town 1 v 6 Cheltenham
Norman 4 2942 *Naylor 39, 63,*
Alsop 44, 74,
Howells 87, Devaney 89
KETTERING: Bowling, Hughes (sub 55 mins Inman), Matthews, Perkins, Norman, Piercewright (sub 82 mins Lenagh), Butcher, Fear, Murray, Watkins, Collins

Macclesfield 2 v 2 Forest Green Rovers
Macclesfield won 11-10 after penalty kicks
Lambert 17, 79 1520 *Meechan 45,*
Cooper 82 (pen)
FOREST GREEN: Perrin, Cousins, Jenkins, Cooper, Impey, Foster (sub 80 mins Daley), Travis, Howey, Odiejayl, Meechan, Langan

Forest Green Rovers 1 v 1 Macclesfield
Cooper 29 1714 *Keen 33*
FOREST GREEN: Perrin, Cousins, Jenkins, Cooper, Impey, Foster M, Travis, Howey, Odiejayl (sub 56 mins Heggs), Meechan, Langan

Northwich Victoria 2 v 5 Hull City
Blundell 73, Mike 80 2285 *Johnsson 13, Matthews 39*
Dudfield 42, Alexander 79
Barnard 83
NORTHWICH: Gibson, Bardsley, (sub 72 mins Quinn), Barnard, Talbot, Burke, Norris, Garvey, Collins (sub 72 mins Skinner), Ingram, Mike, Blundell

Oldham 1 v 1 Barrow
Duxbury 32 5795 *Housham 8*
BARROW: Bishop, Shaw, Maxfield, Hall, Hume, Anthony, Housham, Gaughan, Peverell (sub 70 mins Waters), Warren, Holt

Barrow 0 v 1 Oldham
4368 *Eyres D*
BARROW: Bishop, Shaw, Maxfield, Hall, Hume, Anthony, Housham, Gaughan, Peverrell, Warren, Holt.

Port Vale 3 v 0 Aylesbury United
Burgess 54, Cummins 70 4956
Brooker 90
AYLESBURY:Wheeler, Williams, Risley (sub 72 mins Clarke, S), Gordon,Clark, D (sub 67 mins Joe), Honeyball, Maynard, Silvestri, Marshall (sub 81 mins Clifford), Bangura, Stanbridge

Reading 1 v 0 Welling United
Cureton 61 5338
WELLING: Knight, Hone, Edwards, Watts, Riviere, Lindsay, Rutherford, Overton, Barnes, Abbot(sub 46 mins Fleming), Powell (sub 55 mins Standen)

Staylbridge Celtic 0 v 3 Chesterfield
3503 *Beckett 20,*
Scott 23(OG), D'Auria 70
STALYBRIDGE: Batty, Murphy, Scott, Crookes (sub 36 mins Clements), Woods, Beesley, Peacock, Bushell (sub 78 mins Parr), Courtney, Wood, Pickford

Tamworth 1 v 1 Rochdale
Wilson 42 3199 *Doughty 5*
TAMWORTH : Acton, Warner, Mutchell, Gould, Crocutt, Turner, Foy, Mills (sub 79 mins Hatton), Bailey (sub 73 mins Rickards, Wilson, Colley

Rochdale 1 v 0 Tamworth
Oliver 89 2709
TAMWORTH: Acton, Warner,Mutchell, Gould, Grocutt, Turner, Foy, Mills, Hallam, Bailey (sub 72 mins Hatton), Colley.

Tiverton Town 1 v 3 Cardiff C.
Nancekivell 82 6648 *Brayson 34, Hamilton 55,*
Earnshaw 73
TIVERTON: Edwards, Winter,Saunders (sub 60 mins Chenoweth), Tatterton, Marker, Rogers, Nancekivell, Pears (sub 78 mins Mudge), Everett (sub 60 mins Ovens), Steel, Leonard
played @ Ninian Pk

Tranmere 4 v 1 Brigg Town
Navarro 19, Price 64, 77 7693 *Leech 78*
Flynn 87
BRIGG TOWN: Jordon, Raspin, Nevis, Thompson, Hope, Blanchard, (sub 56 mins Cadman), Rowland, Stones (sub 69 mins Leech), Roach, Drayton (sub 43 mins Wilby), Carter

Whitby Town 1 v 1 Plymouth
Gidea 43 2202 *Phillips 72*
WHITBY: Naisbett, Rennison, Logan, Goodchild, Dixon, Gidea (sub 73 mins Veart), Williams I, Williams G, Robinson, Burt (sub 89 mins Key), Ure (sub 90 mins Ingram)

Plymouth 3 v 2 Whitby Town
Bent 16, Stonebridge 40 5941 *Burt 69, Robinson 72*
Phillips 45
WHITBY: Naisbett, Rennison, Goodchild, Dixon, Logan, Key, Robinson, Williams G, Gidea (sub 51 mins Allen)

Wigan 0 v 1 Canvey Island
3671 *Gregory 88*
CANVEY I: Harrison, Kennedy, Duffy, Chenery, Bodley, Smith, Bennett (sub 85 mins Vaughan), Dicks, Gregory, Miller, Knight (sub 75 mins Boylan)

Worcester City 0 v 1 Rushden & Diamonds
33134 *Hanlon 67*
WORCESTER: McDonnell, Davies A, Jukes, Carty, Weir, Ellis, Bullock, Heeley, Shepherd, Stant (sub 89 mins Burrow), Hyde (sub 77 mins McFarlane)

Hereford United 1 v 0 Wrexham
Wright 9 4107
HEREFORD: Baker, Shirley, Capaldi, Robins Wright, James T, Quiggin, Snape, Voice (sub 66 mins Elmes), Williams G, Parry

Lewes 0 v 2 Stoke - played at Stoke
7081 *Handyside 18,*
Gunnarsson 57
LEWES: Standen, Harris (sub 84 mins Beeston), Johnson C, McCallum, Hack, Cable, Dicker (sub 46 mins Johnson A), Stokes, Francis, Thomsett, Venables (sub 66 mins Shepherd)

Bristol Rovers (Football League Div 3) v Aldershot Town (Ryman Premier) 1-0. Photo: Ian Morsman

Whitby Town (Unibond Premier) v Plymouth Argyle (Football League Div 3) 1-1.
Whitby Town captain D Logan with Plymouth captain P Wotton

Tamworth (Dr Martens Premier) v Rochdale (Football League Div 3) 1-1. Tamworth put the Rochdale defence
under pressure. Photo: Paul Barber

Exeter City   3
(Football League D3)
Cambridge City   0
(Dr Martens Premier)

*Cambridge City's
Rob Nightingale is
just outjumped in a
heading duel with
Exeter skipper Chris
Curran.
Photo: Ken Gregory*

Huddersfield Town (Football League Div 2) v Gravesend & Northfleet (Ryman Premier) 2-1
Gravesend go close against Huddersfield Town with this first minute corner. Photo: Bill Wheatcroft

Barnet (Conference) v Carlisle United (Football League Div 3) 0-0
Barnet's Greg Heald outjumps Carlisle's Mark Winstanley but puts his header just over. Photo: Alan Coomes

SECOND ROUND

Altrincham | 1 | v | 2 | Darlington
Maddox 69 | | 3302 | | *Chillingworth 22, Wainwright 73*

ALTRINCHAM:

Coburn, Locke, Swannick, Maddox, Serton, Hawes, Hulme (sub 45 mins Hargreaves) (sub 88 mins Taylor), Craney, Poland (sub 68 mins Furlong), Thornley, Murphy

---

Exeter City | 0 | v | 0 | Dagenham & Redbridge
| | 4082 | |

DAGENHAM & REDBRIDGE:

Roberts, Janney, Rooney, Smith, Vickers, Broom (sub 52 mins Hazelden) Terry (sub 79 mins Hill), Heffer, Shipp, Stein (sub 86 mins McDougald), Charlery

---

Hinckley United | 0 | v | 2 | Cheltenham Town
| | 2661 | | *Naylor 5, Alsop 49*

HINCKLEY UNITED:

Beattie, Cartwright, Lenton, Penny, Coates (sub 55 mins Gordon), Eustace, Storer, Hunter (sub 75 mins Jenkins), Lucas, Titterton (sub 80 mins Hadland), Wilkes

---

Swindon Town | 3 | v | 2 | Hereford United
Invincible 11 | | 7699 | | *Williams, G 13,*
Edwards, P 53 | | | | *Wright 27*
Howe 76 | | | |

HEREFORD UNITED:

Baker, Clarke, Capaldi, Wright, James, T, Quiggin (sub 83 mins Kevan), Snape, Goodwin, Elmes (sub 83 mins Davidson), Williams, G, Parry

---

Canvey Island | 1 | v | 0 | Northampton Town
Gregory 48 | | 3232 | |

CANVEY ISLAND:

Harrison, Kennedy, Duffy, Chenery, Dicks, Smith, Vaughan (sub 82 mins Boyland), Stimson (sub 75 mins Bennett), Gregory, Miller, Parmenter (sub 89 mins Ward)

AXA SPONSORED F.A. CUP
PRIZE MONEY

	EP	P	1st Q.	2nd Q.	3rd Q.	4th Q.	1	2	TOTAL
Canvey Island				7,500	10,000	20,000	20,000	30,000	87,500
Dagenham & Redbridge						20,000	20,000	30,000	70,000
Altrincham				7,500	10,000	20,000	20,000		57,500
Hinckley United				7,500	10,000	20,000	20,000		57,500
Brigg Town	500	1,000	7,500	7,500	10,000	20,000			46,500
Aylesbury United		1,000	7,500	7,500	10,000	20,000			46,000
Lewes		1,000	7,500	7,500	10,000	20,000			46,000
Hereford United						20,000	20,000		40,000
Aldershot Town				7,500	10,000	20,000			37,500
Barrow				7,500	10,000	20,000			37,500
Bedford Town				7,500	10,000	20,000			37,500
Cambridge City				7,500	10,000	20,000			37,500
Gravesend & Northfleet				7,500	10,000	20,000			37,500
Grays Athletic				7,500	10,000	20,000			37,500
Kettering Town				7,500	10,000	20,000			37,500
Lancaster City				7,500	10,000	20,000			37,500
Newport County				7,500	10,000	20,000			37,500
Tamworth				7,500	10,000	20,000			37,500
Tiverton Town				7,500	10,000	20,000			37,500
Welling United				7,500	10,000	20,000			37,500
Whitby Town				7,500	10,000	20,000			37,500
Worcester City				7,500	10,000	20,000			37,500
Bedlington Terriers		1,000	7,500	7,500	10,000				26,000
Belper Town		1,000	7,500	7,500	10,000				26,000
Cirencester Town		1,000	7,500	7,500	10,000				26,000
Fisher Athletic		1,000	7,500	7,500	10,000				26,000
Harlow		1,000	7,500	7,500	10,000				26,000
Harrogate Railway		1,000	7,500	7,500	10,000				26,000
Mangotsfield United		1,000	7,500	7,500	10,000				26,000
Yeading		1,000	7,500	7,500	10,000				26,000

All Conference clubs entering the competition in the Fourth Qualifying Round and winning one tie received £20,000 and it was good to see a number of Vase level clubs receiving prize money which must have been beyond their imagination in previous years e.g. £16,000 was won by Andover, Bideford, Berkhamsted, Brockenhurst, Hassocks, Horsham, St. Blazey, Stourport Swifts, Stowmarket Town, St. Margaretsbury and Wroxham for their success in the Preliminary and First and Second Qualifying Rounds.

AXA SPONSORED F.A. CUP
ATTENDANCE COMPARISON
Seasons 2000-01 - 2001-02

PRELIMINARY & QUALIFYING ROUNDS

Season	Round	Games	Total Attendance	Average Attendance
2000-01	Extra Preliminary	19	2,515	13
	Preliminary	240	32,688	136
	1st Qualifying	119	19,319	162
	2nd Qualifying	106	37,523	354
	3rd Qualifying	52	23,180	446
	4th Qualifying	42	43,431	1,034
TOTAL		**578**	**158,656**	
2001-02	Extra Preliminary	15	2,135	142
	Preliminary	230	28,444	124
	1st Qualifying	123	20,979	171
	2nd Qualifying	103	40,971	398
	3rd Qualifying	50	30,801	616
	4th Qualifying	43	55,619	1,293
TOTAL		**564**	**178,949**	

COMPETITION PROPER

Season	Round	Games	Total Attendance	Average Attendance
2000-01	1st Proper	48	171,399	3,571
	2nd Proper	26	123,420	4,747
	3rd Proper	40	575,052	14,376
	4th Proper	19	398,241	20,960
	5th Proper	11	250,899	22,809
	6th Proper	4	100,663	25,165
	Semi-Final	2	103,578	51,789
	Final	1	72,500	
TOTAL		**151**	**1,795,752**	
2001-02	1st Proper	52	198,937	3,825
	2nd Proper	24	120,358	5,015
	3rd Proper	38	564,855	14,865
	4th Proper	17	330,365	19,433
	5th Proper	9	244,356	27,151
	6th Proper	5	173,492	34,698
	Semi-Final	2	97,315	48,658
	Final	1	73,963	
TOTAL		**148**	**1,803,641**	

AXA SPONSORED F.A. CUP
TOP GOAL SCORERS

David Seal (Mangotsfield United)
Photo: Pete Norton

11 GOALS
Seal D — Mangotsfield United

8 GOALS
Thornley R — St Margaretsbury

6 GOALS
Clark S — Aylesbury United
Marshall D — Aylesbury United
Milner J — Bedlington Terriers
Ludlow L — Durham City
Newton C — Farsley Celtic
Davey S — Harrogate Railway
Campbell S — Mangotsfield United
Yaku L — Northwood
Mitchell J — Oxford City

5 GOALS
Osgood D — Bracknell Town
Cadman L — Brigg Town
Stone P — Brockenhurst
Naylor T — Cheltenham Town
Fowler J — Croydon Athletic
Liddle S — Croydon Athletic
Godden R — Dartford
McAllister C — Eastleigh
Rose C — Ford United
Thomas N — Grays Athletic
Shepherd D — Lewes

5 GOALS cont.
Greenacre C — Mansfield Town
Ulatowski P — Somersett & A V&E
Richardson D — St Blazey
Booth L — Stouport Swifts
Driver G — Witham Town

4 GOALS
Poland L — Altrincham
Bangura C — Aylesbury United
Holt G — Barrow
Williams J — Bedfont
Slinn K — Bedford Town
Gibb D — Bedlington Terriers
Cunningham C — Belper Town
Rowntree P — Billingham Town
Lytollis P — Brigg Town
Ellington N — Bristol Rovers
Boylan L — Canvey Island
Gregory N — Canvey Island
Alsop J — Cheltenham Town
Wicks N — Chessington & H U
Matthews I — Easington Colliery
Dolby T — Fisher Athletic
Dryden J — Folkestone Invicta
Dobie M — Gretna
Salmon M — Harlow Town
Lucas A — Hinckley United
Wolff C — Hornchurch
Francis S — Lewes
Danks P — Redditch United
Currier D — Rushall Olympic
Court W — Thame United
Koumas J — Tranmere Rovers
Price J — Tranmere Rovers
Moore C — Uxbridge
Defoe J — West Ham United
Ure L — Whitby Town
Toms M — Whitstable Town
Rendell C — Witton Albion
Middleton D — Worcester City
Whitehead L — Worksop Town

Rob Thornley (Altrincham)
Photo: Colin Stevens

Steve Clark (Aylesbury United)
Photo: Andrew Chitty

AXA SPONSORED F.A. CUP
50 HAT-TRICKS (THREE GOALS)

EXTRA PRELIMINARY ROUND - 2

	Woods J	Marske United
	Greenhill R	Newcastle Blue Star

PRELIMINARY ROUND - 19

5	Clark S	Aylesbury United
4	Ulatowski P	Somersett Ambury V & E
4	Moore C	Uxbridge
	Morrow G	Bedfont
	Smith B	Berkhamsted Town
	Osgood D	Bracknell Town
	Wardle P	Cheadle Town
	Fowler J	Croydon Athletic
	Ludlow L	Durham City
	Matthews I	Easington Colliery
	Tomlinson P	Lincoln United
	Mitchell J	Oxford City
	Danks P	Redditch United
	Fearon D	Stocksbridge Park Steels
	Kane C	Tooting & Mitcham United
	Tunnell L	Uxbridge
	Acquah D	Wembley
	Cannie S	Wimborne
	Driver G	Witham

1st QUALIFYING ROUND - 7

Lytollis P	Brigg Town
Belcher M	Cirencester Town
Liddle	Croydon Athletic
McAllister C	Eastleigh
Maddock W	Kendal Town
Brackley P	Lewes
Brierley R	Ramsbottom United
Howard R	St Margaretsbury

2nd QUALIFYING ROUND - 10

5	Seal D	Mangotsfield United
	Thornley R	Altrincham
	Milner J	Bedlington Terriers
	Boylan L	Canvey Island
	Thomas N	Grays Athletic
	Campbell S	Mangotsfield United
	Seal D	Mangotsfield United
	Lunt G	Runcorn FC Halton
	Howard R	St Margaretsbury
	Akuamoah E	Sutton United
	Owen M	Worcester City

3rd QUALIFYING ROUND - 1

Huggins L	Fisher Athletic

4th QUALIFYING ROUND - 6

Marshall D	Aylesbury
Purser W	Barnet
Tilson S	Canvey Island
Piper L	Farnborough Town
Hodges I	Hayes
Powell D	Welling United

1st ROUND PROPER - 1

Poland L	Altrincham

2nd ROUND PROPER - 2

Greenacre C	Mansfield Town
Koumas J	Tranmere Rovers

3rd ROUND PROPER - 2

Ellington N	Bristol Rovers
Moore I	Burnley

AXA SPONSORED F.A. CUP
RESULTS OF THE ROUNDS

1st QUALIFYING ROUND

Squires Gate *North West Counties Div 2*	3	v	2	Ossett Town *Unibond Div 1*
Tooting & Mitcham U *Ryman Div 1*	0	v	2	Corinthian Casuals *Ryman Div 1*
Hertford Town *Ryman Div 3*	0	v	4	St Margaretsbury *Spartan South Midlands*
Evesham United *Dr Martens Western*	1	v	3	Bridgwater Town *Western Premier*

2nd QUALIFYING ROUND

Hassocks *Sussex Div 1*	2	v	0	Bromley *Ryman Div 1*
Moor Green *Dr Martens Premier*	0	v	1	Halesowen Town *Dr Martens Western*
Brockenhurst *Wessex*	2	v	1	Kingstonian *Ryman Premier*
Bath City *Dr Martens Premier*	1	v	3	Bideford Town *Western Premier*

3rd QUALIFYING ROUND

Blyth Spartans *Unibond Premier*	1	v	2	Harrogate Railway *Northern Counties East Premier*
Bedlington Terriers *Northern Div 1*	4	v	1	Runcorn FC Halton *Unibond Premier*
Harlow Town *Ryman Div 1*	3	v	0	Chelmsford City *Dr Martens Premier*
Mangotsfield United *Dr Martens Western*	4	v	1	Merthyr Tydfil *Dr Martens Premier*

4th QUALIFYING ROUND

Boston United *Conference*	0	v	1	Brigg Town *Northern Counties East Premier*
Whitby Town *Unibond Premier*	3	v	1	Scarborough *Conference*
Newport County *Dr Martens Premier*	3	v	1	Woking *Conference*
Grays Athletic *Ryman Premier*	2	v	0	Margate *Conference*

Who will be celebrating this season?

Leatherhead celebrate their victory at Brighton in the 1974-75 season

Burton Albion won at Aldershot in the 1984-85 season. It was Shots first 'home' defeat by non-League opposition since Weymouth in 1949.
Photo: Eric Marsh

Who will be celebrating this season?

A giant bottle of champagne helps the giant-killing players of Whitley Bay celebrate their 2-0 victory over Preston North End in the 1989-90 season. Photo: Alan Pearson

Bath City players relish their moment of FA Cup history in the Second Round after winning 2-1 against Hereford in the 1993-94 season. Photo: Paul Dennis

F.A. UMBRO TROPHY

2001-2002 REVIEW

Yeovil supporters behind the goal at the FA Trophy Final. Photo: Arthur Evans

FIRST ROUND

Saturday 3 November 2001   £700 to each winning club

(DM-W) Bilston Town 1 v 1 Gresley Rovers (DM-W) 199		
Smith 67 *Hutchinson 82*		
Gresley Rovers 0 v 0* Bilston Town 290		
Gresley won 5-4 after penalty kicks.		

(DM-P) Hednesford Tn 5 v 0 R. C. Warwick (DM-W) 405
Lake 33, Francis 55
Lancashire 57,Brown 84
Shakespeare 86

(U-1) Trafford 1 v 1 Ossett Albion (U-1) 158
Weston 45 *Dunderdale 9 (pen)*
Ossett Albion 0 v 3 Trafford 158
Weston 38, Diaczuk 79,83

(U-P) Blyth Spartans 2 v 0 Burscough (U-P) 422
Robson 12,13

(U-1) Workington 0 v 2 Lincoln United (U-1) 266
Burton 75, Hodgson 80 (o.g.)

(U-1) Gateshead 4 v 0 Redditch United (DM) 194
Jones 22, Niblett 43(og)
Ross 55, Preen 82

(U-1) Ashton United 4 v 1 Rocester (DM-W) 160
Johnson 3, Denney 78 *Bussell 45*
Hamlet 85,88

(DM-P) Moor Green 3 v 0 Bamber Bridge (U-P) 325
Crisp 21, Lamey 78
Stanley 87

(U-P) Matlock Town 1 v 1 Marine (U-P) 329
Taylor 90 *Black 29*
Marine 3 v 2 Matlock Town 199
Dolan 78, 82 *Simpson 34, Taylor 60 (pen)*
Cummings 88

(U-1) Ossett Town 1 v 1 Hyde United (U-P) 216
Beaumont 6 *Aspinall 89 (o.g.)*
Hyde United 3 v 2 Ossett Town 223
Nolan 51,Young 54 *Shaw 10, Jackson 33*
Yeo 76

(DM-E) Grantham Town 1 v 0 Stamford (DM-E) 409
Dye 70

(U-1) Gretna 3 v 1 Witton Albion (U-1) 110
Mawson 27 *Morgan 86*
Dobie 77,90

(U-1) Guiseley 0 v 0 Stafford Rangers (DM-P) 337
Stafford Rangers 4 v 2* Guiseley 442
Eccleston 2, 89 *Stuart 3, 43*
Reed 56, Dundas 84

(U-P) Droylsden 1 v 1 Frickley Athletic (U-P) 140
Evans 23 *Evans 66*
Frickley Athletic 1 v 1* Droylsden 176
Duffty 52 *Holmes 37*
Frickley won 4-3 after penalty kicks

(DM-E) Corby Town 0 v 3 Vauxhall Motors (U-P) 111
Fearns 9, 41, Lynch 63

(U-P) Harrogate Town 2 v 0 Colwyn Bay (U-P) 305
Bonsall 13
Smith 72 (o.g.)

(U-1) Radcliffe Borough 0 v 0 AccringtonStanley (U-P) 400
Accrington Stanley 2 v 0 Radcliffe Borough 349
Carden 22, 70

(DM-P) Ilkeston Town 1 v 0 Gainsborough Trinity 468
Knapper 53

(U-1) Chorley 0 v 1 Farsley Celtic (U-1) 187
Spence 5

(U-1) Rossendale Utd 3 v 3 Bedworth United (DM-W) 259
Sargeson 15, 29 *Whitmore 45,Partridge 47, 61*
Patterson 68
Bedworth United 2 v 0 Rossendale United 157
Whitmore 68
Webster 90

(DM-W) Atherstone Utd 1 v 2 Spennymoor Utd. (U-1) 211
O'Toole 12 *Hysen 83, Ainsley 89*

(U-P) Barrow 2 v 1 Halesowen T. (DM-P) 1126
Holt 7, Maxfield 89

(U-1) Kendal Town 3 v 2 Bradford P.A. (U-1) 199
BARNES 3 (27,40,90) *Hayward 43,Thompson 45*

(DM-W) Sutton C'field T 1 v 0 Hucknall Town (U-P) 125
Davies 7

(U-1) North Ferriby Utd 4 v 1 Shepshed D. (DM-E) 123
Farley 65, Dewhurst 68 *Tanner 77*
Powell 76, 81

(DM-P) Hinckley United 2 v 1 Eastwood Town (U-1) 365
Hunter 9, Brennan 31 *White 83*

(DM-W) Bloxwich Utd 2 v 3 Solihull Borough (DM-W) 143
Taylor 45, Ball 49 *Shaw 28, Hall 33, 65*

(U-1) Belper Town 0 v 4 Runcorn (U-P) 303
McNally 23, 32, Watson 67
Price 84

(U-1) Leek Town 0 v 1 Tamworth (DM-P) 500
Warner 36

(DM-E) Spalding Utd 0 v 0 Altrincham (U-P) 307
Altrincham 3 v 2 Spalding United 458
Thornley 11, 79 *Stephenson 40, Williams 67*
Sertori 45

(U-1) Stocksbridge P.S. 1 v 1 Whitby Town (U-P) 181
Biggins 57 *Ure 55*
Whitby Town 2 v 0 Stocksbridge P.S. 264
Williams 37, Burt 90

(R-1) Slough Town 0 v 2 Aylesbury United (R-1) 449
Maynard 61, Stanbridge 73

(R-1) Dulwich Hamlet 3 v 1 Evesham United (DM-W) 237
Edghill 34, Side 41 *Preedy 30*
Allen 85

(DM-W) Chippenham T 1 v 4 Walton & Hersham (R-1) 545
Rawlings 41 *Sweet 23, Dolan 77*
Cory 85, 87

(DM-E) Ashford Town 1 v 3 Bromley (R-1) 275
Hassett 18 *Watts 17, Hughes 56*

(R-1) Barking & E Ham U 1 v 3 Cinderford Town (DM-W) 156
Friend 73 *Trueman 24, Chiverton 39*
Tomkins 81

(DM-E) Dartford 0 v 3 Braintree Town (R-1) 272
Elk 53 (pen), Holt 64 (pen)
Jones 75

(R-1) Northwood 0 v 1 Maidenhead United (R-1) 214
Allen 12

(R-P) Hitchin Yown 1 v 2 Kingstonian (R-P) 383
Marshall 69 *Ball 47, Green 90*

(R-1) Uxbridge 3 v 3 Cirencester Town (DM-W) 80
Tunnell 16 *Miller 6, 45, Gee 55*
Moore 35,65
Cirencester Town 4 v 1 Uxbridge 142
Carter 3, Wollen 40 *Bamford S 89*
Holt 65, 70

Guiseley (Unibond Div 1)   v   Stafford Rangers (Dr Martens Prem)   0-0
Guiseley keeper John Lamb blocks Stafford's Paul Kiely. Photo: Chris Elsey

Chippenham Town (Dr Martens Western)   v   Walton & Hersham (Ryman Div 1)   1-4.
Simon Charity climbs high to head in a cross. Photo: Ken Gregory

Barking & East Ham (Ryman Div 1)   v   Cinderford Town (Dr Martens Western)   1-3.   Cinderford's Adie Harris
(stripes) fires in a shot past Barking's Mark Lord and Kevin Ramsay (right). Photo: Alan Coomes

(DM-P) Worcester City 1 v 1 Mangotsfield U. (DM-W) 862
Hyde 67 / *Summers 24*

Mangotsfield United 2 v 1* Worcester City 317
Summers 25, Seal107 / *Stant 47*

(DM-E) Sittingbourne 1 v 3 Fisher Athletic (DM-E) 232
Gooding 12 / *Dolby 27 (pen), Sammah 75* / *Guest 92 (o.g.)*

(R-1) Whyteleafe 0 v 5 Hampton & Rich. B. (R-P) 152
Williams 33, 90, De Luca 75 / *O'Connor 31, 90*

(DM-E) Tonbridge Angels 3 v 3 Merthyr Tydfil (DM-P) 427
Takalogabhashi 1 / *Davies M 40, 59, Lima 65* / *Cass13, Howell 86*

Merthyr Tydfil 3 v 2 Tonbridge Angels 302
Davies 3, 72 , Rollo 90 / *Greatorex 11, McCann 84*

(R-P) Croydon 3 v 1 Ford United (R-1) 71
McDonnell 31,52 / *Read 24* / *Coleman 88*

(R-P) Bedford Town 4 v 0 Worthing (R-1) 653
Paul 44, Edge 60 / *Dyer 70, Slinn 90*

(DM-P) Crawley Town 0 v 1 Newport I.o.W. (DM-P) 848
Gibbons 36

(R-P) Gravesend & N 2 v 0 Chelmsford City (DM-P) 829
Wilkins 32, Stadhart 68

(R-P) Heybridge Swifts 2 v 3 Erith & Belvedere (DM-E) 196
Parker 74, 90 / *White 52 ,Adams 79,90*

(DM-E) Histon 3 v 1 Weston-s-Mare (DM-W) 116
Walker 28, 69 / *Bevan 66* / *Kennedy 73*

(DM-1) Tooting & Mitch. 3 v 0 Salisbury City (DM-P) 261
Kane 29, Hams 42 / *Webb 74(pen)*

(R-1) Oxford City 2 v 4 Bashley (DM-E) 148
Mitchell 47,58 / *Tilley 25, Blake 28,Hussey 33* / *Gillespie 70*

(DM-E) Banbury United 1 v 0 Windsor & Eton (R-1) 319
Gooderick 21

(R-1) Wealdstone 1 v 1 Bishop's Stortford (R-1) 327
Tilbury 6 / *Shaw 86 (o.g.)*

Bishop's Stortford 3 v 2 Wealdstone 286
Braham 43 / *Deadman 18, Moore 37* / *Southam 64, Paul 74*

(R-1) Carshalton Ath 5 v 1 St.Leonards (DM-E) 212
Elliott 21, Glasgow 49 / *Massey 46 (o.g.)* / *McKenzie 70* / *Hegley 78, Lock 88*

(DM-P) Havant & W'ville 2 v 3 Grays Athletic (R-P) 411
Ferret 21, Hall 90 / *Abraham 48, 90, Rainford 78*

(R-P) Harrow Borough 2 v 3 Dorchester Town (DM-E) 180
Everitt 8, Woodruffe 59 / *O'Hagan 5, 71 Reelfer 29*

(DM-E) Eastbourne Boro 0 v 0 ChathamTown (DM-E) 341
Chatham Town 0 v 1 Eastbourne Borough 217 / *Allen 85*

(DM-P) Bath City 2 v 3 Newport County (DM-P) 877
Foster 21, Gosling 86(p) / *Paul 23, Ryan 43,* / *Shepherd 83*

(DM-P) Cambridge City 4 v 1 Gloucester City (DM-P) 289
Wilkins 35, Challinor 44 / *Burns 30* / *Fox 69, Pope 72*

(DM-E) Rothwell Town 1 v 1 Billericay Town (R-P) 206
McIlwain 85 / *Morgan 2*

Billericay Town 5 v 3* Rothwell Town 273
Simba 46, Moore 110 / *McIlwain 4,109, Mills 108*
CARTHY 3 (95,105,108)

(DM-P) Folkestone Inv. 0 v 1 Tiverton Town (DM-P) 365
Nancekivell 26

(R-P) Enfield 2 v 1 Hastings Town (DM-1) 126
Georgiou 8 Petersen 45 / *Yates 90*

(DM-P) Kettering Town 3 v 1 Swindon Super. (DM-W) 1072
Piercewright 18 / *Winchcombe 39* / *Wilkinson 74* / *Butcher 76*

(R-P) Purfleet 4 v 2 Boreham Wood (R-1) 195
Linger 17, 51 / *Sinclair 12, Lawford 59* / *Marshall 18, 81*

(R-1) Staines Town 1 v 2 Thame United (R-1) 91
Battams 49 / *Potter 76 West 88*

(DM-W) Clevedon Town 3 v 3 Harlow Town (R-1) 256
Allison 38, Cook 63 / *Theodosiou 14,52 ,Salmon 57* / *Bayliss 90*

Harlow Town 5 v 0 Clevedon Town 122
Samuel 12,90 Coley 62 / *Tompkins 29, 80*

(DM-E) Burnham 1 v 1 Yeading (R-1) 55
O'Connor 68 (pen) / *Johnson 65*

Yeading 1 v 2 Burnham 77
Johnson 56 / *Alleyne 14, Jeffrey 43*

(R-P) Hendon 2 v 1 Sutton United (R-P) 287
Hayle 44, Pickett 90 / *Honey 90*

(DM-E) Rugby United 1 v 4 Bognor Regis Town (R-1) 211
O'Brien 72 / *Howell 12, Bright 48* / *Funnell 58, 65*

(DM-E) Wisbech Town 1 v 1 St Albans City (R-1) 376
Hyde 89 / *Ansell 57*

St. Albans City 3 v 0 Wisbech Town 209
Deare 2 (og), Martin 45 / *Evans 85*

FIRST ROUND STATISTICS

Number of Ties: 71
Home Wins: 27 **Away Wins:** 25 **Draws:** 19

First Round Replays
Home Wins: 16* **Away wins:** 3
*Five after extra time and two after penalties.

Top Scoring Clubs
Hednesford Town 5-0 Carshalton Athletic 5-1
Billericay Town 5-3 Harlow Town 5-0
Hampton & Richmond Borough 5-0

Hat Tricks
Barnes (Kendal Town) 3 (Home) v Bradford P.A.
Carthy (Billericay Town) 3 (Home) v Rothwell TowN

Best Attendances
1126 Barrow v Burton Albion
1072 Kettering Town v Swindon Supermarine
877 Bath City v Newport County
862 Worcester City v Mangotsfield United
848 Crawley Town v Newport (I.o.W.)
829 Gravesend & N v Chelmsford City

Lowest Attendances
55 Burnham v Yeading
71 Croydon v Ford United
77 Yeading v Burnham

Average Attendance: 308

SECOND ROUND

Saturday 1 December 2001   £900 to each winning club

(U-P) Accr. Stanley	1 v 1	Altrincham (U-P)	592
Maddox73 (o.g.)		Craney 24	
Altrincham	1 v 1*	Accrington Stanley	417
Hargreaves 67		James 78	

Altrincham won 3-1 after penalty kicks

(DM-P) Moor Green	2 v 1	Trafford (U-1)	343
Crisp 50 Pier 89		Emmett 67	
(U-P) Worksop Town	3 v 2	Marine (U-P)	375
Todd 15		Holmshaw 19 (og)	
Townsend 48, 54(p)		Bainbridge 45	
(U-P) Runcorn F.C.Halt.	4 v 2	Farsley Celtic (U-1)	125
Carrager 20, Gamble 42		Connor 47, Hepworth 63	
Watson 74,76			
(U-1) North Ferriby Utd	4 v 2	Spennymoor United (U-1)	104
Powell 21,78 Farley 27		Ainsley 42, Edgcumbe 76	
Knight 84			
(U-1) Gretna	0 v 1	Emley (U-P)	102
		Day 88	
(DM-P) Stafford Rngrs	0 v 3	Vauxhall Motors (U-P)	555
		Young 25, Fearns 32	
		Haddrell 65	
(U-1) Lincoln United	0 v 1	Solihull Borough (DM-W)	168
		Hall 73	
(U-P) Whitby Town	1 v 2	Blyth Spartans (U-P)	505
Burt 43		Stewart 10, Baker 34	
(DM-W) Bedworth Utd	1 v 4	Gresley Rovers (DM-W)	161
Partridge 27		Bourne 7 ,Woolley 10, 81	
		Parkins 78	
(U-1) Kendal Town	1 v 2	Harrogate Town (U-1)	134
Barnes 71		Dunn 8,15	
(U-P) Lancaster City	2 v 1	Hinckley United (DM-P)	289
Whittaker 65, 9		Gordon 64	
(U-P) Hyde United	0 v 4	Ilkeston Town (DM-P)	355
		Abbott 22, Holmes 72, 90	
		Hemmings 80	
(U-P) Barrow	1 v 1	Burton Albion (U-P)	1521
Anthony 68		Moore 78	
Burton Albion	5 v 0	Barrow	1174
Moore 3,59			

FARRELL 3(17,39,88)

(DM-W) Stourport Swifts	5 v 4	Bishop Auckland (U-P)	297
Booth 7,12 Langford 28		Chillingworth 58,89 Lee 59(p)	
Southwick 44, Hart 79		Salmon 66	
(DM-E) Grantham Town	5 v 1	Frickley Athletic (U-P)	410
Wilson 26,48		Lewis 63	
Ranshaw 33			
Bull 55(p), Taylor 90			
(DM-P) Hednesford Tn	2 v 1	Gateshead (U-P)	252
Lake 7,51		Preen 71	
(DM-W) Sutton Cold. T	0 v 3	Tamworth (DM-P)	371
		Colley 27, Turner 72, Foy 90	
(DM-P) Kings Lynn	4 v 1	Ashton United (U-1)	814
Clarke 38,80		Cornelly 7	
Bloomfield 41, White 70			
(R-P) Kingstonian	6 v 2	Cirencester Town (DM-W)	404
Green 8,60, Mead 48		Carter 45, Terry 70	
Bell 50,52, Sadler 89			
(R-1) Dulwich Hamlet	2 v 1	Billericay Town (R-P)	165
Allen 69, Husbands 90		Carthy 7	
(DM-W) Mangotsfield U	3 v 1	Dorchester Town (DM-E)	313
Edwards 35,85		O"Hagan 75	
Claridge 65			
(DM-E) Fisher Athletic	5 v 1	Merthyr Tydfil (DM-P)	165
Sammah 46 Huggins 48		Beddard 90	
Portway 54,80 Luckett 66			
(R-P) Purfleet	2 v 1	Kettering Town (DM-P)	261
Buglione 47 Brown 82		Piercewright 31	
(DM-P) Tiverton Town	6 v 0	Croydon (R-P)	740
Rogers 7 Gross 15			
Mudge 30			

NANCEKIVELL 3 (26,29,62)

(DM-E) Bashley	1 v 1	Burnham (DM-E)	120
Quirke 32		Potter 90	
Burnham	1 v 4	Bashley	90
O'Connor 76(p)		Jackson 33, Davis 52(p)	
		Tilley 82, Beck 89	
(R-1) Bishops Stortford	1 v 1	Grays Athletic (R-P)	503
John 60		Lock 90	
Grays Athletic	3 v 2	Bishops Stortford	226
Fiddes 25		Hall 4, Southon 7	
Southgate 48,58			
(DM-E) Eastbourne B	0 v 0	Bedford Town (R-P)	518
Bedford Town	1 v 2*	Eastbourne Borough	404
Slinn 70		Pearce 55, Westcott 98	
(R-P) Hampton & Rch B	2 v 2	Harlow Town (R-1)	191
Lee 49, Nade 55		Young 14, Salmon 35	
Harlow Town	1 v 2	Hampton & Ricmond B.	113
Rawlings 19		Nade 16, Lee 55	
(DM-E) Banbury United	0 v 2	Cambridge City (DM-P)	486
		Hann 50, Wilkin 77	
(R-1) Walton & Hersham	2 v 3	Newport County (DM-P)	136
Savage 33, Edgar 49		Paul 45, Whelan 46 (p) Coe 89	
(R-1) Bromley	1 v 1	Tooting & Mitcham (R-1)	315
Taylor 84		Kane 75	
Tooting & Mitcham	3 v 1	Bromley	251
Lawson 42, Kane 85		Bartley 20	
Webb 89			
(DM-P) Welling United	8 v 1	Erith & Belvedere (DM-E)	400

ABBOTT 5(28,42,54,56,82)
Watts 35, Standen43, Powell 38   Adams 13

(R-P) Braintree Town	1 v 1	Basingstoke Town (R-P)	342
Noble 69		Newbury 57	
Basingstoke Town	0 v 2	Braintree Town	236
		Noble 58, Reinelt 72	
(R-1) Carshalton Ath	1 v 0	Newport I.o.W. (DM-P)	266
Elliott 89			
(R-1) Thame United	1 v 5	Bognor Regis Town (R-1)	153
Perna 85 (pen)		Avery 19 (o.g.), Wight 48	
		Birmingham D 78, Hudson 80	
		Birmingam M 90	
(R-P) Chesham United	4 v 0	Weymouth (DM-P)	416
Cooksey 17 Graham 39			
Wootton 49 Hewings 63			
(DM-W) Cinderford Tn	0 v 2	Gravesend & N'fleet (R-P)	245
		Wilkins 60, Hatch 85	
(R-P) Enfield	2 v 1	Histon (DM-E)	121
Walker 3, Rufus 34		Barker 50, Andrews 90	
Histon	3 v 1	Enfield	114
Walker 3, Coburn 48,65		Ayres 23	
(R-P) Maidenhead United1	v 2	Hendon (R-P)	209
Ibe 63		Pickett 1, Yates 62	
(R-1) Aylesbury United	0 v 2	Aldershot Town (R-P)	876
		Harford 22, Payne 58	
(R-P) Canvey Island	5 v 1	St.Albans City (R-P)	480
Parmenter 9 Kennedy 3		Martin 72	
Vaughan 42, 45, Gregory 56			

SECOND ROUND STATISTICS
Number of Ties: 51

Home Wins: 19	Away Wins: 14
Replayed Home Wins: 5*	Replayed Away wins: 4

*One after penalties

Top Scoring Clubs

Welling United 8-0	Tiverton Town 6-0
Kingstonian 6-2	Bognor Regis Town 5-1

Hat Tricks
Abbott (Welling United) 5 (Home) v Erith & Belvedere
Farrell (Burton Albion) 3 (Home) v Barrow
Nancekevill (Tivertonn Town) 3 (Home) v Croydon

Best Attendances
1521 Barrow v Burton Albion   **1174** Burton Alb v Barrow

Lowest Attendances
90 Burnham v Bashley   **102** Gretna v Emley

Histon (Dr Martens Eastern) v Enfield (Ryman Premier) 3-1.
Gary Walker's superb early strike beats Enfield keeper Kenny Addai to put Histon in front. Photo: Gordon Whittington

Bromley (Ryman Div 1) v Tooting & Mitcham United (Ryman Div 1) 1-1
Bromley goalkeeper Danny Harwood takes this cross off the head of Tooting's Luke Ferguson (6). Photo: Alan Coomes

Whitby Town (Unibond Premier) v Blyth Spartans (Unibond Premier) 1-2. Whitby Town v Blyth Spartans. Home keeper Phil Naisbett catches well against a lively Spartans attack. Photo: Graham Brown

THIRD ROUND

Saturday 12 January 2002   £1000 to each winning club

(C) Scarborough 2 v 0 Hednesford T (DM-P)		953
Connell 13, Stamp 90		
(C) Leigh RMI 2 v 0 Emley (U-P)		301
Black 15, Twiss 89	Wilson 34, Hatto75	
Emley 1 v 4 Leigh RMI		374
Bambridge 71	Twiss 19, Maamrid 56,	
	Black 70, Hallows 84	
(U-P) Worksop Town 4 v 3 Tamworth (DM-P)		904
Townsend 15, 53	ROBERTS 3 (14, 42, 89)	
Smith 28, Todd 90		
(C)Chester City 1 v 1 Stourport Swifts (DM-W)		1,006
Haahoff 70	Marsh 75	
Stourport Swifts 0 v 3 Chester City		
(C) Southport 1 v 1 Gresley Rovers (DM-E)		1,100
Jones 21	Cleary 86	
Gresley Rovers 1 v 0 Southport		
(C) Northwich Victoria 3 v 1 Boston United (C)		966
Devlin 17, Quinn 52,89	Clare 57	
(DM-W) Solihull Boro 3 v 0 Runcorn F.C.Halton (U-P)		345
Smith 13,41, Hollis 80		
(C) Stalybridge Celtic 1 v 1 Nuneaton Borough (C)		828
Courtney 35	Charles 28	
Nuneaton Borough 1 v 2 Stalybridge Celtic		1,029
(U-P) Burton Albion 3 v 0 Blyth Spartans (U-P)		1,594
Blount 20 Webster 45(p)		
Glasser 78		
(DM-P) Ilkeston Town 0 v 2 Telford United (C)		792
	Albrighton 2, 17	
(U-P) Vauxhall Motors 4 v 0 Lancaster City (U-P)		278
Cumiskey 15, 53		
Young 60, 86		
(U-1) North Ferriby Utd 3 v 2 Altrincham (U-P)		377
Powell 34 ,Dewhurst 65	Poland 48, 77	
Knight 88		
(C) Morecambe 2 v 0 Kings Lynn (DM-P)		935
Hardiker 38, Norman 55		
(C) Doncaster Rovers 2 v 0 Harrogate Town (U-1)		1886
Paterson 42 Watson 85		
(DM-E) Grantham Town 2 v 1 Moor Green (DM-P)		525
Dye 3,Gilbert 85	Martin 81	
(R-P) Grays Athletic 2 v 4 Welling United (DM-P)		378
Cooper 51 Robinson 80	ABBOTT 4 (5,41,76,90(P))	
(R-P) Chesham United 2 v 2 Hereford United (C)		831
Andrews 35,Fewings 76	Williams G 35, Rodgerson 45	
Hereford United 4 v 0 Chesham United		
Robinson 20, Parry 55		
Williams G 70		
Piearce 80		
(R-1) Dulwich Hamlet 3 v 4 Braintree Town (R-P)		379
Stephenson 5, Side 76	Noble 25, Simpson 41, 90	
Perkins 78	Parratt 85	
(C) Margate 3 v 1 Hayes (C)		625
Collins 10 O'Connell 63	Clark 40	
Lamb 77		

(C) Stevenage Borough 5 v 1 Dover Athletic (C)		1,316
Clarke 31,54 ,Sigers 41	Norman 76	
Jackson 47,51		
(DM-E) Fisher Athletic 0 v 5 Barnet (C)		635
	Bell 15, Purser 42, 72	
	Heald 47, Gower 74	
(DM-E) Histon 1 v 1 Gravesend & N'fl'eet(RP)		216
Munns 69	Barber 82 (o.g.)	
Gravesend & Northfleet 3 v 1 Histon		561
Duku 10, Burton 42	Kennedy 80	
Wilkins76		
(R-P) Hampton & Rich. 2 v 0 Newport County (DM-P)		505
Flitter 48, Ibe 88		
(DM-E) Bashley 2 v 1 Bognor Regis T (R-1)		305
Hussey 41,90	Wyatt 88	
(DM-P) Tiverton Town 1 v 3 Yeovil Town (C)		2,320
Lockwood 83 (o.g.)	Stansfield 15,49, Alford 81	
(C) Dagenham & Red. 1 v 0 Eastbourne B (DM-E)		1,354
Shipp 89		
(C) Forest Green Rvrs 1 v 1 Aldershot Town (R-P)		1,138
Meecham 38	Browne 46	
Aldershot Town 2 v 3 Forest Green Rovers		1,487
Watson 54, Harford 81	Heggs 25 Cooper 37 Shaw85	
(R-P) Canvey Island 2 v 2 Purfleet (R-P)		483
Cobb 30	Martin 77, Linger 80	
Chandler 42 (o.g.)		
Purfleet 0 v 1* Canvey Island		471
	Miller 115	
(DM-W) Mangotsfield U 3 v 2 Tooting & Mitcham (R-1)		369
Loyden 25, Seal 27,57	Onochie 6, Brady 30	
(DM-P) Cambridge City 1 v 1 Hendon (R-P)		404
Wooding 83	Ofori 82	
Hendon 2 v 0 Cambridge City		201
Randall 37, 77		
(C) Farnborough Town 1 v 1 Carshalton Athletic (R-P)		617
Patterson 79	Elliott 90	
Carshalton Athletic 0 v 5 Farnborough Town		372
	Crawshaw 11,14 Vansittart75	
	Piper C 58, 69	
(C) Woking 2 v 1 Kingstonian (R-P)		2,474
Sharpling 7 Patmore 39	Sadler 51	

THIRD ROUND STATISTICS

Number of Ties: 42

Home Wins: 17   Away Wins: 5

First Round Replays

Home Wins: 4   Away wins: 6

Top Scoring Clubs

Stevenage Borough 5-1 (H)   Barnet 5-0 (A)

Farnborough Town 5-0 (A)

Hat Tricks

Roberts (Tamworth) 3 (Away) v Worksop Town

Abbott (Welling United) 4 (Away) v Grays Athletic

Best Attendances

2474 Woking v Kingstonian   2320 Tiverton Town v Yeovil Town

1886 Doncaster Rovers v Harrogate Town

Lowest Attendances

201 Hendon v Cambridge C   216 Histon v Gravesend & N

278 Vauxhall Motors v Lancaster City

Tiverton Town (Dr Martens Prem) v Yeovil Town (Conference) 1-3. Yeovil's Colin Pluck checks Tiverton's Kevin Nancekevill in the Third Round West County derby won 3-1 by the Conference side. Photo: Ken Gregory

Gretna (Unibond Div 1) v Witton Albion (Unibond Div 1) 3-1
Gretna's David Hewson is tackled by Witton Albion's Lee Morgan. Photo: Alan Watson

Forest Green Rovers (Conference) v Aldershot (Ryman Premier) 1-1. Photo: Eric Marsh

FOURTH ROUND

Saturday 2 February 2002   £1500 to each winning club

(C) Morecambe	5 v 0	Gresley Rovers (DM)	984

HAY 4 (29, 30, 43, 77)
Curtis 81

(C) Farnborough Town	1 v 1	Burton Albion(U-P)	1031
Baptiste 16	v	Clough 88	
Burton Albion	3 v 2	Farnborough Town	1706

Clough 13, Bailey 65   Babtree 6, Piper 89
Henshaw 90

Gravesend & Northfleet	2 v 1	Hendon	542

Wilkins 64, Jackson 82   Forbes 86

(C) Chester City	0 v 0	Solihull Borough(DM-W)	1282
Solihull Borough	2 v 4	Chester City	721

Hall 18 Smith 54   **SPINK 3 (45, 72, 90)**
Boland 62

(C) Woking	4 v 2	Welling United (DM-P)	1815

Moore 20, Smith 64   Abbott 61, Standen 77
Saunders 69, Sane 71

(U-1) North Ferriby Utd	4 v 4	Braintree Town (R-P)	381
Powell 5. Perrin 40		**SIMPSON 3 (10, 57, 69)**	
Lowthorpe 43 Knight 87		Blaney 78	
Braintree Town	2 v 2	North Ferriby Utd	580

Owen 29, Simpson 55   Knight 75 Palmer 77
Braintree Town won 4-3 after penalty kicks

(C) Yeovil Town	1 v 1	Doncaster Rovers (C)	2671
Stansfield 71		Barnes 16	
Doncaster Rovers	4 v 5	Yeovil Town	2178

Paterson 6,Gill 22,49   Pluck 57, Alford 75
Owen 88   Stansfield 79,86, Skiverton 89

(C) Margate	2 v 0	Leigh RMI(C)	663

Devlin 10 McConnell 25

(U-P) Vauxhall Motors	0 v 4	Northwich Victoria (C)	1019

Devlin 7, Garvey 34, Illman 56
Collins 88

(C) Dagenham & Red.	0 v 2	Telford United (C)	1256

Smith 32, Quaile 62

(DM-W)Mangotsfield U	0 v 1	Stalybridge Celtic (C)	341

Peacock 61

(C) Forest Green Rvrs	1 v 0	Worksop Town (U-P)	816

Cooper 12

(DM-E) Grantham Town	1 v 4	Canvey Island (R-P)	1222

Taylor 33   Boylan 60,84 ,Duffy 70,72

(C) Hereford United	4 v 1	Hampton & Rich. B(R-P)	1167

Clarke 27 James 52 (p)   Nade 43
Williams 83, Elmes 90

(C) Barnet	0 v 0	Scarborough (C)	1140
Scarborough	2 v 2	Barnet	821

Shields 8, Rennison 97   Purser 4, Strevens 101
Scarborough won 5-3 after penalty kicks

(C) Stevenage Borough	1 v 0	Bashley (DM-E)	1216

Jackson 26

FOURTH ROUND STATISTICS

Home Wins: 10   **Away Wins:** 6   **Draws:** 5
Home goals: 39   **Away goals:** 36

Hat tricks: 3
4 Hay (Stevenage Borough)
Spink (Chester City)
Simpson (Braintree Town)

Best Attendance:
2,671 Yeovil Town v Doncaster Rovers

Average Attendance: 1,121

Stevenage Borough (Conference)   v   Bashley (Dr Martens Eastern)   1-0.   Airborn Bashley keeper Oliver Rastall makes a superb save to thwart Stevenage Borough at Broadhall Way in the FA Trophy tie. Photo: Peter Barnes

Stevenage Borough (Conference)   v   Forest Green Rovers (Conference)   3-2.   Alex Meechan and Simon Futcher (Forest Green) put pressure on the Stevenage goal in the Fifth Round. Photo: Peter Barnes

FIFTH ROUND

Saturday 23 February 2002   £2500 to each winning club

(C) Scarborough 1 v 1 Morecambe (C)		1511
Shepherd 86 (pen) Rigoglioso 37		

Morecambe 3 v 0 Scarborough		801
Curtis 39 Norman 57		
Rigoglioso 63		

(R)Gravesend & N'fleet 0 v 2 Stalybridge Celtic(C)		926
Peacock 16 Wood 54		

(C) Margate 1 v 1 Braintree United (R)		802
Sodje 67 Noble 82		

Braintree Town 1 v 2 Margate		846
Culverhouse 88 Munday 51, Sodje 62		

(C)Stevenage Boro 3 v 2 Forest Green Rvrs (C)		1228
Wormhull 22 Heggs 14, Impey 90		
Cousins (o.g.) 43		
Clarke 74		

(C)Yeovil Town 2 v 1 Canvey Island (R)		3616
Stansfield 16 Cobb 89		
Crittenden (pen) 87		

(U) Burton Albion 3 v 0 Woking (C)		2322
Blount 20 Stride 36,89		

(C) Chester City 2 v 1 Hereford United(C)		1747
Bolland 37 Haarhoff 90 Elmes 76		

(C) Northwich Victoria 3 v 2 Telford United (C)		976
Grant 72, Burke 90 Smith 65 Quayle 81		
Norris 90		

FIFTH ROUND STATISTICS

Home Wins: 6   **Away Wins:** 2   **Draws:** 2

Home goals: 19   **Away goals:** 12

Best Attendance:

3,615 Yeovil Town v Canvey Island

Average Attendance: 1,480

Hat Tricks: 0

Gravesend's Craig Wilkins is under pressure from Stalybridge's Ged Murphy. Photo: Alan Coomes

Gravesend's Nick Burton just nicks the ball off the foot of Stalybridges Gerard Courtney. Photo: Alan Coomes

Stevenage Borough (Conference) v Forest Green Rovers (Conference) 3-2
FA National Game XI Squad players in competition as Simon Wormull (Stevenage - left) and Simon Travis (Forest Green) tussle for possession. Photo: Peter Barnes

Gravesend & Northfleet (Ryman Premier) v Stalybridge Celtic (Conference) 0-2
Stalybridge's Ben Futcher gets in a tackle on Gravesend's Paul Booth at Stonebridge Road. Photo: Alan Coomes

SIXTH ROUND

Saturday 16 March 2002   £3000 to each winning club

| (C) Margate | 1 | v | 2 | Morecambe (C) |

1244

Lamb 86   *Norman 72 76*

Margate: Mitten, Saunders, Lamb, Edwards, O'Connell, Williams, Roddis, Munday, Braithwaite, Sodje, McFlynn Subs not used: Hafner, Porter, Azzopardi, Graham, Turner.

Morecambe: Mawson, McGuire, McKearney, Lightfoot, Murphy, Drummond, Rigoglioso, Thompson, Talbot, Black, Perkins. Subs not used: Carlton, Fensome, Norman, Robinson, Wilcock.

| (C) Norwich Victoria | 0 | v | 2 | Yeovil Town (C) |

1846

Stansfield 35, Alford 45

Northwich Victoria: Gibson, Burke (Grant 74), Ingram, Talbot, Barnard, Owen, Knowles (Quinn 65), Norris, Garvey, Ilman (Devlin 65), Blundell. Subs not used: Sedgemoor, Collins

Yeovil Town: Weale, White, Skiverton, Tonkin, Pluck, O'Brien, (Lockwood 73), Johnson, Crittenden, Brassart (Lindegaard 79), Alford, Stansfield (Giles 45). Subs not used: Sheffield, Way

| (C) Stevenage Borough | 1 | v | 0 | Stalybridge Celtic (C) |

1684

Campbell D 70

Stevenage Borough: Greygoose, Hamsher, Goodliffe, Trott, Riddle, Wormull, McMahon, Stirling, Clarke, Sigere, Jackson. Subs not used: Houghton, D Campbell, Sodje, Wilkerson, J Campbell

Stalybridge Celtic: Fish, Murphy, Perkins, Woods, Futcher, Beesley, Peacock, Parr, Ayorinde, Williamson, Pickford. Subs not used: Wharton, Turley, Barker, Courtney, Wood

| (U) Burton Albion | 2 | v | 0 | Chester City (C) |

3584

Kavanagh 66 Webster 68

Burton Albion: Duke, Hoyle, Henshaw, Kavanagh, Blount, Evans (Wall 77), Stride, Webster, Moore, Clough, Anderson Subs not used: Bailey, Lyons, Glasser, Robinson.

Chester City: W. Brown, Woodyatt, Rose, Lancaster, Bolland, Brabin, Carden, McGorry, Tate (Haarhoff 72), Beesley, McElhatton (D. Brown 72) Subs not used: Spink, Blackburn, Whittaker.

SIXTH ROUND STATISTICS

Home Wins: 2   **Away Wins:** 2   **Draws:** 0

Home Goals: 4   **Away Goals:** 4

Best Attendance: 3,584 Burton Albion v Chester City

Average Attendance: 2,089

Burton Albion (Unibond Premier) v Chester City (Conference) 2-0.
Chester's Chris Tate tackles Terry Henshaw. Photo: Bill Wheatcroft

Stevenage Borough (Conference) v Stalybridge Celtic (Conference) 1-0
Steve Pickford (Stalybridge Celtic) and Sam McMahon (Stevenage Borough) in action at Broadhall Way.
Photo: Peter Barnes

SEMI-FINALS

Played on 6, 13 & 14 April   £6000 to each winning club

FIRST LEG

(C) Yeovil Town   4   v   0   Burton Albion (U)

Att: 5614

Grant 4, Crittendon 53 (pen)
McIndoe 45, Giles 84

Yeovil Town: Weale, Lockwood, Skiverton, Pluck, Tonkin, Crittenden, Way, Johnson, McIndoe, Grant, Stansfield. Subs not used: White, O'Brien, Brassart, Giles, Sheffield.
Burton Albion: Duke, Henshaw, Blount, Wassall, Evans, Stride, Clough, Glasser, Webster, Anderson, Moore. Subs not used: Farrell, Kavanagh, Hoyle, Lyons, Robinson.

SECOND LEG

Burton Albion   2   v   1   Yeovil Town

Att: 4026

Anderson 53, Farrell 72   *Alford 57*

Burton Albion: Duke, Blount, Henshaw, Glasser,Wassall, Evans, Stride, Anderson, Farrell (Moore), Clough (Kavanagh), Webster. Subs not used: Hoyle, Lyons, Robinson
Yeovil Town: Weale, Lockwood, Skiverton, Tonkin, Pluck, Way, Stansfield, Johnson, Alford (Giles), Crittendon, Way, Stansfield, Johns. Subs not used: White, Brassart, O'Brien, Sheffield

Yeovil Town won 5-2 on aggregate

FIRST LEG

(C) Morecambe   1   v   2   Stevenage Borough (C)

Att: 1899

Drummond 76   *McMahon 23*
                                                 Hamsher 90 (pen)

Morecambe: Mawson, McKearney, Colkin, Lightfoot (McGuire 23), Murphy, Drummond, Rigoglioso (Talbot 70), Thompson, Curtis (Carlton 73), Norman, Perkins. Subs not used: Black, Wilcock
Stevenage Borough: Wilkerson, Hamsher, Goodliffe, Trott, Fraser, Fisher, Houghton, Evers, Jackson, George, McMahon. Subs not used: J. Campbell, D. Campbell, Wormull, Greygoose, Stirling

SECOND LEG

Stevenage Borough   2   v   0   Morecambe

Att: 3119

McMahon 50, Campbell D 90

Stevenage Borough: Wilkerson, Hamsher, Goodliffe, Trott, Fraser, Fisher (Stirling 85), Houghton, Evens (Wormull 84), Jackson, George (D. Campbell 77), McMahon. Subs not used: J. Campbell, Greygoose.
Morecambe: Mawson, Fensome, Colkin, McKearney, Murphy, Drummond, Rigoglioso (Curtis 57), Gouck (Black 77), Arnold (Talbot 57) Norman, Thompson. Subs not used: McGuire, Wilcock.

Stevenage Borough won 4-1 on aggregate

Chris Weale (Yeovil Town) makes a good catch at Eaton Park. Photo: Peter Barnes

Nick Crittenden shows remarkable determination for Yeovil Town at Eaton Park. Photo: Peter Barnes

Dale Anderson (on ground) puts Burton Albion ahead in 53 mins at Eaton Park. Photo: Peter Barnes

Kirk Jackson (Stevenage) lays the ball off despite pressure from Andrew Gouck (Morecambe). Photo: Peter Barnes

Liam George (Stevenage) sees a snapshot saved by Craig Mawson (Morecambe). Photo: Peter Barnes

F.A. UMBRO TROPHY AT A GLANCE

THIRD ROUND

Yeovil Town	3
Tiverton Town~	1
Doncaster Rovers	2
Harrogate Town	0
Grantham Town	2
Moor Green	1
Canvey Island	2,0
Purfleet	*2,1
Vauxhall Motors	4
Lancaster City	0
Northwich Victoria	3
Boston United	1
Dagenhanm & Redbridge	1
Eastbourne Borough	0
Ilkeston Town	0
Telford United	2
Farnborough	1,5
Carshalton Athletic	1,0
Burton Albion	3
Blyth Spartans	0
Woking	2
Kingstonian	1
Grays Athletic	2
Welling United	4
Chester City	1,3
Stourport Swifts	1,0
Solihull Borough	3
Runcorn FCH	0
Chesham United	2,0
Hereford United	2,4
Hampton & Rich B.	2
Newport Co.	0
Fisher Athletic	0
Barnet	5
Scarborough	2
Hednesford Town	0
Morecambe	2
King's Lynn	0
Southport	1,0
Gresley Rovers	1,1
Margate	3
Hayes	1
Leigh RMI	2,4
Emley	2,1
North Ferriby United	3
Altrincham	2
Dulwich Hamlet	3
Braintree United	4
Histon	1,1
Gravesend & North.	1,3
Cambridge City	1,0
Hendon	1,2
Mangotsfield United	3
Tooting & Mitcham	2
Stalybridge Celtic	1,2
Nuneaton Borough	1,1
Forest Green Rovers	1,3
Aldershot Town	1,2
Worksop Town	4
Tamworth	3
Bashley	2
Bognor Regis Town	1
Dover Athletic	1
Stevenage Borough~	5

FOURTH ROUND

Yeovil Town	1,5
Doncaster Rovers	1,4
Grantham Town	1
Canvey Island	4
Vauxhall Motors	0
Northwich Victoria	4
Dagenhan & Redbridge	0
Telford United	2
Farnborough Town	1,2
Burton Albion	1,3
Woking	4
Welling United	2
Chester City	0,4
Solihull Borough	0,2
Hereford United	4
Hampton & Rich. Bor.	1
Barnet	0,2
Scarborough	*0,2
(5-3 Pens to Scarborough)	
Morecambe	5
Gresley Rovers	0
Margate	2
Leigh RMI	1
North Ferriby United	4,2
Braintree Town	*4,2
(5-4 Pens to Braintree)	
Gravesend & Northfleet	2
Hendon	1
Mangotsfield Unuted	0
Stalybridge Celtic	1
Forest Green Rovers	1
Worksop Town	0
Bashley	0
Stevenage Borough~	1

FIFTH ROUND

Yeovil Town	2
Canvey Island	1
Northwich Victoria	3
Telford United	2
Burton Albion	3
Woking	0
Chester City	2
Hereford United	1
Scarborough	1,0
Morecambe	1,3
Margate	1,1
Braintree Town	1,1
Gravesend & Northfleet	0
Stalybridge Celtic	2
Forest Green Rovers	2
Stevenage Borough~	3

SIXTH ROUND

Yeovil Town	2
Northwich Victoria ~	0
Burton Albion	2
Chester City	0
Margate	1
Morecambe	2
Morecambe	1,0
Stevenage Borough	2,2
Stalybridge Celtic	0
Stevenage Borough	1

Semi-finals

Yeovil Town	4,1
Burton Albion	0,2
Yeovil Town	2
Stevenage Borough	0

Clubs named first in each pairing were drawn at home (or home just in a semi-final) unless a ~ is shown.

Above: The resplendent band at Villa Park.
Photo: Peter Barnes

Right: It's party time -
Yeovil Town balloons at
Villa Park
Photo: Eric Marsh

Two current England internationals clash - Nick Crittenden (Yeovil Town) and Simon Wormull (Stevenage Borough)
Photo: Peter Barnes

Carl Alford jubilant after scoring Yeovil's first goal.
Photo: Roger Turner

F.A. UMBRO TROPHY
FINAL
Saturday 12th May
at Villa Park
Winners Prize Money: £12,000

Stevenage Borough	0	v	2	Yeovil Town

Alford, Stansfield

Att: 18,809

Stevenage Borough: Paul Wilkerson, John Hamsher, Jason Goodliffe, Rob Trott, Stuart Fraser, Matt Fisher, Simon Wormull (sub Jude Stirling 71st min), Sean Evers (sub Martin Williams 56th min), Kirk Jackson, Jean-Michel Sigere (sub Dudley Campbell 74th min), Adrian Clarke. Subs not used: Jamie Campbell, Dean Greygoose

Yeovil Town: Chris Weale, Adam Lockwood, Anthony Tonkin, Terry Skiverton, Colin Pluck (sub Tom White 51st min), Darren Way, Adam Stansfield, Lee Johnson, Carl Alford (sub Chris Giles 86th min), Nick Crittenden (sub Andy Lindegaard 83rd min), Michael McIndoe. Subs not used: Roy O'Brien, Jon Sheffield

Referee: Mr N Barry (Lincolnshire) assisted by Messrs M S Yerby (Kent) and K P Stround (Dorset). Fourth Official Mr A Bates (Staffordshire)

Pre-match line up at Villa Park, and two English International Captains: Jason Goodliffe, Stevenage Borough (left) and Terry Skiverton, Yeovil Town (right).
Photo: Peter Barnes

Top: Chris Weale in action for Yeovil Town.
Photo: Peter Barnes

Centre: Chris Weale tips over a Stevenage effort in the first minute of the game.
Photo: Graham Brown

Bottom: Adam Stansfield's shot heads goalwards for the second Yeovil goal.
Photo: Graham Brown

AT LAST IT'S YEOVIL

At the thirty third time of asking Yeovil Town, renowned for their F A Challenge Cup exploits over the years, finally found their way to the final of the F A Trophy, and what a day they made it for their hordes of enthusiastic supporters. There was so much green and white, two sides of the ground dominated by it, that red shirted opponents Stevenage Borough, with the stamp of underdogs already in betting terms, must have felt as if they were playing in Yeovil, out-fanned as they were.

Within a dozen minutes of the opening whistle they were further dispirited. Adam Lockwood, appearing in his second consecutive final at Villa Park, having previously represented Forest Green, sent a long throw bouncing into the Stevenage penalty area. With his back to goal Carl Alford's excellent scissor kick sent the ball past a bemused Paul Wilkerson's left hand. Glovers' supporters yelled their approval; Borough's fans looked even glummer.

Alford, whose career had seemed on a downward spiral prior to joining Yeovil, was repaying the faith of manager Gary Johnson in signing him to replace the departed Warren Patmore at the season's start. Johnson had, when Kettering manager, sold Alford to Rushden and Diamonds for £85,000 so he has more than profited from Alford's scoring successes which Stevenage would have recalled since he had two high scoring seasons in their colours, just before the century's turn. "I've still got a lot of great friends there," said Alford, "but I was pleased to score against them."

It had been Stevenage who had come out of the traps the sprightlier. They so nearly got off to a flying start in the first minute when Jean-Michel Sigere's cross was deflected goalwards by Kirk Jackson, bringing out a tremendous muscle stretching tip over from Chris Weale. Unfortunately that was the nearest the Hertfordshire men came to scoring. For all their strength Sigere and the disappointing Jackson, whose reputation for goal scoring while at Worksop had deserted him at Darlington, made few inroads into the Glovers' defence. Skipper Simon Wormull's shooting threatened but always from distances where Weale would have been surprised to be beaten. John Hamsher's and Adrian Clarke's forays down the flanks ensured it was not all one way traffic but it was Yeovil who looked the more potent force throughout.

Whenever a manager selects his own son charges of nepotism are only too predictable but the effective, ener-getic promptings of Lee Johnson silenced any possible criticisms of that kind. Lee's combination with man of the match Adam Stansfield was the clincher. However it was by a different route that Yeovil doubled their lead. A gigantic kick from Weale was headed on by Alford to allow Stansfield to race clear for goal. Wilkerson rushed out to block but Stansfield coolly slid the ball under him. From Elmore of the Screwfix Western League to a Villa Park national final, and a place in John Owen's England team, all in one season has made it a dream year for Stansfield. Now he had also scored in every round of the competition, except the semi-final, that being his seventh Trophy goal.

Stevenage were floored. With two thirds of the game gone they knew their chances of lifting the trophy had slipped away. Manager Wayne Turner tried all permissible substitutes in an attempt to put pressure on the Yeovil back line but it was the Somerset side who could well have extended their lead. Alford just failed to hit the target with what looked an easy chance set up by Michael McIndoe's shot being too fierce for Wilkerson to hold; a top corner seeking free kick from Johnson was turned round by the keeper's outstretched hand and skipper Terry Skiverton had a header from a corner cleared off the line.

Soon West Country fans were applauding the parade of the Trophy. They'll be even more optimistic now about Conference success in the new season and will have expectations of the Football League status they have so long sought. Stevenage too will be after the same prize. They can reflect on their fantastic progress over the last decade, yet will also be looking forward to the possibility of obliterating their rightful wrath at being denied Football League sta-tus in 1996 when they won the Conference title but found their facilities deemed unsuitable for promotion.

Good luck to both teams who contested sportingly with a near perfect football atmosphere.

Arthur Evans

25 in 25

A review of the **F.A. Challenge Trophy** and its participating clubs during the twenty-five year life span of the F.A. Non-League Club Directory (1978 - 2002) will be available in the next year. It will be one of a series of 25 and will contain features, statistics and photos in at least 144 pages dedicated purely to the Trophy competition.

Further details can be found on page 17 so make sure of your copy of this exciting limited edition.

Terry Skiverton lifts the FA Trophy at Villa Park. Photo: Peter Barnes

Above left: Yeovil Manager Gary Johnson with the FA Trophy. Photo: Roger Turner
Above right: Yeovil Town's two goalscorers, Adam Stansfield and Carl Alford. Photo: Roger Turner

PAST F.A. TROPHY FINALS

1970   MACCLESFIELD TOWN 2 (Lyond, B Fidler)   TELFORD UNITED 0   Att: 28,000
        Northern Premier League   *Southern League*
Macclesfield: Cooke, Sievwright, Bennett, Beaumont, Collins, Roberts, Lyons, B Fidler,Young, Corfield, D Fidler.
Telford: Irvine, Harris, Croft, Flowers, Coton, Ray,Fudge, Hart, Bentley, Murray, Jagger.   Ref: K Walker

1971   TELFORD UTD 3 (Owen, Bentley, Fudge)   HILLINGDON BORO. 2 (Reeve, Bishop)   Att: 29,500
        Southern League   *Southern League*
Telford: Irvine, Harris, Croft, Ray, Coton, Carr, Fudge, Owen, Bentley, Jagger ,Murray.
Hillingdon B.: Lowe, Batt, Langley, Higginson, Newcombe, Moore, Fairchild,Bishop, Reeve, Carter, Knox.   Ref: D Smith

1972   STAFFORD RANGERS 3 (Williams 2, Cullerton)   BARNET 0   Att: 24,000
        Northern Premier League   *Southern League*
Stafford R.: Aleksic, Chadwick, Clayton, Sargeant, Aston, Machin, Cullerton, Chapman,Williams, Bayley, Jones.
Barnet: McClelland, Lye, Jenkins, Ward, Embrey, King, Powell, Ferry, Flatt, Easton, Plume .   Ref: P Partridge

1973   SCARBOROUGH 2 (Leask, Thompson)   WIGAN ATHLETIC 1 (Rogers) aet   Att:23,000
        Northern Premier League   *Northern Premier League*
Scarborough: Garrow, Appleton, Shoulder, Dunn, Siddle, Fagan, Donoghue, Franks,Leask (Barmby), Thompson, Hewitt.
Wigan: Reeves, Morris, Sutherland, Taylor,Jackson, Gillibrand, Clements, Oats (McCunnell), Rogers, King, Worswick.   Ref: H Hackney

1974   MORECAMBE 2 (Richmond, Sutton)   DARTFORD 1 (Cunningham)   Att: 19,000
        Northern Premier League   *Southern League*
Morecambe: Coates, Pearson, Bennett, Sutton, Street, Baldwin, Done, Webber,Roberts (Galley), Kershaw, Richmond.
Dartford: Morton, Read, Payne, Carr, Burns,Binks, Light, Glozier, Robinson (Hearne), Cunningham, Halleday.   Ref: B Homewood

1975 **1**   MATLOCK TOWN 4 (Oxley, Dawson, T Fenoughty, N Fenoughty) SCARBOROUGH 0   Att: 21,000
        Northern Premier League   *Northern Premier League*
Matlock: Fell, McKay, Smith, Stuart, Dawson, Swan, Oxley, N Fenoughty, Scott, T Fenoughty, M Fenoughty.
Scarborough: Williams, Hewitt, Rettitt, Dunn, Marshall, Todd, Houghton, Woodall, Davidson, Barnby, Aveyard.   Ref: K Styles

1976   SCARBOROUGH 3 (Woodall, Abbey, Marshall(p))   STAFFORD R. 2 (Jones 2) aet   Att: 21,000
        Northern Premier League   *Northern Premier League*
Scarborough: Barnard, Jackson, Marshall, H Dunn, Ayre (Donoghue), HA Dunn, Dale,Barmby, Woodall, Abbey, Hilley.
Stafford: Arnold, Ritchie, Richards, Sargeant,Seddon, Morris, Chapman, Lowe, Jones, Hutchinson, Chadwick.   Ref: R Challis

1977   Att: 21,500
SCARBOROUGH 2 (Dunn(p), Abbey)   *Northern Premier League*
DAGENHAM 1 (Harris)   *Isthmian League*
Scarborough: Chapman, Smith, Marshall (Barmby), Dunn, Ayre, Deere, Aveyard,Donoghue, Woodall, Abbey, Dunn.
Dagenham: Hutley, Wellman, P Currie, Dunwell,Moore, W Currie, Harkins, Saul, Fox, Harris, Holder.   Ref: G Courtney

1978   Att: 20,000
ALTRINCHAM 3 (King, Johnson, Rogers) *Northern Premier League*
LEATHERHEAD 1 (Cook)   *Isthmian League*
Altrincham: Eales, Allan, Crossley, Bailey, Owens, King, Morris, Heathcote,Johnson, Rogers, Davidson (Flaherty).
Leatherhead: Swannell, Cooper, Eaton, Davies,Reid, Malley, Cook, Salkeld, Baker, Boyle (Bailey).   Ref: A Grey

1979   Att: 32,000
STAFFORD RANGERS 2 (A Wood 2)   *Northern Premier League*
KETTERING TOWN 0   *Isthmian League*
Stafford: Arnold, F Wood, Willis, Sargeant, Seddon, Ritchie, Secker, Chapman, A Wood, Cullerton, Chadwick (Jones).
Kettering: Lane, Ashby, Lee, Eastell, Dixey,Suddards, Flannagan, Kellock, Phipps, Clayton, Evans (Hughes).   Ref: D Richardson

1980 **2**   Att : 26,000
DAGENHAM 2 (Duck, Maycock)   *Isthmian League*
MOSSLEY 1 (Smith)   *Northern Premier League*
Dagenham: Huttley, Wellman, Scales, Dunwell, Mooore, Durrell, Maycock, Horan,Duck, Kidd, Jones (Holder).
Mossley: Fitton, Brown, Vaughan, Gorman, Salter, Polliot, Smith, Moore, Skeete, O'Connor, Keelan (Wilson).   Ref: K Baker

A terrific photo by Bob Thomas showing the determination in the faces of Stan Allan (Altrincham) in stripes and Enfield's Tony Jennings. On this occasion Tony collected the Trophy Winners Medal as Enfield won 1-0 in 1982. But Stan was in the successful Altrincham side that beat Leatherhead in 1978 and both players joined Terry Moore (Bishop's Stortford) as double final winners by picking up Amateur Cup medals when Stan's Skelmersdale United beat Dagenham in 1971 and Tony won with the Hendon who beat Enfield a year later.

Notes:

1   The only occasion three members of the same family played in the same FA Trophy Final team.
2   The first of the Amateurs from the Isthmian League to win the FA Trophy
3   Goalkeeper Terry Moore had also won an Amateur Cup Winners Medal with Bishop's Stortford in 1974

Telford United played in the first two FA Trophy Finals in 1970 and 1971, winning the second. Then between 1983 and 1989 The 'Stags' reached Wembley on three more occasions, winning on two occasions and losing in 1988 after a replay.
This photo shows the celebrations after their 2-1 victory over Northwich Victoria in 1983. Antone Joseph (left of picture) who won medals in all three finals also played in the 1991 final for Kidderminster Harriers.

1981 3   Att:22,578
BISHOP'S STORTFORD 1 (Sullivan)
Isthmian League
SUTTON UNITED 0
Isthmian League
Bishop's Stortford: Moore, Blackman, Brame, Smith (Worrell), Bradford, Abery, Sullivan,Knapman, Radford, Simmonds, Mitchell.
Sutton Utd.: Collyer, Rogers, Green, J Rains,T Rains, Stephens (Sunnucks), Waldon, Pritchard, Cornwell, Parsons.   Ref: J Worrall

1982   Att:18.678
ENFIELD 1 (Taylor)   *Isthmian League*
ALTRINCHAM 0   *Alliance Premier League*
Enfield: Jacobs, Barrett, Tone, Jennings, Waite, Ironton, Ashford, Taylor,Holmes, Oliver (Flint), King.   Ref: B Stevens
Altrincham: Connaughton, Crossley, Davison, Bailey, Cuddy, King (Whitbread), Allan, Heathcote, Johnson, Rogers, Howard.

1983   Att: 22,071
TELFORD UTD 2 (Mather 2)
Alliance Premier League
NORTHWICH VICTORIA 1 (Bennett)
Alliance Premier League
Telford: Charlton, Lewis, Turner, Mayman (Joseph), Walker, Easton, Barnett,Williams, Mather, Hogan, Alcock.
Northwich: Ryan, Fretwell, Murphy, Jones, Forshaw, Ward, Anderson, Abel (Bennett), Reid, Chesters, Wilson.   Ref: B Hill

---

1984   NORTHWICH VICTORIA 1 (Chester)   BANGOR CITY 1 (Whelan)   Att: 14,200
Replay   NORTHWICH VICTORIA 2 (Chesters(p), Anderson) BANGOR CITY 1 (Lunn)   Att: 5,805 (at Stoke)
     Alliance Premier League   *Alliance Premier League*
Northwich: Ryan, Fretwell, Dean, Jones, Forshaw (Power 65), Bennett, Anderson,Abel, Reid, Chesters, Wilson.   Ref: J Martin
Bangor: Letheren, Cavanagh, Gray, Whelan, Banks,Lunn, Urqhart, Morris, Carter, Howat, Sutcliffe (Westwood 105) . Same in replay.

1985   WEALDSTONE 2 (Graham, Holmes)   BOSTON UNITED 1 (Cook)   Att: 20,775
     Alliance Premier League   *Alliance Premier League*
Wealdstone: Iles, Perkins, Bowgett, Byatt, Davies, Greenaway, Holmes, Wainwright,Donnellan, Graham (N Cordice 89), A Cordice.
Boston: Blackwell, Casey, Ladd,Creane, O'Brien, Thommson, Laverick (Mallender 78), Simpsom, Gilbert, Lee, Cook.   Ref: J Bray

1986   ALTRINCHAM 1 (Farrelly)   RUNCORN 0   Att: 15,700
     Gola League   *Gola League*
Altrincham: Wealands, Gardner, Densmore, Johnson, Farrelly, Conning, Cuddy,Davison, Reid, Ellis, Anderson. Sub: Newton.
Runcorn: McBride, Lee, Roberts,Jones, Fraser, Smith, S Crompton (A Crompton), Imrie, Carter, Mather, Carrodus.   Ref: A Ward

1987   KIDDERMINSTER HARRIERS 0   BURTON ALBION 0   Att: 23,617
Replay   KIDDERMINSTER HARRIERS 2 (Davies 2) BURTON ALBION 1 (Groves)   Att: 15,685 (at West Brom)
     Conference   *Southern League*
Kidderminster: Arnold, Barton, Boxall, Brazier (sub Hazlewood in rep), Collins (subPearson 90 at Wembley), Woodall, McKenzie, O'Dowd, Tuohy, Casey, Davies. sub:Jones.
Burton: New, Essex, Kamara, Vaughan, Simms, Groves, Bancroft, Land, Dorsett, Redfern, (sub Wood in replay), Gauden.
Sub: Patterson.   Ref: D Shaw

1988   ENFIELD 0   TELFORD UNITED 0   Att: 20,161, Ref: L Dilkes
Replay   ENFIELD 3 (Furlong 2, Howell)   TELFORD 2 (Biggins, Norris(p))   Att: 6,912 (at W Brom)
     Conference   *Conference*
Enfield: Pape, Cottington, Howell, Keen (sub Edmonds in rep), Sparrow (sub Hayzleden at Wembley), Lewis (sub Edmonds at Wembley), Harding, Cooper, King,Furlong, Francis.
Telford: Charlton, McGinty, Storton, Nelson, Wiggins, Mayman (sub Cunningham in rep (sub Hancock)), Sankey, Joseph, Stringer (sub Griffiths at Wembley, Griffiths in replay), Biggins, Norris.

1989   TELFORD UNITED 1 (Crawley)   MACCLESFIELD TOWN 0   Att: 18,102
     Conference   *Conference*
Telford: Charlton, Lee, Brindley, Hancock, Wiggins, Mayman, Grainger, Joseph, Nelson, Lloyd, Stringer. Subs: Crawley, Griffiths.
Macclesfield: Zelem, Roberts, Tobin, Edwards, Hardman, Askey, Lake, Hanton, Imrie, Burr, Timmons. Subs: Devomshire, Kendall.

     Ref: T Holbrook

1990   BARROW 3 (Gordon 2, Cowperthwaite)   LEEK TOWN 0   Att: 19,011
     Conference   *Northern Premier League*
Barrow: McDonnell, Higgins, Chilton, Skivington, Gordon, Proctor, Doherty (Burgess), Farrell (Gilmore), Cowperthwaite, Lowe, Ferris.
Leek: Simpson, Elsby (Smith), Pearce, McMullen, Clowes, Coleman (Russell),Mellor, Somerville, Sutton, Millington, Norris   Ref: T Simpson

1991 WYCOMBE W. 2 (Scott, West) KIDDERMINSTER H. 1 (Hadley) Att: 34,842
Conference   *Conference*
Wycombe: Granville, Crossley, Cash, Kerr, Creaser, Carroll, Ryan, Stapleton,West, Scott, Guppy (Hutchinson). Ref: J Watson
Kidderminster: Jones, Kurila, McGrath, Weir, Barnett, Forsyth, Joseph (Wilcox), Howell (Whitehouse), Hadley, Lilwall, Humphries

1992 COLCHESTER UTD* 3 (Masters, Smith, McGavin) WITTON ALBION 1 (Lutkevitch) Att: 27,806
Conference   *Conference*
Colchester: Barrett, Donald, Roberts, Knsella, English, Martin, Cook, Masters,McDonough (Bennett 65), McGavin, Smith. Ref: K P Barratt
Witton: Mason, Halliday, Coathup, McNeilis, Jim Connor, Anderson, Thomas, Rose, Alford, Grimshaw (Joe Connor), Lutkevitch (McCluskie)

1993 WYCOMBE W*. 4 (Cousins, Kerr, Thompson, Carroll) RUNCORN 1 (Shaughnessy) Att: 32,968
Conference   *Conference*
Wycombe: Hyde, Cousins, Cooper, Kerr, Crossley, Thompson (Hayrettin 65),Carroll, Ryan, Hutchinson, Scott, Guppy. Sub: Casey.
Runcorn: Williams, Bates, Robertson, Hill, Harold (Connor 62), Anderson, Brady (Parker 72), Brown, Shaughnessy, McKenna, Brabin
                       Ref: I J Borritt

1994 WOKING 2 (D Brown, Hay) RUNCORN 1 (Shaw (pen)) Att: 15,818
Conference   *Conference*
Woking: Batty, Tucker, L Wye, Berry, Brown, Clement, Brown (Rattray 32), Fielder, Steele, Hay (Puckett 46), Walker. Ref: Paul Durkin
Runcorn: Williams, Bates, Robertson, Shaw, Lee, Anderson, Thomas, Connor, McInerney (Hill 71), McKenna, Brabin. Sub: Parker

1995 WOKING 2 (Steele, Fielder) KIDDERMINSTER H. 1 aet (Davies) Att: 17,815
Conference   *Conference*
Woking: Batty, Tucker, L Wye, Fielder, Brown, Crumplin (Rattray 42), S Wye, Ellis, Steele, Hay (Newberry 112), Walker. (Sub: Read(gk)
Kidderminster: Rose, Hodson, Bancroft, Webb, Brindley (Cartwright 94), Forsyth, Deakin, Yates, Humphreys (Hughes 105), Davies,
Purdie. Sub: Dearlove (gk)   Ref: D J Gallagher

1996 MACCLESFIELD TOWN 3 (Payne, OG, Hemmings) NORTHWICH VICTORIA 1 (Williams) Att: 8,672
Conference   *Conference*
Macclesfield: Price, Edey, Gardiner, Payne, Howarth(C), Sorvel, Lyons, Wood (Hulme 83), Coates, Power, Hemmings (Cavell 88).
Northwich: Greygoose, Ward, Duffy, Burgess (Simpson 87), Abel (Steele), Walters, Williams, Butler (C), Cooke, Humphries, Vicary.
Ref: M Reed

1997 WOKING 1 (Hay 112) DAGENHAM & REDBRIDGE 0 Att: 24,376
Conference   *Isthmian League*
Woking: Batty, Brown, Howard, Foster, Taylor, S Wye, Thompson (sub Jones 115), Ellis, Steele (L Wye 108), Walker, Jackson (Hay 77).
Dagenham: Gothard, Culverhouse, Connor, Creaser, Jacques (sub Double 75), Davidson, Pratt (Naylor 81), Parratt, Broom, Rogers,
Stimson (John 65).   Ref: J Winter

1998 CHELTENHAM TOWN 1 (Eaton 74) SOUTHPORT 0 Att: 26,387
Conference   *Conference*
Cheltenham: Book, Duff, Freeman, Banks, Victory, Knight (Smith 78), Howells, Bloomer, Walker (sub Milton 78), Eaton, Watkins. Sub:
Wright.
Southport: Stewart, Horner, Futcher, Ryan, Farley, Kielty, Butler, Gamble, Formby (sub Whittaker 80), Thompson (sub Bollard 88), Ross.
Sub: Mitten.   Ref: G S Willard

1999 KINGSTONIAN 1 (Mustafa 49) FOREST GREEN ROVERS 0 Att: 20,037
Conference   *Conference*
Kingstonian: Farrelly, Mustafa, Luckett, Crossley, Stewart, Harris, Patterson, Pitcher, Rattray, Leworthy (Francis 87), Akuamoah. Subs
(not used): John, Corbett, Brown, Tranter
Forest Green Rovers: Shuttlewood, Hedges, Forbes, Bailey (Smart 76), Kilgour, Wigg (Cook 58), Honor (Winter 58), Drysdale, McGregor,
Mehew, Sykes. Subs (not used): Perrin, Coupe   Ref: A B Wilkie

2000 KINGSTONIAN 3 (Akuamoah 40, 69, Simba 75) KETTERING TOWN 2 (Vowden 55, Norman 64p) Att: 20,034
Conference   *Conference*
Kingstonian: Farelly, Mustafa, Luckett, Crossley, Stewart (Saunders 77), Harris, Kadi (Leworthy 83), Pitcher, Green (Basford 86), Smiba,
Akuamoah. Subs (not used): Hurst, Allan
Kettering Town: Sollit, McNamara, Adams, Perkins, Vowden, Norman (Duik 76), Fisher, Brown, Shutt, Watkins (Hudson 46), Setchell
(Hopkins 81). Subs (not used): Ridgway, Wilson   Ref: S W Dunn

2001 CANVEY ISLAND 1 (Chenery) FOREST GREEN ROVERS 0 at Villa Park Att: 10,007
Isthmian League   *Conference*
Forest Green Rovers: Perrin, Cousins, Lockwood, Foster, Clark, Burns, Daley, Drysdale (Bennett 46), Foster (Hunt 75), Meecham, Slater.
Subs (not used): Hedges, Prince, Ghent
Canvey Island: Harrison, Duffy, Chenery, Bodley, Ward, Tilson, Stimson (Tanner 83), Gregory, Vaughan (Jones 76), Parmenter. Subs (not
used): Bennett, Miller, Thompson.   Ref: A G Wiley

2002 YEOVIL TOWN 2 (Alford, Stansfield) STEVENAGE BOROUGH 0 at Villa Park Att: 18,809
Conference   *Conference*
Yeovil Town: Weale, Lockwood, Tonkin, Skiverton, Pluck (White 51), Way, Stansfield, Johnson, Alford (Giles 86), Crittenden (Lindegaard
83), McIndoe. Subs (not used): O'Brien, Sheffield
Stevenage Borough: Wilkerson, Hamsher, Goodliffe, Trott, Fraser, Fisher, Wormull (Stirling 71), Evers (Williams 56), Jackson, Sigere
(Campbell 74), Clarke. Subs (not used): Campbell, Greygoose   Ref: N S Barry

F.A TROPHY
TOP GOAL SCORERS

9 HAT-TRICKS
(3 GOALS)

10 GOALS
Abbot G   Welling United

8 GOALS
Stansfield A   Yeovil Town

6 GOALS
Simpson N   Braintree Town
Powell V   North Ferriby Utd

5 GOALS
Alford C   Yeovil Town

4 GOALS
Carthy M   Billericay Town
Noble T   Braintree Town
Farrell S   Burton Albion
Wilkins C   Gravesend & Nflt
Barnes K   Kendal Town
Davies M   Merthyr Tydfil
Hay A   Morecambe
Norman J   Morecambe
Knight G   North Ferriby Utd
Hall D   Solihull Borough
Nancekivell K Tiverton Town
Townsend G   Worksop Town

3 GOALS
Purser W   Barnet
Hussey S   Bashley
Reinelt R   Braintree Town
Moore C   Burton Albion
Cobb P   Canvey Island
Elliott G   Carshalton Athletic
Spink D   Chester City
O'Hagen   Dorchester Town
Adams D   Erith & Belvedere
Piper C   Farnborough Town
Woolley B   Gresley Rovers
Nade R   Hampton & Rich B
Lake S   Hednesford Town
Williams G   Hereford United
Walker G   Histon
Ball G   Kingstonian
Green R   Kingstonian
Seal D   Mangotsfield Utd
Linger P   Purfleet
McKwain C   Rothwell Town
Watson L   Runcorn FC Halton
Smith C   Solihull Borough
Clarke A   Stevenage Boro
Jackson K   Stevenage Boro
Kane C   Tooting & Mitch U
Fearns T   Vauxhall Motors
Young N   Vauxhall Motors

1st ROUND - 2

| | Carthy M | Billericay Town |
| | Barnes K | Kendal Town |

2nd ROUND - 3

5	Abbott G	Weling United
	Farrell S	Burton Albion
	Nancekivell K	Tiverton Town

3rd ROUND - 1

| 4 | Abbott G | Welling United |
| | Roberts | Tamworth |

4th ROUND - 3

4	Hay A	Morecambe
	Simpson N	Braintree Town
	Spink D	Chester City

Gary Abbott scores for Welling but this one was in his first spell with the club when playing in the Conference at Telford.
Photo: K Gillard

F.A. CARLSBERG VASE

2001-2002 REVIEW

We've done it! Whitley Bay celebrate with the FA Carlsberg Vase. Photo: SteveAyre

FIRST ROUND QUALIFYING

Saturday 8 September 2001   £150 to each winning club

#	Home		Away	Score	
1	Cheadle Town	v	Washington Nissan	1-2	48
	Clemans		Cogdon (2)		
2	West Auckland Town	v	Ashington	5-2	80
	Anderson, Nicholson, Stanger		Beharral, Lawson		
	Stout, Wheldon				
3	Winterton Rangers	v	North Shields	*3-2	50
	Day (2), Hill		Gibbard, McDonald		
4	Willington	v	Parkgate	2-3	44
	Gillespie, Snow		Smith (3)		
5	Sheffield	v	Rossington Main	*3-3	150
	Moorwood, Owen (2)		Bradley (2), Walker		
	Rossington Main	v	Sheffield	*1-1	96
	Bradley		Fox		
	(Rossington Main won 5-4 after penalties)				
6	Poulton Victoria	v	Pickering Town	0-2	81
			Chapman, Zoll		
7	Glasshoughton Welfare	v	Whickham	2-0	40
	Dickinson, Edwards				
8	Worsbrough Bridge MW	v	Armthorpe Welfare	4-0	45
	Bray (2), Oliver, Watson				
9	Chester-le-Street Town	v	Ramsbottom United	4-1	60
	Blower, Leadbitter, Maddison, Sowerby		Brennan		
10	Norton & Stockton Ancients	v	Nelson	*2-2	26
	Cobain, Roberts		Bannister, Smith		
	Nelson	v	Norton & Stockton Anc.	3-0	51
	Rodriguez (3)				
11	Oldham Town	v	Chadderton	1-4	27
	Black		Barlow (2), Daventry, Gemmell		
12	Maine Road	v	Billingham Synthonia	2-3	45
	Russell (2)		Fawcett, Flanagan (2)		
13	Selby Town	v	Easington Colliery	2-1	68
	Collier		Errington		
14	Maltby Main	v	Peterlee Newtown	*1-1	45
	Winter		Jewson		
	Peterlee Newtown	v	Maltby Main	5-0	62
	Hall (3), Hinton, Jewson				
15	Warrington Town	v	Bottesford Town	9-1	74
	Chadwick, Heverin(3), Moores(2)		Smith		
	Priedt, Trewitt, Warder				
16	Hebburn	v	Esh Winning (@ EW)	1-5	58
	Carmichael		Messer (4), Wray		
17	Walsall Wood	v	North Notts	0-1	45
18	Gedling Town	v	Deeping Rangers	3-2	60
	Frawley, Saunders (2)		Sinclair, Wilson		
19	Rainworth MW	v	Highfield Rangers	*3-2	84
	Clarke, Johnson, Sharman		Rowe (2)		
20	Halesowen Harriers	v	Stourbridge	2-1	170
	Bridge, Williams		Conway		
21	St Andrews	v	Birstall United	*1-1	45
	Cooper		Lord		
	Birstall United	v	St Andrews	0-2	52
			Collins, Purple		
22	Dunkirk	v	Friar Lane OB	1-4	80
	Jeffries		Johnson (2), North, Waldron		
23	Westfields	v	Stratford Town	2-3	24
	Hibbard, Powell		Darroch (2), Halford		
24	Kimberley Town	v	Kidsgrove Athletic	0-3	63
			Lainton, Tobin (2)		
25	Stapenhill	v	Tividale	0-2	47
			Coll, McNaney		
26	Ibstock Welfare	v	Oldbury United	*1-1	73
	Smalley		Grosvenor		
	Oldbury United	v	Ibstock Welfare	1-2	52
	Grosvenor		Beasley, Thompson		
27	Quorn	v	Stafford Town	1-0	123
	Pearson				
28	Marconi	v	Heath Hayes	3-2	22
	Fraser, Moloney (2)		Inskip, Morgan		
29	Gornal Athletic	v	Chasetown	1-2	54
	Burgess		Gilbey, Rutter		
30	Anstey Nomads	v	Cheslyn Hay	1-4	90
	Connelly		Clarke, Dunn, Miller		
31	Beaconsfield SYCOB	v	Brache Sparta	5-1	17
	Callander, Cotton, Polidore,		Ojulah		
	Richardson, Webb				
32	Fakenham Town	v	Needham Market	2-0	118
	Delicat, Mortimer				
33	Chalfont St Peter	v	Thetford Town	2-0	31
	Attrell, Holian				
34	Tring Town	v	Southall	2-0	29
	Kinsley (2)				
35	Norwich United	v	Biggleswade Town	*3-1	74
	Bugdale, Murphy (2)		Phillips		
36	Newmarket Town	v	Wroxham	0-3	76
			Hilton, Johnson, Stock		
37	Bowers United	v	Haringey Borough	4-2	52
	Dirkett, Drant, Williams (2)		Fung, Haastrup		
38	Ford Sports Daventry	v	Biggleswade Utd (@BU)	*3-2	35
	Fretwell, Geary, Kent		Marshall, Tyler		
39	Dunstable Town	v	Ware	2-1	74
	King, Reed				
40	Witney Academy	v	Letchworth	1-2	30
			Campbell, Huntley		
41	Somersham Town	v	Wembley	0-5	89
			Gustave, McGinty (4)		
42	Witham Town	v	Edgware Town	3-1	55
	Bassett, Inglis, Kelly		Harris		
43	Saffron Walden Town	v	Maldon Town	1-11	89
	Porter		Huttley, Newman(2), Warwick(3), Witney(5)		
44	Leyton	v	Hoddesdon Town	0-1	76
			Redford		
45	Kingsbury Town	v	Soham Town Rangers	1-0	63
	Sapiro				
46	Eynesbury Rovers	v	Brook House	0-4	60
			Dell, Gallagher, Hibbert (2)		
47	Ilford	v	Welwyn Garden City	0-1	58
			Fisher		
48	AFC Wallingford	v	Cornard United	3-0	65
	McKinney, Mulvaney, Shildrick				
49	Henley Town	v	Harwich & Parkeston	0-4	101
			Calver, Carmichael, English, Hazel		
50	Mildenhall Town	v	Bugbrooke St Michaels	2-0	104
	McGregor, Salmons				
51	Burnham Ramblers	v	Hertford Town	2-1	57
	Dobson, Greaves		Murt		
52	Haverhill Rovers	v	Woodbridge Town	2-1	115
	Hammond, Holmes		Gilbert		
53	Ringmer	v	Horsham YMCA	2-1	83
	Davies, Randell		Price		
54	VCD Athletic	v	Cray Wanderers	2-0	59
	Bennett, Dimmock				
55	Merstham	v	Southwick	1-2	65
	Watts		Dimneen, Holden		
56	Moneyfields	v	Whitchurch United	6-2	65
	Darnley, Hore, Lafferty, Mould(2), Riddell		Bergalin (2)		
57	AFC Newbury	v	Hillingdon Borough	0-1	71
			Antwi		
58	Lymington Town	v	Walton Casuals	2-0	98
	Beverley (2)				
59	Wick	v	Camberley Town	3-0	95
	Annis, Bridle, Miles				
60	Didcot Town	v	Gosport Borough	1-2	122
	Lawton		Holland, Mann		
61	Erith Town	v	Ash United	0-5	54
			Horton, Johnson(2), Joyce, Woodhouse		
62	Whitstable Town	v	Redhill	0-1	151
			White		
63	Molesey	v	Viking Greenford	1-0	59
	James				
64	Lewes	v	Alton Town	5-1	95
	Harris, Newman, Shepherd(3)		Clothier		
65	Corinthian Casuals	v	Blackfield & Langley	4-2	51
	McDermott, Moorhouse, Waghorn, White		James, Simpkins		
66	Three Bridges	v	Banstead Athletic	2-3	76
	Banks, Massaro		Harding, Hutchinson, Knight		
67	Maidstone United	v	Carterton Town	4-1	350
	Arter, Count, Sinden (2)		King		
68	Elmore	v	Bristol Manor Farm	4-3	66
	Andrews, Reader, Robinson, Stansfield		Cook, Westlake, Williams		
69	Willand Rovers	v	Welton Rovers	*1-2	95
	Pengelly		French, Rogers		
70	Team Bath	v	Corsham Town	3-0	43
	Ball, Lewis (2)				
71	Torrington	v	Pershore Town	*1-1	86
	Madge		Jones		
	Pershore Town	v	Torrington	5-1	105
	Brian, Gregory Maidment(2), Pincher		Vodght		
72	St Blazey	v	Backwell United	*2-0	151
	Richardson (2)				
73	Barnstaple Town	v	Chard Town	1-0	117
	Squire				
74	Bitton	v	Warminster Town	5-0	65
	Cains, Cole(2), Davies(2)				
75	Melksham Town	v	Street	3-2	77
	Messenger, Seals, Staddon		Badman, Morgan		
76	Highworth Town	v	Bridgwater Town	0-2	126
			Knox, Young		
77	Calne Town	v	Shortwood United	2-1	82
	Butler, Davis		Ward		

Round Statistics

Best Home Win
Warrington Town v
Bottesford Town 9-1

Best Away Win
Saffron Walden Town v
Maldon Town 1-11

Best Attendance
Maidstone United v
Carterton Town 350

Average Attendance
75

Selby Town (Northern Counties East) v Easington Colliery (Northern League Div 2) 2-1
Selby Town No 10 scores the second goal for his club against Easington Colliery. Photo: Neil Thaler

Glasshoughton Welfare (Northern Counties East) v Whickham (Northern League Div 2) 2-0
Whickham's Kevin Hay (stripes on left) has his shot blocked. Photo: Bill Wheatcroft

Merstham (Combined Counties) v Southwick (Sussex) 1-2. Goalmouth action as the visitors defend in depth: they went on to win 2-1 with a last minute winner. Photo: Gordon Whittington

SECOND ROUND QUALIFYING
Saturday 22 September 2001   £200 to each winning club

#	Home		Away	Score	
1	Parkgate	v	Cammell Laird	*3-3	48
	Barnfield, Cusworth, Drinc		*Karkin, McGinn 2*		
	Cammell Laird	v	Parkgate	4-2	150
	Bennett,Hagan, McGinn 2		*Dring, Smith*		
2	Newcastle Benfield Saints	v	Peterlee Newtown	2-4	75
	Weatherley, Wilson		*Hall 2, Hinton, Jewson*		
3	Curzon Ashton	v	Atherton Collieries	*5-2	72
	Broome, Flurey, Shiel,		*Fisher, Sloan*		
	Wearden, Worsley				
4	Denaby United	v	Shotton Comrades	*3-2	72
	Hammond 3		*Attewell, Nugent*		
5	Warrington Town	v	Yorkshire Amateur	5-1	105
	Heverin 2, Moores 2, Tickle		*Lewis*		
6	Darwen	v	Bacup Borough	1-5	57
	1 o.g.		*Farnell 2, Hall, Lanns, Stanley*		
7	Billingham Synthonia	v	Horden CW	4-0	117
	Fawcett 2, Flanagan 2				
8	Winterton Rangers	v	Atherton LR	0-1	35
			Massay		
9	Alnwick Town	v	Squires Gate	3-4	60
	Swordy 2, Yeaden		*Catlow, Moss, Noblett, Paynter*		
10	Newcastle Blue Star	v	Glasshoughton Welfare	1-0	66
	Herman				
11	Guisborough Town	v	West Allotment Celtic	2-0	112
	Clarke, McLean				
12	Nelson	v	Garforth Town	8-0	134
13	Blackpool Mechanics	v	Brandon United	3-1	53
	Ashall, Laney, Park		*Cunningham*		
14	Woodley Sports	v	Worsbrough Bridge MW	2-0	83
15	Harrogate Railway	v	Brodsworth	3-1	101
	Hart, McLean 2		*Almunshi*		
16	Great Harwood Town	v	Shildon	0-4	88
			Bolton, Fairhurst, Outhwaite 2		
17	Northallerton Town	v	West Auckland Town	*2-3	68
	Foreman 2		*Johnson 2, Maguire*		
18	Prescot Cables	v	Morpeth Town	2-0	132
	O'Neill 2				
19	Colne	v	Whitley Bay	0-1	79
			Chandler		
20	Louth United	v	Fleetwood Freeport	4-3	55
	Bailey, Grocock, Jones,1 o.g.		*Brooks, Flynn, Riches*		
21	Rossington Main	v	Bridlington Town	2-0	56
	Bradley, Debenham				
22	Flixton	v	Salford City	2-0	60
	Bates, Coyne				
23	Hall Road Rangers	v	Stand Athletic	*3-2	19
	Barnwell, Palmer, Smith		*Ashton, Denham*		
24	Durham City	v	South Shields	4-0	162
	Ludlow 2, Ord, Robertson				
25	Pickering Town	v	Selby Town	*2-0	141
	Connor, Zoll				
26	Holker Old Boys	v	Chester-le-Street Town	0-4	53
			Bowes, Edwards, Morgan, Shiels		
27	Liversedge	v	Thackley	2-3	137
	Sykes, West		*Patterson, Nchardson, Sugden*		
28	Washington Ikeda Hoover	v	Jarrow Roofing Boldon CA	*1-1	63
	O'Donovan		*Perry*		
	Jarrow Roofing Boldon CA	v	Washington Ikeda Hoover	*6-2	80
	Anderson 2, Chow 2, Garrett,		*Burns, Reay*		
	Woodhouse				
29	Thornaby	v	Abbey Hey	4-2	51
			Levendis, Pickering		
30	Pontefract Collieries	v	Castleton Gabriels	1-3	44
	Smith		*Woodyer 2, Hulme*		
31	Goole	v	Hallam	1-3	157
			Bushiri,Goddard, Morris		
32	Chadderton	v	Evenwood Town	0-3	74
			Dutton, Hinton, Murrray		
33	Esh Winning	v	Crook Town	3-1	83
	Marron, Messer 2		*Freary*		
34	Washington Nissan	v	Penrith	4-1	38
	Cogdon 4		*Chapman*		
35	Seaham Red Star	v	Skelmersdale United	1-0	56
	Tierney				
36	Tadcaster Albion	v	Hatfield Main	2-3	55
	Batley, Wilson		*Groome, Lanagan, Miller*		
37	Knypersley Victoria	v	Rainworth MW	*1-3	54
	Atkinson		*Sharman, Williams 2*		
38	Glapwell	v	Pegasus Juniors	1-2	93
	Morgan		*Harris 2*		
39	Cheslyn Hay	v	Kidsgrove Athletic	2-5	51
	Dunn 2		*Mountford, Tobin, Walklett 2*		
40	Long Eaton United	v	Boldmere St Michaels	3-2	62
	Bestwick, Guilor, Heath		*Burgess, Clarke*		

#	Home		Away	Score	
41	Brierley & Hagley Alliance	v	Holwell Sports	*2-1	50
	Perry, Yapp		*Gooding*		
42	Alvechurch	v	Shirebrook Town	0-5	92
			Charlesworth, Johnson, Widdowson 3		
43	Kirby Muxloe	v	Glossop North End	0-2	57
			Hamilton, Nibloe		
44	Ibstock Welfare	v	Holbeach United	1-0	108
	Emery				
45	Lincoln Moorlands	v	Willenhall Town	1-2	93
	Smith		*Bishop, Day*		
46	Causeway United	v	West Midlands Police	2-0	95
	Hall, Parker				
47	Barrow Town	v	Shawbury United	3-0	59
	Pitman, Wardman, 1o.g.				
48	Quorn	v	Grosvenor Park	2-3	86
	Varney 2		*Anifowosi 2, Walker*		
49	Star	v	Halesowen Harriers	3-1	67
	Horler 2, Taylor		*Bridge*		
50	Marconi	v	Bolehall Swifts	*2-2	35
	Gordon, McDonald		*Capaldi, Chawner*		
	Bolehall Swifts	v	Marconi	0-3	32
			Maloney 3		
51	Friar Lane OB	v	Studley BKL	*3-4	85
	James, Kerr, Waldron				
52	South Normanton Athletic	v	Bridgnorth Town	2-3	106
	Coleman, Taylor		*Blakemore, Bullymore*		
53	Nuneaton Griff	v	Downes Sports	0-4	72
			Saunders, Sheedy, Williams 2		
54	Malvern Town	v	Blackstone	1-3	87
	Upton		*Challinor, Saltano, Sharpe*		
55	Ludlow Town	v	Stratford Town	1-6	52
	Finney		*Brant,Sheward,Spacey 2,Stephenson 2*		
56	Dudley Town	v	Cradley Town	*1-2	47
	Gennard		*Smith, Whitehouse*		
57	Collingham	v	Meir KA	2-1	52
	Eade,Gamble		*Bisson*		
58	Handrahan Timbers	v	Buxton	0-4	60
			Bainbridge, Pickford 2, Tibenham		
59	Pelsall Villa	v	Tividale	1-2	97
	King		*Coll, McNaney*		
60	Gedling Town	v	Chasetown	*4-1	50
	Frawley, Marshall 3		*Langston*		
61	Bourne Town	v	North Notts	0-1	106
			Short		
62	Kings Heath	v	St Andrews)	1-2	35
	Rostill		*Martin 2*		
63	Wolverhampton Casuals	v	Staveley MW	*1-1	48
	Miller		*Newton*		
	Staveley MW	v	Wolverhampton Casuals		
	(walkover for Staveley MW – Wolverhampton Casuals withdrawn)				
64	Shifnal Town	v	Leek CSOB	0-4	87
			Hubbard 2, Leaver. Sheldon		
65	Ford Sports Daventry	v	Hullbridge Sports	3-2	35
	Giles 2, Sugrue		*Juson, Mackler*		
66	Wootton Blue Cross	v	Buckingham Town	1-2	67
	Evason		*Abdi, Cox*		
67	Stewarts & Lloyds	v	Wellingborough Town	9-2	25
	Clark, Diver, Drain 3				
	Simmons 2, Torrance 2				
68	Whitton United	v	Rothwell Corinthians	*1-2	78
	Lander		*Cann 2*		
69	Bowers United	v	Leighton Town	2-4	60
	Brant, Williams		*Barnes, Perry 2, Sinnott*		
70	Stowmarket Town	v	St Neots Town	2-3	90
	Jopling 2		*Khune, Meads, Petty*		
71	Felixstowe & Walton Utd.	v	Great Wakering Rovers	1-3	98
	Deasy		*Ewery 2, Sibanda*		
72	Mildenhall Town	v	Haverhill Rovers	*1-1	154
	Long		*Brandt*		
	Haverhill Rovers	v	Mildenhall Town	0-1	148
			Ogilvie		
73	Leyton Pennant	v	Sawbridgeworth Town	2-0	82
	Cove, Richards				
74	Fakenham Town	v	Norwich United	1-3	139
	Delicata		*Hunton, McIntosh, Murphy*		
75	Long Buckby	v	Clapton	2-0	23
	Noel, Tiernan				
76	Concord Rangers	v	St Ives Town	2-1	50
	Clarke, Hobden		*Ewles*		
77	Halstead Town	v	Tring Town	*1-2	121
			Kinsley, Walters		
78	Colney Heath	v	March Town United	11-0	87
	Allen,Garrett 2,Hewing 3,Khan 2				
	Lacey, Parkatides, Townsend				

Hailsham Town (Sussex) v Corinthian Casuals (Ryman Div 3) 1-3. Corinthian Casuals Ian McDermott heads the ball past Hailsham Town's goalkeeper Russell Tanner. Photo: Roger Turner

Ibstock Welfare (Leics Senior) v Holbeach United (United Counties Premier) 1-0.
Martyn Emery heads against the Holbeach bar, then scored with the rebound. Photo: Bill Wheatcroft

Left: Potton United (United Counties Div 1) v Southall (Combined Co) 1-5. Southall Town's Jason Laing jumps well clear of the Potton attack. Photo: Steve Ayre
Right: Nelson (North West Co Div 1) v Garforth Town (Northern Counties East) 8-0. Nelson sub Mick Molyneux blasts his side's fourth goal past Garforth keeper Steve Williams. Photo: Alan Watson

79	Cockfosters v Warboys Town	5-2	64
Grostake, Kennedy, Moniatis 2,1og	*Davis, Setchell*		
80	Southend Manor v Hoddesdon Town	1-2	83
1 og	*Evitt 2*		
81	Wivenhoe Town v Ruislip Manor	1-0	67
Chatters			
82	Royston Town v Brimsdown Rovers	3-2	65
Dobson 2, Easley	*Faulkner 2*		
83	Langford v Maldon Town	1-4	70
Russell	*Warwick, Witney 3*		
84	Brook House v Stanway Rovers	5-0	54
Gill, Galloway 2,Hibbert,Jordan			
85	Kempston Rovers v Wroxham	0-3	46
	Hartle, Johnson. Lewis		
86	Beaconsfield SYCOB v Tilbury	1-2	34
Callender	*Okita, Renshaw*		
87	AFC Wallingford v North Leigh	*5-1	64
McKinvey,Mulraney,Parr,Shildrick	*1 og*		
88	Ipswich Wanderers v Yaxley	2-0	53
Howell, Roberts			
89	Ely City v Letchworth	1-2	96
Eden	*Campbell, Cole*		
90	Tiptree United v Potters Bar Town	7-0	57
Barefield 4,Daly,Powell,Rochester			
91	Milton Keynes City v St Margaretsbury	*1-1	76
Hyde	*Casha*		
	St Margaretsbury v Milton Keynes City	1-5	47
Winger	*Hill, Hyde 4*		
92	Potton United v Southall Town	1-5	27
1og	*Castagnette,Janssen, Smith 3*		
93	Wingate & Finchley v Stansted	*2-2	90
Donn, Levack	*Przedziecki, Thomas*		
	Stansted v Wingate & Finchley	*2-4	52
Lowe,	*Butterfield, Davis, Fitzpatrick 2*		
94	Northampton Spencer v Welwyn Garden City	4-1	85
Coleman 2, Jelley, Underwood	*Woiseman*		
95	Downham Town v Clacton Town	0-8	75
	Bailey, Clewley 2, Farmer, Hepburn		
	Hillier, Hudson 2		
96	Harwich & Parkeston v Dunstable Town	0-2	116
	Carney, 1og		
97	Flackwell Heath v Bedford United	2-1	47
	Kalyan		
98	Chalfont St Peter v Aveley	0-4	40
	Hazle, Leslie 3		
99	Bury Town v Somersett Ambury V&E	4-5	113
	Scripps, Turner 3, Wales		
100	Witham Town v Dereham Town	1-2	79
Driver	*Barrett, Henman*		
101	Harefield United v Harpenden Town	5-4	54
Dunn 3, Herring, Keen	*Bound, Gregory 3*		
102	Kingsbury Town v Great Yarmouth Town	2-1	33
Cooper, Porter	*George*		
103	Holmer Green v East Thurrock United	1-3	62
King	*Dwyer, Hall, St Hilaire*		
104	Leverstock Green v Desborough Town	*0-2	71
	Byrne. McHutchinson		
105	Brentwood v Hanwell Town	2-1	31
Bonham, Cousins	*Elder*		
106	Hadleigh United v Burnham Ramblers	*3-2	76
Willingham 3	*Greaves, Marchant*		
107	Wembley v Cheshunt	3-1	56
Davies 2, Hewitt	*Cox*		
108	Bicester Town v Brightlingsea United	2-0	28
Darch, Marshall			
109	Hythe Town v Bedfont	*1-1	86
Hughes	*Postins*		
	Bedfont v Hythe Town	3-0	54
Morrow, Postins, Stewart			
110	Reading Town v Abingdon Town	1-3	45
Leighton	*Gardner 2, Oram*		
111	Tunbridge Wells v Lordswood	2-5	97
Nicklin 2	*Kacy, Masters 4*		
112	Littlehampton Town v Peacehaven & Telscombe	*3-3	74
Davies, Thornton, 1og	*Durrant 2, Pattendon*		
	Peacehaven & Telscombe v Littlehampton Town	*3-2	72
Lockhart, Pattendon 2	*Templeman 2*		
113	Abingdon United v Epsom & Ewell	2-0	95
Maciak, Smith			
114	Beckenham Town v Wokingham Town	0-3	58
	Blake, Ward 2		
115	VCD Athletic v Godalming & Guildford	5-0	46
Bennett, Brown, Collins, Davis, Kidd			
116	Moneyfields v Molesey	*2-1	80
Boston, Mould	*Nedip*		
117	Arundel v Banstead Athletic	1-5	47
Wincell,	*Moore, Richards 2, Webb, Whelan*		

118	Wick v Slade Green	1-0	92
Loversidge			
119	Metropolitan Police v Ash United	2-3	77
Cormack, Daly	*Brophy , Joyce*		
120	Lancing v Fleet Town	3-2	72
Ford 2, Souter	*Frampton 2*		
121	Greenwich Borough v Chessington United	3-0	40
Scammell, Wallsgrove,1og			
122	Horsham v Chichester City United	1-3	201
French	*Laidlaw, Moore, Thomas*		
123	Whitehawk v Lymington Town	1-0	70
Rowland			
124	Fareham Town v Selsey	0-1	154
	Stephens		
125	Hailsham Town v Corinthian Casuals	1-3	141
Veiga	*Waghorn, White 2*		
126	East Preston v Oakwood	1-4	52
Huckett	*Belgrave,Manvuille,O'Donnell,Simpson*		
127	Chessington & Hook Utd. v Chertsey Town	*4-2	107
Demonlow, Dow, Wicks 2	*Breslyn, Pomroy*		
128	Farnham Town v Redhill	*2-1	60
Morgan 2	*O'Dongo*		
129	Maidstone United v Hungerford Town	4-2	369
Foley, Ribbens, Sinden 2	*Hopkins, Mildenhall*		
130	Hillingdon Borough v Milton United	4-2	40
Howells, O'Neil 2, Yeboa	*Brown, Hartley*		
131	Wantage Town v Lewes	0-1	85
	Shepherd		
132	Dorking v Cobham	3-0	96
Chaagan, Coyle, Lunn			
133	Sandhurst Town v Eastbourne Town	*1-0	73
Watmore			
134	Pagham v Ringmer	0-5	65
	Davies, Grice 3, Randell		
135	Eastbourne United v Bracknell Town	0-3	42
	Edwards, Holzman, Osgood		
136	Thatcham Town v East Grinstead Town	4-1	116
Cook, Green 2, Howard	*Burns*		
137	Hassocks v Chipstead	3-0	115
Graham, Laing, Watkins			
138	BAT Sports v Southwick	3-2	36
Doling, Parrett 2			
139	Gosport Borough v Andover	*2-2	128
Scammell, Walsgrove	*Damen, Dyke*		
	Andover v Gosport Borough	4-2	91
Forbes 2, Rusher2	*Sanderson, Wallsgrove*		
140	Egham Town v Eastleigh	*5-1	85
Farmer, Mernagh 3, Stewart	*Puckett*		
141	Brislington v Team Bath	0-1	69
	Lewis		
142	Bromyard Town v Harrow Hill	4-3	88
Chalmers, Gwynne, Willetts 2	*Barton, Clark 2*		
143	Bournemouth v Bridport	0-2	67
	Gisbourne, Hitchcock		
144	Pershore Town v Frome Town	0-4	76
	Lewis 3, Salter		
145	Portland United v Amesbury Town	*0-0	161
	Amesbury Town v Portland United	0-2	52
146*	Bishop Sutton v Keynsham	4-2	62
Ball, Cripps, Maggs, Saunders	*Harris, Silverthorne*		
147	Wootton Bassett Town v Calne Town	*3-2	126
Newton , Vaughan 2	*Peters, Terry*		
148	Downton v Bridgwater Town	0-3	85
	Knox, Young, 1og		
149	Bideford v Fairford Town	2-1	137
	Walker		
150	Barnstaple Town v Shepton Mallet	3-2	116
Squire, Watts, 1og	*Kayera, Light*		
151	Bitton v Almondsbury Town	0-2	94
	Curtis, Simpson		
152	Devizes Town v Odd Down	2-0	62
Flippance, Lloyd			
153	Melksham Town v Clevedon United	3-1	67
Messenger, Ranger, Sammut	*George*		
154	St Blazey v Gloucester United	1-0	181
Richardson			
155	Minehead Town v Christchurch	2-6	58
Carr, Souden	*Dibba 3, Nicholas 2, Woolner*		
156	Bemerton Heath Harl. v Cullompton Rangers	6-1	76
Chalke,Cole,Palmer 2,Richardson,Cole	*Scott*		
157	Paulton Rovers v Dawlish Town	2-3	110
	Blurton 2, Cliff-Brown		
158	Ilfracombe Town v Welton Rovers	2-0	61
Burns, Shannon			
159	Elmore v Westbury United	3-0	86
Palfrey, Stansfield, Thomas			
160	Tuffley Rovers v Wellington Town	2-1	44
Medcroft 2	*Seymour*		

FIRST ROUND PROPER

Saturday 20 October 2001   £250 to each winning club

1 Nantwich Town v Castleton Gabriels 2-1 65
Scarlett 2 / Hulme

2 Esh Winning v Jarrow Roofing Boldon CA 1-0 73
Drake

3 Hall Road Rangers v Harrogate Railway 2-5 45
Phillips 2 / **Davey 3**, Hart, 1 o.g.

4 Hatfield Main v Guisborough Town 3-4 116
Batchelor, Brown 2 / Clarke 2, Howes, Todd

5 Rossington Main v Curzon Ashton 1-2 92
Bradley / Worsley 2

6 Prescot Cables v Blackpool Mechanics 5-0 132
Jenson, O'Neill, Robinson, Taylor

7 Seaham Red Star v Thornaby 0-1 53
Cole

8 Tow Law Town v Cammell Laird 3-1 189
McKenna, Walker, Wilkinson / Hammond

9 West Auckland Town v Evenwood Town 4-1 81
Ellison 2, Milroy 2 / Raper

10 Dunston Fed. Brewery v Whitley Bay 2-3 203
Bangura, Hogg / Hay, Walton 2

11 Warrington Town v Durham City 1-2 142
Moores / Ord, Taylor

12 Atherton LR v Hallam *1-2 60
Hardman / Hobson, Morris

13 Newcastle Blue Star v Winsford United 0-5 66
Duckworth 2, Shaughnessy, Worthington 2

14 Congleton Town v Shildon 4-2 131
Baker 2, Park, Shaw / Bolton, Outhwaite

15 Mossley v Flixton *3-0 218
Brennan, Clegg, Mallinson

16 Pickering Town v Denaby United *2-0 110
O'Reilly, Wash

17 Chester-le-Street Town v Peterlee Newtown 1-4 71
Bowes / Bendelow, **Hall 3**

18 Squires Gate v Bacup Borough 2-1 105
Catlow, Sugden

19 Thackley v Woodley Sports 1-2 81
Patterson / Kneen, Phillips

20 Louth United v Nelson 1-3 57
Bailey / **White 3**

21 Washington Nissan v Billingham Synthonia *7-9 64
Bolton, **Cogden 3, Johnston 3** / Baker 2, **Flanagan 4**, O'Gorman, Wells

22 Barrow Town v North Notts *2-1 115
Boyles, Wagg / Walker

23 Blackstone v Staveley MW 1-0 57
Mitchell

24 Rainworth MW v Studley BKW 0-5 116
Hands 2, **Pountney 3**

25 Grosvenor Park v Tividale 1-2 55
Anifowosi / Pierpoint, Smith

26 Glossop North End v Raunds Town 1-2 150
Garside / Parker 2

27 Leek CSOB v Kidsgrove Ath 1-7 201
(at Kidsgrove Athletic FC) / Holcroft, Tobin, Twigg, Walker
Pugh / **Wilson-Cunningham 3**

28 Marconi v Rothwell Corinthians 2-1 36
Civzells, Moloney / 1 og

29 Stewarts & Lloyds v Pegasus Juniors 3-0 28
Drain 2, Torrance

30 Buxton v Downes Sports 2-1 161
Lewis 2 / Hewins

31 Shirebrook Town v Causeway United 0-1 223
Parker

32 St Andrews v Bridgnorth Town 2-4 66
Bradley, Orme / Blakemore 2, Bradley, Wilcox

33 Barwell v Willenhall Town 2-0 87
Percival, Warner

34 Heanor Town v Paget Rangers 3-2 111
Preston, Sharp, 1 og / Jones, Roach

35 Cradley Town v Bromsgrove Rovers 0-4 147
Bowen, Ford, McHugh, O'Neill

36 Gedling Town v Alfreton Town *4-4 113
Devonport, Horseman, Sunders 2 / Cheetham, Dolby, Highfield, Wilder
Castledine, France
Alfreton Town v Gedling Town 2-0 174

37 Brierley & Hagley Alliance v Desborough Town 2-4 42
Perry 2 / Byrne 2, Chong, Gilsenan

38 Star v Long Eaton United 2-1 69
Horler, 1 0g / Carson

39 .Boston Town v Collingham 3-2 126
Harrald, Price 2 / Gamble, Hopley

40 Ibstock Welfare v Stratford Town *1-1 97
Freeman / Stephenson
Stratford Town v Ibstock Welfare 3-0 109
Darlison, Darroch, Woodfield

41 Long Buckby v Bromyard Town 1-3 61
McBean / Morris, Willetts 2

42 Great Wakering Rovers v Hoddesdon Town 3-1 141
Hampshire, Sibanda 2 / Pullen

43 Norwich United v Colney Heath 1-2 131
Cooper / Seal, Townsend

44 Tiptree United v Cockfosters 3-1 56
Daly, Powell 2 / Blunsum

45 Wingate & Finchley v Harefield United *1-1 82
Baum / Craft
Harefield United v Wingate & Finchley 2-1 97
Craft, Dunn / Butterfield

46 Tring Town v Southall Town 0-3 45
Christie, Elliott, Smith

47 Somersett Ambury V & E v Barton Rovers 2-3 44
Conway 2 / Jean, Max-Grant 2

48 Diss Town v Concord Rangers *1-1 144
Miller / Vallelly
Concord Rangers v Diss Town *3-2 97
Heale, Hobden 2 / Pauking, Stafford

49 Mildenhall Town v Bicester Town 2-0 149
Head, Salmons

50 Letchworth v London Colney 0-4 76
Ross, Sippetts, Talbot 2

51 Dereham Town v Buckingham Town 4-1 185
King, Maguire, Way 2

52 Hadleigh United v Maldon Town 2-1 66
Francis, Willingham / Witney

53 Flackwell Heath v Clacton Town 0-4 67
Bailey, Hillier, Hudson, Senk

54 Leighton Town v Kingsbury Town 0-2 96
Sapiro 2

55 AFC Sudbury v Hemel Hempstead Town 5-1 227
Bennett 3, Norfolk, Owen

56 Cogenhoe United v Ipswich Wanderers 3-1 76
Harmon 3 / Howell

57 Leyton Pennant v Dunstable Town 6-1 71
Balfour, Campbell, Hughes 2 / Taylor
Shaw, Tilley

58 Brackley Town v Lowestoft Town 5-3 105
Mounsden, **Neal 3**, Purnell / Chenery 2, Reeder

59 Gorleston v Ford Sports Daventry 2-4 185
Ingram 2 / Evans, Sugrue 2, 1 og

60 Wembley v St Neots Town 0-2 86
Khune, 1og

61 Milton Keynes City v Northampton Spencer *3-1 103
Clarke, Hill 2 / O'Conner

62 Wivenhoe Town v Brook House *0-1 86
Gallagher

63 Royston Town v Wroxham *0-1 85
Terrington

64 Bracknell Town v Hillingdon Borough 2-0 72
Osgood, Smith

65 Wokingham Town v Sandhurst Town 1-2 71
Ward / Moore, Mulvaney

66 Lordswood v Corinthian Casuals 0-2 62
Waghorn, Watney

67 Ash United v Leatherhead 7-2 119
Bryant, Horton, **Mitchell 3** / Inglethorpe 2
Woodhouse 2

68 Selsey v Chessington & Hook U 2-0 140
Lee, Stephens

69 AFC Wallingford v Herne Bay 4-2 135
McKinney, Mulvaney, Kildrick 2 / Jones, Keir

70 Greenwich Borough v Wick 7-3 37
Brown, **Gibbs 4**, Muldowney 2 / Schneider 2, Young

71 East Thurrock United v Ringmer 0-3 96
Davies, Lopez, Townsend

72 Burgess Hill Town v Egham Town 4-0 170
Carr 2, Churchill, Edwards

73 Banstead Athletic v Deal Town 3-2 71
Beale, Whelan 2 / Hayes, Tait

74 Sidley United v Hassocks 3-1 105
Ball, Carey, Poole / Rendell

75	Farnham Town Blunden	v	Aveley	*0-1	70
76	Maidstone United Webster	v	Bedfont	1-0	193
77	Abingdon Town Sherwood	v	Peacehaven & Telscombe	1-0	104
78	Dorking Chaason, Moses	v	VCD Athletic Ratchford	2-1	93
79	Saltdean United	v	Abingdon United Henry, Riley, Simms 2, Smith	0-5	49
80	Romford Church, Langer, Mahoney, Rogers	v	Brentwood (@B) Bonham, Stittle, White	4-3	141
81	Tilbury Harrt, Okita 2	v	Whitehawk	3-0	99
82	Lewes Beeston, Byerley, Newman **Shepherd 3**	v	Oakwood Simpson	6-1	128
83	Lancing Gray, Griffin	v	Ramsgate	2-0	91
84	Portland United Fitch 2, Wyton	v	Frome Town	3-0	235
85	Lymington & New Milton Glenister, Keeping, Marwood, Town	v	Bridport	4-0	111
86	Bideford Powell	v	Elmore Palfrey, Stansfield, Woon	1-3	191
87	Almondsbury Town	v	Team Bath Carr, Lewis, Wilmot	0-3	88
88	Chichester City United Barnard, Chandler 2, Laidlaw 1 og, Thomas	v	Barnstaple Town	6-0	125
89	Ilfracombe Town	v	Bishop Sutton Maggs , Shepherd	0-2	78
90	Bemerton Heath Harlequins Chalk, Cole, Harding, Walters	v	Dawlish Town Blurton, 1 og	4-2	107
91	Bridgwater Town Clarke, Young	v	Melksham Town Lardner, Macey, Messinger	2-3	157
92	Moneyfields Boston, Dalton, Milkins, Mould 2	v	Tuffley Rovers	5-0	57
93	Andover Forbes 2	v	Yate Town Minall	2-1	136
94	Wootton Bassett Town	v	St Blazey Pugh, Richardson	0-2	140
95	Devizes Town Coombes, Flippance	v	Christchurch Gogan 2 , Woolner	2-3	80
96	BAT Sports Parrett	v	Thatcham Town Cook, **Green 3**, Howard, McLay 2	1-7	72

Top:
Sidley Utd (Sussex Div 1)   3
Hassocks (Sussex Div 1)   1
Joel Harding, Hassocks goalkeeper, stops a shot from Peter Baker.
Photo: Roger Turner

Centre:
Gedling Town (Northern Co East Div 1)   4
Alfreton Town (Northern Co East Prem)   4
Alfreton's Caine Cheetham (white, right) places his header against the post, with keeper Darren Lowe helpless.
Photo: Bill Wheatcroft

Bottom right:
Dunston Fed Brewery (Northern Div 1)   2
Whitley Bay (Northern Div 1)   3
Whitley Bay's Andy Hay celebrates his first goal for the club.
Photo: Graham Brown

Bottom left:
Bridgwater Town (Western)   2
Melksham Town (Western)   3
Bridgwater winger Steve Sokol evades two Melksham defenders.
Photo: Ken Gregory

SECOND ROUND PROPER

Saturday 10 November 2001   £400 to each winning club

#	Home		Away	Score	Att
1	Marske United *Thompson*	v	Hallam *Morris, O'Carroll*	*1-2	124
2	Winsford United *Miranda, Shaughnessy*	v	St Helens Town *Quirk, Wilde (2)*	2-4	160
3	Durham City **Taylor (3)**	v	Mossley *Mallinson, Thomas*	*3-2	181
4	Harrogate Railway *Haddon*	v	West Auckland Town **Allen (3)**	*1-3	91
5	Guisborough Town *Clarke (2)*	v	Whitley Bay *Dugdale (2)*	*2-2	163
	Whitley Bay *Chandler, Cuggy*	v	Guisborough Town	2-0	184
6	Tow Law Town *Innes, **Wake (4)***	v	Congleton	5-0	201
7	Billingham Town *Bishop, Chapman*	v	Curzon Ashton *Worsley*	2-1	88
8	Squires Gate	v	Billingham Synthonia *Flanagan (2), Wood*	0-3	92
9	Peterlee Newtown *Crosby (2), Jewson*	v	Consett **Thompson (4)**	3-4	52
10	Clitheroe *Reynolds*	v	Nelson *Coldridge*	*1-1	260
	Nelson *Irvine*	v	Clitheroe *Fogerty, Jones, Reynolds*	1-3	302
11	Woodley Sports	v	Pickering Town *O'Reilly, Willgrass, Zoll*	0-3	82
12	Eccleshill United *Cochrane*	v	Bedlington Terriers *Gibb, Milner*	*1-2	103
13	Nantwich Town *Dawson, Gardiner(2), Hampshire*	v	Esh Winning *Davison (2), Emmerson*	4-3	40
14	Thornaby *Reeve*	v	Prescott Cables *Garforth, **Jensen (3)***	1-4	84
15	Barwell *Grassby, Markham, Warner (2)*	v	Borrowash Victoria	4-0	124
16	Brigg Town **Roach(3)**, *Rowland(2), Wilby*	v	Causeway United	6-0	209
17	Arnold Town *Coke, Maddison*	v	Barrow Town *Pitman*	2-1	200
18	Stewarts & Lloyds *McAlwane, **Torrance (4)***	v	Star *Evason, Horler (2)*	*5-3	40
19	Mickleover Sports *Holness*	v	Milton Keynes City *Bevis, Clarke*	*1-2	67
20	Bridgnorth Town *Blackmore, Bradley, Coates*	v	Desborough Town *Byrne*	3-1	96
21	Boston Town	v	Heanor Town *Armstrong, Davis, Flanagan*	0-3	117
22	Blackstone	v	Cogenhoe United **Harmon (3)**	0-3	69
23	Bromsgrove Rovers *Bowen, Moore*	v	Fords Sports Daventry	2-0	301
24	Kidsgrove Athletic *Dicken(2), Holcroft, Mitchell Sanderman, Twigg Wilson-Cunningham*	v	Bromyard Town	7-0	137
25	Rushall Olympic *Piggott (2)*	v	Marconi *Civzelis*	2-1	115
26	Alfreton Town	v	Newcastle Town *Lennon, Stokes*	0-2	172
27	Raunds Town *Anderson(2), Bunting, Dunkley Goodacre, Knight*	v	Stratford Town *Woodfield*	6-1	116
28	Tividale *Coll*	v	Oadby Town *Knight, Miller (2), Warner*	1-4	85
29	Studley BKL *Bailey, Fergie, Hands, **Rowlands(3)***	v	Buxton	*6-1	83
30	Banstead Athletic *George, Greenaway, Shaw, Whelan*	v	Ringmer *Dobbyn, Grice*	4-2	67
31	Brook House *Hibbert Banya, Bennett, Betson, Cheetham, Owen*	v	AFC Sudbury	1-5	110
32	Great Wakering Rovers *Ewers, Hampshire, Sibanda*	v	London Colney *Doolan*	3-1	175
33	Selsey *Lee, Terry*	v	Concord Rangers	2-0	127
34	Brackley Town *Allen, Neal*	v	Berkhamsted Town *Lowe(2), Mullins, Pedder, Richardson*	*2-5	152
35	Wroxham *Carter, Carus, Fox(2), **Stock(3)***	v	Abingdon United *Parsons*	7-1	123
36	Mildenhall Town *Allis, Long, Moore*	v	Maidstone United	3-0	386
37	Aveley *Goldstone, Hazle (2)*	v	Kingsbury Town *Lewis, **Sapiro (3)***	3-4	60
38	Tilbury *Mully, Stubbs*	v	Barton Rovers *Donnelly*	2-1	88
	(after abandoned tie - 81st mn 2-2 att: 62. due to injury to Referee)				
39	Abingdon Town *Border, Charles, Greig*	v	Clacton Town *Farmer, Hillier*	3-2	92
40	Harefield United *Keen*	v	Croydon Athletic *Evans, Johnson*	1-2	54
41	Tiptree United *Darnell, Jackson, Mackrory*	v	Colney Heath *Lacey, Whitehead*	3-2	86
42	Romford	v	St Neots Town *Khine, Petty*	0-3	125
43	Sidley United	v	Dareham Town *Christie, Pert*	1-2	
44	Lewes *Francis (2), Shepherd*	v	Hornchurch *Wolff*	3-1	145
45	Arlesey Town *Broughton, Fontenelle(2), Harding, **Wilkinson (3)***	v	Hadleigh United *Cracknell*	7-1	239
46	Lancing *Ford, Towell*	v	Stotfold *Drury, Saunders (2), Snaylam*	2-4	130
47	Dorking *Lunn, White*	v	Greenwich Borough	2-0	80
48	Corinthian Casuals	v	Burgess Hill Town *Carr, Churchill, Harper*	0-3	156
49	Ashford Town (Middx)	v	Leyton Pennant *Cove (2)*	0-2	75
50	Westfield	v	AFC Wallingford *Shildrick (2)*	0-2	38
51	Thamesmead Town *Williams*	v	Southall Town	1-0	24
52	Cowes Sports *McDonald, Stevens*	v	Christchurch	2-0	83
53	Thatcham Town *Cook, Defraine*	v	Bishop Sutton	*2-0	124
54	Lymington & New Milton *Smith*	v	Wimborne Town *Gill, Lovell*	1-2	218
55	AFC Totton *Mottashed*	v	Melksham Town *Lardner, Messenger*	*1-2	106
56	Cove	v	Bemerton Heath Hqns *Chalk, Cole (2), Guy (2)*	0-5	47
57	Moneyfields *Hopkins, Hore, Jones, Stewart*	v	Portland United *Fitch, Reeve*	*4-2	77
58	Marlow *Ryder (2), Travis*	v	Porthleven *Harvey(2), Hillson, Morrison-Hill*	*3-4	141
59	Andover *Forbes, Webber*	v	Taunton Town *Bastow, Hapgood, Sargent (2)*	2-4	337
60	Ash United *Johnston, **Mitchell (3)***	v	Falmouth Town	4-0	154
61	St Blazey *Daly, Gosling(2), Hooper, Richardson*	v	Elmore *Palfrey, Woon*	5-2	229
62	Team Bath *Carr, Lewis*	v	Bracknell Town	2-0	54
63	Chichester City United *Laidlow, Thomas*	v	Hallen *Cook, Green (2), Sweeney*	2-4	41
64	Brockenhurst *Anderson, Smims (2), Stone*	v	Sandhurst Town *Mulvaney(2), Stairs (2)*	*4-4	68
	Sandhurst Town *Matthews*	v	Brockenhurst *Stone (2)*	1-2	85

Top:
Guisborough Town (Northern Div 1)   2
Whitley Bay (Northern Div 1)   2
Guisborough keeper Waind gathers well
against the twin threat of Whitley Bay's
Fenwick (10) and Chandler (9).
Photo: Graham Brown

Centre:
Team Bath (Western Prem)   2
Bracknell Town (Ryman Div 2)   0
Danny Oliphant of visitors Bracknell is
"apprehended" by Fidell Richards and
Lee Richardson, Team Bath.
Photo: Ken Gregory

Bottom:
Eccleshill United (North Co East)   1
Bedlington Terriers (Northern Div 1)   2
Eccleshill United's James Couborough
takes control of the ball despite the
advancing attention of Bedlington striker
John Milner. Photo: Darren C Thomas

THIRD ROUND PROPER

Saturday 8 December 2001   £600 to each winning club

1	Bedlington Terriers	v	Bridgnorth Town	3-0 531
	Chapman,Gibb,Milner			
2	Prescot Cables	v	Newcastle Town	4-0 82
	Benson, Garforth, Robinson 2			
3	West Auckland Town	v	Nantwich Town	1-0 130
	Milroy			
4	St Helens Town	v	Billingham Synthonia	3-1 129
	Boyd,Cooper,Nester		Wells	
5	Tow Law Town	v	Bromsgrove Rovers	3-1 248
	Nicholson,Wilkinson		Blake	
	Richardson			
	(abandoned in 76th minute 1-0 due to fog)			
6	Cogehoe United	v	Clitheroe	1-5 131
	Harmon		Cryer, **Spencer 3**, Stewart	
7	Arnold Town	v	Consett	2-1 253
	Maddison, Mitchell		Brown	
8	Billingham Town	v	Whitley Bay	1-2 210
	Storr		Hay, Walton	
9	Raunds Town	v	Durham City	*1-1 188
	Bunting		Brightwell	
	Durham City	v	Raunds Town	3-1 224
	Brightwell, Douglas, Ludlow		Anderson	
10	Oadby Town	v	Kidsgrove Athletic	1-2 165
	Warner		Twigg, Walters	
11	Barwell	v	Rushall Olympic	*0-3 121
			Cotterill, Palmer, Wright	
12	Pickering Town	v	Stewarts & Lloyds	2-0 212
	Wash, Willgrass			
13	Heanor Town	v	Hallam	2-1 183
	Armstrong, Preston		Morris	
14	Studley BKL	v	Brigg Town	*2-3 301
	Duncan, Grubb		Carter, Leech, Stones	
15	Croydon Athletic	v	Brockenhurst	5-2 102
	Harrison, **Liddle 3**, Lyward		Jones 2	
16	Thamesmead Town	v	Bemerton Heath Harlequins 0-2 76	
			Kenna, Palmer	
17	Great Wakering Town	v	Thatcham Town	2-0 194
	Hampshire, Munro			
18	Moneyfields	v	Porthleven	*3-4 183
	Hopkins, Hore 2		Burrows, Larsen, Milcock 2	
19	Lewes	v	Hallen	3-0 206
	Francis, Shepherd, Venables			
20	Cowes Sports	v	Tiptree United	1-3 140
	McDonald		Daly, Mackrory, Wareham	
21	Leyton Pennant	v	Mildenhall Town	*1-2 101
	Degaris		Allis, Long	
22	Ash United	v	Stotfold	3-1 172
	Johnston, Joyce, Mitchell		Saunders	
23	Wimborne Town	v	Taunton Town	*1-2 675
	Cannie		Edwards, Laight	
24	AFC Wallingford	v	Abingdon Town	0-1 185
			Scanes	
25	Milton Keynes City	v	St Blazey	3-1 254
	Bevis 2, Hyde		Gosling	
26	Team Bath	v	Arlesey Town	0-1 71
			Meah	
27	AFC Sudbury	v	Berkhamsted Town	4-1 431
	Banya 3, Bennett		Smith	
28	Dorking	v	Kingsbury Town	3-2 133
	Cioni, Lunn 2		Porter, Sapiro	
29	Banstead Athletic	v	Dereham Town	0-2 98
			Barrett, Henman	
30	Tilbury	v	Wroxham	*1-1 96
	Okita		Stock	
	Wroxham	v	Tilbury	*2-1 149
	Carter, Fox		Izzet	
31	Melksham Town	v	St Neots Town	2-3 198
	Ranger, 1 og		Claridge, Petty 2	
32	Burgess Hill Town	v	Selsey	4-0 248
	Downie,Harper,Issac,Levitt			

Top:
Cogenhoe (United Counties)   1
Clitheroe (North West Counties) 5
Clitheroe's Mark Stewart steers his
header inside Cogenhoe keeper
Clint Barker's right hand post for the
visitors' third goal.
Photo: Gordon Whittington

Centre:
Milton Keynes City
(Spartan South Midlands)   3
St Blazey (South Western)   1
Milton Keynes Paul Bevis watches
in case St Blazey's Sid Taylor
makes a mistake.Photo: Steve Ayre

Bottom:
Raunds Town (United Counties)   1
Durham City (Northern Premier) 1
Paul Bennett and Richard Bunting
(Raunds Town) with Kenny
Cramman in possession at Kiln
Park. Photo: Peter Barnes

FOURTH ROUND PROPER
Saturday 19 January 2002   £800 to each winning club

1	Abingdon Town	v	Clitheroe Town	0-3	306
			Cryer 2, Whittingham		
2	Ash United	v	Tow Law Town	0-3	423
			McKenna, Nicholson, Wilkinson		
3	Burgess Hill Town	v	Dorking	*1-1	690
	Harper		*Lunn*		
	Dorking	v	Burgess Hill Town	*1-1	471
	Lunn		*Newman*		
	(Burgess Hill won 3-2 on penalties)				
4	AFC Sudbury	v	Croydon Athletic	5-0	583
	***Bennett 3**, Cheetham ,Owen*				
5	Arlesey Town	v	St Helens Town	1-0	451
	Dellar				
6	Bemerton Heath Harlequins	v	Great Wakering Rovers	0-2	332
			Hampshire, Munro		
7	Kidsgrove Athletic	v	Lewes	0-2	375
			Dicker, Johnson		
8	Bedlington Terriers	v	Brigg Town	1-4	728
	Milner		*Carter 2, Drayton, Raspin*		
9	Pickering Town	v	Tiptree United	0-3	298
			Battell, Mackrory, Parnell		
10	Rushall Olympic	v	St Neots Town	1-2	208
	Currier		*Bloss, Petty*		
11	Whitley Bay	v	Milton Keynes City	5-1	385
	Anderson, Carr 2 Chandler, Fenwick		*Bevis*		
12	Porthleven	v	Mildenhall Town	1-0	485
	Morrison-Hill				
13	Prescot Cables	v	Wroxham	*4-5	296
	Garforth, Riley Robinson, 1 o.g.		*Fox 2, Hill, Hilton, Terrington*		
14	Taunton Town	v	West Auckland Town	3-2	604
	Edwards 2, Kidd		*Milroy 2*		
15	Arnold Town	v	Heanor Town	2-1	437
	Wilkins 2		*Gamble*		
16	Dereham Town	v	Durham City	*2-2	593
	Barrett, Taylor		*Taylor 2*		
	Durham City	v	Dereham Town	2-0	546
	Bennett, Ludlow				

Arnold (Northern Counties East) v Heanor Town (Central Midlands) 2-1
Stefan Gamble heads home Heanor's equalizer at Arnold. Photo: Gordon Whittington

Taunton Town (Western) v West Auckland Town (Northern) 3-2
Steve Kidd knocks in Taunton's opening goal in their 3-2 win over West Auckland Town. Photo: Ken Gregory

Whitley Bay (Northern) v Milton Keynes City (Spartan South Midlands) 5-1
Goalmouth action at Whitley Bay during Milton Keynes best ever Vase run. Photo: Steve Ayres

FIFTH ROUND PROPER

Saturday 9 February 2002   £1000 to each winning club

1	Whitley Bay	3	v	3	Brigg Town
Chandler, Cook, Walton					***Roach 3***
		Att: 642			

	Brigg Town	0	v	3	Whitley Bay
					Walton 2, 1og
		Att: 547			

2	Durham City	2	v	1	St.Neots Town
Healer, Ludlow					
		Att: 537			

3	Wroxham	3	v	1	Arnold Town
Hilton 2, Lewis					*Gadsby*
		Att: 540			

4	Arlesey Town	0	v	3	Clitheroe	603
					Greenwood, Reynolds, Spencer	
		Att: 603				

5	Lewes	4	v	1	Tow Law Town
***Francis 3**, Johnson*					*Maughan*
		Att: 694			

6	AFC Sudbury	2	v	1*	Great Wakering Rovers
	Bennett 2				*Howard*
		Att: 701			

7	Burgess Hill Town	4	v	0	Porthleven	1215
	Carrter 2, Harper Newman					
		Att: 1215				

8	Tiptree United	1	v	1*	Taunton Town
	Barefield				*Laight*
		Att: 518			

	Taunton Town	1	v	2	Tiptree United
	Baston				*Barefield, Parnell*
		Att: 689			

Taunton Town (Western) v Tiptree United (Eastern) 1-2.
Tiptree's super keeper Jason Haygreen beats Ellis Laight to a cross to snuff out a Taunton attack. The goallie performed wonderfully in both games of the replayed tie. Photo: Ken Gregory

Burgess Hill Town (Sussex) v Porthleven (South Western) 4-0
Burgess Hill's Daren Newman challenges this Porthleven player for the ball. Photo: Steve Ayre

Lewes (Ryman Div 2) v Tow Law Town (Northern) 4-1. A header from a Tow Law Town player (stripes) beats
Lewes goalkeeper Ross Standen at The Dripping Pan. Photo: Roger Turner

25 in 25

A review of the **F.A. Challenge Vase** and its participating clubs during
the twenty-five year life span of the F.A. Non-League Club Directory (1978 - 2002) will be
available in the next year. It will be one of a series of 25 and will contain features, statistics
and photos in at least 144 pages dedicated purely to the Vase competition.

Further details can be found on page 17 so make sure of your copy of this exciting limited edition.

SIXTH ROUND PROPER
Saturday 2 March 2002   £2000 to each winning club

Burgess Hill   1   v   2   Tiptree United
Churchill 42

Parnell 26 (pen)
Brady 106

after extra time
Att: 1598

Burgess Hill: Gulle, Brown, Newman, Downey, Churchill, Carp, Williams, Harper, Carter. Subs: Callingham, Isaac, Kirkpatrick, Lewis, Waters.
Tiptree United: Haygreen, Battell, Ford, Houghton, Fish, Brady, Wareham, Daley, Barefield, Parnell, Gillesplton. Subs: Snow, Lodge, Mackrory, Powell, Jackson.

Durham   2   v   1   Wroxham
Ludlow 6
Taylor 89 (pen)

Terrington 68

Att: 954

Durham City: Riches, Lake, Cramman, Walklate, Stephenson, Bennett, Brightwell, Ord, Ludlow, Healer, Irvine. Subs: Taylor, Newton, Douglas, Canavan, Mudd
Wroxham: Fowler, Pauling, Howes, Carus, Carter, Neale, Gill, Fox, Stock, Hilton, Lewis. Subs: Edridge, Hartle, Terrington, Horton, Phillips

---

Lewes   1   v   2   AFC Sudbury
Newman 90 (Pen)

Betson 14
Bennett 79

Att: 1520

Lewes: Standen, Barham, Head, C. Johnson, McCallum, Cable, Dicker, A. Johnson, Francis, Thomsett, Newman. Subs: Beeston, More, Crumplin, Rice.
AFC Sudbury: Nower, Rayner, Bishop, Tracey, Howlett, Devereux, Cheetam, Gardiner, Bennett, Banya, Betson. Subs: Claydon, Hyde, Tanner, Owen, Norfolk.

Clitheroe   1   v   2   Whitley Bay
Cryer 80

Chandler 3
Locker 90

Att: 646

Whitley Bay: Caffery, Sunderland, Middleton, Neil, Anderson, Locker, Carr, Bowes, Chandler, Chay, Walton. Subs: Fenwick, Court, Walmsley, Dugdale, Cuggy.
Clitheroe: Richens, Todhunter, Stewart, Cowring, Sculpher, Greenwood, Aspinall, Reynolds, Cryer, Spencer, Jones. Subs: Fogerty, Gardner, Taylor, Whittingham, Senior.

Lewes v AFC Sudbury 1-2. Gary Bennett (9) puts Sudbury into the Vase Semi-finals with the second goal at Lewes.
Photo: Francis Short

Top:
Lewes (Ryman Div 2)   1
AFC Sudbury (Eastern)   2

Paul Betson, AFC Sudbury No 11,
beats the Lewes defence to score
at the Dripping Pan.
Photo: Roger Turner

Centre: AFC Sudbury all smiles as
they leave the pitch after beating
Lewes at the Dripping Pan.
Photo: Roger Turner

Bottom:
Burgess Hill Town (Sussex)   1
Tiptree United (Eastern)   2

Officials, skippers and mascots
prior to the start of the Burgess
Hill Town v Tiptree United match.
Photo: Arthur Evans

SEMI-FINALS

Saturdays 23 & 30 March 2002   £3,000 to the two winners

FIRST LEG

AFC Sudbury   (0) 0   v   2 (0)   Tiptree United

Daley 49
Wareham 83

Att: 1342

AFC Sudbury: Nower, Rayner, Bishop, Tracey, Howlett, R. Devereux, Cheetam, Gardner, Bennett, Claydon, Betson. Subs not used: Banya, B. Devereux, Hyde, Owen, Tanner.

Tiptree United: Haygreen, Battell, Ford, Houghton, Fish, Brady, Wareham, Daley, Barefield, Wall, Gillespie. Subs not used: Parnell, Tudor, Mackrory, Streetley, Lodge

Whitley Bay   (1) 2   v   1 (1)   Durham City

Fenwick 16   Mudd 15
Cook 83

Att: 1816

Durham City: Riches, Lake, Cramman, Walklate, Stephenson, Bennett, Brightwell, Ord, Ludlow, Mudd, Irvine. Subs not used: Taylor, Newton, Canavan, Douglas, Healer.

Whitley Bay: Caffery, Sunderland, Walmsley, Dixon, Anderson, Locker, Bowes, Walton, Chandler, Middleton, Fenwick. Subs not used: Cuggy, Hay, Cook, Livermore, Dugdale.

SECOND LEG

Durham City   (0) 0   v   0 (0)   Whitley Bay

Att: 2181

Durham City: Riches, Lake, Cramman, Walklate, Stephenson, Bennett, Brightwell, Ord, Ludlow, Healer, Irvine. Subs not used: Taylor, Newton, Canavan, Mudd, Douglas.

Whitley Bay: Caffery, Sunderland, Walmsley, Dixon, Anderson, Locker, Bowes, Walton, Chandler, Middleton, Fenwick. Subs not used: Hay, Dugdale, Cook, Livermore, Neil.

Whitley Bay win 2-1 on aggregate

Tiptree United   (0) 0   v   0 (0)   AFC Sudbury

Att: 1912

Tiptree United: Haygreen, Battell, Ford (Parnell 65), Houghton, Fish, Brady (Streetley 36), Wareham, Daley, Barefield (Powell 43), Wall, Gillespie. Subs not used: Mackrory, Tudor.

AFC Sudbury: Nower, Rayner, Tanner (Hyde 5), Tracey, Bishop (R. Devereux 65), Owen, Cheetam (Norfolk 31), B. Devereux, Bennett, Banya, Betson. Subs not used: Claydon, Boon.

Tiptree win 2-0 on aggregate

Whitley Bay keeper John Caffrey collects under pressure during the tense Second Leg 0-0 draw against Durham City. Photo: Graham Brown

Marc Riches in the Durham goal is challenged by Gary Cook (14) and Michael Fenwick of Whitley Bay at a packed Hillheads Park in the FA Vase Semi-final First Leg. Photo: Graham Brown

Dave Barefield, Tiptree United, fires in a shot at the AFC Sudbury goal during the FA Vase Semi-final Second Leg. Photo: Roger Turner

Carlsberg provided the "showers" for the Tiptree United celebrations at Chapel Road. Photo: Peter Barnes

Pre-match line up at Villa Park with Captains Ian Fish of Tiptree United (left) and Gary Middleton of Whitley Bay (right). Photo: Peter Barnes

FINAL

Tiptree United	0	v	1	Whitley Bay

Chandler 97

after extra time
Att: 4742

Tiptree United: Jason Haygreen, Phil Battell, Colin Wall, Wayne Houghton, Ian Fish, Dave Streetley (sub Adam Gillespie 78th min), Steve Wareham (sub Alex Snow 115th min), Steve Daly, David Barefield, Andy Aransibia (Steve Parnell 78th min), Andy Brady. Subs (not used): Chris Powell, Kevin Ford

Whitley Bay: John Caffrey, Jon Sunderland, Marc Walmsley, Ian Dixon (sub Chris Neil 65th min), Ian Chandler, Kevin Walton, Michael Fenwick (sub Steve Cuggy 79th min). Subs (not used): Gary Cook, Rob Livermore

Referee: Mr A Kaye (West Riding) assisted by Messrs J A Sheffield (Staffordshire) and R M Pollock (Liverpool). Fourth Official: Mr S W Mathieson (Cheshire)

Whitley Bay celebrate with the FA Vase. Photo: Roger Turner

EXTRA TIME WINNER FOR WHITLEY BAY

Out of the 463 entrants to this yearís competition surely no one could have predicted the meeting of modest Tiptree United from the Jewson Eastern Counties League and the Albany Northern Leaguers Whitley Bay, who have experienced some depressing days in recent times, as likely contenders for this year's Villa Park final. Both had started in the Second Qualifying Round way back in September, upsetting previous finalists in Taunton and Sudbury by Tiptree and Guisborough, Brigg and Clitheroe by Whitley Bay, on their way through.

A crowd of less than 5,000 was there to witness the event with the Trinity Road bottom length occupied by Bay's blue and white and the Jam Makers' fans red and black showing in the lower tier of the opposite side. The spectacle of a pre-match release of balloons in the team colours was somewhat marred by the drifting wind which saw a whole cluster of them trapped under the Holte End roof. Later it was all too simplistic to recognise that this had been a prophetic pointer to the game itself which similarly drifted, never ascending to any major heights. Indeed after inflated hopes there was flat disappointment as ninety minutes passed without a score and we floated into extra time.

Yet the Northern Leaguers had been awarded an easier chance to score, four minutes after half time, when presented with a penalty. Marc Walmsley, on an upfield surge, was brought down to earth by Steve Wareham. Referee Kaye immediately pointed to the spot and up stepped Andy Bowes, one of a trio in Bay's ranks who had previously played in a Vase final, for Bedlington Terriers. Facing him was the keeper with the rural novelist's and soap writer's dream name of Jason Haygreen. Bowes had never missed a penalty before but Haygreen was able to give him a new experience. Diving to his left the goalie held Bowes' tame attempt and kept his Essex team in with a chance.

The first half had largely slipped away unnoticed by any but the most fervent of supporters. Tiptree's top scoring David Barefield and new acquisition from Ford United, Andy Aransibia, only a week into life at his new club, never gelled. Aransibia did have one open chance only to put his header yards wide of a yawning goal, whereupon he was substituted by club favourite Steve Parnell who first played for Tiptree twenty years previously before embarking on a career taking in the likes of Halstead, Dagenham, Braintree and Sudbury Town. Goal scoring might be Parnell's forte but there were no openings for him on this sunny Saturday.

Since Bay did the bulk of the attacking most of Tiptree's work was done at the back, where Wayne Houghton and Ian Fish stood firm in front of the staunch Haygreen. Their main opponent was Ian Chandler, who had previously scored six goals in Bay's cup run. Midfielder Kevin Walton was noticeable for his surging runs, bringing one splendid diving save from Haygreen, the latter also tipping over a twenty five yarder from Walmsley. One of Bay's dependable scorers over the years, substitute Steve Cuggy, taking advantage of a rare mistake by Tiptree skipper Fish, whipped over a cross, enabling Chandler to place his header well out of Haygreen's despairing reach. This was in the 97th minute and this single netting was sufficient to see that Andy Gowens, thwarted when a player at Bedlington, could now lift the Vase as manager of the winning team.He was relieved at Chandler's score, thinking that his chances had evaporated with Bowes' penalty miss. "It's a great reward for a great set of people," he declared.

Tiptree's manager, Neil Farlie, who entertained thoughts in his earlier life of becoming a jockey but now earns his living as a long distance lorry driver, still nurses greater ambitions. "Next year I want to come back and lift the Vase," he yearned. He recognises that is a long shot for his longings will be shared by another 400 plus clubs, all vying for the same opportunity.

Arthur Evans

Ian Chandler,
Whitley Bay's
goalscorer
Photo:
Roger Turner

Andy Bowes' despair at having his tame penalty kick saved by Jason Haygreen is mirrored by the delight of the Tiptree fans. Photo: Graham Brown

Tiptree United's Andrew Aransibia's header just goes wide. Photo: Roger Turner

Moments after saving a penalty Tiptree's Jason Haygren saves a Kevin Walton effort to deny Whitley Bay. Photo: Graham Brown

FA CARLSBERG VASE PROGRESS CHART 2001-2002

THIRD ROUND

Tiptree United	3
Cowes Sports ~	1
Pickering Town	2
Stewarts & Lloyds	0
Burgess Hill Town	4
Selsey	0
Dorking	3
Kingsbury Town	2
Moneyfields	*3
Porthleven	4
Leyton Pennant	*1
Mildenhall Town	2
Wimborne	*1
Taunton Town	2
West Auckland Town	1
Nanteich Town	0
Oadby Town	1
Kidsgrove Athletic	2
Lewes	3
Hallam	0
Ash United	3
Stotfold	1
Tow Law Town	3
Bromsgrove Rovers	1
AFC Sudbury	4
Berkhamsted	
Croydon Athletic	5
Brockenhurst	2
Thamesmead Town	0
Bemerton H. H.	2
Great Wakering Rovers	2
Thatcham Town	0
Banstead Athletic	0
Dereham Town	2
Raunds Town	1,1
Durham City	1,3
Barwell	0
Rushall Olympic	3
Melksham Town	2
St. Neots Town	3
Prescot Cables	4
Newcatle Town	0
Tilbury	1,2
Wroxhan	1,1
Arnold Town	2
Consett	1
Heanor Town	2
Hallam	1
Team Bath	0
Arlesey Town	1
St Helens Town	3
Billingham Synthonia	1
AFC Wallingford	0
Abingdon Town	
Cogenhoe Town	1
Clitheroe	5
Bedlington Terriers	3
Bridgnorth	0
Studley BKL	*2
Brigg Town	3
Milton Keynes	3
St. Blazey	1
Billingham Town	1
Whitley Bay	2

FOURTH ROUND

Tiptree United	3
Pickering Town~	0
Burgess Hill Town	1,1
Dorking	1,1
(3-2 Pens to BHT)	
Porthleven	1
Mildenhall	0
Taunton Town	3
West Auckland Town	1
Kidsgrove Athletic	0
Lewes	2
Ash United	0
Tow Law Town	3
AFC Sudbury	5
Croydon Athletic	0
Bemerton H. H.	0
Great Wakering Rovers	2
Dereham Town	2,2
Durham City	2,0
Rushall Olympic	1
St. Neots Town	2
Prescott Cables	*4
Wroxham	5
Arnold Town	2
Heanor Town	1
Arlesey Town	1
St. Helens Town	0
Abingdon Town	0
Clitheroe	3
Bedlington Terriers	1
Brigg Town	4
Milton Keynes	1
Whitley Bay~	5

FIFTH ROUND

Tiptree Town	*1,2
Taunton Town	1,1
Burgess Hill Town	4
Porthleven	0
Lewes	4
Tow Law Town	1
AFC Sudbury	*2
Great Wakering Rovers	1
Durham City	2
St. Neots Town	1
Wroxham	3
Arnold Town	1
Arlesey Town	0
Clitheroe	3
Brigg Town	3,0
Whitley Bay~	*3,3

SIXTH ROUND

Tiptree United	2
Burgess Hill Town ~	*1
Lewes	1
AFC Sudbury	2
Durham City	2
Wroxham	1
Clitheroe	1
Whitley Bay	2

Semi-finals

Tiptree United	2,0
AFC Sudbury ~	0,0
Durham City	1,0
Whitley Bay~	2,0

Final

Tiptree United	0
Whitley Bay	1

Clubs named first in each pairing were drawn at home (or home just in a semi-final) unless a ~ is shown.

* Denotes after extra time

PAST F.A. VASE FINALS

1975   HODDESDON TOWN 2 *(Spartan Sth Mids)*   EPSOM & EWELL 1 *(Surrey Senior)*   Att: 9,500
Sedgwick 2   Wales   Ref: Mr R Toseland
Hoddesdon: Galvin, Green, Hickey, Maybury, Stevenson, Wilson, Bishop, Picking, Sedgwick, Nathan, Schofield
Epsom & Ewell: Page, Bennett, Webb, Wales, Worby, Jones, O'Connell, Walker, Tuite, Eales, Lee

1976   BILLERICAY TOWN 1 *(Essex Senior)*   STAMFORD 0 (aet) *(United Counties)*   Att: 11,848
Aslett   Ref: Mr A Robinson
Billericay: Griffiths, Payne, Foreman, Pullin, Bone, Coughlan, Geddes, Aslett, Clayden, Scott, Smith
Stamford: Johnson, Kwiatowski, Marchant, Crawford, Downs, Hird, Barnes, Walpole, Smith, Russell, Broadbent

1977   BILLERICAY TOWN 1 *(Essex Senior)*   SHEFFIELD 1 (aet) *(Yorkshire)*   Att: 14,000
Clayden   Coughlan og   Ref: Mr J Worrall
Billericay: Griffiths, Payne, Bone, Coughlan, Pullin, Scott, Wakefield, Aslett, Clayden,Woodhouse, McQueen. Sub: Whettell
Sheffield: Wing, Gilbody, Lodge, Hardisty, Watts, Skelton, Kay, Travis, Pugh, Thornhill,Haynes. Sub: Strutt

Replay   BILLERICAY TOWN 2   SHEFFIELD 1   Att: 3,482
Aslett, Woodhouse   Thornhill   at Nottingham Forest
Billericay: Griffiths, Payne, Pullin, Whettell, Bone, McQueen, Woodhouse, Aslett, Clayden, Scott, Wakefield
Sheffield: Wing, Gilbody, Lodge, Strutt, Watts, Skelton, Kay, Travis, Pugh, Thornhill, Haynes

1978   NEWCASTLE BLUE STAR 2 *(Wearside)*   BARTON ROVERS 1 *(South Midlands)*   Att: 16,858
Dunn, Crumplin   Smith   Ref: Mr T Morris
Newcastle: Halbert, Feenan, Thompson, Davidson, S Dixon, Beynon, Storey, P Dixon, Crumplin, Callaghan, Dunn. Sub: Diamond
Barton Rovers: Blackwell, Stephens, Crossley, Evans, Harris, Dollimore, Dunn, Harnaman, Fossey, Turner, Smith. Sub: Cox

1979   BILLERICAY TOWN 4 *(Athenian)*   ALMONDSBURY GREENWAY 1 *(Glos. Co)*   Att: 17,500
Young 3, Clayden   Price   Ref: Mr C Steel
Billericay: Norris, Blackaller, Bingham, Whettell, Bone, Reeves, Pullin, Scott, Clayden,Young, Groom. Sub: Carrigan
Almondsbury: Hamilton, Bowers, Scarrett, Sulllivan, Tudor, Wookey, Bowers, Shehean, Kerr,Butt, Price. Sub: Kilbaine

1980   STAMFORD 2 *(United Counties)*   GUISBOROUGH TOWN 0 *(Northern)*   Att: 11,500
Alexander, McGowan   Ref: Neil Midgeley
Stamford: Johnson, Kwiatkowski, Ladd, McGowan, Bliszczak I, Mackin, Broadhurst, Hall,Czarnecki, Potter, Alexander. Sub: Bliszczak S
Guisborough: Cutter, Scott, Thornton, Angus, Maltby, Percy, Skelton, Coleman, McElvaney,Sills, Dilworth. Sub: Harrison

1981   WHICKHAM 3 *(Wearside)*   WILLENHALL 2 (aet) *(West Midlands)*   Att: 12,000
Scott, Williamson, Peck og   Smith, Stringer   Ref: Mr R Lewis
Whickham: Thompson, Scott, Knox, Williamson, Cook, Ward, Carroll, Diamond, Cawthra,Robertson, Turnbull. Sub: Alton
Willenhall: Newton, White, Darris, Woodall, Heath, Fox, Peck, Price, Matthews, Smith,Stringer. Sub: Trevor

1982   FOREST GREEN ROVERS 3 *(Hellenic)*   RAINWORTH M.W 0 *(Notts Alliance)*   Att: 12,500
Leitch 2, Norman   Ref: Mr K Walmsey
Forest Green: Moss, Norman, Day, Turner, Higgins, Jenkins, Guest, Burns, Millard, Leitch, Doughty. Sub: Dangerfield
Rainworth M.W: Watson, Hallam, Hodgson, Slater, Sterland, Oliver, Knowles, Raine, Radzi, Reah, Comerford. Sub: Robinson

1983   V.S. RUGBY 1 *(West Midlands)*   HALESOWEN TOWN 0 *(West Midlands)*   Att: 13,700
Crawley   Ref: Mr B Daniels
VS Rugby: Burton, McGinty, Harrison, Preston, Knox, Evans, ingram, Setchell, Owen,Beecham, Crawley. Sub: Haskins
Halesowen Town: Coldicott, Penn, Edmonds, Lacey, Randall, Shilvock, Hazelwood, Moss, Woodhouse,P Joinson, L Joinson. Sub: Smith

1984   STANSTED 3 *(Essex Senior)*   STAMFORD 2 *(United Counties)*   Att: 8,125
Holt, Gillard, Reading   Waddicore, Allen   Ref: Mr T Bune
Stanstead: Coe, Williams, Hilton, Simpson, Cooper, Reading, Callanan, Holt, Reeves,Doyle, Gillard. Sub: Williams
Stamford: Parslow, Smitheringate, Blades, McIlwain, Lyon, Mackin, Genovese, Waddicore,Allen, Robson, Beech. Sub: Chapman

1985   HALESOWEN TOWN 3 *(West Midlands)*   FLEETWOOD TOWN 1 *(N W Counties)*   Att: 16,715
L Joinson 2, Moss   Moran   Ref: Mr C Downey
Halesowen: Coldicott, Penn, Sherwood, Warner, Randle, Heath, Hazlewood, Moss (Smith),Woodhouse, P Joinson, L Joinson
Fleetwood Town: Dobson, Moran, Hadgraft, Strachan, Robinson, Milligan, Hall, Trainor, Taylor(Whitehouse), Cain, Kennerley

1986   HALESOWEN TOWN 3 *(West Midlands)*   SOUTHALL 0 *(Isthmian 2 South)*   Att: 18,340
Moss 2, L Joinson   Ref: Mr D Scott
Halesowen: Pemberton, Moore, Lacey, Randle (Rhodes), Sherwood, Heath, Penn, Woodhouse, PJoinson, L Joinson, Moss
Southall: Mackenzie, James, McGovern, Croad, Holland, Powell (Richmond), Pierre,Richardson, Sweales, Ferdinand, Rowe

1987   ST. HELENS 3 *(N W Counties)*   WARRINGTON TOWN 2 *(N W Counties)*   Att: 4,254
Layhe 2, Rigby   Reid, Cook   Ref: Mr T Mills
St Helens: Johnson, Benson, Lowe, Bendon, Wilson, McComb, Collins (Gledhill), O'Neill,Cummins, Lay, Rigby. Sub: Deakin
Warrington: O'Brien, Copeland, Hunter, Gratton, Whalley, Reid, Brownville (Woodyer), Cook,Kinsey, Looker (Hill), Hughes

1988   COLNE DYNAMOES 1 *(N W Counties)*   EMLEY 0 *(Northern Counties East)*   Att: 15,000
Anderson   Ref: Mr A Seville
Colne Dynamoes: Mason, McFafyen, Westwell, Bentley, Dunn, Roscoe, Rodaway, Whitehead (Burke),Diamond, Anderson, Wood (Coates)
Emley: Dennis, Fielding, Mellor, Codd, Hirst (Burrows), Gartland (Cook), Carmody,Green, Bramald, Devine, Francis

1989   TAMWORTH 1 *(West Midlands)*   SUDBURY TOWN 1 (aet) *(Eastern)*   Att: 26,487
Devaney   Hubbick   Ref: Mr C Downey
Tamworth: Bedford, Lockett, Atkins, Cartwright, McCormack, Myers, Finn, Devaney, Moores,Gordon, Stanton. Subs: Rathbone, Heaton
Sudbury Town: Garnham, Henry, G Barker, Boyland, Thorpe, Klug, D Barker, Barton, Oldfield,Smith, Hubbick. Subs: Money, Hunt

REPLAY   TAMWORTH 3   SUDBURY TOWN 0   Att: 11,201
Stanton 2, Moores   at Peterborough
Tamworth: Bedford, Lockett, Atkins, Cartwright, Finn, Myers, George, Devaney, Moores,Gordon, Stanton. Sub: Heaton
Sudbury Town: Garnham, Henry, G Barker, Boyland, Thorpe, Klug, D Barker, Barton, Oldfield,Smith, Hubbick. Subs: Money, Hunt

1990 YEADING 0 *(Isthmian 2 South)* BRIDLINGTON TOWN 0 (aet) *(N Co East)* Att: 7,932
Ref: Mr R Groves
Yeading: Mackenzie, Wickens, Turner, Whiskey (McCarthy), Croad, Denton, Matthews, James(Charles), Sweates, Impey, Cordery
Bridlington: Taylor, Pugh, Freeman, McNeill, Warburton, Brentano, Wilkes (Hall), Noteman,Gauden, Whiteman, Brattan (Brown)

Replay YEADING 1 BRIDLINGTON TOWN 0 Att: 5,000
Sweales at Leeds Utd FC
Yeading: Mackenzie, Wickens, Turner, Whiskey, Croad (McCarthy), Schwartz, Matthews,James, Sweates, Impey (Welsh), Cordery
Bridlington: Taylor, Pugh, Freeman, McNeill, Warburton, Brentano, Wilkes (Brown), Noteman,Gauden (Downing), Whiteman, Brattan

1991 GRESLEY ROVERS 4 *(West Midlands)* GUISELEY 4 (aet) *(Northern Co East)* Att: 11,314
Rathbone, Smith 2, Stokes Tennison 2, Walling, A Roberts Ref: Mr C Trussell
Gresley: Aston, Barry, Elliott (Adcock), Denby, Land, Astley, Stokes, K Smith, Acklam,Rathbone, Lovell (Weston)
Guiseley: Maxted, Bottomley, Hogarth, Tetley, Morgan, McKenzie, Atkinson (Annan),Tennison, Walling, A Roberts, B Roberts

Replay GUISELEY 3 GRESLEY ROVERS 1 Att: 7,585
Tennison, Walling, Atkinson Astley at Bramall Lane
Guiseley: Maxted, Annan, Hogarth, Tetley, Morgan, McKenzie (Bottomley), Atkinson,Tennison (Noteman), Walling, A Roberts, B Roberts
Gresley: Aston, Barry, Elliott, Denby, Land, Astley, Stokes (Weston), K Smith, Acklam, Rathbone, Lovell (Adcock)

1992 WIMBORNE TOWN 5 *(Wessex)* GUISELEY 3 *(Northern Premier Div 1)* Att: 10,772
Richardson, Sturgess 2, Killick 2 Noteman 2, Colville Ref: Mr M J Bodenham
Wimborne: Leonard, Langdown, Wilkins, Beacham, Allan, Taplin, Ames, Richardson, Bridle,Killick, Sturgess (Lovell), Lynn
Guiseley: Maxted, Atkinson, Hogarth, Tetley (Wilson), Morgan, Brockie, A Roberts,Tennison, Noteman (Colville), Annan, W Roberts

1993 BRIDLINGTON TOWN 1 *(NPL Div 1)* TIVERTON TOWN 0 *(Western)* Att: 9,061
Radford Ref: Mr R A Hart
Bridlington: Taylor, Brentano, McKenzie, Harvey, Bottomley, Woodcock, Grocock, A Roberts, Jones, Radford (Tyrell), Parkinson. Sub: Swailes
Tiverton Town: Nott, J Smith, N Saunders, M Saunders, Short (Scott), Steele, Annunziata, KSmith, Everett, Daly, Hynds (Rogers)

1994 DISS TOWN 2 *(Eastern)* TAUNTON TOWN 1 *(Western)* Att: 13,450
Gibbs (p), Mendham Fowler Ref: Mr K. Morton
Diss Town: Woodcock, Carter, Wolsey (Musgrave), Casey (Bugg), Hartle, Smith, Barth, Mendham, Miles, Warne, Gibbs
Taunton Town: Maloy, Morris, Walsh, Ewens, Graddon, Palfrey, West (Hendry), Fowler, Durham, Perrett (Ward), Jarvis

1995 ARLESEY TOWN 2 *(South Midlands)* OXFORD CITY 1 *(Ryman 2)* Att: 13,670
Palma, Gyalog S Fontaine Ref: Mr G S Willard
Arlesey: Young, Cardines, Bambrick, Palma (Ward), Hull, Gonsalves, Gyalog, Cox, Kane,O'Keefe, Marshall (Nicholls). Sub: Dodwell
Oxford: Fleet, Brown (Fisher), Hume, Shepherd, Muttock, Hamilton (Kemp), Thomas, Spittle, Sherwood, S Fontaine, C Fontaine. Sub: Torres

1996 BRIGG TOWN 3 *(N Co East)* CLITHEROE 0 *(N W Counties)* Att: 7,340
Stead 2, Roach Ref: Mr S J Lodge
Brigg: Gawthorpe, Thompson, Rogers, Greaves (Clay), Buckley (Mail), Elston, C Stead, McLean, N Stead (McNally), Flounders, Roach
Clitheroe: Nash, Lampkin, Rowbotham (Otley), Baron, Westwell, Rovine, Butcher, Taylor (Smith), Grimshaw, Darbyshire, Hill (Dunn)

1997 WHITBY TOWN 3 *(Northern)* NORTH FERRIBY UTD. 0 *(N Co East)* Att: 11,098
Williams, Logan, Toman Ref: Graham Poll
North Ferriby: Sharp, Deacey, Smith, Brentano, Walmsley, M Smith, Harrison (Horne), Phillips (Milner), France (Newman), Flounders, Tennison
Whitby Town: Campbell, Williams, Logan, Goodchild, Pearson, Cook, Goodrick (Borthwick), Hodgson, Robinson, Toman (Pyle), Pitman (Hall)

1998 TIVERTON TOWN 1 *(Western)* TOW LAW TOWN 0 *(Northern)* Att: 13,139
Varley Ref: M A Riley
Tiverton: Edwards, Felton, Saunders, Tatterton, Smith J, Conning, Nancekivell (Rogers), Smith K (Varley), Everett, Daly, Leonard (Waters)
Tow Law: Dawson, Pickering, Darwent, Bailey, Hague, Moan, Johnson, Nelson, Suddick, Laidler (Bennett), Robinson.

1999 TIVERTON TOWN 1 *(Western)* BEDLINGTON TERRIERS 0 *(Northern)* Att: 13, 878
Rogers 88 Ref: W. C. Burns
Bedlington Terriers: O'Connor, Bowes, Pike, Boon (Renforth), Melrose, Teasdale, Cross, Middleton (Ludlow), Gibb, Milner, Bond. Subs: Pearson, Cameron, Gowans
Tiverton Town: Edwards, Fallon, Saunders, Tatterton, Tallon, Conning (Rogers), Nancekivell (Pears), Varley, Everett, Daly, Leonard. Subs: Tucker, Hynds, Grimshaw

2000 DEAL TOWN 1 *(Kent)* CHIPPENHAM TOWN 0 *(Western)* Att: 20,000
Graham 87 Ref: E. K. Wolstenholme
Deal Town: Tucker, Kempster, Best, Ash, Martin, Seager, Monteith, Graham, Lovell, Marshall, Ribbens. Subs: Roberts, Warden, Turner
Chippenham Town: Jones, James, Andrews, Murphy, Burns, Woods, Brown, Charity, Tweddle, Collier, Godley. Subs: Tiley, Cutler

2001 TAUNTON TOWN 2 *(Western)* BERKHAMPSTED TOWN 1 *(Isthmian 2)* (at Villa Park) Att: 8,439
Fields 41, Laight 45 Lowe 71 Ref: E. K. Wolstenholme
Taunton Town: Draper, Down, Chapman, West, Hawkings, Kelly, Fields (Groves), Laight, Cann (Tallon), Bastow, Lynch (Hapgood). Subs: Ayres, Parker
Berkhampsted Town: O'Connor, Mullins, Lowe, Aldridge, Coleman, Brockett, Yates, Adebowale, Richardson, Smith, Nightingale. Subs: Ringsell, Hall, Knight, Franklin, Osborne

2002 WHITLEY BAY 1 *(Northern)* TIPTREE UNITED 0 *(Eastern)* (at Villa Park) Att: 4742
Whitley Bay: Caffrey, Sunderland, Walmsley, Dixon (Neil), Chandler, Walton, Fenwick (Cuggy). Subs: Cook, Livermore
Tiptree United: Haygreen, Battell, Wall, Houghton, Fish, Streetley (Gillespie), Wareham (Snow), Daly, Barefield, Aransibia (Parnell), Brady. Subs: Powell, Ford. Ref: A Kaye

All Finals at Wembley unless otherwise shown

F.A. CARLSBERG VASE ROUND BY ROUND STATISTICS

FIRST QUALIFYING ROUND
No of Games: 83   Home Wins: 45
Away Wins: 32   Draws: 6
Best Home Win:
Warrington Tn v Bottesford Tn 9-1
Best Away Win:
Saffron Walden T v Maldon T 1-11
Best Attendance:
Maidstone Utd v Carterton Tn 302

SECOND QUALIFYING ROUND
No. of Games: 170   Home Wins: 83
Away Wins: 77   Draws: 7
Best Home Win:
Colney Heath v March Tn Utd 11-0
Best Away Win:
Downham Town v Clacton Town 0-8
Best Attendance:
Maidstone Utd v Hungerford Tn 359

FIRST ROUND
No. of Games: 148   Home Wins: 100
Away Wins: 44   Draws: 4
Best Home Win:
Chichester C U v Barnstaple T 6-0
Best Away Win:
Leek CSOB v Kidsgrove Ath 1-7
BAT Sports v Thatcham Town 1-7
Best Attendance:
Shirebrook T v Causeway U 232

SECOND ROUND
No. of Games: 67   Home Wins: 33
Away Wins: 31   Draws: 3
Best Home Win:
Kidsgrove Ath v Bromyard Town 7-0
Best Away Win:
Cove v Bemerton Heath Hquns 0-5
Best Attendance:
Mildenhall v Maidstone United 384

THIRD ROUND
No. of Games: 35   Home Wins: 18
Away Wins: 14   Draws: 3
Best Home Win:
Prescot Cables v Newcastle T 4-0
Burgess Hill Town v Selsey 4-0
Best Away Win:
Cogenhoe v Clitheroe 1-5
Best Attendance:
Wimborne v Taunton Town 675

FOURTH ROUND
No. of Games: 18   Home Wins: 7
Away Wins: 9   Draws: 2
Best Home Win:
AFC Sudbury v Croydon Ath 5-0
Best Away Win:
Bedlington Terriers v Brigg Tn 1-4
Best Attendance:
Bedlington Terriers v Brigg Tn 728

FIFTH ROUND
No. of Games: 10   Home Wins: 5
Away Wins: 3   Draws: 2
Best Home Win:
Burgess Hill T v Porthleven 4-0
Best Away Win:
Brigg Town v Whitley Bay 0-3
Arlesey Town v Clitheroe 0-3
Best Attendance:
Burgess Hill T v Porthleven 1215

SIXTH ROUND
No. of Games: 4
Home Wins: 1
Away Wins: 3
Best Attendance:
Burgess Hill T v Tiptree Utd 1598

SEMI-FINALS
No. of Games: 4
Home Wins: 1
Away Wins: 1
Draws: 2
Best Attendance:
Durham City v Whitley Bay 2180

F.A. CARLSBERG VASE ATTENDANCE COMPARISON
Seasons 2000-01 - 2001-02

Season	Round	Games	Total Attendance	Average Attendance
2000-01	1st Qualifying	73	5,814	80
	2nd Qualifying	171*	13,898	81
	1st Proper	104	11,317	109
	2nd Proper	72	9,290	129
	3rd Proper	36	6,059	168
	4th Proper	18	6,036	335
	5th Proper	8	3,909	489
	6th Proper	5	6,431	1,286
	SF (1st Leg)	2	2,595	1,298
	SF (2nd Leg)	2	2,194	1,097
	Final	1	8,439	
TOTAL		492	75,982	
2001-02	1st Qualifying	83	6,213	75
	2nd Qualifying	170*	13,418	79
	1st Proper	99	10,588	107
	2nd Proper	67	8,862	132
	3rd Proper	34	6,603	201
	4th Proper	18	8,188	455
	5th Proper	10	6,686	669
	6th Proper	4	4,700	1,175
	SF (1st Leg)	2	3,161	1,581
	SF (2nd Leg)	2	4,092	2,046
	Final	1	4,742	
TOTAL		490	77,253	

* not including walkovers

F.A. CARLSBERG VASE TOP GOALSCORERS

11 GOALS
Bennett G — AFC Sudbury

10 GOALS
Flanagan L — Billingham Synthonia

9 GOALS
Shepherd D — Lewes
Witney S — Maldon Town
Cogdon G — Washington Nissan

8 GOALS
Hall B — Peterlee Newtown

7 GOALS
Mitchell S — Ash United
Harmon D — Cogenhoe United
Taylor M — Durham City
Sapiro J — Kingsbury Town
Torrance D — Stewarts & Lloyds

6 GOALS
Shildrick A — AFC Wallingford
Roach S — Brigg Town
Lunn S — Dorking
Ludlow L — Durham City
Messer G — Esh Winning
Francis S — Lewes
Moloney S — Marconi
Hyde K — Milton Keynes City
Barefield D — Tiptree United
Chandler I — Whitley Bay
Walton K — Whitley Bay
Stock R — Wroxham

5 GOALS
Forbes A — Andover
Clarke J — Guisborough Town
Wilson-Cunningham D — Kidsgrove Athletic
Mould L — Moneyfields
Robinson N — Prescot Cables
Bradley P — Rossington Main
Richardson D — St Blazey
Petty V — St Neots Town
Horler G — Star
Drain B — Stewarts & Lloyds
Lewis M — Team Bath
Heverin M — Warrington Town
Moores C — Warrington Town
Milroy J — West Auckland Town
Fox J — Wroxham

4 GOALS
Banya S — AFC Sudbury
Johnston D — Ash United
Whelan G — Banstead Athletic
Cole N — Bemerton Heath H
Neal N — Brackley Town
Blackmore C — Bridgnorth Town
Willetts L — Bromyard Town
Hibbert T — Brook House
Harper S — Burgess Hill Town
McGinn C — Cammell Laird
Cryer L — Clitheroe

4 goals cont.
Spencer N — Clitheroe
Thompson A — Consett
Worsley J — Curzon Ashton
Byrne K — Desborough Town
Saunders D — Gedling Town
Hampshire M — Great Wakering Rvrs
Sibanda T — Great Wakering Rvrs
Gibbs C — Greenwich Borough
Willingham B — Hadleigh United
Morris L — Hallam
Dunn B — Harefield United
Tobin S — Kidsgrove Athletic
Masters D — Lordswood
Sinden R — Maidstone United
Warwick T — Maldon Town
Messenger M — Melksham Town
Bevis P — Milton Keynes City
Hore K — Moneyfields
Smith I — Parkgate
Jewson A — Peterlee Newtown
Jensen G — Prescot Cables
Grice S — Ringmer
Smith M — Southall Town
Hands S — Studley BKL
Okita J — Tilbury
Daly S — Tiptree United
Wake B — Tow Law Town
McGinty M — Wembley
Hilton D — Wroxham

62 HAT-TRICKS (THREE GOALS)

FIRST QUALIFYING ROUND - 9
5 Witney S — Maldon Town
4 Messer G — Esh Winning
4 McGinty M — Wembley
Shepherd D — Lewes
Warwick T — Maldon Town
Rodriguez K — Nelson
Smith I — Parkgate
Hall B — Peterlee Newton
Heverin M — Warrington Town

SECOND QUALIFYING ROUND - 21
4 Masters D — Lordswood
4 Hyde K — Milton Keynes City
4 Barefield D — Tiptree United
4 Cogdon G — Washington Nissan
Leslie K — Aveley
Dibba L — Christchurch
Hewing D — Colney Heath
Hammond A — Denaby United
Mernagh G — Egham Town
Lewis G — Frome Town
Marshall J — Gedling Town
Willingham B — Hadleigh United
Dunn B — Harefield United
Gregory C — Harpenden Town

2nd Qualifying Round cont.
Witney S — Maldon Town
Moloney S — Marconi
Grice S — Ringmer
Widdowson L — Shirebrook Town
Turner P — Somersett Ambury
Smith M — Southall Town
Drain B — Stewarts & Lloyds

FIRST ROUND PROPER - 14
4 Flanagan L — Billingham Synthonia
4 Gibbs C — Greenwich Borough
Bennett G — AFC Sudbury
Mitchell S — Ash United
Neal N — Brackley Town
Harmon D — Cogenhoe United
Davey S — Harrogate Railway
Cunningham D — Kidsgrove Athletic
Shepherd D — Lewes
White B — Nelson
Hall B — Peterlee Newton
Pountney C — Studley BKL
Cogden G — Washington Nissan
Johnston A — Washington Nissan

SECOND ROUND PROPER - 13
4 Thompson A — Consett
4 Torrance D — Stewarts & Lloyds
4 Wake B — Tow Law Town
Wilkinson T — Arlesey Town
Mitchell S — Ash United
Roach S — Brigg Town
Harmon D — Cogenhoe United
Taylor M — Durham City
Sapiro J — Kingsbury Town
Jensen G — Prescot Cables
Rowlands K — Studley BKL
Allen R — West Auckland Tn
Stock R — Wroxham

THIRD ROUND PROPER - 3
Banya S — AFC Sudbury
Spencer N — Clitheroe
Liddle S — Croydon Athletic

FOURTH ROUND PROPER - 1
Bennett G — AFC Sudbury

FIFTH ROUND PROPER - 2
Roach — Brigg Town
Francis S — Lewes

ENGLAND SEMI-PROFESSIONAL REPRESENTATIVE FOOTBALL

Since the last of eight Four Nations Tournaments had been contested in Scotland in 1987, the top English players in the huge sector of semi-professional football (now known as the National Game) had been given no competitive international matches.

So when a new look Football Association took the initiative and invited Wales, Ireland and Scotland to join in an end of season tournament, senior levels of non-League football looked forward to a new test for our very best players.

Unfortunately the warm up games against the U.S.A. and Holland couldn't be organised early enough to ensure that the fixtures would be included in a planned season of Conference fixtures. Consequently when England's unbeaten manager John Owens needed to select squads for these fixtures, late in March and April, his starting line ups were far from his first choice.

Both games produced hard won victories and the manager could at least see how a wide selection of players reacted to England training and actual international matches. However, the Wednesday evening fixture at Yeovil against Holland underlined the complete collapse of suitable pre-match preparation.

Conference fixtures were played on the Tuesday evening including one at Yeovil. So the home supporters were given two games in two evenings - not conducive to a big attendance. The home club players of which five were in consideration for the England squad, obviously couldn't be selected, along with those playing for five other clubs involved with Tuesday fixtures. The badly worn Huish Park pitch alsohad to withstand two games in two evenings, so all in all everything was against our last warm up game being a help to the manager before the return of the long awaited competitive tournament.

All credit to the patched up squads achieving a 2-1 victory over U.S.A. and a 1-0 win against the loyal Dutch, who had played us every season since 1995 when we were struggling for fixtures.

So John Owens selected his squad which prepared to meet after the F.A. Trophy Final on the Sunday. Sadly two of the Yeovil players had to pull out after the final, so even then the manager had to include last minutes changes.

The Welsh Semi-Professionals had been building up for this tournament under Tommi Morgan's managership for four seasons and the last two games with England had been very well contested draws.

Ireland had beaten England in Dublin when they last met in 1997, but the Scots chose not to select their squad from the powerful national Junior Football competitions, but to concentrate purely on The Highland and East of Scotland Leagues and this proved to be a bad mistake. they were never likely to be strong enough.

The tournament was played at the grounds of Boston United and Kettering Town and on the first day England grabbed a late equaliser against Wales, but Ireland beat Scotland with a solid performance.

Another Irish success saw them beat England 2-1 at Boston, while Wales made it a miserable three days for Scotland by beating them 2-1 at Kettering.

So on the Saturday, Ireland (six points) were favourites but facing Wales (four points) at Boston, while neither of the two traditional rivals, England (one points) and Scotland (nil points), could achieve anything other than avoidance of the wooden spoon.

Well, England did manage a 2-0 victory against the old enemy even after the really frustrating conditions of the tournament preparations. John Owens, although suffering his first defeat still had the excellent record of Played 14, Won 8, Drawn 5, Lost 1 - Goals 22-10.

At Boston an excellent game, full of fast positive football, saw Wales on top form inspired by an outstanding display from striker Mark Dickeson who hit a splendid hat-trick.

Hopefully this Championship will be repeated next season with England's preparations planned in good time to allow the manager to work with a first choice squad and perhaps even enjoy the occasional training weekend together.

The Welsh and Irish will certainly be keen to take up the challenge again next May and, hopefully a Scottish side representing all of their very strong 'non-League' competitions will come bouncing back to challenge the best.

Tony Williams

England v USA. Back Row: Dr Steve Feldman, Steve Avory (Assistant Coach), Terry Skiverton, Neil Moore, Tim Ryan, Andy Woods, Steve Watson, Leon Braithwaite, Kirk Jackson, Wayne Brown, Mark Stimson, John Owens (Head Coach), Jim Conway (Physio), Mike Appleby (FA Administration). Front Row: Simon Travis, Nick Crittendon, Nick Roddis, Anthony Tonkin, Jason Goodliffe (Captain), Stuart Drummond. Photo: Garry Letts

England v Holland. Back Row: John Owens, Wayne Brown, Neil Moore, Tim Ryan (Captain), Andy Woods, Aaron Webster, Dale Anderson, James Taylor, Greg Heald, Steve Avory, Dr Steve Feldman. Front Row: Jim Conway, Neil Durkin, Mark Quayle, Warren Peyton, Nick Roddis, Tim Hambley, Mark Gower, Darren Stride, Mike Appleby. Photo: Ken Gregory.

25 in 25

A review of **Representative and International Football** during the twenty-five year life span of the F.A. Non-League Club Directory (1978 - 2002) will be available in the next year. It will be one of a series of 25 and will contain features, statistics and photos in at least 160 pages dedicated purely to England Semi-Professional football.

Further details can be found on page 17 so make sure of your copy of this exciting limited edition.

SEMI-PRO FRIENDLIES

ENGLAND	**2**	v	**1**	**USA**
Crittenden 75, Ryan 85 (pen)				*Shulte 32*

At Stevenage Borough

England: Wayne Brown (Andy Woods 61), Simon Travis, Anthony Tonkin, Terry Skiverton, Jason Goodliffe, Tim Ryan, Stuart Drummond (Steve Watson 54), Mark Stimson, Kirk Jackson, Leon Braithwaite (Neil Moore 84), Nick Roddis (Nick Crittenden 65)

John Owens' first choice of attack, Warren Patmore (Woking), Robbie Talbot (Morecambe) and Adam Stansfield (Yeovil Town) all had to pull out through injury and sadly this set the trend for the manager's season.

On the positive side many new faces were seen in England colours and once again the 'never say die' spirit showed as goals from substitute Nick Crittenden and a late penalty from Tim Ryan after Kirk Jackson had been brought down, gave England the victory after losing a 32 minute goal when Mark Shulte scored with a powerful header.

The USA played with style and a lot of talent and hopefully this is a feature that could become an annual event.

ENGLAND	**1**	v	**0**	**HOLLAND**
Anderson 75				

At Yeovil Town

England: Andy Woods, Simon Travis, Tim Ryan (Aaron Webster), Greg Heald (Neil Durkin), Neil Moore, Nick Roddis, Darren Stride (Dale Anderson), Tim Hambley (Warren Peyton), James Taylor, Mark Quayle, Mark Gower

The second 'friendly' international against old friends from Holland was really of little help to the English manager other than to look at a few more potential England players.

On a badly worn pitch, without the local stars who had played the previous evening, it was not surprising that a poor attendance and atmosphere was only livened by the school outings that certainly enjoyed their evening out.

Skipper Tim Ryan had to leave the pitch early on to save aggravating a hamstring injury, but the new look squad settled well and held a young, but hard working Dutch side.

A late goal set up by James Taylor for substitute Dale Anderson gave England the victory, but sadly ti could have been so much better as an international occasion.

FA XIs v LEAGUE XIs
(England trial matches)

FA XI	**3**	v	**4**	**UNIBOND LEAGUE**

FAXI: Andy Woods (Scarborough), Simon Marples (Doncaster), Neil Durkin (Leigh RMI), Martin Clarke (Southport), Paul Beesley (Stalybridge), Andy Scott (Stalybridge), Stewart Drummond (Morecambe), Stewart Elliott (Scarborough), Warren Payton (Nuneaton), Robbie Talbot (Morecambe), Michael Twiss (Leigh RMI). Subs: Stewart Dickinson (Southport) for Woods, Chris Lane (Southport) for Marples, Steve Pickford (Stalybridge) for Payton, Andy Whittaker (Lancaster) for Twiss.

UNIBOND LEAGUE XI: Stuart Coburn (Altrincham), Steve Nicholson (Emley), Mark Sertoi (Altrincham), Mark Hume (Barrow), Scott Maxfield (Barrow), Leigh Warren (Barrow), Darren Stride (Burton Albion), Steven Hawes (Altrincham), Steve Housham (Barrow), Dale Anderson (Burton), Rod Thornley (Altrincham). Subs: Matt Duke (Burton Albion) for Coburn, Graham Anthony (Barrow) for Stride, Gary Townsend (Worksop Town) for Housham, James Wall (Burton) forHume, Simon Yeo (Hyde United) for Hawes.

FA XI	**3**	v	**3**	**DR MARTENS LEAGUE**

(Dr Martens League won 5-3 after penalties)

FAXI: Paul Hyde (Dover), Nathan Bunce (Farnborough), Steve West (Woking), Graham Porter (Margate), Michael Warner (Farnborough), Nick Roddis (Woking), Gary Patterson (Farnborough), Barry Moore (Woking), Anthony Tonkin (Yeovil), Chris Sharpling (Woking), Leon Braithwaite (Margate). Subs: Lee Turner (Margate) for Hyde, Bill Edwards (Margate) for West, Steve Perkins (Woking) for Moore.

DR MARTENS LEAGUE XI: Andy Little (Crawley), Danny Chapman (Folkestone), Ian Wiles (Chelmsford), Anthony Henry (Folkestone), Russell Edwards (Welling), Matthew Halle (Weymouth), John Holloway (Worcester), Danny G Chapman (Folkestone), Tim Hambley (Havant), David Laws (Weymouth), Leigh Phillips (Weymouth). Subs: Glenn Knight (Welling) for Little, David Harlow (Crawley) for Chapman, Jamie O'Rorke (Havant) for Phillips, James Taylor (Havant) for Laws.

FA XI	**0**	v	**2**	**RYMAN LEAGUE**

FAXI: Paul Wilkerson (Stevenage), Simon Travis (Forest Green), Mark Smith (Dagenham), Greg Heald (Barnet), Mark Arber (Barnet), Paul Sturgis (Stevenage), Sam McMahon (Stevenage), Mark Brennan (Dagenham), Dean Clark (Hayes), Ken Charlery (Dagenham), Ben Strevens (Barnet). Subs: Steve Perrin (Forest Green) for Wilkerson, Leon Bell (Barnet) for Brennan, Lee Charles (Nuneaton) for Clarke, Keith Scott (Dover) for Charlery.

RYMAN LEAGUE XI: Lance Key (Kingstonian), Gary Wraight (St Albans), Francis Duku (Gravesend), Aaron Barnett (Gravesend), Ryan Kirby (Aldershot), Jason Chewins (Aldershot), Lee Spiller (Chesham), Dave Rainsford (Grays), Adam Parker (Aldershot), Craig Wilkins (Gravesend), Davis Haule (Hendon). Subs: Darrell Binns (Hendon) for Chawins, Vinnie John (Bishop's Stortford) for Haule, Dean Parrat (Braintree) for Wraight

For FA XI v Universites Match Details see page 1048

FOUR NATIONS TOURNAMENT
at Boston and Kettering 14th - 18th May 2002

Simon Weatherstone

Neil Moore

Stewart Drummond

ENGLAND	1	v	1	WALES
S Weatherstone 90				O'Brien 77

at Boston

England: Wayne Brown, Simon Wormull, Tim Ryan (capt), Neil Moore, Jason Goodliffe, Nick Roddis (Steve Watson 77 mins), Stewart Drummond (Simon Weatherstone 67 mins), Mark Gower, James Taylor (Adam Stansfield 67 mins), Junior McDougald, Aaron Webster (Mark Angel 77 mins)

Wales: Tony Roberts, Mike Flynn, Gary Lloyd, Andrew York (capt) (Matthew Coupe 76 mins), Neil O'Brien, Tony James, Marc Lloyd-Williams (Graham Evans 71 mins), Nathan Davies, Ricky Evans, Gavin Williams (Mark Dickerson 89 mins), Paul Perry

Early pressure from England saw Aaron Webster and Nick Roddis go close and James Taylor only just missed a cross from Simon Wormull. The Welsh had looked solid without creating many chances, but after 77 minutes a long throw from Mike Flynn was neatly flicked in by giant centre half Neil O'Brien past a helpless Wayne Brown. 'Keeper Brown kept his side in the game however with a fine save from Graham Evans and, with the points looking secure for Wales, local hero Simon Weatherstone pounced on a loose ball in midfield, drove forwards towards the Welsh penalty area and smashed a fine low drive into the bottom corner of their net to give England a dramatic equaliser.

Tim Ryan

Wayne Brown

ENGLAND SEMI-PROFESSIONAL REPRESENTATIVE FOOTBALL

IRELAND 2 v 0 **SCOTLAND**
Arkins 40, Molloy 48
at Kettering

Republic of Ireland: Seamus Kelly, Colm Tresson (Brian Shelly 69 mins), David Crawley, Jodie Lynch, Clive Delaney, Tony Gorman, Paul Osam, Trevor Molloy (Tony Grant 77 mins), Kevin McHugh (Jason Byrne 57 mins), Vinny Arkins, Billy Woods (Derek O'Brien 57 mins)

Scotland: Michael Rae, Rod Archibald, Steve Dolan (Scott Anderson 44 mins), Derek Milne, Raleigh Gowrie, Paul McGinlay (William Bennett 57 mins), Ian Murray, Richard Hart, Philip Johnston (Philip O'Neill 60 mins), Scott Hunter (Richard Davidson 75 mins), Michael Stephen (Craig Manson 70 mins)

The experience gained by the Irish squad in recent seasons certainly showed against the Scottish squad playing their first representative match, so it was no surprise when Bill Woods and David Crawley combined to send Vinny Arkins through the Scotland defence and a neatly lobbed goal gave the Irish the lead.

With a goal deficit the Scots came out determined to do better in the second half, but, although a Michael Stephen shot went close, the Irish quickly increased their lead through Trevor Molloy who chipped in beautifully from a free kick while the Scottish defence was getting organised.

This lead was sufficient for the Irish to take their foot off the pedal and enjoy their place at the top of the table.

SCOTLAND 1 v 2 **WALES**
Milne 87   *Lloyd 55, Evans 84*
at Kettering

Scotland: Michael Rae (John Campbell 88 mins), Ross Archibald, Raleigh Gowrie, Derek Milne, Scott Anderson, Paul McGinlay, Ian Murray (Craig Manson 77 mins), Richie Hart (William Bennett 86 mins), Phil Johnson (Phil O'Neill 45 mins), Scott Hunter (Richie Davidson 88 mins), Michael Stephen (Jamie Watt 75 mins)

Wales: Tony Roberts (Pat Mountain 87 mins), Michael Flynn, Gary Lloyd, Mattew Coupe, Neil O'Brien, Tony James, Marc Lloyd-Williams (Graham Evans 58 mins), Nathan Davies (Lee Woodyatt 87 mins), Ricky Evans, Gavin Williams (Mark Dickerson 70 mins), Paul Perry

Although disappointed that they had allowed England a late equaliser, the Welsh were determined to do better against a Scottish side that did battle hard in a close first half.

However, the experienced Gary Lloyd curled in a free kick after 58 minutes and from then the Welsh made no mistakes. Just six minutes later Graham Evans smashed home a powerful shot following an excellent cross from Mark Dickerson.

This looked to be the end of the scoring, but credit to the Scottish spirit, they won a corner with six minutes to go and Derek Milne scored from close in to give the Welsh an uncomfortable last few minutes.

So the Welsh could catch the Irish, but poor Scotland were left pointless at the foot of the table.

ENGLAND 1 v 2 **IRELAND**
Moore 50   *Byrne 21, 30*
at Boston

England: Andy Woods, Adam Lockwood (Nick Roddis 75 mins), Tim Ryan (capt), Jason Goodliffe, Neil Moore (Stewart Drummond 84 mins), Simon Wormull, Simon Weatherstone (James Taylor 75 mins), Mark Gower, Kirk Jackson (Junior McDougald 84 mins), Adam Stansfield, Mark Angel

Republic of Ireland: Kelly, Shelly, Crawley, Lynch, Delaney, Gorman (capt), Osam, Molloy (Tresson 86 mins), O'Brien (Woods 64 mins), Arkins (Grant 82 mins), Byrne

Both sides looked confident in the early exchanges, but it was the Irish who looked the most likely to score, so it was no surprise when David Crawey picked up a loose England pass inside his own half, finding Jason Byrne with a perfect long ball down the middle, and the big striker hammered home an unstoppable shot.

All credit to Simon Weatherstone for continually getting into position to equalise for England, but he just couldn't beat Seamus Kelly in the Irish goal and midway through the first half Byrne scored his and his side's second, with a low shot hooked in under pressure.

England's first defeat under John Owens' managership looked certain, but a powerful header by Neil Moore at the far post from a free kick gave his side hopes and in the closing minutes skipper Tim Ryan and substitute James Taylor went close to equalising. However, it wasn't to be and Ireland deservedly could look forward to the last fixture with a one hundred per cent record.

Above left:
England skipper Tim Ryan just beats Ricky Evans (Wales) to the ball.
Photo: Milton Haworth

Above right:
England's Neil Moore (5) cannot stop Welsh hero Mark Dickerson
Photo: Milton Haworth

Centre left:
Another Welsh goal celebrated
Photo: Milton Haworth

Below:
Scotland keeper Michael Rae clears from England's Junior McDougald

ENGLAND   2   v   0   SCOTLAND
Drummond 55, S Weatherstone 86

at Kettering

England: Wayne Brown, Simon Wormull, Tim Ryan, Neil Moore, Jason Goodliffe, Nick Roddis, Steve Watson (Mark Gower 73 mins), Stewart Drummond (Simon Weatherstone 81 mins), Kirk Jackson (James Taylor 87 mins), Adam Stansfield (Junior McDougald 34 mins), Mark Angel (Aaron Webster 63 mins)

Scotland: Michael Rae, Derek Milne (Ross Archibald 75 mins), Stevie Dolan, Scott Anderson, Raleigh Gowrie, Philip Johnston (Paul McGinlay 75 mins), Ian Murray (Richie Davidson 87 mins), Richie Hart, Philip O'Neill (Jamie Watt 72 mins), Scott Hunter (William Bennett 84 mins), Michael Stephen

The disappointment of featuring at the foot of the four Nation's table obviously affected both countries as they played out a drab first half. England's Adam Stansfield looked lively up front until his injury, but there were no goals at half time despite a dangerous swerving corner giving Scott Anderson a chance at the far post for Scotland.

John Owens obviously lifted his side at half time and it was the persistent Nick Roddis who set up fellow midfielder Stewart Drummond to score from close range within five minutes of the re-start.

This spurred on Scotland and Wayne Brown was called on to save well from Scott Hunter and Philip O'Neill.

England pushed for a second and both Junior McDougald and Kirk Jackson went close before Simon Weatherstone scored his second of the tournament, after the unlucky Michael Rae could only parry a shot into his path. This was substitute Weatherstone's first touch but at least it confirmed his side finished off the bottom of the table with a record of one victory a draw and a defeat. For a side, whose selection was so difficult to plan, maybe this was all that could have been expected.

IRELAND   2   v   5   WALES
Delaney 71, Murphy 78   *Dickerson 44, 55, 72, Evans 47, 58*

at Boston

Wales: Roberts, Flynn, Lloyd, York, N O'Brien, James, N Davies (Woodyatt 68 mins), R Evans (Coupe 89 mins), Parry (Smith 88 mins), Dickerson (Williams 79 mins), G Evans (Lloyd-Williams 85 mins). Subs (not used) Mountain (gk), S Davies

Republic of Ireland: Ryan, Shelly, Crawley (Woods 56 mins), Lynch, Delaney, Gorman, Osam (Murphy 56 mins), Molloy (McHugh 64 mins), D O'Brien (Minnock 56 mins), Arkins, Byrne (Scant 64 mins). Subs (not used) Kelly (gk)

With both counties playing to win The Championship this game proved to be exciting from the start. Two victories gave the Irish the confidence to sail into the attack with good efforts from Vinny Arkins, Jason Byrne and Tony Gorman.

Welsh 'keeper Tony Roberts was kept busy but he stood firm and saved well from Trevor Molloy before Wales hit back with good effect of their own from Paul Parry, Neil O'Brien, Nathan Davies and Gary Lloyd.

The first goal of this entertaining half didn't come until just before the interval when Davies passed to Mark Dickerson, and the big striker crashed a firm shot past Barry Ryan from 20 yards.

This lead gave the Welsh the confidence they needed, but it was a surprise goal from Evans just after half time, which crept up under Ryan, that really inspired 'the reds'. Parry then set up Dickerson for his second and Graham Evans took advantage of a bad mistake to give his side a 4-0 lead.

Welsh supporters and officials couldn't believe this wonderful scoreline and Dickerson and Lloyd didn't help their blood pressure by smacking two more against the Irish woodwork!

However, the Irish didn't deserve to be goalless and it was a relief when Clive Delaney headed in a Billy Woods corner after 71 minutes.

This only spurred on the Welsh however, and Mark Dickerson completed a brilliant hat-trick a minute later and, although Ireland continued the recovery through Alan Murphy twelve minutes from time, a 5-2 scoreline was a tribute to the brilliant Welsh attack.

Tommi Morgan had been steadily building his squad, although the Welsh had played very few games in previous seasons, but his hard work came to fruition at the right time.

Let's hope the Welsh F.A. will be welcoming their three rivals to Wales next May to defend their title at a second tournament at England and Scotland certainly have some points to prove!

Stewart Drummond receives the congratulations after scoring against Scotland

Kirk Jackson heads wide of the goal

Welsh celebration after their victory over the Irish had given them the Championship. Photo: Milton Haworth

ENGLAND SEMI-PRO CAPS 1979 - 2002

Gary Abbott (Welling) **87** v I(s), S(s), 92 W(s)   3
David Adamson (Boston Utd) 79 **v** S, H **80** v I,S, H 5
Tony Agana (Weymouth) **86** v E   1
Carl Alford (Kettering T. & Rushden & Ds) **96** v E,H 2
Dale Anderson (Burton Albion) **02** v H   1
Mark Angel (Boston United) **02** v W(s), E, S 3
Ian Arnold (Kettering Town) **95** v W(s), H 2
Jim Arnold (Stafford Rangers) **79** v S, H 2
Nick Ashby (Kettering & Rushden & Diamonds)
   94 v F, N, **95** v G **96** v E, H 5
Noel Ashford (Enfield & Redbridge Forest.)
   82 v G,H,S. **83 v** I,H,S, **84** W,H,S,I, **85** W,I(s),
   86 E,E, 87 W(s), I,H,S. **90** v W,E **91** I(s) 21
John Askey (Macclesfield) **90** v W 1
Paul Bancroft (Kidderminster H.) **89** v I,W
   90 I,W,E, **91** v W 6
Chris Banks (Cheltenham T.) **98** v H, 99 W 2
Keith Barrett (Enfield) **81** v H,S,I **82 v** G,I,H,S
   83 v I,H,S, **84** v W(s), H, S **85** I,H,S 16
Laurence Batty (Woking) **93** v F(s), **95** v W,H,G 4
Mark Beeney (Maidstone) **89** v I(s) 1
Paul Beesley (Chester C.) **01** v H(s) 1
Dean Bennett (Kidderminster H) **00** v W(s) 1
Graham Benstead (Kettering) **94** v W,F,N(s) 3
Kevin Betsy (Woking) **98** v H(s) 1
Marcus Bignot (Kidderminster H) **97** v H 1
Jimmy Bolton (Kingstonian) **95** v G 1
Steve Book (Cheltenham Town) **99 v** I,H,W 3
Gary Brabin (Runcorn) **94 v** W,F,N 3
Mark Bradshaw (Halifax T.) **98** v H 1
Leon Braithwaite (Margate) **02 v** US 1
Colin Brazier (Kidderminster) **87** v W 1
Stewart Brighton (Bromsgrove) **94** v W 1
Steve Brooks (Cheltenham) **88** v W(s) **90** v W,E 3
Derek Brown (Woking) **94 v** F(s,N 2
Kevan Brown (Woking) **95** v W,H,G **96** v H **97** v E 5
Wayne Brown (Chester C.) **01** v W, H(s),
   02 v US, H(s),W,S. 6
Corey Browne (Dover) **94** v F(s),N(s), **95** v H(s) 3
David Buchanan (Blyth) **86** v E(s,E 2
Brian Butler (Northwich) **93** v F 1
Steve Butler (Maidstone) **88** v W, 89 **v** I,W 3

Gary Butterworth (Rushden & Diamonds)
   97 v E,H **98** **v** H 99 v I,H,W **00** v I 7
Chris Byrne (Macclesfield T.) **97** v H 1
Mark Carter (Runcorn & Barnet) **87** **v** W,I,H,S
   88 v W, 89 **v** I,W, 90 v I,E, **91** v I,W(s) 11
Kim Casey (Kidderminster) **86** v W,E,E(s),
   87 v W,I 5
Paul Cavell (Redbridge) **92** v W **93** v F 2
Lee Charles (Hayes) **99** v I(s), H(s), W(s) 3
Kevin Charlton (Telford) **85** v W,I 2
Ken Charlery (Boston U) **01** vH(s) 1
Andrew Clarke (Barnet) **90** v E,E 2
David Clarke (Blyth Spartans) **80** v I,S(s),H,
   81 v H,S,I, **82** v I,H,S **83** v H,S **84** v H,S,I 14
Gary Clayton (Burton) **86** v E 1
Robert Codner (Barnet) **88** v W 1
John Coleman (Morecambe) **93** v F(s) 1
Darren Collins (Enfield) **93** v F(s), **94** v W,F,N 4
Andy Comyn (Hednesford T.) **98** **v** H(s),
   99 v I(s),H(s),W(s) 4
Steve Conner (Dartford, Redbridge & Dagenham & R)
   90 v I **91** v I,W **92** v W **93** v F 5
David Constantine (Altrincham) **85** v I,H,S **86 v** W 4
Robbie Cooke (Kettering) **89** v W(s), **90** v I 2
Scott Cooksey(Hednesford T.) **97** v E, **98** vH(s)
   01 v W(s),H 4
Alan Cordice(Wealdstone) **83** v I,H,S
   84 vW,S(s), I(s), **85** I,H,S 9
Rob Cousins (Yeovil Town) **00 I v** I(s),H,W 3
Ken Cramman (Gateshead & Rushden & Diamonds)
   96 v E **97** v E,H 3
Nick Crittendon (Yeovil Town) **02** v US (s) 1
Paul Cuddy (Altrincham) **87** v I,H,S 3
Paul Culpin (Nuneaton B) **84** v W, **85** v W(s) ,I,H,S 5
Michael Danzey (Woking) **99** v I,H 2
Paul Davies (Kidderminster H.)
   86 v W, **87** **v** W,I,S, **88** **v** W **89** v W 6
John Davison (Altrincham)
   79 v S,H **80** v I,S, **81** **v** H,S ,I, **82 v** G,I,H,S
   83 I,H,S, **84** W,H,I,S **85** **v** I,H,S 86 **v** W,E,E 24
John Denham (Northwich Victoria) **80** v H 1
Peter Densmore (Runcorn) **88** v W **89** v I 2
Phil Derbyshire (Mossley) **83** v H(s) S(s) 2
Mick Doherty (Weymouth) **86** v W(s) 1
Neil Doherty (Kidderminster H.) **97** v E 1
Stuart Drummond (Morecambe) **00** v I(s),H ,W
   01 v W ,H, **02** v US, W,E(s),S 9
Neil Durkin (Leigh RMI) **02** v H(s) 1
Paul Ellender (Scarborough) **01** v W(s) 1
Lee Endersby (Harrow Bor.) **96 v** H 1
Mick Farrelly (Altrincham) **87** **v** I,H,S 3

Mark Angel

Jason Goodliffe

Junior McDougald

James Taylor

Steve Farrelly (Macclesfield & Kingstonian)
   95 v H(s),G(s), 00 v I,H,W(s)   5
Trevor Finnegan (Weymouth) 81 v H,S   2
Murray Fishlock (Yeovil Town) 99 v H(s)   1
Richard Forsyth (Kidderminster) 95 v W,H,G   3
Ian Foster (Kidderminster H) 00 v W(s)   1
Paul Furlong (Enfield) 90 v I,E,E 91 v I,W   5
Mark Gardiner (Macclesfield T.) 97 v E   1
Jerry Gill (Yeovil T.) 97 v E   1
John Glover (Maidstone Utd) 85 v W,I,H,S   4
Mark Golley (Sutton Utd.)
   87 v H(s),S, 88 v W, 89 v I,W, 92 v W   6
Jason Goodliffe (Hayes) 00 v I, H,W, 01 W
   02 US, W,E,S.   8
Paul Gothard (Dagenham & Redb.)
   97 v E(s), 99 v I(s),W(s)   3
Mark Gower (Barnet) 02   v H, W, E, S(s)   4
Neil Grayson (Cheltenham T.) 98 v H 99 v I,H,W   4
Phil Gridelet (Hendon & Barnet) 89 v I,W,
   90 v W,E,E   5
Steve Guppy (Wycombe W.) 93 v W   1
Scott Guyett (Southport) 01 v H   1
Tim Hambley (Havant & Waterlooville) 02 v H   1
Steve Hanlon (Macclesfield) 90 v W   1
David Harlow (Farnborough T.) 97 v E(s),H   2
Barry Hayles (Stevenage Bor.) 96 v E,H   2
Greg Heald (Barnet) 02 v H   1
Brian Healy (Morecambe) 98 v H   1
Tony Hemmings (Northwich) 93 v F   1
Andy Hessenthaler (Dartford) 90 v I   1
Kenny Hill (Maidstone Utd) 80 v I,S,H   3
Mark Hine (Gateshead) 95 v W(s),H   2
Simeon Hodson (Kidderminster) 94 v W,F,N   3
Colin Hogarth (Guiseley) 95 v W,H   2
Steven Holden (Kettering) 94 v W,F,N(s) 95 v H,G   5
Mark Hone (Welling United) 90 v I 93 v F,
   94 vW(s),F(s),N   5
Gary Hooley (Frickley) 85 v W   1
Dean Hooper (Kingstonian) 98 v H   1
Keith Houghton (Blyth Spartans) 79 v S   1
Barry Howard (Altrincham) 81 v H,S,I 82 v G,I,H,S   7
Neil Howarth (Macclesfield) 95 v H(s) 97 v E   2
David Howell (Enfield) 85 v H(s),S(s) 86 v W,E
   87 v W,IH,S, 88 v W, 89 v I,W 90 v I,E,E   14
Lee Howells (Cheltenham T.) 98 v H 99 v W   2
Lee Hughes (Kidderminster Harriers) 96 v E,H
   97 v E,H   4
Delwyn Humphreys (Kidderminster H.)
   91 v W(s) 92 v W 94 v W,F,N 95 v W,H   7
Steve Humphries (Barnet) 87 v H(s)   1
Nicky Ironton (Enfield) 83 H(s) 84 v W   2
Justin Jackson (Morecambe & Rushden & Diamonds)
   00 v W 01 v W   2
Kirk Jackson (Stevenage Borough) 02 v US, E,S   3
Tony Jennings (Enfield)
   79 v S,H 80 v I,S,H 81 v H,S,I 82 v G,I,H,S   12

Jeff Johnson (Altrincham) 81 v S,I 82 v G,I,H,S
   83 v I,H,S, 84 v H,S,I 84 v I,H,S 86 v W(s),E,E   18
Steve Jones (Leigh RMI) 01 v H   1
Tom Jones (Weymouth) 87 v W   1
Anton Joseph(Telford U. & Kidderm'terH.)84 v S(s),
   85 v W,I,H,S 86 v W(s), 87 W,I(s),H, 88 v W
   89 v I,W 90 v I,E,E   15
Andy Kerr (Wycombe) 93 v W   1
Ged Kimmins (Hyde Utd.) 96 v E(s),H(s) 97 v E(s) 3
Mike Lake (Macclesfield) 89 v I   1
Andy Lee (Telford U. & Witton A.) 89 I(s), 91 IW   3
David Leworthy (Farnborough & Rushden & Diamonds)
   93 W, 94 W 97 EH   4
Adam Lockwood (Yeovil Town) 02 E   1
Kenny Lowe (Barnet) 91 IW   2
Martin McDonald (Macclesfield) 95 G(s)   1
Junior MacDougald (Dagenham & Redbridge)
   01 H(s), 02 W, E(s), S(s)   4
Mark McGregor (Forest Green Rvrs & Nuneaton Boro)
   00 I(s)H(s) 01 W(s)   3
Kevin McIntyre (Doncaster Rovers)
   00 H(s)W, 01 W(s)H   4
John McKenna (Boston Utd)
   88 W(s), 90 IEE, 91 IW, 92 W   7
John Margerrison (Barnet) 87 W   1
Simon Marples (Doncaster Rovers) 00 IH   2
Leroy May (Stafford R.) 95 G(s)   1
Bobby Mayes (Redbridge) 92 W   1
Paul Mayman (Northwich Vic) 80 IS   2
Stewart Mell (Burton) 85 W   1
Neil Merrick (Weymouth) 80 I(s)S   2
Russell Milton (Dover) 94 FN   2
Trevor Morley (Nuneaton) 84 WHSI, 85 WS(s)   6
Neil Moore (Telford United) 02 US (s),H, W, E,S   5
Tarkan Mustafa (Rushden & Diamonds) 01 WH   2
Les Mutrie (Blyth Spartans) 79 SH, 80 ISH   5
Mark Newson (Maidstone U) 84 WHSI, 85 W   5
Doug Newton (Burton) 85 WHS   3
Paul Nicol (Kettering T) 91 IW, 92 W   3
Steve Norris (Telford) 88 W(s)   1
Joe O'Connor (Hednesford T.) 97 EH(s)   2
Eamon O'Keefe (Mossley) 79 SH   2
Frank Ovard (Maidstone) 81 H(s)S(s)I(s)   3
Andy Pape (Harrow Bor. & Enfield) 85 W(s)HS,
   86 W(s)E, 87 WIHS, 88 W, 89 IW, 90 IWE   15
Brian Parker (Yeovil Town) 80 S   1
Warren Patmore (Yeovil Town)
   99 IHW, 00 IH, 01 WH   7
Gary Patterson (Kingstonian) 99 IH, 00 IHW, 01 WH 7
Steve Payne (Macclesfield T.) 97 H   1
Trevor Peake (Nuneaton Bor) 79 SH   2
David Pearce (Harrow Bor) 84 I(s)   1
Warren Peyton (Nuneaton Borough) 02 H(s)   1
Brendan Phillips (Nuneaton Bor. & Kettering T.)
   79 SH, 80 S(s)H   4
Gary Philips (Barnet) 82 G   1
Owen Pickard (Yeovil T.) 98 H(s)   1

Geoff Pitcher (Kingstonian) **99**W, **00** IHW, **01** WH	6
Phil Power (Macclesfield T.) **96** E(s)H(s)	2
Ryan Price (Stafford R. & Macclesfield) **92** W(s) **93** WF **96** EH **97** H	6
Steve Prindiville **98** H(s)	1
Mark Quayle (Telford United) **02** H	1
Simon Read (Farnborough) **92** v W(s)	1
Andy Reid (Altrincham) **95 v** W	1
Carl Richards (Enfield) **86 v** E	1
Derek Richardson (Maidstone U) **83 v** I, **84 v** W, **86** v E	4
Ian Richardson (Dagenham & Red) **95 v** G	1
Kevin Richardson (Bromsgrove) **94** v W,F,N	3
Paul Richardson (Redbridge) **92** v W, **93** v W,F	3
Terry Robbins (Welling) **92** v W, **93** v W,F, **94** v W,F,N	6
Peter Robinson (Blyth S) **83 v** I,H,S **84** W,I **85** v W	6
Nick Roddis (Woking) **01 v** H **02** US,H,W,E(s),S	6
John Rogers (Altrincham) **81 v** H,S,I **82 v** I(s),S	5
Paul Rogers (Sutton) **89** v W, **90** v I, E(2), **91** I,W	6
Colin Rose (Witton Alb.) **96 v** E(s), H	2
Kevin Rose (Kidderminster) **94 v** F(s),N	2
Brian Ross (Marine) **93** v W(s),F(s), **94** v W(s) **95 v** W,H	5
Carl Ruffer (Chester City) **01** v H(s)	1
Tim Ryan (Southport & Doncaster Rovers) **98 v** H, **99 v** I,H,W, **00 v** I,H,W **01** v W,H **02** v US,H,W,I,S	14
Neil Sellars (Scarboro) **81** v H,S,I **82** v G,H(s),S, **83 v** I,H,S	9
Mark Shail (Yeovil T.) **93** v W	1
Simon Shaw (Doncaster Rovers) **99** v I,H	2
Peter Shearer (Cheltenham) **89 v** I(s)	1
Paul Shirtliff (Frickley A. & Boston U.) **86** vE,E **87** v W,I,H, **88** v W **89** v I, W, **90** v I,W,E,E, **92** v W **93** v W,F	15
Paul Showler (Altrincham) **91** v I(s),W	
Gordon Simmonite (Boston United) **79** v S(s,)H(s), **80** v I,S,H	5
Gary Simpson(Stafford R.) **86** v E,E, **87** v I,H,S, **90** v I,W,E,E	9
Wayne Simpson (Stafford) **94** v F,N(s)	2
Terry Skiverton (Yeovil Town) **01 v** W **02 v** US	2
Glenn Skivington (Barrow) **90** v I,W,E **91** v I,W	5
Adrian Smith (Kidderminster H) **00** v I(s),H(s),W	3
Alan Smith (Alvechurch) **82** v G,I,S	3
Ian Smith (Mossley) **80** v I,S,H(s)	3
Mark Smith (Stevenage Bor.) **96** v E,H **98** v H **99** v I,H,W **00** v I,H,W(s)	9
Ossie Smith (Runcorn) **84** v W	1
Tim Smithers (Nuneaton) **85** v W(s),I **86** v W	3
Adam Sollitt (Kettering Town) **00** v I(s),H(s),W	3
Adam Stansfield (Yeovil Town) **02** v W (s), I, S	3
Simon Stapleton (Wycombe) **93** v W	1
Mickey Stephens (Sutton), **82** v G,S(s) **86 v** W,E,E(s)	5
Billy Stewart (Southport) **98** v H	1
Mark Stimson (Canvey Island) **02** v US	1
Bob Stockley (Nuneaton Borough) **80** v H	1
Darren Stride (Burton Albion) **02** v H	1
Steve Stott (Kettering T., Rushden & Ds & Yeovil T.) **95** v W,H(s),G **96** v E,H **99** v H,W(s)	7
James Taylor (Havant & Waterlooville) **02** v H,W, E(s),S(s)	4
Peter Taylor (Maidstone) **84** v HSI	3
Steve Taylor (Bromsgrove R.) **95** v G	1
Shaun Teale (Weymouth) **88** v W	1
Stuart Terry (Altrincham) **95** v W	1
Brian Thompson(Yeovil & Maidstone) **79** v S,H **81** v H,S,I, **82** v I,H,S **83 v** I,H,S **84** v W,H,S,I	15,
Neil Thompson (Scarborough) **87** v W,I,H,S	4
Steve Thompson (Wycombe) **93** v W	1
Kevin Todd (Berwick Rangers) **91** v W	1
Anthony Tonkin (Yeovil Town) **02** v US	1
Simon Travis (Forest Green Rovers) **02 v** US, H.	2
Mark Tucker (Woking) **96** v E	1
Tony Turner (Telford) **85 v** W	1
Paul Underwood (Rushden & D) **99** v I,H **00 v** I **01** v W	4
David Venables(Stevenage B) **94 v** W(s) **95** v H,G, **96 v** E,H(s)	5
Jamie Victory (Cheltenham T.) **98** vH(s)	1
David Waite (Enfield) **82** v G	1
Paul Walker (Blyth) **86** v W,E,E(s), **87** v S(s)	4
Steve Walters (Northwich Victoria) **97** v H	1
Mark Ward (Northwich Victoria) **83** v S(s)	1
Dale Watkins (Cheltenham T.) **98** v H **99** v I(s), **00** v I,H,W	5
John Watson (Wealdstone, Scarborough & Maidstone) **79** v S(s),H **80** v I,S,H **81** v H,S,I **82** v I,H,S **83** v I,H,S, **84** v W(s),H,S,I	18
Steve Watson (Farnborough Town) **02** v US(s), W(s), S	3
Liam Watson (Marine) **95** v W,H(s)	2
Paul Watts (Redbridge Forest) **89** v W **90** v I,E,E **91** v I, **92** v W **93** v W,F	8
Simon Weatherstone (Boston United) **02** v W(s),E,S(s)	3
Paul Webb (Bromsgrove R & Kidderminster H) **93** v F **94** v W,F,N(s) **95** v W,H,G **96** v E,H **97** v E,H	11
Aaron Webster (Burton Albion) **02 v** H(s),W,S(s)	3
Mark West (Wycombe W) **91** v W	1
Steve West (Woking) **01** v W(s)	1
Barry Whitbread (Runcorn & Altrincham) **79 v** S,H **80** v I,S,H, **81 v** I	6
Russ Wilcox (Frickley) **86** v W,E	2
Barry Williams (Nuneaton Borough) **99** v H(s),W	2
Colin Williams (Scarborough & Telford Utd.) **81** v H, S **82** v I,H,S	5
Roger Willis (Barnet) **91** v I(s)	1
Paul Wilson (Frickley) **86** v W	1
Andy Woods (Scarborough) **02** v US,H(s),W,S.	4
Simon Wormull (Dover Athletic) **99** v I(s),W **02 v** W,E,S.	5
Mark Yates (Cheltenham Town) **99** v I, W	2

THE NATIONWIDE CONFERENCE

FOOTBALL CONFERENCE

Founded 1979

President: J C Thompson MBIM, Minst.M

Chairman: W J King   **Chief Executive:** J A Moules

Secretary: Kellie Discipline
Riverside House, 14B High Street, Crayford, Kent DA1 4HG
Tel: 01322 411021   Fax: 01322 550965

The season was dominated by the thrilling championship race which brought together Boston United and Dagenham & Redbridge as first one and then the other appeared to have gained a slight advantage.

The Non-League Newspaper' stoked up the rivalry each week and Sky TV joined in to bring the final stages live into our homes. The competition had never enjoyed such coverage and, despite the media highlighting the rival managers' swings in mood as fortunes varied, it was all good for the non-League game and the Conference Championship duly obliged by remaining in the balance until the very last day.

It is history now that Boston United won on goal difference and, of course, their disciplinary case at the Football Association, although finding them guilty of law breaking, didn't prevent their promotion.

Enough has been said and written about this serious case and it is now all over, but hopefully it won't lead to blatant rulebreaking by clubs comfortable in the knowledge that it's worth risking a feeble slap on the wrist to win trophies and promotion.

Good luck to the players and supporters of Boston and here's to a brilliant season ahead as the Conference clubs all battle for the top five places. The Champions, of course, will go up and what excitement the play offs will create.

It was good to see recently relegated League clubs such as Doncaster Rovers, Scarborough and Chester City looking strong at the end of the season with Morecambe and Stevenage Borough also looking very well prepared for the current campaign.

However, the game that probably gave our level of football its best publicity and promotion last season was the F.A. Umbro Trophy Final in which Yeovil Town and Stevenage Borough produced a thrilling and sporting encounter in front of a splendid crowd which created a brilliant atmosphere at Villa Park.

Gary Johnson's West Country squad were probably the best footballing side on their day last season and deserved to win the Trophy. They are amongst the pre-season favourites, but the standard will probably be higher than ever before as every club has real ambitions to reach those top five places.

Sadly Stalybridge Celtic, Hayes and Dover Athletic lost their membership after a close relegation battle, but who would bet against newcomers Burton Albion challenging at the top, while Kettering Town's immediate return to the Conference reminds us all that they were a power for many seasons.

There are certain clubs who always enjoy proving the doubters wrong and probably Forest Green Rovers, promoted Gravesend & Northfleet and Leigh RMI will be in that category.

The Conference has achieved its two up and two down link with The Football League thanks to The Football Association's backing, but although this will be an historic season there may well be big changes ahead as Division Two and Three of the Football League consider regional football and may well invite some Conference clubs to join them.

We can only wait and see!   TONY WILLIAMS

---

twentyfive in twentyfive twentyfive in twentyfive twentyfive in twentyfive twentyfive in twentyfive

— *25 in 25* —

A review of the progress made by the **Conference** and its member clubs during the twenty-five year life span of the F.A. Non-League Club Directory (1978 - 2002) will be available in the next year. It will be one of a series of 25 and will contain features, statistics and photos in at least 144 pages dedicated purely to the Conference members.

Further details can be found on page 17 so make sure of your copy of this exciting limited edition.

twentyfive in twentyfive twentyfive in twentyfive twentyfive in twentyfive twentyfive in twentyfive

FINAL LEAGUE TABLE 2001-02

		P	W	D	L	F	A	W	D	L	F	A	Pts	GD
1	**Boston United**	42	12	5	4	53	24	13	4	4	31	18	84	42
2	Dagenham & Redbridge	42	13	6	2	35	20	11	6	4	35	27	84	23
3	Yeovil Town	42	6	7	8	27	30	13	6	2	39	23	70	13
4	Doncaster Rovers	42	11	6	4	41	23	7	7	7	27	23	67	22
5	Barnet	42	10	4	7	30	19	9	6	6	34	29	67	16
6	Morecambe	42	12	5	4	30	27	5	6	10	33	40	62	-4
7	Farnborough Town	42	11	3	7	38	23	7	4	10	28	31	61	12
8	Margate	42	7	9	5	33	22	7	7	7	26	31	58	6
9	Telford United	42	8	6	7	34	31	6	9	6	29	27	57	5
10	Nuneaton Borough	42	9	3	9	33	27	7	6	8	24	30	57	0
11	Stevenage Borough	42	10	4	7	36	30	5	6	10	21	30	55	-3
12	Scarborough (-1 point)	42	9	6	6	27	22	5	8	8	28	41	55	-8
13	Northwich Victoria	42	9	4	8	32	34	7	3	11	25	36	55	-13
14	Chester City	42	7	7	7	26	23	8	2	11	28	28	54	3
15	Southport	42	9	6	6	40	26	4	8	9	13	23	53	4
16	Leigh RMI	42	6	4	11	29	29	9	4	8	27	29	53	-2
17	Hereford United	42	9	6	6	28	15	5	4	12	22	38	52	-3
18	Forest Green Rovers	42	7	7	7	28	32	5	8	8	26	44	51	-22
19	Woking	42	7	5	9	28	29	6	4	11	31	41	48	-11
20	Hayes	42	6	2	13	27	45	7	3	11	26	35	44	-27
21	Stalybridge Celtic	42	7	6	8	26	32	4	4	13	14	37	43	-29
22	Dover Athletic	42	6	5	10	20	25	5	1	15	21	40	39	-24

LEADING GOALSCORERS 2001-02

25	Daryl Clare	Boston United	15	Robert Talbot	Morecambe
25	Mark Stein	Dagenham & Redbridge	15	Dean Clark	Hayes
20	Ken Charlery	Dagenham & Redbridge	15	Ian Hodges	Hayes
19	Mark Cooper	Forest Green Rovers	14	Keith Scott	Dover Athletic
18	Gregg Blundell	Northwich Victoria	13	Mark Quayle	Telford United
18	Lenny Piper	Farnborough Town	13	Jon Vansittart	Farnborough
16	Leon Braithwaite	Margate	13	Darryn Stamp	Scarborough
16	Mark Beesley	Chester	12	Dino Maamria	Leigh RMI
16	Simon Parke	Southport	12	Warren Patmore	Woking
16	Michael Twiss	Leigh RMI	12	Steve Whitehall	Southport
16	Jamie Paterson	Doncaster Rovers	12	Simon Weatherstone	Boston United

ATTENDANCES 2001-02

		Highest	Lowest	Average
1	Yeovil	5061	1941	2871
2	Boston United	4200	1694	2434
3	Doncaster Rovers	4027	1489	2408
4	Dagenham & Redbridge	3939	1287	1915
5	Woking	2817	1216	1891
6	Stevenage Borough	2405	1116	1715
7	Hereford United	2210	1205	1551
8	Barnet	2456	787	1456
9	Morecambe	1780	635	1288
10	Nuneaton Borough	2203	726	1277
11	Chester City	2148	605	1274
12	Margate	3676	492	1218
13	Scarborough	2349	616	1194
14	Southport	1732	683	1048
15	Dover Athletic	2325	657	1025
16	Telford United	2168	664	1002
17	Northwich Victoria	1940	579	885
18	Forest Green Rovers	1609	509	840
19	Farnborough Town	1404	479	837
20	Stalybridge Celtic	1226	404	764
21	Hayes	3249	350	736
22	Leigh RMI	788	325	493

RESULTS CHART 20001-02

NATIONWIDE CONFERENCE

		1	2	3	4	5	6	7	8	9	10	11	12	13	14	15	16	17	18	19	20	21	22
1	Barnet	X	0-1	3-1	4-0	2-0	2-0	0-3	0-1	3-1	2-0	1-1	4-1	1-0	1-0	0-1	1-1	0-0	1-2	0-3	0-0	3-0	2-3
2	Boston United	1-1	X	0-1	1-2	2-2	4-2	4-0	6-1	4-1	3-4	2-1	0-1	2-1	3-2	4-1	2-2	0-0	4-1	0-0	3-1	4-0	4-0
3	Chester City	1-0	1-2	X	0-1	1-1	3-0	1-0	2-3	3-1	2-0	1-1	0-3	1-1	1-2	1-0	0-0	0-2	0-0	5-1	2-2	0-2	1-1
4	Dagenham & Redbridge	1-1	1-0	3-0	X	1-0	1-0	2-1	1-1	1-1	1-0	0-1	4-1	3-2	1-1	2-0	4-2	1-1	2-1	1-0	1-5	3-1	1-1
5	Doncaster Rovers	2-3	0-1	2-0	0-0	X	2-1	1-1	5-1	5-2	4-0	25-0	4-1	3-3	2-2	2-2	4-3	1-0	0-1	2-0	1-0	1-1	1-2
6	Dover Athletic	2-2	3-2	1-0	0-1	0-1	X	2-1	1-2	3-2	0-1	0-0	0-0	0-1	2-1	1-2	0-2	0-1	1-0	0-1	0-1	2-2	1-2
7	Farnborough Town	2-1	0-2	1-1	1-2	0-1	1-0	X	3-0	1-2	4-2	3-0	0-0	2-1	4-1	2-1	4-2	0-1	2-0	6-1	1-1	0-1	1-3
8	Forest Green Rovers	2-2	0-3	0-2	2-4	0-2	2-1	1-0	X	2-1	1-1	1-2	3-3	3-1	2-0	1-2	2-2	2-1	0-2	0-0	1-1	2-1	1-1
9	Hayes	0-2	0-2	1-3	2-4	1-5	2-1	0-3	1-1	X	4-1	2-4	2-4	3-1	2-1	1-2	1-2	1-0	0-0	0-2	1-4	4-1	0-4
10	Hereford United	2-1	0-1	1-0	1-0	0-0	3-0	4-2	0-0	0-1	X	0-1	3-0	0-2	1-0	1-1	6-0	0-0	3-0	1-1	0-1	2-2	0-2
11	Leigh RMI	3-3	1-2	3-0	2-0	1-4	1-2	3-0	1-2	1-1	0-1	X	2-2	0-1	1-2	0-1	1-1	1-2	1-0	1-2	3-1	3-1	0-1
12	Margate	0-1	1-1	0-0	1-1	1-1	0-1	2-1	1-1	1-0	2-2	1-2	X	1-1	1-2	1-1	1-1	1-2	8-0	2-1	3-1	4-3	0-1
13	Morecambe	1-0	0-0	0-3	1-1	1-1	0-2	1-1	2-0	2-1	2-2	1-3	2-1	X	2-1	1-0	2-0	2-2	1-0	0-3	2-1	3-1	1-5
14	Northwich Victoria	0-3	1-2	3-1	1-2	2-3	2-1	1-2	2-2	1-0	1-0	0-3	1-1	4-3	X	3-0	1-1	3-1	1-0	2-1	2-2	0-3	1-3
15	Nuneaton Borough	2-3	1-1	1-3	2-0	2-3	3-0	1-1	2-1	0-2	2-0	2-1	0-0	2-3	0-1	X	1-2	3-0	3-1	2-1	1-2	2-0	1-2
16	Scarborough	3-0	2-0	2-1	0-0	0-0	1-1	1-0	1-1	0-1	3-2	2-5	0-2	0-2	1-2	1-2	X	2-0	3-1	1-1	3-1	1-0	0-0
17	Southport	0-1	2-3	3-2	2-2	1-0	0-2	2-5	5-1	2-3	1-1	5-0	1-2	1-1	5-1	1-1	1-0	X	3-1	0-0	0-0	1-0	3-0
18	Stalybridge Celtic	1-1	2-1	0-4	2-3	3-0	0-2	1-2	4-1	1-0	0-2	2-2	2-2	4-3	1-1	4-2	2-3	0-0	X	2-0	0-2	0-2	1-1
19	Stevenage Borough	3-2	1-2	2-1	1-3	0-0	1-3	1-2	4-1	1-1	3-1	0-1	3-1	3-1	1-0	2-2	2-0	2-1	2-0	X	1-1	1-4	2-3
20	Telford United	1-2	2-2	0-3	1-4	3-1	4-3	0-1	0-0	1-2	2-1	3-1	2-0	4-1	1-0	0-2	3-0	1-1	3-1	2-1	X	3-3	2-2
21	Woking	1-3	0-2	2-1	0-2	3-1	4-0	3-2	3-4	0-1	1-0	1-1	0-1	1-3	3-1	0-0	1-2	2-0	1-1	1-1	1-1	X	0-2
22	Yeovil Town	1-2	0-1	0-1	3-3	1-1	2-0	0-1	2-2	2-1	2-1	1-2	1-2	1-1	2-3	2-1	2-2	0-0	0-2	2-1	1-1	1-3	X

MONTHLY AWARDS 2001-02

	Manager of the Month	Goalscorer of the Month	Performance of the Month
August	Jimmy Quinn *Northwich Victoria*	Rocky Baptiste *Farnborough Town*	Dagenham & Redbridge
September	Garry Hill *Dagenham & Redbridge*	Mark Stein *Dagenham & Redbridge*	Dover Athletic
October	Garry Hill *Dagenham & Redbridge*	Lee Charles *Chester City* Warren Patmore *Woking*	Chester City
November	Jake King *Telford United*	Alexander Meechan *Forest Green Rovers*	Stalybridge Celtic
December	Jim Harvey *Morecambe*	Ken Charlery *Dagenham & Redbridge*	Telford United
January	Gary Johnson *Yeovil Town*	Wayne Curtis *Morecambe*	Stalybridge Celtic
February	Jimmy Quinn *Northwich Victoria*	Samuel Ayorinde *Stalybridge Celtic* Michael Twiss *Leigh RMI*	Hereford United
March	Peter Shreeves *Barnet*	Daryl Clare *Boston United*	Woking
April	Garry Hill *Dagenham & Redbridge*	Charlie Griffin *Woking* Mark Cooper *Forest Green Rovers*	Chester City

PROGRAMME OF THE YEAR   Woking FC

FAIR PLAY AWARD   Nuneaton Borough FC

SEQUENCES

CONSECUTIVE VICTORIES
6   Dagenham & Redbridge   Sept 19th - Oct 8th inc

CONSECUTIVE DEFEATS
6   Chester City   Sept 15th - Oct 6th inc

MATCHES WITHOUT DEFEAT
15   Boston United   Sept 22nd - Jan 19th inc

MATCHES WITHOUT SUCCESS
10   Chester City   Sept 1st - Oct 6th inc

CONSECUTIVE DRAWS
4   Doncaster Rovers   Nov 10th - Dec 8th inc

MATCHES WITHOUT DRAWS
16   Stalybridge Celtic   Dec 1st - Apr 1st inc

CONSECUTIVE HOME WINS
6   Dagenham & Redbridge   Feb 23rd - Apr 28th inc

CONSECUTIVE AWAY WINS
7   Dagenham & Redbridge   Aug 25th - Oct 8th inc

WITHOUT CONCEDING A GOAL
5   Barnet   Mar 2nd - Mar 23rd inc

WITHOUT SCORING A GOAL
4   Hereford United   Nov 3rd - Dec 1st inc

JOINT MANAGERS OF THE YEAR 2001-02

Below: Steve Evans (Boston United)
Photo: Peter Barnes

Above: Garry Hill (Dagenham & Redbridge)
Photo: Andrew Chitty

TEAM OF THE YEAR 2001-02 - GOALKEEPER

TONY ROBERTS
Dagenham & Redbridge

TEAM OF THE YEAR 2001-02 - FULL BACK

ANTONY TONKIN
Yeovil Town
Photo: Garry Letts

TEAM OF THE YEAR 2001-02 - FULL BACK

MARK CLIFFORD
Boston United

TEAM OF THE YEAR 2001-02 - CENTRE BACK

GREG HEALD
Barnet

TEAM OF THE YEAR 2001-02 - CENTRE BACK

TERRY SKIVERTON
Yeovil Town
Photo: Garry Letts

TEAM OF THE YEAR 2001-02 - MIDFIELDER

SIMON WEATHERSTONE
Boston United
Photo: Peter Barnes

TEAM OF THE YEAR 2001-02 - MIDFIELDERS

Above:
PAUL TERRY
Dagenham & Redbridge

Below:
JAMIE PATTERSON
Doncaster Rovers

TEAM OF THE YEAR 2001-02 - STRIKER

MARK STEIN
Dagenham & Redbridge

TEAM OF THE YEAR 2001-02 - STRIKERS

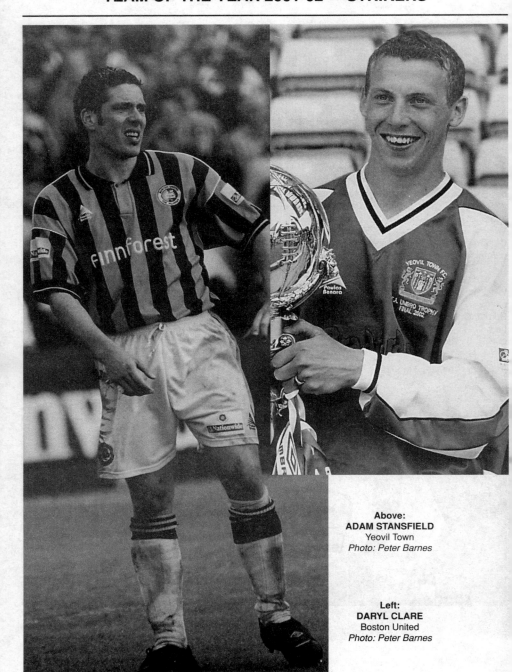

Above:
ADAM STANSFIELD
Yeovil Town
Photo: Peter Barnes

Left:
DARYL CLARE
Boston United
Photo: Peter Barnes

BARNET

Most clubs who have sampled The Football League are anxious to regain their senior status as quickly as possible but however good Barnet's form is this season they cannot gain promotion until they are able to upgrade their facilities in an area of Hertfordshire which is green belt and has a local council which does not wish to change the situation.

Under the experienced guidance of Peter Shreeves and his enthusiastic assistant Martin Allen there is no doubt that The Bees will still contest every competition in which they take part and continue the improvement shown last season, when they finished a very respectable fifth. In mid season the club were drifting a little so some inspiration was needed from the knockout cups . The F.A. Cup campaign began in the Fourth Qualifying Round with a tie at Havant & Waterlooville, which required a replay and brought a pleasing three goal victory and a chance to take on Carlisle United. Sadly a goalless home draw was followed by defeat at Brunton Park by the only goal of the game. The F.A. Trophy also brought a resounding victory, 5-0 at Fisher Athletic followed by a home draw with Scarborough,and then that most frustrating of exits - by penalty shoot out. (3-5)

The Conference brought win doubles against Doncaster Rovers ,Hayes, Margate ,Nuneaton Borough and Woking with only Farnborough Town and Stevenage Borough beating the Bees twice. At the end of the season Greg Heald, Mark Gower and top scorer Wayne Purser were selected for England duty but sadly Purser broke a bone and was not present to see his colleagues play impressively for their country. With luck, he will return this season and the promise of Ben Strevens, Junior Agogo and Neil Midgley up front, plus the quality of Heald, Gower, goalkeeper Lee Harrison and the consistent Mark Arber will give manager Shreeves a very talented basis from which he can build an attractive and effective squad.   T.W.

Left & Right respectively - Ben Strevens & Mark Arber in their FA XI shirts, photographed by Peter Barnes, and Centre - Wayne Purser, last season's top scorer, getting in a cross during the first encounter with Carlisle in the FA Cup last season. Photo: Alan Coomes

BARNET

GROUND DETAILS

Underhill Stadium,Westcombe Drive,Hertfs.EN5 2BE

TEL: 020 8441 6932(office) 8449 6325 (ticket office)
Club Shop: Contact: Melvyn Beresford 0208440 0725
Fax: 020 8447 0655email: info@barnetfc.com
Club Call: 09068 121 544
Refreshments: Bar for all post match and five tea-bars

Match Tickets: From £8 - £15. (£10/£12 for away fans)

Directions: Take junction 23 off the M25, follow signs
for Barnet (A100), the ground is located at the foot of
Barnet Hill. Tube :High Barnet (Northern Line), 400 yds
Train: New Barnet (1.5 miles)

Capacity: 4,057

Founded:	1888
Nickname:	The Bees
Sponsors:	J.B.L.
Colours: Black & amber shirts, black shorts & socks	
Change colours:	All white
Midweek matchday:	Tuesday 7.45
Newsline: 09068 12 15 44 (calls charged at premium rate)	
Reserve League:	None

CLUB OFFICIALS

Chairman: Tony Kleanthous

Directors: A.Adie,G. Slyper, C.Bean

Chief Executive / Secretary Andrew Adie
Tel Nos:01707 872518 (H) 0208441 6932 X204 (W)
07719 287453 (M) 0208447 0655 Fax)
Email: aadie@barnetfc.com

Company Secrrtary: Christopher Bean

P.R.Consultant to the Board: Dennis Signy OBE

Commercial Manager: Ben Keogh
Marketing Manager: Kevin Mullen

MATCHDAY PROGRAMME

Pages: 48   Price: £2.00
Editor: Kevin Mullen
Tel Nos: 020 84416932 (H) 07774132066 (M)
WEBSITE: www.barnetfc.com
Club call: 09068 121 544

FOOTBALL MANAGEMENT TEAM

HEAD COACH   PETER SHREEVES

Date of Appointment	16th March 2001
Date of Birth:	30th November 1940
Place of Birth:	Neath
PREVIOUS CLUBS	
As manager:	Tottenham H (2) ,Sheff Wed (2)
As asst. manager/coach	CharltonA (youth coach),Q.P.R., Watford, Chelsea, Sheff.Wed (2) Nott'm F.
As player	Finchley, Reading,Chelmsford C , Wimbledon,Stevenage
HONOURS	
As manager/coach	U.E.F.A.Cup winners,F.A.Cup & E.Cup Winners Cup Finals. 3rd in Divsion 1
As player	Selected for Wales Under 23
First Team Coach:	Martin Allen
Reserve Team Manager	Paul Wilson
Physiotherapist:	Lee Taylor
Club Playing Status:	Full Time

Season	League	Div.	Pos.	P	Home W	D	L	F	A	Away W	D	L	F	A	Pts	Manager
01-02	Conference	-	5	42	10	4	7	30	19	9	6	6	34	29	67	John Still / Peter Shreeves
00-01	Football Lge	3	24	46	9	8	6	44	29	3	1	19	23	52	45	John Still/Tony Cottee/John Still
99-00	Football Lge	3	6	46	12	6	5	36	24	9	6	8	23	29	75	John Still
98-99	Football Lge	3	16	46	10	5	8	30	31	4	8	11	24	40	55	John Still
97-98	Football Lge	3	7	46	10	8	5	35	22	9	5	9	26	29	70	John Still
96-97	Football Lge	3	15	46	9	9	5	32	23	5	7	11	14	28	58	Terry Bullivant
95-96	Football Lge	3	8	46	13	6	4	40	19	5	10	8	25	26	70	Ray Clemence
94-95	Football Lge	3	12	42	8	7	6	37	27	7	4	10	19	36	56	Ray Clemence
93-94	Football Lge	2	24	46	4	6	13	22	32	1	7	15	19	54	28	Gary Phillips
92-93	Football Lge	3	3	42	16	4	1	45	19	7	6	8	21	29	79	Edwin Stein

HONOURS

FA Amateur Cup 1945-46. Runners-up 1947-48, 1958-59.
FA Trophy runners-up 1971-72.
Athenian League x 5. Athenian Premier Div. x 2.
Southern League Div.1 1965-66. Div. 1 South 1976-77.
Southern League Cup 1976-77.
London League 1897, 1906, 1907.
London Senior Cup x 3. London Charity Cup x 2.
Middlesex Senior Cup x 2. Middlesex Charity Cup x 2.
Herts Senior Cup x 12. Herts Charity Cup x 25.
Wendy Fair Capital League 1988-89.
Clubcall Cup 1988-89.
Football Conference Winners 1990-91.
Football Conference runners-up 1986-87, 1987-88, 1989-90.

PREVIOUS

Leagues: Olympian League, London League, Athenian League, Southern League, Alliance Premier*, Gola League*, Vauxhall Conference*, Football League.

Names: Barnet Alston.

Grounds: Queens Road, Totteridge Lane.

* Same competetion different title.

Past Players who progressed to the Football League

Colin Powell (Charlton Ath), Gary Borthwick (AFC Bournemouth), Graham Pearce (Brighton & H.A), Russell Townsend (Northampton Tn), Colin Barnes (Torquay Utd), Gary Phillips (Brentford), Keith Alexander (Grimsby Town), Nicky Bissett (Brighton & H.A.), Robert Codner (Brighton & H.A.), Lee Payne (Newcastle Utd), Phil Gridelet (Barnsley), david Regis & Paul Harding (Notts County).

CLUB RECORDS

Attendance: 11,026
v Wycombe W., FA Amateur Cup 4th Rnd, 1951-52.

Career Goalscorer: Arthur Morris, 400, 1927-34.

Career Appearances: Les Eason, 648, 1965-74, 1977-78.

Transfer Fee Paid: £130,000
to Peterborough Utd for Greg Heald.

Transfer Fee Received: £800,000
from Crystal Palace for Dougie Freedman.

BEST SEASON

FA Cup: 3rd Round
1964-65, 1970-71, 1972-73, 1981-82, 1990-91, 1991-92, 1993-94.

League Clubs Defeated Newport County (1970-71, a
(as a non-league club) Northampton Town1990-91

FA Trophy: Finalists 1971-72.

League: Conference Champions 1990-91.

LAST SEASON

F.A. Cup:	2nd Round
F.A. Trophy:	4th Round
Conference:	5th
Top Goalscorer:	Wayne Purser

BARNET

	Date	Comp.	Opponents	Att.	Score	Goalscorers
1	18/08	Conf.	Hereford United	2210	1 - 2	Gower 19
2	21/08	Conf.	DOVER ATHLETIC	1377	2 - 0	Midgley 31, Strevens 60
3	25/08	Conf.	SCARBOROUGH	1276	1 - 1	Nower 87
4	27/08	Conf.	Farnborough Town	1126	1 - 2	Strevens 9
5	01/09	Conf.	CHESTER CITY	1197	3 - 1	Nower 43, Midgley 74, Strevens 87
6	04/09	Conf.	Dagenham & Redbridge	1916	1 - 1	Midgley 4
7	08/09	Conf.	SOUTHPORT	1450	0 - 0	
8	11/09	Conf.	Morecambe	1283	0 - 1	
9	15/09	Conf.	Telford United	911	2 - 1	Arber 29[p] 90
10	18/09	Conf.	HAYES	947	3 - 1	Heald 19, Midgley 50, Arber 77
11	22/09	Conf.	NORTHWICH VICTORIA	1364	1 - 0	Bell 63
12	24/09	Herts SC 1	WATFORD	n/k	0 - 2	
13	29/09	Conf.	Margate	1753	1 - 0	Doolan 79
14	02/10	Conf.	YEOVIL TOWN	1583	2 - 3	Flynn 86, Essendoh 90
15	06/10	Conf.	Stalybridge Celtic	525	1 - 1	Purser 90
16	09/10	Conf.	Doncaster Rovers	2935	3 - 2	Flynn 5 74, Purser 7
17	13/10	Conf.	LEIGH RMI	1472	1 - 1	Arber 82
18	16/10	LDV Vans 1S	AFC BOURNEMOUTH	789	2 - 1	Sawyers 54, Essendoh 98
19	20/10	Conf.	BOSTON UNITED	1858	0 - 1	
20	27/10	FA Cup Q4	Havant & Waterlooville	1143	1 - 1	Purser 17
21	30/10	LDV Vans 2S	Northampton Town	2142	1 - 0	Flynn 57
22	03/11	Conf.	Nuneaton Borough	1664	3 - 2	**Strevens** 3 (3 5 14)
23	06/11	FA Cup Q4 R	HAVANT & WATERLOOVILLE	1414	3 - 0	**Purser** 3 (35 37 39)
24	10/11	Conf.	WOKING	1822	3 - 0	Purser 9, Arber 56, Strevens 87
25	17/11	FA Cup 1	CARLISLE UNITED	2277	0 - 0	
26	24/11	Conf.	Forest Green Rovers	984	2 - 2	Strevens 62 Sawyers 85
27	27/11	FA Cup 1 R	Carlisle United	1470	0 - 1	
28	01/12	Conf.	HEREFORD UNITED	1713	2 - 0	Strevens 32 Bell 53
29	04/12	LDV Vans QFS	READING	1171	4 - 1	Strevens 15 80, Arber 30, Berkley 90
30	15/12	Conf.	Dover Athletic	1004	2 - 2	Toms 44, Norman 80[og]
31	26/12	Conf.	STEVENAGE BOROUGH	2456	0 - 3	
32	29/12	Conf.	Scarborough	1051	0 - 2	
33	05/01	LDV Vans SFS	Cambridge United	3108	0 - 2	
34	12/01	FA Trophy 3	Fisher Athletic	635	5 - 0	Bell 15, Purser 42 72, Heald 47, Gower 74
35	19/01	Conf.	Chester City	1421	0 - 1	
36	02/02	FA Trophy 4	SCARBOROUGH	1140	0 - 0	
37	05/02	FA Trophy 4 R	Scarborough	928	2 - 2	Purser 4, Strevens 101 3 5
38	09/02	Conf.	STALYBRIDGE CELTIC	1302	1 - 2	Midgley 90
39	16/02	Conf.	Leigh RMI	458	3 - 3	Berkeley 37 66, Sawyers 75
40	19/02	Conf.	FARNBOROUGH TOWN	787	0 - 3	
41	02/03	Conf.	Hayes	804	2 - 0	Brown 10, Toms 30
42	09/03	Conf.	MORECAMBE	1316	1 - 0	Oshitola 85
43	16/03	Conf.	Southport	946	1 - 0	Purser 23
44	19/03	Conf.	DAGENHAM & REDBRIDGE	1865	4 - 0	Toms 29, Gower 52 78, Midgley 67
45	23/03	Conf.	TELFORD UNITED	1306	0 - 0	
46	25/03	Conf.	Stevenage Borough	2405	2 - 3	Oshitola 58, Doolan 74[p]
47	29/03	Conf.	Boston United	3669	1 - 1	Brown 75
48	01/04	Conf.	NUNEATON BOROUGH	1419	0 - 1	
49	06/04	Conf.	Woking	2035	3 - 1	Toms 2, Purser 8 68[p]
50	13/04	Conf.	FOREST GREEN ROVERS	1302	0 - 1	
51	16/04	Conf.	Yeovil Town	2125	2 - 1	Purser 16, Midgley 41
52	20/04	Conf.	MARGATE	1405	4 - 1	Niven 28, Purser 48, Midgley 77 83
53	22/04	Conf.	DONCASTER ROVERS	1361	2 - 0	Arber 17 36[p]
54	27/04	Conf.	Northwich Victoria	1750	3 - 0	Brown 19, Heald 56, Toms 84

1	2	3	4	5	6	7	8	9	10	11	Substitutes Used
Harrison	Gledhill	Flynn	Goodhind	Heald	Arber	Niven	Strevens	Gower	Midgley	Bell	Brown 2
Harrison	Gledhill	Flynn	Goodhind	Heald	Arber	Niven	Strevens	Gower	Midgley	Bell	Brown 7 Toms 11
Harrison	Gledhill	Flynn	Sawyers	Heald	Arber	Niven	Strevens	Gower	Midgley	Bell	Brown 2 Toms 7
Harrison	Gledhill	Flynn	Sawyers	Heald	Arber	Niven	Strevens	Gower	Midgley	Bell	Toms 2
Harrison	Gledhill	Toms	Goodhind	Heald	Arber	Niven	Strevens	Gower	Midgley	Bell	Flynn 3 Doolan 11 Sawyers 2
Harrison	Goodhind	Sawyers	Bell	Heald	Arber	Niven	Strevens	Doolan	Midgley	Toms	Flynn 11
Harrison	Goodhind	Sawyers	Bell	Heald	Arber	Niven	Strevens	Doolan	Midgley	Toms	Flynn 11 Gledhill 7
Harrison	Goodhind	Sawyers	Bell	Heald	Arber	Niven	Doolan	Strevens	Midgley	Toms	Flynn 11 Brown 7
Harrison	Gledhill	Sawyers	Goodhind	Heald	Arber	Bell	Doolan	Strevens	Midgley	Brown	
Harrison	Gledhill	Flynn	Sawyers	Heald	Arber	Bell	Doolan	Strevens	Midgley	Brown	Niven 11 Taylor 10
Harrison	Gledhill	Flynn	Sawyers	Heald	Darcy	Bell	Gower	Strevens	Midgley	Brown	Niven 9 Oshitola 4 Pluck 6
Harrison	Gledhill	Flynn	Sawyers	Heald	Arber	Gower	Doolan	Strevens	Midgley	Brown	Naisbitt 1 Purser 9
Naisbitt	Gledhill	Flynn	Sawyers	Heald	Arber	Gower	Doolan	Essandoh	Midgley	Brown	Bell 10 Taylor 6 Purches 11
Naisbitt	Gledhill	Flynn	Pluck	Heald	Arber	Gower	Bell	Essandoh	Purser	Brown	Midgley 4 Taylor 9 Purches 11
Naisbitt	Gledhill	Flynn	Sawyers	Heald	Arber	Bell	Purser	Gower	Strevens	Brown	Midgley 10 Essandoh 8
Harrison	Gledhill	Flynn	Sawyers	Heald	Arber	Bell	Purser	Gower	Midgley	Brown	Niven 4 Taylor 10 Essandoh 11
Harrison	Gledhill	Flynn	Sawyers	Heald	Arber	Bell	Purser	Gower	Essandoh	Brown	Wiper 11
Harrison	Gledhill	Flynn	Sawyers	Heald	Arber	Bell	Purser	Gower	Essandoh	Brown	Midgley 11
Harrison	Gledhill	Flynn	Sawyers	Heald	Arber	Bell	Gower	Purser	Strevens	Brown	Midgley 9 Essandoh 10
Naisbitt	Gledhill	Flynn	Niven	Heald	Arber	Bell	Purser	Midgley	Essandoh	Berkley	Strevens 8 Sawyers 2 Taylor 11
Harrison	Gledhill	Flynn	Sawyers	Heald	Arber	Niven	Midgley	Gower	Strevens	Purser	Essandoh 8 Berkley 11
Harrison	Gledhill	Flynn	Sawyers	Heald	Arber	Niven	Bell	Gower	Strevens	Purser	Midgley 9
Harrison	Gledhill	Flynn	Sawyers	Heald	Arber	Niven	Bell	Gower	Strevens	Purser	Midgley 7 Toms 9
Harrison	Gledhill	Flynn	Sawyers	Heald	Arber	Niven	Bell	Gower	Strevens	Purser	
Harrison	Gledhill	Flynn	Sawyers	Heald	Arber	Niven	Bell	Gower	Strevens	Purser	
Harrison	Gledhill	Flynn	Sawyers	Heald	Arber	Niven	Bell	Gower	Strevens	Purser	Midgley 7 Toms 8
Harrison	Gledhill	Flynn	Sawyers	Toms	Arber	Niven	Bell	Gower	Strevens	Purser	Midgley 11 Doolan 5
Naisbitt	Gledhill	Flynn	Toms	Heald	Arber	Doolan	Bell	Midgley	Strevens	Purser	Sawyers 5 Berkley 4
Harrison	Gledhill	Flynn	Sawyers	Heald	Arber	Niven	Bell	Gower	Strevens	Purser	Doolan 7 Toms 3
Harrison	Gledhill	Sawyers	Doolan	Heald	Arber	Gower	Bell	Purser	Strevens	Toms	Midgley 7 Berkley 11
Naisbitt	Gledhill	Arber	Sawyers	Heald	Olayinka	Niven	Bell	Strevens	Midgley	Berkley	Toms 6 Purser 11
Naisbitt	Gledhill	Sawyers	Toms	Heald	Arber	Niven	Bell	Midgley	Strevens	Berkley	Purser 4 Doolan 11
Naisbitt	Gledhill	Sawyers	Bell	Heald	Arber	Berkley	Niven	Purser	Strevens	Gower	Midgley 10 Taylor 7
Naisbitt	Gledhill	Flynn	Niven	Heald	Arber	Gower	Bell	Purser	Strevens	Berkley	Midgley 2 Darcy 7 Toms 8
Naisbitt	Pope	Sawyers	Doolan	Heald	Pluck	Gower	Toms	Midgley	Strevens	Berkley	Purser 11
Naisbitt	Gledhill	Flynn	Sawyers	Heald	Pluck	Doolan	Gower	Strevens	Purser	Toms	Midgley 9 Berkley 8 Niven 7
Naisbitt	Gledhill	Flynn	Sawyers	Heald	Pluck	Gower	Doolan	Purser	Strevens	Toms	Arber 11 Midgley 2 Berkley 7
Harrison	Gledhill	Flynn	Niven	Heald	Arber	Berkley	Bell	Purser	Midgley	Sawyers	Brown 8
Harrison	Gledhill	Sawyers	Doolan	Heald	Arber	Brown	Niven	Purser	Midgley	Berkley	Gower 4
Harrison	Gledhill	Flynn	Gower	Heald	Arber	Brown	Doolan	Purser	Toms	Berkley	Niven 4 Bell 10
Harrison	Gledhill	Flynn	Gower	Heald	Arber	Brown	Doolan	Purser	Toms	Midgley	Niven 11 Sawyers 9 Oshitola 7
Harrison	Gledhill	Flynn	Gower	Heald	Arber	Berkley	Doolan	Purser	Toms	Midgley	Niven 10 Oshitola 9
Harrison	Gledhill	Flynn	Gower	Pluck	Arber	Berkley	Doolan	Purser	Toms	Midgley	Bell 8 Niven 11 Oshitola 9
Harrison	Gledhill	Flynn	Gower	Heald	Arber	Berkley	Doolan	Purser	Toms	Midgley	Niven 7 Oshitola 11
Harrison	Gledhill	Flynn	Gower	Heald	Pluck	Berkley	Doolan	Purser	Toms	Midgley	Yakubu 6 Niven 7 Oshitola 11
Harrison	Gledhill	Flynn	Gower	Heald	Yakubu	Berkley	Niven	Purser	Brown	Midgley	Bell 10 Oshitola 7
Harrison	Gledhill	Flynn	Gower	Heald	Yakubu	Toms	Niven	Purser	Brown	Midgley	Taylor 7 Bell 8 Oshitola 11
Harrison	Gledhill	Flynn	Gower	Heald-	Arber	Toms	Niven	Purser	Brown	Midgley	Pluck 7 Pope 2
Harrison	Pope	Flynn	Gower	Yakubu	Arber	Toms	Niven	Purser	Brown	Midgley	Searle 11 Sawyers 2 Oshitola 7
Harrison	Pope	Flynn	Gower	Pluck	Arber	Searle	Niven	Purser	Brown	Midgley	Sawyers 8 Toms 4
Harrison	Pope	Flynn	Gower	Heald	Arber	Searle	Niven	Purser	Brown	Strevens	Toms 7 Midgley 9 Sawyers 11
Harrison	Pope	Flynn	Gower	Heald	Arber	Gledhill	Niven	Midgley	Strevens	Brown	Toms 10 Searle 8 Pluck 5
Harrison	Pope	Flynn	Gower	Heald	Arber	Gledhill	Niven	Midgley	Toms	Brown	Sawyers 2 Searle 8 Bell 4

BARNET   PLAYING SQUAD

Player	Birthplace	D.O.B.	Previous Clubs

Bold print denotes England semi-professional international.

GOALKEEPERS

Player	Birthplace	D.O.B.	Previous Clubs
Lee Harrison	Billericay	12.09.71	Fulham, Charlton
Danny Naisbitt	Bishop Auckland	25.11.78	Walsall

DEFENDERS

Player	Birthplace	D.O.B.	Previous Clubs
Greg Heald ES	Enfield	26.09.71	Peterborough Utd, Enfield
Lee Flynn	London	04.09.73	Hayes, Hendon, Boreham Wood, Romford
Mark Arber	Johannesburg	08.10.77	Tottenham
Warren Goodhind	Johannesburg	16.08.77	From Trainee

MIDFIELD

Player	Birthplace	D.O.B.	Previous Clubs
Fraser Toms	Ealing	13.09.79	Charlton
John Doolan	Liverpool	07.05.74	Mansfield, Everton
Lee Gledhill	Bury	07.11.80	From Trainee
Lee Pluck	London		From Trainee
Leon Bell	Hitchin	19.12.80	From Trainee
Mark Gower ES, EY,E S-P	Edmonton	05.10.78	Tottenham (£32,500)
David Hillier Eu-21	Blackheath	19.12.69	Bristol R, Portsmouth, Arsenal

FORWARDS

Player	Birthplace	D.O.B.	Previous Clubs
Ben Strevens	Edgware	24.05.80	Wingate & Finchley
Neil Midgley	Cambridge	21.10.78	Kidderminster Harriers, Ipswich
Stuart Niven	Glasgow	24.12.78	Ipswich
Wayne Purser	Basildon	13.04.80	QPR
Junior Agogo	Accra	01.08.79	San Jose Earthquakes, Colorado Rapids, Chicago Fire, QPR, Sheff.Wednesday, Willesden Hawkeye

BURTON ALBION

Of all the clubs promoted to the Conference in the latest campaign Burton Albion achieved that objective in the most convincing fashion with a fifteen point margin over their nearest challengers, Vauxhall Motors, with two `centuries' recorded - 104 match points (only two defeats) and 106 goals scored (with a meagre 30 conceded).

By any standard that is an outstanding set of statistics and suggests few weaknesses, so the only question is whether it can be translated to the Conference.

In a season when top place - never to be lost - was reached in very early autumn no Albion player appeared on the league's list of top scorers, but such strikers as Evans, Moore, Webster, Anderson, Kavanagh and Clough (that name again) appeared regularly on the score sheet, so injuries could be real problems to some teams, but not Albion, who performed the double against Bradford (PA), Hyde United, Gainsborough Trinity, Frickley Athletic , Worksop Town, Colwyn Bay, Barrow, Hucknall Town and runners-up Vauxhall Motor. No-one managed to beat them twice.

Knock-out competitions performances also suggested that the side might be able to live with the best, although the F.A. Challenge Cup run ended at the Fourth Qualifying stage at home to Gravesend & Northfleet (another promoted club) by two clear goals after survival against Arnold Town (1-1 and 4-0) and Berkhamsted Town (2-1 at home).

However, the F.A. Trophy challenge almost went all the way with victories over Barrow (1-1 and 5-0), Blyth Spartans (3-0 at home), Farnborough Town (1-1 and 3-2), Woking (3-0 at home) and Chester City (2-0 at home), which left a semi-final against Yeovil Town, whose four clear goals home performance could not be matched in the return leg - a 2-1 scoreline for the Derbyshire men. But Yeovil did win the final.

Yet another promotion - in effect a great hat-trick - cannot be ruled out and the Clough family has known plenty of success, while an average home attendance of 1,430 is an impressive support basis on which an even bigger following can be attracted . However, it may take the club a few seasons to build the sufficient all round strength that a push for The Football League demands.   W.M

Back row (left to right)**:** Gary Crosby (Assistant Manager), Matthew Brown (Physio), Sean Farrell, Darren Stride, Mark Blount, Darren Wassell, Matthew Duke, Dan Robinson, Andrew Garner, Dale Anderson, Aarron Webster, Colin Hoyle, Steve Booth (Scout) and Roy Hudson (Kit Manager).   **Front row**: Christian Moore, Pat Lyons, Steve Evans, Ben Robinson (Chairman), Nigel Clough (Manager), Terry Henshaw, Paul Wraith, Jason Kavanagh and Tony Kirkland (Football Secretary)

BURTON ALBION

GROUND DETAILS

Eton Park,
Princess Way,
Burton-on-Trent
DE14 2RU
Tel: 01283 565938

Directions: From south M42 - A38 (Lichfield), follow signs forBurton, take 2nd turn for Burton (A5121), right at island - ground on left: From M6 north - jct 15 and follow A50 for Stoke and Uttoxeter, follow A50 signsto Burton, continue under bypass, left into Shakespeare Rd after canal bridge (opp. Navigation Inn), ground at end. From M6 North, leave at Jct 15 .Follow A50 Stoke & Uttoxeter. Leave for A38 South to Burton & Lichfield at Toyota Factory.Leave Burton North A5121 past Pirelli Factory to Island .Turn right ground is on left.

Parking

Capacity:	**4,500**
Cover:	**2,500**
Seats:	**464**

Clubhouse: `The Football Tavern' - open normal pub hours. Full hot & cold menu.
Steward: T.B.A

Club Shop: Yes
Match Tickets:

Founded:	1950
Nickname:	Brewers
Sponsors:	B.I. Industries"
Colours:	Yellow with black trim
Change colours:	Blue
Midweek matchday:	Tuesday
Reserve League:	
Club Websites	www.burtonalbionfc.co.uk www.brewerstreet.com

CLUB OFFICIALS

Chairman: C B Robinson
01283 37272(W)

President:

Vice-Chairman:

Directors:

Secretary: Tony A Kirkland
40 Hurst Drive, Stretton, Burton-on-Trent DE13 0ED
07774 102485 (Mobile)

Commercial Manager: Fleur Robinson

Press Officer: David Twigg (01283 562013)

Pages: 48   Price: £1
Editor: David Twigg (01283 562013)
Clubcall:09066 555 883

Local Press: Burton Daily Mail (01283 43311)
Local Radio: Radio Derby,Centra F.M.

FOOTBALL MANAGEMENT TEAM

MANAGER   **NIGEL CLOUGH**
Date of Appointment: March1999
Date of Birth: 19th March 1966
Place of Birth: Sunderland

PREVIOUS CLUBS
As manager
As asst. manager/coach
As player   Heanor Town, Nottm. Forest, Liverpool

HONOURS
As manager: N.P.L. Champions 2001-02
F.A. Trophy Semi-Finalists 01-02

As player   England - Full & u21 caps

Assistant Manager: Gary Crosby
Physiotherapist: Matthew Brown
Scout: Steve Booth
Club's Playing Status: Part-time.

146

Season	League	Div.	Pos.	Home						Away						Manager
				P	W	D	L	F	A	W	D	L	F	A	Pts	
01-02	N.P.L.	Prem	1	44	17	5	0	59	12	14	6	2	47	18	104	Nigel Clough
00-01	Southern	Prem.	2	42	14	6	1	36	13	11	7	3	40	23	88	Nigel Clough
99-00	Southern	Prem.	2	42	15	3	3	47	15	8	6	7	26	28	78	Nigel Clough
98-99	Southern	Prem.	13	42	7	2	12	29	27	10	5	6	29	25	58	John Barton
97-98	Southern	Prem.	3	42	12	4	5	39	19	9	4	8	25	24	71	John Barton
96-97	Southern	Prem.	6	42	10	7	4	37	32	8	5	8	33	31	66	John Barton

Season	League	Div.	Pos.	P	W	D	L	F	A	Pts	Manager
95-96	Southern	Prem.	16	42	13	12	17	55	56	51	John Barton
94-95	Southern	Prem.	3	42	20	15	7	55	39	75	John Barton
93-94	Southern	Prem.	11	42	15	11	16	57	49	56	Brian Kenning
92-93	Southern	Prem.	7	40	16	11	13	53	50	59	Brian Kenning

HONOURS

Southern League
Lg Cup 63-64 96-97, 99-00 (R-up 88-89),
Div 1 (Nth) R-up 71-72 73-74;

Northern Premier — Champions 2001-02
Lg Chall Cup 82-83 (R-up 86-87),
Presidents Cup R-up 85-86 (SF 86-87);

FA Trophy R-up 86-87;

Birmingham Snr Cup 53-54 70-71 (R-up 86-87);
GMAC Cup SF 86-87;
Bass Charity Vase 81-82 85-86,
Challenge Cup 84-85;
West Mids Lg R-up 53-54;
Staffs Sen Cup 55-56

CLUB RECORDS

Attendance: 5,860
v Weymouth, Southern Lg Cup Final 2nd leg, 1964
(22,500 v Leicester City, F.A. Cup 3rd Rd 1984
- played at Derby County F.C.)

Goalscorer: Ritchie Barker, 157

Appearances: Phil Annable, 567

Win:

Fee Paid: £21,000
to Kidderminster H.for R Jones and J Pearson

Fee Received: £60,000
for Darren Carr to Crystal Palace 1989

PREVIOUS

Leagues:
West Midlands 1950-58
Southern 58-79, 80-2001
Northern Premier 79-80, 01-02

Grounds: Wellington Street 50-57

Names: None

Past Players who progressed to the Football League

L Green & T Parry & S Aston (Hartlepool65/66),
G Hunter (Lincoln 65), D Jones (Newport 68),
R Barker & J Bourne & T Bailey (Derby 67/69/70),
M Pollock & S Buckley (Luton 74),
P Ward (Brighton75), Tony Moore (Sheffield Utd 79),
C Swan & G Clayton (Doncaster 80 & 86),
RJobson (Watford 82), P Haycock (Rotherham 86),
A Kamara (Scarborough 87),
P Groves (Leicester City 88),
S Cotterill & J Gayle (Wimbledon 89),
D Carr(Crystal Pal. 89),
D Smith & D Roberts (Wolves 90 & 92)

BEST SEASON

FA Trophy: R-up 86-87 (SF 74-75)

FA Cup: 3rd Rd Prop 55-56, 84-85. 1st Rd 9 times

League: Champions Northern Prem. 01-02

LAST SEASON

F.A. Cup: Round
F.A. Trophy: Semi-Finals
League: Northern Premier League Champions
Top Goalscorer: Darren Stride
Player of the Year: Darren Stride
Captain: Darren Stride

BURTON ALBION

Match Facts 2001-02

Date	Comp.	Opponents	Att.	Score	Goalscorers
18.08	Unib. P	Bradford Park Avenue	648	4 - 1	Kavanagh 24[p] 80[p], Evans 65, Stride 69
21.08	Unib. P	RUNCORN HALTON	1175	1 - 1	Moore 71
25.08	Unib. P	HYDE UNITED	1102	5 - 1	Stride 24, Evans 35, Farrell 74 77, Clough 81
27.08	Unib. P	Altrincham	1018	2 - 0	Evans 62, Clough 81
01.09	Unib. P	GAINSBOROUGH TRINITY	1204	4 - 2	Anderson 5 35, Wassall 76 81
04.09	Unib. P	Frickley Athletic	513	5 - 0	Glasser 36, Farrell 45, Stride 66 90, Garner 90
08.09	Unib. P	Marine	459	1 - 1	Evans 42
11.09	Unib. P	VAUXHALL MOTORS	1172	2 - 1	Kavanagh 4, Bailey 41
15.09	Unib. P	Gateshead	402	1 - 1	Webster 85
18.09	Unib. P	HUCKNALL TOWN	1108	2 - 0	Bailey 8, Anderson 90
22.09	Unib. P	BURSCOUGH	1361	4 - 0	Moore 2, Henshaw 7, Webster 33, Bailey 74
25.09	Lge Cup G7	Eastwood Town	314	1 - 1	Bailey 78
29.09	FA Cup Q2	Arnold Town	1156	1 - 1	Blount 89
02.10	FA Cup Q2 R	ARNOLD TOWN	1329	4 - 0	Webster 1[p] 18, Stride 31, Wassall 76
05.10	Unib. P	Lancaster City	908	0 - 1	
09.10	Lge Cup G7	LEEK TOWN	529	2 - 2	Bailey 16, Anderson 56
13.10	FA Cup Q3	BERKHAMSTED TOWN	1378	2 - 1	Moore 21, Stride 37
15.10	Unib. P	Hyde United	583	2 - 1	Glasser 22, Stride 67
16.10	Birm SC 1	CRADLEY TOWN	131	1 - 0	Lyons 18
20.10	Unib. P	ACCRINGTON STANLEY	1347	3 - 1	Moore 25, Bailey 77, Anderson 87
23.10	Lge Cup G7	Matlock Town	676	0 - 1	
27.10	FA Cup Q4	GRAVESEND & NORTHFLEET	1647	0 - 2	
30.10	Unib. P	WORKSOP TOWN	1328	1 - 0	Hoyle 41
03.11	Unib. P	Bishop Auckland	371	1 - 1	Hoyle 66
10.11	Unib. P	BAMBER BRIDGE	1366	1 - 1	Anderson 80
13.11	Unib. P	Droylsden	336	7 - 0	Stride 8 77, Kavanagh 15[p] 50[p], Evans 26, Anderson 45, Moore 86
17.11	Unib. P	Runcorn Halton	630	3 - 1	Anderson 64, Webster 70, Farrell 74
20.11	Birm SC 2	SOLIHULL BOROUGH	213	2 - 1	Moore 13 74
24.11	Unib. P	GATESHEAD	1502	5 - 1	Anderson 9 34, Moore 40 42, Farrell 45
27.11	Lge Cup G7	HUCKNALL TOWN	251	0 - 3	
01.12	FA Trophy 2	Barrow	1521	1 - 1	Moore 78
04.12	FA Trophy 2 R	BARROW	1174	5 - 0	Moore 3 59, Farrell 17 39 88
08.12	Unib. P	Emley	703	2 - 3	Webster 8[p], Anderson 29
11.12	Lge Cup G7	BELPER TOWN	158	2 - 0	Bailey 5, Evans 13
15.12	Unib. P	ALTRINCHAM	1712	1 - 1	Stride 19
22.12	Unib. P	Accrington Stanley	1251	3 - 3	Moore 10, Kavanagh 80[p], Clough 90
26.12	Unib. P	BRADFORD PARK AVENUE	2141	3 - 0	Clough 41, Moore 73, Evans 90
08.01	Birm SC 3	Bedworth United	141	3 - 0	Bailey 19, Stride 58, Evans 61
12.01	FA Trophy 3	BLYTH SPARTANS	1594	3 - 0	Blount 29, Webster 44, Farrell 72
19.01	Unib. P	Colwyn Bay	733	3 - 1	Evans 14, Farrell 45, Moore 65
26.01	Unib. P	MARINE	1580	0 - 0	
02.02	FA Trophy 4	Farnborough Town	1031	1 - 1	Clough 88
05.02	FA Trophy 4 R	FARNBOROUGH TOWN	1706	3 - 2	Clough 13, Bailey 65, Henshaw 90
09.02	Unib. P	Gainsborough Trinity	977	1 - 0	Webster 58[p]
12.02	Birm SC QF	Moor Green	305	1 - 3	Lyons 11
16.02	Unib. P	BLYTH SPARTANS	1674	4 - 0	Glasser 33, Stride 37 71, Evans 40
23.02	FA Trophy 5	WOKING	2322	3 - 0	Blount 20, Stride 36 89
02.03	Unib. P	Barrow	1310	2 - 1	Moore 33, Anderson 38
05.03	Unib. P	Hucknall Town	1602	2 - 1	Stride 60 89
09.03	Unib. P	Whitby Town	582	1 - 1	Talbot 90
12.03	Unib. P	EMLEY	1533	2 - 1	Bailey 6, Nicholson 58[og]
16.03	FA Trophy QF	CHESTER CITY	3584	2 - 0	Cavanagh 66, Webster 68
19.03	Unib. P	Worksop Town	1367	1 - 0	Blount 10
23.03	Unib. P	WHITBY TOWN	1434	5 - 1	Kavanagh 45, Blount 76, Evans 88, Webster 89 90
26.03	Unib. P	Bamber Bridge	519	1 - 0	Evans 32
30.03	Unib. P	COLWYN BAY	1591	1 - 0	Evans 21
01.04	Unib. P	Burscough	531	0 - 0	
06.04	FA Trophy SF(1)	Yeovil Town	5614	0 - 4	
09.04	Unib. P	LANCASTER CITY	1512	3 - 0	Anderson 50, Farrell 52, Evans 73
14.04	FA Trophy SF(2)	YEOVIL TOWN	4026	2 - 1	Anderson 54, Farrell 72
17.04	Unib. P	Vauxhall Motors	818	4 - 1	Webster 24, Anderson 34, Moore 59, Kavanagh 74[p]
20.04	Unib. P	DROYLSDEN	2170	1 - 1	Webster 73
22.04	Unib. P	BARROW	1001	4 - 0	Talbot 22 60, Blount 49, Moore 88
27.04	Unib. P	Blyth Spartans	593	1 - 0	Blount 54
30.04	Unib. P	FRICKLEY ATHLETIC	1018	4 - 0	Anderson 22 90, Moore 55, Duke 62[p]
03.05	Unib. P	BISHOP AUCKLAND	1433	3 - 0	Evans 15, Webster 42[p], Henshaw 77

Man of the moment?
Not content with being skipper of
the side who won promotion he
was also top scorer, player of the
year and won his first cap for the
England National Game side.

Darren Stride

Dale Anderson
also won his
first cap last
season.

Photos:
Peter Barnes
Resolute defence
during
the FA Trophy
Semi-Final.

BURTON ALBION

PLAYING SQUAD

Player	Birthplace	D.O.B.	Previous Clubs	
				Bold print denotes England semi-professional international.

GOALKEEPERS

Player	Birthplace	D.O.B.	Previous Clubs
Dan Robinson	Derby	01.09.82	Blackpool, Derby
Matt Duke UP	Derby	16.07.77	Sheffield Utd, Alfreton T, Matlock T

DEFENDERS

Player	Birthplace	D.O.B.	Previous Clubs
Aaron Johnson	Derby	01.11.81	Borrowash V, Doncaster R
Colin Hoyle DMP, UP	Derby	15.01.72	Boston Utd, King's Lynn, Mansfield, Notts Co., Bradford C, Barnsley, Arsenal
Craig Swinscoe	Mansfield	-	Mansfield
Darren Wassall UP	Edgbaston	27.06.68	Birmingham, Derby Co., Nottingham Forest
James Wall UP	Carshalton	21.03.80	Memphis (USA), Burton Alb., Hereford Utd, Derby Co
Jason Kavanagh ES, EY, UP	Birmingham	23.11.71	Cambridge Utd, Stoke, Wycombe, Derby Co, Birmingham
Mark Blount UP	Derby	05.01.74	Gresley R (£5,500), Peterborough, Sheffield Utd, Gresley R, Derby Co
Paul Talbot UP	Gateshead	11.08.79	Gateshead, York, Newcastle Utd
Terry Henshaw UP	Nottingham	29.02.80	Notts Co

MIDFIELD

Player	Birthplace	D.O.B.	Previous Clubs
Aaron Webster ESP, UP	Burton-on-Trent	19.12.80	From Youth team
Andy Sinton ES, E'B', E-Full Int	Newcastle	19.03.66	Wolves, Tottenham Hotspur, Sheffield Wed., QPR, Brentford, Cambridge Utd
Darren Stride ESP, UP	Burton-on-Trent	28.09.75	From Youth team
Neil Glasser UP	Nottingham	17.10.74	Grantham T, Ilkeston, Bromsgrove R, Notts Co., Nottingham Forest
Nigel Clough Eu-21, E 'B', E-Full Int., UP	Sunderland	19.03.66	Manchester C, Liverpool, Nottingham Forest, AC Hunters
Paul Wraith	Burton-on-Trent	31.10.81	Derby Co
Steve Evans UP	Birmingham	12.11.80	Aston Villa

FORWARDS

Player	Birthplace	D.O.B.	Previous Clubs
Andy Garner UP	Stonebroom	08.03.66	Gresley R (£3,500), Blackpool, Derby Co.
Christian Moore UP	Derby	04.11.72	Ilkeston T (£17,000), Forest Green R, Leicester Utd, Belper, Gresley R, Nuneaton B, Stockport, Leicester C
Craig Dudley EY, UP	Newark	12.09.79	Oldham Ath., Notts Co
Dale Anderson UP	Birmingham	10.11.79	Bromsgrove R, Hednesford T, WBA, Nottingham Forest
Glenn Kirkwood	Chesterfield	03.12.76	Ilkeston T, Doncaster R, Eastwood T
Sean Gummer	Derby	14.04.81	Belper T, Mandal (Norway), Belper T, Derby Co

CHESTER CITY

A season that started in turmoil on and off the field finished with justifiable confidence in the future, under the experienced and steady leadership of Mark Wright.

It had been impossible for the previous chairman Terry Smith, managers Gordon Hill and Steve Mungall or the players themselves to produce any sort of consistent form, and as the atmosphere around Deva Stadium deteriorated, City reached rock bottom after losing 0-3 at home to Margate and there were seriouis worries that the club would slip even further away from their cherished Football League membership.

The introduction of Stephen Vaughan as Chairman and Mark Wright as manager lifted the gloom and the distraction of the previous regime ,whatever the rights or wrongs,could be put to one side as the club concentrated on survival.

The F.A.Cup brought no relief from the pressure and City lost at their first hurdle, in front of an impressive attendance of 2,833 at Barrow. So the week in week out battle against relegation was faced bravely and the introduction of Gary Brabin proved to be a masterstroke. Gary had impressed as one of non-league footballs most charismatic characters when playing for Runcorn and the England team before enjoying his spell in The Football League. His impact at the Deva Stadium was obvious for all to see and his contributioin to the clubs' end of season uplift ,brought him a deserved' 'Player of the Year Award' .

City's six F.A.Trophy ties lifted morale and gave everyone a break from the Conference grind but as the season came to a close , Chester City showed their class and pulled away with immaculate timing and a run in of a home draw with Yeovil Town and four straight victories!

A quality manager who may be difficult to keep at the club, an experienced and solid squad with a few inspirational players, in England goalkeeper Wayne Brown,Kevin McIntyre, Michael Twiss and consistant goalscorer Mark Beesley , plus supporters who are just thrilled to be enjoying positive thoughts about the season ahead, all point to a challenge from a much happier Chester City at the right end of the Conference table. T.W.

Back row, left to right: Ryan Sugden, Scott Guyett, Wayne Hatswell, Martyn Lancaster, Carl Ruffer, David Cameron,John Worsnop. Phil Bolland, Wayne Brown, Daniel Collins, Mark Beesley, Michael Brown, Kevin McIntyre, James Kelly and Michael Twiss.**Front row:** Chris Blackburn, James Haarhoff, Stuart Whittaker, Steve Brodie, Joe Hinnigan (Physio), Mark Wright (Manager),Steve Bleasdale (Ass.Man), Alan Cottrell (Chief Scout), Shaun Carey, Ben Davies, Lee Woodyatt and Paul Carden,l

CHESTER CITY

GROUND DETAILS

Deva Stadium, Bumpers Lane, Chester CH1 4LT

Tel: 01244 371376 or 371809
Admin. Office Fax: 01244 390265
emails: mike_CCFC@Hotmail.com
Nicki_CCFC@Hotmail,com
Web site: http://www.chesterfc.co.uk

SIMPLE DIRECTIONS:
Follow signs to Chester, into Town Centre, then follow signs to Queensferry (A548) to Sealand Road. Turn into Bumpers Lane, signed ChesterCity F.C.Two miles to Town centre and British Rail,Chester (01244 340170). Car Parking at ground

MATCH TICKETS: Adults £10-£12   concessions £7-£9
Child   £5 standing £6 sitting

CAPACITY:	5,814
SEATED:	3,094
COVERED TERRACING:	2,640

Refreshments: Six tea bars
Clubhouse: Open matchdays & for private bookings
Contact: The club office on 01244 371376
Function/Banqueting facilities: Yes
Limited guests on match day at #1,50 each
CLUB SHOP: Yes

Founded:	1885
Nickname:	The Blues
Club Sponsors:	Pentagon Glass-Tech.
Club colours:	Royal Blue & White Royal Blue Shorts and Socks
Change colours:	All White
Midweek home matchday:	Tuesday
Reserves' League:	Avon Insurance Division One
Clubcall	0906 8121633

CLUB OFFICIALS

President	T.B.A.
Honory Vice Presidents	J Kane, L Lloyd, M Swallow
Chairman	Stephen Vaughan
Vice Chairman	Fred Williams
Directors	D.Liversage, Richard Lynes
Secretary	Michael Beech
Commercial Manager	Jim Jones

Pages: 36   Price: £2.00
Editor: Rob Ashcroft
Email: alyndalerob@yahoo.co.uk
Tel Nos: 01244 602 111 (H) 01244 680801(H)
Club call: 09068 121 633

Local Press: Chester Chronicle, Evening Leader
Local Radio: Radio Merseyside, Marcher Sound

FOOTBALL MANAGEMENT TEAM

MANAGER:	MARK WRIGHT
Date of Appointment	December 1999
Date of Birth:	1st August 1963
Place of Birth:	Dorchester (Ox.)

PREVIOUS CLUBS
As manager   Southport, Oxford Utd.
As player   Oxford Utd., Southampton, Derby Co., Liverpool
HONOURS
As manager
As player   England: u21: 4; E: 45
FAC '92

*   *

Assistant Manager:	Ted McMinn
Physiotherapist:	Joe Hinnigan
Youth development:	Chas Osula
Community Officer	David James
Club's Playing Status:	Full Time

Season	League	Div.	Pos.	P	W	D	L	F	A	W	D	L	F	A	Pts	Manager
						Home					Away					
01-02	Conference	-	14	42	7	7	7	26	23	8	2	11	28	28	54	G.Hiill, S.Mungall &Mark Wright
00-01	Conference	-	8	42	9	8	4	29	19	7	6	8	20	24	62	Graham Barrow
99-00	Football Lge	3	24	46	5	5	13	20	36	5	4	14	24	43	39	Kevin Ratcliffe/Terry Smith/Ian Atkins
98-99	Football Lge	3	14	46	6	12	5	28	30	7	6	10	29	36	57	Kevin Ratcliffe
97-98	Football Lge	3	14	46	12	7	4	34	15	5	3	15	26	46	61	Kevin Ratcliffe
96-97	Football Lge	3	6	46	11	8	4	30	16	7	8	8	25	27	70	Kevin Ratcliffe
95-96	Football Lge	3	8	46	11	9	3	45	22	7	7	9	27	31	70	Kevin Ratcliffe
94-95	Football Lge	2	23	46	5	6	12	23	42	1	5	17	14	42	29	Mike Pejic/Derek Mann*/Kevin Ratcliffe*
93-94	Football Lge	3	2	42	13	5	3	35	18	8	6	7	34	28	74	Graham Barrow
92-93	Football Lge	2	24	46	6	2	15	30	47	2	3	18	19	55	29	Harry McNally/Graham Barrow

HONOURS

League Division 3N Cup 35-36 36-37; R-up 45-46
Debenhams Cup 77
Welsh Cup Winners 07-08 32-33 46-47
R-up 08-09 09-10 34-35 35-36
52-53 53-54 54-55 57-58 65-66 69-70
Combination 1908-09 R-up 1903-1908 (5 times)
Cheshire County Lge 21-22 25-26 26-27 R-up 30-31
Cheshire Senior Cup 1894-95 96-97 1903-04
07-08 08-09 30-31 31-32
R-up 1887-88 92-93 93-94 1904-05 10-11 28-29
Lancashire League Runners -Up 2001-02

PREVIOUS

Leagues: The Combination 1890-1899, 1901-1910
Lancashire Combination 1910-1914
Cheshire County League 1919-1931
Football League 1931-2000

Grounds: Faulkner St. 1885-98; Old Showground 1898-99
Whipcord Lane 1901-06; Sealand Road. 1906-1990
Moss Rose, Macclesfield (ground share) 90-92

Names: Chester F.C. until 1983

Past Players who progressed to the Football League

not yet applicable

CLUB RECORDS

Attendance: 5,638
v Preston N.E., Div. 3, 2.4.1994
(Sealand Rd.) 20,500 v Chelsea, FAC 16.1.52

Record win: 12-0
v York City, Div. 3N, 1.2.1936

Record defeat: 2-11
v Oldham Ath. (A), Div. 3N, 19.1.1952

Career goalscorer: Stuart Rimmer 135 (84-88 & 91-98)

Career appearances: Ray Gill 406 League Apps. 51-62

Transfer fee paid: £94,000
for Stuart Rimmer, to Barnsley, Aug. 1991

Transfer fee received: £300,000
for Ian Rush from Liverpool, May 1980

BEST SEASON

FA Trophy: Semi Finalists, 2000-01

FA Cup: 5th Round
1890-91, 1976-77, 79-80

As Conference club: 3rd Rd, 2000-01
League Clubs Defeated   Oxford United & Plymouth A
(as non-league club)   0-2001-02
Conference   8th

Nationwide Trophy (Lg Cup)   Winners 2000-01

LAST SEASON

F.A. Cup: 4th Qualifying Round
FA Trophy: Quarter Finals
Conference: 14 th
Top Goalscorer: Mark Beesley
Player of the Year: Gary Brabin
Captain: Carl Ruffer and Gary Brabin

CHESTER CITY

	Date	Comp.	Opponents	Att.	Score	Goalscorers
1	18/08	Conf.	WOKING	745	0 - 2	
2	21/08	Conf.	Southport	1554	2 - 3	Beesley 51, Wright 90
3	25/08	Conf.	Hayes	507	3 - 1	Spink 12, Beesley 30 69
4	27/08	Conf.	NUNEATON BOROUGH	770	1 - 0	Hill 72
5	01/09	Conf.	Barnet	1197	1 - 3	Beesley 68
6	04/09	Conf.	TELFORD UNITED	605	2 - 2	Spink 20 Ruscoe 61
7	08/09	Conf.	Farnborough Town	954	1 - 1	Beesley 90
8	11/09	Conf.	STALYBRIDGE CELTIC	695	0 - 0	
9	15/09	Conf.	BOSTON UNITED	821	1 - 2	Beesley 60
10	18/09	Conf.	Leigh RMI	547	0 - 3	
11	20/09	Ches. SC 1	CONGLETON TOWN	57	2 - 0	Haarhoff Blackburn
12	22/09	Conf.	DAGENHAM & REDBRIDGE	642	0 - 1	
13	29/09	Conf.	Stevenage Borough	1690	1 - 2	Beesley 37
14	02/10	Conf.	Scarborough	783	1 - 2	Ruscoe 55
15	06/10	Conf.	MARGATE	828	0 - 3	
16	09/10	Conf.	HEREFORD UNITED	1142	2 - 0	Haarhoff 74, Ruscoe 90
17	13/10	Conf.	Morecambe	1764	3 - 0	Rose M 34, O'Brien 60,82
18	20/10	Conf.	DONCASTER ROVERS	2148	1 - 1	Ruscoe 59
19	27/10	FA Cup Q4	Barrow	2893	0 - 1	
20	03/11	Conf.	Yeovil Town	2833	1 - 0	Beesley 21
21	06/11	Ches. SC QF	STALYBRIDGE CELTIC	1408	1 - 2	Malkin 84
22	10/11	Conf.	FOREST GREEN ROVERS	1330	2 - 3	Rose 71, Beesley 77
23	24/11	Conf.	Dover Athletic	905	0 - 1	
24	01/12	Conf.	Woking	1793	1 - 2	Blackburn 59
25	08/12	Conf.	MORECAMBE	1466	1 - 1	Beesley 49
26	15/12	Conf.	SOUTHPORT	1473	0 - 2	
27	26/12	Conf.	Northwich Victoria	1940	1 - 3	Blackburn 55
28	29/12	Conf.	HAYES	1250	3 - 1	Ruffer 33, Blackburn 78, Porter 79
29	08/01	Conf.	NORTHWICH VICTORIA	1660	1 - 2	Blackburn 38
30	12/01	FA Trophy 3	STOURPORT SWIFTS	1006	1 - 1	Haarhoff 71
31	15/01	FA Trophy 3 R	Stourport Swifts	630	3 - 0	Brown 40, Beesley 84 90
32	19/01	Conf.	BARNET	1421	1 - 0	Porter 62[p]
33	22/01	Conf.	Telford United	1047	3 - 0	Woodyatt 25, Beesley 47 64
34	02/02	FA Trophy 4	SOLIHULL BOROUGH	1282	0 - 0	
35	09/02	Conf.	Margate	984	0 - 0	
36	12/02	FA Trophy 4 R	Solihull Borough	721	4 - 2	Spink 45 72 90, Bolland 62
37	19/02	Conf.	Nuneaton Borough	760	3 - 1	Woodyatt 2, M Rose 26 56
38	23/02	FA Trophy 5	HEREFORD UNITED	1747	2 - 1	Bolland 37, Haarhoff 90
39	02/03	Conf.	LEIGH RMI	1572	1 - 1	Brabin 7
40	05/03	Conf.	SCARBOROUGH	1475	0 - 0	
41	09/03	Conf.	Stalybridge Celtic	1002	4 - 0	Beesley 36, Tate 54, McElhatton 59 90
42	16/03	FA Trophy QF	Burton Albion	3584	0 - 2	
43	23/03	Conf.	Boston United	2519	1 - 0	Beesley 53
44	26/03	Conf.	Hereford United	1295	0 - 1	
45	30/03	Conf.	Doncaster Rovers	2089	0 - 2	
46	01/04	Conf.	YEOVIL TOWN	1807	1 - 1	Lancaster 55
47	06/04	Conf.	Forest Green Rovers	802	2 - 0	Beesley 77 90
48	13/04	Conf.	DOVER ATHLETIC	1660	3 - 0	D Brown 2, Brabin 67 90
49	16/04	Conf.	FARNBOROUGH TOWN	1386	1 - 0	Whittaker 47
50	20/04	Conf.	STEVENAGE BOROUGH	1866	5 - 1	Whittaker 30 61 67, Brown 68, Ruffer 72
51	28/04	Conf.	Dagenham & Redbridge	3939	0 - 3	

1	2	3	4	5	6	7	8	9	10	11	Substitutes Used
W Brown	S Rose	M Rose	Porter	Ruffer	Blackburn	Hill	Kerr	Wright	Woodyatt	Ruscoe	Hopwood 10 Haarhoff 9 Roberts 2
W Brown	S Rose	M Rose	Porter	Ruffer	Lancaster	Hill	Blackburn	Malkin	Beesley	Ruscoe	Wright 9 Kerr 8 Haarhoff 7
W Brown	S Rose	M Rose	Porter	Ruffer	Lancaster	Hill	Kerr	Spink	Beesley	Ruscoe	Haarhoff 5 Wright 7 Roberts 9
W Brown	S Rose	M Rose	Porter	Spink	Lancaster	Hill	Kerr	Haarhoff	Beesley	Ruscoe	Wright 7 Blackburn 8
W Brown	S Rose	M Rose	Porter	Spink	Lancaster	Hill	Kerr	Haarhoff	Beesley	Ruscoe	Wright 7 Hopwood 9 Woodyatt 5
W Brown	S Rose	Woodyatt	Porter	Ruffer	Lancaster	Hill	Kerr	Spink	Beesley	Ruscoe	Wright 7
W Brown	Woodyatt	M Rose	Porter	Ruffer	Lancaster	Hill	Kerr	Spink	Beesley	Ruscoe	Haarhoff 7 Kilgannon 8 Roberts 2
W Brown	S Rose	M Rose	Porter	Ruffer	Lancaster	Hill	Kilgannon	Spink	Beesley	Ruscoe	Haarhoff 2 Roberts 7
W Brown	Lancaster	Linighan	Porter	Ruffer	Spink	Hill	Kilgannon	McNiven	Beesley	M Rose	Blackburn 4 S Rose 6
W Brown	Lancaster	M Rose	Porter	Ruffer	Linighan	Hill	Blackburn	McNiven	Beesley	Ruscoe	Roberts 11 Kilgannon 8 Hopwood 9
W Brown	Lancaster	M Rose	Porter	Ruffer	Linighan	Hill	Blackburn	McNiven	Beesley	Kerr	Ruscoe 9 Kilgannon 7 Woodyatt 6
W Brown	Roberts	M Rose	Porter	Lancaster	Spink	Hill	Woodyatt	Kerr	Beesley	Ruscoe	S Rose 8 Malkin 2 Lopez 10
W Brown	Lancaster	M Rose	Porter	Woodyatt	Spink	Hill	Kilgannon	Malkin	Beesley	Ruscoe	Lopez 6 Wright 9
W Brown	Woodyatt	M Rose	Lancaster	Halford	Baxter	Ruscoe	C O'Brien	Wright	Beesley	M O'Brien	Porter 7 Kilgannon 6 Hopwood 9
W Brown	Kilgannon	M Rose	Porter	Halford	Lancaster	C O'Brien	Blackburn	Haarhoff	Beesley	M O'Brien	Ruscoe 8 Wright 2
W Brown	Kilgannon	M Rose	Porter	Halford	Lancaster	C O'Brien	Blackburn	Haarhoff	Beesley	M O'Brien	Baxter 3 Ruscoe 10
W Brown	Kilgannon	M Rose	Porter	Halford	Lancaster	C O'Brien	Blackburn	Haarhoff	Spink	M O'Brien	Ruscoe 2 Wright 9
W Brown	Ruscoe	M Rose	Porter	Halford	Lancaster	Ruffer	Blackburn	Haarhoff	Spink	Kerr	Wright 2 Beesley 11
W Brown	Kilgannon	M Rose	Porter	Halford	Ruffer	C O'Brien	Blackburn	Haarhoff	Beesley	M O'Brien	Malkin 9
W Brown	Kilgannon	M Rose	Porter	Ruffer	Lancaster	C O'Brien	Blackburn	Haarhoff	Beesley	M O'Brien	Ruscoe 11 Malkin 9 Kerr 4
W Brown	Ruscoe	M Rose	Porter	Halford	Ruffer	C O'Brien	Kerr	Malkin	Williams	Wright	Higgins 10
W Brown	Ruscoe	M Rose	Porter	Halford	Lancaster	S Rose	Blackburn	Malkin	Beesley	Carden	Williams 9 M O'Brien 11
W Brown	Jenkins	M Rose	Carden	Halford	Lancaster	C O'Brien	Blackburn	Malkin	Beesley	Ruscoe	S Rose 6 Williams 9
W Brown	Jenkins	M Rose	Porter	Halford	Ruffer	Carden	Blackburn	D Brown	Beesley	M O'Brien	Haarhoff 9
W Brown	Carden	Jenkins	Porter	Halford	Spink	C O'Brien	Blackburn	D Brown	M O'Brien	Ruffer	
W Brown	Carden	Jenkins	Porter	Ruffer	Spink	Woodyatt	Blackburn	D Brown	Beesley	Ruscoe	Collins 9 Haarhoff 10
W Brown	Woodyatt	Ruscoe	Jenkins	Ruffer	Lancaster	Blackburn	Carden	D Brown	Beesley	Brabin	Haarhoff 7 Collins 9 Spink 5
W Brown	Woodyatt	Jenkins	Porter	Lancaster	Spink	Blackburn	M Rose	D Brown	Beesley	M O'Brien	Haarhoff 9 Wright 7
W Brown	Woodyatt	M Rose	Lancaster	Jenkins	Spink	Carden	Blackburn	D Brown	Beesley	M O'Brien	Haarhoff 11
W Brown	Lancaster	Carden	Woodyatt	Bolland	Brabin	Porter	Blackburn	D Brown	Beesley	Whittaker	Haarhoff 11
W Brown	Woodyatt	Carden	Lancaster	Bolland	Brabin	Porter	McGorry	D Brown	Beesley	Whittaker	Blackburn 11 Jenkins 2
W Brown	Woodyatt	Carden	Lancaster	Bolland	Brabin	Porter	McGorry	D Brown	Beesley	Whittaker	Spink 7 Haarhoff 9 Blackburn 11
W Brown	Lancaster	M Rose	Carden	Bolland	Brabin	McGorry	Blackburn	D Brown	Beesley	Spink	Porter 9
W Brown	Lancaster	M Rose	Carden	Bolland	Brabin	McGorry	Blackburn	Whittaker	Beesley	Spink	D Brown 10 Woodyatt 4 Porter 9
W Brown	Woodyatt	M Rose	Lancaster	Bolland	Williams	Carey	McGorry	Spink	Beesley	McElhatton	Blackburn 8 Carden 9 Collins 10
W Brown	Woodyatt	Carden	Lancaster	Bolland	Brabin	McGorry	Blackburn	Spink	Beesley	Whittaker	Haarhoff 11
W Brown	Woodyatt	Carden	Lancaster	Bolland	Brabin	Carey	McGorry	Spink	Beesley	McElhatton	Blackburn 8 Malkin 10 Haarhoff 9
W Brown	Lancaster	M Rose	Blackburn	Bolland	Brabin	Carey	McElhatton	Tate	Beesley	Whittaker	Haarhoff 10 Woodyatt 11
W Brown	Woodyatt	M Rose	Williams	Bolland	Brabin	Carey	McGorry	Tate	Beesley	McElhatton	
W Brown	Woodyatt	M Rose	Lancaster	Bolland	Brabin	Carden	McGorry	Tate	Beesley	McElhatton	Haarhoff 11
W Brown	McGorry	M Rose	Lancaster	Bolland	Brabin	Carey	McElhatton	Tate	Beesley	Peacock	Williams 8
W Brown	McGorry	M Rose	Lancaster	Bolland	Brabin	Carey	McElhatton	Tate	Beesley	Peacock	Blackburn 7 Haarhoff 11 D Brown 9
W Brown	Lancaster	M Rose	McGorry	Bolland	Brabin	Carey	McElhatton	D Brown	Beesley	Peacock	Woodyatt 4 Blackburn 8 Spink 9
W Brown	Lancaster	M Rose	Williams	Bolland	Brabin	Carey	McGorry	Spink	Beesley	Peacock	D Brown 9 carden 7 Haarhoff 11
W Brown	Lancaster	M Rose	Woodyatt	Bolland	Brabin	Carden	McGorry	Spink	Beesley	McElhatton	Williams 4 Blackburn 9
W Brown	Lancaster	Carden	Blackburn	Bolland	Brabin	Carey	McGorry	Spink	D Brown	Peacock	Haarhoff 11 Whittaker 10 Collins 9
W Brown	Lancaster	Whittaker	Blackburn	Bolland	Brabin	Carey	McGorry	Collins	Spink	Peacock	Williams 11 Haarhoff 10 M Rose 3
W Brown	Lancaster	M Rose	McGorry	Williams	Brabin	Carey	Blackburn	Collins	D Brown	Whittaker	Ruffer 4 Haarhoff 9 M O'Brien 7
W Brown	Lancaster	M Rose	Carden	Williams	Brabin	Blackburn	McGorry	D Brown	Collins	Whittaker	Ruffer 11 Haarhoff 9 Woodyatt 4

155

CHESTER CITY   PLAYING SQUAD

Player	Birthplace	D.O.B.	Previous Clubs	Bold print denotes England semi-professional international.

GOALKEEPERS

Wayne Brown ESP	Southampton	14.01.77	Weston-Super-Mare, Bristol C

DEFENDERS

Phil Bolland	Liverpool	26.08.76	Oxford Utd (£15,000), Southport, Altrincham, Knowsley U., Trafford, Salford C, Altrincham
Scott Guyett	Ascot	20.01.76	Oxford Utd, Southport, Gresley R, Brisbane C. (Aust)
Steve Harkness EY	Carlisle	27.08.71	Sheff.Wed., Blackburn, Benfica (Port), Liverpool, Carlisle
Wayne Hatswell	Swindon	08.02.75	Oxford Utd, Forest Green R, Witney T, Cinderford T
Martyn Lancaster	Wigan	10.11.08	
Carl Ruffer	Manchester	-	Runcorn, Woodley Sports
Mark Williams	Liverpool	10.11.78	Hereford Utd, Rotherham, Rochdale

MIDFIELD

Chris Blackburn	Chester		From Trainee
Mickey Brown	Birmingham	08.02.68	Boston Utd, Shrewsbury, Preston, Shrewsbury, Bolton, Shrewsbury
Paul Carden	Liverpool	29.03.79	Doncaster R, Chester C, Rochdale, Blackpool
Shaun Carey NC	Kettering	13.05.76	Rushden & Diamonds, Norwich C.
Ben Davies	Birmingham	27.05.81	Kidderminster, Walsall
Jimmy Kelly	Liverpool	14.02.73	Doncaster R, Hednesford T, Wolves, Wrexham
Kevin McIntyre ESP	Liverpool	23.12.77	Doncaster R, Tranmere
Michael Twiss	Salford	26.12.77	Leigh RMI, Port Vale, Sheffield Utd, Manchester Utd

FORWARDS

Mark Beesley	Lancaster	10.01.81	Preston
Steve Brodie	Sunderland	14.01.73	Swansea, Scarborough, Sunderland
David Cameron	Wales	24.08.75	Lincoln C, Worthing, Brighton, St Mirren
Ryan Sugden	Bradford	26.12.80	Scarborough, Oldham
Stuart Whittaker	Liverpool	02.01.75	Southport, Macclesfield, Wigan, Bolton, Liverpool

DAGENHAM & REDBRIDGE

Last Season proved to be Dagenham & Redbridge's best ever as they were denied the Conference Championship by goal difference only and enjoyed great success in the Cup competitions.

Just before the new season began, key defenders, Lee Matthews and Tim Cole were ruled out for the campaign with bad injuries. Garry Hill managed to sign Mark Smith from Stevenage and his experience proved invaluable, earning him the Clubs player-of-the-year trophy. Another close season capture was evergreen striker Mark Stein who notched 24 league goals and finished as runner-up for the Conference golden boot award.

The first two games ended in dull 1-1 draws but 38 points from their next 15 matches saw the Daggers hit top spot in the Conference for the first time ever with a home defeat by Leigh RMI in October, the only blip. Despite this great run they were unable to pull away from Boston, whom they had beaten at York Street, and as early as November the title race looked to be heading for a two-horse race.

Amongst the League games, the Daggers had impressive victories over Leyton Orient and Luton Town in the LDV Vans Trophy before bowing out to Bristol Rovers in the area quarter final. The national media's attention was again caught in the FA Cup when they progressed through to the third round having demolished Football League Exeter City 3-0 en route. In the third round they took the lead against Ipswich Town in front of a record crowd at Victoria Road but unfortunately the Premiership side proved too strong and the Daggers bowed out of the competition 1-4.

At the start of March, still neck and neck with Boston, the two Clubs met at Victoria Road and an Ashley Vickers goal sent the Daggers four points clear. With 13 games still to go, the Daggers seventeen match unbeaten away run in the Conference finally came to an end at Barnet and their form began to stutter, picking up only one point from four games to fall back to second in the table. Coming in to the last game of the season, they needed to beat Chester City and hope Boston failed to win at already relegated Hayes. The Daggers did their part by winning but unfortunately for the Essex side so did Boston to take the title.

The Club did reach the final of the Essex Senior Cup at Southend United but were forced to play their youth team due to league fixtures being played either side of the game. Stalwart goalkeeper, Neville Southall made his debut for the Daggers but despite him rolling back the years to make some breathtaking saves, he was unable to prevent Canvey Island running out easy winners.

Dave Simpson, Press Officer

L-R - Back Row: Steve Perkins, Ollie Berquez, Steve West, Tony Roberts, Paul Gothard, Ashley Vickers, Mark Rooney, Paul Bruce. **Middle Row:** Ross Johnson, Danny Shipp, Mark Smith, Lee Matthews, Steve Heffer, Danny Hill, Mark Stein. **Front Row:** John Keeling, Steve McGavin, Mark Janney, Paul Terry, Lee Goodwin, Danny Hayzelden, Junior McDougall, Steve Vaughan.

DAGENHAM & REDBRIDGE

GROUND DETAILS

Victoria Road, Dagenham,RM10 7XL
Tel: 0208 592 1549   Fax: 0208 593 7227
email: info@daggers.co.uk
web site:www.daggers.co.uk

DIRECTIONS: On A112 between A12 & A13.
Buses 103 & 174,
Dagenham East tube station, turn left and after approximately
500 yards take 5th turning left into Victoria Road.

MATCH TICKETS: Adults £9-£12 concessions £5-£6
No concessions in Carling Stand unless Season Ticket holders
Family(l adult with up to two children) £19 in the family stand

CAPACITY: 6,090
SEATS: 1,028
COVERED: 3,000

CLUBHOUSE: Open 7 days 11am-11pm.
Refreshnments: Hot & cold food available plus three tea bars
Two bars and sponsors bar
Available for Functions: Tony Manhood 0208 592 7194
Shop Contact: SteveThompson 0208 5927194

CLUB SHOP: Open on matchdays
for enquiries on other days contact Steve, above.

Formed: 1992
Nickname: Daggers
Colours: Red and white shirts, red shorts, red socks
Change strip: Blue & white stripes,black shorts and socks.
Midweek matchday: Tuesday
Reserves Lge: Capital League
Sponsors Main: Compass Plumbing Supplies
Kit: Vandanell
Programme: Recorder Group Newspapers
Match Reports: 0930 555840

CLUB OFFICERS

Chairman: Dave Andrews

Joint Presidents: John & Brian East

Vice Chairman: David Ward

Secretary: Derek Almond,
149 Kings Head Hill, Chingford,
London E4 7JG
Tel: 0181 524 2689
Commercial Manager: Steve Thompson c/o Club

Press Officer: Dave Simpson
Tel: 07860 119430

MATCHDAY PROGRAMME

Pages: 48   **Price:** £2.00
Editor: Dave Simpson Tel: 07860 119430 (M)

Clubcall: 09066 555 840

Local Press: Dagenham Post, Ilford Courier,Yellow
Advertiser, Walthamstow Guardian,
Barking & Dagenham Recorder

Local Radio: BBC Radio Essex,
Capital Gold, GLR London Live

FOOTBALL MANAGEMENT TEAM
MANAGER: GARRY HILL

Date of appointment: 7th May 1999
Date of Birth: 15th October 1959
Place of Birth: Essex

PREVIOUS CLUBS
As manager: St. Albans, Heybridge Swifts
As player: None

HONOURS
As manager: Isthmian Prem. League 99-00
As player: N.A.

Asst Manager: Terry Harris
Chief Scout: Mick Loughton
Safety Officer: Phil Milchard
Physio: Richard Harper
Playing Status: Part-t ime

Season	League	Div.	Pos.	Home						Away					Pts	Manager
				P	W	D	L	F	A	W	D	L	F	A		
01-02	Conference	-	2	42	13	6	2	35	20	11	6	4	35	27	84	Garry Hill
00-01	Conference	-	3	42	13	4	4	39	19	10	4	7	32	35	77	Garry Hill
99-00	Isthmian	Prem.	1	42	20	1	0	58	13	12	4	5	39	22	101	Garry Hill
98-99	Isthmian	Prem.	3	42	10	8	3	40	15	10	5	6	31	29	73	Ted Hardy
97-98	Isthmian	Prem.	4	42	11	6	4	43	25	10	4	7	30	25	73	Ted Hardy
96-97	Isthmian	Prem.	4	42	11	3	7	32	21	7	8	6	25	22	65	Ted Hardy

Season	League	Div.	Pos.	P	W	D	L	F	A	Pts	Manager
95-96	Conference	-	21	42	7	12	23	43	73	33	Graham Carr
94-95	Conference	-	15	42	13	13	16	56	69	52	Dave Cusack
93-94	Conference	-	6	42	15	14	13	62	54	59	John Still
92-93	Conference	-	3	42	19	11	12	75	47	67	John Still

HONOURS

(Ryman) Isthmian League Prem. Div. 99-00

(Ryman) Isthmian one2one Charity Shield 2000-01

F.A. Trophy Runners-up 96-97

Essex Senior 97-98

PREVIOUS

Names:

Ilford FC (1881) & Leytonstone (1886) merged in 1979 to form Leytonstone-Ilford.
They & Walthamstow Avenue (1900) merged in 1988 to form Redbridge Forest
who in turn merged with Dagenham (1949) in 1992 to form Dagenham & Redbridge.

Grounds: None

Leagues: GMV Conference 92-96; Isthmian Lge 96-2000

Past Players who progressed to the Football League

Warren Barton (via Maidstone Utd '89 to Wimbledon '90)
Andy Hessenthaler (Watford '91)
Juan Mequel DeSouza (Birmingham C. '94)
Ian Richardson (Birmingham City '95)

CLUB RECORDS

Attendance: 5,500 v Leyton Orient - FA Cup 1st Rnd - 14.11.92
5,492 v Charlton A - F.A.Cup 3rd Rd Replay- 27.01.01
5,949 v Ipswich Town F.A.Cup 3rd Rd -03-01-02

Career goalscorer (all competitions): Paul Cobb 84 (97-01)
Danny Shipp 81 (95-01)

Career appearances (all competitions): Jason Broom - 338
(Steve Corner - 257. Paul Watts - 174)

Win: 8-1 v Woking (A)
GMV Conference 19/4/94
7-0 v Oxford (H) Isthmian Lge1/11/97

Defeat: 0-5
v Stalybridge Celtic (A) GMV Conference 31/4/94
v Northwich Victoria, GMV Conference 3/9/94
v Hyde Utd (H) FA Trophy 2nd Rd.
v Croydon ,Isthmian Lg.Cup(A) 99/00

Transfer fee paid as Dagenham & Redbridge F.C. £15,000
to Purfleet for Paul Cobb in August 1997

Transfer fee received as Dagenham & Redbridge F.C. #65.00
from Birmingham City for Ian Richardson in May 1995

BEST SEASON

FA Cup: Third Round Proper Replay 00-01
0-1 aet v Charlton Ath.(Premier League) (H), after 1-1 (A)

League clubs defeated   Lincoln City 00-01,Exeter C01-02

FA Trophy: Runners-up 96-97

League: Conference Runners-up 01-02

LAST SEASON

F.A. Cup:	Third Round
F.A. Trophy:	Fourth Round
Conference:	2nd
Top Goalscorer:	Mark Stein 25
Player of the Year:	Mark Smith
Captain:	Mark Brennan

DAGENHAM & REDBRIDGE

Match Facts 2001-02

	Date	Comp.	Opponents	Att.	Score	Goalscorers
1	04/08	Essex SC 00-01 F	CANVEY ISLAND	1095	2 - 2	Shipp 69, Goodwin 117 Won 5-4 after pens.
2	18/08	Conf.	SOUTHPORT	1287	1 - 1	Lane 6[og]
3	21/08	Conf.	Margate	1350	1 - 1	Jones 62
4	25/08	Conf.	Telford United	1014	4 - 1	M Smith 27, Stein 62, Shipp 67, Terry 90
5	27/08	Conf.	WOKING	1410	3 - 1	Stein 30, Shipp 31 90
6	01/09	Conf.	Forest Green Rovers	651	4 - 2	Brennan 34, Stein 53 90, McGavin 82[p]
7	04/09	Conf.	BARNET	1916	1 - 1	Heffer 43
8	08/09	Conf.	Stalybridge Celtic	660	3 - 2	Shipp 45, Vickers 78 ,Perkins 81(o.g.)
9	11/09	Conf.	HEREFORD UNITED	1338	1 - 0	Lock 58
10	15/09	Conf.	LEIGH RMI	1370	0 - 1	
11	19/09	Conf.	Boston United	2434	2 - 1	Stein 16, Goodwin 64
12	22/09	Conf.	Chester City	642	1 - 0	Stein 71
13	29/09	Conf.	SCARBOROUGH	1482	4 - 2	**Stein** 3 (20,45,72) Lock 51
14	02/10	Conf.	STEVENAGE BOROUGH	1837	1 - 0	Stein 40
15	06/10	Conf.	Farnborough Town	540	2 - 1	Charley 45 Stein 79
16	08/10	Conf.	Dover Athletic	907	1 - 0	Stein 74
17	13/10	Conf.	YEOVIL TOWN	2163	1 - 1	McGavin
18	16/10	LDV Vans 1S	LEYTON ORIENT	2642	3 - 2	Heffer 61 90, Goodwin 102
19	20/10	Conf.	NUNEATON BOROUGH	1837	2 - 0	Hayzelden 62 Charley 90
20	27/10	FA Cup Q4	Basingstoke Town	1089	2 - 2	Charley 56, Roberts 90
21	30/10	LDV Vans 2S	LUTON TOWN	2433	3 - 2	McGavin 50, Ovendale 76[og], Vickers 94
22	06/11	FA Cup Q4 R	BASINGSTOKE TOWN	1752	3 - 0	McDougald 3, Bristow 42[og], Charley 73
23	10/11	Conf.	NORTHWICH VICTORIA	1780	1 - 1	Stein 21
24	13/11	Essex SC 3	HARWICH & PARKESTON	432	7 - 2	McDougald 12 51 71 84, McGavin 20 90, Hayzelden 40
25	17/11	FA Cup 1	SOUTHPORT	1732	1 - 0	Stein
26	24/11	Conf.	Doncaster Rovers	2529	0 - 0	
27	01/12	Conf.	Southport	951	2 - 2	Stein 66, Charley 88
28	05/12	LDS Vans QFS	Bristol Rovers	3028	1 - 4	Charley 81
29	08/12	FA Cup 2	Exeter City	4082	0 - 0	
30	15/12	Conf.	MARGATE	1742	4 - 1	McGavin 50[p], Stein 52, Clarley 79 85[p]
31	19/12	FA Cup 2 R	EXETER CITY	2660	3 - 0	Janney , McDougald Charley
32	22/12	Conf.	TELFORD UNITED	1559	1 - 5	Charley 28
33	26/12	Conf.	Hayes	820	4 - 2	Charley 27, McDougald 31 48[p], Janney 40
34	05/01	FA Cup 3	IPSWICH TOWN	5949	1 - 4	McDougald 18
35	12/01	FA Trophy 3	EASTBOURNE BOROUGH	1354	1 - 0	Shipp 89
36	15/01	Essex SC 4	FORD UNITED	543	5 - 1	Brennan 22 86, McDougald 45 56 62
37	19/01	Conf.	FOREST GREEN ROVERS	1718	1 - 1	Charley 24
38	02/02	FA Trophy 4	TELFORD UNITED	1256	0 - 2	
39	09/02	Conf.	FARNBOROUGH TOWN	1736	2 - 1	Shipp 9, Stein 38
40	12/02	Conf.	HAYES	1585	1 - 1	Terry 69
41	16/02	Conf.	Yeovil Town	4458	3 - 3	West 29, Goodwin 49, Stein 79
42	19/02	Essex SC QF	Billericay Town	564	2 - 0	Charley 42 56
43	23/02	Conf.	DOVER ATHLETIC	1510	1 - 0	McGavin 43
44	04/03	Conf.	BOSTON UNITED	3805	1 - 0	Vickers 38
45	11/03	Conf.	Stevenage Borough	2101	3 - 1	**Stein** 3 (40 77 82)
46	19/03	Conf.	Barnet	1865	0 - 4	
47	23/03	Conf.	Leigh RMI	492	0 - 2	
48	26/03	Conf.	Morecambe	1235	1 - 1	Charley 54
49	30/03	Conf.	Nuneaton Borough	1551	0 - 2	
50	01/04	Conf.	MORECAMBE	1934	3 - 2	Terry 36, McGavin 76 78
51	06/04	Conf.	Northwich Victoria	744	2 - 1	Hill 16, Stein 90
52	08/04	Conf.	STALYBRIDGE CELTIC	1822	2 - 1	McDougald 9, Hill 41
53	12/04	Conf.	DONCASTER ROVERS	2455	1 - 0	Hill 69
54	15/04	Essex SC F	Canvey Island	n/k		@ Southend United
55	16/04	Conf.	Hereford United	1583	0 - 1	
56	20/04	Conf.	Scarborough	2349	0 - 0	
57	23/04	Conf.	Woking	2817	2 - 0	Stein 32, Smith 58
58	28/04	Conf.	CHESTER CITY	3939	3 - 0	Stein 61 66, Cole 86

1	2	3	4	5	6	7	8	9	10	11	Substitutes Used
Gothard	Rooney	Smith	Goodwin	McGavin	Brennan	Janney	Terry	Shipp	Stein	Jones	Heffer 6 Hill 5 Lock 10
Roberts	Rooney	Smith	Goodwin	Heffer	Hill	Janney	Terry	Shipp	Stein	Jones	Brennan 6 Lock 10
Roberts	Rooney	Smith	Goodwin	Heffer	Hill	Janney	Terry	Shipp	Stein	Jones	Hayzelden 10 Lock 6 Brennan 4
Roberts	Heffer	Vickers	McGavin	Smith	Brennan	Janney	Terry	Shipp	Stein	Jones	Vaughan 6 Lock 10 Hayzelden 11
Roberts	Heffer	Vickers	Lock	Smith	Brennan	Janney	Terry	Shipp	Stein	Jones	Vaughan 6 McGavin 4 Hayzelden 9
Roberts	Heffer	Vickers	Rooney	Smith	Brennan	Janney	Terry	Shipp	Stein	Jones	McGavin 6 McDougald 10
Roberts	Heffer	Vickers	Rooney	Smith	Brennan	Janney	Terry	Shipp	McDougald	Jones	Lock 8 Hayzelden 10 Forbes 9
Roberts	Heffer	Vickers	Rooney	Smith	Brennan	Janney	Terry	Shipp	Lock	Hayzelden	McGavin 10 Forbes 6
Roberts	Rooney	Vickers	Goodwin	Smith	Brennan	Janney	McGavin	Shipp	Lock	Hayzelden	Stein 11 Terry 6 Jones 4
Roberts	Rooney	Vickers	Goodwin	Smith	Heffer	Janney	Terry	Shipp	Stein	Jones	Lock 10 Broom 4
Roberts	Heffer	Vickers	Hill	Smith	Broom	Janney	Terry	Shipp	Stein	Jones	Brennan 8 Forbes 4 Lock 9
Roberts	Heffer	Vickers	Hill	Smith	Broom	Janney	Terry	Lock	Stein	Jones	McGavin 4 Brennan 8 Hayzelden 9
Roberts	Heffer	Vickers	Hill	Smith	Broom	Janney	Terry	Lock	Stein	Jones	McGavin 9 Hill 8 Hayzelden 11
Roberts	Heffer	Vickers	Goodwin	Smith	Broom	Janney	Terry	Charlery	Stein	Jones	McGavin 4 Lock 10 Hayzelden 11
Roberts	Rooney	Vickers	Goodwin	Smith	Broom	Janney	Terry	Charlery	Stein	Heffer	McGavin 7 Jones 10
Roberts	Rooney	Vickers	Goodwin	Smith	Broom	McGavin	Terry	Charlery	Stein	Heffer	Shipp 2 Hayzelden 6
Gothard	Rooney	Vickers	Goodwin	Smith	Heffer	McGavin	Terry	Shipp	Stein	Hayzelden	Cole 2 Hill 8 Broom 12 (Cole)
Roberts	Rooney	Vickers	Goodwin	Smith	Broom	McGavin	Terry	Charlery	Stein	Hayzelden	Shipp 7 Hill 2 Brennan 8
Roberts	Rooney	Vickers	Goodwin	Smith	Broom	Janney	Terry	Charlery	Stein	Hill	McGavin 11 Shipp 9 McDougald 2
Gothard	Rooney	Vickers	Goodwin	Smith	Hill	McGavin	Terry	Shipp	McDougald	Hayzelden	Broom 11 Lock 10 Janney 7
Roberts	McDougald	Vickers	Goodwin	Smith	Hill	McGavin	Terry	Charlery	Stein	Broom	Rooney 3 Shipp 2 Janney 9
Roberts	Rooney	Vickers	Goodwin	Smith	Shipp	Janney	Terry	Charlery	Stein	Broom	McDougald 11 Hayzelden 2 McGavin 7
Roberts	Smith	Vickers	Goodwin	Heffer	Terry	Janney	Shipp	McDougald	Stein	Hayzelden	Charlery 9
Roberts	McDougald	Vickers	Goodwin	Smith	Hill	Janney	Heffer	Shipp	Stein	Hayzelden	Rooney 7 Brennan 6 Charlery 2
Roberts	Rooney	Heffer	Goodwin	Smith	Shipp	Janney	Terry	Charlery	Stein	Hayzelden	Jones 9 McDougald 10
Gothard	Rooney	Broom	Heffer	Goodwin	Hill	McGavin	Shipp	Charlery	Jones	McDougald	Janney 4 Hayzelden 10 Vaughan 6
Roberts	Rooney	Vickers	Shipp	Smith	Heffer	Janney	Terry	Charlery	Stein	Broom	Hayzelden 11 Hill 8 McDougald 10
Roberts	McGavin	Vickers	Goodwin	Smith	Shipp	Janney	Terry	Charlery	Stein	Hayzelden	Rooney 2 McDougald 10 Brennan 8
Roberts	Rooney	Vickers	Heffer	Smith	Shipp	Janney	Terry	Charlery	Stein	Hayzelden	McDougald 10
Roberts	Rooney	Vickers	Heffer	Smith	Shipp	Janney	Terry	Charlery	McDougald	Hayzelden	Hill 2
Roberts	Rooney	Vickers	Heffer	Smith	Shipp	Janney	Terry	Charlery	McDougald	Hayzelden	McGavin 7 Jones 11 Brennan 10
Roberts	Rooney	Vickers	Smith	Goodwin	Terry	Janney	Heffer	Shipp	McDougald	Hayzelden	McGavin 7 Brennan 6 Broom 11
Roberts	Rooney	Broom	Goodwin	Smith	Brennan	Janney	Heffer	Charlery	McDougald	McGavin	Shipp 7 Hayzelden 3 Terry 8
Roberts	Goodwin	Vickers	Rodwell	Smith	Shipp	Janney	Heffer	Charlery	McDougald	Brennan	Terry 2 Hayzelden 11
Roberts	Rooney	Vickers	Rodwell	Heffer	Hill	Janney	Terry	Shipp	Stein	Jones	McGavin 5 Broom 8 Cole 2
Roberts	Hooper	Vickers	West	Smith	Shipp	Janney	Heffer	Charlery	Stein	Jones	McDougald 10 Broom 11 Goodwin 4
Roberts	Hooper	Vickers	West	Smith	Shipp	Janney	Heffer	Charlery	Stein	Jones	Terry 8 McDougald 4 McGavin 7
Roberts	Goodwin	West	Heffer	Smith	Shipp	Hooper	Terry	Stein	McDougald	Jones	Broom 4 Charlery 11 Hill 6
Roberts	Hooper	Vickers	Goodwin	Smith	Heffer	McGavin	Terry	Charlery	McDougald	Broom	Rooney 2 Shipp 10
Roberts	Hooper	Vickers	Goodwin	Smith	Heffer	McGavin	Terry	Charlery	Stein	Jones	McDougald 10 West 2 Broom 7
Roberts	Hooper	Vickers	Goodwin	Smith	Heffer	Shipp	Terry	Charlery	Stein	Jones	Rooney 7 McDougald 9 Broom 11
Roberts	Heffer	Vickers	Goodwin	Smith	Shipp	Hooper	Terry	Charlery	Stein	Broom	Janney 7 Hill 6 McDougald 8
Roberts	Goodwin	Broom	Smith	West	Shipp	Heffer	Terry	Stein	McDougald	Hayzelden	Charlery 3 Gothard 1 Janney 7
Gothard	Goodwin	Hooper	Smith	West	Heffer	Janney	Terry	Charlery	Stein	Jones	Broom 11 Shipp 9 McDougald 10
Gothard	Goodwin	Hooper	West	Smith	Heffer	Janney	Terry	Charlery	Stein	Jones	McDougald 5 Shipp 6 Hill 11
Gothard	Goodwin	Hooper	Rooney	West	Shipp	Hill	Terry	McDougald	Stein	Hayzelden	Cole 2 McGavin 7 Janney 8
Gothard	Cole	West	Rooney	Hooper	Shipp	Hill	Heffer	Stein	McDougald	Hayzelden	McGavin 4 Charlery 7 Smith 3
Gothard	Hill	Hooper	Smith	Shipp	Heffer	Janney	Terry	McDougald	Stein	Jones	Broom 8 Hayzelden 11 McGavin 2
Roberts	Shipp	Hooper	Smith	West	Heffer	Hill	Terry	McDougald	Stein	Jones	Janney 8 McGavin 7 Hayzelden 11
Roberts	Cole	Hayzelden	Goodwin	Smith	Shipp	Janney	Terry	Charlery	Hill	Jones	Broom 10 McGavin 11 Heffer 9
Roberts	West	Hooper	Goodwin	Smith	Heffer	Hill	Terry	Shipp	McDougald	Jones	McGavin 7 Hayzelden 11 Janney 10
Roberts	West	Heffer	Goodwin	Smith	Hill	Janney	Terry	Shipp	Stein	Jones	McGavin 6 McDougald 10 Hayzelden 11
Roberts	West	McGavin	Goodwin	Smith	Shipp	Janney	Terry	McDougald	Stein	Jones	Broom 11 Cole 5 Vickers 2

DAGENHAM & REDBRIDGE — PLAYING SQUAD

Player	Birthplace	D.O.B.	Previous Clubs
			Bold print denotes England semi-professional international.

GOALKEEPERS

Player	Birthplace	D.O.B.	Previous Clubs
Tony Roberts Wales Int.	Holyhead	04.08.69	QPR, Millwall, St.Albans C
Paul Gothard ESP	Essex	24.06.74	Hayes, Dagenham & Red, Grays Ath., Chelmsford C, Colchester

DEFENDERS

Player	Birthplace	D.O.B.	Previous Clubs
Lee Matthews RP	Southend		Southend, Purfleet, £3,000 to Dag & Red
Ashley Vickers RP	Sheffield	14.06.72	Sheffield U, Worcester C, Malvern T, 61 Club, Heybridge S
Lee Goodwin RP	Stepney	05.09.78	West Ham
Tim Cole RP	London		Walthamstow Pennant, Leyton Pennant
Mark Rooney	Lambeth	19.05.78	St.Albans C, Aylesbury Utd, Watford
Mark Smith ESP, NC	Luton	-	Stevenage B, Hitchin, Woking, Hitchin, Letchworth, Hitchin
Ross Johnson	Brighton	02.01.76	Colchester, Brighton
Steve West ESP	Essex	15.11.72	Woking, Enfield, Concord R, East Thurrock Utd, Aveley, Tilbury, Purfleet, Arsenal

MIDFIELD

Player	Birthplace	D.O.B.	Previous Clubs
Mark Janney RP	Romford	02.12.77	Spurs
Steve Heffer RP	London	11.01.73	West Ham, Southend, Swindon, Grays A., Hendon, Boreham Wood
Danny Hazelden	Essex		Grays Ath., Hornchurch, Aveley, Wimbledon (Junior)
Danny Hill Eu-21	Enfield	01.01.74	Cardiff, Oxford Utd, Tottenham
Paul Bruce	London	18.02.78	QPR
Steve Perkins British Univ	Southport	05.11.75	Woking, Stevenage B, Plymouth, Crediton Utd, Burscough

FORWARDS

Player	Birthplace	D.O.B.	Previous Clubs
Junior McDougald ESP, RP	Big Spring	12.01.75	Spurs, Brighton, Rotherham, FC Toulon, Camb.C., Millwall, Camb.C., Leyton O
Paul Terry RP	London		Charlton, Bromley
Danny Shipp RP	Romford	25.09.76	West Ham, Coleraine
Mark Stein EY	Cape Town	29.01.66	Luton, Bournemouth, Chelsea, Stoke, Oxford Utd, QPR, Luton
Steve McGavin NC, FAT	North Walsham	24.01.69	Colchester, Southend, Wycombe, Birmingham, Colchester, Sudbury T

DONCASTER ROVERS

Doncaster Rovers were amongst the clubs fancied for promotion back to league glories, but an early inability to turn draws into victories - six of the first dozen games finished level with four wins and two defeats - saw the club down in twelfth place by the end of September 2001 and the problem never really disappeared over the rest of the season, so that a final fourth place in the Conference was probably seen by fans and management alike as a good recovery but still a little disappointing.

It is true that doubles were achieved against Leigh RMI, Dover Athletic, Hayes and Forest Green Rovers against similar indignities only being imposed by Barnet and Stalybridge Celtic, but with exciting team strengthening a much more consistent season is expected this term.

Last season's knock-out competitions produced pass marks at the best with a narrow Fourth Qualifying Round home win against Emley by the odd goal in five - a thriller by any standards - being followed by a similar scoreline in the First Round proper at home to Scunthorpe United, but exit nonetheless.The F.A. Trophy campaign was also exciting but short-lived.A home victory over Harrogate Town by two clear goals was followed by a visit to Yeovil Town and two shared goals, and the return match should have seen Rovers on their way to Villa Park, but a three-goal lead was squandered and eventually the side finished one short in a nine goal nail-biter - and Yeovil eventually lifted the Trophy!

A goals situation of 69 scored and 43 conceded in the Conference would suggest that not too much is needed for Doncaster Rovers to mount a better challenge for promotion. The Football League always enjoyed the presence of Doncaster Rovers and a reappearance under the club's present direction and refreshed management would be welcome.The defence looks sound, so success may depend on the fitness and goalscoring form of Patterson, Jackson and Barnes.   W.M.

Doncaster Rovers 2002-03
L-R - Back row: Paul Green, Andy Watson, Francis Tierney, Dave Morley, Ricky Ravenhill, Kevin Sandwith, Paul Barnes.
Middle: Justin Jackson, Robert Gill, Mark Albrighton, Andy Warrington, Stuart Nelson, Barry Miller, Tim Ryan, Ross Thompson.
Front: Mickey Walker (assistant manager), Alan Morgan, Jamie Price, Tristram Whitman, Dean Barrick,
Gareth Owen, Jamie Paterson, Simon Marples, Dave Penney (manager)

DONCASTER ROVERS

GROUND DETAILS

Belle Vue Ground, Bawtry Road, Doncaster,
S. Yorks. DN4 5HT

TELEPHONE   01302 539441
                                           Fax 01302 539679
Website: www.doncasterroversfc.co.uk
email: info@doncasterroversfc.co.uk

SIMPLE DIRECTIONS:
From north & west: Into Doncaster town centre and follow
sign to Bawtry (A638) and after 1.2 miles take 3rd exit at
roundabout into Bawtry Road. BR station 2miles
From east: M18, then A630, A18 and A638 (Bawtry Road)
From south: M18 junct 3, A6182, then A18 and A638

MATCH TICKETS:
              Adults:£9-£11, OAPs £6-£7 concessions £3-£6
CAR PARK: Large park at ground (£3)

CAPACITY: 7,219
SEATED: 1,252
COVERED TERRACING: 4,753

SOCIAL FACILITIES: Home members pay £10 for bar
                  membership and visitors £1 admission
CLUB SHOP: Open daily 10-4pm and on matchdays.

Founded:	1879
Nickname:	The Rovers
Sponsors:	Ledger Mobility
Club Colours:	Red & white hoops, red shorts, red socks.
Change Colours:	White with green sleeves/green/green
Midweek matchday:	Tuesday
Reserve Team's League:	Avon Insurance 1st Division

CLUB OFFICIALS

President   Vacant
Chairman   Trevor Milton
Directors: M.Collett, P.Hepworth, K.Chappell,
              S.Highfield, A.Liney, J.Ryan, R.Thomas, P.Wetzel
Club Secretary   Joan Oldale, c/o the club
                                    Tel: 01302 539441
                                    Fax: 01302 539679
                 email: info@doncasterroversfc.co.uk
Press Officer: Steve Uttley
                                    Tel: 07747 612182
Press/Media Executive: Steve Uttley
Commercial Executive   Alick Jeffrey, c/o the club
                                    Tel: 01302 539441
                                    Fax: 01302 539679

MATCHDAY PROGRAMME

DONCASTER ROVERS
Versus
STEVENAGE BOROUGH
Friday 25th January 2002 Kick-off 7.15 pm.
programme £2.00

Ringways Ford support Doncaster Rovers
award-winning match day programme

Pages: 48   **Price:** £2.00
Editor:Michael Harker c/o the club
Tel Nos: 07747 612182(M) 01302 539441(W)
Other club publications:
Supporters' Club Handbook and Two fanzines
Local Press: Doncaster Star; Yorkshire Post
Local Radio: Radio Hallam; Radio Sheffield, Trax FM
Clubcall: 09068121651

FOOTBALL MANAGEMENT TEAM

MANAGER: **DAVE PENNEY**
Date of Appointment   1st January 2002
Date of Birth: 17.08.64
Place of Birth: Wakefield

PREVIOUS CLUBS
As manager: None
As asst. manager/coach: None
As player: Derby Co., Oxford U, Swansea C.
                                  and Cardiff C

HONOURS
As manager
As player: Welsh Cup 1991

*   *   *

First Team Coach/Assistant Manager: Micky Walker
Reserve Manager: Paul Barnes
Physio: Bas Windle
Playing Status: Full Time

Season	League	Div.	Pos.	Home						Away					Pts	Manager
				P	W	D	L	F	A	W	D	L	F	A		
01-02	Conference	-	4	42	11	6	4	41	23	7	7	7	27	23	67	S Wignall /
00-01	Conference	-	9	42	11	5	5	28	17	4	8	9	19	26	58	Steve Wignall
99-00	Conference	-	12	42	7	5	9	19	21	8	4	9	27	27	54	Ian Snodin / Steve Wignall
98-99	Conference	-	16	42	7	5	9	26	26	5	7	9	25	29	48	Ian Snodin

Season	League	Div.	Pos.	P	W	D	L	F	A	Pts	Manager
97-98	F. League	3	24	46	4	8	34	30	113	20	Kerry Dixon
96-97	F. League	3	19	46	14	10	22	52	66	52	Ian Atkins
95-96	F. League	3	13	46	16	11	19	49	60	59	Sammy Chung
94-95	F. League	3	9	42	17	10	15	58	64	58	Sammy Chung
93-94	F. League	3	15	42	14	10	18	44	57	52	Steve Beaglehole
92-93	F. League	3	16	42	11	14	17	42	57	47	Steve Beaglehole

HONOURS

Division 3 N 1934-35, 46-47, 49-50;

Division 4 1965-66, 68-69;

Sheffield County Cup 1890-91, 1911-12,

35-36, 37-38, 55-56, 67-68, 75-76, 85-86;

Yorkshire Electricity Cup 1995-96;

Midland Counties League 1896-97, 98-99;

Northern Intermediate Lge Cup 1984-95, 86-87

Nationwide McMillan Trophy (Conf. Lge Cup) 98-99, 99-00

PREVIOUS

Leagues: Midland Alliance Lge 1890-91;
Midland League 1891-1901, 03-04 & 05-15,20-23;
Football League 1901-3, 04-05, 23-Sept 39, 42-44, 45-98;
Midland Comb. 1915-16; E Midlands War Lge Oct 1939-40;
War Lge North 1940-42, 44-45

Names: None

Ground: 1880-1916 Intake Ground;
1920-22 Benetthorpe Ground;
1922 > Belle Vue (formerly known as Low Pasture)

Past Players

who progressed to the Football League

CLUB RECORDS

Attendance: 37,149 v Hull City, Div. 3N, 2.10.1948

Career Goalscorer: Tom Keetley, 180, 1923-29

Career Appearances: Fred Emery, 417, 1925-36

Win: 10-0 v Darlington (H), Div. 4, 25.01.64

Defeat: 0-12 v Small Heath (A), Division 2, 11.04.03

Transfer Fee Paid: £100,000
to Rushden & Diamonds for Justin Jackson

Transfer Fee Received: £350,000
from Bradford City for Darren Moore, 1997

BEST SEASON

FA Trophy: 4th Rd 99-00 (2nd season)

FA Cup: 5th Rd 1951-52, 53-54, 54-55 & 55-56
League Club defeated: Southend United 1998-99
League Cup: 5th Round 1975-76

League: 7th , League Div. 2, 1901-02

LAST SEASON

FA Trophy: Fourth Round
FA Cup: First Round
League: 4th
Leading Goalscorer: Jamie Paterson
Players' Player of the Year: Gareth Owen
Captain: Gareth Owen
Club Captain: Barry Miller

DONCASTER ROVERS

	Date	Comp.	Opponents	Att.	Score	Goalscorers
1	18/08	Conf.	Farnborough Town	1093	1 - 0	O'Shea 58[og]
2	21/08	Conf.	LEIGH RMI	2433	2 - 0	Whitman 76, Kelly 81[p]
3	25/08	Conf.	YEOVIL TOWN	2796	1 - 2	Whitman 15
4	27/08	Conf.	Stevenage Borough	2352	0 - 0	
5	01/09	Conf.	DOVER ATHLETIC	2044	2 - 1	Sale 2, Paterson 44
6	05/09	Conf.	Boston United	2272	2 - 2	Kelly 65 Owen 85 (pen)
7	08/09	Conf.	WOKING	2598	1 - 1	Carden 23
8	11/09	Conf.	Telford United	1017	1 - 1	Paterson 23
9	15/09	Conf.	Hayes	821	5 - 1	Owen 9, Cauldwell 21, Whitman 22, Paterson 55 77
10	18/09	Conf.	NUNEATON BOROUGH	2623	2 - 2	Campbell 34, Owen 78
11	22/09	Conf.	MORECAMBE	2841	3 - 3	Owen 19, Campbell 45 76
12	29/09	Conf.	Southport	1512	0 - 1	
13	02/10	Conf.	Northwich Victoria	878	3 - 2	Whitman 27, Campbell 38, Miller 69
14	05/10	Conf.	FOREST GREEN ROVERS	2748	5 - 1	Paterson 26,Campbell 57,Whitman 59 Miller 69,Cauldwell 79
15	09/10	Conf.	BARNET	2935	2 - 3	Whitman 42, Owen 78
16	13/10	Conf.	Margate	2087	1 - 1	Jackson 89
17	16/10	LDV Vans 1N	KIDDERMINSTER HARRIERS	1750	0 - 1	
18	20/10	Conf.	Chester City	2148	1 - 1	Campbell 15
19	28/10	FA Cup Q4	EMLEY	2730	3 - 2	Patterson 11[p] 65, Jackson 16
20	03/11	Conf.	STALYBRIDGE CELTIC	2335	0 - 1	
21	06/11	Sheff SC 1	DINNINGTON TOWN	518	6 - 0	Tierney, Hawkins, Penney 2, Barnes, Watson
22	10/11	Conf.	Hereford United	1711	0 - 0	
23	17/11	FA Cup 1	SCUNTHORPE UNITED	6222	2 - 3	Tierney 21, Watson 49
24	24/11	Conf.	DAGENHAM & REDBRIDGE	2529	0 - 0	
25	01/12	Conf.	FARNBOROUGH TOWN	1809	1 - 1	Paterson 70
26	04/12	Sheff SC 2	HALLAM	378	2 - 0	Jackson 38, Whitman 58
27	08/12	Conf.	Yeovil Town	2650	1 - 1	Paterson 56
28	15/12	Conf.	Leigh RMI	546	4 - 1	Sale 28, Paterson 57 70, Watson 75
29	26/12	Conf.	SCARBOROUGH	3279	4 - 3	Paterson 8[p], Watson 61, Owen 70, Whitman 76
30	12/01	FA Trophy 3	HARROGATE TOWN	1886	2 - 0	Campbell 43, Watson 90
31	15/01	Conf.	Scarborough	1789	0 - 1	
32	19/01	Conf.	Dover Athletic	1157	1 - 0	Barnes 13
33	25/01	Conf.	STEVENAGE BOROUGH	2076	2 - 0	Paterson 65, Campbell 75
34	09/02	Conf.	Forest Green Rovers	917	2 - 0	Paterson 37, Sale 90
35	16/02	Conf.	MARGATE	2248	1 - 0	Patterson 75[p]
36	19/02	FA Trophy 4	Yeovil Town	2671	1 - 1	Barnes 16
37	23/02	FA Trophy 4 R	YEOVIL TOWN	2178	4 - 5	Paterson 6[p], Gill 22 49, Owen 88
38	02/03	Conf.	Nuneaton Borough	1461	3 - 2	Barnes 11, Gill 50, Jackson 84
39	05/03	Sheff SC QF	Parkgate	350	3 - 0	Campbell 16 54, Penney 19[p]
40	09/03	Conf.	TELFORD UNITED	2143	1 - 0	Jackson 72
41	12/03	Conf.	BOSTON UNITED	4027	0 - 1	
42	16/03	Conf.	Woking	2133	1 - 3	Campbell 84
43	19/03	Conf.	NORTHWICH VICTORIA	1489	2 - 2	Barnes 49, Tierney 85
44	22/03	Conf.	HAYES	1651	5 - 2	Paterson 12, Squires 42, Gill 58, Green 62, Barnes 70
45	26/03	Sheff SC SF	Frickley Athletic	582	3 - 1	Place 44[og], Ravenhill 45, Barnes 90
46	30/03	Conf.	CHESTER CITY	2089	2 - 0	Gill 34, Barnes 45
47	01/04	Conf.	Stalybridge Celtic	1226	0 - 1	
48	06/04	Conf.	HEREFORD UNITED	1735	4 - 0	Watson 15 30, Squires 57, Green 90
49	12/04	Conf.	Dagenham & Redbridge	2455	0 - 1	
50	20/04	Conf.	SOUTHPORT	2151	1 - 0	Barnes 64
51	22/04	Conf.	Barnet	1361	0 - 2	
52	24/04	Sheff SC F	EMLEY	973	3 - 0	Barnes 47 55, Gill 68 @ Sheffield Wednesday
53	27/04	Conf.	Morecambe	1780	1 - 2	Whitman 34

1	2	3	4	5	6	7	8	9	10	11	Substitutes Used
Richardson	Marples	Barrick	Kelly	Miller	Ryan	Carden	Owen	Campbell	Gill	Caudwell	Sale 10
Richardson	Marples	Barrick	Kelly	Miller	Ryan	Carden	Owen	Campbell	Gill	Caudwell	Sale 9 Whitman 10 Sandwith 3
Richardson	Marples	Sandwith	Kelly	Miller	Ryan	Carden	Owen	Campbell	Whitman	Caudwell	Sale 9 Tierney 7 Paterson 11
Richardson	Marples	Sandwith	Kelly	Miller	Ryan	Carden	Owen	Sale	Whitman	Caudwell	Gill 10 Tierney 7 Paterson 3
Richardson	Marples	Paterson	Kelly	Miller	Ryan	Carden	Owen	Sale	Whitman	Caudwell	Gill 9
Richardson	Marples	Paterson	Kelly	Miller	Ryan	Hawkins	Owen	Campbell	Jackson	Caudwell	Whitman 10 Squires 11 Carden 2
Richardson	Marples	Hawkins	Kelly	Miller	Ryan	Carden	Owen	Campbell	Jackson	Paterson	Whitman 4 Caudwell 11
Richardson	Marples	Hawkins	Kelly	Miller	Ryan	Carden	Owen	Campbell	Jackson	Paterson	Whitman 9
Richardson	Marples	Hawkins	Kelly	Miller	Ryan	Caudwell	Owen	Campbell	Whitman	Paterson	Carden 8 Price 4 Gill 10
Richardson	Marples	Squires	Kelly	Miller	Ryan	Caudwell	Owen	Campbell	Whitman	Paterson	Gill 10
Richardson	Marples	Squires	Carden	Miller	Ryan	Caudwell	Owen	Campbell	Jackson	Paterson	Price 4
Richardson	Marples	Squires	Kelly	Miller	Hawkins	Caudwell	Owen	Campbell	Jackson	Paterson	Barrick 2 Barnes 10
Richardson	Hawkins	Squires	Kelly	Miller	Ryan	Caudwell	Owen	Campbell	Whitman	Paterson	Barrick 7 Carden 11
Richardson	Marples	Squires	Kelly	Miller	Ryan	Caudwell	Owen	Campbell	Whitman	Paterson	Gill 10 Carden 8 Hawkins 2
Richardson	Marples	Squires	Kelly	Miller	Ryan	Caudwell	Owen	Campbell	Whitman	Paterson	Barnes 11 Carden 4 Barrick 3
Richardson	Hawkins	Squires	Kelly	Miller	Ryan	Caudwell	Owen	Campbell	Whitman	Paterson	Carden 4 Barnes 7 Jackson 10
Richardson	Hawkins	Barrick	Kelly	Squires	Ryan	Watson	Owen	Campbell	Whitman	Carden	Barnes 4 Jackson 10 Tierney 7
Richardson	Marples	Barrick	Carden	Hawkins	Ryan	Watson	Owen	Campbell	Whitman	Paterson	Barnes 10 Jackson 7 Caudwell 11
Richardson	Marples	Barrick	Carden	Hawkins	Squires	Tierney	Owen	Campbell	Jackson	Paterson	Barnes 9 Caudwell 7 Penney 12
Richardson	Marples	Barrick	Kelly	Miller	Hawkins	Tierney	Carden	Barnes	Jackson	Paterson	Whitman 8 Watson 7 Sale 2
Richardson	Marples	Barrick	Kelly	Miller	Hawkins	Tierney	Owen	Barnes	Jackson	Paterson	Watson 7
Richardson	Marples	Barrick	Kelly	Miller	Hawkins	Tierney	Owen	Barnes	Jackson	Watson	Whitman 11 Sale 9
Richardson	Marples	Barrick	Kelly	Miller	Squires	Tierney	Owen	Barnes	Campbell	Paterson	Watson 7 Whitman 9 Sale 10
Richardson	Marples	Barrick	Kelly	Miller	Squires	Tierney	Owen	Campbell	Jackson	Paterson	Watson 7
Warrington	Marples	Barrick	Kelly	Miller	Squires	Watson	Owen	Campbell	Sale	Paterson	
Warrington	Marples	Barrick	Kelly	Miller	Squires	Watson	Owen	Campbell	Sale	Paterson	Whitman 9 Sandwith 3 Price 8
Warrington	Marples	Barrick	Kelly	Miller	Squires	Watson	Owen	Campbell	Sale	Paterson	Whitman 10 Price 11
Warrington	Marples	Barrick	Kelly	Miller	Squires	Watson	Owen	Campbell	Whitman	Paterson	Jackson 10 Sandwith 11 Price 2
Warrington	Price	Barrick	Kelly	Miller	Squires	Tierney	Owen	Campbell	Jackson	Paterson	Sale 9 Caudwell 11 Whitman 10
Warrington	Price	Barrick	Kelly	Squires	Ryan	Tierney	Owen	Campbell	Barnes	Paterson	Gill 9 Watson 11
Butler	Price	Barrick	Kelly	Squires	Ryan	Tierney	Owen	Campbell	Barnes	Paterson	Sale 10 Miller 3 Gill 9
Butler	Price	Barrick	Kelly	Squires	Miller	Tierney	Owen	Gill	Barnes	Paterson	Watson 9 Sale 10
Butler	Price	Barrick	Kelly	Squires	Miller	Tierney	Owen	Gill	Barnes	Paterson	Campbell 9 Sale 10
Butler	Price	Barrick	Kelly	Squires	Miller	Tierney	Ravenhill	Gill	Barnes	Paterson	Sale 10 Campbell 9 Sandwith 3
Butler	Price	Barrick	Kelly	Squires	Miller	Tierney	Owen	Gill	Barnes	Paterson	Sale 10 Jackson 9 Sandwith 11
Warrington	Ryan	Barrick	Kelly	Squires	Miller	Tierney	Owen	Gill	Barnes	Jackson	Ravenhill 11 Caudwell 6 Butler 1
Butler	Ryan	Barrick	Kelly	Squires	Miller	Tierney	Owen	Gill	Barnes	Jackson	Ravenhill 8 Paterson 9
Butler	Ryan	Barrick	Kelly	Squires	Miller	Tierney	Owen	Paterson	Barnes	Jackson	Campbell 10 Marples 6 Ravenhill 8
Butler	Ryan	Barrick	Kelly	Squires	Miller	Tierney	Ravenhill	Paterson	Barnes	Jackson	Campbell 3 Marples 5 Gill 8
Butler	Marples	Sandwith	Kelly	Miller	Squires	Tierney	Price	Barnes	Jackson	Paterson	Campbell 10 Gill 11 Green 2
Butler	Price	Sandwith	Kelly	Miller	Squires	Tierney	Green	Barnes	Gill	Paterson	Campbell 9 Ryan 6 Whitman 10
Warrington	Price	Ryan	Kelly	Miller	Squires	Tierney	Owen	Barnes	Gill	Watson	Campbell 9 Green 3 Caudwell 7
Warrington	Price	Ryan	Kelly	Miller	Squires	Watson	Ravenhill	Barnes	Gill	Caudwell	Campbell 11 Sandwith 8 Green 4
Warrington	Price	Ryan	Ravenhill	Miller	Squires	Watson	Green	Barnes	Gill	Whitman	Sandwith 4 Caudwell 7
Warrington	Price	Ryan	Ravenhill	Miller	Squires	Watson	Green	Barnes	Gill	Whitman	Paterson 10
Warrington	Price	Ryan	Ravenhill	Miller	Squires	Watson	Green	Barnes	Gill	Whitman	Paterson 7 Tierney 11 Sandwith 6
Warrington	Price	Sandwith	Penney	Futcher	Ryan	Tierney	Owen	Sale	Paterson	Caudwell	Gill 10 Watson 7 Ravenhill 4
Warrington	Squires	Barrick	Ravenhill	Miller	Futcher	Whitman	Green	Barnes	Gill	Watson	Tierney 11 Campbell 9 Paterson 7

DONCASTER ROVERS   PLAYING SQUAD

Player	Birthplace	D.O.B.	Previous Clubs

Bold print denotes England semi-professional international.

GOALKEEPERS

Player	Birthplace	D.O.B.	Previous Clubs
Andy Warrington	Sheffield	10.0676	York City
Stuart Nelson	Swindon	17.09.81	Oxford C, Des Moines Menace (USA), Millwall, Cirencester

DEFENDERS

Player	Birthplace	D.O.B.	Previous Clubs
Simon Marples ESP	Sheffield		Sheffield Wed., Rotherham, Stocksbridge Park Steels, £12,000 to Doncaster
Tim Ryan ESP	Stockport	10.12.74	Doncaster R, Buxton, Scunthorpe, Southport
Barry Miller	Ealing	29.03.76	Gillingham (£10,000), Farnborough T, Wokingham T
Dean Barrick	Hemsworth	30.09.69	Bury, Preston, Cambridge Utd, Rotherham, Sheff.Wed
Kevin Sandwith	Workington	30.04.78	Telford Utd, Barrow, Carlisle
Alan Morgan	Aberystwyth	02.11.73	Tranmere
David Morley	St Helens	25.09.77	Oxford Utd, Carlisle, Southend, Manchester C
Jamie Price	Normanton	27.10.81	Leeds
Steve Foster	Mansfield	01.10.79	Bristol R, Woking, Telford Utd, Mansfield

MIDFIELD

Player	Birthplace	D.O.B.	Previous Clubs
Andy Watson	Leeds	13.11.78	Garforth Town
Gareth Owen Wales u-21	Chester	21.10.71	Wrexham
Jamie Paterson	Dumfries	26.04.73	Halifax, Scunthorpe, Falkirk, Halifax
Paul Green	Sheffield	10.04.83	Sheffield Wednesday
Ricky Ravenhill	Doncaster	16.01.81	Barnsley, Leeds

FORWARDS

Player	Birthplace	D.O.B.	Previous Clubs
Tristam Whitman	Nottingham		Arnold T, £10,000 to Doncaster R
Francis Tierney	Liverpool	09.10.75	Witton Alb., Exeter, Witton Alb., Notts Co, Crewe
Paul Barnes	Leeds	16.11.67	Bury, Huddersfield, Burnley, Birmingham, York, Stoke C., Notts Co
Brian Quailey St Kitts & Nevis Int.	Leicester	21.03.78	Scunthorpe, WBA, Nuneaton B, Deeping R.
Daniel Bent	Boston	22.02.83	Lincoln C
Justin Jackson ESP, NC, FAT	Nottingham	26.06.75	Rushden & Diamonds (£100k), Morecambe, Halifax, Notts Co., Woking, Morecambe, Ilkeston, Penrith, Ayr Utd, Bolton
Robert Gill	Nottingham	10.02.82	Nottingham Forest

FARNBOROUGH TOWN

There is no doubt that Manager-Owner Graham Westley is a very confident leader. But it is possible that his pre season prophesies last year rebounded a little on him and his players. A consolidating period affected by injuries resulted in a very ordinary start for 'The Boro ,as they took up the challenge of their fourth spell in the Alliance/Conference. They were never lower than thirteenth position but supporters may well have been brainwashed into expecting better.

Established goalscorers in Rocky Baptiste and Gary Crawshaw never really hit their best form as individuals or as attacking combinations but luckily Lenny Piper had a tremendous campaign and the physical presence of Joff Vansittart acted as a good target in the penalty area.. No one could argue with the squad's ball winning potential but the loss, through injury of England skipper Gary Patterson was a tragic blow and left a greater responsibility on Steve Watson, who was rewarded with England caps of his own at the end of the season.

The future of The Stadium was in question for most of the season, with press stories of moving to new grounds, ground sharing and mergers all confusing supporters and obviously not proving good for stability. At all times Westley showed commendable belief in his club's future and after a little flutter in the F.A.Cup with a 4-0 win at Kings Lynn followed by a disappointing 1-2 loss at Halifax, Farnborough were many people's tip for a good run in the F.A.Trophy. A fine 5-0 replay win away to Carshalton Athletic brought them a home tie against Burton Albion.A very late Nigel Clough equalizer earned the visitors a replay and the Unibond leaders won an excellent replay by 3-2.

Hopefully plans for the clubs off field development will be settled and there is no doubt that a little squad strengthening added to Westley'e drive and enthusiasm will once again make Boro a serious Conference contender.

T.W.

FARNBOROUGH TOWN FC 2002-03

Back Row L-R: Nathan Bunce,Barry Laker,Joff Vansittart,Mark Osborn,Graham Benstead (Goalkeeping Coach),Tony Pennock,Christian Lee,Gary Patterson and Gareth Gwillem.**Middle Row:** Martin Kane (Fitness Instructor), Rocky Baptiste,Thomas Ellis,Dean Green, Gary Holloway,Graham Pearce (Coach), Ron Berry (Kit) Leroy Griffiths,Tim O'Shea,Justin Gregory,Lenny Piper and Karl Jones (Physio).**Front Row:** Ken Charley,Darren Annon, Danny Carroll, Steve Watson, Graham Westley (Manager), Chris Piper, Tony Taggart, Michael Warner and Gary Butterworth.

FARNBOROUGH TOWN

GROUND DETAILS

The Aimita Stadium, Cherrywood Road,
Farnborough, Hampshire GU14 8UD

Telephone:	01252 541469
Fax:	01252 372640

Directions: From M3 exit 4, take A325 towards
Farnborough, right into Prospect Ave. (club signpost-
ed), 2nd right into Cherrywood Rd, ground on right.
20-30 min walk from Farnborough Main, Farnborough
North , Frimley BR stations and town centre.
Whippet mini-bus 19 No 12 Bus passes ground.
Parking: 200 spaces at club at £1.00 plus local streets
Match Tickets: Adults £9-10 concessions £5-6

Capacity:	4,163
Seated:	627
Covered Terracing:	1,350

Clubhouse:	Open matchdays. Bar
Refreshments:	Two tea bars

Club Shop:
Boro' Leisurewear shop - all types of club leisurewear
and matchballs (contact Gaye Hoyle 01252 691129)
Supporters Club shop:
Old programmes, scarves, badges etc (contact Paul Doe).

Founded:	1967
Nickname:	The "Boro" or "Town"
Club Sponsor:	AMITA Corporation
Club Colours:	Red & white shirts,
Change colours:	Orange & Blue
Midweek matchday:	Tuesday
Reserves' League:	Capital League
Club Website:	www.ftfc.co.uk

CLUB OFFICIALS

President:	**Charles Mortimer**
Chairman:	**Graham Westley**
Non Executive Directors:	**Matthew Mills, Ron Berry**
	Tony McAleese & John Thridgould
Football Secretary:	**Vince Williams**
	Tel: 01252 541469
Commercial Consultant:	**Michael Warner**
	Tel: 07855 407211
Press Officer:	**Vince Williams**

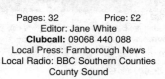

MATCHDAY PROGRAMME

Pages: 32   Price: £2
Editor: Jane White
Clubcall: 09068 440 088
Local Press: Farnborough News
Local Radio: BBC Southern Counties
County Sound

FOOTBALL MANAGEMENT TEAM

MANAGER: **GRAHAM WESTLEY**
Date of Appointment: 1st August 1999
Date of Birth: 4th March 1968
Place of Birth: Isleworth

PREVIOUS CLUBS
  As manager   Enfield, Kingstonian
  As player   QPR, Gillingham, Walton & Hersham

HONOURS
  As manager   Ryman Lge Champs. 2000-01
                              Ryman Lge Cup 99-00

*   *   *

Asst. Manager/Coach:	Graham Pearce
Reserve Team Manager:	
Physio:	Karl Jones
Club Playing Status:	Part Time

Season	League	Div.	Pos.	Home						Away						Manager
				P	W	D	L	F	A	W	D	L	F	A	Pts	
01-02	Conference	-	7	42	11	3	7	38	23	7	4	10	28	31	61	Graham Westley
00-01	Isthmian	P	1	42	14	5	2	43	13	17	1	3	43	14	99	Graham Westley
99-00	Isthmian	P	12	42	8	5	8	25	19	6	6	9	27	36	53	Graham Westley
98-99	Conference	-	22	42	6	5	10	29	48	1	6	14	12	41	32	Alan Taylor
97-98	Conference	-	18	42	10	3	8	37	27	2	5	14	19	43	44	Alan Taylor
96-97	Conference	-	7	42	9	6	6	35	29	7	7	7	23	24	61	Alan Taylor
95-96	Conference	-	10	42	8	6	7	29	23	7	8	6	34	35	59	Alan Taylor
94-95	Conference	-	14	42	8	5	8	23	31	7	5	9	22	33	55	Alan Taylor
93-94	Southern	P	1	42	15	4	2	43	18	10	3	8	31	26	82	Alan Taylor
92-93	Conference	-	21	42	8	5	8	34	36	4	6	11	34	51	47	Ted Pearce

HONOURS

Southern League	Prem. Div. 90-91 93-94,
Isthmian League	Prem. Div. 00-01, R-up 88-89, Div 1 84-85, Div 2 78-79, Lge Cup 99-00,
Athenian Lg	Div 2 78-79,
Spartan Lge	72-73 73-74 74-75 (Lg Cup 74-75),
London Spartan Lge	75-76 (Lg Cup 75-76),
Hants Senior Cup	74-75 81-82 83-84 85-86 90-91 (R-up 93-94)

PREVIOUS

Leagues: Surrey Senior 68-72; Spartan 72-76; Athenian 76-77; Isthmian 77-89 99-01; Alliance Premier (Conference) 89-90 91-93 94-99; Southern 90-91 93-94.

Grounds: Queens Road, Farnborough (1969-1976)

Past Players who progressed to the Football League

Dennis Bailey (Crystal Palace),
Paul Mortimer (Charlton Athletic),
Tommy Jones (Aberdeen),
Allan Cockram (Brentford),
Paul Holsgrove (Millwall),
Maik Taylor (Barnet),
Martin Rowlands (Brentford)

CLUB RECORDS

Attendance: 3,581 v Brentford 22/11/95 (FA Cup)

Win: 11-0 v Chertsey Town (H), Spartan League 72-73

Defeat: 2-10 v Worplesdon (H), Surrey Senior Lge Div. 1 68-69

Career Goalscorer: Simon Read 209, 1986-1994

Career Appearances: Brian Broome 529, 1980-1994

Season Goalscorer: Simon Read 53, 1988-89

Transfer Fee Paid: Undisclosed

Transfer Fee Received: £50,000 from Dover Athletic for David Leworthy, August1993

BEST SEASON

FA Cup: 3rd Rd Proper replay 91-92, 0-1 v West Ham U. (A) after 1-1

League club defeated: Torquay Utd 91-92

FA Trophy: Quarter Final 92-93

FA Vase: Semi-Final 75-76 76-77

League: 5th Conference 91-92

LAST SEASON

F.A. Cup: First Round
F.A. Trophy: Fourth Round
League: 7th Conference
Top Goalscorer: Lenny Piper 19
Player of the Year: Barry Laker & Michael Walker
Captain: Steve Watson

FARNBOROUGH TOWN

	Date	Comp.	Opponents	Att.	Score	Goalscorers
1	11/08	Ryman Shield	Heybridge Swifts	301	4 - 0	Baptiste 18 43[p], Vansittart 73 90
2	18/08	Conf.	DONCASTER ROVERS	1093	0 - 1	
3	22/08	Conf.	Forest Green Rovers	903	0 - 1	
4	25/08	Conf.	Southport	1159	5 - 2	Baptiste 1 32, L Piper 26, O'Shea 63, Vansittart 68
5	27/08	Conf.	BARNET	1126	2 - 1	Baptiste 48 88
6	01/09	Conf.	Stalybridge Celtic	671	1 - 1	L Piper 84
7	04/09	Conf.	MARGATE	797	0 - 0	
8	08/09	Conf.	CHESTER CITY	954	1 - 1	L.Piper 6
9	11/09	Conf.	Yeovil Town	2316	1 - 0	L Piper 61
10	15/09	Conf.	Stevenage Borough	1976	2 - 1	Vansittart 59 90
11	18/09	Conf.	DOVER ATHLETIC	713	1 - 0	Lee 30
12	22/09	Conf.	Leigh RMI	482	0 - 3	
13	29/09	Conf.	BOSTON UNITED	1175	0 - 2	
14	02/10	Conf.	Hereford United	1205	2 - 4	Crawshaw 14 87
15	06/10	Conf.	DAGENHAM & REDBRIDGE	540	1 - 2	Vansittart 20
16	09/10	Conf.	NUNEATON BOROUGH	626	2 - 1	Bunce 78, Piper 81
17	13/10	Conf.	Telford United	948	1 - 0	Vansittart 33
18	20/10	Conf.	HAYES	884	1 - 2	L.Piper 7
19	27/10	FA Cup Q4	King's Lynn	1758	4 - 0	Piper 8 24 65, Vansittart 79
20	03/11	Conf.	Northwich Victoria	717	2 - 1	Laker 35 Vansittart 60
21	07/11	Hants SC 2	PORTSMOUTH ROYAL NAVY	n/k	7 - 1	
22	10/11	Conf.	MORECAMBE	695	2 - 1	Charles 5, L Piper 45
23	17/11	FA Cup 1	Halifax Town	1914	1 - 2	C Piper 51
24	24/11	Conf.	Scarborough	930	0 - 1	
25	01/12	Conf.	Doncaster Rovers	1809	1 - 1	Green 86
26	04/12	Hants SC 3	Aldershot Town	n/k	3 - 4	
27	15/12	Conf.	FOREST GREEN ROVERS	776	3 - 0	L Piper 8[p], Patterson 28, Vansittart 73
28	17/12	Ald. SC 1	SANDHURST TOWN	n/k	3 - 1	
29	26/12	Conf.	Woking	2536	2 - 3	Piper 69 76
30	29/12	Conf.	SOUTHPORT	691	0 - 1	
31	05/01	Conf.	Margate	875	1 - 2	C Piper 89
32	12/01	FA Trophy 3	CARSHALTON ATHLETIC	617	1 - 1	Paterson 79
33	15/01	FA Trophy 3 R	Carshalton Athletic	372	5 - 0	Crawshaw 11 14, C Piper 58 69, Vansittart 75
34	19/01	Conf.	STALYBRIDGE CELTIC	647	2 - 0	Vansittart 64, Lee 83
35	29/01	Ald. SC QF	Ash United	n/k	1 - 2	
36	02/02	FA Trophy 4	BURTON ALBION	1031	1 - 1	Baptiste 16
37	05/02	FA Trophy 4 R	Burton Albion	1706	2 - 3	Baptiste 6, L Piper 89
38	09/02	Conf.	Dagenham & Redbridge	1736	1 - 2	Holloway 2
39	16/02	Conf.	TELFORD UNITED	667	1 - 1	De Souza 68
40	19/02	Conf.	Barnet	787	3 - 0	Holloway 29, Vansittart 75, L Piper 78
41	23/02	Conf.	Nuneaton Borough	728	1 - 1	Williams 80[og]
42	02/03	Conf.	Dover Athletic	1010	1 - 2	Browne 39
43	05/03	Conf.	WOKING	1303	0 - 1	
44	09/03	Conf.	YEOVIL TOWN	1404	1 - 3	Green 87
45	12/03	Conf.	HEREFORD UNITED	479	4 - 2	L Piper 20 89, Taggart 59, Lee 79
46	23/03	Conf.	STEVENAGE BOROUGH	687	6 - 1	Lee 22 49, Taggart 65, L Piper 66, Vansittart 75, Bunce 78
47	30/03	Conf.	Hayes	617	3 - 0	Taggart 30, Lee 75, Vansittart 78
48	01/04	Conf.	NORTHWICH VICTORIA	673	4 - 1	Taggart 44, Green 45, Vansittart 61, Piper 87
49	13/04	Conf.	SCARBOROUGH	843	4 - 2	Taggart 15, C Piper 41 45 90
50	16/04	Conf.	Chester City	1386	0 - 1	
51	20/04	Conf.	Boston United	3764	0 - 4	
52	25/04	Conf.	Morecambe	635	1 - 1	Holloway 33
53	27/04	Conf.	LEIGH RMI	809	3 - 0	L Piper 51, Lee 66, Bunce 87

1	2	3	4	5	6	7	8	9	10	11	Substitutes Used
Farrelly	Warner	Taggart	O'Shea	Annon	Laker	Watson	Jones	Vansittart	Baptiste	C Piper	Darlington 3 Dublin 8 L Piper 11
Farrelly	Warner	Taggart	O'Shea	Annon	Laker	Watson	L Piper	Vansittart	Baptiste	Patterson	Bunce 5
Farrelly	Warner	Taggart	O'Shea	Annon	Laker	Watson	L Piper	Vansittart	Baptiste	Patterson	Crawshaw 9 Darlington 10 C Piper 3
Farrelly	Warner	Taggart	O'Shea	Annon	Laker	Watson	L Piper	Vansittart	Baptiste	Patterson	C Piper 3
Farrelly	Warner	Taggart	O'Shea	Annon	Laker	Jones	L Piper	Vansittart	Baptiste	Patterson	C Piper 7 Bunce 9 Darlington 3
Farrelly	Warner	C Piper	O'Shea	Annon	Laker	Watson	L Piper	Vansittart	Crawshaw	Patterson	Darlington 10
Farrelly	Warner	C Piper	O'Shea	Annon	Laker	Watson	L Piper	Vansittart	Crawshaw	Patterson	Lee 10 Taggart 3
Farrelly	Warner	Annon	O'Shea	Harper	Laker	Watson	L Piper	Vansittart	Lee	C Piper	Darlington 10
Farrelly	Warner	Annon	O'Shea	Harper	Laker	Watson	L Piper	Vansittart	Lee	C Piper	Crawshaw 2 Hodges 11 Jones 10
Farrelly	Warner	Annon	O'Shea	Harper	Laker	Watson	L Piper	Vansittart	Lee	C Piper	Crawshaw 10 Jones 11
Farrelly	Annon	C Piper	O'Shea	Harper	Laker	Watson	L Piper	Vansittart	Lee	Patterson	Baptiste 10 Crawshaw 5
Farrelly	Warner	C Piper	Annon	Harper	Laker	Watson	L Piper	Vansittart	Baptiste	Patterson	Bunce 6 Crawshaw 10 Taggart 5
Farrelly	Warner	Annon	O'Shea	Harper	C Piper	Watson	Patterson	Vansittart	Crawshaw	Taggart	Darlington 9 Jones 11 L Piper 8
Farrelly	Warner	Annon	O'Shea	Harper	C Piper	Watson	L Piper	Vansittart	Dublin	Patterson	Baptiste 16(Jon) Jones 9
Farrelly	Warner	Annon	O'Shea	Harper	Bunce	Watson	C Piper	Vansittart	Dublin	Patterson	Jones 10 L Piper 7 Taggart 5
Farrelly	Warner	Annon	O'Shea	Harper	Bunce	Watson	C Piper	Vansittart	Dublin	Patterson	Crawshaw 10 L Piper 8
Bonfield	C Piper	Annon	O'Shea	Bunce	Laker	Jones	L Piper	Vansittart	Dublin	Patterson	Crawshaw 10 Darlington 9 Taggart 7
Bonfield	Warner	Taggart	Annon	Bunce	Laker	Watson	L Piper	Vansittart	C Piper	Patterson	
Bonfield	Warner	Taggart	Patterson	Bunce	Laker	Watson	L Piper	Vansittart	Charles	C Piper	Baptiste 10 Holloway 3
Bonfield	Warner	Annon	Patterson	Bunce	Laker	Watson	L Piper	Charles	Green	C Piper	
Bonfield	Warner	Annon	Patterson	Bunce	Laker	Watson	L Piper	Baptiste	C Piper	Taggart	Dublin 5 Harper 6
Farrelly	Warner	Gregory	Annon	Harper	Laker	Green	L Piper	Charles	Baptiste	C Piper	Dublin 5 Jones 3 Taggart 10
Bonfield	Warner	Annon	Patterson	O'Shea	Laker	Watson	L Piper	Charles	Green	C Piper	Baptiste 9 Gregory 2 Taggart 8
Benstead	Warner	Annon	Patterson	Bunce	Laker	Watson	L Piper	Vansittart	De Souza	C Piper	Baptiste 9 Crawshaw 10 Green 3
Benstead	Warner	Annon	Patterson	Bunce	Laker	Watson	L Piper	Vansittart	De Souza	C Piper	Baptiste 10 Green 5 Gregory 3
Benstead	Warner	Annon	Patterson	O'Shea	Laker	Watson	L Piper	Vansittart	Green	C Piper	Baptiste 9 Crawshaw 10 Taggart 5
Benstead	Warner	Annon	Green	Patterson	Laker	Watson	L Piper	Vansittart	Baptiste	C Piper	Crawshaw 10 De Souza 4 Gregory 3
Bonfield	Warner	Gregory	Patterson	Annon	Laker	Holloway	L Piper	Vansittart	Crawshaw	De Souza	Baptiste 11 Green 9
Bonfield	Warner	Dublin	Patterson	Annon	Laker	Holloway	L Piper	De Souza	Crawshaw	C Piper	Geen 9 Taggart 4 Vansittart 10
Bonfield	Warner	Gregory	Patterson	Annon	Laker	Holloway	L Piper	Vansittart	Crawshaw	C Piper	Dublin 8 Green 4 Lee 9
Bonfield	Warner	Gregory	Patterson	Annon	Laker	Holloway	L Piper	Baptiste	Crawshaw	C Piper	Dublin 9 O'Shea 11
Bonfield	Warner	Gregory	Patterson	Annon	Laker	Watson	Holloway	Vansittart	Baptiste	Crawshaw	Dublin 9 L Piper 11 Taggart 2
Bonfield	Warner	Gregory	Patterson	Annon	Laker	Watson	Holloway	Baptiste	Crawshaw	C Piper	De Souza 9 L Piper 10
Pennock	Warner	Gregory	Patterson	Annon	Laker	Watson	Holloway	Vansittart	De Souza	C Piper	Crawshaw 9 Green 4 L Piper 11
Pennock	Warner	Gregory	Green	Annon	Laker	Watson	Holloway	Vansittart	De Souza	C Piper	Crawshaw 10 O'Shea 4 L Piper 3
Pennock	Warner	Gregory	O'Shea	Annon	Laker	Watson	Holloway	Vansittart	De Souza	C Piper	Crawshaw 10 Green 4 L Piper 9
Pennock	Warner	Gregory	C Piper	Annon	Laker	Watson	Holloway	De Souza	Crawshaw	Taggart	Dublin 9 Green 11 L Piper 4
Pennock	Warner	Gregory	O'Shea	Harper	Laker	Watson	L Piper	Lee	De Souza	C Piper	Green 10 Taggart 5
Pennock	Warner	Gregory	O'Shea	Harper	Laker	C Piper	L Piper	De Souza	Lee	Patterson	Green 11 Holloway 9 Vansittart 10
Pennock	Warner	Gregory	O'Shea	Harper	Laker	Holloway	L Piper	Vansittart	Green	C Piper	Annon 4 Lee 9 Taggart 5
Pennock	Warner	Gregory	Holloway	Bunce	Laker	Watson	L Piper	Lee	Green	Taggart	C Piper 3 Vansittart 9
Pennock	Warner	Gregory	Holloway	Bunce	Laker	Watson	L Piper	Lee	Green	Taggart	Hicks 10 C Piper 7 Vansittart 8
Pennock	Warner	C Piper	Holloway	Bunce	Harper	Watson	Green	Lee	Vansittart	Taggart	Annon 6 Hicks 8 L Piper 10
Bonfield	Warner	Gregory	C Piper	Bunce	Laker	Watson	L Piper	Lee	Green	Taggart	Annon 6 Vansittart 8
Bonfield	Warner	Gregory	C Piper	Bunce	Harper	Watson	L Piper	Lee	Green	Taggart	Crawshaw 9 Vansittart 8 De Souza 6
Bonfield	Warner	Gregory	C Piper	Bunce	Laker	Watson	Green	Lee	Vansittart	Taggart	Benstead 1 Holloway 3 L Piper 9
Osborn	Warner	Gregory	Holloway	Bunce	Laker	Watson	L Piper	Lee	C Piper	Taggart	Annon 8 De Souza 15 (Gr) Green 9
Osborn	Warner	C Piper	Holloway	Bunce	Laker	Watson	L Piper	Lee	Green	Taggart	Annon 4 Hicks 10 Rose 9

FARNBOROUGH TOWN   PLAYING SQUAD

Player	Birthplace	D.O.B.	Previous Clubs
			Bold print denotes England semi-professional international.

GOALKEEPERS

Tony Pennock WSP, RP	Swansea	10.04.71	Rushden & Diamonds, Yeovil Town, Hereford Utd, Wigan, Stockport

DEFENDERS

Nathan Bunce RP	Hillingdon	02.05.75	Stevenage B, Hayes, Yeading, Brentford
Jim Rodwell NC, DMP	Lincoln	20.11.70	Boston Utd, Rushden & Diamonds, Halesowen T, Nuneaton B, Hednesford T, Bedworth Utd, Boston Utd, Boston T, Bury, Sabam (Malaysia), Darlington
Barry Laker RL	London		Sutton Utd, Banstead Ath., Wimbledon (Junior)
Jim Gardner RL	Beckenham	26.10.78	Exeter, Wimbledon
Justin Gregory RL	Sussex		Dulwich Hamlet, Crawley T, Hastings T, Crawley T, Hastings T, Worthing, Shoreham
Michael Warner RL	Harrogate	17.01.74	Northampton, Tamworth, Redditch Utd
Tim O'Shea Eire Y, RL	Pimlico	12.11.66	Instant Dict (HK), Eastern (HK), Gillingham, Leyton Orient, Tottenham
Tony Taggert RL	London	Brentford	

MIDFIELD

Darron Annon RL	London	17.02.72	Enfield, Kingstonian, Brentford, Carshalton Ath
Danny Carroll	Surrey	-	Crawley T, Dulwich Hamlet, Bromley, Whyteleafe, Chipstead, Whyteleafe
Gary Butterworth ESP, NC, DMP	Peterborough	08.09.69	Rushden & Diamonds, Dag & Red., Peterborough
Gary Holloway	Surrey	-	Hampton & Richmond, Walton & Hersham
Gary Patterson ESP, FAT	Newcastle	27.11.72	Kingstonian, Wycombe, Shrewsbury, Notts Co
Lennie Piper EY, RL	London	08.08.77	St.Albans C, Welling Utd, Gillingham, Wimbledon
Scott Corbett RL	London		Kingstonian, Hampton
Steve Watson ESP; RL	London		Sutton Utd, Croydon, Whyteleafe, Crystal Palace (Junior)

FORWARDS

Chris Piper RL	London		St.Albans C, Charlton
Danny Jones	London		Enfield
Joff Vansittart	Sussex	12.09.74	Dover Ath, Sutton Utd, Crawley T, Brighton
Rocky Baptiste	London		Luton, Hayes, Wealdstone, Willesden Hawkeye, Chelsea (Junior)
Christian Lee	Aylesbury	08.10.76	Eastwood T, Rushden & Diamonds, Farnborough T Bristol R, Rochdale, Northampton, Gillingham, Doncaster R
Dean Green Crawley T, Dulwich Hamlet, Waltham Abbey, Fulham	London	-	Hampton & Richmond, Leyton Pennant, Dulwich Hamlet,
Ken Charley ESP, NC	Stepney	28.11.64	Dag & Red, Boston Utd, Barnet, Stockport, Peterborough, Birmingham, Peterborough, Watford, Peterborough, Maidstone, Fisher Ath., Basildon Utd, Beckton Utd

FOREST GREEN ROVERS

Although tipped as probable strugglers by the pundits, those in the know at The Lawn were more optimistic as the club now had a manager in sole charge who had conducted a clear out and brought in some new young faces. We got off to a reasonable start and we found ourselves sitting dizzily in ninth place and looking forward to a great draw with Macclesfield in the F.A.Cup.

The result of this encounter is now on record but not the fact that we were the better team on both occasions. We lost 10-11 after a memorable penalty shoot out and were deprived of a lucrative draw with Swansea City and possible money from a T.V. conflict.

It proved to be a turning point with worse to come. Performances suffered, we dropped to twelfth place in the new year and then down to fifteenth by the end of January.Goals from forwards had dried up ,and clubs in the lower reaches were easing closer as they fought for Conference existence.

However, our enigmatic skipper Mark,son of legendaryTerry Cooper, took it upon himself to save us with a series of penalties and direct free kicks. He scored seven goals in the last eight games and completed twenty goals in the season from mid field.

Thus we survived by winning our last home game, much the same as the previous season . We celebrated our escape at Southport, only to be drubbed 1-5 which reminded us of our vulnerability.

So to another weed out by the manager and this time some more experienced football campaigners have come to the hamlet at the top of the hill.

Are we optimistic ? Of course we are ! Another reasonable start is needed and must be maintained. The Conference gets stronger all the time and we have to raise our team game and score more goals. If things go our way, gates will improve, money will come in and we need to progress in the F.A.Cup. We will all enjoy our football as usual ,hopefully without fears of relegation. Once again we will be tipped none too favourably but I have a feeling we will be celebrating again in May. **John Dickenson**

FOREST GREEN ROVERS

GROUND DETERMINED DETAILS

'The Lawn',
Nympsfield Road,
Forest Green,
Nailsworth,
Glos. GL6 0ET

TELEPHONE NUMBERS:
01453 834860
(Matchday & Club AdministrationCentre)
Fax: 01453 835291
Lawnside Fitness Suite: 01453 832268
Social Club: 01453 833295

SIMPLE DIRECTIONS:
About 4 miles south of Stroud on the A46 towards Bath.
InNailsworth turn into Spring Hill from the mini roundabout
and the ground is approx. half a mile up the hill on the left.
The nearest BR station is Stroud

CAPACITY: 5,141
COVERED TERRACING: 2500
SEATED: 526

SOCIAL FACILITIES: Clubhouse open every evening.
Bar and lounge. Open before and after Saturday matches.

CLUB SHOP: Open only on matchdays
selling souvenirs and programmes. Contact Andy Whiting.

Pages: 52   Price: £2.00
Editor: Clive White clivewhite@aol.com

Local Press: Stroud News & Journal
Gloucester Citizen

Local Radio: Star FM
BBC Radio Gloucestershire

Founded:	1890
Nickname:	Rovers
Sponsors:	Sheffield Insulations
Club Colours:	Black & white striped shirts, black shorts, red socks.
Change Colours:	Green & White
Midweek matchday:	Tuesday
Reserves' League:	College Academy
Youth League:	Glos. CountyYouth Lge

CLUB OFFICIALS

President	Peter Vick
Vice President	John Duff
Chairman	Trevor Horsley
Secretary	David Honeybill

c/o The lawn, Nympsfield Road,
Forest Green, Nailsworth, Glos. GL6 0ET
Tel: 01453 834860 Fax: 01453 835291

Press Officer Heather Cook
Tel: 01453 823281 Mobile 07775 603287

Marketing & Operations Colin Peake

FOOTBALL MANAGEMENT TEAM

MANAGER: NIGEL SPINK

Date of Appointment June 2001
Date of Birth: 8th August 1958
Place of Birth: Chelmsford

PREVIOUS CLUBS
As manager
As Asst. Man/Coach
As player Chelmsford City, Aston Villa,
West Bromwich Albion, Millwall
HONOURS
As manager FA Trophy R-up (jt)
As player E: 1. B: 2; Eur. Cup; Eur. Super Cup

Coach: Paul Birch
Physio: Bob Baird
Fitness Coach: Tony Daley
Youth Academy: Darren Perrin

Club's Playing Status: Part Time

Season	League	Div.	Pos.	P	W	D	L	F	A	W	D	L	F	A	Pts	Manager
						Home					*Away*					
01-02	Conference	-	18	42	7	7	7	28	32	5	8	8	26	44	51	Nigel Spink
00-01	Conference	-	16	42	6	9	6	28	28	5	6	10	15	26	48	F Gregan/ N. Spink & D. Norton
99-00	Conference	-	19	42	11	2	8	35	23	2	6	13	19	40	47	Frank Gregan
98-99	Conference	-	12	42	9	5	7	28	22	6	8	7	27	28	58	Frank Gregan
97-98	Southern	Prem	1	42	16	3	2	51	20	11	5	5	42	35	89	Frank Gregan

Season	League	Div.	Pos.	P	W	D	L	F	A	Pts	Manager
96-97	Southern	Southern	1	42	27	10	5	87	40	91	Frank Gregan
95-96	Southern	Southern	8	42	22	8	12	85	55	74	Frank Gregan
94-95	Southern	Midland	18	42	11	13	18	56	76	46	Frank Gregan
93-94	Southern	Midland	15	42	12	12	18	61	84	48	Pat Casey
92-93	Southern	Midland	19	42	12	6	24	61	97	42	Geoff Medcroft

HONOURS

FA Trophy R-up 98-99,00-01
FA Vase 81-82,
Southern League - Premier Div . 97-98,
Southern Div . 96-97;
Hellenic Lg 81-82,
Gloucs Nthn Sen Lg 37-38 49-50 50-51,
Gloucs Sen Cup 84-85 85-86 86-87,
Gloucs Sen Amat Cup (N) 26-27 45-46 71-72 75-76 77-78,
Gloucs Sen Prof Cup 84-85 85-86 86-87.

PREVIOUS

Leagues:
Stroud & Dist. 1890-1921,
Glos Northern Snr 22-67,
Glos Co. 67-73,
Hellenic 73-82,
Southern League 82-98,
Conference 98-.

Name: Stroud FC, 1989-92

Ground: None

Past Players who progressed to the Football League

G Rogers (Newport Co. 85)
K Gill (Newport Co. 85),
M England (Bristol Rov 85).
Wayne Hatswell (Oxford Utd. 00)

CLUB RECORDS (since 1998)

Attendance: 3,002
v St. Albans City, FA Umbro Trophy 18.04.99

Win: 8-0
v Fareham Town Southern Lge. Southern Div. 96-97

Defeat: 0-7
v Moor Green, Southern Lge. Midland Div. 85-86.

Career Goalscorer: Karl Bayliss

Career Appearances: Tommy Callinan

Transfer Fee paid: £20,000
for Adrian Randall from Salisbury City

Transfer Fee Received: £35,000
for Marc McGregor to Nuneaton Borough (July 2000)
for Wayne Hatswell to Oxford United (Dec. 2000)

BEST SEASON

FA Cup: 2nd Round 99-00
0-3 v Torquay Utd. (H)

FA Trophy: Runners-up 98-99, 00-01

FA Vase: Winners 81-82.

League: 12th Conference 98-99

LAST SEASON

F.A. Cup: First Round
F.A. Trophy: Fifth Round
Conference: 18th
Top Goalscorer: Mark Cooper 19
Player of the Year: Mark Cooper/ Martin Foster
Captain: Mark Cooper

FOREST GREEN ROVERS

Match Facts 2001-02

	Date	Comp.	Opponents	Att.	Score	Goalscorers
1	18/08	Conf.	Scarborough	1104	1 - 1	Meechan 33
2	22/08	Conf.	FARNBOROUGH TOWN	903	1 - 0	Allen 54
3	25/08	Conf.	BOSTON UNITED	816	0 - 3	
4	27/08	Conf.	Dover Athletic	732	2 - 1	Lightbody 9, Cooper 52
5	01/09	Conf.	DAGENHAM & REDBRIDGE	651	2 - 4	Heggs 40 90[p]
6	04/09	Conf.	Hereford United	1803	0 - 0	
7	08/09	Conf.	MORECAMBE	702	3 - 1	Cooper 3-1 Heggs 67 Shaw 88
8	11/09	Conf.	Hayes	548	1 - 1	Meechan 40[p]
9	15/09	Conf.	Nuneaton Borough	1182	1 - 2	Cooper 90
10	19/09	Conf.	WOKING	756	2 - 1	Travis 41, Heggs 50
11	22/09	Conf.	SOUTHPORT	921	2 - 1	Howey 17, Lightbody 73
12	29/09	Conf.	Northwich Victoria	736	2 - 2	Howie 3 Jenkins 59
13	02/10	Conf.	STALYBRIDGE CELTIC	761	0 - 2	
14	05/10	Conf.	Doncaster Rovers	2748	1 - 5	Ward 53
15	09/10	Conf.	Leigh RMI	405	2 - 1	Travis 27, Lightbody 84
16	13/10	Conf.	STEVENAGE BOROUGH	974	0 - 0	
17	20/10	Conf.	Telford United	835	0 - 0	
18	27/10	FA Cup Q4	Fisher Athletic	420	3 - 1	Howey 15, Futcher 37, Odejayi 88
19	03/11	Conf.	MARGATE	938	3 - 3	Meechan 24 (Pen),59 Travis 26
20	10/11	Conf.	Chester City	1330	3 - 2	Meechan 45 80, Odejayi 68
21	17/11	FA Cup 1	Macclesfield Town	1520	2 - 2	Meechan45, Cooper 82[p]
22	24/11	Conf.	BARNET	984	2 - 2	Meechan 81 Jenkins 89
23	28/11	FA Cup 1 R	MACCLESFIELD TOWN	1714	1 - 1	Cooper 29
24	01/12	Conf.	SCARBOROUGH	751	2 - 2	Heggs 2 Cooper 90
25	15/12	Conf.	Farnborough Town	776	0 - 3	
26	26/12	Conf.	YEOVIL TOWN	1609	1 - 1	Heggs 65
27	29/12	Conf.	Boston United	2190	1 - 6	Langan 65
28	05/01	Conf.	HEREFORD UNITED	1116	1 - 1	Cousins 15
29	13/01	FA Trophy 3	ALDERSHOT TOWN	1138	1 - 1	Meechan 38
30	15/01	FA Trophy 3 R	Aldershot Town	1487	3 - 2	Heggs 25, Cooper 37, Shaw 65
31	19/01	Conf.	Dagenham & Redbridge	1718	1 - 1	Cooper 3
32	22/01	Glos SC 1	MANGOTSFIELD UNITED	154	2 - 5	Daley 17, Middleton 45
33	29/01	Conf.	Yeovil Town	2686	2 - 2	Heggs 32[p] 42
34	02/02	FA Trophy 4	WORKSOP TOWN	816	1 - 0	Cooper 12
35	09/02	Conf.	DONCASTER ROVERS	917	0 - 2	
36	16/02	Conf.	Stevenage Borough	1215	1 - 4	Cooper 11
37	20/02	Conf.	DOVER ATHLETIC	509	2 - 1	Cooper 43, Smith 80[og]
38	23/02	FA Trophy 5	Stevenage Borough	1228	2 - 3	Heggs 14, Impey 90
39	02/03	Conf.	Woking	1638	4 - 3	Meechan 12, Sykes 49, Cooper 58 73
40	09/03	Conf.	HAYES	635	2 - 1	Heggs 25 43
41	16/03	Conf.	LEIGH RMI	636	1 - 2	Lee 87
42	23/03	Conf.	NUNEATON BOROUGH	759	1 - 2	Cooper 25[p]
43	26/03	Conf.	Stalybridge Celtic	512	1 - 2	Cooper 76[p]
44	30/03	Conf.	TELFORD UNITED	642	1 - 1	Cooper 34[p]
45	01/04	Conf.	Margate	845	1 - 1	Cooper 45
46	06/04	Conf.	CHESTER CITY	802	0 - 2	
47	08/04	Conf.	Morecambe	670	0 - 2	
48	13/04	Conf.	Barnet	1302	1 - 0	Cooper 21[p]
49	20/04	Conf.	NORTHWICH VICTORIA	871	2 - 0	Cooper 9[p] 86[p]
50	27/04	Conf.	Southport	737	1 - 5	Cooper 35[p]

1	2	3	4	5	6	7	8	9	10	11	Substitutes Used
Perrin	Cousins	Jenkins	Cooper	Howey	Allen	Shaw	Foster	Heggs	Meechan	Futcher	Lightbody 7
Perrin	Cousins	Jenkins	Cooper	Howey	Allen	Shaw	Foster	Heggs	Meechan	Futcher	Lightbody 7
Perrin	Cousins	Jenkins	Cooper	Howey	Lightbody	Shaw	Foster	Heggs	Meechan	Futcher	Middleton 11 Allen 6 Adams 10
Perrin	Cousins	Jenkins	Cooper	Lightbody	Allen	Shaw	Foster	Heggs	Meechan	Futcher	Middleton 11
Perrin	Cousins	Impey	Cooper	Howey	Allen	Shaw	Lightbody	Heggs	Meechan	Futcher	Daley 10 Middleton 11
Perrin	Cousins	Jenkins	Cooper	Impey	Foster	Shaw	Travis	Heggs	Meechan	Futcher	
Perrin	Cousins	Jenkins	Cooper	Impey	Foster	Shaw	Travis	Heggs	Meechan	Small	
Perrin	Cousins	Small	Jenkins	Cooper	Foster	Travis	Futcher	Heggs	Meechan	Shaw	Daley 6
Perrin	Cousins	Jenkins	Cooper	Impey	Foster	Shaw	Travis	Adams	Meechan	Small	Daley 2 Lightbody 9 Futcher 7
Perrin	Howey	Jenkins	Cooper	Impey	Foster	Shaw	Travis	Heggs	Meechan	Small	Daley 11 Adams 4
Perrin	Howey	Jenkins	Adams	Impey	Foster	Shaw	Travis	Heggs	Meechan	Daley	Futcher 9 Lightbody 10
Perrin	Howey	Jenkins	Cooper	Impey	Foster	Shaw	Travis	Ward	Meechan	Futcher	Cousins 4 Daley 11
Perrin	Cousins	Small	Jenkins	Howey	Foster	Shaw	Travis	Ward	Meechan	Daley	Impey 5 Middleton 3
Perrin	Cousins	Jenkins	Cooper	Impey	Foster	Shaw	Travis	Ward	Meechan	Futcher	Adams 7 Lightbody 9
Perrin	Howey	Jenkins	Cooper	Impey	Foster	Travis	Langan	Ward	Meechan	Futcher	Shaw 4 Lightbody 9
Perrin	Howey	Jenkins	Langan	Impey	Foster	Shaw	Travis	Ward	Meechan	Futcher	Cousins 7 Lightbody 9
Perrin	Cousins	Langan	Howey	Impey	Foster	Shaw	Travis	Odajayi	Meechan	Futcher	Middleton 3
Perrin	Cousins	Jenkins		Howey	Foster	Langan	Travis	Odajayi	Meechan	Futcher	Hayden 11
Perrin	Travis	Jenkins	Cooper	Impey	Foster	Langan	Howey	Odajayi	Meechan	Daley	
Perrin	Cousins	Jenkins	Impey	Howey	Langan	Travis	Cooper	Odajayi	Meechan	Foster	Tearney 11 Shaw 10
Perrin	Cousins	Jenkins	Cooper	Impey	Foster	Travis	Howey	Odajayi	Meechan	Langan	Daley 6
Perrin	Travis	Jenkins	Langan	Cousins	Foster	Shaw	Tearney	Odajayi	Meechan	Daley	Heggs 11 Allen 8
Perrin	Cousins	Jenkins	Cooper	Impey	Foster	Travis	Howey	Odajayi	Meechan	Langan	Heggs 9
Perrin	Cousins	Allen	Cooper	Impey	Foster	Shaw	Odejayi	Heggs	Meechan	Langan	Adams 3 Travis 8
Perrin	Cousins	Jenkins	Cooper	Impey	Howey	Travis	Langan	Heggs	Meechan	Daley	Odejayi 2 Middleton 11 Shaw 10
Perrin	Cousins	Jenkins	Cooper	Impey	Foster	Travis	Langan	Heggs	Meechan	Allen	Shaw 7 Futcher 11
Perrin	Cousins	Jenkins	Cooper	Langan	Foster	Shaw	Travis	Heggs	Meechan	Allen	Futcher 11 Middleton 10 Adams 7
Perrin	Cousins	Jenkins	Cooper	Impey	Foster	Langan	Travis	Heggs	Meechan	Howey	Futcher 6 Adams 10
Perrin	Cousins	Jenkins	Cooper	Foster	Impey	Shaw	Travis	Adams	Meechan	Futcher	Lightbody 9 Allen 11
Perrin	Cousins	Jenkins	Cooper	Impey	Foster	Shaw	Travis	Heggs	Meechan	Futcher	
Perrin	Cousins	Jenkins	Cooper	Impey	Foster	Shaw	Travis	Heggs	Meechan	Sykes	Lightbody 10
Perrin	Cousins	Jenkins	Cooper	Impey	Foster	Shaw	Travis	Heggs	Meechan	Sykes	Langan 7 Tearney 10
Perrin	Cousins	Jenkins	Cooper	Impey	Foster	Langan	Travis	Heggs	Meechan	Futcher	
Perrin	Cousins	Jenkins	Cooper	Impey	Foster	Langan	Travis	Heggs	Meechan	Sykes	Coupe 5 Tearney 8
Perrin	Cousins	Jenkins	Cooper	Coupe	Foster	Langan	Tearney	Heggs	Meechan	Sykes	Travis 8 Daley 10 Futcher 11
Perrin	Cousins	Jenkins	Cooper	Coupe	Foster	Langan	Travis	Heggs	Meechan	Sykes	Futcher 11
Perrin	Cousins	Jenkins	Cooper	Coupe	Foster	Langan	Travis	Heggs	Meechan	Futcher	Impey 3 Tearney 8 Daley 11
Perrin	Cousins	Coupe	Cooper	Impey	Foster	Langan	Tearney	Heggs	Meechan	Sykes	Freestone 10 Allen 8
Perrin	Cousins	Daley	Cooper	Impey	Foster	Tearney	Langan	Heggs	Meechan	Sykes	Allen 7 Travis 3
Perrin	Cousins	Allen	Cooper	Impey	Foster	Langan	Travis	Hopkins	Meechan	Sykes	Lee 2 Futcher 11 Jones 3
Pearcey	Lee	Jenkins	Cooper	Impey	Foster	Tearney	Langan	Hopkins	Meechan	Sykes	Travis 7
Pearcey	Lee	Jenkins	Cooper	Impey	Foster	Tearney	Langan	Hopkins	Meechan	Sykes	Heggs 7 Futcher 11
Perrin	Cousins	Jenkins	Cooper	Impey	Foster	Travis	Langan	Heggs	Meechan	Sykes	Tearney 7
Perrin	Cousins	Jenkins	Cooper	Impey	Foster	Travis	Langan	Heggs	Hopkins	Futcher	Meechan 10 Coupe 2
Perrin	Coupe	Jenkins	Cooper	Impey	Foster	Travis	Allen	Heggs	Meechan	Futcher	Hopkins 8 Tearney 7 Sykes 11
Perrin	Coupe	Jenkins	Cooper	Impey	Foster	Travis	Langan	Heggs	Meechan	Futcher	Hopkins 11 Lee 5
Perrin	Coupe	Jenkins	Cooper	Impey	Foster	Travis	Langan	Heggs	Meechan	Futcher	Lee 8 Allen 11
Perrin	Cousins	Jenkins	Cooper	Impey	Coupe	Travis	Langan	Hopkins	Meechan	Futcher	Tearney 7 Allen 8
Pearcey	Cousins	Jenkins	Cooper	Lee	Coupe	Tearney	Travis	Heggs	Hopkins	Futcher	Adams 8 Perrin 1 Meechan 7

FOREST GREEN ROVERS   PLAYING SQUAD

Player	Birthplace	D.O.B.	Previous Clubs	Bold print denotes England semi-professional international.

GOALKEEPERS

Player	Birthplace	D.O.B.	Previous Clubs
Steve Perrin	Wiltshire		Melksham T, Trowbridge T
Ellis Glassup	Cornwall		St.Austell

DEFENDERS

Player	Birthplace	D.O.B.	Previous Clubs
Kevin Langan	Jersey	07.04.78	Team Bath, Bristol C
Lee Russell	Southampton	03.09.69	Torquay, Portsmouth
Matthew Coupe ES, DMP	St Asaph	07.10.78	Aberystwyth T, Bath C, Clevedon T, Gloucester C, Forest Green R, Bristol C
Steve Jenkins Wales Int.	Bristol	02/01.80	Brentford, Southampton
Jamie Impey	Bournemouth		Dorchester T

MIDFIELD

Player	Birthplace	D.O.B.	Previous Clubs
Alan McLoughlin Rep.of Ireland Int.	Manchester	20.04.67	Rochdale, Wigan, Portsmouth, Southampton, Swindon, Manchester Utd
Alex Sykes British Univ., DMP	Newcastle-under-Lyme	02.04.74	Nuneaton B, Forest Green R, Endsleigh, Cheltenham T, Mansfield, Westfields
Daniel Allen	Swindon	09.09.83	From Youth team
Gary Owers	Newcastle	03.10.68	Notts Co., Bristol C, Sunderland
Rob Cook DMP	Stroud	28.03.70	Basingstoke T, Forest Green R, Cinderford T, Forest Green R, Shortwood Utd
Luke Middleton	Gloucester		Swansea, Southampton, Topsham T
Martin Foster	Rotherham	29.10.77	Doncaster R, Greenock Morton, Leeds

FORWARDS

Player	Birthplace	D.O.B.	Previous Clubs
Tony Daley England Int.	Birmingham	18.11.67	Aston Villa, Wolves, Watford, Walsall
Alex Meechan	Plymouth	29.01.80	Bristol C, Swindon
Carl Heggs	Leicester	11.10.70	Carlisle, Rushden & Diamonds, Northampton, Swansea, WBA, Paget R, Doncaster R, Leicester Utd
Simon Futcher	Swindon		Swindon Supermarine
Adi Adams	Rinteln, Germany	12.06.84	From Youth team
Nathan Lightbody	Swindon	22.12.81	From Youth team
Neil Grayson ESP, NC	York	01.11.64	Cheltenham T, Hereford Utd, Northampton, Boston Utd, Gateshead, Chesterfield, York, Doncaster R, Rowntrees
Trevor Tearney	Birmingham	-	Birmingham

GRAVESEND & NORTHFLEET

It has been a long time since Gravesend & Northfleet were in the elite atmosphere of the top non-League competition, but in the latest campaign they kept their nerves against a really stern challenge from the favourites, Canvey Island, and finished in top position with a four point margin and with a most impressive 90-33 goal difference, although the Island team did even better (108-41) than that!

With such a large number of goals scored and a sound defence mention can be made of the many good contributors such as Smith, Jackson, Stadhart, Wilkins and McKimm - a fine effort. Can they do better in the Conference? The cup form suggest that they might.

In the F.A. Cup the First Round proper was reached from a start in the Second Qualifying Round (1-0 at home to Eastbourne Borough). Dartford (2-0 away) and Burton Albion (2-0 away) followed and a trip to Huddersfield Town ended matters, but by a respectable 1-2 scoreline.

The F.A. Trophy was also impressive starting in Round One at home to Chelmsford City, with success at Cinderford Town (2-0), against Histon (1-1 and 3-1 at home) followed by Hendon (2-1 also at home). A last sixteen home defeat by Stalybridge Celtic brought the run to an end (0-2), but it was no disgrace and allowed the club to concentrate on the important promotion battle.

The basics for a good season in higher company are there. So their loyal fans - the average attendance was in the region of 500 - will be rewarded and are sure to give them every form of encouragement back at the top of the pyramid.

W.M.

L-R - Back Row: Ron Hillyard (goalkeeping coach), Jimmy Strouts, Lew Watts, Mark Bentley, Robert Owen, Jamie Turner, Paul Wilkerson, Craig Wilkins, Liam Hatch, Danny Lye, Paul Booth, Aaron Barnett, Neil Withington (fitness/diet caoch). **Front Row:** Martin Allen (Physio), Lewis Phillip, Adolph Amoko, Steve Mckimm, Justin Skinner, Phil Handford (Assistant Manager), Andy Ford (Manager), Jimmy Jackson (captain), Darren Smith, Austin Berkley, Matt Lee, Eliot Martin (Reserve Team Coach).

GRAVESEND & NORTHFLEET

GROUND DETAILS

Stonebridge Road,
Northfleet,
Kent
DA11 9GN
Tel: 01474 533796

Directions: From A2 take Northfleet/Southfleet exit (B262), follow toNorthfleet then B2175 (Springhead Rd) to junc A226, turn left (The Hill, Northfleet), road becomes Stonebridge Rd, grd on right at bottom of steep hill after 1 mile - car parking for 400-500. 2 mins from Northfleet BR station

Capacity:	4,184
Cover:	3,000
Seats:	500

Clubhouse: Fleet Social Centre. Hot and cold food available at tea bars on matchdays

Club Shop: Sells progs, hats, scarves, badges etc, & other memorabilia. Contact John Still or Angela Still

Formed:	1946
Nickname:	The Fleet
Sponsors:	Shepherd Neame
Colours:	Red/white/red
Change colours:	Silver/black/silver
Midweek matchday:	Tuesday
Youth Team:	P.A.S.E. League
Website:	
Clubcall line:	

CLUB OFFICIALS

Chairman:	Brian Kilcullen
Vice Chairman:	Jason Botley

Directors: Rob Gindley, Brent Ramsell, Bob Gunton, Maurice Norman,Mick Ward and Mark Lindup

Company & Football Secretary: Roly Edwards c/o Football Club

Commercial Manager &Press Officer: Rob Grindley
Tel: 01474 533796 (W) 07940 199166 (M)
email: fleet@stonebridgerd.freeserve.co.uk

Pages: 32 Price: £1.50
Editor: Paul Cossom
Clubcall: 09066 555844
Local Press: Gravesend Reporter,
Kent Messenger. Gravesend Messenger
The News Shopper
Local Radio: Invicta Radio, Radio Kent.

FOOTBALL MANAGEMENT TEAM

MANAGER   **ANDY FORD**

Date of Appointment	September 1997
Date of Birth:	4th May 1954
Place of Birth:	Minehead

PREVIOUS CLUBS
As manager
As asst. manager/coach
As player   Minehead, AFC Bournemouth, Southend U., Swindon T., Gillingham

HONOURS
As manager   Isthmian Lge Premier Div. 01-02, Full Members Cup 00-01, Kent Senior Cup 99-00, 00-01

As player

Assistant Manager: Phil Handford
Coach: Ron Hillyard
Physio: Martin Allen
Club's Playing Status: Part -time

Season	League	Div.	Pos.	Home					Away					Pts	Manager
				P	W	D	L	F	A	W	D	L	F	A		
01-02	Isthmian	Prem.	1	42	14	4	3	43	18	17	2	2	47	15	99	Andy Ford
00-01	Isthmian	Prem.	6	42	12	3	6	32	21	10	2	9	31	25	71	Andy Ford
99-00	Isthmian	Prem.	11	42	9	6	6	36	25	6	4	11	30	42	55	Andy Ford
98-99	Isthmian	Prem.	10	42	11	2	8	31	23	7	4	10	23	30	60	Andy Ford
97-98	Isthmian	Prem.	13	42	10	5	6	41	25	5	3	13	24	42	53	Steve Lovell
96-97	Southern	Prem.	14	42	10	4	7	34	27	6	3	12	29	46	55	Chris Weller

Season	League	Div.	Pos.	P	W	D	L	F	A	Pts	Manager
95-96	Southern	Prem.	11	42	15	10	17	60	62	55	Gary Aldous
94-95	Southern	Prem.	14	42	13	13	16	38	55	52	Gary Aldous
93-94	Southern	South.	1	42	27	11	4	87	24	93	Gary Aldous
92-93	Southern	South	4	42	25	4	13	99	63	79	Gary Aldous

HONOURS

Isthmian League (Rymans)	Champions: 2001-2002
Southern League	Southern League 57
	Southern Div 94-95,
	Div 1 Sth 74-75 R-up 70-71 88-89,
	Lg Cup 77-78 R-up 57-58,
	Champ Cup 77-78;
Kent Sen Cup	48-49 52-53 80-81, 99-00
	R-up 47-48 76-77 90-91 97-98;
Kent Floodlit Cup	69-70 R-up 72-73;
Kent Sen Shield	R-up 47-48 51-52;
Kent Interm Cup	R-up 87-88;
Kent Midweek Lg	95-96, R-up 92-93 93-94 94-95;
Kent Youth Lg	95-96 96-97;
	Lg Cup 82-83 86-87 96-97

PREVIOUS

Leagues:	Kent (Gravesend Utd),
	Southern 46-79, 80-9
	Alliance Prem. 79-80
	Isthmian ??-2002
Names:	Gravesend Utd.and Northfleet Utd
	(merged 1946)
Ground:	Central Avenue (Gravesend Utd)
	(Northfleet always played at StonebridgeRd)

Past Players who progressed to the Football League

Several incl. most recently:
K Baron (Aldershot 60), R Dwight (Coventry 62),
R Cameron (Southend 63), R McNichol (Carlisle 65),
A Humphreys (Mansfield 64), B Thornley (Brentford 65),
P Jeavons (Lincoln 66), B Fry (Orient 66),
B Gordine (Sheffield Utd 68),
T Baldwin (Brentford 77),
L Smelt (Nottm Forest 80),
T Warrilow (Torquay 87),
J.Bullard (West Ham U.98)

CLUB RECORDS

Attendance:	12,036
	v Sunderland, FA Cup 4th Rd 12.2.63.
	26.081
	v Aston Villa FA Cup 3rd Rd 95-96 at Villa Park
Goalscorer:	Steve Portway 150+(92-94, 97-01)
Appearances:	Ken Burrett 537
Win:	8-1
	v Clacton Tn, Sth Lge 62-63,
	(7-0 Godalming 95-96 FAC).
Defeat:	0-9
	v Trowbridge Tn, Southern Lge Prem Div 91-92
Fee Paid:	£8,000
	for Richard Newbery (Wokingham 96),
	& for Craig Williams(Tonbridge 97)
Fee Received:	£35,000
	for Jimmy Bullard (West Ham 1998)

BEST SEASON

FA Cup:	4th Round
	Replay 1963, 2-5 v Sunderland (A), 1-1 (H)
FA Trophy:	Fifth Round
	01-02
League:	5th in The Alliance Premier 79-80

LAST SEASON

F.A. Cup:	First Round
F.A. Trophy:	Fifth Round
League:	Isthmian League Champions
Top Goalscorer:	Che Stadhart 20
Player of the Year:	Justin Skinner
Captain:	Jimmy Jackson

GRAVESEND & NORTHFLEET

Match Facts 2001-02

Date	Comp.	Opponents	Att.	Score	Goalscorers
18.08	Ryman P	Kingstonian	723	1 - 0	Booth 72
21.08	Ryman P	CHESHAM UNITED	391	1 - 4	Booth 89
25.08	Ryman P	HARROW BOROUGH	395	2 - 2	Jackson 75, Wilkins 87
27.08	Ryman P	Aldershot Town	2252	2 - 1	Lye 56, Jackson 85
01.09	Ryman P	Maidenhead United	217	3 - 0	Booth 11, Smith 28, Stadhart 90
04.09	Ryman P	HEYBRIDGE SWIFTS	420	1 - 1	Spiller 45
08.09	Ryman P	ENFIELD	473	3 - 0	Lye 4, Barnett 13, Hatch 81
12.09	Ryman P	Croydon	153	4 - 3	Duku 18, Stadhart 34 41, Jackson 37
15.09	Ryman P	Hampton & Richmond Borough	330	2 - 0	Stadhart 57, Hatch 90
18.09	Ryman P	HENDON	394	3 - 0	Duku 27, Barnett 29, Stadhart 44
22.09	Ryman P	ST ALBANS CITY	604	3 - 2	Wilkins 33 60, Martin 80
25.09	Ryman P	Billericay Town	565	3 - 1	Stadhart 8, Lye 18, Wilkins 66
29.09	FA Cup Q2	EASTBOURNE BOROUGH	510	1 - 0	Wilkins 29
02.10	Ryman P	SUTTON UNITED	582	3 - 1	Booth 4 52, Stadhart 21
09.10	Ryman P	Grays Athletic	453	0 - 2	
13.10	FA Cup Q3	Dartford	1270	2 - 0	Martin 68[p], Owen 74
20.10	Ryman P	BRAINTREE TOWN	779	3 - 0	Wilkins 46, Stadhart 54 85
27.10	FA Cup Q4	Burton Albion	1647	2 - 0	Stadhart 27, McKinn 33
03.11	FA Trophy 1	CHELMSFORD CITY	829	2 - 0	Wilkins 32, Stadhart 68
10.11	Ryman P	BEDFORD TOWN	656	4 - 1	Jackson 7, Wilkins 18 30, Smith 90
13.11	Ryman P	Basingstoke Town	340	4 - 1	Boothe 12, Jackson 63 78, Stadhart 72
17.11	FA Cup 1	Huddersfield Town	6112	1 - 2	Clarke 2[og]
24.11	Ryman P	HITCHIN TOWN	706	2 - 0	Jackson 42, Hatch 86
01.12	FA Trophy 2	Cinderford Town	245	2 - 0	Wilkins 57, Hatch 82
04.12	Lge Cup 1	ARLESEY TOWN	n.k	2 - 1	
11.12	Lge Cup 2	BASINGSTOKE TOWN	n.k	4 - 1	
15.12	Ryman P	KINGSTONIAN	691	2 - 0	Martin 58, Jackson 62
22.12	Ryman P	Boreham Wood	272	2 - 0	Jackson 5, McKimm 71
29.12	Ryman P	Chesham United	424	2 - 2	Wilkins 26, Duku 89
05.01	Ryman P	Heybridge Swifts	266	2 - 1	Smith 14, Barnett 41
08.01	Ryman P	Canvey Island	2111	2 - 0	Jackson 4, Duku 73
16.01	Lge Cup 3	TOOTING & MITCHAM UTD.	n.k	1 - 2	Duku 65
19.01	Ryman P	Enfield	306	5 - 1	Jackson 34 44, McKimm 52, Smith 58, Parker 81
22.01	FA Trophy 3	Histon	214	1 - 1	Barker 83[og]
29.01	FA Trophy 3 R	HISTON	460	3 - 1	Duku 8, Burton 40, Wilkins 76
05.02	FA Trophy 4	HENDON	542	2 - 1	Wilkins 64, Jackson 82
09.02	Ryman P	Hitchin Town	439	4 - 0	Owen 19, McKinn 27 54, Parker 70
13.02	Kent SC QF	Dartford	503	3 - 0	Parker 10 80, Smith 30
16.02	Ryman P	Hendon	364	1 - 1	McKimm 49
19.02	Ryman P	ALDERSHOT TOWN	1216	2 - 1	Barnett 43, Wilkins 46
23.02	FA Trophy 5	STALYBRIDGE CELTIC	926	0 - 2	
02.03	Ryman P	St Albans City	451	3 - 0	Jackson 20 90, Wilkins 83
05.03	Ryman P	MAIDENHEAD UNITED	626	3 - 2	McKimm 6 44, Hatch 64
09.03	Ryman P	BILLERICAY TOWN	862	1 - 0	Wilkins 50
11.03	Ryman P	Purfleet	713	0 - 2	
16.03	Ryman P	Sutton United	689	1 - 0	Stadhart 30
19.03	Ryman P	CROYDON	673	6 - 1	Smith 13 88, Stadhart 24 28 85, Wilkins 64
23.03	Ryman P	GRAYS ATHLETIC	920	2 - 0	Jackson 15, Skinner 49
26.03	Ryman P	CANVEY ISLAND	4098	0 - 1	
30.03	Ryman P	Harrow Borough	381	3 - 0	Smith 22, Stadhart 42[p] 61
01.04	Ryman P	PURFLEET	1085	0 - 0	
06.04	Ryman P	BASINGSTOKE TOWN	802	0 - 0	
09.04	Ryman P	HAMPTON & RICHMOND BOR.	1076	2 - 1	Stadhart 56, Hatch 90
13.04	Ryman P	Braintree Town	663	2 - 0	Lye 54, Booth 87
16.04	Kent SC SF	Fisher Athletic	191	3 - 2	Hatch 54, Booth 77, Wilkins 80
20.04	Ryman P	BOREHAM WOOD	1844	0 - 1	
27.04	Ryman P	Bedford Town	1743	1 - 0	Stadhart 34
06.05	Kent SC F	Margate	2000	5 - 0	Jackson 32, Barnett 37, Duku 80, Booth 85, Lye 88

Left:
Jimmy Jackson, seen here curling another free kick round the wall.
Photo: Alan Coomes

Below:
Robert Owen showing his absolute joy after just two minutes of the FA Cup 1st Round tie against Huddersfield Town at the McAlpine stadium.
Photo: Darren C Thomas

GRAVESEND & NORTHFLEET   PLAYING SQUAD

Player	Birthplace	D.O.B.	Previous Clubs	Bold print denotes England semi-professional international.
GOALKEEPERS				
Jamie Turner RP	Kent	-	Deal T, Greenwich B, Horsham, Welling Utd	
Paul Wilkerson	Hertford	11.12.74	Stevenage B, Welling Utd, Hayes, Slough T, Watford	
DEFENDERS				
Aaron Barnett RP	Kent	-	Erith & Belvedere, Furness, VCD Ath., Charlton	
Craig Wilkins RP	Kent	-	Tonbridge (£7,500), Maidstone Invicta, Maidstone Utd	
Francis Duku Crawley T, RP	London	-	Dulwich Hamletm Grays Ath., Crawley T, Romford, Maidenhead Utd, Collier Row, Reading, West Ham	
Justin Skinner RP	Dorking	17.09.72	Aylesbury Utd, Wimbledon	
Lew Watts	Maidstone	14.09.74	Welling Utd, Fisher Ath., Gravesend	
Matthew Lee RP	Farnborough	13.05.79	Sutton Utd, Gravesend, Charlton	
Nick Burton RP	Bury St.Edmunds	02.10.75	Hampton & Richmond, Aldershot T, Yeovil T, Torquay U., Portsmouth	
MIDFIELD				
Danny Lye RP	Kent	-	Bearsted	
Jimmy Strouts Combined Services Rep.	Yorkshire	21.08.71	Dover Ath., Stevenage B, Dover Ath., Sittingbourne, Harrogate T, Frickley Ath., Harrogate RA	
Jamie Coyle	Kent	-	From Youth team	
Jimmy Jackson RP	Kent	-	Charlton	
Mark Bentley	London	-	Aldershot T, Enfield, Aveley, Enfield	
Robert Owen RP	Kent	-	Sittingbourne, Tonbridge, Sittingbourne, Gillingham	
Steve McKimm RP	London	30.07.75	Kingstonian, Hayes, Farnborough T, Dulwich Hamlet, Molesey, Hendon	
Warren Williams RP	Middlesex	-	Hampton & Richmond, Hanwell T, Viking Greenford	
FORWARDS				
Austin Berkley	Dartford	28.01.73	Barnet, Carlisle, Barnet, Shrewsbury, Swindon, Gillingham	
Che Stadhart RP	London	-	Hampton & Richmond Bor., Chalfont St Peter Leyton Pennant, Stevenage B, Leyton Pennant	
Liam Hatch RP	Kent	-	Herne Bay	
Paul Booth RP	Kent	-	Tunbridge Wells, Tonbridge, Maidstone Utd	
Simon Parker RP	Essex	-	Heybridge Swifts, Stowmarket T, Whitton Utd	

HALIFAX TOWN

Last season could have finished after two games as far as Halifax Town was concerned!

Sitting in sixth position with an away victory and home draw the season looked promising but, sadly the next twelve games brought just four goals and by the end of October 'The Shaymen' had hit rock bottom of the Football League.

From then on the club was never out of the bottom two and after a 2-1 F.A. Cup victory over Farnborough Town and a home draw with Stoke City, defeat in the replay left a long depressing fight against relegation as off the field insecurity did nothing to help the battles on the field.

Halifax had dropped into the Conference before when huge crowds had desperately attended end of season games in an attempt to prevent their fall from grace, with no luck.

This time they were familiar with the drop, the supporters didn't seem to be so worried and the club officials knew relegation wasn't the end of the world.

Perhaps a little more success in the Conference might increase support and boost morale, so it wasn't all gloom and doom. The players and management however, sensed that changes would be made and to a certain extent they have.

The highly successful player manger of all conquering Alfreton Town, Colin Wilder has been given the job of rebuilding the playing squad and new budgets, structures and administration will, hopefully, equip the club satisfactorily for the new challenge of returning to the Football League for a second time.

With Doncaster Rovers, Chester City and Scarborough head of them in the queue it won't be easy, but I suspect they will enjoy themselves more this season than last!

Halifax Town AFC 2003-03 - L-R - Back Row:
Robert Herbert, Paul Stoneman, Adam Quinn, Tom Morgan, Lee Butler, Ryan Poole, Philip Haigh, Steven Kerrigan, Nicky Heinemann.
Middle: Ian Helliwell, Alan Jackson, Alistair Asher, Craig Smith, Phil Clarkson, Stuart Elliott, Gary Birchall, Bobby Barr, Tommy Gildert.
Front: Andy Farrell, Craig Midgley, Steve Bushell, Chris Wilder, Sean McCauley, Ian Fitzpatrick, Neil Grayston.

HALIFAX TOWN

GROUND DETAILS

The Shay Stadium
Halifax
West Yorks.
HX1 2YS
Tel: 01422 341222
Fax: 01422 349487
email: theshay@halifaxafc.co.uk
Website: halifaxafc.co.uk

Directions: M62, J24, head towards the city centre. The ground is on the right signposted "The Shay"
Nearest Railway station: Halifax, 1/2 mile from ground

Capacity:	**9,500**
Covered Seating:	**2,500**
Covered Standing:	**7,000**

Clubhouse: Yes, open during normal licensing hours.

Club Shop: Yes, contact club.

Founded:	1911
Nickname:	The Shaymen
Sponsors:	Nationwide B.S.
Colours:	Blue shirts, white shorts, blue socks
Change colours:	Yellow shirts, blue shorts, white socks
Midweek matchday:	Tuesday 7.45

CLUB OFFICIALS

President:	Bob Holmes
Chairman:	David Cairns
Vice-Chairman:	Adrian Hall
Other Directors:	Bob Bland, T Charlton, Martin Fox, Richard Harrison, Roy Jackson, Phil Jewitt
Chief Executive:	Tony Kniveton
Club Secretary:	Richard Groves c/o the club Tel: 0771 5254323 (M)
Commercial Manager:	Andrew Pinfield Tel: 07753 835449 (M) email: commercial@halifaxafc.co.uk

MATCHDAY PROGRAMME

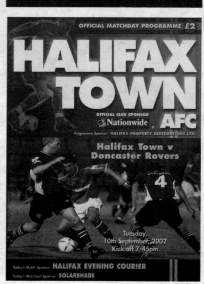

OFFICIAL MATCHDAY PROGRAMME £2

HALIFAX TOWN AFC

OFFICIAL CLUB SPONSOR Nationwide
Programme Sponsor HALIFAX PROPERTY RESTORATIONS LTD.

Halifax Town v
Doncaster Rovers

Tuesday,
10th September, 2002
Kick-off 7-45pm

Today's Match Sponsor HALIFAX EVENING COURIER
Today's Matchball Sponsor SOLARSHADE

Price: £2   Pages: 32
Editor: Andrew Pinfield

FOOTBALL MANAGEMENT TEAM

MANAGER: **CHRIS WILDER**

Date of Appointment	June 2002
Date of Birth:	23rd September 1967
Place of Birth:	Wortley

PREVIOUS CLUBS
As player/manager   Alfreton Town 01-02
As player   Southampton (A), Sheffield Utd., Rotherham Utd., Notts Co., Bradford C., Sheffield Utd., Brighton & H.A., Halifax T., Alfreton T.
HONOURS
As manager   NCE 01-02 - League Championship, League Cup, President's Cup

* * *

Asst Manager:	Lee Butler
Player Coach	Sean McCauley
Youth Team Coach:	Bobby Barr
Youyh Dev. Officer:	Jack Haymer
Physiotherapist:	Alan Jackson

Season	League	Div.	Pos.	P	W	D	L	F	A	W	D	L	F	A	Pts	Manager
						Home (or total)					Away					
01-02	League	Div.3	24	46	5	9	9	24	28	3	3	17	15	56	36	Paul Bracewell/Alan Little
00-01	League	Div.3	23	46	7	6	10	33	32	5	5	13	21	36	47	Paul Bracewell
99-00	League	Div.3	18	46	15	9	22	44	58						54	Mark Lillis
98-99	League	Div.3	10	46	10	8	5	33	25	7	7	9	25	31	66	Kieran O'Regan
97-98	Conference		1	42	17	4	0	51	15	8	8	5	23	28	87	G. Mulhall & K. O'Regan
96-97	Conference		19	42	9	5	7	39	37	3	7	11	16	37	48	J. Carroll/G. Mulhall&K. O'Regan
95-96	Conference		15	42	13	13	16	49	63						52	John Bird/John Carroll
94-95	Conference		8	42	17	12	13	68	54						63	John Bird
93-94	Conference		13	42	13	16	13	55	49						55	Peter Wragg/John Bird
92-93	League	Div.3	22	42	3	5	13	20	35	6	4	11	25	33	36	John McGrath

CLUB RECORDS

Attendance: 36,885
v Tottenham H., FA Cup 5th Rd, 14.02.53

Win: 12-0
v West Vale Ramblers, FA Cup 1st Q. Rd. 13-14

Defeat: 0-13
v Stockport C., Div. 3 North, 33-34

Career Goalscorer: Albert Valentine

Career Appearances: John Pickering

Transfer Fee Paid: £50,000
for Ian Juryeff to Hereford Utd.

Transfer Fee Received: £250,000
for Wayne Allison from Watford

PREVIOUS

Leagues: Yorkshire Comb. 1911-12
Midland League 1912-21
Football League - Division 3 North 1-21-58
- Division 3 1958-63, 69-76, 92
Division 4 1963-69

Grounds: Sandhall Lane 1911-15, Exley 1919-21

Names: None

HONOURS

Conference Champions 1997-98
Promotion to Division 3 1968-69

Past Players
who progressed to the Football League between 93-98

Geoff Horsfield (Fulham)

BEST SEASON

FA Cup: Fifth Round 1913-14, 52-53

FA Trophy: 3rd Round 93-94

Football League: 3rd, Division 3 1969-70

Conference: Champions 1997-98

LAST SEASON

F.A. Cup: 2nd Round Replay

League Cup: 1st Round

L.D.V. Trophy: 1st Round

Football League: 24th Division Three

Leading Goalscorer: Paul Harsley

Captain: Steve Bushell

Player of the Year: Paul Stoneman

Manager: Chris Wilder

HALIFAX TOWN

Match Facts 2001-02

	Date	Comp.	Venue	Opponents	Att.	Score	Goalscorers	
1	11.08	Div.3	A	Lincoln City	3753	2-1	Craig Midgley	
2	18.08	Div.3	H	Exeter City	1937	1-1	Steve Swales	6
3	21.08	Lge. Cup	A	Barnsley	5418	0-2		-
4	25.08	Div.3	A	Southend United	3535	1-4	Neil Redfearn	15
5	27.08	Div.3	H	Oxford United	2271	0-2		15
6	01.09	Div.3	A	York City	2646	0-1		21
7	08.09	Div.3	H	Macclesfield Town	1714	0-0		19
8	15.09	Div.3	A	Swansea City	3794	2-0	Paul Harsley 2	15
9	18.09	Div.3	H	Mansfield Town	1880	1-0	Gary Jones	11
10	22.09	Div.3	H	Leyton Orient	2021	0-0		10
11	25.09	Div.3	A	Rochdale	3410	0-2		12
12	29.09	Div.3	A	Hull City	9572	0-3		18
13	05.10	Div.3	H	Scunthorpe United	2603	0-0		18
14	13.10	Div.3	A	Plymouth Argyle	5088	0-3		21
15	16.10	LDV Trophy	A	Huddersfield Town	3570	0-0	Lost 3-4 after penalties	
16	20.10	Div.3	H	Bristol Rovers	1898	0-0		20
17	23.10	Div.3	H	Luton Town	2140	2-4	Paul Harsley, Ian Fitzpatrick	24
18	27.10	Div.3	A	Carlisle United	3157	0-0		24
19	03.11	Div.3	H	Darlington	2192	2-2	Neil Redfearn, Ian Fitzpatrick	23
20	10.11	Div.3	A	Rushden & Diamonds	3883	1-2	Neil Redfearn	24
21	17.11	F.A.C. 1	H	Farnborough Town	1914	2-1	Craig Middleton, Jamie Wood	-
22	20.11	Div.3	A	Hartlepool United	2963	0-3		24
23	24.11	Div.3	H	Torquay United	1681	2-0	Craig Middleton, Ian Fitzpatrick	23
24	01.12	Div.3	A	Cheltenham Town	3304	1-2	Paul Harsley	24
25	08.12	F.A.C. 2	H	Stoke City	3355	1-1	Paul Harsley	-
26	12.12	F.A.C. 2R	A	Stoke City	4356	0-3		-
27	15.12	Div.3	H	Shrewsbury Town	1730	1-2	Paul Harsley	24
28	26.12	Div.3	A	Macclesfield Town	2421	1-1	Paul Harsley	24
29	29.12	Div.3	A	Oxford United	6046	1-6	Steve Bushell	24
30	12.01	Div.3	A	Exeter City	2785	0-0		24
31	19.01	Div.3	H	Lincoln City	2007	3-0	Gary Jones 2, Ian Fitzpatrick	24
32	22.01	Div.3	A	Kidderminster Harriers	2295	0-2		24
33	26.01	Div.3	A	Scunthorpe United	3465	0-4		24
34	29.01	Div.3	H	Southend United	1251	1-1	Gary Jones	24
35	02.02	Div.3	H	Hull City	3400	0-1		24
36	09.02	Div.3	A	Bristol Rovers	6921	0-2		24
37	12.02	Div.3	H	York City	2818	1-1	Ian Fitzpatrick	24
38	16.02	Div.3	H	Plymouth Argyle	2330	0-2		24
39	23.02	Div.3	H	Swansea City	1601	0-1		24
40	26.02	Div.3	A	Mansfield Town	4513	1-2	Ian Fitzpatrick	24
41	02.03	Div.3	A	Leyton Orient	4748	1-3	Neil Redfearn	24
42	05.03	Div.3	H	Rochdale	2825	1-2	Neil Redfearn	24
43	09.03	Div.3	A	Shrewsbury Town	3729	0-3		24
44	12.03	Div.3	H	Kidderminster Harriers	1227	1-0	Craig Midgley	24
45	16.03	Div.3	H	Cheltenham Town	1870	4-1	Paul Harsley 2, Craig Midgley, Ian Fitzpatrick	24
46	23.03	Div.3	A	Luton Town	6834	0-5		24
47	29.03	Div.3	H	Carlisle United	2728	2-2	Andrew Woodward, Neil Redfearn	24
48	01.04	Div.3	A	Darlington	3041	0-5		24
49	06.04	Div.3	H	Hartlepool United	1838	0-2		24
50	13.04	Div.3	A	Torquay United	2692	4-2	Paul Stoneman, Paul Harsley, Craig Middleton, Matt Clarke	24
51	20.04	Div.3	H	Rushden & Diamonds	2699	2-4	Paul Harsley, Ian Fitzpatrick	24

Lee Butler	Paul Harsley	Dominic Ludden	Andrew Woodward	Chris Clarke	Paul Stoneman	Craig Middleton	Neil Redfearn	Steve Kerrigan	Gary Jones	Craig Midgley	Mark Jules	Barry Richardson	Steve Swales	Graham Mitchell	Matthew Clarke	Alan Reilly	Ian Fitzpatrick	Robert Herbert	Steven Oleksewycz	Jamie Wood	Peter Crookes	Peter Wright	Scott Houghton	Nathan Winder	Steve Bushell	Marc Richards	Andrew Farrell	Nicky Heineman
1	2	3	4	5	6	7	8	9	10	11	12	13	14	15	16	17	18	19	20	21	22	23	25	26	27	28	29	30
X	X		X	X	X		X	X	/9	X	X		X							X		/11						
X	X		X	X	X		X	X	/21	X	X		X							X		/11						
X	X		X	X	X	/6	X	X	/9	X	X		X							X		/11						
X	X		X	X	X	/14	X	X	/21	X	X		X							X		/11						
X	X		X		X	X	X	X	X		X	X								X								
X	X		X	X	X		X	X	X	/10	X		X	X	/9													
X	X		X	X	X		X	X		X			X	X	/24							/14						
X	X		X	X	X		X		X		X		X	X	/24													
X	X		X	X	X		X		X		X		X	X	/24													
X	X		X	X	X	X		X	/7		X		X	X	/17													
X	X			X	X	X	X	/25	X		X		X	X	/10													
X	X			X	X	X		X		X	X		X	X	/5													
X	X			X	X	/10	X	X	X	/5	X		X	X					/9									
X	X			X		X	X	X		X			X	X	X													
X	X			X	X	X	X	X	/2	X		/12	X	X						/9								
X	X			X	X		X	X		X		X	X	X		/7	X			/10								
X	X			X	X		X	/9		X		X	X	X			X			/14								
X	X			X	X	X	X			X		/7	X	X	X		X											
X	X			X	X	X	X	/8		X	X	/6	X	X		X	X			/11								
X	X		X		X	X	X	/18	/7	X	X		X	X			X											
X	X		X		X	X		X		/10	X		X	X			X			X								
X	X	/15	X		X	X	/18	X		/10	X		X	X			X			X								
X	X	X	X	X		X		/18		/21				X	X		X			X						X		
X	X	X	X	X		X	/7	/21		/18				X	X		X			X						X		
X	X	X	X	X			X	X	/18	X				X	X		X	/11				/8						
X	X		X	X			X	X	/11	X	X			X	X		X	/8				/12						
X	X		X		X			/19		/21				X	X	X	X	X	X	X		X			X			
	X		X		X	X		/18		/21	X			X	X	X	X	X		X		X			X			
	X		X		X	X	/9	X	/7					X	X	X		X		X	X		X			X		
	X			X		X	X	X	/9	X	X			X	X	X		X		X			X			X		
	X		X	X	X		X	X		X	X			X	X			X		X			X			X		
	X		X	X	/27	X	X		X	X				X	X			X	X		X		/9		/10	X		
	X	X	X	X		X	X		X	X				X	/10	X	/9			X			X			X		
	X	X	X			X	X		X	X	/12			X		X	X			X			X			X		
	X	X	X	X		X	X		X	X	X			X	X	/25	X			/19	X		X			X		
	X		X			/23			X	X	X			X			X					X	X		X	X			
	X		X				/23	X		X	X	X			X			X					/16	X		X	X		
		X			X	/4	X	X		X	X			X			X					X	X	X	X	X			
	X			X	X	/7	/28	X	X		X	X	X			X					X	X	X	X					
	X			X	X	X	/15	/28	X	X		X			X					X	X	X	X						
	X	X		X	X	X	/11	X	X		X	X			X					/25	X								
	X	X		X	X	X	/11	X	X		X	X	X			X	X			X			X	/18				
	X	X			X	X	X	X	X		X	X				/29	X	X			X	X						
	X	X		/11	X	/29	X	X	X	/16	X	X	X			X					X	X						
	X	X			X		X	X	X	X	X	X	/29	X	/18					X	X							
	X	X			X		X	X	X	X	X	X	/18							X	X	/11						
	X	X		/14	X		X	X	X	X	X	/29	X							C. Smith	X	X	X					
	X			X	X	X	/17	X	X	X	X	X	/7							/2	X	X	X					
	X			X	X	X	/30	X	X	X		X	/7			X					X	X	X					

HALIFAX

PLAYING SQUAD

Player	Birthplace	D.O.B.	Previous Clubs

Bold print denotes
England semi-professional international.

GOALKEEPERS

Lee Butler	Sheffield	30.05.66	Alfreton T, Doncaster R, Halifax T, Dunfermline Ath., Wigan Ath., Barnsley, Aston Villa, Lincoln C, Harworth Cl

DEFENDERS

Alastair Asher	Leicester	14.10.80	Mansfield Town (T)
Chris Wilder	Wortley	23.09.67	Southampton(T), Sheffield Utd., Rotherham U., Notts Co, Bradford City, Sheffield Utd., Halifax T., Alfreton T.
John Beresford **England S, Y, 'B'**	Sheffield	04.09.66	Man. City (A), Barnsley, Portsmouth, Newcastle U., Southampton, Ossett T., Alfreton T.
Neil Grayston	Keighley	25.11.75	Bradford City, Bradford P.A., Southport
Nicky Heinman	Bradford	04.01.85	from trainee
Paul Stoneman	Whitley Bay	26.02.73	Blackpool, Colchester Utd.
Sean McAuley	Sheffield	23.06.72	Manchester U., St. Johnstone, Hartlepool U., Scunthorpe U., Rochdale, Portland Timbers (USA).
Stuart Elliottt	London	27.08.77	Newcastle U., Darlington, Plymouth A., Carlisle U., Durham C., Scarborough, Exeter C.

MIDFIELD

Craig Smith			from trainee
Phil Clarkson	Hambleton	13.11.68	Fleetwood T., Crewe Alexandra, Scunthorpe U., Blackpool
Robert Herbert	Durham	19.08.83	from trainee
Steve Bushell	manchester	28.12.72	York C., Blackpool, Stalybridge Celtic.

FORWARDS

Andy Farrell	Easington	21.12.83	from trainee
Brian Quailey **St. Kitts & Nevis Int.**	Leicester	21.03.78	Deeping Rangers, Nuneaton Bor., W.B.A., Scunthorpe U. Doncaster Rovers
Craig Midgley	Bradford	24.06.76	Bradford C., Hartlepool U.
Ian Fitzpatrick	Manchester	22.09.80	Manchester U., FC Fortune (Ger.).
Simon Parke	Bradford		Bradford P.A., Guiseley
Steve Kerrigan	Bailleston	09.10.72	Albion Rovers, Clydebank, Stranraer, Ayr Utd., Shrewsbury T.,

HEREFORD UNITED

The constant pressure of the financial situation always ensured there was a grey cloud hanging over Edgar Street. Once again the herculian efforts of a few, led by owner- manager Graham Turner, kept the club safely in the Conference. But as the club had only recently been a member of the Football league, this really was a little depressing for all the local fans ,who yearned to see the club challenging to return to Division Three.

The season started brightly with a lucrative televised match at home to Barnet and the Sky audience would have been impressed with a 2-1 victory and spectacular goal from Gavin Williams. In fact only one defeat in the first seven games saw 'The Bulls' in an impressive fourth place. But that was as good as it got and without ever slipping into really dangerous waters, they spent the rest of the season in mid table no-man's-land.

As usual, the club's famous mascot was needed as the F.A. Cup brought another scalp to Edgar Street . Wrexham were beaten by a Wright goal and this brought some much needed income from a trip to Swindon Town . An excellent tie produced a close defeat and five goals for the crowd of 7,699 .

In the F.A.Trophy , two Ryman League clubs, Chesham United and Hampton & Richmond Borough were beaten before an away tie at much improved Chester City brought a 1-2 defeat.

The coming campaign will again be a test for club spirit and determination to overcome the constant financial pressures. Last season Graham Turner stood down to allow PHil Robinson to take up the reigns as he battled with off the field matters. Phil has now moved to Stafford Rangers and Graham is back doing what he loves best. It will be a tough but hopefully rewarding season.   T.W.

Hereford United 2002/2003

L-R - Back Row: Richard Teasdale, Andrew Tretton, Matt Baker, Kenneth Griffiths, Scott Voice, Paul Parry.
Middle Row: Jamie Pitman, Michael Rose, John Grant, Tony James, Matt Clarke, Ben Smith.
Front Row: Robert Purdie, Richard O'Kelly, Ian Wright, Graham Turner and Danny Williams.

HEREFORD UNITED

GROUND DETAILS

Edgar Street,
Hereford.
HR4 9JU

Telephone
Tel: 01432 276666
Fax 01432 341359
Club Call 09068 121645
E-mail HUFCbulls@hotmail.com
Website: http://www.herefordunited.co.uk

SIMPLE DIRECTIONS: From Hereford city centre follow signs to Leominster (A49) into Edgar Street. Car parking for 600 near the ground(60p Sats,free mid week). Nearest railway station Hereford
Match Tickets: Adults £8-£10 concessions £3-£7 plus family combinations.

CAPACITY: 8,843
SEATED: 2,761
COVERED TERRACING: 6,082

SOCIAL FACILITIES: Clubhouse open on matchdays
REFRESHMENTS: Three Tea Bars
CLUB SHOP: Yes

Founded:	1924
Nickname:	The Bulls
Sponsors:	Sun Valley
Club Colours:	White & black shirts, black shorts, white trim; white socks.
Change Colours:	Red shirts; red shorts; red socks
Midweek matchday:	Tuesday

CLUB OFFICIALS

Chairman/Director of Football
Graham Turner

Company Secretary Joan Fennessy

Directors George Hyde Ron Jukes, Grenville Smith, Hugh Brookes, Aidan McGivern.

Club Secretary Joan Fennessy
c/o the club
Tel: 01432 276666 Fax: 01432 341359

FOOTBALL MANAGEMENT TEAM

MANAGER: **GRAHAM TURNER**

Date of Appointment August 1995
Date of Birth: 5th October 1947
Place of Birth: Ellesmere Port

PREVIOUS CLUBS
As manager Shrewsbury T., Aston Villa, Wolverhampton W.
As player Wrexham, Chester City, Shrewsbury T.
HONOURS
As manager League: Div.3 78-79 (Shrewsbury), Div.4 87-88, Div.3 88-89; S.V.T. 87-88 (Wolves)
As player England - Youth cap.

* * *

Coaches:
Chief Scout: Ron Jukes

Physio: Richard O'Kelly
Club Playing Status: Full Time

Pages: 32 Price: £2.00
Editor: Lee Symonds
Clubcall: 09068 121 645

Other club publications: None

Local Press: Hereford Journal; Hereford Times; Worcester Evening News

Local Radio: BBC Hereford & Worcester

Season	League	Div.	Pos.	Home						Away						Pts	Manager
				P	W	D	L	F	A	W	D	L	F	A			
01-02	Conference	-	17	42	9	6	6	28	15	5	4	12	22	38	52	Graham Turner/Phil Robinson
00-01	Conference	-	11	42	6	12	3	27	19	8	3	10	33	27	57	Graham Turner
99-00	Conference	-	8	42	9	6	6	43	31	6	8	7	18	21	59	Graham Turner
98-99	Conference	-	13	42	9	5	7	25	17	6	5	10	24	29	55	Graham Turner
97-98	Conference	-	6	42	11	7	3	30	19	7	6	8	26	30	67	Graham Turner

Season	League	Div.	Pos.	P	W	D	L	F	A	Pts	Manager
96-97	F. League	3	24	46	11	14	21	50	65	47	Graham Turner
95-96	F. League	3	6	46	20	14	12	65	47	74	Graham Turner
94-95	F. League	3	16	42	12	13	17	45	62	49	Graham Turner
93-94	F. League	3	20	42	12	6	24	60	79	42	Greg Downs & John Layton
92-93	F. League	3	17	42	10	15	17	47	60	45	Greg Downs & John Layton

HONOURS

Football League Div. 3 75-76, Div. 4 R-up 72-73;

Southern League R-up 45-46 50-51 71-72

NW Championship 58-59

Div. 1 58-59,

Cup Winners 52 57 59

Welsh Cup Winners 89-90,

R-up 3 times;

PREVIOUS

Leagues: Birmingham League;
Birmingham Combination;
Southern League 39-72;
Football League 72-97

Names: None

Ground: None

Past Players who progressed to the Football League

Since joining the Conference: Gavin Mahon (Brentford)

CLUB RECORDS

Attendance: 18,114
v Sheffield Wed., FA Cup 3rd Rd, 4.1.58

Career Goalscorer: Unknown
Career Appearances: unknown

Win: 6-0 v Burnley (A), Div. 4 24.1.87

Defeat: 0-6 v Rotherham Utd (A), Div. 4 29.4.89

Transfer Fee Paid: £75,000
to Walsall for Dean Smith, 7.94
Transfer Fee Received: £250,000
for Darren Peacock from Q.P.R., 3.91
+ a further £240,000
when he moved to Newcastle Utd. 3.91

BEST SEASON

FA Trophy: Semi-Finals 00-01

FA Cup: 4th Rd 71-72 (as Southern League side),
76-77, 81-82, 89-90, 91-92
League Clubs Defeated (as a non-league club): Exeter C
53-54,Aldershot 56-57,Q.P.R. 57-58,Millwall 65-66,North"ton
T 70-71, Northampton T,Newcastle U71-72,Colchester United
& Brighton & H 97-98,Hartlep'l U&YorkC 99-00 Wrexham01-2

League: 22nd Football League Div.ision 2 1976-77

LAST SEASON

F.A. Cup: Second Round
F.A. Trophy: Fifth Round
Conference: 17th
Top Goalscorer: Gavin Williams
Player of the Year: Gavin Williams
Captain: Ian Wright

CONFERENCE

HEREFORD UNITED

	Date	Comp.	Opponents	Att.	Score	Goalscorers
1	18/08	Conf.	BARNET	2210	2 - 1	Snape 16, G Williams 18
2	21/08	Conf.	Nuneaton Borough	1544	0 - 2	
3	25/08	Conf.	Stalybridge Celtic	851	2 - 0	Elmes 59 74
4	27/08	Conf.	SOUTHPORT	2010	0 - 0	
5	01/09	Conf.	Margate	1010	2 - 2	G Williams 20, Parry 32
6	04/09	Conf.	FOREST GREEN ROVERS	1803	0 - 0	
7	08/09	Conf.	DOVER ATHLETIC	1541	3 - 0	Elmes 14, 88 Williams M 60 (Pen)
8	11/09	Conf.	Dagenham & Redbridge	1338	0 - 1	
9	15/09	Conf.	Morecambe	1462	2 - 2	Elmes 47, Parry 82
10	18/09	Conf.	YEOVIL TOWN	1709	0 - 2	
11	22/09	Conf.	STEVENAGE BOROUGH	1515	1 - 1	Quiggin 73
12	29/09	Conf.	Hayes	634	1 - 4	Voice 25
13	02/10	Conf.	FARNBOROUGH TOWN	1205	4 - 2	Voice 3, Wright 10, Snape 30, G Williams 53
14	05/10	Conf.	Leigh RMI	535	1 - 0	Snape 64
15	09/10	Conf.	Chester City	1142	0 - 2	
16	13/10	Conf.	BOSTON UNITED	1647	0 - 1	
17	20/10	Conf.	SCARBOROUGH	1346	6 - 0	
18	27/10	FA Cup Q4	Dover Athletic	1221	1 - 0	G Williams 33
19	03/11	Conf.	Woking	2107	0 - 1	
20	10/11	Conf.	DONCASTER ROVERS	1711	0 - 0	
21	18/11	FA Cup 1	WREXHAM	4107	1 - 0	Wright 8
22	24/11	Conf.	Northwich Victoria	790	0 - 1	
23	01/12	Conf.	Barnet	1713	0 - 2	
24	08/12	FA Cup 2	Swindon Town	7699	2 - 3	Williams 14 Wright 27
25	15/12	Conf.	NUNEATON BOROUGH	1347	1 - 1	Williams 2
26	26/12	Conf.	Telford United	2168	1 - 0	Goodwin 80
27	29/12	Conf.	STALYBRIDGE CELTIC	1633	3 - 0	Williams 27, Snape 28, Elmes 69
28	05/01	Conf.	Forest Green Rovers	1116	1 - 1	Parry 69
29	12/01	FA Trophy 3	Chesham United	831	2 - 2	Williams 25, Rodgerson 45
30	15/01	FA Trophy 3 R	CHESHAM UNITED	1075	4 - 0	Robinson 20, Parry 55, Williams 70, Pearce 80
31	19/01	Conf.	MARGATE	1474	3 - 0	Goodwin 49, Shirley 60, Elmes 78
32	26/01	Conf.	Southport	970	1 - 1	Rodgerson 46
33	09/02	Conf.	LEIGH RMI	1443	0 - 1	
34	12/02	FA Trophy 4	HAMPTON & RICHMOND B.	1167	4 - 1	Clarke 27, James 52[p], Williams 83, Elmes 90
35	18/02	Conf.	Boston United	3013	4 - 3	Robinson 17 35, Goodwin 23, Elmes 75
36	23/02	FA Trophy 5	Chester City	1747	1 - 2	Elmes 76
37	02/03	Conf.	Yeovil Town	3022	1 - 2	Parry 47
38	05/03	Conf.	TELFORD UNITED	1260	0 - 1	
39	12/03	Conf.	Farnborough Town	479	2 - 4	Wright 12, Robinson 22
40	16/03	Conf.	Dover Athletic	952	1 - 0	Piearce 80
41	23/03	Conf.	MORECAMBE	1408	0 - 2	
42	26/03	Conf.	CHESTER CITY	1295	1 - 0	Wright 6
43	30/03	Conf.	Scarborough	1478	2 - 3	Williams 8, James 90
44	01/04	Conf.	WOKING	1465	2 - 2	Clarke 45, Williams 62
45	06/04	Conf.	Doncaster Rovers	1735	0 - 4	
46	13/04	Conf.	NORTHWICH VICTORIA	1493	1 - 0	Williams 20
47	16/04	Conf.	DAGENHAM & REDBRIDGE	1583	1 - 0	Robinson 89
48	20/04	Conf.	HAYES	1494	0 - 1	
49	27/04	Conf.	Stevenage Borough	1979	1 - 3	Piearce 19

#	1	2	3	4	5	6	7	8	9	10	11	Substitutes Used
1	Baker	Clarke	M Williams	Goodwin	Wright	T James	Rodgerson	Snape	Voice	G Williams	Parry	Elmes 9
2	Baker	Clarke	M Williams	Goodwin	Wright	T James	Rodgerson	Snape	Elmes	G Williams	Parry	Evans 11 Davidson 4
3	Baker	Clarke	M Williams	Webb	Wright	T James	Rodgerson	K James	Elmes	G Williams	Parry	Snape 7 Pearce 8
4	Baker	Clarke	M Williams	Webb	Wright	T James	Piearce	Snape	Elmes	G Williams	Parry	Davidson 7
5	Baker	Clarke	M Williams	Webb	Wright	T James	Davidson	Snape	Elmes	G Williams	Parry	Goodwin 3
6	Barnes	Clarke	M Williams	Webb	Wright	T James	Davidson	Snape	Elmes	G Williams	Parry	Goodwin 3 Pearce 7
7	Baker	Clarke	M Williams	Webb	Wright	T James	K James	Snape	Elmes	G Williams	Parry	
8	Baker	Clarke	M Williams	Webb	Wright	T James	K James	Snape	Elmes	G Williams	Parry	Pearce 7
9	Baker	Clarke	M Williams	Webb	Wright	T James	Goodwin	Snape	Elmes	G Williams	Parry	Sedgemore 5 Pearce 10 K James 7
10	Baker	Clarke	M Williams	Webb	Quiggin	T James	Sedgemore	Snape	Elmes	G Williams	Parry	Pearce 5
11	Baker	M Williams	Capaldi	Webb	Gardiner	T James	Voice	Snape	Elmes	G Williams	Parry	Quiggin 9
12	Baker	Clarke	Capaldi	Webb	Wright	T James	Voice	Snape	Elmes	G Williams	Parry	Goodwin 4 Quiggin 9
13	Baker	Clarke	K James	Webb	Wright	T James	Goodwin	Snape	Voice	G Williams	Parry	
14	Baker	Clarke	K James	Quiggin	Wright	T James	Goodwin	Snape	Voice	G Williams	Parry	
15	Baker	Clarke	Capaldi	Quiggin	Wright	T James	Goodwin	Snape	Voice	G Williams	Parry	Gardiner 7 Elmes 9 Webb 4
16	Baker	Clarke	Capaldi	Webb	Wright	T James	Goodwin	Snape	Voice	G Williams	Parry	Elmes 9
17	Baker	Clarke	Capaldi	Quiggin	Wright	T James	Goodwin	Snape	Elmes	G Williams	Parry	Voice 11 Gardiner 9 K James 10
18	Baker	Clarke	K James	Quiggin	Wright	T James	Goodwin	Snape	Elmes	G Williams	Parry	Voice 9 Shirley 10
19	Baker	Clarke	Capaldi	Quiggin	Wright	T James	Goodwin	Snape	Elmes	G Williams	Parry	Pearce 4 Shirley 8 Davidson 9
20	Baker	Clarke	Capaldi	Quiggin	Wright	T James	Goodwin	Snape	Davidson	G Williams	Parry	Voice 9 Robinson 4
21	Baker	Shirley	Capaldi	Robinson	Wright	T James	Quiggin	Snape	Voice	G Williams	Parry	Elmes *
22	Baker	Clarke	Capaldi	Robinson	M Williams	T James	Kevan	Pearce	Elmes	G Williams	Parry	Voice 9 Quiggin 8
23	Baker	Clarke	Capaldi	Robinson	Wright	T James	Quiggin	Snape	Elmes	G Williams	Parry	M Williams 5 Davidson 9 Kevan 7
24	Baker	Clarke	Capaldi	Robinson	Wright	T James	Quiggin	Snape	Elmes	G Williams	Parry	Davidson * Kevan *
25	Baker	Clarke	Capaldi	Rodgerson	Wright	T James	Goodwin	Kevan	Elmes	G Williams	Parry	Davidson 9 Robinson 8
26	Baker	Clarke	Capaldi	Robinson	Wright	T James	Goodwin	Snape	Elmes	G Williams	Rodgerson	
27	Baker	Clarke	Capaldi	Robinson	Wright	T James	Goodwin	Snape	Elmes	G Williams	Parry	Voice 9
28	Baker	Clarke	Shirley	Robinson	Wright	T James	Goodwin	Snape	Elmes	Quiggin	Parry	Davidson 4
29	Baker	Clarke	Shirley	Robinson	Wright	T James	Rodgerson	Snape	Elmes	G Williams	Parry	Davidson 9
30	Baker	Clarke	Shirley	Robinson	Wright	T James	Rodgerson	Snape	Quiggin	G Williams	Parry	M Williams 2 Kevan 7 Pearce 9
31	Baker	Clarke	Shirley	Robinson	Wright	T James	Rodgerson	Snape	Parry	G Williams	Goodwin	Elmes 9
32	Baker	Clarke	Shirley	Robinson	Wright	T James	Rodgerson	Snape	Parry	Parry	Goodwin	Davidson 9 Pearce 7
33	Baker	Clarke	Shirley	Robinson	Wright	T James	Rodgerson	Snape	Parry	G Williams	Goodwin	Quiggin 7 Elmes 8
34	Baker	Clarke	Shirley	Robinson	Wright	T James	Rodgerson	Snape	Parry	G Williams	Goodwin	Elmes 11
35	Baker	Clarke	Shirley	Robinson	Wright	Hill	Rodgerson	Snape	Parry	G Williams	Goodwin	Elmes 4
36	Baker	Clarke	Shirley	Quiggin	Wright	T James	Rodgerson	Snape	Parry	G Williams	Goodwin	Elmes 4
37	Baker	Clarke	Shirley	Rodgerson	Wright	T James	Goodwin	Snape	Elmes	G Williams	Parry	Quiggin 7
38	Baker	Clarke	Shirley	Rodgerson	Wright	T James	Goodwin	Snape	Elmes	G Williams	Parry	Davidson 9 Pearce 11
39	Jones	Clarke	Shirley	Robinson	Wright	T James	Rodgerson	Snape	Parry	G Williams	Goodwin	Elmes 3
40	Jones	Shirley	Goodwin	Robinson	Wright	T James	Quiggin	Snape	Elmes	G Williams	Parry	Pearce 7
41	Jones	Holmes	Shirley	Robinson	Wright	T James	Goodwin	Pearce	Elmes	G Williams	Rodgerson	Quiggin 11 Davidson 8 Hill 5
42	Jones	Holmes	Barrick	Robinson	Wright	T James	Goodwin	Clarke	Parry	G Williams	Rodgerson	Quiggin 11 Baker 1
43	Baker	Holmes	Barrick	Robinson	Wright	T James	Goodwin	Snape	Parry	G Williams	Rodgerson	Elmes 4 Diamond 11 Hill 5
44	Baker	Holmes	Barrick	Robinson	Clarke	T James	Goodwin	Snape	Parry	G Williams	Diamond	Elmes 11
45	Baker	Holmes	Barrick	Robinson	Clarke	T James	Quiggin	Snape	Elmes	G Williams	Parry	Diamond 7
46	Baker	Holmes	Barrick	Robinson	Wright	T James	Clarke	Snape	Elmes	G Williams	Parry	Quiggin 9 Shirley 2
47	Baker	Holmes	Barrick	Robinson	Wright	T James	Goodwin	Snape	Quiggin	G Williams	Clarke	Shirley 11
48	Baker	Holmes	Barrick	Robinson	Wright	T James	Goodwin	Snape	Quiggin	G Williams	Parry	Pearce 9 Shirley 2
49	Baker	Rodgerson	Goodwin	Robinson	Wright	T James	Quiggin	Snape	Piearce	G Williams	Parry	Elmes 7 Shirley 5

HEREFORD UNITED — PLAYING SQUAD

Player	Birthplace	D.O.B.	Previous Clubs
			Bold print denotes England semi-professional international.

GOALKEEPERS

Player	Birthplace	D.O.B.	Previous Clubs
Matt Baker	Harrogate	18.12.79	Hull
Kenny Griffiths	Devon	-	Torquay

DEFENDERS

Player	Birthplace	D.O.B.	Previous Clubs
Tony James	Birmingham		WBA
Ian Wright	Lichfield	10.03.72	Stoke, Bristol R, Stoke
Matthew Clarke British Univ.	Cardiff		Cradley T, Halesowen H, Halesowen T, Kidderminster H
Paul Parry	Hereford		Youth team
Andy Tretton	Derby	09.10.76	Shrewsbury, Derby
Jamie Pitman FA XI	Trowbridge	06.01.76	Woking, Yeovil T, Hereford Utd, Swindon
Michael Rose	Salford	28.07.82	Chester C, Manchester Utd
Richard Teesdale	Birmingham	-	Walsall
Rob Sawyers	Dudley	20.11.78	Barnet, Wolves

MIDFIELD

Player	Birthplace	D.O.B.	Previous Clubs
Ian Rodgerson	Hereford	09.04.66	Pegasus Jun., Hereford U., Cardiff C., Birmingham C., Sunderland, Cardiff C.
Ben Smith	Chelmsford	23.11.78	Southend, Yeovil T, Reading, Arsenal
Danny Williams	Sheffield	02.03.81	Chesterfield
Robert Purdie	Leicester	-	Leicester

FORWARDS

Player	Birthplace	D.O.B.	Previous Clubs
Scott Voice	Birmingham	12.08.74	Bilston T, Stourbridge, Bilston T, Stourbridge, Wolves
John Grant	Manchester	09.08.81	Crewe
Neil Gough	Harlow	01.09.81	Hampton & Richmond, Leyton Orient
Steve Guinan	Birmingham	24.12.75	Shrewsbury, Plymouth, Camb Utd., Nottingham F

KETTERING TOWN

For a club with ambitions being absent from the Conference for the first time ever was extremely upsetting, but the most recent campaign saw the club finally returning to better things as a result of a very tight competition.

Tamworth led on the last day of the season but only drew 3-3 at Folkestone and missed a penalty, while the East Midlands side won by the odd goal in three at Tiverton Town to take the title by a brace of points with a points difference of 80-42, which was marginally inferior to Tamworth's.

There was never a doubt about Kettering's firepower with several players being regulars on the scoresheets among them Collins, Butcher, Watkins and Norman.

As the Poppies had to start the F.A. Cup competition in the Second Qualifying Round and reached the First Round Proper there was reasonable encouragement from that direction but it took them five matches to arrive at that point with successes against Redditch United (0-0 and 2-0), Northwood (3-0 at home) and Stevenage Borough (0-0 and 2-1), but the denouement came at home to Cheltenham Town, who scored six of the match's seven goals.

The F.A. Trophy challenge ended at Purfleet immediately (1-2), so there were no further distractions with the outcome at the end of the season, The Double had been achieved against Merthyr Tydfil, Salisbury City, Stafford Rangers, Folkestone Invicta, Havant & Waterlooville and Chelmsford City with Cambridge City alone doling out the same medicine in return.

A lucky promotion success? Not really, as The Poppies timed their run in to perfection making their own luck on their way and now it is up to the club to build on it, since the same form may not be good enough for the Conference.

W.M.

L-R - Back Row: Peter Fear, Darren Collins, Wayne Diuk, Carl Lake, Chris Perkins, Gary Hughes, Brett McNamara, Craig Norman. **Middle**: Peter Lake (physio), Martin Matthews, Steve Wilkinson, Ian Bowling, Rob Wild, Steve Lenagh, Brad Piercewright, Jason Lee. **Front**: Andrew Speechley, Soner Zamrutel, Shaun Murray, Carl Shutt (manager), Dale Watkins, Lee Cowling, Rob Yardy

KETTERING TOWN

GROUND DETAILS

Rockingham Road,
Kettering,
Northants, NN16 9AW

COMMUNICATION   Tel: 01536 83028/410815 (Office)
01536 410962 (Social Club)
Fax: 01536 412273
email: info@ketteringtownafc.co.uk
web site: http://www.ketteringtownafc.co.uk

SIMPLE DIRECTIONS:
From south - M1 junction 15, A43 to Kettering use A14 exit
Junct. 7, follow A43 to Corby/Stamford to 1st roundabout, turn
right A6003, ground half a mile.
From north - M1 or M6 use junction 19 then A14 to Kettering.
Exit Junct. 7 then as above.
British Rail - Inter-City Midland - 50 mins from London
(St.Pancras), 20 mins from Leicester

CAPACITY: 6,170
COVERED SEATING: 1,800
COVERED TERRACING: 2,200

CLUB SHOP: Open before and after matches, & office staff
will open on request on non-match days. Situated in front of
main stand. Also Alex Elmores in town centre

SOCIAL FACILITIES: Social Club (Poppies),
Vice-Presidents Bar & Sponsor's Lounge

Pages: 32   Price: £1.50
Editor: Fox Design to Print 0116 222 8500
Clubcall: 09068 101567

Local Press: Evening Telegraph;
Chronicle & Echo; Herald & Post; Citizen
Local Radio: Radio Northampton; Northants 96; KCBC

Founded: 1872

Nickname: Poppies

Club Sponsors: Weldon Plant Ltd.

Club colours: Red & black shirts,
red shorts, black socks

Change colours: Yellow shirts, shorts & socks

Midweek home matchday: Tuesday

CLUB OFFICIALS

President	Sid Chapman
Chairman	Peter Mallinger
Vice Chairman	Michael Leech
Directors	Peter Oliver
Club Secretary/	Graham Starmer
Press Officer	c/o the club

Tel: 01536 483028/410815 Fax: 01536 412273

Assistant Secretary   Andy Thomas

FOOTBALL MANAGEMENT TEAM

MANAGER: Carl Shutt

Date of Appointment: February 2001
Date of Birth: 10th October 1961
Place of Birth: Sheffield

PREVIOUS CLUBS
As manager   .
As asst. man./coach
As player   Spalding U., Sheffield Wed.,
Bristol C., Leeds Utd.,

HONOURS
As manager
As player
                                         *   *   *

Assistant Manager: Ernie Moss
Physio: Peter Lake
Youth & Comunity development: Dominic Genovese

Season	League	Div.	Pos.	P	W	D	L	F	A	W	D	L	F	A	Pts	Manager
						Home					Away					
01-02	Southern	Prem	1	42	12	4	5	41	22	15	2	4	39	19	87	Carl Shuttt
00-01	Conference	-	20	42	5	5	11	23	31	6	5	10	23	31	43	Peter Morris/Carl Shutt
99-00	Conference	-	13	42	8	10	3	25	19	4	6	11	19	31	52	Peter Morris
98-99	Conference	-	2	42	11	5	5	31	16	11	5	5	27	21	76	Peter Morris
97-98	Conference	-	14	42	8	6	7	29	29	5	7	9	24	31	52	Steve Berry
96-97	Conference	-	14	42	9	4	8	30	28	5	5	11	23	34	51	Gary Johnson/Steve Berry

				P	W	D	L	F	A	Pts		
95-96	Conference	-	16	42	13	9	20	68	84	48		Gary Johnson
94-95	Conference	-	6	42	19	10	13	73	56	67		Graham Carr
93-94	Conference	-	2	42	19	15	8	46	42	72		Graham Carr
92-93	Conference	-	13	42	14	13	15	61	63	55		Dave Cusack/Graham Carr

HONOURS

Premier Inter League Cup;
FA Trophy Runners-up 78-79;
Alliance Premier League (Conference) R-up x 4;
Southern League Champions x 4,
County Cup Winners,
Daventry Charity Cup Winners x 2;
Northants Senior Cup x 28;
Maunsell Cup Winners x 12

PREVIOUS

Leagues: Southern League??-79, 01-02
Northants League,
Midland League,
Birmingham League
Central Alliance,
United Counties League
Conference 79-01

Grounds   North Park; Green Lane

Past Players who progressed to the Football League

Billy Kellock(Peterborough), Gary Wood (Notts Co.), Dave Longhurst (Nott'm Forest), Scott Endersby (Ipswich), Steve Fallon (Cambridge U.), Andy Rogers (Plymouth), Martyn Foster (Northampton), Cohen Griffith (Cardiff C.), Andy Hunt (Newcastle), Richard Brown (Blackburn R.) ,Ben Wright (Bristol C.),Kofi Nyamah (Stoke C.) + Adam Sollitt(North'tonT)

CLUB RECORDS

Attendance:	11,536
	Kettering v Peterborough (pre-Taylor report)
Win:	16-0
	v Higham YMCI (FA Cup 1909)
Defeat:	0-13
	v Mardy (Southern League Div. 2, 1911/12)
Transfer fee paid:	£25,000
	to Macclesfield for Carl Alford, 1994
Transfer fee received:	£150,000
	from Newcastle United for Andy Hunt
Career goalscorer:	Roy Clayton 171 (1972 - 1981)
Career appearances:	Roger Ashby

BEST SEASON

FA Trophy:		Runners-up 78-79 99-00
FA Cup:	4th Round	88-89, 1-2 v Charlton Ath.
		91-92, 1-4 v Blackburn R.
League clubs defeated:		Swindon T. 61-62, Millwall 63-64,
		Swansea C. 74-75, Halifax T. 88-89, Bristol Rovers 88-89,
		Maidstone U. 91-92, Hull C. 00-01
League:		Conference Runners-up
		1980-81; 88-89; 93-94; 98-99

LAST SEASON

FA. Trophy:	Second Round
F.A. Cup:	First Round
League:	Southern League Champions
Top Goalscorer:	Dale Watkins
Player of the Year:	Richard Butcher
Captain:	Darren Collins

201

KETTERING TOWN

Date	Comp.	Opponents	Att.	Score	Goalscorers
18.08	DM P	Merthyr Tydfil	725	2 - 0	Murray 40, Watkins 43
21.08	DM P	WORCESTER CITY	1571	4 - 1	Murray 15 54, Watkins 20, Duik 84
25.08	DM P	CRAWLEY TOWN	1545	1 - 3	Norman 37[p]
27.08	DM P	Cambridge City	764	1 - 2	Collins 8
01.09	DM P	NEWPORT COUNTY	1324	1 - 2	Watkins 35
04.09	DM P	Tamworth	803	0 - 1	
08.09	DM P	Newport IOW	650	2 - 0	Watkins 73, Murray 89
11.09	DM P	STAFFORD RANGERS	1214	1 - 0	Watkins 10
15.09	DM P	SALISBURY CITY	1295	4 - 0	Diuk 16, Collins 24, Perkins 61, McNamara 70
17.09	DM P	Worcester City	1152	1 - 1	McNamara 74
22.09	DM P	BATH CITY	1418	0 - 0	
29.09	FA Cup Q2	Redditch United	660	0 - 0	
02.10	FA Cup Q2 R	REDDITCH UNITED	1044	2 - 0	Collins 6, Watkins 73
06.10	DM P	Folkestone Invicta	284	3 - 2	Watkins 35 45, Hughes 40
09.10	DM P	TAMWORTH	1395	1 - 1	Collins 12
13.10	FA Cup Q3	NORTHWOOD	1204	3 - 0	Collins 45, Butcher 57, Watkins 83
20.10	DM P	Welling United	608	1 - 1	Collins 90
23.10	DM P	Stafford Rangers	679	3 - 2	Watkins 1, Cowling 57, Norman 81
27.10	FA Cup Q4	Stevenage Borough	1937	0 - 0	
30.10	FA Cup Q4 R	STEVENAGE BOROUGH	2079	2 - 1	Norman 36, Collins 69
03.11	FA Trophy 1	SWINDON SUPERMARINE	1072	3 - 1	Piercewright 18, Wilkinson 74, Butcher 76
10.11	DM P	Havant & Waterlooville	689	3 - 1	Collins 17, Watkins 49, Butcher 86
13.11	Lge Cup 1	CORBY TOWN	357	3 - 1	Inman 4, Wilkinson 10, Shutt 23
17.11	FA Cup 1	CHELTENHAM TOWN	2942	1 - 6	Norman 4
24.11	DM P	HINCKLEY UNITED	1281	2 - 1	Hughes 30, Inman 77
28.11	Maunsell SF	PETERBOROUGH UNITED	291	1 - 7	Shutt
01.12	FA Trophy 2	Purfleet	261	1 - 2	Piercewright 31
08.12	DM P	Bath City	899	1 - 0	Butcher 76
11.12	Lge Cup 2	King's Lynn	472	1 - 6	Wilkinson 5
15.12	DM P	MERTHYR TYDFIL	1212	3 - 0	Watkins 4, Collins 26 68
22.12	DM P	Crawley Town	2133	2 - 0	Hughes 78, Butcher 85
26.12	DM P	CAMBRIDGE CITY	1957	1 - 2	Norman 44
29.12	DM P	CHELMSFORD CITY	1461	4 - 2	Watkins 34, Norman 60, Butcher 68 90
08.01	N'hants SC 2	WELLINGBOROUGH TOWN	207	10 - 1	Wilkinson 2, Shutt, Lenagh, Inman 3, Lake 3
19.01	DM P	Salisbury City	539	2 - 1	Norman 79[p], Murray 90
29.01	DM P	WELLING UNITED	1175	3 - 1	Howarth 10, Murray 26, Norman 53[p]
02.02	DM P	Weymouth	1005	1 - 3	Howarth 77
09.02	DM P	MOOR GREEN	1458	2 - 1	Watkins 54 63
12.02	DM P	HEDNESFORD TOWN	1455	1 - 1	Watkins 9
16.02	DM P	Newport County	722	2 - 1	Butcher 11, Duik 69
23.02	DM P	TIVERTON TOWN	1441	0 - 0	
25.02	N'hants SC QF	PETERBOROUGH UNITED	177	0 - 2	
02.03	DM P	HAVANT & WATERLOOVILLE	1354	3 - 1	Collins 5, Watkins 16, Norman 62
09.03	DM P	Ilkeston Town	842	2 - 0	Murray 34 70
11.03	DM P	Hednesford Town	920	2 - 1	Watkins 61, Howarth 89
16.03	DM P	KING'S LYNN	1842	3 - 0	Piercewright 18, Collins 41, Butcher 60
19.03	DM P	ILKESTON TOWN	1456	1 - 2	Collins 87
23.03	DM P	Hinckley United	966	1 - 2	Butcher 66
30.03	DM P	FOLKESTONE INVICTA	1394	2 - 1	Watkins 68, Perkins 90
01.04	DM P	Chelmsford City	707	2 - 0	Shutt 24, Cowling 69
06.04	DM P	NEWPORT IOW	1666	1 - 2	Watkins 33
13.04	DM P	Moor Green	586	2 - 0	Butcher 57, Watkins 85
16.04	DM P	King's Lynn	1192	3 - 0	Watkins 46 85, Cowling 87
20.04	DM P	WEYMOUTH	2420	4 - 1	Lenagh 32 56, Collins 52 90
27.04	DM P	Tiverton Town	1996	2 - 1	Norman 9 [p], Lenagh 48

Above:
The pre-match line-up for last season's FA Cup 4th
Qual. Round tie with Stevenage Borough.
L-R Boro Bear, Sam McMahon (Stevenage),
Messrs. Faye, Mellin & Reeve, Martin Matthews
with Peter Morgan the Boro mascot in front.

Left:
Peter Fear and 'keeper Ian Bowling are well
focussed on the ball.

Right:
Chris Perkins ducks to allow 'keeper Ian
Bowling a clear sight of the ball.

Photos: Peter Barnes

KETTERING TOWN — PLAYING SQUAD

Player	Birthplace	D.O.B.	Previous Clubs	
				Bold print denotes England semi-professional international.

GOALKEEPERS

Player	Birthplace	D.O.B.	Previous Clubs
Ian Bowling DMP	Sheffield	27.07.65	Mansfield, Bradford C, Lincoln C, Gainsborough Trinity
Simon Ward	Peterborough	-	Yaxley

DEFENDERS

Player	Birthplace	D.O.B.	Previous Clubs
Craig Norman DMP	Perivale	21.03.75	Chelsea
Chris Perkins DMP	Stepney	01.03.80	Southend
Martin Matthews DMP	Peterborough	22.12.75	King's Lynn, Northampton, Derby
Brad Piercewright DMP	Northampton	-	Scarborough, QPR
Bryan Small Eu-21	Birmingham	15.11.71	Forest Green R, Walsall, Stoke, Bolton, Aston Villa
Garry Hughes DMP	Birmingham	19.11.79	Northampton
Lee Howarth	Bolton	03.01.68	Boston Utd, Stevenage Bor., Barnet, Mansfield T., Peterborough, Chorley
Mark Haran	Rotherham	21.01.77	Hednesford T, Emley, Frickley Ath., Eastwood T, Rotherham

MIDFIELD

Player	Birthplace	D.O.B.	Previous Clubs
Danny Walsh	Manchester	16.09.78	Chesterfield, Oldham
Richard Butcher DMP	Peterborough	22.01.81	Rushden & Diamonds, Northampton
Scott Goodwin	Hull	13.09.78	Hereford Utd, Hednesford T, Grantham T, Shepshed D, Coventry C.
Shaun Murray ES, EY, DMP	Newcastle	07.12.70	Notts Co., Scarborough, Portsmouth, Tottenham
Wayne Duik DMP	Nottingham	26.05.80	Gedling T, Notts Co

FORWARDS

Player	Birthplace	D.O.B.	Previous Clubs
Gez Murphy NC	Leicester	19.12.78	Boston Utd, Telford Utd, Gresley R, Atherstone Utd, Solihull B, VS Rugby Leicester
Niall Inman Rep.of Ire Y & u-21, DMP	Wakefield	06.02.78	Dover Ath., Peterborough
Carl Shutt Premiership, DMP	Sheffield	10.10.61	Darlington, Bradford C, Birmingham, Leeds Utd, Bristol C, Sheff Wed., Spalding Utd
Dale Watkins ESP, NC, DMP	Sheffield	04.11.71	Cheltenham T, Gloucester C, Rushden & Diamonds, Grantham T, Peterborough, Rotherham, Grimsby, Sheff Utd

LEIGH R.M.I.

After a very succesful fifth position in their first season in the Conference few 'experts' gave The Railwaymen much chance to stay in the top half of the table let alone avoid the relegation battleground.

But once again Steve Waywell proved what a sound manager he is and the club officials kept the club up there with the best, despite comparatively poor gates and less revenue that most of their rivals.The doubters had looked to be justified when the club sunk to the bottom two in mid September but character showed through and a 1-0 defeat of highflying Dagenham & Redbridge started a revival which steadily saw them battling into the safety of a mid table place.

The F.A. Cup brought no relief as a very disappointing 2-4 home defeat against Unibond League Worksop Town in front of just 674 was a cruel blow to the confidence. The F.A.Trophy didn't really help either as a replay victory over Emley was followed by defeat at Margate in the Fourth Round.

Ian Monk won the Player of the Year award for a consistent season and the goals of Michael Twiss proved vital but he will have to be replaced next season, and once again the pre season forcasts are not encouraging. It appears that the manager can mould his squad into a very difficult team to beat. When the pressure was on last March his squad produced a run of five undefeated games but can that form be produced on a more consistent basis as they did when they first took the Conference by surprise?

The fun will be in the challenge, as this friendly club are undoubtedly always going to be the underdogs and they enjoy knocking over the 'favourities".

Hopefully they can knock enough over to keep safe.

T.W.

Back Row, left to right: Chris Scott, Dave Ridings, Marcus Hallows, David Felgate, Iain Swan, Andy Heald, Tony Black, Ged Kielty, Rick Harris and Steve Waywell (Manager). **Front Row:** Dino Maamria, Ian Monk, Neil Durkin, Neil Fisher, Nicky Spooner, Dave German, Mick Reynolds and Dave Miller

LEIGH R.M.I.

GROUND DETAILS

**Hilton Park,
Kirkhall Lane,
Leigh WN7 1RN**
Tel: 01942 743743 (Office)
Fax: 01942 768856
Web site: http://www.leigh-rmi.co.uk

DIRECTIONS:
From M61 junction 5, follow the Westhoughton sign to
r'about, then follow signs to Leigh. Keep on main road to
the traffic lights, left into Leigh Road, carry on about 3
miles to the traffic lights. Turn left and first right to the next
set of lights. Right onto Atherleigh Way, A579 at the first
set of traffic lights, turn left (B & Q on right), at the next set
of lights turn right into Kirkhall Lane (Leigh town centre), at
the 2nd opening on right turn into Prescott St., carry on to
top, turn right, ground on left.

CAPACITY: 8000
COVER: 4,000
SEATS: 2,000

CLUBHOUSE: Open matchdays with food available.
Pre-match meals can be arranged.
2 separate function facilities for 200 and 100.

CLUB SHOP: At the ground & open most days. Contact club.

Formed:	1896
Nickname:	Railwaymen
Sponsors:	Widdows Mason
Colours:	Red & white striped shirts
	black shorts and white socks
Change colours:	All Yellow
Midweek home matchday:	Tuesday
Reserve Team	None

CLUB OFFICIALS

Chairman:	T.B.A.
Vice Chairman:	Alan Leach
Directors:	L Berry, K Freer,
	W Taylor,
	G Culshaw
President:	T.B.A.
Secretary:	Alan Robinson
	55 Janice Drive, Fulwood, Preston,
	Lancs. PR2 9TY.
	Tel: 01772 719266 (H)
	01942 743743 (Club)
	07974 651231 (M)
Press Officer:	Secretary

MATCHDAY PROGRAMME

YEOVIL TOWN
SATURDAY, 20th APRIL 2002
KICK OFF 3.00pm

Pages: 32   Price: £2.00
Editor: Secretary

Local Press: Bolton Evening News

Local Radio: Radio Lancs, Red Rose Radio, G.M.R.

FOOTBALL MANAGEMENT TEAM

MANAGER: STEVE WAYWELL
Date of Appointment Aug/Sept 1995
Date of Birth: 4th June 1954
Place of Birth: Bury

PREVIOUS CLUBS
As manager Curzon Ashton
As asst. manager Ashton United
As player Burnley, Stalybridge C., Chorley,
Hyde U., Stalybridge C.

HONOURS
As manager N.P.L. - Prem. Div. 99-00;
Div. 1 R-up 96-97
As asst. manager None
As player F.A.Youth Cup Winners medal
(with Burnley)

Asst Manager Mark Ward
First Team Coach: Gary Thompson
Physiotherapist: Dave Pover
Chief Scout: TBA
Club's Playing Status: Part - time

Season	League	Div.	Pos.	Home					Away					Pts	Manager
				P	W	D	L	F	A	W	D	L	F	A	
01-02	Conference	-	16	42	6	4	11	29	29	9	4	8	27	29	53	Steve Waywell
00-01	Conference	-	5	42	11	5	5	38	24	8	6	7	25	33	68	Steve Waywell
99-00	N.P.L.	Premier	1	44	15	3	4	42	17	13	5	4	49	28	92	Steve Waywell
98-99	N.P.L.	Premier	8	42	6	10	5	30	26	10	5	6	33	28	63	Steve Waywell
97-98	N.P.L.	Premier	3	42	12	6	3	32	15	9	7	5	31	26	76	Steve Waywell

Season	League	Div.	Pos.	P	W	D	L	F	A	Pts	Manager
96-97	N.P.L.	One	2	42	24	11	7	65	33	83	Steve Waywell
95-96	N.P.L.	One	14	40	14	7	19	53	59	49	Steve Waywell
94-95	N.P.L.	Premier	22	42	9	4	29	49	94	31	Mick Holgate
93-94	N.P.L.	Premier	20	42	8	12	22	50	75	*35	Mick Holgate
92-93	N.P.L.	Premier	13	42	14	10	18	72	79	52	Ken Wright

HONOURS

Northern Premier League Champions 1999-2000
NPL League Cup 99-00, Division 1 R-up 96-97;
Premier Inter League (GMAC) Cup 87-88;
Cheshire County Lg 78-79,
Challenge Shield 78-79;
Lancs Combination 57-58
R-up 29-30 55-56 66-67,
Lg Cup 28-29 53-54 56-57 65-66,
Div 2 R-up 48-49 50-51;
West Lancs League 10-11 11-12;
Lancs Junior Cup 24-25 29-30 (R-up x 4);
Lancs Floodlit Trophy 84-85 (R-up 83-84);
Lancs FA Cup 84-85

PREVIOUS

Leagues: Lancashire Alliance 1891-97;
Lancashire League 1897-1900;
Lancashire Combination 17-18, 19-39, 46-68;
Cheshire County League 68-82;
North West Counties League 82-83;
Northern Premier League 83-2000

Name: Horwich R.M.I. until 1995

Ground: Grundy Hill, Horwich until 1994

PastPlayers who progressed to the Football League

Harold Lea (Stockport 58),
David Holland (Stockport 59),
Jim Cunliffe (Stockport 60),
Frank Wignall (Everton 58),
Gary Cooper (Rochdale73),
Tony Caldwell (Bolton 83),
Raymond Redshaw (Wigan 84),
Tony Ellis (Oldham 86),
Paul Jones (Oldham , Nov. 99),
SteveJones (Crewe Alex 01).

CLUB RECORDS

Attendance:
(at Horwich)   8,500 v Wigan Ath Lancs Jnr Cup 54
(at Leigh)   7,125 v Fulham, FAC 98-99

Win: Unknown

Career Appearances: Neil McLachlan

Career Goalscorer: Neil McLachlan

Defeat: 2-9 v Brandon Utd (H)
FA Cup 1998-99

Transfer fee paid: £6,000
to Prescot Cables for Peter Cumiskey 99-00

Transfer fee received: £75,000
from Crewe A. for Steve Jones 2001

BEST SEASON

FA Trophy: Quarter Final 90-91

FA Cup: First Round
28-29, 1-2 v Scarborough (H),
82-83, 0-3 v Blackpool (A)
98-99 (replay), 0-2 v Fulham (H) after 1-1,
00-01, 0-3 v Millwall (H - played away)

FA Vase: N/A

League: 00-01 5th Conference

LAST SEASON

F.A. Cup: Fourth Qualifying Round
F.A. Trophy: Fourth Round
Conference: 16 th
Top Goalscorer: Michael Twiss
Player of the Year: Ian Monk
Captain: Gerry Harrison

LEIGH R.M.I.

	Date	Comp.	Opponents	Att.	Score	Goalscorers
1	18/08	Conf.	HAYES	546	1 - 1	Maamria 18
2	21/08	Conf.	Doncaster Rovers	2433	0 - 2	
3	25/08	Conf.	Margate	815	2 - 1	Hayder 59, Maamria 89
4	27/08	Conf.	NORTHWICH VICTORIA	642	1 - 2	Monk 77
5	01/09	Conf.	Telford United	737	1 - 3	Maamria 54
6	04/09	Conf.	SOUTHPORT	609	1 - 2	Black 67
7	08/09	Conf.	STEVENAGE BOROUGH	584	1 - 2	Maamria 45
8	11/09	Conf.	Nuneaton Borough	973	1 - 2	Monk 68
9	15/09	Conf.	Dagenham & Redbridge	1370	1 - 0	Hallows 52
10	18/09	Conf.	CHESTER CITY	547	3 - 0	Twiss 22 41, Hallows 52
11	22/09	Conf.	FARNBOROUGH TOWN	482	3 - 0	Monk 38, Twiss 90 90
12	29/09	Conf.	Yeovil Town	2835	1 - 2	Hallows 8
13	02/10	Conf.	Morecambe	1263	3 - 1	Twiss 5, Hallows 46 72
14	05/10	Conf.	HEREFORD UNITED	535	0 - 1	
15	09/10	Conf.	FOREST GREEN ROVERS	405	1 - 2	Black 90[p]
16	13/10	Conf.	Barnet	1472	1 - 1	Fisher 56
17	16/10	LDV Vans 1N	SCARBOROUGH	300	2 - 1	Heald 76, Maamria 94[p]
18	20/10	Conf.	WOKING	524	3 - 1	Maamria 40 Twiss 72,82
19	27/10	FA Cup Q4	WORKSOP TOWN	674	2 - 4	Twiss 12, Diggle 86[og]
20	30/10	LDV Vans 2N	Hull City	5226	0 - 3	
21	03/11	Conf.	Scarborough	853	5 - 2	Maamria 14 (Pen),90 Monk 38, Black 50, Newton 12 (og)
22	10/11	Conf.	DOVER ATHLETIC	325	1 - 2	Fisher 55
23	13/11	Lancs MT 1	Chorley	158	4 - 2	Kielty 4, Maamria 53 61, Heald 72
24	24/11	Conf.	Boston United	1940	1 - 2	Twiss 83
25	01/12	Conf.	Hayes	507	1 - 2	Maamria 18
26	08/12	Conf.	MARGATE	439	2 - 2	Fisher 26, Ridings 83
27	15/12	Conf.	DONCASTER ROVERS	546	1 - 4	Twiss 74
28	05/01	Conf.	Southport	1091	0 - 5	
29	08/01	Lancs MT 2	ROSSENDALE UNITED	122	4 - 3	Maamria 30 53 109, Black 112
30	12/01	FA Trophy 3	EMLEY	301	2 - 2	Black 15, Twiss 89
31	14/01	FA Trophy 3 R	Emley	376	4 - 1	Twiss 19, Maamria 56, Black 70, Hallows 84
32	19/01	Conf.	TELFORD UNITED	333	3 - 1	Black 17, Ridings 34, Maamria 44
33	26/01	Conf.	Northwich Victoria	769	3 - 0	Black 52, Maamria 65 84
34	30/01	Lancs MT QF	Accrington Stanley	285	1 - 2	Black 86
35	02/02	FA Trophy 4	Margate	663	0 - 2	
36	09/02	Conf.	Hereford United	1443	1 - 0	Twiss 75
37	16/02	Conf.	BARNET	458	3 - 3	Maamria 33, Twiss 51, Black 59
38	26/02	Conf.	Stalybridge Celtic	404	1 - 0	Twiss 66
39	02/03	Conf.	Chester City	1572	1 - 1	Twiss 42
40	05/03	Conf.	STALYBRIDGE CELTIC	404	1 - 0	Kielty 80
41	09/03	Conf.	NUNEATON BOROUGH	410	0 - 1	
42	12/03	Conf.	MORECAMBE	451	0 - 1	
43	16/03	Conf.	Forest Green Rovers	636	2 - 1	Hallows 37, Heald 57
44	23/03	Conf.	DAGENHAM & REDBRIDGE	492	2 - 0	Twiss 74, Hallows 81
45	30/03	Conf.	Woking	1609	1 - 1	Hallows 34
46	01/04	Conf.	SCARBOROUGH	1465	1 - 1	Twiss 48
47	06/04	Conf.	Dover Athletic	907	0 - 0	
48	13/04	Conf.	BOSTON UNITED	788	1 - 2	Monk 90
49	15/04	Conf.	Stevenage Borough	1116	1 - 0	Hallows 75
50	20/04	Conf.	YEOVIL TOWN	401	0 - 1	
51	27/04	Conf.	Farnborough Town	809	0 - 3	

	1	2	3	4	5	6	7	8	9	10	11	Substitutes Used
1	Felgate	Spooner	German	Durkin	Farrell	Swan	Monk	Ridings	Maamria	Black	Fisher	Hallows 10 Scott 2 Reynolds 4
2	Felgate	German	Heald	Durkin	Farrell	Swan	Monk	Ridings	Maamria	Black	Fisher	Hallows 3 Scott 6 Reynolds 9
3	Felgate	Fisher	German	Durkin	Farrell	Salt	Monk	Ridings	Maamria	Black	Hallows	Heald 11 Hayder 10
4	Felgate	Fisher	German	Durkin	Farrell	Salt	Monk	Ridings	Maamria	Black	Hayder	Reynolds 10 Halows 11
5	Felgate	Fisher	German	Durkin	Farrell	Harris	Monk	Ridings	Maamria	Salt	Heald	Hallows 11 Scott 2 Hayder 6
6	Felgate	Spooner	Fisher	Durkin	Farrell	Harris	Monk	Ridings	Maamria	Black	Salt	Hallows 6 German 8
7	Dootson	Spooner	German	Durkin	Farrell	Harris	Monk	Fisher	Maamria	Black	Salt	Hallows 9 Derbyshire 6
8	Felgate	Spooner	German	Durkin	Farrell	Harris	Monk	Salt	Maamria	Black	Fisher	Hallows 9 Hayder 11 Twiss 10
9	Westhead	Spooner	German	Durkin	Farrell	Harris	Monk	Salt	Maamria	Black	Skinner	Scott 5 Hallows 10 Fisher 6
10	Westhead	Spooner	German	Durkin	Scott	Salt	Monk	Fisher	Hallows	Twiss	Skinner	Hayder 11 Heald 10 Kielty 6
11	Westhead	Spooner	Scott	Durkin	Farrell	Salt	Monk	Fisher	Hallows	Twiss	Skinner	Hayder 11
12	Westhead	Spooner	Scott	Durkin	Farrell	Salt	Monk	Fisher	Hallows	Twiss	Skinner	Kielty 6 Fitzpatrick 11 Swan 10
13	Westhead	Spooner	Scott	Durkin	Farrell	Salt	Monk	Fisher	Hallows	Twiss	Fitzpatrick	Kielty 11
14	Westhead	Spooner	Scott	Durkin	Farrell	Salt	Monk	Fisher	Hallows	Twiss	Skinner	Kielty 11 Maamria 9 Heald 6
15	Westhead	Spooner	Scott	Durkin	Farrell	Salt	Monk	Fisher	Hallows	Twiss	Maamria	Kielty 11 German 3 Black 6
16	Westhead	Spooner	German	Durkin	Swan	Salt	Monk	Fisher	Hallows	Black	Kielty	Maamria 9 Scott 5
17	Westhead	Scott	German	Swan	Farrell	Salt	Black	Fitzpatrick	Maamria	Kielty	Fisher	Hallows 7 Heald 8
18	Westhead	Spooner	German	Durkin	Farrell	Salt	Monk	Fisher	Hallows	Kielty	Black	Maamria 6 Twiss 9 Scott 2
19	Westhead	Spooner	German	Durkin	Farrell	Fisher	Monk	Kielty	Maamria	Twiss	Black	Heald 8 Fitzpatrick 11
20	Westhead	Scott	Heald	Durkin	Farrell	Swan	Fisher	Fitzpatrick	Maamria	Twiss	Kielty	Monk 5 Black 9 Hallows 11
21	Westhead	Scott	Heald	Durkin	Farrell	Fisher	Monk	Fitzpatrick	Maamria	Twiss	Black	German 3 Hallows 10 Spooner 2
22	Westhead	Scott	Heald	Durkin	Swan	Fisher	Monk	Fitzpatrick	Maamria	Twiss	Black	Kielty 8 Hallows 11 German 3
23												
24	Westhead	Spooner	German	Durkin	Swan	Kielty	Monk	Ridings	Maamria	Twiss	Fisher	Hallows 9
25	Westhead	Spooner	German	Durkin	Swan	Harrison	Monk	Ridings	Maamria	Twiss	Fisher	Felgate 1 Black 10 Fitzpatrick 11
26	Westhead	Spooner	German	Durkin	Farrell	Harrison	Monk	Ridings	Maamria	Black	Fisher	Twiss 7 Heald 3
27	Westhead	Spooner	Heald	Durkin	Farrell	Harrison	Monk	Ridings	Maamria	Fisher	Black	Hallows 9 Twiss 10 Swan 11
28	Dootson	Spooner	Fisher	Durkin	Farrell	Kielty	Monk	Ridings	Hallows	Black	Twiss	German 2 Swan 5 Heald 3
29												
30	Westhead	Harrison	German	Durkin	Swan	Kielty	Monk	Ridings	Maamria	Black	Thompson	Fisher 4 Spooner 3 Twiss 9
31	Westhead	Harrison	German	Durkin	Swan	Kielty	Monk	Ridings	Maamria	Black	Twiss	Hallows 9
32	Westhead	Harrison	German	Durkin	Swan	Kielty	Monk	Ridings	Maamria	Black	Twiss	Hallows 11 Heald 3
33	Westhead	Harrison	German	Durkin	Swan	Kielty	Monk	Ridings	Maamria	Black	Twiss	Hallows 10
34												
35	Westhead	Farrell	German	Durkin	Swan	Kielty	Monk	Ridings	Maamria	Black	Twiss	Hallows 9 Heald 3 Fisher 2
36	Westhead	Harrison	German	Durkin	Swan	Kielty	Monk	Ridings	Maamria	Black	Twiss	Fisher 8
37	Westhead	Harrison	German	Durkin	Swan	Kielty	Monk	Fisher	Maamria	Black	Twiss	Farrell 4
38	Westhead	Harrison	German	Durkin	Swan	Kielty	Monk	Ridings	Maamria	Black	Twiss	Hallows 9 Heald 3 Farrell 5
39	Westhead	Harrison	German	Durkin	Swan	Kielty	Monk	Ridings	Hallows	Black	Twiss	
40	Westhead	Harrison	German	Durkin	Swan	Kielty	Monk	Ridings	Maamria	Black	Twiss	Fisher 2 Thompson 8
41	Westhead	Fisher	German	Durkin	Swan	Udall	Monk	Thompson	Hallows	Kielty	Twiss	Heald 6 Spooner 2 Maamria 7
42	Westhead	Harrison	German	Durkin	Swan	Kielty	Monk	Thompson	Maamria	Black	Twiss	Hallows 9 Heald 3
43	Westhead	Harrison	Heald	Durkin	Swan	Kielty	Monk	Thompson	Maamria	Black	Twiss	Fisher 10 Udall 8
44	Westhead	Harrison	German	Durkin	Swan	Kielty	Monk	Ridings	Hallows	Heald	Twiss	
45	Westhead	Harrison	German	Durkin	Swan	Kielty	Monk	Ridings	Hallows	Twiss	Heald	Thompson 11 Archer 9
46	Westhead	Harrison	German	Durkin	Swan	Kielty	Monk	Ridings	Hallows	Twiss	Thompson	Udall 2 Farrell 12 (Ud)
47	Westhead	Harrison	German	Durkin	Swan	Kielty	Monk	Ridings	Hallows	Twiss	Thompson	Heald 3 Spooner 11
48	Westhead	Harrison	German	Durkin	Swan	Kielty	Monk	Ridings	Hallows	Twiss	Heald	Maamria 11 Spooner 1
49	Westhead	Harrison	German	Durkin	Swan	Kielty	Monk	Ridings	Hallows	Twiss	Hallows	Spooner 8 Heald 9
50	Westhead	Harrison	German	Durkin	Swan	Kielty	Monk	Spooner	Hallows	Twiss	Heald	Spencer 7
51	Westhead	Harrison	German	Durkin	Swan	Kielty	Monk	Spooner	Maamria	Twiss	Hallows	Farrell 9 Heald 11 Spencer 8

LEIGH R.M.I.   PLAYING SQUAD

Player	Birthplace	D.O.B.	Previous Clubs
			Bold print denotes England semi-professional international.

GOALKEEPERS

Stuart Coburn	Manchester	05.05.75	Altrincham, Trafford, Irlam T, Maine Road

DEFENDERS

Andy Farrell	Colchester	07.10.65	Colchester, Burnley, Wigan, Rochdale, Morecambe
Jamie Udall	Blackpool		Morecambe, Lancaster C
Neil Durkin	Blackburn		Darwen
Alistair Lindsay	Wigan	11.12.82	From Youth team
Dominic Ludden ES	Basildon	30.03.74	Halifax T, Preston, Watford, Leyton Orient
Neil Fitzhenry	Wigan	24.09.78	Chester C, Wigan
Paul Williams	Leicester	11.09.69	Ilkeston T, Bury, Gillingham, Plymouth, Coventry, Stockport, Leicester

MIDFIELD

Tony Black UP	Barrow	15.07.69	Burnley U, Bamber Bridge, Wigan, Accrington Stanley, Chorley
Ged Kielty UP	Manchester	01.09.76	Manchester C, Cobh Ramblers, Southport, Barrow, Altrincham
Neil Fisher	St.Helens	07.11.70	Chester C, Connah's Quay, Chester C, Bolton
Andy Heald	Manchester	26.07.80	Morecambe
Darren Calland	Billinge	13.12.82	From Youth team
Gerry Harrison	Lambeth	15.04.72	Prestwich Heys, Halifax T, Sunderland, Burnley, Huddersfield, Bristol C, Watford
Peter Connelly	Vancouver, Canada	08.08.83	From Youth team

FORWARDS

Ian Monk GMVC, UP	Burnley	30.06.68	Clitheroe, Ashton U, Macclesfield, Morecambe
Craig Gilligan	Stockport	02.10.83	From Youth team
Damien Whitehead	Whiston	24.04.79	Macclesfield, Warrington T
Noureddine Maamria Tunisia u-21	Tunisia	18.02.74	Southport, Doncaster R, Ayr Utd, Glentoran
Tony Ellis	Salford	20.10.64	Burnley, Rochdale, Stockport, Bury, Blackpool, Preston, Stoke, Preston, Oldham, Nothwich V, Horwich RMI

MARGATE

To reach The Conference was a fine achievement for everyone at the Kent club and for manager Chris Kinnear his steady team building had seen his squad achieve 2nd,3rd and !st in the Dr Martens Premier Division before entering the top flight. A first day away victory brought a 1-0 scoreline at Boston and as the previous season's run in had seen many away wins ground out in similar fashion, the 'experts' prepared for 'The Gate" to endure a gruelling season ahead.

How wrong could they be ? Only one defeat in the first eleven games didn't bring a glut of goals but four successive victories took the club to the top of The Conference and Leon Braithwaite had weighed in with seven singles to set him up for an excellent season and an England cap.

Margate's Conference form, although not often attracting 1,500 attendances certainly kept them in the top ten for practically the whole season and a bumper 3,676 Boxing Day crowd showed what it was like to sample a n exciting atmosphere at Hartsdown Park. Hopefully all the exciting plans for the ground will be completed with as little upheaval as possible, and the steady development of the club will continue as they consolidate at the top of the pyramid.

A disappointing defeat at Grays Athletic in the FA.Cup was forgotten as the club enjoyed it's best ever run in theF.A.Trophy. Two Conference clubs, Hayes and Leigh RMI were beaten at home by 3-1 and 2-0 respectively and then an away replay against Braintree Town brought a tight 2-1 victory and a quarter final tie at home to Morecambe. Sadly only 1,244 turned up to help Margate into the semi-finals and perhaps it wasn't surprising that the chance of progress was missed.

This defeat perhaps deflated morale and so, with no real incentives other than renewed contracts,a run of seven games without a victory was brought to a conclusive end with a spectacular 8-0 victory over a doomed and depressed Stalybridge Celtic.

A full season with the confidence of knowing they can hold their own at this level should improve the club's home form,and with a sound away record of seven wins and seven draws, Margate should be even more consistent this season and they should be very hard to beat.   T.W.

MARGATE FC 2001-02

Back Row, l-r: Steve Hafner, Paul Lamb, Lee Williams, Dean Yorath, Paul Sykes, Mark Munday, Lee Turner, Charlie Mitten, Simon Beard, Graham Porter (captain), Jay Saunders, Paul Lewis, Leon Braithwaite, Tommy Tyne (now Dover Ath.).
Front row: Bill Edwards, Simon Ullathorne, Mo Takalogabhashi, Gary Blackford, Chris Kinnear (manager), Kevin Raine (assistant manager), Phil Collins, John Keister, Mike Azzopardi, Robert Codner.

MARGATE

GROUND DETAILS

Hartsdown Park,
Hartsdown Road,
Margate CT9 5QZ

Telelpone:	01843 221769
Fax:	01843 221769
Email:	office@margatefc.com
Web site:	www.margatefc.com

Directions:
A28 into Margate, turn right opposite Dog & Duck P.H. into Hartsdown Road, proceed over crossroads and ground is on left.
Ten mins walk from Margate (BR)

Capacity: 4,800
Cover: 4,250
Seats: 550

Clubhouse:
Flexible hours, private functions, matchday facilities.

Club Shop:
Contacts: Dave and Debra Canham (01843 221769)

Formed:	1896
Nickname:	The Gate
Sponsors:	A Gomez Ltd.
Newsline:	09068 800 665
Colours:	Royal Blue shirts & shorts, white socks
Change colours:	Red shirts with black shorts and socks
Midweek matchday:	Tuesday
Reserves' League:	Bass Kent Lg. Div 1

CLUB OFFICIALS

Chairman:	Keith Piper
President:	Gordon Wallis
Vice Chairman:	Jim Parmenter
Directors:	K Piper & J Parmenter
Secretary:	Ken Tomlinson

65 Nash Road, Margate , Kent CT9 4BT
Tel & Fax: 01843 291040 (M) 07710033566

Commercial Manager:	Mrs Joscelyn Dodds Tel: 01843 221769
Press Officer:	Jim Parmenter
	01227 832121(W)
	07980 016916 (M)

MATCHDAY PROGRAMME

Margate v Stalybridge £2.00
Saturday 27th April 2002

Pages: 44   Price: £2.00
Editor:Keith Smith (01843 296725)
Clubcall: 09068 800 665
Local Press:
Isle of Thanet Gazette, Thanet Times, Thanet Extra
Local Radio:
Radio Kent, Invicta Radio, TLR

FOOTBALL MANAGEMENT TEAM

MANAGER   CHRIS KINNEAR

Date of Appointment	August 1996
Date of Birth:	10th July 1954
Place of Birth:	Dagenham

PREVIOUS CLUBS
As manager	Dover Athletic
As player	West Ham, Leyton Orient, Wealdstone, Maidstone U., Barnet, Dagenham, Dover A.

HONOURS
As manager   Southern Lge: Prem Div. x 3, R-up x1;
Southern Div. x1, R-up x1; Lge. Cup x2, R-up x1
Kent Senior Cup: x 2, R-up x 1

* * *

Asst. Manager:	Kevin Raine
Physio:	S.Methananda
Chief Scout:	Alan Randall
Reserve Manager:	Mark Harrop
Club's Playing Status:	Part-time

Season	League	Div.	Pos.	P	Home W	D	L	F	A	Away W	D	L	F	A	Pts	Manager
01-02	Conference	-	8	42	7	9	5	33	22	7	7	7	26	31	58	Chris Kinnear
00-01	Southern	P	1	42	17	2	2	47	14	11	5	5	28	13	91	Chris Kinnear
99-00	Southern	P	3	42	13	4	4	33	16	10	4	7	31	27	77	Chris Kinnear
98-99	Southern	S	2	42	13	5	3	44	16	14	3	4	40	17	89	Chris Kinnear
97-98	Southern	S	6	42	14	3	4	37	16	9	5	7	34	26	77	Chris Kinnear
96-97	Southern	S	5	42	11	2	8	36	29	10	7	4	34	18	72	Chris Kinnear
95-96	Southern	S	11	42	11	5	5	36	22	7	0	14	32	40	59	Karl Elsey
94-95	Southern	S	13	42	9	2	10	36	37	6	5	10	24	35	52	Mark Weatherley & Andy Woolford
93-94	Southern	S	9	42	13	2	6	44	25	7	6	8	32	33	68	Mark Weatherley & Andy Woolford
92-93	Southern	S	10	42	9	4	8	30	30	10	3	5	35	28	64	Lee Smelt

HONOURS

HONOURS

Southern Lge 35-36, 00-01
Lge Cp 67-68,97-98, R-up 61-62 74-75,
Div 1 62-63, R-up 66-67, Div 1 Sth 77-78,
East Div R-up 33-34,
Southern Div. R-up: 98-99
Merit Cup 66-67 77-78, Midweek Sect. 36-37,
Kent Lge (4), R-up (5), Div 2 (4), Lge Cp 5),
Kent Senior Cup (5),
Kent Senior Shield (8),
Kent F'lit Cp 62-63 66-67 75-76

PREVIOUS

Leagues: Kent 11-23 24-28 29-33 37-38 46-59;
Southern 33-37, 59-2001

Grounds: Margate College;
Dreamland, Northdown Rd; Garlinge
Name: Thanet Utd 1981-89

Past Players who progressed to the Football League

Over 40 including

J Yeomanson (West Ham 47),
D Bing & G Wright (West Ham 51), T Bing (Spurs 56),
S Foster (C Palace 61), J Fraser (Watford 62),
R Walker (Bournemouth 65), K Bracewell (Bury 66),
T Jenkins & R Flannigan (Reading 69-70),
M Blyth (Millwall 78), M Buglione (St Johnstone 92)

CLUB RECORDS

Attendance:	14,500
	v Spurs, FA Cup 3rd Rd 73
Goalscorer:	Dennis Randall 66 (season 66-67)
CareerAppearances:	Bob Harrop
Win:	8-0
	v Tunbridge Wells (H) 66-67,
	& v Chatham Town (H) 87-88
Defeat:	11-0
	v AFC Bournemouth (A), FAC 1st Rd. 20.11.71
Fee paid:	£5,000
	for Steve Cuggy (Dover Ath93)
Fee received:	Undisclosed
	for Martin Buglione (St Johnstone 92-93)

BEST SEASON

FA Trophy:	Third Round replay 78-79
FA Cup:	Third Round
	72-73 0-6 v Spurs (H),
	36-37 1-3 v Blackpool (A)
League clubs defeated:	Gillingham 29-30,
	Q. P.R., Crystal Palace 35-36,
	Bournemouth & Boscombe Ath. 61-62, Swansea 72-73

LAST SEASON

F.A. Cup:	Fourth Qualifying Round
F.A. Trophy:	Quarter Finals
Conference:	8th
Top Goalscorer:	Leon Braithwaite 16
Player of the Year:	Leon Braithwaite
Captain:	Graham Parker

MARGATE

	Date	Comp.	Opponents	Att.	Score	Goalscorers
1	11/08	DML Shield	WORCESTER CITY	n/k	1 - 1	Tyne 21 5 3
2	18/08	Conf.	Boston United	1909	1 - 0	Braithwaite 72[p]
3	21/08	Conf.	DAGENHAM & REDBRIDGE	1350	1 - 1	Keister 47
4	25/08	Conf.	LEIGH RMI	815	1 - 2	Braithwaite 48
5	27/08	Conf.	Scarborough	886	1 - 0	Braithwaite 69
6	01/09	Conf.	HEREFORD UNITED	1010	2 - 2	Keister 46, Beard 62
7	04/09	Conf.	Farnborough Town	797	0 - 0	
8	08/09	Conf.	TELFORD UNITED	925	3 - 1	Keister 29,Williams 71 Braithwaite 90
9	11/09	Conf.	Woking	1216	1 - 0	Beard 45
10	15/09	Conf.	Southport	1012	2 - 1	Braithwaite 60, Munday 83
11	18/09	Conf.	STEVENAGE BOROUGH	1129	2 - 1	Keister 72, Braithwaite 83
12	22/09	Conf.	Stalybridge Celtic	618	2 - 2	Braithwaite 69, Munday 90
13	29/09	Conf.	BARNET	1753	0 - 1	
14	02/10	Conf.	HAYES	1205	1 - 0	Braithwaite 68
15	06/10	Conf.	Chester City	828	3 - 0	
16	09/10	Conf.	Yeovil Town	2577	2 - 1	Sodje 15, Graham 58
17	13/10	Conf.	DONCASTER ROVERS	2087	1 - 1	Collins 45
18	20/10	Conf.	NORTHWICH VICTORIA	1125	1 - 2	Boardman 68
19	27/10	FA Cup Q4	Grays Athletic	832	0 - 2	
20	03/11	Conf.	Forest Green Rovers	938	3 - 3	Munday 18, Braithwaite 71 (Pen) ,Saunders 80
21	10/11	Conf.	NUNEATON BOROUGH	1211	1 - 1	Beard 90
22	13/11	Kent SC 1	BROMLEY	n/k	3 - 1	Collins Lamb Hafner
23	17/11	Conf.	YEOVIL TOWN	1125	0 - 1	
24	24/11	Conf.	Morecambe	1588	1 - 2	Saunders 76
25	01/12	Conf.	BOSTON UNITED	1745	1 - 1	McFlynn 50
26	08/12	Conf.	Leigh RMI	439	2 - 2	Beard 32, Farrell 36[og]
27	15/12	Conf.	Dagenham & Redbridge	1742	1 - 4	Beard 63
28	26/12	Conf.	DOVER ATHLETIC	3676	0 - 1	
29	05/01	Conf.	FARNBOROUGH TOWN	875	2 - 1	Benstead 9[og], Braithwaite 58
30	12/01	FA Trophy 3	HAYES	625	3 - 1	Collins 9, O'Connell 67, Lamb 80
31	19/01	Conf.	Hereford United	1474	0 - 3	
32	26/01	Conf.	SCARBOROUGH	637	1 - 1	Braithwaite 22[p]
33	02/02	FA Trophy 4	LEIGH RMI	663	2 - 0	McFlynn 10, O'Connell 25
34	09/02	Conf.	CHESTER CITY	984	0 - 0	
35	16/02	Conf.	Doncaster Rovers	2248	0 - 1	
36	23/02	FA Trophy 5	BRAINTREE TOWN	802	1 - 1	Sodje 67
37	02/03	Conf.	Stevenage Borough	1602	1 - 3	Roddis 61
38	05/03	FA Trophy 5 R	Braintree Town	846	2 - 1	Munday 51, Sodje 62
39	09/03	Conf.	WOKING	1061	4 - 3	Flynn 2, Munday 27 67, Sodje 83
40	12/03	Conf.	Hayes	350	4 - 2	McFlynn 15, Munday 20, Taylor 33[og], Sodje 45
41	16/03	FA Trophy QF	MORECAMBE	1224	1 - 2	Lamb 86
42	19/03	Kent SC QF	Folkestone Invicta	314	2 - 1	Sodje 4, Williams 84
43	23/03	Conf.	SOUTHPORT	492	2 - 0	Porter 15, Braithwaite 53
44	25/03	Conf.	Dover Athletic	2325	0 - 0	
45	30/03	Conf.	Northwich Victoria	604	1 - 1	Saunders 61 F
46	01/04	Conf.	FOREST GREEN ROVERS	845	1 - 1	Braithwaite 65[p]
47	06/04	Conf.	Nuneaton Borough	1133	0 - 0	
48	08/04	Conf.	Telford United	708	0 - 2	
49	18/04	Conf.	MORECAMBE	784	1 - 1	Porter 60
50	20/04	Conf.	Barnet	1405	1 - 4	Beard 70
51	23/04	Kent SC SF	ASHFORD TOWN	325	5 - 0	Munday 29 70, Graham 40, McFlynn 81 89
52	27/04	Conf.	STALYBRIDGE CELTIC	757	8 - 0	Roddis 9, Munday 11, Lamb 38, Saunders 55, Braithwaite 58[p] 84, Keister 87,90
53	06/05	Kent SC F	GRAVESEND & NORTHFLEET	2000	0 - 5	

Substitutes Used

#	1	2	3	4	5	6	7	8	9	10	11	Substitutes Used
1												
2	Mitten	Blackford	Lamb	Edwards	Williams	Porter	Keister	Beard	Braithwaite	Munday	Saunders	
3	Mitten	Blackford	Lamb	Edwards	Williams	Porter	Keister	Beard	Braithwaite	Munday	Saunders	
4	Mitten	Blackford	Lamb	Edwards	Williams	Porter	Keister	Beard	Braithwaite	Munday	Saunders	Azzopardi 7 Tako 10
5	Mitten	Blackford	Lamb	Edwards	Williams	Porter	Keister	Beard	Braithwaite	Munday	Saunders	
6	Mitten	Blackford	Lamb	Edwards	Williams	Porter	Keister	Beard	Braithwaite	Munday	Saunders	Yorath 2
7	Mitten	Blackford	Lamb	Edwards	Williams	Porter	Keister	Beard	Braithwaite	Munday	Saunders	Yorath 2
8	Mitten	Yorath	Lamb	Edwards	Williams	Porter	Keister	Beard	Braithwaite	Munday	Saunders	
9	Mitten	Yorath	Lamb	Edwards	Williams	Porter	Keister	Beard	Braithwaite	Collins	Saunders	Azzopardi 10
10	Mitten	Yorath	Lamb	Edwards	Williams	Porter	Keister	Beard	Braithwaite	Munday	Saunders	
11	Mitten	Yorath	Lamb	Edwards	Williams	Porter	Keister	Beard	Braithwaite	Collins	Saunders	Hilaire 7
12	Mitten	Yorath	Lamb	Edwards	Williams	Porter	Munday	Beard	Braithwaite	Collins	Saunders	Azzopardi 2 Hafner 11
13	Mitten	Yorath	Lamb	Edwards	Williams	Porter	Munday	Beard	Braithwaite	Sodje	Saunders	Blackford 2 Collins 7 Turner 1
14	Turner	Blackford	Lamb	Edwards	Williams	Graham	Munday	Beard	Braithwaite	Collins	Saunders	
15	Turner	Blackford	Lamb	Edwards	Williams	Porter	Munday	Graham	Braithwaite	Collins	Saunders	Sodje 10
16	Turner	Blackford	Lamb	Edwards	Williams	Porter	Munday	Graham	Sodje	Collins	Saunders	Hafner 2 Beard 9
17	Turner	Blackford	Lamb	Edwards	Williams	Porter	Munday	Graham	Braithwaite	Collins	Saunders	Sodje 9 Beard 2 Hilaire 10
18	Turner	Hafner	Lincoln	Edwards	Boardman	Porter	Munday	Graham	Braithwaite	Collins	Saunders	Azzopardi 3
19	Turner	Hafner	Lamb	Edwards	Boardman	Porter	Graham	Beard	Braithwaite	Collins	Saunders	Sodje 2 Hilaire 12 (Sod) Munday 10
20	Turner	Boardman	Lamb	Edwards	Williams	Porter	Munday	Beard	Braithwaite	Graham	Saunders	Collins 10
21	Turner	Boardman	Lamb	Edwards	Williams	Porter	Munday	Beard	Braithwaite	Graham	Saunders	Collins 11
22												
23	Turner	Blackford	Lamb	Edwards	Williams	Porter	Graham	Beard	Braithwaite	Collins	Saunders	Munday 2 Sodje 7
24	Turner	Hafner	Lamb	Graham	Williams	Porter	Munday	Beard	Braithwaite	Collins	Saunders	Sodje 7
25	Turner	Blackford	Lamb	Edwards	Williams	Porter	McFlynn	Beard	Braithwaite	Collins	Saunders	Hafner 2 Munday 7
26	Turner	Graham	Lamb	Edwards	Williams	Roddis	McFlynn	Beard	Braithwaite	Collins	Saunders	Sodje 10
27	Turner	Graham	Lamb	Edwards	Williams	Roddis	McFlynn	Beard	Braithwaite	Munday	Sodje	
28	Turner	Graham	Lamb	Edwards	Williams	Porter	McFlynn	Beard	Braithwaite	Sodje	Saunders	Munday 11 Hafner 2 Tako 10
29	Mitten	Graham	Lamb	Edwards	Williams	Porter	McFlynn	Beard	Braithwaite	Collins	Saunders	Munday 10 O'Connell 7
30	Mitten	O'Connell	Lamb	Edwards	Williams	Porter	McFlynn	Beard	Braithwaite	Collins	Saunders	Graham 7 Sodje 9
31	Mitten	O'Connell	Lamb	Edwards	Williams	Porter	McFlynn	Beard	Braithwaite	Collins	Saunders	Roddis 7 Sodje 9
32	Mitten	O'Connell	Lamb	Edwards	Williams	Porter	Roddis	Beard	Braithwaite	Munday	McFlynn	Collins 9
33	Mitten	Hafner	Lamb	Edwards	O'Connell	Porter	Roddis	Munday	Braithwaite	Collins	McFlynn	
34	Mitten	Hafner	Lamb	Edwards	O'Connell	Porter	Roddis	Munday	Braithwaite	Collins	McFlynn	Saunders 2 Graham 11
35	Mitten	Williams	Lamb	Edwards	O'Connell	Porter	Roddis	Beard	Braithwaite	McFlynn	Saunders	Collins 10 Munday 8 Sodje 9
36	Mitten	O'Connell	Lamb	Edwards	Williams	Porter	Roddis	Munday	Braithwaite	McFlynn	Saunders	Graham 11 Sodje 3
37	Mitten	Williams	Lamb	Edwards	O'Connell	Porter	Roddis	Munday	Braithwaite	Sodje	McFlynn	Collins 11 Graham 2
38	Mitten	Saunders	Lamb	Edwards	O'Connell	Porter	Roddis	Munday	Braithwaite	Sodje	McFlynn	Collins 10 Turner 11
39	Turner	Saunders	Lamb	Edwards	O'Connell	Porter	Roddis	Munday	Braithwaite	Sodje	McFlynn	Graham 10
40	Turner	Saunders	Lamb	Edwards	O'Connell	Porter	Roddis	Munday	Braithwaite	Sodje	McFlynn	Williams 6 Hafner 10 Graham 7
41	Mitten	Saunders	Lamb	Edwards	O'Connell	Porter	Roddis	Munday	Braithwaite	Sodje	McFlynn	Graham 11 Turner 1
42												
43	Turner	Graham	Lamb	Edwards	O'Connell	Porter	Roddis	Munday	Braithwaite	Sodje	McFlynn	Williams 7
44	Turner	Williams	Lamb	Edwards	O'Connell	Porter	Graham	Munday	Braithwaite	Sodje	McFlynn	Saunders 10
45	Turner	Williams	Lamb	Edwards	O'Connell	Porter	Graham	Munday	Braithwaite	McFlynn	Saunders	
46	Turner	Williams	Lamb	Edwards	O'Connell	Porter	Graham	Munday	Braithwaite	McFlynn	Saunders	
47	Turner	Graham	Lamb	Edwards	O'Connell	Porter	McFlynn	Munday	Braithwaite	Sodje	Saunders	
48	Turner	Graham	Lamb	Edwards	O'Connell	Porter	McFlynn	Munday	Braithwaite	Roddis	Saunders	Azzopardi 7 Hafner 10
49	Turner	Williams	Lamb	Edwards	O'Connell	Porter	McFlynn	Munday	Braithwaite	Graham	Saunders	
50	Turner	Williams	Lamb	Edwards	O'Connell	Porter	McFlynn	Munday	Braithwaite	Graham	Saunders	Beard 2 Hafner 8
51												
52	Turner	Roddis	Lamb	Edwards	O'Connell	Williams	Graham	Munday	Azzopardi	McFlynn	Saunders	Hafner 6 Braithwaite 9 Keister 2
53												

MARGATE

PLAYING SQUAD

Player	Birthplace	D.O.B.	Previous Clubs

Bold print denotes England semi-professional international.

GOALKEEPERS

Lee Turner DMP	London	04.03.65	Gravesend, Bury T, Corinthian, Sittingbourne, Corinthian, Leyton Orient
Phil Smith	Harrow	14.12.79	Dover Ath., Folkestone Invicta, Millwall

DEFENDERS

Billy Edwards DMP		12.05.75	Sutton Utd, Tooting & Mitcham, Sutton Utd, Fisher Ath
Graham Porter DMP		29.10.74	Ashford T, Erith & Belvedere, Horsham, Maidstone Utd
Iain O'Connell DMP	Southend	09.10.70	Dover Ath (£3,000), Southend
Jay Saunders DMP	Kent	15.01.79	Gravesend, Gillingham
Lee Williams	Kent		Gillingham (Trainee)
Michael Azzopardi	London		Dulwich Hamlet, Tooting & Mitcham
Paul Lamb DMP	Kent	19.04.73	Gravesend, Ramsgate, Margate, Dartford, Ramsgate
Lee Shearer ES	Rochford	23.10.77	Dover Ath., Leyton Orient

MIDFIELD

Simon Beard	Bromley	08.09.72	Dover Ath, Hastings T, Sittingbourne, West Ham
John Keister Sierra Leone Int.	Manchester	11.11.70	Stevenage B, Shrewsbury, Chester C, Walsall, Tigres (Sierra Leone)
Terry McFlynn	Magherafelt	27.03.81	Woking, QPR, Manchester Utd
Mark Munday DMP	Dover	17.02.71	Gravesend, Herne Bay, Ramsgate, Ashford T, Margate

FORWARDS

Phil Collins DMP	Kent	03.07.72	Dartford, Cray W, Sheppey Utd
Leon Braithwaite DMP	London	17.12.72	Welling Utd, St.Patricks Ath., Charlton Ath., Exeter C., Bishop's Stortford
Paul Sykes DMP	Kent	08.11.76	Welling Utd, Gillingham (Trainee)
Akpo Sodke	Nigeria	-	Hayes, Stevenage B
Darren Freeman	Brighton	22.08.73	Brighton, Brentford, Fulham, Gillingham, Horsham, Worthing
Charlie MacDonald	Southwark	13.02.81	Charlton

MORECAMBE

Jim Harvey is one of the most experienced managers in the Conference and at the start of last season the squad he had assembled looked quite capable of challenging for trophies.

And the Shrimps' supporters were not disappointed when, after their first dozen games, third place had been achieved, they had scored in every game and Robbie Talbot looked to be the signing of the year.

Football fortunes are so unpredictable however and although Talbot scored in the next three games, six league games failed to bring a victory and Morecambe were back in fourteenth position.

An F.A.Cup defeat by a single goal against Brentford at Christie Park was a happy distraction during this period. It was a rollercoaster season that must have frustrated all connected with the club.

Another good run brought them up to third place in the new year and then an injury to Talbot reduced the club's firepower considerably. Wayne Curtis did step up and showed distinct promise with a hat trick against Northwich but just what could have been achieved if injuries had been avoided, is open to conjecture.

An exciting F.A.Trophy run began at home to Kings Lynn with a 2-0 victory. This was followed by another home draw and an even better victory, 5-0 v Gresley Rovers. Scarborough away looked a sterner test but a replay gave The Shrimps the chance to take advantage of their good home form and a fine 3-0 victory saw them into the quarter finals at Margate. Two goals from the reliable John Norman set up a two legged semi-final against a very unpredictable Stevenage Borough side and after such a fluctuating season it was a disappointment to the club's supporters when top form deserted their lads just when it mattered. Stevenage won 4-1 on aggregate and a strange season ended with all Shrimps followers knowing that with just a little luck they will do much better in the coming year. T.W.

MORECAMBE FC 2002-03

Back row, left to right: Les Dewhirst (Kitman), Adriano Rigoglioso, Garry Thompson, Stewart Drummond, Michael Stringfellkow, Iain Swan, Jim Bentley, Wayne Curtis and Tommy Sawyer (Kitman)
Middle row: Claudia Manfredi (Sports Therapist), Nick Milner (Fitness & Conditioning Coach), Robbie Talbot, Lee Colkin, Dave McKearney, Craig Mawson, Danny Carlton, Neil Uberschar, Paul Osborne, Jeff Udal (Reserves Manager) and Tony Gribbin (Assistant Reserve Manager)
Front row: Dave Edge (Sports Therapist) Michael Knowles, Ian Arnold, Andy Gouck, Jim Harvey (Manager), Ryan Zico, David Perkins, Nick Rogan, Andy Mutch (Assistant Manager)

MORECAMBE

GROUND DETAILS

Christie Park,
Lancaster Road,
Morecambe,
Lancashire LA4 5TJ

TELEPHONE 01524 411797
Fax: 01524 411797

email: neil@morecambefc.com
Web site: http://www.morecambefc.com

DIRECTIONS:
From south leave M6 motorway at junction 34. Follow signs for Morecambe through Lancaster, on A589, go straight across the first 2roundabouts, and at the third (with the Shrimp pub on your left), follow thesigns for Town Centre - Christie Park is approx. 600 metres on your left

CAPACITY: 6,300
SEATED: 1,200
COVERED TERRACING: 4,300

CLUB SHOP: On ground and open on matchdays. Also commercial office open Monday to Friday 9.00 - 5.00 selling the same goods

SOCIAL FACILITIES: J B's open normal licensing hours

MATCHDAY PROGRAMME

Pages: 48   Price: £2,00
Editor: Sean O'Connor
Other club publications: "Gazetta de la Shrimpa"
Clubcall: 09066 555966

Local Press: Morecambe Visitor; Morecambe Guardian; Lancashire Evening Post; The Citizen

Local Radio: Radio Lancashire;
Red Rose Radio; Bay Radio

Founded: 1920
Nickname: The Shrimps
Club sponsor: Thurnham Leisure Group & Ambulink UK Ltd
Club colours: Red shirts, white shorts, black & white socks
Change colours: White shirts, black shorts and white socks.
Midweek home matchday: Tuesdays, 7.45pm kick-off

Reserve Team's League: Lancashire Lge Div. 1 & North West All. Yth Div.

CLUB OFFICIALS

Honorary President Jim Bowen

Chairman Peter McGuigan

Vice Chairman Graham Hodgson

Directors Peter Cross, Stuart Forrest, Mark Hallam, Rod Taylor Stuart Redman & Neil Marsdin

Company & Club Secretary Neil Marsdin

Commercial Manager Peter Howard

FOOTBALL MANAGEMENT TEAM

MANAGER   JIM HARVEY

Date of Appointment	June 1994
Date of Birth:	2nd May 1958
Place of Birth:	Lurgan, Northern Ireland
PREVIOUS CLUBS	
As manager	None
As asst. manager	Morecambe (Jan - June 1994)
As player	Glenavon, Arsenal, Hereford Utd., Bristol C., Tranmere Rov., Crewe Alex.
HONOURS	
As manager	Spalding Cup 97-98; NPL R-up 94-95
As player	N. Ireland - u23., Leyland Daf Cup, Mercantile Trophy Promotion from Division 4 & Division 3

Assistant Manager Andy Mutch
Second Team Manager Jeff Udall
2nd Team Asst. Manager Tony Gribbins
Football in the Community Derek Quinn
Sports Therapist David Edge

Clb's Playing Staus: Some full time players

Season	League	Div.	Pos.	P	W	D	L	F	A	W	D	L	F	A	Pts	Manager
							Home					Away				
01-02	Conference	-	6	42	12	5	4	30	27	5	6	10	33	40	62	Jim Harvey
00-01	Conference	-	19	42	8	5	8	35	29	3	7	11	29	37	45	Jim Harvey
99-00	Conference	-	3	42	10	7	4	46	29	8	9	4	24	19	70	Jim Harvey
98-99	Conference	-	14	42	9	5	7	31	29	6	3	12	29	47	53	Jim Harvey
97-98	Conference	-	5	42	11	4	6	35	30	10	6	5	42	34	73	Jim Harvey
96-97	Conference	-	4	42	10	5	6	34	23	9	4	8	35	33	66	Jim Harvey

Season	League	Div.	Pos.	P	W	D	L	F	A	Pts	Manager
95-96	Conferece	-	9	42	17	8	17	78	72	59	Jim Harvey
94-95	N.P.L.	Premier	2	42	28	10	4	99	34	94	Jim Harvey
93-94	N.P.L.	Premier	7	42	20	7	15	90	56	67	Bryan Griffiths
92-93	N.P.L.	Premier	3	42	25	11	6	93	51	86	Bryan Griffiths

HONOURS

F.A. Trophy 73-74,
Spalding Cup 97-98,
Northern Premier Lge R-up 91-92 94-95,
Presidents Cup 91-92,
Lancs Combination 24-25 61-62 62-63 66-67 67-68
R-up 1923-24, 25-26,
Lg Cup 26-27 45-46 64-65 66-68;
Lancashire Junior Cup (now ATS Trophy) x8
25-27 61-63 68-69 85-87 92-93, 95-96;
Lancashire Senior Cup 67-68,

PREVIOUS

Leagues: Lancs Combination 1920-68, Northern Premier 1968-1995

Grounds: Woodhill Lane 1920-25, shared with cricket club who still play there

Past Players who progressed to the Football League

Fred Blondel (Bury 1946),
Herbert Harrison (Accrington 1947),
Gordon Milne (Preston 1956),
Ray Charnley (Blackpool 1957),
Geoff Slack (Stockport 1958),
Ron Mitchell (Leeds 1958), Derek Armstrong (Carlisle 1961),
Alan Taylor(Rochdale 1973),
John Coates (Southport via Burscough & Skelmersdale 1975),
Keith Galley (Southport 1975),
Brian Thompson (West Ham 1977),
Malcolm Darling (Bury 1978)
David Eyres (Blackpool), Kenny Lowe (Barnet via Barrow),
Steve Gardner (Bradford City), Dave Lancaster (Chesterfield)

Semi-Professional Capped Players

John Coleman, Mike Bignall, Brian Healy, Stewart Drummond, Justin Jackson

CLUB RECORDS

Attendance: 9,324 v Weymouth FA Cup 4.1.62

Win: 14-0 v Rossendale Utd, Lancs Combination Sept 1967 (Arnold Timmins scored 8)

Defeat: 0-14 v Chorley(A), 19th April 1946

Transfer fee paid: £25,000 to Northwich V. for Steve Walters, July 2000

Transfer fee received: £175,000 from Rushden & Diamonds for Justin Jackson, July 2000

Career Goalscorer: Keith Borrowdale 289 1956-68, 78-79 Lancashire Combination John Coleman 130 1990-1995 (Northern Premier League)

Career Appearances: Steve Done 523 + 7 sub 1968-78

BEST SEASON

FA Cup: 3rd Round 1961-62 v Weymouth (H) 0-1 2000-01 v Ipswich T (H) 0-3

League clubs defeated: Chester City 1961-62, Cambridge Utd.(2000-01)

FA Trophy: Winners 73-74, S-Final: 2001-02 Quarter Final: 72-73, 77-78, 93-94

League: 3rd Conference 1999-2000

LAST SEASON

F.A. Cup: First Round
F.A. Trophy: Semi-Final
Conference: 6th
Top Goalscorer: Robbie Talbot 15
Player of the Year: Stewart Drummond
Club Captain: Dave McKearney

MORECAMBE

	Date	Comp.	Opponents	Att.	Score	Goalscorers
1	18/08	Conf.	NUNEATON BOROUGH	1629	1 - 0	Talbot 44
2	21/08	Conf.	Stalybridge Celtic	874	3 - 4	Gouck 9, Arnold 44[p], Thompson 59
3	25/08	Conf.	Woking	1279	3 - 1	Thompson 25 53, Talbot 50
4	27/08	Conf.	TELFORD UNITED	1342	2 - 1	Lightfoot 61, Arnold 89[p]
5	01/09	Conf.	Hayes	503	1 - 3	Lightfoot 63
6	04/09	Conf.	NORTHWICH VICTORIA	1462	2 - 1	Talbot 6,17
7	08/09	Conf.	Forest Green Rovers	702	1 - 3	Arnold 20
8	11/09	Conf.	BARNET	1283	1 - 0	Talbot 46
9	15/09	Conf.	HEREFORD UNITED	1462	2 - 2	Thompson 66, Norman 79
10	18/09	Conf.	Scarborough	616	2 - 0	Norman 28, Talbot 55
11	22/09	Conf.	Doncaster Rovers	2841	3 - 3	Drummond 13, Gouck 53[p], Black 64
12	29/09	Conf.	DOVER ATHLETIC	1365	2 - 1	Black 41 Thompson G 64
13	02/10	Conf.	LEIGH RMI	1263	1 - 3	Talbot 82
14	06/10	Conf.	Yeovil Town	2404	1 - 1	Talbot 53
15	10/10	Conf.	Boston United	1740	1 - 2	Talbot 77
16	13/10	Conf.	CHESTER CITY	1764	0 - 3	
17	20/10	Conf.	Stevenage Borough	1590	1 - 3	Drummond 16
18	27/10	FA Cup Q4	Harrogate Railway Athletic	900	3 - 2	Drummond 3, Hardiker 34, Curtis 90
19	10/11	Conf.	Farnborough Town	695	1 - 2	Talbot 16
20	17/11	FA Cup 1	Brentford	4026	0 - 1	
21	24/11	Conf.	MARGATE	1588	2 - 1	Talbot 23 Rigoglioso 24
22	01/12	Conf.	Nuneaton Borough	1085	3 - 2	Thompson 63 Talbot 83,90
23	08/12	Conf.	Chester City	1466	1 - 1	Arnold 23[p]
24	15/12	Conf.	STALYBRIDGE CELTIC	1308	1 - 0	Zico-Black 36
25	26/12	Conf.	Southport	1732	1 - 1	Rigoglioso 48
26	29/12	Conf.	WOKING	1308	3 - 1	Norman 24, Talbot 53 73[p]
27	08/01	Lancs MT 2	Darwen	160	2 - 4	Hardiker 15, Thompson 35
28	12/01	FA Trophy 3	KING'S LYNN	939	2 - 0	Hardiker 38, Norman 54
29	19/01	Conf.	HAYES	1149	2 - 1	Curtis 19 20
30	29/01	Conf.	Northwich Victoria	579	3 - 4	Curtis 9 41 57
31	02/02	FA Trophy 4	GRESLEY ROVERS	984	5 - 0	Hay 28 29 43 77, Curtis 80
32	09/02	Conf.	YEOVIL TOWN	1248	1 - 5	Rigoglioso 19
33	23/02	FA Trophy 5	Scarborough	1511	1 - 1	Rigoglioso 37
34	26/02	FA Trophy 5 R	SCARBOROUGH	801	3 - 0	Curtis 39, Norman 57, Rigoglioso 63
35	02/03	Conf.	SCARBOROUGH	1015	2 - 0	Norman 2, Curtis 81
36	09/03	Conf.	Barnet	1316	0 - 1	
37	12/03	Conf.	Leigh RMI	451	1 - 0	Drummond 45
38	16/03	FA Trophy QF	Margate	1224	2 - 1	Norman 72 76
39	19/03	Conf.	SOUTHPORT	1006	2 - 2	Lightfoot 6, Black 47
40	23/03	Conf.	Hereford United	1408	2 - 0	Holmes 69[og], Norman 80
41	26/03	Conf.	DAGENHAM & REDBRIDGE	1235	1 - 1	Thompson 86
42	30/03	Conf.	STEVENAGE BOROUGH	1178	0 - 3	
43	01/04	Conf.	Dagenham & Redbridge	1934	2 - 3	Curtis 62 86
44	03/04	Conf.	Telford United	664	1 - 4	Carlton 77
45	06/04	FA Trophy SF(1)	STEVENAGE BOROUGH	1899	1 - 2	Drummond 76
46	08/04	Conf.	FOREST GREEN ROVERS	670	2 - 0	Gouck 42, G Thompson 82
47	13/04	FA Trophy SF(2)	Stevenage Borough	3119	0 - 2	
48	18/04	Conf.	Margate	784	1 - 1	Arnold 36
49	20/04	Conf.	Dover Athletic	953	1 - 1	Arnold 70[p]
50	23/04	Conf.	BOSTON UNITED	1374	0 - 0	
51	25/04	Conf.	FARNBOROUGH TOWN	635	1 - 1	Norman 87
52	27/04	Conf.	DONCASTER ROVERS	1780	2 - 1	Drummond 4, Arnold 49

1	2	3	4	5	6	7	8	9	10	11	Substitutes Used
Mawson	McKearney	Colkin	Lightfoot	Hardiker	Drummond	Stringfellow	Gouck	Talbot	Arnold	Thompson	Eastwood 9 Norman 11 Rigoglioso 7
Mawson	McKearney	Colkin	Lightfoot	Hardiker	Drummond	Stringfellow	Gouck	Talbot	Arnold	Thompson	Eastwood 11 Norman 10 Rigoglioso 8
Mawson	McKearney	Colkin	Lightfoot	Hardiker	Drummond	McGuire	Gouck	Talbot	Arnold	Thompson	Eastwood 11 Norman 9 Rigoglioso 10
Mawson	Fensome	Colkin	McKearney	Hardiker	Drummond	Lightfoot	Gouck	Talbot	Arnold	Thompson	Eastwood 11 Rigoglioso 8 Stringfellow 7
Mawson	Fensome	Colkin	McKearney	Lightfoot	Drummond	Stringfellow	Gouck	Talbot	Arnold	Thompson	Black 9 Eastwood 11 Rigoglioso 8
Mawson	Fensome	Colkin	Lightfoot	McGuire	Drummond	McKearney	Gouck	Talbot	Arnold	Norman	Curtis 11 Rigoglioso 8 Stringfellow 9
Mawson	Fensome	Colkin	Lightfoot	McGuire	Drummond	McKearney	Gouck	Talbot	Arnold	Norman	Curtis 8 Rigoglioso 3 Stringfellow 4
Mawson	Fensome	Colkin	McKearney	McGuire	Drummond	Rigoglioso	Gouck	Talbot	Norman	Thompson	Curtis 11 Eastwood 9 Uberschar 3
Mawson	Fensome	Colkin	Lightfoot	McGuire	Drummond	McKearney	Gouck	Talbot	Norman	Thompson	Black 8 Perkins 3 Rigoglioso 4
Mawson	Fensome	Perkins	McKearney	McGuire	Drummond	Thompson	Gouck	Talbot	Norman	Black	Crumblehume 7 Eastwood 9 Rigoglioso 10
Mawson	Fensome	Colkin	McKearney	McGuire	Drummond	Hardiker	Gouck	Talbot	Black	Thompson	Eastwood 11 Norman 7 Rigoglioso 9
Mawson	Fensome	Colkin	McGuire	Hardiker	Drummond	McKearney	Gouck	Talbot	Black	Quayle	Black 11 Rigoglioso 16(Tho) Thompson 2
Mawson	Fensome	Colkin	McGuire	Hardiker	Drummond	McKearney	Gouck	Talbot	Norman	Thompson	Black 2 Eastwood 11 Quayle 10
Mawson	Fensome	Hardiker	McGuire	McKearney	Drummond	Rigoglioso	Gouck	Talbot	Thompson	Eastwood	Norman 10 Porter 11
Mawson	Fensome	Hardiker	McGuire	McKearney	Drummond	Rigoglioso	Gouck	Talbot	Eastwood	Thompson	Black 7 Colkin 3 Norman 10
Mawson	Fensome	Colkin	McKearney	McGuire	Drummond	Rigoglioso	Gouck	Talbot	Norman	Black	Arnold 7 Curtis 8 Eastwood 10
Mawson	Fensome	Colkin	McGuire	Lightfoot	Drummond	Hardiker	McKearney	Talbot	Arnold	Black	Curtis 10 Norman 5 Rigoglioso 11
Mawson	Fensome	Colkin	Lightfoot	Hardiker	Drummond	Rigoglioso	Gouck	Talbot	Arnold	Thompson	Black 7 Curtis 11 Norman 9
Mawson	Uberschar	Colkin	Lightfoot	Hardiker	Drummond	McGuire	Gouck	Talbot	Arnold	Thompson	Black 16 (Rig) Rigoglioso 4 Norman 2
Mawson	Fensome	Colkin	McGuire	Hardiker	Drummond	Thompson	Rigoglioso	Talbot	Arnold	Perkins	Curtis 7 Murphy 3
Mawson	Fensome	McKearney	McGuire	Hardiker	Drummond	Thompson	Rigoglioso	Talbot	Arnold	Perkins	Curtis 9 Murphy 8 Norman 10
Mawson	Fensome	McGuire	Murphy	Hardiker	Drummond	Thompson	McKearney	Talbot	Arnold	Perkins	Curtis 5 Black 7 Norman 3
Mawson	Fensome	McKearney	Murphy	Hardiker	Drummond	Rigoglioso	Thompson	Talbot	Arnold	Perkins	Black 11 McGuire 9 Norman 7
Mawson	Fensome	Colkin	McGuire	Hardiker	Drummond	Norman	McKearney	Curtis	Arnold	Black	Murphy 11 Rigoglioso 3 Stanford 9
Mawson	Fensome	Colkin	McGuire	Hardiker	Drummond	Lightfoot	McKearney	Talbot	Norman	Curtis	Black 11 Porter 16 (Rig) Rigoglioso 7
Mawson	Fensome	Colkin	McGuire	Hardiker	Drummond	Rigoglioso	McKearney	Talbot	Norman	Thompson	Black 11 Murphy 9 Porter 7
Mawson	McKearney	Colkin	McGuire	Hardiker	Drummond	Black	Rigoglioso	Talbot	Norman	Perkins	Curtis 9 Murphy 5 Porter 11
Mawson	McKearney	Colkin	McGuire	Hardiker	Drummond	Rigoglioso	Black	Curtis	Norman	Perkins	Fensome 10 Gouck 6 Murphy 4
Mawson	Fensome	Colkin	McGuire	Murphy	Mckearney	Rigoglioso	Thompson	Curtis	Hay	Perkins	Arnold 10 Black 8 Norman 9
Mawson	Fensome	Colkin	McGuire	McKearney	Drummond	Rigoglioso	Thompson	Curtis	Hay	Perkins	Black 11 Stringfellow 5
Mawson	Fensome	Colkin	McGuire	McKearney	Drummond	Rigoglioso	Thompson	Curtis	Hay	Perkins	Black 8 Norman 10 Stringfellow 2
Mawson	Fensome	Colkin	McKearney	Lightfoot	Drummond	Rigoglioso	Gouck	Black	Norman	Perkins	Hay 9 Stringfellow 8
Mawson	McGuire	Colkin	McKearney	Lightfoot	Drummond	Rigoglioso	Black	Curtis	Norman	Perkins	Murphy 5 Stringfellow 7 Thompson 10
Mawson	McGuire	Perkins	McKearney	Murphy	Drummond	Rigoglioso	Black	Curtis	Norman	Thompson	Carlton 10 Fensome 4 Stringfellow 8
Mawson	McGuire	McKearney	Lightfoot	Murphy	Drummond	Rigoglioso	Thompson	Curtis	Norman	Perkins	Carlton 9 Gouck 10 Porter 4
Mawson	McGuire	Perkins	McKearney	Murphy	Drummond	Rigoglioso	Thompson	Talbot	Curtis	Black	Carlton 9 Fensome 10 Norman 8
Mawson	McGuire	McKearney	Lightfoot	Murphy	Drummond	Rigoglioso	Thompson	Talbot	Black	Perkins	Carlton 3 Fensome 12 (Car) Norman 9
Mawson	Uberschar	Perkins	Robinson	Murphy	Lightfoot	Rigoglioso	Crumblehume	Carlton	Thompson	Black	Arnold 9 Gouck 8 Norman 6
Mawson	McGuire	Perkins	McKearney	Murphy	Crumblehume	Rigoglioso	Arnold	Thompson	Norman	Black	Carlton 11 Fensome 2 Thomson 8
Mawson	McGuire	Perkins	Lightfoot	Murphy	Mckearney	Crumblehume	Arnold	Thompson	Norman	Black	Curtis 8 Robinson 11 Thomson 10
Mawson	Fensome	Perkins	Robinson	Murphy	Mckearney	Crumblehume	Arnold	Thomson	Norman	Black	Curtis 11 Porter 10 McGuire 8
Mawson	McGuire	McKearney	Lightfoot	Murphy	Drummond	Rigoglioso	Thompson	Curtis	Norman	Perkins	Arnold 8 Black 11 Gouck 6
Willcock	Fensome	Colkin	McGuire	Robinson	Gouck	Crumblehume	Arnold	Talbot	Thomson	Porter	Carlton 9 Stanford 10 Uberschar 6
Mawson	McKearney	Colkin	Lightfoot	Murphy	Drummond	Rigoglioso	Thompson	Curtis	Norman	Perkins	Carlton 9 McGuire 4 Talbot 7
Mawson	McGuire	Colkin	McKearney	Murphy	Drummond	Arnold	Gouck	Carlton	Norman	Thompson	Black 10 Curtis 9 Rigoglioso 8
Mawson	Fensome	Colkin	McKearney	Murphy	Drummond	Rigoglioso	Gouck	Arnold	Norman	Thompson	Black 8 Curtis 9 Talbot 7
Mawson	McGuire	Colkin	McKearney	Murphy	Drummond	Rigoglioso	Gouck	Curtis	Arnold	Perkins	Carlton 9 Stanford 11 Uberschar 2
Mawson	Uberschar	Colkin	McKearney	Murphy	Drummond	Rigoglioso	Gouck	Arnold	Norman	Black	Carlton 7 Curtis 10 Perkins 11
Mawson	Uberschar	Colkin	McKearney	Murphy	Drummond	Arnold	Gouck	Carlton	Norman	Perkins	Crumblehume 14 (Cur) Curtis 10 Rigoglioso 6
Mawson	Uberschar	Colkin	McKearney	Murphy	Drummond	Arnold	Gouck	Carlton	Norman	Perkins	Curtis 9 Rigoglioso 11
Mawson	Uberschar	Colkin	McKearney	McGuire	Drummond	Rigoglioso	Gouck	Arnold	Norman	Perkins	Black 14 (Cru) Crumblehume 9 Fensome 7

221

MORECAMBE PLAYING SQUAD

Player	Birthplace	D.O.B.	Previous Clubs	
				Bold print denotes England semi-professional international.

GOALKEEPERS

Craig Mawson	Keighley	16.05.79	Halifax T, Burnley

DEFENDERS

Greg Brown	Wythenshawe	31.07.78	Chester C, Macclesfield
Mark Wright Scot.S & Y	Manchester	29.01.70	Everton, Huddersfield, Wigan, Chorley
David McKearney	Liverpool	20.06.68	Prescot Cables, Bolton, Northwich V, Crewe, Wigan, Chorley
David Perkins	Blackpool		From Youth team
Jamie Murphy	Manchester	25.02.73	Halifax, Cambridge Utd, Doncaster R, Blackpool
Nick Coyle ES	Morecambe		From Youth team
Colin Woodthorpe	Liverpool	13.01.69	Bury, Stockport, Aberdeen, Norwich, Chester C
Iain Swan	Glasgow	16.10.79	Leigh RMI, Partick Thistle, Oldham
Jim Bentley	Liverpool	11.06.76	Telford Utd, Manchester C
Keith Hill	Bolton	17.05.69	Cheltenham, Rochdale, Plymouth, Blackburn
Lee Colkin	Nuneaton	15.07.74	Hednesford T, Northampton
Neil Uberschar	Morecambe	16.02.81	From Youth team

MIDFIELD

Stuart Drummond ESP	Preston	11.12.75	Youth team
Andy Gouck	Blackpool	08.06.72	Southport, Rochdale, Blackpool
Michael Knowles	Morecambe	03.03.74	From Youth team
Ryan-Zico Black NI Y	Manchester		From Youth team
Lee Elam	Bradford	24.09.76	Southport, Guiseley
Mike Stringfellow	Lancaster	09.10.81	From Youth team

FORWARDS

Gary Thompson	Kendal	24.11.80	Youth team
Adriano Rigoglioso	Liverpool	28.05.79	Liverpool, Marine
Wayne Curtis	Barrow	06.03.80	Holker OB
Ian Arnold ESP	Durham	04.07.72	Southport, Kidderminster H, Stalybridge C, Kettering T, Carlisle, Middlesbrough
Robbie Talbot	Liverpool		Burscough (£10,000), Marine, Rochdale

NORTHWICH VICTORIA

Northwich Victoria Football Club has established itself as one of the most respected names in non-league football.
The club has contested every season in the Alliance/Conference since it was was formed, they have won the F.A.Trophy at Wembley and they have regularly come through the qualifying rounds of the FA.Cup to take on the League clubs. In fact they have beaten six of them, including local rivals Crewe Alexandra and Chester City.

The club's history is also impressive as they were founded in 1874, they reached the quarter finals of the F.A. Cup in 1983--84 and their famous ' Drill Field 'was known as the ground on which football had been played season by season longer than any other ground. To all outsiders it seems tragic that this ground, of great character, which had been greatly improved in recent seasons is now to be closed down.

No doubt those who have been involved with the politics are even more upset, and we can only hope the famous club comes through this difficult time to give it's supporters many more years of excitement at the top of the pyramid.

In charge at this testing time is Jimmy Quinn, and following an encouraging first season, when The Vics found themselves third after three games, the experienced ex Northern Ireland goalscorer has finally given up playing and will be concentrating on passing his attacking skills onto the youngesters at his disposal. Last season Greg Blundell finished as top scorer and in the second half of the season John Grant scored some vital goals while on loan.

Without ever being in serious danger The Greens also failed to threaten the leaders, until March they had only failed to score on two occasions and then in the run, in with nothing really to play for, they could only score seven times in their last eleven games.The club reached The F.A. Cup First Round once again and faced Hull City who proved too strong on the day and in the F.A. Trophy it took a terrific first half display by the eventual winners,Yeovil Toiwn to bring their challenge to an end.

The coming season will undoubtedly be difficult for everyone involved with Northwich Victoria as they try to come to terms with leaving The Drill Field at a time when the Conference will be awash with ambitious clubs all starting the season with a detrmination to reach those inviting play off positions.

The competition will be at it's most intense and hopefully the morale and character of the club will enable the famous name of Northwich Victoria to remain an ever present in the Conference when the dust settles next May.   T.W.

NORTHWICH VICTORIA FC 2002-03
Back row (l-r): Kevin Street, Phil Trainer, Paul Gibson, Chris Grassie, Andy Woodward & Chris Royle
Middle row: Phil Lea (physio), Steve Walsh, Denny Ingram, Richard Norris, Jake Sedgemore, Dave Cooke (Assistant Manager)
Rob Matthews, Greg Blundell, David McNiven & Steve Davis (Player/Coach)
Front row: Mark Devlin, Greg Rioch, Andy Taylor, Jimmy Quinn (Manager), Val Owen, Danny Griggs & Steve Garvey

NORTHWICH VICTORIA

GROUND DETAILS

Wincham Park,Wincham,Northwich, Cheshire
Tl/Fax:01606 43008

Directions:M6.Jct 19 A556 towardsNorthwich,turn onto A559after three milesat beginning of dual carriageway. Turn left after 3/4 mile opposite BlackGreyhound Inn Ground 1/2 mile onbleft immediately after canal bridge.

CAPACITY	4,000
SEATED	800
COVERED TERRACING	1,500
CLUB SHOP	Located outside ground.Open match days

CLUBHOUSE:
Large social club with members lounge and seperate finctinroom-both available for hire (Tel: 01606 43120) untol 31st Dec 2002. Bass Beer,Pool,Darts, TV etc.
Witton Albion Social Club at Wincham Parkwelcomes all away supporters

Correspondancr to:
Drill Field, Drill Field Rd, Northwich CW9 5HN
Telephone:01606 41450 Fax: 01606 330577.
Club Newsline: 0900802 2713 Web site: www.nvfc.co.uk

Editor: Brian Edge
Pages: 48   Price: £2.00

Other club publications: 'Distant Vics'
(a bi-monthly magazine for exiled Vics' fans)

Local Press: Northwich Guardian (Wed.);
Northwich Chronicle (Wed.); Daily Post;
Manchester Evening News Pink (Sat.)
Local Radio: GMR (BBC Manchester);
Piccadilly Radio; Signal Radio

Founded:	1874
Nickname:	Vics
Club Sponsors:	Britannia Carpets
Club colours:	Green shirts, white shorts and white socks
Change colours:	Sky Blue / navy /navy
Midweek home matchday:	Tuesday
Reserve Team's league:	Lancashire League

CLUB OFFICIALS

Chairman	Dave Stone
Company Secretary	Graham Cookson
Chief Executive	John Stitch
Directors	Derek Nuttall, Jim Rafferty

Associate Directors

Graham Cookson (Co.Sec), Dave Edgeley, Ted Carthy(Gen Man), Peter Garret, Dave Thomas.

President &

Football Secretary	Derek Nuttall c/o the club Tel: 01606 41450 Fax: 01606 330577
Commercial Manager:	Brian Edge Tel : 01606 4145 or 07711 505414

FOOTBALL MANAGEMENT TEAM

MANAGER:	JIMMY QUINN
Date of Appointment	27.07.01
Date of Birth	18.12.59
Place of Birth	Belfast
PREVIOUS CLUBS	
As manager	Reading and Swindon Town
As coach	Peterborough United
As player	Congleton, Oswestry, Swindon, Blackburn Rovers, Leicester City, Bradford City, West Ham United, Bournemouth & B, Reading, Peterborough United,Northwich Victoria, hererford United, Hayes, Nantwich ,Cirencester
HONOURS	
As manager	Division One play off final
As coach	
as player	N.Ireland International 2nd Div Play offWinners 86-7
Assistant Managers:	Steve Davies & Dave Cooke
Physio:	Phil Lea
Res& YouthTeam Manager:	Ted Carthy
Club's Playing Status:	Part-time

Season	League	Div.	Pos.	P	W	D	L	F	A	W	D	L	F	A	Pts	Manager
							Home						**Away**			
01-02	Conference	-	13	42	9	4	8	32	34	7	3	11	25	36	55	Jimmy Quinn
00-01	Conference	-	17	42	8	7	6	31	24	3	6	12	18	43	46	Mark Gardiner/Keith Alexander
99-00	Conference	-	18	42	10	8	3	33	25	3	4	14	20	53	51	Mark Gardiner
98-99	Conference	-	7	42	11	3	7	29	21	8	6	7	31	30	66	Phil Wilson/Mark Gardiner
97-98	Conference	-	9	42	8	9	4	34	24	7	6	8	29	35	60	Phil Wilson
96-97	Conference	-	6	42	11	5	5	31	20	6	7	8	30	34	63	Mark Hancock/ Phil Wilson

Season	League	Div.	Pos.	P	W	D	L	F	A	Pts	Manager
95-96	Conference	-	8	42	16	12	14	72	64	60	Brian Kettle
94-95	Conference	-	10	42	14	15	13	77	66	57	John Williams
93-94	Conference	-	15	42	11	19	12	44	45	52	John Williams
92-93	Conference	-	11	42	16	8	18	68	55	56	Sammy McIlroy/John Williams

HONOURS

Welsh Cup R-up 1881/82,1888-89;
FA Trophy 1983/84, R-up 1982/83 & 1995/96;
Bob Lord Trophy 1979/80, 92/93;
Northern Premier Lge R-up 1976/77;
Northern Premier Lge Cup 1972/73, R-up 1978/79;
Cheshire County Lge 1956/57, R-up 1924/25, 47/48;
Cheshire County Lge Cup 1925/35;
Manchester Lge 1902/03, R-up 1900/01, 03/04, 07/08, 08/09,
11/12; The Combination R-up 1890/91;
Cheshire Senior Cup 1880-81, 81/82, 82/83, 83/84, 84/85,
85/86,1928/29, 36/37, 49/50, 54/55, 71/72, 76/77, 78/79,
83/84, 93/94. R-up 1891/92,96/97, 1905/06, 08/09, 47/48,
50/51, 63/64, 65/66, 69/70, 70/71, 77/78, 85/86; 98/99
Staffordshire Senior Cup 1978/79, 79/80, 89/90,
R-up 1986/87, 90/91;
CheshireAmateur Cup 1901/02, R-up 1898/99, 02/93,
Northwich Senior Cup 1948/49, 58/59,59/60, 63/64, 64/65,
65/66, 67/68, 68/69, 69/70, 71/72, 74/75, R-up x7;
Mid Cheshire Senior Cup 1984/85, 85/86, 87/88, 89/90, 00-01
91/92, 93/94, 94/95, 96/97,98/99,01-02; R-up 1982/83, 83/84,
90/91, 92/93;
North-West Floodlit Lge 1966/67, 75/76;
Cheshire Lge Lancs. Comb. Inter-Lge Cup 1961/62;
Guardian Charity Shield 1985/86, 86/87, 87/88

PREVIOUS

Leagues:
The Combination 1890-1892,
Football League Div.2 1892-94,
The Combination 1894-1898,
The Cheshire League 1898-1900,
Manchester League 1900-12,
Lancashire 1912-19,
Cheshire County League 1919-68,
Northern Premier League 1968-79

Grounds: The Drill Field

Past Players who progressed to the Football League

Tony Hemmings (Wycombe W), Tony Bullock (Barnsley),
Darren Tinson (Macclesfield T) Lee Steele (Shrewsbury
Town),Paul Tait (Crewe Alex),Shaun Teale (Tranmere R &
Aston Villa) , Mark Birch (Carlisle U),Mark Birch (Carlisle U)
and Gary Fletcher (Leyton Orient)

CLUB RECORDS

Attendance: 11,290 v Witton Albion,
Cheshire League, Good Friday 1949

Win: 17-0 v Marple Ass. 15.12.1883
Defeat: 3-10 v Port Vale 7.2.1931

Career Goalscorer: Peter Burns 160 - 1955-65
Career Appearances: 970 by Ken Jones 1969-85

Transfer Fee paid: £12,000
to Hyde United for Malcolm O'Connor - August 1988

Transfer Fee received: £75,000
from Leyton Orient for Gary Fletcher - June 2001

BEST SEASON

FA Cup: Quarter Finals 1883-84
League clubs defeated: Rochdale,Peterborough,Watford
(all 76-7),Chester C (82-3).,Crewe A(84-5) & Bury (00-1)

FA Trophy: Winners 83-84
R-up 82-83 95-96

League: 4th Conference 80-81

LAST SEASON

F.A. Cup: First Round
F.A. Trophy: Quarter Finals
Conference: 13th
Top Goalscorer: Greg Blundell
Player of the Year: Mark Devlin
Captain: Gary Talbot

NORTHWICH VICTORIA

	Date	Comp.	Opponents	Att.	Score	Goalscorers
1	09/08	Mid-Ches.(00-01 F)	WITTON ALBION	n/k	1 - 0	Mike 6
2	18/08	Conf.	Yeovil Town	3290	3 - 2	Brownrigg 32, Burke 41, Blundell 89
3	21/08	Conf.	SCARBOROUGH	760	1 - 1	Norris 31
4	25/08	Conf.	STEVENAGE BOROUGH	821	2 - 1	Mike 24, Jones 38
5	27/08	Conf.	Leigh RMI	642	2 - 1	Blundell 48, Norris 87
6	01/09	Conf.	BOSTON UNITED	1086	1 - 2	Mitchell 44
7	04/09	Conf.	Morecambe	1462	1 - 2	Barnard 79
8	08/09	Conf.	NUNEATON BOROUGH	906	3 - 0	Barnard 3 (Pen), Quinn 30,52
9	11/09	Conf.	Southport	1028	1 - 5	Blundell 59
10	15/09	Conf.	Woking	1331	1 - 3	Mike 65
11	18/09	Ches. SC 1	Altrincham	283	2 - 3	Barnard 13[p], Brownrigg 63
12	22/09	Conf.	Barnet	1364	0 - 1	
13	25/09	Conf.	TELFORD UNITED	739	2 - 2	Burke 4, Garvey 75
14	29/09	Conf.	FOREST GREEN ROVERS	736	2 - 2	Mike 17 Meaker 85
15	02/10	Conf.	DONCASTER ROVERS	878	2 - 3	Talbot 45, Devlin 88[p]
16	06/10	Conf.	Dover Athletic	657	1 - 2	Blundell 90
17	09/10	Conf.	Stalybridge Celtic	711	1 - 1	Mike 6
18	13/10	Conf.	HAYES	698	1 - 0	Blundell 3
19	20/10	Conf.	Margate	1125	2 - 1	Quinn 51 Blundell 65
20	27/10	FA Cup Q4	Telford United	1004	1 - 1	Blundell 35
21	30/10	FA Cup Q4 R	TELFORD UNITED	1063	2 - 1	Mike 30, Devlin 90
22	03/11	Conf.	FARNBOROUGH TOWN	717	1 - 2	Blundell 77
23	10/11	Conf.	Dagenham & Redbridge	1780	1 - 1	Blundell 52
24	17/11	FA Cup 1	HULL CITY	2285	2 - 5	Blundell 73, Mike 80
25	24/11	Conf.	HEREFORD UNITED	790	1 - 0	Devlin 50
26	01/12	Conf.	YEOVIL TOWN	974	1 - 3	Talbot 20
27	15/12	Conf.	Scarborough	986	2 - 1	Dryden 20[og], Blundell 34
28	26/12	Conf.	CHESTER CITY	1940	3 - 1	Devlin 39, Quinn 74, Blundell 80
29	08/01	Conf.	Chester City	1660	2 - 1	Garvey 29 83
30	12/01	FA Trophy 3	BOSTON UNITED	966	3 - 1	Devlin 17, Quinn 53 80
31	19/01	Conf.	Boston United	1981	2 - 3	Blundell 26 88
32	26/01	Conf.	LEIGH RMI	769	0 - 3	
33	29/01	Conf.	MORECAMBE	579	4 - 3	Garvey 1, Illman 79, Owen 85, Talbot 90
34	03/02	FA Trophy 4	Vauxhall Motors	1019	4 - 0	Devlin 7, Garvey 34, Illman 56, Collins 88
35	09/02	Conf.	DOVER ATHLETIC	811	2 - 1	Illman 46, Blundell 70
36	16/02	Conf.	Hayes	543	2 - 1	Grant 43, Norris 62
37	27/02	FA Trophy 5	TELFORD UNITED	916	3 - 2	Grant 17, Burke 89, Norris 90
38	02/03	Conf.	Telford United	929	0 - 1	
39	09/03	Conf.	SOUTHPORT	909	3 - 1	Blundell 27, Teale 32[og], Quinn 90
40	16/03	FA Trophy QF	YEOVIL TOWN	1846	0 - 2	
41	19/03	Conf.	Doncaster Rovers	1489	2 - 2	Blundell 1, Garvey 75
42	23/03	Conf.	WOKING	730	0 - 3	
43	26/03	Mid-Ches. SF	Witton Albion	496	1 - 0	Illman 42
44	30/03	Conf.	MARGATE	604	1 - 1	Grant 25
45	01/04	Conf.	Farnborough Town	673	1 - 4	Grant 41
46	06/04	Conf.	DAGENHAM & REDBRIDGE	744	1 - 2	Grant 13
47	10/04	Conf.	Nuneaton Borough	726	1 - 0	Blundell 73
48	13/04	Conf.	Hereford United	1493	0 - 1	
49	16/04	Conf.	STALYBRIDGE CELTIC	653	1 - 0	Quinn 16
50	20/04	Conf.	Forest Green Rovers	871	0 - 2	
51	22/04	Conf.	Stevenage Borough	1202	0 - 1	
52	27/04	Conf.	BARNET	1750	0 - 3	
53	03/05	Mid-Ches. F	CONGLETON TOWN	n/k	1 - 1	Won 4-3 after pens..

CONFERENCE

	1	2	3	4	5	6	7	8	9	10	11	Substitutes Used
1	✗											
2	Gibson	Knowles	Barnard	Jones	Burke	Talbot	Norris	Browrigg	Blundell	Mike	Devlin	Bailey 2 Garvey 8 Mitchell 10
3	Gibson	Bailey	Barnard	Jones	Burke	Talbot	Norris	Browrigg	Blundell	Mike	Devlin	Garvey 8
4	Gibson	Bailey	Barnard	Jones	Burke	Talbot	Norris	Browrigg	Blundell	Mike	Devlin	Garvey 7 Knowles 8 Mitchell 10
5	Gibson	Bailey	Barnard	Jones	Burke	Talbot	Norris	Browrigg	Blundell	Mike	Devlin	Garvey 8 Walsh 6
6	Gibson	Bailey	Barnard	Jones	Burke	Talbot	Norris	Browrigg	Mitchell	Mike	Devlin	Garvey 8 Dawson 9 Quinn 6
7	Gibson	Knowles	Barnard	Jones	Burke	Garvey	Norris	Bailey	Blundell	Mike	Devlin	Quinn 2
8	Gibson	Bailey	Barnard	Norris	Burke	Talbot	Meaker	Garvey	Blundell	Quinn	Devlin	Brownrigg 4 Mike 10 Mitchell 9
9	Gibson	Bailey	Barnard	Jones	Burke	Talbot	Meaker	Garvey	Blundell	Quinn	Devlin	Norris 4 Mitchell 7
10	Gibson	Bailey	Barnard	Jones	Burke	Talbot	Norris	Meaker	Blundell	Mike	Garvey	Knowles 7 Mitchell 8
	✗											
2	Gibson	Bailey	Barnard	Quinn	Burke	Davis	Garvey	Jones	Blundell	Mike	Devlin	Browrigg 6 Meaker 12 (Bro) Dawson 10
3	Gibson	Bailey	Barnard	Jones	Burke	Talbot	Garvey	Collins	Blundell	Quinn	Devlin	Knowles 3
4	Gibson	Bailey	Barnard	Jones	Burke	Talbot	Garvey	Collins	Blundell	Mike	Devlin	Dawson 10 Meaker 4
5	Gibson	Bailey	Knowles	Garvey	Burke	Talbot	Griggs	Collins	Blundell	Mike	Devlin	Quinn 7
6	Gibson	Sedgemore	Barnard	Ingram	Burke	Talbot	Garvey	Collins	Blundell	Mike	Devlin	Quinn 10 Meaker 8
7	Gibson	Sedgemore	Barnard	Meaker	Ingram	Talbot	Garvey	Collins	Blundell	Mike	Devlin	Burke 10
8	Gibson	Sedgemore	Barnard	Ingram	Owen	Talbot	Garvey	Meaker	Blundell	Mike	Devlin	Collins 8 Quinn 10
9	Gibson	Sedgemore	Barnard	Owen	Burke	Talbot	Garvey	Collins	Blundell	Quinn	Devlin	Mike 9
10	Gibson	Sedgemore	Barnard	Owen	Burke	Ingram	Garvey	Collins	Blundell	Quinn	Devlin	Mike 10 Norris 8
11	Gibson	Sedgemore	Barnard	Owen	Burke	Ingram	Garvey	Collins	Blundell	Quinn	Devlin	Mike 10 Norris 8
12	Gibson	Sedgemore	Barnard	Owen	Burke	Ingram	Garvey	Collins	Blundell	Mike	Devlin	Norris 4
13	Gibson	Bardsley	Barnard	Ingram	Talbot	Burke	Garvey	Collins	Blundell	Mike	Devlin	Quinn 10 Norris 4 Skinner 8
14	Gibson	Bardsley	Barnard	Norris	Burke	Talbot	Garvey	Collins	Blundell	Mike	Ingram	Quinn 2 Skinner 8
15	Gibson	Bardsley	Barnard	Norris	Ingram	Talbot	Garvey	Sedgemore	Blundell	Mike	Devlin	Quinn 10 Collins 8
16	Gibson	Knowles	Barnard	Norris	Ingram	Talbot	Garvey	Sedgemore	Blundell	Quinn	Devlin	Collins 2 Owen 4
17	Gibson	Knowles	Barnard	Owen	Ingram	Talbot	Garvey	Sedgemore	Blundell	Mike	Devlin	Quinn 10 Walsh 2
18	Gibson	Walsh	Barnard	Norris	Ingram	Talbot	Garvey	Sedgemore	Blundell	Quinn	Devlin	Mike 10 Burke 7 Collins 4
19	Gibson	Walsh	Barnard	Owen	Ingram	Talbot	Garvey	Sedgemore	Blundell	Quinn	Devlin	Burke 8
20	Gibson	Walsh	Barnard	Owen	Ingram	Talbot	Garvey	Skinner	Blundell	Quinn	Devlin	Burke 8 Knowles 2
21	Gibson	Walsh	Barnard	Owen	Ingram	Talbot	Garvey	Skinner	Blundell	Quinn	Devlin	Burke 2 Norris 8
22	Gibson	Walsh	Barnard	Owen	Burke	Talbot	Garvey	Skinner	Blundell	Quinn	Devlin	Sedgemore 2 Illman 10 Collins 8
23	Gibson	Sedgemore	Knowles	Owen	Burke	Talbot	Garvey	Collins	Blundell	Illman	Devlin	Quinn 8 Walsh 3
24	Gibson	Knowles	Barnard	Owen	Ingram	Talbot	Garvey	Sedgemore	Blundell	Illman	Devlin	Quinn 10 Norris 7 Collins 8
25	Gibson	Knowles	Barnard	Owen	Ingram	Talbot	Garvey	Sedgemore	Blundell	Illman	Devlin	Norris 11 Walsh 2
26	Gibson	Knowles	Barnard	Owen	Ingram	Burke	Garvey	Sedgemore	Blundell	Grant	Norris	Quinn 10
27	Gibson	Knowles	Burke	Owen	Ingram	Talbot	Garvey	Norris	Blundell	Grant	Illman	Sedgemore 2 Quinn 10
28	Gibson	Knowles	Burke	Owen	Ingram	Talbot	Garvey	Norris	Blundell	Illman	Barnard	Quinn 9
29	Gibson	Knowles	Burke	Owen	Ingram	Talbot	Garvey	Norris	Blundell	Illman	Barnard	Quinn 10 Sedgemore 2 Collins 7
30	Gibson	Knowles	Burke	Owen	Ingram	Talbot	Garvey	Norris	Blundell	Illman	Barnard	Quinn 2 Devlin 10 Grant 3
31	Gibson	Knowles	Barnard	Talbot	Ingram	Owen	Garvey	Norris	Devlin	Blundell	Grant	Collins 2 Burke 3 Sedgemore 9
32	Gibson	Knowles	Barnard	Owen	Ingram	Talbot	Garvey	Sedgemore	Blundell	Grant	Norris	Illman 10 Burke 3 Quinn 8
	✗											
4	Gibson	Royle	Barnard	Porter	Ingram	Talbot	Garvey	Sedgemore	Blundell	Grant	Skinner	Norris 11 Illman 9 Quinn 10
5	Gibson	Talbot	Barnard	Royle	Porter	Burke	Garvey	Sedgemore	Skinner	Grant	Blundell	Norris 2 Illman 7 Knowles 9
6	Gibson	Royle	Barnard	Porter	Ingram	Talbot	Garvey	Norris	Blundell	Grant	Devlin	Sedgemore 8 Quinn 7 Skinner 2
7	Gibson	Royle	Barnard	Porter	Ingram	Talbot	Norris	Sedgemore	Blundell	Grant	Devlin	Garvey 8
8	Gibson	Royle	Barnard	Porter	Ingram	Talbot	Norris	Sedgemore	Blundell	Grant	Devlin	Quinn 4
9	Gibson	Royle	Barnard	Porter	Ingram	Talbot	Norris	Grant	Blundell	Quinn	Devlin	Garvey 9 Owen 7
10	Gibson	Royle	Barnard	Porter	Burke	Talbot	Norris	Owen	Blundell	Quinn	Devlin	Garvey 4
11	Gibson	Royle	Knowles	Porter	Burke	Talbot	Garvey	Owen	Blundell	Grant	Norris	Illman 3 Collins 7
12	Gibson	Royle	Barnard	Owen	Burke	Talbot	Garvey	Porter	Blundell	Grant	Quinn	Norris 2 Sedgemore 9 Illman 8
	✗											

227

NORTHWICH VICTORIA
PLAYING SQUAD

Player	Birthplace	D.O.B.	Previous Clubs	Bold print denotes England semi-professional international.

GOALKEEPERS

Player	Birthplace	D.O.B.	Previous Clubs
Paul Gibson	Sheffield	01.11.76	Notts Co., Manchester Utd

DEFENDERS

Player	Birthplace	D.O.B.	Previous Clubs
Jamie Bates	Manchester		Maine Road, Runcorn, Stalybridge C
Steve Capper	Manchester		From Youth team
Steve Davis EY	Birmingham	26.07.65	Oxford Utd, Barnsley, Burnley, Crewe, Stoke
Andy Woodward	Stockport	23.09.73	Halifax T, Sheffield Utd, Bury, Crewe
Denny Ingram	Sunderland	27.06.76	Scarborough, Hartlepool
Greg Rioch	Sutton Coldfield	24.06.75	Shrewsbury, Macclesfield, Hull, Peterborough, Luton
Jake Sedgemore British Univ.	Birmingham	-	Hereford Utd, Hednesford T, WBA

MIDFIELD

Player	Birthplace	D.O.B.	Previous Clubs
Mark Devlin	Irvine	08.01.73	Stoke, Exeter
Richard Norris	Birkenhead	05.01.78	Marine, Crewe
Andy Taylor	Manchester	-	Manchester Utd
Chris Royle	Manchester	-	Winsford Utd, Congleton T, Witton Alb., Northwich V, Reading
Craig Skinner	Heywood	21.10.70	Leigh RMI, York, Wrexham, Plymouth, Blackburn
Rob Matthews	Slough	14.10.70	Hull, Stockport, Bury, York, Luton, Notts Co., Loughborough Univ.
Val Owen	Manchester	-	Southport, Hednesford T, Northwich V, Hyde Utd

FORWARDS

Player	Birthplace	D.O.B.	Previous Clubs
Gregg Blundell	Liverpool		Vauxhall Motors (£8,500), Tranmere, Kendal Utd
Jimmy Quinn NI Int.	Belfast	18.11.59	Hayes, Highworth T, Hereford Utd, Northwich V, Swindon, Peterborough, Reading, Bournemouth, West Ham, Bradford C, Leicester C, Swindon, Blackburn, Swindon, Oswestry T
Steve Garvey	Stalybridge	22.11.73	Blackpool, Crewe
Danny Griggs	Cheshire	-	Mossley, Nantwich T, Northwich V, Nantwich T, Newcastle T Nantwich T, Middlewich Ath., Crewe
David McNiven	Leeds	27.05.78	Hamilton Acc., Chester C, York, Southport, Oldham
Kevin Street	Crewe	25.11.77	Crewe
Michael Holt	Barnoldswick	-	Rochdale, Preston, Blackburn

NUNEATON BOROUGH

One of the pleasant features of the Conference is that not all the clubs are high profile, but nonetheless give good accounts of themselves on a regular basis and one such outfit is Nuneaton Borough, who also enjoys good loyal support as their average attendance of 1,277 will confirm. Also a position of tenth at the end of the most recent season with goals for and against of 57 each suggesting consistency.

The lowest position achieved by the team was fourteenth at the beginning of September 2001, but in only a few weeks this had improved to fourth, a position held for some time before steady mid-table form was the norm.

The double during the season was gained against Dover Athletic, Leigh RMI, Forest Green Rovers and Scarborough with two reverses each being conceded against Morecambe, Chester City, Yeovil Town and Northwich Victoria - another sign of mid-table form.

However, the one sad feature of the competitive side of the season was the failure to make any impression at all in the knock-out matches with immediate exits from the F.A. Cup (0-3 at lower rated Altrincham in the Fourth Qualifying Round) and at home to struggling Stalybridge Celtic in a Third Round replay of the F.A. Trophy.

As befits a consistent rather than spectacular club, which did not score more than three goals in any match, there were no high goalscorers, but Peyton, Harris, Charles and Thackeray all contributed important strikes.

Nuneaton Borough like any other club probably has ambitions to achieve higher status, but would they benefit from it and would they find such a change enjoyable?

W.M.

NUNEATON BOROUGH 2002-03   Photo courtesy of the Nuneaton Evening Telegraph

Back Row: Warren Peyton, Chris Tullin, Adam Cooper, Steve Hodgson, Chris Mackenzie, Ian Clarkson, Andy Thackeray (Asst. Manager), Alan Cooper (Kit Manager) **Middle**: Paul Egan (Physio), Jamie Lenton, Gary Jones, Richard Lavery, Jason Peake, Michael Love, Jason Harris, Jamie Squires. **Front**: Barry Williams, Terry Angus, Marc McGregor, Steve Burr (Manager), Lee Howey (Coach), Mark Quayle, John Turner

NUNEATON BOROUGH

GROUND DETAILS

Manor Park,
Beaumont Road,
Nuneaton,
Warks. CV11 5HD

Tel.: 02476 385738
Fax: 02476 342690

Simple Directions:
A444 to Nuneaton from M6 junction 3, 2nd exit at 1st round-about, 2nd exit at 2nd r'about, left at 3rd r'bout, 2nd right into Greenmoor Rd, turn right at the end, grd on left. Ground 1 mile from Nuneaton Trent Valley (BR)

Capacity:	6,500
Seated:	520
Terracing -	**Covered:** 3,000
	Uncovered: 3,500

SOCIAL FACILITIES: Clubhouse open every evening, weekend lunchtimes & matchdays.

CLUB SHOP: Sells souvenirs, programmes & club kits
Contact Commercial department

Pages: 56   **Price:** £2.00
Clubcall: 09066 555 848

Editor:Alan Prince
Tel Nos: 01400250332 (H), 07788 800505 (M)

Local Press:
Nuneaton Telegraph & Weekly Tribune
Local Radio: Mercia Sound, BBC CWR

Formed:	1937
Nickname:	The Boro
Club colours:	Blue & white stripes,blue shorts
Change colours:	Navy /gold /navy
Reserve team's league:	Central Conference
Midweek home matchday:	Tuesday 7.45pm

Club Sponsors:
Website: www.nuneatonborough.co.uk

CLUB OFFICIALS

Chairman: Phil Clayton

Executive Directors:
Phil Clayton, Gordon Chislett, Graham Cooper, John Moore,Howard Kerry, David Lee, Dave Radburn, Paul Cleugh,John Phillips,John Wilson,Roger Stanford,
Secretary: Paul Lewis
7 Garfitt Road, Kirby Muxloe,
Leicestershire
Tel: 0116 239 4981 (H) 07711 410642 (M)
Commercial Director: Alan Prince
c/o the club
General Manager: Alan Prince
c/o Club
Press Officers: Phil Clayton
c/o the club

FOOTBALL MANAGEMENT TEAM

MANAGER: **STEVE BURR**
Date of Appointment October 2000
Date of Birth: 12th January 1961
Place of Birth: Aberdeen

PREVIOUS CLUBS
As manager: None
As Asst. Man./Coach Nuneaton Borough 1998
As player: Stafford R,Macclesfield,
Hednesford T

HONOURS
As manager None
As player: Conference, F.A. Trophy x 2
NPL Champions. F.A.XIs

1st Team Coach: Lee Howey
Physio: Helen Cooper
Reserve Team Managers: Ian Charlton &
Graham Wilson
Youth Team Manager: Mick Denis
Scouts: Andy Fern

Season	League	Div.	Pos.	Home						Away					Pts	Manager
				P	W	D	L	F	A	W	D	L	F	A		
01-02	Conference	-	10	42	9	3	9	33	27	7	6	8	24	30	57	Steve Burr
00-01	Conference	-	13	42	9	5	7	35	26	4	10	7	25	34	54	B Phillips/Steve Burr
99-00	Conference	-	15	42	7	6	8	28	25	5	9	7	21	28	51	Brendal Phillips
98-99	Southern	Premier	1	42	16	3	2	52	15	11	6	4	39	18	90	Brendan Phillips
97-98	Southern	Premier	12	42	12	3	6	39	22	5	3	13	29	39	57	Brendan Phillips
96-97	Southern	Premier	7	42	15	2	4	44	20	4	7	10	17	32	65	Brendan Phillips

Season	League	Div.	Pos.	P	W	D	L	F	A	Pts	Manager
95-96	Southern	Midland	1	42	30	5	7	82	35	95	Brendan Phillips
94-95	Southern	Midland	7	42	19	11	12	76	55	68	Elwyn Roberts
93-94	Southern	Premier	22	42	11	8	23	42	66	41	John Barton
92-93	Southern	Midland	1	42	29	5	8	102	45	92	George Rooney/John Barton

HONOURS

Alliance Prem Lge R-up (2) 83-85
Southern Lg Premier Div. 98-99, R-up 66-67 74-75
League Cup Win 95-96
Midland Div 81-82 92-93, Champ 95-96
Lg Cup R-up 62-63, Merit Cup 92-93 (jt)
Birmingham Lg 55-56 (Nth Div 54-55)
Birmingham Comb. R-up 3
Birmingham Snr Cup 7(inc 2001-02), R-up 3

PREVIOUS

Leagues: Central Amateur 37-38; B'ham Comb 38-52; West Mids (B'ham) 52-58;Southern 58-79 81-82 88-99. GM Conference (Alliance Premier & Gola) 79-81 82-8

Names: None

Ground: None

Past Players who progressed to the Football League

A Morton (Fulham 70), R Edwards (Port Vale 72),
K Stephens (Luton 78), T Peake (Lincoln C. 79),
P Sugrue (Man City 80),
M Shotton & T Smithers (Oxford U. 80),
D Thomas (Wimbledon 81), P Richardson (Derby C. 84),
P Culpin (Coventry 85),
R Hill/T Morley/E McGoldrick/A Harris
(Northampton 85/86),
D Bullock (Huddersfield 93)
M Christie (Derby Co. 98)
A Ducros (Kidderminster Harriers) 2000

CLUB RECORDS

Attendance: 22,114 v Rotherham, FA Cup 3rd Rd 1967

Defeat: 1-8 (55-56 & 68-69)

Win: 11-1 (45-46 & 55-56)

Goalscorer: Paul Culpin 201 (Career)
55 (Season - 92/93)

Career Appearances: Alan Jones 545 (62-74)

Transfer Fee Paid: £35,000
for Marc McGregor from Forest Green R. 2000

Transfer Fee Received: £80,000
for Andy Ducros to Kidderminster H. 2000

BEST SEASON

FA Cup: Third Round replay 66-67Rotherham U(H)1-1(A 0-1)
1st Rd 19 times

League Clubs defeated: Watford (53-4),Swansea C(66-67), Oxford U(77-78),Swansea C(93-4) and Stoke City (2001-02)

FA Trophy: Quarter final- 76-77(rep), 79-80, 86-87

League: Runners-up Conference 83-84, 84-85

LAST SEASON

F.A. Cup:	Fourth Qualifying Round
F.A. Trophy:	Third Round
Conference:	10th
Top Goalscorer:	Lee Charles
Player of the Year:	Chris Mackenzie
Captain:	Jason Peake

NUNEATON BOROUGH

	Date	Comp.	Opponents	Att.	Score	Goalscorers
1	18/08	Conf.	Morecambe	1629	0 - 1	
2	21/08	Conf.	HEREFORD UNITED	1544	2 - 0	Thackeray 19, McGregor 53[p]
3	25/08	Conf.	DOVER ATHLETIC	1269	3 - 0	Whitehall 67, Sykes 77, Thackeray 89
4	27/08	Conf.	Chester City	770	0 - 1	
5	01/09	Conf.	YEOVIL TOWN	1484	1 - 2	McGregor 84[p]
6	03/09	Conf.	Stevenage Borough	1665	2 - 2	Whitehall 49, Williams 90
7	08/09	Conf.	Northwich Victoria	906	0 - 3	
8	11/09	Conf.	LEIGH RMI	973	2 - 1	McGregor 40, Charles 84
9	15/09	Conf.	FOREST GREEN ROVERS	1182	2 - 1	Leadbeater 42, Peyton 45[p]
10	18/09	Conf.	Doncaster Rovers	2623	2 - 2	Sykes 26 56
11	22/09	Conf.	Scarborough	890	2 - 1	Whitehall 56, McGregor 76
12	29/09	Conf.	WOKING	1339	2 - 0	McGregor 44 Charles 62
13	02/10	Conf.	SOUTHPORT	1247	3 - 0	Charles 2 6, Whitehall 52
14	06/10	Conf.	Hayes	417	2 - 1	Charles 54 Whitehall 74
15	09/10	Conf.	Farnborough Town	626	1 - 2	Bunce 66[og]
16	13/10	Conf.	STALYBRIDGE CELTIC	1416	3 - 1	Whitehall 25,Peyton 35 (Pen),Charles 90
17	20/10	Conf.	Dagenham & Redbridge	1837	0 - 2	
18	27/10	FA Cup Q4	Altrincham	1306	0 - 3	
19	03/11	Conf.	BARNET	1664	2 - 3	Peyton 36 McGregor 78
20	10/11	Conf.	Margate	1211	1 - 1	Peyton 56
21	17/11	Conf.	Dover Athletic	1007	2 - 1	Clarles 11, Wright 56
22	20/11	Birm SC 2	STOURBRIDGE	206	2 - 1	Sykes 31, Leadbeater 112
23	24/11	Conf.	TELFORD UNITED	1410	1 - 2	McGregor 18
24	01/12	Conf.	MORECAMBE	1085	2 - 3	Charles 36, McGregor 65
25	08/12	Conf.	HAYES	962	0 - 2	
26	15/12	Conf.	Hereford United	1347	1 - 1	Dunkley 89
27	26/12	Conf.	BOSTON UNITED	2203	1 - 1	Charles 40
28	05/01	Conf.	STEVENAGE BOROUGH	1247	2 - 1	Birch 3 82
29	08/01	Birm SC 3	BANBURY UNITED	256	3 - 1	Charles 21, McGregor 48, Sykes 73
30	12/01	FA Trophy 3	Stalybridge Celtic	826	1 - 1	Charles 28
31	15/01	FA Trophy 3 R	STALYBRIDGE CELTIC	1029	1 - 2	Birch 43[p]
32	19/01	Conf.	Yeovil Town	2944	1 - 2	Birch 90
33	02/02	Conf.	Southport	879	1 - 1	Thackeray 46
34	08/02	Birm SC QF	WOLVERHAMPTON W.	563	2 - 2	Peake 85, Thackeray 90 Won 3-2 after pens.
35	16/02	Conf.	Stalybridge Celtic	846	2 - 4	Thackeray 14, Charles 45
36	19/02	Conf.	CHESTER CITY	760	1 - 3	Peyton 84
37	23/02	Conf.	FARNBOROUGH TOWN	728	1 - 1	Harris 89
38	02/03	Conf.	DONCASTER ROVERS	1461	2 - 3	Love 21[p], Peyton 65[p]
39	05/03	Birm SC SF	Moor Green	244	4 - 0	Harkin 7, Peake 13, Harris 15, Charles 89
40	09/03	Conf.	Leigh RMI	410	1 - 0	Peyton 2[p]
41	20/03	Conf.	Boston United	4200	1 - 4	Harkin 89
42	23/03	Conf.	Forest Green Rovers	759	2 - 1	Harris 59 65
43	30/03	Conf.	DAGENHAM & REDBRIDGE	1551	2 - 0	Turner 19, Harris 52
44	01/04	Conf.	Barnet	1419	1 - 0	Thackeray 33
45	06/04	Conf.	MARGATE	1133	0 - 0	
46	10/04	Conf.	NORTHWICH VICTORIA	726	0 - 1	
47	13/04	Conf.	Telford United	1016	2 - 0	Peyton 41[p] 61
48	20/04	Conf.	Woking	2288	0 - 0	
49	27/04	Conf.	SCARBOROUGH	1473	1 - 2	Harris 68
50	02/05	Birm SC F	West Bromwich Albion	n/k	2 - 0	Charles, Turner

1	2	3	4	5	6	7	8	9	10	11	Substitutes Used
MacKenzie	Thackeray	Love	Angus	Weaver	J Williams	Peyton	Whitehall	McGregor	Peake	Sykes	Leadbeater 8 B Williams 11 Charles 9
MacKenzie	Thackeray	Love	Angus	Weaver	B Williams	Peyton	Whitehall	McGregor	Peake	Sykes	Cooper 6
MacKenzie	Thackeray	Love	Angus	Weaver	B Williams	Peyton	Whitehall	McGregor	Peake	Sykes	Leadbeater 6
MacKenzie	Thackeray	Love	Angus	Weaver	B Williams	Peyton	Whitehall	McGregor	Peake	Sykes	Leadbeater 8 Lavery 6 J Williams 11
MacKenzie	Thackeray	Love	Angus	Weaver	B Williams	Peyton	Whitehall	McGregor	Peake	Sykes	Leadbeater 11 Lavery 6 Kennerdale 8
MacKenzie	Thackeray	Love	Angus	Weaver	Lavery	Peyton	Whitehall	McGregor	Peake	J Williams	Crowley 6
MacKenzie	Thackeray	Love	Angus	Weaver	Lavery	Peyton	Whitehall	McGregor	Peake	J Williams	Crowley 10 Kennerdale 7 B Williams 5
MacKenzie	Thackeray	Love	Angus	Weaver	Lavery	Peyton	Charles	McGregor	Crowley	Sykes	Leadbeater 9 B Williams 6
MacKenzie	Thackeray	Love	Angus	Weaver	Lavery	Peyton	Charles	Leadbeater	Crowley	Sykes	Whitehall 9
MacKenzie	Thackeray	Love	Angus	Weaver	Lavery	Peyton	Charles	Leadbeater	Crowley	Sykes	Whitehall 9 B Williams 5
MacKenzie	Thackeray	Love	Angus	B Williams	Lavery	Peyton	Charles	Leadbeater	Crowley	Sykes	McGregor 8 Whitehall 9
MacKenzie	Thackeray	Love	Angus	B Williams	Lavery	J Williams	Charles	McGregor	Crowley	Sykes	Cooper 5 Whitehall 8
MacKenzie	Thackeray	Love	Angus	Cooper	Lavery	J Williams	Charles	McGregor	Crowley	Sykes	Whitehall 9
MacKenzie	Thackeray	Love	Angus	Cooper	Lavery	J Williams	Charles	Whitehall	Crowley	Sykes	Weaver 4 Peake 6 Peyton 7
MacKenzie	Thackeray	Love	Crowley	Cooper	Lavery	Peyton	Charles	Whitehall	Peake	Sykes	Leadbeater 10
MacKenzie	Thackeray	Love	Angus	Cooper	Crowley	Peyton	Charles	Whitehall	Peake	J Williams	Sykes 11 Lavery 6
MacKenzie	Thackeray	Love	Angus	Cooper	Lavery	Peyton	Charles	McGregor	Crowley	J Williams	Whitehall 7 Sykes 11 Weaver 2
MacKenzie	Thackeray	Love	Angus	Cooper	Lavery	Peyton	Charles	McGregor	J Williams	Sykes	B Williams 5 Weaver 10 _FAC_
MacKenzie	Thackeray	Love	Angus	Cooper	Lavery	Peyton	Charles	McGregor	Crowley	Sykes	Leadbeater 11 B Williams 5 Weaver 2
MacKenzie	B Williams	J Williams	Angus	Weaver	Lavery	Peyton	Charles	McGregor	Crowley	Kelly	Cooper 8
MacKenzie	B Williams	Love	J Williams	Weaver	Lavery	Peyton	Charles	McGregor	Crowley	Kelly	Wright 9 _21_
MacKenzie	B Williams	Love	J Williams	Weaver	Lavery	Peyton	Charles	McGregor	Kelly	Wright	Sykes 11 Thackeray 7 Leadbeater 4 _23_
MacKenzie	B Williams	Love	J Williams	Weaver	Lavery	Peyton	Charles	McGregor	Crowley	Sykes	
MacKenzie	Thackeray	Love	B Williams	Weaver	Lavery	Peyton	Charles	McGregor	Crowley	Sykes	Cooper 4 Wright 6 Leadbeater 9
MacKenzie	Thackeray	Love	Angus	B Williams	J Williams	Peyton	Charles	Birch	Crowley	Sykes	Dunkley 7 Wright 6
MacKenzie	Thackeray	Love	Angus	B Williams	Lavery	Wright	Charles	Birch	Crowley	Sykes	
MacKenzie	Thackeray	Love	Angus	B Williams	Lavery	Wright	Charles	Birch	Crowley	Sykes	Harkin 11 Burgess 9 Weaver 5 _28_
MacKenzie	Thackeray	Love	Angus	B Williams	Lavery	Wright	Charles	Birch	Crowley	Peyton	Weaver 5 Harkin 11 _FAT 30_
MacKenzie	Thackeray	Love	Angus	Weaver	Lavery	Burgess	Charles	Birch	Crowley	Harkin	Peake 2 Peyton 11 Sykes 7 _FAT_
MacKenzie	Howey	Love	Angus	Weaver	Lavery	Burgess	Charles	Birch	Crowley	Harkin	
MacKenzie	Weaver	B Williams	Angus	Peake	Lavery	Harkin	Charles	Birch	Peyton	A Turner	Thackeray 6 Love 3 _33_
MacKenzie	Thackeray	Love	Angus	Howey	Crowley	Harkin	Charles	Burgess	Peake	A Turner	Harris 9 Peyton 7 _35_
MacKenzie	Thackeray	Love	Angus	Howey	Lavery	Harkin	Charles	Burgess	Peake	Crowley	Dunkley 7 Peyton 10 Harris 9
MacKenzie	Weaver	Love	Angus	B Williams	Lavery	Thackeray	Charles	Harris	Crowley	Peyton	Dunkley 3 A Turner 8
MacKenzie	Thackeray	Love	Angus	Weaver	B Williams	Lavery	Harkin	Harris	Crowley	Peyton	Peake 7 Burgess 10 _38_
MacKenzie	Thackeray	Love	Angus	Weaver	Howey	Crowley	Harkin	Harris	Peake	Peyton	Charles 8 Lavery 7 _40_
MacKenzie	Thackeray	Love	Angus	Weaver	Howey	Crowley	Harkin	Harris	Peake	Peyton	Charles 7, B Williams 11 sub J Turner)
MacKenzie	Thackeray	Love	Angus	Howey	Crowley	J Turner	Charles	Harris	Peake	Harkin	Lavery 6 Dunkley 11
MacKenzie	Thackeray	Love	Angus	Howey	Lavery	J Turner	Charles	Harris	Peake	Peyton	Dunkley 8
MacKenzie	Thackeray	Love	Angus	Weaver	Lavery	J Turner	Charles	Harris	Peake	Peyton	Dunkley 9
MacKenzie	Thackeray	Love	Angus	Weaver	Lavery	J Turner	Charles	Dunkley	Peake	Harkin	Burgess 10
MacKenzie	Thackeray	Love	Angus	Weaver	Lavery	J Turner	Dunkley	Harris	Peake	Harkin	Charles 9
MacKenzie	Thackeray	Love	Angus	Howey	Lavery	J Turner	Harkin	Harris	Peake	Peyton	
MacKenzie	Tullin	Love	Angus	Howey	Thackeray	J Turner	Harkin	Harris	Peake	Peyton	B Williams 2 Cooper 6
MacKenzie	Cooper	Love	Angus	Howey	B Williams	J Turner	Harkin	Harris	Peake	Peyton	_LP_

233

NUNEATON BOROUGH · PLAYING SQUAD

Player	Birthplace	D.O.B.	Previous Clubs	
Player	*Birthplace*	*D.O.B.*	*Previous Clubs*	Bold print denotes England semi-professional international.

GOALKEEPERS

Chris Mackenzie	Northampton	14.05.72	Corby T, Hereford U, Leyton O
Steve Hodgson	Macclesfield	23.12.81	Macclesfield, Manchester C

DEFENDERS

Terry Angus DMP	Coventry	14.01.66	VS Rugby, Northampton, Fulham, Slough T
Mickey Love	Stockport	27.11.73	Bedworth U, Hinckley T, Hinckley Ath., Wigan, Wycombe, Hinckley Ath., Tamworth,Northampton, Stevenage B
Barry Williams ESP, DMP	Birmingham	06.05.73	Alvechurch, Ely C, Redditch U
Andy Thackeray	Huddersfield	13.02.68	Manchester C, Huddersfield, Newport Co., Wrexham, Rochdale, Halifax T.
Adam Cooper	Coventry	-	From Youth team
James Squires	Preston	15.11.75	Doncaster R, Carlisle, Dunfermline, Preston
Lee Howey	Sunderland	01.04.69	Forest Green R, Northampton, Burnley, Sunderland, Bishop Auckland, Blyth Spartans, Ipswich

MIDFIELD

Jamie Williams	Coventry		Hinckley Utd, Coventry
Jason Peake ES, EY	Leicester	29.09.71	Plymouth, Rochdale, Bury, Brighton, Rochdale, Halifax
Richard Lavery	Coventry	28.05.77	Hinckley Utd, Tamworth, Atherstone Utd, Sutton Coldfield T, Massey Ferguson, Stratford T, Nuneaton B, Hinckley Ath., Bedworth Utd
Craig Woodley	Worcester	04.12.75	Moor Green, Redditch U., Paget R, Solihull B, Rushall Olympic, Sutton Coldfield T, Burton Alb., Sutton Coldfield T, Bromsgrove R
Gary Birch	Birmingham	08.10.81	Walsall
John Turner	Blackburn	22.01.80	Coalville T, Loughborough Dynamo, Shepshed Dynamo, Bamber Bridge, Blackburn, Preston

FORWARDS

Marc McGregor ESP	Southend	30.04.78	Oxford U, Endsleigh, Forest Green R, £35,000 to Nuneaton B
Warren Peyton			Bury, Rochdale
Gary Jones	Huddersfield	06.04.69	Halifax T, Hartlepool, Notts Co., Southend, Boston Utd, Kettering T, Grantham T, Doncaster R, Rossington Main
Jason Harris	Sutton	24.11.76	Harrogate T, Southend, Hull, Preston, Leyton O., Crystal Pal.
Mark Quayle	Liverpool	02.10.78	Telford Utd, Morecambe, Altrincham, Ilkeston T, Leigh RMI, Halifax T, Notts Co., Everton

SCARBOROUGH

Not so long ago Scarborough were a Football League club, who were deprived of their status because Carlisle United's goalkeeper scored a freak last ditch goal, but in their latest campaign they were happy just to survive in the Conference after a nightmare of a season, from which they only finally managed to awake in mid-March.

In fact as the year 2002 began the team occupied the bottom spot and had only won four of its matches, one being the last one of the year against anther former Football League club, Barnet, by three clear home goals, while some wins in mid-January against Doncaster Rovers and Woking (both by single strikes) did slightly relieve the pressure.

However, the next victory did not occur until Stalybridge Celtic were visited in mid-March with another away success at Hayes four days later lifting the side out of a relegation place and after that the final eight matches produced four victories, three draws and only one defeat (away to Farnborough Town), so twelfth place and respectability was attained.

The knock-out competitions provided little real joy with the F.A. Cup challenge ending in the Fourth Qualifying Round at Whitby Town (1-3), but the F.A. Trophy was altogether better with success at home against Hednesford Town (2-0) being followed by two draws against Barnet (0-0 away and 2-2 at home) and advancement through penalties (5-3).

Highflying Morecambe then left Scarborough after sharing two goals, but scored three without reply on their own pitch and a club, whose name was once almost a permanent feature of the competition, was out of it.

A goals story of 55 for and 63 against would suggest that the side was weak in both departments, which was the case before the late revival, when various players, notably Stamp, Blunt, Rose and Sugden, contributed bravely and helped to bring about the ultimate mid-table position, but those supporters, who avoided ultimate and terminal cardiac arrest, will be anxious for something like the most recent season not to recur.

W.M.

SCARBOROUGH FC 2002-03

ck Row: Brian Hodgson (Kit Manager); Kevin Farley (Physiotherapist); Anthony Ormerod; Steve Baker; Richard Tracey (released); Shaun Rennison; Andy Woods; Leigh Walker; Keith Scott; Neil Campbell; Richard Dryden; David Henderson;
Mitch Cook (Centre of Excellence Director); Ian Kerr (Youth Team Manager)
Front: Paul Shepherd; Andy Wright; David Pounder; Darren Connell; Karl Rose; Russell Slade (Manager);
Mark Patterson (Assistant Manager); Gareth Stoker; Olivier Brassart; Jason Blunt; Scott Jordan; Mark Hotte.
Player not shown – Nick Henry

SCARBOROUGH

Founded:	1879
Nickname:	The Seadogs
Club Sponsors:	OCM Ltd
Colours	Red& white shirts, black or whiteshorts, red socks
Change colours:	Yellow/yellow/blue
Midweek Matchday:	Tuesday
Youth League	Youth Aliance

GROUND DETAILS

McCain Stadium
Seamer Road
Scarborough
N. Yorkshire YO12 4HF

TELEPHONE
Tel: 01723 375094
Fax: 01723 366211
Newsline: 0891 121650

SIMPLE DIRECTIONS The ground is situated on the main
Scarborough to York road (A64), about half a mile
beyond B&Q on the left as you go into Scarborough.
Scarborough central (BR) about 2 miles.
Car Parking: Ample in streets around the ground.

CAPACITY	5,900
SEATING	3,500
COVERED TERRACING	1,000

CLUB SHOP: Monday to Friday 09.00-17.00
and matchdays

SOCIAL FACILITIES: Clubhouse - open matchdays only

MATCHDAY PROGRAMME

Pages: 44 Price: £1.50
Editor: James Hunter

Other club publications: None

Local Press:
Scarborough Evening News; The Mercury

Local Radio: Radio York; Y.C.R. Radio

CLUB OFFICIALS

Chairman Malcolm Reynolds
President John R Birley
Company Secretary Philip Webster

Directors: M.Reynolds, J Birley & P Webster,

Secretary,Press Officer

& Commercial Manager Kevin Philliskirk

Tel Nos: 01723 375094 (W) 07798 538318 (M)

01723 366211 (Fax) Email:scarboroughfc@

zoom.co.uk. Correspondance to club.

FOOTBALL MANAGEMENT TEAM

MANAGER: RUSSELL SLADE

Date of Appointment: November 2001
Date of Birth: 10.10.60
Place of Birth: Wokingham

PREVIOUS CLUBS
As manager: Notts County, Jt Manager Sheff.Utd
As coach: Northampton T, Notts C,Sheff U.
As player: Notts County

Firts Team Coach Mark Patterson
Physiotherapist Kevin Farley
Centre of Excellence Director Mitch Cook
Youth Team Manager Ian Kerr

Season	League	Div.	Pos.	P	W	D	L	F	A	W	D	L	F	A	Pts	Manager
							Home					**Away**				
01-02	Conference	-	12	42	9	6	6	27	22	5	8	8	28	41	*55	Neil Thompson
00-01	Conference	-	10	42	7	9	5	29	25	7	7	7	27	29	58	C. Addison/ Neil Thompson
99-00	Conference	-	4	42	10	6	5	36	14	9	6	6	24	21	69	Colin Addison
98-99	F. League	3	24	46	8	3	12	30	39	6	3	14	20	38	48	Mike Wadsworth

Season	League	Div.	Pos.	P	W	D	L	F	A	Pts	Manager
97-98	F. League	3	6	46	19	15	12	67	58	72	Mike Wadsworth
96-97	F. League	3	12	46	16	15	15	65	68	63	Mike Wadsworth
95-96	F. League	3	23	46	8	16	22	39	69	40	Ray McHale
94-95	F. League	3	21	42	8	10	24	49	70	34	Philip Chambers
93-94	F. League	3	14	42	15	8	19	55	61	53	Philip Chambers
92-93	F. League	3	13	42	15	9	18	66	71	54	Ray McHale

HONOURS

FA Trophy 72-73 75-76 76-77
Vauxhall Conference 86-87
Bob Lord Trophy 83-84
NPL Lge Cup 76-77
North Eastern Cos Lge 62-63, Lge Cup 62-63
Midland Lge 29-30
Scarborough & Dist. Lge 45-46
E. Riding Cup x 8; N. Riding Sen. Cup x 17

PREVIOUS

Leagues:
Northern 1898-1910 14-26
Yorkshire Combination 10-14; Yorkshire 26-27;
Midland 27-40 46-60 63-68
Scarborough & Dist. 45-46
Northern Counties 60-62; North Eastern 62-63;
Northern Premier 68-79
Alliance Premier 79-87 99-
Football League 87-99

Name: None

Past Players who progressed to the Football League

Not yet applicable

CLUB RECORDS

Attendance: 11,162
v Luton Town, FAC 3rd Rd, 1938

Victory: 6-0 v Rhyl Athletic, FA Cup 29.11.30

Defeat: 0-8 v Mansfield Town (H), FA Cup 22.11.52

Career Goalscorer: Unknown

Career Appearances: 196 Steve Richards 87-91

Transfer Fee Paid: £100,000
for Martin Russell to Leicester C., Feb. 87

Transfer Fee Received: £350,000
for Craig Short from Notts Co. (£150K 7/89 + £250K9/92)

BEST SEASON

FA Cup: 3rd Round 30-31 37-38 75-76 77-78

League Clubs Defeated (as non-league club):LincolnC(30-1)
York C (32-3), Darlington (37-8), Bradford C(64-5),Oldham A
(72-3),Crewe A(73-4), P.N.E(75-6),Crewe A & Rochdale (77-8)

FA Trophy: Winners 72-73 75-76 76-77

Football League: 5th in Division 4, 88-89

League Cup: 4th Round 92-93

LAST SEASON

F.A. Cup:	Fourth Qualifying Round
F.A. Trophy:	Fifth Round
Conference:	12th
Top Goalscorer:	
Player of the Year:	
Captain:	
Highest League Attendance:	

SCARBOROUGH

	Date	Comp.	Opponents	Att.	Score	Goalscorers
1	25/07	N Rid SC SF	MIDDLESBROUGH	n/k	0 - 3	
2	18/08	Conf.	FOREST GREEN ROVERS	1104	1 - 1	Stamp 83
3	21/08	Conf.	Northwich Victoria	760	1 - 1	Pounder 23
4	25/08	Conf.	Barnet	1276	1 - 1	Brodie 56
5	27/08	Conf.	MARGATE	886	0 - 1	
6	01/09	Conf.	Woking	1244	2 - 1	Stamp 8 45
7	04/09	Conf.	STALYBRIDGE CELTIC	867	1 - 1	Brodie 77
8	08/09	Conf.	HAYES	896	1 - 2	Burt 80
9	10/09	Conf.	Stevenage Borough	1794	0 - 2	
10	15/09	Conf.	Yeovil Town	2390	2 - 2	Brodie 22, Wilford 34
11	18/09	Conf.	MORECAMBE	616	0 - 2	
12	22/09	Conf.	NUNEATON BOROUGH	890	1 - 2	Stamp 57
13	29/09	Conf.	Dagenham & Redbridge	1482	2 - 4	Stamp 26, Stoker 44
14	02/10	Conf.	CHESTER CITY	783	2 - 1	Stamp 12, Rennison 90
15	06/10	Conf.	Boston United	1700	2 - 2	Blunt 49 Windross 61
16	09/10	Conf.	Southport	701	0 - 1	
17	13/10	Conf.	DOVER ATHLETIC	870	1 - 1	Windross 88
18	16/10	LDV Vans 1N	Leigh RMI	300	1 - 2	Pounder 48
19	20/10	Conf.	Hereford United	1346	0 - 6	
20	27/10	FA Cup Q4	Whitby Town	1862	1 - 3	Stamp 8
21	03/11	Conf.	LEIGH RMI	853	2 - 5	Brodie 43 Elliott 60
22	09/11	Conf.	Telford United	859	0 - 3	
23	24/11	Conf.	FARNBOROUGH TOWN	930	1 - 0	Windross 23
24	01/12	Conf.	Forest Green Rovers	751	2 - 2	Pounder 40, Dryden 60
25	15/12	Conf.	NORTHWICH VICTORIA	986	1 - 2	Pounder 71
26	26/12	Conf.	Doncaster Rovers	3279	3 - 4	Rennison 5, Miller 52[og], Blunt 88
27	29/12	Conf.	BARNET	1051	3 - 0	Shepherd 22, Shields 45, Rose 56
28	12/01	FA Trophy 3	HEDNESFORD TOWN	951	2 - 0	Connolly 13, Stamp 90
29	15/01	Conf.	DONCASTER ROVERS	1789	1 - 0	Blunt 6
30	19/01	Conf.	WOKING	1238	1 - 0	Rose 68
31	26/01	Conf.	Margate	637	1 - 1	Shepherd 49[p]
32	29/01	North RSC 1	Whitby Town	363	3 - 3	Shields 11, Connell 51, Henderson 110 Lost 1-4 after pens.
33	02/02	FA Trophy 4	Barnet	1140	0 - 0	
34	05/02	FA Trophy 4 R	BARNET	928	2 - 2	Shields 8, Rennison 97 Won 5-3 after pens.
35	16/02	Conf.	Dover Athletic	1005	2 - 0	Shields 33, Stamp 90
36	23/02	FA Trophy 5	MORECAMBE	1511	1 - 1	Shepherd 86[p]
37	26/02	FA Trophy 5 R	Morecambe	801	0 - 3	
38	02/03	Conf.	Morecambe	1015	0 - 0	
39	05/03	Conf.	Chester City	1475	0 - 0	
40	09/03	Conf.	STEVENAGE BOROUGH	1188	1 - 1	Blunt 57
41	12/03	Conf.	Stalybridge Celtic	626	3 - 2	Murphy 15[og], Blunt 37, Stamp 77[p]
42	16/03	Conf.	Hayes	631	2 - 1	Rose 30 43
43	23/03	Conf.	YEOVIL TOWN	1379	0 - 0	
44	30/03	Conf.	HEREFORD UNITED	1478	3 - 2	Blunt 32, Baker 41[p], Sugden 46
45	01/04	Conf.	Leigh RMI	1465	1 - 1	Rose 90
46	06/04	Conf.	TELFORD UNITED	1439	3 - 1	Rennison 45, Stamp 52, Sugden 78
47	10/04	Conf.	SOUTHPORT	1254	2 - 0	Rose 13, Jordan 86
48	13/04	Conf.	Farnborough Town	843	2 - 4	Connell 13, Stamp 45
49	16/04	Conf.	BOSTON UNITED	2228	2 - 0	Pounder 24, Stamp 47
50	20/04	Conf.	DAGENHAM & REDBRIDGE	2349	0 - 0	
51	27/04	Conf.	Nuneaton Borough	1473	2 - 1	Stamp 62, Connell 77

Woods	Short	Fitzsimmons	Rennison	Faure	Ingram	Blunt	Fickling	Stamp	Burt	Pounder	Brodie 10 Stoker 2
Woods	Short	Fitzsimmons	Rennison	Faure	Ingram	Blunt	Fickling	Stamp	Brodie	Pounder	Stoker 10 Turley 5 Sherwood 11
Woods	Atkinson	Fitzsimmons	Rennison	Faure	Ingram	Blunt	Fickling	Stamp	Brodie	Stoker	Turley 10 Sherwood 5
Woods	Short	Fitzsimmons	Rennison	Fickling	Ingram	Blunt	Stoker	Stamp	Brodie	Pounder	Burt 3 Sherwood 4
Woods	Short	Fitzsimmons	Rennison	Fickling	Ingram	Blunt	Stoker	Stamp	Brodie	Burt	Barnwell-Edinboro 10
Woods	Short	Fitzsimmons	Rennison	Fickling	Ingram	Blunt	Stoker	Stamp	Brodie	Burt	Barnwell-Edinboro 11 Atkinson 2
Woods	Atkinson	Fitzsimmons	Faure	Fickling	Ingram	Wilford	Blunt	Stamp	Brodie	Barnwell-E	Rennison 5 Stoker 4 Burt 7
Woods	Wilford	Fitzsimmons	Rennison	Faure	Ingram	Blunt	Stoker	Barnwell-E	Brodie	Sherwood	Pounder 11 Henderson 9
Woods	Atkinson	Fitzsimmons	Rennison	Faure	Ingram	Blunt	Stoker	Wilford	Brodie	Pounder	Turley 11 Burt 10
Woods	Atkinson	Fitzsimmons	Rennison	Faure	Ingram	Blunt	Stoker	Wilford	Brodie	Pounder	Turley 3 Burt 8
Woods	Atkinson	Fitzsimmons	Rennison	Faure	Ingram	Blunt	Wilford	Stamp	Brodie	Pounder	Turley 8
Woods	Atkinson	Keegan	Rennison	Faure	Ingram	Blunt	Stoker	Stamp	Brodie	Wilford	Swales 2 Fitzsimmons 3 Jewell 8
Woods	Atkinson	Keegan	Rennison	Faure	Ingram	Blunt	Wilford	Stamp	Brodie	Pounder	Windross 9 Hogg 5 Jewell 8
Woods	Swales	Fitzsimmons	Rennison	Atkinson	Keegan	Blunt	Elliott	Windross	Brodie	Pounder	
Woods	Swales	Fitzsimmons	Rennison	Atkinson	Keegan	Blunt	Elliott	Windross	Brodie	Pounder	Wilford 9 Jewell 11
Woods	Atkinson	Fitzsimmons	Wilford	Jones	Faure	Blunt	Elliott	Windross	Brodie	Pounder	Stoker 10 Swales 2
Woods	Stoker	Fitzsimmons	Wilford	Jones	Faure	Blunt	Elliott	Windross	Torpey	Pounder	Atkinson 10 Newton 2
Woods	Atkinson	Fitzsimmons	Faure	Jones	Keegan	Blunt	Elliott	Stamp	Stoker	Pounder	Windross 6 Swales 2 O'Riordan 3
Woods	Atkinson	Pounder	Rennison	Faure	Jones	Blunt	Elliott	Stamp	Stoker	Windross	Swales 2 Fitzsimmons 10 O'Riordan 11
Newton	Swales	Fitzsimmons	Rennison	Wilford	Atkinson	Blunt	Elliott	Stamp	Brodie	Pounder	Windross 9 Crawford 3
Woods	Atkinson	Pounder	Rennison	Faure	Bennett	Blunt	Elliott	Windross	Brodie	Jones	Jewell 8 Swales 2
Smith	Blunt	Jordan	Faure	Rennison	Jones	Baker	Patterson	Windross	Shields	Pounder	Sherwood 3 Jewell 10
Smith	Jordan	Dryden	Baker	Rennison	Jones	Blunt	Patterson	Shields	Stamp	Pounder	Windross 9 Elliott 4 Sherwood 2
Smith	Stoker	Dryden	Baker	Rennison	Jones	Shepherd	Patterson	Stamp	Shields	Pounder	Jordan 10 Elliott 4 Windross 5
Smith	Jordan	Dryden	Stoker	Shepherd	Rennison	Blunt	Patterson	Rose	Shields	Pounder	Baker 8 Faure 2 Windross 10
Woods	Blunt	Dryden	Stoker	Rennison	Shepherd	Jordan	Patterson	Rose	Shields	Pounder	Stamp 10
Woods	Jordan	Faure	Stoker	Rennison	Shepherd	Blunt	Baker	Rose	Connell	Pounder	Keegan 5 Stamp 10
Woods	Hotte	Jordan	Shepherd	Rennison	Stoker	Blunt	Patterson	Rose	Shields	Pounder	Stamp 2 Connell 10 Baker 8
Woods	Hotte	Burley	Stoker	Rennison	Shepherd	Blunt	Patterson	Stamp	Shields	Pounder	Baker 11 Connell 10 Rose 8
Woods	Hotte	Burley	Stoker	Rennison	Shepherd	Blunt	Patterson	Stamp	Rose	hields	Baker 10 Pounder 11
Woods	Baker	Burley	Stoker	Rennison	Shepherd	Blunt	Patterson	Rose	Shields	Pounder	Connell 10 Stamp 9
Woods	Pounder	Baker	Stoker	Rennison	Shepherd	Blunt	Patterson	Stamp	Shields	Connell	Rose 2 Burley 11 Hotte 8
Woods	Jordan	Hotte	Stoker	Faure	Baker	Salt	Sugden	Stamp	Shields	Burley	Rose 10 Pounder 8
Woods	Pounder	Hotte	Stoker	Baker	Shepherd	Blunt	Salt	Stamp	Sugden	Rose	Jorda 11 Connell 10
Woods	Baker	Hotte	Stoker	Shepherd	Jordan	Blunt	Salt	Stamp	Sugden	Pounder	Connell 11 Rennison 2
Woods	Jordan	Hotte	Stoker	Rennison	Shepherd	Blunt	Patterson	Sugden	Mann	Pounder	Stamp 9
Woods	Jordan	Hotte	Stoker	Rennison	Shepherd	Blunt	Patterson	Stamp	Sugden	Pounder	Rose 10 Pounder 8
Woods	Jordan	Hotte	Stoker	Rennison	Shepherd	Blunt	Patterson	Stamp	Sugden	Mann	Pounder 10 Tracey 11 Rose 16 (Tra)
Woods	Jordan	Baker	Stoker	Rennison	Shepherd	Blunt	Patterson	Stamp	Rose	Pounder	Hotte 6
Woods	Jordan	Hotte	Stoker	Rennison	Baker	Blunt	Salt	Stamp	Rose	Pounder	Sugden 9 Faure 8
Woods	Jordan	Hotte	Stoker	Rennison	Baker	Blunt	Salt	Stamp	Rose	Pounder	Sugden 7
Woods	Jordan	Hotte	Stoker	Rennison	Baker	Blunt	Salt	Sugden	Rose	Wright	Patterson 8 Pounder 11 Henderson 7
Woods	Jordan	Hotte	Stoker	Rennison	Baker	Blunt	Salt	Sugden	Rose	Pounder	Patterson 8 Faure 6 Brunton 4
Woods	Jordan	Hotte	Salt	Rennison	Baker	Blunt	Patterson	Stamp	Rose	Wright	Pounder 11 Sugden 8
Woods	Jordan	Hotte	Salt	Rennison	Baker	Blunt	Patterson	Stamp	Rose	Wright	Connell 10 Sugden 11
Woods	Jordan	Hotte	Salt	Rennison	Faure	Blunt	Patterson	Stamp	Sugden	Connell	Pounder 10 Jones 6
Woods	Jordan	Hotte	Salt	Rennison	Baker	Blunt	Patterson	Stamp	Sugden	Pounder	Connell 10
Woods	Jordan	Hotte	Salt	Rennison	Baker	Blunt	Patterson	Stamp	Sugden	Pounder	Connell 10
Woods	Jordan	Hotte	Baker	Rennison	Salt	Blunt	Rose	Wright	Stamp	Pounder	Connell 9

SCARBOROUGH | PLAYING SQUAD

Player	Birthplace	D.O.B.	Previous Clubs

Bold print denotes England semi-professional international.

GOALKEEPERS

Player	Birthplace	D.O.B.	Previous Clubs
Andy Woods	Colchester	15.01.76	Halifax, Doncaster R
Leigh Walker	Sheffield	27.02.81	Stalbridge Celtic, Emley, South Normanton Ath., Barnsley, Sheffield Utd

DEFENDERS

Player	Birthplace	D.O.B.	Previous Clubs
Shaun Rennison	Northallerton	23.11.80	From Trainee
Mark Hotte	Bradford	27.09.78	Oldham
Richard Dryden Div 4	Stroud	14.06.69	Luton, Southampton, Bristol C, Birmingham, Notts Co., Exeter, Bristol R
Steve Baker	Pontefract	08.09.78	Middlesbrough

MIDFIELD

Player	Birthplace	D.O.B.	Previous Clubs
Gareth Stoker	Bishop Auckland	22.02.73	Leeds, Hull, Hereford U, Cardiff, Rochdale
Jason Blunt	Penzance	16.08.77	Blackpool, Leeds
Scott Jordan	Newcastle	19.07.75	York
Andy Wright	Leeds	21.10.78	Fortuna Sittard (Holl), Reading, Leeds
Anthony Ormerod EY	Middlesbrough	31.03.79	Middlesbrough
David Pounder	Newcastle	03.02.80	From Trainee
Nick Henry Div 2	Liverpool	21.02.69	Tranmere, Walsall, Sheffield Utd, Oldham
Olivier Brassart	Noisy-le-Sec (Fra.)	20.05.77	Yeovil T, Stuttgart Kickers (Ger), RAEC Bergen (Belg), FC Denderleeuw (Belg), Royal Antwerp (Belg), RC Lens (Fra.)
David Hendrson	Newcastle	28.09.1982	From Youth team

FORWARDS

Player	Birthplace	D.O.B.	Previous Clubs
Keith Scott NC, FAT	London	09.06.67	Dover Ath., Colchester, Reading, Wycombe, Norwich, Stoke, Swindon, Wycombe, Lincoln C, Leicester Utd
Neil Campbell	Middlesbrough	26.01.77	Doncaster R, Southend, Scarborough, York
Paul Shepherd	Leeds	17.11.77	Oldham, Luton, Scunthorpe, Ayr Utd, Leeds
Darren Connell	Blackpool	03.02.82	Macclesfield, Blackpool
Karl Rose	Barnsley	12.10.78	Barnsley

SOUTHPORT

The departure of Mark Wright to Oxford United and introduction of Phil Wilson who had guided Stalybridge Celtic back to the Conference obviously meant that the reasonably settled playing squad would be disrupted, and, as expected, it took half the season for the 'new' Southport to settle down.

The hardest aspect to get right when moulding a new squad is goalscoring, and this was certainly the case at Haig Avenue. The Sandgrounders failed to score on twelve occasions before Christmas and the club drifted down to fifteenth place.

However, on the completion of a double over neighbours Chester City and a draw with Morecambe, victories followed against Farnborough Town and Leigh RMI (5-0) and Southport rocketed up to fourth place in the first week of the new year. Simon Parke scored in three of these games and his goals turned out to be vital as he finished top scorer in a low scoring season.

During this period of development The F.A.Cup had brought a victory over local rivals Marine after a replay, but an unfortunate First Round draw took Southport down to a rampant Dagenham & Redbridge where they lost to a Stein penalty - the only goal of the game. The F.A.Trophy didn't bring any better luck as a disappointing defeat was suffered in a Third Round replay at Gresley Rovers.

Having achieved a top five position it looked as if the club had consolidated by mid March and could happily build for the year ahead. Perhaps a lack or urgency and non involvement with the excitement at either end of the table brought on a relapse, but nine games without a victory brought the club right down to the edge of the relegation battle, before a final day 5-1 defeat of Forest Green enabled the end of season party to be enjoyed. Better things will be expected in the year ahead!

T.W.

SOUTHPORT 2002-03

L-R - Bac: Dean Howell, Steve Dickinson, Mark Winstanley, Kevin Welsby, Andy Scott
Middle: Tony Sullivan, Chris Lane, Steve Jones, Barry Jones, John Robertson, Gary Bauress, Peter Thomson, James Connolly, Steve Pickford, Bret Harris (Physio)
Front: Neil Gibson, Steve Whitehall, Peter Ward (Assistant Manager) Steve Soley (Captain) Phil Wilson (Manager), Martin Clark, Marc Lloyd-Williams

SOUTHPORT

GROUND DETAILS

Haig Avenue,
Southport,
Merseyside. PR8 6JZ

TELEPHONE: Ground: 01704 533422
Ticket Office: 01704 533422
Fax: 01704 533455

SIMPLE DIRECTIONS:
From M6 - M58 through Ormskirk (A570) to Southport.
Straight on at Tesco/McDonalds roundabout.
Right at the mini roundabout and the ground is on the right

CAPACITY: 6,008
SEATED: 1,660
COVERED TERRACING: 1,100

SOCIAL FACILITIES:
Clubhouse open 6.00-11.00 every night and match days.
Tel: 01704 530182

CLUB SHOP: New shop opened 1999.
Scarves, replica kits and large range of souvenirs for sale.
Contact D Hitchcock, c/o Southport F.C or
e-mail: derek@hitchcock98.freeserve.co.uk

Founded:	1881
Nickname:	The Sandgrounders
Club Sponsors:	V K Vodka Kick
Club colours:	Old Gold / black /black
Change colours:	All white
Midweek home matchday:	Tuesday
Reserves' League:	Lancashire League

CLUB OFFICIALS

President T.B.A.

Chairman Charles Clapham
Directors C Clapham,S Shrouder (Vice Chairman), B J
Hedley, A Pope, P Abrams,T Medcroft, S Porter, G.Tait

Football Secretary Ken Hilton
34 Mill Lane, Burscough, Ormskirk, Lancs. L40 5TS
Tel: 01704 894504 (H) 07802 661906 (M)

**Sales &
Marketing Manager** Derek Hitchcock
Tel: 07976 555782
e-mail: derek@hitchcock98.freeserve.co.uk
Press Officer Derek Hitchcock

FOOTBALL MANAGEMENT TEAM

MANAGER: PHIL WILSON
Date of Appointment June 2001
Date of Birth: 6th December 1950
Place of Birth: Wallasey

PREVIOUS CLUBS
As manager Caernarfon T., Stalybridge Celtic, Leek T.
Northwich Vics., Stalybridge C.
As player New Brighton, Runcorn, Mossley,
Altrincham, Northwich Victoria.
HONOURS
As manager N.P.L. Championship 91-92, 00-01
As player Conference Championship,
N.P.L. Championship x 2;
F.A. Trophy Winner, R-up x 2

* * *

Assistant Manager: Peter Ward
Reserve Team Coach: Tony Murphy
Physiotherapist: Brett Harris

Club's Playing Status: Part-time

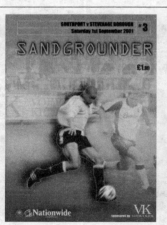

MATCHDAY PROGRAMME

Pages: 40 Price: £1.50

Editor: Derek Hitchcock (07976 555782)
Clubcall: 09066 555 875

Local Press: Southport Visiter; The Champion
Local Radio: Dune F.M.; Radio Merseyside; Red
Rose, Radio City; Radio Lancashire

Season	League	Div.	Pos.	Home P	W	D	L	F	A	Away W	D	L	F	A	Pts	Manager
01-02	Conference	-	15	42	9	6	6	40	26	4	8	9	13	23	53	Phil Wilson
00-01	Conference	-	4	42	9	5	7	33	24	11	4	6	25	22	69	Mark Wright
99-00	Conference	-	9	42	10	5	6	31	21	5	8	8	24	35	58	Paul Futcher / Mark Wright
98-99	Conference	-	18	42	6	9	6	29	28	4	6	11	18	31	45	Paul Futcher
97-98	Conference	-	16	42	9	5	7	32	26	4	6	11	24	32	50	Paul Futcher
96-97	Conference	-	11	42	8	5	8	27	28	7	5	9	24	33	55	Steve Joel / Ronnie Moore

Season	League	Div.	Pos.	P	W	D	L	F	A	Pts	Manager
95-96	Conference	-	6	42	18	12	12	77	64	66	Billy Ayre
94-95	Conference	-	3	42	21	9	12	68	50	72	Brian Kettle/Billy Ayre
93-94	Conference	-	4	42	18	12	12	57	51	66	Brian Kettle
92-93	N.P.L.	Premier	1	42	29	9	4	103	31	96	Brian Kettle

HONOURS

FA Trophy R-up 97-98;

Football League Division Four Champions 1972/73
Runners-up 1966/67;

Third Division North Section Cup 1937/38;

Northern Premier League 1992/93
League Cup 1990/91, League Shield 1993/94;

Liverpool Senior Cup 1930/31, 1931/32, 1943/44,
1957/58 (shared), 1963/64 (shared), 1974/75,
1990/91, 1992/93, 1998/99;

Lancashire Senior Cup 1904/05;
Lancashire Junior Cup 1919/20, 1992/93, 1996-97,
1997-98

PREVIOUS

Leagues: Northern Premier League,
Football League,
Lancashire Combination

Grounds: Ash Lane

Names: Southport Central; Southport Vulcan

Past Players who progressed to the Football League

Shaun Teale,
Andy Mutch,
Steve Whitehall,
Tony Rodwell

CLUB RECORDS

Attendance: 20,010 v Newcastle United
FA Cup - 1932

Record win: 8-1 v Nelson - 01.01.31

Record defeat: 0-11 v Oldham - 26.12.62

Career goalscorer: Alan Spence 98

Career appearances: Arthur Peat 401 - 1962-72

Transfer fee paid: £20,000
for Martin McDonald from Macclesfield Town - 1995

Transfer fee received: £25,000
from Rochdale for Steve Whitehall - 1991

BEST SEASON

FA Cup: Quarter Final, 1930-31.Lost to Everton (A) 1-9
(The first Division 3 North team to reach the Quarter Finals)

League club defeated: Mansfield Town (1998-9)
(as a non-league club)
FA Trophy: Runners-up 97-98,
0-1 v Cheltenham Town

League: Football League Div. 3 23rd 73-74

LAST SEASON

F.A. Cup: First Round

F.A. Trophy: Third Round

Conference: 15th

Top Goalscorer: Simon Parke 16

Player of the Year: Barry Jones

Captain: Martin Clark

SOUTHPORT

	Date	Comp.	Opponents	Att.	Score	Goalscorers
1	31/07	L'pool SC 00-01 F	Burscough	n/k	0 - 1	
2	18/08	Conf.	Dagenham & Redbridge	1287	1 - 1	Teale 26
3	21/08	Conf.	CHESTER CITY	1554	3 - 2	Teale 1, Parke 67, S Jones 77
4	25/08	Conf.	FARNBOROUGH TOWN	1159	2 - 5	Parke 70, Elam 90
5	27/08	Conf.	Hereford United	2010	0 - 0	
6	01/09	Conf.	STEVENAGE BOROUGH	1003	0 - 0	
7	04/09	Conf.	Leigh RMI	609	2 - 1	Jones 31, Leadbeater 73
8	08/09	Conf.	Barnet	1450	0 - 0	
9	11/09	Conf.	NORTHWICH VICTORIA	1028	5 - 1	Sullivan 16 45, Parke 36 55, Lane 65
10	15/09	Conf.	MARGATE	1012	1 - 2	Parke 20
11	18/09	Conf.	Stalybridge Celtic	806	0 - 0	
12	22/09	Conf.	Forest Green Rovers	921	1 - 2	B Jones 39
13	29/09	Conf.	DONCASTER ROVERS	1512	1 - 0	S.Jones 90
14	02/10	Conf.	Nuneaton Borough	1247	0 - 3	
15	06/10	Conf.	TELFORD UNITED	819	0 - 0	
16	09/10	Conf.	SCARBOROUGH	701	1 - 0	Lane 64
17	13/10	Conf.	Woking	1478	0 - 2	
18	16/10	LDV Vans 1N	Rochdale	1411	0 - 2	
19	20/10	Conf.	DOVER ATHLETIC	863	0 - 2	
20	27/10	FA Cup Q4	Marine	1305	1 - 1	Lane 5
21	30/10	FA Cup Q4 R	MARINE	1145	2 - 1	R Jones 24, L Jones 61
22	03/11	Conf.	Boston United	1694	0 - 0	
23	09/11	Conf.	YEOVIL TOWN	944	3 - 0	Whitehall 2, Parke 9, B Jones 46
24	17/11	FA Cup 1	Dagenham & Redridge	1736	0 - 1	
25	24/11	Conf.	Hayes	528	0 - 1	
26	01/12	Conf.	DAGENHAM & REDBRIDGE	951	2 - 2	Whitehall 62,90
27	04/12	L'pool SC QF	St Helens Town	195	2 - 1	Parke 77 79
28	08/12	Conf.	Dover Athletic	861	1 - 0	Whitehall 27
29	15/12	Conf.	Chester City	1473	2 - 0	Whitehall 80, Parke 87
30	26/12	Conf.	MORECAMBE	1732	1 - 1	Elam 50
31	29/12	Conf.	Farnborough Town	691	1 - 0	Parke 23
32	05/01	Conf.	LEIGH RMI	1091	5 - 0	Lane 19[p], Whitehall 45, Parke 67, Howell 71, Eastwood 89
33	08/01	Lancs MT 2	LANCASTER CITY	311	2 - 1	Sullivan 9 18
34	12/01	FA Trophy 3	GRESLEY ROVERS	1100	1 - 1	Jones 21
35	16/01	FA Trophy 3 R	Gresley Rovers	776	0 - 1	
36	19/01	Conf.	Stevenage Borough	1504	1 - 2	Eastwood 8
37	26/01	Conf.	HEREFORD UNITED	970	1 - 1	Elam 45
38	02/02	Conf.	NUNEATON BOROUGH	879	1 - 1	Teale 41
39	05/02	Lancs MT QF	BARROW	184	0 - 2	
40	09/02	Conf.	Telford United	977	1 - 1	Jones 57
41	16/02	Conf.	WOKING	985	2 - 0	Parke 34 47
42	02/03	Conf.	STALYBRIDGE CELTIC	1144	3 - 1	S Jones 20, Parke 72, Grayston 76
43	09/03	Conf.	Northwich Victoria	909	1 - 3	Teale 70
44	16/03	Conf.	BARNET	946	0 - 1	
45	19/03	Conf.	Morecambe	1006	2 - 2	Parke 33, S Jones 90
46	23/03	Conf.	Margate	492	0 - 2	
47	01/04	Conf.	BOSTON UNITED	1295	2 - 3	Lane 10, Parke 65
48	10/04	Conf.	Scarborough	1254	0 - 2	
49	13/04	Conf.	HAYES	683	2 - 3	Teale 45, Parke 80
50	16/04	L'pool SC SF	EVERTON	n/k	1 - 3	Elam
51	20/04	Conf.	Doncaster Rovers	2151	0 - 1	
52	23/04	Conf.	Yeovil Town	1941	0 - 0	
53	27/04	Conf.	FOREST GREEN ROVERS	737	5 - 1	S Jones 15 57 80, Parke 46, Elam 79

	1	2	3	4	5	6	7	8	9	10	11	Substitutes Used
1												
2	Dickinson	Lane	Macauley	Teale	Robertson	Clark	Bauress	Elam	S Jones	Parke	Grayston	McGorry 7
3	Dickinson	Lane	Macauley	Teale	Robertson	Clark	Bauress	Elam	S Jones	Parke	Grayston	Obong 9 McGorry 3
4	Dickinson	Lane	Macauley	Teale	Robertson	Clark	Bauress	Elam	S Jones	Parke	Grayston	B Jones 2 McGorry 11
5	Dickinson	B Jones	Macauley	Teale	Robertson	Clark	Bauress	Elam	S Jones	Parke	Grayston	
6	Dickinson	B Jones	Grayston	Teale	Robertson	Clark	Bauress	Elam	S Jones	Parke	McGorry	Leadbetter 9 Sullivan 11 Lane 8
7	Dickinson	Lane	Macauley	Teale	Robertson	Clark	B Jones	Obong	S Jones	Sullivan	Grayston	Leadbetter 8
8	Dickinson	Lane	Macauley	B Jones	Robertson	Clark	Elam	Sullivan	S Jones	Parke	Grayston	Leadbetter 8 Whittaker 12 (Lea)
9	Dickinson	Lane	Owen	B Jones	Robertson	Clark	Elam	Sullivan	S Jones	Parke	Grayston	Whittaker 7 Macauley 11 Leadbetter 8
10	Dickinson	Lane	Owen	B Jones	Robertson	Clark	Elam	Sullivan	S Jones	Parke	Grayston	Whittaker 7 Macauley 11 McGorry 4
11	Dickinson	Lane	B Jones	Teale	Robertson	Clark	Owen	Sullivan	S Jones	Parke	Grayston	Macauley 7 McGorry 3 Whittaker 9
12	Dickinson	Lane	Macauley	Teale	Robertson	Clark	McGorry	B Jones	Sullivan	Parke	Grayston	S Jones 9 Whittaker 5
13	Dickinson	Lane	Macauley	Teale	B Jones	Clark	Sullivan	McGorry	Parke	Elam	Grayston	S Jones 11 Whittaker 7 Bauress 8
14	Dickinson	Lane	Macauley	Teale	B Jones	Clark	Elam	McGorry	Parke	S Jones	Williams	Bauress 10
15	Dickinson	Lane	Macauley	B Jones	Robertson	Clark	Bauress	McGorry	Parke	Williams	Elam	Whittaker 10
16	Dickinson	Lane	Macauley	Bauress	Robertson	Clark	B Jones	McGorry	Parke	Obong	Elam	Williams 10 Teale 7 Whittaker 3
17	Dickinson	Lane	Macauley	Teale	Robertson	B Jones	McGorry	Bauress	Parke	Williams	Elam	Sullivan 10
18	Dickinson	Lane	Macauley	Teale	Robertson	Clark	Bauress	B Jones	Parke	Eastwood	Elam	
19	Dickinson	Lane	Macauley	Teale	Robertson	Clark	Bauress	S Jones	Parke	Eastwood	Elam	Sullivan 5 Leadbetter 11
20	Dickinson	Lane	Macauley	B Jones	Connolly	Clark	Bauress	S Jones	Parke	Leadbetter	Elam	Grayston 5 Whittaker 10
21	Dickinson	Lane	Macauley	B Jones	Robertson	Clark	Grayston	S Jones	Parke	Sullivan	Elam	Whittaker 3 Leadbetter 10
22	Dickinson	Lane	Macauley	B Jones	Robertson	Clark	Grayston	S Jones	Parke	Whitehall	Elam	
23	Dickinson	Lane	Macauley	Teale	B Jones	Clark	Grayston	S Jones	Parke	Whitehall	Elam	Whittaker 9
24	Dickinson	Macauley	Grayston	Teale	Robertson	Clark	Bauress	S Jones	Parke	Whitehall	Elam	Whittaker 5 Sullivan 7 Leadbetter 10
25	Dickinson	Lane	Macauley	Teale	Robertson	Clark	B Jones	S Jones	Parke	Whitehall	Grayston	Elam 9 Sullivan 3
26	Dickinson	Lane	Howell	Teale	B Jones	Clark	Elam	S Jones	Parke	Whitehall	Grayston	Sullivan 3
27												
28	Dickinson	Lane	Howell	B Jones	Robertson	Clark	Elam	S Jones	Parke	Whitehall	Grayston	
29	Dickinson	Lane	Howell	Teale	B Jones	Clark	Elam	S Jones	Parke	Whitehall	Grayston	Sullivan 8
30	Dickinson	Lane	Howell	Teale	B Jones	Clark	Elam	S Jones	Parke	Whitehall	Grayston	Eastwood 9
31	Dickinson	Macauley	Howell	Teale	B Jones	Clark	Elam	S Jones	Parke	Whitehall	Grayston	Eastwood 10
32	Dickinson	Lane	Howell	Teale	B Jones	Clark	Elam	S Jones	Parke	Whitehall	Grayston	Robertson 6 Macauley 7 Eastwood 10
33												
34	Dickinson	Lane	Howell	Teale	Robertson	B Jones	Elam	S Jones	Parke	Whitehall	Grayston	Macauley 3
35	Dickinson	Lane	Howell	Teale	Robertson	B Jones	Elam	S Jones	Parke	Whitehall	Grayston	Sullivan 7 Eastwood 9
36	Dickinson	Lane	Howell	Teale	B Jones	Clark	Macauley	S Jones	Parke	Eastwood	Elam	Sullivan 10
37	Dickinson	Lane	Howell	Teale	B Jones	Clark	Elam	S Jones	Parke	Whitehall	Grayston	Eastwood 10
38	Dickinson	Macauley	Howell	Teale	B Jones	Clark	Elam	S Jones	Parke	Eastwood	Grayston	Sullivan 3 Scott 10
39												
40	Dickinson	Macauley	Howell	Teale	B Jones	Clark	Elam	S Jones	Parke	Eastwood	Grayston	Sullivan 10
41	Dickinson	Lane	Howell	Teale	B Jones	Clark	Elam	S Jones	Parke	Whitehall	Grayston	Sullivan 10
42	Dickinson	Lane	Howell	Teale	B Jones	Clark	Elam	S Jones	Parke	Whitehall	Grayston	
43	Dickinson	Lane	Howell	Teale	B Jones	Clark	Elam	S Jones	Parke	Whitehall	Grayston	Sullivan 10 Eastwood 3
44	Dickinson	Lane	Howell	Teale	B Jones	Clark	Elam	S Jones	Parke	Eastwood	Grayston	Sullivan 10
45	Dickinson	Lane	Howell	Teale	B Jones	Clark	Elam	S Jones	Parke	Sullivan	Grayston	Eastwood 3
46	Dickinson	Lane	Howell	Teale	Robertson	Clark	Elam	S Jones	Parke	Sullivan	Grayston	Eastwood 10 Bauress 5
47	Dickinson	Lane	Howell	Teale	Robertson	Clark	Elam	S Jones	Parke	Ward	Grayston	Scott 11
48	Dickinson	B Jones	Howell	Teale	Robertson	Clark	Elam	S Jones	Parke	Ward	Grayston	Macauley 11 Scott 3 Whitehall 10
49	Dickinson	Macauley	Howell	Teale	B Jones	Clark	Elam	S Jones	Parke	Ward	Grayston	Robertson 8 Whitehall 10 Eastwood 2
50												
51	Dickinson	Lane	Scott	Teale	B Jones	Clark	Macauley	Howell	Parke	Whitehall	Grayston	Elam 2 Mulvaney 8
52	Dickinson	Lane	Scott	Teale	B Jones	Clark	Elam	Macauley	S Jones	Whitehall	Grayston	Parke 8 Mulvaney 10
53	Dickinson	Lane	Scott	Teale	B Jones	Clark	Elam	S Jones	Parke	Whitehall	Grayston	Morgan 10 Mulvaney 7 Howell 5

SOUTHPORT   PLAYING SQUAD

Player	Birthplace	D.O.B.	Previous Clubs	
				Bold print denotes
				England semi-professional international.

GOALKEEPERS

Steve Dickinson	Bradford		Bradford C, Guiseley
Kevin Welsby	Crewe	10.07.79	Leek T, Crewe

DEFENDERS

Martin Clark	Accrington	12..09.70	Preston, Lancaster C, Accrington Stanley, Crewe
Barry Jones	Prescot	20.06.70	York, Wrexham, Liverpool, Prescot Cables
Gary Bauress UL	Liverpool	19.01.71	Stalybridge C, Barrow, Leek T, Stalybridge C, Ashton Utd, Stalybridge C, Tranmere, Everton
James Connelly	Preston		Preston
John Robertson	Liverpool	08.01.74	Northwich V, Lincoln, Wigan
Dean Howell	Nottingham	-	Crewe, Notts Co
Mark Winstanley	St Helens	22.01.68	Carlisle, Shrewsbury, Burnley, Bolton

MIDFIELD

Chris Lane	Liverpool	24.05.79	Hereford Utd, Everton
Steve Jones UL	Stoke		Stalybridge C, Leek T, Eastwood Hanley, Stafford R, Stoke
Andy Scott EY	Manchester	27.06.75	Stalybridge Celtic, Rochdale, Cardiff, Blackburn
Neil Gibson	St Asaph	10.10.79	Sheffield Wed., Tranmere
Steve Pickford UP	Manchester	-	Stalybridge Celtic, Glossop NE, Leigh RMI, Glossop NE
Steve Soley	Widnes	22.04.71	Carlisle, Portsmouth, Leek T, Warrington T, Avon Ath

FORWARDS

Marc Lloyd-Williams W 'B' & SP	Bangor	08.02.73	Bangor C, York, Halifax T, Bangor C, Colwyn Bay, Altrincham, Stockport, Bangor C, Porthmadog, Llanberis
Peter Thomson	Bury	30.06.77	Luton, NAC Breda (Holl), Lancaster C, Chorley, Bury
Steve Whitehall	Bromborough	08.12.66	Nuneaton B, Chester C, Oldham, Mansfield, Rochdale, Southport

STEVENAGE BOROUGH

Only one defeat in the first eight league games augered well for manager Paul Fairclough as he strove to repeat the excitement and success of his previous glorious spell at Broadhall Way. Steady results until the new year gave hope, but a disappointing F.A.Cup result in a replay at Kettering prevented any chance of renewing their giant killing reputation while a slip into the bottom half of the table persuaded the board to look for a new manager and Wayne Turner was brought in from Peterborough. He took up the reigns in the F.A.Trophy and when the scalps of Conference colleagues Forest Green Rovers and Stalybridge Celtic were added to those of DoverAthletic and Bashley, supporters began to seriously think of a first ever national cup final.

The club had enjoyed regular success as they rose through the divisions under Fairclough. They had then been unfairly deprived of League Football despite winning the Conference and the bubble had burst as everyone suffered a depresing anti climax. Now there was a glimmer, and a very real hope of excitement to match their smart and beautifully equipped stadium. Morecambe seemed very reasonable semi final opponents and so they proved to be as Boro eased comfortably into a final with favourites Yeovil Town at Villa Park.

Twenty thousand decked out in red or green on a lovely sunny Sunday morning produced a festival atmosphere and a thrilling cup tie. Sportsmanship and sheer quality gave non-league football a great advertisement as the game was enjoyed live on Sky TV and Boro although second best on the day proved they have every possibilty of a return to the glory days in the seasons ahead.   T.W.

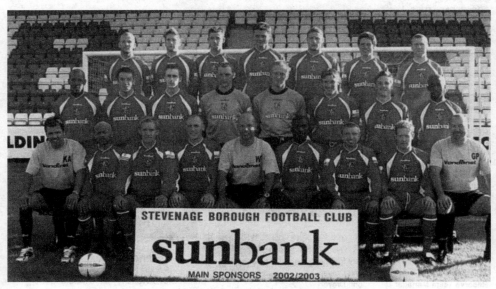

L-R - Back: Stuart Fraser, Richard Howell, Adam Furness, Robin Trott, Matt Fisher, Adrian Clarke, Simon Wormull.
Middle: Jean Michel Sigere, John Dreyer, Jack Midson, Mark Westhead, Phil Wilson,
Kirk Jackson, Sam McMahon, Martin Williams.
Front: Keith Allinson (Physio), DJ Campbell, Jamie Campbell, Jason Goodliffe, Wayne Turner (Manager),
Jude Stirling, Scott Houghton, Simon Travis, Gary Phillips (Assistant Manager).

STEVENAGE BOROUGH

GROUND DETAILS

Stevenage Stadium,
Broadhall Way,
Stevenage,
Herts SG2 8RH
Tel: 01438 223223
Fax: 01438 743666
email: austinmakin@aol.com
Web site: http://www.stevenageborofc.com

Nickname:	Boro'
Club Sponsors:	Sun Banking Corporation
Club colours:	Red/red/white
Change colours:	All Yellow
Midweek home matchday:	Monday
Reserve Team's League:	Capital League

SIMPLE DIRECTIONS:
Stevenage South exit off A1(M) - ground on right at second roundabout.Spectators are however advised to go straight on at this roundabout and park inthe Showground opposite the stadium. The stadium is one mile from Stevenage BRstation. Buses SB4 and SB5

CAPACITY: 7,107

SEATED: 3,404
(included away stand all seater)

COVERED TERRACING: 3,703
Groundsman: Ken Watters
CLUB SHOP: Mon - Sat 9-5.30. Broadhall Way, Stevenage. 01438 218061. Sells a complete range of club merchandise including a customising service. Mail Order, credit cards accepted, contact Tracey Levy (01438 218061)

SOCIAL FACILITIES:
Tel.: 01438 218079. Clubhouse at ground open Monday to Friday 7 - 11pm,Saturday noon - 2.00 & 4.30 - 11pm, Sunday: All day from noon. Contact: Jenny Cairns
Clubcall: 09066 555982

CLUB OFFICIALS

Chairman: Phillip Wallace

Club Administrator: Roger Austin
01438 218072

Commercial Manager: Clive Abrey
01438 218073
Press Officer: Steve Watkins
Tel Nos: 01438 218072 (W) 07771 523661 (M)

FOOTBALL MANAGEMENT TEAM

MANAGER: WAYNE TURNER
Date of Appointment: February 2002
Date of Birth: 9th March 1961
Place of Birth: Luton

PREVIOUS CLUBS
As manager
As coach : Peterborough United
As player : Luton Town, Lincoln City (L), Coventry and Brentford City

HONOURS
As manager
As player None
Assistant Manager Gary Phillips
1st Team Coach John Dreyer
Reserve Team Manager John Dreyer
Physiotherapist Keith Allinson
Chief Scout Alan Carrington
Scouts Paul Hardstaffe, Ray Aggio, Colin Morris and Gary Isott
Club's Playing Status: Some Full time players

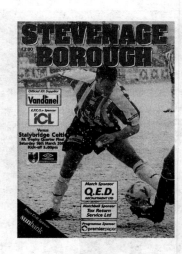

PROGRAMME
Pages: 36 Price: £2.00
Editor: Steve Watkins Tel: 01438 318891
Other club publications: The Borough Yearbook

Local Press: Stevenage Gazette; Comet;
Stevenage Mercury; Herald
Local Radio: Chiltern Radio;
BBC Three Counties Radio and Hertbeat

Season	League	Div.	Pos.	Home						Away					Pts	Manager
				P	W	D	L	F	A	W	D	L	F	A		
01-02	Conference	-	11	42	10	4	7	36	30	5	6	10	21	30	55	P. Fairclough / W.Turner
00-01	Conference	-	7	42	8	7	6	36	33	7	11	3	35	28	63	Paul Fairclough
99-00	Conference	-	10	42	8	5	8	26	20	8	4	9	34	34	57	R./ Steve Wignall /P Fairclough
98-99	Conference	-	6	42	9	9	3	37	23	8	8	5	25	22	68	Paul Fairclough / Richard Hill
97-98	Conference	-	15	42	8	8	5	35	27	5	4	12	24	36	51	Paul Fairclough
96-97	Conference	-	3	42	15	4	2	53	23	9	6	6	34	30	82	Paul Fairclough

Season	League	Div.	Pos.	P	W	D	L	F	A	Pts	Manager
95-96	Conference	-	1	42	27	10	5	101	44	91	Paul Fairclough
94-95	Conference	-	5	42	20	7	15	68	49	67	Paul Fairclough
93-94	Isthmian	Prem.	1	42	31	4	7	88	39	97	Paul Fairclough
92-93	Isthmian	Prem.	7	42	18	8	16	62	60	62	Paul Fairclough

HONOURS

GM Vauxhall Conference 95-96,
Isthmian Lge Prem 93-94,
Div 1 91-92, Div 2 (North) 85-86 90-91;
Utd Counties Lg Div 1 80-81 (Div 1 Cup 80-81),
Herts SnrCup R-up 85-86, 93/94;
Herts Charity Cup R-up 93-94,
Herts Charity Shield R-up83-84,
Televised Sports Snr Floodlit Cup 89-90,
Eastern Professional F'lit Cup Group winner
81-82 85-86 86-87 88-89 90-91 91-92,
South Co's Comb. Cup 91-92;
Essex & Herts Border Comb.(Reserves) 94/95
Essex & Herts (Western Div) 95-96

PREVIOUS

Leagues: Chiltern Youth 76-79;
Wallspan South Combination 79-80;
United Counties 80-84;
Isthmian 84-94

Grounds: King George V Playing Field 1976-80

Past Players who progressed to the Football League

Richard Wilmot & NeilTrebble (Scunthorpe Utd) 1993,
Simon Clark (Peterborough United) 1994,
Leo Fortune West (Gillingham) 1995,
Phil Simpson (Barnet) 1995,
Barry Hayles (Bristol Rovers) 1997)

CLUB RECORDS

Attendance: 6,489 v Kidderminster H.,
GM Vauxhall Conference 25.1.97

Win: 11-1 v British Timken Athletic (H),
United Counties League Div.1, 1980-81

Defeat: 0-7 v Southwick (H),
Isthmian League Div. 1, 1987-88

Career goalscorer: Barry Hayles

Career appearances: Martin Gittings

Transfer fee paid: £20,000
for Richard Leadbetter to Hereford United 1999

Transfer fee received: £300,000
for Barry Hayles (Bristol R.) July 97

BEST SEASON

FA Cup: Fourth Round replay 97-98.
1-2 v Newcastle Utd. (A) after 1-1
also 3rd Round 1996-97.
0-2 v Birmingham City (A)
League clubs defeated: Leyton Orient 96-97;
Cambridge Utd., Swindon Town 97-98

FA Trophy: Runners-up 01-02

League: Conference Champions 95-96

LAST SEASON

F.A. Cup:	Fourth Qualifying Round
F.A. Trophy:	Runners-up
Conference:	11th
Top Goalscorer:	J.M.Sigere
Player of the Year:	Jason Goodliffe
Captain:	Jason Goodliffe
Highest League Attendance:	2,352

STEVENAGE BOROUGH

	Date	Comp.	Opponents	Att.	Score	Goalscorers
1	18/08	Conf.	STALYBRIDGE CELTIC	1772	2 - 0	Hamsher 18[p], Williams 59
2	21/08	Conf.	Hayes	685	2 - 0	Campbell 10 36
3	25/08	Conf.	Northwich Victoria	821	1 - 2	Armstrong 71
4	27/08	Conf.	DONCASTER ROVERS	2352	0 - 0	
5	01/09	Conf.	Southport	1003	0 - 0	
6	03/09	Conf.	NUNEATON BOROUGH	1665	2 - 2	Goodliffe 75 90
7	08/09	Conf.	Leigh RMI	584	2 - 1	Clarke 56 (Pen)Tate 85
8	10/09	Conf.	SCARBOROUGH	1794	2 - 0	Tate 58, Clarke 66
9	15/09	Conf.	FARNBOROUGH TOWN	1976	1 - 2	Sodje 89
10	18/09	Conf.	Margate	1129	1 - 2	McMahon 60
11	22/09	Conf.	Hereford United	1515	1 - 1	Sodje 75
12	29/09	Conf.	CHESTER CITY	1690	2 - 1	Hay 47.59
13	02/10	Conf.	Dagenham & Redbridge	1837	0 - 1	
14	05/10	Conf.	Woking	2554	1 - 1	Hay 25
15	08/10	Conf.	TELFORD UNITED	1370	1 - 1	Wormull 70 (Pen)
16	13/10	Conf.	Forest Green Rovers	974	0 - 0	
17	15/10	LDV Vans 1S	SOUTHEND UNITED	1114	1 - 4	Sigerre 55
18	20/10	Conf.	MORECAMBE	1590	3 - 1	Hay 46,Sigere 69,Hamsher 78 (Pen)
19	27/10	FA Cup Q4	KETTERING TOWN	1937	0 - 0	
20	30/10	FA Cup Q4 R	Kettering Town	2079	1 - 2	Wormnull 39
21	03/11	Conf.	Dover Athletic	1319	1 - 0	Hay 69
22	10/11	Conf.	BOSTON UNITED	2078	1 - 2	Fisher 80
23	13/11	Herts SC 2	Hoddesdon Town	n/k	2 - 0	Sigerre 48, Bridge 68
24	17/11	Conf.	Telford United	914	1 - 2	Wormull 24
25	24/11	Conf.	Yeovil Town	2468	1 - 2	Fisher 71
26	01/12	Conf.	Stalybridge Celtic	674	0 - 2	
27	15/12	Conf.	HAYES	1572	1 - 1	Hay 77
28	26/12	Conf.	Barnet	2456	3 - 0	Campbell 19, McMahon 52, Sigerre 68
29	05/01	Conf.	Nuneaton Borough	1247	1 - 2	Sigere 59
30	08/01	Herts SC QF	Hitchin Town	n/k	1 - 3	
31	12/01	FA Trophy 3	DOVER ATHLETIC	1316	5 - 1	Clarke 31 54, Sigerre 42, Jackson 47 51
32	19/01	Conf.	SOUTHPORT	1504	2 - 1	McMahon 11, Hamsher 22[p]
33	25/01	Conf.	Doncaster Rovers	2076	0 - 2	
34	02/02	FA Trophy 4	BASHLEY	1218	1 - 0	Jackson 26
35	09/02	Conf.	WOKING	2170	1 - 4	Sigere 86
36	16/02	Conf.	FOREST GREEN ROVERS	1215	4 - 1	Clarke 9 26, Williams 38, Shields 88
37	23/02	FA Trophy 5	FOREST GREEN ROVERS	1228	3 - 2	Wormull 22, Cousins 43[og], Clarke 74
38	02/03	Conf.	MARGATE	1602	3 - 1	Sigere 4 57, Jackson 90
39	09/03	Conf.	Scarborough	1188	1 - 1	Wormull 4
40	11/03	Conf.	DAGENHAM & REDBRIDGE	2101	1 - 3	Sigere 75
41	16/03	FA Trophy QF	STALYBRIDGE CELTIC	1684	1 - 0	D Campbell 70
42	23/03	Conf.	Farnborough Town	687	1 - 6	McMahon 76
43	25/03	Conf.	BARNET	2405	3 - 2	Clarke 25, Sigere 32 47
44	30/03	Conf.	Morecambe	1178	3 - 0	Jackson 4 27, Sigere 8
45	01/04	Conf.	DOVER ATHLETIC	1604	1 - 3	Clarke 14
46	06/04	FA Trophy SF(1)	Morecambe	1899	2 - 1	McMahon 23, Hamsher 90[p]
47	08/04	Conf.	Boston United	3841	0 - 0	
48	13/04	FA Trophy SF(2)	MORECAMBE	3119	2 - 0	McMahon 50, D Campbell 90
49	15/04	Conf.	LEIGH RMI	1116	0 - 1	
50	18/04	Conf.	YEOVIL TOWN	1275	2 - 3	Jackson 28 87
51	20/04	Conf.	Chester City	1866	1 - 5	Jackson 85
52	22/04	Conf.	NORTHWICH VICTORIA	1202	1 - 0	Williams 53
53	27/04	Conf.	HEREFORD UNITED	1979	3 - 1	Jackson 62, Goodliffe 71, Stirling 86
54	12/05	FA Trophy F	Yeovil Town	18809	0 - 2	@ Aston Villa F.C.

#	1	2	3	4	5	6	7	8	9	10	11	Substitutes Used
1	Wilkerson	Arnott	Goodliffe	Dreyer	Sturgess	Hamsher	McMahon	Walters	Clarke	Hay	Williams	Armstrong 11 Illman 10 Smith 8
2	Wilkerson	Arnott	Goodliffe	Dreyer	Sturgess	Hamsher	McMahon	Walters	Clarke	DJ Campbell	Williams	Armstrong 11 Illman 10
3	Wilkerson	Arnott	Goodliffe	Dreyer	Sturgess	Hamsher	McMahon	Walters	Clarke	DJ Campbell	Williams	Armstrong 10 Trott 3 Illman 5
4	Wilkerson	Arnott	Sodje	Dreyer	Sturgess	Illman	McMahon	Walters	Clarke	Hay	Williams	Armstrong 6 Trott 5 Smith 10
5	Wilkerson	Arnott	Goodliffe	Dreyer	Sodje	Lincoln	McMahon	Armstrong	Clarke	Hay	Morgan	Fitzpatrick 11 Illman 8 Trott 2
6	Wilkerson	Sodje	Goodliffe	Dreyer	Sturgess	Fitzpatrick	McMahon	Walters	Morgan	DJ Campbell	Williams	Hay 10 Illman 5 Clarke 6
7	Wilkerson	Sodje	Goodliffe	Dreyer	Sturgess	Tate	McMahon	Walters	Clarke	DJ Campbell	Williams	Morgan 9 Hay 15 (Arm) Armstrong 10
8	Wilkerson	Watts	Goodliffe	Dreyer	Sturgess	Tate	McMahon	Walters	Clarke	DJ Campbell	Williams	Armstrong 10 Smith 8
9	Wilkerson	Watts	Goodliffe	Dreyer	Sturgess	Sodje	McMahon	Walters	Clarke	Tate	Williams	Trott 3 Morgan 2 Smith 9
10	Wilkerson	Arnott	Sodje	Trott	Sturgess	Tate	McMahon	Walters	Clarke	Williams	Illman	Armstrong 11 Morgan 10
11	Wilkerson	Arnott	Goodliffe	Trott	Sturgess	Sodje	McMahon	Walters	Clarke	Williams	DJ Campbell	Illman 11
12	Wilkerson	Hamsher	Goodliffe	Dreyer	Sturgess	Sodje	McMahon	Castle	Clarke	Williams	Tate	Armstrong 11 Hay 2
13	Greygoose	Hamsher	Goodliffe	Dreyer	Sturgess	Illman	McMahon	Castle	Clarke	Williams	Tate	Morgan 9 Hay 6
14	Greygoose	Sodje	Goodliffe	Trott	Sturgess	Wormull	McMahon	Castle	Clarke	Hay	Sigere	Williams 10
15	Greygoose	Sodje	Goodliffe	Dreyer	Sturgess	Wormull	McMahon	Castle	Williams	Hay	Sigere	Illman 9
16	Greygoose	Sodje	Goodliffe	Dreyer	Sturgess	Wormull	McMahon	Clarke	Williams	Hay	Sigere	Castle 8 Illman 10 Armstrong 14 (Ill)
17	Greygoose	Sodje	Goodliffe	Dreyer	Hamsher	Wormull	McMahon	Clarke	Williams	Sigere	Armstrong	Scarlett 8
18	Greygoose	Hamsher	Sodje	Dreyer	Sturgess	Castle	McMahon	Luckett	Williams	Hay	Sigere	Clarke 8 Illman 10 Fisher 11
19	Greygoose	Sodje	Goodliffe	Dreyer	Sturgess	Wormull	McMahon	Castle	Williams	Illman	Sigere	Fisher 8 DJ Campbell 10 Abbey 6
20	Greygoose	Sodje	Goodliffe	Dreyer	Sturgess	Wormull	McMahon	Castle	Williams	Illman	Sigere	Fisher 8 DJ Campbell 10 Abbey 6
21	Greygoose	Hamsher	Trott	Sodje	Dreyer	Fisher	Williams	McMahon	DJ Campbell	Hay	Wormull	Clarke 4 Castle 6 Abbey 10
22	Greygoose	Hamsher	Goodliffe	Trott	Sturgess	Fisher	Williams	McMahon	DJ Campbell	Hay	Wormull	Sigere 10 Illman 4
23												
24	Greygoose	Hamsher	Goodliffe	Trott	Sturgess	Fisher	Williams	McMahon	DJ Campbell	Sigere	Wormull	Hay 9
25	Greygoose	Hamsher	Goodliffe	Trott	Dreyer	Fisher	Williams	McMahon	Hay	Sigere	Wormull	DJ Campbell 2 Illman 10
26	Wilkerson	Sturgess	Goodliffe	Trott	Dreyer	Fisher	Williams	McMahon	Hay	Illman	Wormull	Sigere 9 Midson 7 Clarke 3
27	Greygoose	Hamsher	Dreyer	Trott	Sturgess	Wormull	Fisher	Carey	Clarke	Sigere	Illman	Hay 11 Williams 9
28	Wilkerson	Hamsher	Goodliffe	Trott	Dreyer	Wormull	Carey	McMahon	Clarke	Sigere	DJ Campbell	Williams 10
29	Wilkerson	Hamsher	Goodliffe	Dreyer	Sturgess	Wormull	Carey	McMahon	Clarke	Sigere	DJ Campbell	Armstrong 9 Jackson 11 Williams 5
30												
1	Wilkerson	Hamsher	Goodliffe	Trott	Dreyer	Wormull	Carey	McMahon	Clarke	Sigere	Jackson	DJ Campbell 10 Fisher 7
2	Wilkerson	Hamsher	Goodliffe	Trott	Dreyer	Wormull	Fisher	McMahon	Clarke	Sigere	Jackson	Williams 10
3	Wilkerson	Hamsher	Goodliffe	Trott	Dreyer	Wormull	Fisher	McMahon	Clarke	Sigere	Jackson	Shields 7 Sodje 4 Williams 9
4	Wilkerson	Hamsher	Goodliffe	Dreyer	Sturgess	Wormull	Fisher	McMahon	Clarke	DJ Campbell	Jackson	Sodje 4 Williams 10
5	Wilkerson	Hamsher	Goodliffe	Sodje	Sturgess	Wormull	Fisher	McMahon	Clarke	Jackson	Sigere	Williams 7 Hay 5 Tagro 9
6	Greygoose	Hamsher	Goodliffe	Stirling	Riddle	Williams	McMahon	Shields	Clarke	Sigere	Jackson	Hay 11 Wormull 6
7	Greygoose	Hamsher	Goodliffe	Stirling	Riddle	Wormull	McMahon	Shields	Clarke	Williams	Jackson	Hay 11
8	Greygoose	Hamsher	Goodliffe	Trott	Riddle	Wormull	McMahon	Stirling	Clarke	Sigere	Williams	Hay 11 Jackson 8 Sturgess 9
9	Greygoose	Hamsher	Riddle	Trott	Goodliffe	Wormull	J Campbell	McMahon	Jackson	Sigere	Houghton	Sodje 3 Fisher 6 Hay 10
0	Greygoose	Hamsher	Goodliffe	Trott	Riddle	J Campbell	Williams	Stirling	Hay	Sigere	Houghton	Clarke 6 Jackson 9
1	Greygoose	Hamsher	Goodliffe	Trott	Riddle	Wormull	McMahon	Stirling	Clarke	Sigere	Jackson	Houghton 9 D Campbell 10 J Campbell 6
2	Greygoose	Hamsher	Sodje	Trott	Riddle	J Campbell	Houghton	Stirling	Jackson	DJ Campbell	Clarke	McMahon 5 Sigere 10 Armstrong 11
3	Wilkerson	Hamsher	Goodliffe	Trott	Sturgess	Fisher	Houghton	McMahon	Jackson	Sigere	Clarke	Stirling 5
4	Wilkerson	Hamsher	Stirling	Trott	Fraser	Fisher	Houghton	Evers	Jackson	Sigere	Clarke	McMahon 8 George 10 DJ Campbell 9
5	Wilkerson	Hamsher	Goodliffe	J Campbell	Fraser	Evers	Wormull	McMahon	DJ Campbell	George	Clarke	Fisher 6 Jackson 7 Houghton 11
6	Wilkerson	Hamsher	Goodliffe	Trott	Fraser	Fisher	Houghton	Evers	George	Jackson	McMahon	Wormull 8 DJ Campbell 9
7	Greygoose	Howell	Sturgess	Dreyer	Sodje	Stirling	Wormull	J Campbell	Midson	DJ Campbell	Armstrong	Dean 3 Smith 11 Evers 8
8	Wilkerson	Hamsher	Goodliffe	Trott	Fraser	Fisher	Houghton	Evers	Jackson	George	McMahon	Stirling 6 Wormull 8 DJ Campbell 10
9	Greygoose	Sodje	J Campbell	Trott	Fraser	Stirling	Howell	Evers	DJ Campbell	George	Armstrong	Houghton 8 McMahon 7 Jackson 11
0	Wilkerson	Hamsher	J Campbell	Trott	Stirling	Evers	Wormull	McMahon	Jackson	DJ Campbell	George	Sodje 7 Armstrong 11
1	Greygoose	Sodje	Goodliffe	J Campbell	Fraser	Fisher	Wormull	McMahon	Williams	Armstrong	DJ Campbell	Jackson 10 Evers 6 Hamsher 9
2	Wilkerson	Hamsher	Goodliffe	Trott	Dreyer	Williams	Wormull	Evers	Jackson	DJ Campbell	McMahon	Stirling 6 Midson 10 J Campbell 11
3	Wilkerson	Hamsher	Goodliffe	Trott	Fraser	Wormull	Evers	Fisher	Jackson	Williams	Clarke	Stirling 11 Midson 7 DJ Campbell 9
4	Wilkerson	Hamsher	Goodliffe	Trott	Fraser	Fisher	Wormull	Evers	Jackson	Sigere	Clarke	Stirling 7 Williams 8 DJ Campbell 10

STEVENAGE BOROUGH   PLAYING SQUAD

Player	Birthplace	D.O.B.	Previous Clubs	Bold print denotes England semi-professional international.

GOALKEEPERS

Mark Westhead	Blackpool	19.07.75	Leigh RMI, Wycombe, Kidderminser, Telford Utd, Bolton W., Blackpool Mechs
Phil Wilson	Oxford	17.10.82	Oxford C, Oxford Utd

DEFENDERS

Robin Trott	Orpington	17.08.74	Gillingham, Welling U, £8,000 to Stevenage B
Jason Goodliffe ESP	Hillingdon	07.03.74	Hayes, Brentford
Paul Sturgess	Dartford	04.08.75	Hereford Utd, Brighton, Millwall, Charlton
Jamie Campbell	Birmingham	21.10.72	Exeter, Brighton, Cambridge Utd, Barnet, Luton
John Dreyer	Alnwick	11.06.63	Cambridge Utd, Bradford C, Stoke, Luton, Oxford Utd, Wallingford T
Jude Stirling	Enfield	29.06.82	Luton
Simon Travis ESP, British Univ.	Preston	22.03.77	Forest Green R, Telford Utd, Stockport, Holywell T, Torquay
Stuart Fraser	Edinburgh	09.01.80	Luton

MIDFIELD

Sam McMahon	Newark	10.02.76	Leicester, Camb.U
Matt Fisher	Mansfield		Kettering T, Gedling T, Ashfield Utd, Army
Neil Smith	Lambeth	30.09.71	Reading, Fulham, Gillingham, Tottenham
Richard Howell	Hitchin	29.08.82	Crystal Palace
Scott Houghton ES, EY	Hitchin	22.10.71	Halifax T, Leyton Orient, Southend, Peterborough, Walsall, Luton, Tottenham
Simon Wormull ESP, NC	Crawley	01.12.76	Rushden & Diamonds, Dover Ath., Brentford, Tottenham

FORWARDS

Adrian Clarke ES	Cambridge	28.09.74	Arsenal, Southend
Martin Williams	Luton	12.07.73	Reading, Luton, Leicester
DJ Campbell	London		Chesham Utd, Aston Villa (Trainee)
Graeme Tomlinson	Watford	10.12.75	Exeter, Macclesfield, Manchester Utd, Bradford C
Jean-Michel Sigere NC	France	26.01.77	Rushden & Diamonds, Bordeaux (France)
Kirk Jackson ESP	Barnsley	16.10.76	Darlington (£10,000), Worksop T, Chesterfield, Scunthorpe U., Sheffield Wed.

TELFORD UNITED

With the relegation of Ketteriing Town in the previous season, Telford United found themselves as one of the last two 'ever presents' who had never left the Alliance/Conference since its inception in 1979.

The club had enjoyed some wonderful years in the F.A.Cup, reaching the Second Round three times, plus the Third Round, Fourth Round and Fifth Rounds between 1982 and 1992,and in the F.A. Trophy with five finals including three wins.

But now it was difficult to decide which way 'The Bucks' were going, great plans had been announced for their famous Bucks Head ground to be developed into a magnificent stadium, an ambitious Chairman had great ideas, but was there the support to bring in the necessary income to make the scheme economically viable?

Last season a quiet start was gradually improved upon but neither the ground nor the team really made the dramatic improvements that had been prophecied. At the end of the year United had reached fourth spot and a 5-1 victory at much fancied Dagenham & Redbridge showed what was possible.

Mark Quayle took the honours in the attack while stalwart Jim Bentley once again produced a great season's work. Ironically it was the Conference's other longest serving member, Northwich Victoria who prevented 'The Bucks ' from enjoying any cup glory as they knocked Jake King's side out of the F.A.Cup after a replay in the Fourth Qualifying Round and inflicted another defeat at the Drill Field in the F.A. Trophy Fifth Round.

Hopefully, the ground will be steadily developed to match the wonderful original plans, without detracting from the quality of squad that will be needed to cope with an ever improving Conference.

T.W.

TELFORD UNITED FC 2002-03
Back row L-R: Gary Fitzpatrick, Matthew Bloomer, Peter Smith, Grant Brown, Paul Edwards, Craig Jones, Tony Lormor, Mark Foran, Richard Scott.
Front Row: David Brown, Gareth Hanmer, Paul Moore, Kevin Jobling, Jake King, Steve Palmer, Ashley Wooliscroft, Jordan King, Kevin Davies

TELFORD UNITED

GROUND DETAILS

New Bucks Head Stadium
The Bucks Way,
Telford,
Shropshire TF12TJ

Tel: 01952 640064
Fax: 01952 640021
email: telford.united@lineone.net
web site: www.telford.united-fc.co.uk

SIMPLE DIRECTIONS:
Leave M54 Junction 6.and takeA518.At second island take second exit,then left at third island and turn right immediately after railway bridge.

Due to contruction of a new stadium on the same site the following details apply for season 2002-03

CAPACITY:	4,101
SEATED:	554
COVERED TERRACING:	2,960

SOCIAL FACILITIES:
During 2002-03 season - in concourses

CLUB SHOP:
Telephone 01952 640064for details

MATCHDAY PROGRAMME

Pages: 32   Price: £1.80
Editor: Mike Ferriday

Clubcall: 09066 555 982

Local Press: Shropshire Star; Telford Journal,Telford News,Local Radio: BBC Radio Shropshire;Beacon Radio; Telford FM; WABC

Founded:	1876
Nickname:	The Bucks
Club Sponsors:	Personal Resource Centre
Club colours:	Red.Blue.Red
Change colours:	Yellow/blue/yellow or white
Midweek home matchday:	Monday

CLUB OFFICIALS

President	Gerald Smith
Chairman	Andy Shaw
Directors:	Andy Shaw, Rob Cave,
	Mike Ferriday and Paul Booth
Football Secretary	Mike Ferriday
	c/o the club
	01952 640064
Commercial Manager	Robin Eaves
Press Officer	Robert Cave
	0771 0227337

FOOTBALL MANAGEMENT TEAM

MANAGER: **JAKE KING**
Date of appointment: March 2000
Date of Birth: 29th January 1955
Place of Birth: Glasgow

PREVIOUS CLUBS
as manager   Telford Utd (11.96-5.97),
                Shrewsbury Town (97-2000)
as player   Shrewsbury T., Cardiff C., Wrexham

HONOURS
as manager   None
as player   Football League 3rd Div. Championship;
                4th Div. Runners-up

• • •

Assistant Manager:	Kevin Jobling
Coach:	Roger Preece
Physio:	Brin May

Club's Playing Status: Some full time players

Season	League	Div.	Pos.	P	W	D	L	F	A	W	D	L	F	A	Pts	Manager
					Home					**Away**						
01-02	Conference	-	9	42	8	6	7	34	31	6	9	6	29	27	57	Jake King
00-01	Conference	-	6	42	13	1	7	33	23	6	7	8	18	28	65	Jake King
99-00	Conference	-	16	42	12	4	5	34	21	2	5	14	22	45	51	Alan Lewer / Jake King
98-99	Conference	-	17	42	7	8	6	24	24	3	8	10	20	36	46	Jimmy Mullen / Alan Lewer
97-98	Conference	-	20	42	6	7	8	25	31	4	5	12	28	45	42	Steve Daly / Jimmy Mullen
96-97	Conference	-	9	42	6	7	8	21	30	10	3	8	25	26	58	Wayne Clarke

Season	League	Div.	Pos.	P	W	D	L	F	A	Pts	Manager
95-96	Conference	-	13	42	15	10	17	51	56	55	Wayne Clarke
94-95	Conference	-	19	42	10	16	16	53	62	46	Gerry Daly / George Foster
93-94	Conference	-	17	42	13	12	17	41	49	51	Gerry Daly
92-93	Conference	-	15	42	14	10	18	55	60	52	Gerry Daly

HONOURS

FA Trophy Winners 71-72, 82-83, 88-89.
R-up 69-70, 87-88;
Birmingham League1920-21, 1934-35, 1935-36;
Cheshire League 1945-46, 1946-47, 1951-52;
Edward Case Cup 1952-53, 1954-55;
Welsh Cup 1901-02, 1905-06, 1939-40;
BirminghamSenior Cup 1946-47;
Walsall Senior Cup 1946-47;
Birmingham League Challenge Cup 1946-47;
Shropshire Senior Cup (30);
Southern League Cup 1970-71;
Midland Floodlit Cup 1970-71, 1982-83, 1988-89,
Runners-up 1969-70, 1987-88

CLUB RECORDS

Attendance:	13,000 v Shrewsbury Town
	Birmingham League - 1936
Win:	**Unknown**
Defeat:	**Unknown**
Career appearances:	**Unknown**
Career goalscorer:	Jack Bentley
Transfer fee paid:	£20,000
	to Wrexham for Jake Edwards
Transfer fee received:	£50,000
	from Scarborough for Stephen Norris

PREVIOUS

Leagues:	Southern League,
	Cheshire League,
	Birmingham League
Name:	Wellington Town (prior to 1969)
Grounds:	None

BEST SEASON

FA Cup: 5th Round 84-85, 0-3 v Everton (A), 47,402.
Also 4th Rd. 83-84, 3rd Rd.86-87,2nd Rd. 82-83,85-86,91-92

League clubs defeated: Wigan (82-3), Rochdale, Stockport
C.& Northampton T(83-4)Bradford C, Darlington,Lincoln C.&
P.N.E. (84-85),Stockport C (85-6),Burnley (86-7) and Stoke
City (91-92)

FA Trophy: Winners 70-71, 82-83, 88-89.
R-up 69-70, 87-88

League: 3rd Conference 81-82

Past Players who progressed to the Football League

A.Walker (Lincoln City),G.French (Luton Town),
K.McKenna (Tranmere Rovers), S.Norris (Scarborough),
David Pritchard (Bristol Rovers) 1994,
Sean Parrish (Doncaster Rovers) 1994,
Steve Foster (Bristol R.);
Peter Wilding, Roger Preece, Mark Williams & Martyn Naylor
- all to Shrewsbury 1997
Neil Moore (Mansfield Town)

LAST SEASON

F.A. Cup:	Fourth Qualifying Round
F.A. Trophy:	Fifth Round
Conference:	9th
Top Goalscorer:	Mark Quayle
Player of the Year:	Jim Bentley
(Club) Captain:	Jim Bentley
Highest League Attendance:	2,168

TELFORD UNITED

Match Facts 2001-02

	Date	Comp.	Opponents	Att.	Score	Goalscorers
1	21/07	Shrops SC 1	Shifnal Town	204	4 - 0	Palmer 12, Smith 50[p], Edwards 55 75
2	01/08	Shrops SC F	SHREWSBURY TOWN	1841	1 - 3	Edwards 16
3	18/08	Conf.	Dover Athletic	1001	1 - 0	Smith 37
4	21/08	Conf.	YEOVIL TOWN	1203	2 - 2	Hanmer 28, Scott 71
5	25/08	Conf.	DAGENHAM & REDBRIDGE	1014	1 - 4	J Edwards 90
6	27/08	Conf.	Morecambe	1342	1 - 2	Jobling 62
7	01/09	Conf.	LEIGH RMI	737	3 - 1	Quayle 25 33 75
8	04/09	Conf.	Chester City	605	2 - 2	Davies 65 Edwards 87
9	08/09	Conf.	Margate	925	1 - 3	Quayle 37
10	11/09	Conf.	DONCASTER ROVERS	1017	1 - 1	Quayle 30
11	15/09	Conf.	BARNET	911	1 - 2	Albrighton 38
12	22/09	Conf.	Woking	1524	1 - 1	Edwards 49
13	25/09	Conf.	Northwich Victoria	739	2 - 2	Quayle 44 84[p]
14	29/09	Conf.	STALYBRIDGE CELTIC	965	3 - 1	Hammer48 Bentley 52,81
15	02/10	Conf.	BOSTON UNITED	1113	2 - 2	Palmer 8, N Moore 87
16	06/10	Conf.	Southport	819	0 - 0	
17	08/10	Conf.	Stevenage Borough	1370	1 - 1	Fitzpatrick 86
18	13/10	Conf.	FARNBOROUGH TOWN	948	0 - 1	
19	20/10	Conf.	FOREST GREEN ROVERS	835	0 - 0	
20	27/10	FA Cup Q4	NORTHWICH VICTORIA	1004	1 - 1	Smith 30
21	30/10	FA Cup Q4 R	Northwich Victoria	1063	1 - 2	Edwards 66
22	03/11	Conf.	Hayes	629	4 - 1	Albrighton 40, **J. Edwards 3** (44,55,79)
23	09/11	Conf.	SCARBOROUGH	859	3 - 0	J Edwards 51, Smith 64 86
24	17/11	Conf.	STEVENAGE BOROUGH	914	2 - 1	Hanmer 46, Fitzpatrick 77
25	24/11	Conf.	Nuneaton Borough	1410	2 - 1	Martindale 56,Fitzpatrick 70
26	01/12	Conf.	DOVER ATHLETIC	974	4 - 3	Martindale 8 (Pen),55 Albrightoon 32 Fitzpatrick 45
27	15/12	Conf.	Yeovil Town	2454	1 - 1	Martindale 63
28	22/12	Conf.	Dagenham & Redbridge	1559	5 - 1	Hammer15, Fitzpatrick 50, Bentley 66 Martindale 74, Moore 80
29	26/12	Conf.	HEREFORD UNITED	2168	0 - 1	
30	12/01	FA Trophy 3	Ilkeston Town	792	2 - 0	Albrighton 2 17
31	19/01	Conf.	Leigh RMI	333	1 - 3	Smith 30
32	22/01	Conf.	CHESTER CITY	1047	0 - 3	
33	02/02	FA Trophy 4	Dagenham & Redbridge	1256	2 - 0	Smith 32, Quayle 62
34	09/02	Conf.	SOUTHPORT	977	1 - 1	Bentley 52
35	16/02	Conf.	Farnborough Town	667	1 - 1	Quayle 21
36	27/02	FA Trophy 5	Northwich Victoria	916	2 - 3	Smith 65, Quayle 81
37	02/03	Conf.	NORTHWICH VICTORIA	929	1 - 0	Quayle 13
38	05/03	Conf.	Hereford United	1260	1 - 0	Smith 53
39	09/03	Conf.	Doncaster Rovers	2143	0 - 1	
40	16/03	Conf.	Boston United	2265	1 - 3	Albrighton 21
41	23/03	Conf.	Barnet	1306	0 - 0	
42	30/03	Conf.	Forest Green Rovers	642	1 - 1	Moore 90
43	01/04	Conf.	HAYES	762	1 - 2	Bentley 80
44	03/04	Conf.	MORECAMBE	664	4 - 1	Edwards 29, Quayle 36 57, Fensome 38[og]
45	06/04	Conf.	Scarborough	1439	1 - 3	Moore 33
46	08/04	Conf.	MARGATE	708	2 - 0	Quayle 34, Bentley 47
47	13/04	Conf.	NUNEATON BOROUGH	1016	0 - 2	
48	20/04	Conf.	Stalybridge Celtic	698	2 - 0	Quayle 48, King 90
49	27/04	Conf.	WOKING	1259	3 - 3	Bentley 34 82, Albrighton 64

1	2	3	4	5	6	7	8	9	10	11	Substitutes Used
Price	Albrighton	Hanmer	N Moore	Bentley	Fowler	Scott	Jobling	Smith	J Edwards	Palmer	
Price	Albrighton	Hanmer	N Moore	Bentley	Fowler	Scott	Jobling	Smith	J Edwards	Palmer	Davies 5 Fitzpatrick 9
Price	Albrighton	Hanmer	N Moore	Bentley	Fowler	Scott	Jobling	Smith	J Edwards	Palmer	Fitzpatrick 8 Crowe 2 Preece 9
P Edwards	Davies	Hanmer	N Moore	Albrighton	Fowler	Scott	Jobling	Palmer	J Edwards	Preece	Martindale 9
Price	Davies	Hanmer	N Moore	Albrighton	Fowler	Scott	Jobling	Quayle	J Edwards	Palmer	Fitzpatrick 8 Preece 11
Price	Davies	Hanmer	N Moore	Albrighton	Fowler	Scott	Jobling	Quayle	J Edwards	Palmer	
Price	Davies	Hanmer	N Moore	Albrighton	Fowler	Scott	Jobling	Quayle	J Edwards	Palmer	Fitzpatrick 11 Preece 3 King 2
Price	Wooliscroft	Hanmer	N Moore	Albrighton	Fowler	Scott	Jobling	Quayle	P Moore	Preece	Fitzpatrick 8
Price	Davies	Hanmer	N Moore	Albrighton	Fowler	Scott	Jobling	Quayle	J Edwards	Preece	Fitzpatrick 11
Price	Wooliscroft	Davies	N Moore	Preece	Fowler	Scott	Fitzpatrick	Quayle	J Edwards	Hanmer	Palmer 5
Price	Wooliscroft	Davies	N Moore	Preece	Fowler	Scott	Fitzpatrick	Quayle	J Edwards	Hanmer	Smith 7 Palmer 5
Price	Wooliscroft	Davies	Hanmer	Bentley	Fowler	Scott	Fitzpatrick	Smith	J Edwards	Palmer	Martindale 9 P Moore 10
Price	Wooliscroft	Hanmer	N Moore	Bentley	Fowler	Scott	Fitzpatrick	Smith	J Edwards	Palmer	Martindale 2 Albrighton 5
Price	Wooliscroft	Hanmer	N Moore	Albrighton	Fowler	Scott	Fitzpatrick	Smith	J Edwards	Palmer	Martindale 9
Price	Wooliscroft	Hanmer	N Moore	Albrighton	Fowler	Scott	Fitzpatrick	Martindale	P Moore	Palmer	
Price	Wooliscroft	Hanmer	Palmer	Albrighton	Fowler	Scott	Fitzpatrick	Martindale	J Edwards	Smith	P Moore 11
Price	Wooliscroft	Hanmer	N Moore	Scott	Fowler	Smith	Fitzpatrick	Martindale	J Edwards	Palmer	Jobling 11 P Moore 9
Price	Wooliscroft	Hanmer	N Moore	Bentley	Fowler	Scott	Fitzpatrick	Martindale	Smith	Palmer	Jobling 7 Davies 6
Price	Wooliscroft	Hanmer	N Moore	Bentley	Albrighton	Jobling	Fitzpatrick	Smith	J Edwards	Palmer	
Price	Wooliscroft	Hanmer	N Moore	Bentley	Albrighton	Jobling	Fitzpatrick	Smith	J Edwards	Palmer	P Moore 9 Scott 7
Price	Wooliscroft	Hanmer	N Moore	Bentley	Albrighton	Jobling	Fitzpatrick	Smith	J Edwards	Palmer	Davies 3 P Moore 10 King 7
Price	Wooliscroft	Davies	N Moore	Bentley	Jobling	Fitzpatrick	Scott	Smith	P Moore	Hanmer	Martindale 11 Preece 2
P Edwards	Wooliscroft	Hanmer	N Moore	Bentley	Fowler	Fitzpatrick	Jobling	Smith	Martindale	Palmer	P Moore 10
P Edwards	Wooliscroft	Hanmer	N Moore	Bentley	Albrighton	Fitzpatrick	Jobling	Smith	Martindale	Palmer	P Moore 10 Scott 11
P Edwards	Wooliscroft	Hanmer	N Moore	Bentley	Albrighton	Fitzpatrick	Jobling	Smith	Martindale	Palmer	
P Edwards	Wooliscroft	Hanmer	N Moore	Bentley	Albrighton	Fitzpatrick	Jobling	Quayle	Martindale	Palmer	King 8 P Moore 9 Davies 11
P Edwards	Wooliscroft	Hanmer	N Moore	Bentley	Albrighton	Fitzpatrick	Jobling	Smith	Martindale	Palmer	Quayle 9 P Moore 10
P Edwards	Wooliscroft	Hanmer	N Moore	Bentley	Albrighton	Fitzpatrick	Jobling	Smith	Martindale	Palmer	J Edwards 9 Quayle 10
P Edwards	Wooliscroft	Hanmer	N Moore	Bentley	Albrighton	Fitzpatrick	Jobling	Smith	Martindale	Palmer	P Moore 9 Quayle 10 J Edwards 8
P Edwards	Wooliscroft	Hanmer	N Moore	Bentley	Albrighton	Fitzpatrick	Jobling	Quayle	J Edwards	Palmer	Martindale 9 Smith 2 P Moore 10
P Edwards	Davies	Hanmer	N Moore	Bentley	Albrighton	Fitzpatrick	Jobling	Quayle	Smith	Palmer	P Moore 9
P Edwards	Davies	Hanmer	N Moore	Bentley	Albrighton	Fitzpatrick	Jobling	Quayle	Smith	Palmer	Wooliscroft 8 J Edwards 10 Martindale 9
P Edwards	Davies	Hanmer	N Moore	Bentley	Albrighton	Fitzpatrick	Fowler	Quayle	Smith	Palmer	P Moore 9 King 5
P Edwards	Davies	Hanmer	N Moore	Bentley	Albrighton	Fitzpatrick	Jobling	Smith	Quayle	Palmer	
P Edwards	Davies	Hanmer	N Moore	Bentley	Albrighton	Fitzpatrick	Jobling	Quayle	Smith	Palmer	Martindale 9 P Moore 10 Wooliscroft 7
P Edwards	Davies	Hanmer	N Moore	Bentley	Albrighton	King	Jobling	Quayle	Smith	King	Scott 11
P Edwards	Davies	Hanmer	N Moore	Bentley	Albrighton	King	Jobling	Quayle	Smith	Palmer	Scott 11
P Edwards	Davies	Hanmer	N Moore	Bentley	Albrighton	Fitzpatrick	Jobling	Quayle	Smith	Scott	Martindale 6 King 11 P Moore 10
P Edwards	Wooliscroft	Hanmer	N Moore	Bentley	Fowler	Fitzpatrick	Jobling	Quayle	Smith	Davies	Martindale 10 P Moore 9
P Edwards	Wooliscroft	Davies	N Moore	Bentley	Fowler	Fitzpatrick	Jobling	Smith	Martindale	Hanmer	P Moore 11 Scott 8 J Edwards 9
P Edwards	Wooliscroft	Davies	N Moore	Bentley	Fowler	Fitzpatrick	Jobling	Martindale	J Edwards	Hanmer	P Moore 3 Smith 9
P Edwards	Wooliscroft	Davies	N Moore	Fowler	Scott	Fitzpatrick	Jobling	Quayle	J Edwards	Hanmer	King 8 P Moore 9 Smith 10
P Edwards	Wooliscroft	Davies	N Moore	Bentley	Scott	Fitzpatrick	Jobling	Quayle	J Edwards	Hanmer	King 7 Smith 11 P Moore 10
P Edwards	Wooliscroft	Hanmer	N Moore	Bentley	Albrighton	Fitzpatrick	Jobling	Quayle	J Edwards	King	Davies 3 Smith 11 P Moore 10
P Edwards	Wooliscroft	Hanmer	N Moore	Bentley	Albrighton	Fitzpatrick	Jobling	Quayle	J Edwards	King	Davies 3 Smith 10 P Moore 11
Hateley	Wooliscroft	Davies	N Moore	Hanmer	Albrighton	King	Jobling	Quayle	P Moore	Palmer	Fitzpatrick 8 J Edwards 5 Smith 10
Hateley	Wooliscroft	Hanmer	N Moore	Bentley	Albrighton	Fitzpatrick	King	Quayle	Smith	Palmer	P Moore 9 J Edwards 10 Davies 3

257

TELFORD UNITED   PLAYING SQUAD

Player	Birthplace	D.O.B.	Previous Clubs
			Bold print denotes England semi-professional international.

GOALKEEPERS

Player	Birthplace	D.O.B.	Previous Clubs
Paul Edwards	Liverpool	22.02.67	Shrewsbury, Crewe, Leek T
Craig Jones	Birmingham	-	Walsall

DEFENDERS

Player	Birthplace	D.O.B.	Previous Clubs
Gareth Hanmer	Shrewsbury	12.01.73	Shrewsbury, WBA, Newtown
Kevin Davies	Sheffield	15.11.78	Sheffield Utd
Lee Fowler	Eastwood	21.06.69	Halifax, Doncaster R, Preston, Stoke
Ashley Wolliscroft	Stoke	28.12.79	Stoke
Dean Spink	Halesowen	22.01.67	Chester C, Wrexham, Shrewsbury, Aston Villa, Halesowen T
Grant Brown	Sunderland	19.11.69	Lincoln C, Leicester C
Mark Foran	Aldershot	30.10.73	Bristol R, Crewe, Peterborough, Sheffield Utd, Millwall
Nick Porter	Newport	-	From Youth team

MIDFIELD

Player	Birthplace	D.O.B.	Previous Clubs
Roger Preece	Much Wenlock	09.06.69	Coventry, Wrexham, Chester, Telford U, Shrewsbury
Steve Palmer	Birmingham		Wednesfield
Gary Fitzpatrick Eire Y	Birmingham	05.08.71	Leicester C, VS Rugby, Moor Green, Hednesford T, £15,000 to Telford U
Kevin Jobling	Sunderland	01.01.68	Leicester, Grimsby, Shrewsbury
Richard Scott	Dudley	29.09.74	Peterborough, Shrewsbury, Birmingham
Jordan King	Telford	-	From Youth team

FORWARDS

Player	Birthplace	D.O.B.	Previous Clubs
Ben Henshaw	Wolverhampton		Oxford U
Peter Smith	Rhuddlan	15.09.78	Crewe
David Brown	Bolton	02.10.78	Chester C, Torquay, Hull, Manchester Utd
Paul Moore	Birmingham	-	Bromsgrove R, Stourport Swifts, Paget R, Redditch Utd, Bromsgrove R, Stourbridge, Bromsgrove R, Kidderminster, Walsall
Tony Lormor	Ashington	29.10.70	Hartlepool, Mansfield, Preston, Chesterfield, Peterborough, Lincoln C, Newcastle

WOKING

Woking had been drifting into mid table in recent seasons , although an old favourite in Colin Lippiatt had revived ambitions and boosted hopes among their many supporters who had become used to much better fare. A terrible start to the season saw The Cards in twenty first position by the end of August and despite the arrival of England centre forward Warren Patmore from Rushden & Diamonds, a n improved spell in October was followed by a severe goal draught and an early embarrassing exit from The F.A.Cup at Newport County.

The return of Geoff Chapple to link up with his old friend sadly didn't bring a happy or successful reunion and very soon Colin Lippiatt left the club and a long end of season battle was fought against an ever threatening dangerous involvement with the three relegation places.

A hint of an F.A.Trophy run was encouraging and hopes were justifiably lifted as their manager was,after all, the most sucessful in Trophy history, and a defeat of local rivals and Chapple's recent club Kingstonian, really set Woking alight. Sharpling and Patmore provided the goals and four goals at home to Welling United really got the fans talking about the possibility of another final.

It wasn't to be however, as a visit to a very confident Burton Albion side brought an abrubt exit by three goals to nil. So it was back to the grind of survival and although three victories in four games early in March lifted the pressure, The Cards couldn't ever rise higher than eighteenth. In fact thirteen goals in five games raised hopes and certainly entertained the fans ,with Charlie Griffin finishing the season in encouraging form and a final position of nineteenth was safe but disappointing.

Despite the experienced Chapple strengthening his squad extensively, the bookies didn't fancy Woking's chances and for once The Cards started the season as underdogs !   T.W.

Back Row: David Piper, Nicky Banger, Stuart Reeks, Jon Boardman, Warren Patmore, Lee Sandford, Chris Collins, Rob Hollingdale, Anthony Allman
Middle Row: Ian Burns (Youth Team Manager), Matt Crossley (Asst Coach), Stuart Baverstock, Steve Farrelly, Tony Tucker, Ron Rawlings (Kitman), Barry Kimber (Physio)
Front Row: Grant Payne, Scott Smith, Chris Sharpling, Scott Steele, Glenn Cockerill (Head Coach), Geoff Chapple, Manager, Ben Abbey, Jon Brady, Barry Moore, Robert Kember

WOKING

GROUND DETAILS

Kingfield Stadium,
Kingfield Road,
Woking,
Surrey. GU22 9AA.

Tel: 01483 772470
Fax: 01483 888423
Football Office Fax: 01483729230
Web site: http://www.wokingfc.co.uk

Simple Directions:
M25 J10 or 11, signposted from outskirts of Town. Ground 1 mile. Woking B.R. Station & buses from Woking.

Capacity:	6,000
Seated:	2,500
Terracing -	**Covered:** 1,400
	Uncovered: 2,100

SOCIAL FACILITIES:
Clubhouse open on matchdays. Food available.

CLUB SHOP: Phone 01483 772470 for details.

Pages: 48 **Price:** £2.00
Editor: Paul Beard 01344 482018
Clubcall: 09066 555 070

Other club publications:
"Winning isn't Everything" (fanzine)
Local Press: Woking News & Mail; Woking Herald; Surrey Advertiser
Local Radio: BBC Surrey Sussex; County Sound; BBC Southern Counties

Founded:	1889
Nickname:	The Cards
Club colours:	Red & white halved shirts, & white shorts and red & white socks.
Change colours:	All Yellow
Midweek home matchday:	Tuesday 7.45pm.
Club Sponsors:	T.B.A.
Newsline	09066 555070

CLUB OFFICIALS

Chairman: Chris Ingram
Directors: Chris Ingram, Phil Ledger JP, Bob Drennan, John Buchanan, Julian Golding and Mike Bidmead (Company Secretary)

Managing Director Brian Blower
Tel No: 01483 772470

Football Director Phil J Ledger J.P.
19 Ainsdale Way, Woking, Surrey. GU21 3PP.
Tel: 01483 725295 (H), 07831 271369 (M)

Press Officers Phil Ledger & Brian Blower
Club Administrator Sue Day

FOOTBALL MANAGEMENT TEAM

MANAGER: GEOFF CHAPPLE
Date of Appointment 2001-2002
Date of Birth: 7th November 1945
Place of Birth: Farnham, Surrey
PREVIOUS CLUBS
As manager Windsor & Eton, Woking, Kingstonian.
As player Woking, Guildford City, Windsor & Eton
HONOURS
As manager FA Trophy 93-94, 94-95, 96-97, 98-99, 99-00
Isthmian League - Premier Div. 91-92, 97-98, Div. 1 R-up 89-90, Div. 2 S 86-87, League Cup 90-91, Charity Shield 91-92; Conference - R-up 94-95, 95-96, Championship Shield 94-95, R-up 95-96.

Coach: Glen Cockerill
Youth Team Manager: Ian Burns
Physio: Barry Kimber
Club's Playing Status: Part time

Season	League	Div.	Pos.	P	W	D	L	F	A	W	D	L	F	A	Pts	Manager
					Home					Away						
01-02	Conference	-	19	42	7	5	9	28	29	6	4	11	31	41	48	Colin Lippiatt/Geoff Chapple
00-01	Conference	-	14	42	5	10	6	30	30	8	5	8	22	27	54	Colin Lippiatt
99-00	Conference	-	14	42	5	6	10	17	27	8	7	6	28	26	52	Brian McDermott/Colin Lippiatt
98-99	Conference	-	9	42	9	5	7	27	20	9	4	8	24	25	63	John McGovern/Brian McDermott
97-98	Conference	-	3	42	14	3	4	47	22	8	5	8	25	24	74	John McGovern
96-97	Conference	-	5	42	10	5	6	41	29	8	5	8	30	34	64	Geoff Chapple

Season	League	Div.	Pos.	P	W	D	L	F	A	Pts	Manager
95-96	Conference	-	2	42	25	8	9	83	54	83	Geoff Chapple
94-95	Conference	-	2	42	21	12	9	76	54	75	Geoff Chapple
93-94	Conference	-	3	42	18	13	11	58	58	67	Geoff Chapple
92-93	Conference	-	8	42	17	8	17	58	62	59	Geoff Chapple

HONOURS

FA Trophy 93-94, 94-95, 96-97
FA Amateur Cup 57-58
GM VauxhallConference R-up 94-95, 95-96
Isthmian League: 91-92, R-up 56-57
Div.2 South 86-87
Isthmian Lge Cup: 90-91, R-up 89-90
Surrey Senior Cup: 12-13, 26-27, 55-56, 56-57,
71-72, 90-91, 93-94, 95-96, 99-00;
London Senior Cup R-up 82-83
Isthmian League Charity Shield 91-92, 92-93
Vauxhall Championship Shield 94-95, R-up 95-96.

PREVIOUS

Leagues: Isthmian 1911-92

Grounds: Wheatsheaf, Ivy Lane (pre 1923)

Past Players who progressed to the Football League

Ray Elliott (M'wall 46), Charlie Mortimore (A'shot 49),
Robert Edwards (Chelsea 51), Ron Newman (Portsmouth 55),
Mervyn Gill (Southampton 56),John Mortimore (Chelsea 51),
Reg Stratton (Fulham 59), George Harris (Newport Co. 61),
Norman Cashmore (A'shot 63), Alan Morton (C. Palace 67),
William Holmes (Millwall 70), Richard Forbes (Exeter 79),
Kevin Rattray (Gillingham 95), Steve Foster (Bristol Rov. 97),
Justin Jackson (Notts Co. 98), Kevin Betsy (Fulham 98).

CLUB RECORDS

Attendance: 6,000
v Swansea, FA Cup - 1978/79
v Coventry C., FA Cup - 1996-97

Win: 17-4 v Farnham, 1912-13

Defeat: 0-16 v New Crusaders, 1905-06

Career Goalscorer: C Mortimore 331, 1953-65

Career Appearances: B Finn 564, 1962-74

Transfer Fees
Paid: £60,000 for Cris Sharpling
(C.Palace) - 2001

Received: £150,000 for Steve Foster
(Bristol Rovers) - May 1997
£150,000 for Kevin Betsy (Fulham)

BEST SEASON

FA Cup: 4th Round 90-91,0-1 v Everton (A) Att 34,724
League clubs defeated: West Bromwich Albion (90-91)
Cambridge United & Millwall (96-97)

FA Trophy: Winners 93-94, 94-95, 96-97.

FA Amateur Cup: Winners 75-58

League Conference Runners-up 94-95, 95-96

LAST SEASON

F.A. Cup:	Fourth Qualifying Round
F.A. Trophy:	Fifth Round
Conference:	19th
Top Goalscorer:	Warren Patmore
Player of the Year:	Barry Moore
Captain:	Scott Smith & Scott Steele
Highest League Attendance:	2,288

WOKING

	Date	Comp.	Opponents	Att.	Score	Goalscorers
1	18/08	Conf.	Chester City	745	2 - 0	Haughton 2, Moore 39
2	21/08	Conf.	BOSTON UNITED	1701	0 - 2	
3	25/08	Conf.	MORECAMBE	1279	1 - 3	Griffin 20
4	27/08	Conf.	Dagenham & Redbridge	1410	1 - 3	Huckerby 23
5	01/09	Conf.	SCARBOROUGH	1244	1 - 2	Huckerby 7
6	04/09	Conf.	Yeovil Town	3157	3 - 1	Huckerby 33,Griffin 34,Kadi 85
7	08/09	Conf.	Doncaster Rovers	2598	1 - 1	Roddis 9
8	11/09	Conf.	MARGATE	1216	0 - 1	
9	15/09	Conf.	NORTHWICH VICTORIA	1331	3 - 1	Patmore 17, West 63, McFlynn 84
10	19/09	Conf.	Forest Green Rovers	756	1 - 2	Patmore 90
11	22/09	Conf.	TELFORD UNITED	1524	1 - 1	Haughton 22
12	29/09	Conf.	Nuneaton Borough	1339	0 - 2	
13	02/10	Conf.	DOVER ATHLETIC	1546	4 - 0	Perkins 32, Patmore 42 90[p], Carruthers 52[og]
14	05/10	Conf.	STEVENAGE BOROUGH	2554	1 - 1	Patmore 71 (Pen)
15	09/10	Conf.	Hayes	818	1 - 4	Patmore 90
16	13/10	Conf.	SOUTHPORT	1478	2 - 0	West 49 Moore 86
17	20/10	Conf.	Leigh RMI	524	1 - 3	Patmore 23
18	27/10	FA Cup Q4	NEWPORT COUNTY	2119	0 - 0	
19	29/10	FA Cup Q4 R	Newport County	1431	1 - 3	Chandler 30
20	03/11	Conf.	HEREFORD UNITED	2107	1 - 0	Steele 81
21	10/11	Conf.	Barnet	1822	0 - 3	
22	24/11	Conf.	STALYBRIDGE CELTIC	2033	1 - 1	Smith 59 (Pen)
23	01/12	Conf.	CHESTER CITY	1793	2 - 1	West 13,25
24	15/12	Conf.	Boston United	1949	0 - 4	
25	26/12	Conf.	FARNBOROUGH TOWN	2536	3 - 2	Sharpling 2 79, Patmore 15
26	29/12	Conf.	Morecambe	1308	1 - 3	Patmore 22
27	05/01	Conf.	YEOVIL TOWN	2516	0 - 2	
28	08/01	Surrey SC 4	BANSTEAD ATHLETIC	265	3 - 1	
29	12/01	FA Trophy 3	KINGSTONIAN	2474	2 - 1	Sharpling 7, Patmore 39
30	19/01	Conf.	Scarborough	1238	0 - 1	
31	02/02	FA Trophy 4	WELLING UNITED	1815	4 - 2	Moore 20, Smith 64, Saunders 69, D'Sane 71
32	09/02	Conf.	Stevenage Borough	2170	4 - 1	Steele 21, Sharpling 29, Patmore 40, Perkins 67
33	16/02	Conf.	Southport	985	0 - 2	
34	23/02	FA Trophy 5	Burton Albion	2322	0 - 3	
35	26/02	Surrey SC QF	CHERTSEY TOWN	n/k	9 - 1	
36	02/03	Conf.	FOREST GREEN ROVERS	1638	3 - 4	Sharpling 4 68, Patmore 83[p]
37	05/03	Conf.	Farnborough Town	1303	1 - 0	Moore 14
38	09/03	Conf.	Margate	1061	3 - 4	Moore 20, S Steele 72, Pitcher 89
39	16/03	Conf.	DONCASTER ROVERS	2133	3 - 1	Griffin 45, D'Sane 49, Moore 86
40	19/03	Surrey SC SF	TOOTING & MITCHAM UNITED	467	3 - 1	D'Sane 22, Haughton 69, Patmore 74
41	23/03	Conf.	Northwich Victoria	730	3 - 0	Perkins 11, Griffin 26 87
42	26/03	Conf.	HAYES	2202	0 - 1	
43	30/03	Conf.	LEIGH RMI	1609	1 - 1	Moore 56
44	01/04	Conf.	Hereford United	1465	2 - 2	Boardman 20, Pitcher 90
45	06/04	Conf.	BARNET	2035	1 - 3	Griffin 10
46	08/04	Conf.	Dover Athletic	1121	2 - 2	Griffin 48 65
47	13/04	Conf.	Stalybridge Celtic	1180	2 - 0	D'Sane 28, Griffin 84[p]
48	20/04	Conf.	NUNEATON BOROUGH	2288	0 - 0	
49	23/04	Conf.	DAGENHAM & REDBRIDGE	2817	0 - 2	
50	27/04	Conf.	Telford United	1259	3 - 3	D'Sane 20, Griffin 32, Haughton 80
51	30/04	Surrey SC F	CRYSTAL PALACE	n/k	0 - 3	@ Metropolitan Police FC

	1	2	3	4	5	6	7	8	9	10	11	Substitutes Used
1	Tucker	Piper	Hollingdale	West	P Steele	McFlynn	Pitman	Moore	S Steele	Griffin	Haughton	Graham 3 Huckerby 11 Kadi 9
2	Tucker	Piper	Hollingdale	West	P Steele	McFlynn	Pitman	Moore	S Steele	Griffin	Haughton	Graham 6 Huckerby 10 Smith 11
3	Tucker	Piper	Hollingdale	West	P Steele	Smith	Pitman	Moore	S Steele	Griffin	Haughton	Huckerby 9 Kadi 5 Allman 11
4	Tucker	Piper	Smith	West	P Steele	Fowler	Pitman	Moore	Kadi	Griffin	Huckerby	S Steele 6 Allman 9 Randall 10
5	Tucker	Piper	Hollingdale	West	P Steele	Fowler	Pitman	Moore	D'Sane	Griffin	Huckerby	Kadi 6 Reeks 11 S Steele 3
6	Tucker	Piper	Hollingdale	West	P Steele	Kadi	Chandler	Moore	S Steele	Griffin	Huckerby	Reeks 11 Haughton 9
7	Tucker	Piper	Hollingdale	West	P Steele	Chandler	Roddis	Moore	Kadi	Griffin	Huckerby	Perkins 3 Randall 10 Haughton 11
8	Tucker	Piper	Hollingdale	West	P Steele	Chandler	Roddis	McFlynn	Moore	Griffin	Huckerby	Perkins 3 Randall 8 Haughton 10
9	Tucker	Piper	Graham	West	P Steele	Chandler	Roddis	Perkins	Patmore	Haughton	Moore	McFlynn 3 Huckerby 10 Reeks 5
0	Tucker	Piper	Moore	West	Reeks	Chandler	Perkins	Roddis	Patmore	Haughton	Graham	Griffin 7 McFlynn 10
11	Tucker	Piper	Hollingdale	West	Reeks	Chandler	Perkins	Roddis	Patmore	Haughton	Moore	McFlynn 8 Huckerby 10 Graham 7
12	Tucker	Piper	Hollingdale	West	Reeks	Chandler	Moore	McFlynn	Patmore	Haughton	Graham	Roddis 3 Griffin 10 S Steele 5
13	Tucker	Piper	Hollingdale	West	Reeks	Chandler	Perkins	Fowler	Patmore	Sharpling	Moore	Pitman 7
14	Tucker	Piper	Hollingdale	West	Reeks	Chandler	Perkins	Fowler	Patmore	Sharpling	Pitman	Griffin 1 S Steele 7
15	Tucker	Piper	Hollingdale	West	Reeks	Chandler	Moore	Fowler	Patmore	Sharpling	Pitman	S Steele 3 McFlynn 5
16	Tucker	Piper	Pitman	West	Smith	Chandler	Roddis	Fowler	Patmore	Sharpling	Moore	Griffin 10 McFlynn 7 Reeks 3
17	Tucker	Piper	Pitman	West	Smith	Chandler	Roddis	McFlynn	Patmore	Sharpling	Moore	Griffin 3 Perkins 8 Reeks 4
18	Tucker	Piper	Moore	Reeks	Smith	Chandler	Perkins	Pitman	Patmore	Sharpling	Huckerby	Griffin 11 Fowler 4
19	Tucker	Piper	Pitman	West	Smith	Chandler	Perkins	Moore	Patmore	Sharpling	S Steele	Griffin 3 Haughton 11 Fowler 8
20	Tucker	Piper	Pitman	West	Smith	Chandler	Roddis	Fowler	Patmore	Sharpling	S Steele	Haughton 10 Kadi 8
21	Tucker	Piper	Pitman	West	Smith	Chandler	Roddis	Moore	Patmore	Sharpling	S Steele	Haughton 9 Perkins 7
22	Tucker	Piper	Reeks	Saunders	Smith	Moore	Perkins	Roddis	Haughton	Sharpling	Pitman	
23	Tucker	Piper	Pitman	Saunders	Smith	Moore	Perkins	Fowler	West	Sharpling	Kadi	Haughton 11 Reeks 8
24	Tucker	Piper	Pitman	Saunders	Smith	Webber	Perkins	D'Sane	West	Sharpling	Kadi	Griffin 9 Moore 11
25	Tucker	Piper	Pitman	Saunders	Smith	Moore	Perkins	D'Sane	Patmore	Sharpling	S Steele	Webber 8
26	Tucker	Piper	Pitman	Saunders	Smith	Webber	Perkins	Moore	Patmore	Sharpling	S Steele	Kadi 3 P Steele 5 West 12 (P St)
27	Tucker	Piper	Moore	Saunders	Smith	McGorry	Perkins	Webber	Patmore	Sharpling	S Steele	West 9 Griffin 10 D'Sane 11
28												
29	Tucker	Piper	Hollingdale	West	Smith	Pitman	Perkins	D'Sane	Patmore	Sharpling	S Steele	Webber 7
30	Tucker	Piper	Hollingdale	West	Smith	Saunders	McGorry	Pitcher	Patmore	Sharpling	S Steele	D'Sane 4 Haughton 11
31	Tucker	Piper	Hollingdale	Saunders	Smith	Moore	D'Sane	Pitcher	Patmore	Sharpling	S Steele	Haughton 10 Perkins 11
32	Tucker	Piper	Hollingdale	Saunders	Smith	Moore	D'Sane	Pitcher	Patmore	Sharpling	S Steele	Perkins 3 Griffin 9 Haughton 10
33	Tucker	Piper	Hollingdale	Saunders	Smith	Perkins	D'Sane	Pitcher	Patmore	Sharpling	S Steele	Haughton 7 Huckerby 2 Boardman 3
34	Tucker	Piper	Reeks	Boardman	Smith	Pitcher	Kadi	Perkins	Griffin	Sharpling	S Steele	Reece 7
35												
36	Tucker	Piper	Reece	Pitcher	Smith	Boardman	D'Sane	Perkins	Griffin	Sharpling	S Steele	Patmore 7 Saunders 5 Haughton 2
37	Tucker	Piper	Reece	Pitcher	Saunders	Boardman	Perkins	Moore	Griffin	Sharpling	S Steele	Patmore 9 Haughton 10
38	Tucker	Piper	Reece	Pitcher	Smith	Saunders	Griffin	Moore	Patmore	Sharpling	S Steele	Haughton 9 D'Sane 11
39	Bevan	Piper	Reece	Pitcher	Saunders	Smith	Perkins	Moore	Griffin	Sharpling	S Steele	D'Sane 11 Pitman 7
40												
41	Bevan	Piper	Reece	Pitcher	Saunders	Boardman	Perkins	Moore	Griffin	Sharpling	Smith	Patmore 9 Haughton 10
42	Bevan	Piper	Reece	Pitcher	Saunders	Boardman	Perkins	Moore	Griffin	Sharpling	Smith	Patmore 9 D'Sane 4 Haughton 5
43	Bevan	Piper	Reece	Pitcher	Boardman	Smith	Perkins	Moore	Patmore	Sharpling	Griffin	Pitman 7 Haughton 10
44	Bevan	Piper	Reece	Pitcher	Saunders	Boardman	Pitman	Moore	Patmore	Sharpling	Smith	Griffin 7 Haughton 10
45	Tucker	Piper	Reece	Pitcher	Saunders	Boardman	Perkins	Moore	Griffin	Sharpling	Smith	Patmore 5 D'Sane 7 Haughton 10
46	Tucker	Piper	Reece	Pitcher	Saunders	Boardman	Perkins	Moore	Griffin	D'Sane	Smith	Sharpling 9
47	Bevan	Piper	Reece	Pitman	Reeks	Boardman	Perkins	Moore	Griffin	D'Sane	Smith	Haughton 10 Sharpling 9
48	Bevan	Piper	Reece	Pitman	Reeks	Boardman	Perkins	Moore	Griffin	D'Sane	Smith	Haughton 3 Sharpling 5
49	Tucker	Piper	Reeks	Pitman	Smith	Boardman	Perkins	Moore	Griffin	D'Sane	Sharpling	Haughton 2 Saunders 4
50	Tucker	Piper	Reece	Pitman	Reeks	Boardman	Perkins	Moore	Griffin	D'Sane	Smith	Sharpling 7 Haughton 9 Saunders 4
51												

WOKING
PLAYING SQUAD

Player	Birthplace	D.O.B.	Previous Clubs
			Bold print denotes England semi-professional international.

GOALKEEPERS

Player	Birthplace	D.O.B.	Previous Clubs
Steve Farrelly ESP, FAT	Liverpool	27.03.65	Hampton & Richmond, Farnborough T, Kingstonian, Barrow, Rotherham, Macclesfield, Chester C
Stuart Baverstock	Surrey	-	From Youth team
Anthony Tucker	London		Fulham

DEFENDERS

Player	Birthplace	D.O.B.	Previous Clubs
Scott Smith New Zealand Int.	Christchurch	06.03.75	Rotherham, Kettering T
Michael Danzey ESP	Widnes	08.02.71	Nottingham F, Peterborough, St.Albans C, Camb.U, Aylesbury U. £15,000 to Woking
David Piper	Bournemouth	31.10.77	Yeovil T, Southampton
Paul Steele	Wiltshire		Yeovil T, Chippenham T
Chris Collins	Chatham	26.09.79	Newport IOW, Stevenage B, Southampton
Lee Sandford EY, Div 2	Basingstoke	22.04.68	Sheffield Utd, Stoke, Portsmouth
Jonathan Boardman	Reading	27.01.81	Crystal Palace

MIDFIELD

Player	Birthplace	D.O.B.	Previous Clubs
Scott Steele FAT, SS	Motherwell	19.09.71	Airdrie
Barry Moore	London	04.02.77	Hayes, Hampton
Rob Hollingdale	London		Boreham Wood (£15,000), Wembley
Jon Brady NC	Newcastle (Aust)	14.01.75	Rushden & Diamonds, Hayes, Mjolner (Norw), Hayes, Wycombe, Brentford, Swansea, Adamstown Rosebuds (Aust)
Robert Kember	Wimbledon	21.08.81	Crystal Palace
Nicky Banger	Southampton	25.04.71	Merthyr Tydfil, Torquay, Merthyr Tydfil, Plymouth, Dundee, Oxford Utd, Oldham, Southampton

FORWARDS

Player	Birthplace	D.O.B.	Previous Clubs
Charlie Griffin	Bath	25.06.79	Swindon (£25,000), Chippenham T
Ben Abbey	London	13.05.78	Crawley T, Southend Utd., Oxford Utd, Crawley T, Maidenhead Utd, Osterley
Chris Sharpling	Bromley	21.04.81	Crystal Palace (£60,000)
Warren Patmore ESP, RP	Kingsbury	14.08.71	Rushden & Diamonds, Yeovil T, Ards, Northampton, Millwall, Cambridge Utd, Northwood
Grant Payne	Woking	25.12.75	Aldershot T, Woking, Wimbledon

YEOVIL TOWN

Despite their wonderful record in the F.A.Cup ,Yeovil Town had never even reached an F.A. Trophy let alone won the competition. So an appearance at Villa Park was an historic occasion for all involved with the famous non-league club .There was massive excitement as they worked their way through the rounds past Tiverton Town (3-1 away), Doncaster Rovers in an away replay with an amazing 5-4 victory after trailing 0-3 , holders Canvey Island (2-1 at home) and Northwich Victoria (2-0 away), before producing a brilliant 4-0 home victory against much fancied Burton Albion in the semi-final first leg. This big lead produced a rather flat atmosphere in the second leg as Albion won 2-1 and Yeovil took their place in their first national final. But there was nothing flat about the wonderful atmosphere at Villa Park as both sides produced a superb spectacle in the Spring sunshine . The Glovers deserved their victory with two excellent goals from heroes Carl Alford and Adam Stansfield and the quality and sportmanship on show were a credit to both clubs.

In the Conference ,Yeovil's home form probably prevented them from seriously challenging the top two but on their day Gary Johnson's very well coached squad produced some of the best football seen in last seasons competition. Skipper Terry Skiverton enjoyed a superb season and along with Antony Tonkin, Nick Crittendon, Adam Lockwood and Adam Stansfield represented England . Indeed the fairy story of the season must have been Stansfield 's amazing rise from Elmore in the Western League, to the England team in the Four Nations Tournament and Man of the Match in the Trophy Final. Despite a first game defeat in the F.A.Cup at Hayes and the slightly disappointing non involvement with the promotion battle, Yeovil Town are favourites for a very exciting season.T.W.

L-R - Back Row: Tom White, Abdoulai Demba, Steve Collis, Chris Weale, Jon Sheffield, Roy O'Brien, Chris Giles.
Middle Row: Stuart Housley (youth team coach), Tony Farmer (physio), Colin Pluck, Carl Alford, Anthony Tonkin, Gavin Williams, Adam Lockwood, Adam Stansfield, Stephen Reed, Ian Linney, Maurice O'Donnell (reserve team manager), Tony Trott (kit manager), Steve Thompson (assistant manager). **Front:** Kim Grant, Andy Lindegaard, Michael McIndoe, Nick Crittenden, Gary Johnson (manager), Terry Skiverton, Darren Way, Lee Johnson, Olivier Brassart.

YEOVIL TOWN

GROUND DETAILS

Huish Park,
Lufton Way,
Yeovil
Somerset, BA22 8YF

TELEPHONE 01935 423662
Fax 01935 473956
Web site: http://www.ytfc.net

SIMPLE DIRECTIONS:
Leave A303 at Cartgate roundabou, take A3088 towards
Yeovil. First exit at next roundabout, then first exit at next
roundabout into Lufton Way.
Railway station - Yeovil Pen Mill (Bristol/Westbury to
Weymouth) 2.5 miles from ground.
Bus service from station on Saturday

CAPACITY: 9,107
SEATED: 5,253
COVERED TERRACING: 3,854

SOCIAL FACILITIES: Matchdays hot + cold food available.
Meals can be ordered provided advance notice is given.
All weather astro turf pitch available for bookings 9am-10pm

CLUB SHOP: Open matchdays & 10-4 weekdays, selling a full
range of souvenirs, match programmes, scarves, hats,
replica kits and badges

Pages: 48   Price: £2.00

Editor: Adrian Hopper

Clubcall: 09066 555 850
Other club publications: "100 Huish Heroes" £3; Centenary
Book £14.99 (Both available from the club)

Local Press: Western Gazette; Western Daily Press; Bristol
Evening Post; Sunday Independent; Yeovil Express & Clarion
Local Radio: Radio Bristol; Somerset Sound; Orchard FM

Founded   1895

Nickname: Glovers

Sponsors: Bradfords Building Supplies

Club Colours: Green & white shirts
                           white shorts & green socks

Change Colours: White with green trim/green/white

Midweek matchday: Tuesday

CLUB OFFICIALS

Chief Executive: John Fry

President   S N Burfield M.B.E.

Company Secretary   George Smith

Club Secretary   Jean Cotton
                               c/o the club

Commercial Sales Manager   Alan Skirton
                               c/o the club

FOOTBALL MANAGEMENT TEAM
MANAGER: GARY JOHNSON

Date of Appointment   June 2001
Date of Birth: 28th September 1955
Place of Birth: London

PREVIOUS CLUBS
As manager   Newmarket Town, Cambridge Utd.,
                 Kettering Town, Latvia
Youth Academy
Director   Watford
As coach   Cambridge Utd.
As player   Watford, Malmo, Newmarket Town

* * *

First Team Coach/Ass.Man.   Steve Thompson
Reserve team manager: Maurice O'Donnell
Youth development: Stuart Housley
Chief Scout: Frank Leworthy
Physio: Tony Farmer

Club's Playing Status: Full Time

eason	League	Div.	Pos.	P	W	D	L	F	A	W	D	L	F	A	Pts	Manager
						Home					*Away*					
01-02	Conference	-	3	42	6	7	8	27	30	13	6	2	39	23	70	Gary Johnson
00-01	Conference	-	2	42	14	3	4	41	17	10	5	6	32	33	80	D Webb/ Colin Addison
99-00	Conference	-	7	42	11	4	6	37	28	7	6	8	23	35	64	C.Lippiatt/Steve Thompson/Dave Webb
98-99	Conference	-	5	42	8	4	9	35	32	12	7	2	33	22	71	Colin Lippiatt
97-98	Conference	-	11	42	14	3	4	45	24	3	5	13	28	39	59	Graham Roberts/Colin Lippiatt
96-97	Isthmian	Prem.	1	42	17	3	1	49	17	14	5	2	34	17	101	Graham Roberts

Season	League	Div.	Pos.	P	W	D	L	F	A	Pts	Manager
95-96	Isthmian	Prem.	4	42	23	11	8	83	51	80	Graham Roberts
94-95	Conference	-	22	42	8	14	20	50	71	*37	Brian Hall/Graham Roberts
93-94	Conference	-	19	42	14	9	19	49	62	51	Steve Rutter/Brian Hall
92-93	Conference	-	4	42	18	12	12	59	49	66	Steve Rutter

HONOURS

Southern Lge 54-55, 63-64, 70-71
R-up 23-24, 31-32, 34-35, 69-70, 72-73
Southern Lge Cup 48-49, 54-55, 60-61, 65-66
Vauxhall-Opel Lge (Isthmian) 87-88, R-up 85-86, 86-87
ICIS Prem. (Isthmian) 96-97;
AC Delco Cup 87-88.
Bob Lord Trophy 89-90
R-up 93-94
F.A. Trophy 01-02

PREVIOUS

Leagues: Western League, London Combination, Southern League, Alliance Premier 79-85, Isthmian 85-88, GMV Conference 88-95, Isthmian 95-97

Names: Yeovil & Petters Utd

Ground: Pen Mill ground 1895-1921, Huish 1921-1990

Past Players who progressed to the Football League

Over 40 players & 18 managers including, since 1985:-

Nigel Jarvis (Torquay), Ian Davies (Bristol Rovers),
Alan Pardew (Crystal Palace), Paul Miller (Wimbledon)
Guy Whittingham (Portsmouth), Mark Shail (Bristol City),
Malcolm McPherson (W.H.U)
Howard Forinton & Jerry Gill (B'hamC)
Barrington Belgrave & Ben Smith (Southend U)

ACHIEVE BY UNITY

CLUB RECORDS

Attendance:	8,868
	v Rushden & Diamonds 21-04-01
Career Goalscorer:	Dave Taylor 285 1960-69
Career Appearances:	Len Harris, 691, 1958-72
Win:	10-0
	v Kidderminster Harriers (H), Southern Lge. 27.12.1955
	v Bedford Town (H), Southern Lge. 4.3.61
Defeat:	0-8
	v Manchester Utd., FA Cup 5th Rd.
	12.2.49 at Maine Rd. (81,565)
Transfer Fee Paid:	Undisclosed ,May 2002
	to Hereford United for Gavin Williams
Transfer Fee Received:	£75,000
	for Mark Shail from Bristol City

BEST SEASON

FA Cup   5th Rd 48-49

v ManchesterU (at Maine Rd) Att.81,565
League clubs defeated: C.Palace, Exeter C (34-5);
Brighton (38-9); Bury, Sunderland (Div1) (48-9);
Gillingham (49-50); Southend (58-9); Walsall (60-1);
C. Palace & Southend U (63-64); Bournemouth (70-1);
Brentford (72-3); Cambridge U (87-8); Walsall (91-2);
Hereford U & Torquay U (92-93); Fulham (93-94);
NorthamptonT (98-99); Blackpool & Colchester U (00-1).
A record TWENTY victories.

FA Trophy: Winners 2001-0002
League: Conference Runners-up 00-01

LAST SEASON

F.A. Cup:	4th Qualifying Proper
F.A. Trophy:	Winners
Conference:	3rd
Top Goalscorer:	Adam Stansfield
Captain:	Terry Skiverton
Player of the Year:	Michael McIndoe

YEOVIL TOWN

Match Facts 2001-02

	Date	Comp.	Opponents	Att.	Score	Goalscorers
1	18/08	Conf.	NORTHWICH VICTORIA	3290	2 - 3	McIndoe 12, Giles 90
2	21/08	Conf.	Telford United	1203	2 - 2	Ramsay 53, Crittenden 65
3	25/08	Conf.	Doncaster Rovers	2796	2 - 1	Way 53, Giles 90
4	27/08	Conf.	HAYES	2782	2 - 1	Turner 36, Belgrave 74
5	01/09	Conf.	Nuneaton Borough	1484	2 - 1	Alford 68, Belgrave 73
6	04/09	Conf.	WOKING	3157	1 - 3	Alford 45
7	08/09	Conf.	Boston United	2282	0 - 4	
8	11/09	Conf.	FARNBOROUGH TOWN	2316	0 - 1	
9	15/09	Conf.	SCARBOROUGH	2390	2 - 2	Johnson 47, Giles 77
10	18/09	Conf.	Hereford United	1709	2 - 0	Alford 40, Johnson 48
11	22/09	Conf.	Dover Athletic	1015	2 - 1	Alford 14, Giles 30
12	29/09	Conf.	LEIGH RMI	2835	2 - 1	Way 65 (Pen),Ramsey 85
13	02/10	Conf.	Barnet	1583	3 - 2	Crittenden 39, Johnson 56, Ramsay 82
14	06/10	Conf.	MORECAMBE	2404	1 - 1	Crittenden 90
15	09/10	Conf.	MARGATE	2577	1 - 2	Alford 45
16	11/10	Som. PC 1	MINEHEAD TOWN	n/k	3 - 0	Parkinson 7, Thompson 42, Giles 56
17	13/10	Conf.	Dagenham & Redbridge	2163	1 - 1	Ramsey 25
18	16/10	LDV Vans 1S	QUEENS PARK RANGERS	2879	3 - 0	Giles 37 90, Grant 80
19	20/10	Conf.	Stalybridge Celtic	829	1 - 1	Alford 10
20	27/10	FA Cup Q4	Hayes	1182	1 - 3	Turner 38
21	31/10	LDV Vans 2S	Bristol Rovers	4301	1 - 1	McIndoe 27 4 5
22	03/11	Conf.	CHESTER CITY	2833	0 - 1	
23	09/11	Conf.	Southport	944	0 - 3	
24	17/11	Conf.	Margate	1125	1 - 0	Pluck 20
25	21/11	Som. PC 2	STREET	225	0 - 1	
26	24/11	Conf.	STEVENAGE BOROUGH	2468	2 - 1	Broad 22 Alford 39
27	01/12	Conf.	Northwich Victoria	974	3 - 1	Talbot 16 (og),McIndoe 65, Stansfield 81
28	08/12	Conf.	DONCASTER ROVERS	2650	1 - 1	McIndoe 87
29	15/12	Conf.	TELFORD UNITED	2454	1 - 1	McIndoe 27
30	26/12	Conf.	Forest Green Rovers	1609	1 - 1	Grant 41
31	05/01	Conf.	Woking	2516	2 - 0	Thompson 10, Stansfield 90
32	12/01	FA Trophy 3	Tiverton Town	2320	3 - 1	Stansfield 15 49, Alford 81
33	19/01	Conf.	NUNEATON BOROUGH	2944	2 - 1	Stansfield 79, McIndoe 88
34	26/01	Conf.	Hayes	708	4 - 0	Grant 26, Johnson 41, Brassart 66, Stansfield 71
35	29/01	Conf.	FOREST GREEN ROVERS	2686	2 - 2	Pluck 7, Grant 11
36	09/02	Conf.	Morecambe	1248	5 - 1	McIndoe 16, Grant 40 50, Johnson 45, Stansfield 69
37	16/02	Conf.	DAGENHAM & REDBRIDGE	4458	3 - 3	McIndoe 24, Stansfield 30, Giles 85
38	19/02	FA Trophy 4	DONCASTER ROVERS	2671	1 - 1	Stansfield 79
39	23/02	FA Trophy 4 R	Doncaster Rovers	2178	5 - 4	Pluck 57, Alford 75, Stansfield 79 86, Skiverton 89
40	02/03	Conf.	HEREFORD UNITED	3022	2 - 1	Crittenden 45, Lindegaard 90
41	05/03	FA Trophy 5	CANVEY ISLAND	3616	2 - 1	Stansfield 17, Crittenden 79[p]
42	09/03	Conf.	Farnborough Town	1404	3 - 1	O'Shea 53[og], Giles 86, Stansfield 90
43	16/03	FA Trophy QF	Northwich Victoria	1846	2 - 0	Stansfield 35, Alford 45
44	23/03	Conf.	Scarborough	1379	0 - 0	
45	26/03	Conf.	BOSTON UNITED	5061	0 - 1	
46	30/03	Conf.	STALYBRIDGE CELTIC	3064	0 - 2	
47	01/04	Conf.	Chester City	1807	1 - 1	Skiverton 42
48	06/04	FA Trophy SF(1)	BURTON ALBION	5614	4 - 0	Grant 4, Crittenden 37[p], McIndoe 45, Giles 84
49	14/04	FA Trophy SF(2)	Burton Albion	4026	1 - 2	Alford 57
50	16/04	Conf.	BARNET	2125	1 - 2	Way 70
51	18/04	Conf.	Stevenage Borough	1275	3 - 2	Giles 12, Kumbar 26 45
52	20/04	Conf.	Leigh RMI	401	1 - 0	Kumber 13
53	23/04	Conf.	SOUTHPORT	1941	0 - 1	
54	27/04	Conf.	DOVER ATHLETIC	2852	2 - 0	Alford 19, Stansfield 45
55	12/05	FA Trophy Final	STEVENAGE BOROUGH	18809	2 - 0	Alford 12, Stansfield 65 @ Aston Villa F.C.

1	2	3	4	5	6	7	8	9	10	11	Substitutes Used
Sheffield	Johnson	Tonkin	Skiverton	Pluck	Way	Belgrave	Turner	Ramsay	Crittenden	McIndoe	Alford 8 White 9 Giles 7
Sheffield	Johnson	Tonkin	White	Pluck	Way	Belgrave	Poole	Ramsay	Crittenden	McIndoe	Alford 7 Thompson 8
Sheffield	Johnson	Tonkin	Skiverton	White	Way	Belgrave	Ramsay	Alford	Crittenden	McIndoe	Turner 7 Giles 8
Sheffield	Johnson	Tonkin	Skiverton	White	Way	Turner	Ramsay	Alford	Crittenden	McIndoe	Belgrave 8 Giles 9
Sheffield	Johnson	Tonkin	Skiverton	White	Way	Turner	Ramsay	Alford	Crittenden	McIndoe	Belgrave 8
Sheffield	Johnson	Tonkin	Skiverton	White	Way	Turner	Ramsay	Alford	Crittenden	McIndoe	Belgrave 8 O'Brien 4 Giles 7
Sheffield	Johnson	Tonkin	Skiverton	White	Way	Belgrave	Ramsay	Alford	Crittenden	McIndoe	O'Brien 8 Giles 7
Sheffield	Johnson	Tonkin	Skiverton	White	Way	Turner	Ramsay	Alford	Crittenden	McIndoe	Belgrave 6 O'Brien 2 Giles 7
Sheffield	Johnson	Tonkin	Skiverton	White	O'Brien	Turner	Ramsay	Alford	Crittenden	McIndoe	Lindegaard 6 Bent 12 (Lin) Giles 8
Sheffield	Lockwood	Tonkin	Skiverton	White	Way	Johnson	Giles	Alford	Crittenden	McIndoe	Turner 11
Sheffield	Lockwood	Tonkin	Skiverton	White	Way	Turner	Giles	Alford	Crittenden	Johnson	Ramsay 9 Thompson 8
Sheffield	Lockwood	Tonkin	Skiverton	White	Way	Turner	Giles	Alford	Crittenden	Johnson	Thompson 7 Ramsay 8
Sheffield	Lockwood	Tonkin	Skiverton	White	Way	Turner	Ramsay	Alford	Crittenden	Johnson	Pluck 4
Sheffield	Lockwood	Tonkin	Pluck	White	Way	Turner	Ramsay	Alford	Crittenden	Johnson	Lindegaard 7 Giles 9
Weale	Lockwood	Tonkin	Pluck	White	Way	Johnson	Ramsay	Alford	Crittenden	McIndoe	Schram 4 Giles 8
Weale	Schram	Pluck	Haveron	White	Lindegaard	Johnson	Ramsay	Alford	Crittenden	McIndoe	Grant 9 Turner 3 Giles 6
Weale	Schram	Tonkin	Haveron	White	Giles	Turner	Johnson	Alford	Crittenden	McIndoe	Grant 9
Weale	Schram	Tonkin	Skiverton	White	Giles	Turner	Johnson	Alford	Crittenden	McIndoe	Grant 6 Lockwood 7 Ramsay 9
Weale	Lockwood	Tonkin	Skiverton	White	Schram	Turner	Grant	Alford	Crittenden	McIndoe	Pluck 5 Thompson 7 Thompson 10
Weale	Lockwood	Tonkin	Skiverton	White	Schram	Grant	Johnson	Alford	Crittenden	McIndoe	Way 6 Thompson 12 (Way) Giles 9
Weale	Lockwood	Tonkin	White	Skiverton	Schram	Ramsay	Johnson	Alford	Crittenden	McIndoe	Thompson 6 Turner 8 Giles 7
Weale	Lockwood	Tonkin	Haveron	Pluck	Grant	Stansfield	Johnson	Giles	Crittenden	McIndoe	Cooper 5
Weale	Lockwood	Tonkin	Thompson	Pluck	Grant	Stansfield	Johnson	Alford	Crittenden	McIndoe	Haveron 6 Giles 9
Weale	Lockwood	Tonkin	Thompson	Pluck	Grant	Stansfield	Broad	Alford	Crittenden	McIndoe	Haveron 4 Turner 6 Giles 9
Weale	Lockwood	Tonkin	Thompson	Pluck	Turner	Stansfield	Broad	Alford	Crittenden	McIndoe	Poole 4 Giles 9
Weale	Lockwood	Tonkin	Thompson	Pluck	Turner	Stansfield	Broad	Alford	Crittenden	McIndoe	White 8 Way 6 Giles 9
Weale	Lockwood	Tonkin	Thompson	Pluck	Turner	Stansfield	Broad	Alford	Crittenden	McIndoe	Way 6 Grant 9 Giles 8
Weale	Lockwood	Tonkin	Thompson	Pluck	Way	Stansfield	Johnson	Grant	Crittenden	McIndoe	White 4 Alford 9 Giles 7
Weale	Lockwood	Tonkin	Thompson	Pluck	Way	Stansfield	Johnson	Alford	Grant	McIndoe	White 4 Turner 10 Giles 9
Weale	Lockwood	Tonkin	Thompson	Pluck	Way	Stansfield	Johnson	Alford	Crittenden	Grant	White 4 Turner 6 Giles 11
Weale	Lockwood	Tonkin	Thompson	Pluck	Grant	Stansfield	Johnson	Alford	Crittenden	McIndoe	White 5 Turner 6 Giles 9
Weale	Lockwood	Tonkin	Thompson	Pluck	Brassart	Stansfield	Johnson	Grant	Crittenden	McIndoe	White 4 Skiverton 5 Alford 9
Weale	Lockwood	Tonkin	Thompson	Pluck	Brassart	Stansfield	Johnson	Grant	Crittenden	McIndoe	White 6 Alford 9 Giles 4
Weale	Lockwood	Tonkin	Thompson	Pluck	Brassart	Stansfield	Johnson	Grant	Crittenden	McIndoe	White 4 Alford 9 Giles 7
Weale	Lockwood	White	Brassart	Skiverton	Way	Stansfield	Johnson	Grant	Crittenden	McIndoe	Alford 9 Giles 4
Weale	Lockwood	Tonkin	Skiverton	Thompson	Way	Stansfield	Johnson	Grant	Crittenden	McIndoe	White 5 Alford 4 Giles 9
Weale	Lockwood	Thompson	Skiverton	Pluck	Way	Stansfield	Brassart	Grant	Crittenden	McIndoe	White 8 Alford 6 O'Brien 3
Weale	Lockwood	Tonkin	Skiverton	White	O'Brien	Stansfield	Brassart	Giles	Crittenden	McIndoe	Alford 9 Lindegaard 5
Weale	Lockwood	Tonkin	Skiverton	White	O'Brien	Stansfield	Johnson	Grant	Crittenden	McIndoe	Thompson 8 Alford 9
Weale	O'Brien	Tonkin	Skiverton	White	Brassart	Stansfield	Johnson	Alford	Crittenden	McIndoe	Pluck 8 Giles 9
Weale	White	Tonkin	Skiverton	Pluck	Brassart	Stansfield	Johnson	Alford	Crittenden	O'Brien	Lockwood 11 Lindegaard 6 Giles 7
Weale	White	Tonkin	Skiverton	Pluck	Brassart	Stansfield	Johnson	Alford	Crittenden	O'Brien	Lockwood 11 Way 8 Giles 9
Weale	White	Tonkin	Skiverton	Pluck	Brassart	Stansfield	Johnson	Giles	Crittenden	O'Brien	Way 6 Grant 11 Alford 9
Weale	White	Tonkin	Skiverton	Pluck	Way	Stansfield	Johnson	Brassart	Crittenden	Kumbar	Lockwood 2 Grant 11 Giles 9
Weale	Lockwood	Tonkin	Skiverton	Pluck	Brassart	Kumbar	Johnson	Grant	Crittenden	McIndoe	Way 6 O'Brien 9 Thompson 7
Weale	Lockwood	Tonkin	Skiverton	Pluck	Way	Stansfield	Johnson	Grant	Crittenden	McIndoe	Giles 9
Weale	Lockwood	Tonkin	Skiverton	Pluck	Way	Stansfield	Johnson	Alford	Crittenden	McIndoe	Giles 9
Weale	Lockwood	Tonkin	White	Pluck	Way	Stansfield	Johnson	Alford	Crittenden	McIndoe	Lindegaard 5 Giles 9
Collis	Lockwood	Tonkin	O'Brien	White	Brassart	Lindegaard	Kumbar	Giles	Grant	McIndoe	Stansfield 9 Crittenden 11 Alford 9
Weale	O'Brien	Tonkin	Brassart	White	Way	Stansfield	Johnson	Grant	Crittenden	Kumbar	McIndoe 11 Lockwood 4 Alford 9
Weale	Lockwood	Kumbar	Skiverton	Pluck	Way	Stansfield	Johnson	Grant	Crittenden	McIndoe	Tonkin 9 Brassart 11 Giles 3
Weale	Lockwood	Tonkin	Skiverton	Pluck	Way	Stansfield	Johnson	Alford	Lindegaard	McIndoe	White 5 Brassart 10 Grant 7
Weale	Lockwood	Tonkin	Skiverton	Pluck	Way	Stansfield	Johnson	Alford	Crittenden	McIndoe	White 5 Giles 9 Lindegaard 10

YEOVIL TOWN   PLAYING SQUAD

Player *Birthplace*   *D.O.B.* *Previous Clubs*

Bold print denotes
England semi-professional international.

GOALKEEPERS

Chris Weale FAT	Yeovil		From Youth team
Jon Sheffield	Bedworth	01.02.69	Plymouth, Peterborough, Cambridge Utd, Norwich

DEFENDERS

Anthony Tonkin British Univ., FAT			Falmouth T., Plymouth Arg.
Terry Skiverton ESP, FAT	Mile End	26.06.75	Welling Utd, Wycombe, Chelsea
Adam Lockwood ESP, FAT	Wakefield	26.10.81	Reading
Colin Pluck FAT	London	06.09.78	Dover Ath., Hayes, Stevenage B, Morton, Watford
Tom White FAT	Bristol	26.01.76	Bristol R

MIDFIELD

Nick Crittenden FAT	Ascot	11.11.78	Chelsea
Steve Thompson ESP, FAT, GMVC, RP	Plymouth	12.01.63	Bristol C, Torquay, Saltash U, Slough T, Wycombe, Woking £5,000 to Yeovil T
Andy Lindegard FAT	Dorset		Westlands Sports
Roy O'Brien Rep.of Ire S & Y	Cork	27.11.74	Arsenal, Wigan, Bournemouth, Dorchester T
Darren Way ES, FAT	Plymouth	21.11.79	Norwich
Jamie Willmott	Bristol		Bristol R
Lee Johnson FAT	Newmarket	07.06.81	Watford
Michael McIndoe FAT	Edinburgh	02.12.79	Hereford Utd (£25,000), Luton

FORWARDS

Carl Alford ESP, FAT	Denton	11.02.72	Doncaster R, Stevenage B, Rushden & Diamonds, Kettering T, Macclesfield, Witton Alb., Burnley, Stockport, Rochdale
Gavin Williams WSP	Merthyr Tydfil	20.07.80	Hereford Utd
Abdou Demba Mali Int.	Mali	02.11.76	KV Ostende (Belg), El Kahlij (UAE)
Adam Stansfield ESP, FAT	Devon	10.09.78	Elmore, Cullompton R, Tiverton T, Cullompton T
Chris Giles FAT	Milborne Port	16.04.82	Sherborne
Howard Forinton RP	Boston	18.09.75	Torquay, Peterborough, Birmingham, Yeovil T, Oxford C, Abingdon T, Oxford Utd
Kim Grant Ghana Int.	Ghana	25.09.72	Scunthorpe, Lommel (Belg), Millwall, Luton, Charlton

NORTHERN PREMIER LEAGUE

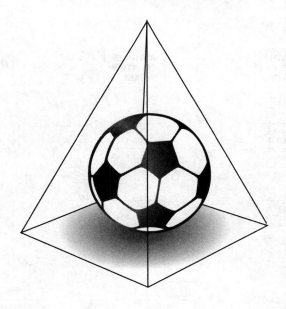

PYRAMID SECTION

UniBond
NORTHERN PREMIER

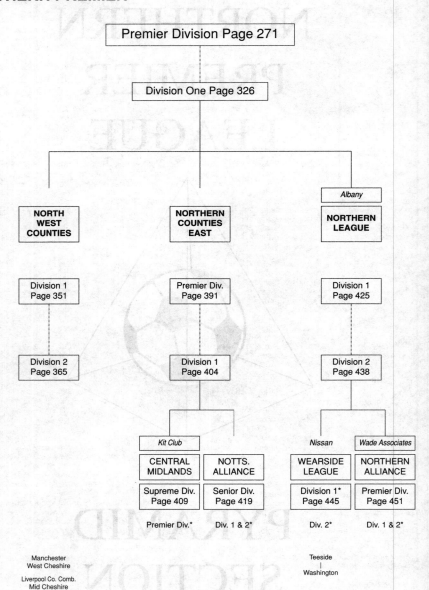

Premier Division Page 271

Division One Page 326

NORTH WEST COUNTIES	NORTHERN COUNTIES EAST	*Albany* NORTHERN LEAGUE

| Division 1 Page 351 | Premier Div. Page 391 | Division 1 Page 425 |

| Division 2 Page 365 | Division 1 Page 404 | Division 2 Page 438 |

Kit Club CENTRAL MIDLANDS	NOTTS. ALLIANCE	*Nissan* WEARSIDE LEAGUE	*Wade Associates* NORTHERN ALLIANCE
Supreme Div. Page 409	Senior Div. Page 419	Division 1* Page 445	Premier Div. Page 451
Premier Div.*	Div. 1 & 2*	Div. 2*	Div. 1 & 2*

Manchester
West Cheshire

Liverpool Co. Comb.
Mid Cheshire
West Lancashire
Staffs Senior
Lancs & Cheshire

Teeside
|
Washington

UniBond League

President: N White F.S.C.A.

Chairman: Ken Marsden

Secretary & Treasurer: R D Bayley
22 Woburn Drive, Hale, Altrincham, Cheshire WA15 8LZ
Tel: 0161 980 7007   Fax: 0161 904 8850

Press Secretary: P Bradley
7 Guest Road, Prestwich, Manchester M25 7DJ
Tel: 0161 798 5198   Fax: 0161 773 0930

The season was dominated by Burton Albion who led the Premier Division table virtually from start to finish losing only twice as they created a new UniBond League record of 104 points on the way to booking their Conference ticket. Nigel Clough's side also reached three figures in the "goals for" column, scoring seventeen more goals than any other team whilst the 30 goals conceded was 23 fewer than anyone else managed. Amazingly it was the Brewers' first Championship of any description and they will have been delighted at making their move from the Dr Martens League so successful and will now hope to emulate Boston United, who a few seasons earlier had made the reverse trip and are now in the Football League!

For half the campaign both Altrincham and Lancaster City threatened to keep pace with Burton's dominance but both fell away alarmingly in the New Year, leaving Vauxhall Motors to continue their meteoric rise up the Pyramid and emerge in second spot at the first attempt following their consecutive promotions from the NWCL in 2000 and the UniBond First Division in 2001. Finishing joint third with Lancaster were Worksop Town and the word is that the Tigers are looking for big things next term with financial backing coming from the wealthy Raymond family.

At the opposite end of the table Bamber Bridge hit cash problems and were marooned in the bottom two virtually throughout the campaign. It looked for much of the campaign as through they would be joined in the relegation spots by Hyde United and indeed they were, until fate intervened. Bishop Auckland had earlier announced they were to leave their Kingsway ground which had been their home for over a century and to ground share at Shildon. Bishop's application was agreed by the League with the proviso that the necessary ground improvements to bring their temporary home up to Premier Division standards were completed by 30th April. Unfortunately Bishop's missed the deadline and the League were left with no alternative but to demote the famous old club to the First Division which gave a reprieve to Hyde.

It was a very similar tale in the First Division where Harrogate Town were the dominant force taking the title a long way from home before dropping points once the heat was off. For much of the campaign they had been chased hard by Radcliffe Borough but just as Lancaster City and Altrincham in the top flight had faded, so did Borough who in the end almost missed the newly introduced "play-offs". Ossett Town invested in experienced players and finished runners-up but, like Bishop Auckland, failed to meet the deadline date for ground improvements and were thus not promoted. Their disappointment gave Bamber Bridge a lifeline as the Preston based club now went into the play-offs rather than face automatic relegation. The play-offs were without doubt a success story in keeping many clubs in both Divisions with meaningful fixtures until very late in the season and then producing two and three times the normal attendances for the play-off matches themselves.

The beneficiaries of the new system were Ashton United, although surely nobody could begrudge the Hurst Cross outfit their promotion by the back door after they had finished third for the sixth time in ten seasons! After they had overcome a rejuvenated Spennymoor United in the semi-final they won the play-off final at Bamber Bridge, who had disposed of Radcliffe Borough in the other semi-final.

At the bottom newcomers Ossett Albion enjoyed themselves but go straight back to the NCEL determined to bounce immediately up again whilst Kendal Town, who have struggled against the drop for several seasons finally succumbed and will play next term in the NWCL. Replacing the Lake District side are Kidsgrove Athletic and the League also welcomes old friends Alfreton Town who lost their UniBond status in 1999.

One of the most famous names in football, Accrington Stanley, took the League Challenge Cup in an epic encounter over two legs against another former Football League outfit, Bradford Park Avenue. Stanley used no fewer than three keepers (including two outfield players) in the first half of the first leg and despite playing with nine men for much of the game, held out until virtually stoppage time before conceding a goal. They pulled that deficit back on their own ground but couldn't force a winner leaving the final to be decided on penalties for the second successive season. Stanley proved to be the masters of the penalty shoot out as they then went on to beat Burton Albion in the same manner to lift the Peter Swales UniBond League Challenge Shield between the Champion Club and the Cup-Winners, as well as knocking Altrincham out of the FA Umbro Trophy in similar fashion.

After lifting the Chairman's Cup in 2001, Barrow went on to take this season's President's Cup with the only goal of the final against Gainsborough Trinity, coming as the match approached stoppage time. The Chairman's Cup this time was captured by Worksop Town who just held out against a ferocious late assault from Droylsden to win 2-1.

In the AXA Sponsored FA Cup UniBond clubs gave excellent accounts of themselves and although Worksop Town went down at Bournemouth, Barrow and Whitby Town held Oldham Athletic and Plymouth Argyle respectively to 1-1 draws before narrowly losing the replays by the odd goal. Altrincham reached the Second Round Proper and made Darlington work every inch of the way for a 2-1 victory. Both Altrincham and Whitby, however, had the satisfaction of receiving cheques for £40,000 each with their matches being amongst the games featured on BBC's "Match of the Day".

Burton Albion carried the UniBond flag proudly in the FA Umbro Trophy and put no fewer than three Conference clubs out of the competition. Farnborough Town, Woking and Chester City all fell as the Brewers marched into the semi-finals, only to go down at the final hurdle over two legs to Yeovil Town.

FINAL LEAGUE TABLES 2001-02
PREMIER DIVISION

		P	W	D	L	F	A	GD	Pts
1	Burton Albion	44	31	11	2	106	30	76	104
2	Vauxhall Motors	44	27	8	9	86	55	31	89
3	Lancaster City	44	23	9	12	80	57	23	78
4	Worksop Town	44	23	9	12	74	51	23	78
5	Emley	44	22	9	13	69	54	15	75
6	Accrington Stanley	44	21	9	14	89	64	25	72
7	Runcorn FC Halton	44	21	8	15	76	53	23	71
8	Barrow	44	19	10	15	75	59	16	67
9	Altrincham	44	19	9	16	66	58	8	66
10	Bradford Park Avenue	44	18	5	21	77	76	1	59
11	Droylsden	44	17	8	19	65	78	-13	59
12	Blyth Spartans	44	14	16	14	59	62	-3	58
13	Frickley Athletic	44	16	11	17	63	69	-6	58
14	Gateshead	44	14	14	16	58	71	-13	56
15	Whitby Town	44	15	8	21	61	76	-15	53
16	Hucknall Town	44	14	9	21	49	68	-19	51
17	Marine	44	11	17	16	62	71	-9	50
18	Burscough	44	15	5	24	69	86	-17	50
19	Gainsborough Trinity	44	13	10	21	61	76	-15	49
20	Colwyn Bay	44	12	11	21	49	82	-33	47
21	Bishop Auckland	44	12	8	24	46	68	-22	44
22	Hyde United	44	10	10	24	61	87	-26	40
23	Bamber Bridge	44	7	10	27	38	88	-50	30

PLAY-OFFS

SEMI-FINALS

Bamber Bridge v Radcliffe Borough 3-2   Ashton United v Spennymoor United 3-1

FINAL

Bamber Bridge v Ashton United 1-2

LEADING GOALSCORERS

in order of League goals

		Lge	Cup	Tot.			Lge	Cup	Tot.
					Rod Thornley	Altrincham	17	16	33
Terry Fearns	Vauxhall Motors	27	9	36	Darren Day	Emley	17	6	23
Andy Whittaker	Lancaster City	26	6	32	Jason Maxwell	Bradford Park Ave	16	8	24
Paul Mullin	Accrington Stanley	22	12	34	Steve Preen	Gateshead	16	7	23
Lutel James	Accrington Stanley	21	2	23	Paul McNally	Runcorn FC Halton	16	5	21
Andy Hayward	Bradford Park Ave	20	11	31	Steve Housham	Barrow	16	4	20
Glen Robson	Blyth Spartans	20	7	27	Richie Townsend	Marine	16	2	18

AVERAGE ATTENDANCES

	00/01	01/02		00/01	01/02		00/01	01/02
Accrington Stanley	613	529	Burton Albion	-	1430	Hyde United	427	341
Altrincham	597	638	Colwyn Bay	287	295	Lancaster City	334	384
Bamber Bridge	272	255	Droylsden	311	217	Marine	277	271
Barrow	1065	1116	Emley	536	297	Runcorn FC Halton	287	297
Bishop Auckland	206	223	Frickley Athletic	190	222	Vauxhall Motors	144	260
Blyth Spartans	328	432	Gainsborough Trinity	393	393	Whitby Town	322	309
Bradford Park Avenue	262	316	Gateshead	213	196	Worksop Town	495	438
Burscough	230	232	Hucknall Town	246	288			

MONTHLY SPONSORSHIP AWARDS

	CLUB OF MONTH	FAIR PLAY			
Aug	Lancaster City	Vauxhall Motors	Dec	Accrington Stanley	Burton Albion
Sep	Altrincham	Burton Albion	Jan	Bradford P.A.	Worksop Town
Oct	Altrincham	Whitby Town	Feb	Burton Albion	Gainsborough Tr.
Nov	Accrington Stanley	Gateshead	Mar	Burton Albion	Colwyn Bay
			Apr/May	Bradford P.A.	Burton Albion

PREMIER DIVISION RESULTS & ATTENDANCES CHART 2001-02

Each cell shows the home result and the attendance. Rows are home teams; columns are away teams. Blank cells are the diagonal (team vs itself).

Team	Wor	Whi	Vau	Run	Mar	Lan	Hyd	Huc	Gat	Gai	Fri	Eml	Dro	Col	B A	Bur	Bra	Bly	Bis	Bar	Bam	Alt	Acc
Accrington S	5-0 505	2-3 502	2-3 505	1-1 481	3-1 488	3-2 349	2-0 470	1-2 582	2-1 330	1-1 384	1-1 403	0-1 511	5-2 285	3-0 316	3-3 1251	3-0 415	5-1 674	0-0 479	1-1 518	0-3 671	2-0 603	0-0 919	
Altrincham	2-0 709	0-1 646	0-1 472	0-2 469	0-1 768	2-3 438	2-0 639	2-0 498	3-1 659	1-1 567	0-2 632	1-2 452	3-3 217	4-0 680	0-1 1018	0-3 557	0-1 644	2-1 714	1-1 745	2-1 770	4-3 537		3-1 625
Bamber B	0-0 170	3-0 195	1-3 183	1-6 242	0-1 226	1-1 311	1-3 216	1-4 273	1-4 173	1-0 238	0-2 218	2-1 240	0-0 796	1-2 135	0-1 519	2-3 274	2-1 320	0-1 174	1-2 188	1-0 409		1-1 211	0-1 484
Barrow	1-0 829	2-0 1133	1-2 861	2-1 1247	0-0 695	1-1 2032	1-3 1053	6-1 1411	4-1 1113	3-0 1198	3-1 1100	1-3 936	3-3 721	1-1 964	1-2 1310	2-1 1280	2-3 1351	4-1 569	3-1 1199		1-1 1445	2-2 1212	0-4 891
Bishop Auck.	1-2 185	1-0 283	3-4 180	1-3 191	0-0 186	1-1 238	0-2 206	0-2 176	1-2 307	0-1 207	1-1 188	1-0 192	6-2 165	1-2 172	1-1 371	2-1 152	0-4 452	1-1 256		1-2 276	2-1 159	2-1 180	1-2 179
Blyth Sprtns	2-2 411	2-1 286	0-1 356	2-2 322	0-0 312	1-0 444	2-0 461	1-2 278	2-1 810	2-2 488	0-0 345	1-3 519	0-0 326	2-0 324	0-1 593	2-1 381	4-1 404		1-1 256	1-1 466	3-1 445	0-3 479	1-1 398
Bradford P.A.	1-5 438	1-1 361	1-3 274	3-1 304	1-3 308	1-1 285	3-1 216	0-1 213	3-5 185	2-0 220	3-0 325	1-1 391	1-3 253	5-0 265	1-4 648	0-2 260		2-2 337	2-2 221	3-2 244	5-2 298	4-1 306	1-2 420
Burscough	2-3 228	3-1 205	2-3 184	1-3 22	1-1 182	0-6 263	0-2 276	1-3 156	2-2 195	3-1 175	1-0 205	2-1 223	2-0 186	4-0 191	0-0 531		0-2 213	1-2 185	0-2 654	4-0 1001	5-0 185	0-2 322	3-2 327
Burton Alb	1-0 1328	5-1 1434	2-1 1172	1-1 1175	0-0 1580	1-1 1512	5-1 1102	2-0 1108	5-1 1502	4-2 1204	4-0 1018	2-1 1533	6-2 2170	0-0 1591		4-0 1361	3-0 2141	4-0 1674	3-0 1433	0-5 nk	1-1 1366	3-1 1712	3-1 1347
Colwyn Bay	0-3 295	1-1 229	1-0 266	0-1 249	0-0 295	1-2 295	4-4 209	1-1 288	1-2 227	2-1 224	1-5 262	1-0 205	1-0 385		1-3 733	2-1 187	1-2 309	1-1 265	1-2 262	2-0 372	0-0 260	2-5 457	3-0 290
Droylsden	0-2 216	2-3 177	3-2 167	0-1 119	0-2 238	2-0 201	2-0 484	3-0 121	0-1 245	1-2 141	1-0 177	3-2 175		3-2 202	0-7 336	3-1 120	1-0 386	0-0 201	1-0 82	2-1 362	0-0 204	2-0 402	1-5 259
Emley	1-1 465	0-2 216	1-1 231	1-1 227	2-4 247	1-4 193	2-2 272	3-0 192	2-2 172	2-1 321	2-1 474		1-0 254	2-0 241	3-2 703	3-0 171	0-0 447	2-1 124	0-1 257	2-3 258	5-0 243	3-1 388	0-3 311
Frickley Ath	4-0 319	1-4 243	1-0 160	2-4 158	3-3 173	3-2 255	2-2 169	0-1 152	0-0 149	3-1 256		1-1 302	3-0 149	2-1 131	0-5 513	3-0 125	4-1 398	1-5 168	2-1 157	0-1 475	3-1 234	3-1 296	1-3 194
Gainsboro T	0-2 876	2-0 315	2-1 310	1-4 385	3-0 273	1-2 195	4-1 265	0-1 309	1-1 310		2-2 266	1-2 278	3-1 311	2-1 288	1-1 977	1-1 305	0-7 130	1-1 334	1-1 290	0-0 125	1-0 175	1-3 450	5-2 475
Gateshead	0-3 156	2-0 202	0-2 135	0-2 141	2-4 205	1-1 327	3-1 249	1-1 123		1-0 148	0-0 259	2-0 235	2-0 145	3-3 201	1-2 402	0-2 128	1-0 186	1-1 426	3-0 138	2-1 278	3-2 234	0-2 172	0-0 206
Hucknall Tn	0-1 266	0-1 195	1-0 202	1-2 235	2-2 212	1-1 251	4-2 365		0-0 267	1-4 283	3-4 212	0-4 162	0-3 126	1-2 186	1-2 1602	1-2 155	2-0 389	1-1 191	2-3 175	1-2 241	1-0 291	1-1 425	1-3 191
Hyde United	3-3 425	1-1 316	0-2 218	0-1 527	2-2 341	4-4 291		0-2 261	1-3 301	1-1 308	0-0 307	2-3 333	0-3 432	1-2 267	1-2 523	3-2 322	4-0 437	3-1 266	1-3 344	3-3 1028	2-0 152	3-2 437	2-4 416
Lancaster C	2-1 391	3-1 353	0-2 239	1-1 423	3-0 330		2-1 269	1-0 257	1-3 279	5-2 379	0-2 260	0-1 245	2-2 320	2-1 357	0-0 908	0-3 280	1-2 274	4-2 315	1-0 245	3-2 323	1-0 173	1-0 477	1-0 349
Marine	1-1 352	0-3 210	1-1 283	0-0 232		0-2 391	3-1 202	2-0 223	1-1 217	4-0 208	4-0 236	2-0 223	2-0 218	1-1 214	1-1 459	1-2 251	0-2 269	0-2 283	3-1 202	1-3 275	1-0 214	1-0 334	2-5 306
Runcorn	0-1 340	0-2 184	1-2 214		4-1 348	1-4 219	2-1 281	2-1 271	4-1 202	4-0 151	3-1 241	2-0 468	2-0 380	1-2 211	1-3 630	4-0 268	1-0 206	1-2 275	3-0 170	2-0 250	0-1 268	0-1 301	1-0 361
Vauxhall M	3-2 347	4-1 237		3-2 207	4-1 310	0-2 199	1-2 324	2-1 201	2-3 402	0-4 245	3-1 275	1-1 274	1-0 174	1-0 357	1-4 818	3-2 202	1-1 358	2-2 276	2-0 254	2-4 336	1-0 291	2-1 252	1-0 220
Whitby Town	0-2 305		1-2 271	2-2 295	1-2 295	0-1 499	3-2 85	1-0 384	2-3 218	4-0 453	4-1 288	4-1 288	3-0 326	1-0 239	1-1 582	1-3 309	3-2 361	2-2 228	2-0 254	0-1 454	2-0 352	2-3 371	2-1 309
Worksop Tn		2-0 317	3-3 414	1-1 417	1-1 353	1-1 251	2-1 353	1-0 403	2-1 507	4-0 453	1-1 370	1-1 475	0-1 347	1-0 349	0-1 1367	3-1 412	1-1 358	3-0 331	2-1 367	0-1 454	2-0 352	2-0 421	5-0 421

UNIBOND LEAGUE CUP TABLES 2001-02

GROUP ONE	P	W	D	L	F	A	Pts
Blyth Spartans4	3	0	1	10	6	9	
Gateshead	4	2	0	2	8	7	6
Spennymoor Utd	4	1	2	1	9	7	5
Bishop Auckland	4	1	2	1	5	7	5
Gretna	4	0	2	2	6	11	2

GROUP TWO	P	W	D	L	F	A	Pts
Kendal Town	4	4	0	0	14	7	12
Barrow	4	2	0	2	9	10	6
Bamber Bridge	4	2	0	2	5	6	6
Lancaster City	4	1	0	3	10	11	3
Workington	4	1	0	3	4	8	3

GROUP THREE	P	W	D	L	F	A	Pts
Bradford Park Ave	4	4	0	0	11	1	12
Guiseley	4	3	0	1	7	3	9
Harrogate Town	4	1	1	2	5	6	4
Farsley Celtic	4	1	0	3	2	7	3
Whitby Town	4	0	1	3	2	10	1

GROUP FOUR	P	W	D	L	F	A	Pts
Accrington Stanley	5	4	0	1	11	7	12
Burscough	5	3	0	2	9	4	9
Chorley	5	2	1	2	8	9	7
Rossendale Utd	5	2	0	3	6	8	6
Marine	5	1	2	2	6	8	5
Radcliffe Borough	5	1	1	3	6	10	4

GROUP FIVE	P	W	D	L	F	A	Pts
Trafford	5	4	0	1	7	3	12
Altrincham	5	3	0	2	6	5	9
Vauxhall Motors	5	2	2	1	9	8	8
Witton Albion	5	2	1	2	7	5	7
Runcorn FC Hal.	5	0	3	2	7	11	3
Colwyn Bay	5	0	2	3	6	10	2

GROUP SIX	P	W	D	L	F	A	Pts
Emley	5	4	0	1	11	7	12
Ashton United	5	3	1	1	22	13	10
Droylsden	5	3	1	1	16	9	10
Ossett Town	5	2	1	2	8	10	7
Hyde United	5	1	1	3	9	13	4
Ossett Albion	5	0	0	4	4	18	0

GROUP SEVEN	P	W	D	L	F	A	Pts
Matlock Town	5	2	2	1	7	7	8
Leek Town	5	1	4	0	8	6	7
Hucknall Town	5	2	1	2	8	8	7
Belper Town	5	2	1	2	7	6	7
Eastwood Town	5	1	2	2	7	8	5
Burton Albion	5	1	2	2	5	7	5

GROUP EIGHT	P	W	D	L	F	A	Pts
North Ferriby Utd	5	3	1	1	7	7	10
Gainsborough Tr.	5	3	0	2	9	7	9
Worksop Town	5	2	1	2	8	6	7
Frickley Athletic	5	2	0	3	11	11	6
Stocksbridge PS	5	1	3	1	5	6	6
Lincoln United	5	1	1	3	8	11	4

Group winners qualify for League Challenge Cup, Runners-up for President's Cup and third place for Chairman's Cup

LEAGUE CHALLENGE CUP

QUARTER FINALS

Accrington Stanley	1*0	Emley
Bradford Park Avenue	7-1	Blyth Spartans
Kendal Town	2-3	Trafford
Matlock Town	2*1	North Ferriby United

SEMI-FINALS

Accrington Stanley	2-1	Trafford
Matlock Town	1-2	Bradford Park Avenue

FINAL (Two Legs)

Bradford Park Avenue	1-0	Accrington Stanley
Accrington Stanley	5p1*0p4	Bradford Park Avenue

PRESIDENT'S CUP

QUARTER FINALS

Altrincham	1-2	Gainsborough Trinity
Barrow	2-1	Gateshead
Burscough	1-3	Ashton United
Leek Town	0-1	Guiseley

SEMI-FINALS

Ashton United	4*5	Barrow
Gainsborough Trinity	5-1	Guiseley

FINAL

Barrow	1-0	Gainsborough Trinity

at Hyde United FC

CHAIRMAN'S CUP

QUARTER FINALS

Droylsden	3p3*3p2	Chorley
Harrogate Town	2-0	Bamber Bridge
Spennymoor United	4*2	Hucknall Town
Vauxhall Motors	0-3	Worksop Town

SEMI-FINALS

Harrogate Town	0*1	Droylsden
Spennymoor United	0-1	Worksop Town

FINAL

Droylsden	1-2	Worksop Town

at Droylsden FC

FAIRPLAY AWARD 2001-02

PREMIER DIVISION

	Cautions	Dismissals	Total
Accrington Stanley	84	6	102
Altrincham	60	6	78
Bamber Bridge	59	10	89
Barrow	82	4	94
Bishop Auckland	71	1	74
Blyth Spartans	78	7	99
Bradford Park Avenue	71	7	92
Burscough	70	11	103
Burton Albion	22	2	28
Colwyn Bay	71	4	83
Droylsden	60	7	81
Emley	70	5	85
Frickley Athletic	66	5	81
Gainsborough Trinity	49	6	67
Gateshead	49	7	70
Hucknall Town	58	4	70
Hyde United	82	7	103
Lancaster City	52	6	70
Marine	59	3	68
Runcorn	66	1	69
Vauxhall Motors	43	2	49
Whitby Town	59	3	68
Worksop Town	48	3	57
Total	1429	117	

FIRST DIVISION

	Cautions	Dismissals	Total
Ashton United	59	6	77
Belper Town	48	0	48
Chorley	52	6	70
Eastwood Town	71	9	98
Farsley Celtic	48	5	63
Gretna	40	2	46
Guiseley	61	3	70
Harrogate Town	40	3	49
Kendal Town	57	5	72
Leek Town	45	2	51
Lincoln United	62	4	74
Matlock Town	59	8	83
North Ferriby United	56	3	65
Ossett Albion	65	9	92
Ossett Town	71	2	77
Radcliffe Borough	62	5	77
Rossendale United	49	3	58
Spennymoor United	52	3	61
Stocksbridge Park Steels	43	1	46
Trafford	70	4	82
Witton Albion	66	2	72
Workington	43	4	55
Total	1219	89	

Caution: 1 point   Dismissal: 3 points

ACCRINGTON STANLEY

CLUB OFFICIALS

Chairman: **Eric Whalley**
President: **J C Prescott/J Hudson**
Secretary: **Philip Terry**
8 Princess Street, Colne, Lancs BB8 9AN.
Tel: 01286 866768 (H), 01282 864000 (B).
Commercial Director: **John de Maine**

FOOTBALL MANAGEMENT TEAM

Manager: John Coleman
Asst Manager: Jimmy Bell
Osteopath: Martin Dixon D.O.
Physio: Paul Jones

FACT FILE

Formed: 1968
Nickname: Reds
Sponsors: Red Rose Assurance
Colours: Red/red/red
Change colours: All White
Midweek home matchday: Tuesday
Youth Lge: Lancs Youth Floodlit League.
Reserves: Lancashire League

2001-2002
Player of the Year: Paul Mullin
Captain: Peter Cavanagh
Top Scorer: Paul Mullin
YoungP.o.Y.: Peter Cavanagh
Reserve P.o.Y.: Danny Thorpe

GROUND Crown Ground, off Livingstone Road, Accrington.Tel: 01254383235.
Club Website: www.accrington stanley.co.uk **EMail Address:** info@accringtonstanley.co.uk
Directions: Arriving on A680 from Clayton-le-Moors Livingstone Rd is on left 50 yds past
Crown Hotel. From M62/M66, through town centre on A680 -Livingstone Rd 500 yds on right
after Victoria Hospital. 1 1/2 miles from Accrington(BR).
Capacity: 5,000   Cover: 2,000   Seats: 1,200
Clubhouse: Open five nights and matchdays. Private functions. Well stocked tea-bar in ground.
Club Shop: Sells replica kits, sweaters,etc Contact: Liz Rackstraw (01254 397869)

Programme - Pages: 44 Price: £1.20
Editor: P Terry. (01282 866768)
Local Press: Accrington Observer, Lancashire
Evening Telegraph. Local Radio: Radio
Lancashire, Red Rose Radio.

PREVIOUS   **Leagues:** Lancs Combination 70-78; Cheshire County 78-82; North West Counties 82-87. **Names:** None **Grounds:**, None
                     CLUB RECORDS   Attendance: 2,465 v Farsley Celtic 06.05.01 Unibond Division One.
                     (10,081 v Crewe Alexandra, F.A. Cup Second Round Proper 5/12/92 - played at Ewood Park,Blackburn).
                     Career Goalscorer: David Hargreaves 328. **Career Appearances:** Chris Grimshaw 362.
                     Win: 10-0 v Lincoln United 99-00, 9-0 v Ashton Town 75-76
                     Fee Paid : £15,000 Paul Mullin from Radcliffe Borough 00-01**Fee Received :** £60,000 for Gary Williams from Doncaster R
BEST SEASON   **FA Trophy:** 2ndt Rd 99-00 **F.A.Cup:** 2nd Rd 92-93 1-6 v Crewe Alexandra (H) League clubs defeated: None.
HONOURS   Unibond Challenge Cup 01-02, Unibond Challenge Shield 01-02,N West Counties Lg R-up 86-87; Cheshire County Lg Div
2 80-81 (R-up 79-80);Lancs Comb 73-74 77-78 (R-up 71-72 75-76), Lg Cup 71-72 72-73 73-74 76-77;George Watson Trophy 71-72 73-74 ; John
Duckworth Trophy 85-86; Lancs Junior Cup (now MarsdenTrophy) 01-02, R-up 83-84 96-97; Lancs U18 Cup 89-90;N.W.All Div Cup 94-95; Anglo-
Barbados Cup 95. , IVW Alliance Cuo Finalists 95-96, Lancs Floodlit Youth League 2001-02.

Players Progressing: David Hargreaves (Blackburn R. 77), Ian Blackstone (York C.), Gus Wilson (Crewe), Glen Johnstone (Preston),
DarrenLyons (Bury), Martin Clark (Crewe 92-93), Mark Wright (Wigan 93-94), Paul Collings (Bury 93-94),   Brett Ormerod (Blackpool 96-97),
Harvey Cunningham (Doncaster R.).Gareth Seddon (Bury)

Back row left to right: Paul Mullin,Dave Robinson, Andy Procter, Jonathon Smith, Jamie Speare, Jimmy Bell (Assistant Manager),
Steve Halford, Robbie Williams, Barry Hart and Daniel Thorpe.
Front row: Simon Carden, John Colemen (Manager), Paul Burns, Lee Buggie, Steve Flitcroft and Lutel James.

NORTHERN PREMIER LEAGUE PREMIER DIVISION

Date	Comp.	Opponents	Att.	Score	Goalscorers
18.08	Unib. P	Gainsborough Trinity	475	2 - 5	G Williams 55, Flitcroft 82
22.08	Unib. P	BARROW	671	0 - 3	
25.08	Unib. P	BURSCOUGH	415	3 - 0	G Williams 48, James 85 88
27.08	Unib. P	Marine	306	5 - 2	Williams 20, Mullin 45, James 48 54 90
01.09	Unib. P	VAUXHALL MOTORS	505	2 - 3	Mullin 88 89
04.09	Unib. P	Colwyn Bay	290	0 - 3	
12.09	Unib. P	DROYLSDEN	285	5 - 2	Smith 2, James 44 78, Cavanagh 49, Mullin 51
15.09	Unib. P	Frickley Athletic	194	3 - 1	Flitcroft 1, Mullin 87 90
17.09	Unib. P	Emley	311	3 - 0	James 17 52, Carden 78
22.09	Unib. P	WHITBY TOWN	502	2 - 3	Carden 63, Smith 77
26.09	Lge Cup G4	CHORLEY	215	2 - 3	Robinson 1, Mullin 51
29.09	FA Cup Q2	Pickering Town	224	2 - 1	Mullen 25 50
03.10	Unib. P	WORKSOP TOWN	505	5 - 0	Smith 3, Mullin 17 58, James 66, Flitcroft 74
07.10	Unib. P	ALTRINCHAM	919	0 - 0	
09.10	Lge Cup G4	Marine	145	2 - 1	Mullin 70 85
13.10	FA Cup Q3	Emley	433	0 - 1	
17.10	Unib. P	COLWYN BAY	316	3 - 0	Flitcroft 55, Carden 58, Brennan 85
20.10	Unib. P	Burton Albion	1347	1 - 3	James 65
24.10	Lge Cup G4	BURSCOUGH	247	2 - 1	Mullin 24, Smith 27
27.10	Unib. P	BISHOP AUCKLAND	518	1 - 1	James 45
30.10	Unib. P	Altrincham	625	1 - 3	Bowden 56
03.11	FA Trophy 1	Radcliffe Borough	400	0 - 0	
07.11	FA Trophy 1 R	RADCLIFFE BOROUGH	349	2 - 0	Carden 27 70
10.11	Unib. P	Vauxhall Motors	220	2 - 1	Mullin 28 59
13.11	Lancs MT 1	Castleton Gabriels	52	7 - 0	Shirley, Carden, Howarth, Mullen, Bell 3
17.11	Unib. P	BLYTH SPARTANS	479	0 - 0	
24.11	Unib. P	Droylsden	259	5 - 1	Carden 12 43 65 85, James 13
27.11	Lge Cup G4	Rossendale United	344	2 - 1	Carden 11, Mullin 70
01.12	FA Trophy 2	ALTRINCHAM	592	1 - 1	Maddox 73[og]
04.12	FA Trophy 2 R	Altrincham	417	1 - 1	James 78 1 3
08.12	Unib. P	BRADFORD PARK AVENUE	674	5 - 1	James 5[p], Mullin 25 72, Carden 43, Flitcroft 76
12.12	Lge Cup G4	RADCLIFFE BOROUGH	149	3 - 1	Mullin 58, Carden 66 70
15.12	Unib. P	Hucknall Town	191	3 - 1	Carden 18 60, Cavanagh 45
22.12	Unib. P	BURTON ALBION	1251	3 - 3	Mullin 26, Cavanagh 32[p], Smith 75
26.12	Unib. P	Bamber Bridge	484	1 - 0	Carden 57
09.01	Lancs MT 2	ATHERTON COLLIERIES	159	4 - 1	Carden 19, Smith 25, James 70, G Williams 87
12.01	Unib. P	Burscough	327	2 - 3	Carden 60, James 76
18.01	Unib. P	Hyde United	416	4 - 2	Mullin 66 86, Williams 71, James 75
26.01	Lge Cup QF	EMLEY	596	1 - 0	Payne 108
30.01	Lancs MT QF	LEIGH RMI	285	2 - 1	Mullin 32 48
02.02	Unib. P	HUCKNALL TOWN	582	1 - 2	Halford 43
09.02	Unib. P	Blyth Spartans	398	1 - 1	Flitcroft 61
16.02	Unib. P	Runcorn Halton	361	0 - 1	
19.02	Lancs MT SF	Burscough	178	1 - 0	G Williams 90
23.02	Unib. P	FRICKLEY ATHLETIC	403	1 - 1	Carden 2
02.03	Unib. P	Gateshead	206	0 - 0	
05.03	Unib. P	Lancaster City	349	0 - 1	
09.03	Lge Cup SF	TRAFFORD	546	2 - 1	Halford 32, Brennan 53
12.03	Unib. P	GATESHEAD	330	2 - 1	Mullin 54, James 90
16.03	Unib. P	Bradford Park Avenue	420	2 - 1	Flitcroft 18, Proctor 33
20.03	Unib. P	LANCASTER CITY	349	3 - 2	Halford 44, Carden 75, Burns 90
23.03	Unib. P	Bishop Auckland	179	2 - 1	Cavanagh 23, James 58[p]
27.03	Unib. P	GAINSBOROUGH TRINITY	384	1 - 1	Hurst 46
30.03	Unib. P	Barrow	891	4 - 0	Cavanagh 54, Mullin 73, James 89 90
01.04	Unib. P	BAMBER BRIDGE	603	2 - 0	Mullin 35 85
06.04	Unib. P	HYDE UNITED	470	4 - 1	Mullin 12 87, Procter 42, Williams 83
10.04	Lge Cup F(1)	Bradford Park Avenue	471	0 - 1	
13.04	Unib. P	EMLEY	511	0 - 1	
15.04	Unib. P	Worksop Town	371	0 - 5	
20.04	Unib. P	RUNCORN HALTON	481	1 - 1	Buggie 81
24.04	Lancs MT F	BARROW	1330	2 - 0	Mullin 23, Carden 63 — Morecambe
27.04	Unib. P	Whitby Town	309	1 - 2	James 88
30.04	Lge Cup F(2)	BRADFORD PARK AVENUE	1107	1 - 0	Mullin 64 5 4
03.05	Unib. P	MARINE	488	3 - 1	G Williams 38, Smith 67, Mullin 90

PLAYING SQUAD

Goalkeepers: James Speare (Sligo), Bobby Harris (Padiham), Danny Thorpe (Daisy Hill)

Defenders: Barry Shuttleworth (Macclesfield), Jay Flannery (Lancaster), Jonathon Smith (Gt. Harwood), Peter Cavanagh (Liverpool), Robbie Williams (St Dominics), Steve Caswell (Droylsden), Steve Halford (Chester), Steve Hollis (Ashton Utd), Paul Burns (Morecambe)

Midfield: Steve Flitcroft (Blackburn), Andy Proctor (Gt. Harwood), Dave Robinson (Runcorn), Dean Calcutt (Bradford PA), John Doolan (Ashton Utd), Mark Brennan (St Helens), Mike Marsh (Boston Utd), Simon Carden (Radcliffe B)

Forwards: David Gray (Rossendale), Lutel James (Bury), Lee Buggie (Bury), Mark Ceraolo (Ashton Utd), Paul Mullin (Radcliffe B), Russell Payne (Ashton Utd)

ALTRINCHAM

CLUB OFFICIALS		FACT FILE	
Chairman:	Geoffrey Goodwin	Formed:	1903
President:	Noel White	Nickname:	The Robins
Directors:	Graham Rowley, Andrew Shaw		
	and Geoff Goodwin	Sponsor:	Hillcrest Homes
Secretary:	Graham Heathcote	Colours:	Red & white striped/black/white
Press Officer:	John Pollit	Change colours:	Yellow/green/green
Match Secretary:	George Heslop	Midweek matchday:	Tuesday

FOOTBALL MANAGEMENT TEAM

Reserves' League: Lancashire League

Manager: Bernard Taylor
Coach: Andy May
Physiotherapist: Gary Thompson

Youth League: North West Youth Alliance
Local Press: Sale & Altrincham Messenger;
Sale & Altrincham Express;
Manchester Evening News

GROUND: Moss Lane, Altrincham, Cheshire WA15 8AP
Tel: 0161 928 1045 Fax: 0161 926 9934

Directions: M6 junction 19; A556/M56 (Manchester Airport) to junction 7; signs Hale and Altrincham; through 1st traffic lights then 3rd right into Westminster Road and continue into Moss Lane. Ground on right.

CAPACITY: 6,085 **COVER:** Yes **SEATS:** 1,154
Clubhouse: Bar under the stand open on match days only. Two snack bars on ground for pies, crisps, soft drinks etc **Club Shop:** Yes

Programme - Pages: 36 Price: £1.20
Editor: Graham Rowley, Tel: 0161 928 1045

Local Radio: GMR (BBC); Signal Radio;
Piccadilly Radio

PREVIOUS **Leagues:** Manchester 03-11, Lancashire Comb. 11-19, Cheshire County 19-68, Northern Premier 68-79, 97-99; Conference 79-97 99-00 **Grounds:** Pollitts Field -1903-1910 **Names:** None

RECORDS **Attendance:**10,275 Altrincham Boys v Sunderland Boys,English Schools Shield 3rd Round 28.02.25
Goalscorer: Jack Swindells 252 - 1965-71 **Appearances:** JohnDavison 677 - 1971-86
Win: 9-2 v Merthyr Tydfil,Vauxhall Conference, Feb 1991 **Defeat:** Unknown
Fee Paid: £15,000 to Blackpool for Keith Russell
Fee Received: From Scarborough for Paul Ellender 2000

BEST SEASON **FA Trophy:** Winners 77-78, 85-86 **League:** Conference Champions 1979-80, 80-81
FA Cup: 85-86 4th Round, 0-2 v York City (A) League clubs defeated:15

HONOURS FA Trophy 77-78, 85- 86; Alliance Premier League 79-80, 80-81; Bob Lord Trophy 80-81;
Northern Prem. Lge: Champions 98-99; Lge.Cup 69-70 97-98; N.P.L. Shield 79-80;
Cheshire County League: Champions 65-66, 66-67; Lge Cup 50-51, 52-53, 63-64; Cheshire Senior Cup 04-05, 33-34, 66-67,81-82; Manchester League 04-05; Cheshire Amateur Cup 03-04.

Players Progressing: Several, most recent being G Barrow (Wigan Ath. 81), J Rogers(Wigan Ath., 82), P Conning (Rochdale, 86), E Bishop (Tranmere R. 88), P Edwards (Crewe, 88), A Kilner (Stockport C. 90), P Showler (Barnet, 91), S Johnson & A Reid (Bury 92), C Freeman (Doncaster R. 93), T Carke (Shrewsbury T. 93),Nicky Daws (Bury), Kevin Ellison (Leicester City), Danny Adams (Macclesfield Town)

Back row left to right: Mark Maddox, Mark Sertori, Ian Craney, Stuart Coburn, Paul Taylor, Terry Bowker, and Gary Scott. **Middle row:**Gary Thompson(physio) , Keith Mairs (snr), Kevin Hulme, Jason Gallagher, Danny Murphy, Carl Furlong, Chris Adama, Graham Heathcote Coach),and Graham Wright (Reserves Manager).**Front row:** Dave Swannick, Keith Mairs, Steve Hawes (Captain), Bernard Taylor (Manager), Mark Harris (Chairman), Rod Thornley, Lee Poland and Jeremy Illingworth.

Match Facts 2001-02

Date	Comp.	Opponents	Att.	Score	Goalscorers
18.08	Unib. P	WHITBY TOWN	646	1 - 0	Furlong 53
21.08	Unib. P	Worksop Town	421	2 - 1	Hulme 26, Craney 72
25.08	Unib. P	Colwyn Bay	457	5 - 2	Hayes 9, Thornley 26 36 90, Craney 44
27.08	Unib. P	BURTON ALBION	1018	0 - 2	
01.09	Unib. P	Lancaster City	477	1 - 1	Hulme 79
04.09	Unib. P	HUCKNALL TOWN	498	2 - 0	Furlong 70, Craney 90
08.09	Unib. P	BRADFORD PARK AVENUE	644	1 - 0	Thornley 68
10.09	Unib. P	Emley	388	1 - 2	Thornley 18[p]
15.09	Unib. P	Burscough	322	2 - 0	Hulme 52, Thornley 62[p]
18.09	Ches. SC 1	NORTHWICH VICTORIA	283	3 - 2	Poland 39, Thornley 58[p], Murphy 69
22.09	Unib. P	GATESHEAD	659	3 - 1	Murphy 11, Gallagher 66, Thornley 90
26.09	Lge Cup G5	Runcorn Halton	235	2 - 0	Illingworth 64, Furlong 89
29.09	FA Cup Q2	FRICKLEY ATHLETIC	537	4 - 1	Hulme 30, Thornley 54 65 85
02.10	Unib. P	BARROW	770	2 - 1	Hulme 52, Furlong 66
07.10	Unib. P	Accrington Stanley	919	0 - 0	
09.10	Lge Cup G5	TRAFFORD	235	0 - 1	
13.10	FA Cup Q3	WITTON ALBION	841	4 - 1	Murphy 20, Thornley 35[p], Hawes 66, Poland 85
20.10	Unib. P	BLYTH SPARTANS	714	2 - 1	Hulme 13, Thornley 45[p]
23.10	Lge Cup G5	Witton Albion	234	0 - 3	
27.10	FA Cup Q4	NUNEATON BOROUGH	1306	3 - 0	Thornley 45[p] 65, Hulme 63
30.10	Unib. P	ACCRINGTON STANLEY	625	3 - 1	Scott 26, Thornley 37 47
03.11	FA Trophy 1	Spalding United	307	0 - 0	
06.11	FA Trophy 1 R	SPALDING UNITED	458	3 - 2	Thornley 10 79, Sertori 34
13.11	Ches. SC QF	Woodley Sports	128	8 - 1	Poland 4, Hargreaves, Finney 2, Craney
17.11	FA Cup 1	LANCASTER CITY	2076	1 - 1	Thornley 6[p]
24.11	Unib. P	Frickley Athletic	296	1 - 3	Hulme 83
27.11	FA Cup 1 R	Lancaster City	1934	4 - 1	Poland 41 106 120[p], Thornley 119[p]
01.12	FA Trophy 2	Accrington Stanley	592	1 - 1	Craney 24
04.12	FA Trophy 2 R	ACCRINGTON STANLEY	417	1 - 1	Hargreaves 67 3 1
08.12	FA Cup 2	DARLINGTON	3302	1 - 2	Maddox 69
11.12	Lge Cup G5	VAUXHALL MOTORS	114	2 - 0	Thornley 48, Murphy 63
15.12	Unib. P	Burton Albion	1712	1 - 1	Carney 60
18.12	Lge Cup G5	COLWYN BAY	176	2 - 1	Thornley 14, Craney 9
22.12	Unib. P	DROYLSDEN	796	2 - 2	Hulme 2 77
12.01	FA Trophy 3	North Ferriby United	377	2 - 3	Poland 48 77
15.01	Ches. SC SF	MACCLESFIELD TOWN	496	2 - 0	Poland 26, Thornley 35
19.01	Unib. P	Whitby Town	371	3 - 2	Taylor 3, Carney 17, Hulme 89
22.01	Unib. P	Runcorn Halton	301	1 - 0	Hulme 13
29.01	Unib. P	Marine	334	0 - 1	
02.02	Unib. P	COLWYN BAY	680	4 - 0	Craney 5, Furlong 28, Thornley 39[p], Schueuber 71
05.02	Pres. Cup QF	GAINSBOROUGH TRINITY	239	1 - 2	Haws 52
09.02	Unib. P	Barrow	1212	2 - 2	Thornley 7, Craney 75
12.02	Unib. P	BAMBER BRIDGE	537	4 - 3	Poland 23 65[p], Ryan 29, Lin 36[og]
16.02	Unib. P	MARINE	768	1 - 0	Thornley 21
23.02	Unib. P	Blyth Spartans	479	3 - 0	Thornley 17, Murphy 59, Poland 89
02.03	Unib. P	BISHOP AUCKLAND	745	1 - 1	Thornley 45
05.03	Unib. P	Droylsden	402	0 - 2	
09.03	Unib. P	FRICKLEY ATHLETIC	632	0 - 2	
13.03	Unib. P	Bishop Auckland	180	1 - 2	Furlong 61
16.03	Unib. P	GAINSBOROUGH TRINITY	567	1 - 1	Furlong 27
19.03	Ches. SC F	CREWE ALEXANDRA	625	0 - 3	Northwich Victoria
23.03	Unib. P	Hucknall Town	425	0 - 0	
26.03	Unib. P	HYDE UNITED	639	1 - 2	Haws 25
30.03	Unib. P	BURSCOUGH	557	0 - 3	
01.04	Unib. P	Bradford Park Avenue	306	1 - 4	Hulme 56
03.04	Unib. P	Bamber Bridge	211	1 - 1	Haws 50
06.04	Unib. P	Gateshead	172	2 - 0	Thornley 35, Hulme 43
09.04	Unib. P	RUNCORN HALTON	469	0 - 2	
13.04	Unib. P	Hyde United	437	2 - 3	Strange 34, Murphy 50
16.04	Unib. P	LANCASTER CITY	438	2 - 3	Hulme 31, Craney 54
20.04	Unib. P	Gainsborough Trinity	450	3 - 1	Thornley 1, Craney 53, Sertori 56
22.04	Unib. P	EMLEY	452	1 - 2	Wood 54[og]
27.04	Unib. P	WORKSOP TOWN	709	2 - 0	Shuttleworth 22, Daniel 76
30.04	Unib. P	Vauxhall Motors	252	1 - 2	Daniel 17
03.05	Unib. P	VAUXHALL MOTORS	472	0 - 1	

PLAYING SQUAD

Goalkeepers: Andy Moore (Squires Gate)
Defenders: Gary Talbot (Northwich), Mark Maddox (Barrow), Neil Ryan (Portland Timbers), Steve Rose (Chester), James Wilkinson (Macclesfield), Paul Taylor (Hyde), Steve Spencer (Youth), Neil Murphy (Blackpool)
Midfield: Andy MacDonald (Witton), Jason Gallagher (Hyde), Danny Murphy (Mossley), Ian Craney (Runcorn), Simon Woodford (Ramsbottom), Marc Whiteman (Bury)
Forwards: Adewale Ajet (Hednesford), Rod Thornley (Congleton), Andy Tunnicliffe (Manchester C), Peter Band (Hyde)

ASHTON UNITED

CLUB OFFICIALS

Chairman: Terry Styring
President: R.Thomasson
Vice Chairman: J Milne
Directors: Mike Cummings,David Wright (Financial),Dickie Day, Kevin O'Carroll,Arthur Mycroft, Jim Pinder,Jim Sutherland and Stuartr Jones (Administration)
Secretary: Stuart Jones
7 Rufford Close,Ashton-under-Lyne,Lancs. OL6 8XA. H/Fax: 01613441170
Mobile; 07788 613608
Press Officer: M.Crabtree

FACT FILE

Formed: 1878   Nickname: Robins
Club Sponsors: Wheelbrook Services
Colours: Red & white halves/black/red
Change colours: Amber & Blue/blue/amber & blue
Midweek matchday: Tuesday
Website: www.aufc4.freeserve.co.uk

FOOTBALL MANAGEMENT TEAM

Manager: Gerry Quinn
Physio: Martin Grose

OFFICIAL MATCHDAY PROGRAMME
ASHTON UNITED versus GUISELEY
Friday, 3rd May, 2002 - Kick-off: 7-45 p.m.
Programme £1.00

PROGRAMME
Pages: 22 Price: £1
Editor:Ken & Steve Lee
Local Press: Ashton Reporter, Ashton Advertiser Local Radio: GMR

GROUND   Surrey Street, Hurst Cross, Ashton-u-Lyne OL6 8DY.
Tel: 0161339 4158. (office) 01613 301511 (Social Club). Fax 0161 339 4158
Directions:M62 jct 20, A627(M) to Oldham, keep in right hand 2 lanes, leave at Ashton sign after 2 miles passing Belgrade Hotel, take A627 at next island,keep in left lane and take slip road signed Ashton-under-Lyme, at island follow Stalybridge/Park Road sign, go straight ahead for 3 miles to ground at Hurst Cross. BR to Charles Street (Ashton), or Stalybridge. Buses 331, 332, 337, 408(Ashton-Stalybridge) all pass ground
Capacity: 4,500   Seats: 250   Cover: 750
Clubhouse: Open 11am-11pm. Refreshment bar open matchdays
Club Shop: Yes - contact Ken or Steve Lee (0161 330 9800)
PREVIOUS   **Leagues:** Manchester; Lancs Comb 12-23, 48-64, 66-68; Midland 64-66; Cheshire Co. 23-48, 68-82; Nth West Count 82-92.
Name: Hurst 1878-1947. Ground: Rose Hill 1878-1912
CLUB RECORDS Attendance: 11,000 v Halifax Town, FA Cup First Round 1952.
Scorer: Mark Edwards, 37   **Appearances:** Micky Boyle, 462.
Win: 11-3 v Staylbridge Manchester Interm Cup 55   **Defeat:** 11-1 v Wellington Town Cheshire Lge 46-47.
Fee Paid: £9,000 for Andy Whittaker (Netherfield, 1994)   **Fee Received:** £15,000 for Karl Marginson (Rotherham, Mar. 1993)
BEST SEASON   **FA Trophy**: Qtr Final v Dagenham (0-1) (A0 96-97
FA Cup: 1st Rd replay 52-53, 1-2 v Halifax T (A), after 1-1. Also 1st Rd 55-56, 1-6 v Southport (A)
HONOURS   Northern Prem Lge Div 1 Cup 94-95; Manchester Sen Cup 1884-85 13-14 75-76 77-78; Manchester Lge 11-12; Lancs Comb. Div 2 60-61 (Lge Cup 62-63);Manchester Prem. Cup 79-80 82-83 92-93 00-01,01-02; North West Counties Lge 91-92;Challenge Cup 91-92, Div 2 87-88; Floodlit League 90-91; Challenge Shield 92-93; Manchester Chall Shield 35-36 38-39 49-50 53-54 (R-up 34-35 39-40), Manchester Interm Cup 58-59 62-63 65-66, R-up 60-61 64-65; Manchester Jnr Cup 1894-95 10-12 32-33; Unifilla Div 1 Cup 96-97,98-99
Players progressing: A Ball (Blackpool), J Mahoney (Stoke C.), B Daniels(Manchester C.), R Jones (Rotherham U.), A Arrowsmith (Liverpool), N Stiffle(Crystal Palace), K Marginson (Rotherham U), P Wilson (Plymouth Argyle)

Back row left to right: Greg Challender,Darren Royle, James Riordan, Andy Johnson, Phil Denney, Alex Green, Jason Dormer, Lee Blackshaw, Gareth Hamlet and Gareth Morris.
Front row: Gerry Quinn (Managher), Peter Carty, Fredrick Maiomi, Chris Connelly, Lee Calvert, Paul Garvey and Martin Grose (physio)

NORTHERN PREMIER LEAGUE PREMIER DIVISION

Date	Comp.	Opponents	Att.	Score	Goalscorers
18.08	Unib. 1	FARSLEY CELTIC	136	5 - 2	Gomersall 7, Miller 23 84 90, Cornelly 78[p]
21.08	Unib. 1	Leek Town	268	3 - 2	Morris 28 51, Royle 31
25.08	Unib. 1	North Ferriby United	171	1 - 1	Miller 54
27.08	Unib. 1	HARROGATE TOWN	190	1 - 1	Cornelly 33[p]
01.09	FA Cup P	Esh Winning	105	3 - 0	Cornelly 1, Garvey 53, Gomersall 58
08.09	Unib. 1	CHORLEY	167	0 - 2	
11.09	Unib. 1	Kendal Town	128	2 - 2	Cornelly 39, Morris 81
15.09	FA Cup Q1	SKELMERSDALE UNITED	132	4 - 2	Morris 1, Miller 8, Cornelly 39, Garvey 73
22.09	Unib. 1	Spennymoor United	173	6 - 2	Miller 4, Denney 22 35 64, Garvey 28, Cornelly 62
25.09	Lge Cup G6	OSSETT ALBION	112	6 - 2	Paladino 6, Hamlet 7 11 68, Denney 20, Riordan 87
29.09	FA Cup Q2	STOCKSBRIDGE PARK STEELS	193	1 - 1	Hamlet 89
02.10	FA Cup Q2 R	Stocksbridge Park Steels	239	1 - 2	
06.10	Unib. 1	OSSETT ALBION	132	2 - 1	Denny 27 43
09.10	Lge Cup G6	Droylsden	139	5 - 2	Garvey 44, Miller 55 64, Denney 58, Cornelly 65
13.10	Unib. 1	EASTWOOD TOWN	179	3 - 2	Cornelly 38 48, Miller 66
16.10	Unib. 1	GRETNA	142	6 - 2	France 13, Cornelly 14, Garvey 18, Dormer 76, Miller 82, Denney 85
20.10	Unib. 1	Lincoln United	146	1 - 2	Cornelly 7
23.10	Lge Cup G6	Ossett Town	160	3 - 3	Calvert 1 78, Carty 40
27.10	Unib. 1	STOCKSBRIDGE PARK STEELS	148	3 - 0	Denney 8, Miller 76, Ludlam 78[og]
30.10	Unib. 1	Workington	242	1 - 1	Cornelly 26
03.11	FA Trophy 1	ROCESTER	160	4 - 1	Johnson 3, Denney 78, Hamlet 85 88
10.11	Unib. 1	Farsley Celtic	94	1 - 1	Johnson 22
13.11	Unib. 1	WITTON ALBION	182	4 - 2	Denney 25 35 81, Cornelly 78
17.11	Unib. 1	MATLOCK TOWN	178	0 - 1	
24.11	Unib. 1	Eastwood Town	128	1 - 1	McDonald 90
27.11	Lge Cup G6	HYDE UNITED	221	6 - 3	Morris 12, Blackshaw 13 18 67, Denney 46, Ashwell 47[og]
01.12	FA Trophy 2	King's Lynn	814	1 - 4	Cornelly 7
04.12	Unib. 1	BELPER TOWN	136	3 - 1	Riordan 4, Denney 37 58
08.12	Unib. 1	LEEK TOWN	214	4 - 1	Morris 11 71, Green 15, Blackshaw 55
10.12	Lge Cup G6	Emley	174	2 - 3	Morris 35, Denney 41
15.12	Unib. 1	Harrogate Town	406	0 - 3	
29.12	Unib. 1	Witton Albion	358	1 - 1	Dormer 41
12.01	Unib. 1	Belper Town	224	1 - 1	Denney 32
15.01	Manc PC QF	TRAFFORD	150	2 - 0	Green 37, Cornelly 71[p]
19.01	Unib. 1	SPENNYMOOR UNITED	158	2 - 3	Beasley 7[og], Green 50
26.01	Pres. Cup QF	Burscough	176	3 - 1	Cornelly 31 39, Dormer 90
02.02	Unib. 1	Ossett Town	254	2 - 2	Hamlet 65, Aspinall 78[og]
09.02	Unib. 1	NORTH FERRIBY UNITED	144	1 - 3	Fisher 63[og]
16.02	Unib. 1	Chorley	207	1 - 1	Cornelly 90[p]
27.02	Manc PC SF	Abbey Hey	74	2 - 1	Denney 73, Riley 93[og]
02.03	Unib. 1	Guiseley	180	0 - 2	
05.03	Unib. 1	RADCLIFFE BOROUGH	161	2 - 1	Green 39, Denney 44
09.03	Pres. Cup SF	BARROW	228	4 - 5	Denney 22 36 64, Morris 27
16.03	Unib. 1	LINCOLN UNITED	138	3 - 0	Garvey 34, Carty 43, Green 48
19.03	Unib. 1	KENDAL TOWN	107	3 - 2	Cornelly 24 71, Green 54
23.03	Unib. 1	Ossett Albion	128	5 - 1	Green 10, Morris 37, Riordan 68, Hamlet 85, Raynor 90[og]
26.03	Unib. 1	Stocksbridge Park Steels	208	3 - 3	Cornelly 1, Miller 20, Hamlet 61
30.03	Unib. 1	Gretna	115	0 - 2	
01.04	Unib. 1	TRAFFORD	178	1 - 3	Green 18
06.04	Unib. 1	Radcliffe Borough	204	3 - 2	Blackshaw 51, Calvert 63, Miller 75
09.04	Unib. 1	OSSETT TOWN	147	1 - 1	Calvert 74
13.04	Unib. 1	Trafford	310	3 - 1	Cornelly 15, Calvert 48, Miller 71
16.04	Unib. 1	Rossendale United	191	2 - 1	Dormer 60, Miller 71
20.04	Unib. 1	WORKINGTON	177	1 - 0	Denney 78
23.04	Unib. 1	Matlock Town	305	3 - 0	Denney 27, Garvey 45, Cornelly 54
26.04	Manc PC F	SALFORD CITY	319	3 - 1	Denney 29 84, Challender 67 Oldham Athletic
30.04	Unib. 1	ROSSENDALE UNITED	130	3 - 2	Miller 1, Denney 28 90
03.05	Unib. 1	GUISELEY	246	2 - 1	Cornelly 49, Denney 80
06.05	Play-off SF	SPENNYMOOR UNITED	407	3 - 1	Cornelly 31, Denney 43, Blackshaw 90
09.05	Play-off F	Bamber Bridge	n.k	2 - 1	Denney, Own-Goal

PLAYING SQUAD

Goalkeepers: Andy Johnston (Great Harwood), David Pierce (Winsford)

Defenders: Darren Royle (Flixton), Gareth Morris (Youth), Jamie Riordan (Ossett Alb), Greg Challender (Leek), Lee Connor (Farsley Celtic), Phil Bayliss (Trafford), Mike Jefferson (Youth)

Midfield: Dean Johnson (Ossett Alb), Mike Carmody (Altrincham), Ashley Partington (Youth), Phil Cooney (Skelmersdale), Arron Sutcliffe (Youth), Lee Calvert (Ossett Alb)

Forwards: Chris Cornelly (Ossett Alb), Craig Fleury (Curzon Ashton), Jason Dormer (Hyde), Phil Denney (Bradford PA), Paul Garvey (Flixton), Jamie Miller (Liversedge), Gareth Hamlet (Emley)

BARROW

BARROW AFC SEASON

CLUB OFFICIALS

President: Alan Dunn
Chairman: Brian Keen
Match Secretary; Neil McDonald
Birchfield, 6A Salthouse Rd., Barrow-in-Furness, Cumbria Tel: 01229 828227 (H)
07703 499482 (M)
Press Officer: Phil Yelland
83 Camus Drive, Edinburgh EH10 6QY
Tel: 0131 445 1010 (H) & Fax
0131 476 8131 (B)
Manager: Kenny Lowe
Assistant Manager: Lee Turnbull

FACT FILE

Founded: 1901
Nickname: Bluebirds
Sponsors: Canaltime
Club Colours: Blue & white/blue/blue
Change Colours: White/black/black
Midweek matchday: Tuesday
Barrow Soccer Hotline: 09066 555820
Local Press: North West Evening Mail,
Barrow & West Cumberland Advertiser
Local Radio: BBC Radio Furness, BBC Radio
Cumbria, Red Rose Radio, Bay Radio

Saturday 19th
January 2002

**FRICKLEY
ATHLETIC**

UniBond
Premier
Kick Off
3.00pm

Today's Sponsors
Match:
Unison Town Hall
Match Ball:

Man of the Match:

Official
Programme
£1.40

GROUND: Holker Street Stadium, Wilkie Road, Barrow-in-Furness, CumbriaLA14 5UW
Tel: 01229 820346
Directions: M6 to junction 36, A590 to Barrow, enter Barrow on Park Road and after about 2 miles turn left into Wilkie Rd - ground on right. B.R.1/4 mile
Capacity: 4,500 **Seated:** 1000 **Covered Terracing:** 1,200
Clubhouse: Barrow F.C. Cross Bar next to ground. Open matchdays and Functions only.
Snack bars on ground **Club Shop:** Situated on the ground.
2001-002: Captain: Mark Hume P.o.Y.: Grant Holt Top Scorer:Grant Holt

Pages: 44   Price: £1.40

Editorial Team:
Darren Gardner, Phil Yelland, & Russell Dodd

PREVIOUS **Leagues:** Lancs Comb 01-21; Football League 21-72; Northern Premier 72-79, 83-84,86-89, 92-98; 99- GM Vauxhall Conference 79-83, 84-86, 89-92, 98-99 **Grounds:** The Strawberry & Little Park, Roose **Names:**None

RECORDS **Attendance:** 16,854 v Swansea Town, FA Cup 3rd Rd. 1954
Career Appearances: Colin Cowperthwaite 704 **Career Goalscorer:** Colin Cowperthwaite 282 (Dec '77-Dec '92).
Defeat: 1-10 v Hartlepool Utd, Football Lge Div 4, 1959 **Win:** 12-0 v Cleator, FA Cup 1920.
Transfer Fee Paid: £9,000 for Andy Whittaker (Ashton Utd, July 94).
Transfer Fee Received: £40,000 for Kenny Lowe (Barnet, Jan 91)

BEST SEASON **FA Trophy:** Winners 1989-90, Semi-Final 87-88
FA Cup: Third Round Proper 9 times including once as a non-League club 90-91, 0-1 v Bolton Wanderers (A)

HONOURS F.A. Trophy Winners 89-90, Northern Premier League 97-98, 88-89, 83-84; Lge Cup R-up 87-88, Lge Shield 84-85 R-up 89-90 98-99; Bob Lord Trophy R-up 90-91, Cumbrian Cup 82-8383-84 (R-up 84-85), Lancs Floodlit Cup R-up 86-87, Lancs Sen Cup 54-55 (R-up 51-52 65-66 66-67 69-70), Lancs Challenge Trophy 80-81 (R-up 81-82 84-85 01-02), Lancs Comb 20-21, R-up 13-14, Div 2 R-up 04-05 10-11. Unibond Chairman's Cup (00-01)President's Cup 01-02

Players progressing: I McDonald, N McDonald, J Laisby, B Diamond, F Gamble, B Knowles, G Skivington, P Byron, L Edwards, K Lowe, M Dobie, T Rigby, N Doherty.

Back row left to right: Scott Maxfield, Anthony Hall, Lee Warren, Lee Rogers, Mark Hume, Simon Bishop, Wayne Bullimore, Grant Holt, Ian Duerden, Simon Shaw and Steve Gaughan. Front row, Graham Anthony, Neil Doherty, Mike McKenzie, Carl Waters, Kenny Lowe (Manager), Brian Keen (Chairman) Lee Turnbull (Assistant Manager), Andy Hill, Steve Hausham and Gareth Jones

Match Facts 2001-02

Date	Comp.	Opponents	Att.	Score	Goalscorers
18.08	Unib. P	HUCKNALL TOWN	1411	6 - 1	Housham 10 30, Duerden 25, Holt 40, Jones 80, Hall 88
22.08	Unib. P	Accrington Stanley	671	3 - 0	Duerden 24[p], Holt 55 65
25.08	Unib. P	Droylsden	372	0 - 2	
27.08	Unib. P	BAMBER BRIDGE	1445	1 - 1	Hulme 58
01.09	Unib. P	BURSCOUGH	1280	1 - 0	Jones 63
08.09	Unib. P	Whitby Town	336	4 - 2	Hume 3, Housham 25 30 56
11.09	Unib. P	RUNCORN HALTON	1247	2 - 1	Gaughan 19[p], Holt 39
15.09	Unib. P	GAINSBOROUGH TRINITY	1198	3 - 0	Maxfield 12, Hume 56 84
18.09	Unib. P	Marine	323	2 - 3	Holt 51, Hume 81
22.09	Unib. P	Frickley Athletic	258	3 - 2	Peverill 6, Hume 24, Housham 45
25.09	Lge Cup G2	BAMBER BRIDGE	519	2 - 0	Waters 32, Jones 90
29.09	FA Cup Q2	KENDAL TOWN	1180	3 - 0	Holt 1, Gaughan 13, Peverill 41
02.10	Unib. P	Altrincham	770	1 - 2	Housham 90
05.10	Unib. P	BISHOP AUCKLAND	1199	3 - 1	Peverill 44, Holt 45 82
09.10	Lge Cup G2	Workington	225	0 - 2	
13.10	FA Cup Q3	ROSSENDALE UNITED	1325	1 - 1	Peverill 19
16.10	FA Cup Q3 R	Rossendale United	1023	3 - 3	Hume 14, Holt 58 103 Lost 5-3 after pens.
20.10	Unib. P	Emley	362	1 - 2	Maxfield 19
23.10	Lge Cup G2	Kendal Town	151	3 - 5	Linard 14, Holt 72 82
27.10	FA Cup Q4	CHESTER CITY	2893	1 - 0	Holt 58
30.10	Unib. P	Burscough	244	2 - 3	Gaughan 41, Housham 84
03.11	FA Trophy 1	HALESOWEN TOWN	1126	2 - 1	Holt 7, Maxfield 89
06.11	Unib. P	COLWYN BAY	964	1 - 1	Housham 78
10.11	Unib. P	Blyth Spartans	466	1 - 1	Gaughan 31
13.11	Lancs MT 1	SKELMERSDALE UNITED	308	3 - 2	Jones 12, Waters 44, Peverill 71
17.11	FA Cup 1	Oldham Athletic	5795	1 - 1	Housham 4
24.11	Unib. P	Gainsborough Trinity	475	1 - 0	Doherty 33
27.11	FA Cup 1 R	OLDHAM ATHLETIC	4368	0 - 1	
01.12	FA Trophy 2	BURTON ALBION	1521	1 - 1	Anthony 68
04.12	FA Trophy 2 R	Burton Albion	1174	0 - 5	
08.12	Unib. P	Bishop Auckland	276	2 - 1	Ellison 23, Holt 79
15.12	Unib. P	GATESHEAD	1113	4 - 1	Ellison 37 90, Gowan 68[p], Duerden 84
18.12	Lge Cup G2	Lancaster City	173	4 - 3	Duerden 27, Jones 33, Housham 54, Waters 66
21.12	Unib. P	Hyde United	241	2 - 1	Housham 23, Gaughan 78
26.12	Unib. P	LANCASTER CITY	2032	0 - 0	
29.12	Unib. P	BRADFORD PARK AVENUE	1351	2 - 3	Anthony 22, Holt 55
08.01	Lancs MT 2	Bamber Bridge	139	1 - 0	Hume 57
12.01	Unib. P	WHITBY TOWN	1133	2 - 0	Ellison 20 51
15.01	Unib. P	Lancaster City	1028	3 - 3	Ellison 25 69, Hume 42
19.01	Unib. P	FRICKLEY ATHLETIC	1100	3 - 1	Housham 23, Holt 28 84
26.01	Pres. Cup QF	GATESHEAD	704	2 - 1	Duerden 2, Peverill 72[p]
02.02	Unib. P	Bamber Bridge	409	0 - 1	
05.02	Lancs MT QF	Southport	184	2 - 0	Peverill 1, Holt 86
09.02	Unib. P	ALTRINCHAM	1212	2 - 2	Hume 69 89
16.02	Unib. P	HYDE UNITED	1053	0 - 0	
23.02	Unib. P	Hucknall Town	278	1 - 2	Holt 50
02.03	Unib. P	BURTON ALBION	1310	1 - 2	Housham 67
05.03	Unib. P	MARINE	695	1 - 1	Doherty 39
09.03	Pres. Cup SF	Ashton United	228	5 - 4	Holt 38, Waters 40 61, Ellison 71, Housham 119
12.03	Lancs MT SF	CLITHEROE	612	3 - 0	Hall 23, Bullimore 35, Waters 70
16.03	Unib. P	EMLEY	936	1 - 1	Bullimore 65[p]
19.03	Unib. P	DROYLSDEN	721	1 - 2	Waters 41
23.03	Unib. P	Colwyn Bay	293	5 - 0	Gaughan 2, Housham 66 76, Holt 70, Jackson 90
26.03	Unib. P	VAUXHALL MOTORS	861	1 - 2	Bullimore 89[p]
30.03	Unib. P	ACCRINGTON STANLEY	891	0 - 4	
01.04	Unib. P	Runcorn Halton	275	3 - 1	Holt 3, Housham 4, Bullimore 43
06.04	Unib. P	Bradford Park Avenue	411	0 - 2	
10.04	Unib. P	Gateshead	125	0 - 0	
13.04	Unib. P	Worksop Town	454	1 - 0	Holt 74
16.04	Pres. Cup F	GAINSBOROUGH TRINITY	488	1 - 0	Holt 89 @ Hyde United
20.04	Unib. P	WORKSOP TOWN	829	1 - 0	Bullimore 88
22.04	Unib. P	Burton Albion	1001	0 - 4	
24.04	Lancs MT F	Accrington Stanley	1330	0 - 2	@ Morecambe
27.04	Unib. P	Vauxhall Motors	250	0 - 2	
30.04	Unib. P	BLYTH SPARTANS	569	4 - 1	Holt 16, Jones 26, Housham 28, Waters 81

PLAYING SQUAD

Goalkeepers: Neil Bennett (Airdrie), Simon Bishop (Dunston Fed)
Defenders: Andy Hill (Vickers SC), Anthony Hall (Gateshead), Ian McGuckin (Oxford), Lee Turnbull (Halifax), Lee Rogers (Grantham), Lee Warren (Doncaster), Simon Shaw (Doncaster), Mark Hume (Doncaster)
Midfield: Graham Anthony (Carlisle), Nigel Pepper (Scunthorpe), Stee Gaughan (Halifax), Tony Hopper (Carlisle), Scott Maxfield (Doncaster), Troy Bennett (Gainsborough Trinity), Wayne Bullimore (Grantham)
Forwards: Neil Tarrant (Boston Utd), Alex Nesovic (Dundalk), Carl Waters (Holker OB), Grant Holt (Sengkang Marine - Singapore), Steve Gill (Barrow Rangers), Gareth Jones (Dalton Utd), Nicky Peverill (Blyth)

BLYTH SPARTANS

CLUB OFFICIALS

Chairman:**Tommy Hedley**
Secretary: **Joe Hobin**, 23 Princes Gdns,
Malvins Close, Blyth, Northumberland,
NE24 2HJ. Tel: 01670 360820.
Press Officer: **Ken Teasdale**

FACT FILE
Formed: 1899 Nickname: Spartans
Sponsors: Federation Brewery.
Colours:Green & white stripes/black
Change colours: Yellow
Midweek Matches: Wednesday
Local Press:Newcastle Journal &
Evening Chronicle.

FOOTBALL MANAGEMENT TEAM

Manager: John Charlton
Assistant Manager: Graeme Clarke

GROUND: Croft Park, Blyth, Northumberland. Tel: 01670 354818 FAX: 01670 545592
Website: www.spartans.freeserve.co.uk
Directions: Through Tyne tunnel heading north on A19, take Cramlington turn A1061, follow
signs for Newsham/Blyth. Right fork at railway gates in Newsham, down Plessey Rd, ground
can be seen on left. Buses X24, X25, X26, X1 from Newcastle.
Capacity: 6,000   Seats: 300   Cover: 1,000
Clubhouse: Open every night plus Saturday & Sunday lunch & matchdays. Available for
wedding functions. Pies & sandwiches available.
Souvenir Shop: Large selection. Contact: Bob Bell (01670 545592)

Pages: 64 Price: £1
Editor: Brian Grey Tel: 0191 2650119

PREVIOUS	Leagues: Northumberland 01-07; Northern Alliance 07-13, 46-47; North Eastern13-14 19-39 47-58 62-64; Northern Combination 45-46; Midland 58-60; Northern Counties 60-62; Northern 62-94. Names: None Grounds: None
CLUB RECORDS	Fee Received: £30,000 for Les Mutrie (Hull City) 1979. Fee Paid:
BEST SEASON	**FA Trophy:** Quarter-Final replay 79-80 82-83. **FA Amateur Cup:** Semi-Final 71-72. **FA Cup:** 5th Rd replay 77-78 (lost to Wrexham). 1-1 (A) 1-2 (H) at Newcastle United Gillingham 22-23, Crewe Alexandra,Stockport County 71-72, Chesterfield, Stoke City 77-78, Bury 95-96.
HONOURS	Nth Lg(10) 72-73 74-76 79-84 86-88 94-95, (R-up 71-72 73-74 77-78 84-85 94-95),Lg Cup(5) 72-73 77-79 81-82 91-92 94-95, Presidents Cup 96-97; Nth Eastern Lg35-36 (R-up 22-23, Lg Cup 49-50 54-55); Northumberland Lg 03-04; Northern All.08-09 12-13 (R-up 46-47); Northumberland Snr Cup (19); Shields Gazette Cup 95-96.

Players Progressing: William McGlen (Manchester Utd 46), Joe Roddom (Chesterfield 48), Henry Mills (Huddersfield 48), John Allison (Reading 49), James Kelly (Watford 49), Robert Millard (Reading 49), Jim Kerr (Lincoln 52), James Milner (Burnley 52), John Hogg (Portsmouth 54), John Allison(Chesterfield 55), John Inglis (Gateshead 57), John Longland (Hartlepool 58),Alan Shoulder (Newcastle 79), Les Mutrie (Hull City 79), Steve Carney(Newcastle 80), Craig Liddle (Middlesbrough 94), Paul O'Connor (Hartlepool 95). Gustavo Di Lella (Hartlepool 98)

Match Facts 2001-02

Date	Comp.	Opponents	Att.	Score	Goalscorers
18.08	Unib. P	BAMBER BRIDGE	445	3 - 1	Keegan 15, Robson 82, Hutton 88
22.08	Unib. P	Gateshead	426	1 - 1	Robson 56
25.08	Unib. P	Frickley Athletic	168	5 - 1	Innes 18 24, Robson 57 67[p], Radigan 73
27.08	Unib. P	BISHOP AUCKLAND	654	2 - 1	Pepper 77, Skelton 88
01.09	Unib. P	Bradford Park Avenue	337	2 - 2	Skelton 36, Radigan 88
04.09	Unib. P	EMLEY	519	1 - 3	Robson 44
08.09	Unib. P	HYDE UNITED	461	2 - 0	Forster 27, Pepper 85
11.09	Unib. P	Lancaster City	315	2 - 4	Robson 7, Skelton 77
15.09	Unib. P	Runcorn Halton	275	2 - 1	Robson 46, Skelton 75
22.09	Unib. P	Droylsden	201	0 - 0	
25.09	Lge Cup G1	BISHOP AUCKLAND	319	4 - 1	C Pepper 44[p], Stewart 70, Skelton 82, Scroggins 88
29.09	FA Cup Q2	ECCLESHILL UNITED	499	5 - 0	Radigan 15, Innes 35, Stewart 42, Robson 79 84
02.10	Unib. P	Bishop Auckland	256	1 - 1	Radigan 79
05.10	Unib. P	GAINSBOROUGH TRINITY	488	2 - 2	Robson 8 10
09.10	Lge Cup G1	Spennymoor United	148	2 - 0	Robson 15 26[p]
13.10	FA Cup Q3	HARROGATE RAILWAY ATHLETIC	670	1 - 2	Martin 38
16.10	Unib. P	FRICKLEY ATHLETIC	345	0 - 0	
20.10	Unib. P	Altrincham	714	1 - 2	Pepper 78
27.10	Unib. P	Hyde United	266	1 - 3	Stewart 90
30.10	N'humbs SC 1	WHITLEY BAY	358	5 - 1	Skelton 11 61, Hutton 43, Robson 55, Perry 66
03.11	FA Trophy 1	BURSCOUGH	422	2 - 0	Robson 12 13
10.11	Unib. P	BARROW	466	1 - 1	Skelton 70
13.11	Lge Cup G1	GRETNA	215	3 - 1	Skelton 9, Perry 22, Pepper 54
17.11	Unib. P	Accrington Stanley	479	0 - 0	
24.11	Unib. P	BURSCOUGH	381	2 - 1	Stewart 9, Pepper 88
28.11	Lge Cup G1	Gateshead	134	1 - 4	Jones 20[og]
01.12	FA Trophy 2	Whitby Town	505	2 - 1	Stewart 10, Baker 34
08.12	N'humbs SC QF	West Allotment Celtic	240	0 - 2	
15.12	Unib. P	Worksop Town	331	0 - 3	
22.12	Unib. P	Vauxhall Motors	276	2 - 2	Stewart 20, Radigan 75
26.12	Unib. P	GATESHEAD	810	2 - 1	Baker 28 37
29.12	Unib. P	Colwyn Bay	265	1 - 1	Scroggins 57
12.01	FA Trophy 3	Burton Albion	1594	0 - 3	
19.01	Unib. P	Hucknall Town	191	1 - 2	Skelton 90
22.01	Unib. P	WHITBY TOWN	286	2 - 1	Robson 39, Skelton 48
30.01	Lge Cup QF	Bradford Park Avenue	133	1 - 7	Pepper 81
02.02	Unib. P	BRADFORD PARK AVENUE	404	4 - 1	Robson 28 47[p], Pepper 55, Innes 80
09.02	Unib. P	ACCRINGTON STANLEY	398	1 - 1	Robson 39
16.02	Unib. P	Burton Albion	1674	0 - 4	
19.02	Unib. P	HUCKNALL TOWN	278	1 - 2	Scroggins 34
23.02	Unib. P	ALTRINCHAM	479	0 - 3	
02.03	Unib. P	RUNCORN HALTON	322	2 - 2	Robson 2, Williams 25
05.03	Unib. P	Bamber Bridge	174	1 - 0	Robson 89
09.03	Unib. P	Burscough	185	2 - 1	Robson 6[p], Scroggins 81
16.03	Unib. P	VAUXHALL MOTORS	356	0 - 1	
20.03	Unib. P	Whitby Town	228	2 - 2	Perry 16, Forster 61
23.03	Unib. P	DROYLSDEN	326	0 - 0	
30.03	Unib. P	LANCASTER CITY	444	1 - 0	Robson 48
01.04	Unib. P	Gainsborough Trinity	334	1 - 2	Robson 16
06.04	Unib. P	WORKSOP TOWN	411	2 - 2	Forster 2, Martin 51
10.04	Unib. P	Emley	124	1 - 2	McMahon 27
13.04	Unib. P	Marine	283	2 - 0	Robson 35[p] 63
16.04	Unib. P	MARINE	312	0 - 0	
20.04	Unib. P	COLWYN BAY	324	2 - 0	Martin 45, Radigan 90
27.04	Unib. P	BURTON ALBION	593	0 - 1	
30.04	Unib. P	Barrow	569	1 - 4	Martin 73

PLAYING SQUAD

Goalkeepers: Paul Gilmore (Seaham Red Star)

Defenders: Andy Martin (Queen of the South), Colin Morton (Hibernian), Graham Pepper (Gateshead), John Hutton (Darlington), Paddy Little (Jarrow), Richard Forster (Hartlepool), Ian Irving (Morpeth)

Midfield: Carl Pepper (Darlington), Gareth Williams (Whitley Bay), Lee Scroggins (Darlington), Justin Keegan (Darlington), Scott Emerson (York)

Forwards: Phil Brumwell (Darlington), Gary Innes (Seaham), Steve Stewart (Durham), Glen Robson (Harrogate T), David McMahon (Queen of the South), Paul Baker (Durham)

BRADFORD PARK AVENUE

MARINE

Bradford versus
MARINE UniBond
Monday 26 August 2002
Premier Division Programme £1.20

CLUB OFFICIALS

Chairman: **Frank Thornton**
President: **Charlie Atkinson**
Secretary: **Steven Burnett** , 21 Edward
Turner Close,Low Moor,Bradford BD12 0AS
Tel: 01274 608344(H) 07866076220 (M)
Press Officer: **Tim Clapham**
Commercial Manager: **Geoff Cope**

FOOTBALL MANAGEMENT TEAM

Manager: Trevor Storton
Asst Manager: Ian Thompson
Physio: Ray Killick

FACT FILE

Formed: 1907
Reformed: 1988
Nickname: Avenue
Club Sponsor: Ham Construction
Colours: White & Green/white/ white
Change colours Yellow
Midweek Matches: Wednesday
Reserves' league: Lancashire League

GROUND

Horsfall Stadium, Cemetery Road, Bradford, West Yorks BD6 2NG (01274 604578)

Directions: M62 Jct 26. Along M606 to the end. At roundabout takeA6036 (signed Halifax) and pass Odsal Stadium on left hand side. At next roundabout take 3rd exit A6036 (Halifax), in approx. 1 mile turn left into Cemetery Rd (by Kings Head Pub). Ground 150 yards on left
Capacity: 5,000   Cover: 2,000   Seats: 1,247
Club Shop: Yes - contact Russell Foulds (c/o Ground) or 01924 440901 **Clubhouse:** Yes

Programme
Pages: 36 Price: £1.20
Editor: James Northin   01924 384477

Local Press: Telegraph & Argus
Local Radio: Radio Leeds

PREVIOUS   **Leagues:** Southern 07-08; Football League 08-70; Northern Premier 70-74; West Riding County Amtr 88-89; Central Mids 89-90; N. W. Counties 90-95
Grounds: Park Avenue 07-73; Valley Parade 73-74; Manningham Mills 88-89; Bramley R.L.F.C., McLaren Field 89-93; Batley 93-96
CLUB RECORDS   **Attendance:** 1,007 v Bradford City 97 (Centenary Chall). 32,810 v Blackpool, War Cup 1944
Win: 11-0 v Denby Dale FAC 1908   **Defeat:** 0-7 v Barnsley 1911
Scorer: Len Shackleton 171 1940-46   **Appearances:** Tommy Farr 542 1934-50
Fee Received: £34,000 for K Hector (Derby County 1966)
Fee Paid: £24,500 for L Leuty (Derby County 1950)
BEST SEASON   **FA Vase:** 2nd Rd Prop 94-95   **FA Trophy:** 3rd Rd 98-99
FA Cup: Qtr finals 1912-13 v Aston Villa (0-5), 19-20 v Bristol City (A) 0-2, 45-46 v Birmingham City 2-2 (H) 0-6 (A) Agg 2-8
HONOURS   Football Lge Div 2 R-up 1914; 3rd Div N 28; Yorkshire Lge 21, 23; Midland Lge 32; West Riding Snr Cup 11,13, 25, 27, 32,36, 51, 53, 63; West Riding County Cup 28-29, 90-91; N.W.C. Lg 94-95, Challenge Trophy 94-95. N.P.L. (Unibond) Division One Champions 2000-01

Bradford (Park Avenue) AFC 2002-03 - L-R - Back Row: D Wilson (kit man), Andy Hayward, Matt Daly, Graham Mitchell, Ross Turner, Jason Maxwell, Robbie Painter, James Stansfield. **Front:** Dean Martin, Phil Atkinson, Andy Quinn, Wayne Benn, Rory Prendergast, Phil Lindley, Richard Tracey.

NORTHERN PREMIER LEAGUE PREMIER DIVISION

Date	Comp.	Opponents	Att.	Score	Goalscorers
18.08	Unib. P	BURTON ALBION	648	1 - 4	Bagshaw 31
22.08	Unib. P	BURSCOUGH	260	0 - 2	
25.08	Unib. P	Worksop Town	361	2 - 3	Thompson 8, James 51[p]
27.08	Unib. P	Whitby Town	358	1 - 1	Hayward 47
01.09	Unib. P	BLYTH SPARTANS	337	2 - 2	Hancock 57, Lindley 79
04.09	Unib. P	Gainsborough Trinity	398	1 - 4	O'Brien 20
08.09	Unib. P	Altrincham	644	0 - 1	
12.09	Unib. P	BISHOP AUCKLAND	221	0 - 2	
15.09	Unib. P	MARINE	308	2 - 3	Hayward 2, Maxwell 81
18.09	Unib. P	Droylsden	143	2 - 2	Hayward 76 78
22.09	Unib. P	Bamber Bridge	320	1 - 2	Maxwell 90
26.09	Lge Cup G3	HARROGATE TOWN	156	3 - 1	Thompson 38, Nazha 72[p], Maxwell 90
29.09	FA Cup Q2	DROYLSDEN	297	3 - 2	Brunskill 22[og], Hayward 35, Calcutt 55
02.10	Unib. P	Hucknall Town	186	0 - 1	
06.10	Unib. P	FRICKLEY ATHLETIC	325	3 - 0	Nazha 28, James 54[p] 58[p]
09.10	Lge Cup G3	Farsley Celtic	121	2 - 0	Calcutt 23, James 71
13.10	FA Cup Q3	Marine	371	2 - 4	Maxwell 29, Hayward 90
17.10	Unib. P	EMLEY	391	2 - 1	Calcutt 82 90
20.10	Unib. P	Lancaster City	437	0 - 4	
27.10	Unib. P	DROYLSDEN	253	3 - 1	Hayward 33, Bairstow 42, Thompson 55
03.11	FA Trophy 1	Kendal Town	199	2 - 3	Hayward 43, Thompson 65
07.11	Unib. P	GAINSBOROUGH TRINITY	220	2 - 0	Maxwell 35, Nazha 73
10.11	Unib. P	Colwyn Bay	309	2 - 1	Calcutt 46, O'Brien 89[p]
17.11	Unib. P	VAUXHALL MOTORS	274	1 - 3	Nazha 75
21.11	Unib. P	GATESHEAD	186	3 - 5	Thompson 47, Hayward 54, Stanfield 64
24.11	Unib. P	Marine	274	2 - 1	Maxwell 25, Hancock 38
01.12	Lge Cup G3	Guiseley	225	1 - 0	Maxwell 71
08.12	Unib. P	Accrington Stanley	674	1 - 5	Maxwell 32
11.12	W Rid SC 2	Ossett Albion	92	6 - 3	Maxwell 7 35, Hayward 12 32 44 62
15.12	Unib. P	HYDE UNITED	216	3 - 1	Hayward 14 80, O'Brien 90
26.12	Unib. P	Burton Albion	2141	0 - 3	
29.12	Unib. P	Barrow	1351	3 - 2	Thompson 3 56, Maxwell 17
09.01	Lge Cup G3	WHITBY TOWN	107	5 - 0	Calcutt 10 75 85, Potter 53, Maxwell 58
19.01	Unib. P	RUNCORN HALTON	304	3 - 1	Hayward 3, Stansfield 17, Maxwell 90
23.01	Unib. P	BAMBER BRIDGE	298	5 - 2	Hancock 9, James 20[p], Maxwell 23, Potter 66, Hayward 90
30.01	Lge Cup QF	BLYTH SPARTANS	133	7 - 1	Potter 18, Hayward 20 43 48 73, Maxwell 37 69
02.02	Unib. P	Blyth Spartans	404	1 - 4	O'Brien 33[p]
09.02	Unib. P	Emley	386	0 - 1	
16.02	Unib. P	WORKSOP TOWN	438	1 - 5	Hayward 12
23.02	Unib. P	Burscough	213	2 - 0	Maxwell 68, Hayward 74
27.02	W Rid SC QF	Garforth Town	n.k	2 - 1	James 15[p], Potter 90
02.03	Unib. P	LANCASTER CITY	285	1 - 0	Hayward 51
09.03	Lge Cup SF	Matlock Town	443	2 - 1	Thompson 42, Potter 45
12.03	W Rid SC SF	Farsley Celtic	122	0 - 1	
16.03	Unib. P	ACCRINGTON STANLEY	420	1 - 2	Hayward 71
19.03	Unib. P	Frickley Athletic	447	0 - 0	
23.03	Unib. P	Hyde United	389	0 - 2	
27.03	Unib. P	HUCKNALL TOWN	213	0 - 1	
30.03	Unib. P	Vauxhall Motors	206	1 - 2	Lindley 73
01.04	Unib. P	ALTRINCHAM	306	4 - 1	Martin 15, Hayward 39 72, Maxwell 59
03.04	Unib. P	Gateshead	130	7 - 0	Hayward 21 26, Martin 25, James 30, Calcutt 59 87, Richards 80
06.04	Unib. P	BARROW	411	2 - 0	Hayward 43, Hancock 71
10.04	Lge Cup F(1)	ACCRINGTON STANLEY	471	1 - 0	James 89
20.04	Unib. P	Bishop Auckland	452	4 - 0	Calcutt 20, Hayward 58, Martin 59, Maxwell 64
23.04	Unib. P	Runcorn Halton	269	2 - 0	Hayward 6, Calcutt 75
27.04	Unib. P	COLWYN BAY	265	5 - 0	Maxwell 25 58 77, Martin 45, Lindley 79
30.04	Lge Cup F(2)	Accrington Stanley	1107	0 - 1	Lost 4-5 after pens.
03.05	Unib. P	WHITBY TOWN	361	1 - 1	Maxwell 90

PLAYING SQUAD

Goalkeepers: Rob Montgomery (Vauxhall Motors), Joel Armstrong (Chesterfield)
Defenders: Graham Mitchell (Halifax), James Stansfield (Liversedge), Matt Daly (Guiseley), Mike Thompson (Frickley), Martin James (Winsford), Neil Lacey (Emley), Neil Bagshaw (Rotherham)
Midfield: Dean Martin (Lancaster), Andy Quinn (Gainsborough Trinity), Wayne Benn (Halifax), Ian Richards (Halifax), Phil Lindley (Youth), Rory Prendergast (Frickley)
Forwards: Jason Maxwell (Gainsborough Trinity), Andy Hayward (Frickley), Michael Nunn (Army), Robbie Painter (Gateshead)

BURSCOUGH

CLUB OFFICIALS
Chairman: **Frank Parr**
Vice Chairman: **Stuart Heaps**
President: **Rod Cottam**
Secretary/Press Off. **Stan Strickland**
109 Redgate, Ormskirk, Lancs L39 3NW
H 01695574722 B 01695 574722
M 07970 030588
Email sstrick@109redgate.freeserve.co.uk

FOOTBALL MANAGEMENT TEAM
Manager: Shaun Teale
Asst Manager: Ray Stafford
Physio: Mel Jingleton

FACT FILE
Founded: 1946
Nickname: Linnets
Sponsors: Nationwide Produce Ltd.
Colours: Green/white/green
Change colours: T.B.A.
Midweek Matches: Tuesday
Reserves: Lancashire League

2001-02
Captain:Ged Nolan
Top Scorer: Lee McEvilly 19
P.o.Y.: Matty Taylor

Pages:44 Price £1.20
Editor: Stan Strickland
(01695 574722)
Local Radio: Radio Lancs,Red Rose.

GROUND: Victoria Park, Bobby Langton Way, Mart Lane, Burscough, Ormskirk, Lancs L40 0SD Tel: 01704 893237   Website: www.burscoughfc.co.uk
Directions: M6 Jct 27, follow signs thru Parbold A5209, right into Junction Lane (signed Burscough & Martin Mere) to lights, right onto A59 to Burscough Village, 2nd left over canal bridge into Mart Lane to ground. 200 yards from Burscough Bridge BR station (Wigan-Southport line). Half mile from Burscough Junction (Ormskirk Preston line)
Capacity: 2,500   **Seats:** 270   **Cover:** 1,000
Clubhouse: `Barons Club' (privately owned, access outside grd). Mon-Thurs 7-11pm, Fri 4-11pm, Sat 1-11pm, Sun noon-3 & 7-10.30pm. No food   **Club Shop:** Yes

PREVIOUS   **Leagues:** Liverpool Co Comb. 46-53, Lancs Comb. 53-70, Cheshire Co.70-82, North West Cos 82-98, Unibond NPL98-01
CLUB RECORDS   **Attendance:** 4,798 v Wigan Athletic,F.A.Cup 3rd Qual.Rd.1950-51
Goalscorer: Johnny Vincent 60 53-54. Most Goals in Game: Louis Bimpson 7. In Career: Wes Bridge 188
Win: 10-0 v Cromptons Recreation 1947 & v Nelson 1948-49, both Lancs. Comb.
Defeat: 0-9 v Earlstown,Liverpool County Comb.1948-49   **Fee paid:** £2,500 Stuart Rudd (Skelmersdale Utd 00-01)
Fee Received: £20,000 from Rochdale for Lee McEvilly 2001-02
BEST SEASON   **FA Cup:** 1st Rd 59-60 77-78 79-80 80-81
FA Trophy: 1982-83 99-00
FA Vase: 1994-95 (Last 16)

HONOURS   Liverpool Challenge Cup 47-48 50-51,54-55; George Mahon Cup 47-48; Liverpool County Comb Div 1, 49-50 (Div 2 53-54, 67-68); Lancs Comb.Div 2 53-54; Lancs Comb Div 1 55-56 69-70; Lord Wavertree Cup 67-68; Cheshire County Lge R-up 70- 71, League Cup 74-75 (R-up 73-74); Lancs Jnr Cup 47-48&49-50 66-67; Liverpool Non-Lg Snr Cup 55/56, 71-72; North West Counties Lge 82-83, Lge Cup 92-93 95-96(R-up 91-92), Challenge Shield 82-83, 95-96; Liverpool Senior Cup R-up 92-93,95-96, 99-00., Liverpool Junior Cup 00-01

Players progressing: L Bimpson, B Parker (Liverpool 53), B Pilson (Stoke 53-54), A Green (Huddersfield), K Waterhouse (Preston), F Gamble (Derby 80), Tony Rigby (Bury), S Teale (Aston Villa), L Watson (Preston), K Formby A Russell (Rochdale 94),G Martindale (Bolton 94), S Perkins (Plymouth A. 97), M.Yates (Dundee 99), L. Trundle (Wrexham, R. Lowe (Shrewsbury T.), L McEvilly (Rochdale 02)

L-R Back:
Andy Barlow,
Joe Taylor,
Matt Taylor,
Kris McHale,
Michael White.

Middle:
Ryan Bowen,
Mike Sawtell,
Jeff Underwood,
Scott McAuley,
John Norman,
Steve Hussey,
Gary Martindale.

Front:
Peter Wright,
Marin Molyneux (team captain),
Ray Stafford (Asst Man.),
Bernard O'Malley (Group Chairman, Club Sponsors Nationwide Produce PLC),
Shaun Teale (Manager),
Carl Macauley (club captain),
John Lawless.

Match Facts 2001-02

Date	Comp.	Opponents	Att.	Score	Goalscorers
31.07	L'pool SC 00-01 F	SOUTHPORT	n.k	1 - 0	McEvilly 37
18.08	Unib. P	FRICKLEY ATHLETIC	205	1 - 0	Cassidy 31
22.08	Unib. P	Bradford Park Avenue	260	2 - 0	Molyneaux 64, McEvilly 78
25.08	Unib. P	Accrington Stanley	415	0 - 3	
27.08	Unib. P	LANCASTER CITY	263	0 - 6	
01.09	Unib. P	Barrow	1280	0 - 1	
04.09	Unib. P	BAMBER BRIDGE	185	5 - 0	Bowen 10, Evans 60, Knowles 66 84, Lawless 87
08.09	Unib. P	EMLEY	223	1 - 1	McEvilly 84[p]
11.09	Unib. P	Marine	251	3 - 3	Lawless 8, Furlong 62 84
15.09	Unib. P	ALTRINCHAM	322	0 - 2	
18.09	L'pool SC 1	LIVERPOOL	272	1 - 7	Howarth 87
22.09	Unib. P	Burton Albion	1361	0 - 4	
25.09	Lge Cup G4	ROSSENDALE UNITED	112	2 - 0	Cassidy 39, Furlong 73
29.09	FA Cup Q2	Harrogate Town	391	1 - 1	Bowen 76
02.10	FA Cup Q2 R	HARROGATE TOWN	187	2 - 2	Lost 4-5 after pens.
06.10	Unib. P	MARINE	182	1 - 1	Dugdale 51
09.10	Lge Cup G4	Chorley	130	2 - 0	Innes 67, Bowen 87
13.10	Unib. P	COLWYN BAY	191	4 - 0	Bowen 12 75, Knowles 25, Stanton 89
16.10	Unib. P	VAUXHALL MOTORS	184	2 - 3	McEvilly 59, Furlong 60
20.10	Unib. P	Bishop Auckland	152	1 - 2	McEvilly 22[p]
24.10	Lge Cup G4	Accrington Stanley	247	1 - 2	McEvilly 67
27.10	Unib. P	GAINSBOROUGH TRINITY	175	3 - 1	Birch 49, Knowles 60, Furlong 90
30.10	Unib. P	BARROW	244	3 - 2	McEvilly 6 31 35
03.11	FA Trophy 1	Blyth Spartans	422	0 - 2	
07.11	Unib. P	Runcorn Halton	268	0 - 4	
10.11	Unib. P	HUCKNALL TOWN	156	1 - 3	Dugdale 80
17.11	Unib. P	DROYLSDEN	186	6 - 2	Birch 45, Bowen 52[p], McEvilly 55 65 79[p], Dugdale 75
24.11	Unib. P	Blyth Spartans	381	1 - 2	Lawless 31
01.12	Unib. P	Hucknall Town	155	2 - 1	Dugdale 45, Knowles 72
04.12	Unib. P	Vauxhall Motors	202	2 - 3	McEvilly 8, Birch 33
06.12	Lancs MT 1	Blackpool Mechanics	50	3 - 0	McEvilly 37 71, Knowles 42
08.12	Unib. P	WHITBY TOWN	205	3 - 1	McEvilly 67 77 87
11.12	Lge Cup G4	Marine	103	1 - 2	McMullen 90
15.12	Unib. P	Bamber Bridge	274	3 - 2	McEvilly 35, Furlong 43 47
18.12	Lge Cup G4	RADCLIFFE BOROUGH	106	3 - 0	Furlong 52 54 89
26.12	Unib. P	Colwyn Bay	187	1 - 2	Knowles 57
29.12	Unib. P	HYDE UNITED	276	0 - 2	
08.01	Lancs MT 2	SQUIRES GATE	102	3 - 1	Furlong 10, Birch 17, Bowen 50
12.01	Unib. P	ACCRINGTON STANLEY	327	3 - 2	Molloy 68, Dugdale 75 77
19.01	Unib. P	Gainsborough Trinity	305	1 - 3	Lawless 78
26.01	Pres. Cup QF	ASHTON UNITED	176	1 - 3	Mason 78
29.01	Lancs MT QF	DARWEN	79	4 - 1	Nolan 28, Dugdale 47, Molloy 50, Furlong 81
02.02	Unib. P	GATESHEAD	195	2 - 2	Molyneux 39, Nolan 90
09.02	Unib. P	BISHOP AUCKLAND	202	1 - 0	Stanton 3
16.02	Unib. P	Whitby Town	309	3 - 1	Furlong 1 21, Dugdae 36
19.02	Lancs MT SF	ACCRINGTON STANLEY	178	0 - 1	
23.02	Unib. P	BRADFORD PARK AVENUE	213	0 - 2	
04.03	Unib. P	Hyde United	322	2 - 3	Malloy 50, Knowles 89
09.03	Unib. P	BLYTH SPARTANS	185	1 - 2	Leahey 4
16.03	Unib. P	Worksop Town	412	1 - 3	Furlong 63
23.03	Unib. P	WORKSOP TOWN	228	2 - 3	Birch 38, Dann 83
30.03	Unib. P	Altrincham	557	3 - 0	Furlong 46, Knowles 76, Mason 90
01.04	Unib. P	BURTON ALBION	531	0 - 0	
09.04	Unib. P	Droylsden	120	1 - 3	Mason 58
13.04	Unib. P	RUNCORN HALTON	229	1 - 3	Furlong 21
15.04	Unib. P	Emley	171	0 - 3	
20.04	Unib. P	Gateshead	128	0 - 2	
27.04	Unib. P	Frickley Athletic	125	0 - 3	
03.05	Unib. P	Lancaster City	280	3 - 0	Alty 11, Mason 70, Birch 84

PLAYING SQUAD

Goalkeepers: Gary Maguire (Stockport), Matty Taylor (Preston)

Defenders: Shaun Teale (Southport), Carl Macauley (Telford), Jeff Underwood (Southport), Ryan Bowen (Youth), Tommy Molloy (Youth)

Midfield: Marvin Molyneux (Youth), Peter Wright (Halifax), Ray Birch (Congleton), Steve Hussey (Everton), John Lawless (Youth)

Forwards: Gary Martindale (Telford), John Norman (Morecambe), Lee Furlong (Southport), Kris McHale (Marine)

COLWYN BAY

CLUB OFFICIALS

Chairman: Henry Chapman

Directors: M.Roberts,R.Hayley,C.Chambers, I.Saunders,Miss M Jones, Miss M Martin,Miss J.E.Jones

Secretary / Press Officer: Mike Roberts, 18 Belgrave Road,Colwyn Bay, N.Wales Tel Nos:01492 534724(H) 07887 782565 (M)

FOOTBALL MANAGEMENT TEAM
Manager: Colin Caton
Assistant Manager: Dean Martin
Physio: Colin Edwards

FACT FILE

Formed: 1885
Nickname: `Bay' or `Seagulls'
Sponsors: Bay View Centre
Colours: All Sky Blue.
Change colours: Tangerine
Reserve Team:
Midweek home matchday: Tuesday

2000-01 Captain: Graham Roberts
P.o.Y.: James McIlvogue
Top scorer: Deiniol Graham 25

Colwyn Bay
Clwb Pêl Droed Bae Colwyn

BAY VS **GATESHEAD**
UNIBOND LEAGUE PREMIER DIVISION

Saturday 16th March 2002
KO 3:00pm

Pages: 28 Price: £1
Editor: Andy Owens (01614316938)
Local Press: North Wales Weekly News, North Wales Pioneer.
Club Website: www.cbfc.skynow.co.uk

GROUND Llanelian Road, Old Colwyn, N.Wales.   Tel: 01492 514581
Email Address:mikerobs@cbfc.freeserve.co.uk
Directions: M55 North Wales Coast - approaching Colwyn Bay take 1st exit signposted Old Colwyn, left at bottom slip road, straight over r'bout into Llanelian Rd - ground half mile on right. 2 miles from Colwyn Bar BR station.
Capacity: 2,500   Seats: 250   Cover: 700
Clubhouse: Open matchdays only.
Club Shop: Yes - contact: A Holden 01492 534287 Metal Badges: Yes

PREVIOUS	Leagues: Nth Wales Coast 01-21 33-35; Welsh National 21-30; Nth Wales Comb. 30-31; Welsh Lg (Nth) 45-84; North West Counties 84-91
	Grounds: Eiras Park 1930-82; Llanelian Road 82-92; Northwich Victoria FC 92-93; Ellesmere Port Stadium 94-95 (2 years in exile thro' dispute with FAW re League of Wales).
CLUB RECORDS	**Attendance:** 5,000 (at Eiras Park) v Borough United, 1964.
	Goalscorer: Peter Donnelly **Appearances:** Bryn A Jones
BEST SEASON	**FA Trophy:** Quarter Finals 96-97.
	F.A Cup: Second Round Proper 95-96 v Blackpool (A) 0-2. League club defeated: Wrexham(Welsh Cup)
HONOURS	Northern Premier Lg Div 1 91-92 (Div 1 Cup 91-92); North West Counties Lg R-up90-91 (Div 3 R-up 83-84, Lg Cup 88-89, Floodlit Cup 90-91; Welsh Cup SF 91-92;Welsh National Lg R-up 27-28 29-30; Nth Wales Comb. 30-31; Welsh Lg Nth 64-65 82-83 83-84 (R-up 35-36 45-46 63-64), Lg Cup 27-28; Alves Cup 63-64; Cookson Cup 73-74 79-80 80-81 81-82 83-84; Barritt Cup 79-80 81-82 83-84; Nth Wales Coast Chal. Cup 30-31 31-32 81-82 82-83 83-84 95-96 97-98; Nth Wales Coast Jnr Cup 1898-99. North Wst Coast Cup 99-00.

Players progressing: Peter Suddaby (Blackpool), Gareth Davies (Wrexham).

Left to Right,
Back:
James McIlvogue,
Alun Evans,
Jason Jones,
Glen Graham,
Paul Smith,
Dean Williams,
Paul Jones,
Owain Roberts,
Colin Caton.

Front:
Deiniol Graham,
Craig Lawton,
Craig Hogg,
Stuart Scheuber,
Robbie Williams.

Photo: Ian Saunders

Match Facts 2001-02

Date	Comp.	Opponents	Att.	Score	Goalscorers
18.08	Unib. P	LANCASTER CITY	295	1 - 2	Limbert 66
21.08	Unib. P	Droylsden	202	2 - 3	J Jones 46, McIlvogue 60
25.08	Unib. P	ALTRINCHAM	457	2 - 5	Evans 22[p] 38
27.08	Unib. P	Vauxhall Motors	357	1 - 1	Evans 80
01.09	Unib. P	Hyde United	267	2 - 1	J Jones 39, D Graham 50
04.09	Unib. P	ACCRINGTON STANLEY	290	3 - 0	Limbert 17 86, D Graham 57
08.09	Unib. P	HUCKNALL TOWN	288	1 - 1	Evans 68
11.09	Unib. P	Bamber Bridge	135	2 - 1	D Graham 46[p], McIlvogue 88
15.09	Unib. P	BISHOP AUCKLAND	262	1 - 2	D Graham 87
18.09	Unib. P	RUNCORN HALTON	249	1 - 0	Cross 22
22.09	Unib. P	Emley	241	0 - 2	
25.09	Lge Cup G5	Witton Albion	165	0 - 1	
29.09	FA Cup Q2	FARSLEY CELTIC	392	2 - 2	McIlvogue 68, Caton 90
02.10	FA Cup Q2 R	Farsley Celtic	187	1 - 3	
05.10	Unib. P	VAUXHALL MOTORS	266	1 - 0	Barton 45
09.10	Lge Cup G5	RUNCORN HALTON	220	3 - 3	Cross 26, Barton 52 85
13.10	Unib. P	Burscough	191	0 - 4	
17.10	Unib. P	Accrington Stanley	316	0 - 3	
20.10	Unib. P	WORKSOP TOWN	295	0 - 3	
23.10	Lge Cup G5	VAUXHALL MOTORS	145	2 - 2	McIlvogue 17 38
27.10	Unib. P	Gateshead	201	3 - 3	Williams 24, McIlvogue 40, D Graham 45
30.10	Unib. P	HYDE UNITED	209	4 - 4	McIlvogue 13 25, J Jones 54, D Graham 86
03.11	FA Trophy 1	Harrogate Town	305	0 - 2	
06.11	Unib. P	Barrow	964	1 - 1	D Graham 34[p]
10.11	Unib. P	BRADFORD PARK AVENUE	309	1 - 2	Limbert 67
17.11	Unib. P	Hucknall Town	186	1 - 1	J Jones 76
20.11	Unib. P	Runcorn Halton	211	2 - 1	J Jones 14, Limbert 65
24.11	Unib. P	BAMBER BRIDGE	260	0 - 0	
01.12	Unib. P	Gainsborough Trinity	288	2 - 1	McIlvogue 72, Evans 83
08.12	Unib. P	FRICKLEY ATHLETIC	262	1 - 5	McIlvogue 34
11.12	Lge Cup G5	TRAFFORD	94	0 - 2	
15.12	Unib. P	Whitby Town	239	0 - 1	
18.12	Lge Cup G5	Altrincham	176	1 - 2	Scheuber 21
26.12	Unib. P	BURSCOUGH	187	2 - 1	Williams 45, J Jones 67
29.12	Unib. P	BLYTH SPARTANS	265	1 - 1	Lawton 65
12.01	Unib. P	Bishop Auckland	172	2 - 1	D Graham 29[p], McIlvogue 65
19.01	Unib. P	BURTON ALBION	733	1 - 3	D Graham 38
02.02	Unib. P	Altrincham	680	0 - 4	
09.02	Unib. P	Worksop Town	349	1 - 2	G Graham 49
16.02	North WCC 3	Bodedern	100	2 - 0	Evans 4, Graham 41
23.02	Unib. P	Lancaster City	357	1 - 2	Roberts 74
02.03	Unib. P	WHITBY TOWN	229	1 - 1	D Graham 69[p]
07.03	North WCC 5	RHYL	190	3 - 1	D Graham 25 30 40
16.03	Unib. P	GATESHEAD	227	1 - 2	Scholber 45
19.03	Unib. P	Marine	214	1 - 1	Lawton 34
23.03	Unib. P	BARROW	293	0 - 5	
30.03	Unib. P	Burton Albion	1591	0 - 1	
01.04	Unib. P	MARINE	295	1 - 1	Scheuber 65
06.04	Unib. P	Frickley Athletic	131	1 - 2	McIlvogue 52
13.04	Unib. P	GAINSBOROUGH TRINITY	224	2 - 1	Evans 16 66
15.04	North WCC QF	BANGOR CITY	140	5 - 1	D Graham 15, McIlvogue 23 27, Roberts 66[p], S Jones 74
17.04	Unib. P	EMLEY	205	1 - 0	Furlong 24
20.04	Unib. P	Blyth Spartans	324	0 - 2	
24.04	North WCC SF	CAERNARFON TOWN	n.k	1 - 2	D Graham @ Conwy United
27.04	Unib. P	Bradford Park Avenue	265	0 - 5	
03.05	Unib. P	DROYLSDEN	385	1 - 0	Limbert 35

PLAYING SQUAD

Goalkeepers: Matthew Boswell (Rocester)
Defenders: Adrian Moody (Wrexham), Colin Caton (Witton), Craig Hogg (Everton), Dewi Parry (Rhyl), Gary Curtiss (Rhyl), Lee Coathup (Rhyl), Neil Rigby (Rhyl)
Midfield: Craig Lawton (Holywell), Graham Roberts (Macclesfield), Marc Limbert (Altrincham), John Stannard (Rhyl), Owain Roberts (Ruthin), Andy Jones (Rhyl), Stuart Scheuber (Altrincham)
Forwards: Alun Evans (Ebbw Vale), James McIlvogue (Conwy), Carl Furlong (Rhyl), Deniol Graham (Cwmbran), Lee Kissock (Radcliffe B), Jon Fisher-Cooke (Rhyl), Danny Barton (Caernarfon)

DROYLSDEN

DROYLSDEN FOOTBALL CLUB

CLUB OFFICIALS

Chairman: **David Pace**

Secretary: **Alan Slater**
83 King Edward Rd.,Hyde,
Cheshire SK14 5JJ
Tel & Fax: 0161 368 3687

FOOTBALL MANAGEMENT TEAM
Manager: David Pace
Asst Manager: Aeon Lattie
Physio Alan Cross

FACT FILE
Formed: 1892 Nickname: The Bloods
Sponsors:Alpha Court Windows
Colours: Red /black/black
Change colours: Yellow/Blue/Blue
Midweek matchday: Monday
2001-02
Captain : Paul Phillips
P.o.Y.: Adam Farley
Top Scorer: Nigel Evans

BLOOD'S REVIEW
Programme Sponsored by Alpha Group

GROUND The Butchers Arms Ground, Market Street, Droylsden, Manchester M43 7AY
Tel: 0161 370 1426/8341 FAX: 0161 370 8341
Directions: The ground lies 4 miles east of Manchester via the A662 Ashton New Road,
behind Butchers Arms Hotel.From M60 Jct 23 (opening August 2000) Follow A662 to
Doylsden. Right at lights in town centre through mini roundabout and ground on left.
Capacity: 3,500 **Cover:** 2,000 Seats:500

Pages: 24 Price: £1.00
Editor: T.B.A.Local Press: Tameside Reporter,
Tameside Advertiser
Local Radio: BBC Manchester
Club Website: wwwdroylsdenfc.fsnet.co.uk

Clubhouse: Pub hours except matchdays. Pool and darts **Shop:** Yes Metal Badges

PREVIOUS **Leagues:** Manchester; Lancs Com 36-59, 50-68; Cheshire County 39-50, 68-82; NW Counties 82-87

CLUB RECORDS **Attendance:** 4,250 v Grimsby, **FA Cup** 1st rd 1976
Scorer: E Gillibrand 78 (1931-32) **Win:** 13-2 v Lucas Sports Club
Fee Received: £11,000 for Tony Naylor (Crewe)

BEST SEASON **FA Cup:** 2nd Rd 78-79 v Altrincham (H) 0-2. League clubs defeated: Rochdale 78-79
FA Vase: **FA Trophy:**

HONOURS Northern Prem Lge Div 1 98-99, R-up 89-90, Div 1 Cup 87-88, R-up 88-9, 98-9 NPL President's Cup 98-99 Chairmans Cup
R-up: 01-02; NW Counties Lge Div 2 86-87; Cheshire County Lge R-up 39-40 45-46, Lge Cup 77-78 (R-up 76-77); Lancs Comb Div 2 R-up 55-56
58-59 62-63; Manchester Lge 30-31 32-33 (Lge Cup 23-24 33-34); Manchester Prem Cup 80-81 (R-up 83-84 90-91 93-94); Man Sen Cup 72-73
75-76 78-79 (R-up 72-73 75-76 78-79); Manchester Interm Cup 59-60 64-65 69-70; Manchester Chall Shield 46-47

Players progressing: Albert Butterworth & F Letchford (Blackpool 1931), William Davies & Maurice Randall (Crewe 1947), William Mellor (Accrington 1950),
Geoff Tonge (Bury 1960), David Campbell (WBA 1962), Kevin Randall (Bury 1965), Peter Litchfield (Preston 1979), Tony Naylor (Crewe 1990)

Back row, left to right: Aeori Lattie, Nigel Evans, Harvey Cunningham, James Glendenning, Robert Pell, Adam Farley,
Robert Trees, Mark Bradshaw, David Kerr, Iain Brunskill and Alan Cross (Physio).
Front row: Neil Hall, Darren Wright, Danny Warner, Paul Phillips, Steve Porter, Scott Willis and Steve Quinn

Date	Comp.	Opponents	Att.	Score	Goalscorers
21.08	Unib. P	COLWYN BAY	202	3 - 2	Richardson 14 78, Moore 33
25.08	Unib. P	BARROW	372	2 - 0	Evans 42, Warner 80
27.08	Unib. P	Runcorn Halton	380	0 - 2	
01.09	Unib. P	Worksop Town	347	3 - 0	Green 12, Pell 28, Warner 55
04.09	Unib. P	HYDE UNITED	484	3 - 2	Evans 40 77, Warner 67
08.09	Unib. P	GATESHEAD	245	0 - 1	
12.09	Unib. P	Accrington Stanley	285	2 - 5	Evans 27 53
15.09	Unib. P	Hucknall Town	126	0 - 1	
18.09	Unib. P	BRADFORD PARK AVENUE	143	2 - 2	Pell 7, Evans 81
22.09	Unib. P	BLYTH SPARTANS	201	0 - 0	
25.09	Lge Cup G6	Ossett Town	117	2 - 0	Kinney 66, Richardson 75
29.09	FA Cup Q2	Bradford Park Avenue	297	2 - 3	Kinney 25 30
02.10	Unib. P	EMLEY	175	3 - 2	Evans 3 70, Moore 76
07.10	Unib. P	Hyde United	432	3 - 0	Glendenning 24, Kinney 35 60
09.10	Lge Cup G6	ASHTON UNITED	139	2 - 5	Cunningham 50, Bradshaw 90
13.10	Unib. P	Bishop Auckland	165	2 - 1	Evans 30, Kinney 55
16.10	Unib. P	Lancaster City	320	2 - 2	Holmes 38 55
20.10	Unib. P	WHITBY TOWN	177	2 - 3	Holmes 10 37
22.10	Lge Cup G6	Hyde United	258	3 - 3	Evans 67 72, Richardson 79
27.10	Unib. P	Bradford Park Avenue	253	1 - 3	Holmes 54
30.10	Manc PC 1	Abbey Hey	90	1 - 2	Pell 88
03.11	FA Trophy 1	FRICKLEY ATHLETIC	140	1 - 1	Evans 23
06.11	FA Trophy 1 R	Frickley Athletic	176	1 - 1	Holmes 37Lost 3-4 after pens.
10.11	Unib. P	Frickley Athletic	149	1 - 3	Evans 32
13.11	Unib. P	BURTON ALBION	336	0 - 7	
17.11	Unib. P	Burscough	186	2 - 6	Molyneux 29[og], Evans 70
24.11	Unib. P	ACCRINGTON STANLEY	259	1 - 5	Hayder 89
01.12	Unib. P	Bamber Bridge	217	3 - 3	Brunskill 25, Pell 75, Warner 89
08.12	Unib. P	VAUXHALL MOTORS	167	3 - 2	Glendenning 29 67, Pell 63
15.12	Unib. P	GAINSBOROUGH TRINITY	141	1 - 2	Pell 34
18.12	Lge Cup G6	EMLEY	89	3 - 0	Lattie 13, Kerr 75, Phillips 90[p]
22.12	Unib. P	Altrincham	796	2 - 2	Kent 45, Lattie 48
08.01	Lge Cup G6	Ossett Albion	80	6 - 1	Evans 6, Pell 45 66, Wright 59, Hamilton 80 89
12.01	Unib. P	BAMBER BRIDGE	204	0 - 0	
19.01	Unib. P	Marine	218	4 - 2	Peel 10, Porter 18 76, Evans 74
29.01	Chair. Cup QF	CHORLEY	77	3 - 3	Hamilton 30, Richardson 86[p], Glendenning 115 Won 3-2 after pens.
02.02	Unib. P	Emley	254	2 - 4	Pell 59, Warner 67
12.02	Unib. P	HUCKNALL TOWN	121	3 - 0	Evans 51, Willis 72, Pell 81
16.02	Unib. P	Gateshead	145	0 - 2	
02.03	Unib. P	Gainsborough Trinity	311	3 - 1	Bradshaw 33, Wright 37, Evans 82
05.03	Unib. P	ALTRINCHAM	402	2 - 0	Wright 40, Evans 54
09.03	Chair. Cup SF	Harrogate Town	364	1 - 0	Hall 104
12.03	Unib. P	RUNCORN HALTON	119	0 - 1	
16.03	Unib. P	LANCASTER CITY	201	2 - 0	Glendenning 54, Pell 80
19.03	Unib. P	Barrow	721	2 - 1	Pell 7, Willis 75
23.03	Unib. P	Blyth Spartans	326	0 - 0	
26.03	Unib. P	WORKSOP TOWN	216	0 - 2	
30.03	Unib. P	FRICKLEY ATHLETIC	177	1 - 0	Lattie 84
03.04	Unib. P	Vauxhall Motors	174	0 - 1	
09.04	Unib. P	BURSCOUGH	120	3 - 1	Malloy 13[og], Porter 38, Wright 76
13.04	Unib. P	Whitby Town	326	0 - 3	
17.04	Chair. Cup F	WORKSOP TOWN	470	1 - 2	Pell 70
20.04	Unib. P	Burton Albion	2170	1 - 1	Willis 69
27.04	Unib. P	MARINE	238	0 - 2	
30.04	Unib. P	BISHOP AUCKLAND	82	1 - 0	Willis 45
03.05	Unib. P	Colwyn Bay	385	0 - 1	

PLAYING SQUAD

Goalkeepers: Paul Phillips (Curzon Ashton)

Defenders: Adam Farley (Altrincham), Aeon Lattie (Flixton), Danny Warner (Curzon Ashton), Dave Ashton (Curzon Ashton), Gary Burke (Northwich), Ged Murphy (Stalybridge), James Glendinning (St Helens), Stuart Locke (Accrington Stanley)

Midfield: Neil Hall (Hyde), Steve Porter (Burscough), Steve Quinn (Woodley Sports), Lloyd Richardson (Salford C)

Forwards: Darren Wright (Chester), Leon Hamilton (Curzon Ashton), Nigel Evans (Stalybridge), Wael Nazha (Ossett T)

FRICKLEY ATHLETIC

FRICKLEY ATHLETIC F.C

OFFICIAL CLUB PROGRAMME · PRICE £1.20
SEASON 2002/03

FRICKLEY A F C

The Blues
v
BARROW A.F.C.

UniBond Premier League
31st August 2002
Kick Off 3.00pm

CLUB OFFICIALS

Chairman: Peter Bywater
Directors:K.Day,P.Draper,S.Pennock, T.Corke and L.Beckett
Financial Secretary: A.Steele
Tel: 0114 2460218
Secretary : Ruth Simpson,67 Brooksfield Court, South Kirby, Pontefract,.WF9 3DL
Tel No: 01977 641116

FOOTBALL MANAGEMENT TEAM

Manager: Phil Sharpe
Assistant Manager: Mark Hancock

FACT FILE

Formed: 1910   Nickname: The Blues

Sponsors: Next Distributions

Colours: All blue with white stripe on shirt

Change colours: Yellow & black.

Midweek home matchday: Tuesday

Reserves' League: Doncaster Senior

Website: www.frickleyafc.co.uk

2001-02

Captain: Steve Price P.o.Y.:Simon Collins

Top Goalscorer: Andy Evans

GROUNDWestfield Lane, South Elmsall, Pontefract   Tel/Fax: 01977 642460
Email Address: steve@ frickleyafc.co.uk
Directions: Follow signs for South Elmsall from A1 and A638. Left at Superdrug warehouse, right at T junction and immediately left up Westfield Lane. Left into Oxford Road (opposite Westfield Hotel) - ground at bottom on right. Two miles from South Elmsall (BR).
Capacity: 6,000   **Cover:** 2,500   **Seats:** 800
Clubhouse: On ground open matchdays, food available.
Club Shop: Yes

Pages: 40 Price: £1
Editor: S Pennock Tel: 01302 835956

Local Press: South Yorks Times,
Hemsworth & South Elmsall Express.
Local Radio: Radio Sheffield, Radio
Hallam, Radio Leeds and Ridings F.M.

PREVIOUS   Leagues: Sheffield; Yorkshire 22-24; Midland Counties 24-33 34-60 70-76;Cheshire County 60-70;
Northern Premier 76-80; GMV Conference (Alliance Premier) 80-87.   Name: Frickley Colliery

CLUB RECORDS   **Attendance:** 6,500 v Rotherham United, FA Cup First Round 1971.
Goalscorer: K Whiteley.   **Defeat:** 0-12 v Worksop 2000-01 Unibond Premier   **Fee Paid:** £1,800.
Fee Received: £12,500 for Paul Shirtliff (Boston Utd) & £12,500 for Russ Wilcox (Northampton)

BEST SEASON   **FA Cup:** 3rd Rd 1985-86 (1-3 v Rotherham H).2nd Rd 84-85. (0-1 at Darlington). 1st Rd 36-37 57-58 63-64 71-72 73-74
83-84 86-87 88-89 00-01. League clubs defeated: Hartlepool United 85-86.   **FA Trophy:** Quarter-Finals 84-85.

HONOURS   Alliance Premier Lg R-up 85-86, Midland Counties Lg R-up 72-73 (Lg Cup 75-76),Yorkshire Lg R-up 23-24, Sheffield &
Hallamshire Senior Cup 27-28 56-57 60-6162-63 66-67 78-79 85-86 87-88 89-90 99-00, Sheffield Assoc. Lg 20-21 (R-up 11-12).
Players Progressing: Dennis Smith & Jack Brownsword (Hull1946), Stan Scrimshaw (Halifax 1947), William Callaghan (Aldershot 1949), Leo Dickens 1950), John Ashley & Graham Caulfield (York 1950 & 67), Ron Barritt(Leeds 1951), John Pickup (Bradford PA 1955), Tom Hymers & Arthur Ashmore &Stewart Gray (Doncaster 1958 & 66 & 78), Colin Roberts (Bradford City 1959),Derek Downing (Middlesbrough 1965), Graham Reed & Russell Wilcox (Northampton1985 & 86), Will Foley (Swansea 1986), Gary Brook (Newport 1987), Wayne Scargill (Bradford City 94-95), Andy Hayward (Rotherham Utd.).

Back row, left to right: Antony Jackson, Phil Sharpe (Manager), Robert Peel, Pete Myers, Craig Marsh, Jon Wordsworth, Craig Elkin, Andy Evans, Mark Hine, Paul Marquis and Ronnie Akers (Physio). **Front row:** Lee Morris, Remo Nesa, David Jones, Mark Hancock (Assistant Manager), Ryan Williams, Chris Gowen, Mark Wilkinson and Paul Bruke.

NORTHERN PREMIER LEAGUE PREMIER DIVISION

Date	Comp.	Opponents	Att.	Score	Goalscorers
18.08	Unib. P	Burscough	205	0 - 1	
21.08	Unib. P	WHITBY TOWN	243	1 - 4	Fothergill 79
25.08	Unib. P	BLYTH SPARTANS	168	1 - 5	Bernard 46
01.09	Unib. P	Gateshead	259	0 - 0	
04.09	Unib. P	BURTON ALBION	513	0 - 5	
08.09	Unib. P	Vauxhall Motors	275	1 - 3	Santos 25
11.09	Unib. P	Worksop Town	370	1 - 1	Lewis 65
15.09	Unib. P	ACCRINGTON STANLEY	194	1 - 3	Collins 74
18.09	Unib. P	Whitby Town	178	3 - 1	Lewis 10 25 90
22.09	Unib. P	BARROW	258	2 - 3	Savic 65, Hanby 77
25.09	Lge Cup G8	Stocksbridge Park Steels	171	1 - 2	Fothergill 5
29.09	FA Cup Q2	Altrincham	537	1 - 4	Fothergill 83
02.10	Unib. P	GAINSBOROUGH TRINITY	256	3 - 1	Own-Goal 17, Price 58[p] 79
06.10	Unib. P	Bradford Park Avenue	325	0 - 3	
09.10	Lge Cup G8	NORTH FERRIBY UNITED	99	4 - 1	Savic 50 68, Scott Collins 83, Simon Collins 84
13.10	Unib. P	HYDE UNITED	169	2 - 2	Price 28[p], Lewis 65
16.10	Unib. P	Blyth Spartans	345	0 - 0	
20.10	Unib. P	BAMBER BRIDGE	162	2 - 0	Lewis 71, Evans 89
23.10	Lge Cup G8	Gainsborough Trinity	307	1 - 2	Lewis 76
27.10	Unib. P	Runcorn Halton	241	0 - 1	
30.10	Unib. P	BISHOP AUCKLAND	157	2 - 1	Fothergill 26, Evans 40
03.11	FA Trophy 1	Droylsden	140	1 - 1	Evans 66
06.11	FA Trophy 1 R	DROYLSDEN	176	1 - 1	Duffty 52 4 3
10.11	Unib. P	DROYLSDEN	149	3 - 1	Evans 13 57, Price 48[p]
13.11	Sheff SC 1	Sheffield	179	3 - 1	Fothergill 13 28, Myers 75
16.11	Unib. P	Hyde United	307	0 - 0	
24.11	Unib. P	ALTRINCHAM	296	3 - 1	Collins 13 28, Myers 24
27.11	Lge Cup G8	WORKSOP TOWN	239	1 - 4	Price 28[p]
01.12	FA Trophy 2	Grantham Town	410	1 - 5	Lewis 62
04.12	Sheff SC 2	MEXBOROUGH MAIN STREET	n.k	3 - 2	Evans 40, Duffty 70, Oleksewycz 80
08.12	Unib. P	Colwyn Bay	262	5 - 1	Oleksewycz 41 64 88, Evans 52 80
11.12	Lge Cup G8	LINCOLN UNITED	76	4 - 2	Fothergill 4 38, Price 27, Scott Collins 30
15.12	Unib. P	LANCASTER CITY	193	1 - 4	Evans 50
21.12	Unib. P	Gainsborough Trinity	266	2 - 2	Price 12, Collins 46
26.12	Unib. P	Emley	474	1 - 2	Simon Collins 62
12.01	Unib. P	Hucknall Town	212	4 - 3	Evans 32, Jones 88, Price 89[p], Prendergast 90
19.01	Unib. P	Barrow	1100	1 - 3	Chambers 83
26.01	Unib. P	RUNCORN HALTON	158	2 - 4	Evans 65 85
02.02	Unib. P	Bishop Auckland	188	1 - 1	Evans 70
09.02	Unib. P	Marine	236	0 - 4	
16.02	Unib. P	VAUXHALL MOTORS	160	1 - 0	Gowan 22
19.02	Unib. P	WORKSOP TOWN	319	4 - 0	Simon Collins 12, Chambers 60 89, Myers 70
23.02	Unib. P	Accrington Stanley	403	1 - 1	Myers 70
02.03	Unib. P	HUCKNALL TOWN	152	0 - 1	
05.03	Sheff SC QF	Stocksbridge Park Steels	129	1 - 0	Myers 52
09.03	Unib. P	Altrincham	632	2 - 0	Chambers 31, Evans 48
16.03	Unib. P	MARINE	173	3 - 0	Chambers 22, Collins 65, Lewis 80
19.03	Unib. P	BRADFORD PARK AVENUE	447	0 - 0	
26.03	Sheff SC SF	DONCASTER ROVERS	582	1 - 3	Evans 48
30.03	Unib. P	Droylsden	177	0 - 1	
01.04	Unib. P	EMLEY	302	1 - 1	Myers 49
06.04	Unib. P	COLWYN BAY	131	2 - 1	Prendergast 11, Simon Collins 57
13.04	Unib. P	Lancaster City	260	2 - 0	Chambers 52, Prendergast 71
20.04	Unib. P	Bamber Bridge	218	2 - 0	Price 54, Chambers 77
27.04	Unib. P	BURSCOUGH	125	3 - 0	Collins 56 68, Prendergast 78
30.04	Unib. P	Burton Albion	1018	0 - 4	
03.05	Unib. P	GATESHEAD	149	0 - 0	

PLAYING SQUAD

Goalkeepers: Mark Wilkinson (Stocksbridge), Chris Howe (Rossington Main)
Defenders: Phil Sharpe (Guiseley), Chris Gowen (York), Paul Marquis (Bradford PA), Mark Hancock (Bradford PA), Nicky Limber (Gainsborough Trinity), Andy Gregory (Emley)
Midfield: Keiron Darlow (Harrogate T), Mark Hine (Armthorpe), Richard Bashforth (Youth), Matt Russell (Pickering), Duncan Milligan (Harrogate T)
Forwards: Andy Evans (Stalybridge), Graham Lewis (Northwich), Paul Burke (Harrogate T), Lee Morris (Hallam), Adam Russell (Barry), Craig Marsh (Matlock), Gary Duffty (Matlock)

GAINSBOROUGH TRINITY

GAINSBOROUGH TRINITY
versus
BRADFORD
PARK AVENUE
2001/02 SEASON
4th September 2001

T
H
E

B
L
U
E
S

Main Club Sponsor
T BLAND
WELDING

OFFICIAL PROGRAMME £1.20

CLUB OFFICIALS

Chairman: **Pat Lobley** Pres: **Ken Marsden.**
Directors:T.Hanson(Commercial),Nicholson
,T.Johnson,S.Horsley,A.Lobley,M.Hewson
R.Coleman and D.Keeley
Secretary/Press Officer: Frank Nicholson
9 North Street, Morton,
Gainsborough, Lincs DN213AS.
Tel. 01427 615239, Fax 01427 615239

FACT FILE

Formed: 1873
Nickname: The Blues
Sponsors: T Bland Welding
Colours: All Blue
Change colours: Yellow/black/yellow
Midweek home matchday: Tuesday
Youth League: Northern Youth Alliance

FOOTBALL MANAGEMENT TEAM
Manager:Phil Stant
Asst Manager: Colin Benson
Physio: Peter Jellett

2001-02
Captain: John Reed
P.o.Y.: Chris Hurst
Leading Goalscorer: Lee Ellington 23

GROUND   The Northolme, Gainsborough, Lincs DN21 2QW
Tel: 01427 - 613295 (office) 679109 (club) 613295 (Fax)
email: nicholsons.northstreet@virgin.net
Directions: The Northolme is situated opposite the Texaco and Fina petrol stations on the
A159 Gainsborough to Scunthorpe road. Two miles from Lea Road (BR)
Capacity: 4,000   Cover: 2,500   Seats: 1,015
Clubhouse: Executive `Club on the Park' (01427 679109) open Saturday matchday
lunchtimes. Restaurant facilities.
Club Shop: Souvenirs - Wendy Godley (01427 611612)
Programmes - Nigel Tasker (01522 542014)

PROGRAMME
Pages: 44   Price: £1.20
Editor: Basil Godley   Tel: 01427 611612

Local Press: Gainsborough News,
Lincolnshire Echo.
Local Radio: BBC Radio Lincs, Lincs FM

PREVIOUS   **Leagues:** Midland Counties 1889-96, 12-60, 61-68, Football Lge 1896-1912, Central Alliance 60-61.
Names: None   Grounds: None

CLUB RECORDS   **Attendance:** 9,760 v Scunthorpe Utd. Midland Lge. 1948.
Fee Paid: £3,000 for Stuart Lowe (Buxton 89-90).   **Fee Received:** £30,000 for Tony James (Lincoln 1988).
Win: 7-0 v Fleetwood Town and Great Harwood Town.   **Defeat:** 2-7 v Hyde Utd.

BEST SEASON   **FA Cup:** 3rd Rd 1886-87 v Lincoln C (A) 0-1 after 2-2, 1st Rd on 33 occasions.   **FA Trophy:** 2nd Rd, 2nd replay86-87.

HONOURS   Northern Premier Lge Cup 81-82 96-97 (R-up 71-72); Midland Co's Lge 1890-91,1927-28, 48-49, 66-67 (R-up 1891-92,
1895-96, 13-14, 28-29); Lincs Senior Cup 1889-90, 92-93, 94-95, 97-98, 1903-05, 06-07, 10-11, 46-49, 50-51, 57-59, 63-64

Players Progressing: Since 1980 - Stewart Evans (Sheffield Utd 80), Tony James, Ian Bowling & John Schofield (Lincoln 88), Dave
Redfern(Stockport 91), Richard Logan (Huddersfield 93), Glenn Humphries (Hull City).

Back row, left to right: Danny Brown, Chris Hurst, Andy Brownrigg, Dan Barrett, Barry Richardson, Alex Allen, Neil Allison, Max
Nicholson and John Reed. **Front row:** Lee Ellington, Luke Staton, Mark Anderson, Peter Jellett (Physio), Phil Stant (Manager), Colin
Benson (Assistant Manager), Dean Walling (Player/ Coach), Darren Knowles and Neil Mann.   **Photo:**Chris Etchells

NORTHERN PREMIER LEAGUE PREMIER DIVISION

Date	Comp.	Opponents	Att.	Score	Goalscorers
01.08	Lincs SC 1	GRANTHAM TOWN	n.k	0 - 0	Lost 2-4 after pens.
04.08	Lincoln Chall Tphy	Lincoln United	n.k	3 - 0	
18.08	Unib. P	ACCRINGTON STANLEY	475	5 - 2	Reed 10[p], Brown 45 47, Hirst 74, Watts 84
21.08	Unib. P	Hucknall Town	283	4 - 1	Gore 22, Ellington 50 73, Brown 75
25.08	Unib. P	Emley	321	1 - 2	Reed 80
27.08	Unib. P	WORKSOP TOWN	876	0 - 2	
01.09	Unib. P	Burton Albion	1204	2 - 4	Allison 55, Ranshaw 56
04.09	Unib. P	BRADFORD PARK AVENUE	398	4 - 1	Ellington 18, Reed 30, Holmes 70, Watts 85
08.09	Unib. P	BAMBER BRIDGE	393	5 - 0	Ellington 7 51, Allison 44, Watts 78, Ranshaw 81
10.09	Unib. P	Hyde United	308	1 - 1	Stanhope 44
15.09	Unib. P	Barrow	1198	0 - 3	
18.09	Unib. P	GATESHEAD	310	1 - 1	Bassinder 15
25.09	Lge Cup G8	North Ferriby United	140	1 - 2	Watts 37
29.09	FA Cup Q2	DUNSTON FEDERATION BREWERY	328	5 - 1	Gore 40, Ellington 55 90, Stanhope 62, Own-Goal 89
02.10	Unib. P	Frickley Athletic	256	1 - 3	Watts 13
05.10	Unib. P	Blyth Spartans	488	2 - 2	Watts 47 71
09.10	Lge Cup G8	WORKSOP TOWN	397	2 - 1	Ellington 40[p], Bassinder 49
13.10	FA Cup Q3	Worksop Town	756	0 - 4	
16.10	Unib. P	Whitby Town	245	4 - 0	Watts 33, Bassinder 34 48, McNamara 47
20.10	Unib. P	RUNCORN HALTON	385	1 - 4	Watts 15
23.10	Lge Cup G8	FRICKLEY ATHLETIC	307	2 - 1	Ellington 83 85
27.10	Unib. P	Burscough	175	1 - 3	Ellington 73
30.10	Unib. P	WHITBY TOWN	315	2 - 0	Hall 24, Hurst 77
03.11	FA Trophy 1	Ilkeston Town	468	0 - 1	
07.11	Unib. P	Bradford Park Avenue	220	0 - 2	
09.11	Unib. P	BISHOP AUCKLAND	290	1 - 1	Stanhope 34
17.11	Unib. P	Bishop Auckland	207	1 - 0	Watts 39
24.11	Unib. P	BARROW	475	0 - 1	
27.11	Lge Cup G8	Lincoln United	119	2 - 3	Hurst 20, Hall 90
01.12	Unib. P	COLWYN BAY	288	1 - 2	Ball 33
08.12	Unib. P	MARINE	273	0 - 0	
11.12	Lge Cup G8	STOCKSBRIDGE PARK STEELS	109	2 - 0	Williams 75, Ellington 86
15.12	Unib. P	Droylsden	141	2 - 1	Hurst 19, Raynor 47
21.12	Unib. P	FRICKLEY ATHLETIC	266	2 - 2	Ellington 30 80
12.01	Unib. P	Marine	236	1 - 1	Ellington 76
19.01	Unib. P	BURSCOUGH	305	3 - 1	Ellington 29[p] 60, Gonshall 52
02.02	Unib. P	HYDE UNITED	375	1 - 0	Brown 41
05.02	Pres. Cup QF	Altrincham	239	2 - 1	Hurst 80, Ellington 89[p]
09.02	Unib. P	BURTON ALBION	977	0 - 1	
12.02	Unib. P	Worksop Town	453	0 - 4	
16.02	Unib. P	Lancaster City	379	2 - 5	Williams 44, Brown 90
23.02	Unib. P	Bamber Bridge	238	0 - 1	
25.02	Unib. P	EMLEY	278	1 - 2	Brown 41
02.03	Unib. P	DROYLSDEN	311	1 - 3	Hurst 49
09.03	Pres. Cup SF	GUISELEY	328	5 - 1	Hurst 20, Ellington 31 51 58, Connell 65
12.03	Unib. P	LANCASTER CITY	255	3 - 2	Ellington 6 32, Williams 31
16.03	Unib. P	Altrincham	567	1 - 1	Hurst 48
19.03	Unib. P	HUCKNALL TOWN	309	0 - 0	
23.03	Unib. P	VAUXHALL MOTORS	310	2 - 1	Stanhope 56, Connell 68
27.03	Unib. P	Accrington Stanley	384	1 - 1	Payne 52
30.03	Unib. P	Gateshead	148	0 - 1	
01.04	Unib. P	BLYTH SPARTANS	334	2 - 1	Connell 10 25
06.04	Unib. P	Runcorn Halton	208	0 - 4	
13.04	Unib. P	Colwyn Bay	224	1 - 2	Ellington 53
16.04	Pres. Cup F	Barrow	488	0 - 1	@ Hyde United
20.04	Unib. P	ALTRINCHAM	450	1 - 3	Gowshall 59
23.04	Unib. P	Vauxhall Motors	151	0 - 4	

PLAYING SQUAD

Goalkeepers: Barry Richardson (Halifax)

Defenders: Alex Allen (Brodsworth), Darren Knowles (Northwich), Dean Walling (Camb Utd), Wayne Hall (York), Ian Gore (Boreham Wood), Neil Allison (Geyland Utd - Singapre)

Midfield: Chris Hurst (Frickley), Darren Holmes (Hallam), John Reed (Ethnikos Perez - Greece), Luke Staton (Merthyr), Neil Bray (Long Eaton), Mark Anderson (Scunthorpe), Frazer McHugh (Tamworth)

Forwards: Phil Stant (Hinckley Utd), Max Nicholson (Woodlands Wellington - Singapore), Lee Ellington (Exeter), Mark Guest (Dinnington), Paul Eshelby (Worksop)

GATESHEAD

Gateshead
FOOTBALLCLUB
Tynesider Matchday Magazine
Season 2001/2002
Gateshead v Lancaster City £1.00
Premier Division

CLUB OFFICIALS

Chairman: **John Gibson**

Vice Chairman: **Mike Coulson**

General Manager: **Mike Coulson**

Secretary: : **Mike Coulson**

Press Officer: **Dean Ranyard**

FOOTBALL MANAGEMENT TEAM

Managers : Gary Gill & Steve Agnew

Physio: Bev Dougherty

FACT FILE

Founded: 1930
Nickname: The Tynesiders
Sponsors: Cameron Hall Developments Ltd
Colours: White with black trim/ black/ white
Change colours: All red
Midweek home matchday: Wednesday
Supporters' Unofficial Website:
www.gatesheadfc.co.uk
Season 2001-02
Captain: Sam Kitchin
Top Scorer: Steve Preen 23
P.o.Y.: Steve Preen

GROUND International Stadium, Neilson Road, Gateshead, NE10 0EF.
Tel: 0191 478 3883 Fax : 0191 477 1315.
Directions: From the South follow A1(M) to Granada services (Birtley),take right hand fork marked A194(M) (Tyne Tunnel, South Shields) follow A194 to first roundabout, turn left onto A184 - then 3 miles to stadium. Turn right at traffic lights into Neilson Road. BY RAIL to Newcastle Central Station,transfer to the Metro System and then to Gateshead Stadium.
Capacity: 11,795 Seats: 11,795 Cover: 3,300
Clubhouse: Bar inside Tyne & Wear stand open before, during and after matches
Club Shop: Sells full range of souvenirs, badges, programmes & fanzines. Contact: Stella Dickenson (0191 478 3883)

Pages: 24 Price: £1.00
Editor: Dean Ranyard 07715 124588

Local Press: Gateshead Post, Newcastle Chronicle & Echo, Sunderland Echo, Sunday Sun. Local Radio: BBC Radio Newcastle, Metro FM, Century Radio.

PREVIOUS **Leagues:** Football League - Div. 3 N. 30-58, Div.4 58-60, Northern Counties League 60-62, North Regional League 1962-1968, Northern Premier 68-70, 73-83,85-86, 87-90; Wearside 70-71; Midland Lge 71-72; Alliance Premier (Conference)83-85, 86-87, 90-98. **Grounds:** Redheugh Park - 1930-1971

CLUB RECORDS **Attendance:** 11,750 v Newcastle United (Pre-Season Friendly. 7th August 95)
Win: 8-0 v Netherfield, Northern Premier League. **Defeat:** 0-9 v Sutton United, 22.09.90, GMVC.
Career goalscorer: Bob Topping **Career appearances:** Simon Smith, 450, 85-94
Fee paid: £9,000 for Paul Cavell (Dagenham &Redbridge). **Fee received:** For Kenny Cramman from Rushden & D.

BEST SEASON FA Cup: Quarter Final, 1952-53. v Bolton W (H) 0-1 **FA Trophy:** Quarter Final, 0-1 v Wycombe W. (A) 13.3.93

HONOURS Football League Div. 3 North R-up 31-32, 49-50; Northern Premier - Champions82-83, 85-86; Runners-up 89-90; Northern Premier League Cup R-up 89-90;Multipart Shield 85-86.

Players Progressing: Osher Williams(Southampton, Stockport, Port Vale, Preston), John McGinley (Sunderland,Lincoln), Billy Askew (Hull City, Newcastle United), Lawrie Pearson (Hull City,Port Vale), Ian Johnson (Northampton Town), Ken Davies (Stockport), Kenny Lowe(Birmingham C., Barnet, Darlington, Stoke C.)

Back row left to right: R.Howe (Kit Manager), S. Preen, L.Ellison, R.Bowman, P.Thompson and R.Jones. **Middle Row:** T.Miller (Press Officer),A Waggott (Director), S.Bowey, J.Mohan, L.Fitzgerald, Triallist, A.Swan, C, Lynch,B. Dougherty (Physio)., T.Buckingham, M.Coulson,(Secretary) and T.Bone (Director). **Front row:** S.Johansen, G De Lella, P.Ross, S.Agnew, J.Gibson (Chairman), G.Gill (Asst Manager), R Watson,W. Edgcumbe G.McAlindon and R.Alderson

Date	Comp.	Opponents	Att.	Score	Goalscorers
18.08	Unib. P	Marine	279	3 - 1	Preen 22, Alderson 24, Painter 71
22.08	Unib. P	BLYTH SPARTANS	426	1 - 1	Thompson 44
25.08	Unib. P	Whitby Town	402	3 - 2	Preen 2, Pitts 38[og], Jones 56
27.08	Unib. P	EMLEY	235	2 - 0	Thompson 12, Painter 64
01.09	Unib. P	FRICKLEY ATHLETIC	259	0 - 0	
04.09	Unib. P	Bishop Auckland	307	2 - 1	Painter 46, Ross 79
08.09	Unib. P	Droylsden	245	1 - 0	Preen 25
12.09	Unib. P	WHITBY TOWN	202	2 - 0	Painter 44, Preen 87
15.09	Unib. P	BURTON ALBION	402	1 - 1	Agnew 22
18.09	Unib. P	Gainsborough Trinity	310	1 - 1	Preen 32
22.09	Unib. P	Altrincham	659	1 - 3	Hawes 17[og]
26.09	Lge Cup G1	SPENNYMOOR UNITED	97	0 - 4	
29.09	FA Cup Q2	RUNCORN HALTON	242	2 - 4	Nelson 79, Preen 89
05.10	Unib. P	Bamber Bridge	173	4 - 1	Agnew 12, Preen 50 81, McAlindon 55
09.10	Lge Cup G1	Gretna	102	3 - 0	Nelson 65 90, McAlindon 70
13.10	Unib. P	BAMBER BRIDGE	173	1 - 1	Thompson 18
17.10	Lge Cup G1	Bishop Auckland	102	1 - 2	Preen 76
20.10	Unib. P	Vauxhall Motors	202	1 - 4	Painter 68
24.10	Durham CC 1	WEST AUCKLAND TOWN	103	4 - 2	McAlindon 21, Jameson 34, Preen 56, Nelson 89
27.10	Unib. P	COLWYN BAY	201	3 - 3	Preen 14 85, Ross 48
03.11	FA Trophy 1	REDDITCH UNITED	194	4 - 0	Jones 22, Niblett 43[og], Ross 55, Preen 82
14.11	Durham CC 2	BRANDON UNITED	115	3 - 2	Thompson 66, Morrell 68, Ross 105
17.11	Unib. P	MARINE	205	2 - 4	Painter 27, Agnew 72
21.11	Unib. P	Bradford Park Avenue	186	5 - 3	Morrell 10 14, Preen 20 75, Jones 24
24.11	Unib. P	Burton Albion	1502	1 - 5	Thompson 57
28.11	Lge Cup G1	BLYTH SPARTANS	134	4 - 1	Preen 17, Alderson 25, Jones 46, Painter 67
08.12	Unib. P	HYDE UNITED	265	4 - 1	Preen 7 89, Agnew 12, Morrell 46
10.12	FA Trophy 2	Hednesford Town	252	1 - 2	Preen 71
15.12	Unib. P	Barrow	1113	1 - 4	McAlindon 48
26.12	Unib. P	Blyth Spartans	810	1 - 2	Bowey 42[p]
09.01	Durham CC QF	CROOK TOWN	122	7 - 2	Alderson 12, Preen 26, Thompson 55, Bowey 70[p] 78 89, McAlindon 79
12.01	Unib. P	Hyde United	301	1 - 2	Morrell 75
19.01	Unib. P	LANCASTER CITY	195	1 - 2	Preen 15
26.01	Pres. Cup QF	Barrow	704	1 - 2	McAlindon 89
02.02	Unib. P	Burscough	195	2 - 2	Bowey 67, Preen 90
05.02	Durham CC SF	Billingham Town	n.k	0 - 1	
09.02	Unib. P	VAUXHALL MOTORS	135	0 - 2	
16.02	Unib. P	DROYLSDEN	145	2 - 0	Preen 63, McAlindon 70
02.03	Unib. P	ACCRINGTON STANLEY	206	0 - 0	
06.03	Unib. P	WORKSOP TOWN	156	0 - 3	
09.03	Unib. P	Runcorn Halton	217	1 - 1	McAlindon 53
12.03	Unib. P	Accrington Stanley	330	1 - 2	Jones 72
16.03	Unib. P	Colwyn Bay	227	2 - 1	Anthony 6, Alderson 85
20.03	Unib. P	BISHOP AUCKLAND	138	1 - 0	Alderson 57
23.03	Unib. P	RUNCORN HALTON	141	0 - 2	
30.03	Unib. P	GAINSBOROUGH TRINITY	148	1 - 0	Thompson 41
01.04	Unib. P	Worksop Town	507	1 - 2	Painter 13
03.04	Unib. P	BRADFORD PARK AVENUE	130	0 - 7	
06.04	Unib. P	ALTRINCHAM	172	0 - 2	
10.04	Unib. P	BARROW	125	0 - 0	
13.04	Unib. P	Hucknall Town	267	0 - 0	
17.04	Unib. P	HUCKNALL TOWN	123	1 - 1	Jones 67
20.04	Unib. P	BURSCOUGH	128	2 - 0	Jones 89, Bowman 90
23.04	Unib. P	Lancaster City	253	0 - 2	
29.04	Unib. P	Emley	172	2 - 2	Anthony 5, Lawson 56
03.05	Unib. P	Frickley Athletic	149	0 - 0	

PLAYING SQUAD

Goalkeepers: David Campbell (Bishop Auckland), Richard Siddall (Sheff Wed)

Defenders: David Goodchild (Whitby), David Morgan (Grimsby), Mark Sunley (Spennymoor), Nicky Mohan (Hull), Rob Bowman (Bohemians), Simon Bates (Spennymoor), Robert Jones (Spennymoor)

Midfield: Paul Thompson (Stevenage), Alex Lawson (Ashington), Neil Bishop (Billingham T), Neil Radigan (Blyth), Steve Agnew (York)

Forwards: David Colvin (Sheff Utd), Lee Flanagan (Billingham Synthonia), Steve Preen (Queen of the South), Gareth McAlinden (Scarborough), David Southern (Crook)

HARROGATE TOWN

CLUB OFFICIALS

Chairman: Bill Fotherby
Vice Chairman: Howard Matthews
President: Leslie Silver
Club/Company Secretary
Brian Russell 24 Hall Lane, Harrogate,
HG13DK Tel/Fax: 01423 525341
Managing Director: Nigel Pleasants

FOOTBALL MANAGEMENT TEAM
Team Manager: John Reed
Player/Coach: Neil Aspin

FACT FILE
Formed: 1919
Nickname: Town
Colours: All yellow
Change colours:All white
Midweek home matchday: Tuesday

2000-01
Leading goalscorer: Robbie Williams 27
Captain: Robbie Williams
Supporters' & Players'P.O.Y: Neil Aspin
Supporters Club P.O.Y:Ashley Grimes

GROUND: Wetherby Road, Harrogate.Tel:01423 883671 Clubhse, 01423 880675 Office&Fax
Sec.& Admin.Tel. & Fax: 01423 525341   Website:www.harrogatetownafc.co.uk
Directions: From Leeds turn right at traffic lights (Nid Vale Motors) into Hookstone Road,
continue to Woodlands Hotel (traffic lights) turn left into Wetherby Road, ground on the right.
From Harrogate (BR), turn left and left again, cross road (Odeon Cinema), proceed for about
400yds to main road, crossover to The Stray (open land) using footpath which leads to
Wetherby Rd, ground 200yds on left. From A61 turn right onto southern by pass then left on
to A661.Ground 400 yds on right after Sainsburys, lights and Woodlands Hotel.
From the West on A59 straight on to Wetherby Rd from Empress roundabout. ground on left.
From North: A59 exit from M1 then southern bypass to Wetherby Rd
Capacity: 3,800   Cover: 900   Seats: 450 Shop Yes (Phil Harrison 01423 525211)
Clubhouse: On ground, open every match day and for functions & special events.

Pages: 40   Price: £1.40
Editor: Bob Head
01423 549153 - 07799 834918M

Local Press: Yorkshire Post Group
Harrogate Advertiser Series
Local Radio: Radio Leeds, Radio York
Stray FM.

PREVIOUS   **Names:** Harrogate FC1919-32, Harrogate Hotspurs 35-48   **Ground:** Starbeck Lane 1919-20
Leagues: West Riding 1919-20 Yorkshire 20-21, 22-31, 57-82; Midland 21-22; Northern 31-32;
Harrogate & District 35-37 7 40-46 WRCAL 37-40 West Yorkshire 46-57; Northern Counties East 82-87

CLUB RECORDS **Attendance:** 4,280 v Railway Athletic, Whitworth Cup final 1950.
Win: 13-0 v Macklefield   **Defeat:** 1-10 v Methley United 1956

BEST SEASON   **FA Vase:** 4th Round 89-90 **FA Cup:** 3rd Qual. Rd Replay 87-88(0-2 at Bishop Auck after(1-1 draw) & 01-2 v Vauxhall M.0-3
F.A.Trophy: 3rd Rd Replay v Spennymoor United 99-00 & 2001-02 v Doncaster Rovers (away) 0-2

HONOURS   Unibond Div 1 Champions 2001-02,Northern Premier Lge Div 1 Cup 89-90; Northern Counties (East) Div 1(Nth) R-up 84-85
plus 3rd 85-86 & promoted. (Reserve Div 85-86, Reserve Div Cup 86-87); Yorkshire League Div 1 26-27 R-up 62-63 Div 2 81-82, Div 3 R-up 71-
72 80-81; West Riding County Cup 62-6372-73 85-86; 01-02 West Riding Challenge Cup 24-25 26-27

Players progressing: Tony Ingham (Leeds 47), Stewart Ferebee (York C. 79),Tim Hotte (Halifax T. 85), Andy Watson (Halifax T. 88),
Ian Blackstone(York C. 95) , Eric Stephenson (Leeds United1932)

Back row: Brian Russell (Company Secretary), Ian Marshall (Physio), Matt Alberty, Neil Aspin (Coach), Michael Ord, Chris Hudson, Ian
Blackstone, Scott Bairstow, Ashley Connor, Chris Hill, Michael McNaughton, Scott Bonsall, Craig Elliott,David Donaldson,Neil Sykes, Nigel
Pleasants (Managing Director) **Front Row:** Scott Conlon, Peter Atkinson, Duncan Richards, Robbie Whellans, John Reid (Manager),Bill Fotherby
(CHairman), Stephen Ball, Iain Dunn, Dave Morris, Colin Hunter, Martin Walker, (Kit Manager), and Mascot Francesca Briggs.

Date	Comp.	Opponents	Att.	Score	Goalscorers
18.08	Unib. 1	Lincoln United	140	1 - 2	Ord 9
21.08	Unib. 1	STOCKSBRIDGE PARK STEELS	218	2 - 0	Hall 52, Elliott 69
25.08	Unib. 1	WITTON ALBION	307	0 - 0	
27.08	Unib. 1	Ashton United	190	1 - 1	Whellans 75
01.09	FA Cup P	West Auckland Town	110	2 - 2	Atkinson 27, Albury 37
04.09	FA Cup P R	WEST AUCKLAND TOWN	220	4 - 1	McNaughton 30, Albery 33, Ball 60 65
08.09	Unib. 1	TRAFFORD	244	1 - 0	Dunn 85
11.09	Unib. 1	Farsley Celtic	171	3 - 0	Whellans 7, Atkinson 45[p], Albury 57
15.09	FA Cup Q1	Salford City	112	3 - 2	Whellans 26 45, Ball 35
18.09	Unib. 1	GUISELEY	316	2 - 0	Ball 52, Dunn 77
22.09	Unib. 1	Rossendale United	338	2 - 1	Blackstone 73 88
26.09	Lge Cup G3	Bradford Park Avenue	156	1 - 3	Blackstone 13
29.09	FA Cup Q2	BURSCOUGH	391	1 - 1	Ord 60
02.10	FA Cup Q2 R	Burscough	187	2 - 2	Won 5-4 after pens.
05.10	Unib. 1	North Ferriby United	194	3 - 1	Allerby 59 65, Merriss 83
09.10	Lge Cup G3	WHITBY TOWN	247	1 - 1	Severn 10
13.10	FA Cup Q3	Vauxhall Motors	409	1 - 3	Brazier 15[og]
16.10	Unib. 1	Eastwood Town	128	2 - 2	Aspin 16, Whellans 80
20.10	Unib. 1	RADCLIFFE BOROUGH	308	1 - 0	Blackstone 46
22.10	Lge Cup G3	Guiseley	161	1 - 2	Bonsall 90
27.10	Unib. 1	Matlock Town	289	1 - 1	Whellans 11
30.10	Unib. 1	FARSLEY CELTIC	303	5 - 3	Dunn 21, Bonsall 22, Blackstone 31, Whellans 69[p] 90
03.11	FA Trophy 1	COLWYN BAY	305	2 - 0	Bonsall 13, Smith 72[og]
10.11	Unib. 1	Gretna	94	3 - 0	Whellans 10 83, Bonsall 63
13.11	Unib. 1	OSSETT ALBION	276	0 - 0	
17.11	Unib. 1	LINCOLN UNITED	304	5 - 1	Whellans 26 51 70[p], Hudson 58, Merris 88
24.11	Unib. 1	KENDAL TOWN	402	1 - 0	Whellans 58
08.12	Unib. 1	Trafford	158	2 - 1	McNaughton 45, Elliott 62
15.12	Unib. 1	ASHTON UNITED	406	3 - 0	Bonsall 8, Elliott 24, Harris 54
18.12	FA Trophy 2	Kendal Town	134	2 - 1	Dunn 8 15
29.12	Unib. 1	LEEK TOWN	507	1 - 0	Hunter 70
08.01	W Rid SC 2	HARROGATE RAILWAY ATHLETIC	629	3 - 0	Whellans 9, Dunn 19, Elliott 72
12.01	FA Trophy 3	Doncaster Rovers	1886	0 - 2	
15.01	Lge Cup G3	FARSLEY CELTIC	222	2 - 0	Elliott 3, Fell 38
19.01	Unib. 1	GRETNA	401	2 - 1	Hunter 5, McNaughton 86
29.01	Chair. Cup QF	BAMBER BRIDGE	194	2 - 0	Pryers 15[og], Elliott 32
09.02	Unib. 1	Ossett Albion	197	4 - 2	Elliott 24, Ord 52 87, Whellans 85
12.02	W Rid SC QF	GUISELEY	294	2 - 1	Elliott 1, Whellans 38
16.02	Unib. 1	Kendal Town	201	3 - 1	Ord 22, Whellans 37, Merris 50
19.02	Unib. 1	Workington	214	2 - 0	Stansfield 24, Elliott 88
23.02	Unib. 1	EASTWOOD TOWN	525	0 - 0	
02.03	Unib. 1	Radcliffe Borough	392	3 - 4	Elliott 24, Hunter 52, Whellans 61
05.03	Unib. 1	Chorley	182	2 - 0	Whellans 76, Bonsall 90
09.03	Chair. Cup SF	DROYLSDEN	364	0 - 1	
12.03	W Rid SC SF	LIVERSEDGE	258	2 - 0	Stansfield 72, Merris 90
16.03	Unib. 1	Stocksbridge Park Steels	225	1 - 0	Albery 89
19.03	Unib. 1	ROSSENDALE UNITED	370	6 - 1	Blackstone 15 28, Ord 16, Merris 33, Albery 83, Dunn 85
23.03	Unib. 1	MATLOCK TOWN	457	3 - 2	Whellans 37 64, Blackstone 44
26.03	Unib. 1	CHORLEY	471	0 - 1	
30.03	Unib. 1	Ossett Town	512	0 - 0	
01.04	Unib. 1	SPENNYMOOR UNITED	413	2 - 0	Provett 45[og], Blackstone 79
06.04	Unib. 1	Leek Town	294	0 - 0	
09.04	Unib. 1	Belper Town	210	4 - 3	McNaughton 5, Whellans 52 76, Fell 67
13.04	Unib. 1	OSSETT TOWN	756	1 - 1	Atkinson 24
15.04	Unib. 1	Guiseley	338	1 - 2	Albery 77
17.04	W Rid SC F	FARSLEY CELTIC	470	4 - 0	Blackstone 25, Whellans 63 66, Hunter 90
Woodlesford					
20.04	Unib. 1	Witton Albion	375	0 - 0	
25.04	Unib. 1	NORTH FERRIBY UNITED	416	1 - 1	Blackstone 65
27.04	Unib. 1	BELPER TOWN	330	6 - 0	Whellans 8, Fell 32, Bonsall 52 90, Milligan 62, Blackstone 79
30.04	Unib. 1	Spennymoor United	228	0 - 1	
03.05	Unib. 1	WORKINGTON	1109	0 - 2	

Match Facts 2001-02

PLAYING SQUAD

Goalkeepers: Chris Hill (Bridlington)

Defenders: Duncan Richards (Barnsley), John Fielding (York), Mark Bowes (Hamilton), Michael Nelson (Bury), Mike McNaughton (Frickley), Paul Sykes (Ossett T), Sean Roberts (Hull), Simon Sturdy (Pickering), Neil Aspin (Hartlepool)

Midfield: Andy Wright (Doncaster), Ben Rhodes (York), Colin Hunter (Morecambe), Dave Merris (Guiseley), Nick Richardson (York), Marc Thompson (York), Simon Watson (Doncaster), Scott Bonsall (Hednesford), Scott Conlon (Canberra Cosmos)

Forwards: Clint Marcelle (Darlington), Craig Elliott (Farsley Celtic), Scott Jackson (Ossett T), Iain Dunn (Gainsborough T), Robbie Whellans (Farsley Celtic)

HUCKNALL TOWN

CLUB OFFICIALS

Chairman: Brian Holmes
Vice-Chairman: Glen Lathell
President: Andy Stewart
Secretary: Paul Dobson,15 Abbey
Court,Beeston,Nottingham NG9 2RB
Tel No: 01158753185 (H) 07718269541(M)
General Manager: David Green
Press Officer: Andy Donaldson

FOOTBALL MANAGEMENT TEAM

Manager: Phil Starbuck
Assistant Manager: Steve Prindiville
Physio: Jason Truscott

FACT FILE

Founded: 1987
Nickname: The Town
Sponsors: Doff-Portland
Colours: Yellow/black/yellow
Change colours: Allblue
Midweek matches: Tuesday
Reserves' League: Central Conference

2001-02

Captain: Paul Mitchell
P.o.Y.: Danny Mayman
Top Scorers: Gary Ricketts

THE TOWN
The Official Matchday Programme of
Hucknall Town Football Club
2001-2002 Season
£1.30

Saturday 9th. March 2002 Kick Off 3.00pm
MARINE
UniBond League Premier Division

GROUND	Watnall Road, Hucknall, Notts NG15 7LP Tel: 0115 956 1253
Directions:	M1 jct 27, A608 to lights, right onto A611 to Hucknall, right at r'bout (new by-pass), over next r'bout, right at next r'bout into Watnall Rd -grd on right. From M1 jct 26 follow Nottm signs to lights on island, left onto A610, right at Three Ponds Pub onto B600 towards Watnall, 200 yds past Queens Head turn right signed Hucknall, follow over m'way and past Rolls Royce -ground on left. Nearest station Hucknall

Pages: 92   Price: £1.20
Editor: Drew Baker(07989 320280)
Local Press: Hucknall & Bulwell Dispatch;
Nottm Evening Post; Nottm Football Post
Club Website: www.hucknalltownfc.co.uk
EMAIL address: swmatters@virgin.net

Capacity: 5,000   **Seats:** 270   **Cover:** 2,200   **Floodlights:** Yes
Clubhouse: Every night and weekend lunchtimes   **Club Shop:** Yes, (Lynne Taylor)

PREVIOUS	**Leagues:** Bulwell & Dist. 46-59 60-65; Central All. 59-60; Notts Spartan 65-70; Notts All. 70-89; Central Midlands 89-92 Northern Counties East 92-97, Unibond 97- **Ground:** Wigwam Park 46-54 Name: Hucknall Colliery Welfare (until pit closure 1988)
CLUB RECORDS	**Attendance:** 1,436 v Ilkeston Town, FA Cup 4th Qual 28/10/00 **Appearances:** Dave McCarthy 282,Paul Tomlinson 240 **Goals:** Maurice Palethorpe approx 400 (80s & 90s)
BEST SEASON	**FA Cup:** 4th Q Rd v Ilkeston Town 00-01 lost 0-1 and 2001-02 v Cambridge City (A) 1-3 after 1-1 **FA Vase:** Quarter Final 85-86 **FA Trophy:** 3rd Rd v Redditch 98-99 , Leigh RMI 00-01
HONOURS	Northern Counties (East) Lg Div 1 R-up 92-93 (Lg Cup 93-94 96-97 97-98) Presidents Cup 96-97; Central Mids Lg x2 89-91 R-up 91-92, Lg Cup x3 89-92; Notts All.Sen (4) 76-78 87-89, Div 1 Div 1 72-73 80-81 86-87 Div 2 70-71; Intermediate Cup 72-73 78-81 84-84; Lge Cup 78-79; Notts Snr Cup 84-85 90-91 97-98 99-00, R-up 83-84 85-86 87-88 89-90 98-99 00-01 Unibond Lg.: Div 1 R-Up 98-99

Back row,left to right: Steve Prindiville (Assistant Manager), Phil Starbuck (Manager), Stuart Hicks, Michael McLarnon, Paul Burke, Craig Gaunt, Ryan Young, Simon Brown, Dale Wright, Steve Roebuck, Aran Gibbs, Sammy Chapman and Ken Burton. **Front row:** Ian Griffiths, Ian Duerden, Danny Mayman, Nathan Hollingworth, Paul Mitchell, Simon Newell, Daniel Bainbridge and Rusell Cooke

NORTHERN PREMIER LEAGUE PREMIER DIVISION

Date	Comp.	Opponents	Att.	Score	Goalscorers
18.08	Unib. P	Barrow	1411	1 - 6	Ricketts 90
21.08	Unib. P	GAINSBOROUGH TRINITY	283	1 - 4	Ricketts 89
25.08	Unib. P	BISHOP AUCKLAND	175	2 - 3	Chambers 7 35
27.08	Unib. P	Hyde United	261	2 - 0	Ricketts 16, Bignall 90
01.09	Unib. P	WHITBY TOWN	195	0 - 1	
04.09	Unib. P	Altrincham	498	0 - 2	
08.09	Unib. P	Colwyn Bay	288	1 - 1	Chambers 60
15.09	Unib. P	DROYLSDEN	126	1 - 0	Miller 60
18.09	Unib. P	Burton Albion	1108	0 - 2	
22.09	Unib. P	VAUXHALL MOTORS	202	1 - 1	Brown 13
25.09	Lge Cup G7	Matlock Town	244	2 - 2	Bignall 16, Mayman 50
29.09	FA Cup Q2	Eastwood Town	422	1 - 0	Ricketts 86
02.10	Unib. P	BRADFORD PARK AVENUE	186	1 - 0	Clarke 70
05.10	Unib. P	Runcorn Halton	271	1 - 2	Rankin 43
09.10	Lge Cup G7	EASTWOOD TOWN	159	1 - 3	Ricketts 64
13.10	FA Cup Q3	STOURPORT SWIFTS	289	2 - 0	Ricketts 34, Chambers 65
16.10	Unib. P	Worksop Town	403	0 - 1	
20.10	Unib. P	Marine	223	0 - 2	
23.10	Lge Cup G7	BELPER TOWN	94	2 - 1	Ricketts 5, Wood 44[og]
27.10	FA Cup Q4	CAMBRIDGE CITY	593	1 - 1	Sherlock 47
29.10	FA Cup Q4 R	Cambridge City	598	1 - 3	Miller 38
03.11	FA Trophy 1	Sutton Coldfield Town	142	0 - 1	
10.11	Unib. P	Burscough	156	3 - 1	Chambers 15, Mayman 72, Cooke 77
13.11	Unib. P	EMLEY	162	0 - 4	
17.11	Unib. P	COLWYN BAY	186	1 - 1	Clarke 27
24.11	Unib. P	Vauxhall Motors	201	1 - 3	Mayman 80
27.11	Lge Cup G7	Burton Albion	251	3 - 0	Bignall 25, Ricketts 45, Cooke 63
01.12	Unib. P	BURSCOUGH	155	1 - 2	Wright 7
11.12	Lge Cup G7	LEEK TOWN	85	0 - 2	
15.12	Unib. P	ACCRINGTON STANLEY	191	1 - 3	Starbuck 90
29.12	Unib. P	BAMBER BRIDGE	214	1 - 1	Brown 90
12.01	Unib. P	FRICKLEY ATHLETIC	212	3 - 4	Kennerdale 10, Mayman 44, Newall 55
19.01	Unib. P	BLYTH SPARTANS	191	2 - 1	Burke 35, Mitchell 52
26.01	Chair. Cup QF	Spennymoor United	117	2 - 4	Newell 14, Ricketts 85
02.02	Unib. P	Accrington Stanley	582	2 - 1	Starbuck 70, Ricketts 77
06.02	Notts SC 3	TEVERSAL	171	4 - 1	Burke 13, Mayman 52 55, Ricketts 65
09.02	Unib. P	RUNCORN HALTON	235	1 - 2	Ricketts 35
12.02	Unib. P	Droylsden	121	0 - 3	
16.02	Unib. P	Bishop Auckland	176	2 - 0	Duerden 33, Ricketts 70
19.02	Unib. P	Blyth Spartans	278	2 - 1	Duerden 68, Starbuck 90
23.02	Unib. P	BARROW	278	2 - 1	Duerden 80, Starbuck 90
02.03	Unib. P	Frickley Athletic	152	1 - 0	Mitchell 52
05.03	Unib. P	BURTON ALBION	1602	1 - 2	Ricketts 10
09.03	Unib. P	MARINE	212	3 - 2	Duerden 14, Ricketts 70, Hicks 72
16.03	Unib. P	Bamber Bridge	273	4 - 1	Duerden 32 90, Fryers 45[og], Starbuck 46
19.03	Unib. P	Gainsborough Trinity	309	0 - 0	
23.03	Unib. P	ALTRINCHAM	425	0 - 0	
27.03	Unib. P	Bradford Park Avenue	213	1 - 0	Burke 51
30.03	Unib. P	Whitby Town	384	2 - 2	Mitchell 29, Starbuck 52[p]
01.04	Unib. P	LANCASTER CITY	327	0 - 1	
13.04	Unib. P	GATESHEAD	267	0 - 0	
17.04	Unib. P	Gateshead	123	1 - 1	Ricketts 87
20.04	Unib. P	HYDE UNITED	249	3 - 1	Ricketts 42, Cooke 60, Newell 83
27.04	Unib. P	Lancaster City	257	0 - 1	
30.04	Unib. P	WORKSOP TOWN	266	0 - 1	
03.05	Unib. P	Emley	192	0 - 3	

PLAYING SQUAD

Goalkeepers: Ryan Young (Nuneaton)

Defenders: Craig Gaunt (Moor Green), Jermaine Bailey (Eastwood T), Kieran Begley (Local), Nathan Hollingsworth (Teversal), Simon Brown (Notts Co), Steve Prindiville (Stafford R), Stuart Hicks (Mansfield)

Midfield: Dale Wright (Ilkeston), Danny Farthing (Pickering), Jamie Roberts (Eastwood T), Paul Mitchell (Arnold), Steve Lenagh (Ilkeston)

Forwards: Phil Starbuck (Burton Alb), Andy Woodcock (Youth), Gary Ricketts (Hinckley Utd), Jason Tee (Sheffield), Scott Huckerby (Hinckley Utd)

HYDE UNITED

UNIBOND PREMIER LEAGUE

HYDE UNITED

FOOTBALL CLUB LTD

The official programme of Hyde United Football Club - Season 2002 - 2003 - £1.20

CLUB OFFICIALS

Chairman: S C Hartley

Secretary: Tony Beard,
30 Fishermans Close,Winterley, Sandbach,
Cheshire. CW11 4SW
Tel & Fax: 01270 212473
07778 792502 (M) See email below.

Commercial Manager: Paul Harrop
Tel No: 0161 368 1031

FOOTBALL MANAGEMENT TEAM

Manager: David Nolan

Physio: Tony Carroll

FACT FILE

Formed: 1919

Nickname: The Tigers

Club Sponsors: T.M.I.Metals

Colours: Red/white/red

Change White/red/white

Midweek home matchday: Monday

Website: www.hydeunited.co.uk

2001-02

Captain: Peter Band

P.o.Y. : Matthew Taylor

Top Scorer: Simon Yeo 17

WELCOME TO
Ewen Fields Home of the Tigers

Pages: 32 Price: £1.
Editor: M Dring

Local Press: Tameside Advertiser
& Hyde Reporter.
Local Radio: GMR, Key 103

GROUND

Tameside Stadium, Ewen Fields, Walker Lane, Hyde SK14 5PL (0161 368 1031).
Directions: On entering Hyde follow signs for Tameside Leisure Park - in Walker Lane take 2nd car park entrance nr Leisure Pool, follow road around to the stadium. Quarter of a mile from Newton (BR). Train from Manchester (15 minutes)
Capacity: 4,130   **Cover:** 2,000   **Seats:** 660
Clubhouse: (0161 368 1621). Open most nights, 150 seats. +Sponsors Lounge for 70
Club Shop: Replica shirts, scarves, sports shirts, baseball caps, bronx hats,badges.
Contact Tony Beard (0161 3681031) or Email: beard@fishermans.fslife.co.uk

PREVIOUS **Leagues:** Lancs & Cheshire 19-21; Manchester 21-30; Cheshire County 30-68, 70-82; Northern Prem. 68-70
CLUB RECORDS **Att** 9,500 v Nelson, FA Cup 1952. **Scorer:** P O'Brien 247. **Appearances:** S Johnson 623.
Defeat: (as Hyde F.C.) 0-26 v Preston North End, F.A. Cup.
Fee Paid: £8,000 for Jim McCluskie (Mossley, 1989). **Fee Received:** £50.000 for Colin Little (Crewe Alexandra) 1995.

BEST SEASON **FA Cup:** 1st Rd 54-55(1-5 v Workington(A), 83-84 0-2 v Burnley (H), 94-95 1-3 v Darlington. (H)
FA Trophy: Semi Final 88-89 94-95 95-96

HONOURS Prem Inter-Lge Cup R-up(2) 88-90; NPL R-up(2) 87-89, 99-00 (Lg Cup 85-86 88-89 95-96(R-up 83-84 94-95), Chal. Shield 96-97, (R-up 86-87 90-91); Cheshire Co. Lg(3)54-56 81-82 (Lg Cup 33-34 52-53 54-55 72-73 81-82, Lg Chal. Shield(2) 80-82; Manchester Lg(5) 20-23 28-29 29-30 (Lg (Gilgryst) Cup(4) 27-29 49-50 70-71);Cheshire Snr Cup 45-46 62-63 69-70 80-81 89-90 96-97; Manchester Prem. Cup 93-94, 94-95, 95-96, 98-99,Snr Cup 74-75, Int Cup 55-56 56-57(jt), Jnr Cup 21-22 68-69;Lancs & Cheshire F'lit Cup(2) 54-56; Ashton Chal. Cup(6) 30-34 39-40 47-48;Hyde Chal Cup(2) 27-29; Reporter Cup(3) 72-74 75-76; Gavin Nicholson Mem Trophy79-80; Lancs F'lit Trophy(2) 86-88; Edward Case Cup(4), Unifilla Cup Winners: 99-00.
Players Progressing: C McClelland ,J Webber,P Barry (B'burn 1946 & 47 & 48),L Battrick (Man.City 1968), J Hilton (Wrexham 1950), D Teece (Hull 1952), R Calderbank & William Bell & Neil Colbourne (R'dale 1953 & 74 & 80), Jeff Johnson (Stockport 1976), David Constantine & Donald Graham (Bury 1979), George Oghani (Bolton 1983), Kevin Glendon (Burnley 1983), Peter Coyne (Swindon 1984),Colin Little (Crewe Alex. 1995),Lutel James (Bury) Simon Yeo (Llincoln City 2002)

Match Facts 2001-02

Date	Comp.	Opponents	Att.	Score	Goalscorers
18.08	Unib. P	BISHOP AUCKLAND	344	1 - 3	M Taylor 76
20.08	Unib. P	Emley	272	1 - 2	Yeo 19
25.08	Unib. P	Burton Albion	1102	1 - 5	Matthews 87
27.08	Unib. P	HUCKNALL TOWN	261	0 - 2	
01.09	Unib. P	COLWYN BAY	267	1 - 2	Salmon 10
04.09	Unib. P	Droylsden	484	2 - 3	Salmon 13, Band 63
08.09	Unib. P	Blyth Spartans	461	0 - 2	
10.09	Unib. P	GAINSBOROUGH TRINITY	308	1 - 1	Hawtin 85
14.09	Unib. P	BAMBER BRIDGE	268	0 - 1	
17.09	Ches. SC 1	WARRINGTON TOWN	187	0 - 1	
22.09	Unib. P	Lancaster City	365	2 - 4	Foster 45, Ashwell 89
24.09	Lge Cup G6	EMLEY	221	1 - 2	McCreadie 16
29.09	FA Cup Q2	Vauxhall Motors	318	1 - 2	Yeo 42
02.10	Unib. P	Bamber Bridge	216	3 - 1	Foster 50 58 89
07.10	Unib. P	DROYLSDEN	432	0 - 3	
09.10	Lge Cup G6	Ossett Albion	85	1 - 0	Matthews 13
13.10	Unib. P	Frickley Athletic	169	2 - 2	Critchley 26, Foster 38
15.10	Unib. P	BURTON ALBION	583	1 - 2	Yeo 20
22.10	Lge Cup G6	DROYLSDEN	258	3 - 3	Yeo 30 38, Nolan 42
27.10	Unib. P	BLYTH SPARTANS	266	3 - 1	Yeo 4[p], Filson 25, Young 45
30.10	Unib. P	Colwyn Bay	209	4 - 4	Band 48, Doherty 59, Critchley 66 89
03.11	FA Trophy 1	Ossett Town	216	1 - 1	Aspinall 89[og]
08.11	FA Trophy 1 R	OSSETT TOWN	223	3 - 2	Nolan 51, Young 54, Yeo 76
10.11	Unib. P	Worksop Town	289	2 - 3	Obong 36, Yeo 66[p]
16.11	Unib. P	FRICKLEY ATHLETIC	307	0 - 0	
24.11	Unib. P	Bishop Auckland	206	2 - 0	Yeo 3, Young 73
27.11	Lge Cup G6	Ashton United	221	3 - 6	Obong 4, Howard 16, Rowe 86
01.12	FA Trophy 2	ILKESTON TOWN	355	0 - 4	
08.12	Unib. P	Gateshead	265	1 - 4	Obong 90
15.12	Unib. P	Bradford Park Avenue	216	1 - 3	Foster 47
17.12	Lge Cup G6	OSSETT TOWN	112	1 - 2	Matthews 44
21.12	Unib. P	BARROW	241	1 - 2	Foster 62
29.12	Unib. P	Burscough	276	2 - 0	Leadbeater 52, Yeo 90
12.01	Unib. P	GATESHEAD	301	2 - 1	Obong 3, Evans 21
18.01	Unib. P	ACCRINGTON STANLEY	416	2 - 4	Yeo 42 68
02.02	Unib. P	Gainsborough Trinity	375	0 - 1	
08.02	Unib. P	LANCASTER CITY	251	1 - 1	Filson 47
11.02	Unib. P	MARINE	341	2 - 2	Nolan 68 84
16.02	Unib. P	Barrow	1053	0 - 0	
02.03	Unib. P	Marine	269	1 - 2	Nolan 45
04.03	Unib. P	BURSCOUGH	322	3 - 2	Evans 45, Madin 67, Yeo 84
11.03	Unib. P	WORKSOP TOWN	425	3 - 3	Yeo 64 84, Filson 90
16.03	Unib. P	Whitby Town	324	2 - 1	Band 48, Madin 56
19.03	Unib. P	Runcorn Halton	202	1 - 3	Foster 2
23.03	Unib. P	BRADFORD PARK AVENUE	389	2 - 0	Foster 36, Crookes 77
26.03	Unib. P	Altrincham	639	2 - 1	Evans 40, Foster 71
29.03	Unib. P	RUNCORN HALTON	527	0 - 1	
01.04	Unib. P	Vauxhall Motors	281	1 - 2	Yeo 10
06.04	Unib. P	Accrington Stanley	470	1 - 4	Foster 68
10.04	Unib. P	VAUXHALL MOTORS	218	0 - 0	
13.04	Unib. P	ALTRINCHAM	437	3 - 2	Foster 7 50[p], Crookes 64
20.04	Unib. P	Hucknall Town	249	1 - 3	Yeo 17
22.04	Unib. P	WHITBY TOWN	316	1 - 1	Madin 83
27.04	Unib. P	EMLEY	333	2 - 3	Madin 48, Nolan 56

PLAYING SQUAD

Goalkeepers: Peter Crookes (Halifax)

Defenders: Dave Swannick (Altrincham), Danny Webster (Vauxhall Motors), Dominic Crookes (Stalybridge), Paul Lin (Bamber Bridge), Stuart Taylor (Christchurch - NZ), Paul Maguire (Morecambe), Paul Challinor (Ilkeston)

Midfield: Dave Nolan (Droylsden), Ged Smith (Marine), Josh Howard (Stalybridge), Leon Smith (Atherton LR), Neil Critchley (Leigh), Richard Eyre (Kidsgrove), Martin Doherty (Leek)

Forwards: Anthony Hargreaves (Bamber Bridge), Lee Maden (Preston), Gareth Rowe (Alsager), Steve Foster (Blackburn), Lee Evans (Caernarfon)

LANCASTER CITY

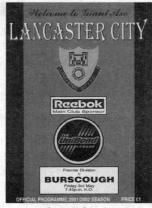

Welcome to Giant Axe

LANCASTER CITY

Reebok Main Club Sponsor

THE UniBond LEAGUE

Premier Division
BURSCOUGH
Friday 3rd May
7.45p.m. K.O.

OFFICIAL PROGRAMME 2001/2002 SEASON   PRICE £1

CLUB OFFICIALS

Chairman:**Ron Moore** Pres: **M Woodhouse**

Chief Executive: **M.Parkinson**

Secretary: **Barry Newsham**
13 Kingsdale Road, Lancaster LA1 5NE
Tel No: 01524 64024

Match Secretary: **Mike Sparks**

Email : mike@sparks13.freeserve.co,uk

Commercial Man.: **Bill Byrne**

FOOTBALL MANAGEMENT TEAM
Manager: Tony Hesketh
Coach: Barrie Stimpson
Physio: S.Riley, D Hughes

FACT FILE

Formed: 1902
Nickname: Dolly Blues
Sponsors: Reebok
Colours:Sky Blue/Navy/Navy
Change colours: All white
Midweek matchday: Tuesday
Reserve League: Lancashire League
Club Website: www.lancastercityfc.com

2001.02
Captain: K.Mayers
Top Scorer: A.Whittaker 32
P.o.Y:Farrell Kilbane

GROUND Giant Axe, West Road, Lancaster LA1 5PE Tel: 01524 382238 (Office).
Capacity: 3153   Cover: 900   Seats: 513
Directions: M6 junc 33, follow into city, left at lights immediately after Waterstones bookshop,
2nd right, pass railway station on right, follow road down hill, ground 1st right. 5 mins walk
from both bus & rail stations
Clubhouse: "The Dolly Blue Tavern" just outside the ground. Also a new tea bar inside
ground serving food and drinks.   **Club Shop:** Inside ground, selling metal badges,
pennants, programmes and other souvenirs etc. Contact Dave Crawford at club.

Pages: 32 Price: £1
Editor: Bill Byrne

Local Press: Lancaster Guardian, Morecambe Visitor,
Lancashire Evening Post, Lancaster Citizen.
Local Radio:
Red Rose, Radio Lancashire, Bay Radio

PREVIOUS	**Leagues:** Lancs Combination 05-70; Northern Premier 70-82; North West Counties82-87. **Name:** Lancaster Town. **Ground:** Quay Meadow 05-06 (club's 1st 2 games only!)
CLUB RECORDS	**Attendance:** 7,500 v Carlisle, FA Cup 1936. **Goalscorer:** David Barnes 130 League & cup. **Appearances:** Edgar J Parkinson, 591 league & cup. **Win:** 8-0 v Leyland Motors (A), 83-84. **Defeat:** 0-10 v Matlock T, NPL Division One, 73-74
BEST SEASON	**FA Vase:** Second Rd 86-87 90-91. **FA Cup:** 2nd Rd 46-47 (1-4 (A) v Gateshead) 72-73 (1-2 (A) v Notts County) **FA Trophy:** Third Rd 74-75 75-76. League Clubs defeated: Barrow, Stockport County 21-22
HONOURS	Northern Prem. Lg Cup R-up 79-80 (Div 1 Cup R-up 90-91), Lancs Combination 21-22 29-30 34-35 35-36 (R-up 19-20 22- 23 27-28 51-52, Lg Cup 21-22, Div 2 R-up14-15), Lancs Jun. Cup (ATS Challenge Trophy) 27-28 28-29 30-31 33-34 51-52 74-75 (R-up 06-07 08-09 19-20 26-27,00-01), Lancs Yth (u18) Cup 87-88 88-89 (R-up 86-87 89-90), President's Cup 1994- 95 Unibond Div 1 95-96, Div 1 Lge Cup 95-96., Lg.Challenge Cup 99-00 , 00-01

Players Progressing: J McNamee (Workington 75), B O'Callaghan (Stoke C.), I Stevens (Stockport Co. 86), G Johnstone (P.N.E. 93), M Clark & W
Collins (Crewe Alex.), G Wilson (Crewe Alex.). P.Thomson (NAC Breda 99) Chris Ward (Birmingham City)

NORTHERN PREMIER LEAGUE PREMIER DIVISION

Date	Comp.	Opponents	Att.	Score	Goalscorers
18.08	Unib. P	Colwyn Bay	295	2 - 1	Whittaker 89 90
21.08	Unib. P	VAUXHALL MOTORS	239	2 - 0	Whittaker 37 90
25.08	Unib. P	MARINE	330	2 - 1	Welch 80, Kilbane 90
27.08	Unib. P	Burscough	263	6 - 0	Whittaker 6[p] 62 71, Welch 18, Clitheroe 31, Potts 79
01.09	Unib. P	ALTRINCHAM	477	1 - 1	Whittaker 19
04.09	Unib. P	Runcorn Halton	391	2 - 0	Whittaker 18[p], Martin 89
08.09	Unib. P	Bishop Auckland	238	1 - 1	Potts 67
11.09	Unib. P	BLYTH SPARTANS	315	4 - 2	Whittaker 16 60, Clitheroe 72, Potts 90
18.09	Unib. P	Bamber Bridge	311	1 - 1	Butler 15
22.09	Unib. P	HYDE UNITED	365	4 - 2	Potts 1, Whittaker 3 39, Clitheroe 85
25.09	Lge Cup G2	WORKINGTON	141	4 - 2	Holliday 1, Butler 6, Welch 79, Whittaker 79
29.09	FA Cup Q2	Durham City	289	0 - 0	
02.10	FA Cup Q2 R	DURHAM CITY	215	2 - 1	Welch Haddow ??
05.10	Unib. P	BURTON ALBION	908	1 - 0	Whittaker 33
09.10	Lge Cup G2	Kendal Town	213	3 - 4	Potts 45, Welch 45, Martin 84
13.10	FA Cup Q3	STOCKSBRIDGE PARK STEELS	339	2 - 1	Welch 16, Whittaker 27
16.10	Unib. P	DROYLSDEN	320	2 - 2	Whittaker 45 64
20.10	Unib. P	BRADFORD PARK AVENUE	437	4 - 0	Kilbane 5, Whittaker 19 60, Potts 42
23.10	Peter Swales Sh.	Stalybridge Celtic	284	0 - 11	
27.10	FA Cup Q4	VAUXHALL MOTORS	630	2 - 2	Mayers 10, Welch 52
30.10	FA Cup Q4 R	Vauxhall Motors	601	1 - 0	Whittaker 40
03.11	Unib. P	Worksop Town	499	1 - 0	Kilbane 87
10.11	Unib. P	RUNCORN HALTON	423	1 - 1	Mayers 23
17.11	FA Cup 1	Altrincham	2076	1 - 1	Whittaker 12
24.11	Unib. P	Emley	330	1 - 2	Mayers 88
27.11	FA Cup 1 R	ALTRINCHAM	1934	1 - 4	Mayers 22
01.12	FA Trophy 2	HINCKLEY UNITED	289	2 - 1	Whittaker 65 90
08.12	Unib. P	WORKSOP TOWN	391	2 - 1	Whittaker 17[p] 54
11.12	Lge Cup G2	Bamber Bridge	182	0 - 1	
15.12	Unib. P	Frickley Athletic	193	4 - 1	Whittaker 2 83, Clitheroe 45, Welch 85
18.12	Lge Cup G2	BARROW	173	3 - 4	Rigby 37, Middleton 40, Clitheroe 76
26.12	Unib. P	Barrow	2032	0 - 0	
08.01	Lancs MT 2	Southport	311	1 - 2	S Clitheroe 65
12.01	FA Trophy 3	Vauxhall Motors	278	0 - 4	
15.01	Unib. P	BARROW	1028	3 - 3	Holliday 44, Welch 89 90
19.01	Unib. P	Gateshead	195	2 - 1	Martin 42, Mayers 48
29.01	Unib. P	BISHOP AUCKLAND	245	1 - 0	Brown 6
02.02	Unib. P	WHITBY TOWN	353	2 - 3	Yates 15[p] 49
08.02	Unib. P	Hyde United	251	1 - 1	Butler 34
12.02	Unib. P	Vauxhall Motors	219	1 - 4	Yates 26
16.02	Unib. P	GAINSBOROUGH TRINITY	379	5 - 2	Yates 19 29, Welch 61, Butler 64, Birks 71
23.02	Unib. P	COLWYN BAY	357	2 - 1	Butler 25 65
02.03	Unib. P	Bradford Park Avenue	285	0 - 1	
05.03	Unib. P	ACCRINGTON STANLEY	349	1 - 0	Welch 70
12.03	Unib. P	Gainsborough Trinity	255	2 - 3	Mayers 81, Lyons 88
16.03	Unib. P	Droylsden	201	0 - 2	
20.03	Unib. P	Accrington Stanley	349	2 - 3	Welch 21, Whittaker 31
23.03	Unib. P	BAMBER BRIDGE	233	4 - 1	Mayers 31, Whittaker 39 52[p], Welch 67
26.03	Unib. P	EMLEY	245	0 - 1	
30.03	Unib. P	Blyth Spartans	444	0 - 1	
01.04	Unib. P	Hucknall Town	327	1 - 0	Kevam 56
09.04	Unib. P	Burton Albion	1512	0 - 3	
13.04	Unib. P	FRICKLEY ATHLETIC	260	0 - 2	
16.04	Unib. P	Altrincham	438	3 - 2	Welch 37, Butler 51, Birks 81
20.04	Unib. P	Marine	291	4 - 4	Potts 22 77, Welch 58 80
23.04	Unib. P	GATESHEAD	253	2 - 0	Mayers 11, Yates 87
27.04	Unib. P	HUCKNALL TOWN	257	1 - 0	Yates 73
30.04	Unib. P	Whitby Town	199	2 - 0	Kilbane 72, Whittaker 86
03.05	Unib. P	BURSCOUGH	280	0 - 3	

PLAYING SQUAD

Goalkeepers: Mark Thornley (Barrow)

Defenders: Farrell Kilbane (Stafford R), Jimmy Graham (Guiseley), Paul Sparrow (Rochdale), Andy Fensome (Morecambe), Paul Rigby (Kendal), Stewart Clitheroe (Port Vale)

Midfield: Alex Kevan (Hereford), Andy Lyons (Morecambe), Chris Perkins (Stalybridge), Lee Clitheroe (Oldham), Paul Haddow (Barrow), Graeme Atkinson (Rochdale), Brian Butler (Leigh)

Forwards: Andy Whittaker (Bamber Bridge), Michael Yates (Dundee), Phil Brown (Kendal), Brian Welch (Clitheroe), Neil Morton (Morecambe)

MARINE

CLUB OFFICIALS

Chairman: Tom Culshaw
President: Dennis Hargreaves
Secretary: John Wildman
4 Ashbourne Avenue, Blundellsands,
Liverpool L23 8TX   Tel: 0151 924 5248
Press Officer: David Wotherspoon

FOOTBALL MANAGEMENT TEAM

Manager: Roly Howard
Asst Mgr/Coach: Roger Patience
Physio: John Bradshaw

FACT FILE

Formed: 1894
Nickname: The Mariners
Sponsors: Johnsons the Cleaners
Colours: White/black/black
Change colours: Yellow & Green
Midweek matchday: Tuesday
Reserves' League: Lancs. League Div. One

PROGRAMME
Pages: 24 Price: 80p
Editor: David Wotherspoon
Local Press: Crosby Herald, Liverpool Echo,
Daily Post Local Radio: BBC Radio
Merseyside, Radio City

GROUND Rossett Park, College Road, Crosby, Liverpool(Tel: 0151 924 1743)
Directions: College Road is off main Liverpool-Southport road (A565) in Crosby. Ground ten minutes walk from Crosby & Blundellsands (Mersey Rail). Bus No. 92
Capacity: 2,800   Cover: 1,400   Seats: 400

Clubhouse: Open daily. Concert Hall (250 seats), Members Lounge (100 seats).
Club Shop: Sells replica kit and range of souvenirs.Metal Badges in home and away colours. Contact Dave Rannard 0151474 9848

PREVIOUS   **Leagues:** Liverpool Zingari; Liverpool Co. Comb.; Lancs Combination 35-39, 46-69; Cheshire County 69-79.
                  Name: Waterloo Melville   **Ground:** Waterloo Park1894-1903

CLUB RECORDS **Attendance:** 4,000 v Nigeria, Friendly 1949
                  Goalscorer: Paul Meachin 200   **Win:** 14-2 v Rossendale Utd (A), Cheshire County Lge 25/2/78
                  Appearances: Peter Smith 952   **Defeat:** 2-11 v Shrewsbury Town F.A.Cup 1st Rd 1995
                  Fee Paid: £6,000 for Jon Penman (Southport Oct. 1995)   **Fee Received:** £20,000 for Richard Norris (Crewe 96)

BEST SEASON   **FA Trophy:** Semi Final 83-84, 91-92   **FA Amateur Cup:** Runners up 31-32 (SF 46-47)
                  FA Cup: 3rd Rd 92-93, 1-3 v Crewe Alex. (A)   League clubs defeated: Barnsley 75-76, Halifax T. 92-93

HONOURS   FA Amateur Cup R-up 31-32; Northern Prem Lg 94-95, R-up 85-86 91-92, Lg Cup 84-85 91-92 (R-up 80-81 85-86);
                  Presidents Cup R-up 83-84 86-87; Cheshire Co. Lg73-74 75-76 77-78 (R-up 72-73); Lancs Comb. R-up 46-47 (Lg Cup 46-47
                  63-64 68-69); Liverpool Comb. 27-28 30-31 33-34 34-35 (Lg Cup 30-31); Lancs Tphy 87-88 90-91; Lancs Jnr Cup 78-79;
                  Lancs Amtr Cup (5); Liverpool Snr Cup 78-79 84-8587-88 89-90 94-95 99-00; Liverpool Non-Lge Cup 68-69 75-76 76-77;
                  Liverpool Chal. Cup 42-43 44-45 71-72.

Players Progressing: A Sharrock, S Brooks (Southport 73 &77), A Jones (Leeds 60), G Williams (Preston 72), J Lacy (Fulham), P Beesly (Sheffield Utd), M Kearney (Everton 81), A Finlay (Shrewsbury 81), P Cook (Norwich), P Edwards (Crewe), I Nolan (Tranmere), J McAteer(Bolton W.), R Norris (Crewe 96).

Back row,left to right: Club Doctor, Keith Johnson (Physio), Kevin Formby, Mark Nulty, Jon Wareing, Chris Clarke, Rick Bainbridge, Eddie Hussin, Dave Thompson, Anton Lally,Will Dolan, Roly Howard (Manager) and Roger Patience Asst.Manager. **Front Row:**John Bradshaw (physio), Ann Fisher (Physio), Phil MacDiarmiad, Stuart Gelling, Jon Gautrey ,mascot, Richie Townsend, John Morgan, Chris Fitzimmons and Will Black.

Date	Comp.	Opponents	Att.	Score	Goalscorers
18.08	Unib. P	GATESHEAD	279	1 - 3	Townsend 86
21.08	Unib. P	Bamber Bridge	226	1 - 0	Morgan 21
25.08	Unib. P	Lancaster City	330	1 - 2	Townsend 33
27.08	Unib. P	ACCRINGTON STANLEY	306	2 - 5	Gautrey 18, Bainbridge 55
04.09	Unib. P	Vauxhall Motors	310	1 - 4	Wareing 77
08.09	Unib. P	BURTON ALBION	459	1 - 1	Morgan 50
11.09	Unib. P	BURSCOUGH	251	3 - 3	Townsend 31, Hussin 78, Douglas 89
15.09	Unib. P	Bradford Park Avenue	308	3 - 2	Townsend 21, Black 28 86
18.09	Unib. P	BARROW	323	3 - 2	Morgan 31, Bainbridge 53, Thornley 83
22.09	Unib. P	WORKSOP TOWN	352	1 - 1	Morgan 76[p]
25.09	Lge Cup G4	Radcliffe Borough	129	1 - 1	Morgan 70[p]
29.09	FA Cup Q2	Maine Road	228	2 - 0	Gautrey 42, Townsend 88
02.10	L'pool SC 1	Runcorn Halton	n.k	0 - 3	
06.10	Unib. P	Burscough	182	1 - 1	Wareing 84
09.10	Lge Cup G4	ACCRINGTON STANLEY	145	1 - 2	Dolan 45
13.10	FA Cup Q3	BRADFORD PARK AVENUE	371	4 - 2	Randles 25, Morgan 28 85, Douglas 68
20.10	Unib. P	HUCKNALL TOWN	223	2 - 0	Townsend 8, Hussin 71[p]
23.10	Lge Cup G4	ROSSENDALE UNITED	137	0 - 2	
27.10	FA Cup Q4	SOUTHPORT	1305	1 - 1	Townsend 21
30.10	FA Cup Q4 R	Southport	1145	1 - 2	Hussin 90
03.11	FA Trophy 1	Matlock Town	329	1 - 1	Black 29
06.11	FA Trophy 1 R	MATLOCK TOWN	199	3 - 2	Dolan 78 82, Cummings 88
10.11	Unib. P	WHITBY TOWN	210	0 - 3	
13.11	Lancs MT 1	Squires Gate	122	1 - 2	Hussin 85
17.11	Unib. P	Gateshead	205	4 - 2	Robinson 2, Black 67 86 89
20.11	Unib. P	BAMBER BRIDGE	175	0 - 1	
24.11	Unib. P	BRADFORD PARK AVENUE	274	1 - 2	Morgan 71
27.11	Lge Cup G4	Chorley	117	2 - 2	Bainbridge 53, Dolan 71
01.12	FA Trophy 2	Worksop Town	362	2 - 3	Holmshaw 19[og], Bainbridge 34
08.12	Unib. P	Gainsborough Trinity	273	0 - 0	
11.12	Lge Cup G4	BURSCOUGH	103	2 - 1	Bainbridge 81, Morgan 90
15.12	Unib. P	EMLEY	223	2 - 0	Dolan 75, Townsend 86
26.12	Unib. P	VAUXHALL MOTORS	283	1 - 1	Black 90
12.01	Unib. P	GAINSBOROUGH TRINITY	236	1 - 1	Hussin 90
19.01	Unib. P	DROYLSDEN	218	2 - 4	Black 22, Douglas 87
26.01	Unib. P	Burton Albion	1580	0 - 0	
29.01	Unib. P	ALTRINCHAM	334	1 - 0	Townsend 35
02.02	Unib. P	Runcorn Halton	348	1 - 1	Black 80
09.02	Unib. P	FRICKLEY ATHLETIC	236	4 - 0	Black 1 4, Gautrey 44, Bainbridge 66
11.02	Unib. P	Hyde United	341	2 - 2	Townsend 50 63
16.02	Unib. P	Altrincham	768	0 - 1	
23.02	Unib. P	Worksop Town	353	1 - 2	Townsend 73
02.03	Unib. P	HYDE UNITED	269	2 - 1	Bainbridge 5, Hussin 72
05.03	Unib. P	Barrow	695	1 - 1	Townsend 24
09.03	Unib. P	Hucknall Town	212	2 - 3	Bainbridge 5, Robinson 35
16.03	Unib. P	Frickley Athletic	173	0 - 3	
19.03	Unib. P	COLWYN BAY	214	1 - 1	Rimmer 48
23.03	Unib. P	Emley	247	3 - 3	Townsend 12 55, Rimmer 73 Welfare Ground
30.03	Unib. P	BISHOP AUCKLAND	291	2 - 3	Townsend 62, Bainbridge 69
01.04	Unib. P	Colwyn Bay	295	1 - 1	Townsend 57
03.04	Unib. P	RUNCORN HALTON	232	2 - 0	Morgan 5, Randles 35
06.04	Unib. P	Whitby Town	295	1 - 2	Morgan 9
10.04	Unib. P	Bishop Auckland	186	0 - 0	
13.04	Unib. P	BLYTH SPARTANS	283	0 - 2	
16.04	Unib. P	Blyth Spartans	312	0 - 0	
20.04	Unib. P	LANCASTER CITY	291	4 - 4	Bainbridge 13, Hussin 21, Dolan 51, Gautrey 90
27.04	Unib. P	Droylsden	238	2 - 0	Taylor 21, Gautrey 28[p]
03.05	Unib. P	Accrington Stanley	488	1 - 3	Taylor 68

PLAYING SQUAD

Goalkeepers:	Billy Stewart (Rhyl), Chris Clarke (Chorley)
Defenders:	Gary Randles (Runcorn), Lee Mullin (Tranmere), Jon Gautrey (Southport), Kevin Formby (Southport), Jon Wareing (Wigan), Steve Rimmer (Hyde)
Midfield:	Eddie Hussin (Winsford), Anthony Bowden (Accrington Stanley), Mike Douglas (Ashville), Ricky Bainbridge (Local), Paul McNally (Runcorn), Stuart Gelling (Colwyn Bay), Anton Lally (Kendal), Will Dolan (Youth)
Forwards:	Tommy Taylor (Youth), David Thompson (Southport), John Morgan (Southport), Alan Bailey (Burton Alb), Karl Robinson (Bamber Bridge), Ritchie Townsend (Cwmbran), Neil Black (Tranmere)

RUNCORN F.C. HALTON

CLUB OFFICIALS

Chairman: **Dr David Robertson**

Vice Chairman: Ian Burgess
Secretary: **Debbie Quaile**, 57 The
Moorings, Lydiate,Liverpool L31 2PR
Tel No: 0151 531 1296 (H)
0161 200 4925 (W)
07970 175652 (M)

FOOTBALL MANAGEMENT TEAM

Manager: Liam Watson
Assistant Manager: Neil Whalley

FACT FILE

Formed: 1918
Nickname: The Linnets
Midweek matchday: Tuesday
Colours: Yellow/&green/yellow
Change colours: All red
Reserve's league: Lancashire
Youth's league: Northwest Alliance
Website: www.runcornfc.co.uk

GROUND HaltonStadium, Lowerhouse Lane, Widnes, Cheshire. WA8 7DZ
Tel No: Matchdays only 0151 5106000 Fax matchdays only 0151 510 6001
Directions: From M62 take junction 7 and follow signs to Widnes and Autoquest Stadium.
Follow Widnes by -pass and then turn right onto Ashley Way. At roundabout take second exit
and go straight onto the next roundabout where the Stadium ia on the right.
Capacity: 12,500 Covered Seats: 12,500
Clubhouse: Open on matchdays. Light snacks available.
Club Shop: Phone club.

PROGRAMME
Pages: 36 Price: £1.20
Editor: Secretary
Local Press: Runcorn Weekly News,
Liverpool Echo, Runcorn World, Manchester
Evening News.
Radio: Radio Merseyside, GMR.Wire F.M

PREVIOUS **Leagues:** Lancs Combination; Cheshire Co. Lg; Northern Prem. Lge. 68 -81; Alliance Premier (Conference) 81-96.
Names: Runcorn **Grounds:** None

CLUB RECORDS **Attendance:** 10,111 v Preston - FA Cup 1938-39.
Goalscorer: Alan Ryan (66 goals in 64 appearances 67-68).
Win: 11-1 v Congleton Town 64-65. **Defeat:** 0-9 v Wellington 46-47.
Fee Paid: £17,000 for Simon Rudge, Hyde Utd, 1989. **Fee Received:** £80,000 for Ian Woan, Nottm Forest, 1990.

BEST SEASON **FA Trophy:** Runners-up 85-86, 92-93, 93-94. **FA Cup:** Second Round Replay 85-86,0-4 v Wigan Ath. (A), after 1-1.
Second Round also 47-48, 67-68, 77-78, 86-87,87-88, 88-89. League clubs defeated: Scunthorpe Utd. 1947-48, Notts. Co
(1967-68), Chester City 1987-88, Wrexham 1988-89.

HONOURS Lancs Jnr Cup 1918-19; Cheshire Lg 1919-20, 36-37, 38-39, 39-40, 62-63;Cheshire Snr Cup 24-25, 35-36, 61-62, 64-65,
67-68, 73-74, 74-75, 84-89 (5times), R-up 93-94; Cheshire Co. Bowl 37-38; Northern Premier Lg 75-76, 80-81(R-up 74-75);
NPL Chall Cup 74-75, 79-80, 80-81; NPL Challenge Shield 80-81,81-82; Alliance Premier Lg 81-82, Gola Lg Championship
Shield 82-83, 85-86; Bob Lord Trophy 82-83, 84-85, R-up 91-92. FA Trophy R-up 85-86, 92-93, 93-94.NPL Pres.Cup 98-99

Players Progressing: Mark McCarrick, Eddie Bishop, Jim Cumbes, Graham Abel,Barry Knowles, Mark Jones, Don Page, David Pugh, Ian Woan,
Gary Brabin, Paul Robertson, Mike Smith,Mark Carter

Back row left to right: Mal Liptrot (Kit Manager), John Ryder, David Robinson, Mark Winstanley, Mike Tomlinson, David Ness and David Gamble.
Middle row: Gary Lunt, Michael Short, Neil Whalley (Assistant Manager), Liam Watson (Player/Manager) and Steve Latrham.
Front row: Steve Carragher, Alan Cowley, Tony Ward, John McAllister and Chris Price

Date	Comp.	Opponents	Att.	Score	Goalscorers
18.08	Unib. P	EMLEY	468	2 - 0	Ness 1, Robinson 79
21.08	Unib. P	Burton Albion	1175	1 - 1	McNally 86
27.08	Unib. P	DROYLSDEN	380	2 - 0	Watson 43, Lunt 88
01.09	Unib. P	Bamber Bridge	242	6 - 1	McNally 3 19 70 75, Gamble 29, Watson 61
04.09	Unib. P	LANCASTER CITY	391	0 - 2	
08.09	Unib. P	WORKSOP TOWN	340	0 - 1	
11.09	Unib. P	Barrow	1247	1 - 2	Lunt 56
15.09	Unib. P	BLYTH SPARTANS	275	1 - 2	Watson 44
18.09	Unib. P	Colwyn Bay	249	0 - 1	
22.09	Unib. P	Bishop Auckland	191	3 - 1	McNally 33 60, Carragher 75
26.09	Lge Cup G5	ALTRINCHAM	235	0 - 2	
29.09	FA Cup Q2	Gateshead	242	4 - 2	Carragher 5, Lunt 20 26 71
02.10	L'pool SC 1	MARINE	n.k	3 - 0	
05.10	Unib. P	HUCKNALL TOWN	271	2 - 1	Leadbeater 26, Watson 65
09.10	Lge Cup G5	Colwyn Bay	220	3 - 3	Whalley 57, Carragher 64, Watson 76[p]
13.10	FA Cup Q3	BEDLINGTON TERRIERS	396	2 - 2	McNally 36, Watson 49[p]
17.10	FA Cup Q3 R	Bedlington Terriers	821	1 - 4	Latham 72
20.10	Unib. P	Gainsborough Trinity	385	4 - 1	Price 10 24, McAlister 48, McNally 65
24.10	Lge Cup G5	TRAFFORD	123	1 - 3	Lunt 89
27.10	Unib. P	FRICKLEY ATHLETIC	241	1 - 0	McNally 31
03.11	FA Trophy 1	Belper Town	303	4 - 0	McNally 23 32, Watson 67, Price 84
07.11	Unib. P	BURSCOUGH	268	4 - 0	Price 23, McNally 38 48, Watson 50
10.11	Unib. P	Lancaster City	423	1 - 1	McNally 38
13.11	Lge Cup G5	Vauxhall Motors	128	2 - 2	Cowley 40, Tomlinson 66
17.11	Unib. P	BURTON ALBION	630	1 - 3	Price 56
20.11	Unib. P	COLWYN BAY	211	1 - 2	McNally 55
24.11	Unib. P	Whitby Town	295	2 - 2	Tomlinson 15, McNally 86
28.11	L'pool SC QF	EVERTON	282	1 - 2	Latham 32
08.12	Unib. P	BAMBER BRIDGE	234	3 - 2	Watson 12, Carragher 51, Price 86
11.12	Lge Cup G5	Witton Albion	153	1 - 1	Cowley 60
08.01	Unib. P	Vauxhall Motors	207	2 - 3	McNally 45, Carragher 60
12.01	FA Trophy 3	Solihull Borough	346	0 - 3	
19.01	Unib. P	Bradford Park Avenue	304	1 - 3	Carragher 60
22.01	Unib. P	ALTRINCHAM	301	0 - 1	
26.01	Unib. P	Frickley Athletic	158	4 - 2	Lunt 20, Tomlinson 25, Leadbeater 31 63
02.02	Unib. P	MARINE	348	1 - 1	McNally 20
09.02	Unib. P	Hucknall Town	235	2 - 1	Lunt 69, Watson 72
16.02	Unib. P	ACCRINGTON STANLEY	361	1 - 0	Tomlinson 21
23.02	Unib. P	Emley	227	0 - 1	
02.03	Unib. P	Blyth Spartans	322	2 - 2	Lunt 52, Watson 79
05.03	Unib. P	VAUXHALL MOTORS	214	1 - 2	Leadbeater 44
09.03	Unib. P	GATESHEAD	217	1 - 1	Tomlinson 82
12.03	Unib. P	Droylsden	119	1 - 0	Price 40
19.03	Unib. P	HYDE UNITED	202	3 - 1	Gamble 20, Leadbeater 82 85
23.03	Unib. P	Gateshead	141	2 - 0	Leadbeater 14, Lunt 31
29.03	Unib. P	Hyde United	527	1 - 0	Carragher 88
01.04	Unib. P	BARROW	275	1 - 3	Lunt 64
03.04	Unib. P	Marine	232	0 - 2	
06.04	Unib. P	GAINSBOROUGH TRINITY	208	4 - 0	Watson 28, Lunt 58, Cowley 73, McNeil 84
09.04	Unib. P	Altrincham	469	2 - 0	Cowley 28, Maddox 36[og]
13.04	Unib. P	Burscough	229	3 - 1	McNeil 5, Cowley 47 90
16.04	Unib. P	WHITBY TOWN	237	4 - 1	Cowley 24, Price 38, Carragher 78, Ryder 90
20.04	Unib. P	Accrington Stanley	481	1 - 1	Carragher 83
23.04	Unib. P	BRADFORD PARK AVENUE	269	0 - 2	
27.04	Unib. P	BISHOP AUCKLAND	202	3 - 1	Carragher 50, McNeil 53, Watson 71
03.05	Unib. P	Worksop Town	417	1 - 1	Lunt 70

PLAYING SQUAD

Goalkeepers: Mark Winstanley (Prescot)
Defenders: Anthony McMillan (Wigan), Chris Price (Morecambe), Ian Baines (St Helens), David Ness (Youth), Steve Aspinall (Bamber Bridge), Mike Tomlinson (Warrington), Peter Ellis (Knowsley), Steve Carragher (Accrington Stanley), Tony Ward (Chorley)
Midfield: Andy Morris (Wigan), Dave Gamble (Marine), Francis McMahon (Wigan), Chris Lightfoot (Morecambe), Dominic Morley (Droylsden), Gary Lunt (Crewe), Steve Lathom (Youth)
Forwards: Kevin Leadbeater (Southport), Matt McNeil (Stalybridge), Liam Watson (Accrington Stanley), Wes Kinney (Droylsden)

Match Facts 2001-02

STALYBRIDGE CELTIC

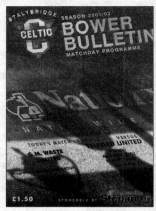

CLUB OFFICIALS

President: Roy Oldham
Chairman: Peter Dennerly
Vice Chairman: Dorothy Norton
Directors: B McCallum, G Crossley, G Greenwood, E Stafford, J.Dillon, R.Gorski, P.Fenton

Football Secretary & Commercial Manager: John Hall
Tel Nos: 0161 4560765(H) 0161 338 2828(W) 07813 864492 (M)
Press Officer: Keith Trudgeon
Tel: 0161205 7631 (B) 0161 304 8934 (H)

FACT FILE
Formed: 1909
Nickname: Celtic
Sponsors: Stepan & Tameside T.M.B.C.
Club colours: Blue & white shirts, blue shorts, blue socks
Change colours: All Gold
Midweek matchday: Tuesday
Reserves' League: None
Club Website: www.stalybridgeceltic.co.uk

FOOTBALL MANAGEMENT TEAM
Manager: David Miller
Assistant Manager: Gerry Luczka
Sports Therapist: David Power
Chief Scout: David Stewart

Pages: 40 Price: £1.50
Editor: Nick Shaw Tel: 0161 633 1117

GROUND Bower Fold, Mottram Road, Stalybridge, Cheshire SK15 2RT
Telephone: 0161 338 2828 Fax: 0161 338 8256.

Directions: From Stockporet ansd South: M60,M67 to end of Motorway through large round-about to traffic lights.Then left to mini roundabout and left again into Mottram Road.Follow signs to Stalybridge, down hill and ground is on left next to Hare & Hounds pub.
Capacity: 6,108 **Seats:** 1,200 **Cover:** 1,200
Clubhouse: Open matchdays only. Food available
Club Shop: Contact Bob Rhodes Tel No: 01457 764044 (H)

Local Press: Manchester Evening News, Manchester Evening News Pink (Sat.eve.), Aston Reporter, Ashton Advertiser
Local Radio: G.M.R. (BBC Manchester), 96.2 The Revolution

PREVIOUS **Leagues:** Lancashire Combination 1911-12, Central League 1912-21, Football League 1921-23, Cheshire County Lge 1923-1982, North West Counties 1982-87, Northern Premier 1987-92, 98-01, Conference 92-98, 01-02.
Grounds: None **Names:** None
CLUB RECORDS **Attendance:** 9,753 v WBA, FA Cup replay, 22-23
Win: 16-2; v Manchester NE 1.5.26; v Nantwich 22/10/32 **Defeat:** 0-6 v Northwich Victoria **Career goalscorer:** Unknown
Career appearances: Kevin Booth 354 **Goalscorer (season):** Chris Camden 45, 91-92
Fee paid: £15,000 to Kettering Town for Ian Arnold 95 **Fee received:** £16,000 for Lee Trundle from Southport
BEST SEASON **FA Cup:** Second Round 93-94, 1-3 v Carlisle Utd.(A); 99-00 1-2 v Chester City (H). League clubs defeated: None
FA Trophy: Third Round 1991-92, 0-1 v Witton Albion (A). **League:** 12th Conference 92-93
HONOURS Northern Premier League Prem Div 91-92, 00-01, R-up 90-91; Div.1 R-up 87-88; Cheshire County Lg 79-80, R-up 77-78 Lg Cup 21-22 R-up 46-47,81-82; Challenge Shield 77-78, R-up 79-80, Res Div R-up 81-82; N.W. Cos Lg 83-84, 86-87, Lge Cup R-up 83-84, Champions v Cup Winners Trophy 83-84; Lancs Comb Div 2 11-12; Cheshire Snr Cup 52-53, R-up 54-55, 80-81; Manchester Snr Cup 22-23, Intermediate Cup 57-58, 68-69, R-up 56-57, 67-68, 69-70; Challenge Shield 54-55, (Junior Cup 62-63); Lancs Floodlit Cup 88-89, R-up 89-90; Reporter Cup R-up 74-75; Edward Case Cup 77-78
Players progressing: Too numerous to list. but includes recently Eamoon O'Keefe, John Anderson, Lee Trundle

Stalybridge Celtic 2002-03
Back row (left to right):
Dave Ridings; Marcus Hallows; Scott Westwood; Craig Dootson; Jerome Fitzgerald; Chris Timons; Phil Eastwood.
Middle:
Allan Short kit manager; Steve Wynne; Kevin Parr; Gerry Luczka, asst. manager; Dave Miller, Manager; Kenny Mayers; Terry Bowker; Ian Senior, coach.
Front:
Colin Potts; Dave German; Nathan Wharton; Glyn Barker.

NORTHERN PREMIER LEAGUE PREMIER DIVISION

Date	Comp.	Opponents	Att.	Score	Goalscorers
18/08	Conf.	Stevenage Borough	1772	0 - 2	
21/08	Conf.	MORECAMBE	874	4 - 3	Courtney 41, Steele 78 85, Pickford 79
25/08	Conf.	HEREFORD UNITED	851	0 - 2	
29/08	Conf.	Boston United	2015	1 - 4	Evans 90
01/09	Conf.	FARNBOROUGH TOWN	671	1 - 1	Woods 41
04/09	Conf.	Scarborough	867	1 - 1	
08/09	Conf.	DAGENHAM & REDBRIDGE	660	2 - 3	
11/09	Conf.	Chester City	695	0 - 0	
15/09	Conf.	Dover Athletic	1008	0 - 1	
18/09	Conf.	SOUTHPORT	806	0 - 0	
22/09	Conf.	MARGATE	618	2 - 2	Futcher 37, Kelly 84
29/09	Conf.	Telford United	965	1 - 3	
02/10	Conf.	Forest Green Rovers	761	2 - 0	Pickford 38[p], Kelly 90
06/10	Conf.	BARNET	525	1 - 1	
09/10	Conf.	NORTHWICH VICTORIA	711	1 - 1	Courtney 90
13/10	Conf.	Nuneaton Borough	1416	1 - 3	
17/10	Ches. SC 1	TRANMERE ROVERS	197	2 - 1	Bushell 9 42[p]
20/10	Conf.	YEOVIL TOWN	829	1 - 1	
23/10	Peter Swales Sh.	LANCASTER CITY	284	11 - 0	Turley 7, Clements 14, Wharton 25, Pickford 30 58 75, McNeil 40 77
27/10	FA Cup Q4	BEDLINGTON TERRIERS	812	2 - 1	Clements 10, Pickford 65
03/11	Conf.	Doncaster Rovers	2335	1 - 0	
06/11	Ches. SC QF	Chester City	1408	2 - 1	O'Neil 11, Parr 118
10/11	Conf.	HAYES	660	1 - 0	Peacock 40
17/11	FA Cup 1	CHESTERFIELD	3503	0 - 3	
24/11	Conf.	Woking	2033	1 - 1	
01/12	Conf.	STEVENAGE BOROUGH	674	2 - 0	
15/12	Conf.	Morecambe	1308	0 - 1	
29/12	Conf.	Hereford United	1633	0 - 3	
12/01	FA Trophy 3	NUNEATON BOROUGH	826	1 - 1	Courtney 36
15/01	FA Trophy 3 R	Nuneaton Borough	1029	2 - 1	Parr 88, Ayorinde 99
19/01	Conf.	Farnborough Town	647	0 - 2	
22/01	Ches. SC SF	CREWE ALEXANDRA	n/k	2 - 7	Pickford 75, Courtney 88
26/01	Conf.	BOSTON UNITED	1023	2 - 1	Ayorinde 38, Courtney 63
05/02	FA Trophy 4	Mangotsfield United	314	1 - 0	Peacock 61
09/02	Conf.	Barnet	1302	2 - 1	Murphy 15, Peacock 32
16/02	Conf.	NUNEATON BOROUGH	846	4 - 2	Ayorinde 18 84 85, Courtney 78
23/02	FA Trophy 5	Gravesend & Northfleet	926	2 - 0	Peacock 16, Wood 54
26/02	Conf.	LEIGH RMI	404	0 - 1	
02/03	Conf.	Southport	1144	1 - 3	Parr 79
05/03	Conf.	Leigh RMI	404	0 - 1	
09/03	Conf.	CHESTER CITY	1002	0 - 4	
12/03	Conf.	SCARBOROUGH	626	2 - 3	Ayorinde 45, Pickford 63
16/03	FA Trophy QF	Stevenage Borough	1684	0 - 1	
23/03	Conf.	DOVER ATHLETIC	658	0 - 2	
26/03	Conf.	FOREST GREEN ROVERS	512	2 - 1	Parr 1 36
30/03	Conf.	Yeovil Town	3064	2 - 0	Courtney 16, Shandran 79
01/04	Conf.	DONCASTER ROVERS	1226	1 - 0	Ayorinde 10
06/04	Conf.	Hayes	510	0 - 0	
08/04	Conf.	Dagenham & Redbridge	1822	1 - 2	Courtney 8
13/04	Conf.	WOKING	1180	0 - 2	
16/04	Conf.	Northwich Victoria	653	0 - 1	
20/04	Conf.	TELFORD UNITED	698	0 - 2	
27/04	Conf.	Margate	757	0 - 8	

Match Facts 2001-02

PLAYING SQUAD

Goalkeepers: Craig Dootson (Leigh)

Defenders: Chris Timons (Ilkeston), David German (Leigh), Danny Caldicott (Atherton LR), Jerome Fotzgerald (Rossendale), Gary Parkinson (Blackpool) , Terry Bowker (Bamber Bridge)

Midfield: Dave Ridings (Leigh), Glyn Barker (Rochdale), Darren Bowman (Rossendale), Kenny Mayers (Lancaster), Nathan Wharton (Radcliffe B), Kevin Parr (Glossop), Scott Westwood (Leigh)

Forwards: Phil Eastwood (Southport), Chris Denham (Stand Ath), Ged Courtney (Marine), Colin Potts (Lancaster), Marcus Hallows (Leigh)

VAUXHALL MOTORS F.C.

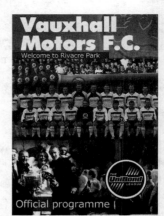

CLUB OFFICIALS

President: F G Ward

Chairman: Tony Woodley

Vice Chairman: Mal Grimshaw

Treasurer: Steven McInerney

Secretary: Mal Grimshaw, 23 Depenbech
Close, Malpas, Cheshire SY14 8QS
Fax/ Tel: 01948 860774

FOOTBALL MANAGEMENT TEAM

Manager: Alvin McDonald
Asst. Manager: Peter Carroll

FACT FILE
Formed: 1987
Re-formed 1995
Nickname: Motormen
Club Sponsors: Lookers Wirral
Colours: White/navy blue/white
Midweek Matchday: Tuesday
Reserves' Lge: Wset Cheshire Lge.
Club Website: www.vauxhall.co.uk
2001-02
Captain: Phil Brazier
P.o.Y.: Terry Fearns
Top Scorer: Terry Fearns 36

Welcome to Rivacre Park

Official programme |

36 Pages
Programme Website Editor: Andy Wilson

GROUND Vauxhall Sports Ground, Rivacre Road, Hooton, Ellesmere Port, South Wirrall.
Tel: 0151 328 1114 (Ground) 0151 327 2294 (Club) Email: admin@vauxhallfc.co.uk

Directions: M 53 junction 5, take the A41 to Chester. At the first set of lights (at Chimneys pub) turn left into Hooton Green. Follow to end and turn left at T-junction, to the end & right at the T-junction into Rivacre Rd, ground is 250 yards on right.
Floodlights: Yes
Clubhouse: Yes **Club Shop:** Yes

HONOURS West Cheshire Lge 86, 95, R-up 84, W. Ches. Lge Bowl 68, Pyke Cup 2000, R-up 73,
N.W.C. Lge. 2nd Div 88-89 95-96; Raab Karcher Chall Cup 90-91;.NWC Challenge Cup 98-99, Division 1 99-00,
Floodlit Trophy Winners 99-00. Cheshire Amateur Cup R-up 87 94
Wirral Senior Cup 87, R-up 83, 84, 95, 00; Wirrall Amateur Cup 86 R-up 87; Wirral Junior Cup 83

PREVIOUS **Leagues:** Ellesmer Port Lge., Wirral Combination, West Cheshire League 66-87, 92-95; North West Counties Lg 87-92, 95-00;
Names: Vauxhall Motors 63- 87, Vauxhall GM 88-92, 95-99

BEST SEASON **FA Vase:** S-Final 99-00 v ChippenhamTown 0-1 aet (2 legs) **F.A.Trophy:** 4th Round 2001-02
F.A Cup: 4th Qualifying Round 2001-02 v Lancaster City (H) 0-1 after 2-2

RECORDS **Attendance:** 1,500 v English F.A. XI, 1987

Back row left to right: Wayne McDermott, Terry Fearns, Phil Brazier (captain), Nicky Young, Liam Croxton, Steve Hilton, Chris Holmes, Matt Haddrell, Rob Lawton, Peter Cumiskey and Brad Cullen **Front row:** Carl Nesbitt, Paul Hart, Carl Spellman, Kevin Lynch, Alvin McDonald (Manager), Jon Paul Stanhope, Neil Rigby, Ian Horrigan and Kevin Thompson.

Match Facts 2001-02

Date	Comp.	Opponents	Att.	Score	Goalscorers
18.08	Unib. P	WORKSOP TOWN	347	3 - 2	Fearns 13 30 65
21.08	Unib. P	Lancaster City	239	0 - 2	
25.08	Unib. P	Bamber Bridge	183	3 - 1	Cullen 35, Vicary 46, Lynch 89
27.08	Unib. P	COLWYN BAY	357	1 - 1	Stanhope 47
01.09	Unib. P	Accrington Stanley	505	3 - 2	Cumisky 45 81, Young 90
04.09	Unib. P	MARINE	310	4 - 1	Fearns 25 57, Young 60, Stanhope 90
08.09	Unib. P	FRICKLEY ATHLETIC	275	3 - 1	Lynch 7, Fearns 21 57
11.09	Unib. P	Burton Albion	1172	1 - 2	Young 69
15.09	Unib. P	EMLEY	274	1 - 1	Fearns 45
22.09	Unib. P	Hucknall Town	202	1 - 1	Stanhope 55
25.09	Lge Cup G5	Trafford	74	2 - 0	Croxton 18, Fearns 59
29.09	FA Cup Q2	HYDE UNITED	318	2 - 1	Lynch 20, Fearns 81
02.10	Ches. SC 1	Macclesfield Town	n.k	1 - 2	
05.10	Unib. P	Colwyn Bay	266	0 - 1	
09.10	Lge Cup G5	WITTON ALBION	122	3 - 2	Fearns 19 41, Haddrell 65
13.10	FA Cup Q3	HARROGATE TOWN	409	3 - 1	Young 20, Fearns 35 70
16.10	Unib. P	Burscough	184	3 - 2	Young 34, Haddrell 64, Lynch 90
20.10	Unib. P	GATESHEAD	202	4 - 1	Cumiskey 19 29[p] 54, Young 52
23.10	Lge Cup G5	Colwyn Bay	145	2 - 2	Young 60 68
27.10	FA Cup Q4	Lancaster City	630	2 - 2	Cumiskey 30[p] 53
30.10	FA Cup Q4 R	LANCASTER CITY	601	0 - 1	
03.11	FA Trophy 1	Corby Town	111	3 - 0	Fearns 9 41, Lynch 63
10.11	Unib. P	ACCRINGTON STANLEY	220	1 - 2	Stanhope 81
13.11	Lge Cup G5	RUNCORN HALTON	128	2 - 2	Lawton 38, Haddrell 81
17.11	Unib. P	Bradford Park Avenue	274	3 - 1	Haddrell 10, O'Brien 60[og], Young 83
24.11	Unib. P	HUCKNALL TOWN	201	3 - 1	Lynch 20, Young 79, Fearns 85
01.12	FA Trophy 2	Stafford Rangers	555	3 - 0	Young 25, Fearns 32, Haddrell 65
04.12	Unib. P	BURSCOUGH	202	3 - 2	Fearns 5 71, Young 39
08.12	Unib. P	Droylsden	167	2 - 3	Young 13, Aldridge 80
11.12	Lge Cup G5	Altrincham	114	0 - 2	
15.12	Unib. P	BISHOP AUCKLAND	170	3 - 0	Fearns 48[p] 66, Nesbitt 89
22.12	Unib. P	BLYTH SPARTANS	276	2 - 2	Fearns 10, Lynch 88
26.12	Unib. P	Marine	283	1 - 1	Cumiskey 15[p]
08.01	Unib. P	RUNCORN HALTON	207	3 - 2	Fearns 33 83 85
12.01	FA Trophy 3	LANCASTER CITY	278	4 - 0	Cumiskey 53 63, Young 60 86
19.01	Unib. P	Worksop Town	414	3 - 3	Fearns 7 27, Brazier 90
26.01	Chair. Cup QF	WORKSOP TOWN	305	0 - 3	
03.02	FA Trophy 4	NORTHWICH VICTORIA	1019	0 - 4	
09.02	Unib. P	Gateshead	135	2 - 0	Young 31, Thompson 70
12.02	Unib. P	LANCASTER CITY	219	4 - 1	Haddrell 3, Fearns 27 84, Young 73
16.02	Unib. P	Frickley Athletic	160	0 - 1	
23.02	Unib. P	WHITBY TOWN	184	0 - 2	
02.03	Unib. P	Emley	231	1 - 1	Fearns 59
05.03	Unib. P	Runcorn Halton	214	2 - 1	Young 10, McDermott 65
16.03	Unib. P	Blyth Spartans	356	1 - 0	Cumiskey 37
19.03	Unib. P	BAMBER BRIDGE	152	1 - 0	Haddrell 68
23.03	Unib. P	Gainsborough Trinity	310	1 - 2	Fearns 90
26.03	Unib. P	Barrow	861	2 - 1	Thompson 26, Young 63
30.03	Unib. P	BRADFORD PARK AVENUE	206	2 - 1	Cumiskey 15 51[p]
01.04	Unib. P	HYDE UNITED	281	2 - 1	Fearns 24, Cumiskey 86
03.04	Unib. P	DROYLSDEN	174	1 - 0	Haddrell 40
06.04	Unib. P	Bishop Auckland	180	4 - 3	McDermott 1, Fearns 22 24, Haddrell 65
10.04	Unib. P	Hyde United	218	0 - 0	
17.04	Unib. P	BURTON ALBION	818	1 - 4	Fearns 90
20.04	Unib. P	Whitby Town	271	2 - 1	Lawton 59, McDermott 74
23.04	Unib. P	GAINSBOROUGH TRINITY	151	4 - 0	Wright 13, Haddrell 57, Cullen 84, Lawton 89
27.04	Unib. P	BARROW	250	2 - 0	Haddrell 46, Brazier 67
30.04	Unib. P	ALTRINCHAM	252	2 - 1	Haddrell 33, Lynch 89
03.05	Unib. P	Altrincham	472	1 - 0	Lynch 25

PLAYING SQUAD

Goalkeepers: Andrew Ralph (Kidsgrove), Steve Hilton (Marine)
Defenders: Andy McMullen (Burscough), Derek Ward (TNS), Ian Horrigan (Rhyl), Kevin Thompson (Heswall), Phil Brazier (Rochdale), Wayne McDermott (Leek)
Midfield: Carl Nesbitt (Poulton V), Carl Spellman (Curzon Ashton), Jimmy Collins (Northwich), Kevin Lynch (Prescot), Laim Croxton (Radcliffe B), Robbie Lawton (Caernarfon), Matthew Hogg (Bamber Bridge), Stuart Wright (Shell)
Forwards: Terry Fearns (St Helens), Nicky Young (Bromborough Pool), Darren Vicary (Stalybridge), Paul Hart (Altrincham), Nicky Welton (Rhyl), Peter Cumiskey (Leigh)

WAKEFIELD & EMLEY

CLUB OFFICIALS

Chairman: **Peter Matthews.**
President: **Peter Maude**

Secretary/Press Officer: **Richard Poulain**
17, Smithy Lane, Skelmanthorpe,
Huddersfield HD89DF.
Tel:01484 860323 H,07711 620726 M&B

FOOTBALL MANAGEMENT TEAM
Manager: Ronnie Glavin.
First Team Coach: John Peachey
Asst Manager: Jimmy Martin
Physio: Daryl Brook.

FACT FILE
Formed: 1903
Nickname: 'The Pewits
Sponsors: Eurotrail
Colours: Maroonblue/white/maroon
Change Colours. White/navy/navy
Mid week matchday: Tuesday
Reserves' Lge: N. Co's E
Web: www.emlyyafc.free-online.co.uk
E.Mail:richard.poulain@btopenworld.com
2001-02
Captain: Steve Nicholson
Top Scorer:Danny Day
P.o.Y.: Ryan Crossley

GROUND	Wakefield Wildcats RLFC., Belle Vue Stadium, Doncaster Rd., Wakefield
	Tel. No: 01924 211611
Directions:	Jct 39 M1 ,follow A636 to Wakefield, then A638 Doncaster Road
	1 mile from town centre.

Capacity: 11,000   Cover: 5,000   Seats: 1,050
Clubhouse: (01924 848398). Members' social club open seven nights a week and Saturday
& Sunday. Bingo, discos, occasional cabaret.
Club Shop: Yes .Contact Diane Glavin

Pages: 34 Price: £1
Editor: Alan Blackman (01924 403959)
Local Press: Hudd'field Examiner, Hudd'field
& Dist't Chronicle.,Wakefield Express
Local Radio: Radio Leeds, Radio Sheffield,
Pulse FM, Huddersfield FM.,Ridings F.M.

HONOURS	FA Vase Runners-up 87-88; Northern Premier Lge Div 1 R-up 90-91; Northern Counties E Lge 87-88, 88-89 (R-up 85-86); Yorkshire Lg 75-76 77-78 79-80 81-82(R-up(5) 72-74 76-77 78-79 80-81, Lg Cup 69-70 78-79 81-82, Div 2 R-up 69-0; Sheffield & Hallamshire Senior Cup 75-76 79-80 80-81 83-84 88-89 90-91 91-9297-98; Huddersfield Challenge Cup 82-83 83-84 85-86; Huddersfield Lg(4) 65-69.
PREVIOUS	Leagues: Huddersfield; Yorkshire 69-82; Northern Counties East 82-89.
	Names: Emley FC 1903-2002 Grounds: Emley Welfare Sports Ground
CLUB RECORDS	Attendance: 5,134 v Barking, Amateur Cup 3rd Proper 1/2/69.
	18,629 v West Ham Utd, at Upton Pk, 3rd Rd Proper 3/1/99.
	Win: 12-0 v Ecclesfield Red Rose9-6-97 Defeat: 7-1 v Altrincham 25-4-98.
	Goalscorer: Mick Pamment 305. Appearances: Ray Dennis 762.
	Fee Received: £60,000 for Michael Reynolds (Ayr Utd 98)
BEST SEASON	FA Amateur Cup: Third Round replay 69-70.
	FA Vase: Runners-up 87-88 (Semi-Final86-87).
	FA Trophy: Quarter Final 98-99
	FA Cup: Third Round Proper 97-98 (1-2 v West Ham Utd) League Club Defeated: Lincoln City 1997-98
Players progressing:	A Sweeney (Hartlepool Utd 79), G Cooper(Huddersfield Tn 84), J Francis (Sheffield Utd 88), S Smith (Crewe Alexandra1992), C Alcide (Lincoln City 95), C Hurst (Huddersfield Tn 97), G Hurst (Ayr Utd 98), M.Reynolds (Ayr United 1998)

Back row left to right: Daryl Brook (Physio), Ronnie Glavin (Manager), Paul David, Gary Hatto, Ryan Crossley, Mickey Norbury, Andy Wilson, Paul Cuss, Simeon Bambrook, Danny Day, Jimmy Martin (Assistant Manager) and John Peachey (Coach). **Front row:** Lee Ryan, Michael Reynolds, Steve Nicholson (Captain), Robert Tonks, MilesThorpe and Nicky Wood

NORTHERN PREMIER LEAGUE PREMIER DIVISION

Date	Comp.	Opponents	Att.	Score	Goalscorers
18.08	Unib. P	Runcorn Halton	468	0 - 2	
20.08	Unib. P	HYDE UNITED	272	2 - 1	Bambrook 44 77
25.08	Unib. P	GAINSBOROUGH TRINITY	321	2 - 1	Day 11, Bambrook 75
27.08	Unib. P	Gateshead	235	0 - 2	
01.09	Unib. P	BISHOP AUCKLAND	257	0 - 1	
04.09	Unib. P	Blyth Spartans	519	3 - 1	M Wilson 2 15, Edge 28
08.09	Unib. P	Burscough	223	1 - 1	M Wilson 39
10.09	Unib. P	ALTRINCHAM	388	2 - 1	Hatto 30, A Wilson 32[p]
15.09	Unib. P	Vauxhall Motors	274	1 - 1	Edge 79
17.09	Unib. P	ACCRINGTON STANLEY	311	0 - 3	
22.09	Unib. P	COLWYN BAY	241	2 - 0	Bambrook 22, Day 67
24.09	Lge Cup G6	Hyde United	221	2 - 1	Bambrook 13, A Wilson 61
29.09	FA Cup Q2	BAMBER BRIDGE	307	1 - 0	Norbury 71
02.10	Unib. P	Droylsden	175	2 - 3	Norbury 2, Thorpe 82
05.10	Unib. P	Worksop Town	475	0 - 0	
08.10	Lge Cup G6	OSSETT TOWN	223	4 - 0	Norbury 4, Day 7 76 85
13.10	FA Cup Q3	ACCRINGTON STANLEY	433	1 - 0	Norbury 61
17.10	Unib. P	Bradford Park Avenue	391	1 - 2	Day 72
20.10	Unib. P	BARROW	362	2 - 1	Wilson 21, Norbury 41[p]
22.10	Lge Cup G6	OSSETT ALBION	239	2 - 1	Robinson 45, Robshaw 55
28.10	FA Cup Q4	Doncaster Rovers	2730	2 - 3	Hatto 23[p], Day 83
07.11	Unib. P	Bishop Auckland	192	0 - 1	
10.11	Sheff SC 1	DAVY	94	2 - 1	Robshaw 55, Tonks 90
13.11	Unib. P	Hucknall Town	162	4 - 0	Reynolds 14, Day 43 44 89
17.11	Unib. P	Bamber Bridge	240	1 - 2	Hatto 11[p]
24.11	Unib. P	LANCASTER CITY	330	2 - 1	Day 11[p], Norbury 50
01.12	FA Trophy 2	Gretna	102	1 - 0	Day 88
04.12	Sheff SC 2	PARRAMORE SPORTS	97	1 - 0	Wilson 84
08.12	Unib. P	BURTON ALBION	703	3 - 2	Thorpe 30, Tonks 40, Robshaw 88
10.12	Lge Cup G6	ASHTON UNITED	174	3 - 2	Coleano 56, Norbury 59, A Wilson 70
15.12	Unib. P	Marine	223	0 - 2	
18.12	Lge Cup G6	Droylsden	89	0 - 3	
26.12	Unib. P	FRICKLEY ATHLETIC	474	2 - 1	Robshaw 8, Reynolds 44
12.01	FA Trophy 3	Leigh RMI	301	2 - 2	Wilson 34, Hatto 75
14.01	FA Trophy 3 R	LEIGH RMI	376	1 - 4	Bambrook 71
19.01	Unib. P	BAMBER BRIDGE	243	5 - 0	Norbury 11 54, Ryan 36, Hatto 17 34[p]
26.01	Lge Cup QF	Accrington Stanley	596	0 - 1	
02.02	Unib. P	DROYLSDEN	254	4 - 2	Day 43 48, Norbury 61 69
09.02	Unib. P	BRADFORD PARK AVENUE	386	1 - 0	Norbury 28
23.02	Unib. P	RUNCORN HALTON	227	1 - 0	Norbury 49
25.02	Unib. P	Gainsborough Trinity	278	2 - 1	Bambrook 40, Lee 90
02.03	Unib. P	VAUXHALL MOTORS	231	1 - 1	Norbury 23
05.03	Sheff SC QF	ELM TREE	167	2 - 0	Coleano 42, Ryan 73
12.03	Unib. P	Burton Albion	1533	1 - 2	Day 48
16.03	Unib. P	Barrow	936	1 - 1	Ryan 24
23.03	Unib. P	MARINE	247	3 - 3	Wilson 32, Reynolds 60, Day 66 @ Welfare Ground
26.03	Unib. P	Lancaster City	245	1 - 0	Hatto 60[p]
29.03	Unib. P	WORKSOP TOWN	465	1 - 1	Bambrook 73[p]
01.04	Unib. P	Frickley Athletic	302	1 - 1	Day 71
03.04	Unib. P	Whitby Town	288	1 - 4	Thorpe 34
08.04	Unib. P	WHITBY TOWN	216	0 - 2	
10.04	Unib. P	BLYTH SPARTANS	124	2 - 1	Day 24 38
13.04	Unib. P	Accrington Stanley	511	1 - 0	Adams 13
15.04	Unib. P	BURSCOUGH	171	3 - 0	Bambrook 10 73 90
17.04	Unib. P	Colwyn Bay	205	0 - 1	
20.04	Sheff SC SF	RENISHAW JUNIORS	251	4 - 1	Wood 3 90, Day 34, Thorpe 84
22.04	Unib. P	Altrincham	452	2 - 1	Smith 70, Bambrook 90
24.04	Sheff SC F	Doncaster Rovers	973	0 - 3	Sheffield Wednesday
27.04	Unib. P	Hyde United	333	3 - 2	Ryan 22 28, Coleano 35
29.04	Unib. P	GATESHEAD	172	2 - 2	Day 63, Hatto 77
03.05	Unib. P	HUCKNALL TOWN	192	3 - 0	Day 32 55, Adams 39

Match Facts 2001-02

PLAYING SQUAD

Goalkeepers: Paul Cuss (Huddersfield)

Defenders: Nicky Wood (Huddersfield), Alex Higgins (Stalybridge), Steve Nicholson (Farsley Celtic), Richard Walker (Youth), Ryan Crossley (Stevenage)

Midfield: Andy Wilson (Ossett Alb), Gary Hatto (Frickley), Chris Prasher (Youth), Robert Tonks (Local), Paul David (Bradley R), Simeon Bambrook (Garforth), Miles Thorpe (Frickley)

Forwards: Danny Day (Ossett Alb), Michael Reynolds (Leigh), Steve Smith (Sheffield), Rudi Coleano (Garforth)

WHITBY TOWN

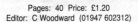

CLUB OFFICIALS

Chairman: Graham Manser.
President: Brooks Mileson
Secretary: Charlie Woodward
6 Westlands Ave, Whitby,
North Yorks YO21 3DZ Tel: 01947 602312
Press Officer: Secretary

FOOTBALL MANAGEMENT TEAM

Manager: Harry A Dunn
Asst Manager: David Logan
Physio: P.Watt

FACT FILE
Formed: 1926
Nickname: Seasiders
Sponsors: Sports Net.
Colours: All Royal Blue
Change Colours: All white.
Midweek matchday: Tuesday
Reserve League: Teeside League

2001-02
Captain: David Logan
P.o.Ys.:Phil Naisbett & Alex Gildea
Top scorer: Lee Ure 18

AXA FA CUP 1st ROUND PROPER
WHITBY TOWN
V
PLYMOUTH ARGYLE
SATURDAY 17th NOVEMBER 2001
K.O. 1.00 p.m.

£2.00

GROUND   Turnbull Ground, Upgang Lane, Whitby, North Yorks
Fax: 01947 603779   Tel: 01947 604847

Directions: Take the A174 road from town centre.
Ground on offside travelling towards Sandsend.

Capacity: 3,200   Cover: 500   Seats: 300

Clubhouse: Mon-Fri 7-11pm, Sat 12-11pm, Sun 12-2 & 7-10.30.   **Club Shop:** Yes

Pages: 40 Price: £1.20
Editor: C Woodward (01947 602312)

Local Press: Whitby Gazette, Northern Echo.
Local Radio: Yorkshire Coast Radio

PREVIOUS   **Leagues:** Northern League 1926-97.   **Name:** Whitby United (pre 1950).   **Grounds:** None
CLUB RECORDS   **Attendance:** 4,000 v Scarborough, N Riding Senior Cup 18.4.65
Win: 11-2 v Cargo Fleet Works 1950   **Defeat:** 3-13 v Willington 24.3.28
Career Goalscorer: Paul Pitman (382)   **Career Appearances:** Paul Pitman (468)
Transfer Fee Paid: £2,500 for John Grady (Newcastle Blue Star 90)
Fee Received: £5,000 for Graham Robinson (Gateshead 97)

BEST SEASON   **FA Vase:** Winners 97.   **FA Amateur Cup:** Runner-up 1964-6 **FA Trophy:** QuarterFinals 1983-84
FA Cup: 2nd Round 83-84 v Wigan A (a) 0-1,1985-86 v York C (a) 1-3 League Clubs beaten: Halifax Town 1983-84

HONOURS :   F.A Amateur Cup R-up 64-65; FA Vase 96-97; NPL Div 1 97-98; Northern Lge 92-93 96-97 (R-up 27-28 63-64 67-68 81-82
82-83), Lg Cup 28-29 63-64 69-70 76-77 84-85 95-96; Rothmans National Cup 75-76 77-78; Nth Riding SnrCup 64-65
67-68 82-83 89-90, 98-99; N Riding Bene Cup 92-93; J R Cleator Cup 84-85 92-93 95-96 96-97;
Mickey Skinner Trophy [5], Unibond Presidents Cup R-up 99-00

Players Progressing: Malcolm Poskett (Hartlepool), Sammy Kemp (Huddersfield), Jimmy Mulvaney (Hartlepool, Barrow, Stockport), Bobby Veart
(Hartlepool), Derek HamptonJ amie Burt, Trevor Smith, John Linacre & Phil Linacre (Hartlepool), Mark Hine (Grimsby). David Logan (Mansfield)
Jamie Burt (Chesterfield).

Back row left to right: Graham Rennison, Danny Wood, Aaron Wilford, Graham Robinson, Phil Naisbett, Kevin Graham,Craig Rand, Graeme
Williams, Paul Watt (Physio) and Denis Wheeler (Coach) **Front row:** Harry Dunn (Manager), Lee Ure, Danny Key, Alex Gildea, Richard Dunning,
David Logan (Captain), Craig Skelton and Craig Veart

Date	Comp.	Opponents	Att.	Score	Goalscorers
18.08	Unib. P	Altrincham	646	0 - 1	
21.08	Unib. P	Frickley Athletic	243	4 - 1	Dawson 36, Robinson 35 45, Booth 82
25.08	Unib. P	GATESHEAD	402	2 - 3	Robinson 54 79
27.08	Unib. P	BRADFORD PARK AVENUE	358	1 - 1	Logan 89[p]
01.09	Unib. P	Hucknall Town	195	1 - 0	Sankey 2
04.09	Unib. P	WORKSOP TOWN	305	0 - 2	
08.09	Unib. P	BARROW	336	2 - 4	Robinson 15, Dixon 53
12.09	Unib. P	Gateshead	202	0 - 2	
15.09	Unib. P	Worksop Town	317	0 - 2	
18.09	Unib. P	FRICKLEY ATHLETIC	178	1 - 3	Robinson 53
22.09	Unib. P	Accrington Stanley	502	3 - 2	Dunning 10, Williams 13 51
25.09	Lge Cup G3	GUISELEY	175	1 - 2	Ure 4
29.09	FA Cup Q2	RAMSBOTTOM UNITED	256	5 - 2	Dunning 34 61, Ure 43 89, Rennison 46
09.10	Lge Cup G3	Harrogate Town	247	1 - 1	Burt 30
13.10	FA Cup Q3	SPENNYMOOR UNITED	411	3 - 0	Ingram 26, Ore 85, Burt 87
16.10	Unib. P	GAINSBOROUGH TRINITY	245	0 - 4	
20.10	Unib. P	Droylsden	177	3 - 2	Dixon 45, Robinson 83, Ure 87
27.10	FA Cup Q4	SCARBOROUGH	1862	3 - 1	Williams 15, Ure 57, Burt 90
30.10	Unib. P	Gainsborough Trinity	315	0 - 2	
03.11	FA Trophy 1	Stocksbridge Park Steels	181	1 - 1	Ure 55
06.11	FA Trophy 1 R	STOCKSBRIDGE PARK STEELS	264	2 - 0	Williams 37, Burt 90
10.11	Unib. P	Marine	210	3 - 0	Ure 15, Williams 27 89
17.11	FA Cup 1	PLYMOUTH ARGYLE	2202	1 - 1	Gildea 43
20.11	Lge Cup G3	FARSLEY CELTIC	144	0 - 2	
24.11	Unib. P	RUNCORN HALTON	295	2 - 2	Burt 70, March 85
27.11	FA Cup 1 R	Plymouth Argyle	5914	2 - 3	Burt 70, Robinson 72
01.12	FA Trophy 2	BLYTH SPARTANS	505	1 - 2	Burt 43
08.12	Unib. P	Burscough	205	1 - 3	Logan 62[p]
12.12	North RSC P2	Northallerton Town	66	3 - 1	Veart 29, Burn 59, Allen 90
15.12	Unib. P	COLWYN BAY	239	1 - 0	Ure 80
09.01	Lge Cup G3	Bradford Park Avenue	107	0 - 5	
12.01	Unib. P	Barrow	1133	0 - 2	
19.01	Unib. P	ALTRINCHAM	371	2 - 3	Goodchild 26, Ure 45
22.01	Unib. P	Blyth Spartans	286	1 - 2	Williams 74
29.01	North RSC 1	SCARBOROUGH	363	3 - 3	Willgrass 76, Gildea 90, Allen 107 Won 4-1 after pens.
02.02	Unib. P	Lancaster City	353	3 - 2	Dixon 21, Logan 44[p], Ure 59
09.02	Unib. P	BAMBER BRIDGE	291	1 - 0	Ure 68
16.02	Unib. P	BURSCOUGH	309	1 - 3	Logan 75[p]
23.02	Unib. P	Vauxhall Motors	184	2 - 0	Gildea 13, Robinson 57
02.03	Unib. P	Colwyn Bay	229	1 - 1	Gildea 66
05.03	Unib. P	BISHOP AUCKLAND	254	2 - 0	Marchant 30, Dunning 85
09.03	Unib. P	BURTON ALBION	582	1 - 1	Logan 57
12.03	Unib. P	Bamber Bridge	195	0 - 3	
16.03	Unib. P	HYDE UNITED	324	1 - 2	Logan 15
20.03	Unib. P	BLYTH SPARTANS	228	2 - 2	Marchant 45, Gildea 82
23.03	Unib. P	Burton Albion	1434	1 - 5	
26.03	North RSC SF	BEDALE ATHLETIC	226	7 - 1	Robinson 11 27 68, Graham 12, Watts 35, Gildea 41, Ure 86
30.03	Unib. P	HUCKNALL TOWN	384	2 - 2	Logan 60[p], Skelton 74
01.04	Unib. P	Bishop Auckland	283	0 - 1	
03.04	Unib. P	EMLEY	288	4 - 1	Skelton 3, Gildea 9, Robinson 13, Denning 24
06.04	Unib. P	MARINE	295	2 - 1	Skelton 41, Ure 81
08.04	Unib. P	Emley	216	2 - 0	Ure 71 88
13.04	Unib. P	DROYLSDEN	326	3 - 0	Gildea 52, Skelton 54, Wood 75
16.04	Unib. P	Runcorn Halton	237	1 - 4	Ure 51
20.04	Unib. P	VAUXHALL MOTORS	271	1 - 2	Robinson 2
22.04	Unib. P	Hyde United	316	1 - 1	Veart 71
27.04	Unib. P	ACCRINGTON STANLEY	309	2 - 1	Skelton 18, Veart 30[p]
30.04	Unib. P	LANCASTER CITY	199	0 - 2	
03.05	Unib. P	Bradford Park Avenue	361	1 - 1	Logan 88
08.05	North RSC F	MIDDLESBROUGH	n.k	3 - 3	Robinson 24 64, Skelton 42 Los 2-4 after pens.

PLAYING SQUAD

Goalkeepers:	Adam Dowell (Sunderland), Phil Naisbett (Exeter)
Defenders:	Aaron Wilford (Scarborough), Allan Price (Fishburn), Craig Rand (Sheff Wed), Ben Dixon (Woodlands Wellington - Singapore), David Logan (Bishop Auckland), Graeme Williams (Guisborough), Kevin Graham (Rowntrees), Michael Laws (Northallerton), Steve Swales (Halifax), Tom Reid (Harrogate T)
Midfield:	Adam Jewell (Scarborough), Alex Gildea (Scarborough), Craig Veart (Spennymoor), Danny Richmond (Shildon), Dave Anderson (Chester-le-Street), Martin Gray (Darlington)
Forwards:	Craig Skelton (Blyth), Graeme Robinson (Gateshead), Lee Ure (Norton), Stefan Zoll (Pickering), Glen Smith (Staithes), Richard Dunning (Blackburn),

321

WORKSOP TOWN

Welcome to Sandy Lane • 2000/2001 Season

CLUB OFFICIALS

Chairman:NeilHood
Club Secretary: Keith Illett, 2 Mount Ave.,
Worksop, Notts (01909 487934)
Company Secretary & Commercial Manager: Lisa Hamilton-Clark
Press Officer: Mel Bradley

FOOTBALL MANAGEMENT TEAM

Team Manager: Paul Mitchell
Assistant Manager: Peter Rinkcavage
Physio: Graham Bacon

FACT FILE

Formed: 1861   Nickname:The Tigers
Sponsors: D.T.H. Engineers/Eyres of Worksop/Norwood Fisheries/Erriccsons

Colours: All Amber
Change colours: All Blue
Midweek home matchday: Tuesday.
Reserves' Lg: Central Midlands Reserves:
Under 19's: F.A.Northern Academy
Youth Teams' Lge: Central Mid.Res
U18s Notts Imp.

2001-02 Captain: Linden Whitehead
P.o.Y.: Gavin Smith
Leading Scorer: Gavin Smith 19

WORKSOP TOWN F.C.

Tigers

v Accrington Stanley
Saturday 5th May 2001
3.00pm
(UniBond League Premier Division)

Guardian NEWSPAPERS Official Match Day Programme £1

GROUND

Babbage Way, off Sandy Lane, Worksop, Notts S80 1UJ (01909 501911).
Directions: M1 jct 31 (from north) jct 30 (from south), follow Worksop signs,join A57 and follow signs for Sandy Lane Industrial Estate - ground on left. 5mins walk from station.
Capacity: 3,000   Cover: 1,000   Seats: 900
Clubhouse: Tigers Club. Normal licensing hours. Pool, quiz nights, disco etc.
Club Shop: `The Tigershop' 30 page catalogue from
Steve Jarvis, 10 Wood End Drive, Ravenshead, Notts NG15 9EJ.

Pages: 28-32   Price: £1
Editor: Mel Bradley (01909 500491/500500)
Local Press: Worksop Guardian, Worksop
Star, Nottingham Football Post.
Local Radio: Radio Sheffield, Radio Hallam,
Radio Lincoln.,Trax FM

PREVIOUS   **Leagues:** Midland (Counties)1896-98 1900-30 49-60 61-68 69-74, Sheffield Assoc. 1898-99 1931-33, Central Comb. 33-35, Yorkshire 35-39, Central All. 47-49 60-61, Northern Premier 68-69,74-

Grounds: Netherton Road, Bridge Meadow, Central Ave. (pre 1989), The Northolme (Gainsborough Trin. - shared) 89-92.

CLUB RECORDS   **Attendance:** 2,100 v Chris Waddle XI Linden Whitehead's testimonial 0 7.05.01
Goalscorer: Kenny Clark, 287   **Appearances:** Kenny Clark 347
Win: 20-0 v Staveley, 1/9/1894   **Defeat:** 1-11 v Hull City Res., 55-56.
Fee Received: £47,000 for Jon Kennedy, Sunderland May 2000 **Paid:** £5,000 for Kirk Jackson to Grantham Town, 98-99

BEST SEASON   **FA Cup:** 3rd Rd: 07-08 v Chelsea (A) 1-9, 21-22 v Southend (H) 1-2, 22-23 v Spurs (A) 0-0, 0-9, 55-56 v Swindon (A) 0-1.
2nd Rd: 25-26, 1st Rd: 20-21, 26-27, 61-62, 78-79. **League Clubs defeated:** Rotherham T. 1894-95, Grimsby T. 94-95, Nelson 1921-22, Chesterfield 22-23, Coventry C. 25-26, Bradford C. 55-56. **FA Trophy:** Q,Final 1-2 v Forest Green 00-01

HONOURS   N.P.L. Presidents Cup 85-86 95-96, Unibond Div One Runners-up 97-98, Unibond Premier Div. Runners-up 98-99,Unibond
Chairman"s Cup:2001-02 Sheffield Assoc. Lg 1898-99, Sheffield & Hallamshire Snr Cup 23-24 52-53 54-55 65-66 69-70 72-73 81-82 84-85 96-97,
Mansfield Charity Cup 22-23; Midland Cos Lg 21-22 65-66 72-73 (R-up 62-6366-67 73-74).
Players P rogressing: J Brown (Sheff Wed), G Dale (Chesterfield 48), A Daley (Doncaster 50), K Wood (Grimsby 51), H Jarvis (Notts Co. 51),
B Taylor (Leeds 51), S Rhodes 51, D Gratton 52, A Hodgkinson 53, J Harrison 67 (Sheffield Utd), S Lloyd & P Marshall (Scunthorpe 54),
A Rhodes (QPR 54), R Moore (Rotherham 55), H Mosby (Crewe 56), L Moore (Derby 57), H Bowery (Nottm Forest 75), T Moore (Rochdale 84), S
Adams (Scarborough 87), D Moss (Doncaster 93), Jon Kennedy (Sunderland 00), K Jackson (Darlington 01).

Back row, left to right: Mark Barnard, Darren Roberts, Adam Walker, Shaun Varley, Adam Valente, Gary Townsend, Gavin Smith, Darren Bradshaw and Andy Todd. **Front row:** Richard Peacock, Steven Hawes, Danny McPherson, Matthew Cauldwell, Linden Whitehead (Captain), Ryan Ludlam, Andy Smith and Ryan Davis

NORTHERN PREMIER LEAGUE DIVISION ONE

Date	Comp.	Opponents	Att.	Score	Goalscorers
18.08	Unib. P	Vauxhall Motors	347	2 - 3	Whitehead 76, Townsend 88
21.08	Unib. P	ALTRINCHAM	421	1 - 2	Townsend 65
25.08	Unib. P	BRADFORD PARK AVENUE	361	3 - 2	Whitehead 36 75, Smith 60
27.08	Unib. P	Gainsborough Trinity	876	2 - 0	Smith 15, Cropper 85
01.09	Unib. P	DROYLSDEN	347	0 - 3	
04.09	Unib. P	Whitby Town	305	2 - 0	Cropper 15, Kotylo 44
08.09	Unib. P	Runcorn Halton	340	1 - 0	Cropper 11
11.09	Unib. P	FRICKLEY ATHLETIC	370	1 - 1	Jones 71[og]
15.09	Unib. P	WHITBY TOWN	317	2 - 0	Cropper 6, Eshelby 45
19.09	Unib. P	Bishop Auckland	185	2 - 1	Cropper 74, Townsend 80
22.09	Unib. P	Marine	352	1 - 1	Kotylo 85
25.09	Lge Cup G8	LINCOLN UNITED	313	1 - 0	Todd 56
03.10	Unib. P	Accrington Stanley	505	0 - 5	
05.10	Unib. P	EMLEY	475	0 - 0	
09.10	Lge Cup G8	Gainsborough Trinity	397	1 - 2	Hindley 82[p]
13.10	FA Cup Q3	GAINSBOROUGH TRINITY	756	4 - 0	Whitehead 29, Cropper 37, Townsend 61, Goddard 88
16.10	Unib. P	HUCKNALL TOWN	403	1 - 0	Whitehead 7
20.10	Unib. P	Colwyn Bay	295	3 - 0	Graham 26[og] 63[og], Todd 49
23.10	Lge Cup G8	STOCKSBRIDGE PARK STEELS	292	1 - 1	Townsend 71
27.10	FA Cup Q4	Leigh RMI	674	4 - 2	Townsend 4, Whitehead 32, Cropper 39, Smith 72
30.10	Unib. P	Burton Albion	1328	0 - 1	
03.11	Unib. P	LANCASTER CITY	499	0 - 1	
06.11	Sheff SC 1	PARKGATE	236	0 - 1	
10.11	Unib. P	HYDE UNITED	289	3 - 2	Cropper 50 56 80
17.11	FA Cup 1	AFC Bournemouth	4414	0 - 3	
27.11	Lge Cup G8	Frickley Athletic	239	4 - 1	Todd 36, Gray 71 81, Townsend 82
01.12	FA Trophy 2	MARINE	362	3 - 2	Todd 15, Townsend 48 54[p]
08.12	Unib. P	Lancaster City	391	1 - 2	Smith 38
11.12	Lge Cup G8	NORTH FERRIBY UNITED	224	1 - 2	Kotylo 47
15.12	Unib. P	BLYTH SPARTANS	331	3 - 0	Todd 3, Townsend 74, Holmes 85
12.01	FA Trophy 3	TAMWORTH	904	4 - 3	Townsend 15 53, Smith 28, Todd 90
19.01	Unib. P	VAUXHALL MOTORS	414	3 - 3	Waddle 54, Townsend 61, Linnigan 89
26.01	Chair. Cup QF	Vauxhall Motors	305	3 - 0	Whitehead 31, Townsend 54, Gray 90
02.02	FA Trophy 4	Forest Green Rovers	816	0 - 1	
09.02	Unib. P	COLWYN BAY	349	2 - 1	Eshelby 15, G Smith 85
12.02	Unib. P	GAINSBOROUGH TRINITY	453	4 - 0	Todd 20, G Smith 25 26 90
16.02	Unib. P	Bradford Park Avenue	438	5 - 1	Eshelby 2, Davis 30, Smith 45, Ludlam 63[p], Varley 90
19.02	Unib. P	Frickley Athletic	319	0 - 4	
23.02	Unib. P	MARINE	353	2 - 1	Linigan 19, Todd 39
02.03	Unib. P	BAMBER BRIDGE	352	2 - 0	Ludlam 33, Todd 89
06.03	Unib. P	Gateshead	156	3 - 0	Linighan 41, G Smith 45, Whitehead 54
09.03	Chair. Cup SF	Spennymoor United	233	1 - 0	Linighan 74
11.03	Unib. P	Hyde United	425	3 - 3	Whitehead 37, Holmes 47, Todd 87
16.03	Unib. P	BURSCOUGH	412	3 - 1	Smith 35, Cropper 57, Todd 58
19.03	Unib. P	BURTON ALBION	1367	0 - 1	
23.03	Unib. P	Burscough	228	3 - 2	Smith 59 81, Todd 86
26.03	Unib. P	Droylsden	216	2 - 0	Smith 52[p] 85
29.03	Unib. P	Emley	465	1 - 1	G Smith 70
01.04	Unib. P	GATESHEAD	507	2 - 1	Todd 57, Kotylo 87
06.04	Unib. P	Blyth Spartans	411	2 - 2	Cropper 63, G Smith 83
09.04	Unib. P	Bamber Bridge	170	0 - 0	
13.04	Unib. P	BARROW	454	0 - 1	
15.04	Unib. P	ACCRINGTON STANLEY	371	5 - 0	Diggle 6, Todd 26, Gray 56, C Smith 77, Marsh 90
17.04	Chair. Cup F	Droylsden	470	2 - 1	G Smith 20 64
20.04	Unib. P	Barrow	829	0 - 1	
23.04	Unib. P	BISHOP AUCKLAND	367	2 - 1	G Smith 19, Whitehead 40
27.04	Unib. P	Altrincham	709	0 - 2	
30.04	Unib. P	Hucknall Town	266	1 - 0	Townsend 85
03.05	Unib. P	RUNCORN HALTON	417	1 - 1	Towsend 90

PLAYING SQUAD

Goalkeepers: Dave McCarthy (Hucknall), Ross Turner (Alfreton)

Defenders: Brian Linighan (Gainsborough T), Darren Beesley (Harrogate), Darren Bradshaw (Stevenage), Mark Barnard (Northwich), Ryan Ludlam (Sheff Utd), Martin Diggle (Hallam), Ryan Davis (Luton)

Midfield: Gavin Smith (Sheff Wed), Andy Smith (Lincoln), Andy Todd (Eastwood T), Linden Whitehead (Alfreton), Richard Peacock (Chester), Krystof Kotylo (Nuneaton), Matty Caudwell (Doncaster), Steve Hawes (Altrincham)

Forwards: Andy Gray (Grantham), Darren Roberts (Tamworth), Gary Townsend (Youth)

Match Facts 2001-02

BAMBER BRIDGE

Date	Comp.	Opponents	Att.	Score	Goalscorers
18.08	Unib. P	Blyth Spartans	445	1 - 3	Leaver 68
21.08	Unib. P	MARINE	226	0 - 1	
25.08	Unib. P	VAUXHALL MOTORS	183	1 - 3	Robinson 90
27.08	Unib. P	Barrow	1445	1 - 1	Aspinall 72
01.09	Unib. P	RUNCORN HALTON	242	1 - 6	Robinson 14
04.09	Unib. P	Burscough	185	0 - 5	
08.09	Unib. P	Gainsborough Trinity	393	0 - 5	
11.09	Unib. P	COLWYN BAY	135	1 - 2	Moran 14
14.09	Unib. P	Hyde United	268	1 - 0	Burton 6
18.09	Unib. P	LANCASTER CITY	311	1 - 1	Moran 53
22.09	Unib. P	BRADFORD PARK AVENUE	320	2 - 1	Robinson 42, Burton 72
25.09	Lge Cup G2	Barrow	519	0 - 2	
29.09	FA Cup Q2	Emley	307	0 - 1	
02.10	Unib. P	HYDE UNITED	216	1 - 3	Aspinall 8
05.10	Unib. P	GATESHEAD	173	1 - 4	Robinson 25
10.10	Unib. P	Bishop Auckland	159	0 - 2	
13.10	Unib. P	Gateshead	173	1 - 1	Cooper 59
20.10	Unib. P	Frickley Athletic	162	0 - 2	
23.10	Lge Cup G2	WORKINGTON	116	3 - 0	Cooper 44, Denham 53, Aspinall 57
03.11	FA Trophy 1	Moor Green	325	0 - 3	
10.11	Unib. P	Burton Albion	1366	1 - 1	Moran 84
17.11	Unib. P	EMLEY	240	2 - 1	Leaver 76, Bowker 86
20.11	Unib. P	Marine	175	1 - 0	Aspinall 23
24.11	Unib. P	Colwyn Bay	260	0 - 0	
27.11	Lge Cup G2	Kendal Town	94	1 - 4	Smith 78
01.12	Unib. P	DROYLSDEN	217	3 - 3	Nezianya 2 35, Moran 3
08.12	Unib. P	Runcorn Halton	234	2 - 3	Moran 37, Smith 47
11.12	Lge Cup G2	LANCASTER CITY	182	1 - 0	Moran 33
15.12	Unib. P	BURSCOUGH	274	2 - 3	Moran 20 49
26.12	Unib. P	ACCRINGTON STANLEY	484	0 - 1	
29.12	Unib. P	Hucknall Town	214	1 - 1	Ryan 75
08.01	Lancs MT 2	BARROW	139	0 - 1	
12.01	Unib. P	Droylsden	204	0 - 0	
19.01	Unib. P	Emley	243	0 - 5	
23.01	Unib. P	Bradford Park Avenue	298	2 - 5	Smart 29, Fryer 84
29.01	Chair. Cup QF	Harrogate Town	194	0 - 2	
02.02	Unib. P	BARROW	409	1 - 0	Ryan 75
09.02	Unib. P	Whitby Town	291	0 - 1	
12.02	Unib. P	Altrincham	537	3 - 4	Cooper 18, Smith 26, Bowker 59
23.02	Unib. P	GAINSBOROUGH TRINITY	238	1 - 0	Ryan 29
02.03	Unib. P	Worksop Town	352	0 - 2	
05.03	Unib. P	BLYTH SPARTANS	174	0 - 1	
12.03	Unib. P	WHITBY TOWN	195	3 - 0	Ryan 37 63, Bray 75
16.03	Unib. P	HUCKNALL TOWN	273	1 - 4	Halliwell 59
19.03	Unib. P	Vauxhall Motors	152	0 - 1	
23.03	Unib. P	Lancaster City	233	1 - 4	Skeogh 65
26.03	Unib. P	BURTON ALBION	519	0 - 1	
01.04	Unib. P	Accrington Stanley	603	0 - 2	
03.04	Unib. P	ALTRINCHAM	211	1 - 1	Craney 88[og]
09.04	Unib. P	WORKSOP TOWN	170	0 - 0	
13.04	Unib. P	BISHOP AUCKLAND	188	1 - 2	Cooper 45
20.04	Unib. P	FRICKLEY ATHLETIC	218	0 - 2	
06.05	Play-off SF	RADCLIFFE BOROUGH	n.k	3 - 2	
09.05	Play-off F	ASHTON UNITED	n.k	1 - 2	

BISHOP AUCKLAND

Date	Comp.	Opponents	Att.	Score	Goalscorers
18.08	Unib. P	Hyde United	344	3 - 1	Shaw 30, Foster 47, Chillingsworth 55
25.08	Unib. P	Hucknall Town	175	3 - 2	Rowe 2, Lee 50, Chillingsworth 60
27.08	Unib. P	Blyth Spartans	654	1 - 2	Chillingsworth 69
01.09	Unib. P	Emley	257	1 - 0	Chillingsworth 44
04.09	Unib. P	GATESHEAD	307	1 - 2	Shaw 47
08.09	Unib. P	LANCASTER CITY	238	1 - 1	Chillingsworth 90
12.09	Unib. P	Bradford Park Avenue	221	2 - 0	Bayles 40, Brunskill 77
15.09	Unib. P	Colwyn Bay	262	2 - 1	Lee 17, Bayles 78
19.09	Unib. P	WORKSOP TOWN	185	1 - 2	Bell 45
22.09	Unib. P	RUNCORN HALTON	191	1 - 3	Ellison 27
25.09	Lge Cup G1	Blyth Spartans	319	1 - 4	Ellison 35
29.09	FA Cup Q2	Workop Town	441	1 - 3	Lee 53
02.10	Unib. P	BLYTH SPARTANS	256	1 - 1	Chillingworth 64
05.10	Unib. P	Barrow	1199	1 - 3	Bayles 20
10.10	Unib. P	BAMBER BRIDGE	159	2 - 0	Salmon 28, Bromley 49
13.10	Unib. P	DROYLSDEN	165	1 - 2	Shaw 41
17.10	Lge Cup G1	GATESHEAD	102	2 - 1	Milroy 19, Shaw 34
20.10	Unib. P	BURSCOUGH	152	2 - 1	Bromley 2, Lee 81[p]
24.10	Durham CC 1	ESH WINNING	95	2 - 1	Shaw 20, Brunskill 41
27.10	Unib. P	Accrington Stanley	518	1 - 1	Hutt 51
30.10	Unib. P	Frickley Athletic	157	1 - 2	Chillingsworth 54
03.11	Unib. P	BURTON ALBION	371	1 - 1	Salvin 14
07.11	Unib. P	EMLEY	192	1 - 0	Chillingsworth 79
09.11	Unib. P	Gainsborough Trinity	290	1 - 1	Shaw 25
13.11	Durham CC 2	Dunston Federation Brewery	173	2 - 1	Chillingsworth 42 58
17.11	Unib. P	GAINSBOROUGH TRINITY	207	0 - 1	
24.11	Unib. P	HYDE UNITED	206	0 - 2	
01.12	FA Trophy 2	Stourport Swifts	251	4 - 5	Brunskill 59, Lee 60[p], Bell 67, Shaw 90
08.12	Unib. P	BARROW	276	1 - 2	Brunskill 26
15.12	Unib. P	Vauxhall Motors	170	0 - 3	
18.12	Lge Cup G1	Gretna	62	1 - 1	Shaw 20
08.01	Durham CC QF	Jarrow Roofing Boldon CA	153	4 - 2	Chillingsworth 22 84, Bromley 26, Lydon 56
12.01	Unib. P	COLWYN BAY	172	1 - 2	Bromley 88
16.01	Lge Cup G1	SPENNYMOOR UNITED	201	1 - 1	Shoulder 39
29.01	Unib. P	Lancaster City	245	0 - 1	
02.02	Unib. P	FRICKLEY ATHLETIC	188	1 - 1	Shaw 9[p]
05.02	Durham CC SF	South Shields	193	7 - 0	Shaw 7 62, Chillingsworth 19 38 51, Lee 66, Salmon 78
09.02	Unib. P	Burscough	202	0 - 1	
16.02	Unib. P	HUCKNALL TOWN	176	0 - 2	
02.03	Unib. P	Altrincham	745	1 - 1	Brunskill 90
05.03	Unib. P	Whitby Town	254	0 - 2	
13.03	Unib. P	ALTRINCHAM	180	2 - 1	Shaw 25, Rowe 36
20.03	Unib. P	Gateshead	138	0 - 1	
23.03	Unib. P	ACCRINGTON STANLEY	179	1 - 2	Rowe 35
29.03	Durham CC F	BILLINGHAM TOWN	300	1 - 0	Shaw 77 Durham City
30.03	Unib. P	Marine	291	3 - 2	Salmon 38, Skedd 66, Proudlock 76
01.04	Unib. P	WHITBY TOWN	283	1 - 0	Quinn 44
06.04	Unib. P	VAUXHALL MOTORS	180	3 - 4	Chillingsworth 9 89, Proudlock 37
10.04	Unib. P	MARINE	186	0 - 0	
13.04	Unib. P	Bamber Bridge	188	2 - 1	Shaw 9 20
20.04	Unib. P	BRADFORD PARK AVENUE	452	0 - 4	
23.04	Unib. P	Worksop Town	367	1 - 2	Quinn 37
27.04	Unib. P	Runcorn Halton	202	1 - 3	Chillingworth 41
30.04	Unib. P	Droylsden	82	0 - 1	
03.05	Unib. P	Burton Albion	1433	0 - 3	

Match Facts 2001-02

DIVISION ONE FINAL LEAGUE TABLE 2001-02

	P	W	D	L	F	A	Pts		P	W	D	L	F	A	Pts
Harrogate Town	42	25	11	6	80	35	86	North Ferriby Utd	42	14	16	12	71	60	58
Ossett Town	42	21	13	8	73	44	76	Chorley	42	16	9	17	59	57	57
Ashton United	42	21	12	9	90	63	75	Matlock Town	42	15	9	18	49	48	51
Spennymoor United	42	22	6	14	75	73	72	Trafford	42	14	9	19	64	80	51
Radcliffe Borough	42	20	8	14	73	51	68	Workington	42	12	12	18	51	57	48
Leek Town	42	20	8	14	67	51	68	Farsley Celtic	42	12	11	19	64	78	47
Gretna	42	19	7	16	66	66	63	Belper Town	42	12	11	19	49	66	47
Eastwood Town	42	17	11	14	61	59	62	Lincoln United	42	11	14	17	62	80	47
Rossendale United	42	17	10	15	69	58	61	Stocksbridge PS	42	12	9	21	55	76	45
Witton Albion	42	17	10	15	72	68	61	Kendal Town	42	9	9	24	52	76	36
Guiseley	42	18	7	17	60	67	61	Ossett Albion	42	8	8	26	43	92	32

DIVISION ONE FINAL RESULTS CHART 2001-02

		1	2	3	4	5	6	7	8	9	10	11	12	13	14	15	16	17	18	19	20	21	22
1	Ashton Utd	X	1-1	0-2	3-2	5-2	6-2	2-1	1-1	3-2	4-1	3-0	0-1	1-3	2-1	1-1	2-1	3-2	2-3	3-0	1-3	4-2	1-0
2	Belper Tn	1-1	X	3-1	1-0	2-2	0-2	0-1	3-4	2-1	3-2	0-0	1-1	2-2	1-0	0-1	0-1	2-3	1-2	1-0	0-3	2-3	0-0
3	Chorley	1-1	1-1	X	2-2	3-2	5-4	0-1	0-2	4-2	0-0	2-0	0-0	2-0	3-0	2-2	1-2	0-2	2-1	1-0	3-2	1-2	1-2
4	Eastwood T	1-1	1-0	0-2	X	1-1	1-2	2-2	2-2	2-0	2-1	1-2	2-1	1-1	2-1	1-2	0-0	1-0	2-1	3-3	3-1	4-5	0-2
5	Farsley C	1-1	3-0	2-0	1-0	X	3-1	1-2	0-3	3-2	3-3	3-4	3-0	2-0	2-4	2-5	1-3	0-1	0-0	2-1	3-0	0-2	1-0
6	Gretna	2-0	0-0	1-0	4-1	1-0	X	3-1	0-3	0-0	0-2	2-2	1-2	2-1	2-0	2-1	1-2	0-4	0-1	2-1	4-0	1-3	2-2
7	Guiseley	2-0	5-4	4-1	0-1	1-0	1-2	X	2-1	1-0	1-2	3-2	0-2	1-1	4-1	0-2	2-1	0-1	3-0	0-2	1-1	1-1	3-3
8	Harrogate	3-0	6-0	0-1	0-0	5-3	2-1	2-0	X	1-0	1-0	5-1	3-2	1-1	0-0	1-1	1-0	6-1	2-0	2-0	1-0	0-0	0-2
9	Kendal T	2-2	2-1	1-1	2-3	3-2	1-2	1-1	1-3	X	1-2	1-2	1-3	1-3	5-1	1-5	4-1	0-3	3-1	1-1	0-2	4-2	1-1
10	Leek Town	2-3	0-1	0-2	2-1	2-0	1-0	1-2	0-0	2-0	X	2-0	2-0	1-1	1-0	1-0	0-3	4-1	1-3	5-0	5-0	3-2	0-0
11	Lincoln U	2-1	1-3	2-1	0-3	2-2	1-2	2-2	2-1	1-1	4-2	X	1-0	2-2	5-0	1-1	1-1	1-1	2-4	3-3	2-2	1-1	0-1
12	Matlock T	0-3	2-0	0-1	1-1	2-1	1-1	0-1	1-1	1-2	1-1	5-0	X	4-2	0-0	0-1	1-0	0-1	0-2	2-0	1-1	5-1	1-2
13	N Ferriby U	1-1	3-2	2-2	1-3	2-2	6-1	3-0	1-3	2-1	0-0	1-4	0-2	X	3-1	0-1	0-1	2-0	3-2	2-3	1-1	1-1	2-0
14	Ossett Alb	1-5	0-0	1-0	1-4	2-2	1-1	1-2	0-4	1-0	1-1	3-1	0-2	3-5	X	2-0	1-1	0-4	3-1	0-1	3-5	3-1	0-3
15	Ossett Tn	2-2	0-2	1-3	3-1	1-2	3-1	3-0	0-0	1-0	0-1	5-1	2-0	0-0	2-0	X	2-2	2-1	2-0	3-2	0-0	3-2	2-1
16	Radcliffe B	2-3	0-1	2-1	2-1	1-1	3-2	4-1	4-3	0-1	3-1	0-2	2-0	0-0	4-1	0-3	X	1-3	1-2	5-0	6-1	5-0	1-1
17	Rossendale	1-2	0-0	0-3	1-1	5-2	1-0	5-1	1-2	0-0	2-2	0-3	1-3	2-0	1-1	0-1	3-3	X	3-3	0-0	3-4	1-2	1-2
18	Spennymoor	2-6	2-2	2-1	1-2	2-1	0-2	3-0	1-0	1-1	0-2	2-1	2-0	2-1	3-2	3-3	2-1	1-1	X	2-1	4-1	4-2	5-4
19	Stocksbridge	3-3	2-1	2-0	0-1	0-1	2-2	2-1	0-1	5-1	1-2	0-0	2-0	1-4	3-0	2-3	3-2	0-1	1-2	X	3-2	1-3	0-0
20	Trafford	1-3	1-2	3-1	0-1	2-2	1-4	1-4	1-2	0-1	2-1	3-1	3-0	3-2	1-1	1-0	0-1	3-3	1-2	3-1	X	0-1	1-1
21	Witton Alb	1-1	2-0	1-1	4-0	0-0	1-2	3-1	0-0	2-0	0-4	2-1	1-1	0-0	0-1	1-3	0-2	0-3	5-0	7-2	0-1	X	3-0
22	Workington	1-1	2-3	0-3	0-1	4-0	0-2	0-1	2-1	2-4	1-0	1-1	4-0	1-1	1-1	0-2	2-1	0-1	2-3	1-3	X

LEADING GOALSCORERS

in order of League goals

		Lge	Cup	Tot.
Mark Dobie	Gretna	24	8	32
Jody Banim	Radcliffe Borough	24	3	27
Andy Mason	Chorley	22	7	29
Robbie Whellans	Farsley Celtic	21	7	28
Carl Cunningham	Belper Town	21	6	27
Carl Rendell	Witton Albion	21	5	26
Phil Denney	Ashton United	19	11	30
Chris Newton	Farsley Celtic	19	7	26
Gavin Knight	North Ferriby U	18	9	27
Dave Whittaker	Leek Town	18	2	20

AVERAGE ATTENDANCES

	00/01	01/02		00/01	01/02		00/01	01/02
Ashton United	177	162	Harrogate Town	216	421	Radcliffe Borough	169	217
Belper Town	199	192	Kendal Town	130	168	Rossendale Utd	-	230
Chorley	215	201	Lincoln United	113	125	Spennymoor Utd	135	160
Eastwood Town	136	132	Matlock Town	261	275	Stocksbridge PS	167	184
Farsley Celtic	108	111	North Ferriby Utd	160	147	Trafford	139	155
Gretna	89	97	Ossett Albion	-	138	Witton Albion	307	284
Guiseley	191	202	Ossett Town	112	243	Workington	315	245

MONTHLY SPONSORSHIP AWARDS

	CLUB OF MONTH	FAIR PLAY			
Aug	Ossett Town	Spennymoor Utd	Dec	Rossendale Utd	Chorley
Sep	Harrogate Town	Ossett Albion	Jan	Spennymoor Utd	Workington
Oct	Ashton United	Belper Town	Feb	Spennymoor Utd	Workington
Nov	Harrogate Town	Farsley Celtic	Mar	Ossett Town	Stocksbridge PS
			Apr/May	Ashton United	Leek Town

ALFRETON TOWN

CLUB OFFICIALS
Chairman: Wayne Bradley
Vice Chairman: Sam Egan
Dev. Manager: Glen Waudby
Secretary: Roger Taylor
9 Priory Rd, Alfreton, Derbys. DE55 7JT
Tel: 01773 835121

FOOTBALL MANAGEMENT TEAM
Manager:David Lloyd
Assistant Manager: Charlie Wiliamson
Physio: Mick Jenkins

FACT FILE
Formed: 1959   Nickname: The Reds
Sponsors: Impact Marketing & Publicity Ltd
Colours: all red   Change colours: all white
Midweek home matchday: Tuesday
Res League: Mid Regional Alliance + Under
19s,18s, 16s, 15s, 13s, & 12s

2001-02
Leading Goalscorer: Mick Godber
Captain: Darren Brookes
P.o.Y. - Manager's: Mark Highfield
Players' Steve Heath Supp. Chris Wilder

GROUND: Town Ground, North St., Alfreton, Derbys Tel: 01773 521734 Admin.
Club Website: alfretontownfc.com
Directions: M1 junction 28 and follow A38 towards Derby for 1 mile,left onto B600, right at main road to town centre and after half a mile turn left down North Street - ground on right. Half mile from Alfreton (BR) station.Buses 242 & 243 from both Derby and Mansfield
Capacity: 5,000   Cover: 1,000   Seats: 350   Floodlights: Yes

Clubhouse: H & C food & drinks on ground.
Supporters Club bar outside ground open every day.
Club Shop: Programmes & club souvenirs. Contact Brian Thorpe Tel: 01773 836251

PROGRAMME - Pages: 32   Price: £1
Editor: Chris Tacey (01302 722415)

Newsline: 01773 830277
Local Radio: Radio Derby
Local Press: Derbyshire Times; Derby Evening
Telegraph; Chad, Ripley & Heanor News

PREVIOUS	**Leagues:** Central All.(pre-reformation 21-25) 59-61; Midland (Counties) 25-27 61-82; N.C.E. 82-87; Northern Premier 87-99
BEST SEASON	**FA Trophy:** 1st Rd Proper 94-95. **FA Vase:** 5th Round 99-00 **FA Cup:** 1st Rd 3rd replay 69-70. Also 1st Rd 73-74. - League clubs defeated: Lincoln 24-25
RECORDS	**Attendance:** 5,023 v Matlock Tn, Central All 60. **Scorer:** J Harrison 303 **Win:** 15-0 v Loughborough, Midland Lge. 69-70 **Appearances:** J Harrison 560 **Defeat:** 1-9 v Solihull FAT 97, 0-8 v Bridlington 92. **Fees - Paid:** £2,000 for Mick Goddard (Worksop Town)) **Received:** £7,000 for Paul Eshelby (Ilkeston Tn 96-97)
HONOURS:	N.C.E. Lg 84-85,2001-02 (Lg Cup 84-85,01-02); Midland Co. Lg 69-70 73-74 76-77 (R-up 71-72 80-81 81-82), Lg Cup 71-72 72-73 73-74; Derbyshire Sen Cup (7) and Runners -up (8) Div Cup (N) 64-65; Evans Halshaw Floodlit Cup 87-88 95-96; Cent All Lg.R-Up 63-64; NPL Div 1 R-Up 95-96 NCE Presidents Cup Winners 2001-02

Players progressing: M Wright (68), A Kowalski (73), A Henson (81), Philip Greaves (86) (All Chesterfield), A Woodward (Grimsby T. 70), A Taylor (Chelsea72), R Greenhough (Chester C. 85), K Smith (Exeter C. 89) M Duke (Sheff.Utd 99)

Back row ,left to right:Ian Askey,Steve Heath, Mick Godber, Ross Turner,Brad Elam, Steve Circuit and Ryan Hadley.

Middle row: Darren Schofield, Darren Brookes (Captain), Ryan France, Mick Goddard and Steve Johnson.
Front row: Mark Highfield, Gary Thorpe, Mick Jennings, (physio),Chris Wilder (Player-Man), David Lloyd (Coach), Chris Dolby ,Adam Fretwell.

Trophies: N.C.E.L Presidents Cup,N.CE.L. League Cup,N.C.E.L . Championship & Derbyshire Senior Cup

BAMBER BRIDGE

CLUB OFFICIALS

President: **Arthur Jackson**
Chairman: **David Spencer**
Secretary : **David Rowland**
c/o B.B.F.C.
Commercial Manager: **Keith Brindle**

FACT FILE

Founded: 1952
Nickname: Brig
Sponsors: T.B.A.
Colours: White/black/black
Change Colours: Yellow/blue/yellow
Midweek Matches: Tuesday
Reserves' League: Lancashire Legue
Website: www.bamberbridge-fc,co.uk

BAMBER BRIDGE
FOOTBALL CLUB

DIVISION ONE
Official
Programme
2002-2003
Season

PRICE
£1.00

v KENDAL TOWN
UniBond League First Division
Saturday 21st September 2002
3.00pm KICK-OFF

FOOTBALL MANAGEMENT TEAM

Manager: **Paul Byron**
Asst Manager: **Andy Farley**
Physio: **T.B.A.**

PROGRAMME

Pages: 36   Price: £1
Editor: Dave Rowland (01772 312987)

GROUND   Irongate, Brownedge Road, Bamber Bridge, Preston, Lancs.PR5 6UX
Tel Nos: Club Office 01772-909690; Social Club 01772-909695; Fax No. 01772-909691

Directions: M6 Junct 29, A6 (Bamber Bridge Bypass) towards Walton-le-Dale, to r'bout, A6
London Road to next r'bout, 3rd exit signed Bamber Bridge (Brownedge Road) and first right.
Ground 100 yds at end of road on left. Just over a mile from Bamber Bridge (BR).
Capacity: 3,000   Seats: 1008   Cover: 800   Club Shop: Yes
Clubhouse: On ground. Open all day Saturday matchdays, every evening and Sunday
lunch. Refreshment cabin on ground serves hot & cold drinks & snacks etc during matches.

PREVIOUS   **Leagues:** Preston & District 52-90; North West Counties 90-93.
             Grounds: King George V Ground, Higher Walton 1952-86. **Names:** None

CLUB RECORDS **Attendance:** 2,300 v Czech Republic, Pre-Euro 96 Friendly.
             Win: 8-0 v Curzon Ashton N.W.Co. 94-95.   **Defeat:** Unknown
             Fee Paid: £10,000 to Horwich R.M.I.for Mark Edwards.
             Fee Received: £15,000 from Wigan Athletic for Tony Back, 1995.

BEST SEASON   **FA Vase:** Semi Final 91-92 (lost 0-2 on agg to Wimborne Tn).
             FA Cup: 2nd Round Proper, 99-00, v Cambridge United (A) Lost 0-1

HONOURS   Nth West Co's Lge R-up 92-93 (Div 2 91-92, F'lit Cup R-up 91-92); Preston &Dist Lge(4) (R-up 3); Guildhall Cup 78-79 80-
             81 84-85 89-90, R-up 77-78 79-80 87-88; Lancs Amtr Shield 81-82, R-up 80-81 89-90; Lancastrian Brigade Cup 76-77 89-90
             90-91; A.T.S.Lancs Trophy 94-95, R-Up 95-96; NPL Chall Cup 94-95; NPL 1st Div R-Up 94-95; NPL Prem Div Champ 95-96.

Back row, left to right: Lee Pryers, David Sutch, Andy Pollit, Matty Hind, Cyril Shorrock, Stewart Clitheroe, Paul Kelly and Dean Cooper.
Middle row: Karl Hankinson, Paul Ryan, Stuart Shepherd, David Holliwell, Simon Woodward, Alex Porter, Steve Wallace, Bradley Lyons.
Front row: Dave Leaver, Andy Forley, Paul Byron(Manager), Dave Froggart (Second Team Manager) Andy Hosgood (Physio), Chris
Blakeman and Peter Smith.

BELPER TOWN

CLUB OFFICIALS

Chairman: Phil Varney
President: Alan Benfield
Secretary: Bryan Rudkin
121 Marsh Lane, Belper, Derbys, DE56
1GU. Tel: 01773 827091 Mobile: 07710
444195
Press Officer: Nigel Oldrini

FACT FILE

Formed: 1883
Nickname: Nailers
Colours: Yellow/black/black & yellow
Change colours: All white
Midweek home matchday: Tuesday
Reserves' League: Midlands Reg All

OFFICIAL MATCHDAY PROGRAMME
SEASON 2001/02
£1.00

Unibond League Division One
BELPER TOWN
Vs.
GRETNA
Saturday 2nd February, 2002
K.O. 3.00pm

*Members of the Unibond League
Division One*

1951 - 2001 50TH ANNIVERSARY SEASON

FOOTBALL MANAGEMENT TEAM

Manager: Gary Marrow
Asst Manager/ Coach: Mark Ogley

2000-2001

Captain: Steve Kennedy
P.o.Y.: Steve Kennedy
Top scorer: Carl Cunningham 27

GROUND

Address: Christchurch Meadow, Bridge Street, Belper DE56 1BA (01773825549).

Directions: From M1 North, Jnct 28 onto A38 towards Derby, turn off at A610

(Ripley/Nottingham), then 4 exit at roundabout towards Ambergate. At junction with A6 (Hurt

Arms Hotel) left to Belper. Ground on right past traffic lights. 400 yards from Belper (BR)

Capacity: 2,640   Cover: 1,000   Seats: 200

Clubhouse: Open matchdays and for functions with bar and hot and cold food available.

Pages: 32 Price £1.00
Editor:Dave Laughlin 01773 856556

Local Press: Belper News, Derby Evening
Telegraph, Belper Express
Local Radio: BBC Radio Derby

PREVIOUS	**Leagues:** Central Alliance 57-61; Midland Co's 61-82, Northern Counies East 1982-97
	Grounds: Acorn Ground prior to 1951
	Names: None
CLUB RECORDS	**Attendance:** 3,200 v Ilkeston Town, 1955
	Goalscorer: Mick Lakin 231 **Appearances:** Gil Rhodes
	Fee Received: #2,000 for Craig Smith from Hinckley United **Fee Paid:** £2,000 to Ilkeston Town for Jamie Eaton. 2001
	Victory: 15-2 v Nottingham Forest 'A'1956 **Defeat:** 0-12 v Goole Town 1965
BEST SEASON	**FA Vase:** Semi-final 94-95 **FA Amateur Cup:** Not entered
	FA Trophy: 3rd Qual Rd 97-98
	FA Cup: 1st Rd Prop 1887-88 v Sheff Wed. (H) 2-3 (4th Qual. Rnd 1957-58, 00-01 ,01-02)
HONOURS	Northern Counties East Lge 84-85, Midland Counties Lg 79-80; Central Alliance Lge 58-59;
	Derbys Snr Cup 58-59 60-61 62-63 79-80

Players progressing: None

Back Row L-R: Mick Gilbert (physio), Mark Ogley (Asst. Mananger), Niall McNamara, Gary Reece, Graham Lewis, Dean Jones, Gary Ingham, Leroy Chambers, Liam Walshe, Michael Allsop, Steve Kennedy (Capt.), Paul Bennett (Kit Man), Gary Marrow (Manager)
Front Row: Craig Smithurst, Mark Wilson, 2002/03 Sponsors - Belper Gas (2 people), Chris Hilton, Jamie Eaton, Russell White.

Photo: Billl Wheatcroft

BISHOP AUCKLAND

The **Two Blues**
at Dean Street

Season
2002/2003

THE
OFFICIAL MATCH
PROGRAMME OF
BISHOP AUCKLAND F.C.

Bishop Auckland F.C.

CLUB OFFICIALS

Chairman: Terry Jackson
Vice-Chairman: T.B.A.
Secretary/Press Off.: Tony Duffy,
90 Escomb Road, Bishop Auckland,
Co. Durham, DL14 6TZ
Commercial Manager: T.B.A.

FOOTBALL MANAGEMENT TEAM

Manager: Alan Shoulder
Asst Mgr: Tony Boylan
Physio: Dave Nesbitt

FACT FILE

Formed: 1886
Nickname: Bishops
Sponsors:Helios Properties PLC
Colours: All Sky & Navy blue
Change colours: Red & white.
Midweek home matchday: Wednesday.
Reserve Team: None.

Local Press: Northern Echo,
Evening Gazette, Newcastle Journal.
Local Radio: Radio Cleveland, Radio
Metro, Radio Newcastle, Century Radio

GROUND DETAILS

Address: C/o Shildon F.C. Dean Street, Shildon, Co.Durham Tel No: 01388 773877
Directions: As for Shildon F.C.
Clubhouse: Yes, B.A. Social Club 0138 8603686

Pages: 28 Price: £1.
Editor: Bobby Wake (01388 609428)

PREVIOUS	Leagues: N East Counties 1889-90/ Northern Alliance 1890-91/ Northern 1893-1988.
CLUB RECORDS	**Attendance:** 17,000 v Coventry, FA Cup 2nd Rd 6/12/52. **Appearances:** Bob Hardisty.
	Win: 12-3 v Kingstonian, Amateur Cup 55. **Defeat:** 0-7 v Halifax Tn FA Cup 2nd Rd66-67.
	Fee Paid: £2,000. Fee Received: £9,000 for David Laws from Weymouth.
BEST SEASON	**FA Amateur Cup:** Winners 10 times **FA Trophy:** Quarter Finals 78-79, 88-89, 96-97, 99-00
	FA Cup: 4th Rd 54-55, 1-3 v York City (H). League clubs defeated: Crystal Palace, Ipswich 54-55, Tranmere 56-57.
HONOURS	FA Amateur Cup 1895-96, 1899-1900 13-14 20-22 34-35 38-39 54-56 57-58 (R-up(8)01-02 05-06 10-11 14-15 45-46 49-51 53-54); Northern Lg(19) 1898-99 1900-02 08-10 11-12 20-21 30-31 38-39 46-47 49-52 53-5666-67 84-86, R-up (17) 78-79 86-87 96-97, Lg Cup(7) 49-51 53-55 59-60 66-67 75-76); D'ham Chall Cup 1891-92 98-99 1930-31 38-39 51-52 55-56 61-62 66-67 84-8585-86 87-88 96-97, 98-99 HFS Loans Lg Div 1 R-up 88-89. Plus tournaments in Isle of Man, Spain, Portugal etc

Players Progressing: B Paisley (Liverpool), F Richardson & S O'Connell (Chelsea 46 & 54), R Hardisty & K Williamson (Darlimgton 46 & 52), WShergold (Newport 47), N Smith (Fulham 48), R Steel & K Murray (Darlington 50),A Adey (Doncaster 50), F Palmer & A Stalker (Gateshead 51 & 58), A Sewell(Bradford City 54), G Barker (Southend 54), J Major (Hull 55), H Sharratt(Oldham 56), F McKenna (Leeds 56), J Barnwell (Arsenal 56), D Lewis (Accrington Stanley 57), C Cresswell (Carlisle 58), W Bradley (Man Utd), L Brown(Northampton), P Baker (Southampton), M Gooding (Rotherham), K Nobbs & A Toman(Hartlepool), P Hinds (Dundee Utd), Jeff Smith (Bolton W.) 2001.

L-R - Back row; Rory Barker, Steven Jones, Kevin Shoulder, Stuart Dixon, Brian Rowe, Keith Finch, Craig Lake, Chris Hoyles, Barry Poskett, Jamal, Chris Ndkmu. **Front Row;** Tony Boylan, Craig Marley, Craig Wilkinson, Anthony Skedd, Wayne Edgcumbe, Michael Quinn, Jon King, Brian Nelson, Baz Mundy, Alan Shoulder.

Photo: Bill Wheatcroft

CHORLEY

CLUB OFFICIALS

Chairman: Jack Kirkland

Commercial Manager: T.B.A.

Secretary / Press Officer:
Mick Wearmouth
6 Avondale Rd, Chorley, Lancs. PR7 2ED
Tel: 01257 271395

FOOTBALL MANAGEMENT TEAM

Player - Manager: Mark Molyneaux
Reserve Team Manager: Mark Cox

FACT FILE

Formed: 1883
Nickname: The Magpies
Sponsors: Lex - Auto
Colours:
White & black stripes/black/black & white
Change colours: All yellow
Midweek matchday: Tuesday
Reserve League: Alliance League

2001-02
Leading goalscorer: Andy Mason 29
Captain: Paul Fleming
P.o.Y.: Andy Mason

THE BLACK & WHITE
Magpies Review
Official Match Day Programme

CHORLEYFC.COM

LEX Auto Logistics
Official Sponsors of Chorley F.C.

BELPER
TOWN F.C.
Members of the UNIBOND LEAGUE FIRST DIVISION
SEASON ~ 2001/2002

PROGRAMME £1

GROUND   Victory Park, Duke Street, Chorley, Lancs   Tel: 01257 263406
Directions: M61 jct 6, A6 to Chorley, going past Yarrow Bridge Hotel on Bolton Rd turn left
at 1st lights into Pilling Lane, 1st right into Ashley St.,,ground 2nd left. From M6; jct 27, follow
signs to Chorley, left at lights,continue for 2 1/2 miles on A49, right onto B5251, on entering
Chorley turn right into Duke Street 200yds after Plough Hotel. 1/4 mile from Chorley (BR).
Capacity: 4,100   Cover: 2,800   Seats: 900
Clubhouse: 01257 275662. Open every evening. Weekend entertainment, Snacks available
Club Shop: Yes.

Pages: 32 Price: £1.
Editor: Mike Neild
Local Press: Lancs Evening Post,
Chorley Guardian.
Local Radio: Radio Lancs.

PREVIOUS   Leagues: Lancs Alliance 1890-94; Lancs 94-1903; Lancs Comb. 03-68, 69-70;Northern Premier 68-69, 70-72, 82-88;
Cheshire County 72-82; GMV Conference 88-90.
Grounds: Dole Lane 1883-1901; Rangletts Park 01-05; St George's Park 05-20.   Name: None

CLUB RECORDS   **Attendance:** 9,679 v Darwen, 1931-32. **Goalscorer:** Peter Watson.
Fee Paid: Undisclosed to Marine for Brian Ross 1995. **Fee Received:** £22,500 for Paul Mariner (Plymouth, 1973).

BEST SEASON   **FA Cup:** 2nd Rd 86-87 v P.N.E. (A) 0-5 after 2-2 at Blackburn, 90-91 v Shrewsbury Town (A) 0-1
League Clubs defeated in F.A. Cup : Wolverhampton W 1986-87 and Bury 1990-91 **FA Trophy:** Semi-Final 1995-96.

HONOURS   Northern Premier Lg 87-88, Cheshire Co. Lg 75-76 76-77 81-82, Lancs Comb. 19-2022-23 27-28 28-29 32-33 33-34 45-46
59-60 60-61 63-64 (R-up 21-22 26-27 48-4962-63 64-65 65-66), Lg Cup 24-25 58-59 62-63), Lancs Lg 1896-97 98-99,
Lancs Alliance 1892-93 (R-up 94-95), Lancs Jnr Cup 1894-95 1908-09 23-24 39-40 45-4657-58 58-59 60-61 63-64 64-65
75-76 79-80 81-82 82-83.

Players Progressing: Charles Ashcroft (Liverpool 1946),William Healey (Arsenal 49), Stan Howard (Huddersfield 52), Derek Hogg (Leicester 52),
William Norcross (Southport 59), Micky Walsh (Blackpool 71),Paul Mariner (Plymouth 73), Graham Barrow (Wigan 76), Steve Galliers
(Wimbledon77), Kevin Tully (Bury 80), Geoff Twentyman (Preston 83), Gary Buckley (Bury84), Chris Hunter (Preston 84).

Back row left to right: Scott Bradford, David Eatock, Mark Court, Danny Mills and Ian Leather.
Middle row: Julie Anderson (Physio), Graham Hill (coach), Glyn Williams, Mark Schofield, Lee Moyneux, David Eatock, Paul Eatock,
Simon Marsh, Ian Dickenson, Chris Blakeman, David Sutch and Dave Haslam (Coach).
Front row: Neil Mitchell, Mick Williams, Paul Fleming (captain), Ken Wright (Manager), Andy Mason, Danny Kent and Peter Smyth.

EASTWOOD TOWN

EASTWOOD TOWN FOOTBALL CLUB

CLUB OFFICIALS
President: **George Belshaw**
Chairman: **Gary Hardy**
Vice Chairman: **Roy Cheatle**
President:
Secretary / Press Officer: **Paddy Farrell**
7 Primrose Rise, Newthorpe,
Notts.NG16 2BB Tel/Fax: 01773 786186

FACT FILE
Formed: 1953
Nickname: The Badgers
Sponsors: T.B.A.
Colours: White with black trim/black/black
Change Colours: Yellow/blue/yellow
Midweek matchday: Tuesday
Club's EMAIL : patriciafarrell@barbox.net

MAIN SPONSOR
HAYLEY
CONFERENCE CENTRES
EASTWOOD HALL
UNIBOND LEAGUE - DIVISION 1

HAYLEY
CONFERENCE CENTRES

EASTWOOD TOWN v CHORLEY
Saturday 22nd December, 2001. Kick-off 3pm
OFFICIAL PROGRAMME
Price £1

FOOTBALL MANAGEMENT TEAM
Manager: Bryan Chambers
Ass.Manager: Coach:
Physio: Rudy Funk

2001-02
Captain .: Paul Gould
Top Goalscorer: Marc Smith 12
P.o.Y.: Danny Bryant

Pages: 50   Price: £1.00
Editor: Paddy Farrell 01773786186

Local Press: Eastwood Advertiser
Nottingham Evening Post, Derby Telegraph
Local Radio: Radio Nottingham, Radio Trent

GROUND   Coronation Park, Eastwood, Notts. Tel: 01773 715823

Directions: From North - M1 jct 27, follow Heanor signs via Brinsley to lights in Eastwood. Turn left then first right after Fire Station - ground entrance on Chewton Street. From South - M1 jct 26, A610 to Ripley, leave at 1st exit(B6010), follow to Eastwood, left at lights, first left at `Man in Space' -ground entrance on Chewton Street. Nearest station - Langley Mill. Buses every10 mins (R11, R12 or R13) from Victoria Centre, Nottingham - approx 40 mins
Capacity: 5,500   Cover: 1,150   Seats: 650
Clubhouse: Social club open normal licensing hours (Sat 11am-11pm, midweek matches 6.30-11pm). Hot & cold food available. Steward; Jane Rowley
Club Shop: Sells programmes, mugs, scarves, badges etc. Contact R K Storer - 0115 9199596

PREVIOUS   **Leagues:** Notts Alliance 53-61; Central Alliance 61-67; East Midlands 67-71; Midland Counties 71-82; N.C.E. 82-87.
       Names: None -predecessors Eastwood Collieries disbanded in 1953
       Ground: Coronation Park 1953-65 - previous pitch now town bowling green
CLUB RECORDS   **Attendance:** 2,723 v Enfield, FA Amateur Cup, February 1965.
       Goalscorer: Martin Wright. Appearances: Arthur Rowley, over 800 1st team games, but not a single booking, 1955-76
       Win: 21-0 v Rufford Colliery 26/10/54 & Ilkeston Town 10/5/69   **Defeat:** 0-8 v Hucknall Town (a) 13/02/01
       Fee Paid: £500 for Jamie Kay, Gainsborough Trin.90-91   **Fee Received:** £72,500 for Richard Liburd, Middlesbrough 92-93
BEST SEASON   **FA Amateur Cup:** Third Round replay 1967-68.   **FA Trophy:** First Round1978-79
       FA Cup: 1st Round Proper 99-00, v Exeter City (A)
HONOURS   Northern Counties (East) Lg R-up 82-83 84-85; Midland Counties Lg 75-76(R-up 74-75 77-78), Lg Cup 77-78 79-80; Central Alliance 63-64 (R-up 64-65);Notts Alliance 56-57 (R-up 53-54 54-55 55-56 57-58 58-59 59-60), Lg Cup 55-56;East Midlands Lg R-up 68-69; Notts Senior Cup (winners 9 and R-up 5);Evans Halshaw Floodlit Cup 94-95R-up 89-90 97-98; Notts Intermediate Cup 86-87;98-99.99-00 Ripley Hospital Charity Cup(6)76-81.Mid Regional All (Prem) 99-00 R-up 97-8,98-9. MRAChallenge Cup 2001-02

Players progressing: J Butler (Notts Co 57), A Woodcock A Buckley Andrew Todd (Nottm F), P Richardson (Derby), S Buckley (Luton), R Liburd (Middlesbrough 92-93), Martin Bullock (Barnsley 94-95), Neil Illman (Plymouth 95-96), Lee Marshall (Scunthorpe 97), Glenn Kirkwood(Donc"ter R)

L-R Back:

George Belshaw,
President

Dave Davies,
Sportsman of the Year

Debbie Sandeman of
'Joblot' (sponsors of the
man-of the match award)

Paul Gould,
Players' Player

Bryan Chambers,
Manager

Rudy Funk
Asst. Man. & chief coach

Front:

James Hutchinson,
Most Promising Player

Danny Bryant
*Manager's choice and
Player of the Year*

FARSLEY CELTIC

CLUB OFFICIALS

Chairman: John E. Palmer

Secretary: Nicholas Gill,4 Victoria Gardens,Pudsey, Leeds LS28 7SP.
Tel No: 0113 2361633 (H)
07929 000872 (M)

FOOTBALL MANAGEMENT TEAM

Manager: Martin Haresign
Reserves Manager: Gary Stokes
Coach: John Deacy

FACT FILE

Formed: 1908
Nickname: Villagers
Colours: All Royal Blue
Change colours: All Yellow
Midweek home matchday: Tuesday
Reserves' League: Lancashire

2001-02

Captain: Damien Henderson
Top scorers :Chris Newton
& Robbie Whellans both 21
P.O.Y.: Andy Shields

Leek AFC
12th January 2002

Pages: 32   Price £1
Les WoodHoward Stevenson

Local Press: Yorkshire Evening Post,
Telegraph & Argus, Pudsey Times
Local Radio: Radio Leeds, Radio Aire,
Radio Pennine

GROUND: Throstle Nest, Newlands, Farsley, Pudsey, Leeds LS28 5BE
Club Email: phil@yorkshirefolk.fsnet.co.uk Tel: 01532 561517
Directions: From North East: A1 south to Wetherby, A58 to Leeds, at 1st island (approx 8 miles) take 3rd exit (A6120 ring-rd), follow Bradford signs to 12th r'bout (approx 12 miles) - 1st exit (B6157 Stanningley). From M62 jct 26, M606 (Bradford) to r'bout, 4th exit (A6177) passing McDonalds on left, continue on Rooley Lane - Sticker Lane passing Morrisons store on left to lights (approx 3 miles) - right onto A647 (Leeds) to 2nd r'bout, 2nd exit (B6157 Stanningley). Continue 800yds passing Police & Fire Stations on left.Turn left down New Street at Tradex warehouse before turning right into Newlands. Ground at bottom of road. One mile from New Pudsey (BR)
Capacity: 4,000   Cover: 1,500   Seats: 300
Clubhouse: Lounge, games room and committee room Open every evening and Friday and weekend lunchtimes. New multi-purpose Leisure Centre available evenings and afternoons
Club Shop: League & non-League progs & magazines. Club badges, scarves,ties, sweaters, training suits, polo & T-shirts. Various souvenirs & photos. Contact: Brian Falkingham, 27 Rycroft Ct., Leeds LS13 4PE. 0113 255 0749 e-mail: clubshop@breathemail.net

PREVIOUS	**Leagues:** West Riding County Amateur; Leeds Red Triangle; Yorkshire 49-82; Northern Counties East 82-87
	Grounds: Red Lane, Farsley; Calverley Lane, Farsley (prior to 1948)
CLUB RECORDS	**Attendance:** 11,000 (at Elland Road) v Tranmere Rovers, FA Cup 1st Rd 1974
BEST SEASON	**FA Amateur Cup:** Third Round, 34-35
	FA Cup: 1st Rd 74-75 (see above). Lost 0-2. **FA Vase:** Quarter Final 87-88
HONOURS	West Riding County Cup 57-58 59-60 66-67 70-71 83-84 87-88 95-96 96-97 00-01; Yorkshire League 59-60 68-69 (R-up 57-58 58-59 70-71 71-72); Div 2 51-52;League Cup 62-63 63-64 66-67 96-97

Players progressing: Barry Smith (Leeds 1951), Paul Madeley (Leeds 1962),William Roberts (Rochdale 1988), Stuart McCall (Bradford City)

Back row left to right: Damien Place, Gary Shaw, Liam Sutcliffe, Damien Henderson, Paul Cuthbertson and Andy Lamb
Front row: Simon Brooker, Richard Hepworth, Liam Gray, Andy Shields and Chris Newton

GUISELEY

CLUB OFFICIALS

Chairman: Philip Rogerson
Secretary: Bruce Speller
71 Oxford Avenue, Guiseley,
Leeds LS20 9BY
Tel: 01943 874534
Email: bruce.speller@virgin.net
Club Website: www.guiseleyafc.co.uk

Press Officer: John Martin
Tel: 01943 879473
Directors: P. Rogerson, S.Allen

FACT FILE

Formed: 1909   Sponsors: T.B.A.
Cols:White/navy/white Change:Yellow/Navy
Midweek home matchday: Monday
Reserves' League: Lancashire League
2001-02
Leading goalscorer: Mark Stuart
Captain: James Nettleton
P.o.Y.: Mark Stuart Young P.o.Y.: John Lamb

FOOTBALL MANAGEMENT TEAM

Manager: Neil Parsley
Assistant Manager: Clive Freeman
Physio: Benn Gallagher

GROUND: Nethermoor, Otley Road, Guiseley, Leeds LS20 8BTTel: 0943 873223
Directions: Via M1 to M62 jct 28, follow Airport signs to junction of A65 at Horsforth. R-about turn left onto A65 through Rawdon to Guiseley centre. Ground 1/4 mile past traffic lights, on the right,entrance on A65 opposite Silver Cross factory. Further car parking available,frst right after ground, off Ings Crescent. 5 mins walk from Guiseley (BR/Metro) station.
Capacity: 3,000   Cover: 1,040   Seats: 427
Clubhouse: (01943 872872) Open before and after all games (closes 11pm). Snack bar within ground open before and during matches.
Club Shop: Sells programmes, various items of clothing, key rings, badges, mugs etc. Phone Jennifer Rogerson 01943 879236

Programme
Pages: 40   Price: £1
Editor: Rachel O'Connor

Local Press: Yorkshire Evening Post, Bradford Telegraph & Argus, Airedale &Wharfedale Observer, Wharfe Valley Times.

PREVIOUS   **Leagues:** West Riding Co. Amtr; West Yorks; Yorkshire 68-82; Northern Co's East82-91.

CLUB RECORDS   **Attendance:** 2,486 v Bridlington Town, FA Vase Semi Final 1st Leg 89-90.

BEST SEASON   **FA Cup:** First Round Proper 1994-95, 1-4 v Carlisle Utd. (at Valley Parade); 99-00, v Forest Green Rov. (A)
FA Vase: Winners 1990-91 (R-up 91-92, S.F. 94-95).
FA Trophy: Semi-Final 1994-95.

HONOURS   FA Vase 90-91 (R-up 91-92), Northern Premier Lg Div 1 94-95 (Presidents Cup 94-95, Div 1 Cup 92-93), Northern Counties (East) Lg 90-91 (Lg Cup 90-91), West Riding County Cup(5 inc 94-95), Yorkshire Lg R-up 79-80 81-82 (Lg Cup 79-80).

Players Progressing: Keith Walwyn (York City), Frank Harrison (Halifax Town),Dean Walling (Carlisle United), Richard Annan (Crewe Alexandra). Dave Hanson (Halifax Town), Geoff Horsfield (Birmingham City)

KENDAL TOWN

CLUB OFFICIALS

Chairman: David Willan
President: M Macklin
Secretary: Craig Campbell,
34 High Sparrowmire, Kendal,
Cumbria LA9 5PD
Tel: 01539 734209 (H)
Press Officer: Peter Savage
Tel: 01539 726488
Match Sec: John Wharton,
3 Vickers Hill, Kendal, Cumbria.
Tel: 01539 734209

FOOTBALL MANAGEMENT TEAM

Manager: Peter Smith
Asst Manager: Bruce Richardson
Physio: Stan Casey

Programme

Pages: 32   Price: £1.00
Editor: John Wharton (01539734209)

FACT FILE

Formed: 1920
Nickname: Town
Colours:
Black & white stripes/black/black
Change colours:
All yellow
Midweek home matchday:
Tuesday
Local Press:
Westmorland Gazette
Lancaster Evening Post
Local Radio:
Radio Cumbria, The Bay.

GROUND   Parkside Road, Kendal, Cumbria Tel: 01539 727472

Directions: M6 junction 36, follow signs for Kendal (South), right at lights, left at r-bout to `K' Village - Parkside Rd on right opposite factory main offices - ground 400 yds. A mile & a half from Oxenholme (BR) station - bus service to `K' village, No 41 or 41A
Capacity: 2,490   Cover: 1,000   Seats: 250

Clubhouse: The Park, open all matchdays. Pies & pasties available   **Club Shop:** No

PREVIOUS   Leagues: Westmorland; North Lancs; Lancs Combination 45-68; Northern Premier 68-83; North West Counties 83-87

CLUB RECORDS   **Attendance:** 5,184 v Grimsby Town, FA Cup 1st Rd 1955
Goalscorer: Tom Brownlee. **Win:** 11-0 v Great Harwood 22/3/47. **Defeat:** 0-10 v Stalybridge Celtic 1/9/84
Fee Paid: Undisclosed for Tom Brownlee (Bradford C., 66). **Fee Received:** £10,250 for Andy Milner (Man. City 95)

BEST SEASON   **FA Vase:** 3rd Rd 89-90   **FA Trophy:** 2nd Rd 80-81.
FA Cup: 2nd Rd replay 63-64, 1-4 v Chesterfield(A) after 1-1. 2nd Rd 49-50, 1st Rd 45-4648-49 52-53 54-55 55-56 64-65

HONOURS   Lancs Comb. 48-49 64-65 (R-up 45-46 53-54 61-62 63-64, Lg Cup 55-56 60-61), Westmorland Snr Cup(12) 24-25 31-33 35-36 46-48 63-64 65-66 71-72 86-8789-89 90-91

Players progressing: John Laidlaw (Carlisle 1946), Louis Cardwell (Crewe 1947), Herbert Keen (Barrow 1953), Alec Aston (Preston 1955), Horace Langstreth (Torquay 1956), John Simpson (Lincoln 1957), Dennis Rogers (Accrington 1959), Tom Brownlee (Bradford City 1965), Peter McDonnell (Bury 1973), Keith Silken (Workington 1973), Roger Wicks (Darlington 1981), Andy Milner (Man City)

Back row (left to right); Kyle Hayton, Chris Park, Bruce Richardson (assisant manager), Ian Simpson, Richard Close, Lee Ward, Phil Hodgson, Damien Corcoran, Stuart Cliff, Neil Murphy (assistant manager), Stan Casey (coach).
Front row: Mike McKecknie, Lee Blamire, Mike Smith, Ryan Close (mascot), Jamie Close, David Foster, Mark Crichley, Lee Pennington, James Shepherd.   Picture courtesy of the Westmorland Gazette.

KIDSGROVE ATHLETIC

CLUB OFFICIALS
Chairman: Terry Hillman
Vice Chairman: Stan Brown
President: Ernie Langford
Secretary: Alan Thompson
7 Sandown Road, Crewe, Cheshire CW1 3TE
Tel: 01270 256588 (H) 07712 956400 (M)

FOOTBALL MANAGEMENT TEAM
Manager: Kevin Langley
Physio: Graham Plant

FACT FILE
Formed: 1952
Nickname: "The Grove"
Colours: All Royal Blue
Change Colours: All yellow
Midweek Matches: Wednesday

2001-02
Captain: John Diskin
Player of The Year: Darren Twigg
Top Goalscorer: Darren Twigg 23

KIDSGROVE ATHLETIC F.C.

Out of the Blue

V Buxton F.C.
F.A. Cup 1st Round Preliminary

Unibond Division 1 · Season 2002/2003

PROGRAMME
Pages: 32   Price: £1
Editor: Mr. J Neisbett

GROUND: Clough Hall, Hollinswood Road, Kidsgrove, Stoke-on-Trent, Staffs
Tel: 01782 782412

Directions: M6 Jct 16, A500 towards Stoke, 2nd jctn onto A34 towards Manchester,
turn right at 1st lights down hill, rt at lights into Cedar Rd , 2nd right into Lower
Ash Rd, 3rd left into Hollinwood Rd to ground.   BR Kidsgrove (5mins)
Capacity: 4,500   Seats: 400   Cover: 600   Floodlights: Yes

Clubhouse: Yes. Food matchdays. Seating 180 with Sky TV, Big Screen

HONOURS NWC Div. 1 97-98, 01-02; NWC Chall. Cup 97-98;
Mid Cheshire Lg 70-71,78-79 86-87 87-88, R-up 68-69 85-86; Lg Cup 67-68 69-70 85-86, R-up 84-85 86-87;
Staffs County Lge; Burslem & Tunstall Lge. Floodlit Trophy R-up: 1999

PREVIOUS **Leagues:** Burslem & Tunstall 1953-63, Staffordshire County 63-66, Mid Cheshire Lge. 66-90, North West Counties 90-2002.
Ground: Vickers & Goodwin 1953-60

BEST SEASON **FA Cup:** 1995, 1st Qualifying Round, 1-3 v Hinckley   **FA Vase:** Semi-Final 1997-98, 2-3 agg. v Tiverton Town

RECORDS **Attendance:** 1,903 v Tiverton Town, FA Vase S-F 1998 **Career Goalscorer:** Scott Dundas 53 1997-98
Victory: 23-0 v Cross Heath W.M.C., Staffs Cup 1965 **Defeat:** 2-7 v Glossop N.E., NWCL Div 1 93-94.
Transfer Fee Received: Richard Mitchell 2001-02 £3,000
Players Progressing: Mark Bright (Crystal Palace), Ronnie Jepson (Port Vale).

L-R - Back Row: Dave Eaton, Darren Twigg, Chris Holmes, Wayne Mountford, Phil Traynor, Dale Hawtin.
Front Row: Paul Robertson, Steve Ashton, Danny Worthington, Steve Tobin, Andy Porter   **Photo:** Bill Wheatcroft

LEEK TOWN

CLUB OFFICIALS

President: D.J.Bray
Chairman: Paul Burston
Directors: Paul Burston,Alan Clarke,Andy Wain,Dave Stringer and Paul Ogden
Secretary: Christine Osmond: 10 Corporation Street,Stoke on Trent Staffs. ST44AU (01782 847936 (H)
Commercial Manager: Ken Warburton
Press Officer: Mike Cope

FOOTBALL MANAGEMENT TEAM

Manager: John Ramshaw

Coach: Paul Cox   Physio: Bill Allen

FACT FILE

Founded: 1946
Nickname: The Blues
Club Sponsors: Kerrygold
Colours: Blue with yellow trim
Change colours: Yellow with blue trim
Reserve team league: Manchester League
Midweek home matchday: Monday

Newsline: 0930 55 54 53
Local Press: Leek Post & Times, Evening Sentinel
Local Radio: Radio Stoke, Signal Radio

Programme
Pages: 40   Price: £1.00
Editors: Steve Reynolds & Tracy Cope

GROUND   Harrison Park, Macclesfield Road, Leek ST13 8LD
Tel: 01538 399278 Fax: 01538 399826

Directions: Opposite Courtaults chemical works on A523 Macclesfield to Buxton
road half a mile out of Leek heading towards Macclesfield.

Capacity: 3,600   Seated: 625   Covered Terracing: 2,675
Club Shop: Contact club on 01538 399278.
Clubhouse: `Blues' Bar openmatch days. Functions by request (01538 383734)

PREVIOUS   **Leagues:** Staffs County, Manchester 51-54 57-73, West Mids (B'ham) 54-56,Cheshire County 73-82, North West Counties 82-87, Northern Premier 87-94 95-97,Southern League 94-95, Conference 97-99
Names: Abbey Green Rovers/ Leek Lowe Hamil.   **Grounds:** None
CLUB RECORDS Attendance: 5,312 v Macclesfield Town, F.A. Cup Second Qualifying Round 73-74   **Win:** Unknown   **Defeat:** Unknown
Transfer fee paid: £2,000 for Simon Snow (Sutton Town)   **Transfer fee received:** £30,000 for Tony Bullock (Barnsley)
Career goalscorer: Dave Suttons 144   **Career appearances:** Gary Pearce 447.
BEST SEASON   FA Cup: 2nd Rd 90-91, 0-4 v Chester (A) after 1-1   League clubs defeated: Scarborough 90-91.
FA Trophy: Runners-up 89-90, Q-F 85-86.
HONOURS   FA Trophy R-up 89-90; Northern Premier Lg 96-97, R-up 93-94 (Div 1 89-90, Div 1Cup R-up 88-89, Presidents Cup R-up 93-94, Lg Shield 90-91); North West Co's LgCup 84-85 (Charity Shield 84-85); Cheshire County Lg 74-75 (Challenge Shield74-75); Manchester Lg 51-52 71-72 72-73 (Lg Cup 72-73); Staffs Snr Cup 95-96,R-up 54-55 81-82 95-96, Jnr Cup 51-52 70-71 (R-up 47-48 48-49 49-50)); StaffsCo. Lg 50-51 69-70 70-71 73-74 (R-up 47-48 49-50, Lg Cup 70-71 73-74); LeekPost Charity Shield 46-47; Leek Cup 47-48 52-53 70-71 71-72 (R-up 46-47); MayBank Cup 47-48 50-51 71-72; Hanley Cup 48-49 70-71 (R-up 49-5); Mid Cheshire LgDiv 2 87-88 (Div 2 Cup 87-88); Evans Halshaw Floodlit Cup Winners 93-94 94-95; Southern Lge Cup R-up 94-95; Unibond Lge Chall Cup R-up 95-96
Players progressing: Geoff Crosby (Stockport 52), Bill Summerscales (70), Mark Bright (81) & Martyn Smith (84) allto Port Vale,
Paul Edwards (Crewe 89), Tony Bullock (Barnsley 97)

Back row, left to right: Lee Martin, Melvin Wilkes (Coaches), J.Marrow, P.Berry, G.Liddle, K.Welsby, W.Johnson, D.Macpherson, F.M. M'Fomo with directors A.Clarke and M.Clarke.
Front row: M.Bulllock, M. Ridley, S.Taaffe, J.Hassell, S.Callear, A.Danylyk and Secretary, C.Osmond.

LINCOLN UNITED

CLUB OFFICIALS

Chairmen: Robin Taylor & Maurice Bull
President: Phil Morley
Vice Chairman: W.White
Commercial Manager: Roy Parnham

Secretary/Press Officer: Tom Hill, 4,Westwood Drive, Swanpool, Lincoln LN6 0HJTel Nos: 01522 683630 (H) 07885 020797 (M)

FOOTBALL MANAGEMENT TEAM

Managers: Garry Goddard
Physio: Anthony Adams

FACT FILE

Formed: 1938
Nickname: United
Colours: All white
Change Colours: All light blue
Midweek home matchday: Tuesday
Reserves ' League: Lincolnshire
2000-2001
Captain: Chris White
Top Goalscorer: Ian Williams 14
P.o.Y.: Ian Williams

GROUND Ashby Avenue, Hartsholme, Lincoln Tel: 01522 690674
Directions: From Newark A46 onto Lincoln relief road (A446), right at 2nd r'bout for Birchwood (Skellingthorpe Rd), go for 1 mile passing lake and Country Park, 1st right 10yds after 30mph sign into Ashby Ave., ground entrance200 yds, opposite Old Peoples home. From north follow A57 via Saxilby until reaching A46 Lincoln Relief Road - continue on this and turn left at r'bout signed Birchwood then as above. 3 miles from Lincoln Central (BR)
Capacity: 2,714 **Seats:** 400 **Covered:** 1,084
Clubhouse: Open daily normal licensing hours. Matchday snack bar -hot &cold food & drinks
Club Shop: Yes. Contact:Secretary

Programme
Pages: 40 Price:#1.00
Editor:Roy Parnham TelNo: 01522 687543

Local Press: Lincolnshire Echo
Lincoln Standard

PREVIOUS	**Leagues:** Lincs 45-48 60-67; Lincoln 48-60; Yorks 67-82; Northern Co'sEast 82-86, 92-95; Central Mids 82-92 **Grounds:** Skew Bridge (40s); Co-op Sports Ground (to mid 60s); Hartsholme Cricket Ground (to 82) **Name:** Lincoln Amateurs (until an ex-pro signed in 1954)
CLUB RECORDS	**Attendance:** 2,000 v Crook Town, FA Amateur Cup 1st Rd Proper, 1968 **Scorer:** Tony Simmons 215 **Appearances:** Steve Carter 447 **Win:** 12-0 v Pontefract Colls 95. **Defeat:** 0-7 v Huddersfield Town FA Cup 1st Round Proper16-11-91 **Fee Paid:** £1000 for Paul Tomlinson (Hucknall Town ,Dec 2000) **Fee Received:** £3,000 for Dean Dye (Charlton Ath., 7.91)
BEST SEASON	**FA Cup:** First Round Proper 91-92 (0-7 at Huddersfield Town), 97-98 v Walsall (0-2 Away) **FA Trophy:** 3rd 3Rd **F.A.Vase:**
HONOURS	Northern Counties East - Prem Div. 94-95, Div 1 92-93, Div 1 Sth 82-83,Div 2 85-86, Presidents Cup 94-95; Yorks Lg 70-71 73-74 (Lg Cup 70-71); Lincs Lg 63-64; Lincs Snr `A' Cup 72-73 85-86 95-96, R-up 91-92 94-95, `B' Cup 63-6470-71; Central Mids Lg 91-92 (Wakefield Cup 90-91); Evans Halshaw Floodlit Cup R-up 92-93; Lincs I'mediate Cup(7) 67-73 80-81; Blankney Hunt Inter Lge 95-96,Cup 95-96 Lincs Sen Cup: R-up 97-98 Uniflla Div 1 Cup R-up 97-98

Back Row, left to right: Tom Hill (Secretary), Robin Taylor (Director), Paul Titcombe (Asst. Manager), Paul Burton, Kev Riley, Adam Gilbert, Paul Ward, Steve Curry, Simon Daniels, Ben Brown, James Drinkall, Lee Soar, Tony Adams (Trainer), Kev Hilton (Match Secretary) and Phil Morley (President). **Front Row:** Chris Hudson, Dave Frecklington, Paul Tomlinson, Richard Taylor, Jason Sedland, Pete Doyle (Chairman), Chris White, Allen Crombie (Manager),Gary Walters, Danny Hargreaves, Dominic Revill and Chris Ellis (Committee)

MATLOCK TOWN

CLUB OFFICIALS

Chairman: **Donald Carr**
Vice Chairman: **Michael Tomlinson**
Secretary: **Keith Brown**
'Barncroft', 1 Malvern Gardens
Matlock, Derbyshire DE4 3JH
01629 584231 (H) 01335 390301 (B)
Press Officer: **Ian Richardson**
Commercial Manager: **Tom Wright**

FOOTBALL MANAGEMENT TEAM

Manager: Ernie Moss
Physio: Michael Cunningham

GROUND

FACT FILE

Formed: 1885
Nickname: The Gladiators
Sponsors: Westons of Wirksworth
& Panasonic/ Tarmac
Colours: Royal Blue/white/blue
Change colours: All yellow
Midweek home matchday: Tuesday
Local Press: Matlock Mercury
Derbyshire Times, Derby Evening Telegraph,
Chesterfield Express & Sheffield Star
Local Radio: Radio Derby & Peak 107 F.M.

Causeway Lane, Matlock, Derbyshire
Tel: 01629 583866 (& Fax)

Directions: On A615, 500 yds from town centre and Matlock (BR)
Capacity: 7,500   Cover: 2,000   Seats: 240
Clubhouse: Gladiators Social Club, on ground, open matchdays only
Club Shop: Yes. Contact: Sue Tomlinson (01629 583866)

PROGRAMME
Pages 40   Price £1.00
Editor: Mike Tomlinson (01629 583866)
Website: www.matlocktownnfc.co.uk

PREVIOUS	**Ground:** Hall Leys (last century). **Leagues:** Midland Counties 1894-96; Matlock & District; Derbys Senior; Central Alliance 24-25 47-61; Central Combination 34-35; Chesterfield & District 46-47; Midland Counties 1961-69
CLUB RECORDS	**Attendance:** 5,123 v Burton Albion, FA Trophy 1975 **Win:** 10 v 0 Lancaster (A) **74** **Defeat:** 0-8 v Chorley (A) 71 Career **Goalscorer:** Peter Scott. **Career Appearances:** Mick Fenoughty **Fee Paid:** £2,000 for Kenny Clarke 1996 **Fee Received:** £10,000 for Ian Helliwell (York)
BEST SEASON	**FA Trophy:** Winners 1974-75 **FA Cup:** 3rd Rd 76-77. 1st Rd 1885-86 86-87 86-8787-88 1959-60 74-75 75-76 89-90 League clubs defeated: Mansfield Town 76-77
HONOURS	Northern Prem Lge R-up 83-84, Lge Cup 77-78, Shield 78-79; Midland Counties Lge 61-62 68-69; Central All (North) 59-60 60-61, R-up 61-62 62-63,Div 1 Cup R-up 61-62, Div 2 59-60, Div 2 Cup 59-60 60-61; Derbyshire Sen Cup74-75 76-77 77 78 80-81 83-84 84-85 91-92, R-up 60-61 72-73 73-74 75-76 80-8181-82 82-83 89-90 93-94 97-98; Derbyshire Div Cup (North) 61-62 R-up 62-63;Evans Halshaw Floodlit Cup 88-89 91-92; Anglo-Italian Non-League Cup 79

Players progressing: Keith Haines (Leeds 1959), Wayne Biggins (Burnley 1984),Darren Bradshaw (Chesterfield 1987), Les McJannet (Scarborough 1987), Ian Helliwell (York 1987)

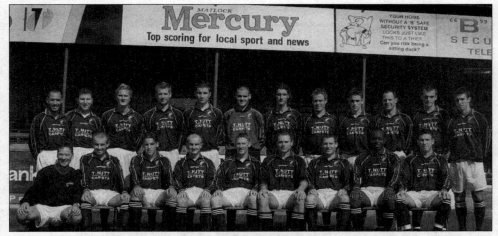

Back row, left to right: Chris James, Dave McNicholas, Andy Simpson, Mark Willgoose, James Lukic, Kevin Tye,Will Davies, Gareth Williams, Matt Varley, Steve Charles, James Lomas and Stuart Clarke. **Front row:** Mick Cunningham (Physio), Phil Brown, Danny Holland, Lee Handbury, Nick Tilly (Captain), Richard Taylor, Wayne Fairclough and Ian Clarke.

NORTH FERRIBY UNITED

£1.20p

CLUB OFFICIALS
President: Brian Thacker
Chairman: Les Hare
Vice Chairman: John Greenly
Press Officer: Mike O'Brian
Secretary: Stephen Tather
16 Peasholme, Heads Lane, Hessle,
E Yorks HU13 0NY
Tel: 01482 642046 (H) Fax 01482 647244;
01482 351903 (B)

FOOTBALL MANAGEMENT TEAM

Manager: Brian France
Asst Mgr: Paul Olsson
Physio: Martin Woodmansey

FACT FILE

Founded: 1934
Nickname: United
Sponsors: Dransfield Developments
Colours: All white
Change colours: All yellow
Midweek matches: Tuesday
Reserves League: Humber Premier
2001-02
Captain: Rob Dewhurst
P.o.Y.: Gavin Mnight
Top Scorer: Gavin Knight 27

EAST RIDING SENIOR CUP WINNERS POST WAR RECORD 1996-2001

NORTH FERRIBY UNITED
v
ROSSENDALE UNITED
Tuesday, 5th March 2002
UNIBOND LEAGUE DIVISION 1 SEASON 2001/2002
OFFICIAL MATCHDAY PROGRAMME

GROUND: Grange Lane, Church Road, North Ferriby HU14 3AA   Tel: 01482 634601
Directions: Main Leeds-Hull road A63 or M62, North Ferriby is 8 miles west of Hull. Into
North Ferriby, thru village passed the Duke of Cumberland Hotel, right down Church Rd,
ground half mile on left. One mile from North Ferriby (BR)

Programme
Pages: 40   Price: £1.20
Editor: Dave Simmons
Tel & Fax: 01430 827390
Local Press: Hull Daily Mail

Capacity: 3,000   Seats: 250   Cover: 1,000   Floodlights: Yes

Clubhouse: Bar, lounge, TV, pool open every night   **Club Shop:** Yes

HONOURS   FA Vase Finalist 96-97; Yorkshire Lg R-up 75-76, Lg Cup 74-75, Div 2 70-71;
N.C.E. Prem Div : Champions 99-00 R-up 97-98, Div 1 85-86 (Lg Cup R-up) 90-91 97-98,
Presidents Cup 90-91, 98-99, 99-00 Div 1 (North), R-up 82-83, Res. Div R-up 90-91;
E. Riding Snr Cup (10), E. Riding Church Lg 37-38

PREVIOUS   **Leagues:** East Riding Church; East Riding Amateur; Yorks 69-82

BEST SEASON   **FA Cup:** 3rd Q 97-98,98-99   **F.A.Trophy:** 4th Ropund 2001-02   **FA Vase:** R-up 96-97, SF 88-89, QF 89-90

RECORDS   **Attendance:** 1,800 v Tamworth, FA Vase Semi-Final, 1989
Goalscorer: Andy Flounders 50, 98-99   **Appearances:** Richard Woomble, 74-94
Win: 9-0 v Hatfield Main, N.C.E. Lge Prem 97-98.   **Defeat:** 1-7 v North Shields,N.C.E. Lge Prem 91.
Fee received: £6,000 for Dean Windass (Hull City,1988)

Players progressing: T Hotte (Hull) 88, I Ironside (Halifax) 88, D France, D Windass & M Matthews (Hull) 91.

Back row, left to right: Alan Stevenson (Kitman), Nathan Steed, Andy Thompson, Adam Lowthorpe, Michael Price, Paul Farley, Ian Fenton and Martin Woodmansey (physio).

Middle row: Paul Foot, David Botham, Gavin Knight, Paul Sharp, Vill Powell, Steve Fisher, Graham Botham and Ben Sherwood.

Front row: Martin Wood, Steve Perrin,,Dave Frisby (Captain), Brian France (Manager), Paul Olsson (Assistant Manager), Carl Wood and Danny Sherwood

Macot: Alex Walkeley

OSSETT TOWN

CLUB OFFICIALS

President: Paul Jervis
Chairman: Graham Firth
Football Chairman: Peter Wilkinson
Commercial Manager: Graham Willis
Secretary: Steve Andrews
74 Park View, Flocton, Nr Wakefield WF4 4AF
email: steveandrews@ossetttown.fsnet.co.uk

FOOTBALL MANAGEMENT TEAM
Manager: Gary Brook
Asst Manager: B. Crawther
Coach: Nigel Yarrow

FACT FILE
Founded: 1936
Sponsors:: Builders Supply(Wakefield) Ltd
Colours:Red with white trimd
Change colours: All sky
Midweek matches: Tuesday
Reserves' League: Lancashire League

Website: www.ossetttown.freeserve.co.uk

Pages: 56   Price: £1.00
Editor: Andrew Wilkinson
email: arwilko@ahoo.co.uk
Local Press: Dewsbury Reporter,
Wakefield Express

GROUND: Ingfield, Prospect Road, Ossett, Wakefield WF5 8AN Tel: 01924 272960
Directions: M1 jct 40, B6129 to Ossett, left into Dale Street, left again at lights opposite bus station on ring road, ground on left. Nearest stations Dewsbury or Wakefield Westgate - both three miles from. Buses 116, 117, 126 and127 from Wakefield, buses 116, 126 and 127 from Dewsbury, buses 117, 118 or 216 from Leeds
Capacity: 4,000   Seats: 360   Cover:1,000   Floodlights: Yes
Clubhouse: Open Fri & Sun lunchtimes, all day Sat and every evening. Pie & peas, chips, soup from tea bar   **Club Shop:** Yes (Graham Willis (h) 01924 266393)

PREVIOUS   **Leagues:** Leeds 36-39; Yorkshire 45-82; N.C.E. 83-99   **Ground:** Fern House (pre-1958)

RECORDS   **Attendance:** 2,600 v Manchester Utd, friendly 1988
Win: 10-1 v Harrogate RA (H), N.C.E. Lge Prem. Div. 27/4/93
Defeat: 0-7 v Easington Colliery, FA Vase 8/10/83
Fee received: £1,350 for Derek Blackburn (Swansea 1957)
Appearances: Steve Worsfold   **Goalscorer:** Dave Leadbeater

HONOURS   Northern Counties East - Lg Cup 89-90, Div 2 88-89, Res. Div 88-89, Res.Cup 87-88 88-89;
West Riding County Cup 58-59 81-82.

Players progressing: Arnold Kendall (Bradford C.) 1949, Ron Liversidge(Bradford C.) 56, Derek Blackburn (Swansea) 57, Simon Lowe (Barnsley) 83, Gary Chapman (Bradford C.) 88, Mick Norbury (Scarborough) 1989, Mike Williams(Sheffield W.) 90, Dean Trott (Northampton) 98, Paul Cuss (Huddersfield Town) 98.

L-R - Back row: John Brown, James Walshaw, James Featherstone, Simon Fuller, Mark Lambert, Rob Bloomfield, Lee Bracey, David Briggs, Chris Annan, Carl Fothergill, Dave Hanson.   **Front row:** Steve Olekseuycz, Kieron O'Brien, Ross Wood, Paul Fleming, Ryan Gray, Craig Boardman (Capt.), Chris Beaumont, Alan Barker, Graham Marchant, Brendan Aspinall.

Photo: Bill Wheatcroft

RADCLIFFE BOROUGH

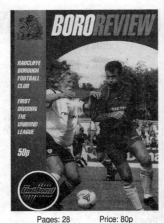

CLUB OFFICIALS

Chairman: Bernard Manning (Junior)

President: Bernard Manning (Senior)

Vice Chairman: J. Ryan

Company Secretary: Graham E Fielding
Football Secretary: Ian Hannay
Both c/o Radcliffe Borough

FOOTBALL MANAGEMENT TEAM
Manager: Kevin Glendon
Coach: Mike Farrelly
Physio: Roy Davies

FACT FILE
Formed: 1949
Sponsors: T.B.A.
Nickname: Boro'
Colours: All blue
Change colours: Green & white hoops
Midweek home matchday: Tuesday
Reserve Team: No
2001-02
Captain: David Bean
P.o.Y.: Danny Hurst
Top scorer: Jody Banim 28

GROUND: Stainton Park, Pilkington Road, Radcliffe, Lancs., M26 3PE 0161 724 5937 (club).
0161 724 8346 (Office) 0161 723 3178(Fax) Website: www.radcliffeborough.co.uk
Directions: M62 junction 17 - follow signs for Whitefield and Bury. Take A665 to Radcliffe.
Thro' town centre, turn right into Unsworth St. (opposite Turf Hotel). Ground on left half mile
Colshaw Close East. 1/2 mile from Radcliffe(BR)
Capacity: 3,000 Cover: 1,000 Seats: 350
Clubhouse: (0161 724 5937) 'The Boro' - public house on ground with food available
Club Shop: Yes

Pages: 28   Price: 80p
Editor: Roy Swinbank

Local Press: Radcliffe Times, Bolton
Evening News, Manchester Evening News
Local Radio: GMR, Piccadilly

PREVIOUS **Leagues:** South East Lancs; Manchester 53-63; Lancs Comb. 63-71; Cheshire County 71-82; North West Counties 82-87
Ground: Bright Street 1949-70.

CLUB RECORDS **Attendance:** 2,495 v York City (F.A.C 1st Round 2000-01)
Goalscorer: Ian Lunt **Appearances:** Chris Lilley.
Fee Paid: £5,000 for Gary Walker(Buxton, 1991). **Fee Received:** £15,000 for Paul Mullin (Accrington Stanley 2000-01)

BEST SEASON **FA Trophy:** 3rd Rd v Gateshead 1995-96
FA Cup: 1st Round Proper, 00-01 v York City 1-4) **FA Vase:** 4th Rd v Boston Town 93-94

HONOURS Unibond Lge Div One Champ 96-97; North West Counties Lg 84-85 (Div 2 82-83); Lancs Combination Lg. Cup 69-70;
Manchester Lg R-up 55-56 (Lg Cup 58-59 joint); Manchester Prem. Cup R-up 97-98

Players progressing: Jim Hayman (Bury 50), Ian Wood (Oldham Athletic 65), Robert Hutchinson (Rochdale 74),
Gary Haworth (Rochdale 84), Kevin Hulme (Bury 89), Neil Hardy (Stockport County)

Back row, left to right: Richard Landon, Richard Battersby, Danny Hurst, Simon Kelly and Eamonn Kelly.
Front row: Tony Whealing, Lee Kissock, Mark Dempsey (Captain), Jamie Price, Eamonn Elliot and Ryan Cain.

ROSSENDALE UNITED

ROSSENDALE UNITED
FOOTBALL CLUB

Sponsored by SWINBURNE JAMES

CLUB OFFICIALS
Chairman: A Connelly **V Chair:** LeeBrierley
President: David White
Press Offcer: Kevin Procter
Secretary: Kevin Procter,5 Booth Street,
Waterfoot, Rossendale, Lancs BB4 9AL
Tel No: 01706 223405
Email Address: rossendaleunited@zen.co.uk

FOOTBALL MANAGEMENT TEAM
Manager: James McCluskie
Ass. Man. Andy Grimshaw Coach: David
White.Physios: Billy Howarth&Chris Connelly

FACT FILE
Founded: 1898 Nickname: The Stags
Sponsors: Hurstwood Developments
Colours: Blue & white stripes/blue/blue
Change cols: Red&yellow stroipes/red/red
Midweek matchday: Tuesday
Reserves ' League: Lancashire
Website: www.nip.to@zen.co.uk
2000-01
Captain: Gary Rishton
P.o.Y.: Jason Heffernan`
Top Scorer: Craig Sargeson 39

Today's Opponents:
V Chorley
League Cup Group

North West
Counties Football
League Champions
2000/2001 Season

2001/2002 Season

GROUND	Dark Lane, Staghills Rd, Newchurch, Rossendale, Lancs BB4 7UA
	Tel: 01706 215119 (Ground); 01706 213296 (Club)
Directions:	M60 Junc 18, M66 north following signs for Burnley, then A682 to Rawstenstall,
	take 2nd exit sign Burnley A682, at 1st lights turn right into Newchurch Rd,
	1.5 miles turn right into Staghills Rd, grd 800 yards right
Capacity:	2,500 Cover: Yes Seats: 500 Floodlights: Yes
Clubhouse:	Evenings & matchdays. Hot snacks. Pool, satellite TV, concert room
Club Shop:	Yes

Programme: 28 pages-£1.00
Editor: David Howarth

Local Radio: Red Rose, Radio Lancashire.
Local Press: Lancs Evening Telegraph,
Rossendale Free Press

PREVIOUS **Leagues:** N.E. Lancs Comb.; Lancs Comb. 1898-99 1901-70; Central Lancs 1899-1901; Cheshire County 70-82;
NWC 82-89 93-01; N.P.L. 89-93. **Grounds:** None

RECORDS **Attendance:** 12,000 v Bolton Wanderers FA Cup 2nd Rd 71
Appearances: Johnny Clarke 770, 1947-65 **Goalscorer:** Bob Scott
Fee Paid: £3,000 for Jimmy Clarke (Buxton, 1992)
Fee Received: £1,500 for Dave O'Neill (Huddersfield Town, 1974)
Win: 17-0v Ashton Town, Lancs Comb.1911-12
Defeat: 0-14 v Morecambe, Lancs Comb. 67-68

BEST SEASON **FA Cup:** 2nd Rd 71-72, 1-4 v Bolton W. at Bury FC. Also 1st Rd 75-76   Also 1st Rd 75-76, 0-1 v Shrewsbury T. (H)
FA Trophy : 2nd Rd 81-82   **FA Vase:** 5th Rd 86-87,88-89

HONOURS N.W.C. Lg Div 1 88-89 00-01(R-up 87-88 93-94), Div 2 R-up 85-86, Chall Cup 93-94

Players progressing: T Lawton, G Smith (Bradford C 52), E Hartley & W O'Loughton (Oldham 56/60), C Blunt (Burnley 64), F Eyre (Bradford PA
69), D O'Neill (Huddersfield), C Parker (Rochdale 92).

Back row, left to right: Andrew Grimshaw, Mick Hilton, Carl Howarth, Richard Harris, Chris Scott, Mark Andrews, Gareth Gardiner,
Gerome Fitzgerald, Lee Fitzpatrick, Ged Walsh, David Gray, League Registration Secrtary ,Andrew Connelly (Chairman), Jim
McCluskie (Manager) and League Secretary Duncan Bayley.
Front row: Darren Bowman, Paul Lynch, Jason Heffernan, Craig Sargeson, Matt Houldsworth and Troy Hayder.

SPENNYMOOR UNITED

The MOORS
£1

OFFICIAL MATCHDAY MAGAZINE

Chairman & Press Off: Barrie Hindmarch
Vice Chairman: P. Fletcher
Football Match Secretary
Brian Boughen,141 Durham Rd,
Spennymoor, Co.Durham. DL16 6JU Tel
No: 01388 81187
Com Man: Des Beamson
Gen Sec: Tom Metcalfe (01388 811561)

FOOTBALL MANAGEMENT TEAM
Manager: Tony Lee
Physio: Peter Carey
Coach: Tim Wattis

FACT FILE
Founded: 1904
Nickname: The Moors
Sponsors: T.B.A.
Club colours: Black & white
stripes/black/white.
Change colours: All red
Midweek home matches: Tuesday
Reserve Team: None
2000-01
Captain:Jason Ainsley P.o.Y.: Jason Ainsley
Top scorers: Lee Adamson & Wayne
Edgecombe 15 each

UNIBOND LEAGUE
FIRST DIVISION
8th Dec 2001 3:00pm
v
GRETNA

GROUND Brewery Field, Durham Road, Spennymoor, County Durham DL16 6JN Tel: 01388
811934 Directions: From South; A1(M), A167, A688,straight on at mini-r'bout, 3rd exit at
next large r'bout (St Andrews church opposite), pass Asda on left, straight on at junction, pass
Salvin Arms (Durham Rd), ground 200 yds on left. From A167North - leave at Croxdale
(N.E.S.S. factory), right at cemetery on left - this is Durham Rd - ground half mile on right.
Nearest rail stations are Durhamand Bishop Auckland (via Darlington)-buses from there.
Capacity: 7,500   **Seats:** 300   **Cover:** 2,000
Clubhouse: (01388 814100) Open eves. 7-11pm, Sat 12-11pm (matchdays only), Sun12-2 &
7-10.30pm. Bar snacks. Private functions. Tea bar in ground.   **Club Shop:** Sells replica kit,
memorabilia, programmes etc. Contact Peter Fletcher (01388 814100).

Pages: 44 Price: £1
Editor: Gary Nunn

Local Press: Northern Echo; The Journal

PREVIOUS
Leagues: Northern 05-08 60-90; North Eastern 08-37 38-58; Wearside 37-38;Midland Counties 58-60;
Northern Counties East 90-93.   **Ground:** Wood Vue 1901-1904.   **Names:** None.

CLUB RECORDS
Attendance: 7,202 v Bishop Auckland, Durham County Challenge Cup 30/3/57.
Win: 19-0 v Eden Colliery, North Eastern Lge 6/2/37. **Defeat:** 0-16 v Sunderland`A', Durham Snr Cup 4.1.02 (H.T.: 0-10)
Goalscorer: Dougie Humble 200+.   **Appearances:** Ken Banks 600+.
Fee Paid: £3,500 for Don Prattie (Gretna).   Fee Received: £20,000 for Michael Heathcote (Sunderland, 88).

BEST SEASON
FA Trophy: Semi Final 77-78
FA Cup: 3rd Rd 36-37, 1-7 v West Bromwich Albion(A).   League clubs defeated : Hartlepool 27-28, Southport 75-76.

HONOURS
Northern Premier Lg Cup 93-94 (Div 1 R-up 93-94); Northern Lg(6) 67-68 71-7273-74 76-79 (R-up(3) 74-75 79-81), Lg
Cup(5) 65-66 67-68 79-81 86-87; Turney Wylde Cup 80-81; J R Cleator Cup 80-81 86-87; Northern Counties (East) Lg 92-
93(Lg Cup 92-93); Durham Challenge Cup 29-30 44-45 45-46 53-54 62-63 67-68 72-7373-74 74-75 75-76 78-79 82-83 93-94 94-95 95-96 97-98;
Durham Benevolent Bowl26-27 29-30 31-32 47-48 58-59 60-61; North Eastern Lg(4) 09-10 44-46 56-57 (Lg Cup 28-29).
Players Progressing: Over fifty, including: H. Hubbick (Burnley, 3.25), T .Dawson (Charlton, 3.39), T. Flockett (Charlton, 4.49), J. Smallwood(Chesterfield,
12.49), J. Oakes (Aldershot, 5.54), J. Adams (Luton Town, 53),Alan Moore (Chesterfield), Michael Heathcote (Sunderland, 5.87), Jason Ainsley(Hartlepool,
94), Richie Alderson (York City 97), Graeme Paxton (Newcastle Utd 97)

Back row left to right: Peter Carey (Physio), Tony Lee (Manager), Jim Prvitt, Jason Ainsley, Gary Williamson, Carl Beasley, Graham Liddle,
Leigh Grant , Steve Robson and Jim Watts (Coach). **Front row:** Jarrod Suddick, Steve Pickering, Stephen Ball, Wayne Edgecombe, Ritchie
Watson, Anthony Lee and Matty Hysen

STOCKSBRIDGE PARK STEELS

CLUB OFFICIALS

President: J.Newton
Chairman: Alan Bethel
Vice-Chairman: M Grimmer
Secretary: Michael Grimmer
48 Hole House Lane, Stocksbridge
Sheffield S36 1BT Tel: 0114 288 6470
Press Officer: Edwin O'Sullivan
Commercial Manager: Andrew Horsley
Tel: 0114 288 3867

FOOTBALL MANAGEMENT TEAM
Manager:Wayne Biggins
Asst Manager: Graham Furness
Physio: Sean Hird

FACT FILE

Formed: 1986
Nickname: Steels
Sponsors:John Crawshaw (Butchers)
Colours: Yellow/ blue/yellow
Change colours: All blue
Midweek matches: Tuesday
Reserves' League: SheffieldCounty Senior

2001-02
Captain: Jon Brown
P.o.Y.: Jimmy Flynn
Top Scorer: Wayne Biggins 11

Pages: 28   Price:1.00
Editor: Edwin O'Sullivan
Tel: 0114 288 4218

Local Press:
Look local, Green'un, The Star

GROUND	Bracken Moor Lane, Stocksbridge, Sheffield. Tel: 0114 288 2045
	Fax: 0114 288 8305 Club Website: http://members.aol.com/spsfc/
Directions:	M1 jct 35a (from S), 36 (from N), A616 to Stocksbridge.
	On arrival in Stocksbridge turn left into Nanny Hill under the Clock Tower
	and continue up the hill for about 500 yds - ground on left

Capacity: 3,500   **Cover:** 1,000   **Seats:** 450
Clubhouse: Open 7 days (lunchtime & evenings). No food. Separate foodbar for matches
Club Shop:(H.O'Sullivan 0114 2884218) badges, mugs, shirts, progs,watches and scarves .

PREVIOUS	**Ground:** Stonemoor 49-51 52-53 **Names:** Stocksbridge Works, Oxley Park;clubs merged in 1986
	Leagues: Sheffield Amateur/ Sheffield Association/Yorkshire 49-82
CLUB RECORDS	**Attendance:** 2,000 v Sheffield Wed., Floodlight opening Oct '91
	Fee Received: £15,000 for Lee Mills (Wolves, 1992) **Fee Paid:** Nil
	Win: 5-0 v Warrington Town NPL 96-97 **Defeat:** 2-7 Witton Albion 2001-02
	Scorer: Trevor Jones (145) **Appearances:** Not known
BEST SEASON	**FA Cup:** 4th Q 50-1, 56-7 **FA Trophy:** 3rd Q 96-97 **FA Vase:** 4th Rd 95-96.
HONOURS	Northern Co's East Prem Div 93-94, R-up 95-96, Div 1 91-92, Lg Cup 94-95; Sheffield Snr Cup 92-93 95-96,98-99.
	Oxley Park F C: County Sen Div 1 85-86:Stocksbridge Works FC: Yorkshire Lge Div 1 51-52 54-55 55-56 56-57 57-58
	61-62 62-63, Div 2 50-51 64-65, Div 3 70-71 74-75, Lge Cup 61-62 Sheffield Snr Cup 51-52

Players progressing: Peter Eustace (Sheffield Wednesday) 1960 (from Stocksbridge Works) , Lee Mills (Wolverhampton W.) 1992

Back row, left to right: J. Beggs, J. Flynn, D. Fearon, S. Morfitt, D. McCarthy, R. Green,T. Jones and P. Jackson.
Front row: C. Hilton, C. Ludlam, L. Robinson, Wayne Biggins (Manager), J. Brown, M. Horne, G. Hurlstone, J. Illingworth and R. Ashton

TRAFFORD

CLUB OFFICIALS

Chairman: **Tom Walmsley**

President: **David Roberts**

Secretary: **Graham Foxall**
90 Grosvenor Road, Urmston M41 5AQ
Tel: 0161 747 4502

FOOTBALL MANAGEMENT TEAM

Manager: Joey Dunn
Asst Manager: Stuart Humphries
Coach: T.B.A.

FACT FILE

Formed: 1990
Nickname: The North
Sponsors: Caffro Construction Ltd
Colours: All White
Change colours: All Yellow
Midweek Matchday: Tuesday
Reserve League: Mid Cheshire Div 2
2001-02
Captain: Chris Patterson
P.o.Y.: Anthony Hogan
Top Scorer: Darren Emmett 15

TRAFFORD F.C. REVIEW

Season 2001-2002

£1.00

Shawe View
Pennybridge Lane

Main Sponsor
CAFFRO
Construction

Unibond First Division
Trafford v Radcliffe Borough

GROUND:
Shawe View, Pennybridge Lane, Flixton, Urmston, Manchester M41 5DL Tel: 0161 7471727
Website: www.traffordfc.freeserve.co.uk   Email: dave-murray@traffordfc.freeserve.co.uk
Directions: M60 jct 9, B5158 towards Urmston, at 1st r/about take 1st exit, 1st lights turn
right into Moorside Road, at nextr/about 2nd exit into Bowfell Rd, at next lights turn sharp left,
then immediately right into Pennybridge Lane next to Bird-in-Hand Pub parking on left 100yds
Capacity: 2,500   Cover: 740   Seats: 292
Clubhouse: Yes   **Club Shop:** Yes

Pages: 44   Price: £1
Editor: David Murray (0161 775 7509)

Local Press: Stretford & Urmston
Messenger, Manchester Evening News
Local Radio:
GMR Talk, Key 103, Century 105

PREVIOUS   **Leagues:** Mid Cheshire 90-92; North West Counties 92-97.   **Name:** NorthTrafford 90-94.

CLUB RECORDS   **Attendance:** 803 v Flixton (NPL Div 1 27/12/97)
Goalscorer: Garry Vaughan 88   **Appearances:** Garry Vaughan293
Win: 10-0 v Haslingden St Mary's (LancsAmt Shield 91)   **Defeat:** 0-6 v Oldham Town (NWCL Div 2 93)
Fee Paid: Undisclosed for Jock Russell (Radcliffe Borough)   **Fee Received:** Undisclosed for Mike Turner (Witton A.)

BEST SEASON   **FA Vase:** 5th Rd 95-96   **FA Trophy:** 3rd Round 2000-01
FACup: 2nd Rd Qual 95-96,99-00

HONOURS   Lamont Pils Trophy 93-94; NWCL Div 1 96-97, Div 2 R-up 93-94, Lge ChallCup R-up 96-97; Res Div 93-94; Carling Chall
Cup R-up 94-95; Manchester PremCup R-up 94-95, R-up 96-97, Res Div Champ 96-97, Cup 96-97; Manchester Amt
Cup 96-97,01-02 Unifilla 1st Div Cup 97-98 Unibond Presidents Cup 99-00 Mid Cheshire Div 2 99-00

Players progressing: Anthony Vaughan (Ipswich, Manchester City & Nott'm Forest)

L-R - Back Row: Joey Dunn (manager), Dave Mayes, John McAllister, Mike Harris, John Moss, Dave Collins, Andy Morris,
Richard Irving, Stuart Humphreys (asst. manager).
Front Row: Steve Sutcliffe, Mark Phillips, Paul Johnson, Paul Burke, Ian Horton, Colin Flood, Alan Cowley.

WITTON ALBION

albionreview

CLUB OFFICIALS

President: T Stelfox

Chairman: M Worthington

Secretary: Phil Chadwick
29 Jack Lane, Davenham, Northwich,
Cheshire CW9 8LF Tel: 01606 44845

FACT FILE
Formed: 1887
Nickname: The Albion
Colours: Red & white stripes/ black/red
Change colours: All yellow
Midweek matchday: Tuesday
Reserve League: Altrincham U21

FOOTBALL MANAGEMENT TEAM

Manager: Benny Phillips
Physio: Steve Crompton

GROUND Bargain Booze Stadium, Wincham Park, Chapel St, Wincham, Northwich. Tel/Fax:
01606 43008 Email: bp-uh-2000@aol.com
Website~: www.wittonalbion.co.uk
Directions: M6 junc 19. A556 towards Northwich, after 3 miles turn onto A559 at beginning of
dual carriageway, after 3/4 mile turn left opposite Black Greyhound Inn, grd 1/2 mile on left
immediately after crossing Canal Bridge
Capacity: 4,500   **Seated:** 650   **Cover:** 2,300
Clubhouse: Concert room and Vice-Presidents room open matchdays, Tuesday,Thursday,
Friday evenings. Food available for private functions   **Club Shop:** Yes

Stocksbridge Park Steels FC
Saturday, 12th January 2002, Kick Off: 3pm

Pages: 32   Price: £1
Editor: Secretary
Local Press: Northwich Guardian,
Northwich Chronicle
Local Radio: BBC GMR, BBC Radio Stoke

PREVIOUS   **Leagues:** Lancs Comb.; Cheshire County -79; Northern Premier 79-91, GMV Conference 91-94
Grounds: Central Ground, Witton Street, Northwich

CLUB RECORDS   **Attendance:** 3,940 v Kidderminster Harriers - FA Trophy Semi-Final 13.4.91 (Wincham Road)
9,500 v Northwich Victoria - Cheshire League 7.4.50 (Cenral Ground)
Win: 13-0 v Middlewich (H) NS Cup .**Defeat:** 0-9 v Macclesfield Town (a) 18.9.65
Fee Paid: £12,500 to Hyde Utd for Jim McCluskie 91   **Fee Received:** £11,500 for Peter Henderson from Chester City.
Goalscorer: Frank Fidler 175 (1947-1950)   **Appearances:** Alf Ashley 556 (1946-1958)

BEST SEASON   **FA Trophy:** Runners-up 91-92, Semi-Finals 90-91, 92-93
FA Cup: 91-92 Second Round 91-92, 1-5 v Preston North End (A). League clubs defeated: Halifax Town91-92

HONOURS   Northern Prem Lge 90-91; Cheshire County Lge 48-49 49-50 53-54 (R-up 50-51),Lge Cup 53-54 75-76; Cheshire County
Sen Cup (7); FA Trophy R-up 91-92 (SF 90-91 92-93)

Players progressing: P Henderson (Chester C.), Chris Nicholl (Burnley - ex-Southampton manager), Phil Power (Crewe), Neil Parsley &
Mike Whitlow (Leeds), Geoff Horsfield (Halifax Town ,Fulham), Robert Trees (Bristol Rovers).

WORKINGTON

CLUB OFFICIALS
Chairma: Dale Brotherton
President: Minnie Thexton
Vice Chairman: Humphrey Dobie
Match Sec.: Steve Durham (01946 61380)
Secretary: Dale Brotherton
Lime House, Holm Hill, Dalston, Carlisle
CA5 7BX Tel: 07977 759903

FOOTBALL MANAGEMENT TEAM
Manager:Tommy Cassidy
Asst. Man: Keith Mason
Physio: Les Sharkey

FACT FILE
Formed: 1884 (reformed 1921)
Nickname: Reds
Sponsors:Print Express
Colours: All red
Change colours: yellow & black/black/yellow
Midweek matchday: Tuesday
Reserves' League: Cumberland County
2001-02
CaptainStuart Williamson
P.o.Y.: Kevin Wolfe
Top Scorer :Graham Goulding 12

GROUND: Borough Park, Workington, Cumbria CA14 2DT   Tel: 01900 602871
Website: www.workingtonredsafc.co.uk
Directions: A66 into town, right at `T' junction, follow A596 for 3/4 mile - ground is then visible and signposted. Ground is north of town centre 1/4 mile from Workington (BR) station &1/2 mile from bus station
Capacity: 2,500   Cover: 800   Seats: 300   Floodlights: Yes
Clubhouse: Open matchdays and for private functions. Food on matchdays restricted menu
Club Shop: Sells programmes, badges, magazines, pennants, photographs, replica kit, T-shirts. etc.   Contact Keith Lister (01900 812867)

Pages: 36   Price: £1
Press Off/ Ed: Steve Durham (01946 61380)

Local Press:
Evening News & Star, Times & Star
Local Radio: BBC Radio Cumbria, C.F.M

HONOURS Football League: 5th in Div 3 65-66, 3rd Div 4 63-64, Cumberland County Cup 1886-91(x5) 95-00(x5) 1906-08(x2) 09-10 24-25 34-35 36-38(x2) 49-50 53-54 67-68 85-86 95-96, 99-00 (R-up 1885-86 91-92 1899-1901(x2) 02-03 08-09 11-12 23-24 26-27 29-30, 46-47 68-69 78-79) Football League Cup QF 63-64 64-65; N.P.L. Presidents Cup 83-84; North Eastern Lge R-up 38-39, Lge Cup 34-35 36-37 R-up 37-38; N.W. Trains Lg Div 1 98-99

PREVIOUS **Leagues:** Cumberland Assoc. 1890-94; Cumberland Sen. Lge 94-1901, 03-04; Lancashire Lge 1901-03; Lancashire Comb. 04-10; North Eastern 10-11, 21-51; Football League 51-77
Grounds: Various 1884-1921, Lonsdale Park 21-37

BEST SEASON FA Cup: 4th Rd 33-34. 1st Rd - 53 occasions.
FA Trophy: Q. Final 99-00   **FA Vase:** 6th Rd, 98-99 (1st season)

RECORDS **Attendance:** 21,000 v Manchester Utd, FA Cup 3rd Rd 4/1/58
Goalscorer: Billy Charlton 193   **Win:** 17-1 v Cockermouth Crusaders, Cumb-erland Sen. Lge 19/1/01
Appearances: Bobby Brown 419   **Defeat:** 0-9 v Chorley (A), NPL Prem. Div., 10/11/87
Fee Paid: £6,000 for Ken Chisholm (Sunderland,'56)   **Fee Received:** £33,000 for Ian McDonald (Liverpool, '74)

Players progressing: Numerous, the best known being John Burridge.

Back row left to right: Alan Blair, Damian Maw, Craig Lewis, Stuart Williamson, Kevin Wolfe, Will Varty, Barry Irving and John Wharton. **Front row:** Arthur Peers, Robert Ennis, Craig Johnston, Ryan McCluskey, Matty Lea and Marc Green.

It hasn't always been easy to get a Bamber Bridge team photo, but this group was only too pleased.
Photo: Peter Barnes

The players of Newcastle Blue Star and Hebburn are reminded of 'The Wheatsheafs' proximity to Newcastle Airport.
Photo: Graham Brown

GROUNDTASTIC

The Football Grounds Magazine

Groundtastic is the acclaimed magazine featuring news, articles and special features on football grounds at all levels from the Premiership to non-league. Each glossy 80-page edition carries regular development updates, including 6 pages of non-league news, together with articles and photos chronicling the rich history of non-league grounds. The magazine usually retails at £3.50 but to receive a free sample issue send 2 first class stamps to: 21 Tiptree Grove, WICKFORD, SS12 9AL. To obtain details of back issues and our other publications, please visit our website at www.groundtastic.ukgateway.net

THE NORTH WEST COUNTIES FOOTBALL LEAGUE

President: W J King   **Chairman:** D Tomlinson

Secretary: Geoff Wilkinson, 46 Oaklands Drive,
Penwortham, Preston PR1 0YY   Tel: 01772 746312

Press Officer: Paul Lawler, 61 Cable Street,
Formby, Merseyside L37 3LU   Tel/Fax: 01704 875575

A twenty-three club First Division of the North West Counties looked particularly strong as the season got underway with Prescot Cables becoming early favourites.

There was certainly no shortage of goals in the league (a total of 1763) as three clubs registered over a hundred and four clubs conceded a three figure total.

As the season settled down it was clear that Salford City and Kidsgrove Athletic who had come through some rebuilding after the 1997-98 F.A. Vase Semi-Final excitement, both looked capable of catching Prescot Cables.

There were no outstanding F.A. Cup runs for member clubs last season, but once again the F.A. Vase brought out the best in Clitheroe who reached the Quarter Finals before losing to Whitley Bay, the eventual winners.

With a month to go before the end of the season Kidsgrove brought in Congleton Town manager Kevin Langley to replace Dave Sutton in a bold move that luckily for the club chairman actually worked. The league was won by five points and deadline transfer arrival from Winsford United, Danny Worthington scored eight goals in the final month and won the last 'Player of the Month' award of the season.

So Kidsgrove Athletic will compete in the Unibond Division One for the first time with Prescot Cables finishing as runners-up and League Cup winners.

Great Harwood Town finished at the foot of the table and will be relegated with Maine Road and Flixton, but Division Two champions Stand Athletic's ground did not meet the required criteria so only Alsager Town and Squires Gate will be moving up to the First Division.

2001-02 HONOURS LIST

First Division Champions
Kidsgrove Athletic
Runners Up
Prescot Cables
Relegated to Second Division
Flixton, Maine Road, Great Harwood Town

Second Division Champions
Stand Athletic
Runners Up
Alsager Town
Promoted to First Division
Alsager Town, Squires Gate

Worthington Challenge Trophy Winners
Prescot Cables
Runners Up
Atherton Collieries

Reserve Division Champions
Woodley Sports Reserves
Runners Up
Skelmersdale United Reserves

Reserve Division Cup Winners
Woodley Sports Reserves
Runners Up
Maine Road Reserves

Atherton Collieries celebrate winning BW FC Goldline Trophy at the Reebok Stadium 1-0 v Charnock Richard.
Attendance: 950

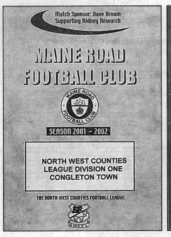

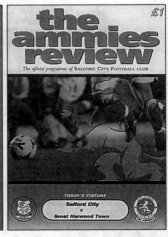

OFFICIAL LEAGUELINE: 09066 555 944   www.nwcfl.co.uk

FINAL LEAGUE TABLES 2001-02
FIRST DIVISION

	P	W	D	L	F	A	Pts	GD			P	W	D	L	F	A	Pts	GD
Kidsgrove Athletic	44	31	9	4	125	47	102	78		Curzon Ashton	44	16	7	21	74	72	55	2
Prescot Cables	44	29	10	5	110	42	97	68		Fleetwood F'port	44	13	13	18	70	86	52	-16
Salford City	44	29	10	5	91	40	97	51		Nantwich Town	44	12	15	17	63	90	51	-27
St Helens Town	44	28	6	10	101	44	90	57		Congleton Town	44	13	11	20	71	79	50	-8
Clitheroe	44	22	10	12	73	53	76	20		Atherton Collieries	44	13	8	23	66	91	47	-25
Newcastle Town	44	22	11	11	97	66	77	31		Abbey Hey	44	12	11	21	62	101	47	-39
Winsford United	44	19	12	13	72	71	69	1		Glossop Nth End	44	13	7	24	78	105	46	-27
Mossley	44	18	14	12	82	63	68	19		Atherton LR	44	11	11	22	62	88	44	-26
Skelmersdale Utd	44	19	5	20	87	89	62	-2		Flixton	44	11	9	24	61	112	42	-51
Woodley Sports	44	16	12	16	58	65	60	-7		Maine Road	44	8	7	29	68	115	31	-47
Warrington Town	44	16	11	17	78	72	59	6		Great Harwood T	44	5	11	28	39	99	26	-60
Ramsbottom Utd	44	15	10	19	75	73	55	2										

SECOND DIVISION

	P	W	D	L	F	A	Pts	GD
Stand Athletic	40	30	5	5	110	47	95	63
Alsager Town	40	24	9	7	77	31	81	46
Squires Gate	40	24	9	7	103	60	81	43
Stone Dominoes	40	25	3	12	71	40	78	31
Formby	40	21	14	5	76	39	77	37
Bootle	40	19	7	14	82	64	64	18
Norton United	40	19	7	14	56	51	64	5
Blackpool Mechs	40	18	9	13	69	48	63	21
Nelson	40	18	9	13	73	63	63	10
Leek CSOB	40	17	8	15	62	65	59	-3
Darwen	40	15	10	15	77	73	55	4
Bacup Borough	40	13	13	14	52	66	52	-14
Padiham	40	14	8	18	69	66	50	3
Colne	40	14	8	18	61	72	50	-11
Chadderton	40	15	5	20	65	81	50	-16
Ashton Town	40	13	6	21	65	85	45	-20
Cheadle Town	40	10	8	22	66	85	38	-19
Castleton Gabriels	40	10	3	27	61	95	33	-34
Holker Old Boys	40	7	9	24	43	79	30	-36
Daisy Hill	40	8	4	28	49	114	28	-65
Oldham Town	40	7	4	29	50	113	25	-63

RESERVE DIVISION

	P	W	D	L	F	A	Pts	GD
Woodley Sports	32	25	4	3	97	30	79	67
Skelmersdale Utd	32	20	5	7	103	33	65	70
Padiham	32	19	5	8	89	57	62	32
Curzon Ashton	32	19	3	10	69	55	60	14
Maine Road	32	18	4	10	71	46	58	25
Clitheroe	32	18	3	11	61	54	57	7
Ashton Town	32	17	5	10	69	43	56	26
Atherton LR	32	16	6	10	77	63	54	14
Squires Gate	32	15	6	11	77	58	51	19
Glossop Nth End	32	12	9	11	53	54	45	-1
Salford City	32	11	6	15	65	58	39	-7
Nelson	32	11	6	15	51	70	39	-19
Stand Athletic	32	7	7	18	45	72	28	-27
Cheadle Town	32	7	5	20	44	94	26	-50
Chadderton	32	5	5	22	42	99	20	-57
Atherton Collieries	32	2	9	21	29	79	15	-50
Daisy Hill	32	3	6	23	39	116	15	-77

Colne Reserves resigned - record expunged

LEADING GOALSCORERS 2001-02

FIRST DIVISION

		L	C	T
Andy Bott	Newcastle Town	41	7	48
Neil Robinson	Prescot Cables	29	11	40
Danny Worthington	Kidsgrove Athletic	32	5	37
	(inc 30 for Winsford)			
Lee Cooper	St Helens Town	28	7	35
Russell Brierley	Ramsbottom Utd	29	5	34
Darren Twigg	Kidsgrove Athletic	28	6	34
Jock Russell	Maine Road	28	6	34
	(inc 1 for Salford)			
Gary Jensen	Prescot Cables	23	8	31
Stuart Rudd	Skelmersdale Utd	24	4	28
Chris Moores	Warrington Town	19	8	27
Bradley Wosahlo	Mossley	24	2	26
Kevin Garforth	Prescot Cables	19	5	24

SECOND DIVISION

		L	C	T
Lee Catlow	Squires Gate	38	6	44
Paul Baker	Darwen	29	5	34
Chris Denham	Stand Athletic	27	2	29
Ian Pilkington	Padiham	27	0	27
Neal Smith	Formby	26	0	26
Paul Fildes	Bacup Borough	23	2	25
	(inc 15 for Colne)			
Ronald Morgan	Bootle	24	0	24
Colin Fletcher	Stone Dominoes	23	1	24
Colin Bennett	Chadderton	18	2	20
Rob Park	Blackpool Mechs	18	1	19
Andy Dutton	Norton United	15	2	17
	(inc 4 for Alsager)			
Chris Barlow	Alsager Town	15	2	17
	(inc 16 for Chadderton)			

FIRST DIVISION RESULTS CHART 2001-02

#	Team	1	2	3	4	5	6	7	8	9	10	11	12	13	14	15	16	17	18	19	20	21	22	23
1	Abbey H	X	2-0	2-6	1-1	0-0	0-3	2-1	1-0	2-2	2-2	0-2	3-0	1-3	2-2	0-1	0-4	0-0	0-4	0-2	3-1	1-2	2-2	0-1
2	Ath. Coll	3-1	X	4-2	0-0	2-1	5-1	0-4	0-2	3-4	4-1	2-2	6-2	1-2	1-1	2-0	3-2	3-2	1-2	0-3	1-2	2-0	2-2	1-1
3	Ath. LR	0-1	3-1	X	1-1	2-0	0-4	0-0	2-0	1-3	3-1	0-2	3-2	3-0	4-0	3-4	0-3	0-0	0-3	0-5	0-5	3-3	3-0	1-1
4	Clitheroe	7-0	2-1	3-0	X	3-1	1-1	0-1	3-2	1-0	1-0	2-3	1-0	1-3	4-1	1-1	1-2	0-0	2-1	1-2	0-2	2-4	3-1	3-0
5	Cong'ton	0-3	2-1	4-3	4-4	X	1-3	0-0	2-1	2-0	2-0	0-2	3-3	3-2	2-3	1-1	1-2	1-2	0-2	5-2	2-4	3-3	0-1	4-0
6	Curzon	1-1	2-1	3-1	1-0	2-1	X	0-2	2-4	5-2	3-1	0-1	2-1	1-5	2-2	2-3	0-1	3-1	0-2	0-2	6-0	1-1	4-1	1-2
7	F'wood	4-3	1-1	3-3	0-1	0-1	4-0	X	1-1	5-5	2-2	1-4	2-0	2-0	1-5	2-1	1-4	4-1	0-2	1-1	0-2	1-7	1-1	1-1
8	Flixton	1-1	2-0	1-1	1-1	0-3	0-7	2-3	X	1-0	1-3	4-3	0-4	3-3	3-5	1-4	1-2	6-2	0-3	0-3	0-0	5-1	0-3	1-4
9	Glossop	2-3	2-0	1-1	1-2	2-1	2-2	3-1	1-4	X	6-0	1-2	3-2	1-4	2-2	2-1	0-4	4-3	1-2	2-2	3-1	2-4	1-3	3-2
10	Harwood	1-1	1-2	1-0	1-2	0-2	2-1	1-1	0-1	1-1	X	0-3	1-2	1-1	1-1	3-2	0-4	0-2	0-5	0-2	0-6	2-1	3-3	1-1
11	K'grove	2-3	7-4	5-1	3-0	2-0	1-0	2-2	13-0	4-0	2-1	X	3-1	2-1	3-2	3-1	1-3	1-1	1-1	1-1	3-3	2-0	3-0	4-0
12	Maine Rd	1-2	0-0	2-0	1-3	1-1	3-1	2-4	0-1	4-5	4-1	1-6	X	3-1	0-0	3-5	3-4	5-4	0-5	0-1	4-2	0-3	1-3	2-4
13	Mossley	1-1	5-1	1-2	1-2	2-2	2-2	1-1	4-2	3-2	1-0	0-0	3-1	X	3-2	1-0	1-1	1-1	1-1	3-1	2-3	2-0	1-1	0-1
14	Nantwich	3-2	1-1	1-2	2-0	1-1	1-0	0-4	3-1	2-3	2-2	0-3	2-1	0-4	X	1-1	0-5	0-0	1-0	1-1	2-1	0-1	2-4	0-2
15	N'castle	9-2	4-0	2-2	1-2	2-1	2-0	3-0	3-1	4-3	2-1	0-0	3-3	1-1	7-2	X	0-1	3-2	2-1	1-1	4-1	2-1	0-1	2-2
16	Prescot	6-2	3-0	2-0	0-1	5-1	4-2	2-0	1-1	3-0	4-1	3-1	4-1	1-1	1-1	2-2	X	1-2	3-4	0-0	0-0	2-1	6-1	1-1
17	R'bottom	5-1	1-2	2-1	1-4	3-2	1-2	0-0	1-1	2-1	5-0	3-5	4-1	2-4	1-2	0-1	0-0	X	0-2	0-1	3-2	2-0	6-0	1-1
18	St H'ens	5-2	4-0	3-1	0-2	2-3	3-1	3-1	1-2	3-1	3-0	1-2	4-0	2-1	5-2	2-2	0-1	2-1	X	0-2	6-2	3-1	2-2	1-0
19	Salford	2-1	4-1	2-1	0-0	1-0	2-0	2-1	7-1	2-0	1-0	1-1	4-2	3-1	0-2	1-6	1-1	1-0		X	6-0	3-0	3-0	2-1
20	Sk'dale	1-3	1-2	2-1	2-3	2-6	1-2	6-1	4-1	1-0	2-0	0-4	5-0	2-3	0-0	2-1	1-1	2-1	0-3	3-4	X	2-3	2-3	2-1
21	Warr'ton	3-0	3-0	1-1	3-0	1-1	0-0	3-0	2-2	8-1	3-2	1-6	2-2	1-2	1-1	1-2	0-3	1-3	0-0	0-2	0-2	X	2-1	4-1
22	Winsford	1-4	2-3	3-0	1-3	0-1	1-0	1-3	4-0	1-0	1-1	1-3	1-0	2-0	2-2	4-2	3-0	2-0	1-1	1-1	1-2	0-0	X	2-1
23	Woodley	4-1	1-1	1-1	2-1	1-1	1-0	4-3	1-0	1-0	1-2	0-0	1-1	3-1	1-3	2-3	0-1	1-2	2-1	0-3	0-2	2-1		X

SECOND DIVISION RESULTS CHART 2001-02

#	Team	1	2	3	4	5	6	7	8	9	10	11	12	13	14	15	16	17	18	19	20	21
1	Alsager Town	X	3-0	2-0	1-1	3-0	4-1	6-0	0-4	2-0	2-1	2-3	2-2	1-0	2-0	4-0	1-0	0-1	1-1	1-0	1-2	2-0
2	Ashton Town	0-4	X	0-2	2-0	2-5	3-0	6-2	3-2	1-2	3-3	0-0	1-1	1-1	2-0	2-4	1-2	1-1	3-2	1-3	0-4	3-0
3	Bacup Borough	0-2	1-0	X	0-2	2-1	0-1	1-1	2-2	1-1	3-2	3-2	2-2	0-1	1-1	0-2	2-1	0-0	2-2	1-2	1-2	0-2
4	Blackpool Mechs	2-2	4-2	2-0	X	1-2	3-1	3-0	3-3	0-1	3-1	0-1	0-0	3-0	4-0	1-1	2-1	2-0	3-0	0-0	1-2	2-3
5	Bootle	0-2	3-1	1-1	0-3	X	3-0	5-2	1-0	5-1	4-0	3-1	3-0	1-1	2-0	2-2	0-0	0-4	3-3	1-0	0-2	
6	Castleton Gab.	0-0	3-2	2-5	2-3	3-0	X	1-0	2-0	2-0	0-2	1-1	1-5	2-3	0-2	2-3	4-0	2-3	0-1	1-4	3-5	1-2
7	Chadderton	0-2	1-1	2-0	2-1	0-5	3-1	X	2-2	7-0	4-0	3-2	1-0	3-4	1-3	0-1	1-1	2-2	2-4	4-3	0-0	
8	Cheadle Town	2-2	1-2	2-4	0-2	3-2	3-2	3-0	X	0-0	2-1	1-2	0-1	3-2	2-1	1-0	1-3	1-3	3-4	2-4	0-3	0-0
9	Colne	3-1	2-3	2-1	0-0	2-2	7-5	2-3	3-2	X	2-0	3-3	0-1	3-1	2-3	2-1	0-2	5-1	1-1	0-3	2-3	1-2
10	Daisy Hill	0-3	0-2	2-3	1-2	3-1	0-3	2-0	4-2	2-2	X	1-1	3-0	1-5	5-0	0-1	1-0	0-5	1-2	1-7	1-3	
11	Darwen	2-1	4-1	0-1	3-3	2-2	4-0	3-1	0-1	6-3	X	1-4	1-1	2-1	2-1	0-1	4-1	1-2	3-2	2-4	1-3	
12	Formby	0-1	2-0	1-1	2-2	2-2	2-0	2-1	0-0	4-1	2-2	X	1-1	2-1	2-1	0-0	5-2	3-0	1-1	2-3	1-0	
13	Holker OB	1-2	2-1	0-0	0-2	2-3	3-2	2-1	0-0	2-4	1-1	X	0-1	0-1	2-0	2-1	1-1	0-3	0-1	1-2	1-3	
14	Leek CSOB	0-0	3-2	1-1	4-1	0-3	3-7	1-4	4-3	2-1	1-0	4-1	0-2	2-0	X	1-1	3-2	3-0	1-1	0-3	2-1	1-0
15	Nelson	2-0	1-2	2-2	2-0	3-4	1-0	0-2	3-0	2-1	9-1	2-1	1-1	3-0	1-2	X	5-1	3-2	1-1	0-3	2-1	1-0
16	Norton Utd	1-1	2-0	2-0	2-0	2-1	2-0	0-1	2-1	0-2	5-1	1-3	1-4	3-0	1-1	1-3	X	3-0	2-0	2-2	1-1	1-0
17	Oldham Town	0-6	1-5	2-2	1-4	2-6	1-2	0-2	4-3	0-1	3-1	2-2	1-2	4-2	1-1	1-3	0-3	X	3-1	1-5	1-6	0-2
18	Padiham	0-1	1-2	0-1	0-2	2-4	5-0	5-3	4-4	1-3	6-0	3-2	0-0	5-1	4-0	1-1	0-2	3-2	X	0-1	0-4	0-1
19	Squires Gate	0-4	5-2	7-0	3-1	3-2	3-1	3-1	2-3	3-2	4-0	1-1	2-3	4-2	1-1	3-2	2-1	5-3	2-1	X	2-2	3-1
20	Stand Athletic	1-1	4-1	2-5	2-1	2-1	3-1	1-0	3-1	2-1	2-2	3-0	3-1	5-1	2-1	0-1	6-0	4-0	0-1	4-2	X	2-1
21	Stone Dominoes	1-2	4-1	6-0	1-0	2-0	2-0	1-0	2-1	2-0	4-0	1-2	2-1	2-1	4-0	1-1	4-0	2-3	1-2	1-3		X

ABBEY HEY

Secretary: Gordon Lester, 6 Newhaven Avenue, Hr.Openshaw, Manchestewr M11 1HU
Tel Nos: 0161 370 0270 (H) 0161 200 4630 (W)

Ground: Abbey Stadium, Goredale Avenue, Gorton, Manchester 18
Tel: 0161 231 7147 (Club)   Fax: 01823 490281

Directions: A57 towards Hyde, right into Woodland Avenue approx one & a half miles
past Belle Vue junction, right again into Ryder Brow Rd, 1st left after bridge
into Goredale Ave. **Nearest Railway Station:** Ryder Brow
Capacity: 1000   Seats: 100   Cover: 300   Floodlights: Yes

Honours Manchester Amat. Lge 65-66: S.E. Lancs Lge 66-67, 68-69 R-up 67-68;
Div.2 68-69; Lge Shield 65-66: Manc. Co. Amat. Cup 64-65, 67-68, 68-69,
R-up 63-64: Manchester Lge Prem. Div. 81-82, 88-89, 90-91, 93-94, 94-95;
Div. 1 70-71; Div.2 88-89, 92-93, 93-94; Gilcryst Cup 76-77, 88-89,
R-up 97-88; Open Tphy 78-79,79-80, 92-93: Manchester Chall. Tphy 82-83,
95-96, 96-97. N.W. Trains Div 2 R-up 98-99

Previous Leagues: Manchester Amateur; South East Lancs; Manchester Lge.
Record Attendance: 400 v Manchester City XI oct 99

FACT FILE

Formed: 1902
Colours:Red& white/red/red & white
Midweek matchday: Tuesday

CLUB PERSONNEL

Chairman: James Whittaker
0161 445 0036

Emergency Contact; G.Lester
0161 370 0270 or 0161 236 3311 ext 2800

ALSAGER TOWN

FACT FILE

Secretary: Pauline Matthews, 43 Ellgreave Street, Dalehall, Stoke -0n-Trent, ST6 4DJ
Tel No: 01782 834296

Ground: The Town Ground, Wood Park, Alsager. Tel: 01270 882336

Directions: M6, Junction 16, A500 towards Stoke. Leave A500 at 2nd exit (A34 to Congleton),
at 2nd set of lights turn left for Alsager. Turn right opposite Caradon/Twyfords   (500
yds), into Moorhouse Ave., Woodland Court 1/2 mile on right.
Nearest Railway station: Alsager
Floodlights: Yes

HONOURS Joint Runners -up Mid Cheshire Div. 2, Runners-up Springbank Vending Lge.

PREVIOUS Leagues: Mid Cheshire Div. 2; Springbank Vending Lge.

RECORD Attendance: 110 v Formby Sept 99, League 200 v Port Vale (friendly)

Founded: 1968
Colours: Black & white/black/black
Change colours: Yellow & sky blue/yellow/yellow
Midweek Matches: Wednesday

CLUB PERSONNEL

Chairman: Peter Clegg
Tel: 01270 876013
1st Team Sec.: Pauline Matthews
Tel: 01782 834296H

2001-02
Leading goalscorer: Kark Bayley
Captain: Mark Timms
P.o.Y.: Wayne Brotherton
Goalkeeper Rob Powner achieved 24 clean
sheets in 2001-2002 season

ATHERTON COLLIERIES

FACT FILE

Secretary: Emil Anderson, 109 Douglas St, Atherton M46 9EB Tel Nos: 01942 879209 (H)
0161 288 6355 (W) 0792 937461 (M) Email: geocities.com/ath-c-g-c
Ground: Atherton Colls Football Ground,Alder St., Atherton, Gt ManchesterTel:01942884649.
Directions: M61 Jct 5, follow sign for Westhoughton, left onto A6, right ontoA579 (Newbrook
Rd/Bolton Rd) into Atherton. At first set of lights turn leftinto High Street, 2nd left into Alder St. to
ground. Quarter mile from AthertonCentral (BR).
Seats: 300   Cover: 1,000   Capacity: 2,500   Floodlights: Yes
Clubhouse: Open Mon-Fri 7-11pm, Sat 11am-11pm, Sun noon-3 & 7-10.30pm. Hot &cold food
on matchdays. **Club Shop:** No, but programmes & badges are available
PREVIOUS Leagues: Bolton Combination 20-50, 52-71; Lancs Combination 50-52, 71-78;
Cheshire County 78-82.

HONOURS: BNWCFL 3rd Div Champ 86/87; Bridge Shield 85/86; Lancs County FA
Shield19/20, 22/23, 41/42, 45/46. 56/57, 64/65; Tennents F/lit Trophy Finalist
94/95; NWCFL Div 2 R/up 95/96 Gpldline Trophy 2001-02 Worthington
Challenge Trophy R-up 2001-02

RECORDS Attendance: 3,300 in Lancs Combination, 1920's
Players Progressing: J Parkinson (Wigan), Russell Beardsmore(Manchester Utd).

Founded: 1916
Nickname: Colls
Club Sponsors: Kensite
Colours: Black & white stripes/black/black.
Change colours: Yellow/blue/yellow
Reserves'·Lge: NWTL Res Div
Midweek Matches: Monday
Programme: 40 pages, £1
Editor: Secretary
2001-02 Captain: Paul Dowle
Club Website:
geocities@frank35.freeserve.co.uk

CLUB PERSONNEL

Chairman: Steve Payne
Vice Chairman:
President: T.B.A.
Foster Feste
Physio: Chris Roberts

ATHERTON L.R.

Secretary: Steve Hartle,165 Bolton Road, Atherton, Gtr Manchester M46 9AD (01942 870253)

Ground: Crilly Park, Spa Road, Atherton, Greater Manchester (01942 883950).
Directions: M61 to Jct 5, follow signs for Westhoughton, left onto A6, right onto A579 (Newbrook Rd/Bolton Rd) over the railway bridge, right into Upton Rd passing Atherton Central Station, left into Springfield Rd and left again into Hillside Rd into Spa Rd and ground.
Capacity: 3,000   **Seats:** 250   **Cover:** 3 sections   **Floodlights:** Yes
Clubhouse: Open normal licensing hours.   **Club Shop:** No

PREVIOUS	**Name:** Laburnum Rovers 56-80 **Grounds:** Laburnum Road 56-58 Hagfold 58-66 **Leagues:** Bolton Comb.; Cheshire County 80-82; NWCL 82-94; NPL 94-97.
RECORDS	**Attendance:** 1,856 v Aldershot Town, FA Vase Quarter-Final replay 5/3/94.
	Appearances: Jimmy Evans **Fee Paid:** £500 for Joey Dunn from Warrington T.
	Scorer: Shaun Parker **Fee Received:** £1,500 for Stuart Humphries to Barrow
BEST SEASON	**FA Cup:** 3rd Qual Rd 96-97, 0-2 v Bamber Bridge
	FA Vase: Semi-Final rep. 94-95, 1-2 v Diss Town **FA Trophy:** 1st Qual Rd 96-97
HONOURS	North West Co Lge 92-93 93-94, Champs Trophy 92-93 93-94, F/Lit Trophy 93-94; N.P.L.Div.1 Cup R-up 95-96,Goldline Trophy 98-99, Bolton Hosp Cup: 84-85; 01-02 W.Houghton Ch C 81-82

Players progressing to Football League: Barry Butler (Chester), Lee Unsworth(Crewe).

FACT FILE
Formed: 1956
Nickname: The Panthers
Sponsors: Bolton Evening News
Colours: Yellow & Navy
Change colours: Green & White
Midweek Matches: Tuesday
Reserves' League: North West Co Res Div
Prog: 48 pages £1.0 (Best in league 3rd year)
Editor: Tim Lees
Local Radio: GMR

CLUB PERSONNEL
Chairman:Alan Grundy
Financial Director: Terry Poole
Manager: Alan Lord Ass Manr: Jason Holroyd
Coach: Danny Johnson

CLITHEROE

Secretary: Colin Wilson, 4 Moss Street, Clitheroe, Lancs BB7 1DP
Tel/Fax: 01200 424370 Mobile: 07714 382232

Ground: Shawbridge, Clitheroe, Lancs (01200 423344).
Directions: M6 jct 31, A59 to Clitheroe (17 miles), at 5th r'bout continue for half a mile and turn left at Pendle Road. Ground one mile, behind Bridge Inn' on the right. 11 miles from Blackburn BR station: Clitheroe
Capacity: 2,000   **Seats:** 300   **Cover:** 1200   **Floodlights:** Yes
Clubhouse: Open during matches. Snacks available   **Club Shop:** Yes.

HONOURS	FA Vase Runners-up 95-96; Lancs Comb. 79-80, Lg Cup 34-35; Lancs Challenge Tphy 84-85; NW C Lge 85-86, Div 2 84-85, Div 3 83-84; East Lancs Floodlit Trophy 94-95.N.W.Trains Floodlit Cup: 98-99
PREVIOUS	Leagues: Blackburn & Dist.; Lancs Comb. 03-04 05-10 25-82.
BEST SEASON	FA Cup: FA Vase: Runners-up 95-96
RECORDS	Attendance: 2,000 v Mangotsfield, FA Vase Semi/F 95-96.
	Goalscorer: Don Francis Appearances: Lindsey Wallace.

Players progressing Ray Woods (Leeds 1950), Chris Sims (Blackburn 1960), Lee Rogerson (Wigan Ath), Carlo Nash (Crystal Palace).

FACT FILE

Formed: 1877.
Nickname: The Blues
Colours: Blue & white /blue/blue
Change colours: All yellow
Midweek matchday: Tuesday
Reserves' Lge: N.W.C.L

Chairman: David Burgess

CONGLETON TOWN

Secretary and Press Officer: Paul kelly, 19 Melrose DDrive,Crewe,Cheshire CW1 3YD
Tel Nos: 01270 21599 (H) 01270 612250 (W)

GROUND Booth Street Ground, Crescent Road, Congleton, Cheshire Tel: 01260 74460
Directions: On approach to Congleton via Clayton bypass take second right after fire
station, into Booth Street. Two miles from Congleton (BR)
Capacity: 5,000   **Cover:** 1,200   **Seats:** 250
Clubhouse: Open match days only   **Club Shop:** Yes. Contact:Gerry Brocklehurst

PREVIOUS	**Leagues:** Crewe & Dist; North Staffs; Macclesfield; Cheshire 20-39, 46-65, 78-82; Mid Cheshire 68-78; Nth West Co 82-87, N.P.L. 87-01
	Name: Congleton Hornets (prior to current club's formation in 1901)
CLUB RECORDS	**Attendance:** 7,000 v Macclesfield, League 53-54 **Fee Paid:** None.
	Goalscorer: Mick Biddle 150+ **Fee Received:** £5,000 for D Frost (Leeds)
	Appearances: Ray Clack 600+ & Graham Harrison 600+
BEST SEASON	**FA Trophy:** 3rd Qual. Rd 89-90 90-91. **FA Vase:** 4th Rd 76-77 80-81
	FA Cup: 1st Rd 89-90, 0-2 v Crewe A. (A) League clubs defeated: None
HONOURS	North West Counties League R-up 85-86; Cheshire County League R-up 20-2121-22 (Div 2 81-82); Mid Cheshire League 73-74 75-76 77-78, (R-up 69-70 71-72 76-77, League Cup 71-72; Cheshire Senior Cup 20-21 37-38

Players progressing: Ron Broad (Crewe 55), Jack Mycock (Shrewsbury 58),Steve Davies (Port Vale 87), L Hamlet (Leeds), Jimmy Quinn (West Ham), Ian Brightwell (Man City)

FACT FILE
Formed: 1901 Nickname: Bears
Colours:White &blacktrim/black/black & white
Change colours:Red & White
Midweek home matchday: Tuesday
Website:http://members.aol.com/beartown
Programme: Pages: 48 Price: £1.00
Editor: Ken Mead c/oClub
Local Radio: Radio Stoke, Signal.Local Press:
Congleton Chron, Staffs Eve Sentinel

CLUB PERSONNEL
Chair: Peter EvansV- Chair: Steve Burgess
Press Officer: Ken Mead-07710405674(M)
Manager:Bryan Griffith
Asst Mans: Adrian Riely & Gary Bickerstaff
Coach: John Brown
Physio: Paul Kelly
2001-02
Captain: Steve Callear
P.O.Y:A drian Rielly
Top Scorer: Dave Shaw 18

CURZON ASHTON

Secretary: Robert Hurst, 36 Russell Road, Partington, Manchester M31 4DZ
Tel: 0161 775 3883 Fax 0161 775 8787 Mob 0771 325 2310 Email:curzonashton@byford.co.uk
Ground: National Park, Katherine Street, Ashton-under-Lyne OL7 6DA (0161 330 6033)
Directions: M60 Jct 23 to Ashton- u -Lyme on Manchester Rd (A635) then turn into Williams
Street.Ground at bottom of road.One and a half miles from Ashton-under-Lyne (BR)
Capacity: 5,000   **Cover:** 450   **Seats:** 350   **Floodlights:** Yes
Clubhouse: Every night. Food on matchdays. **Club Shop:** Contact Roy Howe, 0161 220 8345

PREVIOUS	**Leagues:** Manchester Amat.; Manchester (-1978); Cheshire Co. 78-82; N.W C. 82-86 Northern Prem. Lge. 87-97, N.C.E. 97-98, N.W.C. 98-01	
BEST	**FA Cup:** 3rd Qual. Rd replay 89-90, 1-3 v Mossley (A) after 1-1	
SEASON	**FA Vase:** Semi-Final 79-80 **FA Trophy:** 2nd Qual. Rd 82-83, 84-85	
HONOURS	**NWC Lge Div.2 r-up 99-00;** Cheshire Co. Lge Div 2 R-up 78-79: Manchester Lge 77-78, R-up 74-75 75-76; Lge Cup 77-78, R-up 74-75 75-76; Murray Shield R-up 75-76: Manchester Amat. Lge 63-64 65-66, R-up 64-65: Manchester Prem. Cup x 5	
RECORDS	**Attendance:** 1,826 v Stamford, FA Vase SF 1980	
	Goalscorer: Alan Sykes **Appearances:** Alan Sykes 620	
	Win: 7-0 v Ashton United **Defeat:** 0-8 v Bamber Bridge	

FACT FILE
Formed: 1963 Nickname: The Blues
Colours: All Blue Change colours: All Red
Midweek matches: Monday
Programme: 40pages £1.00
Editor: Robert Hurst (0161 775 3883)
2000-01 Capt: M Wearden P.o.Y.: P Wearden
Top Scorer: Josh Mittan
Website: www.curzon-ashton.co.uk
CLUB PERSONNEL
Chairman: Harry Galloway
Vice Chairman: R.onnie Capstick
Chief Executive: Harry Twamley
President: Peter Mayo
Press Officer:Graham Shuttleworth
Treasurer: Sam Shuttleworth
Manager: Gary Lowe
Assistant Manager: Derek Hall
Physio: Martin Rothwell

FLEETWOOD TOWN

Secretary:	Kevin Pennington, 1 Carlisle Avenue, Fleetwood, Lancs. FY7 8LP. Tel: 01253 771602 (H); 01253 822626 (B) 07967 192843 (M) Email Address: fleetwoodfreeport@btinternet .com or:kevin@fffcfreeserve.co.uk
Ground:	Highbury Stadium, Park Avenue, Fleetwood, Lancs (01253 770702)
Directions:	From M55, junction 3, follow signs (A585) to Fleetwood. At Nautical College campus (onleft) traffic island take first left, at second island take 6th exit. Stadium is 3/4 mile on left.
	Floodlights: Yes
PREVIOUS	**Leagues:** None **Names:** Fleetwood Wanderers (97-98)
RECORD	**Attendance:** 6,150 v Rochdale F.A.Cup 1st Round 65-66
HONOURS	NWCFL v 2 Champions: 98-99 Div 2 trophy Winners: 98-99

FACT FILE
Founded: 1997
(amalgamation of Fleetwood F.C. and
Fleetwood Town who had disbanded at the
end of season 1995-96)
Colours: Red & white/black/red
Midweek Matchday: Tuesday
Club Website: www.fleetwoodfreeportfc.co.uk
CLUB PERSONNEL
Chairman: Jim Betmead
Manager Mick Hoyle
2000-01
Captain & P.O.Y.: Steve Hartley
Top Goalscorer:Kevin Barnes 26

FLIXTON

Secretary: Terry Langford, 56 Garstang Ave, Bolton, BL2 6JN Tel: 07939 557261 (M)
Ground: Valley Road, Flixton, Manchester M41 8RQ Tel: 0161 748 2903
Directions: Leave M60 take B5214 signed Urmston. At 2nd R'about take 3rd exit. Take right
only lane on the exit into Davyhulme Rd. Follow road to Valley Rd, just after a left hand bend
after 1.5 miles. Ground is at the other end of the road. Coaches as above and carry on to the
next R'about take 4th exit (Woodbridge Rd). The ground is at the bottom of this road.
Capacity: 2,000   **Cover:** 650   **Seats:** 250
Clubhouse: Open daily 1.00pm-11pm. Sandwiches available most eves **Club Shop:** No

PREVIOUS	**Leagues:** South Manchester & Wythenshawe 60-63; Lancs & Cheshire 63-73; Manchester 73-86; North West Counties 86-96; Northern Premier 97-00
CLUB RECORDS	**Attendance:** 1,543 v Brigg Town FA Vase Semi-Final 95-96
	Goalscorer: John Mitchell **Appearances:** John Mitchell & Stan Matthews
	Win: 10-2 Irlam 94-95 **Defeat:** 1-10 v Knowsley Utd 90-91
BEST SEASON	**FA Cup:** 1st Qual. Rd replay 91-92, 1-2 v Mossley (A) after 1-1
	FA Vase: Semi-final 95-96 v Brigg Town
HONOURS	N.W.Co Div I 95-96, Div 2 94-95 Lg.Cup 94-95 95-96 (R-up 87-88), Div 3 R-up 86-87; Manc. Lg R-up 78-79 81-82 85-86, Div 1 77-78, Open Tphy 80-81; Lancs Amtr Cup 79-80 (R-up 80-81); Manc. Chal. Tphy 83-84 (R-up x2 84-86); Manc. Prem. Cup R-up 86-87 91-92; Manc. Amtr Cup R-up 88-89

FACT FILE
Formed: 1960
Nickname: Valley Roaders
Colours: Blue & white stripes/blue/blue
Change Colours: Gold/black/black
Midweek home matchday: Tuesday
Reserves' League: North West Alliance
Programme - Pages: 36 Price: £1.00
Editor: T.B.A.

CLUB PERSONNEL
Chairman: Dave Trow
President: F H Eadie
Manager: Alan McGreevy
Club Email: footytel@cwcom.net
Matchday Tel: - As Secretary

Whitley Bay on the attack against Clitheroe in the Quarter Final of the FA Vase. Photo: Graham Brown

Salford City. Back Row (l-r): Karl Margison, Chris Robertson, Mattie Hughes, Dave Chadwick, Tony Cullen, Phil Melville, Ross Hartford, Gary Vaughan, Dave Brown (capt), Gary Buckley (Asst Manager), Phil Taylor, Mickey Dunn (Physio). Front Row: Rhodri Giggs, Francis Vaughan, Andy Brown (Manager), Keith Evans, George Switzer, Loz Greenhalgh, Gary Bainbridge (Trainer)

Woodley Sports keeper Steve Morris manages to get above Thackley striker Stuart Taylor to punch the ball away from danger in the First Round of the FA Vase. Photo: Darren C Thomas

GLOSSOP NORTH END

Secretary: Peter Hammond, 15 Longmoor Road, Simmondley, Glossop, Derbys SK139NH
Tel: 01457 863852(H) 01457 854411(B)

Ground: Surrey Street, Glossop, Derbys (01457 855469).

Directions: A57 to Glossop.Left at traffic lights (near Tresco sign) into Glossopbrook Road then Follow road to top of hill and ground is on right. Buses 236 and 237 from Manchesterpass ground. Railway Station: Glossop Central.

Capacity: 2,374	Seats: 209	Cover: 509	Floodlights: Yes

Clubhouse: Licensed bar. Hot & cold drinks and pies etc on matchdays.   **Club Shop:** Yes

HONOURS	NWC Lge Lamot Pils Tphy 90-91; Manchester Lg 27-28(Gilgryst Cup 22-23 29-30 34-35 74-75); FA Amateur Cup QF 08-09. Manchester Premier Cup 1997 and 1998. Derbyshire Senior Cup 2000-01.
PREVIOUS	**Leagues:** Midland 1896-98; Football Lge 1898-1915; Manchester Lge 15-56 66-78; Lancs Combination 56-66; Cheshire County 78-82. **Names:** Glossop North End 1886-1898; Glossop FC 1898-1992.
BEST SEASON	**FA Cup:** Quarter Final 1909 **FA Vase:**
RECORDS	**Attendance:** 10,736 v Preston North End, FA Cup 1913/14 **Fee paid:** £3,000 for Andy Gorton (Lincoln City, 1989). **Fee received:** £3,000 for Andy Gorton (Oldham Athletic, 1990).

Players progressing: Jimmy Rollands (Rochdale), Ray Redshaw (Wigan Athletic).

FACT FILE
Founded: 1886 Re-formed 1992
Nickname: Hillmen
Sponsor: T.B.A.
Colours: All Royal Blue
Change colours: AllGold.
Midweek Matches: Tuesday
Reserves' League: N.W.Co Res Lg
Programme: 32 pages, 50p
Editor: John Hamilton (01457 866216)

CLUB PERSONNEL
Chairman: Syd White
President: C T Boak
Press Officer: Secretary
Manager: Micky Boyle
Asst Manager: Ian Boyle
Physio:Mick Parr

MOSSLEY

Secretary: David Buckley, 18 Chellow Dene, Mossley, Ashton-under-Lyne, Lancs. OL5 0NB.
Tel: 01457 835989   Email:bobbuckley@mossleyafc.fsnet.co.uk
Ground: Seel Park, Market Street, Mossley, Lancs. (Grd 01457 832369), (Club 01457 836104)
Directions: From north; M60 J.23, then A635 to Ashton-U-Lyne, A670 Mossley to town centre Grd behind market place. From south; M6 Junc 19, A556, M56 to Junc 3, A5103 to M'chester, then Mancunian Way (A57M) to A635. Follow Ashton signs 5m, the Mossley signs via A670 to town centre. Rail: Mossley BR. Buses 153 from Manchester, 343 from Oldham, 350 from Ashton

Capacity: 4,500	Cover: 1,500	Seats: 200	Floodlights: Yes

Clubhouse: Open nights and matchdays   **Club Shop:** Yes

HONOURS	FA Trophy Runners-up 79-80; Northern Premier League 78-79 79-80 (R-up 80-81 81-82 82-83, Chall Cup 78-79; NWC Floodlit Trophy R-up 95-96 NWTL Div 1 R-up 98-99
BEST SEASON	**FA Cup:** 2nd Rd replay 49-50, also 2nd Rd 80-81 & 1st Rd 6 times. **FA Trophy:** Runners-up 79-80 **FA Vase:** 6th Rd 96-97, 99-00
PREVIOUS	**Leagues:** Ashton; South East Lancs; Lancs Comb. 18-19; Cheshire County 19-72; Northen Prem. **Names:** Park Villa 03-04; Mossley Juniors 04-09.
RECORDS	**Attendance:** 7,000 v Stalybridge 1950 **Fee Paid:** £2,300 **Fee Received:** £25,000 for Eamon O'Keefe (Everton, 1979)

FACT FILE
Formed: 1903   Nickname: Lilywhites
Colours:Black & white stripes/black/black
Change: Yellow/blue/blue
Midweek matchday: Tuesday
Programme: 28 Pages £1.00
Editor: John A. Cawthorne
Local Press : Oldham Evening Chronicle/
Mossley & Saddleworth Reporter/Manchester Evening News/Tameside Advertiser/Pink Final
Local Radio: BBC GMR/Key 103/
96.2 Revolution
CLUB PERSONNEL
Chair: Sam Rigby   Pres.: J Wharmby
Manager: Benny Phillips
Website: www.welcometo/mossleyafc
www.mossley.20m.com
Email: mossleyafc@hotmail.com

NANTWICH TOWN

Secretary:	Bernard Lycett, 'Rivington", Clay lane, Haslington, Crewe CW11 5SE Tel: 01270 584066 (H) 07876320280 Email Address: blycett@aol
Ground:	Jackson Avenue, off London Road, Nantwich, Cheshire. Tel: 01270 624098
Directions:	M6 Jct 16, A500 for Nantwich (about 8 miles), continue on A52 over railway crossing (London Rd), second right after railway crossing into Jackson Ave. From Chester, use the A51. Three miles from Crewe (BR).

Capacity: 1,500	Seats: 150	Cover: 555	Floodlights: Yes

Clubhouse: Every night except Sunday 8pm-11pm. Hot pies available   **Club Shop:** Yes

HONOURS	Cheshire Co. Lg 80-81; Ches. Snr Cup 75-76; N.W. Co.Lg.Cup 94-95
PREVIOUS	**Leagues:** Shropshire & Dist.; The Combination 1892-94; Lancs Comb. 12-15; Cheshire Combination 19-38; Manchester; Mid-Cheshire; Cheshire County 68-82. **Name:** Nantwich FC (pre 1973)
RECORDS	**Attendance:** 2,750 v Altrincham, Cheshire Senior Cup 66-67 **Fee r eceived:** £4,000 from Stafford Rangers for D.Dawson **Record Goalscorer in Season:** Gerry Duffy, 42 in 61-62

FACT FILE
Founded: 1884
Nickname: Dabbers
Club Sponsors: Jim Barrie Plant Hire
Colours: Black & white/black/black
Change colours: All green
Midweek matchday: TuesdayReserves'
League:Springbank Midland
Programme: 18 pages, 65
Editor: Che Kerrin (01270 624098)

Club Website: www.nantwichtownfc.co.uk
CLUB PERSONNEL
Chairman: Clive Jackson
6 Spencer Close, Crewe CW2 8DT
01270 664469 (H) 07970 546238 (B)
Manager: Nigel Cleghorn
Captain: Mark Gardiner
Physio: Ivan Robertson

NEWCASTLE TOWN

Secretary: John F Cotton, 293 Weston Rd., Weston Coyney, Stoke-on-Trent, Staffs. St3 6HA
Tel: 01782 333445 (H) 07977516879(M)
Ground: Lyme Valley Parkway Stadium, Lilleshall Rd, Clayton, Newcastle-under-Lyne, Staffs
(01782 662351) (Club 01782 662350 also a fax)
Directions: M6 jct 15, A500 for Stoke, left at r'bout A519 for Newcastle, right at 2nd r'bout into
Stafford Ave., 1st left into Tittensor Road to ground. 3miles from Stoke-on-Trent (BR).
Seats: 300   **Cover:** 1,000   **Capacity:** 4,000   **Floodlights:** Yes   **Club Shop:** Yes
Clubhouse: Saturday matchdays 12-7.30pm, midweek 5-11pm. Hot & cold food available.
HONOURS: Nth West Co's Lg Div 1 R-up 95-96 96-97,99-00 Div 2 R-up 91-92, Challenge Cup
96-97, R-up 99-00 F/Lit Trophy R-up 96-97; Lamot Pils Tphy 91-92; Mid Cheshire Lg Div1 85-86,
R-up 86-78, Div 2 82-83, 90-91, Lge Cup 84-85; Walsall Snr Cup 93-94 94-95 R-up 95-96;
Sentinel Cup 94-95; Tennents Floodlit Trophy 92-93 95-96; Staffs Snr Cup R-up 95-96, 01-02;
Staffs M/W F/Light Lge 94-95 R-up 95-96; Umbro Over 35 Chall Cup 94-95.
RECORDS - **Attendance:** 3,948 v Notts County FA Cup Nov 96 **Win:** 8-0v Skelmersdale U.
Defeat: 0-5 v Eastwood Hanley (A) **Appearances:** Neil Pesteridge 385 (Lg only)
Goalscorer: Shaun Wade 105 (NWCL only) **F.A.Vase:** S-Final 99-00
PREVIOUS - **Leagues:-** Hanley & Dist. Sunday; North Staffs Sunday; Potteries & Dist.Sunday;
Res Refuge Ass Mid; Newcastle & Dist/ Staffs Co.; Mid Cheshire.
Names: Parkway Hanley (founded 1964, later Clayton Park, ParkwayClayton); Newcastle Town
(founded 1980) - clubs merged in 1986.

FACT FILE
Founded: 1964 Nickname: Castle.
Sponsors: Bristol Street Ford Ltd
Colours: All Royal Blue/blue/white
Change colours: All yellow
Midweek Matches: Tuesday
Reserve Team: SpringbankVending.Midland
Programme: 40 pages,£1.00
Editor: Peter Tindall 01260 280983 (H)
Website: www.nitvision.net/newcastletownfc
2001-02
Captain & P.o.Y.: Dean Gillick
Top Scorer: Andy Bott 48

CLUB PERSONNEL
Chairman: J W Walker
Vice-Chairman: K G Walshaw
Press Officer: Ray Tatton (01782 644916)
Manager: Jimmy Wallace
Asst Manager: Michael Bates
Physios: Martin Brown & Eddie Silk

PRESCOT CABLES

Secretary: Doug Lace,20 Cable Road, Prescott,Merseyside L35 5AW
Ground: Valerie Park, Hope Street, Prescot. L34 6HD (Tel No: 0151 430 0507)
EMail: kenderbyshire@blueyonder.co.uk
Ground:Directions: M62 Jct 7. A57 to Prescot. Take 3rd exit at roundabout after two and a half
miles. Turn right after another 1/2 mile. Right at Hope & Anchor pub, into Hope Street..
Capacity: 4,400   **Seats:** 200   **Cover:** 550   **Floodlights:** Yes
Clubhouse: Refreshment bar, open matchdays/evenings for hot & cold refreshments
Club Shop: No but ties & metal badges available.

HONOURS	Lancs Comb. 56-57 (Lg Cup 47-48); Ches. Lg Div 2 76-77; Mid Ches. Lg 76-77; L'pool Non-League Cup(4) 51-53 58-59 60-61; L'pool Chal. Cup(5) 28-30 48-4961-62 77-78; George Mahon Cup 36-37.
PREVIOUS	Leagues: Liverpool Co. Comb.; Lancs Comb. 1897-98 18-20 27-33 36-67; Ches. Co. 33-36 78-82; Mid Cheshire 67-78.
	Names: Prescot Athletic; Prescot Cables 46-65 80-90; Prescot Town 65-80.
BEST SEASON	**FA Cup:** 2nd Rd 57-58 59-60 **FA Vase:** 2nd Rd 1998-99
RECORDS	**Attendance:** 8,122 v Ashton National, 1932

FACT FILE
Founded: 1886
Nickname: Tigers
Colours: Gold/black/gold
Change colours: All blue
Midweek Matches: Tuesday
Programme: 30 pages,70p
Editor: Ken Derbyshire

CLUB PERSONNEL
President: Mr B F Taylor
Chairman: Ted Mercer
Vice Chairman: G.Hayward
Commercial Manager: Arthur McCumiskey
Manager:Tommy Lawson
Asst Manager: Andy Gray

2001-02
Leading goalscorer: Neil Robinson 40

RAMSBOTTOM UNITED

Secretary: John Maher,12 Lilburn Close,Ramsbottom, Lancs. Tel: 01706 822458

Ground: Riverside Ground, Acre Bottom, Ramsbottom. Tel: 01706 822799(Cricket Club)
        Answe Phone: 01706 822458 (for match details)   **Floodlights**: Yes
Email Sddress: final.inspection@madison filter.com
Directions: M66(North) to junction 1, take A56 towards Ramsbottom. After one mile turn left
into Bury New Road. Turn left after theMondi Paper Mill along the road running parallel with the
East Lancs Railway. From North: M65- A56 Follow signs ro Ramsbottominto town centre.

HONOURS:	Bolton Comb. Div. One Champs 72-73; Bolton Comb. Prem Div. 76-77, 86-87; Manchester Lge Div. One Champs 90-91; Manchester Lge Div. 1 Cup Winners 90-91; Gilgryst Cup Winners 94-95; NWCFL Div 2 Champ 96-97, Trophy 95-96
RECORDS	**Attendance:** 829 v Southport F.A.C. 3Q 98-99 NWCFL Div 2 29/3/97
PREVIOUS	**Leagues:** Bury Amateur League, Bolton Combination, Manchester Lge.
BEST SEASON:	**F.A. Cup:** 3rd Q 1998-99 **F.A. Vase:** 2nd Round 98-99, 99-00

FACT FILE

Formed: 1966
Colours: Blue with white trim/blue/white
Midweek Matchday: Tuesday
Club website: fittp.//members,xoom

CLUB PERSONNEL

Chairman: H Williams (01706 822799)

2001-02
Captain: Warren Brierley
P.o.Y.: Phil Porter
Top Goalscorer: Russell Brierley 34

Cheadle Town F.C.

Park Road Stadium, Cheadle, Cheshire

GRASMERE ROVERS
40 YEARS
1961 2001
CHEADLE TOWN

NORTH WEST COUNTIES FOOTBALL LEAGUE

Division Two - Season 2001 - 2002

Tue 5th Feb 2002
v
WUHAN RED HEART K
K.O. 7.30pm

Official Match Day Programme

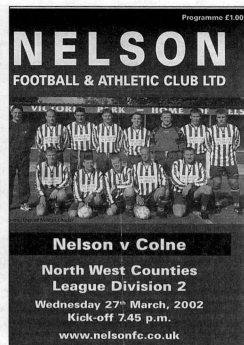

Programme £1.00

NELSON

FOOTBALL & ATHLETIC CLUB LTD

VICTORIA PARK — HOME OF ELS

Nelson v Colne

North West Counties League Division 2

Wednesday 27th March, 2002
Kick-off 7.45 p.m.

www.nelsonfc.co.uk

Squirrel Review

The Official Matchday Magazine of Formby Football Club

DKS
PACKAGING

Worthington Trophy Winners 2001

www.formbyfc.co.uk

NWCFL

NORTH WEST COUNTIES LEAGUE DIVISION TWO 3pm

FORMBY A.F.C. V DAISY HILL A.F.C

SATURDAY 23RD FEBRUARY 2002   PROGRAMME £1

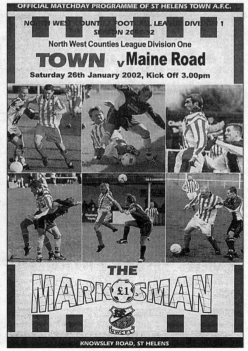

OFFICIAL MATCHDAY PROGRAMME OF ST HELENS TOWN A.F.C.

NORTH WEST COUNTIES FOOTBALL LEAGUE DIVISION 1
SEASON 2001-2002

North West Counties League Division One

TOWN v Maine Road

Saturday 26th January 2002, Kick Off 3.00pm

THE
MARKSMAN
£1

NWCFL

KNOWSLEY ROAD, ST HELENS

SALFORD CITY

Secretary: Frank McCauley, 22 Beverley Road, Pendlebury, Salford M27 4HY
Tel: 0161 736 0021   E mail: mccauley@yahoo.co.uk **Ground:** Moor Lane, Kersal, Salford, Manchester. Tel: 0161 792 6287

Directions: M62 jct 17, A56 Bury New Road to Manchester, continue thro' 4 sets of lights, right into Moor Lane, ground 500 yds left. 4 miles from Manchester Victoria (BR). Buses 96, 139, 94, 95 to Moor Lane

Capacity: 8,000   **Seats:** 260   **Cover:** 600   **Floodlights:** Yes

Clubhouse: Open matchdays only. Hot snacks

HONOURS	Lancashire Amateur Cup 72-73 74-75 76-77; Manchester Senior Cup, Manchester Challenge Cup, Manchester Lg 74-75 75-76 76-77 78-79. Reserve Division North 2000-01. Reserve Division North Cup 2000-01.
PREVIOUS	**Leagues:** Manchester 63-80; Cheshire Co. 80-82. **Names:** Salford Central 40-63; Salford Amateurs 1963 until merger with Anson Villa; Salford FC. **Ground:** Crescent, Salford
BEST SEASON	**FA Cup:** **FA Vase:**
RECORDS	**Attendance:** 3,000 v Whickham FA Vase 1981

FACT FILE

Founded: 1940
Nickname: Ammies
Colours: White with blue trim/blue/blue
Change colours: Yellow and sky blue
Midweek Matches: Tuesday
Reserves' League: NWC Res. Div. S.
Programme: 24 pages, £1.00
Editor: Dave Cooper
CLUB PERSONNEL

Chairman: DavidTaylor
Manager: Andy Brown
Press Officer: Secrtary
Commercial Manager: Stevie Plant

SKELMERSDALE UNITED

Secretary: Bryn Jones, 34 Bromilow Road, Skelmersdale, Lancs. WN8 8TU
Ground: White Moss Park, White Moss Road, Skelmersdale, Lancs   Tel: 01695 722723

Directions: M58 Jct 3, at 2nd r'bout take 3rd exit towards Skelmersdale, continue for approx 1 mile, ground on the right. 4 miles from Ormskirk (BR)

Capacity: 10,000   **Seats:** 250   **Cover:** 1,000   **Floodlights:** Yes

Clubhouse: None. Matchday food bar sells hot drinks, soup, pies & pasties etc
Club Shop: No, but badges available in two colours.

HONOURS	FA Amateur Cup 70-71 R-up 66-67; Ches. Co. Lg 68-69 69-70, Jubilee Cup 69-70; Lancs F'lit Cup 69-70; Lancs Jnr Cup 69-70 70-71; Ashworth Cup 70-71; Barassi Anglo-Italian Cup 70-71; Lancs Non-Lge Cup 73-74 74-75; North West Co's Lg Cup: 99-00 R-up 82-83.N.W.Co Div 2 R-Up: 97-98
PREVIOUS	**Leagues:** Liverpool County Comb., Lancashire Comb. 1891-93, 03-07, 21-24 55-68, 76-78, Cheshire County 68-71 78-82, Northern Premier 71-76.
BEST SEASON	**FA Cup:** 1st Rd 67-68, 0-2 v Scunthorpe(A), 68-69, 0-2 v Chesterfield(A), 71-72, 0-4 v Tranmere R. (H) **FA Amateur Cup:** Winners 70-71
RECORDS	**Attendance:** 7,000 v Slough, FA Amat Cup Q-F '67

FACT FILE
Founded: 1882
Nickname: Skem
Sponsors:Matalan
Colours: Blue & white stripes/blue/blue
Change colours: Red & white stripes/red/red
Midweek Matches: Tuesday
Reserves play North West Counties Res. Div.
Programme: 32 pages, £1
Editor: Peter McGee
CLUB PERSONNEL
President: D.Tomlinson
Managing Director: A.Gore -
Press Officer: Secretary
Manager: Paul Gallagher
Asst Manager: Mick Budey
Coach: CliffTalbot Physio: Billy Leigh
2001-02
Leading goalscorer: Stuart Rudd 28
Captain: Stuart Rudd
P.o.Y.: John Brownrigg

SQUIRES GATE

Secretary:	Jeff Webster, 168 Highcross Road, Poulton-Le-Fylde, FY6 8DA. Tel/Fax: 01253 890846. Mobile 077406 44335
Ground:	School Road, Marton, Blackpool, Lancs. Tel: 01253 798584
Directions:	M6 to M55 jct 4, left onto A583, right at 1st lights (Whitehall Rd) follow signs for airport. Ground approx 1.5 miles on right. Nearest station Blackpool South.
Capacity: 1000	**Seats:** 2 new stands (100 seats) **Cover:** One side **Floodlights:** Yes
Clubhouse: Yes	
HONOURS	West Lancs Lg: Div 2 80-81, Richardson Cup 86-87, N.W.C.L 2nd Div Trophy winners 2000/01
PREVIOUS	**Leagues:** W. Lancs (pre-1991)
RECORD	**Attendance:** 600 v Everton 95

FACT FILE

Formed: 1948
Colours: Royal/black/royal
Midweek Matches: Tuesday
Programme: 20 pages

CLUB PERSONNEL

Chairman: P Mack (01772 339955)
Life Vice President: Wilf Carr

Manager: Gordon Fell
Assistant Manager: Joe Dewhurst
Reserves Manager: Dean Whitehead

ST HELENS TOWN

Secretary: John McKiernan,35 Royston Gardens,Peasley Cross,St Helens WA 1RJ Tel No: 01744 635826 **Ground:** St Helens R.L.F.C. , Knowsley Road, St Helens **Directions: From South:** M62 Jct 7-5th exit (St Helens) 3rd r'about (Sherdley), follow Town Centre signs. Left at r'about to L'pool & Prescot.Rt at lights then left at Black Bull after 1 mile. Ground on right. **From North:** M6.Jct 23 take A580 to L'pool.7 mile left to A570 and 1st Rt into Bleak Hilll Road.Left at right hand bend after 1 mile into Mill Brow. At T jct left at Black Bull, turn right -ground on left. **Capacity:** 19,100 **Seats:** 2,362 **Cover:** 12,408 **Floodlights:** Yes

Clubhouse: Weekdays 8-11pm, Saturday matchdays 2-6.30pm. **Club Shop:** Yes

HONOURS: FA Vase 86-87; George Mahon Cup 49-50; Lancs Comb. 71-72, Div 2 50-51, Lg Cup R-up 70-71;Liverpool Snr Non Lge Cup R-up 76-77; Lancs Jnr Cup R-up 66-67; Bass Charrington Cup 73-74; Carling Chall Cup r-up 93-94; N.W.C. Floodlit Trophy r-up 97-98.

PREVIOUS **Leagues:** Lancs Comb. 03-14 49-75; Liverpool County Comb. 49-74; Cheshire County 74-82. **Grounds:** Park Road 01-52; City Road 52-53.

BEST SEASON FA Cup: 4th Q Rd 85-86 **FA Vase:** Winners 86-87

RECORDS **Gate:** 4,000 v Manchester City, Bert Trautmann transfer match,April 1950. **Goalscorer:** S Pennington **W in:** 10-4 v Everton `B' 1952 **Appearances:** Alan Wellens **Defeat** : 1-8 v Liverpool Res., L'pool Snr Cup 1950

FACT FILE
Founded: 1946
Nickname: `Town'
Colours: Red & white/white/red
Change colours: Royal blue & white/white/royal blue
Midweek Matches: Tuesday
Programme: 24 pages, 50p
Editor: John McKiernan (01744 600612)
Local Press: Reporter, Star, Echo.
CLUB PERSONNEL
Chairman/Press Officer: Jim Barrett
Public Liaison Officer: John McKiernan 01744 635826 (H) 01744 24348 (W)
Manager: John Davison
Asst Manager: G Walker
Coach: John Neary

WARRINGTON TOWN

Secretary: Barry Thorpe, 46 Greenheys Road,Little Hulton,Manchester M389TP(01617990423) **Ground:** Cantilever Park, Common Lane, Latchford, Warrington WA4 2RS Tel: 01925 631932 (Club), 01925-653044 (FAX). **Directions:** M6 junction 20, then A50 towards Warrington. After 2 miles turn left immediately after swing bridge into Station Road, ground 600yds on left. From town centre travel 1 mile south on A49, left at lights into Loushers Lane, ground quarter mile on right. 2miles from Warrington Bank Quay (BR) **Capacity:** 2,000 **Cover:** 650 **Seats:** 350 **Floodlights:** Yes **Club Shop:** Yes (Barry Thorpe) **Clubhouse:** Weekdays 1-11pm, Sat. 12-11pm, Sun. 12-11 p.m. Bar food on matchdays **PREVIOUS** **Leagues:** Warrington & Dist. 49-52; Mid-Cheshire 52-78; Cheshire Co. 78-82; N.W.C. 82-90; N.P.L 90-97. **Name:** Stockton Heath 1949-62. **RECORDS** **Attendance:** 2,600 v Halesowen T., FA Vase S-F 1st leg 85-86. **Goalscorer:** Steve Hughes 167 **Fee Received:** £60,000 for Liam Watson (Preston N. E.) 92-93 **BEST SEASON FA Cup:** 4th Qual. Rd 94-95 replay with Hyde Utd.. **FA Vase:** Runners-up 86-87 **FA Trophy:** Quarter-Finalists 92-93 **HONOURS:** FA Vase R-up 86-87; N.W.C. Lge 89-90 (Lg Cup 85-86 87-88 88-89 (R-up 89-90), Div 2 00-01R-up 86-87, Div 3 R-up 82-83; Mid-Cheshire Lg 60-61 R-up 57-58, Lg Cup 54-55 55-56 11-12 72-73, Altrincham Amat. Cup 54-55, Players progressing recently: M Leonard (Everton), N Whalley & L Watson (P.N.E.) 92-93.

FACT FILE
Formed: 194 8 Nickname: The Town
Colours: Blue & yellow/blue/blue
Change colours: Orange/black/black
Midweek matchday: Tuesday
Reserves' League: Mid-Cheshire
Programme: 48-60 Pages £1.00
Editor: Paul Roach, 55 Moorcroft, New Brighton, Mold, Flintshire CH7 6RU
Tel: 01352 752489, 07740 430190 (M))
CLUB PERSONNEL
Chairman: Harry Boden
Vice Chairman: D.J.Hughes
Press Officer: Colin Serjent
Manager: Alan Blair Asst Man Dave Hughes
Coach: Derek Brownbill
Top Scorer 2001-02: Chris Moores 27

WINSFORD UNITED

Secretary: Peter Warburton, 3 Massey Avenue, Winsford, Cheshire CW7 3DU (01606554295) **Ground Address:** Barton Stadium, Wharton, Winsford, Cheshire CW7 3EU (01606 593021). **Directions:** From north; M6 junction 19, A556 towards Northwich to Davenham,then A5018 to Winsford. From south; M6 junction 18, A54 through Middlewich to Winsford. Ground quarter mile off main road in Wharton area of town. 1 mile from Winsford (BR). **Capacity:** 6,000 **Cover:** 5,000 **Seats:** 250 **Clubhouse:** Mon-Sat 8-11pm, Sun 8-10.30pm **Club Shop:** Yes, contact Kay Lomas **PREVIOUS** **Name:** Over Wanderers (pre 1914). **Leagues:** The Combination 02-04; Cheshire Co. 19-40, 47-82; N.W.C. 82-87, N.P.L 87-01. **CLUB RECORDS** **Attendance:** 7,000 v Witton Albion 1947.**Goalscorer:** Graham Smith 66. **Apps:** Edward Harrop 400.**Fee Paid:** Nil. **Fee Received:** £6,000 for Neville Southall from Bury. **BEST SEASON** **F.A. Cup:** 2nd Rd 1887-88. 1st Rd 1975-76 1991-92 **F.A. Trophy:** Qtr Finals 77-78. League clubs defeated: None. **HONOURS** N.P.L. R-up 92-93, Div 1 R-up 91-92, Lg Cup 92-93, Presidents Cup 92-93; Cheshire Co. Lg 20-21 76-77 (R-up 74-75 79-80),Lg Cup x 7 R-up x 3; Cheshire Snr Cup 58-59 79-80 92-93; Mid-Cheshire Snr Cup 90-91 92-93 (R-up 88-89); Cheshire Amateur Cup 00-01 02-03; Lancs Comb/Cheshire County Inter-Lg Cup 62-63. Players P rogressing recently: Mark Came (Bolton W. 84), Dave Bamber (Blackpool), Bob Sutton (W.H.U.), Richardson (Sheff. U.), Stanley Wood (W.B.A.), R Pearce (Luton T.). Andy Oakes (Derby C),Darren Sheridan (Barnsley),Jon Whitley(Lincoln C), Wayne Collins(Sheff W)

FACT FILE
Founded: 1883
Nickname: Blues
Colours: Royal blue & White/white/blue
Change colours: All Maroon
Midweek matchday: Tuesday
Programme: Pages: 24 Price: £1.00
Editor: R. Astles Tel: 01270 661623
Local Press: Winsford Chronicle, Winsford Guardian.
Local Radio: Signal, Piccadilly.
CLUB PERSONNEL
Chairman: Mark Loveless President: A Bayliss
Vice Chairman: David Taylor
Manager: Alan Walker

WOODLEY SPORTS

FACT FILE
Founded: 1970
Colours: Royal Blue/White/Red
Midweek Matchday: Tuesday

Secretary: Ian Woodhouse, 4 Firethorn Drive, Godley, Hyde SK14 3SN
Tel: 0161 3511631 (H), 0161 330 6837 (B) 07775 688277 (M)

Ground: Lambeth Grove Stadium, Lambeth Grove, Woodley, Stockport.
Tel: 0161 494 6429   Floodlights: yes

Directions: M60 Jct 25, follow signs (A560) Bredbury, take left filter at lights which
brings you onto A560 Stockport Road for approx 1 mile, turn left at pub,
Lowes Arms into Mill Street which goes into Mill Lane. Over bridge take 2nd
right into Woodlands Avenue, then 1st left into Lambeth Grove.
Ground 200 yards ahead.
Floodlights: Yes

HONOURS NWC Div 2 99-00

RECORD **Attendance:** 1,500 v Stockport County

PREVIOUS **Leagues:** Lancashire & Cheshire, Manchester League.

BEST SEASON **FA Cup:** 99-00   **FA Vase:** 1st Round 1998-99

CLUB PERSONNEL
Chairman: Ian Campbell
14 Gloucester Rd., Gee Cross, Hyde.
Tel: 0161 368 4060(H)

*Carlisle United Reserves' Michael Dickinson bursts between Carlisle City's Alan Hodgson (left) and Mike Algeo in the
Cumberland Senior Cup Final at Raydale Park, Gretna when United won 2-0. Photo: Alan Watson.*

ASHTON TOWN

Secretary: Stephen Barrett, 11 Clement Avenue, Atherton M46 0PT
Tel Nos: 01942 889492 (H)   01942 529312 (W)
Ground: Edge Green Street, Ashton-in-Makerfield, Wigan WN4 8SY (01942 510677)
Directions: M6 Jct 23, A49 to Ashton-in-M. Right at lights onto A58 towards Bolton.
After 3/4 mile turn right at `Rams Head' P.H. into Golbourne Rd. After 200
yds right into Edge Green Str. Ground at end.
Floodlights: No

HONOURS Warrington Lg Guardian Cup.

PREVIOUS **Leagues:** Warrington, Lancs Comb. 03-11 71-78, Ches. Co. 78-82.

BEST SEASON **FA Vase:** Prelim. Rd 84-85

RECORD **Gate:** 600 v Accrington Stanley 76-77

FACT FILE
Founded: 1962
Colours: Red with white trim/red/red
Change colours: All sky blue
Midweek Matches: Tuesday

CLUB PERSONNEL
President: W Pomfrett
Chairman: Len Riley
Manager: Norman Hickson

BACUP BOROUGH

Secretary: Frank Manning, 38 Acre Avenue, Stacksteads, Bacup OL13 0HN
Tel: 01706 877460 (H)
Ground: West View, Cowtoot Lane, Blackthorn, Bacup, Lancashire (01706 878655).
Directions: From M62, M66 onto A681 through Rawtenstall to Bacup centre, leftonto A671
towards Burnley, after approx 300 yds right (immed. before the IrwellInn) climbing Cooper
Street, right into Blackthorn Lane then first left intoCowtoot Lane to ground.
Capacity: 3,000   **Seats:** 500   **Cover:** 1,000   Floodlights: Yes
Clubhouse: Open matchdays and private functions (for which buffets can beprovided). Pies and
sandwiches on matchdays.   **Club Shop:** Not yet
HONOURS Lancs Jnr Cup 10-11 (R-up 22-23 74-75); Lancs Comb. 46-47 (Lg Cup R-
up46-47 80-81; NW Co's Lg Div 2 R-up 89-90.
PREVIOUS **League:** Lancs Comb. 03-82Name: Bacup FC.Grounds: None
BEST SEASON **FA Cup:** **FA Vase:**
RECORD **Gate:** 4,980 v Nelson 1947   **Scorer:** Jimmy Clarke

FACT FILE
Founded: 1875
Nickname: The Boro
Club Sponsors:B&EBoys Ltd
Colours:White with black trim,black,black
Change colours:Yellow,Blue,Blue
Midweek Matches: Wednesday
Programme: 22Pages 50p
Editor: D Whatmough (0706 875041)
CLUB PERSONNEL
President: W.Shufflebottom
Chairman: Ken Peters
Vice Chairman: D.Whatmough
Manager: Brent Peters
Assistant Manager: Simon Holding

BLACKPOOL MECHANICS

Secretary: Brian Wood,7 Kendal Avenue,Blackpool FY3 7LG (01253 391079)
Ground: Jepson Way, Common Edge Rd, Blackpool, Lancs FY4 5DY (01253 761721).
Directions: M6 to M55, follow Airport signs. Left at r'bout along A583 (Preston New Rd) to
lights, right into Whitehill Rd, becomes School Rd, to lights.Straight over main road & follow
signs for Blackpool Mechanics F.C. to ground.Rail to Blackpool North - then bus 11c from Talbot
Rd bus station (next to rail station) to Shovels Hotel, Common Edge Rd.
Capacity: 2,000   **Seats:** 250   **Cover:** 1,700   Floodlights: Yes
Clubhouse: Match days, training nights. Dancehall. Matchday, hot food.
Club Shop: Manager Andrew Sneddon (01253 729962). Ties, sweaters, old programmes, badges.
HONOURS Lancs Comb Bridge Shield 72-73; NW Co's. Lg Div 3 85-86; W Lancs Lg 60-
61 62-63; Lancs County FA Shield 57-58 60-61:
PREVIOUS **Leagues:** Blackpool & Fylde Comb., West Lancs, Lancs Comb. 62-68.
Grounds: Stanley Pk 47-49
RECORD **Gate:** 1,200 v Morecambe, Lancs Comb, August 1968
2000-01 **Captain:** John Oliver **P.o.Y.:** Keith Johnstone **Top Scorer:** Rob Park 23

FACT FILE
Founded: 1947   Nickname: Mechs
Sponsors: Bloomfield Bakery Blackpool.
Club colours: Tangerine/white/tangerine
Change colours: All blue
Midweek matchday: Wednesday
Programme: 10 pages, 50p
Editor: David Gore

CLUB PERSONN
Chairman: John Sanderson
President: Gregory Gregorio
Commercial Manager: John Sanderson
Manager: Brian Wilson
Asst Man.: Stuart Parker
Coach: William Singleton.

BOOTLE

Secretary: William Jones, 36 Rydecroft, Woolton, Liverpool L25 7UT
Tel Nos: 0151 428 2203(H) 0793 912893 (W)
Ground: Bucks Park, Northern Perimeter Rd, Netherton, Bootle. L307PT (0151 526 1850)
Directions: End of M57 & M58 follow signs to Bootle and Docks A5063.
Turn right at next lights by Police station. Entrance 100 yds on right.
Old Roan station 300yds. Bus 55 (150yds from grd), 302 341 345 350 (350yds).
Capacity: 5,000   **Seats:** 400   **Cover:** 1,400   Floodlights: Yes
Clubhouse: Normal pub hours. Darts & pool   **Club Shop:** Yes
HONOURS N.W.C. Lge Div 2 R-up 92-93 (R'lit Trophy 93-94), Liverpool Chall. Cup 64-65 75-76
78-79, Liverpool Amtr Cup 65-66 67-68 73-74, Lancs Amtr Cup 69-70, Liverpool Co. Comb. (x9)
64--66 67-74, George Mahon Cup (x6) 66--68 70-72--74, Lancs Comb. 75-76 76-77, Lge Cup
75-76, Cheshire County Lge Div 2 78-79.
PREVIOUS Leagues: Liverpool Shipping, Liverpool Co Comb., Lancs Comb. 74-78, Cheshire Lge
78-82. **Name:** Langton 1953-73 **Grounds:** Edinburgh Park 1953-73, Orrell Mount Park 73-8

FACT FILE
Founded: 1954
Nickname: Bucks
Sponsors: Taximex
Colours: All royal blue with amber trim
Change colours: Yellow/black/black
Midweek matchday: Tuesday
Reserves' League: Liverpool Co. Combination
Programme: 32 pages, 50p
Editor: Secretary
CLUB PERSONNEL
Chairman: Frank Doran
Manager: T.B.A.

CASTLETON GABRIELS

Secretary: David Lord, 34 Fairway, Castleton, Rochdale OL11 3BU   Tel: 01706 522719
Ground: Butterworth Park, Chadwick Lane, off Heywood Rd., Castleton, Rochdale. Tel: 01706
527103)   **Directions:** M62 Jct 20, A6272M to r'bout. Left towards Castleton (A664Edinburgh
Way) to next r'bout, keeping Tesco Superstore to the left, take 1st exit to next r'bout, take 2nd
exit into Manchester Rd (A664), after just under mile turn right at `Top House' P.H. into Heywood
Rd., to end & ground on right
Capacity: 1,500   Seats: 400   Cover: 650   Floodlights: Yes
Clubhouse: Open seven nights a night and all day Saturday. Pie & peas and sandwiches available matchdays (pie & peas only at Reserve matches)   **Club Shop:** No
HONOURS   Manchester Lge 86-87, Murray Shield 86-87; Res Div Cup 95-96.
PREVIOUS   **Leagues:** Rochdale Alliance 24-84; Manchester 84-89.
                     Name: St Gabriels (pre-1960s)   **Ground:** Park pitches; Springfield Pk 60-81.
RECORDS   **Gate:** 640 v Rochdale, pre-season friendly 1991   **Win:** 8-0 v Squires Gate
                     N.W.Co.Div 2 94   **Defeat:** 1-10 v Blackpool Mechanics N.W.Co.Div 2 95

FACT FILE
Founded: 1924   Nickname: Gabs
Club Sponsors: Kick Off
Colours: Sky & Navy Blue/Sky & Navy/Navy
Change colours: All red
Midweek matchday: Tuesday
Reserves ' League: N.W.C. Res. Div.
Programme: 28 pages, 50p
Editor: David Jones (01942 730220 -W)

CLUB PERSONNEL
Chairman: Rod Harling
Vice Chairman: R Butterworth
Press Officer: Secretary
Manager/Coach:David Jones
Assistant Manager:Roy Grundy
Coach: Neil Mills

CHADDERTON

Secretary: Ronald Manton,77 Denton Lane, Chadderton, Oldham OL9 9AC
Ground: Andrew Street, Chadderton, Oldham, Lancs (0161 624 9733)   **Capacity:** 2,500
Directions: M62 Jct 20, A627(M) to M'chester.. M'way becomes dual carriageway. Left at 1st
major traffic lights A669 Middleton Rd, then first left into Butterworth Street. Andrew Street is
second right. Oldham Werneth (BR) 1 m or Mills Hill (BR) l m.Buses 24,181,182 to Middleton Rd
from Lever Street of Piccadilly Gardens. **Seats:** 200   **Cover:** 600   **Floodlights:** Yes
Clubhouse: Matchdays only. Hot & cold snack during & after games **Club Shop:** No
HONOURS M'chester Am Lg 62-63, North Div 55-56, M. Prem Cup R-up 82-83, Chall Tphy 71-
72, R-up 72-73, M. Lg Div 1 66-67, Div 2 64-65, Gilgryst Cup 69-70, Murray Shield 65-66, Lancs
Comb. Cup R-up 81-82, Alf Pettit & Hulme Celtic Cup 61-62, NWC F/lit Tphy R-up 92-93
Manchester Umbro International Cup Winners 2000
RECORD Gate: 1,500 v Guinness Ex'ts 1969 **Appearances:** Billy Elwell 750+ (64-90)
Players progressing: (include) David Platt (Crewe, Arsenal), John Pemberton (Crewe,Leeds U)
Graham Bell(Oldham), Paul Hilton (Bury), Don Graham (Bury).

FACT FILE
Founded: 1947   Nickname: Chaddy
Sponsors: T.B.A.
Colours: All red Change colours: All Yellow
Midweek Matches: Tuesday
Programme: 28-32 pages Editor: David Greaves
Previous Leagues:Oldham Am,Manchester
Am,Manchester 64-80,Lancs Comb 80-82

2001-02
Top Scorer & P.o.Y.: Colin Bennett
Captain: Gary Kelly
CLUB PERSONNEL
Chairman: Harry Mayall
President: Derek Glynn
Press Officer: John Fitton
Manager: Mike Lester

CHEADLE TOWN

Secretary: David Busby, 9 Tatton Road, Handforth, Wilmslow, Cheshire Sk9 3QZ
Tel Nos: 01625 524116 ((H) o7932 634630 (M)
Ground: Park Road Stadium, Park Road, Cheadle, Cheshire SK8 2AN (0161 4282510).
Directions: M60 Jct 2, follow signs towards Cheadle (A560), first left after lights into Park Road,
ground at end. 1 mile from Gatley (BR), buses from Stockport.
Capacity: 2,500   Seats: 300   Cover: 300   Floodlights Yes
Clubhouse: Open every night. Food available   **Club Shop**: No
HONOURS   Manchester Lg Div 1 79-80 (R-up 80-81 81-82); Manchester Amtr Cup 79-
                     80;Lamot Pils R-up 90-91; NWCFL Div 2 Trophy R-up 95-96:
PREVIOUS   **Leagues:** Manchester (pre 1987)
RECORD   **Attendance :** 1,700 v Stockport County, August 1994.
                     Scorer: Peter Tilley   **Appearances:** John McArdle
Players progressing: Ashley Ward (Crewe), Steve Bushell (York), Dean Crowe(Stoke).
2000-01- **Captain:** Chris Williams **Top Scorer:** Paul Wardle 14

FACT FILE
Founded: 1961
Colours: White/black/black
Change colours: All blue.
Midweek Matches: Tuesday
Reserves' Lge: NW Counties Lge
Programme: 24 pages,80p.
Editor: Stuart Crawford

CLUB PERSONNEL
President: Freddie Pye
Chairman: Chris Davies
Vice-Chairman: Clive Williams
Press Officer: Chris Davies (0161 428 2510).
Manager: Martin Wardle
Player/ Coach: Paul Wardle

COLNE F C

Secretary: Ray Davies,11 Robinson Street,Colne, Lancs BB8 9PU (01282 859120)

Ground: Holt House Stadium, Holt House, Colne. (Tel: 01282 862545)
Directions: Enter Colne from M65 to roundabout, keep left follow signs for Keighley. At next
roundabout turn left, continue on Harrison Drive over mini roundabout & follow road to ground.
Nearest Railway station - Colne.
Capacity: 1,800   Seats: 100   Cover: 1000   Floodlights: Yes

Clubhouse: Yes,Small Lounge Bar open on matchdays   **Club Shop:** No
HONOURS   BEP Cup Winners 96-97
BEST SEASON   **FA Cup:**   **FA Vase:**
RECORDS   **Attendance:** 240 v Nelson 97-98
                     Scorer: Geoff Payton   **Appearances:** Nick Roscoe
PREVIOUS   **Leagues:** East Lancashire League

FACT FILE

Formed: 1996
Colours: All red
Change colours: All yellow
Midweek Matchday: Wednesday
Programme: Yes   Editor: Ray Moore

CLUB PERSONNEL

Chairman: Dave Blacklock
Press Officer: Ray Moore(01282 868857)
Manager:Denzil Hart

Garforth's Lee Beaton tackles Nelson's Nigel Coates (stripes) in the Second Qualifying Round of the FA Vase.
Photo: Alan Watson

Alsager Town FC captain Mark Timms is presented with the Division Two Runners Up Trophy by League Chairman David Tomlinson

Leek CSOB

DAISY HILL

Secretary: Bob Naylor, 8 Bailey Fold, Westhoughton, Bolton, Lancs BL5 3HH   01942 813720
Ground: New Sirs, St James Street, Westhoughton, Bolton, Lancs.   01942 818544
Directions: M61 Jct 5, A58 (Snydale Way/Park Road) for 1.5 miles, left into Leigh Road
(B5235) for 1 mile, right into village then left between Church and School into St James Street.
Ground 250 yds on the left. Half mile from Daisy Hill (BR)

Capacity: 2,000   Seats: 200   Cover: 250   Floodlights: No   Club Shop: No
Clubhouse: Open normal licensing hours during any football activity. Snacks on matchdays

HONOURS	Bolton Comb Prem Div 62-63 72-73 75-76 77-78, Lg Cup 59-60 61-62
	71-72 72-73; Lancs Shield 61-62 71-72 86-87:
PREVIOUS	**Leagues:** Westhoughton; Bolton Comb.; Lancs Combination. 78-82.
	Name: Westhoughton Town **Record Goals & Apps:**Alan Roscoe 300-450
BEST SEASON	**FA Cup:** **FA Vase:**
RECORD	**Attendance:** 2,000 v Horwich RMI,Westhoughton Charity Cup Final 79-80

PLAYERS PROGRESSING: Barry Butler (Chester C)+ Phil Priestley (Rochdale)via AthertonLR

FACT FILE
Founded: 1894(first known records)
Reformed: 1952
Colours: All royal blue   Change: All red
Midweek Matches: Tuesday
Reserves' Lge NWCL Res Div
Programme: 40 pages 80p
Editor: T.B.a.
CLUB PERSONNEL
Chairman:Tony Veitch
Manager:Joe Paladino

2001-02
Leading Scorer: S.Brockley
P.o.Y.: Adi Veitch

DARWEN

Secretary: Lynn Atkinson, 14 Prospect Gardens,Darwen, Lancs (01254 708158)
Ground: Anchor Ground, Anchor Road, Darwen, Lancs BB3 0BB, (01254 705627)
Directions: A666 Blackburn / Bolton road, 1 mile north of Darwen town centre,turn right at
Anchor Hotel, ground 200 yds on left. One and a half miles from Darwen (BR), bus 51 to
Anchor Hotel.From M65 Jct 4 signs to Darwen.Left at A666,1/2 mile left at anchor Hotel. ground
200 yds on left Capacity: 4,000   Seats: 250   Cover: 2,000   Floodlights: Yes
Clubhouse: Matchday only   **Club Shop:** No

HONOURS	Lancs Comb 31 32 73 75: Comb Cup 30 31 75; Lancs Jun Cup 73; Geo
	Watson Trophy 73; LFA Yth Cup 75; NWC Cup 83; Lancs F/Lit Trophy 90; NWC Res Div Cup
	94; Blackburn & Dist Yth Lge 94 95 97, Cup 94 95 97; NW All Chall Cup 96.
PREVIOUS	**Leagues:**Football Alliance 1889-91, Football Lg 1891-99, Lancs Lg 99-
	03,Lancs Comb. 03-75, Ches. Co. 75-82. **Ground:** Barley Bank
RECORD	**Gate:** (Anchor Ground) 10,000 v Fleetwood Lancs Jun Cup 1920
BEST SEASON	**FA Cup:** Semi Finals 1881

FACT FILE
Founded: 1875
Sponsors:
Colours: Red & white/red/red
Change colours: All blue
Midweek Matches: Tuesday
Reserves' League: NWC Res. Div.
Programme: 20 pages, £1.00 Editor: S.Hart
Local papers: Lancs Evening Telegraph
CLUB PERSONNEL
President: E Devlin
Chairwoman: Mrs K Marah
Manager: S Wilkes
Asst Manager: M Atkinson
Physio: Mick Sharples

FORMBY

Secretary: Dave Dickinson,2 Seafield,Formby,Merseyside L374EL Tel : 01704 870944
Ground: Altcar Road ,Formby,Merseyside (01704 833505)
Directions: Turn right at lights opposite Tesco into Altcar Road. Through mini roundabout and
ground is on the rigt next to refuse tip

Capacity: 2,000   Seats: 220   Cover: 500   Floodlights: November 2002
Clubhouse: None. Matchday refreshment bar stocks hot food & drinks
Club Shop: Sells programmes, badges & souvenirs. **HONOURS** Liverpool Co. Comb. 48-49, R-
up 64-65; Liverpool Senior Cup 77-78, R-up 84-85; Challenge Cup 52-53 63-64 67-68, R-up 64-
65; Amtr Cup 29-30 47-48 48-49;Lamot Pils Trophy 94-95; George Mahon Cup 64-65, R-up 55-
56 56-57; Lancs Co FA Amt Cup 34-35, Woirthingtobn Trophy 00-01
PREVIOUS Leagues: Liverpool Co. Comb. 19-68/ Lancs Comb. 68-71, Ches. Co. 71-82.
BEST SEASON   FA Cup: 1st Rd 73-74, 0-2 v Oldham Ath. (H)   **FA Trophy:** 1st Rd 73-74,
lost to Stalybridge Celtic **FA Vase:** 2nd Rd 96-97, lost to Tetley Walker

Founded: 1919   Nickname: Squirrels
Club Sponsors: DKS Packaging
Colours: Yellow/blue/yellow
Change:Green/black/black
Midweek Matches: Tuesday
Reserves : Liverpool Co.unty Comb Div 2
Prog: 36 pages, £1.00 Ed:Dave Cookson
(01772 311681) Website: www.formbfc.co.uk
CLUB PERSONNEL
Chairman: Chris Welsh
Comm. Man.:Dave Dickinson (01704 870944)
Managers: Peter Hennerty & Mike Scott
Physio: Barry O'Connor
2001-02
Capt. : Howard Rubbery P.o.Y.: Tom Spearitt
Top scorer: Neal Smith

GREAT HARWOOD TOWN

Secretary: Mark Jones, 15 Elm Close, Rishton,Blackburn, BB1 4HN Tel: 01254 876822(H)
Ground: The Sportsmans, Wood Street, Great Harwood, Lancs Tel: 01254 883913
Directions: M66 from Manchester to Haslingden exit, A680 through Baxenden, Accrington to
Clayton-le-Moors, left at the Hyndburn Bridge Hotel into Hyndburn Road and right into Wood
Street to ground. 3miles from Rishton (BR), 6 miles from Blackburn (BR). Various buses from
Heyes Lane & Park Road to Blackburn & Accrington

Capacity: 2,500   Cover: 700   Seats: 200   Floodlights: Yes
Clubhouse: The Sportsman just outside ground. Normal licensing hours. Full bar facilities.
Squash courts and gym. Hot & cold snacks & drinks on matchdays from tea bar in ground
Club Shop: Sells programmes, badges, key rings, shirts. Contact: J McKay (c/o club)
HONOURS N.W.C. R-up 91-92, Div 2 90-91, Lamot Pils Tphy 89-90, R-up 90-91, Tennents F'lit
Trophy 91-92, Lancs ATS Chall. Trophy 91-92, R-up 90-91
PREVIOUS Leagues: West Lancashire; Lancs Comb. 79-82; N.W.C. 82-92; N.P.L. 92-99
Record Gate: 5,397 v Manchester Utd, 1980. **Best Season - FA Cup:** 1st Qual. Rnd replay 92-
93, 1-2 v Atherton LR (H), after 1-1 **FA Vase:** Quarter Finals 90-91, 1-2 v Littlehampton Town (A)

FACT FILE
Formed: 1965   Nickname: Robins
Club Sponsors: None
Colours: All red
Change colours: All blue
Midweek Matches: Monday
Reserves' league: West Lancs Lge
Programme: Pages: 20 Price: 20p
Editor: D Bennet

CLUB PERSONNEL
Chairman: William Holden
Press Officer: K Lambert
Commercial Manager: Mark Smith
Manager: M Crabbe
Asst Manager: Dave Sargent

HOLKER OLD BOYS

Secretary: John Adams, 20 Middlefield,Barrow in Furness, Cumbria. LA14 4AU(01229 431121)

Ground: Rakesmoor Lane, Hawcoat, Barrow-in-Furness, Cumbria (01229 828176)

Directions: M6 Jct 36, A590 to Barrow-in-Furness, on entering Barrow, continue across r'bout, 2nd right (Dalton Lane) to top of road, right into Rakesmoor Lane, ground on right.

Capacity: 2,500   Seats: 220   Cover: 500   Floodlights: Yes

Clubhouse: Mon-Fri 8-11pm, Sat noon-11pm, Sun normal licensing. Pies & peas on matchdays

Club Shop: No

HONOURS	W Lancs Lg 86-87, R-up 85-86; Lancs Junior Shield 88-89 90-91.
PREVIOUS	**Leagues:** North Western; Furness Premier; West Lancs 70-91.
RECORDS	**Attendance:** 1240 v Barrow ATS Trophy 95-96 **Win:** 12-0
	Defeat: 1-8 v Newcastle T. (H) 91-92 **Scorer:** Dave Conlin
2000-01	**Captain:** Mike Brown **P.o.Y.:**Gary Waters **Top Scorer:** Carl Waters 34

FACT FILE
Founded: 1936   Nickname: Cobs
Club Sponsors: Kitchen Design Studio
Colours: Green & white stripes/green/green
Change colours: Blue/red
Midweek Matches: Tuesday
Programme: 8 pages, 30p
CLUB PERSONNEL
President: R Brady
Chairman: Allan Wilson
Vice Chairman: Ray Sharp
Press Officer: John Taylor
Manager: Dereck Birrell
Asst Manager: Jim Capstick
Coach: Jim Ballantyne
Physio: Mark Hetherington

LEEK C.S.O.B.

Secretary: Stan Lockett, 5 Fitzherbert Close, Swynnerton, Stone, Staffs ST150PQ,
Tel: 01782 796062 (H) 0944 493106 (M)

Ground: Harrison Park, Macclesfield Road, Leek, Staffs,   Tel: 01538 383734
Club Email: stan@slockett.freeserve.co.uk

Directions: M6 south Junc 17, A534 to Congleton - follow signs for Leek (A54), carry on to junction with A523, right onto A523, this road is direct to Leek, ground 8 miles on right just into Leek.

Capacity: 3,600   Seating: 625   Covered Terracing: 2,675   Floodlights: Yes

PREVIOUS	**Leagues:** Leek & Moorland Lge, Staffs County North, Refuge Midland Lge.
RECORDS	**Attendance:** 293 v Tamworth F.A.Cup 1998-99
BEST SEASON	**FA Cup:** 3rd Q 98-99 **FA Vase:**
HONOURS	Refuge Midland Lge 95-96. Lge Cup 94-95 95-96; Leek Cup 94-95 95-96; Midland Ref Charity Shield 95-96; Sportsline Chall Cup 95-96. NWCL Div. 1 winners - Programme of the Year 2000/01

FACT FILE
Founded: 1945
Colours: Red & white stripes/white/red
Change colours: All Yellow
Midweek Matchday:Tuesday
Programme: Yes   Editor: Stan Lockett
CLUB PERSONNEL
Chairman: K J Hill, 11 Springfield Drive, Leek,
Staffs ST13 Tel: 01538 371859
Manager: Chris McMullen
Asst Man: Andrew Walters
Physio: Keith Tatton & Paul Tatton
2001-02
Leading goalscorer: Lee Fower 10
Captain: Simon Tweats P.o.Y.: Russell Clarke

MAINE ROAD

Secretary: Derek Barber, Flat 4, Maple Court, 259 Wellington Rd., Heaton Moor, Stockport SK4 5BS (0161 431 8243) **Ground:** Manchester County FA Ground, Brantingham Rd., Chorlton-cum-Hardy, Manchester M21 0TT (0161 861 0344) **Directions:** M60 Jct 7, A56 towards City Centre, right onto A5145 Chorlton/Stockport, thro' lights, left at next lights into Wilbraham Rd (A6010) to Chorlton, thro' lights for approx 1 mile. Left into Withington Rd, first left into Brantingham Rd, ground 300 yds on left. 2 miles from Stretford (Metrolink (tram)), 3 miles from Piccadilly & Victoria , Virgin & First North Western trains. Buses16 16A 85 87 87A 168 188 275.

Clubhouse: Matchdays (Snacks on ground) **Shop:** No.

Capacity: 2,000   Seats: 200   Cover: 700   Floodlights: Yes.

HONOURS	Manc. Prem. Lg(4) 82-86, Cup 82-83 83-84;98-98 Man.Co Prem. Cup 87-8 Chal. Cup(4) 82-83 84-87; NW Co's Lg Div 2 89-90 (R-up 88-89).
Previous Leagues:	Rusholme Sunday 55-66; Manchester Amtr Sunday 66-72; Manchester 72-87
BEST SEASON	**FA Cup:** 2nd Qual. 2nd replay 92-93 **FA Vase:** 4th Rd 94-95
RECORDS	**Attendance:** 875 v Altrincham, FA Cup 2nd Qual. Rd 29/9/90

FACT FILE
Founded: 1955 Nickname: Blues
Sponsors:Parry's Jewellers
Colours: Blue/blue/yellow
Change Colours: Yellow, Green,Yellow
Midweek matchday: Tuesday
Reserves ' League: NW Co's Lge Res. Div.
Programme: 48 pages £1.00
Editor: Mr P,Ramsden (0161 448 1659)
CLUB PERSONNEL
Chairman: R Meredith
President: F G Thompson
Press Officer: P Ramsden
Manager: Chris Simms
Physio: E Jenkinson

NELSON

Secretary: Paul Wilson, 56 Gisburn Road,Barrowford, Nelson BB9 8NG (01282 618803)

Ground: Victoria Park, Lomeshaye Way, Nelson, Lancs (01282 613820)

Directions: M65 jct 13, 1st left (A6068 Fence), 2nd left (B6249 for Nelson),2nd right sign Lomeshaye Village to grd

Capacity: 1500   Seats:150Cover: 200   Floodlights: Yes

Clubhouse: Bar open matchdays   **Club Shop:** Yes

HONOURS	Lancs Lge 54-55; Lancs Comb. 1949-50 51-52; Lg Cup 49-50 50-51 59-60; Bridge Shield 75-76 81-82; Lancs Jnr Cup 54-55; N.W.C. Div 2 Cup 96-97.
BEST SEASON	**FA Cup:** 2nd Rd Proper 30-31(replay) **FA Vase:** 2nd Prelim Rd 2001-02
PREVIOUS	**Leagues:** Lancashire 1889-98 1900-01; Football League 1898-1900; Lancashire Comb. 01-16 46-82; N.W.C. 82-88; West Lancashire 88-92.

FACT FILE
Founded: 1881
Nickname: Blues
Colours: Blue & white stripes/bluek/blue
Change colours: Gold and blue.
Midweek matchday: TuesdayReserve League:
N.W.C. Res. Div.
Website: www.nelsonfc.co.uk

CLUB PERSONNEL
Director: A.Pickering
Club Secretary: L.Treitl
Treasurer: S.Smith
Manager: John Bailey
Assistant Manager:Andy Wych

NORTON UNITED

Secretary: Dennis Vicker, 86 Ford Green Road, Smallthorne, Stoke-on-Trent ST6 1NX
Tel: 01782 822727 (H) 01785 354200 (B)

Ground: Norton CC & MWI, Community Drive, Smallthorne, Stoke-on-Trent
Tel: 01782 838290

Directions: M6 J16, A500 to BUrslem/Tunstall, turn off on A527, bear right at traffic island to Burslem,

through lights to Smallthorne, take 3rd exit on mini roundabout, turn right by pedestrian crossing into Community Drive, ground 200 metres on left.
Nearest Station: Stoke-on-Trent (mainline) Longport (local)

PREVIOUS **League:** Midland League to 2001

RECORDS **Attendance:** 165 v Alsager Town 2002

HONOURS Midland League - Champions 00-01 98-99 96-97, League Cup 00-01 96-97 91-92;
Staffs FA Senior Vase 98-99

FACT FILE
Founded: 1989
Colours: Black & white stripes/black/black
Change Cols.: Red & black stripes/white/white
Midweek Matchday: Wednesday
Programme:

CLUB PERSONNEL
Chairman
Stephen Beaumont
8 Maitland Grove, Trentham, Stoke-on-Trent.
Tel: 01782 642321 (H)

OLDHAM TOWN

Secretary: Billy O'Niel,WhitebankStadium, Whitebank Road,Oldham.OL8 3JH (0161 624 2689)
Ground: Whitebank Stadium, Whitebank Rd, Hollins, Oldham, Lancs OL8 3JH(0161 624 2689)
Directions: M62 jct 18, M66 to Heaton Pk, right on to A576, left at 2nd lights on to A6104, follow Victoria Ave. on to Hollinwood Ave. under bridge to roundabout take 2nd exit onto Hollins Road, follow Hollins Rd for one & a half miles to Fire Station, left on through gate leading onto Elm Rd and follow to next left, Whitebank Rd on left.

Capacity: 1,000 Seats: 101 Cover: Yes Floodlights: Yes
Clubhouse: Open evenings and matchdays
HONOURS NWC: Div 2 97-98, R-up 94-95; Div 3 R-up 85--86; Lg.Champions 97-98
Res Div R-up 94-95, Cup 94/95:

PREVIOUS **Leagues:** Manchester Amateur; Lancashire Comb. 81-82.

BEST SEASON FA Cup: FA Vase:

RECORD **Attendance:** 495 v Halifax Town, 1996.

FACT FILE
Founded: 1964
Colours: Blue,white,blue
Change Colours:
Midweek Matches: Tuesday
Programme: 16 pages, 50p
Editor: Secretary

CLUB PERSONNEL
Chairman: Ken Hughes
Manager: Len Cantello

PADIHAM

Secretary: Alan Smith,242 Burnley Road, Padiham, Lancs. BB112 8SS (01282 771963)
Ground: Arbories Memorial Sports Ground, Well Street, Padiham, Lancs. BB12 8LE
Tel: 01282 773742   e-mail: brooks@household60.freeserve.co.uk

Directions: M65, J8, then follow A6068 (signed Clitheroe & Padiham). At lights at bottom of hill, turn right into Dean Range/Blackburn Road towards Padiham. At the next junction turn into Holland street opposite church, then into Well Street at the side of the Hare & Hounds pub to the ground. Nearest rail station: Burnley
Floodlights: No

Honours Lancs Amateur Cup R-up 66, Lancs Amateur Shield R-up 97, Burnley, Pendle & Rossendale Hosp. Cup 96, R-up 91; Lancs Comb. Trophy 81, R-up 82; NWC Div. 3 R-up 83-84; W. Lancs Div.1 99-00, Div.2 71-72 76-77 R-up 96-97, Pres. Cup R-up 79 94 97; E. Lancs Amat Lge R-up 06-07 **Best Season:** FA Cup: Third Rd., 1883-84
PreviousLeagues: Lancashire Comb.; NW Counties; West Lancs.; N.E. Lancs;
NE Lancs Combination; East Lancs Amateur Lge.

FACT FILE
Formed: 1878
Colours: Royal blue & white/white/red
Change: Red & black/black/black
Midweek Matchday: Wednesday

Chairman: Mick Muldoon
Brook Foot Farm Barn, Grove Lane,
Padiham, Lancs.
Tel: 01282 778831

STAND ATHLETIC

Secretary: Dave jackson, 26 BrookdeneRoad, Unsworth,Bury Bl9 8ND (061796 0353)
Football & Fixture Secretary: Alan C Davis, 86 Polefield Rd., Prestwich, Manchester M25 2QW
0161 773 9196 (H) 0161 773 9191 (F) 07957 638332 (M)

Ground: Ewood Bridge, Manchester Road, Haslingden, Lancs. BB4 6JY
Tel: 01706 217814
Directions: M66 northbound, exit at Blackburn/Clitheroe turn-off. keep in left hand lane to roundabout, turn left passing Haslingden Cricket Club on rhs, follow road to bottom of hill, around a sharp left-hand bend. Ground is 100 yards on right.
Capacity: Floodlights: Yes
PREVIOUS **Leagues:** Bury Amateur, South East Lancs., Lancs & Cheshire, Manchester to 01.
HONOURS Manchester League Prem Div. 98-99 99-00 00-01, Div.1 94-95
Manchester Chall. Trophy 94-95; Manchester County Cup R-up 95-96;
Lancs. Amateur Shield R-up 00-01

FACT FILE
Founded: 1964
Colours: Blue & yellow/blue/blue
Change cols: Red & black stripes/black/black
Midweek Matchday: Tuesday

CLUB PERSONNEL
Chairman: Pat Walsh

STONE DOMINOES

Secretary: Vicky Turner, Springbank House, Station Road, Barlaston, Staffs ST12 9DE
Tel No: 01782 373298 (H) 07866 096198 (M)

Ground: Springbank Park, Yarnfield Lane, Yarnfield, nr Stone, Staffs. Tel: 01785 761891
Directions: M6 South , J15, take A500 to A34, take south route to Stone (5 miles), through
traffic lights to Walton Hotel (still on A34), turn right to Yarnfield Lane, approx. 2
miles over M6, ground on left before entering village
Nearest rail station: Stoke/Stone　　　　　　　Floodlights: Yes

Honours: Midland League Div. 1 99-00, Div. 2 R-up 96-97,
Div.1 Cup 98-99, Div. 2 Cup 96-97, Charity Shield 00

Previous League: Midland League

Record Attendance: 124 v Audley, Staffs. Vase Nov. 99

FACT FILE

Formed: 1987
Colours: Red/black/black
Midweek Matchday: Tuesday

Chairman: Bob Bowers
Springbank House, Station Road,
Barlaston, Staffs.
Tel: 01782 373298 (H) 01785 815551 (B)

Billingham Town's Stuart Jackson clears from Bishop Auckland's Tony Nelson in the Durham Senior Cup Final, which Bishop Auckland won 1-0. Photo: Alan Watson

Leigh Grant (9) fires past Ripley Town's Shaun Machin to pull his side Graham St Prims back to 4-5 in the Derbyshire Senior Cup. Ripley Town won the tie 7-4. Photo: Bill Wheatcroft

Kirkham & Wesham FC, winners of the West Cheshire League Premier Division 1999-00, 2000-01 and 2001-02

Eric Crompton (Chairman) and Graham Randle (Secretary) of Charnock Richard FC, winners of the Lancashire FA Challenge Shield 2001-02 against the holders, Kirkham & Wesham

Lytham St Annes, winners of the Tavern Cup, 5-0 against Milnthorpe Corinthians. Back Row (l-r): Steve Ramsdale, Paul Allen, Andy Lavin, Paul Wright, Matt Hodson, Paul Maddison, Tom Grey, Tom Duerden, Mark Williams (Manager), Mike Wilson. Front Row: Mike Ewart, Dave Barrow, Steve Lilley (Capt), Danny Hetherington

LIVERPOOL COUNTY FOOTBALL COMBINATION

President: Lord Pendry   **Chairman:** H E Humphries
Secretary: J F Deal, 24 The Pastures, Crossens, Southport PR9 8RH   Tel: 01704 211955

2001-02 was another incident packed season for the Frank Armitt Liverpool County Combination with success achieved on the field of play but failure off the pitch with the collapse of the merger talks with the I Zingari League.

The season started in optimistic mood with the reformation of a Second Division after a two year absence with the introduciton of four new clubs. In order to re-establish the Second Division, the bottom three from the First Division were relegated to provide for a seven-club division. This was hardly an ideal number but just enough to get the new division off the ground.

Once again our clubs showed their domination of amateur football in Liverpool. This was most clearly seen in the Liverpool County FA Challenge Cup where we had six representatives in the quarter-finals and all four in the semi-finals.

Saint Aloysius had their greatest season in their 68 year history, heading the First Division virtually from start to finish and achieved a tremendous level of consistency throughout the season and deservedly won the championship with a six point margin. In their first season in the Liverpool County FA Challenge Cup they edged out South Liverpool in the final by a deflected sizzling shot from Danny Walker in extra time.

In the Second Division Tuebrook went one better than the Aly's, a terrific treble saw them take the Second Division title by a healthy seven point margin, the Second Division League Cup with a 4-0 win and most prestigious of all, the Liverpool County FA Junir Cup with a 2-1 win over Aintree Villa Reserves in the final.

It was Saint Dominics turn to win the Lancashire Amateur Cup, defeating Manweb from the West Cheshire League by the only goal in the final. Waterloo Dock came within a whisker of taking the Northern Counties Championship, going down 2-1 in the final to Northbank of the Northern Alliance, while the previous season's team of the season, Yorkshire Copper Tube, found some consolation during a season disrupted by injury and suspensions by taking The President's Cup with a 3-1 win over Mossley Hill Athletic.

Whilst things went very well on the field there were several disappointments off it, most notably the failure of the merger proposals with the I-Zingari League. In the short term, this is a disaster for the health of the amateur game in Liverpool as the development of a pyramid structure is a necessity to ensure that teams play at the correct level fc. their facilities and playing strength. Nevertheless, as the city's representative at "level four" of the non-league game, the County Combination will continue to make great efforts to achieve innovations required for the game in the city.

The other main disappointment was the demise of Crawfords in October. One of the mainstays of the league for the last twenty years or so, the loss of many of their best players in theclose season and a poor start to the new season. The end came suddenly after a 6-1 thrashing by Saint Aloysius. It was a sad day for the game in Liverpool.

FINAL LEAGUE TABLE 2001-02

FIRST DIVISION

| | | P | Home | | | | | Away | | | | | | |
			W	D	L	F	A	W	D	L	F	A	GD	Pts
1	Saint Aloysius	24	10	1	1	34	15	7	3	2	30	12	37	55
2	Speke	24	6	2	4	25	20	9	2	1	23	13	18	49
3	Waterloo Dock	24	5	5	2	37	18	7	3	2	45	16	48	44
4	Yorkshire Copper Tube	24	8	1	3	35	14	6	1	5	20	11	30	44
5	Saint Dominics	24	7	2	3	25	16	6	2	4	38	28	19	43
6	Lucas Sports	24	6	3	3	35	16	6	3	3	29	15	33	42
7	South Liverpool	24	4	2	6	18	20	6	4	2	17	10	5	36
8	Halewood Town	24	5	2	5	23	20	5	1	6	17	30	-10	33
9	Mossley Hill Athletic	24	5	2	5	22	22	4	3	5	22	24	-2	32
10	Royal Seaforth	24	3	6	3	21	20	2	2	8	21	34	-12	23
11	Ford Motors	24	2	1	9	13	27	2	1	9	21	59	-52	14
12	Prescot Leisure	24	3	1	8	17	40	1	1	10	13	42	-52	14
13	Marconi	24	2	1	9	23	52	0	2	10	14	44	-59	11

SECOND DIVISION

| | | P | Home | | | | | Away | | | | | | |
			W	D	L	F	A	W	D	L	F	A	GD	Pts
1	Tuebrook	24	8	2	2	49	19	9	2	1	37	17	50	55
2	Birchfield	24	7	1	4	28	21	8	2	2	34	14	27	48
3	REMYCA United	24	6	1	5	29	18	8	2	2	38	19	30	45
4	Cheshire Lines	24	8	4	0	28	15	5	1	6	18	27	4	44
5	South Sefton Borough	24	2	4	7	25	31	3	2	7	28	29	-7	20
6	Earle	24	1	1	10	14	39	2	4	6	16	33	-42	14
7	Formby Reserves	24	2	1	9	10	44	2	0	10	16	44	-62	13

LEADING GOALSCORERS

FIRST DIVISION

		Lge	Cup	Tot.
Brian Burns	Yorkshire CT	23	17	40
Jeff Dodd	Saint Dominics	26	12	38
Lee Battle	Waterloo Dock	28	8	36
John Conway	Saint Aloysius	17	8	25
Alex Bishop	South Liverpool	12	9	21
Mark Carney	Saint Dominics	9	12	21
Terry Jones	Saint Aloysius	16	2	18
James Kelle	Mossley Hill Athletic	11	7	18

		Lge	Cup	Tot.
James Hodgson	Lucas Sports	16	1	17
John Edwards	Waterloo Dock	13	4	17
Steve Scales	Yorkshire CT	5	11	16
Adam Williams	Waterloo Dock	10	5	15
Chris McGrath	Mossley Hill Athletic	8	7	15

SECOND DIVISION

		Lge	Cup	Tot.
Gary Hughes	Tuebrook	34	16	50
Colin Toole	REMYCA Utd	31	7	38
Terry Murphy	Birchfield	22	2	24

DIVISION ONE RESULTS CHART 2002-02

		1	2	3	4	5	6	7	8	9	10	11	12	13	14
1	Crawfords UB	X	-	-	1-3	-	-	-	0-6	-	2-1	-	-	-	-
2	Ford Motors	-	X	3-4	0-1	5-0	0-2	2-0	0-6	0-0	2-3	1-5	0-8	0-7	0-1
3	Halewood Town	-	3-0	X	1-0	7-1	2-2	3-1	2-2	0-1	0-2	2-0	2-5	0-4	1-2
4	Lucas Sports	-	9-1	4-0	X	5-2	1-2	4-1	6-0	0-0	0-0	0-0	4-2	2-4	0-4
5	Marconi	-	4-6	7-2	0-9	X	1-0	5-3	3-5	0-2	0-4	2-7	2-4	0-8	0-2
6	Mossley Hill Athletic	-	1-1	3-1	1-2	3-1	X	3-0	4-3	0-1	2-2	1-4	2-4	1-3	1-0
7	Prescot Leisure	-	3-2	1-2	0-6	2-1	1-5	X	2-0	1-1	2-3	1-3	3-4	0-6	1-7
8	Royal Seaforth	2-2	4-0	0-1	1-1	2-2	1-4	2-2	X	2-1	1-2	2-1	3-3	2-2	1-1
9	South Liverpool	-	2-5	1-2	0-1	2-2	1-1	2-1	5-0	X	0-1	0-1	2-0	2-6	1-0
10	Speke	-	2-0	1-2	2-1	5-3	3-1	1-2	2-1	2-3	X	1-1	5-2	1-1	0-3
11	St Aloysius	3-3	4-2	4-1	2-2	3-2	4-1	5-2	2-0	2-1	0-2	X	2-0	4-1	2-0
12	St Dominics	5-2	5-2	3-0	2-2	2-0	4-2	1-0	2-1	1-3	0-1	0-2	X	3-3	2-0
13	Waterloo Dock	3-2	6-1	1-1	5-2	7-0	1-1	5-0	3-3	1-1	2-3	3-3	1-3	X	2-0
14	Yorkshire C T	-	6-1	2-1	1-2	1-0	5-1	9-1	3-0	1-3	4-0	0-3	2-2	1-0	X

Crawfords United Biscuits withdrew during the season. Their records are shown in the chart above but have been expunged from the league table.

CONSTITUTION 2002-03

BIRCHFIELD
Edge Hill College, St Helens Road,
Ormskirk, Merseyside
Tel: 01695 575171

CHESHIRE LINES
Southmead Road, Allerton,
Liverpool, Merseyside
Tel: 0151 427 7176

EARLE
Arncliff Centre, Earle, Liverpool,
Merseyside

FORD MOTORS
Ford Sports & Social Club, Cronton
Lane, Widnes
Tel: 0151 424708

FORMBY RESERVES
Brows Lane, Formby, Merseyside
Tel: 01704 833505

HALEWOOD TOWN
Hollies, Hollies Road, Halewood,
Merseyside
Tel: 0151 443 2063

LUCAS SPORTS
Arncliff Centre, Earle, Liverpool

MARCONI
Whitefield, Roby Road, Huyton
Tel: 0151 489 1031

MOSSLEY HILL ATHLETIC
Athletic Club, Mossley Hill Road,
Liverpool
Tel: 0151 724 4377

PRESCOT LEISURE
Wood Lane, Prescot, Merseyside

REMYCA UNITED
Pimbley Field, Maghull, Liverpool

ROYAL SEAFORTH
Edinburgh Park, Townsend Lane,
Liverpool, Merseyside
Tel: 0151 263 5185

SOUTH LIVERPOOL
The Pavilions Sports Ground,
Sandy Lane, Weston Point,
Runcorn, Cheshire
Tel: 01928 590508

SOUTH SEFTON BOROUGH
Orrell Mount, Liverpool, Merseyside

SPEKE
Speke Hall Avenue, Speke,
Liverpool, Merseyside
Tel: 0151 486 1588

ST ALOYSIUS
Edinburgh Park, Townsend Lane,
Liverpool, Merseyside
Tel: 0151 263 5267

ST DOMINICS
St Dominics School, Lordens Road,
Huyton, Merseyside
Tel: 0151 489 2798

TUEBROOK
Bootle Sports Centre, Maguire
Avenue, Bootle, Merseyside

WATERLOO DOCK
Edinburgh Park, Townsend Lane,
Liverpool, Merseyside
Tel: 0151 263 5267

CARLSBERG WEST CHESHIRE A.F.L.
Founded 1892
President: Ken Halsall
Chairman & Hon. Treasurer: Ray Prescott
Hon. General & Fixtures Secretary: Arthur Green, 46 Bertram Drive, Meols, Wirral CH47 0LH
Tel/fax: 0151 6324946   Email: arthurlgreen@hotmail.com   www.west-cheshire.org.uk

Not until the final whistle blew in their last game, when a late goal by opponents Heswall would have seen Cammell Lairds retaining their title, were Christleton confirmed as League champions.

Earlier in the campaign such a thrilling finale had not appeared likely with Lairds building up a significant advantage only for Christleton to string together a long sequence of wins, culminating with a vital one over their rivals. From then on neither side seemed keen to take the title with both dropping vital points before that final dramatic evening.

Christleton also had their regular success in the Chester Senior Cup while Lairds had considerable consolation in lifting the Pyke and Wirral Senior Cups.

Too many drawn games cost third placed Poulton Vics a stake in the title race, while they had to be content with being losing finalists in the Wirral Senior. Newton had their best season for many years, coupling fourth spot with a journey to the Cheshire Amateur Cup final. Vauxhall Reserves, finishing just below Newton, also lost out to them in the Cheshire semis, while Aintree Villa completed their first season in Division One in a creditable sixth spot. Immediately below them were fellow promoted side Manweb, who also fought their way to the Lancashire Amateur Cup final, while Shell improved on last season's position by three places. Heswall had a mediocre campaign by their standards and Maghull slipped back into mid table having finished fourth twelve months earlier.

A number of teams were casting anxious looks over their shoulders as the season entered its closing stages. Helsby lost their three year grip on the Runcorn Senior and also lost out in the Pyke final, but were able to maintain Division One status, while an excellent run-in took General Chemicals (Runcorn Senior Cup winners on penalties) clear of danger and Stork were always just above the drop zone. Ashville's change of managers still couldn't prevent a bottom two finish, while Mond Rangers lingered as table trailers virtually throughout the whole campaign, picking up just two wins all season.

HONOURS BOARD 2001-02

	Winners	Runners Up
Division One	Christleton	Cammell Laird
Division Two	Mallaby	Castrol Social
Division Three	Maghull Reserves	Aintree Villa Reserves
Pyke Challenge Cup	Cammell Laird	Helsby
West Cheshire Bowl	Christleton Reserves	Heswall Reserves
West Cheshire Shield	New Brighton Reserves	Grange Athletic
Cheshire Amateur Cup	Barnton	Newton
Lancashire Amateur Cup	St Dominics	Manweb
Chester Senior Cup	Christleton	Chester Nomads
Liverpool Junior Cup	Tuebrook	Aintree Villa Reserves
Runcorn Challenge Cup	General Chemicals	Helsby
Wirral Senior Cup	Cammell Laird	Poulton Victoria
Wirral Amateur Cup	Castrol Social	Grange Athletic
Bill Weight Memorial Cup	Aintree Villa/Cammell Laird (shared)	
Carlsberg Shoot Out	Maghull	Newton
Cooper Smith Trophy	Mid-Cheshire AFL	West Cheshire AFL

FINAL LEAGUE TABLES 2001-02

DIVISION ONE

	P	W	D	L	F	A	Pts
Christleton	30	20	6	4	57	32	66
Cammell Laird	30	20	4	6	71	40	64
Poulton Victoria	30	17	9	4	70	35	60
Newton	30	15	4	11	53	42	49
Vauxhall M Res	30	13	7	10	54	38	46
Aintree Villa	30	12	8	10	51	52	44
Manweb	30	11	9	10	51	51	42
Shell	30	12	4	14	46	46	40
Heswall	30	12	3	15	45	51	39
Maghull	30	10	8	12	44	48	38
Helsby	30	10	6	14	56	61	36
General Chemicals	30	10	6	14	46	64	36
Stork	30	10	5	15	49	52	35
Mersey Royal	30	10	4	16	49	62	34
Ashville	30	8	7	15	47	60	31
Mond Rangers	30	2	6	22	30	85	12

DIVISION TWO

	P	W	D	L	F	A	Pts
Mallaby	30	22	4	4	103	35	70
Castrol Social	30	17	5	8	50	31	56
Blacon YC	30	15	6	9	61	40	51
West Kirby	30	12	10	8	56	45	46
Christleton Reserves	30	14	5	11	53	43	47
Pavilions	30	13	7	10	50	49	46
Poulton Vics Res	30	13	6	11	61	54	45
New Brighton	30	14	3	13	54	49	45
Capenhurst Villa	30	10	11	9	56	58	40
Upton AA	30	11	3	16	49	55	36
Manor Athletic	30	11	3	16	51	62	36
Merseyside Police	30	11	3	16	45	64	36
Cammell Laird Res	30	8	11	11	44	53	35
Heswall Res	30	8	7	15	52	69	31
Mersey Royal Res	30	9	4	17	53	92	31
Ashville Reserves	30	7	2	21	41	80	23

DIVISION ONE RESULTS CHART 2001-02

		1	2	3	4	5	6	7	8	9	10	11	12	13	14	15	16
1	Aintree Villa	X	0-4	1-3	0-1	2-2	4-0	1-1	0-4	1-1	2-1	2-1	0-4	4-3	2-0	3-2	1-1
2	Ashville	1-1	X	2-2	0-2	0-1	3-1	1-4	1-2	2-5	0-2	1-1	1-2	1-1	2-1	1-0	2-2
3	Cammell Laird	2-0	3-0	X	4-2	4-2	4-1	3-0	3-2	2-2	4-1	3-1	2-1	1-2	1-0	3-1	2-1
4	Christleton	1-0	2-1	1-2	X	0-1	1-1	2-0	1-1	2-2	2-0	2-2	2-0	2-2	2-1	3-2	3-2
5	General Chemicals	2-2	0-0	3-3	2-1	X	1-6	0-1	6-0	2-3	0-3	4-1	0-4	0-4	2-1	2-1	1-3
6	Helsby	2-4	5-1	0-0	1-3	1-1	X	1-3	0-5	0-1	3-2	1-1	1-2	2-3	1-2	3-2	1-1
7	Heswall	0-3	3-5	4-2	1-0	0-1	1-3	X	0-0	4-1	0-2	3-1	2-1	0-4	1-6	2-4	1-2
8	Maghull	0-3	1-2	1-3	1-0	4-3	1-2	0-2	X	0-0	2-1	4-0	0-1	1-1	1-1	1-1	3-1
9	Manweb	2-2	2-1	1-0	1-2	1-2	1-1	1-0	2-4	X	3-3	0-2	5-2	2-2	2-1	1-2	0-2
10	Mersey Royal	0-3	2-1	3-0	2-4	3-0	2-5	0-5	1-1	4-1	X	4-1	1-2	3-5	1-3	2-1	0-1
11	Mond Rangers	1-2	1-6	1-4	1-5	1-3	2-8	1-0	1-2	1-3	2-2	X	0-7	1-4	0-2	0-1	2-2
12	Newton	3-2	1-1	0-3	1-3	3-2	1-3	3-0	0-0	1-2	1-1	3-1	X	2-1	1-1	2-1	2-0
13	Poulton Victoria	3-1	4-0	2-4	0-0	2-0	4-0	1-1	4-1	3-1	2-0	1-1	0-1	X	2-1	3-2	1-1
14	Shell	0-3	1-4	1-2	1-2	5-1	1-0	1-2	2-1	0-0	2-0	3-2	3-2	0-3	X	1-1	2-1
15	Stork	2-2	4-3	0-2	1-2	1-1	4-0	0-3	3-1	1-5	1-2	2-0	3-0	0-1	3-1	X	1-0
16	Vauxhall	5-0	4-0	3-1	1-2	4-1	0-3	0-2	3-0	2-0	5-1	1-0	1-0	2-2	1-2	2-2	X

CARLSBERG MANAGERS OF THE MONTH

August	Mark Yeardsley	Grange Athletic	January	John McHugh	Capenhurst Villa
September	Mike Keeley	Cammell Laird	February	John Brett	Mallaby
October	John McInnes	Maghull Reserves	March	Gary Moore	General Chemicals
November	Peter Fearon	Heswall	April	Peter Kavanagh	Castrol Social
December	Dave Tills	Christleton			

TOP SCORERS 2001-02

(League and Cup)

Chris McGinn	Cammell Laird	38	Chris Herbert	St Werburghs (Div 3)	24
Craig Cartwright	Mersey Royal	31	Lee Hunt	Helsby	24
Gary Tyrrell	Helsby	28	Scott Johnson	Manweb	24
Chris Barrow	Mallaby	*27	Mike Wilde	West Kirby	**24
Gordon Harrison	Heswall	27	John Goodall	Mallaby	23
Alan Hooley	St Werburghs (Div 3)	26	Mark Galer	Mallaby	22
Mike Riley	Poulton Victoria	25			
Robbie Cowley	Newton	24	* 2 with Poulton Victoria		
			**4 with Ashville		

AINTREE VILLA
Chairman: John Gregson   Formed: 1954
Secretary: Alf Shepherd, 154 Altway, Aintree, Liverpool L10 6LG
Tel: 0151 526 9287 (H)
Ground: Aintree racecourse.
Colours: Tangerine/white/white
Sponsors: Woolton Carpets/Aintree Conservative Club

ASHVILLE
Chairman: Eddie Parker   **Club Formed:** 1949
Secretary: Dave Walton, 15 Wellesley Road, Wallasey, Wirral,
Merseyside, L445UR Tel: 0151 639 9196
Ground: Villa Park, Cross Lane, Wallasey Village, Wallasey,
Tel: 0151 638 2127   Colours: White & black/black/black
Sponsors: Kelly Sports & West Wallasey Van Hire.

CAMMELL LAIRD
Chairman: Ray Steele
Secretary: Anthony R wood, 25 Prenton Park Rd,Prenton,Birkenh'd,
MerseysideCh42 8JR Tel Nos: 0151 608 0591(H) 07931 761429 (M)
Ground: Kirklands, St Peters Road, Rock Ferry, Birkenhead
Tel: 0151 645 5991   Colours: All blue   Formed: 1906
Sponsors:Hallmark Cleaning SAervices

CHRISTLETON
Chairman: Ron Mayers
Secretary: Ken Price, 35 Canadian Ave, Hoole, Chester CH2 3HQ
Tel: 01244 313513
Ground: Little Heath, Christleton Tel: 01244 332153
Colours: Red/black/red   Formed 1897 Re-Formed: 1966
Sponsors: Allans Skip Hire

GENERAL CHEMICALS
Chairman: Dave Robinson
Secretary: Tony Riley 171 Cotton Lane, Runcorn, Cheshire WA7 5JB
Tel: 01928 565390
Ground: Picow Farm Road, Runcorn
Colours: Blue & white/blue/blue & white   Formed: 1958
Sponsors: Maltacourt Ltd

HELSBY
Chairman: John Close
Secretary: John Evans, 35 Hill View Ave., Helsby, Ches. WA6 0ES
Tel: 01928 724817 (H)
Ground: Helsby Sports & Social Club Tel: 01928 722267
Colours: White/green/green   Formed: 1895
Sponsors: Brand - Rex EVC. & Helsby Sports & Social Club

HESWALL
Chairman: Brian Flanagan
Secretary: Jake Horan ,13 Reedville Rd, Bebington, Wirral L63 2HS
Tel: 0151 644 0459
Ground: Gayton Pk,Brimstage Rd, Heswall, Wirral Tel:01513428172
Colours: Yellow/royal blue/yellow   Formed: 1891
Sponsors: Pyramids Shopping Centre

MAGHULL
Chairman: Les Jacques **Secretary:** Danny Sherlock, 14 Alexander
Drive, Lydiate, Merseyside L31 2NJ Tel: 0151 526 2306
Ground: Old Hall Field, Hall Lane, Maghull, Merseyside (0151 526
7320) **Directions:** M57 or M58 to end (Switch Island), A59 towards
Preston (Northway)to lights at Hall Lane, right following signs for
Maghull BR. then 200 yds on the left.1/2 m from Maghull (Merseyrail)
Colours: Blue & red stripes/blue/blue **Sponsors:** Soldier of Fortune

MANWEB
Chairman: James Parry   Formed: 1932
John Shimmin, 54 Gonville Rd., Bootle, Merseyside L20 9LR
tel: 0151 933 5763 (H)
Ground: Manweb Sports & Social Club, Thingwall Rd., Liverpool L15
7LB Tel: 0151 281 5364   Colours: White/navy/white
Sponsors: Comasec yate Ltd

MERSEY ROYAL
Chairman: Tony Nelson   **Secretary:** Dave Lawson 7 Mount Park,
Higher Bebington, Wirral L63 5RD Tel: 0151 608 2261
Ground: Bromborough Pool Village, The Green, South View Rd.,
Bromborough Pool. Tel: 0151 645 3476
Colours: Navy & light blue striped shirts   Formed: 1946
Sponsor: E.Casey

MOND RANGERS
Chairman: David Holland
Secretary: Steve Kinsella, 3 Bramble Way, Beechwood, Runcorn,
Cheshire WA7 3HN Tel Nos: 01928 715178 (H) 07867 972919 (W)
Ground: Pavilions Club, Sandy Lane, Weston Point, Runcorn WA7 5EX
Tel: 01928 590508 **Colours:** Blue & black stripes   Formed:1967
Sponsors: Rocksavage Power Co. & Domestic Boiler Services

NEWTON
Chairman: John Murray
Secretary: Alan Dabner, 79A Eleanor Road, Bidston, Wirral CH43
7RW. Tel Nos: 0151 653 2151 (H) 0151 993 2151 (B)
Ground: Millcroft, Frankby Road, Greasby, Wirral Tel: 0151 677 8382
Colours: Yellow/green/yellow   Formed: 1933
Sponsors: Cory Brothers Shipping Ltd.

POULTON VICTORIA
Chairman: Thonas Quinn
Secretary: George Cooper,1 Foxhey Road, Wallasey, Wirral CH44
2ES. Tel Nos: 0151 201 2072 (H) 0151 638 9112 (W)
Ground: Victoria Park, Rankin Street, Wallasey Tel: 0151 638 3559
Colours: All Royal Blue   Formed: 1935
Sponsors: Carlsberg & Bass

SHELL F.C.
Chairman: Gerry Fraser
Secretary: Steven Foden, 23 Hornbeam Avenue, Great Sutton, South
Wirral Ch65 7AQ. Tel Nos: 0151 356 8837 (H) 07941 187632 (M)
Ground: Chester Road, Whitby, Ellesmere Port, South Wirral
Tel: 0151 200 7080 **Colours:** Yellow /navy/navy   Formed: 1924
Sponsors: Abba Security Systems Ltd.

STORK
Chairman: Brian Favengen
Secretary: Steve Carter
7 Elm Road, Bebington, Wirral L63 8PF Tel: 0151 645 6697
Ground: Unilever Sports Ground, Bromborough
Colours: All green   Formed: 1920
Sponsors: The Village Leisure Hotel

VAUXHALL MOTORS RESERVES
Chairman: Tony Woodley
Secretary: Carole Paisey, 26 South Road, West Kirby, Wirral L48
3HQ (0151 6256 936)
Ground: Vauxhall Sports Ground, Rivacre Road, Hooton, Ellesmere
Port (0151 3281114)
Colours: White/royal blue/white   Formed: 1963

BLACON YOUTH CLUB
Chairman: Peter Barnes
Secretary: Colin Lawson,54 Adelaide Rd., Blacon, Chester CH1 5SZ
Tel: 01244 375508 (H)
Ground: Cairns Crescent Playing Fields, Cairns Crescent, Blacon,
Chester. **Colours:** Black & white stripes/black/black **Formed:** 1964
Sponsors: George Starkey Painter & Decorator & McDonalds

CAPENHURST VILLA   Formed: 1952
Chairman: Brian Heyes
Secretary: Martin Williams, 157 Hope Farm Road, Great Sutton,
South Wirral L662TJ Tel: 0151 339 8935
Ground: Capenhurst Sports Ground, Capenhurst Lane, Capenhurst
Tel: 0151 339 4101   **Colours:** All maroon
Sponsors: Handbridge Decorators & Commercial Properties

CASTROL SOCIAL FC   Formed: 1954
Secretary: Mike Caulfield, 2 Weaver Road, Whitby, Ellesmere Port
CH66 2JJ. Tel: 0151 355 5966 (H)
Ground: Castrol Sports & Social Club, Chester Road, Whitby,
Ellesmere Port(0151 355 1730)
Colours: Royal & emerald/royal/white

MALLABY FC   Formed: 1965
Chairman: G M Langan
Secretary: Tommy Kenny, 11 Seeley Ave., Claughton, Birkenhead
CH41 0BX Tel: 0151 653 5925 (H)
Ground: Balaclava, Birkenhead Park.
Colours: Red & black stripes/black/red

MANOR ATHLETIC   Formed: 1968
Chairman: Tony Bell
Secretary: Stewart Galtress, 3 Centurion Close, Meols, Wirral CH47
7BZ Tel: 0151 632 3211 email: s-galtress@hotmail.com
Ground: Unilever Sports Ground, Bromborough
Colours: All royal blue

MERSEYSIDE POLICE   Formed: 1885
Secretary: Gary Dinsmore, 3 Chaffinch Close, West Derby, Liverpool
L12 0NX Tel: 0151 220 0285 (H)
Ground: Police Club, Fairfield, Prescot Road, Liverpool L7 0JD
Tel: 0151 228 2352
Colours: All navy b lue with red trim.

NEW BRIGHTON   Formed: 1993
Secretary: Carl Gidman. 64 Ford Road, Upton, Wirral CH49 0TG Tel:
0151 678 1858 (H/B)
Ground: Harrison Drive, Wallasey Village, Wallasey
Colours: Red & white/white/red & white

PAVILIONS   Formed: 1998
Secretary: Beverley Crilly, 26 Perrin Ave., Weston Point, Runcorn WA7
4BJ Tel: 01928 575938 (H)
Ground: Pavilions Complex, Sandy Lane, Weston Point, Runcorn
Tel: 01928 590508
Colours: Blue & white stripes/blue/blue

UPTON ATHLETIC ASSOC. Formed: 1964
Secretary: Barry Gaulton, 24 St Marks Crescent, Whitby, Ellesmere
Port L66 2XD (0151 339 1504)
Ground: Cheshire County Council Sports & Social Club, Plas Newton
Lane, Chester (01244 318367)
Colours: All blue

WEST KIRBY   Formed: 1895
Secretary: Roy Williamson, 85 Wood Lane, Greasby, Wirral CH49 2PX
Tel: 0151 677 4860 (H)
Ground: Johnston Recreation Ground, Neston Road, Willaston, South
Wirrall.
Colours: White/black/black

plus

Ashville Reserves; Cammell Laird Reserves; Christleton Reserves;
Heswall Reserves; Mersey Royal Reserves; Poulton Victoria Reserves.

25 in 25

A review of the progress made by non-League football and its member clubs during
the twenty-five year life span of the F.A. Non-League Club Directory (1978 - 2002) will be
available in the next year in a series of 25 books containing features, statistics
and photos. The featured Leagues will be:

Western League	South Western League
United Counties	West Midlands
N.W. Counties	Midland Combination
Eastern Counties	Kent
Wessex League	Northern
Midland Alliance	F.A. Cup
F.A. Vase	N.Co. East
Conference	Isthmian League
F.A. Trophy	Northern Premier Lge
England Representative	Southern League
Combined Counties	Spartan S. Midlands
Essex Senior	Sussex League
Hellenic League	

To book your copies of 25 - 25 please use the form at the back of this Directory

THE BASS/WPRC
MID CHESHIRE ASSOCIATION FOOTBALL LEAGUE
Founded 1948

President: R Atherton   **Chairman:** J Walton
Hon. Secretary: G Edgeley, 61 Harris Road, Lostock Gralam,
Northwich, Cheshire CW9 7PE   Tel: 01606 352799

In a season when the weather has been particularly kind the league programme commenced and concluded as planned. Barnton, after a difficult winter period when it seemed they weren't going to be the force of previous years and having been rocked by the sudden resignation of Manager Mark Emmerson, finally rose to the occasion as the year turned to secure the First Division championship with ease. By the end of the season they had also won the elusive Cheshire Amateur Cup, beating West Cheshire rivals Newton FC in a scrappy, ill-tempered final at Chester City.

Rylands came from a comfortable mid-table slot to pip Cheadle Heath Nomads for the runners-up prize, which both pleased, and surprised, even their own followers.

The Final of the Division One Cup, played at Witton Albion on a very wet night, saw Knutsford outplay a strong Padgate St Oswalds team to win 2-0, Padgate having one player sent off.

In Division Two it was a battle of the Warrington-based clubs for honours. New entrants Crosfields and Daten were neck and neck for several weeks behind Golborne Sports, but as the pressure of the end of season approached it all came down to the final games. Crosfields pipped Daten for the coveted Division Two championship trophy by one goal in an exciting season. Daten, meanwhile, having finished second and gained promotion were also the Cinderella club in losing the Division Two Cup Final by 2-1 to Golborne Sports, the latter gaining some comfort for missing out on promotion.

Whilst Trafford Reserves won the Manchester County FA Cup final, the star effort went to Poynton who, having defeated Bollington Athletic on penalties in the Presidents Cup Final, then went on to defeat Cheadle Heath Nomads 24 hours later by a Golden Goal 2-1 scoreline.

During the season the Mid-Cheshire League Representative team humbled their West Cheshire rivals (comprised wholly of Cammell Laird players) 4-0 to retain the Cooper Smith Trophy.

At the League's AGM in June the Vice Chairman Brian Dowd and Treasurer Brian Riley were presented with momentos in becoming Life Members for 21 years service to the League. Knutsford were voted the Team of the Year for excellent administration and players Peter Withers (Crosfields) and Duncan Warrender (Poynton) share the Player of the Year Award.

DIVISION ONE FINAL LEAGUE TABLE 2001-02

			HOME				AWAY						
		P	W	D	L	F	A	W	D	L	F	A	GD	Pts
1	Barnton	28	11	3	0	36	7	7	4	3	29	18	40	61
2	Rylands	28	8	3	3	34	20	7	4	3	31	19	26	52
3	Cheadle Heath	28	8	4	2	26	14	7	3	4	32	21	23	52
4	Knutsford	28	9	2	3	25	12	6	4	4	20	13	20	51
5	Linotype	28	7	1	6	24	22	7	3	4	23	18	7	46
6	Crewe FC	28	4	5	5	23	31	8	2	4	27	28	-9	43
7	Styal	28	6	4	4	26	20	5	4	5	24	25	5	40
8	Pilkington	28	4	4	6	19	25	6	5	3	18	15	-3	39
9	Padgate St Oswalds	28	5	4	5	23	24	5	2	7	25	34	-10	36
10	Poynton	28	4	2	8	21	28	4	5	5	18	24	-13	31
11	Broadheath Central	28	4	3	7	18	27	4	2	8	18	23	-14	29
12	Garswood United	28	4	4	6	15	19	2	4	8	24	37	-17	26
13	Middlewich Town	28	2	5	7	20	21	3	5	6	10	19	-10	25
14	Chorlton Town	28	3	3	8	23	36	4	1	9	17	26	-22	25
15	Trafford REs	28	2	4	8	20	29	3	3	8	19	33	-23	22

DIVISION TWO FINAL LEAGUE TABLE 2001-02

			HOME					AWAY						
		P	W	D	L	F	A	W	D	L	F	A	GD	Pts
1	Crosfields	30	10	2	3	50	23	10	4	1	49	19	57	66
2	Daton	30	9	5	1	54	23	10	4	1	46	21	56	66
3	Golborne Sports	30	9	6	0	47	23	10	2	3	37	14	47	65
4	Malpas	30	7	2	6	41	24	9	2	4	32	28	21	52
5	Whitchurch Alport	30	6	5	4	30	18	8	4	3	45	22	35	51
6	Lostock Gralam	30	7	2	6	27	25	6	6	3	27	23	6	47
7	Bollington Athletic	30	4	4	7	23	27	8	4	3	35	21	10	44
8	Chester Nomads	30	6	3	6	27	29	7	1	7	25	25	-2	43
9	Warrington Bro	30	8	2	5	26	25	5	2	8	25	31	-5	39
10	Linotype Reserves	30	4	5	6	26	34	6	0	9	35	39	-12	35
11	Garswood United Res	30	6	1	8	28	34	3	6	6	21	25	-10	34
12	Poynton Reserves	30	3	5	7	25	35	4	6	5	27	25	-8	32
13	Pilkington Reserves	30	5	3	7	30	41	4	5	6	25	41	-27	32
14	Rylands Reserves	30	4	2	9	21	29	1	2	12	10	56	-54	19
15	Cheadle Heath Reserves	30	3	2	10	24	55	2	2	11	21	52	-62	19
16	Middlewich Town Reserves	30	3	3	9	18	33	1	2	12	18	55	-52	17

DIVISION ONE RESULTS CHART 2001-02

		1	2	3	4	5	6	7	8	9	10	11	12	13	14	15
1	Barnton	X	2-1	3-0	3-0	3-0	2-1	0-0	3-1	3-0	2-2	4-0	4-0	3-1	0-0	4-1
2	Broadheath Central	0-2	X	1-5	0-2	2-4	3-4	2-0	1-2	1-1	3-2	1-0	1-1	0-3	1-1	2-0
3	Cheadle Heath	2-2	2-0	X	2-1	2-3	4-1	2-1	0-0	3-1	2-0	0-1	2-0	0-0	3-3	2-1
4	Chorlton Town	4-4	2-0	0-0	X	1-4	1-5	1-2	1-4	3-1	2-1	0-3	1-2	2-4	3-4	2-2
5	Crewe FC	2-4	3-2	0-6	3-2	X	3-3	1-1	2-2	0-0	0-1	4-2	1-1	2-4	0-2	2-1
6	Garswood United	0-3	1-0	3-1	2-1	0-1	X	0-1	0-1	2-2	0-2	0-0	0-0	2-2	4-2	1-3
7	Knutsford	1-3	0-3	1-1	3-2	5-0	3-0	X	3-1	1-0	2-0	0-1	1-1	1-0	2-0	2-0
8	Linotype	3-1	3-0	3-1	3-1	1-2	2-0	1-4	X	0-2	0-1	0-1	4-3	1-1	2-1	1-4
9	Middlewich Town	1-1	1-1	1-3	1-2	0-1	4-1	0-0	0-2	X	4-4	0-0	1-2	0-2	1-2	6-0
10	Padgate St Oswalds	2-1	1-1	2-4	1-0	1-1	3-1	2-1	1-3	0-1	X	2-2	5-1	1-1	0-4	2-3
11	Pilkington	1-0	2-1	1-2	2-2	2-4	1-1	2-2	1-2	2-0	2-4	X	1-4	0-3	2-0	0-0
12	Poynton	2-3	0-3	1-1	2-3	3-1	2-0	2-1	0-2	0-0	2-3	1-4	X	3-4	1-2	2-1
13	Rylands	0-4	3-1	1-3	3-0	3-0	3-3	0-3	2-1	4-1	6-2	0-0	0-0	X	4-1	5-1
14	Styal	0-0	2-3	3-1	1-0	3-3	3-3	0-1	3-1	0-1	4-2	1-2	2-1	2-0	X	2-2
15	Trafford REs	0-1	1-2	1-4	0-1	2-3	3-1	0-3	1-1	0-0	5-1	2-2	1-2	2-6	2-2	X

CUP RESULTS 2001-02

DIVISION ONE CUP FINAL
Knutsford   2   v   0   Padgate St Oswalds

CHESHIRE AMATEUR CUP
Winners: Barnton

DIVISION TWO CUP FINAL
Golborne Sports   2   v   1   Daten

MANCHESTER COUNTY FA CUP
Winners: Trafford Reserves

PRESIDENTS CUP FINAL
Poynton   1   v   1   Bollington Athletic
Poynton won 4-2 on penalties

LEAGUE REPRESENTATIVE MATCH
Mid Cheshire   4   v   0   West Cheshire
Played at Trafford FC

HONOURS BOARD

DIVISION ONE

	League Champions	Runners Up	League Cup Winners	Runners Up
2001-02	Barnton	Rylands	Knutsford	Padgate St Oswalds

DIVISION TWO

	League Champions	Runners Up	League Cup Winners	Runners Up
2001-02	Crosfields	Daton	Golborne Sports	Daten

BILL GRAY TROPHY - CLUB OF THE SEASON
2001-02   Knutsford

PLAYER OF THE SEASON
2001-02   Peter Withers (Crosfields)
Duncan Warrender (Poynton)

DIVISION ONE CLUBS

BARNTON AFC
Chairman: William Perrin **Manager:** Mark Emmerson
Secretary: Michael Webster, 92 Church Road, Barnton CW8 4JE (01606 782960)
Ground: Townfield, Townfield Lane, Barnton
Colours: Black & White Stripes/Black
Change Colours: Blue & yellow /blue

BROADHEATH CENTRAL FC
Chairman: Ian Beresford **Manager:** Peter Cavanagh
Secretary: David Murphy,113 Downs Drive,Timperley, Altrincham Wa14 5QU (0161 718 0523)
Ground: Viaduct Road, Broadheath, Altrincham
Colours: Black & Red Stripes/Black
Change Colours: Blue & White Stripes/White

CHEADLE HEATH NOMADS
Chairman: Roy Welsh **Manager:** Peter Blundell
Secretary: George Gibbons, 20A Gillbent Road,Cheadle Hulme,SK8 6NB Tel No: 0161 440 9951
Ground: The Heath, Norbreck Ave, Cheadle, Stockport
Colours: Maroon & Sky blue,Maroom/maroon
Change Colours: Yelow & Green/Green/Green

CHORLTON TOWN
Chairman: Peter Grogan **Manager:** Sandy Slater
Secretary: Jim Calderbank, 21 South Meade, Timperley, Altrincham, Cheshire WA15 6QL
Ground: Parkway Ground, Rylstone Avenue,Chorlton
Colours: Red & Black/White/white
Change Colours: Yellow or Blue/Blue/Red

CREWE FC
Chairman: Patrick Slack **Manager:** Ian O'Reilly
Secretary: Mrs M Vickers, 59 Hall-o-Shaw St, Crewe (01270 581578)
Ground: Cumberland Sprts Grnd, Thomas St, Crewe
Colours: Sky Blue/Marooon/White
Change Colours: Yellow/Black/Blue

CROSSFIELDS FC
Chairman: Michael Hickey **Manager:** Derek Evans
Secretary: Frank Whitehouse, 153 Birdwell Drive, Gt. Sankey, Warrington Tel: 01925 728710 (H) 01925 625750 (B)
Ground: Hood Lane Rec., Gt. Sankey, Warrington
Colours: Primrose & blue
Change Colours: Orange & black

DATEN FC
Chairman: Trevor Farrington
Manager: Robert Jones
Secretary: Michael Henshall, 21 Upwood Rd., Lowton, Warrington WA3 2RL Tel: 01942 724471 01772 321800 (B)
Ground: Culcheth Sports Club, Charnock Rd., Culcheth Tel: 01925 763096
Colours: Sky & royal blue
Change Colours: Blue & white stipes/navy

GARSWOOD UNITED FC
Chairman: Barry Mavers **Manager:** Alan Clarke
Secretary: Tony McKeown,44 Dunsdale Drive, Ashton, Wigan WN4 8PT Tel No: 01942 724259
Ground: The Wooders, Simms Lane End, Garswood
Colours: Blue & White Halves/Blue/Blue
Change Colours: All Yellow

KNUTSFORD FC
Chairman: Ken Harrison **Manager:** Srewart Dow
Secretary: Kevin Deeley, 28 East Street, Guide Bridge, Manchester, M34 5DX (0161 320 9650)
Ground: Manchester Road, Knutsford
Colours: Red /Black/Black
Change Colours: Black & White stripes/White/White

LINOTYPE FC
Chairman: James Barry **Manager:** Glyn Williams
Secretary: Brian McGuiness, 36 Barrington Road, Altrincham, Cheshire (0161 929 0021)
Ground: British Airways Club, Clay Lane, Timperley
Colours: White/Black
Change Colours: Red & Black/White/red

MIDDLEWICH TOWN FC
Chairman: Steven Morris **Manager:** David Twite
Secretary: Philip Hassell,1 Whitegate `Close,Middlewich,Cheshire CW10 0RF Tel Nos: 01606 832185 (H) 01606832734 (W)
Ground: Seddon Street, Middlewich (01606 835842)
Colours: Red/Black/Red
Change Colours: White/black

PADGATE ST OSWALDS FC
Chairman: Graham Millins **Manager:** Nick Armitage
Secretary: Brian Hughes, 13 Jubilee Ave, Padgate, Warrington WA1 3JY (01925 490924)
Ground: Bennets Rec. Ground, Station Rd, Padgate
Colours: White /Black/White
Change Colours: Yellow/Green/Yellow

PILKINGTON AFC
Chairman: Barry Meadows **Manager:** David Burrows
Secretary: Kevin Guy,22 Ennerdale Avenue,Ashton -in-Makerfield WN4 5BA Tel No: 01942 723693
Ground: Ruskin Drive, St Helens
Colours: Sky blue 7navy,navy/navy
Change Colours: Red & black/red/red

POYNTON
Chairman: David Corcoran **Manager:** Charlie Jones
Secretary: Mark Warburton, 27 Alderley Close, Hazel Grove, Stockport SK7 6BS (01625 873872)
Ground: London Road North, Poynton
Colours: Red & Black/Black/Red
Change Colours: Blue & White/Blue/Blue

RYLANDS FC
Chairman: Alan Jackson **Manager:** Terry Selby
Secretary: Ian Finchett, 31 Elizabeth Drive, Padgate, Warrington WA1 4JQ (01925 816911)
Ground: Rylands Rec. Club, Gorsey Lane, Warrington
Colours: Blue & Black/Black/Black
Change Colours: Red & Black/Black/Red

STYAL FC
Chairman: Barry Green **Manager:** Jim Vince
Secretary: Alan Jones, 1 Oak Brow Cottages, Altrincham Rd, Styal, Wilmslow SK9 4JE (01625 530270)
Ground: Altrincham Road, Styal
Colours: Yellow/Black/Black
Change Colours: Blue/White/White

SPRINGBANK VENDING
MIDLAND LEAGUE

President: T Myatt   **Chairman:** P Savage

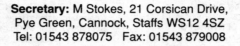

Secretary: M Stokes, 21 Corsican Drive,
Pye Green, Cannock, Staffs WS12 4SZ
Tel: 01543 878075 Fax: 01543 879008

FINAL LEAGUE TABLE 2001-02

	P	W	D	L	F	A	Pts
Eccleshall	36	24	6	6	89	35	
Audley	36	20	11	5	72	37	
Redgate Clayton	36	22	4	10	72	46	70
Adderley Green	36	20	9	7	79	45	69
Stallington	36	20	5	11	72	60	65
Brocton	36	17	12	7	64	39	63
Milton Rangers	36	18	7	11	58	46	61
Hanford	36	14	12	10	58	47	54
Abbey Hulton Utd	36	15	8	13	71	59	53
Hanley Town	36	12	12	12	54	46	48
Vale Juniors	36	13	9	14	67	69	48
Newcastle Town	36	12	11	13	44	48	47
Leoni AG	36	10	10	16	49	75	40
Dominoes FC	36	9	9	18	49	61	36
Alsager AFC	36	9	9	18	49	76	36
Wolstanton Utd	36	6	12	18	41	77	30
Ball Haye Green	36	7	6	23	48	83	27
Foley	36	5	12	19	38	78	27
Cheadle Town OB	36	3	8	25	33	80	17

RESULTS CHART

		1	2	3	4	5	6	7	8	9	10	11	12	13	14	15	16	17	18	19
1	Abbey Hulton	X	0-3	1-0	2-0	0-3	1-1	3-2	1-2	4-0	2-2	1-1	8-1	0-0	1-0	1-5	7-1	4-1	2-2	1-1
2	Adderley Green	3-1	X	2-2	2-2	3-1	2-2	3-0	0-1	6-2	3-0	0-3	4-1	4-1	5-2	1-0	2-0	1-0	0-2	4-0
3	Alsager	0-2	0-3	X	0-1	1-5	4-4	0-1	1-2	0-0	1-1	3-1	1-1	0-0	4-2	2-1	1-5	1-6	1-0	1-2
4	Audley	4-0	4-0	6-1	X	1-0	0-0	2-2	1-1	1-1	1-0	1-4	2-5	4-0	0-0	1-0	1-5	1-1	2-1	3-0
5	Ball Haye Green	5-4	1-1	1-1	2-3	X	0-1	3-1	0-4	3-2	0-2	1-2	0-3	3-4	0-1	0-1	1-2	2-0	0-3	1-2
6	Brocton	1-1	3-1	2-1	0-3	0-0	X	6-1	2-0	2-0	1-0	0-3	1-2	2-2	0-0	3-1	2-1	1-1	1-2	4-0
7	Cheadle Town OB	0-3	0-1	2-6	1-2	1-2	2-3	X	1-2	0-1	0-0	1-2	0-0	1-2	1-1	0-2	1-3	0-5	1-1	3-2
8	Eccleshall	5-2	1-0	5-0	2-3	4-0	1-1	3-0	X	4-0	0-1	4-2	4-2	3-0	0-2	0-3	7-0	3-0	3-1	1-1
9	Foley	0-5	0-2	2-1	1-1	4-2	1-2	2-1	1-6	X	1-2	1-1	2-4	0-0	2-2	2-4	1-2	0-1	1-2	1-0
10	Hanford	3-2	1-1	1-2	2-2	2-2	1-1	2-1	0-1	5-2	X	2-2	3-3	0-2	2-0	1-1	0-3	4-0	2-1	2-1
11	Hanley Town	1-0	2-2	0-1	0-0	5-0	1-3	1-0	0-1	1-1	0-1	X	1-1	1-1	1-1	1-1	3-2	1-1	3-3	3-0
12	Leoni AG	0-2	1-1	2-1	0-2	5-2	1-4	1-1	1-4	1-1	2-1	0-4	X	1-0	1-1	1-3	1-2	0-0	0-2	1-1
13	Milton Rangers	2-0	5-1	4-2	1-2	3-3	2-1	2-0	2-1	3-1	0-1	2-1	3-0	X	0-0	3-0	1-2	2-0	3-1	1-2
14	Newcastle Town	0-2	2-3	3-3	0-3	3-0	1-2	1-2	1-1	3-0	2-1	1-0	2-0	0-2	X	0-3	0-1	2-1	0-0	1-1
15	Redgate Clayton	3-1	1-3	1-0	1-0	1-0	1-0	2-1	0-3	1-1	4-3	2-0	2-1	3-1	3-2	X	5-3	1-0	2-2	3-0
16	Stallington	3-0	0-4	1-2	0-1	2-1	1-0	2-2	1-1	4-2	1-2	3-0	4-1	2-0	1-2	4-2	X	2-0	2-2	3-2
17	Dominoes	1-2	0-3	0-2	2-2	3-2	0-3	1-1	0-2	2-0	1-1	2-1	1-2	3-1	0-1	3-1	2-2	X	2-3	2-2
18	Vale Juniors	1-3	2-5	5-2	0-3	2-0	0-4	5-1	4-4	0-0	1-1	3	5-2	0-1	1-2	1-7	0-1	2-5	X	3-1
19	Wolstanton Utd	2-2	2-2	1-1	0-4	2-2	1-1	3-1	1-3	2-2	0-6	0-2	0-1	1-2	1-3	1-0	1-1	3-2	2-4	X

LEAGUE CUP 2001-02

THIRD ROUND

Eccleshall	v	Hanford	0-1
Leoni AG	v	Brocton	0-2
Cheadle Town OB	v	Audley	0-1
Stallington	v	Adderley Green	1-0

SEMI-FINALS

Audley	v	Hanford	1-2
Brocton	v	Stallington	1*1, 2p4

FINAL

Hanford	v	Stallington	0*0, 4p2

THE ASDA LOGIC
WEST LANCASHIRE FOOTBALL LEAGUE

President: D Procter Esq.
Chairman & General Secretary: W Carr Esq.
60 Selby Avenue, Blackpool FY4 2LZ   Tel: 01253 348450

The challengers for the Asda Logic West Lancashire League Premier Division crown were nearly lucky third time around as they tried to wrestle the title from the grasp of Kirkham & Wesham. Chased all the way to the final few weeks, Kirkham had just enough to hold off the challenge of Charnock Richard and take the Championship for the third consecutive season.

The front two were set in their positions right from the start of the season and their battle for top spot was rarely interrupted. Kirkham held pole position for the first couple of months although Charnock's unbeaten run lasted longer, moving them above their rivals in September. Already by October, the pair were six points ahead of the rest of the divisionwho only had a battle for third to fight.

Into the New Year, the title looked to be Kirkham's as the Fylde side opened up a four point lead. However, credit to Charnock as they moved back to the top at the end of February, albeit having played two games more. With three games left, only a point separated the pair and a further twenty were between them and Dalton United in third. But that was as close as it got as Kirkham's experience of the tense finale told and they ended up with 72 points compared to Charnock's 66.

The competition for third place also went down to the wire. In the end, Wyre Villa deservedly took the third spot after being consistent throughout the year. Fulwood Amateurs made a late run into fourth place led by new manager Tony Greenwood, who parted company with UniBond League side Bamber Bridge earlier in the season. Last season's runners up, Dalton United, failed to build on their success and they finished fifth.

The first relegation spot was clear cut from the New Year onwards as Garstang failed to adapt to a second season in the top division. A wretched run in to the end of the season left them thirteen points adrift of the other team to be relegated, Tempest United, who went back from where they came last summer.

Charnock Richard did manage to get some revenge on Kirkham & Wesham by winning the final of the Lancashire Challenge Shield as the West Lancashire League again provided both finalists. Charnock also won the final of the Richardson Cup, beating Barnoldswick United.

Replacing Garstang and Tempest United in the Premier Division are Milnthorpe Corinthians and Turton who managed to beat off tough opposition to take the promotion places.

The lead changed hands a number of times in Division One, but in the end Corinthians took the title. Fleetwood Hesketh and Carnforth Rangers failed to keep up the momentum towards the end of the season allowing Turton to sneak into second place, having finally caught up their games in hand. Corinthians also took the President's Cup beating local rivals Carnforth Rangers to claim the first Division double.

Coppull United and Bootle will be in the First Division next season but no team was relegated due to league restructuring and the decision to terminate the membership of Wigan SMR.
Steven Hewitt

HONOURS LIST 2001-02

Premier Division	Champions: Kirkham & Wesham	Runners up: Charnock Richard
Division One	Champions: Milnethorpe Corinthians	Runners up: Turton
Division Two	Champions: Coppull United	Runners up: Bootle
Richardson Cup	Winners: Charnock Richard	Runners up: Barnoldswick United
President's Cup	Winners: Milnthorpe Corinthians	Runners up: Carnforth Rangers
Tavern Cup	Winners: Thornton Cleveleys	Runners up: BAC/EE Preston
Houston Cup	Winners: Lytham St Annes	Runners up: Milnethorpe Corinthians
Lancashire Challenge Shield	Winners: Charnock Richard	Runners up: Kirkham & Wesham
Westmorland Senior Cup	Winners: Milnethorpe Corinthians	Runners up: Kendal Town

FINAL LEAGUE TABLES 2001-02

PREMIER DIVISION

	P	W	D	L	F	A	Pts
Kirkham & Wesham	30	22	6	2	90	20	72
Charnock Richard	30	19	9	2	69	28	66
Wyre Villa	30	16	6	8	58	47	54
Fulwood Amateurs	30	15	7	8	63	46	52
Dalton United	30	16	2	12	70	48	50
Barnoldswick Utd	30	14	4	12	60	68	*43
Burnley United	30	13	4	13	65	79	43
Blackrod Town	30	10	8	12	53	49	38
Freckleton	30	11	5	14	42	49	38
Eagley	30	10	7	13	46	48	37
Blackpool Wren R	30	11	3	16	51	55	36
Springfields	30	11	2	17	52	62	35
Norcross & Warbreck	30	9	6	15	42	67	33
Bae Barrow S C	30	7	10	13	49	66	31
Tempest United	30	9	4	17	51	61	*28
Garstang	30	4	3	23	33	101	15

DIVISION ONE

	P	W	D	L	F	A	Pts
Milnethorpe Corinths	26	19	3	4	66	39	60
Turton	26	17	5	4	62	24	*53
Fleetwood Hesketh	26	15	6	5	58	38	51
Carnforth Rangers	26	13	6	7	65	35	45
Hesketh Bank	26	11	6	9	67	52	39
Crooklands Casuals	26	11	6	9	68	63	39
Whinney Hill	26	10	8	8	42	41	38
Wigan SMR	26	9	9	8	43	52	36
Poulton Town	26	9	5	12	44	45	32
Haslingden St Marys	26	9	6	11	49	57	*30
Feniscowles	26	6	8	12	42	49	*23
Millom	26	6	3	17	41	72	21
Lancashire Constab	26	5	5	16	43	79	20
Burnley Belvedere	26	2	4	20	32	76	10

* points adjustment

PREMIER DIVISION CLUBS 2002-03

BARNOLDSWICK UNITED FC
Secretary: Mrs L James, 37 Long Ing Lane, Barnoldswick, Colne, Lancs BB18 6BJ. Tel: 01282 815361
Ground: West Close, Victory Park, Barnoldswick
Colours: White & blue/blue/blue

BAE BARROW SPORTS CLUB FC
Secretary: Mrs B Knagg, Hibbert Road, Barrow in Furness, Cumbria LA14 5AF. Tel: 01229 831785
Ground: Hawcoat Lane, Barrow
Colours: Maroon & white/maroon/maroon

BLACKROD TOWN FC
Secretary: Mr D Almond, 40 Landedmans, Westhoughton, Bolton BL5 2QJ. Tel: 01942 793122
Ground: Blackrod Community Centre, Vicarage Rd, Blackrod
Colours: Blue/white/blue

BLACKPOOL WREN ROVERS FC
Secretary: Mr P Kimberly, 34 Priory Gate, Blackpool FY4 2QE. Tel: 01253 349853
Ground: School Rd/Whitehill Rd, Blackpool
Colours: Red/red/red

BURNLEY UNITED FC
Secretary: Mr K Blackburn, 13 Salus Street, Burnley. Tel: 01282 415711
Ground: Barden Sports Ground, Barden Lane, Burnley
Colours: Red/black/red

CHARNOCK RICHARD FC
Secretary: Mr G Randle, 63 Broad Oak Lane, Penwortham, Preston PR1 0UY. Tel: 01772 496782
Ground: Charter Lane, off Chorley Lane
Colours: Green & white/black/black

DALTON UNITED FC
Secretary: Mr A Ogilvie, 20 Meadowlands Ave, Barrow in Furness LA13 0AR. Tel: 01229 822928
Ground: Railway Meadow, Beckside Rd, Dalton in Furness
Colours: Red & black/black/black

EAGLEY FC
Secretary: Mr M Hackin, 260 Darwen Rd, Bromley Cross, Bolton BL7 9JG. Tel: 01204 595863
Ground: Eagley Sports Complex, Dunscar Ind Estate
Colours: Yellow/blue/blue & yellow

FRECKLETON FC
Secretary: Mrs L O'Reilly, 41 Windene Grove, Freckleton PR4 1DE. Tel: 01772 634773
Ground: Hodgson Memorial Ground, Bush Lane, Freckleton
Colours: Red/black/red

FULWOOD AMATEUR FC
Secretary: Mr A Peterson, 89 Dukes Meadow, Ingol, Preston PR2 6AU. Tel: 01772 734327
Ground: Lightfoot Lane, off A6 Preston - Lancaster
Colours: Blue & white/black/blue & black

KIRKHAM & WESHAM FC
Secretary: Mr E Picton, 14 St Michaels Rd, Kirkham, Preston PR4 2TQ. Tel: 01772 686264
Ground: Coronation Rd, off A585 - B5219
Colours: All blue

MILNETHORPE CORINTHIANS FC
Secretary: Mr C Davidson, 27 Beetham Rd, Milnthorpe, Cumbria LA7 7QN. Tel: 01539 562884
Ground: Strands Lane, Milnethorpe
Colours: Red & white/white/red

NORCROSS & WARBRECK FC
Secretary: Mr T Dickinson, 10 Loxley Place, Whitehome, Blackpool FY5 3HH. Tel: 01253 866004
Ground: Thornton
Colours: Yellow & green/green/yellow & green

SPRINGFIELDS FC
Secretary: Mr F Yates, 123 Alder Close, Leyland PR26 7TT. Tel: 01772 496074
Ground: SSRA Sports Ground, Dodney Drive, Preston
Colours: Tangerine/blue/tangerine

TURTON FC
Secretary: Mr E Charnock, 15 Crown Point, Edgeworth, Turton BL7 0BD. Tel: 01204 852608
Ground: Thomasson Fold, Edgworth Village
Colours: Yellow/black/black

WYRE VILLA FC
Secretary: Mr G Bradley, Park Farm, Burned House Lane, Preesall, Poulton le Fylde FY6 0PQ. Tel: 01253 810637
Ground: Shard Bridge, Stalmine Village
Colours: Blue & white/blue/blue

DIVISION ONE CLUBS

Bootle (Cumbria) AFC
Carnforth Rangers FC
Crooklands Casuals FC
Fleetwood Hesketh FC
Haslingden St Mary's FC
Lancashire Constabulary FC
Poulton Town FC
Whinney Hill FC
Burnley Belvedere FC
Coppull United FC
Feniscowles FC
Garstang FC
Hesketh Bank FC
Millom FC
Tempest United FC

DIVISION TWO CLUBS

Askam United FC
Bae Canberra FC
Crosshills FC
Furness Cavaliers FC
Lytham St Annes FC
Pennington FC
Thornton Cleveleys FC
BAC/EE Preston FC
Barrow Rangers FC
Euxton Villa FC
GSK Ulverston Rangers FC
Mill Hill St Peters
Stonelough FC
Todmorden Borough FC

AIR MILES
MANCHESTER
FOOTBALL LEAGUE

Honorary President: Norman Noder

League Secretary: Joe Hall, 31 Sunhill Close, Rochdale, Lancashire OL16 4RU.
Tel. 01706 719829   Fax. 01706 719828   Email – jj.hall@zoom.co.uk

The big story of 2001/2002 season in the AIR MILES Manchester League was the transformation of Stockport Georgians from perennial relegation strugglers to League and Cup double winners.

After collecting the Premier Division title with a 4-1 victory over Rochdale Sacred Heart, Georgians then defeated the same opponents 1-0 in a thrilling Gilgryst Cup Final.

Wythenshawe Amateurs finished as runners-up for the second year running despite putting together a phenomenal run of eighteen league games without defeat, which stretched from mid-November to the end of the season.

Third placed Prestwich Heys equalled their previous best performance since rejoining the League in the mid 1980s and fourth place for Leigh Athletic represents a highly satisfactory start to life in the Premier Division, as they were the previous season's First Division Champions.

New Mills slotted into Premier Division life without any rival to claim a fifth place finish and consolidation after promotion, as well as retaining the Derbyshire Divisional Cup in front of a 1000 plus gate at Buxton when they defeated neighbours Whaley Bridge 2-0.

Elton Fold side were a surprise package as they claimed a best ever sixth place after a very good season, though East Manchester will have hoped for better than seventh spot, but they did win the Manchester Challenge Trophy with a 4-1 win over Belden.

Irlam Mitchell Shackleton had to settle for a mid-table spot in a season that promised better things, whereas Springhead pieced together a great late run to climb up the table to ninth.

The enigma of the campaign was Atherton Town, who looked like Championship material before a poor run saw them slip to tenth, while Rochdale Sacred Heart recovered well to steer themselves clear of relegation worries, and were also unlucky beaten finalists in a highly entertaining Gilgryst Cup Final.

Beneath Hearts in twelfth, Dukinfield Town will want to put the last nine months behind them after a campaign where they found little consistency, but Monton Amateurs and Willows saw their relegation worries eased with the resignation of Failsworth Town, but both will look for better form next term

And what can you say about poor Pennington? The Jubilee Park side failed to win any of their first twelve games, and collected only three points from their last seventeen games to finish bottom.

For the second season running, a debutant club went on to claim the First Division title as Royton Town ended the most exciting promotion race in years as worthy Champions and Wilmslow Albion finished runners-up, partly due to the prolific Mickey Beirne who hammered in 53 goals in a success-strewn season in which Albion also claimed the Murray Shield with a 2-1 win over Hindsford

Hollinwood impressed with a third place finish, Leland Mayall transforming the Oldham side into a credible promotion contender, and Breightmet United once again pressed their claim for elevation to the top flight before finishing fourth, while Ashton Athletic recorded a best ever fifth place finish, earning respect throughout the Division in the process, and Hindsford AFC started off well but fell away towards the end of a gruelling campaign to finish sixth, losing out to Wilmslow in the Murray Shield.

Belden looked a good outside bet before April defeats ended the Blackley side's chances, and they also relinquished their hold on the Manchester Challenge Trophy with defeat to East Manchester in the Final.

Whalley Range enjoyed another highly creditable season to finish eighth, just ahead of the unpredictable Wythenshawe Town, and Whitworth Valley started well enough but slipped away in the second half of the season, and Old Alts recovered to escape re-election worries to claim eleventh position.

For Avro, Milton, Tintwistle Villa and Warth Fold, there is always next season after stop-start campaigns saw them finish in the lower reaches of the Division, but Unsworth and Manchester Royal must seek re-election, although both can take some solace from contributing to the most competitive First Division season for many years.

FINAL LEAGUE TABLES 2001-02

PREMIER DIVISION

	P	W	D	L	F	A	Pts
Stockport Georgians	28	20	3	5	66	27	63
Wythenshawe Am	28	19	5	4	61	33	62
Prestwich Heys	28	16	3	9	77	43	51
Leigh Athletic	28	15	6	7	61	49	51
New Mills	28	14	7	7	51	37	49
Elton Fold	28	14	4	10	56	47	46
East Manchester	28	13	5	10	54	52	44
Irl. Mitch. Shack.	28	11	9	8	55	41	42
Springhead	28	13	2	13	65	63	41
Atherton Town	28	10	6	12	48	36	36
Rochdale S Hrt	28	8	10	10	52	54	34
Dukinfield Town	28	6	7	15	40	55	25
Monton Amateurs	28	5	4	19	40	81	19
Willow	28	5	4	19	32	74	19
Pennington	28	1	5	22	20	86	8

* points adjustment

DIVISION ONE

	P	W	D	L	F	A	Pts
Royton Town*	32	23	4	5	130	55	76
Wilmslow Albion*	32	22	5	5	132	66	68
Hollinwood	32	19	7	6	106	60	64
Breightnet United	32	20	4	8	91	56	64
Ashton Athletic	32	18	9	5	71	38	63
Hindsford	32	18	5	9	79	53	59
Belden*	32	19	2	11	92	77	56
Whalley Range	32	18	1	13	80	72	55
Wythenshawe Town*	32	16	8	8	92	60	53
Whitworth Valley	32	13	5	14	74	67	44
Old Altrinchamians	32	9	5	18	53	87	32
Avro*	32	10	4	18	43	68	31
Milton	32	6	7	19	46	98	25
Tintwhistle Villa	32	6	4	22	56	100	22
Warth Fold	32	7	0	25	55	112	21
Manchester Royal	32	4	5	23	49	102	17
Unsworth	32	4	5	23	55	133	17

PREMIER DIVISION RESULTS CHART

		1	2	3	4	5	6	7	8	9	10	11	12	13	14	15	16
1	Atherton Town	X	0-0	0-1	4-0	3-0	0-1	2-2	5-0	1-2	3-0	2-3	1-2	3-4	1-2	1-2	1-1
2	Dukinfield Town	1-1	X	0-1	1-3	2-2	0-5	7-1	3-1	5-2	2-1	2-2	1-2	4-1	1-6	0-0	1-2
3	East Manchester	1-3	1-0	X	1-3	-	1-1	4-2	4-2	3-2	2-0	1-2	1-1	1-2	0-4	3-1	1-3
4	Elton Fold	2-1	5-1	1-4	X	-	3-5	1-2	4-2	2-1	3-1	2-0	2-2	4-2	0-1	3-2	1-2
5	Failsworth Town	-	0-3	0-5	2-2	X	2-0	0-7	-	-	3-1	2-4	1-1	2-1	-	-	1-1
6	Irlam Mitchell Shack.	0-0	1-1	3-3	0-1	3-0	X	1-2	4-2	3-0	6-2	2-0	3-1	1-1	0-0	2-1	1-2
7	Leigh Athletic	1-0	4-2	2-0	3-0	-	2-2	X	4-1	2-3	4-1	2-1	2-5	3-2	3-1	2-2	2-1
8	Monton Amateurs	0-4	2-1	2-4	1-1	-	0-3	2-2	X	0-1	2-1	0-4	2-1	0-2	2-5	3-1	0-4
9	New Mills	2-0	0-0	1-2	0-0	2-1	3-1	2-2	3-0	X	5-0	3-1	4-4	2-0	0-1	2-1	2-2
10	Pennington	0-1	1-1	1-1	1-3	-	1-3	0-2	2-0	0-1	X	0-7	1-1	0-3	0-7	1-1	1-3
11	Prestwich Heys	3-4	4-0	3-3	1-2	-	2-0	5-2	4-3	0-1	6-0	X	2-1	3-0	1-1	3-1	4-0
12	Rochdale Sacred H	3-3	1-0	2-1	5-2	-	2-2	0-0	4-4	1-2	1-1	2-3	X	3-2	0-2	0-1	0-2
13	Springhead	2-0	2-1	6-4	2-0	-	3-2	2-3	4-4	2-4	7-1	2-4	2-4	X	2-3	2-0	1-3
14	Stockport Georgians	0-3	3-0	2-1	1-0	-	3-1	1-0	2-1	0-0	4-0	2-1	4-1	3-4	X	2-1	0-3
15	Willows	1-3	1-5	1-2	0-7	2-0	4-1	0-5	0-3	2-1	4-1	1-6	1-1	1-2	0-6	X	1-5
16	Wythenshawe Am	0-1	2-0	2-3	1-1	3-2	1-1	1-0	4-1	2-2	3-2	4-2	3-2	2-1	1-0	2-1	X

NB. Failsworth Town withdrew during the season. Their results are shown but have been expunged from the league table.

GILGRYST CUP 2001-02

QUARTER-FINALS

| Atherton Town | v | Monton Amateurs | 2-1 | Dukinfield Town | v | Irlam Mitchell Sh. | 1-2 |
| Rochdale Sacred Hrt | v | East Manchester | 4*3 | Stockport Georgians | v | Elton Fold | 1-0 |

SEMI-FINALS

Rochdale Sacred Hrts v Irlam Mitchell Shack. 5-2   Stockport Georgians v Atherton Town 3-0

FINAL

Rochdale Sacred Hrt v Stockport Georgians 0-1   at Elton Fold

MURRAY SHIELD 2001-02

QUARTER-FINALS

| Ashton Athletic | v | Hindsford | 0-5 | Breightmet United | v | Whalley Range 8p7, 1*1 |
| Old Altrinchamians | v | Wilmslow Albion | 0-7 | Tintwhistle Villa | v | Breightmet United | 6-2 |

SEMI-FINALS

Hindsworth v Tintwhistle Villa 7-0   Wilmslow Albion v Breightmet United 6-2

FINAL

Hindsford v Wilmslow Albion 1-2   at Stockport Georgians

OPEN TROPHY 2001-02

FINAL

Irlam Mitch. Sh. Res v New Mills Reserves 0-1   at Avro

ATHERTON TOWN
Formed: 1964
Secretary: Gerald Butler, 43 Hope Fold Ave., Atherton, Lancs
M29 0BW Tel: 01942 870326
Ground: Howe Bridge Spts Centre, Howe Bridge, Atherton
Tel: 01942 884882
Directions: A579 Atherton to Leigh road - Sports Centre 800
yds on left
Colours: Royal/white/royal

DUKINFIELD TOWN
Formed: 1948
Secretary: Paul Bishop, 21 Church Walk, Stalybridge,
Cheshire Tel: 0161 303 0398
Ground: Blocksages Playing Fields, Birch Lane, Dukinfield.
Directions: From Ashton centre follow Kings St, turn left into
Chapel St. thenright turn into Foundry St/Birch Lane. Ground
880 yds on right, behind publicbaths.
Colours: All yellow

EAST MANCHESTER
Formed: 1960 (called ICL until 1985)
Secretary: D Wilkinson, 76 Sandy Lane, Dukinfield, Cheshire
SK16 5NL Tel: 0161 330 4450
Ground: The Butchers Arms, Droylsden
Directions: From Manchester take A662 (Ashton New Road) to
junct with Market St. in Droylsden. Left into Market St. at lights,
over the mini r'about. Ground entrance on the left.
Colours: All royal blue

ELTON VALE
Formed: 1957 (Formerly Elton Fold >2002)
Secretary: Guy Mallinson, 14 Lonsdale St, Bury BL8 2QD
Tel: 0161 797 7090
Ground: Elton Vale Road, Bury
Directions: A58 from Bury to Boltonto junction with Ainsworth
Road (B6196). Approx. 3/4 mile right into Elton Vale Road.
Ground is 150 yards on left after Foulds Ave.
Colours: Blue & black/black/black

IRLAM MITCHELL SHACKLETON
Formed: 1970 (called Mitchell Shackleton until 2001)
Secretary: Ian Street, 11 Senior Road, Peel Green, Eccles,
M30 7PZ Tel: 0161 789 7061
Ground: Salteye Park, Peel Green, Eccles Tel: 0161 788 8373
Directions: Leave M63 at Peel Green r'bout (jct 2), take A57
Liverpool Roadtowards Irlam, ground entrance half mile on left
behind Kara Cafew opposite Barton airport. Or, follow A57 from
Manchester via Salford & Eccles, then follow Irlam signs.
Colours: Blue & white

LEIGH ATHLETIC
Formed: 1959
Secretary: Rick Wilson. Tel: 01942 518328
Ground: Madley Park, Charles St., Leigh Tel: 01942 673500
Directions: Exit A580 at junction with A574 onto Warrington
Road and follow into Leigh town centre. Turn right into King
Street and turn right into Church Street (Boars Head Public
House). Take sixth left into Charles Street and ground straight
ahead.
Colours: Yellow/ Blue/ Blue

MONTON AMATEURS
Formed: 1916
Secretary: Tony Lee, 28 Wheatley Rd, Swinton, Manchester
M27 3RW Tel: 0161 793 8033

Ground: Granary Lane, Worsley
Directions: From Eccles Centre turn right into Worsley Rd at
Patricroft Bridge.Ground approx 1 mile on left, entrance just
before Bridgewater Hotel
Colours: All royal blue

NEW MILLS
Formed: 1987 (re formed)
Secretary: Barry Land, 165 Lowleighton Road, New Mills,
High Peak SK22 4LR Tel: 01663 746174
Ground: Church Lane, New Mills (01663 747435).
Directions: From A6 (Buxton Road), turn into Albion Road
(A6015) at New Mills Newtown Train Station. Follow to junction
of Church Road/Church Lane and ground on left.
Colours: Amber/black/black

PRESTWICH HEYS
Formed: 1938
Secretary: Norman Deardon Tel: 0161 959 1305
Ground: Sandgate Rd, Whitefield Tel: 0161 773 8888
Directions: Follow Old Bury Rd (A665) from Manchester to
Prestwich, right intoHeywood Rd, 3rd left into Mount
Rd/Sandgate Rd - ground on right.
Colours: Red & white/red/red

ROCHDALE SACRED HEART
Formed: 1955
(called Robinson's >1985; RSH>87 & Sacred Heart>2001)
Secretary: Joe Devlin, 61 Buersil Ave., Rochdale, Lancs. OL16
4TR Tel: 01706 712602
Ground: Fox Park, Belfield Mill Lane, Rochdale
Directions: From Rochdale town centre follow the A640 to
Milnrow, at Kingsway junction turn left into Albert Royds Street
and turn right again into Bellfield Mill Lane.
Colours: All red

ROYTON TOWN
Secretary: Phil Dean (0161 287 8436)
Ground: Crompton Cricket Club, Glebe Road, Shaw
Directions: J20, M62 onto A627(M) signed Oldham. At 1st exit
follow A663 (broadway) onto A66 (Shaw Road). At r'about take
2nd exit (Crompton Way), and then 1st left onto Rochdale
Road. Glebe Road is 4th turning on right and ground is at end
of the road.
Colours: Yellow and Black

SPRINGHEAD
Formed: 1926
Secretary: Alex Simmons
Tel: 0161 620 0959 or 07764 836918
Ground: St John St, Lees, Oldham (0161 627 3760).
Directions: From Oldham (Mumps r'bout) follow A669 towards
Lees for approx onemile, left into St John St, ground 500yds on
right.
Colours: Black & red/black/black

STOCKPORT GEORGIANS
Formed: 1987
Secretary: Ged Newcombe, 7 Chiltern Close, Hazel Grove,
Stockport SK7 5BQ Tel: 0161483 0004
Ground: Cromley Rd, Stockport, Tel: 0161 483 6581
Directions: Follow A6 from Stockport centre, turn right at
Cemetery intoBranhall Lane. After 1 mile turn left at r/about into
Woodsmoor Lane. Take 1st right Flowery Fields then right into
Cromley Road
Colours: Red and black

WILLOWS
Formed: 1977
Secretary: Frank Miller, 11 Edmund Street, Salford,
Manchester Tel: 0161 737 2411 or 07761 486146
Ground: Agecroft Sports Ground, Salford.
Directions: From Manchester, follow signs for A580(East
Lancs Road) and exit at IRlas o' th' Height. At r'about take 4th
exit, following signs for A666 (Kearsley/Bury). At 1st set of
lights, right onto Agecroft Road (at Henry Boddington P.H.).
Travel down approx. 1/3 mile and ground on the left.
Colours: Red and white

WILMSLOW ALBION
Formed: 1919
Secretary: Norma Winn, 236 Derbyshire Lane, Stretford,
Manchester (0161 2869520)

Ground: Oakwood Farm, Styal Road, Wilmslow
Directions: From J5, M56 follow signs for Wilmslow. Turn right
at the end of Ringway Road into Styal Road (B5166). Take 3rd
right onto Altrincham Road and ground on right.
Colours: Yellow and blue

WYTHENSHAWE AMATEURS
Formed: 1959
Secretary: John Sobierajsh, 5 Wensley Drive, Withington,
Manchester Tel: 0161 445 3415
Ground: Longley Lane, Northenden Tel: 0161 998 7268
Directions: Princess Parkway from Manchester to Post House
hotel, via PalatineRd & Moor End Rd to Longley Lane - ground
entrance opposite Overwood Rd.
Colours: Blue & white stripes/blue/blue

DIVISION ONE CLUBS

ASHTON ATHLETIC
Secretary: Steve Halliwell, 20 Kings Road, Golborne,
Warrington Tel: 01942 517728 (H) 07774 180165 (M)
Ground: Brocstedes Park, Farm Road, Ashton-in-Makerfield
Tel: 01942 716360.
Colours: Orange and navy blue

AVRO
Secretary: Karen Birch, 27 Brooks Drive, Failsworth,
Manchester M35 0L5 Tel: 0161 682 6731
Ground: Lancaster Club, Broadway, Failsworth
Colours: Red & black/red/red

BELDEN (previously (B.I.C.C.)
Secretary: Rob Fuller, Tel: 0161 681 6948 or 07971 177475
Ground: Belden Works, Blackley New Road, Blackley.
Tel: 0161 740 9151
Colours: Maroon and blue

BREIGHTMET UNITED
Secretary: Roy Haslam, Tel: 01204 535933 or 07796 134093
Ground: Moss Park, Back Bury Rd, Breightmet, Bolton
Tel: 01204 533930
Colours: Black & white stripes/black/red

HIGHFIELD UNITED
Secretary: Jackie Lomax, Tel: 0161 764 9986
Ground: Seedfield Sports Club, Parkinson Street, Bury
Colours: Jade and black

HINDSFORD
Secretary: Eddie Evans, 17 Belmont Avenue, Atherton M46
9RR RTel Nos: 01942 895869 (H) 07767 492411 (M)
Ground: Squires Lane, Tyldesley
Colours: Red /blue/red & blue

HOLLINWOOD
Secretary: Ken Evans, 20 Meadow Rise, High Crompton,
Shaw, Oldham OL2 7QG Tel: 01706 840987 or 07740 442818.
Ground: Lime Lane, Hollinwood, Oldham (0161 681 3385).
Colours: Yellow & Navy/ Navy / Navy

MANCHESTER ROYAL
Secretary: Steve Jackson.
Tel: 01457 868571 or 07974 108266
Ground: Kings Road, Whalley Range, Manchester. Tel: 0161
613 5467
Colours: Red & black/black/black

MILTON
Secretary: Andrew Cole, 21 Whittle Drive, Shaw, Oldham OL2
8TJ Tel Nos: 01706 291973 (H) 07754 482393 (M)
Ground: Athletic Stadium, Springfield Park, Rochdale.
Colours: Green& Black,Black/Black

OLD ALTRINCHAMIANS
Secretary: Phil Lewis, 10 Woodfield Grove, Sale, M33 6JW
Tel: 0161 973 7082 or 07796 475550 (M))
Ground: Crossford Bridge Playing Fields, Meadows Rd, Sale.
Colours: Black & white stripes/black/black

TINTWISTLE VILLA
Secretary: Bill Higginbottom, 61 West Drive, Tintwistle,
Glossop Tel: 01457 852467
Ground: West Drive, Tintwistle
Colours: Black & white stripes/black/black

UNSWORTH
Secretary: Suzanne Angle Tel: 0161 766 4073 or 07775 522351
Ground: Hillock Playing Fields, Mersey Close, Whitefield
Colours: Blue and Yellow

WARTH FOLD
Secretary: Felix Daniel. Tel: 0161 232 0392 or 077877 880407
Ground: The Elms, Whitefield
Colours: Yellow and blue

WHALLEY RANGE
Secretary: Paul Pestell. Tel: 0161 881 5297 or 07712 840125
Ground: Kings Rd, Whalley Range, Manchester. Tel: 0161 613
5467
Colours: Red & black stripes/black/black

WHITWORTH VALLEY
Secretary: Alan Riley, 31 John Street, Whitworth, Rochdale
OL12 8BT Tel: 01706 852619 (H) 07930 543924 (M)
Ground: Rawstron Street, Whitworth Tel: 01706 853045.
Colours: Black & white/black/red

WYTHENSHAWE TOWN
Secretary: Norman Hardman. Tel: 0161 437 8236.
Ground: Ericstan Park, Timpson Rd, Wythenshawe,
Manchester. Tel: 0161 998 5076.
Colours: All royal Blue

WIGAN & DISTRICT AMATEUR FOOTBALL LEAGUE

General Secretary: K Whitehead, 62 Crediton Drive, Platt Bridge, Wigan   Tel: 01942 862373

FINAL LEAGUE TABLES 2001-02

PREMIER DIVISION

	P	W	D	L	F	A	Pts
Highfield	24	20	1	3	84	31	61
Hindley Town	24	15	4	5	53	30	49
Newburgh United	24	13	4	7	71	52	43
Winstanley St Aidans	24	16	6	6	67	40	42
Downall Green Utd	24	13	2	9	57	38	41
Whelley	24	11	3	10	43	47	36
Burscough Bridge	24	10	2	12	46	55	32
Shevington	24	10	0	14	48	58	30
Hindley Green	24	7	8	9	50	61	29
Standish St Wilfrids	24	9	1	14	47	48	28
Wigan Rovers	24	8	4	13	37	49	28
Pemberton	24	6	3	15	38	87	21
Ashworth Hospital	24	1	4	19	30	76	4

FIRST DIVISION

	P	W	D	L	F	A	Pts
Bickerstaffe	22	16	4	2	69	31	52
Worsley Mesnes	22	15	5	2	65	24	50
Royal Bank	22	14	5	3	57	25	47
Newburgh Res.	22	12	4	6	77	40	40
Ince Central	22	11	2	9	65	49	35
St Jude's	22	9	5	8	57	53	32
Marus Bridge	22	6	5	11	45	65	23
Douglas Valley	22	8	3	11	43	63	21
Springfield	22	5	5	12	41	53	20
Goose Green	22	5	2	15	38	60	17
Winstanley St A. Res	22	4	4	14	34	79	16
Standish St W Res	22	4	2	16	34	79	14

Scholes resigned without completing their programme

WESTMORLAND ASSOCIATION FOOTBALL LEAGUE

Hon Secretary/Treasurer: Ron Wilkinson, High Sampool Farmhouse, Levens, Kendal LA8 8EQ   Tel: 01539 552267

FINAL LEAGUE TABLES 2001-02

DIVISION ONE

		P	W	D	L	F	A	W	D	L	F	A	Pts
1	Wetheriggs United	26	9	3	1	40	8	10	2	1	39	11	62
2	Appleby	26	10	2	1	44	24	8	1	4	48	23	57
3	Coniston	26	10	1	2	33	10	8	1	4	33	18	56
4	Staveley United	26	10	2	1	29	12	7	2	4	24	17	55
5	Sedbergh Wanderers	26	10	1	2	43	25	7	0	6	25	27	52
6	Kendal County	26	8	1	4	40	16	5	4	4	26	26	44
7	Burneside	26	6	3	4	18	14	4	2	7	20	29	35
8	Lunesdale United	26	5	1	7	29	28	4	3	6	21	29	31
9	Keswick	26	4	3	6	21	29	4	3	6	20	29	30
10	Windermere SC	26	3	4	6	16	29	4	3	6	20	34	*25
11	Ambleside United	26	3	1	9	21	40	4	2	7	26	31	24
12	Shap	26	4	0	9	23	42	3	1	9	17	38	22
13	Carvetii United	26	2	0	11	17	37	3	2	8	14	43	17
14	Greystoke	26	1	4	8	20	31	0	0	13	12	39	7

DIVISION TWO

		P	W	D	L	F	A	W	D	L	F	A	Pts
1	Carleton Rovers	24	12	0	0	41	2	11	1	0	38	5	70
2	Victoria SC	24	9	3	0	32	10	10	1	1	34	11	61
3	Ibis	24	8	0	4	30	17	8	1	3	35	15	49
4	Appleby Reserves	24	6	2	4	26	18	6	1	5	33	20	39
5	Dent	24	5	2	5	28	31	6	3	3	24	19	38
6	Kirkoswald	24	6	1	5	24	25	4	3	5	15	22	34
7	Ullswater United	24	5	3	4	25	21	4	2	6	18	29	32
8	Wetheriggs United Res	24	5	2	5	29	23	4	1	7	25	27	30
9	Kendal County Res	24	6	2	4	32	25	1	3	8	22	44	26
10	Grasmere	24	1	3	8	16	29	4	2	6	19	30	20
11	Endmoor KGR	24	4	1	7	38	32	1	2	9	10	33	18
12	Burneside Reserves	24	2	3	7	14	24	1	3	8	15	36	15
13	Carvetii United Res	24	3	2	7	18	40	0	1	11	9	62	12

NORTH WESTERN FINAL LEAGUE TABLES 2001-02

STAFFS COUNTY LEAGUE

	P	W	D	L	F	A	Pts
Stallington Res	32	22	5	5	88	45	71
Goldenhill Wndrs	32	21	6	5	117	33	69
Redgate Clayton Res	32	22	2	8	89	43	68
Wedgwood S & S	32	19	3	10	98	49	60
Bradeley	32	17	7	8	88	49	58
Chatterley Whitfield	32	17	5	10	87	50	56
Stone Old Alleynians	32	16	6	10	72	45	54
Milton Rg Res	32	16	3	13	68	60	51
Abbey Hulton U Res	32	14	7	11	77	59	49
Holt JCB	32	13	5	14	47	55	44
Alsagers Bank	32	13	4	15	69	76	43
Hanley Town Res	32	12	6	14	68	66	42
Ward Wanderers	32	12	3	17	66	64	39
Congleton Vale	32	11	4	17	69	70	37
Foley Res	32	7	5	20	46	87	26
Abbey Hulton Youth	32	3	3	26	26	145	12
Gnosall Horns	32	0	0	32	24	203	0

ROCHDALE ALLIANCE

PREMIER DIVISION

	P	W	D	L	F	A	Pts
Spotland Reform	16	13	1	2	86	21	40
New Vic	16	10	3	3	71	30	33
Asia	16	10	2	4	51	34	32
Sudden Websters	16	8	3	5	49	31	27
Nightingale Fk	16	7	3	6	58	53	24
Milnrow	16	6	2	8	33	49	20
Kirkholt WMC	16	5	4	7	42	43	19
Whittles S Thyme	16	3	0	13	32	77	9
Thrum Hall*	16	1	0	15	20	104	2

DIVISION ONE

	P	W	D	L	F	A	Pts
Welfield WMC	16	14	2	0	79	28	44
Kingsway	16	12	1	3	59	30	37
Foth & Harvey	16	9	2	5	56	40	29
Belfield Rangers *	16	8	0	8	40	49	23
King William IV	16	6	1	9	40	48	19
St Albans	16	6	0	10	43	58	18
S Websters Res *	16	5	4	7	39	29	17
Brickcroft SC	16	5	2	9	37	54	17
Birch Hill	16	1	0	15	21	78	3

NORTH LEICESTER LEAGUE

PREMIER DIVISION

	P	W	D	L	F	A	Pts
Hathern	22	17	5	0	58	19	56
West End Rangers	22	15	3	4	81	28	48
Sileby United WMC	22	14	5	3	60	33	47
Ashby Ivanhoe	22	12	4	6	58	27	40
Ingles	22	9	6	7	47	44	33
Bagworth Colliery	22	9	5	8	43	39	32
Kegworth Town	22	8	3	11	44	51	27
Markfield	22	7	2	13	41	70	23
Shelthorpe KC	22	5	6	11	35	55	17
Woodhouse Imperial	22	4	5	13	32	70	17
Loughborough Town	22	3	7	12	29	64	16
Shepshed Amateurs	22	1	5	16	25	53	8

LANCASHIRE & CHESHIRE AMATEUR LEAGUE

DIVISION ONE

	P	W	D	L	F	A	Pts
Heaton Mersey	26	18	7	1	86	25	61
Denton Town	26	16	4	6	62	49	52
Old Ashtonians	26	12	8	6	60	34	44
Rochdalians	26	11	9	6	56	50	42
Bedians	26	10	10	6	59	50	40
Hooley Bridge	26	10	8	8	54	55	38
Oldham Albion	26	10	5	11	56	58	35
Hazel Grove	26	10	4	12	55	64	34
Heywood Town	26	8	6	12	52	57	30
Old Stoconians	26	9	3	14	38	55	30
Cheadle Hulme	26	7	8	11	39	47	29
Wardle	26	7	7	12	66	85	28
Metro	26	5	7	14	64	89	22
Old Standians	26	4	4	18	39	68	16

DIVISION TWO

	P	W	D	L	F	A	Pts
Moss Amateurs	26	24	1	1	119	29	73
Beechfield United	26	22	2	2	84	36	68
Hollingworth	26	13	6	7	63	53	45
Disley Amateurs*	26	12	5	9	63	49	38
Hollingworth OB	26	11	5	10	45	49	38
West Didsbury	26	10	4	12	48	56	34
South Manchester	26	8	7	11	43	46	31
Old Chorltonians	26	9	4	13	44	56	31
Oldham Victoria	26	9	4	13	48	62	31
St Margaret Marys	26	9	3	14	55	74	30
Romiley	26	8	4	14	37	57	28
Newton	26	7	2	17	53	76	23
Oldham Teachers	26	5	7	14	36	60	22
Moston Brook OB	26	6	4	16	41	76	22

CHESTERFIELD & DISTRICT SUNDAY LEAGUE

DIVISION ONE

	P	W	D	L	F	A	Pts
Shirebrook Northern	20	17	1	2	96	24	52
Doe Lea	20	12	2	6	59	46	38
Anvil	20	10	5	5	66	39	35
Brimington Boys	20	9	5	6	43	44	32
Hillstown CC	20	8	6	6	56	49	30
D A Sports	20	8	3	9	32	50	27
Holmewood MW	20	7	5	8	56	62	26
Renishaw SC	20	6	5	9	56	62	23
Parkhouse	20	4	4	12	40	58	15
Grassmoor Sports	20	5	1	14	32	66	15
Newbold WMC	20	3	5	12	29	65	14

MANCHESTER AMATEUR SUNDAY LEAGUE

PREMIER DIVISION

	P	W	D	L	F	A	Pts
Moss Side	18	15	2	1	77	36	47
Timperley Bigshorts	18	14	2	2	68	14	44
Nello James	18	9	3	6	51	50	30
Withington Posh	18	9	2	7	35	30	29
Maudeth	18	8	4	6	51	35	28
Boundary	18	7	3	8	36	32	24
Oakhill	18	7	2	9	36	41	23
MUSC	18	3	4	11	30	68	13
Olympic Belgrave	18	3	1	14	44	71	10
Melchester	18	3	1	14	25	76	10

NORTHERN COUNTIES EAST FOOTBALL LEAGUE

FEEDER TO: NORTHERN PREMIER LEAGUE

President: H F Catt   **Chairman:** Tom Dixon
Secretary/Treasurer: B Wood, 6 Restmore Avenue, Guiseley, Leeds LS20 9DG
Tel & Fax: 01943 874558

The League and its fixture planners breathed a huge sigh of relief this season after the problems encountered the year before when nearly 290 matches were postponed. It was not entirely trouble free, though, with the mid-winter wet spell causing flooding difficulties at Tadcaster Albion again, for example, but generally the weather was a little kinder and the League's fixtures finished on time on the first Saturday in May. Those clubs who did get behind with their matches were often the successful ones with a backlog caused by Cup progress and a number of long distance evening away fixtures had to be played at the end of the season.

With Brigg Town failing to gain promotion at the end of last season when second-placed Ossett Albion were promoted, it was likely that the North Lincs club would again put in a strong challenge for the championship, but their early League fixtures were 'put on hold' somewhat due to plenty of FA Cup and Vase action.

The early running was taken up by several clubs with Selby Town and Hallam being prominent. Another side who became caught up in FA matches was Pickering Town, the promoted club from Division One, who had played only twelve league matches by the beginning of December. For the eventual winners of the Premier Division perhaps 23rd October was the main date of significance. It was on that day that the club, who had always nurtured ambitions to return to the Unibond League, made the decision to replace boss, Jason Maybury, with their own full back Chris Wilder, and from then on the club continued to progress in a number of competitions, losing just one further league match during the rest of the campaign.

Even with that good record, though, it was by no means certain that the championship would return to Alfreton, who last won the trophy back in the 1986-87 season. Both Brigg Town and Pickering Town were the main challengers and a crucial game for Brigg came on 27th March when Alfreton gained a vital 5-1 away victory at The Hawthorns and Pickering's challenge fell away, due in part to their tough end of season fixture list. Eventually, Brigg's push for the title also faltered a little at the end and Alfreton won the championship by six points and with it a return to the Unibond League, which has been richly deserved for their consistency of performance.

Sheffield, playing for the first time at their new Dronfield home, ended the season in mid-table whilst Borrowash Victoria, who had been promoted along with Pickering Town from Division One, were hampered by a poor playing surface and had to use Derby Council's Moorways Stadium for some matches. A number of clubs struggled to avoid the relegation zone which, due to a number of factors, will not operate this season. Garforth Town had a poor season and finished in bottom place with Buxton just above them in the final table.

This Premier Division report would not be complete without a record of thanks to everyone at Denaby United both on the playing and administration side of the club. Under notice to quit their Tickhill Square ground from the local Miner's Welfare organisation at the end of the season, they were determined to leave the League with dignity and achieved this in very difficult circumstances and without finishing in the bottom two. As Secretary Barrie Dalby said: "We've been at Tickhill Square in the Midland, Yorkshire and NCE Leagues since 1912 and it's very sad that we've been forced out of business by local people." Although the club has now gone their eminently proud past history will remain in the records of non-League soccer in the area and beyond.

Taking Alfreton's place in the Premier Division will be Ossett Albion, who return to the NCE after just one season in the higher Unibond League, whilst there will be no relegation from the Premier Division to Division One because of Denaby's demise and only Bridlington Town being suitably graded for promotion.

It was the newly-promoted club in Division One, Lincoln Moorlands, who proved successful in the early matches with Gedling Town and Mickleover Sports also picking up points and Worsbrough Bridge MW not far behind at the turn of the year. The challenge of Bridlington Town was slow to start and a 5-2 defeat by the eventual champions, Gedling Town, in early December seemed to have galvanised the team as that proved to be their final defeat of the season as they went on to enjoy an eighteen match unbeaten run.

By early April it was clear that Gedling woud be champions but the runners-up position was between Brid and Worsbrough who themselves had put together a run of matches since late October with just one defeat in that period. Eventually the seasiders reached the elusive promotion position with a two point margin over their Barnsley rivals and will be promoted to the Premier Division. Sadly, Gedling will not be moving up as their ground does not yet meet the higher standards required.

Pontefract Colls. and Staveley MW must seek re-election to the Division. Rather surprisingly, the Chesterfield club had another poor season after being relegated from the Premier Division. Joining the Division will be CML champions club Shirebrook Town from Mansfield.

To add to their Premier Division success, Alfreton Town had a marvellous season winning the NCE League Cup (4-0 against Armthorpe Welfare), the President's Cup (runners up: Bridlington Town) and the Derbyshire Senior Cup. Our Wilkinson Sword Trophy was won by Bridlington Town, who were also beaten finalists in the East Riding Senior Cup. Lincoln Moorlands won the Lincs Senior 'A' Cup and Gedling Town the Notts Senior Cup. Thackley Reserves were 2-1 winners of the Reserve Division Cup against Selby Town Reserves. There is no doubt who deserves the plaudits in FA national competitions with Brigg Town reaching the First Round Proper of the FA Cup before going out at Tranmere Rovers, whilst the Lincs club also reached the Fifth Round of the FA Vase before losing in a replay to the eventual winners, Whitley Bay.

HONOURS LIST 2001-02

Premier Division	Winners	Alfreton Town	Runners Up	Brigg Town
Division One	Winners	Gedling Town	Runners Up	Bridlington Town
Reserve Division	Winners	Emley Reserves	Runners Up	Farsley Celtic Reserves
League Cup	Winners	Alfreton Town	Runners Up	Armthorpe Welfare
President's Cup	Winners	Afreton Town	Runners Up	Bridlington Town
Wilkinson Sword Trophy	Winners	Bridlington Town	Runners Up	Lincoln Moorlands
Reserve Division Cup	Winners	Thackley Reserves	Runners Up	Selby Town Reserves
Derbyshire Senior Cup	Winner	Alfreton Town		
East Riding Senior Cup			Runners Up	Bridlington Town
Lincs Senior 'A' Cup	Winners	Lincoln Moorlands		
Nottinghamshire Senior Cup	Winners	Gedling Town		

FINAL LEAGUE TABLES 2001-02

PREMIER DIVISION

	P	W	D	L	F	A	Pts
Alfreton Town	38	27	5	6	94	36	86
Brigg Town	38	25	5	8	90	46	80
Hallam	38	21	6	11	72	62	69
Pickering Town	38	20	8	10	70	38	68
Harrogate Railway Ath	38	17	10	11	83	61	61
Armthorpe Welfare	38	17	7	14	56	58	58
Selby Town	38	14	12	12	47	47	54
Thackley	38	14	11	13	48	47	53
Sheffield	38	14	10	14	54	62	52
Arnold Town	38	13	10	15	53	55	49
Liversedge	38	14	6	18	59	66	48
Goole	38	13	9	16	43	51	48
Eccleshill United	38	13	9	16	60	72	48
Glapwell	38	12	10	16	66	71	46
Brodsworth MW	38	13	9	16	68	74	*45
Borrowash Victoria	38	10	13	15	49	57	43
Glasshoughton Welfare	38	10	10	18	49	62	40
Denaby United	38	11	5	22	47	78	38
Buxton	38	8	13	17	43	61	37
Garforth Town	38	8	4	26	46	83	28

DIVISION ONE

	P	W	D	L	F	A	Pts
Gedling Town	30	21	5	4	75	42	68
Bridlington Town	30	20	4	6	73	25	64
Worsbrough Bridge MW	30	18	8	4	70	37	62
Lincoln Moorlands	30	15	6	9	52	41	51
Mickleover Sports	30	16	2	12	51	42	50
Maltby Main	30	15	3	12	54	44	48
Winterton Rangers	30	14	6	10	44	36	48
Rossington Main	30	12	7	11	44	46	43
Hall Road Rangers	30	12	7	11	54	57	43
Hatfield Main	30	10	7	13	50	47	37
Louth United	30	10	5	15	36	46	35
Yorkshire Amateur	30	8	6	16	32	47	30
Tadcaster Albion	30	9	3	18	40	62	30
Parkgate	30	8	3	19	53	80	27
Staveley MW	30	4	12	14	32	60	24
Pontefract Colllieries	30	4	4	22	23	71	16

* Points adjustment

PREMIER DIVISION RESULTS CHART 2001-02

		1	2	3	4	5	6	7	8	9	10	11	12	13	14	15	16	17	18	19	20
1	Alfreton Town	X	0-2	1-1	8-0	1-0	5-0	1-0	2-1	2-1	2-1	1-1	4-2	3-0	3-4	3-1	3-0	3-0	2-0	4-1	2-1
2	Armthorpe Welf.	3-0	X	1-0	2-4	1-2	1-2	1-2	4-1	1-1	2-0	3-2	1-1	4-1	2-1	2-1	0-2	1-3	0-0	2-2	1-1
3	Arnold Town	0-2	3-0	X	2-0	1-2	0-2	4-0	1-2	1-3	4-1	2-0	4-2	0-3	0-2	1-4	2-1	0-3	0-2	1-0	1-0
4	Borrowash Victoria	1-3	1-0	1-1	X	1-3	0-0	0-2	3-1	3-3	1-1	2-1	0-0	1-1	1-2	2-2	0-2	0-0	0-1	2-0	1-2
5	Brigg Town	1-5	2-3	5-1	4-1	X	1-0	6-2	4-0	4-0	4-3	6-1	1-1	0-1	3-0	2-3	2-1	0-1	2-2	4-0	3-1
6	Brodsworth MW	0-1	2-2	1-4	2-2	1-2	X	3-0	7-3	2-2	0-1	3-2	2-2	1-0	7-2	0-4	1-2	0-2	3-1	1-2	0-4
7	Buxton	0-1	5-0	4-3	0-0	1-2	0-3	X	1-0	2-0	2-3	1-1	0-1	0-1	1-1	1-3	0-1	1-1	1-1	0-0	0-0
8	Denaby Utd	2-4	3-0	1-1	1-2	1-0	1-6	0-4	X	4-0	1-0	2-0	0-2	3-1	2-0	2-4	1-1	0-1	0-3	2-0	2-4
9	Eccleshill United	0-4	1-2	0-1	1-1	1-3	1-3	1-2	1-2	X	2-1	3-1	1-0	1-0	1-2	1-0	4-1	2-1	1-1	3-0	1-3
10	Garforth Town	2-6	0-3	3-0	2-4	1-1	1-2	2-0	3-1	X	3-7	1-2	4-1	0-2	1-1	5-1	0-3	0-3	3-2	1-2	
11	Glapwell	1-0	1-0	2-1	3-1	2-2	2-2	4-1	3-1	3-5	3-0	X	5-0	2-1	0-3	2-2	1-0	2-2	0-2	1-4	2-3
12	Glasshoughton W	0-0	0-1	2-2	1-4	1-2	2-2	2-2	0-1	2-2	0-1	0-1	X	0-3	1-2	2-1	4-1	0-1	3-0	2-0	1-2
13	Goole	2-0	3-0	1-1	2-0	0-1	2-1	1-0	0-1	2-0	1-1	2-2	0-2	X	2-1	1-3	1-0	1-1	0-0	1-1	1-2
14	Hallam	4-4	1-1	1-1	2-0	1-2	3-2	4-1	2-1	1-5	0-3	3-2	1-1	5-1	X	1-3	1-2	2-1	2-1	3-0	2-1
15	Harrogate Railway	1-1	3-1	1-1	0-1	0-1	1-1	4-2	2-2	7-3	4-1	2-1	0-2	4-4	1-3	X	4-2	1-2	1-0	1-2	5-2
16	Liversedge	0-2	4-1	2-0	6-3	3-0	0-3	2-2	4-0	2-2	1-0	2-2	4-6	0-1	1-2	2-2	X	2-0	0-2	1-4	1-2
17	Pickering Town	0-2	1-2	1-3	0-1	2-2	8-1	0-0	4-1	3-0	3-1	2-0	5-1	2-0	3-0	1-2	1-1	X	2-1	0-2	2-1
18	Selby Town	2-1	2-3	0-0	2-2	1-5	1-0	1-1	1-1	1-3	1-0	2-2	1-0	2-1	2-1	3-2	0-2	1-3	X	1-2	0-0
19	Sheffield	1-4	0-2	2-2	3-2	1-3	6-1	3-0	3-2	1-1	3-1	2-1	1-0	0-0	3-3	1-1	1-0	0-4	1-1	X	0-0
20	Thackley	0-4	0-1	0-0	1-1	1-3	1-1	1-1	0-0	2-1	1-0	0-0	3-1	2-0	0-1	1-2	1-2	1-1	0-2	2-0	X

LEAGUE CUP 2001-02

FIRST ROUND

Mickleover Sports	v	Parkgate	1-4		Rossington Main	v	Tadcaster Albion	6-4
Worsbrough Bridge	v	Gedling Town	2-3		Yorkshire Amateur	v	Staveley MW	2-3

SECOND ROUND

Arnold Town	v	Thackley	2-1		Borrowash Victoria	v	Staveley MW	1-2
Brodsworth MW	v	Armthorpe Welfare	2-3		Buxton	v	Pickering Town	1-2
Garforth Town	v	Eccleshill United	3-0		Gedling Town	v	Alfreton Town	1-2
Glapwell	v	Maltby Main	2-0		Goole	v	Selby Town	1-0
Glasshoughton Welf	v	Denaby United	3-1		Hall Road Rangers	v	Hallam	4-5
Hatfield Main	v	Pontefract Colls	4-3		Lincoln Moorlands	v	Liversedge	0-3
Parkgate	v	Brigg Town	2-7		Rossington Main	v	Bridlington Town	0-4
Sheffield	v	Louth United	9-0		Winterton Rangers	v	Harrogate Railway	2-6

THIRD ROUND

Alfreton Town	v	Liversedge	2-1		Armthorpe Welfare	v	Sheffield	2-0
Arnold Town	v	Hatfield Main	2-0		Bridlington Town	v	Hallam	2-3
Brigg Town	v	Harrogate Railway	0-2		Glapwell	v	Garforth Town	1-0
Glasshoughton Welf	v	Pickering Town	3-2		Staveley MW	v	Goole	2-2, 0-4

FOURTH ROUND

Alfreton Town	v	Goole	1-0		Armthorpe Welfare	v	Glasshoughton Welf	4-0
Arnold Town	v	Harrogate Railway	1-0		Glapwell	v	Hallam	1-3

SEMI-FINALS

Alfreton Town	v	Hallam	3-1		Armthorpe Welfare	v	Arnold Town	1-0

FINAL

Alfreton Town	v	Armthorpe Welfare	4-0		at Worksop Town

PRESIDENT'S CUP 2001-02

FIRST ROUND

Alfreton Town	v	Mickleover Sports	2-1		Borrowash Victoria	v	Arnold Town	3-4
Gedling Town	v	Sheffield	3-1		Goole	v	Brigg Town	2-1
Hall Road Rangers	v	Thackley	2-3		Hatfield Main	v	Parkgate	1-1, 1-0
Pickering Town	v	Hallam	0-2		Selby Town	v	Bridlington Town	0-2

SECOND ROUND

Arnold Town	v	Hatfield Main	0-0,1-1,5p4		Gedling Town	v	Bridlington Town	1-5
Goole	v	Thackley	2-0		Hallam	v	Alfreton Town	0-3

SEMI-FINALS

Arnold Town	v	Alfreton Town	0-1		Bridlington Town	v	Goole	2-1

FINAL 1st Leg

Bridlington Town	v	Alfreton Town	2-1

FINAL 2nd Leg

Alfreton Town	v	Bridlington Town	1-0	Aggregate score 2-2. Alfreton won on away goals

WILKINSON SWORD TROPHY 2001-02

FIRST ROUND

Bridlington Town	v	Yorkshire Amateur	4-2	Lincoln Moorlands	v	Mickleover Sports	2-0
Louth United	v	Gedling Town	2-1	Maltby Main	v	Winterton Rangers	1-2
Parkgate	v	Tadcaster Albion	2-3	Rossington Main	v	Hall Road Rangers	1-0
Staveley MW	v	Hatfield Main	4-0	Worsbrough Bridge	v	Pontefract Collieries	4-0

SECOND ROUND

Bridlington Town	v	Staveley MW	9-0	Lincoln Moorlands	v	Louth United	1-0
Tadcaster Albion	v	Rossington Main	3-0	Worsbrough Bridge	v	Winterton Rangers	2-1

SEMI-FINALS

Bridlington Town	v	Tadcaster Albion	5-0	Lincoln Moorlands	v	Worsbrough Bridge	2-1

FINAL 1st Leg

Bridlington Town	v	Lincoln Moorlands	4-0

FINAL 2nd Leg

Lincoln Moorlands	v	Bridlington Town	0-6	Bridlington Town won 10-0 on aggregate

RESERVE DIVISION CUP 2001-02

FIRST ROUND

Eccleshill Utd Res	v	Brigg Town Res	2-0	Emley Reserves	v	Thackley Res	1-1, 2-3
Farsley Celtic Res	v	Pontefract Colls Res	3-0	Glasshoughton W Rs	v	Garforth Town Res	2-4
Liversedge Res	v	Selby Town Reserves	1-2	Pickering Town Res	v	Yorkshire Am Res	0-2
Rossington Main Res	v	Ossett Albion Res	0-3	Tadcaster Albion Res	v	Harrogate Rail Res	1-2

SECOND ROUND

Farsley Celtic Res	v	Eccleshill Utd Res	2-1	Harrogate Rail Res	v	Garforth Town Res	0-2
Ossett Albion Res	v	Selby Town Res	1-2	Thackley Reserves	v	Yorkshire Am Res	2-1

SEMI-FINALS

Farsley Celtic Res	v	Selby Town Res	1-2	Thackley Reserves	v	Garforth Town Res	1-0

FINAL

Thackley Reserves	v	Selby Town Reserves	2-1	at Ossett Albion

LEADING GOALSCORERS 2001-02

PREMIER DIVISION			DIVISION ONE		
Michael Godber	Sheffield/Alfreton Town	33	Duncan Bray	Worsbrough Bridge	24
Michael Goddard	Hallam/Alfreton Town	32	Phillip Harrison	Bridlington Town	21
Stephen Davey	Harrogate Railway	31	Paul Palmer	Hall Road/Bridlington	21
Lee Morris	Hallam	25	James Richardson	Bridlington Town	18
Simon Drayton	Brigg Town	20	Stephen Batley	Tadcaster Albion	17
Gareth Collinson	Sheffield/Brodsworth	18	Craig Burdick	Bridlington Town	17
Simon Johnson	Armthorpe Welfare	18	Martin Thacker	Bridlington Town	17
Simon Roach	Brigg Town	18	Kevin Duckworth	Tadcaster Albion	16
Stephen Dillon	Glapwell	17	Lee Harper	Bridlington Town	16
Lee Borman	Brigg Town	15	Norman Limb	Gedling Town	15
Stefan Zoll	Pickering Town	14	Andrew Frawley	Gedling Town	12
Karl Cochrane	Eccleshill United	12	Darren Phipps	Hatfield Main	12
			Duncan Smith	Lincoln Moorlands	12

ARMTHORPE WELFARE

Secretary: Maureen Cottam, The Orchards, Whiphill Lane, Armthorpe, Doncaster DN3 3JP.
Tel: 01302 832514 (H)
Ground: Welfare Ground, Church St, Armthorpe, Doncaster DN3 3AG.Tel:(M) 07771 853899-
(match days only)
Directions: M18 junc 4, A630, left at r'bout then proceed to next r'bout and turn right. Ground
400yds on left behind Plough Inn. Doncaster (BR) 2 1/2 miles. Buses A2, A3 & 181 pass ground
Capacity: 2,500   **Seats:** 200   **Cover:** 400   **Floodlights:** Yes   **Club Shop:** No

Clubhouse: No. Refreshments on ground. Wheatsheaf Hotel used after matches

HONOURS   Northern Co's East Lg R-up 87-88, Lg Cup R-up 91-92, Div 1 R-up 83-84,
East Central Div 1 84-85; Doncaster & Dist. Lg 82-83, Div 1 81-82, Div 2 79-80, Div 3 78-79; Lg
Cup 79-80 80-81 81-82 82-83; Challenge Cup 82-83; West Riding Chall. Cup 81-82 82-83;
Goole & Thorne Dist. Cup 82-83
PREVIOUS   League: Doncaster Senior
RECORD   **Attendance :** 2,000 v Doncaster R., Charity match 85-86
    Appearances: Gary Leighton   **Scorer:** Martin Johnson
    Win: 7-0 v Stocksbridge PS NCE 84-85 & Brodsworth MW NCE 00-01
    Defeat: 0-7 v Belper Town NCE 86-87
BEST SEASON   **FA Vase:** 3rd Round 84-85   **FA Cup:** 3rd Qual. Rd. 86-87

FACT FILE
Founded: 1926
(Disbanded 1974, re-formed 1976)
Nickname: Wellie
Club Sponsors: Houston Transport
Colours: Green & white hoops,green green.
Change colours: Navy/white/navy
Midweek matches: Tuesday
Programme: 24 pages
Editor: John Morgan, 01302 834475 (H)
Local paper: Doncaster Evening Star

CLUB PERSONNEL
Chairman: Stephen Taylor (01302 371995)
Vice Chairman: James Houston
Comm. Manager: Peter Camm
Press Officer: Sharon Morgan
Manager: Carl Leighton
Asst Manager: John McKeown
Coach: Steve Taylor
Physio: Joey Johnson

ARNOLD TOWN

Secretary: Tony Beale, 6 Elms Gardens, Ruddington, Nottm NG11 6DZ (0115 921 1451)
Ground: King George V Recreation Ground, Gedling Rd, Arnold, Notts (0115 9263660)
Directions: From M1 jct 26, take A610 to B6004 (Stockhill Lane) 3 miles to A60. Right at A60,
immediate left (St Albans Rd), thru lights by Wilkinsons left onto Hallams Lane. Ground on right
opposite market. From A1(M)/A614/A60 to lights (Harvester on right), left thru lights to, St.
Albans Rd then as above. Nottingham Midland (BR) 4 miles. Buses 55,57.58, 59 pass ground.
From A6514 left onto A60 for 1/4 m then rt onto Nottingham Rd to town centre by Wilkinsons.
Capacity: 3,400   **Seats:** 150   **Cover:** 950   **Floodlights:** Yes   **Club Shop:** Sells progs,
scarves, badges, mugs , replica shirts and baseball caps etc.(Martin Williams 0115 9598759)
Clubhouse: Licensed bar open matchdays & training nights. Also tea-bar on matchdays.

HONOURS (Arnold & Arnold Town): Central Mids Lg 92-93 (R-up 88-89, Lg Cup 87-88 (R-up 90-
91), F/lit Cup 89-90); NCE Lg 85-86, R-up 83-84, 94-95; Div 1 94-95; Presidents Cup 94-95;
Central 62-63; Notts Snr Cup x9, r-up x 5; Midland Co's Lg R-up 70-71 75-76, Lg Cup 74-75
(R-up 68-69 70-71 80-81). **PREVIOUS Leagues:** Central Mids 89-93. Arnold FC: Bulwell & Dist,
Notts Spartan, Notts Comb (pre 55), Central All. 55-63/ Midland 63-82/ NCE 82-86/ Central Mids
86-89. Kingswell: Notts Yth/ Notts Amat./Notts Spartan/ E. Mids Reg.(pre'76)/Midland 76-82/
NCE 82-86/ Central Mids 86-89. **Names:** Arnold FC (founded 1928 as Arnold St Marys) merged
with Arnold Kingswell(founded 1962) 1989 **BEST SEASONS: FA Cup:**1st Rd replay 77-78
FA Vase.: 5th Rd 01-02 **FA Trophy:** 2nd Rd Replay 71-2

FACT FILE
Founded: 1989   Nickname: Eagles
Sponsors: Mapperley Sports/Neartone Printers
Colours: Yellow (blue trim)/blue/yellow
Change Colours:All red
Midweek matches: Tuesday
Programme:44 pages £1
Editor: Mel Draycott (0115 926 1574)
2001-02 Captain: Chris Hudson
Top Scorers : Mark Gadsby & Paul Mitchell 12
P.o.Y :. Lee Broster
CLUB PERSONNEL
President: Alan Croome Chairman: David Law
Vice-Chairman: Roy Francis
General Manager: Ray O'Brien
Comm. Manager: Len Robinson
Team Manager: Iain McCulloch
Asst Man: Bill Brindley Physio: Trevor Wells
Press Officer: Brian Howes (0115 9856986)
Website: www.arnoldfc.com
Email: mail@arnoldfc.com

BORROWASH VICTORIA

Secretary.: Ian Collins, 30 Margreave Road, Chaddesden, Derby DE21 6JD
    Tel: 01332 739437
Ground: Robinson Construction Bowl, Borrowash Road, Spondon, Derby
    Tel: 01332 669688.
Directions: M1 jct 25, A52 towards Derby, 3rd left off by-pass into Borrowash Rd, ground 400
    yds on left. 2 miles from Spondon (BR). Nottingham to Derby buses pass nearby.
Capacity: 5,000   **Seats:** Yes   **Covered:** 500   **Floodlights:** Yes
Clubhouse: Normal pub hours. Hot & cold food.   **Club Shop:** No

PREVIOUS   **Leagues:** Derby Sun. School & Welf. 52-57; Derby Comb.; Midland 79-82;
    N.C.E.; Cen Mid Lg.   **Ground:** Dean Drive 1911-84

RECORDS   **Attendance:** 2,000 v Nottim Forest,(floodlight opening 22/10/85)
    Win: 11-1 **Defeat:** 3-8 **Goalscorer:** Paul Acklam **Appearances:** Neil Kellogg
BEST SEASON   FA Cup 3rd Qual. Rd 91-92   FA Vase: 4th Rd 90-91,00-01
HONOURS   N.C.E. Lg Div 1 00-01,Div 1 Sth 83-84 (R-up 84-85, Div 2 Sth R-up 82-83),
    Derby Comb. 77-78 (R-up(10) 65-66 68-74 75-77 78-79, Lg Cup 68-69 75-76
    (R-up 63-64 66-67), Midland Co's Lg Div 80-81 (Div 1 Cup 80-81),
    Derbys Snr Cup R-up 90-91, Derbys Div. Cup 73-74 (R-up 70-71 72-73),
    Cen. Midl Lg B E Webbe Cup R-up 88-89 (Res. Cup 94-95)

FACT FILE
Founded: 1911
(Reformed 1963)
Nickname: Vics
Club Sponsors: Robinson Construction
Colours: Red & white stripes/black/black
Change Colours: Navy blue/sky/sky
Mid matches: Tues Prog: 16 pages, 50p
Editor: Max Anderson (01332 669688)

CLUB PERSONNEL
Chairman: Ian Anderson
Press Officer: Secretary
Manager/Coach:Bob Sykes
Asst Man:John Kinane

2001-02
Top Scorer: Tom Widdison 7
Capt: LeeThomas

BRIDLINGTON TOWN

Secretary: Chris Bemrose, 16 North Back Lane, Bridlington, E. Yorks. YO16 7BA
Tel: 01262 604036 (H & Fax) 01262 676836(B) e-mail Admin@brudtownafc.freeserve.co.uk

Ground Queensgate Stadium, Queensgate, Bridlington YO16 7LN **Tel:** 01262 606879
Capacity: 3,000 **Seats:** 742 **Covered Standing** 150 **Executive Boxes:** 2 **Floodlights:** Yes
Directions From south on A165 - Pass golf course, straight over lights. Turn right at r'about by
B&Q. Turn left at next lights & over rlwy bridge. At r'about bear left and then straight on up Quay
Road. After lights turn right into Queensgate & ground is 800yds on right.**From south & west** via
A614 (formerly A166) - Straight on at lights (Hosp. on right). At r'about straight on to mini-r'about &
take 2nd exit rt.. Over the first lights,left at next lights into Queensgate.Ground 800yds on rt.
Clubhouse: Open every evening & all day Sat & Sun   **Club Shop:** Yes, matchdays

HONOURS:E. Riding Sen. Co. Cup 96-97,01-02. E Riding Co. Lg Div. 1 95-96, Sen. Cup 98-99
NCE Div1 R-up 2001-02,Presidents Cup R-up 01-02,WilkinsonSword Trophy .01-02.
RECORD   **Attendance:** 432 for an F.A. Sunday Cup Semi-Final 3.3.2000
                 Appearances: Neil Grimson 200+ (87-97)
                 Goalscorer: Neil Grimson
                 Win: 15-1 v Rudston (A), Driffield Lg Cup 94-95
BEST SEASON **FA Cup:** 2nd Qual. Rd 00-01**FA Vase:** 1st Round 99-00
PREVIOUS   **Leagues:** Driffield Lg.; East Riding County Lg.
                 Names: Grays Inn 1986, Greyhound F.C. 1988

FACT FILE

Founded: 1994
Sponsors: Barton Engineering &
PBS Construction (N.E.) Ltd
Colours: All Red Change Colours: All Blue
Midweek Matchday: Tuesday

Programme: 40 pages Price £1.00
Prog. Editor: Jonathon Bemrose
Website: www.bridtownafc.freeserve.co.uk

CLUB PERSONNEL

Chairman: Barrie Garton
Tel: 01262 850827(H)
Vice Chairman: Don Bemrose
Match Sec.: Jonathon Bemrose
Tel: 01262 673995 (H) 01262 408224 (B)

BRIGG TOWN

Secretary: Robert B Taylor, `Highfield House', Barton Rd, Wrawby, Brigg, Lincs DN20 8SH
Tel: 01652 652284 (H) 01724 402749 (W) **Email Address:** bobtaylor60@aol.com

Ground: The Hawthorns, Hawthorn Avenue, Brigg (01652 652767) Office: 01652 651605

Directions: From M180 Junc 4 Scunthorpe East, A18 through Brigg leaving on Wrawby Rd, left
into recreation ground and follow road into BTFC.
Capacity: 4,000   **Seats:** 250   **Cover:** 2 Stands   **Floodlights:** Yes

Clubhouse: Licensed club open matchdays

HONOURS   F.A. Challenge Vase 95-96; Northern Co's East Lg Presidents Cup R-up 91-
92 92-93, R-up 95-96; Lincs Lg 49-50 53-54 73-74 75-76 (Div 1 68-69 69-70 70-71 71-72, Lg
Cup 49-50 65-66 68-69 69-70 72-73); Mids Co's Lg 77-78 (Lg Cup 77-78); Lincs `A' Snr Cup 75-
76 76-77 94-95 99-00; Lincs `B' Snr Cup (5), NCE (Premier) 00-01
PREVIOUS   **Leagues:** Lindsey; Lincs 48-76; Midland Counties 76-82
                 Grounds: Manor House Convent, Station Rd (pre 1939); Brocklesby Ox 1939-59

BEST SEASON FA Vase: Winners 95-96   **FA Cup:** 4th Rd Q

RECORD   Attendance: 2,000 v Boston U. 1953 (at Brocklesby Ox)

FACT FILE

Formed: 1864 Nickname: Zebras
Colours: Black & white stripes/black/red
Change colours: Yellow/Blue
Midweek Matchday: Wednesday
Programme: 24 pages
Editor: Match Secretary
Club Website: zebras@briggtown.co.uk

CLUB PERSONNEL

President: M.Harness
Chairman: David Crowder, Tel: 01724 864742 (H)
Match Sec: John Martin. Tel: 01652 654526 (H)
Manager: Ralph Clayton
Coach:Dave McLean
2000-01
P.o.Y. & Top Scorer: Simon Roach
Captain: Phil Rowland

BRODSWORTH WELFARE

Secretary: Nigel Hyde, 33 Grosvenor Crescent, Arksey, Doncaster DN5 0SX
Tel Nos: 01302 820738 (H) 01302 820738 (FAX) 07713 140632 (M)
Ground: Welfare Ground, Woodlands, Nr. Doncaster (01302 728380).

Directions: From A1 take A638 to Doncaster, take left after Woodlands Pub into Welfare
Road, ground 50yds on left.
Regular bus service from North Bridge Bus Station, Doncaster.
Capacity: 3,000   Seats: 228   Cover: 500   Floodlights: Yes
Clubhouse: Yes, Matchday drinks and snacks   **Club Shop:** Yes
HONOURS   Yorks Lg 24-25, Donc. & Dist. Lg 84-85 (Lg Cup 85-86, Div 2 78-79, Div 2Cup
78-79), Sheffield Jnr Cup 83-84, Mexborough Montagu Cup 91-92 92-93.R-up N.C.E. Div 1 98-
99
PREVIOUS **Leagues:** Doncaster Snr; Sheffield; Yorkshire.
              Name: Brodsworth Main, Brodsworth Miners Welfare

BEST SEASON FA Cup: 4th Qual. Rd 26-27   **FA Vase:** 3rd Rd 97-98

RECORD   **Win:** 9-0 v Blidworth MW, NCE 97-98
              Fee received: £2,550 (+ Payments for apps) for Danny Schofield
                 fromHuddersfield Town, Jan 99

FACT FILE

Founded: 1912
Nickname: Broddy
Colours: Navy & light blue/royal blue/royal blue
Change colours: Yellow & black
Midweek home matchday: Wednesday
Programme: 50 pages
Editor: Mark Bell

CLUB PERSONNEL

Chairman: Gordon Jennings Tel: 01302 781121
Press Officer Mark Bell (0797 779 4893)
Tel: 01302 725794H)   07720 832147 (M)
Manager: AlanRradford
Physio: Eric Beaumont
2001-02
Captain: Terry Taylor
Top Goalscorer: Gareth Collinson

Arnold Town. Back Row (l-r): Peter Davey, Jon Boulter, Nathan Fletcher, Tony Brown, Chris Hudson, Mark Gadsby, Charlie Bannister. Middle Row: Jim Walters (Academy Coach), Nigel Baily, Tony Simpson, Jason Belcher, David Wilkins, David Law (Chairman), Lee Broster, Stuart Coke, Arran Mohammed, Wayne Manners, Nick Scott (Kitman). Front Row: Bryn Gunn, Darren Bogan, Bill Brindley (Assistant Manager), Paul Mitchell, Iain McCulloch (Manager), Giorgio Vitale, Brett Williams.

Maltby Main. Back Row (l-r): Wilf Race (Manager), Ian Proctor, Lee Winfindale, Chris Bentley, Lee Manderson, Brian Cusworth, Brett Wasden, Gary Liversidge, Russ Evans, Matt Szczepkowski. Front Row: Vinnie Brady (Assistant Manager), Simon Motyka, Jon Noble, Matt Telling, Darryl Winter, Scott Somerville, Paul Staniforth, Russ Ward, Nathan McHale.

BUXTON

Secretary: Sarah Barton,20 Danesway,Chapel en-le-Frith,High Peak SK23 0RF
Tel: No & Fax : 01298 813268 (please telephone before faxing).email:mike@buxtonfc.co.uk
Ground : The Silverlands, Buxton, Derbyshire (01298 24733)

Directions: 200 yards of Buxton Market Place, opp. County Police HQ. Buxton (BR) 1/2 mile.
Capacity: 4,000   **Cover:** 2,500   **Seats:** 490   **Floodlights:** Yes
Club Shop: Yes, Mike Barton,01298 813268
Clubhouse: (01298 23197). Open nightly + Sunday lunchtimes. licensed, no hot food

HONOURS   N.P.L Lg Cup 90-91, Presidents Cup 81-82; Cheshire County 72-73(R-up 46-47 62-63, Lg Cup 56-57 57-58 68-69); Manchester Lg 31-32 (R-up 04-05 28-29 29-30 30-31, Lg Cup 25-26 26-27); Derbys. Sen. Cup 38-39 44-45 45-46 56-57 59-60 71-72 80-81 85-86 86-87.

PREVIOUS   **Leagues:** The Combination 1891-99; North Derbyshire; E Cheshire; Manchester 07-32; Cheshire County 32-73; NLP 73-98.]

BEST SEASON   **FA Trophy:** Qtr Finals 70-71 71-72.   **FA Vase:** 98-99
FA Cup: 3rd Rd 51-52. 2nd Rd 58-59, 1st Rd 62-63League clubs defeated: Aldershot 51-52

RECORDS   **Attendance:** 6,000 v Barrow, FA Cup 1st rd 51-52
Goalscorer: Dave Herbert 104 in 263 games   **Fee Paid:** £5,000 for Gary Walker (Hyde Utd)
Appearances: David Bainbridge 635Fee Received: £23,500 for Ally Pickering (Rotherham 89)

FACT FILE

Formed: 1877
Nickname: The Bucks
Sponsors: Holmfield Bakery
Colours: Royal blue & white /royal/royal
Change colours: All yellow with blue trim
Midweek matchday: Tuesday
Programme: 36 pages £1.00
Editor: Tony Tomlinson
Website: www.buxtonfc.co.uk
Local Press: Buxton Adverftiser and Matlock
Mercury. Local Radio: Radio Derby

CLUB PERSONNEL
Chairman: Tony Tomlinson
Manager: Ronnie Wright
Director of Football: Kenny Johnson
Asst Manager/Coach: David Bainbridge
Res Managers:Barry Nash & JohnCohen
Physio: Dave Percival
Player of the Year: Danny White

ECCLESHILL UNITED

Secretary: LyndaAndrews,46 Stott Terrace,Eccleshill, Bradford BD2 2DX (01274 640346)
Ground: Plumpton Park, Kingsway, Wrose, Bradford BD2 1PN (01274 615739)

Directions: M62 jct 26 onto M606, right on Bradford Ring Road A6177, left on to A650 for Bradford at 2nd r'bout. A650 Bradford Inner Ring Road onto Canal Rd,branch right at Staples (Dixons Car showrooms on right), fork left after 30mph sign to junction with Wrose Rd, across junction - continuation of Kings Rd, 1st left onto Kingsway - ground 200 yds on right. 2 miles from Bradford (BR). Buses 624 or 627 for Wrose
Capacity: 2,225   **Seats:** 225   **Cover:** 415   **Floodlights:** Yes
Clubhouse: Open normal licensing hours. Bar, lounge, games room, hot &cold snacks
Club Shop: Sells range of souvenirs.
HONOURS   N.C.E.Div 1 96-97, Div 2 R-up 86-87, Res Div 86-87 89-90, R-up 87-88 94-95; Bradford Amtr Lg Cup 61-62; Bradford & Dist. Snr Cup 84-85; Bradford & Dist. FA Snr Cup 85-86; W. Riding County Amat. Lg 76-77; West Riding Cup R-up 99-00
PREVIOUS   **Leagues:** Bradford Amat; W Riding Co Amat   **Name:** Eccleshill FC
            Ground: Myers Lane
BEST SEASON   **FA Vase:** 99-00, 5th Rd
RECORDS Attendance: 715 v Bradford C 96-97   **Win:** 10-1 v Blackpool Mechs (H), F.A.C /IQ
Defeat: 0-6 v Rossington Main (A), N.C.E. Lge Cup 2nd Rd 92-93, &   v Gt. Harwood T. (A), FA Cup Prel. Rd 91-92

FACT FILE
Founded: 1948
Nickname: Eagles
Colours: Blue & white stripes/blue/blue
Change colours: All yellow
Midweek matches: Tuesday
Reserves' Lge: NCE Res. Div
Programme: 24-28 pages, 50p
Editor: Lynda Andrews
Tel: 01274 640346
Local Press: Bradford Telegraph & Argus,
Bradford Star Free Press

CLUB PERSONNEL
Chairman: Keith Firth Tel: 01274 787057 (H)
Press Officer: Bill Rawlings (01274 635753)
Manager: Tony Brown
Physio: Gordon Raynor

Player to Progress:Terry Dolan (Hudd'sfied U)

GARFORTH TOWN

Secretary: Paul Bracewell, 24 Coupland Rd, Garforth, Leeds LS25 1AD
            Tel: 0113 286 3314 (H) 0113 214 1800 (B) 07931 900260 (M)

Ground: Wheatley ParkStadium,Cedar Ridge,B rierlands Lane,Garforth, Leeds LS25 2AA
            Tel: 0113 286 4083   Website: www.garforth.town.freeserve.co.uk

Directions: M1 junction 47. Take turning signed 'Garforth' (A642). Approx 200 yards turn left into housing estate opposite White Ho. (Cedar Ridge). Stadium at end of lane.
Capacity: 3,000   **Seats:** 278   **Cover:** 200   **Floodlights:** Yes
Clubhouse: Full Licensing Hours   **Club Shop:** Yes

HONOURS   N.C.E. Lg Div 1 97-98, R-up 96-97, Div 2 R-up 85-86, Lge Cup 99-00; Yorks Lg Div 3 R-up 79-80; Barkston Ash Snr Cup 80-81 84-85 85-86 86-87 92-93 94-95; Wilkinson Sword Trophy 96-97; West Riding County FA Cup 97-98 99-00
PREVIOUS   **Leagues:** Leeds Sunday Comb 64-72; West Yorks 72-78; Yorks 78-82.
            Names: Miners Arms 64-78, Garforth Miners 78-79
BEST SEASON   **FA Vase:** Q-F 85-86   **FA Cup:** 2nd Qual. Rd. 91-92, 97-98
RECORDS   **Attendance:** 1,014 Brendan Ormsby Testimonial v Comb. Leeds/A. Villa XI
            Goalscorer: Vinnie Archer   **Appearances:** Philip Matthews (82-93)
            Record Fee Received: £25,000 for Andy Watson to Doncaster Rovers 1999
            Win: 11-0 v Blidworth W,.Div.1 97-98**Defeat:**1-8 v GlasshoughtonWR Cup 00-01

FACT FILE
Founded: 1964
Nickname: The Miners
Sponsors: Mansfield Breweries
Colours: Yellow/Blue/Yellow
Change colours: Red/black/red
Midweek matches: Tuesday
Reserves' League: NCE Res. Div.
Programme: 32 pages, 50p
Editor: Chris Mather 0113 286 3453 (H)

CLUB PERSONNEL
President: Norman Hebbron
Chairman: Stephen Hayle
Press Officer: Ian Coultard 0113 286 8827
Manager/Coach: Dave Harrison
Asst Manager: Phil Hutchinson
Physio: Paul Cavell
Coach: Brendon Ormsby

GLAPWELL

Secretary: Ellen Caton, 111 The Hill, Glapwell, Chesterfield. S44 5LU.
Tel: 01246 854648 (H & Fax) 07976 838423 (M)
Email: ellen@decaton.fsnet.co.uk

Ground: Hall Corner, Glapwell, Chesterfield, Derbyshire   Tel: 01623 812213

Directions: M1 Junc. 29 A617 towards Mansfield, after Young Vanish Inn take filter lane left onto Bolsover Road, ground facing, use rear entrance next to garden centre
Floodlights: Yes

HONOURS Central Midlands Lg 93-94, Floodlit Cup 93-94, Evans Halshaw Floodlit Cup 96-97 Derbyshire Senior Cup 97-98 R-Up 00-01 (lost onpenalties)   NCE Lg. Cup Finalists 99-00.

BEST SEASON   **FA Vase:** 2nd Rd 96-97

FACT FILE
Founded: 1985
Colours: Black & white stripes/white/white
Change colours: All yellow
Midweek matches: Tuesday
Programme: 48 pages £1.00
Editor: Paul Harrison
01623 842588 (H) 07966 500521 (M)
Web site: www.glapwellfc.co.uk
CLUB PERSONNEL
Chairman: Roger Caton
Manager:Andy Kirk
Assistant Manager: Junior Glave
Commercial Manager: Andrew Saunders

2001-02
Leading goalscorer: Steve Dillon 18
Captain: Simon Poxon
P.o.Y.: John Redfern

GLASSHOUGHTON WELFARE

Secretary: Eric Jones, `Marrica', Westfields Ave, Cutsyke, Castleford WF10 5JJ.
Tel: 01977 556257 (H) 01977 514157(B)

Ground: Glasshoughton Welfare, Leeds Rd, Glasshoughton, Castleford (01977518981)

Directions: From M62 use either Junct. 31 or 32 towards Castleford. From Junction 32 the road comes into Glasshoughton. From Junct. 31 turn right at 2nd roundabout at Whitwood Tech. College. The ground is on the left in Leeds Road. Car park on ground. Castleford (BR) 1 mile.
Capacity: 2,000   Seats: None   Covered: 250   Floodlights: Yes

Clubhouse: Bar & refreshment facilities   **Club Shop:** No

HONOURS   West Riding County Cup 93-94

PREVIOUS   **League:** West Yorkshire   **Name:** Anson Sports 1964-76
Ground: Saville Park 1964-76

RECORD   **Attendance:** 300 v Bradford C, 90
Win: 8-1 v Garforth Town, WR Cup 00-01
Defeat: 0-8 v Hucknall Town, NCE 97-98

BEST SEASON   **FA Cup:** 2nd Qual Rd. 98-99   **FA Vase:** 2nd Round 00-01

FACT FILE
Founded: 1964
Club colours: All Blue
Change colours: All yellow
Midweek Matchday: Tuesday
Reserves' Lge: N.C.E. Res. Div.
Programme: 20 pages, 20p
Prog. Editor: Nigel Lee (0113 247 6186)-W

CLUB PERSONNEL
President: R Rooker
Chairman: Gordon Day
Tel: 01977 514178 (H)
Match Sec: Barry Bennett
Tel: 01977 682593 (H)
Manager: Wayne Day
Asst Manager/Coach: M Ripley

GOOLE AFC

Secretary: Malcolm Robinson, 55 Clifton Gardens, Gools, E.Yorks. DN14 6AR
Tel: 01405 761078 (H) 07801 092952 (M) Email: malrob@lineone.net
Match Secretary: Graeme Wilson, 12 Thorntree Close, Goole, E. Yorks DN14 6LN
Tel: 01405 763316 (H)

Ground: Victoria Pleasure Grounds, Marcus St, Goole DN14 6AR
Tel: 01405 762794 Website: www.gooleafc.freeserve.co.uk
Directions: M62 to Junc 36, then follow signs for town centre.
Turn right at 2nd lights into Boothferry Rd, then after 300 yards turn right again into Carter St, and the ground is at the end of road.
Capacity: 3000   Seats: 200   Cover: 800   Floodlights: Yes
Club Shop: Yes   **Clubhouse:** Matchdays only

HONOURS   NCE Div. 1 99-00, Div. 1 Trophy 99-00; Cen. Mids. Lge. 97-98
PREVIOUS   **League:** Central Midlands 97-99
RECORDS   **Attendance:** 964 v Leeds Utd. 99
Appearances: Phil Dobson 187 (1999-2001)   **Goalscorer:** Kevin Stevens
(97-01)
BEST SEASON   **FA Vase:** 4th Round 98-99   **FA Cup:** 2nd Qual. Rd. 00-01

FACT FILE
Founded: 1997
Colours: Red/ white/ black.
Change Colours: Gold/black/gold & black
Midweek Matchday: Tuesday
Programme Editor: Malcolm Robinson
CLUB PERSONNEL
Chairman: Geoffrey Bruines
49A Pinfold Street, Howden, nr Goole,
East Yorks. DN14 7DE
Tel: 01430 430048 (H) 07790 952790 (M)
Manager:Steve Richards
2001-02
Top Goalscorer: Andy Saville 13 Captain :
Captain: Andy Saville

HALLAM

Secretary: Mrs Susan Muzyczka, 24 Meadow Bank Avenue, Sheffield, S7 1PB.
Tel: 0114 255 3173(H) Club Email: hallamfc@supanet.co.uk Website:www.sportsworldwide.co.uk
Ground: Sandygate, **(The oldest club ground in the world 1860)** Sandygate Road,
Crosspool, Sheffield S10.Tel: 0114 230 9484.   Two new stands and full access & facilities for
wheelchair users. New changing rooms and Social Club. Plus Refreshmants Canteen.
Directions: A57 Sheffield to Glossop Rd, left at Crosspool shopping area signed`Lodge Moor' on
to Sandygate Rd. Ground half mile on left opposite Plough Inn. 51 bus from Crucible Theatre

Capacity: 1,000   **Seats:** 250   **Cover:** 400   **Floodlights:** Yes   **Club Shop:** Yes
Clubhouse: No, use Plough Inn opposite. Hot & cold snacks on ground for matches

HONOURS: Northern Counties (East) Lg Div 1 R-up 90-91 94-95, Yorkshire Lg Div 2 60-61
(R-up 56-57), Sheffield & Hallamshire Snr Cup (4) Finalists 01-02

BEST SEASON   **FA Vase:** 5th Rd 80-81   **FA Cup:** 3rd Qual. Rd 1957
PREVIOUS   League: Yorkshire 52-82
CLUB RECORDS   **Attendance:** 2,000 v Hendon, FA Amtr Cup 3rd Rd 59
                        13,855 v Dulwich at Hillsborough, FA Amtr Cup 55)
                  Goalscorer: A Stainrod 46   **Appearances:** P Ellis 500+
                  Win: 7-0 v Hatfield Main (H) 92-93, & v Kiveton Park (H) 69-70
                  Defeat: 0-7 v Hatfield Main (A) 88-89

FACT FILE
Formed: 1860   Nickname: Countrymen
Sponsors: Hallamshire Holdings Ltd.
Colours: Blue & white hoops/white/blue
Change colours: Red/black/black
Midweek Matches: Wednesday
Programme: Yes 50p
Editor: Mark Radford (Press Off.)
Local Press: Star, Green'Un, Sheffield
Telegraph, Yorkshire Post
CLUB PERSONNEL
Chairman: Tony Scanlan - 01246 415471H
Vice Chairman:R.Merry
President: A Cooper
Press Officer: Mark Radford
Tel: 0114 249 7287 (H)
Manager: S.Hird
Physio:J.Beachall
2001-02 Leading goalscorer: Lee Morris 31
Captain: Tim Willis

HARROGATE RAILWAY ATHLETIC

Secretary: W Douglas Oldfield, 80 Stonefall Ave., Harrogate, Nth Yorks HG2 7NP
               Tel: 01423 540786

Ground: Station View, Starbeck, Harrogate. Tel: 01423 885539 & 01423 883104 (Fax)

Directions: A59 Harrogate to Knaresborough road. After approx 1.5 miles turn left just
               before railway level crossing. Ground is 150 yds up the lane
               Adjacent to Starbeck (BR).
               Served by any Harrogate to Knaresborough bus.
Capacity: 3,000   **Seats:** 300   **Cover:** 600   **Floodlights:** Yes
Clubhouse: Games, TV room, lounge. Open normal pub hours. Hot food available.
Club Shop: Yes
HONOURS   N.C.E. Div 1 98-99, Div. 2 North 83-84, Lg Cup 86-87
PREVIOUS   Leagues: West Yorkshire; Harrogate District; Yorkshire 55-73 80-82.
               Names: Starbeck LNER
RECORD   **Attendance:** 1,400; 1962 FA Amateur Cup
BEST SEASON   **FA Cup:** 4th Qual. Rd. 90-91,01-02   **FA Vase:** 4th Round 88-89
               FA Amateur Cup: 2nd Round 52-53
2001-02   **Captain :** Danny Ames **Top scorer:** Steve Davey 35 **P.o.Y.:** Phil Walker

FACT FILE
Founded: 1935   Nickname: The Rail
Sponsors: Calvert Carpets
Colours: Red /green/red
Change: All white
Midweek matchday: Monday
Programme Editor: Gordon Ward
Tel: 01423 880423 (H) 01423 880423 (Fax)
Local Press: Yorkshire Post, Harrogate Herald
& Advertiser, York Press

CLUB PERSONNEL
President: J Robinson
Chairman: Dennis Bentley
Comm. Man: T.B.A.
Press Officer/Prog. Editor: Gordon Ward
Tel: 01423 880423 (H)
Manager: P.Marshall
Assistant.Man.: M.Margis
Physio: P.Scarth

LIVERSEDGE

Secretary: Michael Balmforth, 7 Reform St., Gomersal, Cleckheaton BD19 4JX (01274 862123)
Ground: Clayborn Ground, Quaker Lane, Hightown Rd, Cleckheaton, W. Yorks (01274 862108)
Directions: M62 jct 26, A638 into Cleckheaton, right at lights on corner of Memorial Park,
         through next lights & under railway bridge, 1st left (Hightown Rd) and Quaker
         Lane is approx 1/4 mile on left and leads to ground. From M1jct 40, A638 thru
         Dewsbury and Heckmondwike to Cleckheaton, left at Memorial Park then
         as above. Buses 218 & 220 (Leeds-Huddersfield) pass top of Quaker Lane
Capacity: 2,000   Seats: 250   Cover: 750   Floodlights: Yes
Clubhouse: Matchdays, Tues, Thursday. Pool, TV. Snacks **Club Shop:** No
HONOURS   W. Riding Co. Chal. Cup 48-49 51-52 69-70; W. Riding County Cup 89-90;
           North Counties East Lg Div 1 R-up 89-90 (Div 2 R-up 88-89);
           West Riding Co.Amtr Lg(6) 23-24 25-27 64-66 68-69 (Lg Cup 57-58 64-65).
PREVIOUS   Leagues: Spen Valley; West Riding County Amateur 22-72; Yorkshire 72-82.
           Ground: Primrose Lane, Hightown.   **Name:** None
BEST SEASON FA Cup: 2nd Qual. Rd. 93-94 97-98 99-00
           FA Vase: 2nd Round 74-75 91-92 93-94 98-99
RECORD   **Attendance:** 986 v Thackley
Players progressing: Garry Briggs (Oxford), Martin Hirst (Bristol City) Leigh Bromby (Sheffield Wed)

FACT FILE
Founded: 1910   Nickname: Sedge
Colours: All blue Change: Gold & Black
Midweek Matches: Tuesday
Reserves League: NCEL Res. Div.
Programme: 28 pages, 50p
Editor: Secretary
Local Press: Yorkshire Evening Post,
Telegraph & Argus, Spenbrough Guardian

CLUB PERSONNEL
Chairman: Robert Gawthorpe
Press Officer: Secretary
Manager: Wayne Bruce
Coach: Phil Smith

2001-02
Top Goalscorer: Adam Goldthorpe 13
Captain: Paddy Kerr
P.O.Y.: Steve West

OSSETT ALBION

Secretary: David Chambers, 109 South Parade, Ossett, Wakefield, WF5 0BE. Tel:01924 276004 (
GROUND: Dimple Wells, Ossett (01924 273618-club, 01924 280450-grd)
Directions: M1 jct 40. Take Wakefield road, right at Post House Hotel down Queens Drive. At end right then second left down Southdale Rd. At end right,then first left down Dimple Wells (cars only). Coaches take second left following the road for 200yds bearing left twice. Four miles from both Wakefield and Dewsbury BR stations. Buses 116 and 117
Capacity: 3,000   **Seats:** 200   **Cover:** 500   **Floodlights:** Yes
Clubhouse: 3 bars + function room, open 7 days per week - catering available
Club Shop: Selling various souvenirs & programmes. Contact chairman
PREVIOUS   Leagues: Heavy Woollen Area 44-49; West Riding Co. Amtr 49-50; West Yorks 50-57; Yorks 57-82. **Ground:** Fearn House
RECORDS   Attendance: 1,200 v Leeds Utd, floodlight opening 1986
Win: 12-0 v British Ropes(H), Yorks. Lge Div. 2 6/5/59
Defeat: 2-11 v Swillington (A), W. Yorks. Lge Div. 1 25/4/56
Goalkeeper: John Balmer   **Appearances:** Peter Eaton, 800+ (22 yrs)
HONOURS: Yorks Lg 74-75 R-up 59-60 61-62, Lg Cup 75-76, 76-77, Div 2 78-79, 80-81 R-up 58-59; N.C.E. Prem. Div. R-up 00-01 Div 1 86-87 Lg Cup 83-84; West Yorks Lg 53-54 55-56 Div 2 52-53, Lg Cup 52-53; W. Riding County Cup 64-65 65-66 67-68; Wheatley Cup 56-57 58-59
Players progressing: Gary Brook (Newport, Scarborough, Blackpool) 1987, Ian Ironside (Barnsley, Middlesbrough, Scarborough) 1980.

FACT FILE
Founded: 1944   Nickname: Albion
Sponsors: Arco
Colours: Old gold & black/black/gold
Change colours: All white
Midweek matches: Wednesday
Reserves' Lge: NCEL Res Div
Prog: 44 pages Price: £1
Editor: N Wigglesworth (01924 275630)
Website: www.pyke42.freeserve.co.uk
2000-01 - Captain: C. Shaw
P.o.Y.: M. Carter Top Scorer: M. Carter 16

CLUB PERSONNEL
President: Miss Helen Worth
Chairman: Neville A Wigglesworth
Vice-Chairman: S B Garside
Commercial Man.: D Riley 01924 240247
Press Officer: Neville Wigglesworth
01924 275630
Manager: Eric Gilchrist
Physio: Nicky Davies Coach: Tony Passmore

PICKERING TOWN

Secretary: David Chapman, 29 The Avenue, Norton Malton, N. Yorks, YO17 9EF.
        Tel: 01653 693486(H)
Ground: Recreation Club, Mill Lane (off Malton Rd), Pickering, North Yorkshire
        Tel: 01751 473317
Directions: A169 from Malton. On entering Pickering take 1st left past Police Station and
        B.P. garage into Mill Lane, ground 200 yards on right
Capacity: 2,000   **Seats:** 200   **Cover:** 500   **Floodlights:** Yes
Clubhouse: Open 1.30pm for Saturday games, 6pm for midweek games.
        Food available from Football Club Kitchen at half-time and after games.
Club Shop: No
PREVIOUS   Leagues: Beckett; York & District; Scarborough & District; Yorkshire 72-82.
RECORD   Attendance: 1,412 v Notts County, friendly, August 1991
HONOURS   Northern Co's East Lg R-up 92-93 Div 2 87-88, Div 1 R-up 91-92, 00-01,
        Yorks Lg Div 3 73-74, Div 2 R-up 74-75 North Riding Snr Cup R-up 93-94 94-95,
        N. Riding Co. Cup 90-91, Wilkinson Sword Trophy 2000-01.
BEST SEASON   FA Cup: 2nd Qual. Rd. 99-00,01-02   **FA Vase:** 4th Round 01-02
Players progressing: Chris Short (Stoke City), Craig Short (Everton) both via Scarborough

FACT FILE
Founded: 1888
Nickname: Pikes
Club Sponsors: Flamingoland
Colours: Royal bluewhite/royal blue
Change colours: All Green
Midweek matches: Tuesday
Reserves' League: N.C.E. Res. Div.
Programme: 48 pages, 80p
Editor: Gerry Gregory (01751 473818)

CLUB PERSONNEL
Chairman: Anthony Dunning (01751 473697)
President: J.P.Jennison
Manager: Steve Brown
Assist. Manager: Richard Rose
Physio: Clive Reynolds
Coach: Steve Brown

2001-02
Leading goalscorer: Stefan Zoll 19
P.o.Y: Danny Farthing
Captain: Simon Sturdy

SELBY TOWN

Secretary: Thomas Ardley,176 Abbots Rd,Selby, N.Yorks.O8 8AZ Tel: 01757 700356 H)
07974691437(M) Email Address: toonarkley@hotmail.com
Ground: Flaxley Rd Ground, Richard St, Scott Rd, Selby, N YorksYO8 0BS.Tel: 01757 210900
Directions: From Leeds, left at main traffic lights in Selby down Scott Rd.then 1st left into Richard St. From Doncaster go straight across main traffic lights into Scott Road then 1st left. From York right at main traffic lights into Scott Rd, and 1st left. 1 mile from Selby (BR)
Capacity: 5,000 **Seats:** 220 **Cover:** 350 **Floodlights:** Yes
Clubhouse: Bar at ground open first and second team matchdays   **Club Shop:** Yes
HONOURS   Yorkshire Lg 32-33 34-35 35-36 52-53 53-54 (R-up 24-25 25-26 27-28 28-29
        30-31 31-32 50-51 55-56, Div 3 R-up 74-75, Lg Cup 37-38 53-54 54-55 62-63);
        N.C.E. Div 1 95-96, Div 2 R-up 89-90, Presidents Cup 00-01; W. Riding Snr
        Cup 37-38; W. Riding Co Cup 27-28 48-49; W. Riding Chall. Cup 34-35 35-36
PREVIOUS   League: Yorkshire (1920-82) **Ground:** Bowling Green, James St. 1920-51
BEST SEASON FA Cup: Second Round Proper 54-55   **FA Vase:** 4th Round 95-96
RECORD   Attendance: 7,000 v Bradford Park Avenue (FA Cup 1st Rnd 1953-54)
Goalscorer: Graham Shepherd 158 (63-82)
Win: 14-1 v Altoffs, W. Rid. Cup 35
Defeat: 0-14 v Bradford PA Res. Yorkshire Lge 28

FACT FILE
Founded: 1918 Nickname: The Robins
Sponsors: A>D>D> Computers
Colours: All red
Change colours: Amber/black/amber
Midweek Matches: Tuesday
Reserves' League: N.C.E. Res. Div.
Programme: 30 pages, 50p
Editor: Richard Pickering (01757 706486)
Local Newspaper: Selby Times
CLUB PERSONNEL
Chairman: David Maguire (01757 290456)
President: J.Belbin
Match Sec: Jason Whiteley
Manager: B Lyon
Asst Manr/Coach: G.Cygan
2001-02
Catain: Andy Hart
P.o.Y.: Dominic Moyles
Top Scorer: Peter Collier 11

SHEFFIELD

Secretary: Stephen Hall, 23 Regent Court, Bradfield Rd, Hillsborough, Sheffield S6 2BT
Tel: 0114 233 4441 (H), 01246 258918 (B)
Ground: Coach & Horses Ground, Sheffield Road, Dronfield. Sheffield
Directions: M1, J 29, A617 into Chesterfield. At traffic island turn right onto dual carriageway A61 (Sheffield). Follow over two islands and at third island follow sign 'Dronfield/Gosforth Valley'. At entrance to Dronfield, The Coach & Horses ground is at bottom of hill on the right.
Capacity: 2,000   **Seats:** 250   **Floodlights:** Yes
Clubhouse: Licensed Bar   **Club Shop:** No

PREVIOUS   League: Yorks 49-82   **Grounds:** Abbeydale Park, Dore (1956-1989);
Sheffield Amateur Sports Club, Hillsborough Park 1989-91; Sheffield International (Don Valley) Stadium 1991-94; Sheffield Sports Stadium Don Valley 94-97.
HONOURS   FA Amateur Cup 02-03; FA Challenge Vase Runners-up 76-77;
Northern Co's East Lg Cup 94-95 ,Div 1 88-89 90-91;
Yorkshire Lg Div 2 76-77, Lg Cup 77-78
BEST SEASON   FA Cup: 4th Qual. Rd 00-01   **FA Vase:** R-up 76-77
FA Amateur Cup: Winners 1903-04
RECORD   Attendance: 2,000 v Barton Rovers, FA Vase SF 76-77
Player progressing: Richard Peacock, Hull 94-95,

FACT FILE

Founded: 24th October1857
Nickname: The Club
Sponsors: Bumford Heating
Colours: Red & black /black/red
Change: All blue
Midweek matchday: Tuesday
Programme: 16 pages, 50p
Editor:Craig Williamson(0114 258 1108)

CLUB PERSONNEL

Chairman: Richard Tims
Tel: 0114 2728888 (B)
President: Alan Methley

Manager: David McCarthy
Asst Manager: Lee Walshaw
Physio: Steve Naylor

THACKLEY

Secretary: Stewart Willingham, 3 Kirklands Close, Baildon, Shipley, Yorks BD17 6HN
Tel: 01274 598589
Ground: Dennyfield, Ainsbury Avenue, Thackley, Bradford (01274 615571).
Directions: On main Leeds/Keighley A657 road, turn off at Thackley corner which is 2 miles from Shipley traffic lights and 1 mile from Greengates lights.Ainsbury Avenue bears to the right 200yds down the hill. Ground is 200yds along Ainsbury Avenue on the right. 3 miles from Bradford Interchange (BR), 1.5 miles from Shipley (BR). Buses to Thackley corner (400 yds)
Capacity: 3,000   **Seats:** 300   **Cover:** 600   **Floodlights:** Yes
Clubhouse: Tue-Sun evenings,matches and w/e lunchtimes. Hot & cold snacks on matchdays
Club Shop: Progs, Metal badges- £2.50 + s.a.e.Contact Geoff Scott (01274 611520)

HONOURS   N.C.E. Lg R-up 94-95, Lg Cup R-up 94-95; Yorks Lg Div 2 73-74; West Yorks Lg 66-67; W. Riding Co. Amtr Lg (x3) 57-60; W. Riding Co. Cup 73-74 74-75; W. Riding Co. Chal. Cup 63-64 66-67, R-up 94-95; Bradford & Dist. Snr Cup 12.
PREVIOUS   Leagues: Bradford Amateur, W. Riding County Amateur, W. Yorks, Yorks 67-82.
Name: Thackley Wesleyians 1930-39
BEST SEASON   FA Vase: 5th Rd 80-81 (01-2 v Whickham)   **FA Cup:** 2nd Qual. Rd.(x3)
RECORD   Attendance: 1,500 v Leeds Utd 1983
Players progressing: Tony Brown (Leeds), Ian Ormondroyd (Bradford City).

FACT FILE

Founded: 1930
Sponsors: Diamond International Shipping
Colours: Red & white/white/red
Change colours: All white
Midweek matches: Tuesday
Programme: 20 pages, 50p Editor: Secretary
Local Press: Bradford Telegraph & Argus,
Bradford Star, Aire Valley Target.

CLUB PERSONNEL

Chairman: Secretary (acting)
Treasurer: Steven Paley
Manager/Coach: Andrew Taylor
Asst Manager: Warren Fletcher
Physio: John Laidler
2000-01
Captain: Craig Sugden P.o.Y.: Bryan Brooks
Top Scorer: Andrew Patterson 12

Pickering Town's Kevin Martin manages to palm away this Alfreton shot but the visitors won 2-0.
Photo: Bill Wheatcroft

Above left: Glasshoughton Welfare's Jamie Heath takes the ball past Whickham's Kevin Hay. Photo: Bill Wheatcroft

Above right: Woodley Sports Andy McDonald tussles in midfield with Thackley's Amjad Iqbal during their clash at Dennyfield. Photo: Darren C Thomas

Below: Whitley Bay's Gary Cook (11) puts in an early cross during the Fifth Round FA Vase tie against Brigg Town which produced a thrilling 3-3 draw. Photo: Graham Brown

GEDLING TOWN

Secretary: Tony White, 9 Bourne Street, Netherfield, Nottingham NG4 2FJ(0115 911 1961)
Ground: Riverside Ground, (rear of Ferryboat Inn), Stoke Lane, Stoke Bardolph, Nott'm NG14 5HX
Directions: A612 Nottingham-Lowdham-Southwell road. Just before Burton Joyce turn right into Stoke Lane to Ferryboat P.H. Approx 1.5 miles. Ground at rear of pub.
Capacity: 2,000   **Seats:** None   **Cover:** 500   **Floodlights:** Yes
Clubhouse: Matchdays only. Refreshments. Licensed bar.   **Club Shop:** No
Honours: Central Mids Lg Prem 97-98 R-up 91-92, Div 1 90-91, (Res Prem 96-97 97-98); Wakefield Floodlit Trophy 92-93 R-up 95-96; Ken Marsland Cup (Res) 93-94; Notts Amtr Lg 89-90 (Snr Cup R-up 89-90).Res Lg & Cp Winners 98-99, NCECup 01-02, Notts Cup 01-02
Best season FA Vase: 3rd Rd 96-97
RECORDS   **Attendance:** 250 v Arnold Town.
Win: 11-0 v Radford 91-92   **Defeat:** 2-5 v Staveley MW 93-94.
Goalscorer: Rob Orton 98 in 124 **Appearances:** Gary Ball 300+

FACT FILE
Founded: 1986
Colours: Blue & yellow/blue&yellow/blue
Midweek Matchday: Tuesday
Prog 32 pages 50p
Editor:Tony White

Chairman: T.B.A.

Managers: Gary Haywood
Assistant Manager: darren Davies
Physio: Dick Henton

HALL ROAD RANGERS

Secretary: Neil Winsor,168 Blenheim Street,Princes Avenue, Hull, East Yorks. 01482 491045(H)
Ground: Dene Park, Dene Close, Beverley Rd, Dunswell, Nr Hull (01482 850101).
Directions: M62 to A63, turn left before Humber Bridge onto A164 to Beverley,after approx 5 miles turn right onto A1079. In 2 miles turn left at large roundabout to ground 20 yards on right.
Capacity: 1,200   Seats: 250   Cover: 750   Floodlights: Yes
Clubhouse: Open all week for drinks and bar snacks, snooker, pool and darts.   **Shop:** Yes

HONOURS   N.C.E. Lg Div 2 90-91, Yorks Lg Div 3 72-73 79-80, E. Riding Snr Cup 72-73 93-94.

PREVIOUS   **Leagues:** East Riding Co.; Yorks 68-82   **Ground:** Hull Co-Op (to 1968)

BEST SEASON   **FA Cup:** Never entered   **FA Vase:** 3rd Round 99-00

RECORDS   **Attendance:** 1,200 v Manchester City Aug 93
Goalscorer: G James   **Appearances:** G James

Players progressing: Gerry Ingram (Blackpool, Sheff Wed). Mark Greaves (Hull City)

FACT FILE
Founded: 1959   Nickname: Rangers
Sponsor: Admiral Signs of Hull Ltd.
Colours: Blue & white hoops/ blue/ blue.
Change : Red & Black Stripes,black/black
Midweek Matches: Wednesday
Reserves' League: East Riding Co.League
Programme: 36 pages, 50p
Editor/Press Officer: Secretary
Local Press: Hull Daily Mail

CLUB PERSONNEL
Chairman:Robert Smailes (01482 821354 (H))
Manager: Nigel Dalee
Asst Mgr: Jamie Barnwell
Coach: Ian Davis

HATFIELD MAIN

Secretary: Stuart Bagnall, 53 Walnut Road, Thorne, Doncaster, S.Yorks. DN8 4HN
TeL: 01405 740424 (H) 07788 730804 (M)
Ground: Dunscroft Welfare Ground, Dunscroft, Doncaster, S. Yorks Tel: 01302 841326
Directions: From Doncaster (A18) Scunthorpe Rd to Dunsville, left at Flarepath Hotel down Broadway. Ground half mile on right.
Stamforth & Hatfield (BR) 1/2 mile. Buses every 15 mins. from Doncaster.
Capacity: 4,000   Seats: 200   Cover: 600   Floodlights: Yes
Clubhouse: Full licensing hrs. Hot/cold drinks/snacks **Club Shop:** Yes
HONOURS   Northern Counties East Prem Div 95-96, R-up 88-89, Div One 94-95; Yorks Lge Div 1 R-up 65-66; W Riding Cup 61-62 63-64.
PREVIOUS   **League:** Doncaster Dist, Yorkshire 55-82
RECORDS   **Gate:** 1,000 v Leeds, A Jones testimonial. Competitive: 750 v Bishop Auckland.
Appearances: Lal Dutt   **Fee received:** £1,000 for Mark Hall (York City)
Players progressing: Mark Atkins (Scunthorpe), Wayne Hall (York)

FACT FILE
Founded: 1936   Nickname: The Main
Sponsors: Manor Tyres, (Stainforth)
Colours: All red   Change Colours: All blue
Midweek matchday: Tuesday
Reserves' League: None
Programme: 25 pages, 50p
Editor: Tony Ingram (01302 842795)

CLUB PERSONNEL
President: R. Wright   Chairman: Peter Wright
Treasurer: Russel Wright
Commercial Manager: Stuart Robinson
Manager: Colin Douglas
Asst Manager:Glenn Hodgit &Stuart Dowing
Physio: Shaun McDonald

LINCOLN MOORLANDS

Secretary: Stuart Gordon,35 Rochester Drive,Hampton Park,Lincoln LN6 0XQ (01522828894)
Ground: Moorland Sports Ground, Newark Rd, Lincoln LN5 9LY
Tel: 01522 520184   Office & Fax: 01522 874111
Directions: From north A1 to Markham Moor. Take A57 until Lincoln by-pass and then turn right onto A46. At 3rd r'about left into Doddington Rd. Continue until Newark Rd. - ground on left after 800 yards.
From Newark enter Lincoln on A1434, go past Forum Shopping Centre for approx. 3/4 mile. Ground on left signposted 'Moorlands Club'.
Capacity: **Seats:** 100   **Cover:** 200   **Floodlights:** Yes
Clubhouse: Yes   **Club Shop:** No
HONOURS Central Midlands Supreme 99-00, R-up 00-01, Lincolnshire Senior A 00-01

2000-01   **Leading Goalscorer:** Steve Bull 14
Captain: Darren Chapman   **P.o.Y.:** Jamie Chesman

FACT FILE
Founded: 1989

Nickname: The Moors
Colours: Sky Bue + Navy trim/Navy/ Sky Blue
Change colours: Orange/black/orange
Midweek Matchday: Wednesday
Programme: 2 pages price 75p
Editor: Kevin Griffin 01522 720940 (H)

CLUB PERSONNEL
Chairman: Graham Longhurst
Manager: Garry Goddard

LONG EATON UNITED

Secretary: Jim Fairley, 13 Redland Drive,Chilwell, Nottingham NG9 5JZ9726343.
Tel No: 0115 9199447 (HO

Ground: Grange Park, Station Road, Long Eaton, Nottingham (0115 973 5700).

Directions: M1 Junc 25, take A52 towards Nottingham, to island by `Bardills Garden Centre', left onto B6003 to t/lights. Right A453, 2nd left Station Rd. Entrance on left opposite the Speedway Stadium

Capacity: 5,000　Seats: None　Cover: 500　Floodlights: Yes

Clubhouse: Open matchdays, snacks available
Club Shop: None

Record Honours **Attendance:** 2,000 1973 FA Cup
Derbys Snr Cup 64-65 75-76, Midland Co's Lg R-up 76-77,
Central Alliance Div South 58-59, Northern Co's (East) Div 1 South 84-85.

FACT FILE
Founded: 1956
Nickname: Blues
Sponsor: Beeston Suite Co
Colours: All Blue
Change colours: Red/black/black
Midweek Matchday: Tuesday
Programme: 20 pages 50p
Editor: G Whitehead

CLUB PERSONNEL
Chairman: J C Fairley
Manager:Adam Bamford
Physio: John Burns

LOUTH UNITED

Secretary: Albany Jordan,180 High Holme Road,Louth, Lincs. LN110JX Tel No: 01507 607356
Ground: Park Avenue, Louth, Lincs Tel: 01507 607351 FAX: 01507 607351
Directions: A16 To Louth Market Place, exit via Eastgate/Eastfield Rd, to Fire Station turn right into Park Avenue. Ground at bottom of avenue of prefabricated bungalows.
Capacity: 2,500　Seats: None　Cover: 400　Floodlights: Yes　**Club Shop:** No
Clubhouse: Weekdays 6.30-11.45, Sat 12-11.45. Full bar facilities. Snacks available.

HONOURS Lincs Lg Prem 72-73 85-86 86-87 (Div 1 57-58 66-67 67-68; Lg Challenge Cup 73-74 86-87; Lg Charity Cup 55-56 56-57 67-68; Central Mids Lg Cup R-up 92-93; Wakefield F'lit Cup R-up 91-92; Lincs Snr `A' Cup 77-78. R-Up 00-01 Lincs Sen Cup R-up: 98-99
PREVIOUS Leagues: Lincs 47-75 82-88; Central Midlands 88-93.
Names: Louth Nats & Louth Town - merged　Grounds: None
BEST SEASON FA Cup: 3Rd Q 0-2 v Emley **F.A Vase:** 4th Rd v Halesowen Town 85-86
RECORDS: Goalscorers: Peter Rawcliffe 39 Appearances: Steve Newby 510 Att:: 2,500

FACT FILE
Founded: 1947　Nickname: The Lions
Sponsors: 'Brother'
Colours: Blue with red trim/blue/blue
Change:All Yellow
Midweek matches: Tuesday
Reserves League: Lincolnshire
Prog:50p ED/ PressOff: Albany Jordan
CLUB PERSONNEL
Chair: Jim Waumsley V-Chair: Albany Jordan
Ch Exec:Jim Walmsley Pres: Dave Fairburn
Commercial Manager: Simon Hewson
Man: Steve Newby Coach: Nigel Fanthorpe.
Physio: Kenny Vincent
2000-01 Capt: James Marshall P.o.Y.: & Top Scorer Simon Bailey 23

MALTBY MAIN

Secretary: Dave Morris, 2 Buckingham Way, Maltby. S66 7EA Tel No: 01709 814400
Email: david@morris1984.fsnet.co.uk
Ground: Muglet Lane, Maltby , Rotherham. Tel: 017941 057883
Directions: Exit M18 at junct 1 with A631. Two miles into Maltby, right at traffic lights at Queens Hotel turn onto B6427 Muglet Lane. Ground 3/4mile on left. Bus 101 from Rotherham stops at ground. Bus 287 from Sheffield to Queens Hotel, then follow as above
Capacity: 2,000　Seats: 150　Cover: 300　Floodlights: Yes
Clubhouse: No, Miners Welfare Club opposite　**Club Shop:** No
HONOURS Sheff. & Hallamshire Snr Cup 77-78, N.C.E. Lge Presidents Cup 92-93, Mexborough Montague Cup 76-77 80-81 90-91,Yorks Lg R-up 77-78, Sheff. Wharncliffe Cup 80-81.
CLUB RECORDS Attendance: 1,500 v Sheffield Wed., June 91-92 (friendly)
PREVIOUS Leagues: Sheffield County Senior; Yorkshire 73-82.
Name: Maltby Main 1916-65 (disbanded); Maltby Miners Welfare 1970-96
2001-02 Captain: Brett Wasden Top Scorer: Russ Ward 9

FACT FILE
Founded: 1916　Nickname: Miners
Sponsors: Millgate Computer Systems
Colours: Red/white/red　Change: All yellow
Midweek matchday: Wednesday
Programme: 36 pages, 70p
Editor: Nick Dunhill Tel: 017941 057 883
CLUB PERSONNEL
Chairman: Gary Kitching
Vice Chairman: Graham McCormick
President: H Henson
Match Sec: Dave Morris (01709 814400)
Manager:Wilf Race
Asst. Man: Vinnie Brady
Coach: Les Harris

MICKLEOVER SPORTS

Secretary: Tony Shaw, 80 Onslow Road, Mickleover, Derbys. DE3 5JB
Tel: 01332 512826 (H & Fax)
Club Website: www.mickleoversports.fsnet.co.uk
Ground: Mickleover Sports Ground, Station Rd, Mickleover, Derby (01332 521167).
Directions: Derby ring road A38 to A52, turn off at Markeaton Park Island.Take turn to Ashbourne A52, then 2nd left into Radbourne Lane. Take 3rd left into Station Road, ground on corner.

Capacity: 1,500　Seats: 280　Cover: 200

Clubhouse: Open Thursdays and Fridays (7-11 p.m) Saturdays and Sundays (11am-11pm) Snacks available only on Matchdays
Club Shop: No
2000-01 Top Goalscorer: Justin O'Reilly 7 **Captain :** Corin Holness **P.o.Y.** Corin Holness

FACT FILE
Founded: 1948
Colours: Red & White shirts/black/red
Change Colours: All blue
Midweek Matchday: Tuesday
Programme Editor: Stephen Pritchard
Tel: 01332 516271

CLUB PERSONNEL
Chairman Keith Jenkinson (01332 516 271-H)
Match Sec.: Cath Grant (01332 511359)
Manager: Mark Kelsey

PARKGATE

Secretary: Bruce Bickerdike, 2 Cardew Close, Rawmarsh, Rotherham S62 6LB
Tel: 01709 522305 Fax: 01709 528583.
Ground: Roundwood Sports Complex, Green Lane, Rawmarsh, Rotherham S62 6LA
Tel: 01709 826600   Website: www.parkgatefc.co.uk   Email: bruce@parkgatefc.co.uk
Directions: From Rotherham A633 to Rawmarsh. From Doncaster A630 to Conisbrough, then
A6023 through Swinton to Rawmarsh. Grd at Green Lane - right from Rotherham, left from
Conisbrough at the Crown Inn. Grd 800yds right
Capacity: 1,000   Seats: 300   Cover: 300   Floodlights: Yes   **Club Shop:** No.
Clubhouse: Licensed bar, 2 lounges. Meals available lunchtime Wed-Sat.
HONOURS   S&HSC Finalists 0-3 v Emley 97-98, Wilkinson Sword Trophy R-up 98-99
PREVIOUS   **Leagues:** Sheffield County Senior Lge; Yorkshire 74-82   **Ground:** None
    Names: BSC Parkgate (82-86); RES Parkgate (pre-1994).
RECORD   **Attendance:** v Worksop 1982
BEST SEASON   **FA Cup:** 2nd Qual. Rd 97-98   **FA Vase:** 1st Round, 6 times

FACT FILE
Founded: 1969
Nickname: The Gate or The Steelmen
Kit Sponsors: JBB Investigations
Colours: All red   Change: Blue & yellow
Midweek matches: Tuesday
Programme: 20 pages, £1.00
Editor: Stuart Bisby (01709 545219)
CLUB PERSONNEL
President: Paul Cristinacce
Chairman: Neil Freeman
Vice Chairman: Les Taylor
Press Officer: Secretary
Manager: Stewart Evans
Asst Man: Vincent Brady
Physio: David Proctor

PONTEFRACT COLLIERIES

Secretary: Frank Maclachlan, 188 Watling Road, Ferry Fryston, Castleford WF102QY
,Tel: 01977 512085 (H), 01977 601327 (B), 07710 586447 (M) Email: rod@erick.fsnet.co.uk
Ground: Skinner Lane, Pontefract, West Yorkshire (01977 600818)
Directions: M62 jct 32 towards Pontefract. Left at lights after roundabout for park entrance and
retail park. Traffic thro town should follow racecouse signs thro lights to roundabout and back to
lights. Monkhill (BR) 1/2 mile. Bahhill (BR) 1 mile. Tanshelf (BR) 1/2 mile .All Leeds and Castleford
buses pass ground. **Capacity:** 1,200 **Seats:** 300 **Cover:** 400 **Floodlights:** Yes
Clubhouse: Fully licensed. Hot & cold snacks. Open before and after games   **Club Shop:** No
HONOURS   N.C.E. Lg Div 1 83-84 95-96 (Div 2 R-up 82-83); Floodlit Comp 87-88 88-89;
Yorks Lg Div 3 81-82; W. Riding Co. Cup R-up 87-88 90-91;Embleton Cup 82-83 86-87 95-96; 99-
00 Castleford FA Cup 82-83 86-87,94-95; Wilkinson Sword 95-96
PREVIOUS Leagues: West Yorkshire 58-79; Yorkshire 79-82 **RECORD Attendance:** 1,000 v
Hull City, floodlight opening 1985.   **Players progressing:** David Penney (Derby Co., 85),
Andy Hayward (Rotherham U) and Dean Trott (Northampton Town)

FACT FILE
Founded: 1958   Nickname: Colls
Sponsors: Liverno
Colours: Blue & black halves/black/black
Change :All green Midweek Matches: Tuesday
Programme: 36 pages 70p
Editor:Rod Taylor(01977 602266
Local Press: Pontefract & Castleford Express
Website: www.nce-league.freeserve.co.uk
CLUB PERSONNEL
Chairman: Steve Lloyd 01977 795581 (H)
Manager: Gary Batley   Asst Mgr: David Vase
Physio: Mick Slater
2000-01 Capts: Andy Hardy (P.o.Y.)
& Dave Brook
Top Scorer: Ricardo Gabbiadini 10

ROSSINGTON MAIN

Secretary: Gerald Parsons, 15 Seaton Gardens, Rossington, Doncaster DN11 0XA
Tel: 01302 867542 (H)
Ground: Welfare Ground, Oxford Street, Rossington, Doncaster   Tel: 01302 865524
Directions: Enter Rossington and go over the railway crossings. Pass the Welfare Club on
right, Oxford Street is next right - ground is at bottom.8miles from Doncaster (BR)
Capacity: 2,000   Seats: 200   Cover: 500   Floodlights: Yes
Clubhouse: Evenings & matchdays, Sandwiches, rolls, satellite TV, pool.   **Club Shop:** No
HONOURS   Cen. Mids. Prem Div. 84-85, Lg. Cup 83-84 84-85;
    Doncaster Sen Lge 44-45, Lg. Cup 44-45; DDSALShield 90-91 R-up 89-90.
PREVIOUS   **Leagues:** Doncaster Sen, Yorkshire Lge, Sheffield County Sen, Cent Mids.
RECORDS   **Attendance:** 864 v Leeds United 8/91.
    Goalscorer: Mark Illman   **Appearances:** Darren Phipps
BEST SEASON   **FA Cup:** 2nd Qual. Rd. 25-26   **FA Vase:** 2nd Round 88-89

FACT FILE
Founded: 1920   Nickname: The Colliery
Sponsor: RJB Mining
Colours: All blue
Change colours: Blue & black
Midweek matches: Tuesday
Reserves' League: Beefeater County Sen
Programme: 50p
Editor:Peter Murden
CLUB PERSONNEL
Chairman: Gerald Murden (01302 867542)
Joint Managers: D Ridley & L Ostle
Physio: J White

SHIREBROOK TOWN

Secretary: L. Graham, 10 Saville Way, Warsop, Mansfield, Notts. NG20 0DZ
Tel: 01623 844299
Ground: BRSA Sports Ground, Langwith Rd, Shirebrook, Mansfield(01623 742535).
Directions: M1 jct 29, A617 to Mansfield, 2.5 miles, onto B6407 to Shirebrook,
    then through town to Langwith Rd.
Capacity: 2,000 **Seats:** None **Cover:** 400 **Floodlights:** Yes
Clubhouse with refreshments at the ground.
Club Shop: No
Honours: Central Midlands Supreme Champions 00-01 01-2 R-Up 99-00 Lg Cup winners 00-
01 Res Prem Div 94-95 95-96. Floodlit Cup winners 97-98
Records Most Appearances :G.Quincey 26
2001-2   Captain:T.Starkey   **PoY.:/ Top Scorer:** L Widdowson

FACT FILE
Founded 1985
Sponsors: Warsop Tyre Service
Colours: All Red & black
Change : All Blue
Midweek Matchday: Wednesday

Programme 12 pages 50p
Editor: G.Howarth

CLUB PERSONNELL
Chairman: Mr S.T. Brown
Tel: 01623 748375
Manager:Gary Quincey

STAVELEY MINERS WELFARE

Secretary: Keith Burnard, 2 Woodland Grove, Clowne, Chesterfield S43 4AT   Tel: 01246 811063
Ground: Inkersall Road, Staveley, Chesterfield, Derbyshire   Tel: 01246 471441
Directions: M1 jct 30, follow A619 Chesterfield - Staveley is 3 miles from jct30. Turn left at GK Garage in Staveley town centre into Inkersall Rd - ground 200yds on right at side of Speedwell Rooms. Frequent buses (47, 70, 72, 75, 77) from Chesterfield stop in Staveley town centre - 3 mins walk to ground
Capacity: 5,000   **Cover:** 400   **Seats:** 220   **Floodlights:** Yes
Clubhouse: The Staveley Miners Welfare, 500 yds from ground, open before and after games
Club Shop: Yes, contactRod Walker 01246 473655
HONOURS   County Sen Lg Div 2 92-93, Div 3 91-92, Chesterfield & D. Amat Lg R-up89-
                          90 90-91, Byron (Lge) Cup 89-90, R-up 90-91.NCE Div 1 R-up 97-98
PREVIOUS   Leagues: Chesterfield & D. Amat 89-91; County Sen 91-93.
BEST SEASON   FA Cup: FA Vase: 98-99, 3rd Rd at least
RECORDS   **Attendance:** 280 v Stocksbridge, Sheffield Snr Cup 22/1/94
                          Goalscorer: Mick Godber   **Appearances:** Shane Turner

FACT FILE
Founded: 1989   Nickname: The Welfare
Colours: All Blue
Change colours: All yellow
Midweek matches: Tuesday
Reserves' League: Beauvale Midlan Regional
Alliance: Premier Division
Programme: 32pages, #1.00
Editor: Steve Cooper (0713 572253)
CLUB PERSONNEL
Chairman: Dennis Burnand
Tel: 01246 475644 (H)
2000-01
Captain & P.o.Y.: Asa Ingall
Top Scorer: Ian Clarke 7

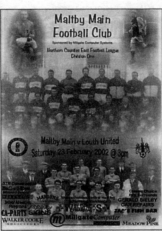

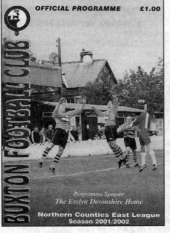

TADCASTER ALBION

Secretary: Howard Clarke,17 Springhill Court,Tadcaster,N.Yorks.LS24 8DN (0193735017)
Ground: The Park, Ings Lane, Tadcaster, LS24 9AY. Tel: 01937 834119
Directions: From West Riding and South Yorks, turn right off A659 at John Smith's
Brewery Clock.
From East Riding turn left off A659 after passing over river bridge and pelican
crossing (New Street).
Capacity: 1,500 **Seats:** Planned this season **Cover:** 400 **Floodlights:** Yes
Clubhouse: No **Club Shop:** No
HONOURS None
RECORD **Attendance:**1,200 v Wincanton F.A.Vase 4th Rd 1996-7
Win: 13-0 v Blidworth MW, NCE 97-98 **Defeat:** 2-10 v Thackley
PREVIOUS **Leagues:** York, Harrogate, Yorkshire (73-82)
BEST SEASON FA Cup: 2nd Qual. Rd. 98-99 **FA Vase:** 5th Round 77-78

FACT FILE
Founded: 1892
Colours: Navy & Red trim/navy & red/navy
Change colours: Green & Yellow halves
Midweek Matchday: Tuesday
Programme: 20 pages
Programme Editor: Mrs Angela Burnett (Sec.)

CLUB PERSONNEL
Chairman: Michael Burnett
Tel No: 01973 832802
President: Lord Edward Stourton
Match Sec: 01937 835017 (H/B)
Manager: Wayne Day

WINTERTON RANGERS

Secretary: G Spencer, 2 Dale Park Ave.,Winterton,Scun'pe,N Lincs.DN15 9UY (01724 732039)
Ground: West Street, Winterton, Scunthorpe, South Humberside (01724 732628).
Directions: From Scunthorpe take A1077 Barton-on-Humber for 5 miles. On entering Winterton take
3rd right (Eastgate), 3rd left (Northlands Rd)and 1st right (West St.). Ground 200yds on left
Capacity: 3,000 **Seats:** 200 **Covered:** 200 **Floodlights:** Yes **Club Shop:** No.
Clubhouse: Open matchdays & evenings Mon-Sat, hot & cold food available on matchdays
HONOURS Lincs Jnr Cup 47-48 61-62; Lincs Snr `B' Cup 69-70; Yorks Lg 71-72 76-77
78-79 (Lg Cup 80-81); N.C.E. Div 2 89-90; S'thorpe Lg & Cup many times.
PREVIOUS **Leagues:** Scunthorpe & Dist. 45-65; Lincs 65-70; Yorkshire 70-82.
BEST SEASON **FA Vase:** QF 76-77 **FA Cup:** 4th Qual Rd replay 76-77, 2-3 after 3-3
RECORD **Attendance:** 1,200 v Sheffield Utd, official floodlight opening, Oct. 78
Fee received: £5,000 for Henry Smith (Leeds United, 1979)
Players progressing Henry Smith (Leeds), Keith Walwyn (Chesterfield), Rick Greenhough(Chester)

FACT FILE
Founded: 1930 Nickname: Rangers
Colours: Blue & white/Black/Blue
Change colours: All red
Midweek matches: Wednesday
Programme: 28-36 pages, 50p
Editor: Mark Fowler (01724 734570)

CLUB PERSONNEL
Chairman: Ian Grimshaw
Vice Chairman: A Smith
Press Officer: as Secretary
Manager: J. Wilkinson
2001-02- Top goalscorer: Vas Nikoladis
Captain: Simon Green
P.O.Y: Phil Doyle

WORSBROUGH M.W. & ATHLETIC

Secretary: Garry Wiggan, 9 Pantry Well, Worsbrough Bridge, Barnsley, S. Yorks S70 4SW
Tel: 01226 247023 (H) 01226 247023 (Fax) 07817 068752 (M)
Ground: Park Road, Worsbrough Bridge, Barnsley Tel: 01226 284452
Directions: On the A61 Barnsley-Sheffield road two miles south of Barnsley, 2miles from M1 jnt
36 opposite Blackburns Bridge. Two and a half miles from Barnsley (BR). Yorkshire Traction run
buses every 10 mins thru Worsbrough Bridge.
Capacity: 2,000 **Seats:** 175 **Cover:** 175 **Floodlights:** Yes
Clubhouse: Yes **Club Shop:** No
HONOURS Northern Co's East Div 1 R-up 90-91 (Div 3 R-up 85-86); Sheffield SnrCup
R-up 72-73; County Snr Lg 65-66 69-70 (R-up 62-63, Lg Cup 65-66); Barnsley Lg 52-53 58-59
59-60, Lg Cup 56-57 58-59 (R-up 53-54), Beckett Cup 57-58.
PREVIOUS **Leagues:** Barnsley 52-61; Sheffield County Snr 62-71; Yorkshire 71-82.
RECORD **Attendance:** 1,603 v Blyth Spartans, FA Amateur Cup 1971
BEST SEASON **FA Cup:** 1st Qual. Rd 78-79 79-80 80-81 **FA Vase:** 3rd Round 90-91

FACT FILE
Founded: 1923
Reformed: 1947
Colours: All red
Change colours: Yellow/blue
Midweek Matchday: Wednesday
Programme: 60 pages, 50p
Editor: Secretary

CLUB PERSONNEL
Chairman: John Wright
Press Officer: T.B.A.

YORKSHIRE AMATEUR

Secretary: David Packham, 30 Roxholme Avenue, Leeds LS7 4JF (0113 262 0758)
Ground: The Bracken Edge, Roxholme Road, Leeds LS8 4DZ Tel: 0113 262 4093
Directions: From South M1 to Leeds, then A58 Wetherby Road to Fforde Green Hotel, left at
lights and proceed to Sycamore Ave. (on right). From East A1 to Boot & Shoe Inn then to
Shaftesbury Hotel, turn right into Harehills Lane, then to Sycamore Avenue. Two and a half
miles from Leeds (BR). Buses 2, 3 & 20 from Briggate to Harehills Ave.
Capacity : 1,550 **Seats:** 200 **Cover:** 160 **Floodlights:** Yes **Club Shop:** Yes
Clubhouse: Bar, tea bar, games, lounge. Every night 8.30-11, Sat matchdays 11, Sun 12-3.
HONOURS FA Amtr Cup SF 31-32; West Riding Co. Cup(3); Yorks Lg 31-32, Div 2 58-
59 (R-up 52-53 71-72), Div 3 77-78, Lg Cup 32-33; Leeds & Dist. Snr Cup.
PREVIOUS **League:** Yorks 20-24 30-82. **Ground:** Elland Road 1919-20
RECORD **Attendance:** 4,000 v Wimbledon, FA Amateur Cup QF 1932.
Players progressing: Gary Strodder & Stuart Naylor (W.B.A.), Peter Swan (Leeds U) Brian
Deane (Doncaster R)

FACT FILE
Founded: 1918 Nickname: Ammers
Sponsors: Screeching Parrot
Colours: White/navy/red
Change colours: All red
Midweek Matches: Tuesday
Programme: 12 pages, 50p
Editor: Charles Sharman (0113 293 8894)
Local Press: Yorkshire Post, Yorkshire Evening
Post and North Leeds Advertiser

CLUB PERSONNEL
Chairman: Andrew Wilkinson (0113 2650841)
President: Rayner Barker
Manager: Denis Metcalfe
Coach:Jim McKay Physio: Terry Davies

KitClub
CENTRAL MIDLANDS LEAGUE
FEEDER TO: NORTHERN COUNTIES LEAGUE

President: Mr R Holmes   **Vice President:** Mr D Capenerhurst
Chairman & General Secretary: Frank Harwood
103 Vestry Road, Oakwood, Derby DE21 2BN
Tel: 01332 832372   Fax: 01332 835004   e-mail: frankharwood@onetel.co.uk

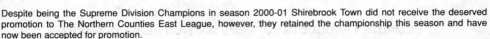

Despite being the Supreme Division Champions in season 2000-01 Shirebrook Town did not receive the deserved promotion to The Northern Counties East League, however, they retained the championship this season and have now been accepted for promotion.

Like the previous season the Championship was decided in their last game of the season and they successfully held off the challenge of Hucknall Rolls.

The previous season Shirebrook had achieved the double, also winning the League Challenge Cup. This season they were removed from the competition due to playing an ineligible player and the eventual winners were Retford United who defeated Thorne Colliery 1-0 at Alreton Town's ground. Retford United also won the R&R Scaffolding Premier Division title and they too had to wait until the final game before clinching the title from Barton Town Old Boys and Dinnington Town.

Incidentally, the League Challenge Cup final featured two Premier Division sides, the first time this has happened in the League's thirty year existence.

After the previous season when the Phoenix Trophies (previously MJT Promotions) Floodlit Cup competition had to be abandoned due to the weather, thanks to the League Fixture Secretary Tony Baugh who arranged the earlier rounds to be played in the early part of the season, the competition went its full course and South Normanton Athletic retained the trophy with a 2-1 victory in the final.

Again it can be recorded that all the finals were well attended and the CMFL express their thanks to Alfreton Town Football Club, Dunkirk Football Club and South Normanton Athletic Football Club for the loan of their grounds and facilities for the finals.

Member clubs again distinguished themselves and the League in outside cup competitions with Heanor Town achieving the honour of receiving the Team of the Round award in the FA Vase in three successive rounds, a feat that has not been achieved before. A special presentation was made to the club by the Football Association.

In County Cup competitions the highlight was the fine results achieved by Sneinton (now Carlton Town) and Teversal in the Nottinghamshire FA Senior Cup competition, both accounted for clubs higher in the pyramid system, Sneinton knocked out the holders Arnold Town before going out in the Semi-final against the eventual winners Gedling Town, who are an ex-CMFL side.

The League extends its thanks to all the sponsors. The main sponsors Redfern Removers, who have been with the League for eight years, unfortunately a change of directors as meant that they have withdrawn the sponsorship but the CMFL remain very grateful for their support. KitClub, a Southampton based company have stepped into the 'breach', Computer Products continue as the Supreme Division sponsors, as do R&R Scaffolding in the Premier Division. Phoenix Trophies, who took over the company MJT Promotions, continue to sponsor the Floodlit Cup competition and Reserves League Cup competition and new sponsors have been obtained for both the League Challenge Cup and both of the Reserve Divisions, Humber Inspection Services Limited are taking the League Challeng Cup and Lee's Fishing, Hardware and Garden Centre is sponsoring the Reserves Divisions.

Frank Harwood, League Chairman/General Secretary

COMPUTER PRODUCTS SUPREME DIVISION FINAL LEAGUE TABLE 2001-02

	P	W	D	L	F	A	Pts		P	W	D	L	F	A	Pts
Shirebrook Town	38	29	3	6	105	25	90	Sandiacre Town	38	15	7	16	71	68	52
Hucknall Rolls	38	26	8	4	93	39	86	Holbrook FC	38	15	6	17	70	63	51
Long Eaton United	38	26	6	6	84	39	84	Graham St Prims	38	15	3	20	55	76	48
South Normanton Ath	38	22	6	10	82	51	72	Askern Welfare	38	12	11	15	58	54	47
Sneinton Fc	38	20	5	13	73	42	65	Clipstone Welfare	38	11	8	19	45	76	41
Greenwood Meadows	38	19	7	12	78	55	64	Collingham	38	10	9	19	59	63	39
Heanor Town	38	18	8	12	69	52	62	Bottesford Town	38	10	7	21	41	79	*36
North Notts FC	38	17	9	12	63	52	60	Nettleham	38	9	4	25	43	85	31
Dunkirk	38	17	6	15	62	70	57	Kimberley Town	38	3	9	26	27	98	18
Teversal	38	15	11	12	75	61	56	Selston	38	3	3	32	37	142	12
								* points adjustment							

R & R SCAFFOLDING PREMIER DIVISION FINAL LEAGUE TABLE

	P	W	D	L	F	A	Pts		P	W	D	L	F	A	Pts
Retford United	38	27	6	5	106	32	87	Ollerton Town	38	15	7	16	63	65	52
Barton Town Old Boys	38	26	4	8	104	49	82	Kiveton Park	38	14	6	18	70	73	48
Dinnington Town	38	25	6	7	110	44	81	Blidworth Welfare	38	11	6	21	53	80	39
Ripley Town	38	25	6	7	109	52	81	Welbeck MW	38	10	9	19	53	94	39
Blackwell Miners Welf	38	25	3	10	110	48	78	Radford FC	38	10	6	22	50	82	36
Thorne Colliery	38	23	8	7	94	46	77	Shardlow St James	38	9	8	21	40	76	35
Forest Town	38	20	10	8	71	57	70	Gad Khalsa Sports	38	9	8	21	34	75	35
Stanton Ilkeston	38	18	6	14	78	67	60	Yorkshire Main	38	8	5	25	42	101	29
Bentley Colliery	38	19	1	18	90	84	58	Harworth CI	38	4	6	28	32	116	18
Thoresby Coll Welf	38	16	9	13	53	49	57	Kirkby Town SFC	38	5	2	31	42	114	17

COMPUTER PRODUCTS SUPREME DIVISION RESULTS CHART

		1	2	3	4	5	6	7	8	9	10	11	12	13	14	15	16	17	18	19	20
1	Askern Welfare	X	0-1	0-0	2-2	4-0	0-1	0-1	2-1	2-1	2-1	0-0	1-4	5-1	1-0	2-0	5-0	0-1	1-1	1-2	1-1
2	Bottesford Town	2-2	X	0-2	0-2	2-2	1-4	1-3	1-1	1-1	1-3	1-1	1-3	3-1	1-0	1-3	3-0	1-5	0-4	1-4	2-2
3	Clipstone Welfare	1-1	1-2	X	1-4	3-1	0-2	2-4	0-4	2-4	0-1	2-2	0-2	1-1	2-0	0-2	2-0	1-1	1-3	0-0	1-1
4	Collingham	1-1	1-3	3-0	X	1-1	1-2	0-3	2-2	4-2	1-4	0-0	3-1	1-2	1-3	1-2	5-1	0-2	0-2	0-2	1-1
5	Dunkirk	2-1	2-0	3-1	0-4	X	1-3	2-1	4-2	3-2	0-4	3-1	1-2	0-3	1-2	1-0	5-2	3-0	1-1	0-6	1-1
6	Graham St Prims	0-0	1-2	2-5	1-1	2-5	X	1-3	1-2	3-1	1-4	1-0	0-3	2-1	4-0	3-1	2-3	1-3	0-2	0-5	3-1
7	Greenwood Mdws	4-0	3-0	0-1	2-0	0-3	1-0	X	2-3	2-1	2-2	5-0	1-4	0-0	1-3	3-4	0-1	1-3	1-0	1-1	2-1
8	Heanor Town	4-0	2-1	1-0	0-2	0-4	0-1	0-3	X	3-0	0-1	1-0	0-1	1-2	1-1	2-2	6-0	4-2	1-0	2-0	2-
9	Holbrook	0-0	4-0	2-3	3-2	3-0	3-1	1-2	0-5	X	1-1	10-1	1-1	2-0	2-2	0-3	5-0	0-2	0-2	4-0	4-
10	Hucknall Rolls	1-0	5-0	5-2	2-1	3-0	2-0	3-2	3-3	2-0	X	2-2	2-1	3-0	1-0	0-3	4-2	1-1	2-0	1-0	2-1
11	Kimberley Town	1-1	0-1	1-2	2-1	1-2	0-2	0-2	1-2	1-2	0-6	X	0-5	1-0	0-4	1-3	4-0	0-4	0-2	2-3	0-3
12	Long Eaton Utd	1-0	3-0	1-0	3-2	0-0	2-3	2-2	0-0	3-0	2-1	3-0	X	1-0	3-2	3-1	5-2	0-4	1-1	2-1	2-2
13	Nettleham	0-3	0-0	1-0	1-2	1-3	2-5	1-3	0-3	0-3	4-0	0-3		X	1-2	0-5	1-3	1-2	1-6	4-3	3-2
14	North Notts	1-4	4-1	1-1	1-3	3-2	1-0	4-0	4-0	3-0	2-2	4-2	0-3	3-2	X	1-2	1-0	1-1	0-0	0-0	1-1
15	Sandiacre Town	2-3	1-2	3-1	1-1	2-1	3-0	1-1	2-1	0-1	2-2	1-1	1-4	2-3	2-2	X	7-1	2-1	1-4	0-2	0-2
16	Selston	1-5	0-2	0-2	2-4	0-4	1-3	1-8	3-3	4-2	0-5	1-1	1-4	0-1	0-5	2-3	X	1-7	1-3	0-5	1-1
17	Shirebrook Town	2-0	2-0	12-0	1-0	2-1	5-0	3-0	3-0	1-0	1-0	8-0	0-2	2-0	4-0	4-1	2-0	X	1-0	0-1	1-3
18	Sneinton	3-3	2-0	1-2	1-0	1-3	5-0	2-1	0-1	0-1	0-1	3-0	2-1	3-1	0-1	4-2	5-2	0-2	X	1-5	2-3
19	South Normanton	2-1	2-1	2-1	4-2	1-2	2-1	1-1	2-1	2-2	5-3	0-0	2-0	4-2	2-0	4-1	5-2	0-5	1-4	X	1-2
20	Teversal	5-4	3-2	3-0	2-2	5-0	1-1	5-1	1-1	1-2	2-2	4-0	1-3	1-1	1-2	0-2	3-0	0-5	0-3	1-0	X

R & R SCAFFOLDING PREMIER DIVISION RESULTS CHART

		1	2	3	4	5	6	7	8	9	10	11	12	13	14	15	16	17	18	19	20
1	Barton Town OB	X	4-1	2-1	6-3	2-2	4-1	2-0	6-1	5-1	4-1	2-0	4-1	1-2	4-3	2-0	3-1	2-1	2-3	0-0	2-1
2	Bentley Colliery	2-0	X	1-2	2-3	3-5	3-4	1-2	4-3	4-3	2-1	3-2	6-2	2-4	1-2	3-1	1-3	1-3	2-3	2-1	4-0
3	Blackwell Miners W	1-3	2-1	X	4-1	2-1	3-3	3-1	6-0	8-2	4-0	3-0	6-0	3-1	1-2	7-1	1-4	0-0	1-3	3-0	8-0
4	Budworth Welfare	0-5	1-3	0-1	X	1-3	1-2	1-1	4-1	2-0	0-5	2-3	2-0	1-1	3-1	0-1	1-1	1-2	3-2	1-1	3-1
5	Dinnington Town	9-0	2-0	1-2	3-2	X	7-0	3-0	7-0	3-0	3-1	4-1	5-3	0-2	5-4	6-0	2-1	2-1	2-3	4-0	2-2
6	Forest Town	2-4	2-3	2-1	2-1	3-1	X	0-0	3-0	3-1	2-1	4-1	0-2	1-2	0-3	3-0	0-0	4-2	2-0	4-2	
7	Gad Khalsa Sports	0-1	1-5	1-0	2-1	0-1	1-1	X	3-0	2-5	0-0	0-1	2-0	0-3	0-3	0-2	1-3	0-1	0-2	0-0	2-5
8	Harworthy Coll Inst	0-5	0-5	1-3	1-4	0-3	0-2	0-4	X	0-3	1-3	1-1	2-0	1-2	0-3	0-1	1-1	1-1	1-0	2-4	1-0
9	Kirkby Town	1-0	2-3	2-3	0-1	0-1	0-0	1-2	2-2	X	0-3	0-4	0-1	3-1	0-2	2-5	3-2	1-2	2-6	0-2	2-4
10	Kiveton Park	0-2	1-2	0-4	1-2	2-2	2-2	4-1	5-3	8-0	X	3-2	1-2	0-4	2-2	4-1	0-0	1-0	0-3	6-2	3-1
11	Ollerton Town	1-8	4-1	4-4	5-0	1-1	1-2	1-1	4-1	3-1	3-1	X	0-2	0-3	4-1	3-0	1-2	0-2	2-1	0-2	2-1
12	Radford	1-4	3-2	4-1	1-1	2-1	0-1	0-1	3-1	3-2	6-0	0-3	X	3-2	0-1	1-1	4-0	1-4	0-2	1-1	2-0
13	Retford United	2-2	0-0	2-0	2-0	1-1	3-3	7-0	1-1	6-0	1-0	3-1	2-1	X	2-0	6-1	6-0	4-0	1-2	6-1	2-0
14	Ripley Town	2-5	9-3	3-1	3-1	1-0	1-1	4-0	7-2	6-0	1-0	2-0	X	3-2	1-1	3-1	2-2	4-1	6-0		
15	Shardlow St James	2-0	2-0	1-4	0-2	0-3	0-1	2-2	0-0	2-0	1-2	0-0	0-0	1-6	X	0-1	0-1	0-4	3-0	1-1	
16	Stanton Ilkeston	1-2	2-6	1-4	2-1	1-2	2-3	3-0	3-6	0-2	1-1	2-1	4-1	1-3	5-4	2-1	X	2-0	1-3	5-0	5-0
17	Thoresby Coll Welf	1-0	0-1	1-2	3-0	0-3	2-2	0-0	2-0	2-1	4-0	3-0	2-2	0-3	1-4	1-1	3-0	X	1-1	0-1	3-2
18	Thorne Colliery	1-0	1-3	2-1	5-0	1-1	0-3	2-0	6-0	2-1	1-1	2-2	1-2	1-1	4-1	2-2	2-1	X	8-1	3-0	
19	Welbeck Miners Welf	0-6	3-1	0-2	2-2	1-5	0-2	5-0	5-1	3-0	2-1	1-1	4-2	0-6	1-4	2-2	2-3	2-3	2-2	X	0-3
20	Yorkshire Main	0-0	1-3	1-5	2-1	1-4	0-2	2-4	0-3	1-1	0-2	0-2	1-0	1-8	2-3	2-0	0-4	1-1	0-4	1-1	X

LEAGUE CUP 2001-02

FIRST ROUND

Forest Town	v	Holbrook	0-3	Gad Khalsa Sports	v	Yorkshire Main	4-2
Graham St Prims	v	Barton Town Old Boys	3-4	Kiveton Park	v	Hucknall Rolls	3-3, 1-3
Long Eaton United	v	Sandiacre Town	0-1	Shardlow St James	v	Blidworth Welfare	2-0
Shirebrook Town	v	Radford	4-1	Sneinton	v	Dinnington Town	3-2

SECOND ROUND

Askern Welfare	v	Greenwood Meadows	1-2	Barton Town OB	v	Blackwell M W	2-5
Bottesford Town	v	Nettleham	0-3	Clipstone Welfare	v	North Notts	1-1, 2-3
Harworth Coll Inst	v	Bentley Colliery	1-3	Heanor Town	v	Kimberley Town	9-0
Hucknall Rolls	v	Selston	4-0	Kirkby Town	v	Ripley Town	0-5
Retford United	v	Welbeck M W	4-0	Shardlow St James	v	Gad Khalsa Sports	2-1
Shirebrook Town	v	Sneinton	2-0	Sth Normanton Ath	v	Collingham	2-1
Stanton Ilkeston	v	Holbrook	0-3	Teversal	v	Dunkirk	3-3, 3*1
Thoresby Coll Welf	v	Sandiacre Town	1-3	Thorne Colliery	v	Ollerton Town	2-0

THIRD ROUND

Blackwell M W	v	Bentley Colliery	8-4	Greenwood Mdws	v	Sandiacre Town	1-2
Heanor Town	v	Shirebrook Town	1-1, 2V6	Holbrook	v	Thorne Coll	2-2,2*2,3p5
Hucknall Rolls	v	Shardlow St James	2-0	North Notts	v	Teversal	0-3
Retford United	v	Nettleham	2-2, 3-0	Sth Normanton Ath	v	Ripley Town	3-3, 4-1

Shirebrook Town and Heanor Town expelled for playing ineligible players

FOURTH ROUND

Sandiacre Town	v	Retford United	3-3, 0-1	Sth Normanton Ath	v	Teversal	4-4, 5*3
Thorne Colliery	v	Blackwell M W	1-0	Hucknall Rolls			walkover

SEMI FINALS

Hucknall Rolls	v	Thorne Colliery	0-1	Retford United	v	Sth Normanton Ath	2-1

FINAL

Retford United	v	Thorne Colliery	0-1	at Alfreton Town FC

PHOENIX TROPHIES FLOODLIT CUP 2001-02

SEMI FINALS

Clipstone Welfare	v	Sth Normanton Ath	1-5 agg	Shirebrook Town	v	Blackwell M W	7-1 agg

FINAL

Shirebrook Town	v	Sth Normanton Athletic	1-2	at Dunkirk FC

LEADING GOALSCORERS 2001-02

COMPUTER PRODUCTS SUPREME DIVISION			R & R SCAFFOLDING PREMIER DIVISION		
L Widdowson	Shirebrook Town	36	K Mabon	Ripley Town	40
M Nangle	Hucknall Rolls	34	L Cartledge	Dinnington Town	38
L Aldred	Sandiacre Town	26	J Slinger	Blackwell Miners Welfare	33
R Coleman	South Normanton	20	G Nattriss	Retford United	33
L Grant	Graham St Prims	19	R Blake	Barton Town	32
J Webster	Holbrook FC	18	D Palmer	Bentley Colliery	26
			M Downing	Blackwell Miners Welfare	26

ASKERN WELFARE

Chairman: John Metcalfe **President:** R.Redhead
Secretary: Jon Stewart, 43 Sutton Road, Askern,Doncaster,S.Yorks. DN6 0AG
& Match Sec Tel Nos: 01302 702502 (H) 01302 703035 (W)
Ground: Askern Welfare Sports Ground, Doncaster Road, Askern,Doncaster
Tel: 01302 700957. Clubhouse open normal hours and all day Saturdays
Directions: A1/A639 Pontefract. Follow sign for Askern/Campsall.At T-junction turn right.
Left at Anne Arms, right at Supersave, ground on right.
Capacity: 3,000 **Cover** 200**Floodlights** Yes **Club shop:**Yes(01226 771900)
Prog: 30 Pages £1. **Editor & Com Man:** Martin Terrell (01302 701964)

Formed: 1924 **Nickname:** The Welly
Colours: Black & white stripes/black/black
Change colours: All Red with white trim
Midweek Matchday: Wednesday
Reserves Lg: Doncaster & Dist. Sen. Prem.
Manager: Paul Curtis **Capt:** Simon Roberts
Asst Man/Coach: Martin Terrell
Physio: Kevin Lewis

BARTON TOWN OLD BOYS

Secretary: Peter Mitchell, 56 Brigg Rd., Barton-on-Humber, North Lincs. DN18 5DR
Tel: 01682 632382 (H) 07900 105204 (M)

Ground: Marsh Lane Football Ground, Marsh Lane, Barton-on-Humber, North Lincs.
Tel: 07900 105204 (Secretary's Mobile)
Directions: Approaching from south on A15, Barton is the last exit before Humber Bridge.
Follow A1077 into town. Right at mini r'about, at bottom of hill onto 'Holydyke'.
2nd left onto George St., then into King St. Marsh Lane is opp. junction of King
St. & High St.

Colours: Light blue/dark blue/dark blue
Change colours: Red & black
stripes/black/black

Manager: Leigh Palin

BLACKWELL MINERS WELFARE

Secretary: Steve Harris, 6 Pennine Close, Newton, Alfreton, Derbys DE55 5UD.
Tel: 01773 779172(H) 01246 501561(W) 01773 779173 (F)
Email: steve-harris@bdrmg.co.uk
Club Website: www.blackwellmwfc.org.uk - Club Email: manor@globalnet.co.uk

Ground: Welfare Ground, Primrose Hill, Blackwell, Derbyshire DE55 5JE. Tel: 01773 811295.

Directions: M1 Junc 28, A38 towards Mansfield, left onto B6406, left again at Hilcote Arms,
ground 1 mile on left just past Miners Welfare. Matchday Tel: 07890 198776

Colours: Red & white stripes/red/red
Change cols: White/black/black
Midweek Matchday: Wednesday

Manager: Paul Jones
Tel: 01623 405608 (H)

BOTTESFORD TOWN

Secretary: Tony Reeve,61 Skelton Road,Scunthorpe,North Lincolnshire DN17 1RB
Tel No 01724 352939 (H)
Ground: Birch Park, Ontario Road, Bottesford, Scunthorpe, N. Lincs.
Tel: 01724 871833
Directions: Exit M180 via M181 - Scunthorpe. At r'about right into Scotter Road.
Over next r'about then 2nd left into South Park Rd., on to Sunningdale Rd.
Right into Goodwood Rd, ground at end.

Colours: Orange/Black/Black
Change: Blue & Yellow/blue/yellow
Manager: Vic Jubber

CARLTON TOWN

Secretary: Paul Shelton, 28 Freda Close, Gedling,Nottingham NG4 4GP.
Tel Nos: 0115 9877527 (H) 07808 160630 (M)
Ground & Directions: Stoke Lane Gedling, Nottingham. (0115 9873583). A612 Nottingham to
Southwell Road. Stoke Lane is situated off A612 between Gedling & Burton Joyce(signed Stoke
Bardolph). Ground 200 yards on left over level crossing. BR. Nearest Station is Carlton.
Capacity: 1000 **Seats:** 20 **Cover:** 200 **Floodlights:** Yes **Club Shop:** No **Clubhouse:**
Yes (0115 9402531) **Previous Name:** Sneiton F.C.
Honours: Notts Alliance Div 1 92-93, Notts Alliance Div 2 84-85 Notts Intermediate Cup 91-92

Founded: 1904
Colours: Yellow/Blue/Blue
Change Colours: All Red
Midweek Matchday: Tuesday
Programme: £1.00 Editor: Martin Bell
Chief Executive: Mick Garton
President: John W. Stokeld
Head Coach: Tom Brookbanks
Asst. Managers: Dave Nairn & Brian Franks
Physio: Martin Jepson

CLIPSTONE WELFARE

Secretary: Barry Clarke, 40 Church Road, Clipstone, Mansfield, NG21 9DG (01623640829).
Ground & Directions: Clipstone Lido Ground Clipstone Road West, Mansfield,Notts (01632
655674). B6030 from Mansfield, between Forest Town & Clipstone, on left entering Clipstone.
Capacity: 3000 **Seats:** 90 **Cover:** 200 **Floodlights:** Yes **Club Shop:** No
Honours: Notts Snr Cup 85-86 94-95, Notts Alliance 72-73 73-74 74-75 92-93 94-95 (Lg Cup
72-73 73-74 74-75 94-95 (R-up 92-93)), Notts I'mediate Cup 55-56. Central Midlands Premier
Championship 94-95 96-97

Founded 1927
Colours: Red/black/black
Change Colours: All B lue
Midweek Matchday: Tuesday or Wednesday
Programme: Yes

Chairman: Carl Hardwick
Manager: Steve Bingley

Retford United, Central Midland League Cup Winners 2001-2002. Photo: Bill Wheatcroft

Sandiacre Town. Back Row (l-r): Mel Williams (Secretary), Brian Howden, Tony Maddocks, Matt Clowes, Paul Wilson, Dean Whiley, Andy Marlow, Danny Hale, Chris Murdock, Tony Roe (Manager). Front Row: Gary Kelly, Nathan Boddey, Robbie Wooldridge, Matt Berry, Adi Young, Harvey Brown.

Kirkby Town. Back Row (l-r): Mark Gwynne (Physio-Coach), Dave Lester, Mark McCallum, Darren Palfrey, Owen Williams, Steve Boot, Jimi Bottomore, Ben Woodward, Mark Burton, Dave Howard (Manager), Jonathon Scott. Front Row: Stuart Bosworth, Spencer Winfield, Richard Parsons, Mohammed Gagarawa, Darren Chambers, Mark Sheldon, David Ward. Photo: Gordon Whittington

COLLINGHAM

Secretary: Gerry Williams, 47 Dykes End, Collingham, Newark, Notts NG23 7LD
Tel No: 01636 892189 (H)
Ground & Directions: Collingham FC, Station Road, Collingham, Newark, Notts. (01636 892303) Take A46 Newark to Lincoln road (Newark bypass). Turn left into Collingham on the A1133 road. In village turn right at traffic lights.Ground 100 yards on left.

Colours:Amber/ Black/Black
Change Colours: White/blue
Midweek Matchday: Tuesday

Manager: Paul Tichcombe

DINNINGTON TOWN

Secretary: Wallace Chambers, 26 Mackenzie Way,Kiveton Park, Sheffield S26 6QMM
Tel No: 07932 677881

Ground: Resource Centre, 131 Laughton Road, Dinnington.
Tel: 01905 518555

Directions: M1 J31 onto A57 towards Worksop. At 1st lights turn left to Dinnington. Follow road into town centre and the ground is on the left.

Colours: Yellow/black/black
Change: Green & Black/white/white

Manager: Steve Toyne
Tel: 01142 347584 (H)
07960 616129 (B)

DUNKIRK

Secretary: Steve Throssell, 24 Kingfisher Wharf, Castle Marina, Nottingham NG71GA (0115 9473903 or 07903 322446
Ground & Directions: The Ron Steel Sports Ground, Trentside Farm, Clifton Bridge, Nottingham (0115 9850803). Ring Road - Clifton Bridge (North End),Ind Estate, Lenton Lane.
Honours: FA Vase 5th Rd 93-94; Cen Mid Sup Div R-up 96-97, Prem Div R-up 95-96,KO Cup 97-98; Notts Alliance Div 1 84-85, Div 2 82-83, Lg Cup R-up 84-85; Notts I'mediate Cup 83-4
Capacity:1,500 **Seats:** No **Cover:** 200 **Floodlights:** Yes **Shop:** No **Clubhouse:** Yes
Record Attendance: 821 v Tiverton Town, F.A.Vase 5th Rd 93-94

Founded: 1946
Colours: Red/black/black
Change Colours: All Blue
Midweek Matchday: Tuesday
Programme : Yes
Chairman:Jack Riley
Manager: Andy Freeman
Assistant Manager: Ian Henry
Players Progressing: Roger Willis and Matthew McKemzie (Grimsby T), Wes Morgan (Nottm F)

GRAHAM STREET PRIMS

Secretary: Mrs E Wright, 6 Athol Close, Sinfin Moor, Derby DE24 9LZ
Tel. Nos.: 01332 606837 (H) 01332 340131 x6855 (B)
Match Secretary: D.J.Tice, North Bank Cottage,Church Lane,Swarkestone, Derbys. DE73 1JB
Tel. No.: 01332 704054
Ground: Asterdale Sports Centre, Borrowash Road, Spondon, nr Derby. Tel: 01332 668656
Directions: M1 Junc 25, take A52 to Derby. 3rd left Borrowash Road - golf driving range on left, approx 400m further turn left into Asterdale Sports Centre. Ground at rear.
Capacity: 1,000 Seats: No Cover: Yes Floodlights: Yes Club shop: No Clubhouse: Yes

Formed: 1904
Colours: Red & white stripes/black/black
Change Colours: Yelow/red/red
Midweek Matchday: Tuesday
Programme: Yes

Manager: Gerry McElhinney

GREENWOOD MEADOWS

Secretary: Peter Hynes,64 Wallis Street,Basford,Nottingham NG6 0EP
0115 9705132
Ground: Greenwood Meadows, Lenton Lane, Clifton, Nottingham.
Tel: 0115 986 5913
Directions: M1 Junc 24 take A453Nottingham-Clifton Bridge to Lenton Ind Estate.
Left into Old Lenton Lane.Ground second on right on lane.

Colours: Green & white/black/green
Change: Red & black.black/black

Managers: Brian Cawthorn & Chris Nicholson

HEANOR TOWN

Secretary: Keith Costello, 45 Stainsby Avenue, Heanor, Derbys. DE75 7EL(01773 719446).
Ground & Directions: The Town Ground, Mayfield Avenue, Heanor (01773713742/715815).
M1 (J26), take A610 onto A608, ground 200yds from Market Square
Capacity: 3,000 and new stand being built `Cover:` 1,000+ new stand **Floodlights:** Yes
Honours: Central Midlands League Cup 94-95 (Runners-up 86-87 92-93, B E Webbe Removals Cup 88-89), West Midlands Reg. League Runners-up 72-73; Midland Co's League Runners-up 65-66 67-68; Derbys Senior Cup(9) 1892-94 1946-47 65-69 70-7178-79; FA Cup 1st Rd 58-59 63-64.Central Midlands Supreme Champions:94-5,96-7 Central All.Lg(2) R-up4

Nickname: The Lions
Colours: Black& white Halves/black/black
Change Colours: All Red
Midweek Matchday: Wednesday
Programme: 32pages £1.00 Ed: Stan Wilton
01332 880199 (H) & 01332 881049 (Fax)
Club House: On ground.Hot food (match days)
Chair: John McCulloch Manager: Bill Fossey
F.A.Vase 2001-02 Result of Round Rd 1,2+3

CENTRAL MIDLANDS LEAGUE SUPREME DIV.

HOLBROOK

Secretary: Alan Pace,5 Belvedere Close,Swanwick,Derbys. DE56 1BY Tel No: 01773 528224
Ground: The Welfare Ground, Shaw Lane, Holbrook, Derbyshire Tel: 07932 930298
Directions: From A38 take B6179 for Kilburn, turn left at lights for Belper. 1mile on left at Bulls Head for Holbrook. 2 miles on turn right at Venturegarage into Shaws Lane.
Capacity: 1,000 **Seats:** None **Cover:** 250 **Floodlights:** No
Clubhouse: Holbrook Miners Welfare, Shaw Lane.(01332 880259) **Shop:** No
Honours: Central Midlands Premier Division 99-00

Founded: 1996
Nickname: The Brookies
Colours:Blue & black halves/black/black
Change:All Yellow
Midweek Matchday:Wednesday
Programme: Yes / 24pages 50price

Chairman: T.B.A.
Manager: Mark Webster

RETFORD UNITED

Secretary: John Hodgkinson, Richmond Ho., York St., East Markham, Notts. NG22 0QW
Tel: 01777 870773 (H) 07850 975978 (B)

Ground: Cannon Park, Leverton Rd., Retford, Notts.
Tel: 0794 9454694

Directions: From A1 take A620 past Ranby Prison and into Retford. At large r'about take 3rd exit. Pass Morrisons superstore to lights. Right at lights, then left at next set. Follow Leverton Rd. out of town. Cannon Park on RHS after two bridges.

Colours: Black & white stripes/black/black
Change colours: Yellow/blue/white

Manager: Neil Pointon
Tel: 01942 322506 (H)

RIPLEY TOWN

Secretary: Michael E Boam, 5 Valley Drive, Newthorpe, Notts. NG16 2DT.
Tel: 01773 715277 (H) 0374 876794 (B)

Ground: Hanson Brick Works, Peasehill Road, Ripley, Derbys.
Tel: 01773 742200

Directions: M1, J 28, A38 south to A610 signed Nottingham. Continue approx. 1 mile. Turn right into Steam Mill Lane, continue to Peasehill Road to brickworks.

Colours: Blue & White/ Blue/ Blue
Change: White/black/white

Manager: Paul MacFarland
Tel: 01773 609030 (H)

ROLLS ROYCE LEISURE F.C.

Secretary: Gary Warbrick, 20 Balmoral Road, Hucknall, Nootts. NG15 8ES
Tel. No: 0115 9640384 (H) 07732426283 (M)
Ground & Directions: Rolls Royce Sports & Social Club, Watnall Road, Hucknall Notts (0115 963 0134). M1 Junc 27. Follow sign A611 to Hucknall. Turn right onto by-pass. 2nd r/about turn right on to Watnall Road. Take 2nd left after fire station on R.R. Sports Ground.
Capacity: 1,000 **Cover:** yes **Floodlights:** No **Clubhouse:** Social Club always open with food

Colours: All Blue
Change colours: Yellow/yellow/white
Midweek Matchday: Wednesday
Programme: Yes

Chairman: Darryl Claypole
Manager: Phil Towle
Reserves: Peter Needham & Paul Hopkins

SANDIACRE TOWN

Secretary: Mel Williams, 38 Pasture Rd.,Stapleford, Nottingham NG9 8GL Tel: 0115 9174079
Ground: St Giles Park, Stanton Road, Sandiacre, Nottingham NG105EP Tel:0115 9392880.
Directions: M1 jct 25, follow signs to Sandiacre passing Post House on right, straight over crossroads into Rushy Lane and towards Stanton Rd, 1st right after 1000yds into Stanton Rd, ground at bottom after another1000yds. **Web:** homepage.ntlworld.com/sandiacretownfc
Capacity: 2,000 Seats: None Cover: 250 Floodlights: Yes Shop: No
Clubhouse: Members Club 8-11pm. Sunday lunch, Saturday1.30-11pm. Snacks available
Honours: Central Mids Lg Premier Div 92-93 (Lg Cup 92-93), Midlands Regional Alliance R-up 91-92, Central Mids Lge Cup R-up 95-96.

Founded: 1978 Nickname: Saints
Cols:Red/navy/red Change: Yellow/sky/yellow
Midweek Matchday: Tuesday
Programme: 44 pages 50p
Ed.i/Press Off: Mel Williams (0115 917 4079)
Manager: Tony Roe and Mark Harvey
2001-02 Leading goalscorer: Lee Aldred 32
Captain: Danny Hale
P.o.Y.: Lee Aldred

SOUTH NORMANTON ATHLETIC

Secretary: Kevin Taylor, 65 Downibng Street, South Normanton,Alfreton, Derbyshire. DE55 2HF
Tel No: 07763 465663
Ground & Directions: South Normanton Athletic FC, Lees Lane, South Normanton,Derby (01773 581491). M1 June 28, B6019 towards South Normanton, right after 1mile (in South Normanton) at BP garage into Market Street, after quarter mile turn left immediately after The Clock pub into Lees Lane, ground at bottom on right. (Food available on matchdays)
Capacity: 3000 **Seats:** 150 **Cover:** 300 **Floodlights:**Yes
Clubhouse Yes - open on matchdays **Club Shop:** No

Formed: 1875
Colours: Yellow/navy/yellow
Change colours: Black & white/black/white
Programme: Yes - The Shiner
Midweek Matchday: Tuesday

Chairman: Glindon Davison
Manager: Rob Aitkin
Asssistant Manager: Marcus Brameld

415

SUTTON TOWN

Secretary: Keith Mayes, 22 Allington Drive, mansfield, Notts. NG19 6NA
Tel: 01623 437938 (H) 07949 786422 (M)

Ground: Mansfield Hosiery Mills, Huthwaite Road, Sutton-in-Ashfield, Notts. NG17 3LA
Tel: 01623 552376
Directions: M1 Jct. 28 - A38 towards Mansfield. Take the A38 at Kings Mill Island,
1st left (Sutton sign), then 1st rt into Hosiery Mills ground.
Clubhouse: 01623 405660
Previous Name: North Notts

Colours: White/navy/red
Change: All royal blue - socks & shorts with
yellow trim

Manager: Les McJannett
Tel: 01623 655834 (H) 07951 061236 (M)

TEVERSAL

Secretary: Kevin Newton, 8 Vere Ave., Sutton in Ashfield, Notts NG17 2ES
Tel: 01623 461145

Ground: Teversal Grange Country Inn, Carnarvon Street, Teversal, Sutton-in-Ashfield, Notts.
Tel: 01623 442021

Colours: Red & white/ black/red
Change: Blue / white/white
Managers: John Courtie

Directions: M1, J28, A38 towards Mansfield. At r'about take A6075 Mansfield Woodhouse.
Next lights left B6014, Stanton Hill. At r'about take A6014 Tibshelf.
2nd on right Carnarvon St., ground at the top.

BENTLEY COLLIERY
Secretary: James P Tooth, 38 East St., Darfield, Barnsley, South Yorks. S73 9AE Tel: 01226 754012 (H/Fax)
Ground: Bentley Miners' Welfare, The Avenue, Bentley, Doncaster, S. Yorks. Tel: 01302 874420 **Directions:** North from Doncaster on A19: Selby Road. In Bentley turn right at mini r'about on Arksey Lane. Left at shops onto The Avenue and the ground is 60 yards on left.
Colours: All Yellow　　**Change colours:** White & Claret/claret/claret　　**Manager:** Roy Butterworth

BLIDWORTH WELFARE
Secretary: Graham Redfern, 1 Dennbigh Close,Rainworth,Notts NG21 0HY Tel No: 01623 403019
Ground: Welfare Ground, Mansfield Rd, Blidworth, Mansfield (01623 793361). **Directions:** On B6020, Rainworth side of Blidworth. From M1 jct 27 take A608 to Kirby at lights follow A611 to Kirby then take B6020through Ravenshead to Blidworth -thru village and up hill ground on right. From A1 follow A614 /A617 to Rainworth, left at lights 1st right on to B6020 to Blidworth - ground on left at top of hill.
Colours: Orange/black/orange　　**Change colours:** Blue/whiteblue.　　　　**Manager:** Rudi Funk

FOREST TOWN
Secretary: Jan Nieloojadio, 14 Bransdale Avenue, Forest Town, Mansfield, Notts. NG19 0LZ Tel No: 01623 648588
Ground: Forest Town Welfare Sports Ground, Clipstone Rd West, Forest Town, Mansfield, Notts. Tel: 01623 624678
Directions: From Mansfield follow signs for Clipstone/Forest Town. The ground is situated at the Mansfield end of Forest Town on the right.
Colours: All blue　　**Change Colours:** All red　　　　　　　　**Manager:**Mat Vardy

G.A.D. KHALSA SPORTS
Secretary: Karnijit Singh Khatkar, 29 Cloverdale Drive, Sinfin, Derby DE24 3JP
　　　　　Tel: 01332 607380 (H) 07973 640230 (B) email: gadkhalsa@hotmail.com
Ground: The Wharf, Shardlow, Derby. Tel: 01332 799135 (Matchday only)　　**Directions:** M1 J24 on to A6 Derby road. Into Shardlow past garage. Right at corner paper shop of wharf. Down to village hall. Ground adjacent.
Colours: Orange/black/orange　　**Change colours:** Gold & blue/navy/navy　　**Manager:** Karnijt Singh Khatkar

GEDLING M.W.
Secretary: Norman Hay, 182 Gedling Rd., Arnold, Nottingham NG5 6NY. Tel: 0115 926 5598 (H)
Ground: Plains Sports & Social, Plains Road, Mapperly, Nottingham. Tel: 0115 926 6300
Location: The ground is situated on the B684 in Mapperley
Colours: Yellow/blue/yellow　　**Change:** Blue/white/blue　**Manager:** Mark Allison Tel: 0115 931 2650 (H)

HARWORTH COLLIERY INSTITUTE
Secretary: Tom Brogan, 30 Lindsey Road, Harworth, Doncaster, Sth Yorks DN11 8QH Tel: 01302 750132.
Ground: Recreation Ground, Scrooby Rd, Bircotes, Doncaster Tel: 01302 750614.
Directions: Off A1(M) at Blyth, head towards Bawtry for approx 2 miles, 3rd left, ground in village at top of hill on left. Or, from Doncaster to Bawtry then head for A1(M) and turn left after caravan site - ground at top of hill.
Colours: Amber & black/black/amber & black **Change Cols:** Claret and Blue **Midweek Matchday:** Wednesday **Manager:** Alan Needham

KIMBERLEY TOWN　　Website: info@kimberleytownfc.co.uk
General Manager/Match Secretary: Mrs Patricia Critchley, 21 Rowborn Drive,Oughtbridge, Sheffield S35 0JR Tel: 0114 2517742
Ground & Directions: Stag Ground, Nottingham Road, Kimberley Tel: 0115 938 2788. Thro' Nuthall from M1 J 26 to Kimberley, ground entrance 150 yds after Stag Inn.　　**Capacity:** 2,500　　**Seats:** None　　**Cover:** 150　　**Floodlights:** Yes
Clubhouse: Evenings (Except Sun) & matchdays. Hot & cold snacks available　　　**Colours:** All Blue　　**Change colours:** Red/white/white
Chairman/Manager: Graeme Critchley

KIVETON PARK
Secretary: Kevin Hull,3 Chapel way, Kiveton Park, Sheffield S26 6QTTel No: 01909 772152
Ground: Hard Lane, Kiveton Park, Sheffield. Tel: 0797 4247074.　　　　　**Directions:** M1 Junct. 31. Take A57 Worksop road, first right to Todwick, at T junct. turn right. Follow road to Kiveton crossroads. Go over and ground is on right after approx 100m.
Colours: Green & Blue/Blue/Green.　　**Change Colours::** All Red　**Manager:** Stuart Holmes

NETTLEHAM
Secretary: Andrew Bandelow,104 Wragby Road,Bardney,Lincoln.LN3 5XW Tel: 01522 790023 (H) 01522 530363 (W)
Ground & Directions: Mulsanne Park, Field Close, Nettleham (01522 750007). A46 3 miles north of Lincoln, right at Brown Cow Pub, past Church 2nd turning on right, ground at end　　**Honours:** Central Mids Lg Premier Div. Cup R-up 87-88, Village Tphy, Nursing Cup, Kelly Read Cup, Blankney Hunt Cup, Lincoln & Dist. Amtr Cup R-up, Joe Miller Tphy(2).
Colours: All Navy Blue　　**Change:** Yellow/Black/Yellow　　　**Midweek Matchday:** Tuesday　　　　**Manager:** Jim Masterton

OLLERTON TOWN
Gen. Secretary: Les Brown,14 Holly Rise,New Ollerton, Notts NG22 9UZ Tel No: 01623 836023
Secretary: Les Brown, 14 Holly Rise, New Ollerton, Notts. NG22 9UZ Tel: 01623 836023 (H)
Ground: Walesby Lane, New Ollerton, Notts
Directions: From Ollerton r'about om A614 take A6075 to Ollerton. At r'about first left & after 30m left into Walesby Lane
Colours: All red   **Change colours:** Blue/white/blue   **Manager:** Alan Owen

PELICAN
Secretary: Neil Swift, 21 Lancaster Way, Strelley, Nottingham NG8 6PH. Tel: 0115 929 4728 (H) 0776 77778765 (B)
Ground: Brian Wakefield Sports Ground, Lenton Lane, Nottingham   Tel: 0115 986 8255
Directions: M1 J26 take A610 to ring road. Follow signs A52 Grantham. Go under Clifton Bridge, Ground last on Lenton Lane.
Colours: All Blue   **Change:** Red/black/black   **Manager:** Glen Russell   **Honours:** Notts Alliance Lg Cup 90-91(R-up 91-92 93-94).

RADFORD
Secretary: Miss Joanne Smith, 63 Hilcot Drive, Aspley, Nottingham NG8 5HS Tel No: 0794 9091477
Ground: Radford FC, Berridge Rd. West, off Radford Road, Radford, Nottm (0115 943250).   **Directions:** M1 Junc 26,take A610 to Nottingham,
at duel carriageway turn left. Move to right lane andgo immediately right into Wilkinson St. At top turn right & right again at 2nd crossing.
Colours: Claret & sky blue/claret/claret **Change:** Red & Blue stripes/red/red **Manager:** Matt Keetley   **Midweek Matchday:** Tuesday

SELSTON
Secretary: George Elliott, 3 Derwent Drive,Selston, Notts. NG16 6QU9 Tel: 01773 781540 (H) 07786 574452 (M)
Ground: The Parish Hall Ground, Mansfield Road, Selston, Notts   Tel: 01773 812540 **Directions:** J27 M1. Take A608 (Heanor). 1st right onto
B600 (Alfreton/Selston). Into Selston & take 2nd right onto B6018 (Kirby-in-Ashfield). Ground 600 yds on left.
Colours: Black & white/white/white   **Change:** Navy & sky halves/navy/black   **Manager:** John Dawn

SHEFFIELD CITY
Secretary: John Wilson, Whitewalls Farm, Swinston Hill Rd, Dinnington, Sheffield S25 2RY. Tel: 01909 563466 (H) 01909 569973 (B)
Ground: Meadowhall Stadium, 101 Ferrers Road, Tinsley, Sheffield S9 1RZ. **Directions:** J34, M1 South exit Tinsley Viaduct. Take
A6178 to Templeborough/Rotherham. 2nd road on rt. past "Fox & Duck" P.H., is Ferrers Rd. Ground at bottom.
Colours: Red/black/black   **Change:** Blue/white/white   **Manager:** Mick Dakin

STANTON ILKESTON
Secretary: Mrs Helen Taylor, 2 West Avenue, Sandiacre,Notts. Ng9 5FT Tel No: 0115 9490945
Ground & Directions: Hallam Fields Sports Ground, Stanton Club, Hallam Fields,Nr Ilkeston, Derbys (0115 9323244), M1 (J26), take A52
Nottingham, then A6002for Ilkeston. Follow road through t/lights, turn right at next lights. Followroad to Rutland Windows. Turn left into Thurman
St, to top turn left ground 200yds right. **Manager:**Jim Thornehill & Stuart Whitworth   **Midweek Matchday:** Mon. or Wed.
Colours: All blue & white   **Change:** Yellow & Black

THORESBY COLLIERY WELFARE
Secretary: Barry Reece, 125 Henton Rd., Edwinstone, Mansfield, Notts. NG21 9LD Tel: 01623 822415 (H) 01623 491422 (B)
Ground: Thoresby Colliery Sports Ground, 4th Avenue, Edwinstone, Notts. Tel: 01623 822283 (Ground & Clubhouse)
Directions: A614 Ollerton r'about take A6075 Mansfield/Edwinstone. Turn left opposite 'Manvers Arms' onto 5th Avenue. Opposite Nursing Home
turn right onto 4th Ave. Ground entrance ahead.
Colours: Blye & white/ blue/blue **Change Colours:** Gold/black/black   **Manager:** Mick Heron

THORNE COLLIERY
Secretary: Glyn Jones, 21 Haynes Close, Thorne,Doncaster, S Yorks DN8 5HR Tel No: 01405 741062
Ground & Directions: Miners Welfare, Grange Road, Moorends, Thorne, Doncaster.(01374 996474), M18 Junc 6, in THorne, turnat lights to
Moorends, go almostthrough village, Grange Road on right.
Manager: Graham Jones **Colours:** All Navy   **Change:** Green & Navy/green/green **Midweek Matchday:** Tuesday

WELBECK WELFARE F.C.
Secretary: Gillian Gibbonbs,21 Cumberland Avenue,Warsop, Mansfield, Notts. NG20 0JJ Tel No: 01623 844616
Ground: Elksley Road, Meden Vale, Mansfield. (01623 842611)   **Directions:** 1 1/2 miles off A60 between Worksop and Mansfield. Signed
Meden vale. (do NOT follow signs for Welbeck Colliery.) Turn off at Warsop Church.
HONOURS: Notts Alliance Div 2 93-94 (Intermediate Cup 93-94), Chesterfield & Dist. Lg 92-93
Colours: All black/white   **Change colours:** Grey/grey/red   **Manager:** Neil Gibbons

YORKSHIRE MAIN
Secretary: Dennis Tymon, 22 Pamela Drive, Warmsworth, Doncaster DN4 9RP   Tel: 01302 852455
Ground: Yorkshire Main Welfare, Edlington Lane, Edlington, Doncaster Tel: 01709 864075
Directions: A1M junc 36. Proceed on A630 towards Rotherham. At 1st lights turn on to B6376. Ground on left after Fire Station.
Colours: Yellow/green/yellow   **Change Colours:** Red/black/red   **Manager:** Derek Wynne

NOTTS FOOTBALL ALLIANCE
Founded 1894
Chairman: Alan Wright
10 Faraday Road, Mansfield NG18 4ES   Tel: 01623 624379
Treasurer: Godfrey Stafford
7 The Rushes, Gotham, Nottingham NG11 0HY   Tel: 01509 820737

FINAL LEAGUE TABLES 2001-02

SENIOR DIVISION

		P	W	D	L	F	A	Pts	GD
1	Pelican	30	22	6	2	66	22	72	44
2	Southwell City	30	21	4	5	80	35	67	45
3	Wollaton	30	20	6	4	68	37	66	31
4	Radcliffe Olympic	30	18	6	6	76	34	60	42
5	Newark Flowserve	30	17	2	11	68	45	53	23
6	Kimberley Miners W.	30	15	5	10	86	55	50	31
7	Boots Athletic	30	14	5	11	60	45	47	25
8	Rainworth Miners W.	30	11	8	11	55	48	41	7
9	Notts Police	30	11	5	14	52	62	38	-10
10	Keyworth United	30	11	3	16	64	67	36	-3
11	Cotgrave Colliery W.	30	9	7	14	57	66	34	-9
12	Clifton	30	10	3	17	42	81	33	-39
13	Ruddington United	30	9	5	16	48	63	32	-15
14	Attenborough	30	5	7	18	30	65	16	-35
15	Linby Colliery Welfare	30	3	7	20	43	94	16	-51
16	Woodhouse	30	1	7	22	27	103	10	-76

FIRST DIVISION

		P	W	D	L	F	A	Pts	GD
1	Kingswell	30	24	1	5	88	30	73	58
2	Awsworth Villa	30	17	7	6	66	41	58	25
3	Boots Athletic Res.	30	18	4	8	51	37	58	14
4	Newark Flowserve Res.	30	16	6	8	62	41	54	21
5	Chaffoteaux	30	14	10	6	55	34	52	21
6	Southbank	30	14	5	11	59	49	47	10
7	ASC Dayncourt	30	14	5	11	56	54	47	2
8	Magdala Amateurs	30	12	4	14	47	68	40	-21
9	Bestwood Miners Welf.	30	10	9	11	55	58	39	-3
10	Gedling Miners Welf.	30	11	4	15	64	70	37	-6
11	Melton Mowbray	30	10	5	15	57	63	35	-6
12	Southwell City Res.	30	9	8	13	51	60	35	-9
13	Calverton Miners Welf.	30	9	5	16	44	68	32	-24
14	Wollaton Res.	30	8	6	16	39	54	30	-15
15	Basford United	30	6	3	21	39	70	21	-31
16	Matrixgrade	30	4	6	20	34	70	18	-36

DIVISION TWO

	P	W	D	L	F	A	Pts
Bilborough	30	23	2	5	108	37	71
AC Bulwell	30	20	7	3	91	38	67
Stapleford Borough	30	21	4	5	81	45	67
Bilsthorpe	30	20	6	4	70	29	66
Keyworth United Res.	30	20	4	6	103	50	64
Kimberley M W Res.	30	16	3	11	76	58	51
Chaffoteaux Res.	30	13	8	9	58	45	47
Pegasus	30	13	3	14	70	58	42

DIVISION TWO cont.

	P	W	D	L	F	A	Pts
Pelican Res.	30	11	8	11	76	52	41
East Leake Athletic	30	11	5	14	57	67	38
Kirton Brickworks	30	10	2	18	32	48	32
Bottesford St Mary's	30	7	8	15	52	64	29
Ruddington United Res.	30	7	5	18	45	73	26
Newark Town	30	5	4	21	46	120	19
Sandhurst	30	5	2	23	43	90	17
Pinxton North End	30	2	1	27	29	163	7

NOTTS FOOTBALL ALLIANCE

SENIOR DIVISION RESULTS CHART 2001-02

		1	2	3	4	5	6	7	8	9	10	11	12	13	14	15	16
1	Attenborough	X	2-1	3-0	2-0	0-4	1-8	1-1	2-2	1-3	0-1	1-5	0-3	0-0	1-8	0-2	0-0
2	Boots Athletic	1-0	X	4-0	1-1	2-0	3-1	2-0	1-4	2-2	1-4	1-1	3-1	4-2	1-1	2-3	3-0
3	Clifton	2-1	1-0	X	2-2	4-3	4-6	1-3	1-0	3-0	0-2	0-3	2-1	2-1	2-1	0-3	5-1
4	Cotgrave Colliery Welfare	3-0	2-0	3-4	X	3-5	4-2	5-4	3-4	2-0	1-2	1-1	1-2	3-1	0-2	0-2	8-1
5	Keyworth United	3-0	1-4	2-1	4-1	X	2-3	5-0	2-4	1-2	0-4	3-5	2-2	2-0	0-3	0-3	3-3
6	Kimberley Miners Welfare	2-1	1-2	5-1	4-4	1-3	X	1-0	0-2	3-1	0-1	3-3	3-3	2-2	3-2	0-2	7-0
7	Linby Colliery Welfare	2-7	0-4	2-2	2-3	4-4	1-8	X	1-4	2-2	0-3	2-4	1-2	0-1	2-6	3-4	2-2
8	Newark Flowserve	0-1	3-0	4-2	3-1	2-1	1-2	0-2	X	2-1	0-1	1-2	3-1	3-1	2-2	1-3	6-1
9	Notts Police	2-1	3-2	5-0	0-1	1-2	1-7	2-0	3-4	X	2-5	0-3	2-2	1-0	0-3	3-2	3-2
10	Pelican	0-0	1-4	6-0	3-0	2-0	1-0	2-2	3-2	2-1	X	2-1	2-1	0-0	1-0	4-0	2-2
11	Radcliffe Olympic	3-1	3-2	2-0	5-0	3-1	0-3	2-0	1-3	2-2	1-1	X	1-0	1-0	4-0	3-1	6-0
12	Rainworth Miners Welfare	0-0	0-1	4-2	1-1	2-1	1-2	3-0	3-1	1-1	1-2	3-1	X	6-3	0-2	2-3	2-0
13	Ruddington United	3-1	1-1	5-0	3-3	2-4	3-1	7-2	0-3	1-5	0-6	1-0	2-4	X	4-1	1-2	2-0
14	Southwell City	3-2	1-0	3-0	4-0	4-2	4-1	5-1	2-1	2-0	2-0	1-0	2-2	3-0	X	2-1	4-2
15	Wollaton	2-0	4-2	5-0	1-1	2-1	2-2	2-2	1-0	3-1	1-1	0-0	3-1	3-0	2-2	X	3-2
16	Woodhouse	1-1	2-6	1-1	1-0	0-3	0-5	0-2	1-3	1-3	0-2	1-10	1-1	0-2	1-5	1-3	X

SENIOR CUP

FIRST ROUND

ASC Dayncourt	v	Boots Athletic	1-2	Attenborough	v	Linby CWe	5-1
Awsworth Villa	v	Keyworth United	5-3	Bestwood Miners Welfare	v	Newark Flowserve	2-3
Chaffoteaux	v	Basford Utd	3-4, 1*1	Gedling Miners Welfare	v	Southbank	5-4
Kimberley Miners Welfare	v	Cotgrave C W	5-2, 4*4	Kingswell	v	Woodhouse	3-1
Notts Police	v	Ruddington United	2-1	Pelican	v	Magdala Amateurs	10-1
Rainworth M W	v	Melton Mowbray	4-2	Wollaton	v	Radcliffe Olympic	5*3

SECOND ROUND

Attenborough	v	Boots Athletic	2-1	Awsworth Villa	v	Newark Flowserve	2-3
Basford United	v	Calverton MW	3-2	Clifton	v	Notts Police	3-4
Matrixgrade	v	Kingswell	0-6	Rainworth MW	v	Gedling MW	3-1
Southwell City	v	Pelican	3-2	Wollaton	v	Kimberley M Welf.	4-0

QUARTER-FINALS

Attenborough	v	Basford United	3-2	Kingswell	v	Notts Police	2-1
Newark Flowserve	v	Rainworth MW	0-2	Southwell City	v	Wollaton	4*1

SEMI-FINALS

Kingswell	v	Attenborough	2-0	Rainworth	v	Southwell	0-1

FINAL

Southwell City	v	Kingswell	5-1	at Calverton Miners Welfare

INTERMEDIATE CUP

QUARTER-FINALS

Gedling MW Res.	v	Radcliffe O. Res.	4-2	Keyworth United Res.	v	Bilborough	1-3
Pelican Res.	v	Boots Athletic Res.	0-4	Wollaton Res.	v	AC Bulwell	3*5

SEMI-FINALS

Bilborough	v	Gedling Res.	5-3	Boots Res.	v	AC Bulwell	0-1

FINAL

AC Bulwell	v	Bilborough	2*2	at Cotgrave CW

REPLAY

AC Bulwell	v	Bilborough	3-1	at Rainworth

ATTENBOROUGH

Secretary: Terry Allen, 5 Coningsby Road,Woodthorpe, Nottingham NG54LG Tel: 0115 920 0698
Ground & Directions: The Village Green, The Strand, Attenborough, Beeston,Nottingham. Midway between Beeston & Long Eaton on A6005 - adjacent to NatureReserve (via Attenborough Lane).
Colours: All Royal Blue
Change colours: White/black/black.

AWSWORTH VILLA

Secretary: Paul Wilkinson
15 Barlow Drive North, Awsworth, Nottingham NG16 2RQ.
Tel: 0115 930 4905 (H) 0115 932 8721 (B)

Ground: Shilo Park, off Attewell Road, Awsworth, Nottm.

Colours: Red & white/red/red.

BOOTS ATHLETIC

Secretary: Ian Whitehead
21 Rosthwaite Close, West Bridgford, Nottingham NG26RA
Tel: 0115 981 2830 (H) 0115 968 7535 (B)
Ground: Lady Bay, West Bridgford, Nottingham Tel: 0115 981 2392
Colours: Blue&white stripes, bue,blue.

Honours: Notts Alliance Div 1 91-92 (Lg Cup 91-92), Notts Snr Cup R-up 93-94,Notts Inter R-up 91-92.

CLIFTON

Secretary: Mrs Pat Brodie, 21 Cerne Close, Clifton, Nottingham.
Tel: 0115 9215113

Ground: Green Lane, Clifton Est., Nottm Tel: 0115 984 4903

Colours: All white(Blue trim)

COTGRAVE COLLIERY WELFARE

Secretary: Kevin Whitehead, 51 Crosshill, Cotgrave, Nottinham.
NG12 3NB Tel: 0115 989 4043

Ground: Woodview, Cotgrave, Nottingham
Colours: Red/blue/blue

KEYWORTH UNITED

Secretary: Stuart Douglas
29 Ashley Crescent, Keyworth, Nottm. NG12 5GF
Tel: 0115 937 5358

Ground: Platt Lane, Keyworth (0115 937 5998)

Colours: Green/black/green

KIMBERLEY MINERS WELFARE

Secretary: Stephen Hobster
35 Truman Street, Kimberley, Nottingham NG16 2HA
Tel Nos: 0115 938 4067 (H) 07866 777376 (M)

Ground: Digby Street, Kimberley, Nottingham (0115 938 2124)

Colours: Black & red/black/black & red

KINGSWELL

Secretary: Phil Smith
1 Mowbray Rise, Arnold, Nottm NG5 5DW
Tel: 0115 956 9585 (H) 07977 633051 (M)
Ground: Williams Lee Memorial Ground
Park Road, Calverton, Nottingham Tel: 0115 965 3097

Colours: Red & White (home) All blue (away)

LINBY COLLIERY WELFARE

Secretary: J.Riley,70 Bolingey Way, Hucknall, Notts.NG15 6TQ
Tel No: 0115 953 3025

Ground: Church Lane, Linby, Nottingham (07971 023622)

Colours: Red ,black& white/red & black shorts

NEWARK FLOWERSERVE

Secretary: Kevin Presland, Appleby Lodge, Barnby Road, Newark, Nottingham NG24 2NE Tel: 01636 704606, 07771 507065

Ground: Lowfield Works, off hawton Lane, Balderton, Newark, Nottingham. Tel: 01636 702672

Colours: Orange/blue/orange

NOTTINGHAMSHIRE POLICE

Secretary: John Beeston   **Club Colours:** All Red
17 Alandene Ave, Watnall, Nottingham NG16 1HH
Tel: 0115 938 2110
Ground: Calverton Recreation Centre, Hollingwood Lane, Calverton, Nottingham (0115965 4390)
Honours: Notts Snr R-up 91-92, Notts All. Div 1 & Lge Snr Cup R-up 85-86, PAANNat. K-O Comp 63-64.

RADCLIFFE OLYMPIC

Secretary: C Johnson, 2 The Firs, Holme Pierrepoint, Nottingham NG12 2LT Tel: 0115 933 3791

Ground: Wharf Lane, Radcliffe-on-Trent, Nottingham

Colours: All Black with Beige & red trim

RAINWORTH MINERS WELFARE

Secretary: Alan Wright, 10 Faraday Road, Mansfield NG18 4ES
Tel: 01623 624379 (H) 01623 553237 (B)
Ground: Kirklington Road, Rainworth, Notts
Directions: On A617 Mansfield - Newark Road
Colours: All white
Honours: Notts Alliance 77-78 78-79 79-80 80-81 81-82 82-83 (R-up
93-94, Lg Cup 81-82), Notts Snr Cup 80-81 81-82 (R-up 82-83 92-93),
FA Vase R-up 82-82, ThornEMI F'lit Cup R-up 82-83 83-84 84-85

RUDDINGTON UNITED

Secretary: John Fisk, 3 Savages Rd., Ruddington, Nottm NG11 6EW
Tel: 0115 9842552
Ground & Directions: The Elms Park Ground, Loughborough Road,
Ruddington (0115 984 4976) On A60 Nottm to Loughborough, 5 miles
out of Nottingham.
Colours: Yellow & blue/blue/blue
Honours: Notts Comb. Lg 79-80, Lg Cup 70-71 76-77 80-81

SOUTHWELL CITY

Secretary: Pat Johnson
                    63 The Ropewalk, Southwell, Notts NG25 0AL
                    Tel: 01636 812594

Ground: War Memorial Recreation G round, Bishops Drive,
Southwell, Notts. 01636 814386

Colours: Black& White stripes/black/black.

WOLLATON

Secretary: Paul King, 18 Lancaster Way, Strelley, Nottingham NG8 6PH
Ground: Wollaton Sports Association, Wollaton Village, Nottm
                    Tel: 0115 9133 134
Colours: **All** Sky Blue
Honours: Notts All. Div 1 R-up 92-93, Div 2 91-92,
                    I'mediate Cup R-up 91-92.

DIVISION ONE CLUBS

ASC DAYNCOURT

Secretary: Adrian Cridge, 3 Regina Close, Radcliffe on Trent,
Nottingham NG12 2EL. Tel: 0115 933 4771 (H) 07831 680687 (M)
Ground: Bingham Road Playing Fields, Radcliffe on Trent,
Nottingham
Colours: Navy & white/navy/navy

BASFORD UNITED

Secretary: Maria Smith, 17 Snenfield Gardens, Rise Park,
Nottingham NG5 5BH (0115 955 8045)
Ground: Greenwich Ave., Bagnall Rd, Basford, Nottm (0115
942 3918).
Directions: M1, J26 follow signs A610 Nottingham then B6004
Arnold into Mill St.
Colours: Yellow/black/yellow

BESTWOOD MINERS WELFARE

Secretary: Alan Fisher,5 Skipton Close, Ilkeston, Derbyshire
DE7 9HX (0115 932 7717)
Ground: Bestwood Workshops, Park Rd, Bestwood
Colours: Red/navy blue/navy blue.

BILSTHORPE

Secretary: Duncan Costin, 12 Calstock ~Road, Woodthorpe,
Nottingham. NG5 4FH Tel: 0115 919 9371 (H) 0115 949 5232
(B) 07989 596001 (M)
Ground: Birchover Park, Brindley Road, Bilborough,
Nottingham. Tel: 0115 928 7662
Colours: red shirts, navy shorts

BOOTS ATHLETIC RESERVES

CALVERTON M.W.

Secretary: John Daniel, 13 Renals Ways, Calverton,
Nottingham NG14 6PH 0115 965 4447 (H) 0771 5306032 (M)
Ground: Calverton Recreation Centre, Hollingwood Lane,
Calverton, Nottingham Tel: 0115 965 4390
Colours: Sky Blue&navy/navy

CHAFFOTEAUX

Secretary: Mark Nicholls, 31 Telford Drive, Newthorpe, Nottm.
NG16 3NN 01773 534169 (H) 0115 942 2400(B)
Ground: Basil Russell Playing Fields, Maple Drive, Nuthall,
Nottingham 0115 938 4765
Colours: Red & black/red&black/black

MAGDALA AMATEURS

Secretary: Alan Gilmour, 9 Adbolton Grove, West Bridgford,
Nottingham NG2 5AR Tel: 0115 982 1071
Ground: Civil Service Sports Ground, Wilford Lane, W
Bridgford.
Colours: Amber/Black/Tangerine

MATRIXGRADE

Secretary: Stephen Farmery (0115 910 6694 (H) 07979
238209 (M)
Ground: Carrington Sports Ground, Mansfield Rd., Nottm.
Colours: Yellow & black/black/black

NEWARK FLOWERSERVE RESERVES

SOUTHBANK

Secretary: Gerry Bishop, 4 Foxearth Ave., Clifton, Nottm.
NG11 8JQ Tel: 0115 984 2363
Ground: Carlton Hill, Nottingham
Colours: Red & White Stripes/White/Red

SOUTHWELL CITY RESERVES

STAPLEFORD BOROUGH

Secretary: Tony Iacovitti, 1 Edward Street, Stapleford,
Nottingham NG9 8FH Tel: 0115 949 7598 (H) 07974 088210
(M)
Ground: The University Sports Ground, University Boulevard,
Nottingham.
Colours: Blue & black/black/blue

WOLLATON RESERVES

WOODHOUSE

Secretary: Tony Dove, 1 Greenwood Close, Sutton-in-
Ashfield, Nottm. Tel: 01623 554466
Ground: Debdale Lane, mansfield Woodhouse, Nottm.
Tel: 01623 631747
Colours: Red & blue stripes/blue/blue & red

Basford United. Back Row (l-r): Marc Barnaby, Simon Allcock, Lee Carter, Darren Hanmans, Nigel Cann, Lance Swinago-Robertson, Garry Holmes, Matthew Wheat, Fred Kirk (Manager). Front Row: Martin Smith, Simon Martin, Karl Smith, Matthew Hudson, Alistair Brown, Andrew Dawkins. Photo: Gordon Whittington

Gedling MW. Photo: Gordon Whittington

Eynesbury Rovers, Huntingdonshire Senior Cup winners after beating St Neots 3-0 in the Final.
Photo: Gordon Whittington

NORTHERN LEAGUE
Founded 1889

President: George Courtney MBE   **Chairman:** Mike Amos
Hon. Secretary & Treasurer: A Golightly, 85 Park Road North, Chester-le-Street, Co Durham DH3 3SA
Tel: 0191 388 2056   Fax: 0191 3891 1385   E-mail: tonygol@northernlge.fsnet.co.uk

There are old heads in the Albany Northern League - and younger ones, too - who long for the Amateur Cup glory days when a Northern League team seemed always to be running around Wembley with the old pot.

Certainly the competition was dominated in the twenty years after the war by teams within twenty miles of Durham and twenty miles of London, but it's 1954-55 - a twice replayed final between Bishop Auckland and Crook - since two NL sides met in the final.

There were mixed feelings, therefore, when Durham City and Whitley Bay both reached the semi-finals of the FA Carlsberg Vase. Many hoped that they would be drawn apart, in the hope of another all North-East affair in the final; the more cautious - caffey hearted, as they say in these parts - wanted them together, so that one finalist would be guaranteed.

Fate threw them together. The two semi-final legs say Whitley Bay win 2-1 at home, and hold out for a relatively comfortable goalless draw at Durham. Two seasons ago they were struggling at the foot of the Unibond: a return to the League they had left in 1988 coincided with new faces (and new money) in the boardroom and a welcome resurgence in fortune.

The final was not, as the euphemists say, a classic. Villa Park was hugely welcoming but mostly empty, the match itself disappointing until Ian Chandler's header in extra time saw the Sea Horses - as now they are curiously styled - to ecstatic victory.

They were the fourth Northern League finalists in the past six seasons and the second winners. Familiarity breeds nothing but elation. The Vase is a tremendous competition, right from the early rounds and already Whitley Bay are planning a pre-season game - a friendly in every sense - with Tiptree, the defeated finalists.

Perhaps distracted by the Vase run, or bogged down by a fixture backlog - the rainy season again lasted about four months in this part of the world - Whitley Bay were unable, however, to make a big impression on the First Division. Bedlington Terriers were champions for a record equalling fifth successive season, and will be all the more anxious to clinch the title for a sixth time because the record is now held jointly by their neighbours and rivals Blyth Spartans.

The Terriers again declined to apply for elevation, promoting only tittle-tattle among the ignorant that ANL clubs are insular, unambitious and not interested in the Pyramid. It's rot, and that's being euphemistic, too.

The fact of the matter is that the Unibond First Division, into which the ANL promotes, had just one club - Spennymoor United - in the North East of England. For the Unibond's other two feeders, promotion would still mean plenty of local derbies and relatively few journies amounting to much more than an hour across the Pennines.

For the Albany Northern League champions, or runners up, promotion would mean a vastly increased travel bill and midweek trips often ending in the early hours. A club considering promotion costed coach travel and was quoted £12,000 for the season - a huge expense. It's financial prudence, not lack of ambition, which makes our clubs baulk.

With the League's increased geographic isolation from the rest of the Pyramid in mind, we have pressed through-out a season of national restructuring talks with the FA for a redefining of boundaries - regardless of the level at which the League might operate.

We have pressed for a Northern League which would serve an area between Tweed and Humber but not much west of the A1 - a halfway house in terms of geography and rationality and a principle which clubs at a special general meeting approved with just one dissenting vote. Where it will end, of course, is another matter entirely - at the time of writing, the FA still hasn't sorted out Level Two.

The worry is that for the Northern League, and others at Level Three, it will be a case of devil take the hindmost. The bigger fear is that the opportunity to address the North-East's problems, shared probably with the south Western League, will be lost forever. Like Ben Gunn, or the Swiss Family Robinson or whoever it was, we shall be marooned.

We are also apprehensive about the FA-driven changes to the refereeing system, particularly as they will affect our Second Division, but reserve judgement.

With Bedlington long time leaders in the First Division, much the greater excitement was in the Second. Eight or nine clubs had realistic hopes of promotion in March and, with three games remaining, any one of four could have

been champions and any of them in fourth place. Penrith were the most popular nomination for the title but lost their last three matches and missed out altogether. Shildon won the division with Prudhoe and Esh Winning also promoted - the latter for the first time since joining the new Northern League Second Division in 1982. They're still partying up there.

Shildon, resurgent, also reached both major cup finals. In the League Cup they lost to a "golden goal" - good rule, that - by Durham City and in the Craven Cup final for Second Division clubs went down to Prudhoe Town (Prudhoe's chairman, Alex Waters, has spent tens of thousands of his own money on developing the ground and pitch - built on top of a rubbish tip - but has never seen them play. Too stressful, he insists, and, though he has a Newcastle United season ticket, he's never seen them, either.)

At the bottom of the First Division, Seaham Red Star - runners up just two seasons ago - failed to shine for most of the season and were relegated. Struggling for helpers like so many more, the club gave precautionary notice of resignation but, happily, were able to withdraw it.

Thornaby, now a real yo-yo club, and Ashington - joyously promoted just twelve months earlier - join them back in the Second Division.

For reasons connected with ground grading, the ANL's automatic promotion and relegation agreements with its feeders are suspended. Though the League indicated to the FA its willingness to increase Second Division member ship in order to accommodate clubs marooned through no fault of their own, a series of frustrating bureaucratic delays prevented that happening. For Wearside League champions North Shields it was particularly galling. We hope next season that automatic promotion and relegation may be resumed.

Once again the League was much blessed by very substantial sponsorship from the Albany Group, headed by former four minute miler and would-be Carlisle United owner Brooks Mileson. Brooks also personally sponsors the Performance of the Week and Fair Play and Good Conduct awards - Consett the only club not to collect a red card in League games.

Evenwood Town were also able to resurrect an old agreement, claiming a match ball for going three months without out a caution. Because of the prevailing North-East climate, they'd played just four games in that time.

The Northern League Club - established four years ago to promote interest and information about the League again achieved record membership, as it has every season. Annual membership remains at £10, which includes an enamel lapel badge, and £7.50 thereafter. Details are available from Martin Howarth, 17 The Turn, Morpeth, Northumberland NE61 2DU.

A Northern League Club subscription also includes copies of Northern Ventures Northern Gains, the League's highly acclaimed and ludicrously inexpensive 24 page magazine. It's otherwise available from Peter Lax, 21 Carlton Avenue, Billingham, Cleveland - £3.50 for six issues, including postage.

The magazine has had much to occupy it in the past twelve months and doubtless will again. As always we look forward to the new season, and to two teams in the final of the Vase.

Mike Amos

FINAL LEAGUE TABLES 2001-02

DIVISION ONE

	P	W	D	L	F	A	Pts	GD
Bedlington Terriers	40	28	8	4	104	35	92	69
Tow Law Town	40	26	7	7	90	44	85	46
Dunston Federation	40	22	9	9	86	53	75	33
Marske United	40	21	8	11	56	48	71	8
Whitley Bay	40	20	8	12	78	49	68	29
Durham City	40	19	11	10	87	62	68	25
West Auckland T	40	19	11	10	80	57	68	23
Billingham Town	40	16	9	15	67	66	57	1
Brandon United*	40	17	8	15	68	53	56	15
Billingham Synth.	40	15	10	15	79	75	55	4
Guisborough Town*	40	16	9	15	68	63	54	5
Jarrow Roofing BCA	40	15	8	17	62	74	53	-12
Peterlee Newtown	40	14	10	16	54	60	52	-6
Chester-le-Street	40	14	7	19	63	68	49	-5
Washington I.H.	40	13	5	22	54	74	44	-20
Consett	40	11	10	19	60	65	43	-5
N'castle Blue Star*	40	13	6	21	56	80	42	-24
Morpeth Town	40	10	10	20	48	70	40	-22
Ashington*	40	11	8	21	62	98	38	-36
Thornaby	40	8	5	27	48	96	29	-48
Seaham Red Star*	40	6	5	29	38	118	20	-80

DIVISION TWO

	P	W	D	L	F	A	Pts	GD
Shildon	38	28	4	6	135	51	88	84
Prudhoe Town	38	26	7	5	104	32	85	72
Esh Winning	38	27	4	7	93	39	85	54
Penrith	38	26	4	8	101	42	82	59
Easington Coll.	38	24	5	9	87	47	77	40
Horden CW	38	21	9	8	87	55	72	32
Washington Nissan	38	23	3	12	95	68	72	27
South Shields	38	18	8	12	62	41	62	21
Northallerton T	38	17	10	11	59	52	61	7
Kennek Ryhope CA	38	17	8	13	65	47	59	18
Crook Town*	38	16	6	16	53	60	51	-7
Norton & Stockton	38	14	7	17	66	71	49	-5
Alnwick Town	38	12	12	14	63	74	48	-11
Hebburn Town	38	12	6	20	52	97	42	-45
Evenwood Town	38	8	5	26	46	96	29	-50
Whickham	38	7	5	26	50	90	26	-40
Willington	38	6	6	26	52	114	24	-62
Murton	38	5	7	26	34	108	22	-74
Eppleton CW*	38	6	6	26	42	91	18	-49
Shotton Comrades	38	4	4	30	45	116	16	-71

points deducted

DIVISION ONE RESULTS CHART 2001-02

		1	2	3	4	5	6	7	8	9	10	11	12	13	14	15	16	17	18	19	20	21
1	Ashington	X	1-3	3-2	3-0	1-0	3-3	0-2	3-3	1-3	2-7	0-4	1-1	3-0	2-1	2-2	8-0	2-1	2-2	1-1	3-2	0-3
2	Bedlington T.	5-2	X	3-2	3-1	2-0	4-1	0-1	0-0	3-0	3-1	3-1	3-1	3-0	3-0	2-1	1-0	3-0	4-0	2-1	1-1	0-0
3	Billingham S.	2-1	1-3	X	1-1	4-1	2-1	3-2	1-2	3-3	3-1	0-1	4-1	0-2	0-1	1-0	2-2	3-1	2-2	1-0	2-2	0-3
4	Billingham T.	4-2	1-1	1-4	X	0-3	1-0	3-1	0-3	0-4	1-2	2-2	3-1	1-1	5-1	3-0	2-0	0-0	1-2	3-0	2-2	2-3
5	Brandon Utd	2-1	2-1	1-1	0-1	X	2-0	4-2	0-1	0-5	1-1	3-0	3-0	1-0	2-1	1-1	2-0	3-1	0-1	8-2	3-4	0-1
6	Chester le St	4-0	0-2	4-1	2-1	2-0	X	1-3	2-3	4-0	2-2	2-2	1-2	0-0	1-5	2-1	2-3	2-1	1-5	1-1	2-0	0-2
7	Consett	1-2	1-2	2-2	5-2	0-0	1-1	X	0-2	2-0	0-0	0-2	0-1	3-3	1-1	3-0	2-2	2-3	1-2	1-2	0-2	2-0
8	Dunston Fed.	2-1	3-2	4-3	2-3	2-2	2-2	4-0	X	0-4	1-3	2-1	1-0	1-1	3-0	2-3	5-0	1-0	1-1	5-0	1-1	0-3
9	Durham City	5-0	1-3	3-1	4-3	0-2	2-1	1-1	4-1	X	1-0	4-3	1-2	0-3	4-1	1-1	2-2	3-3	2-3	4-0	1-1	1-1
10	Guisboro T	2-1	1-2	1-1	1-2	2-2	3-2	1-1	0-4	3-4	X	4-0	0-1	3-0	2-2	0-3	3-1	3-1	1-1	2-1	0-1	2-1
11	Jarrow Rfng	3-3	3-1	1-2	3-0	1-5	0-3	0-2	4-3	0-1	2-1	X	2-2	0-0	0-0	1-4	0-3	4-1	0-3	1-0	0-5	2-1
12	Marske Utd	3-0	1-1	1-0	2-0	2-2	2-1	1-0	0-4	3-1	1-2	3-1	X	2-1	2-0	2-3	3-0	2-1	1-0	1-3	1-1	2-1
13	Morpeth T	3-0	1-6	1-1	0-2	1-2	1-4	3-1	2-2	1-0	3-0	1-3	0-1	X	3-1	2-4	1-2	0-0	0-3	1-4	0-3	2-1
14	Newcastle BS	0-1	0-3	2-5	2-5	0-4	2-4	2-1	1-1	2-2	0-0	2-0	0-1	2-0	X	6-0	1-3	4-1	2-1	0-3	1-2	3-2
15	Peterlee N	0-0	1-1	5-1	0-0	1-0	1-0	1-2	2-1	1-1	1-5	1-1	2-1	1-0	3-0	X	1-1	0-1	1-2	0-1	0-2	0-0
16	Seaham R S	1-3	0-8	1-4	1-1	2-1	0-1	0-3	1-4	2-6	2-3	1-4	0-1	0-4	0-1	0-5	X	0-4	1-4	2-3	1-0	0-3
17	Thornaby	2-0	1-6	2-4	2-3	0-3	0-2	0-6	0-3	0-1	4-1	1-3	0-0	1-3	0-1	1-2	3-1	X	0-4	2-0	1-2	3-7
18	Tow Law T	4-1	1-1	2-0	1-0	0-0	2-0	1-0	2-1	1-3	2-1	0-3	2-1	3-3	4-1	2-0	5-0	9-2	X	2-1	2-0	2-0
19	Washington IH	2-1	1-5	4-1	1-1	2-1	0-1	5-0	0-3	2-3	0-1	2-2	2-3	0-0	1-3	2-0	3-0	0-2	1-4	X	0-2	0-1
20	West Auckland	9-2	2-2	1-6	0-2	4-0	2-1	2-2	1-2	2-2	2-1	0-2	1-1	3-1	4-2	3-2	5-0	1-0	4-3	0-1	X	0-3
21	Whitley Bay	4-0	0-3	3-3	1-4	3-2	4-0	4-3	0-1	0-0	1-2	3-0	0-0	3-0	1-2	4-0	4-3	2-2	1-0	3-2	1-1	X

LEADING GOALSCORERS 2001-02

DIVISION ONE

Andrew Fletcher	Dunston FB	35
Lee Flanagan	Billingham Synthonia	30
John Milner	Bedlington Terriers	27
Paul Rowntree	Billingham Town	27
Roy Allen	West Auckland Town	26
Lee Ludlow	Durham City	26

DIVISION TWO

John Outhwaite	Shildon	30
Nigel Bolton	Shildon	29
Marc Nash	Prudhoe Town	27
Tony Hanson	Easington Colliery	25
Adam Johnston	Washington Nissan	23

Whitley Bay, FA Vase Winners 2001-02. Back Row (l-r): Gary Cook, Andrew Wilson (Kit man), Jon Sunderland, Andy Hoggarth, Andy Hay, Andy Gowen (Manager), Danny Anderson, Mark Cameron (Asst Manager), Ian Chandler, Chris Neil, Mark Walmsley. Front Row: Steve Logger, Mark Taylor, Rob Livermore, Gary Middleton (Capt), Andy Dugdale, Michael Fenwick, Yosuke Suzuki.

ALBANY LEAGUE CUP 2001-02

FIRST ROUND

Esh Winning	v	Willington	1-0	Evenwood Town	v	Alnwick Town	1-2
Shotton Comrades	v	Morpeth Town	2-4	Tow Law Town	v	Murton	5-0
Whitley Bay	v	Easington Colliery	3-0	Crook Town	v	Jarrow Roofing	0-1
Hebburn Town	v	Horden CW	2-1	Peterlee	v	Northallerton	3-2
Washington I H	v	Kennek Ryhope CA	4-1				

SECOND ROUND

Dunston Federation	v	Billingham Synthonia	5-0	Guisborough	v	Consett	1-2
Newcastle Blue Star	v	Prudhoe Town	0-1	Penrith	v	Brandon United	2-2
Seaham Red Star	v	Ashington	2-4	South Shields	v	Washington Nissan	4-3
Tow Law Town	v	Alnwick Town	6-1	Whickham	v	Marske United	1-0
Whitley Bay	v	Chester le Street	3-2	Bedlington Terriers	v	Billingham Town	0-1
Eppleton CW	v	Hebburn Town	1-2	Jarrow Roofing	v	Thornaby	2-0
Shildon	v	West Auckland	2-1	Washington IH	v	Durham City	1-2
Esh Winning	v	Peterlee	0-1	Norton & SA	v	Morpeth Town	0-0

Brandon United and Norton & SA won on penalties

THIRD ROUND

Ashington	v	Norton & SA	2-1	Dunston Federation	v	Brandon United	2-1
Consett	v	Peterlee Newtown	0-2	Durham City	v	Hebburn Town	6-2
Jarrow Roofing	v	Prudhoe Town	1-0	Shildon	v	South Shields	2-1
Whickham	v	Tow Law Town	1-3	Whitley Bay	v	Billingham Town	4-2

FOURTH ROUND

Tow Law Town	v	Ashington	3-0	Durham City	v	Dunston Federation	1-0
Whitley Bay	v	Peterlee N	4p3, 2-2	Jarrow Roofing	v	Shildon	2-3

SEMI FINALS

Durham City	v	Whitley Bay	2-0	Tow Law Town	v	Shildon	1-3

FINAL

Durham City	v	Shildon	3-2	at Durham City	

CRAVEN CUP 2001-02

SEMI FINALS

Penrith	v	Prudhoe Town	0-2	Shildon	v	Washington Nissan	3-2

FINAL

Prudhoe Town	v	Shildon	1-0	at Esh Winning	

twentyfive in twentyfive twentyfive in twentyfive twentyfive in twentyfive twentyfive in twentyfive

25 *in* 25

A review of the progress made by the **Northern League** and its member clubs during the twenty-five year life span of the F.A. Non-League Club Directory (1978 - 2002) will be available in the next year. It will be one of a series of 25 and will contain features, statistics and photos in at least 160 pages dedicated purely to the Northern League members.

Further details can be found on page 17 so make sure of your copy of this exciting limited edition.

twentyfive in twentyfive twentyfive in twentyfive twentyfive in twentyfive twentyfive in twentyfive

ASHINGTON

Secretary: Brian Robinson, 80 Milburn Road, Ashington, N/thumberland NE63 0PG
Tel: 01670 852832 (H) 01670 521212 (B) FAX: 01670 852832
Ground: Portland Park, Ashington NE63 9XG (01670 811991 Social Club)
Directions: 200 yds north at traffic lights in centre of town
Capacity: 2,000   Seats: 350   Cover: 2,200   Floodlights: Yes
Clubhouse: Open 6-11 evening & from11am on Tuesdays (market days)
Not open Weds and Sun, darts, jukebox, snacks etc.
Club Shop No but jumpers, baseball caps etc. behind bar

PREVIOUS **Leagues:** Northern Alliance 1892-93 1902-14 69-70; Football League;
North Eastern 14-21 29-58 62-64; Midland 58-60; Northern Counties 60-62;
Wearside 64-65; N.P.L. 68-69., Northern Lg. Div 2 Champions 2000-01

RECORD **Attendance:** 13,199 v Rochdale, FA Cup 2nd Rd 9/12/50
Fee Received: £2,500 from W.B.A. for Tony Lowery

BEST SEASON **FA Cup:** 3rd Rd 26-27   League Clubs defeated: Halifax Town 50-51
FA Amateur Cup SF 73-74

HONOURS Northumberland Snr Cup (9) , Northumberland Chall. Bowl (6) ,
Midland Lg 58-59, North Eastern Lg Cup 33-34 (jt Sunderland Res.) 39-40;
Northern Alliance x 4, R-up x 6; Lg Cup 47-48, Craven Cup Winners 98-99
Players progressing: Tony Lowery (W.B.A.), Les Mutrie (Colchester), R Cummins (Aberdeen),
David Walton (Sheff Utd.)

FACT FILE
Formed: 1883
Nickname: The Colliers
Sponsors: T.B.A.
Club colours: Black & white stripes/black/black
Change colours: Green/white/green
Midweek Matches: Tuesday
Programme: Yes, 50p
Editor: A Marchett (01670 854585)

CLUB PERSONNEL
Chairman: Tom Reed
Joint Presidents:
Sir Bobby Charlton & Jackie Charlton OBE
Press Officer: Brian Bennett (01670 856606)
Manager: Tony Harrison
Asst.Manager: Paul Anderson
Physio: Mick Harrison

BEDLINGTON TERRIERS

Secretary: Shaun Campbell,106 Wright St., Blyth. Northumberland NE24 1HG
Tel: 01670 353823 (H) 07703 529869 (M)
Ground: Welfare Park, Park Rd., Bedlington, Northumberland. Tel: 01670 825485
Directions: Into Bedlington, turn left at `Northumberland Arms' on Front St., then 2nd Right,
ground on right 100 yds .   Club Website: www.btfc.fsnet.co.uk
Capacity: 3,000   Seats: 300   Cover:500   Floodlights: Yes
Clubhouse: Open every evening, 7-11pm Sat. & Sun lunch. Pool, darts etc Club Shop: Yes
Record Att: 2,400 v Colchester Utd   **Record Seasons Scorer:** John Milner 63 , 98-99
HONOURS Northern League Div One 97-98 98-9 99-00 00-01 01-02 R-up: 85-86 9596 Div 2
94-95 (R-up 84-85), Northern Alliance 66-67 (R-up 67-68 69-70 71-72) Lg Cup 57-58 66-67 69-
70 81-82, Lge Chall Cup 96-97 00-01,Northumberland Sen Cup 96-97. 97-98 01-02Cleator Cup
97-88, 98-99, 99-00

PREVIOUS **Leagues:** Northern Alliance   **Names:** Bedlington Mechanics 49-53;
Colliery Welfare 53-56; Mechanics 56- 61; Bedlington United 61-65;
Bedlington Colliery 65-68; Bedlington Town 68-74.

BEST SEASON **FA Cup:** 2nd Rd v Scunthorpe(a) 0-1 **FA Vase:** Final 98-9 VTiverton T 0-1

RECORDS **Attendance:** 1,013 v Blyth Spartans, Northern Lg 85-86
Win: 11-0 v West Auckland, (H) Lge 96-97   **Scorer:** John Milner63

FACT FILE
Formed: 1949
Colours: Red & white/red&white/white
Change colours: Blue & whitw/blue&white/blue
Midweek Matches: Wednesday
Programme: 50 pages, £1.00
2001-02
Captain: Warren Teasdale
Top Scorer: John Milner (37)
P.o.Y.: Martin Kirkby
CLUB PERSONNEL

Chairman: David Perry
(0468 195350)
Vice Chairman: John Feary
Press Officer: Bill Lowery (01670 713099)
Managers: Keith Perry & Tony Lowrey
Coach: Melvyn Harmison
Physio: Dave Robertson

BILLINGHAM SYNTHONIA

Secretary: Graham Craggs, 10 Embleton Grove, Wynard,Stockton on TeesTS22 5SY
Tel No: 01740 645367
Ground: The Stadium, Central Avenue, Billingham, Cleveland (Press Box 01642 532348)
Directions: Turn off A19 onto A1027 signposted Billingham, Norton (this applies from either
north or south), continue straight on along Central Avenue, ground on left
opposite office block. 1 mile from Billingham (BR)
Capacity: 1,970   Seats: 370   Cover: 370   Floodlights: Yes
Clubhouse: Onthe ground. Normal club hours   **Club Shop:**Yes(Lapel Badges)
HONOURS Northern Lg 55-57 88-89 89-90 95-96, R-up 49-50 50-51 51-52, Lg Cup 51-
52 87-88 89-90, Div 2 86-87, Teeside Lg 36-37 (Lg Cup 34-35 38-39),
Durham Chall. Cup 88-89 90-91, North Riding Snr Cup 66-67 71-72, North
Riding Amat. Cup 38-39 56-57 62-63 63-64.

PREVIOUS **League:** Teeside (1923-War)   **Name:** Billingham Synthonia Recreation

BEST SEASON **FA Amateur Cup** 4th Rd 48-49   **FA Vase:** 3rd Rd 01-02
FA Trophy: Q-F replay 93-94, 1-2 v Woking after 1-1 (A)
FA Cup:1st Rd 48-49 51-52 56-57 57-58 87-88 89-90

RECORDS **Attendance:** 4,200 v Bishop Auck. 6/9/58
Scorer: Tony Hetherington **Appearances:** Andy Harbron

FACT FILE
Founded: 1923
Nickname: Synners
Sponsors: Darlington Building Society
Colours: Green & White quarters/white/white
Change colours: Blue & White
Midweek Matches: Tuesdays
Programme: 20 pages (+ads),50p
Editor: David Lealman (01642 559540)
2001-02
Captain: Andrew Harbron
Top Scorer &P.o.Y.: : Lee Flanagan 41

CLUB PERSONNEL
Chairman: Stuart Coleby
President: Frank Cook
Press Officer: Secretary
Manager: Stuart Coleby
Physio: Chris Rooney
Coach: Lenny Gunn

BILLINGHAM TOWN

Secretary: Glen Youngman,13 Blackthorne Grove, fairfield, Stockton, Cleveland TS19 7DG
Tel/Fax: 01642 655516 and Tel: 01642 862058

Ground: Bedford Terrace, Billingham, Cleveland. Tel: 01642 560043

Directions: Leave A19 on A1027 (signed Billingham). Turn left at 3rd r/bout,over bridge 1st left,
1st left again to grd

Capacity: 3,000	Seats: 176	Cover: 600	Floodlights: Yes

Clubhouse: Open matchdays. Hot & cold food **Club Shop**: No

HONOURS	Durham Cup 76-77 77-78, R-up: 01-02Teesside Lg 77-78 81-82, Nth Riding Snr Cup R-up 76-77 81-82, Stockton & Dist. Lg(3)
PREVIOUS	**Leagues :** Stockton & Dist. 68-74; Teesside 74-82.
	Name: Billingham Social Club (pre-1982) **Ground :** Mill Lane (pre-1974)
BEST SEASON	**FA Cup:** 1st Rd Proper 55-56
	FA Vase: 5th Rd Proper
RECORDS	**Attendance:** 1,500 v Manchester City, FA Youth Cup 1985
	Scorer: Paul Rowntree 396 (1990-2001)
	Appearances: Paul Rowntree 505 (including 2000-01)

Players progressing: Gary Pallister (Middlesbrough), Gerry Forrest (Southampton), Dave Robinson (Halifax),
Tony Barratt (Hartlepool), Mark Hine (Grimsby), Tony Hall(Middlesbrough), Graham Hall (Arsenal).

FACT FILE
Founded: 1967   Nickname: The Social
Colours: All Blue
Change colours: Yellow/green/green
Midweek Matches: Tuesday
Reserves' Lge: Stockton & Dist Sunday
Programme: 28 pages, 50p
Editor:Peter Martin
2001-02
P.o.Y.:Shaun Gregory
Captain & Top Scorer: Paul Rowntree 34
CLUB PERSONNEL
Chairman: Tommy Donnelly
Hon. President: F Cook M.P.
President: G A Maxwell
Press Officer: Tom Donnelly
(01642 555332(H) 01642 370101(W)
Fax : 01642 651033
Manager: Alan Robinson
Asst Manager: Michael Watson
Coaches: Lee Tucker

BRANDON UNITED

Secretary:	Brian Richardson, Flat 2, 30 Commercial St, Brandon, Durham DH7 8PL
	Tel: 0191 378 1373
Ground:	Welfare Ground, rear of Commercial St., Brandon, Durham Tel: 0191 378 2957
Directions:	A690 - 3 miles west of Durham City. Buses 49 & 49A from Durham

Capacity: 3,000	Seats: 200	Cover: 300	Floodlights: Yes	Club Shop: No

Clubhouse: Open every day, lunch & evening. Pool Entertainment at weekends

HONOURS	FA Sunday Cup 75-76, Northern Lg Div 2 84-85 99-00Northern All.(2) 77-79, Lg Cup 77-78 79-80 Sunderland Shipowners Cup 81-82, Durham Co. Sunday Cup 73-74 75-76 76-77,Durham & Dist Sunday Lg(4) 73-77 (Div 2 69-70, Div 3 68-69), Staffieri Cup 75-76
PREVIOUS	**Leagues:** Durham & Dist. Sunday 68-77; Northern All. 77-80;
	Northern Amtr 80-81; Wearside 81-83.
BEST SEASON	**FA Cup:** 1st Rd replay 88-89 (lost to Doncaster). Also 1st Rd 79-80
	FA Vase: QF 82-83 83-84 **FA Trophy:** 3rd Qual. Rd 87-88 89-90
RECORD	**Gate:** 2,500, FA Sunday Cup SF
	Record Goalscorer: Tommy Holden
	Most Appearances: Derek Charlton 1977-86

Players progressing: Bryan Liddle (Hartlepool 1984) Dean Gibb (Hartlepool 1986),
Paul Dalton (Manchester Utd 1988), Neil Richardson (Rotherham).

FACT FILE
Founded: 1968
Nickname: United
Sponsors: Bramble Down Landscapes
Colours: All red   Change colours: All blue
Midweek Matches: Wednesday
Programme: 40 pages, 30p
Editor: Keith Nellis (0191 378 0704)

2001-02
Top Scorer: Michael Cunningham 17
P.o.Y: Mark Patterson
Team Captain: Richard Pitt

CLUB PERSONNEL
Chairman: Neil Scott
Vice Chairman: John Dickinson
President: Brian Hewitt
Press Officer: Secretary

Manager: Ken Lindoe
Physio: Keith Glendenning

CHESTER-LE-STREET TOWN

Secretary: Melvyn Atkinson, 1 St Marys Close, Chester-le-Street, Co Durham DH2 3EG
Tel: 0191 288 3664
Ground: Moor Park, Chester Moor, Chester-le Street, County Durham (0191 388 3363)
Directions: Ground lies approx 2 miles south of town on A167 (C.-le-S. to Durham). Regular
buses from C.-le-S. and Durham pass ground. Railway station 2 miles distant in town centre

Capacity: 3,500	Seats: 150	Cover: 1,500	Floodlights: Yes

Open Matchdays- midweek 6.30p.m.- 11.00 p.m. Saturday 12.00p.m.-7.00.Open Monday 7..30-
11.00pm **Club Shop:** No, but old programmes available from editor
GROUNDS Ravensworth Welfare, Low Fell 72-73; Riverside Pk 73-78; Sacriston Welfare 78-79.
HONOURS Northern Lg Div 2 83-84 97-98; Wearside Lg 80-81 (R-up 82-83);
Monkwearmouth Cup 80-81 81-82; Washington Lg; Durham Minor Cup; Washington AM Cup.

PREVIOUS	**Leagues:** Newcastle City Amtr 72-75; Washington 75; Wearside 77-83
	Names: Garden Farm 72-78
BEST SEASON	**FA Cup: 4th Qual. Rd. 86-87, 2-3 v Caernarfon Town (H)**
	FA Vase : 5th Rd v Fleetwood Town 84-85 (1-1,2-0,0-3)
RECORD	**Gate:** 893 v Fleetwood FA Vase 18/2/85,
	(3000 Sunderland v Newcastle,Bradford appeal match 85)
	Appearances: Colin Wake 313
	Win: 9-0 v Washington N.L. 28/2/98 **Defeat:** 0-7 v Consett 6/11/96

FACT FILE
Founded: 1972 Nickname: Cestrians
Colours: Blue & white hoops/white/white
Change colours: All yellow
Midweek Matches: Tuesday
Programme: 40 pages, 50p
Editor/Press Officer:J.Thornback
2001-02Captain & P.o.Y.: Colin Wake
Top Scorer: Martin Bowes 21
CLUB PERSONNEL
Chairman: John Tomlinson
Vice Chairman: Jack Thornback
President: John Holden
Press Off.: Jack Thornback (0191 3883554)
Manager: Stuart Sherwood
Asst Manager: tony Heslop Stuart Sherwood
Physio: Mark Parkinson

CONSETT

Secretary: Ian Hamilton, 29 Grange Street, Delves Lane, Consett, Co. Durham DH87AG
Tel: 01207 509366
Ground: Belle Vue Park, Ashdale Road, Consett, County Durham (01207 503788)
Directions: Quarter of mile north of town centre - along Medomsley Rd, left down Ashdale Rd, ground 100m yards on left. Follow signs for Sports Centre and Baths
Capacity: 4,000   Seats: 400   Cover: 1,000   Floodlights: Yes
Clubhouse: Matchdays, and evenings on request. Darts & pool   **Club Shop:** No

HONOURS   North Eastern Lg 39-40 (Div 2 26-27, Lg Cup 50-51(jt) 53-54), Durham Challenge 5, (R-up 2), Northern Lg R-up 76-77 (Div 2 88-89, Lg Cup 78-79 80-81), Northern Counties Lg 61-62, Sunderland Shipowners Cup 67-68, Monkwearmouth Charity Cup 67-68, Wearside Lg R-up 68-69 69-70.
PREVIOUS   Leagues: Northern Alliance 19-26 35-37; North Eastern 26-35 37-58 62-64; Midland 58-60; Northern Counties 60-62; Wearside 64-70
          Grounds: Vicarage Field (pre-1948); Leadgates Eden Colliery 48-50
BEST SEASON   FA Cup: 1st Rd 58-59, 0-5 v Doncaster Rov. (A)
          FA Trophy: 2nd Rd 78-79.   **FA Vase:**
RECORD Gate: 7,000 v Sunderland Reserves, first match at Belle Vue, 1950.
Players progressing: Tommy Lumley (Charlton), Alan Ellison (Reading), Laurie Cunningham (Barnsley), Jimmy Moir (Carlisle), Jackie Boyd (West Bromwich Albion).

FACT FILE
Founded: 1899Nickname: Steelmen
Colours: Red with black & white trim/black/red
Change colours: Sky blue/dark blue/sky blue
Midweek Matches: Wednesday
Programme: 16 pages, 30p
Programme Editor: Andrew Pearson
Local Press: Journal, Northern Echo,
Consett Advertiser.
2000-01
Top scorer: Tony Halliday 27
Captain & P.o.Y.: Jeff Sugden

CLUB PERSONNEL
Chairman: D.Nicholls
Vice Chairman: Stuart Moffat
President: John Hirst
Press Officer: Andrew Pearson
Tel: 01207 506194
Manager: Colin Carr
Physios: Brian Nicholson & Jim Vipond

DUNSTON FEDERATION BREWERY

Secretary: Bill Montague, 12 Dundee Close, Chapel House, Newcastle-upon-Tyne NE51JJ
Tel: 0191 2672250
Ground: Federation Park, Wellington Road, Dunston, Gateshead   Tel: 0191 493 2935
Directions: Dunston/Whickham exit off A1(M), grd 400 yds north. along Dunston Rd on L. 1 mile from Dunston or Metrocentre stations. Buses from Gateshead & Metrocentre stop outside ground
Capacity: 2,000   Seats:120   Cover: 400   Floodlights: Yes
Clubhouse: Matchdays only. Hot & cold snacks, darts.   **Club Shop:** No
HONOURS Northern Lge Div 1 R-up 00-01, Div 2 92-93, Challenge Cup 97-8, 98-9, 99-00; Northern Amtr Lg 77-78 R-up 2, Lg Cup 77-78 78-79 R-up 75-76, Lg Shield 78-79 79-80, Wearside Lg 88-89, 89-90. R-up 90-91, Lg Cup 90-91, N. Comb. 86-87 R-up 3, Lg Cup 83-84, 86-87 R-up 3, Sunderland Shipowners Cup 87-88, Durham Co Tphy 81-82 R-up 2, Minor Cup 79-80 R-up 78-79, Gateshead Chy Cup 77-78 80-81, Heddon Homes Cup 80-81. Cleator Cup 00-01
PREVIOUS   Ground: Dunston public park 75-86
          Names: Whickham Sports; Dunston Mechanics Sports
BEST SEASON   FA Vase: Quarter-Finals 92-93, 0-2 v Gresley Rov. (A)
          FA Cup: 3rd Qual. Rd 92-93, 0-3 v Northallerton T.
RECORDS   Attendance: 1,550 - Sunderland Shipowners Cup Final 1/4/88
Win: 13-0 v Crook T. (H), Northern Lge Div. 1, 00-01   **Scorer:** Paul King
Defeat: 1-6 v Billingham Synthonia (A), Northern Lge Div. 1, 94-95   **Appearances:** Paul Dixon

FACT FILE
Founded: 1975   Nickname: The Fed
Sponsors: Federation Brewery
Colours: All blue with white trim
Change colours :Yellow/black
Midweek matchday: Tuesday
Reserve s' League : None
Programme: 28 pages   50p
Editor: Ian McPherson (0191 420 5583)
CLUB PERSONNEL
Chairman: Malcolm James
Vice-Chairman: Fred Fowles
President: John Smart
Press Officer: Ian McPherson (0191 420 5583)
Commercial Secretary: Malcolm James
Manager: Bobby Scaife
Asst Manager: Perry Briggs
Physio: Matt Annan
2001-02 Leading Club & League goalscorer:
Andy Fletcher40
Captain: Billy Irwin P.o.Y.: Andy Fletcher

DURHAM CITY

Secretary: Kevin Hewitt, 21 Cerrytree Drive, Langley Park,Co Durham DH7 9FX
          Tel: 0191 3733878 (H & FAX) 0191 383 4200 (W)
Ground: Archibalds Stadium, Durham
Directions: At J62 on A1M take A690 towards Durham City. Follow signposts for
          Belmont Industrail Estate.
Capacity: Seats: 300 **Cover:** 700   **Floodlights:** Yes
HONOURS   Northern Lg 94-95 (R-up 70-71, Div 2 R-up 30-31 91-92), Durham
          Benevolent Bowl 55-56, Durham Challenge Cup R-up (2).Northern Div 2
          Champions 98-99, Div 2 Champions 98-99 Durham Challenge Cup R-up (3)
PREVIOUS   **Leagues:** Victory 18-19; N Eastern 19-21 28-38; Football Lge 21-28;
          Wearside 38-39 50-51.
          Grounds: Holliday Park 21-38; Ferens Park 49-94. NB club disbanded in 1938
BEST SEASON **FA Cup:** 2nd Rd 25-26 57-58 (Also 1st Rd 27-28 55-56)
          FA Vase: SF 01-02, QF 87-88   **FA Amateur Cup:** 2nd Rd rep. 57-58
          FA Trophy: 1st Rd 83-84, 94-95
RECORD   **Appearances:** Joe Raine, 552

Players progressing: Harry Houlahan (Newcastle 51), Derek Clark (Lincoln 51),
          Leo Dale & David Adamson (Doncaster 54/70), Stan Johnstone (Gateshead 54),
          Dennis Coughlan (Barnsley 57), John Wile (Sunderland 66), Brian Taylor(Coventry 68),
          Paul Malcolm (Rochdale 84), Gary Pearson (Darlington 02)

FACT FILE
Reformed: 1949
Nickname: City
Sponsors: Sportsnet
Colours: Blue & gold halves/blue & gold stripe/
blue with gold top socks
Change colours: Red & black stripes
Midweek Matches: Tuesday
Programme: 30 pages
Editor: Gordon Wright
Local Press: Northern Echo,
Sunderland Echo, Evening Chronicle
CLUB PERSONNEL
Chairman: Stewart Dawson
Vice Chairman: David Asbery
President: Stewart Dawson
Commercial Manager: Richrd Rodden
Press Officer: Secretary
Manager: Brian Honour
Asst Manager/Coach: Derek Bell
Physio: Alan Trennery

Durham City away to Dereham Town in the FA Vase. Back Row (l-r): Keith Douglas, Lee Ludlow, Gary Bennett, Paul Stephenson, Mark Riches, Craig Lake, Derek Bell (Asst Manager). Front Row: Stuart Brightwell, Stuart Irvine, Richard Ord, Kenny Cramman, Michael Taylor. Photo: Arthur Evans

Whitley Bay: Caffrey, Bowes, Dixon, Anderson, Walmsley, Sunderland, Locker, Fenwick, Chandler, Walton, Middleton
Photo: Graham Brown

Chester-Le-Street Town FC. Back Row (l-r): Andy Blower, Chris Burn, Lee Compton, Ian Aitken, Steven Leadbitter, Martin Bowes. Front Row: Gary Shields, Jamie Morgan, David Turner, Colin Wake, Gary Andison, Phil Sowerby

ESH WINNING

Secretary: Roli Bell,12 Park Rd.Central, Chester-le-Street, Co Durham 0191 388 1458 (H)

Ground: West Terrace, Waterhouses, Durham Tel: 0191 373 3872 (Fax: 0191 387 1983)

Directions: Durham to Ushaw Moor, to Esh Winning; ground 1 mile further at Waterhouses
Capacity: 3,500   Seats: 160   Cover: 500   Floodlights: Yes
Clubhouse: Open daily. Snacks served   **Club Shop:** No
HONOURS   Durham & Dist. Sunday Lg 78-79 79-80, Durham Co. Sun. Cup R-up 78-79,
Staffieri Cup 74-75, Guards Cup 72-73, N. Durham Yth Lg 94-95, Auckland Yth Lge 94-95.

PREVIOUS   **Leagues:** Durham & Dist Sunday; Northern Alliance 81-82.
            Grounds: None   **Names:** Esh Winning Pineapple (pre-1982)

BEST SEASON   **FA Cup:** 2nd Qual Rd 90-91   **FA Vase:** 2nd Round 83-84

RECORDS   **Gate:** 900 v Liverpool Fantail, FA Sunday Cup 1982
        Goalscorer: Mark Drake   **Appearances:** Paul Hewitson 40
        Win: 11-0 v Norton (H)   **Defeat:** 0-10 v Shotton Comrades
        Fee Paid: #350 for Mark Drake**Received:** £500 for Paul Ward (Brandon U)

FACT FILE

Formed: 1967
Nickname: `Esh'
Sponsors:Lumsden & Carroll
Colours: Yellow/green/green/ green
Change colours: Green & Navy
Midweek Matches: Wednesday
Programme: 20 pages, 50p
Editor: Nigel Quinn

CLUB PERSONNEL

Chairman: Charles Ryan
Vice Chairman: David Parkinson
President: Jack Lumsden
Press Officer: Secretary

Manager:Barrie Fleming
Physio:Trevor Best

GUISBOROUGH TOWN

FACT FILE
Founded: 1973   Nickname: Priorymen
Sponsors: Hensons Windows & Conservatories
Colours: Red & white stripes/Black/Red
Change colours:Yellow
Midweek matchday:Wednesday
Reserves ' League: Teesside Strongarm
Programme: 32pages, 50p
Editor: Stuart Burns
Local Press: Northern Echo,
Middlesbrough Evening Gazette
2001-02
Captain: Darron Mowbray
Top Goalscorer: Jamie Clarke 17
CLUB PERSONNEL
Chairman: Richard Corden
Vce Chairman: Keith Watson
Press Officer: Stuart Burns
Manager: Steve Corden
Asst Manager: Tiger Wyke
Physio: Gary Hinchley

Secretary: Keith Smeltzer, 212 Woodhouse Road, Guisborough, Cleveland TS14 6LP
        Tel: 01642 226181 (W) 01287 201561 (H) 07811 850388 (M)
Ground: King George V Ground, Howlbeck Rd, Guisborough, Cleveland (01287 636925)

Directions: From west: bear left at 2nd set of lights, left into Howlbeck Rd after quarter mile,
ground at end. Buses from Middlesbrough
Capacity: 3,500   Seats: 150   Cover: 400   Floodlights: Yes   Club Shop: Yes
Clubhouse: Open evenings & weekends. Hot & cold snacks & drinks from kitchen on matchdays

HONOURS   FA Vase R-up 79-80; Northern Lg Cup 87-88 (Div 2 R-up 86-87),
        Northern Alliance 79-80 (R-up 78-79, Lg Cup 78-79);
        N. Riding Sen. Cup 89-90 90-91 91-92 92-93 94-95.
PREVIOUS   **Leagues:** Middlesbrough & District; South Bank; Northern Alliance 77-80;
        Midland Counties 80-82; Northern Counties (East) 82-85.
BEST SEASON   **FA Cup:** 1st Round Proper 88-89, 0-1 v Bury   **F.A.Vase:** Finalists 79-80
        FA Trophy: 1st Rd Proper 90-91 91-92 92-93
CLUB RECORDS Gate: 3,112 v Hungerford, FA Vase SF, 1980
        (at Middlesbrough FC - 5,990 v Bury, FA Cup 1st Rd 1988)
        Goalscorer: Mark Davis 341   **Appearances:** Mark Davis 587
        Win: 6-0 v Ferryhill & v Easington   **Defeat:** 0-4 v Billingham Synthonia

JARROW ROOFING BOLDON C.A.

FACT FILE
Founded: 1987Nickname: Roofing
Sponsors: Jarrow Roofing Co
Colours: Yellow with Blue trim shirts,
Royal Blue & Yellow sjhorts and socks
Change colours: Red & Black
Midweek matchday: Tuesday
Programme: 20 pages, free with entry
Editor: Brian Marshall (0191 4217011)
2000-01
Top Goalscorer: C.How 33
Captain & P.o.Y: Scott Garrett
CLUB PERSONNEL
Chairman: Richard McLoughlin
Press Officer/Treasurer: Rose McLoughlin
Manager/ Secretary: Richard McLoughlin
Coach: Colin Richardson
Physio: John Cullen

Secretary/Manager: Richard McLoughlin, 8 Kitchener Terrace, Jarrow NE32 5PU
        Tel: 0191 489 9825

Ground: Boldon CA Sports Ground, New Road, Boldon Colliery (0191 519 1391)

Directions: A19 to junction with A184 (Sunderland/Newcastle). Follow signs to Boldon Asda
stores, then to North Road Social Club. Ground behind. East Boldon(BR) 800 yds.
Capacity: 3,500   Seats: 150   Cover: 800   Floodlights: Yes   Club Shop: Yes
Clubhouse: Open eves.& w/e lunchtimes. Hotdogs, burgers etc from tea bar on matchdays

HONOURS   Wearside Lg Div 2 R-up 91-92 95-96; Sunderland Shipowners Cup R-up
        93-94, 94-95; Tyneside Amtr Lg R-up 90-91, Chal. Shield 90-91 (R-up 89-
        90); Bill Dixon Cup 90-91; Mid-Tyne Lg 87-88; Fred Giles Cup R-up 87-88;
        Gateshead Charity Cup SF 90-91; Monkwearmouth Cup 94-95;
        Craven Cup 96-97, Northern League Div One Cup R-Up 98-98

PREVIOUS   **Leagues:** Mid-Tyne; Tyneside Amtr 88-91; Vaux Wearside

RECORD   **Attendance:** 500 v South Shields
        Appearances: Mick Haley **Goalscorer:** Paul Chow

Consett keeper James Platten punches clear against Newcastle Blue Star.
Photo: Alan Watson

Bedlington Terriers striker John Milner holds off the challenge of Eccleshill United joint player-manager Martin Pattison in their FA Vase Second Round tie.
Photo: Darren C Thomas

Steve Kidd fires home Taunton's opening goal in their 3-2 win over West Auckland Town in the Fourth Round of the FA Vase.
Photo: Ken Gregory

MARSKE UNITED

Secretary: Ian Rowe, 19 High Row, Loftus, Saltburn By The Sea, Cleveland. TS134SA
& Press Officer   Tel: 01287 643440 (H) 01642 230546 (B) 01642 241273 (Fax)
Ground: Mount Pleasant, Mount Pleasant Ave., Marske, Redcar, Cleveland. Tel: 01642 471091
Directions: From A19 take A174 exit marked Yarm, Teesport, Redcar, Whitby and head east
towards Saltburn until Quarry Lane r/about. Take 1st left (A1085) into Marske, 1st right (Meadow
Rd) then 1st left (Southfield Rd),then 1st left again Mount Pleasant Ave directly into car park.
      By train: Darlington to Saltburn, Marske station 300 yds from ground.
Capacity: 2,500   Seats: 169   Cover: 300   Floodlights: Yes
Clubhouse: Open every night and weekend lunchtimes. Food served after all games
  Contact : Janet Pippen (01642 474985)
HONOURS   N Riding Sen Cup 94-95; N Riding County Cup 80-81 85-86; Teesside Lg
80-81 84-85; Wearside Lg 95-96, R-up 93-94 94-95 96-97, Cup 92-93 94-95 95-96; M/mouth
Charity Cup 93-94 95-96; Sunderland Ship. Cup 95-96 96-97.N.Lg Cup R-up: 00-01
PREVIOUS   **Leagues:** Cleveland & South Bank 56-76, Teesside 76-85, Wearside 85-97.
BEST SEASON   **FA Cup:** 2nd Qual Rd., 00-01   **FA Vase:** Qtr Final replay, 00-01
RECORDS   **Attendance:** 1,359 v Bedlington Terriers (F.A.Vase) **Win:** 16-0 v North Shields
      Defeat: 3-9   **Goalscorer:** Chris Morgan 169 **Appearances:** John Hodgson 476
Players progressing: Peter Beagrie (Middlesbrough), Tony Butler (Blackpool),
      Roy Hunter (Northampton), Dave Logan (Mansfield T.)

FACT FILE
Founded: 1956   Nickname: The Seasiders
Colours: Yellow/royalblue/white
Change: Royal/sky/yellow
Midweek matchday: Tuesday
Programme: 60 pages £1.00
Editor: Moss Holtby (01642 475612)
Local Press: Sunday Sun, Middlesbrough
Evening Gazette, Northern Echo

CLUB PERSONNEL
Chairman: John Hodgson
Vice Chairman: John Corner
President: Raymond Jarvis
Commercial Manager: Steve Davies
Manager: Charlie Bell
Assistant Manager: Stephen Dowling
Physios: Eric Barrett & Owen Hughes
Coaches: Charlie Bell & Stephen Dowling
Kit Manager: Colin Gilbert

NEWCASTLE BLUE STAR

GROUND: Wheatsheaf Sports Ground, Woolsington, Newcastle-on-Tyne. NE13 8DF
Tel: 0191 286 0425 **Email Address:** nbsfc@blueyonder**Club Website:** www.nbsfc,co,uk
Directions: From central station follow airport signs for 7 miles - ground next to Wheatsheaf Hotel
on left, approx. 800yds before airport. Callerton Parkway metro station is 400yds from ground
Capacity: 2,000   Seats: 300   Cover: 500   Floodlights: Yes **Club Shop:** Yes
Clubhouse: Open every day
HONOURS   FA Vase 77-78; Northern Lg R-up 87-88, Lg Cup 85-86, R-up(1), Div 2 85-86;
Wearside Lg 73-74 75-76 82-83 83-84 84-85, R-up 74-75 77-78 79-80, Lg Cup76-77 79-80 80-81
82-83 83-84; Sunderland Shipowners Cup 82-83 84-85; Monkwearmouth Charity Cup 74-75 79-80
82-83 88-89; Northern Comb. 62-63 68-69, Lg Cup 66-67 71-72; Northumberland Snr Cup 76-77
82-83 85-86 87-88, R-up 74-75 78-79 80-81, Minor Cup 64-65; J R Cleator Cup 86-87.
PREVIOUS   **Leagues:** Newcastle Business Houses 32-38; North East Amateur;
      Tyneside Amateur; Northern Comb.; Wearside 75-85
BEST SEASON FA Trophy: Qtr-finals 88-89, 1-4 v Telford Utd (H)
      FA Vase: Winners 77-78, SF 81-82   **FA Cup:** 1st Rd 84-85, 0-2 v York C. (A)
RECORD Attendance: 1,800 v Almondsbury Greenway, FA Vase SF 77-78
      Appearances & Goalscorer: Ian Crumplin
Players progressing: Ian Crumplin & Tony Robinson (Hartlepool 1976 & 1986), Barry Dunn
(Darlington 1979), Ian McInerney (Huddersfield Town 1988) Peter Weatherson (Queen o South)
Andy Morrell (Wrexham 1999)

FACT FILE
Founded: 1930 Nickname: `Star'
Sponsors: T.B.A.
Colours: All Blue
Change colours: Red/Black/red
Midweek matchday: Tuesday
Reserves' League: None
Programme:44 pages,60p Editor: M.Gault
CLUB PERSONNEL
Secretary: Jim Anderson
38 Western Ave.,West Denton,
Newcastle-on-Tyne NE5 5BU
Tel: 0191 243 1025
Chairman: Derek Sayers
Press Officer: Secretary
Manager/Coach: S.Leeming
Assistant Manager: T.B.A.
Physio: T.B.A.
2001-02
Captain: Warren Fisher
Top Goalscorer :Ross Greenhill
P.o.Y.: Paul Bennett

PETERLEE NEWTOWN

Secretary: Danny Cassidy, 23 Melbury Str, Seaham, Co. Durham SR7 7NF
Tel Nos: 0191 581 4591 (H) 07904 398824 (M)

Ground: Eden Lane, Peterlee, County Durham (0191 586 3004)

Directions: From town centre Fire Station, turn left into Edenhill Rd, thenright into Robson Ave.
Left at the next junction and ground is on the right

Capacity: 6,000   Seats: 50   Cover: 200   Floodlights: Yes
Clubhouse: Open normal licensing hours. Sandwiches etc available **Club Shop:** No

HONOURS   Northern Lg Div 2 82-83, North Eastern F'lit League, 4th Qual Rd FA Cup
PREVIOUS   **Leagues:** Northern Alliance 76-79; Wearside 79-82

RECORD   **Attendance:** 2,350 v Northern, Hillsborough Fund match 1989
      Scorer : Keith Fairless   **Appearances** : Keith Bendelow

BEST SEASON   **FA Cup:** 4th Qual. Rd replay 85-86   **FA Vase:**

Players progressing: Keith Fairless (Scarborough) 1986, Brian Honour(Hartlepool) 1988

FACT FILE
Formed: 1976
Nickame: Newtowners
Sponsors: Artix Ltd
Colours: Sky/navy/sky
Change colours: Yellow/black/yellow
Midweek Matches: Wednesday
Programme: 10 pages, 30p
Editor: Secretary
Local Press: Hartlepool Mail,
Sunderland Echo, Northern Echo

CLUB PERSONNEL
Chairman: Carl Paylor
Vice-Chairman: Bill Burnett
President: David Brown
Press Officer: Ray Matthews (0191 523 8566)
Manager: Tommy Smith
Asst Manager: Eddie Freeman
Physio: Ron Lamdrel

PRUDHOE TOWN

Secretary: Chris Lowther, 10 Westhills,Tantobie, Stanley, Co.Durham DH9 9RZ
Tel: 01207 230108

Ground: Kimberley Park, Broomhouse Road, Prudhoe, Northumberland NE42 5EH
Tel/Fax: 01661 835900

Directions: To Prudhoe along A695, turn right at `Falcon' Inn, 200 yds down Eastwood
Rd., left into Broomhouse Rd., ground on right

Capacity: 5,000   Seats: 150   Cover: Yes   Floodlights: Yes

Clubhouse: Open every evening plus Sat/Sun lunchtimes

HONOURS Hexham & Dist. Lg 68-69 (Lg Cup 68-69), Newcastle & Dist. Lg 69-70 70-71,
Lg Cup 69-70, Charity Shield 69-70 70-71), Northern Comb. 79-80, Northern
AmtrLg 71-72, Clayton Charity Cup 68-69, Northumberland Minor Cup 78-79,
Northumberland Benevolent Bowl 79-80, Heddon Homes Charity Cup 81-82

PREVIOUS **Leagues:** Hexham & Dist 59-69; Newcastle & Dist 69-71; N. Comb.; N.Amtr;
Northern All. 84-88   **Names:** Ovington 1969-75; Prudhoe East End 75-94
Grounds: Farm field, Ovington 59-68; Mickley Welfare 68-69

RECORD **Attendance:** 2,500 v Blyth, Northumberland Snr Cup 1981

FACT FILE

Founded: 1959
Nickname: Citizens
Sponsors: Swinton Insurance
Colours: Orange and blue
Change: White & blue chevrons/navy/sky
Midweek Matches: Tuesday
Programme: 8 pages, 50p
Editor: Rev.Frank Campbell

CLUB PERSONNEL

Chairman: Alex Waters
Press Officer:ErnieGoodfellow(01661 836941)

Manager: Steve Smith
Asst Manager: Shaun McKenna
Physio: Ernie Goodfellow

SHILDON

Secretary /Press Officer: Mike Armitage, 22 Hambleton Court, Byerley Park, Newton Aycliffe,
Co.Durham DL5 7HR   Tel: 01325 316322

Ground: Dean Street, Shildon, County DurhamTel: 01388 773877   **Directions:** In the town
centre 1 mile from BR station and 300yds from Darlington-Bishop Auckland bus stop

Capacity: 4,000   Seats: 480   Cover: 1000   Floodlights: Yes   **Club Shop:** No

Clubhouse: Every eve. 7.30-11pm (earlier match nights).Matchdays.

HONOURS Northern Lg 33-34 34-35 35-36 36-37 39-40 (R-up 32-33 38-39, Div 2 Champions
2001-02 Lg Cup 33-34 34-35 37-38 38-39 39-40 52-53), Durham Challenge Cup 07-08 25-26
71-72,   Durham Amateur Cup 01-02 02-03, Durham Benevelopment Bowl 24-25

PREVIOUS **Leagues:** Auckland & District 1892-96; Wearside 96-97; North Eastern 07-32.

BEST SEASON FA Cup: 2nd Rd 36-37 1st Rd 27-28 29-30 34-35 36-37 55-56 59-60 61-62

FA Trophy: 3rd Qual. Rd 74-75   **FA Amateur Cup:** 4thRd 58-59   **FA Vase:** 1st Rd 86-87

RECORDS **Attendance:** 13,000 - Leeholme v Perkinsville, schoolboys game, 1920s.
(Shildon game); 11,000 Shildon v Ferryhill Ath., Durham Sen. Cup 1922
Appearances: Bryan Dale   **Goalscorer:** Jack Downing, 61 (1936-37)

Players progressing: Ken Whitfield (Wolves 47), James Smith(Chelsea 51),
Mike Peacock, Philip Shute, Nigel Bolton (Darlington 60, 84, 95),
Kevin Stonehouse (Blackburn 79), Alan White (Middlesbrough 93).

FACT FILE

Founded: 1890
Nickname: Railwaymen
Sponsors:
Colours: Purple/black/black
Change: Yellow/blue/blue
Midweek Matches: Wednesday

Programme: 48 pages, 50p
Editor: Secretary

CLUB PERSONNEL

Chairman: Gordon Hampton
Vice Chairman: G. Elliott
President: John Atkinson

Manager: Ray Gowan
Assistant Manager: David Bayles
Physio: Neil Jennings

TOW LAW TOWN

Secretary: Bernard Fairbairn, 3 Coppice Walk, Mowden Park, Darlington, Co. Durham DL3 9DP
Tel: 01325 350743

Ground: Ironworks Road, Tow Law, Bishop Auckland Tel: 01388 731443

Directions: Just of High Street in Tow Law town centre

Capacity: 6,000   Seats: 200   Cover: 300   Floodlights: Yes

Clubhouse: Every evening 8.30 -10.30   **Club Shop:** Yes

HONOURS FA Vase R-up 97-98; Rothmans National Cup 1977,
Northern League Champions 23-24 24-25 94-95, R-up 28-29 88-89, Lg Cup 73-74;
Rothmans Overseas Cup 76-77, Durham Chal. Cup 1895-96, Durham Amtr Cup 1892-93.

PREVIOUS **Leagues:** None

BEST SEASON **FA Cup:** 2nd Rd rep. 67-68, 2-6 v Shrewsbury T. (A) after 1-1. Also 1st Rd
68-69 84-85 89-90.   League Clubs defeated:Mansfield Town 67-68
FA Amateur Cup: 3rd Rd rep. 70-71   **FA Trophy:** 2nd Rd rep. 82-83
FA Vase: Runners-up 1997-98

RECORD **Gate:** 5,500 v Mansfield Town, FA Cup 1967

Players progressing: Reuben Cook & Ralph Guthrie (Arsenal 1951 & 53), Gordon Hughes, Terry Melling
& Chris Waddle (Newcastle 1956 & 65 & 80), EricJohnstone & Kevin Dixon (Carlisle 1963 & 83), Keith
Adamson (Barnsley 1966),Tom Henderson (Bradford PA 1969), Vincent Chapman (Huddersfield 1988)

FACT FILE
Founded: 1890
Nickname: Lawyers
Colours:
Black & white stripes/black/black & white
Change colours: Red & white
Midweek Matches: Tuesday
Programme: Yes
Editor:Chairman
Local Press : Northern Echo

CLUB PERSONNEL
Chairman: John Flynn
Press Officer: John Flynn (01388 730525)
Manager: Graeme Forster
Assistant Manager: Andy Sinclair

2000-01
Leading goalscorer: Nigel Bolton 27
Captain: Michael Bailey
P.o.Y.: Scott Nicholson

WASHINGTON IKEDA HOOVER

Secretary: George Abbott,14 Grosvenor St, Southwick, Sunderland, Tyne & Wear SR5 2DG
Tel Nos: 0191 5491384 (H) 0191 4177779 (W)

Ground: Albany Park, Spout Lane, Concord, District 11, Washington
Tel: 0191 417 7779

Directions: Ground situated opposite bus station.

Capacity: 3,000 Seats: 25 Cover: Yes Floodlights: Yes Club Shop: No

Clubhouse: Open normal licensing hours, with live entertainment, pool etc

PREVIOUS **Leagues:** Washington Amateur; Northern Alliance 67-68; Wearside 68-88

Ground: Usworth Welfare Park

RECORD **Gate:** 3,800 v Bradford Park Avenue, FA Cup 1970

FACT FILE

Founded: 1949
Nickname: Mechanics
Colours: All red
Change colours: All blue
Midweek Matches: Wednesday
Programme: 8 pages, 10p
Editor: Secretary

CLUB PERSONNEL

Chairman: Derek Armstrong
Tel: 0191 416 3956 (H)
Press Officer: Ray Lish
Tel: 0191 415 7071

WEST AUCKLAND TOWN

Secretary: Allen Bayles, 11 Edith Terrace, West Auckland, Co.Durham.DL14 9JT
Tel: 01388 833783 (H) & FAX, 01388 605221 (B) 01388 661366

Ground: Darlington Road, West Auckland, Co.Durham Tel: 01388 834403

Directions: Leaving West Auckland take A68-ground on right before leavingvillage. Bus route via Bishop Auckland fron Newcastle or Darlington

Capacity: 3,000 Seats: 250 Cover: 250 Floodlights: Yes **Club Shop:** No

Clubhouse: On Gound. (The Thomas Lipton Trophy is on display at the local Working Mans Club five minutes away). Tel No: 01388 661366

HONOURS FA Amateur Cup Finalists 60-61; Northern League Champions 59-60, 60-61
Div 2 90-91,Lg Cup 59-60,62-639r-UP;48-49,61-62,63-64)
Durham Challenge Cup 63-64 Durham Benevolent Bowl 62-63; Sir Thomas
Lipton Tphy`First World Cup'(as featured in `The Captains Tale') 1909, 1911.

PREVIOUS **League:** Auckland & District
Names: St Helens Utd (1919 only), West Auckland Town.

BEST SEASON **FA Cup:** 1st Rd 58-59, 61-62,98-99 **FA Trophy:** 3rd Rd. 77-78
FA Vase: 4th Rd. 2001-02 **FA Amateur Cup:** Runners-up 60-61; Q-F 59-60

RECORD **Gate:** 6,000 v Dulwich Hamlet, FA Amateur Cup 58-59
Victory: 11-0 in Durham County Cup

FACT FILE

Founded: 1892
Nickname: West
Sponsors:Rushlift Mechanical Handling and
F.Hudson Transport
Colours: White with black & amber band and
black collar & cuffs.
Change Colours: All Yellow
Midweek Matches: Tuesday

CLUB PERSONNEL

Chairman: Jim Polfreyman
Press Officer:Stuart Alderson
Manager: Allan Oliver
Ass.Manager & Coach: Paul Cross

WHITLEY BAY

Secretary: Derek Breakwell 27 Kings Rd, Whitley Bay, Tyne & Wear, NE26 3BD 0191 252 7940

GROUND Hillheads Park, Rink Way off Hillheads Road, Whitley Bay, Tyne& Wear NE25 8HR
0191 291 3637 Club. Fax & matchday office 0191 291 3636 Website: www.whitleybayfc.co.uk

Directions: 1 mile walk from bus station - leave St Pauls Church southward, turn right at r-about, ground 3rd left at rear of ice rink.Whitley Bay (25mins from Newcastle) or Monkseaton metro stations, both 1 mile. Email: derek.breakwell@whitleybayfc.com

Capacity: 4,500 Cover: 650 Seats: 450

Clubhouse: Open 4-11pm Mon-Fri, 12pm 11pm Sat, 7pm 10.30 pm Sun.Bar,Darts,Pool.functions

Club Shop: Sells progs, scarves, hats, metal badges etc. Contact Tom Moody (0191 291 1618)

PREVIOUS **Leagues:** Tyneside 09-10, Northern All. 50-55, North Eastern Lge 55-58,
Northern Lge 58-88; N.P.L. 88-00 **Name:** Whitley Bay Athletic 1950-58

CLUB RECORDS **Attendance:** 7,301 v Hendon, FA Amateur Cup 1965

Win: 12-0 v Shildon 1961 **Defeat:** 1-8 v Bishop Auckland 1979 **Goalscorer:** Billy Wright 307

Appearances: Bill Chater 640 **Fee Paid:** £500 for Paul Walker from Blyth Spartans

Fee Received: £10,000 for Kevin Todd from Berwick Rangers

BEST SEASON **FA Amateur Cup:** Semi Final 65-66 68-69 **FA Trophy:** 3rd Rd 86-87

FA Cup: 3rd Rd 89-90 (0-1 v Rochdale [A]). **F.A.Vase:** Winners 2001-02

HONOURS: Northern Premier Lg Div 1 90-91 (Div 1 Cup 88-89 90-91), Northern Lg 64-65 65-66
(R-up 59-60 66-67 68-69 69-70), Lg Cup 64-65 70-71 (R-up 67-68); Northern Alliance 52-53 53-54
(Lg Cup 52-53 53-54); Northumberland Sen. Cup x10, R-up x7

FACT FILE

Formed: 1897
Nickname: The Bay
Colours: Blue & white stripes/white/white
Change colours: Yellow or white
Midweek home matchday: Tuesday
Programme Pages: 24 Price: £1.00
Website: www.whitleybayfc.co.uk

CLUB PERSONNEL

Chairman: Fred Iredale
Vice Chairman: Peter Siddle
President: T.B.A.
Press Officer: Peter Fox (0779 933654 (M)
Manager: Andy Gowens
Asst Manager/Coach: Mark Cameron
Physio: David Burton

2000-01

Leading goalscorer: Stee Cuggy 25
Captain: Gary Middleton
P.o.Y.: Danny Anderson

ALNWICK TOWN

Secretary: Darren Middleton, 1 Fire Station Houses, Alnwick, NE66 2PB(1665 603781)
Ground: St James' Park, Alnwick, Northumberland Tel: 01665 603162
Directions: 35 miles north of Newcastle on A1, take the slip road to Alnwick,then first left. At roundabout turn left, ground is then on your left.
Capacity: 2,500   Seats: 100   Cover: 200   Floodlights: Yes
HONOURS   Northern Lg Div 2 R-up 88-89, Northern Alliance 37-38 62-63 63-64 65-66 67-68 68-69 69-70 70-71 71-72 (R-up 59-60 61-62 66-67 72-73, Lg Cup 61-62 65-6667-68 68-69 70-71, Subsidiary Cup 80-81), Durham Central Lg Cup 64-65, Northumberland Benevolent Bowl 86-87, Northumberland SNR Cup R-up 61-62,Northumberland Amtr Cup 71-72.
PREVIOUS   League: Northern Alliance 35-39 46-64 64-82
                        Names: Alnwick United Services; Alnwick United.
BEST SEASON   FA Cup: 3rd Qual. Rd 51-52 (3-4 at Blyth), 57-58 (4-6 at Easington Coll.).
                        FA Trophy: 3rd Qual. Rd 90-91.
RECORD   Attendance: 600 v Bedlington Terriers, Northern Alliance 1971.

FACT FILE
Founded: 1879
Colours: Black & white stripes/black/black
Change colours: Green and yellow
Midweek Matches: Tuesday

Local Press: Northumberland Gazette

CLUB PERSONNEL
Chairman:Iain Burns
Manager: Malcolm Beusle
Press Officer: Iain Burns

Players progressing: George Turnbull (Grimsby 1950) and Brian Pringle (1973)

CROOK TOWN

Secretary/Press Officer: Alan Stewart, 29 Sycamore Gardens,Crook, Co. Durham DL15 9LR
      Tel/Fax: 01388 764 216 (H). 0191 384 3388 (W). Mobile: 07971 375095.
Ground: Millfield Ground, West Road, Crook, County Durham (01388 762959)
Directions: 400 yds west of town centre on Wolsingham Road (A689). Nearest BR station is Bishop Auckland (5 miles). Buses 1A & 1B from Bishop Auckland or X46& X47 from Durham
Capacity: 3,500   Seats: 400   Cover: 300   Floodlights: Yes
Clubhouse: Lic Bar open matchdays. Hot & Cold Food available from Shop   **Club Shop:** Yes
PREVIOUS   Leagues: Auckland & Dist. 1894-96; Northern 1896-28 29-30; Durham Central 28-29; North Eastern 30-36; Wartime Durham & Northumberland 40-41;Durham Cen. 41-45.
BEST SEASON   FA Trophy: 3rd Rd 76-77 **FA Cup:** 3rd Rd, v Leicester 31-32. 2nd Rd (4), 1st Rd.(10) **FA Vase:** 4th Rd 99-00 **FA Amateur Cup:** Winners 5 times, plus S-F x 3
HONOURS   FA Amateur Cup Winners 00-01 53-54 58-59 61-62 63-64; Northern Lg 5, (R-up 4) Lg Cup 3, (R-up 4); Durham Chall. Cup 26-27 31-32 54-55 59-60; Durham Benevolent Bowl 6; Ernest Armstrong Mem Trophy 97.
2001-02 Leading Goalscorer: Martin Blythe - 16 **Captain:** Paul Dawson **P.o.Y.:** Paul Dawson

FACT FILE
Formed: 1889   Nickname: Black & Ambers
Sponsors: NEMS
Colours: Amber/black/black
Change colours: All White
Midweek Matches: Wednesday
Programme: Yes   Editor: Secretary

CLUB PERSONNEL
Chairman: Stephen Buddle
Vice-Chairman:William Neil
Chief Executive: Tom Chopra
President: Sir Tom Cowie O.B.E.
General Manager: David Buchanan
Manager: Ronan Liddane
Asst. Manager: Dennis Pinkney
Physio: Dave Southern

EASINGTON COLLIERY

Secretary: Alan Purvis, 12 Wark Crescent, Jarrow, Tyne & Wear, NE32 4SH (0191 489 6930)
Ground: Easington Colliery Welfare Ground, CW Park, Easington, Co Durham. (0191 527 3047)
Directions: A19 Easington turn-off, B1284 thru Easington to Black Diamond PH (next to zebra crossing), ground on the right
Capacity: 2,450   Seats: 175   Cover: 475   Floodlights: Yes   **Club Shop:** No
Clubhouse: Normal licensing hours. Pies, soup and sandwiches available
HONOURS   Northern Lg Div 2 R-up 85-86; Wearside Lge 29-30 31-32 32-33 47-48 48-49, R-up 28-29 46-47 73-74, Lg Cup 32-33 45-46 61-62; Monkwearmouth Cup 30-31 47-48 75-76; Sunderland Shipowners Cup 74-75 79-80.
PREVIOUS   Leagues: Wearside 13-37 39-64 73-88
BEST SEASON   FA Cup: 1st Round Proper 55-56
                        FA Trophy: 2nd Qual. Rd replay 88-89   **FA Vase:** 4th Rd replay 82-83
RECORD   Attendance: 4,500 v Tranmere Rovers, FA Cup 1st Round 1955
                        Scorer: Andrew McKenna   **Appearances:** David Howard

FACT FILE
Founded: 1913   Nickname: The Colliery
Colours: Green & white stripes/green/green
Change colours: Yellow/black/yellow
Midweek Matches: Tuesday
Programme: Yes   Editor: Charlie Dodds

CLUB PERSONNEL
Chairman: Tommy Goodrum
Press Officer: Alan Purvis
Manager: Tony Metcalfe
Asst Manager: Paul Pringle

2000-01
Leading Goalscorer: Ian Matthews 15
Captain: Andrew Davies P.o.Y.: Stephen Salvin

EPPLETON COLLIERY WELFARE

Secretary: John Tweddle, 40 Station Road, Hetton le Hole, Tyne & Wear DH50AT
Tel No: 0191 526 9633
Ground: Eppleton Welfare Park, Park View, Hetton-le-Hole, Tyne & Wear (01915261048)
Directions: Situated behind Front Street Post Office & directly behind Hetton swimming baths, Hetton-le-Hole on A182. Buses 194, 535, 231, X5, X94 in Front Street. 8 miles from Durham BR station; buses 154 and 254 from Durham
Capacity: 2,500   Seats: 250   Cover: 500   Floodlights: Yes
Clubhouse: Bar & lounge on ground. Normal opening hours. Whitbread beers
Club Shop: Club sweaters, polo shirts, metal lapel badges available
HONOURS   Northern Lg Div 2 R-up 92-93, Wearside Lg 90-91 91-92 (Lg Cup 74-75 78-79 87-88, Sunderland Shipowners Cup 47-48 85-86 90-91 (R-up 91-92), Monkwearmouth Charity Cup 89-90 90-91 91-92), Durham Challenge Cup 89-90.
PREVIOUS   Leagues: Wearside 51-65 74-92; Houghton & District 65-74.
RECORD   Attendance: 1,250 - Monkwearmouth Charity Cup Final 1987-88

FACT FILE
Founded: 1929
Nickname: Welfare
Club Sponsors: E & N Ritchie
Colours: Black & sky/black/black
Change colours : Yellow/green/green
Midweek matchday: Wednesday
Programme: 16 pages,50p Editor:

CLUB PERSONNEL
Chairman: Ralph Lawson
President: J.Storey
Commercial Mgr: Secretary
Press Officer: Secretary
Manager: Vin Pearson
Asst Manager: John Cullen

EVENWOOD TOWN

Secretary: Paull Tucker,1 Kiddlewood Ave, St Helen Auckland, Bishop Auckland DL14 9DJ
Tel No: 01388 607181

Ground: Welfare Ground, Stones End, Evenwood, County Durham Tel: 01388 832281

Directions: In village centre by Sports & Social club in Stones Rd

Capacity: 3,500   Seats: 32   Cover: 200   Floodlights: Yes

Clubhouse: Open lunch & evening every day

HONOURS Northern Lg 48-49 69-70 70-71 (Lg Cup 35-36), Durham Challenge Cup 69-70.

PREVIOUS **Leagues:** Barnard Castle & Dist. 1894-95; Auckland & Dist. 1894-96 1903-04
08-23 28-31; Wear Valley 1896-99 1904-06 24-25; Gauntlett Valley 06-07;
South Durham 27-28.   Names: None

BEST SEASON   FA Cup: 1st Rd 1936   FA Vase:

RECORD   Gate: 9,000 v Bishop Auckland, FA Amtr Cup 1931

FACT FILE
Founded: 1890
Nickname: The Wood
Sponsors: C A Roofing
Club colours: All blue
Change:Orange and white
Midweek Matches: Tuesday
Programme: 50p Editor: Rev .Frank Campbell

CLUB PERSONNEL
Chairman: Craig Latcham
President: N Colegrove
Press Officer: Secretary
Manager: Ken Houlahan
Assistant Manager: Morc Coulson

HEBBURN TOWN

Secretary: Tom Derrick, 63 Staneway, Felling, Gateshead, NE10 8LS.Tel: 0191 442 1563

Ground: Hebburn Sports & Social Ground, Victoria Road West, Hebburn Tel: 0191 483 5101

Directions: On the main road through the town about 1 mile from railway station. Hebburn lies on the Metroline - excellent bus service from Heworth Metro

Capacity: 2,000   Seats: 153   Cover: 420   Floodlights: Yes   **Club Shop:** No

Clubhouse: Open 7-11pm weekdays, Sat 11am-1pm, Sun noon-2.30pm. Pool, darts etc

PREVIOUS **Leagues:** Jarrow & Dist. Jnr 12-14; S Shields Comb. 19-22; Tyneside Comb. 22-27;
Tyneside 27-39; Northern Comb. 41-44 45-59; North Eastern 44-45 59-60; Wearside 60-89.
Names: Reyrolles; Hebburn Reyrolles (pre-1988), Hebburn 88-00

HONOURS Shields Gazette Cup 91-92, Wearside Lg 66-67 (Monkwearmouth Charity Cup 68-69),
Durham Challenge Cup 42-43 91-92, Tyneside Lg 38-39, Northern Comb. 43-44, Gateshead
Charity Cup 35-36 37-38, Palmer Hospital Cup 27-28, Hebburn Aged Miners Cup 35-36, Heddon
Homes Cup 42-43, Hebburn Infirmary Cup 35-36 36-37 37-38 38-39, Craven Cup 99-00.

BEST SEASON FA Vase: 2nd Rd 91-92 **FA Cup:** 2nd Qual. Rd rep. 89-90, 0-3 v South Bank (A)

RECORD Attendance: 503 v Darwen, FA Cup Prel. Rd replay 7/9/91 **Win:** 10-1 **Defeat** 3-10

FACT FILE
Founded: 1912
Nickname: Hornets
Colours: Yellow /navy blue/yellow
Change colours:Blue and White stripes/black
Midweek Matches: Wednesday
Programme: 24 pages, 30p
Editor: Steve Newton

CLUB PERSONNEL
Chairman: Bill Laffey
Vice-Chairman: Brian Errington
Press Officer: Alan Armstrong 0191 483 2046
Manager: Tony Robinson
Coach: Norman Dryden

HORDEN COLLIERY WELFARE

Secretary: Robert Wood, 29 Morpeth St., Horden, Peterlee, County Durham SR84BE
Tel: 0191 586 8802

Ground: Welfare Park Ground, Park Road, Horden, Peterlee, Co. Durham Tel: 0191 587 3549

Directions: A19 to Peterlee, signposted from there   (Club)

Capacity: 3,000   Seats: 220   Cover: 370   Floodlights: Yes

Clubhouse: Normal licensing hours. Hot & cold snacks, darts, pool

HONOURSDurham Challenge Cup 35-36 63-64 80-81 81-82, Durham Benevolent Cup 33-34,
Wearside Lg 11-12 12-13 13-14 33-34 64-65 67-68 69-70 70-71 71-72 72-73 (Lg Cup 33-34 49-50, Monkwearmouth Charity Cup 12-13 23-24 32-33 69-70 72-73,Sunderland Shipowners Cup 65-66 72-73), North Eastern Lg 37-38 63-64 (`Non-Reserve' Medal 50-51).

PREVIOUS **Leagues:** Wearside 07-35 63-75; N. Eastern 35-58 62-64; Midland
(Co's)58-60; Northern Co's 60-62.   **Names:** Horden Athletic

BEST SEASON FA Cup: 2nd Rd 38-39, 2-3 v Newport Co. (H)

RECORD Attendance: 8,000 - FA Cup 1937   Player progressing: Paul Dobson (Hartlepool Utd)

FACT FILE
Reformed : 1980
Nickname: Colliers
Colours: Red/black/red
Change colours:Sky,navy,navy
Reserves League: Wearside Div 2
Midweek Matches: Tuesday
Programme: 10 pages, 50p

CLUB PERSONNEL
Chairman: Norman Stephens
Press Officer: M.Burgon (041 089 064417)

KENNEK RYHOPE C.A.

Secretary: Rob Jones,17Aspatria Avenue, Blackhall, Hartlepool TS27 4EG
Tel No: 0191 5870949

Ground: Meadow Park, Stockton Road, Ryhope, Sunderland (0191 523 6555)

Directions: From Sunderland follow signs for A19 South, ground adj to Cherry
Knowle Hopital in Ryhope

Capacity: 2,000   Seats: 150   Cover: 200   Floodlights: Yes

HONOURS Wearside Lg 61-62 62-63 63-64 65-66(Lg Cup 63-64 77-78),
Durham Chal.Cup 77-78, Monkwearmouth Charity Cup 09-10 65-66 66-67,
Sunderland Shipowners Cup 61-62 (S.C.Vaux) 86-87

PREVIOUS **Names:** Ryhope C.W. (est.1898, prev.Ryhope Villa) merged with Sporting Club
Vaux (est.1968 as Monkwearmouth, later Bishopwearmouth, South Hetton) in 1988; Sunderland
Vaux Ryhope C.W. 88-93. **Leagues:** S. C. Vaux: Tyne & Wear; N.Eastern Amat.

BEST SEASON   FA Cup 1st Rd Proper 67-68   **FA Vase** 1st Rd 81-82

RECORD   Gate: 2,000; Ryhope Colliery Welfare v Workington, FA Cup 1967

FACT FILE
Founded: 1988
Colours: Red & white stripes/black/red Change
colours: All Blue

CLUB PERSONNEL
Chairman: W.Mathieson
Tel: 0191 534 5496 (H)
Press Officer: Secretary

MORPETH TOWN

Chairman: Ken Beattie Tel.: 01670 515271 (H), 01670 520565 (B)
Secretary/Press Officer: Les Scott,1 Bennetts Walk, Morpeth, Northumberland NE61 1TP
Tel Nos: 01670 517390 (H) 0780 3483509 (M)
Ground: Craik Park, Morpeth Common, Morpeth, Northumberland. (01670 513785)
Directions: Morpeth is signed off the A1 onto A197. Take the B6524, right at Mitford sign, then right after about a mile into the ground, next to Morpeth Common

Capacity: 1000	Seated: 150	Cover: 150	Floodlights Yes

Clubhouse: Yes **Club Shop:** No
HONOURS Northern Alliance 83-84, 93-94 (R-up 37-38, 65-66, 73-74, 81-82, 84-85);
Challenge Cup Winners 38-39, 85-86, 93-94 (R-up 36-37, 62-63, 73-74).

PREVIOUS **Leagues:** Northern Alliance pre 1994 **Ground:** Storey Park, Morpeth. pre 1992
BEST SEASON **FA Cup:** 4th Q Rd v Burton Albion 1998-99
FACT FILE Colours: Amber & black stripes/black/black Change colours: Blue,white,blue
Midweek Matchday: Tuesday Programme: Yes

MURTON

Secretary: Chris Fahey, 16 D'Arcy Square, Murton, Seaham, Co. Durham SR7 9LZ
Tel No: 0191 5171355
Ground: Recreation Park, Church Lane, Murton, Co. Durham (0191 517 0814)
Directions: Exit A19 onto B1285 heading west into Murton - Church Lane on left opposite catholic church

Capacity: 3,500	Seats: 100	Cover: 320	Floodlights: Yes	Club Shop: No

Clubhouse: `The International' 300 yards from ground on B1285. Normal pub hours. Restaurant upstairs. Matchday snacks at ground
HONOURS Northern Lg Div 2 89-90, Wearside Lg 28-29 36-37 59-60 (Lg Cup 58-5970-71), Sunderland Shipowners Cup 59-60 69-70 70-71, Monkwearmouth Charity Cup 21-22 28-29 34-35 35-36 63-64 70-71 87-88, Durham Chall. Cup 92-93, Durham Jnr Cup 50-51.
PREVIOUS **Leagues:** Wearside 13-46 51-88; North East Counties 46-51.
RECORD **Gate:** 3,500 v Spennymoor Utd, Durham Challenge Cup 1951
Appearances: Robert Welch 500 (1962-78)

FACT FILE
Founded: 1904 Nickname: Gnashers
Club Sponsors: John Hellyns
Colours: All white with red trim
Change colours: Red/black/red
Midweek matchday: Wednesday
Programme: 12 pages, 30p
Programme Editor: Stuart Upperton
CLUB PERSONNEL
Chairman: Tom Torrence
Vice Chairman: J Hudson
President: John Hellens
Press Officer: Secretary
Commercial Mgr: T Carr
Manager: Jeff Cranson
Asst Mgr: Brian Burlinson
Coach: Richie Madden Physio: Vince Symmonds

NORTHALLERTON TOWN

Secretary: Ken Lomer, 28 Aysgarth Grove, Romanby, Northallerton, N. Yorks DL7 8HY
Tel: 01609 779686(H) 01609 773970 (W) **Website:** www.northallertontown.co.uk
Ground: Ainderby Rd, Romanby, Northallerton, N. Yorks. Tel: 01609 772418
Directions: Leave A1 at Leeming Bar (A684) follow signs to Northallerton,approaching town take B1333 signed Romanby - ground 250yds on left. 3/4 a mile from Northallerton BR station - local bus from town centre(1 1/2 miles) passes ground

Capacity: 3,000	Seats: 150	Cover: 500	Floodlights: Yes

Clubhouse: Mon-Fri 7.30-11pm, Sat noon-7.30pm, Sun 12-2 & 7.30-10.30pm
Club Shop: Yes, Contact Nigel Taylor 07990 948574
HONOURS Northern Lg Cup 93-94, Div 2 96-97 R-up 89-90, Harrogate & Dist. Lg.;
N.Riding Snr Cup R-up 83-84; Harrogate Invit; Alverton Trophy.
PREVIOUS **Leagues:** Allertonshire; Vale of Mowbray; Ripon & Dist.; Teesside; North Yorks;
Darlington & Dist.; Harrogate & Dist. **BEST SEASON FA Cup:** 4th Qual. Rd 92-93
RECORD Gate: 671 v Farnborough, FAT 3rd Rd 20/2/93 **FA Trophy:** 3rd Rnd 92-93

FACT FILE
Founded: 1994 Nickname: Town
Colours: Black & White stripes,black
Change colours: All Yellow
Midweek matchday: Tuesday
Reserves ' League: Harrogate & District
Prog.: 16 pages, 50p Ed: Ian Bolland
CLUB PERSONNEL
Chairman: Ralph Alderson
Vice Chairman: Les Hood
Press Officer: Ian Bolland (01609 776900)
Manager: Peter Mulcaster
Physio: T.B.A.
01-02 Captain: Mark Forster P.o.Y.: Darren Poole Top Scorer:Ross Foreman

---

NORTON & STOCKTON ANCIENTS

Secretary: Danny Day,186 Braemar Road, Billingham, TS23 2AR (01642 899506)
Email Address: linda.day 2@ntlworld.com
Ground: Norton (Teesside) Sports Complex,Station Road, Norton, Stockton-on-Tees, Cleveland (01642 530203) Clubhouse (01642 5540310
Directions: Norton village 2 miles from Stockton centre, turn into Station Road on outskirts of village

Capacity: 2,000	Seats: 200	Cover: Yes	Floodlights: Yes

Clubhouse: Full bar facilities, 150 yds from ground
HONOURS Northern Lg Cup 81-82
PREVIOUS **Leagues:** Teesside (pre-1982) **Name:** Norton & Stockton Cricket Club Trust
BEST SEASON **FA Cup:** 1st Qual Rd(4) 88-89 90-93 **FA Vase:**
RECORD **Attendance:** 1,430 v Middlesbrough, Friendly 88

FACT FILE
Formed: 1959 Nickname: Ancients
Colours: Ambe& black stripes/black &
amber/black
Change: Red with green trim/red socks
Midweek Matches: Wednesday
Programme: 12 pages with entry
Club Website: nortonfootball .co.uk
CLUB PERSONNEL
Chairman: Steve Warnes
President: Barry Lee
Press Officer: Secretary
2000-01
Catain: Michael Pugh P.o.Y.: Peter Conway
Top Goalscorer: Gary Alford

Top:
Thistlwaite scores the second goal of his hat trick during South Shields' 4-1 win over Shotton Comrades.
Photo: Graham Brown

Centre:
Penrith's Phil Thornton gets in a header on goal against Evenwood Town.
Photo: Alan Watson

BAY WATCH

THE OFFICIAL MATCHDAY PROGRAMME OF WHITLEY BAY F.C

Whitley Bay V Durham City
F.A. CARLSBERG VASE
7th Round
Semi-Final First Leg
Saturday 23rd
March 2002

£1.00

PENRITH

Secretary: John Balmer, 58 Castle Hill Road, Penrith, Cumbria   Tel: 01768 866736
Ground: Southend Road Ground, Penrith, Cumbria   Tel: 01768 895990
Directions: M6 Jct 40, onto dual carriageway to Appleby & Scotch Corner,
first left at next r'bout, approx 1/2 mile into Penrith on A6 into town,
take 1st left for ground. 3/4 mile from Penrith (BR)
Capacity: 4,000   Seats: 200   Cover: 1,000   Floodlights: Yes   Club Shop: No
Clubhouse: Open Thurs, Fri & Sat 9.30pm-2am, & Sat 2-6pm, Wed match nights 6.30-10.30pm
HONOURS   Northern Lg R-up 61-62; NW Co's Lg R-up 83-84; NW Co's F/Light Trophy 95-96
96-97; Cumberland Snr Cup [12], 46-48 50-51 60-66 70-71 72-73 74-75
PREVIOUS   Leagues: Carlisle & Dist., Northern 48-82, N.W.C. 82-87, 90-97, N.P.L. 87-90.
BEST SEASON   FA Cup: 2nd Rd 81-82   League Clubs beaten: Chester 81-82
RECORDS   **Attendance:** 2,100 v Chester 1981
Goalscorer: C Short   **Appearances:** Lee Armstrong
Win: 13-2 v Parton Utd   **Defeat:** 0-13 v Bishop Auckland

FACT FILE
Founded: 1894   Nickname: Blues
Sponsors: British Gypsum
Colours: Blue/white/blue
Change colours: White/red/white
Midweek Matches: Wednesday
Reserve team: None
Programme: 24 pages, 50p
Press Officer: Secretary
Local Press: Cumberland & Westmorland
Herald, Cumberland News

CLUB PERSONNEL
Chairman: Walter Brogden
Vice Chairman: M Robson
Manager: Geoff Byers
Physio: Les Cornwell

SEAHAM RED STAR

Secretary: John Smith, 33 Frederick St., Seaham, Co.Durham.SR7 7HX   Tel: 0191 5810423

Ground: Seaham Town Park, Stockton Road, Seaham, Co. Durham (0191 581 1347)
Directions: From Tyne Tunnel: A19 Teeside approx 8 miles; B1404 Seaham slip road, left at top
of slip road. Right at traffic lights & first left past school into ground
Capacity: 4,000   Seats: 60   Cover: 200   Floodlights: Yes   **Club Shop:** No
Clubhouse: Mon-Sat 11am-11pm, Sun 12-2, 7-10.30pm   Bars & restaurant, snooke & pool

HONOURS   Northern Lg Cup 92-93, Phillips F'lit Tphy 78-79, Durham Chal. Cup 79-80,
Wearside Lg 81-82 (Lg Cup 81-82, Div 2 R-up 87-88, Monkwearmouth Charity Cup R-up 79-80).
PREVIOUS   Name: Seaham Colliery Welfare Red Star 78-87
Leagues: Sunday f'tball; Houghton & Dist. 73-74; Northern Alliance74-79; Wearside 79-83.
BEST SEASON   FA Cup: **FA Vase:** 5th Rd 78-79   **FA Trophy** 2nd Rd 89-90
RECORDS Gate: 1,500 v Guisborough, Wearside Lg & v Sunderland, floodlight opener 1979
Scorer: Tom Henderson   **Appearances:** Michael Whitfield

FACT FILE
Formed: 1973   Nickname: The Star
Colours: All Red
Change colours: All blue
Midweek Matches: Wednesday
Reserves ' League: Banks Youth League
Programme: 20 pages
Editor: David Copeland (0191 581 8514)

CLUB PERSONNEL
Chairman: JohnSmith
President: Michael English
Press Officer: D.Copeland (0191 5818514)
Manager: Chris Copeland
Asst Man.: Paul Walker
Physio: Allan Jackson

SHOTTON COMRADES

Secretary: Billy Banks, 30 Hamilton Court, Shotton Colliery, Durham DH6 2NL (0191 526 7134)
Ground: Shotton Rec. Ground, Station Road, Shotton Colliery, Co. Durham(0191 526 2859)
Directions: A19 to Peterlee to Shotton, right at the War Memorial t-junction,
follow round 800yds, ground on right
Capacity: 1,700   Seats: 80   Cover: 400   Floodlights: No   **Clubhouse:** No   **Club Shop:** No
HONOURS   Houghton & District Lg 78-79, Lg Cup x 2, Northern Alliance Lg Cup SF,
Hetton Charity Cup 78-79, Peterlee Sunday Lg 75-76, Div 2 74-75;
Northern Lg.Div 2 Cup R-up 94-95.
PREVIOUS   Leagues: Peterlee Sunday 74-76; Houghton & Dist. 76-80; Northern Alliance 80-83
BEST SEASON FA Cup: 2nd Qual. Rd 85-86, 0-2 v Wingate(H)   **FA Vase** 1st Rd 86-87 90-91
RECORDS   **Attendance:** 1,726 v Dennis Waterman XI
Goalscorer: Keith Willets 50   **Win:** 8-0 v Bedlington Ter. (H), '92
Appearances: J Cudlip   **Defeat:** 1-7 v Brandon Utd (A), FA Cup Prel. Rd 91-92
Transfer Fee received: £500 for G Gudlip (Shildon)

FACT FILE
Formed: 1973   Nickname: Coms
Colours: Red & white stripes/black/black
Change colours: All orange
Midweek matches: Wednesday
Reserves' Lge: Banks u-19 Yth
Programme: 12 pages, 20p Editor: E A Jones

CLUB PERSONNEL
Chairman: Colin Jobes
Vice Chairman: T Robinson
President: G Taylor
Press Officer: Secretary

Manager: B Huntingdon
Physio: W Banks

SOUTH SHIELDS F.C.

Secretary: David Fall, 50 Basil Way, South Shields NE34 8UD   Tel: 0191 426 2135

Ground: Mariners Club, Filtrona Park, Shaftesbury Avenue, Jarrow, Tyne & Wear NE34 9PH.
Tel: 0191 427 9839

Directions: From A1(M) take A194(M) to South Shields, A194 town centre road for 5 miles,
ignore A1300 (Sunderland & coast) & turn left at next lights beside Co-op store
into Simonside Ind. Est. (Shaftesbury Ave.), ground at bottom
Capacity: 2,500   Seats: 150   Cover: 400   Floodlights: Yes
Clubhouse: Two function suites, club kitchen   **Club Shop:** Yes
HONOURS   Northern Lge Div 2 R-up 95-96, Northern Alliance 74-75 75-76, Wearside Lg 76-
77 92-93 94-95, Monkwearmouth Charity Cup 86-87 (R-up 94-95), Shipowners Cup 92-93 (R-up
83-84)), Durham Chal. Cup 76-77 R-up 94-95. **BEST SEASON**   **FA Vase** QF 75-76
PREVIOUS   Leagues: Northern Alliance 74-76   **Ground:** Jack Clarke Park 74-92
RECORD   **Attendance:** 1,500 v Spennymoor, Durham Challenge Cup Final 94-95

FACT FILE
Founded: 1974   Nickname: Mariners
Colours: Claret & blue/white/white
Change: All white
Midweek matchday: Tuesday
Reserve team: None
Programme: 50p Editor: Steve Leonard

CLUB PERSONNEL
Chairman: John Rundle
Vice Chairman: George Scott
Press Officer: Secretary
Manager: David Clark
Asst Manager:Paul Brown
Physio: Jim Wilkinson

THORNABY

Secretary: Peter Morris, 20 Wheatear Lane, Ingleby Barwick, Stockton-on-Tees,
                   Cleveland TS17 0TB Tel: 01642 760779
Ground: Teesdale Park, Acklam Road, Thornaby, Stockton-on-Tees TS17 8TZ (01642 606803)
Directions: A19 to Thornaby turn off, ground half mile on right. One mile from Thornaby
                   BR station. Any Stockton-Middlesbrough bus - stop at Acklam Rd, Thornaby
Capacity: 5,000   Seats: 150   Cover: 350   Floodlights: Yes   **Club Shop:** No
Clubhouse: 150+ seater social club open eves. & w/e lunch.
               Sandwiches avail. in bar, canteen in ground sells pies, burgers, soup, drinks etc

PREVIOUS   **Leagues:** Stockton & District 80-81; Wearside 81-85.
RECORD   **Attendance:** 3,000 v Middlebrough, pre-season friendly August 1986
                 Appearances: Michael Watson
BEST SEASON **FA Vase:** 3rd Rd 89-90   **FA Trophy:** 3rd Rd 92-93
                 FA Cup: 4th Qual. Rd replay 92-93,1-2 v Blyth (H) after 1-1
HONOURS   Northern Lg Div 2 87-88 91-92, Nth Riding Co. Cup 85-86, Craven Cup 94-95.

FACT FILE
Formed: 1980
Colours:Yellow and blue/Navy & white/yellow
Change colours: All sky
Midweek Matches: Wednesday
Reserves' Lge: Wearside & Teesside Lgs
Programme: 24 pages, 50p
Editor: Peter Morris (01642 585625)
Local Press: Northern Echo, Evening Gazette

CLUB PERSONNEL
Chairman: Lol Lyons
Press Officer: Peter Morris
Manager: Michael Watson
Asst Mgr: Peter May
Coach: Paul Sharkey

WASHINGTON NISSAN

Secretary: Harry English, 22 Rushcliffe, Fulwell , Sunderland SR6 9RG
                   Tel: 0191 548 7194 (H) 0191 415 2340 (W) 07889 469961 (M)

Ground: Nissan Sports Complex, Washington Road, Sunderland SR5 3NS
                   Tel: 0191 415 2354 or 0191 415 2773
Directions: North along A1 (M) use A690 (signed Sunderland) connect with A19,
                   north on A19, after passing the A1231 turn off, plant on the left.
                   Past plant & follow signs 'Nissan Offices'.
Clubhouse: Open Mon-Fri 5-11pm, Sat 11am-11pm, Sun noon-3 & 7-10.30pm

PREVIOUS   **League:** Wearside to 2001
HONOURS: Wearside Lg Div 1 93-94 (Lg Cup R-up 91-92, Div 2 Cup 92-93 93-94),
                   Nissan European Trophy 3.

FACT FILE
Founded: 1988
Colours: Blue & black stripes/ blue/blue
Change colours: Red & white/white/white.

CLUB PERSONNEL
Chairman: Alan Hill
Treasurer: J.Taylor
Press Officer: Paul Curry
Manager: Stan Fenwick
Assistant Manager: Keith Robertson.
Coach: Darren Ward

WHICKHAM

Secretary: Harry Hodgson, 2, Dockendale Hall, Dockendale Lane, Whickham,
               Newcastle upon Tyne,NE16 4EN   Tel: 0191 488 2493
Ground: Glebe Ground, Rectory Lane, Whickham (0191 420 0186)   **Directions:** A692
(Consett) from A69. Left at r'bout signed Consett/Whickham. Uphill and right at mini-r'bout.
Continue along & turn left into Rectory Lane (by Lloyds Bank) for 500 yds, clubhouse on right
Capacity: 4,000   Seats: 100   Cover: Yes   Floodlights: Yes
Clubhouse: Mon-Fri. 12-3 & 7-11, Sat.11-11, Sun. 12-2, 7.30-11   Souvenir Shop: No
HONOURS   FA Vase 80-81, Wearside Lg 77-78 87-88 (R-up 80-81 84-85, Lg Cup 86-87,
               Monkwearmouth Charity Cup 76-77, Sunderland Shipowners Cup 77-78 80-81),
               Northern Comb. 69-70 72-73 73-74 (Lg Cup 60-61 73-74)
PREVIOUS   **Leagues:** Derwent Valley -55; Northern Comb. 55-57 59-74; Tyneside Amtr 57-
               59; Wearside 74-88   **Ground:** Rectory Rec. Field
BEST SEASON   **FA Cup:** 1st Qual. Rd. 89-90   **FA Vase:** Winners 80-81
RECORD   Gate: 3,165 v Windsor & Eton, F.A. Vase SF 81

FACT FILE
Founded: 1944
Colours: Black & White stripes/ Black/Black
Change colours: All white
Midweek Matches: Wednesday
Programme: 20p
Local Press : Newcastle Journal, Sunday Sun,
Evening Chronicle
2000-01 Top Goalscorer: Paul Wlson 22
Captain & P.o.Y.: Kriss Holmes

CLUB PERSONNEL
Chairman: Tommy Thompson
Manager: Steve Higgins
Press Officer: Secretary

WILLINGTON

Secretary: Bob Nichols, 46 Cavendish Ct, Brandon,Durham DH7 8UW Tel/ FAX 0191378 1981
Ground: Hall Lane, Hall Lane Estate, Willington, County Durham (01388 746221
Website: www.willingtonafc.free-online.co.uk
Directions: Willington is on A690 7 miles west of Durham City & 2 miles east of Crook. Northern
Bus Co. operates a service through Willington from Crook or Durham City
Capacity: 2,680   Seats: 350   Cover: 400   Floodlights: Yes   Club shop: Occasionally
Clubhouse: Open eves 7-11pm &Sat. matchdays 1-11pm. Bar facilities.Tea shop on matchdays
HONOURS   FA Amateur Cup 49-50, R-up 38-39; Northern League 13-14 25-26 29-30,
               R-up 12-13 57-58 75-76, Lge Cup 24-25 25-26 27-28 30-31 31-32 48-49 56-57 74-75;
               Durham Benevolent Cup 48-49 50-51 57-58.
BEST SEASON FA Cup: 1st Rd rep. 73-74, 1-6 v Blackburn R (A) after 0-0.Also 1st Rd 45-46
         FA Trophy 3rd Rd 75-76   **FA Amat. Cup:** Winners 49-50   & 50-51
PREVIOUS   **Leagues:** Auckland & Dist. 1906-11   **Names:** Willington Temperance 1906-11
RECORD Attendance: 10,000 v Bromley, FA Amateur Cup 2nd Rd 24/1/53   **Goalscorer:** J
`Boxer' Taylor 55-69 150 approx.**Appearances:** S Rutherford 47-61 & G.Brown51-64 both 350+

FACT FILE
Founded: 1906 Nickname: Blue & Whites
Sponsor:T.B.A.
Colours: Blue & white stripes/blue/blue
Change colours: Yellow/green/green
Midweek Matches: Tuesday
Youth League: Auckland & Dist League
Programme: 50p Editor: Keith Newton

CLUB PERSONNEL
Chairman: John Phelan
Vice-Chair: Anne Robson
President: Hilary Armstrong M.P.
Press Officer: Sec Manager :Dave Styles
2001-02 Captain & P.o.Y.: Brett Cummings.
Top Scorer: Chris Taylor 20

JARROW ROOFING
BOLDON C.A. FOOTBALL CLUB

HAWAY THE ROOFERS

Members of the Albany Northern League Division One

Official Matchday Programme 70p

WILLINGTON A.F.C.

ALBANY
THE JOBRELATED LOAN RECOVERY SERVICE

NORTHERN LEAGUE

50p

SUPPORT WILLINGTON A.F.C.
W.A.F.C.

WELCOME TO HALL LANE
Official Programme

SHILDON AFC
Founded 1890
(THE RAILWAYMEN)

Ashfield

SEASON 2001 / 2002

THE ALBANY
NORTHERN LEAGUE
DIVISION TWO

ALBANY NORTHERN LEAGUE
NEWCASTLE BLUE STAR F.C.
OFFICIAL MATCHDAY PROGRAMME

M METRO

THE WHEATSHEAF GROUND, WOOLSINGTON
NEAR CALLERTON PARK WAY METRO STATION

NISSAN WEARSIDE LEAGUE

FEEDER TO:
ARNOTT INSURANCE NORTHERN LEAGUE

President: W Robson   **Chairman:** P J Maguire

Secretary: T Clark, 55 Vicarage Close, New Silksworth, Sunderland SR3 1JF
Tel: 0191 5211 242   Email: tclark2@virgin.net

FINAL LEAGUE TABLE 2001-02

	P	W	D	L	F	A	GD	Pts
North Shields	32	25	3	4	94	31	63	78
New Marske S C	32	21	7	4	81	37	44	70
Darlington Rail Ath	32	21	4	7	75	43	32	67
Windscale	32	18	9	5	74	44	30	63
Redcar Town*	32	19	5	8	88	45	33	59
Birtley Town	32	16	9	7	86	58	28	57
Wolviston	32	14	6	12	66	59	7	48
Stokesley S C	32	13	7	12	69	61	8	46
S. Shields H & W	32	11	9	12	72	61	11	42
Boldon Comm Assoc.	32	11	3	18	57	82	-25	36
S Shlds Cleadon SC	32	9	7	16	50	63	-13	34
Ryhope Coll Welfare	32	9	6	17	47	70	-23	33
Jarrow	32	8	9	15	41	70	-29	33
Annfield Plain	32	7	5	20	47	84	-37	26
Whitehaven Amat	32	6	8	18	48	86	-38	26
Stanley United	32	4	8	20	49	77	-28	20
Ferryhill Athletic*	32	6	3	23	41	114	-73	18

* points adjustment

RESULTS CHART

		1	2	3	4	5	6	7	8	9	10	11	12	13	14	15	16	17
1	Annfield Plain	X	0-3	1-3	1-4	2-1	1-1	2-5	0-3	1-5	2-1	1-5	1-2	0-1	4-7	4-1	0-0	3-0
2	Birtley Town	2-2	X	5-3	4-0	10-1	4-1	1-2	1-5	2-2	2-2	1-0	3-3	2-1	2-2	7-2	2-2	2-1
3	Boldon Community Assoc.	5-1	2-4	X	0-3	4-4	3-1	0-5	0-7	1-5	3-4	3-2	1-0	2-0	6-2	1-1	0-1	2-1
4	Darlington Railway Athletic	1-0	3-1	4-1	X	1-0	4-0	0-0	2-1	2-0	3-0	3-2	4-4	2-1	2-0	2-0	1-2	2-2
5	Ferryhill Athletic	3-0	1-4	1-4	0-7	X	5-1	0-1	0-3	1-3	5-1	0-3	2-1	3-3	3-1	3-1	3-3	0-2
6	Jarrow	2-1	0-2	1-0	4-3	3-1	X	1-1	0-0	2-2	3-1	3-3	0-6	0-1	2-2	2-2	0-4	3-4
7	New Marske Sports Club	4-2	3-1	4-2	3-3	4-0	2-0	X	0-4	0-3	2-0	2-0	4-0	2-2	4-1	7-0	4-1	0-2
8	North Shields	1-2	5-3	3-0	3-2	4-1	3-0	2-2	X	1-1	7-0	2-0	1-0	3-1	2-3	4-2	2-1	4-2
9	Redcar Town	4-1	6-0	2-0	5-1	10-0	3-2	2-2	0-1	X	4-1	1-0	0-1	3-1	1-3	3-1	2-0	3-0
10	Ryhope Colliery Welfare	2-3	0-3	4-1	1-3	6-0	0-1	3-3	0-2	2-0	X	2-1	3-3	3-0	1-1	4-2	0-3	1-2
11	South Shields Cleadon SC	3-1	2-0	3-0	0-2	2-1	1-2	0-3	0-1	2-6	3-0	X	0-4	2-2	4-3	4-2	1-3	0-4
12	S. Shields Harton & Westoe	6-2	2-4	4-1	3-2	4-1	2-0	0-1	2-3	3-3	4-0	1-1	X	2-2	1-3	3-3	1-2	1-2
13	Stanley United	1-1	1-2	0-1	1-2	5-0	3-4	1-3	1-6	3-1	1-2	1-1	4-5	X	2-4	1-2	1-2	3-3
14	Stokesley SC	1-3	0-0	4-1	1-2	4-1	1-1	1-2	1-0	2-1	1-1	5-1	1-0	4-2	X	0-1	1-2	4-0
15	Whitehaven Amateurs	3-2	3-3	1-4	0-3	5-1	0-0	0-3	1-6	1-3	2-1	1-1	3-0	1-1	2-2	X	0-2	2-4
16	Windscale	1-1	1-1	3-2	3-1	7-0	2-1	2-1	2-3	7-2	0-0	2-2	1-1	3-1	3-1	4-3	X	1-2
17	Wolviston	3-2	1-5	1-1	0-1	5-0	3-0	1-2	1-2	1-2	0-1	1-1	3-3	6-1	4-3	1-0	4-4	X

LEAGUE CUP 2001-02

FIRST ROUND

Wolviston	v	Whitehaven Amateurs	3-0

SECOND ROUND

Boldon C A	v	Ferryhill Athletic	0-4	Darlington Rail Ath	v	Wolviston	3-2
Jarrow	v	Ryhope Colliery Welf	3-0	New Marske S C	v	Windscale	2-4
North Shields	v	Birtley Town	1-2	Redcar Town	v	Annfield Plain	1-0
SS Harton & Westoe	v	Stanley United	0-3	Stokesley SC	v	Sth Sh Cleadon SC	6-0

QUARTER-FINALS

Birtley Town	v	Stanley United	3-2	Darlington Rail Ath	v	Ferryhill Athletic	3-1
Jarrow	v	Redcar Town	3-1	Stokesley SC	v	Windscale	3-2

SEMI-FINALS

Darlington Rail Ath	v	Stokesley SC	0-6	Jarrow	v	Birtley Town	0-1

FINAL

Birtley Town	v	Stokesley SC	2-1	at Wolviston

SUNDERLAND SHIPOWNERS CUP 2001-02

FIRST ROUND

Sth Sh Cleadon SC	v	Jarrow	0-1

SECOND ROUND

Birtley Town	v	Redcar Town	3-0	Darlington Rail Ath	v	S S Harton & Westoe	3-2
Jarrow	v	Annfield Plain	3-0	New Marske S C	v	Whitehaven Amateurs	3-0
North Shields	v	Ryhope C W	4-1	Stanley United	v	Wolviston	3*6
Stokesley SC	v	Boldon C Assn	1-0	Windscale	v	Ferryhill Athletic	3-2

QUARTER-FINALS

Birtley Town	v	New Marske SC	4p2,2*2	Darlington Rail Athl	v	North Shields	3-2
Jarrow	v	Stokesley SC	2-1	Windscale	v	Wolviston	0-1

SEMI-FINALS

Birtley Town	v	Darlington Rail Ath	2-0	Jarrow	v	Wolviston	4*2

FINAL

Jarrow	v	Birtley Town	4p2, 2*2	at Jarrow

MONKWEARMOUTH CHARITY CUP 2001-02

FIRST ROUND

Stanley United	v	Wolviston	0-4

SECOND ROUND

Birtley Town	v	Sth Sh Cleadon SC	2-0	Darlington Rail Ath	v	SS Htn & Westoe	2p4,1*1
New Marske SC	v	Annfield Plain	2-0	North Shields	v	Boldon CA	5-1
Redcar Town	v	Ferryhill Athletic	10-1	Ryhope CW	v	Windscale	3-1
Stokesley SC	v	Jarrow	3-1	Whitehaven Amats	v	Wolviston	3-2

QUARTER-FINALS

North Shields	v	New Marske SC	11p10,2*2	Ryhope C W	v	Redcar Town	0-3
S S Harton & Westoe	v	Stokesley SC	3-0	Whitehaven Amats	v	Birtley Town	1-2

SEMI-FINALS

Birtley Town	v	Harton & Westoe	5-0	North Shields	v	Redcar Town	0-1

FINAL

Birtley Town	v	Redcar Town	5-2	at Birtley Town

ANNFIELD PLAIN

Secretary: M Lawson, 24 Northgate, Anfield Plain, Stanley, Co. Durham DH9 7UY
Tel: 01207
Ground: Derwent Park, Annfield Plain. **Directions:** On A693 road to Consett, 200yds west of junction with A6067. Ground behind new housing estate. 6 miles fromDurham (BR). Buses from Sunderland, Newcastle & Durham.
Capacity: 6,000   Seats: 20   Cover: 200   Floodlights: No
HONOURS   Wearside Lg 84-85 (Monkwearmouth Charity Cup 92-93),
FA Cup: 1st Rd 26-27 28-29 64-65.

Founded: 1890.
Colours: Claret/white/blue
Change colours: All blue.
Programme: 16 pages, 20p

Chairman: Frank Ross
Treasurer :Marshall Lawson
Manager: D Longstaff
Press Officer: Frank Ross

BARNARD CASTLE GLAXO

Ground: Glaxo Sports & Social Club, Harmire Road, Barnard Castle, Co. Durham
Tel: 01833 638926

BIRTLEY TOWN

Secretary: Kevin McConnell, 8 Laybourn Place, Birtley DH3 1PL Tel No: 0191 4100 495
Commercial Manager: Ray Stafford.
Ground: Birtley Sports Complex. **Directions:** (From Durham) Off A1(M) signpstedfor Chester-le-Street, take 2nd turn off r-bout signed Birtley, take last turnoff next r-bout (still signed Birtley), after one and a half miles take 1stleft after AEI Cables - ground at rear of sports complex.
Capacity: Unknown   Seats: None   Cover: None   Floodlights: No.
Clubhouse: Matchdays only
HONOURS: Wearside Lg 45-46 (Lg Cup 35-36), Northern Alliance 23-24 (R-up 13-14).

Founded: 1890   Reformed: 1986
Colours: Green&white hoops/white/green
Change colours: Yellow/blue/red.
Midweek matches: Wednesday
Sponsors: C & C Coachworks
Chairman: John Heslington
Vice-Chairman: J Grainger
Manager: Barry Fleming
Asst Manager: David Smith
Coach: Malcolm Thompson

BOLDON COMMUNITY ASSOCIATION

Secretary: Tom Robson, 16 Hardie Drive, West Boldon ,Tyne & Wear NE36 0JH.
Ground: Boldon Community Association, New Road, Boldon Colliery.
Directions: A19 to junc A184 Sunderland/Newcastle. Follow signs to Boldon Asdastores, then to North Road Social Club (SHACK). Ground behind. 800 yds fromEast Boldon (BR). Buses 533, 531, 319, 528.
Capacity: 3,500   Seats: 100   Cover: 400   Floodlights: No
Clubhouse: Matchdays only. Bar snacks
HONOURS: Wearside Lg 3, (Lg Cup 3), M/mouth Char Cup 2, Shipowners Cup 6.

Founded: 1892.   Nickname: Villa
Colours: Black & Blue Stripes/ Black/Blue
Change: Scarlet & black
Chairman:Kevin Oliver
Vice Chairman: G Smith
President: A Brewster.
Manager: Bill Newham
Asst Manager: P Quinn
Coach: Tommy Frazer.
Press Off. / Comm. Man.: Secretary

DARLINGTON RAILWAY ATHLETIC

Secretary: Martyn Jackson, 6 Westlands Rd., Darlington,Co.Durham DL3 9JJ
          Tel Nos: 01325 240495 (H) 0870 370095 (M)
Ground: Railway Social Club, Brinkburn Road,Darlington, Co Durham
          Capacity: 1,000 **Seats:** None **Cover:** 50 **Floodlights** : Planned
Directions: Take A68 off A1 towards Darlington. Turn left opposite pub on right into Brinkburn
          Road and ground is 400 yards on left.
Clubhouse: Yes. It serves all sports at complex.
Honours: Auckland & Dist Lg & Cup, Darlington & The SacristonCharity Cups, 00-01

Reformed 1996

Colours: Dark blue & light blue stripes,
blue shorts and socks.
Change Colours: Red & black quarters,
black shorts and socks.

Manager: Dave Woodcock
Programme : Yes Editor: Robert Harman

FERRYHILL ATHLETIC

Secretary: Norman Bellwood, 49 Rush Park, Bishop Auckland DL14 6NS
          Tel: 01388 451065 (H)
Football Secretary: Rob Ridley, 31 Ravensworth Road, Ferryhill Tel: 0780 3803335
Ground: Dean Bank Recreation Ground
Directions: The ground is situated on the old Dean & Chapter Colliery Welfare site west of the old Athletic ground at Darlington Road. From the top of Darlington Road with the Black Bull on your right, pass over the bridge crossing the A167 cutting. Dean Bank school is immediately on your left, turn left at the one way traffic restriction. Follow the signs to Dean Bank Rec.

Colours: Black & amber/amber/black & amber
Change: Red & white/red/red & white

Chairman: Secretary
Press Officer: Jimmy O'Sullivan
Tel: 01740 635524

JARROW

Secretary: Susan Scott,46 Breamish Street, Jarrow. NE32 5SH (0191 4248610)

Ground: Perth Green Community Centre.
Directions: From A19 or A1(M) followdrections to South Shields, right onto John Reid Road.
First slip road ontoBrockley Whinns Estate, follow road past Red Hackle pub, third left left
ontoInverness Road, then right into Perth Green Community Centre.

HONOURS: Sth Tyne Lg & Lg Cup, Washington Lg R-up 89-90 (Lg Cup 90-91, Aged Peoples
Tphy R-up 90-91), Gateshead Charity Cup 90-91, Durham Tphy R-up 90-91.

Founded: 1980.
Colours: Blue & white/blue/blue
Change: Green/black/green

Chairman: B.Tyreman
Treasurer: Jimmy Kane

NEW MARSKE

Secretary: Peter Livingstone,5 Guisborough Rd,Thornaby on Tees TS17 8BE
Tel Nos: 01642 646428(H) 01642 606803 (B)

Ground: Gurney Street, New Marske, Redcar
Directions: A19 south onto A174 Redcar- Teesport. Follow A174 towards Saltburn turn right
at roundabout with footbridge over road. Ground 500 yds on left.

Colours: Yellow & black/navy/navy or white
Change colours: Blue & black/navy/navy

Charmain: Errol Richter
Tel: 01947 600296
Press Officer: Tony Saunders

NORTH SHIELDS

Secretary: Dave Thompson, 38 Barnstable Road, North Shields. Tel: 0191 259 0249
Ground: Ralph Gardner Park, West Percy Rd., N.Shields, Tyne & Wear, NE29 OES
Directions: A19 northbound through Tyne Tunnel. Take 1st slip round to 1str/about & take 3rd
exit & over next r/about. Take 3rd exit again at nextr/about into Waterville Rd. Over another
r/about and 2nd left into Silkey'sLane. 1st right into West Percy Rd, grd on right.
Clubhouse: None
HONOURS: FA Amateur Cup 68-69, Northern Lge 68-69, N.C.E. Prem. Div. 91-92,
R-up 89-90, 90-91, Lge. Cup 90-91, Presidents Cup 91-92.

Founded: 1896
Nickname: New Robins
Sponsors: Wilkinson Stores
Colours: All red
Change colours: Blue & black/black/blac

Chairman: Alan Matthews.
Treasurer:Mike Taylor
Manager: Bob Weir.Coach: Wilf Keilty.

REDCAR TOWN

Secretary: Keith Markman, 2 Riccall Court , Redcar, Cleveland TS10 4HL
Tel: 01642 481966
Ground: British Steel Club, South Ave., Dormanstown, Redcar.
Directions: Take the A19 South, then the A66 to Middlesbrough. Stay on the A66 following
Teeside/Redcar. When A66 ends, at A1053 r'about, take right to Redcar.
At next r'about, bear left onto A1085 to Redcar. Over next r'about, right at next
r'about into Dormanstown. 1st right along the Fleet, 1st left into South Ave.,
ground 200 yds on right.

Colours: All red
Change colours: All royal blue

Chairman: Fred Blackburn 01642 471773
Press Officer: Allan Monghan
Tel: 01642 470962

RYHOPE C.W.

Secretary: George McKitterick, 8 Kilburn Close, Ryhope Village, Sunderland. SR2 0QU
Tel: 0191 523 8436)
Ground: Ryhope Recreation Park, Ryhope Street, Ryhope, Sunderland Tel: 0191 521 2843
Directions: Take A19 (3 miles south of Sunderland centre) to Ryhope village, atVillage Green turn
into Evelyn Terrace/Ryhope Street and carry on up bank pastPresto's for 600 yds - ground
appears on left. 3 miles from Sunderland Central(BR), bus every 10 mins from Sunderland centre.
Capacity: 1,000 **Seats:** No **Cover:** No **Floodlights:** Yes
HONOURS: Wearside Lg 4, (Lg Cup 2), Durham Chall Cup 77-78, M/mouth Charity Cup3,
S/land Shipowners Cup 2

Founded: 1988.

Colours: Yellow/black/black & red
Change colours: Red/white/red & white

Chairman:: G. Routledge
Press Officer: Peter Grainge

SOUTH SHIELDS CLEADON F.C.

Secretary: Douglas Keys,3 Paragon Way,Holder Hause Estate, South Shields. NE34 8TA
Tel No: 0191 536 7434
Ground: Jack Clarke Park, South Shields.
Directions: Enter South Shields on A194 to r'bout taking you on to A1300 JohnReid Rd. 2nd left
at 3rd r'bout into King George Rd then Sunderland Rd, rightat lights into Grosvenor Rd, left into
Horsly Hill Rd. Ground on right
Clubhouse: Cleadon Social Club, Fulwell Ave, S Shields. Normal pub hours except Saturday.
HONOURS: Wearside Lg Div 2 90-91, Shields & Dist. Lg, Washington Lg 77-78 84-85

Nickname: The Club
Sponsors: Cleadon & Dist. Soc. Club
Colours: Yellow/black/black
Change: All red
Midweek matches: Wednesday
Chairman: Gordon Ferries
Vice-Chairman/Press Off . /Manager:
David Wood (0191 455 4607).
Asst Man: Steve Duguid
Commercial Manager: Joan Wood

SOUTH SHIELDS HARTON & WESTOE

Colours: All Blue
Change colours: All red

Secretary: Alan Bell, 31 Meldon avenue, South Shields, Tyne & Wear NE34 0EL
Tel Nos: 0191 4218233 (H) 0191 4301446 (W)
Groun: Harton Colliery Welfare.

Chairman: Ronald Wightman
Treasurer: Gordon Smith

Directions: A1M at Whitemare Pool take A194 to South Shields for 2 1/2 miles.
At third roundabout turn right onto A1300. At 2nd roundabout turn left onto
Boldon Lane. Ground 50 yards on right

STANLEY UNITED

Nickname: The Nops
Sponsors: Company Cars Direct
Colours: Red & white stripes/black/red
Change colours: Sky/navy/navy

Secretary: Vince Kirkup, 9 Brookes Rise, Regents Green, Langley, Durham DH7 8XY
Tel: 0191 378 0921
Ground: High Road, Stanley, near Crook (nicknamed Hill Top Ground). **Directions:** Teeside on
A689 to Bishop Auckland and onto Crook, turn left atMarket Place then 1st right for Tow Law to
Billy Row and Stanley, right at topof bank then 1st left, grd 250 yards on left.
Clubhouse: Open matchdays.   **Club Shop:** No
HONOURS: Northern Lg 3, R-up 62-63, Lg Cup 3,
BEST SEASON: FA Cup 1st Rd 53-54.   FA Amateur Cup Semi Final 19-20.

President: A Westgarth
Chairman: Barry Waiting.
Asst Manager/ Coach: K Finnegan
Physio: J Burn

STOKESLEY SPORTS CLUB

Colours: Red & black/black/black
Change: White/red/red

Secretary: Peter Grainge, 77 Darnton Drive, Easterside, Middlesbrough TS4 3RF
Tel: 01642 273934
Ground: Stokesley Sports Ground, Broughton Road, Stokesley
Directions: A19 to Middlesbrough, then A174 turn to Whitby/Teesport. At 3rd turning up slip
road A172 to Stokesley. Over 1st r'about, next r'about turn to Stokesley, 5 miles. At next r'about
keep left to next r'about. Ground 100 yards on left.

Chairman: Eric Taylor 01642 273934
Press Officer: secretary

WHITEHAVEN AMATEURS

Colours: Yellow/blue/yellow
Change colours: White/navy/white

Secretary: Richard Stamp, Johnson House, Hillcrest Avenue, Whitehaven, CA28 6SU
Tel No: 01946 61877
Ground: Whitehaven County Ground, Coach Road, Whitehaven
Directions: Barrow on A595, ignore branch to town centre at B.P. garage turnright at t/lights on
A5094. 1/2 mile turn left at Esso garage into Coach Rd.Narrow lane ent immed after l/ crossing
to grd behind Rugby Lge Stadium.
HONOURS: Cumberland Cup 90-91, County League 87-88 88-89, Wearside Lg Div 2
Cup R-up 93-94.

Chairman: Bill Robson.
Press Officer: Secretary
Manager: Ian Green
Assistant Manager: Ian Atkins

WINDSCALE

Founded: 1950
Colours:White & Navy Blue/ Navy/White
Change: Blue & white/royal/royal

Secretary: Craig Heggie, 12 Bookwell, Egremont, Cumbria CA2 2LS
Tel Nos: 01946 823587 (H) 01946 788337 (W)
Ground: Falcon Field, Egremont.
Directions: A66 to Bridgefoot. A595 Barrow,bottom of hill approaching Egremont take
3rd turn off island (signed)Smithfield/Gillfoot, ground in housing estate
HONOURS: Furness Senior Cup 1985-86

Chairman: R Napier
Press Officer: Secretary
Treasurer: A Barwise

WOLVISTON

Founded: 1910   Nickname: Wolves
Sponsors: R.C.I. Industrial Cleaners
Colours: Royal blue/blue/white
Change: Red & white/red/white

Secretary: Keith Simpson, 14 Lodore Grove, Acklam, Middlesbrough TS5 8PB 01642 823734
Ground: Metcalfe Way, Wynyard Road, Wolviston, Billingham, Cleveland TS22 5NE.
Directions: On Wynyard Road between Thorpe Thewles & Wolviston. A19 onto A689 into Wolviston
village, take Wynyard Road towards Thorpe Thewles, grd left before Sir John Halls Estate.
Capacity: 2,000   Seats: None   Cover: 200   Floodlights: No   Club Shop: No.
Clubhouse: Licensed bar. Hot & cold meals. Open 11am-11pm on matchdays.
HONOURS: Wearside Lg Div 2 89-90, Lg Cup R-up 92-93, Teeside Lg R-up 84-85, Lg Cup 86-
87, Durham FA Trophy R-up 89-90, Stockton & Dist. Lg 3, LgCup 3, Lg Charity Cup 79-80.
Record Gate: 500 v Middlesbrough 27/7/93

Chairman: Eddie Poole   President: Bob Smith
Vice Chairman: Derek Stockton
Press Officer: Andy Anderson
Manager: John Johnson
Asst Manager: Kevin Smith
Coach: Alan Lucas

Amble United (in stripes) put on the pressure at home to Seaton Delavel in the Northern Alliance. Photo: Alan Watson

Wearside League Champions North Shields take on Windscale at Ralph Gardiner Park. Photo: Graham Brown

Northern Alliance action from West Allotment Celtic v Northbank. Celtic's Benjamin (hoops) climbs highest in a closely contested encounter. Photo: Graham Brown

WADE ASSOCIATES NORTHERN
FOOTBALL ALLIANCE

President: Les Todd   **Chairman:** George Dobbins
Secretary: John McLackland, 92 Appletree Gardens
Walkerville, Newcastle upon Tyne NE6 4SX   Tel: 0191 2621636
Press Officer: Bill Gardner   Tel/Fax: 0191 4883422   Email: bill.gardner@eidosnet.co.uk

HONOURS LIST 2001-02

Premier Division Champions	West Allotment Celtic	Runners-up	Shankhouse
Division One Champions	Bedlington Terriers A	Runners-up	Newcastle Procter & Gamble
Division Two Champions	Haydon Bridge United	Runners-up	University of Northumbria
League Cup Winners	West Allotment Celtic	Finalists	Carlisle City
Challenge Cup Winners	Shankhouse	Finalists	Northbank Carlisle
Combination Cup Winners	Newcastle Procter & Gamble	Finalists	Heaton Stannington
Amateur Cup Winners	University of Northumbria	Finalists	Haydon Bridge United

FINAL LEAGUE TABLES 2001-02

PREMIER DIVISION

	P	W	D	L	F	A	Pts
West Allotment Celtic	28	19	5	4	65	29	62
Shankhouse	28	18	7	3	57	16	61
Newcastle Benfield Snts	28	19	2	7	69	34	59
Carlisle City	28	14	6	8	49	33	48
Amble United	28	13	8	7	48	36	47
Walker Central*	28	12	8	8	62	39	41
Ponteland United	28	12	5	11	55	48	41
Harraby Catholic Club*	28	12	8	8	45	38	41
Northbank Carlilse*	28	12	5	11	48	41	35
Winlaton	28	8	7	13	36	47	31
Spittal Rovers	28	8	4	16	30	67	28
Newcastle University *	28	8	4	16	30	39	25
Ryton	28	5	8	15	39	56	23
Percy Main Amateurs	28	6	2	20	30	76	20
Seaton Delaval Ams*	28	3	3	22	24	88	9

DIVISION ONE

	P	W	D	L	F	A	Pts
Bedlington Terriers 'A'	26	20	3	3	87	14	63
N Procter & Gamble	26	16	8	2	68	23	56
Cullercoats	26	16	2	8	64	29	50
Heaton Stannington	26	13	6	7	61	38	45
Chopwell Top Club	26	13	4	9	45	46	43
Wallington	26	10	5	11	42	46	35
Walker Fosse	26	10	5	11	47	62	35
Wark *	26	10	7	9	57	53	34
Newbiggin Central W	26	10	4	12	57	56	34
Rutherford Newcastle	26	10	2	14	46	65	32
Hebburn Reyrolle	26	9	2	15	50	64	29
Cramlington Town	26	8	1	17	42	69	25
Cowgate Sports Club	26	5	7	14	38	65	22
Prudhoe RTH	26	3	2	21	29	103	11
* points adjustment							

DIVISION TWO

	P	W	D	L	F	A	Pts
Haydon Bridge United	22	15	7	0	94	28	52
University of N'umbria	22	16	3	3	60	21	51
Walker Stack FOS	22	12	3	7	59	49	39
Newcastle EE R C	22	11	5	6	61	43	38
Ashington Colliers	22	10	4	8	49	35	34
Otterburn	22	9	5	8	52	45	32
New Birtley *	22	10	4	8	66	48	31

	P	W	D	L	F	A	Pts
Benwell *	22	8	5	9	53	57	26
Newcastle Brit Telecom	22	6	2	14	38	58	20
Forest Hall	22	6	2	14	47	69	20
Wallsend Town	22	5	3	14	39	91	18
Highfields United *	22	1	3	18	20	94	3
* points adjustment							

NORTHERN FOOTBALL ALLIANCE

PREMIER DIVISION RESULTS CHART 2001-02

		1	2	3	4	5	6	7	8	9	10	11	12	13	14	15
1	Amble United	X	4-2	2-3	0-2	3-0	0-0	0-0	1-1	3-2	5-0	2-0	5-2	0-3	4-2	1-0
2	Carlisle City	1-1	X	5-1	1-2	1-0	0-0	1-1	2-0	3-0	4-0	0-1	0-0	2-2	0-6	0-2
3	Harraby Catholic Club	3-1	1-2	X	0-2	2-0	2-1	4-1	0-0	0-0	3-2	1-4	3-0	0-0	0-1	4-0
4	Newcastle Benfield Saints	2-0	3-2	0-0	X	2-0	1-2	2-1	2-1	3-0	3-1	1-4	7-0	4-4	1-2	4-2
5	Newcastle University	0-1	0-1	2-3	0-4	X	2-2	2-0	1-2	3-0	1-2	1-2	0-1	0-2	1-4	1-1
6	Northbank Carlisle	0-2	0-1	1-1	4-2	0-2	X	4-1	5-4	2-1	4-0	1-4	4-0	4-3	0-1	2-1
7	Percy Main Amateurs	1-4	0-3	1-3	1-4	0-1	3-2	X	0-4	4-3	3-1	0-6	3-1	1-4	0-1	1-2
8	Ponteland United	2-1	1-3	1-2	2-1	0-3	0-1	5-3	X	4-2	1-3	2-3	3-2	3-2	5-1	1-2
9	Ryton	1-1	2-3	4-2	1-3	1-1	0-0	3-0	1-3	X	6-1	1-1	2-0	1-1	1-3	1-1
10	Seaton Delaval Amateurs	1-2	1-3	1-3	0-5	0-4	0-7	1-2	1-3	1-1	X	1-1	2-0	1-2	1-1	0-2
11	Shankhouse	0-1	0-0	2-0	1-0	1-0	1-0	7-0	1-1	1-0	1-0	X	4-0	1-1	0-1	0-0
12	Spittal Rovers	0-0	2-1	1-1	1-4	2-1	2-1	2-1	1-3	2-1	4-2	1-3	X	1-3	2-3	2-0
13	Walker Central	3-3	0-3	2-2	0-1	1-2	0-1	2-1	1-0	1-2	8-0	0-4	6-0	X	2-0	3-0
14	West Allotment Celtic	4-0	2-1	1-0	4-1	1-1	3-0	4-0	2-2	4-0	2-0	1-1	4-1	2-2	X	5-1
15	Winlaton Hallgarth	1-1	1-4	1-1	0-3	0-1	4-0	0-1	1-1	5-2	7-1	0-3	0-0	0-4	2-0	X

STAN SEYMOUR LEAGUE CUP

FIRST ROUND

Cowgate Sports	v	Hebburn Reyrolle	2-1	Cullercoats	v	Benwell	1-0
Forest Hall	v	Horden CW Athletic	1-0	Heaton Stann.	v	Bedlington 'A'	1-4
Highfields Utd	v	Haydon Bridge Utd	1-5	Newcastle BT	v	Walker Stack FOS	3-2
Northern SC	v	Cramlington Town	2-3	Otterburn	v	Ashington Colliers	0-1
Univ. of Northumbria	v	New Birtley	0-3	Wallington	v	Newcastle P & G	2-1
Wark	v	Wallsend Town	8-5				

SECOND ROUND

Amble United	v	Forest Hall	6-1	Ashington Colliers	v	Ryton	2-4
Carlisle City	v	Cullercoats	4-1	Cowgate Sports	v	Spittal Rovers	4-2
Haydon Bridge Utd	v	Chopwell TC	1-2	New Birtley	v	Newcastle EE Rail	3-5
Newcastle Benfield St	v	Wark	5-2	Newcastle BT	v	Bedlington 'A'	0-7
Northbank Carlisle	v	Walker Fosse	4-0	Percy Main Ams	v	Harraby CC	1-0
Prudhoe RTH	v	Newbiggin CW	2-3	Rutherford N'castle	v	Ponteland	0-2
Seaton Delaval Am	v	W Allotment	1-4	Shankhouse	v	Cramlington Town	4-0
Wallington	v	Newcastle University	0-2	Winlaton Hallgarth	v	Walker Central	1-4

THIRD ROUND

Bedlington 'A'	v	W. Allotment	2-3	Carlisle City	v	Percy Main Ams	3-0
Cowgate Sports	v	Ryton	1-3	Newbiggin CW	v	Newcastle Univ.	1-4
Newcastle Benfield Sts	v	Amble	4-1	Northbank Carlisle	v	Ponteland	4-2
Shankhouse	v	Newcastle EE Rail	7-1	Walker Central	v	Chopwell TC	6-2

QUARTER-FINALS

Carlisle City	v	Shankhouse	2-1	Northbank Carlisle	v	Newcastle Benfield Sts	1-0
Ryton	v	Walker Central	2-1	West Allotment Cltic	v	Newcastle University	2-1

SEMI-FINALS

Carlisle City	v	Northbank	3p1, 5*5	Ryton	v	West Allotment Celtic 2-3

FINAL

West Allotment Cltc v Carlisle City 1-0 at Heaton Stannington

CHALLENGE CUP

SEMI-FINALS

Northbank Carlisle	v	Harraby Catholic Club	1-0
Shankhouse	v	Newcastle Benfield Sts	2-0

FINAL

Northbank Carlisle v Shankhouse 1-2

COMBINATION CUP

SEMI-FINALS

Heaton Stannington	v	Chopwell TC	2-1
Newcastle P & G	v	Bedlington 'A'	3-0

FINAL

Heaton Stannington v Newcastle P & G 0-1

AMBLE UNITED

Secretary: Kevin Lewis, 2 Park Close, North Broomhill,Northumberland NE65 9YN(01670 761162)
Ground: Amble Welfare Park, Coquet High School, Amble..
Directions: Enter Amble after industrial estate on right. One undred yards past the zebra crossing turn left before 'The Masons arms'. Continue as if leaving Amble and Coquet High school and the ground are on the left.

Colours: Orange & Black stripes/black
Change colours: Blue & whitw/white
Chairman: Rod Henderson
Manager/Coach: Keith Douglas

BEDLINGTON TERRIERS 'A'

Secretary: Shaun Campbell,106 Wright St., Blyth. Northumberland NE24 1HG
Tel: 01670 353823 (H) 07703 529869 (M)
Ground: Welfare Park, Park Rd., Bedlington, Northumberland. Tel: 01670 825485
Directions: Into Bedlington, turn left at `Northumberland Arms' on Front St., then 2nd Right, ground on right 100 yds . Club Website: www.btfc.fsnet.co.uk

Colours: Red & white/red&white/white
Change colours:
Blue & whitw/blue&white/blue

Chairman: David Perry

CARLISLE CITY

Secretary: Jackie Williamson,14 Etterby Street, Stanwix, Carlisle Tel No: 01228 523798
Ground: The Sheepmount Sports Complex, Carlisle (01228 265599).
Directions: B6264 Brampton-Carlisle road & follow Workington signs, dual-c'way down hill (Carlisle Castle on right), where road intersects double back on yourself and take turning left just before castle, follow down hill keeping left until ground.

Colours: Sky & Navy hoops/navy
Change colours: White/navy

Chairman: Jackie Ewbank
Manage/Coach: Willie Armstrong.

HARRABY CATHOLIC CLUB 1999

Colours:All white
Change colours: Old gold and black

Secretary: Mike Little, 34 Springfield Road, Harraby, Carlisle CA1 3QR (01228 512887)
Ground: Harrowby Community Centre, Edghill Road,Harraby
Directions: A69 over M^ to Rosehill roundabout.Second ledft on Eastern Way. First left after 3/4 mile into Arnside Road. End of road left into Edghill Road

Chairman/Press Officer: Richard Wilson
Manager/Coach: Bobby Rutherford & Kevin Robson

NEWCASTLE BENFIELD SAINTS

Secretary: Tony Baird, 3 Rathmore Gardens, North Shields, Tyne & Wear NE30 2SX
Ground: Benfield Park, Benfield Rd, Newcastle-upon-Tyne.
Directions: From Newcastle towards coast take 2nd exit after Corner House pub lights, right into Benfield Rd, ground on left opp. Walkergate Hosp. & adjacent to school.

Colours: All Navy Blue
Change colours:All White

Chairman: Jimmy Rowe
Manager: Allan Bell Coach: Steve Burn

NEWCASTLE UNIVERSITY

Secretary: Simon Kent, 8/10 Myrtle Grove,JesmondNewcastle -u-TyneNE2 3HT(0191 2093609)
Ground: Cochrane Park, Etherstone Avenue, Newcastle -u-Tyne
Directions: From Newcastle via Jesmond to coast road.Take first slip road after Jesmond Dene and immediately after lights at the Corner House.Then take first slip road and left again onto A188 and right at first roundabout at the garage into Etherstone Avenue. Ground is 200 metres on left

Colours: All blue
Change colours: White/navy

Chairman: Simon Kent
Manager: T.B.A.

NORTHBANK CARLISLE

Secretary: David Bell,4 Carlislwe Road, Dalston ,Cumbria CA5 7NG (01228 711095)
Ground: Sheepmount Sports Complex, Carlisle
Directions: B6264 from Bampton to Carlisle, follow Workington sign, past Carlisle Castle on right. Where dual carriageway intersects take next right and travel back towards Castle. Turn left before castle & keeping left follow the road to Complex

Colours: Red & white/red
Change colours: Yellow & navy/navy

Chairman: Kenny Brown
Manager: Bob Lancaster

PERCY MAIN AMATEURS

Secretary: Len Renham, 7 Stanley Crescent, Whitley Bay, Tyne & wear NE26 2 EB
Tel No: (0191 2902768)
Ground: Purvis Park , St John's Green,Percy Main, North Shields.
Directions: A19 Tyne tunnel follow signs for Royal Quays and take seconsd left after school Ground is first turning on the right adjacent to Percy Main cricket club.t after Percy Main schol

Colours: Claret & blue/claret
Change colours: All Blue

Chairman: G.Marsh
ManagerBob Rodgerson
Coach: John Humbertson

PONTELAND UNITED

Secretary: L McMahon, 1 Wardle Drive, Annitsford, Cramlingham NE23 7DB (0191250 0463).
Ground: Ponterland leisure Centre Ponteland (01661 825441)
Directions: Left at lights entering Ponteland from N'castle, ground 100m on left adjacent to Leisure Centre.
Colours: Black & White stripes/Black   **Change Colours:** All yellow

Chairman:Alan Birkinshaw
Manager : Barry Wardrobe
Coach:Steve Baxter

RYTON

Secretary: Les Robson, 31 Park View Gardens, Runhead, Ryton, Tyne & wear NE40 3JD
Tel: 0191 413 7628
Ground: Kingsley Park, Crawcrook, (Tel No: 0191 413 4448)
Directions: West from Newcastle, over Scotswood Bridge and take A695to Blaydon roundabout. A617 and go through Ryton until traffic lights at Crawcrook. Turn righ when signposted to Wylam and Clara Vale ground is 400 yds on right.

Colours: Blue & black/black
Change colours: Orange/black

Chairman: Michael Williams
Manage Stevan Kendall
Coach: K.Dixon

SEATON DELAVAL AMATEURS

Secretary: Bill Fellows, 11 Ridley Street, Klondyke, Cramlington NE23 6RH (01670 731833)
Ground: Wheatridge Park, Seaton Delaval.
Directions: A189 from Newcastle, at Annitsford r'bout A190 to Seaton Delaval,left at r'bout entering village, ground 450yds on right next to Deal Garage and behind Market Garden. 3 miles from Cramlington BR station. Bus 363 from Newcastle passes ground.

Colours: Sky/black
Change colours: Yellow/blue

Chairman: Tom Ashburn
Manager/Coach: Steve Armstrong

SHANKHOUSE

Secretary: Syd Ramsey, 6 Brinkburn Ave, Cramlington, Northumberland NE23 6TB
Tel: 01670 715943
Ground: Action Park, Dudley.
Directions: Tyne Tunnel A19 to Moor Farm roundabout at Anitsford. A1 exit to Morpeth and leave at first slip road.Left at junction (to Dudley) turn right to Seaton Burn at roundabout.Then immediate right after Weetslade club and ground is signposted.

Colours: Yellow/blue
Change colours: White/blue

Chairman: George Davison
Manager: Garry Kirkup

SPITTAL ROVERS

Secretary: G Burn, 7 Sea Road, Spittal, Berwick-on-Tweed TD15 1RN (01289306049).

Ground: Newfields, Berwick-on-Tweed.
Directions: From south take Berwick by-pass to 3rd r'bout. Safeway Store on right - pitch reached by taking 2nd left on r'bout.

Chairman: Noel Evans
Vice Chairman: Paul Renton
Manager/Coach: Carl Hudson

Colours: Black & white stripes/black
Change colours: Green/Black

WALKER CENTRAL

Secretary: BobMulroy, 31 Dalton Cres., Byker Wall, Newcastle-upon-Tyne NE62DA
Tel: 0191 265 7803

Ground: Monkchester Recreation Ground, Walker, Newcastle.
Directions: From City: Shields Rd to Union Rd, to Welbeck Rd, right into Monckchester Rd, left into pitch (between houses) opposite Norbury Grove.

Club colours: White and black
Change colours: All Blue
Chairman: R T McClellan
Manager/Coach: Ray Mulroy/Billy Johnson

WEST ALLOTMENT CELTIC

Secretary: Mark Hedley,12 Co-operative Terrace,West Allotment, Tyne and Wear NE27 0DU
Tel No: 0191 2702178
Ground: Blue Flames Sports Ground, Benton
Directions: From Newcastle take A189 to the roundabout at junction with A191. Folllow road east for one and a half miles.Immediatley after Station Road (B1317) junction and traffic lights, turn right into ground.

Colours: Green& white hoops, green,green
Change colours: All Blue

Chairman: Joe Mather
Manager: Terry Mitchell

WINLATON HALLGARTH

Secretary: Robert Young, Alwinton, 21B California, Winlaton Tyne & Wear NE21 6NG
Tel No: 0191 4144363)
Ground: Shibdon Park, Shibdon Road, Blaydon-on-Tyne, Tyne & Wear.
Directions: From north, over A1 Scotswood Bridge to 1st slip road, take Swalwell and Consett road to r'bout, right, Blaydon Baths car park and ground 400yds on right. From South past Metro Centre to Swalwell, then on to Blaydon and the Blaydob Baths car park.

Colours: Green & Black
Change colours: Blue & white/blue
Chairman: R obertYoung
Manager/CoachStephen Brown

SOUTH CLEVELAND GARAGES TEESSIDE FOOTBALL LEAGUE

FEEDER TO: NORTHERN LEAGUE

President: J Corner   **Chairman:** L Crossman

Secretary: R D Marsay, 12 Aislaby Court, Wilton Lane, Guisborough, Cleveland TS14 6TG

Tel: 01287 637087   Fax: 01287 281051   Email: dmarsay@ntlworld.com

HONOURS LIST 2001-02

League Champions	Grangetown BC	JV Madden Trophy Winners	Grangetown BC
Runners up	Nunthorpe Athletic	Finalists	Acklam Steelworks
Macmillan Bowl Winners	Thornaby FC	Player of the Year	Lee Atkinson
Finalists	Nunthorpe Athletic		(Acklam Steelworks)
RT Raine Trophy Winners	Bedale Athletic	Match Official of the Year	Bill Mounter
Finalists	Stokesley SC		(Billingham)

FINAL LEAGUE TABLE 2001-02

		P	W	D	L	F	A	Pts	GD
1	Grangetown BC	34	25	4	5	97	41	79	56
2	Nunthorpe Athletic	34	24	7	3	96	45	79	51
3	Carlin How	34	23	3	8	99	48	72	51
4	Fishburn Park	34	19	7	8	80	50	64	30
5	Acklam Steelworks	34	21	0	13	102	61	63	41
6	Bedale Athletic	34	20	2	12	103	69	62	34
7	Cargo Fleet	34	18	8	8	90	60	62	30
8	Thornaby YC	34	18	7	9	83	45	61	38
9	Richmond Town	34	18	5	11	81	54	59	27
10	Wolviston Reserves	34	13	6	15	72	81	45	-9
11	BEADS FC	34	13	3	18	65	75	42	-10
12	Hollybush United	34	12	6	16	59	72	42	-13
13	New Marske SC	34	10	5	19	50	73	35	-23
14	Thornaby*	34	10	6	18	67	69	33	-2
15	Stokesley SC	34	10	3	21	46	93	33	-47
16	Whitby Town Reserves	34	8	2	24	53	90	26	-37
17	Mackinlay Park	34	4	2	18	32	109	14	-77
18	Guisborough Town Reserves	34	0	4	30	30	169	4	-139

* three points deducted

RESULTS CHART

		1	2	3	4	5	6	7	8	9	10	11	12	13	14	15	16	17	18
1	Acklam SW	X	0-2	1-4	4-1	2-3	5-2	1-6	9-1	5-0	3-1	3-0	3-2	4-2	6-0	3-1	1-2	3-1	2-0
2	Beads FC	1-4	X	0-5	3-0	1-2	0-3	0-1	4-0	1-2	5-1	3-0	1-4	3-6	2-3	2-0	2-1	2-0	7-1
3	Bedale Ath	0-5	4-2	X	3-0	3-1	5-1	1-4	9-1	4-1	4-2	4-0	2-3	3-0	3-0	4-3	4-0	5-2	2-2
4	Cargo Fleet	0-1	6-1	6-4	X	2-0	1-2	3-0	8-1	4-0	3-1	4-1	1-1	3-1	2-2	1-1	4-2	2-2
5	Carlin How	5-3	4-0	7-2	1-1	X	3-4	5-0	4-0	3-0	3-0	2-1	1-1	2-1	6-0	3-0	0-3	4-0	4-0
6	Fishburn Park	3-1	2-1	3-1	1-1	1-2	X	0-2	2-2	1-1	9-3	1-0	4-1	0-3	2-0	2-1	2-1	2-1	5-0
7	Grangetown	2-0	1-0	1-4	1-1	3-1	2-1	X	11-1	6-0	3-1	2-1	2-3	3-1	3-1	4-0	2-0	2-0	5-2
8	Guisboro Tn Rs	2-11	1-8	1-1	1-8	2-3	0-5	0-5	X	0-1	0-0	0-1	1-3	2-7	0-3	0-4	1-5	1-4	2-4
9	Hollybush Utd	2-3	5-1	6-2	1-2	2-3	1-5	1-1	4-1	X	2-0	3-1	2-2	0-1	1-1	1-1	1-4	3-1	6-2
10	Mackinlay Park	2-0	1-0	0-5	0-3	1-2	2-2	1-2	4-2	1-2	X	1-3	1-4	1-2	1-4	1-4	1-9	0-4	0-4
11	New Marske SC	0-4	1-1	4-2	0-2	3-1	1-1	3-6	2-3	3-1	X	1-2	1-3	4-1	2-0	1-1	1-1	3-3
12	Nunthorpe Ath	5-3	1-1	2-0	0-2	2-1	1-0	3-5	5-0	5-2	3-0	4-2	X	4-1	2-0	3-1	3-0	6-1	3-2
13	Richmond Town	1-3	7-0	5-1	2-3	1-2	1-1	0-2	6-1	1-0	5-0	3-0	0-0	X	4-1	3-1	1-0	3-1	1-1
14	Stokesley SC	2-0	1-2	0-1	0-3	0-7	1-3	0-5	2-2	1-1	3-2	3-0	1-5	0-2	X	4-3	0-1	3-0	3-1
15	Thornaby SC	0-1	3-1	1-5	4-1	2-7	1-1	2-4	11-2	1-0	3-0	1-2	3-2	2-8	1	X	0-1	1-1	3-1
16	Thornaby YC	3-0	2-2	4-0	2-3	3-3	4-2	3-3	4-1	2-2	4-0	6-1	2-3	3-1	4-1	0-0	X	1-0	4-0
17	Whitby Town Res	2-1	2-4	0-6	6-4	2-1	0-4	0-3	5-1	2-3	0-1	4-0	1-5	2-3	5-2	1-2	0-3	X	1-5
18	Wolviston Res	3-7	1-2	1-0	10-4	1-3	1-3	1-2	2-0	1-0	4-1	2-1	2-2	6-1	1-1	1-0	3-0	2-1	X

455

PREVIOUS HONOURS

LEAGUE CHAMPIONS
2001-02 Grangetown BC
2000-01 Acklam Steelworks
1999-00 Grangetown Boys Club
1998-99 Grangetown Boys Club
1997-98 Acklam Steelworks
1996-97 Acklam Steelworks
1995-96 Acklam Steelworks

R T RAINE TROPHY WINNERS
2001-02 Bedale Athletic
2000-01 Bedale Athletic
1999-00 Nunthorpe Athletic
1998-99 Cargo Fleet
1997-98 Dormans Athletic
1996-97 BSC Redcar
1995-96 BSC Redcar

PLAYER OF THE YEAR
2001-02 Lee Atkinson
Acklam SW
2000-01 Adam Bramley
Bedale Athletic
1999-00 Nicholas Agiadis
Acklam Steelworks
1998-99 John Newton
Whitby Town Reserves

MACMILLAN BOWL WINNERS
2001-02 Thornaby SC
2000-01 Grangetown Boys Club
1999-00 Grangetown Boys Club
1998-99 Nunthorpe Athletic
1997-98 Acklam Steelworks
1996-97 Acklam Steelworks
1995-96 Acklam Steelworks

J V MADDEN TROPHY
2001-02 Grangetown BC
2000-01 Acklam Steelworks
1999-00 Nunthorpe Athletic
1998-99 Acklam Steelworks
1997-98 Acklam Steelworks
1996-97 Acklam Steelworks
1995-96 Tees Components

MATCH OFFICIAL OF THE YEAR
2001-02 Bill Mounter
Billngham
2000-01 Gary Coxon
Middlesbrough
1999-00 Mark Tilling
Guisborough
1998-99 Chris Lane
Hutton Rugby

CLUBS IN MEMBERSHIP 2000-01
FIRST DIVISION CLUBS

ACKLAM STEELWORKS
Gary Bell, 10 Avalon Court, Hemlington, Middlesbrough
TS8 9HU Tel: 01642 276736

B.E.A.D.S.
Dave Kane, 27 Edgeworth Court, Hemlington,
Middlesbrough TS8 9EP Tel: 01642 280586

BEDALE ATHLETIC
Mike Allen, 1 Sycamore View, Nosterfield, Bedale, North
Yorks DL8 2QR Tel: 01677 470739

CARLIN HOW WMC
Simon Whitwell, 10 Harebell Close, North Skelton,
Saltburn TS12 2FE Tel: 01287 652135

FISHBURN PARK
Richard & Karen Hutton, 14 Abbots Road, Whitby, North
Yorks YO22 4EB Tel: 01947 602537

GRANGETOWN BOYS CLUB
Kevin Larkin, 19 Braemar Grove, Teesville,
Middlesbrough TS6 0AN Tel: 01642 452095

HOLLYBUSH UNITED
Michael Griffiths, 7 Penryn Close, Skelton, Saltburn
TS12 2ND Tel: 01287 651381

MACKINLAY PARK
Martin Coats, 221 High Street, Marske, Redcar TS11
7LR Tel: 01642 475707

NEW MARSKE SC
Peter Livingstone, 5 Guisborough Road, Thornaby
TS17 8EE Tel: 01642 646428

NUNTHORPE ATHLETIC
Kevin Levitt, 131 Burlam Road, Middlesbrough TS5 5AX
Tel: 01642 824332
RICHMOND TOWN
Wendy Prosser, 19 Glebe Court, Melsonby, Richmond,
North Yorks DL10 5NU Tel: 01325 718924

STOKESLEY SC
Peter Grainge, 77 Darnton Drive, Easterside,
Middlesbrough TS4 3RK Tel: 01642 273934

THORNABY FC
Dave Watson, 13 Mainside, Redmarshall, Stockton
TS21 1HY Tel: 01740 631028

THORNABY YOUTH CLUB
Geoff Kirk, 9 Tipton Close, Thornaby, Stockton TS17
9QF Tel: 01642 676516

WHITBY TOWN RESERVES
Willie Morton, 24 Pembroke Way, Whitby, North Yorks
YO21 1NT Tel: 01947 600641

WOLVISTON RESERVES
Keith Simpson, 14 Lodore Grove, Acklam,
Middllesbrough TS5 8PB Tel: 01642 823734

SECOND DIVISION CLUBS

Billingham Wanderers
Darlington Cleveleand Bridge
Darlington Railway Athletic
Reserves
Darlington SRM SC

Dormans
Guisborough Town Reserves
Huntsman
SMG Redstripe
Teesside - Arriva

Teesside Athletic
Teesside Link
Whinney Banks

SHEFFIELD COUNTY SENIOR LEAGUE

President: M Matthews Esq.   **Chairman:** A Goodison Esq.

Secretary & Treasurer: Brian Gould   **Press Officer:** Bill Ownsworth

This season was a very entertaining one as Wombwell Main completed the League and Cup double. South Kirby Colliery finished runners-up in Division One to gain promotion yet again, two seasons running, and will now play Premier Division football.Wickersley who went up as Champions regained their Premiership place once again.

In Division Two Elm Tree, who only joined the League at the start of this season won the league at the first attempt. The surprise package were Renishaw Juniors from Division Two who reached the Semi-final of the Sheffield Senior Cup with a fantastic cup run as they knocked out three teams from the Northern Counties East League that play in a contributory league.

This season coming see the Premier League and Division One both get supply league status for Referees marks as this league is class as the top league in South Yorkshire.

In Division Two the League has been extended to an extra nine new clubs. This is good for the league as this division was looking as though it was going to have to fold as numbers were starting to dwindle. But as they say in football, "it's a funny old game". This season it will now run with sixteen teams.

The League also appoints match officials to the FA Premier League Academy with clubs from Sheffield Wednesday and Sheffield United.

So this season looks very promising and I for one cannot wait for it to start.

Mark Carratt

HONOURS LIST 2001-02

Premier Division Champions	Wombwell Main
Runners Up	Athersley Recreation
Division One Champions	Wickersley FC
Runners Up	South Kirby Colliery
Division Two Champions	Elm Tree FC
Runners Up	Hollinsend Ams
League Cup Winners	Wombwell Main
Runners Up	Hallam Reserves FC
Leading Goalscorer	David Streaker
	South Kirby Colliery
Most Sporting Team	Penistone Church Reserves
Referee of the Season	Paul Windle

FINAL LEAGUE TABLES 2001-02

PREMIER DIVISION

	P	Home					Away					Total					Pts	GD
		W	D	L	F	A	W	D	L	F	A	W	D	L	F	A		
Wombwell Main	26	12	1	0	48	10	8	3	2	39	22	20	4	2	87	32	64	55
Athersley Recreation	26	12	0	1	42	11	8	0	5	24	15	20	0	6	66	26	60	40
Phoenix	26	8	2	3	30	20	6	3	4	26	22	14	5	7	56	42	47	14
Mex Main Street	26	5	4	4	38	29	7	1	5	23	21	12	5	9	61	50	41	11
Hallam Reserves	26	7	3	3	27	16	5	1	7	29	20	12	4	10	56	36	40	20
Swinton Athletic	26	6	2	5	21	20	6	1	6	16	29	12	3	11	37	49	39	-12
Penistone Church	26	5	5	3	19	12	5	3	5	22	21	10	8	8	41	33	38	8
Parkgate Reserves	26	3	4	6	23	23	6	3	4	26	17	9	7	10	49	40	34	9
Hare & Hounds	26	4	2	7	12	26	4	4	5	20	29	8	6	12	32	55	30	-23
Thorpe Hesley	26	5	0	8	19	29	4	1	8	15	34	9	1	16	34	63	28	-29
Groves Social	26	6	0	7	26	21	2	3	8	14	33	8	3	15	40	54	27	-14
Ecclesfield Red Rose	26	4	1	8	15	26	3	5	5	24	27	7	6	13	39	53	27	-14
The Wetherby	26	3	3	7	19	27	4	2	7	16	30	7	5	14	35	57	26	-22
Frecheville	26	2	3	8	10	32	2	0	11	8	29	4	3	19	18	61	15	-43

DIVISION ONE

	P	Home					Away					Total					Pts	GD
		W	D	L	F	A	W	D	L	F	A	W	D	L	F	A		
Wickersley	26	10	1	2	47	18	11	0	2	38	12	21	1	4	85	30	64	55
South Kirkby Colliery	26	11	2	0	50	15	7	6	0	39	24	18	8	0	89	39	62	50
Grapes Roy Hancock	26	10	1	2	44	27	9	0	4	32	21	19	1	6	76	48	58	28
Stocks Park Reserves	26	7	1	5	41	16	8	3	2	38	13	15	4	7	79	29	49	50
Georgia Pacific	26	5	4	4	31	28	9	2	2	50	31	14	6	6	81	59	48	22
Oughtibridge WMSC	26	7	3	3	22	12	5	0	8	24	31	12	3	11	46	43	39	3
Parramore Sports	26	4	2	7	26	29	7	2	4	33	25	11	4	11	59	54	37	5
Sheffield Lane Top	26	7	0	6	30	26	4	3	6	22	34	11	3	12	52	60	36	-8
Avesta Polarit	26	3	2	8	32	42	6	2	5	24	31	9	4	13	56	73	31	-17
Caribbean Sports	26	4	4	5	32	27	4	2	7	31	29	8	6	12	63	56	30	7
The Forum	26	3	1	9	30	54	6	1	6	28	33	9	2	15	58	87	29	-29
High Green Villa	26	2	2	9	24	45	2	4	7	19	43	4	6	16	43	88	18	-45
Davy	26	1	3	9	19	40	1	1	11	23	49	2	4	20	42	89	10	-47
Denaby United Res	26	2	1	10	16	44	0	1	12	22	68	2	2	22	38	112	8	-74

DIVISION TWO

	P	Home					Away					Total					Pts	GD
		W	D	L	F	A	W	D	L	F	A	W	D	L	F	A		
Elm Tree	28	10	0	4	42	14	9	2	3	26	15	19	2	7	68	29	59	39
Hollinsend Amateur	28	10	1	3	33	14	7	4	3	35	19	17	5	6	68	33	56	35
HSBC	28	8	2	4	40	21	9	2	3	34	16	17	4	7	74	37	55	37
Renishaw Juniors	28	9	3	2	34	18	5	1	8	20	34	14	4	10	54	52	46	2
NCB Maltby	28	7	3	4	35	24	5	0	9	13	30	12	3	13	48	54	39	-6
Sheffield Central	28	5	3	6	20	18	2	4	8	14	32	7	7	14	34	50	28	-16
Dinnington T Res	28	4	2	8	15	26	3	1	10	18	48	7	3	18	33	74	24	-41
Penistone Ch Res	28	0	3	11	12	39	2	3	9	14	37	2	6	20	26	76	12	-50

WEST YORKSHIRE ASSOCIATION FOOTBALL LEAGUE

Founded 1928

President: J Hill   **Chairman:** B Chaplin

Secretary: Kevin Parkinson, 9 Lake Lock Drive, Stanley, Wakefield WF3 4HN   Tel: 01924 825491

HONOURS LIST 2001-02

	League Champions	**League Runners-Up**
PREMIER DIVISION	Horsforth St Margaret's	Carlton Athletic
DIVISION ONE	Baildon Trinity Athletic	Tadcaster Magnet Sports
DIVISION TWO	Upper Armley Old Boys	Curwell Lions

	League Cup Winners	**League Cup Runners Up**
PREMIER DIVISION	Pudsey	Beeston
DIVISION ONE	Baildon Trinity Athletic	Methley Rangers
DIVISION TWO	Woodhouse Hill WMC	Upper Armley Old Boys

FINAL LEAGUE TABLES 2001-02

PREMIER DIVISION

	P	W	D	L	F	A	Pts
Horsforth St Margaret's	30	23	1	6	87	33	70
Carlton Athletic	30	22	1	7	78	46	67
Whitkirk Wanderers	30	21	4	5	62	39	67
Aberford Albion	30	19	3	8	68	24	60
Pontefract Srts & Soc	30	15	6	9	74	59	51
Pudsey	30	15	5	10	60	49	50
Nestle Rowntrees	30	15	3	12	83	52	48
Nostell Miners Welfare	30	12	9	9	90	62	45
Knaresborough Town	30	11	7	12	52	49	40
Beeston	30	11	5	14	68	69	38
Ripon City Magnets	30	11	4	15	54	69	37
Wetherby Athletic	30	7	9	14	47	74	30
Wakefield	30	7	7	16	40	66	28
Bardsey	30	6	3	21	39	98	21
Mount St Mary's	30	3	7	20	53	97	16
Armley Athletic	30	2	6	22	33	102	12

DIVISION ONE

	P	W	D	L	F	A	Pts
Baildon Trinity Athletic	24	14	6	4	73	33	48
Tadcaster Magnet Spts	24	15	3	6	66	38	48
Ossett Common Rovers	24	14	5	5	49	20	47
Sandy Lane	24	13	6	5	51	36	45
Kirk Deighton Rngrs*	24	10	5	9	55	56	38
Barwick*	24	11	5	8	54	46	35
Rothwell Town	24	10	5	9	32	29	35
Howden Clough	24	9	7	8	52	46	34
Robin Hood Athletic	24	8	6	10	42	48	30
East End Park	23	6	8	9	40	46	26
Methley Rangers	23	6	3	14	36	64	21
Featherstone Colliery	24	5	1	18	42	82	16
Rothwell Athletic	24	2	4	18	26	74	10

East End Park v Methley Rangers unplayed
* points adjustment

DIVISION TWO

	P	W	D	L	F	A	Pts
Upper Armley Old Boys	26	21	5	0	107	28	68
Churwell Lions	26	19	5	2	109	51	62
Sherburn White Rose	26	18	3	5	85	47	57
Woodhouse Hill WMC	26	15	5	6	88	39	50
Kippax Welfare	26	14	3	9	71	51	45
Stanley United	26	11	5	10	52	58	38
Kellingley Welfare	26	10	4	12	67	62	34

	P	W	D	L	F	A	Pts
Camerons	26	9	6	11	60	73	33
Hartshead Senior	26	9	2	15	56	74	29
Great Preston	26	7	5	14	50	85	26
Dewsbury Moor Ath	26	5	9	12	50	71	24
Boston Spartans	26	7	3	16	43	87	24
Kippax Athletic	26	4	5	17	55	75	17
Pontefract Town	26	2	2	22	37	129	8

PREMIER DIVISION RESULTS CHART 2001-02

		1	2	3	4	5	6	7	8	9	10	11	12	13	14	15	16
1	Aberford Albion	X	8-0	3-1	2-0	0-1	0-1	2-0	4-1	1-1	2-0	1-3	2-0	3-0	3-0	2-0	4-1
2	Armley Athletic	L-W	X	1-1	1-4	4-2	0-3	1-1	1-1	3-5	0-8	3-5	0-3	1-4	0-1	2-2	0-1
3	Bardsey	0-5	2-1	X	0-3	2-3	0-2	0-1	6-4	0-7	1-5	0-5	0-5	1-3	4-5	3-1	1-2
4	Beeston	0-4	4-1	3-2	X	1-3	1-4	2-1	7-1	4-1	3-3	0-3	1-1	5-3	1-0	2-2	4-4
5	Carlton Athletic	0-2	6-1	1-0	2-1	X	2-1	3-1	5-2	W-L	3-1	5-1	3-2	3-5	2-1	1-2	2-2
6	Horsforth St Margaret's	2-1	7-1	9-1	5-1	0-2	X	2-0	5-2	2-5	0-1	5-2	1-2	2-1	6-1	3-0	2-1
7	Knaresborough Town	3-2	2-0	1-2	3-2	0-1	3-3	X	2-0	3-6	2-2	1-2	1-1	4-2	2-0	6-1	1-1
8	Mount St Mary's	1-2	4-4	2-2	2-9	1-6	0-1	0-4	X	2-4	0-2	1-2	1-1	2-0	1-1	7-1	1-1
9	Nestle Rowntrees	1-3	4-0	7-0	1-1	1-3	0-2	1-2	1-3	X	4-0	3-2	5-0	5-1	3-0	1-2	2-3
10	Nostell Miners Welfare	3-3	6-0	11-2	9-3	3-5	1-3	2-1	6-3	3-3	X	3-3	3-2	4-1	2-2	1-1	2-3
11	Pontefract Sports & Soc	0-0	2-0	1-0	3-5	1-3	0-3	4-1	4-2	2-1	2-2	X	4-1	5-1	3-2	2-2	1-2
12	Pudsey	1-0	2-3	3-2	3-0	0-3	2-1	1-0	3-2	2-3	0-3	2-1	X	4-3	0-0	5-0	4-1
13	Ripon City Magnets	3-2	1-0	1-0	W-L	5-1	0-3	1-3	5-3	3-1	3-0	3-3	0-0	X	0-3	1-1	0-1
14	Wakefield	0-4	5-5	0-2	1-0	3-1	1-4	2-2	1-0	2-3	2-2	2-2	0-4	4-1	X	0-2	1-3
15	Wetherby Athletic	0-3	6-0	2-2	3-1	1-5	1-3	1-1	2-2	1-3	4-2	2-4	3-4	2-2	1-0	X	1-4
16	Whitkirk Wanderers	1-0	2-0	1-2	1-0	2-1	1-2	2-0	5-2	2-1	1-0	3-2	3-2	3-1	3-0	2-0	X

DIVISION ONE RESULTS CHART 2001-02

		1	2	3	4	5	6	7	8	9	10	11	12	13	14
1	Baildon Trinity Athletic	X	2-2	1-1	5-1	3-0	5-0	10-0	2-0	5-1	2-0	1-1	2-1	1-6	n/a
2	Barwick	3-3	X	0-2	4-1	2-2	1-2	1-2	1-0	8-2	3-1	0-1	5-4	1-1	7-4
3	East End Park	2-2	5-5	X	3-2	2-6	0-1	n/p	1-1	3-2	2-3	0-1	1-1	3-3	2-2
4	Featherstone Colliery	3-5	1-5	1-2	X	3-4	3-6	4-2	0-1	1-3	3-1	2-6	2-3	0-3	n/a
5	Howden Clough	4-0	5-0	3-1	6-2	X	0-2	2-3	0-2	1-0	W-L	2-2	0-3	2-4	8-3
6	Kirk Deighton Rangers	1-2	1-2	4-3	2-2	3-3	X	3-2	1-3	2-1	2-2	2-1	2-2	1-3	1-3
7	Methley Rangers	1-5	0-1	1-1	2-4	2-2	3-1	X	2-0	0-2	2-5	4-1	3-4	1-2	3-4
8	Ossett Common Rovers	2-1	0-3	0-0	10-0	0-0	4-2	2-1	X	2-1	6-0	1-0	2-1	0-1	7-2
9	Robin Hood Athletic	2-1	1-3	3-2	2-1	3-3	5-5	0-0	1-1	X	2-0	2-1	1-2	1-4	n/a
10	Rothwell Athletic	0-7	0-2	0-5	1-3	0-1	3-7	1-2	0-6	0-5	X	1-1	4-4	1-3	n/a
11	Rothwell Town	0-3	1-0	2-0	4-1	2-2	0-3	2-0	2-3	0-0	1-0	X	0-1	1-0	n/a
12	Sandy Lane	0-0	2-1	0-1	2-0	3-1	4-2	5-2	0-0	1-1	2-0	1-0	X	3-2	n/a
13	Tadcaster Magnet Spts	2-5	7-1	4-0	0-2	4-3	2-0	6-1	0-3	2-1	3-3	0-2	4-2	X	n/a
14	York Railway Institute	1-6	n/a	n/a	n/a	n/a	n/a	n/a	n/a	1-11	6-2	0-3	2-2	1-8	X

York Railway Institute withdrew during the season. Their results are shown above but have been expunged from the League table.

PREMIER DIVISION CUP

FIRST ROUND

Aberford Albion	v	Beeston	8-1	Bardsey	v	Pontefract S & S	3p4, 4*4
Horsforth St Margaret's	v	Wakefield	6-0	Knaresborough Tn	v	Pudsey	1-2
Mount St Mary's	v	Ripon City Magnets	1-3	Nestle Rowntrees	v	Nostell Miners Welfare	2-3
Wetherby Athletic	v	Carlton Athletic	1-2	Whitkirk Wanderers	v	Armley Athletic	3-1
(Aberford expelled)							

QUARTER-FINALS

Beeston	v	Pontefract S & S	4p3, 2*2	Carlton Athletic	v	Horsforth St Margaret's	1-2
Nostell Miners Welfare	v	Pudsey	0-2	Whitkirk Wanderers	v	Ripon City Magnets	6-1

SEMI-FINALS

Beeston	v	Horsforth St Margaret's	3-1	Pudsey	v	Whitkirk Wanderers	4-1

FINAL

Beeston   v   Pudsey   0-1   at Nostell Miners Welfare

DIVISION ONE CUP FINAL   DIVISION TWO CUP FINAL

Methley Rangers   v   Baildon Trinity Ath 3p5, 0*0   Upper Armley O B   v   Woodhouse Hill WMC1-2

MUMTAZ WEST RIDING COUNTY AMATEUR FOOTBALL LEAGUE

President: J Jones Esq.

General Secretary: Stuart Marsden, 28 Church View, Crigglestone, Wakefield WF4 3PF
Tel: 01924 253095

On December 29th 2001, two of the League's sides, Littletown and Storthes Hall, met at Beck Lane Heckmondwike in a Premier Division Round One Cup-tie. After 90 minutes play the scores were level at 1-1, extra time took place and with no further score a penalty shoot-out commenced. Following 34 consecutive conversions and with the score level at 17-17, the referee, Mr Bob Hargreaves (Halifax), abandoned the game due to darkness (there being no floodlights at the ground). An application was submitted to Guinness World Records to have the shoot out ratified as a possible record and on April 10th 2002 Guinness confirmed that the claim was an official Guinness World Record. Both clubs and and the League received certificates, and to commemorate the achievement the League have presented individual certificates to the players, the referee and his two assistants.

FINAL LEAGUE TABLES 2001-02

PREMIER DIVISION

	P	W	D	L	F	A	Pts		P	W	D	L	F	A	Pts
Brighouse Town	26	20	2	4	81	29	62	Campion AFC	26	10	4	12	49	55	34
Silsden AFC	26	17	4	5	66	30	55	Littletown AFC	26	8	7	11	41	48	31
Ovenden West Riding	26	17	2	7	64	33	53	Wibsey AFC	26	8	4	14	39	69	28
Lower Hopton AFC	26	15	4	7	68	39	49	Keighley Phoenix	26	8	3	15	49	67	27
Hemsworth MW	26	12	6	8	49	38	42	Storthes Hall AFC	26	5	7	14	32	57	22
Golcar United	26	13	3	10	54	55	42	Marsden AFC	26	4	6	16	34	53	18
Otley Town AFC	26	11	2	13	44	58	35	Stump Cross 2000	26	4	6	16	23	62	18

DIVISION ONE

	P	W	D	L	F	A	Pts		P	W	D	L	F	A	Pts
Tyersal AFC	30	19	4	7	75	43	61	Rawdon Old Boys	29	12	6	11	67	66	42
Bay Athletic AFC	30	18	6	6	68	32	60	Ardsley Celtic	30	12	6	12	73	76	42
Steeton AFC	30	19	3	8	78	43	60	Halifax Irish	30	10	5	15	56	73	35
Keighley Shamrocks	30	16	6	8	71	44	54	Heckmondwike Town	29	9	5	15	67	76	32
Altofts AFC	30	15	7	8	80	54	52	Dudley Hill Athletic	30	9	3	18	49	74	30
Hall Green United	30	15	5	10	83	64	50	Salt Old Boys	30	8	6	16	46	80	30
Eastmoor AFC	30	14	4	12	63	50	46	Farnley AFC	30	9	1	20	44	77	28
Dudley Hill Rangers	30	13	3	14	80	75	42	Crag Road United	30	4	4	22	42	114	16

DIVISION TWO

	P	W	D	L	F	A	Pts		P	W	D	L	F	A	Pts
Wakefield City	22	15	4	3	72	29	49	Barclays AFC	22	9	5	8	42	42	32
Hunsworth AFC	22	14	5	3	66	32	47	Westbrook Wanderers	22	8	6	8	61	52	30
Salts AFC	22	12	5	5	56	35	41	Robertown AFC	22	7	6	9	44	46	27
Morley Town AFC	22	12	5	5	72	54	41	Ventus/Yeadon Celtic	22	4	3	15	28	73	15
Bowling AFC	22	11	6	5	57	35	39	Dynamoes AFC	22	4	1	17	47	88	13
Westwood AFC	22	10	7	5	55	39	37	Green Lane AFC	22	0	0	22	21	92	0

PREMIER DIVISION RESULTS CHART 2001-02

		1	2	3	4	5	6	7	8	9	10	11	12	13	14
1	Brighouse Town	X	2-3	4-1	4-0	2-1	2-3	1-0	3-1	5-2	1-2	2-0	5-0	3-2	7-1
2	Campion	1-3	X	0-4	2-1	4-0	2-2	1-3	2-1	2-1	1-3	0-2	2-1	2-2	1-1
3	Golcar United	2-3	3-2	X	3-0	3-3	2-0	1-3	1-0	0-4	1-4	1-1	3-1	2-1	3-2
4	Hemsworth MW	0-4	1-0	6-1	X	5-2	1-3	2-2	4-2	2-3	1-1	3-3	0-0	8-0	3-1
5	Keighley Phoenix	3-6	3-2	0-2	0-1	X	1-1	4-2	5-4	5-2	1-0	0-2	3-0	0-1	2-3
6	Littletown	1-1	2-4	1-4	1-2	5-1	X	4-1	1-0	0-2	0-3	1-3	1-2	0-3	1-0
7	Lower Hopton	3-2	3-0	2-3	1-0	3-2	3-3	X	1-1	5-0	3-2	1-3	5-0	4-0	6-1
8	Marsden	1-1	1-2	1-1	1-2	0-1	2-2	2-1	X	1-1	0-5	1-1	3-2	2-3	0-1
9	Otley Town	0-3	2-1	2-3	1-0	4-2	1-3	1-6	4-2	X	3-2	1-3	0-2	0-1	1-0
10	Ovenden W Riding	0-3	3-2	6-2	0-1	3-0	3-1	2-3	2-1	3-2	X	2-0	2-0	2-0	5-0
11	Silsden	0-2	6-1	3-2	0-1	6-3	2-1	1-1	3-1	4-1	4-0	X	3-2	3-1	6-0
12	Storthes Hall	1-6	1-4	2-1	1-1	3-3	0-0	0-3	0-1	3-4	1-2	2-1	X	1-1	5-1
13	Stump Cross	0-4	1-5	0-2	0-0	1-3	3-3	0-3	1-4	0-2	0-0	0-3	0-0	X	1-3
14	Wibsey	1-2	3-3	4-3	2-4	2-1	0-1	3-0	3-1	0-0	2-7	0-3	2-2	3-1	X

PREMIER DIVISION CUP 2001-02

FIRST ROUND

Golcar United	v	Otley Town	2-3	Hemsworth MW	v	Silsden	2-1
Littletown	v	Storthes Hall	1-2, 1*1	Marsden	v	Campion	6p5, 2*2
Stump Cross	v	Lower Hopton	1-2	Wibsey	v	Ovenden W Riding	1-4

QUARTER-FINALS

Lower Hopton	v	Hemsworth MW	1-2	Marsden	v	Brighouse Town	1-3
Otley Town	v	Keighley Phoenix	1-4	Storthes Hall	v	Ovenden W Riding	1-3

SEMI-FINALS

Hemsworth MW	v	Ovenden W Riding	1*0	Keighley Phoenix	v	Brighouse Town	0-5

FINAL

Brighouse Town	v	Hemsworth M W	2p4, 1*1	at Littletown

DIVISION ONE CUP 2001-02

SEMI-FINALS

Halifax Irish Club	v	Altofts	0-3	Keighley Shamrocks	v	Rawdon Old Boys	0-2

FINAL

Altofts	v	Rawdon Old Boys	3*2

LEAGUE CONSTITUTION FOR 2002-03

PREMIER DIVISION	DIVISION ONE	DIVISION TWO
Bay Athletic	Altofts	Barclays
Brighouse Town	Ardsley Celtic	Bowling
Campion	Dudley Hill Athletic	Crag Road United
Golcar United	Dudley Hill Rangers	Dynamoes
Hemsworth Miners Welfare	Eastmoor	Green Lane
Keighley Phoenix	Halifax Irish Club	Farnley
Littletown	Hall Green United	Morley Town
Lower Hopton	Heckmondwike Town	Roberttown
Otley Town	Hunsworth	Salts
Ovenden West Riding	Keighley Shamrocks	Ventus & Yeadon Celtic
Silsden	Marsden	Westbrook Wanderers
Storthes Hall,Tyersal	Rawdon Old Boys	Westwood
Wibsey	Salt Old Boys	
	Steeton	
	Stump Cross	
	Wakefield City	

LINCOLNSHIRE FOOTBALL LEAGUE

Hon. Secretary: Colin Barraclough
14 Lichfield Road, Bracebridge Heath, Lincoln LN4 2SS
Tel: 01522 560912

FINAL LEAGUE TABLE 2001-02

	P	W	D	L	F	A	Pts
Lincoln United Res	26	20	3	3	64	17	63
Grimsby & Imm Am.	26	16	7	3	72	33	55
Wyberton	26	16	5	5	63	33	53
Grantham Town Res	26	12	5	9	43	37	41
Sleaford Town	26	11	6	9	58	60	39
Lincoln Moorlands Res	26	10	4	12	45	52	34
Skegness Town	26	8	9	9	42	45	33
Alstom Sports	26	9	5	12	52	53	32

	P	W	D	L	F	A	Pts
Limestone Rangers	26	7	8	11	59	69	29
Louth United Res*	26	8	6	12	45	57	29
Hykeham Town	26	7	6	13	40	63	27
Horncastle Town	26	5	10	11	28	51	25
Appleby Frodingham Ath	26	6	5	15	36	54	23
Retford Town	26	5	5	16	33	56	20

* points deducted

LEAGUE CUP 2001-02

FIRST ROUND

Alstom Sports	v	Louth United Res	2-1	Appleby Frod Ath	v	Horncastle Town	3-2
Grantham Town Res	v	Lincoln Moorlands Rs	2-0	Hykeham Town	v	Lincoln United Res	0-3
Limestone Rangers	v	Wyberton	1-2	Retford Town	v	Barrowby United	4-3
Skegness Town	v	Grimsby & Immingham	1-3				

QUARTER-FINALS

Alstom Sports	v	Grimsby & Immingham	2-3	Grantham Town Res	v	Sleaford Town	3-1
Retford Town	v	Appleby Frodingham	2-3	Lincoln United Res	v	Wyberton	0-2

SEMI-FINALS

Appleby Frodingham	v	Grantham Town Res	1-4	Wyberton	v	Grimsby & Imm. Am.	6-5

FINAL

Grantham Town Res	v	Wyberton	7-1	at Boston United	

SUPPLEMENTARY CUP 2001-02

SEMI-FINALS

Lincoln United Res	v	Alstom Sports	4-2	Skegness Town	v	Sleaford Town	0-1

FINAL

Lincoln United Res	v	Sleaford Town	2-3

League
Champions
Lincoln United
Reserves

NORTH EASTERN FINAL LEAGUE TABLES 2001-02

HUMBER PREMIER LEAGUE

	P	W	D	L	F	A	Pts
Reckitts	24	22	1	1	83	18	67
Sculcoates Amateurs	24	15	5	4	69	36	50
Westella & Willerby	24	12	6	6	60	40	42
Beverley Town	24	12	5	7	60	41	41
North Ferriby Utd Res	24	12	4	8	61	35	40
Hutton Cranswick Utd	24	11	5	8	53	46	38
Easington United	24	11	4	9	60	39	37
Hider Foods	24	9	4	11	40	50	31
Hall Road Rngrs Rs	24	9	2	13	44	45	29
Driffield	24	8	4	12	35	46	28
Bridlington Town Rs	24	4	3	17	24	74	15
Hedon United	24	3	4	17	44	94	13
Bridlington S C	24	3	3	18	25	94	12

STOKESLEY & DISTRICT LEAGUE

DIVISION ONE

	P	W	D	L	F	A	Pts
Dorman	20	15	2	3	93	27	47
Ennis Square	20	13	2	5	52	33	41
Teeside Athletic	20	11	5	4	64	37	36
Redcar Coke Ovens	20	11	2	7	58	36	35
B & H Kings Head	20	11	2	7	48	29	35
The Grenadier	20	10	4	6	55	43	34
Marlborough P O	20	9	2	9	64	53	29
Woodman's Arms	20	6	4	10	34	44	22
Stokesley SC	20	6	1	13	35	51	19
Lingdale	20	2	3	15	24	95	9
Bull's Head	20	1	3	16	21	98	6

WRAGG OVER 35'S LEAGUE

PREMIER DIVISION

	P	W	D	L	F	A	Pts
Tomtreddlehoyle	22	17	3	2	52	15	37
Norton Woodseats	22	14	4	4	50	19	32
FC Main	22	14	2	6	55	35	30
Mosborough Trinity	22	12	3	7	49	42	27
Ecclesfield Ball	22	11	3	8	45	40	25
Thurcroft Corinthians	22	9	4	9	43	37	22
Dearne Comm OB	22	10	1	11	39	40	21
Wickersley O. Village	22	8	1	13	32	43	17
Barrel	22	6	3	13	38	62	15
Railway Tavern	22	5	4	13	36	53	14
Sherwood AFC	22	4	5	13	33	59	13
Stocksbridge PS	22	5	1	16	27	54	11

EAST RIDING AMATEUR LEAGUE

PREMIER DIVISION

	P	W	D	L	F	A	Pts
East Hull Amateurs	20	14	4	2	67	35	46
Keyingham AFC	20	12	4	4	49	30	40
Discount Carpets	20	12	1	7	68	47	37
Auto Matrix	20	10	4	6	54	40	34
Kinloss	20	8	5	7	53	47	29
Withernsea	20	8	2	10	35	38	26
Nightjar	20	8	1	11	39	53	25
Malet Lambert YC	20	6	6	8	38	37	24
Gra Knowles Wolf	20	6	4	10	39	54	22
Kingburn AFC	20	4	3	13	31	59	15
Hider Foods	20	3	4	13	30	63	13

GAINSBOROUGH & DISTRICT LEAGUE

DIVISION ONE

	P	W	D	L	F	A	Pts
Clumber Inn	20	15	2	3	55	29	47
Boat Inn	20	15	1	4	62	27	46
Bircotes	20	14	0	6	88	37	39
AFC Friendship	20	12	2	6	70	41	35
Misterton United	20	10	2	8	41	43	32
Wroot	20	9	4	7	42	38	31
Marshalls Sports	20	8	4	8	38	40	28
Blacksmiths	20	6	3	11	32	48	21
Epworth Town	20	4	4	12	30	53	16
Crowle Colts	20	3	1	16	27	76	6
Harworth	20	1	3	16	27	76	6

LEEDS RED TRIANGLE LEAGUE

PREMIER DIVISION

	P	W	D	L	F	A	Pts
Wyebeck Arms	22	18	2	2	77	26	56
Street Works SA	22	14	2	6	69	40	44
FC Headingley	22	13	0	9	66	42	39
Shoulder of Mutton	22	11	3	8	67	50	36
Central Ex-Service	22	10	5	7	73	54	35
Old Griffin Head	22	11	2	9	46	40	35
Pudsey Shamrock	22	9	5	8	53	44	32
Lowside WMC	22	10	2	10	51	51	32
AFC Stanningley Al	22	8	3	11	55	77	27
Scott Hall Steel	22	4	3	15	49	79	15
Main Line SC	22	5	2	15	43	79	14
Seacroft WMC	22	3	3	16	24	91	12

LEEDS SUNDAY LEAGUE

PREMIER DIVISION

	P	W	D	L	F	A	Pts
East Leeds BC	22	17	4	1	91	15	55
Goose 87	22	16	2	4	64	32	50
Diamond Sports	22	12	3	7	56	38	39
Kippax Welfare	22	11	3	8	52	47	36
Whistlestop	22	10	4	8	51	37	34
Halton Moore	22	9	5	8	48	48	32
Vesper Gate	22	9	2	11	46	54	29
Cranmer Bank	22	8	3	11	48	51	27
Manston Hotel	22	7	6	9	41	49	27
Adel	22	6	1	15	29	64	19
Moorgate	22	5	3	14	38	68	18
St Nicholas	22	3	2	17	26	71	11

ROTHERHAM & DISTRICT SUNDAY LEAGUE

PREMIER DIVISION

	P	W	D	L	F	A	Pts
Brinsworth Athletic	22	15	3	4	67	28	48
Clifton Hotel	22	15	4	3	80	30	46
Joker	22	14	2	6	47	27	44
Maltby M W	22	13	4	5	61	29	43
Swallownest M W	22	11	5	6	58	37	38
Thurcroft Hotel	22	11	4	7	41	27	37
KCM Fighting Cocks	22	11	3	8	53	43	36
Lord Conyers Arms	22	7	4	11	37	42	25
East Herringthorpe	22	8	0	14	47	77	24
Aughton Robin Hood	22	6	2	14	34	57	20
FC Kiveton	22	4	2	16	45	70	11
Maltby Haynook	22	0	1	21	20	123	1

SOUTHERN
LEAGUE

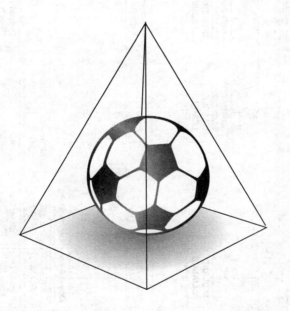

PYRAMID
SECTION

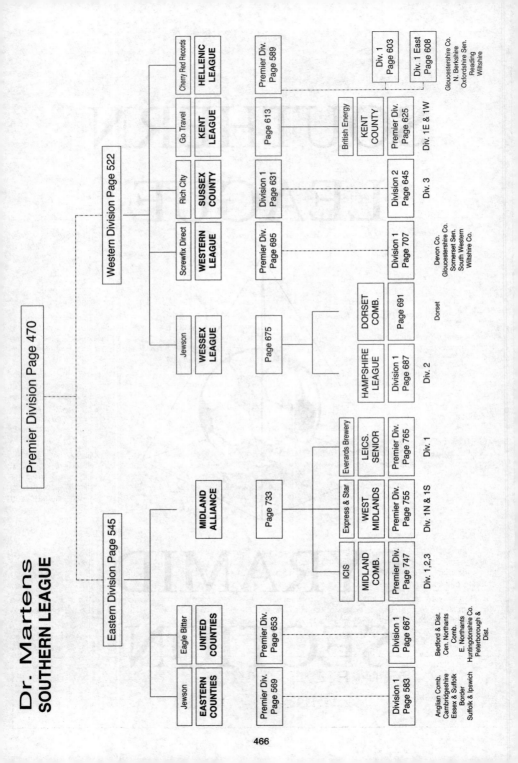

Dr. Martens
SOUTHERN LEAGUE

Premier Division Page 470

Western Division Page 522

Eastern Division Page 545

Western Division Page 522

Cherry Red Records	Go Travel	Rich City	Screwfix Direct	Jewson
HELLENIC LEAGUE	**KENT LEAGUE**	**SUSSEX COUNTY**	**WESTERN LEAGUE**	**WESSEX LEAGUE**

Premier Div. Page 589

Page 613

Division 1 Page 631

Premier Div. Page 695

Page 675

British Energy
KENT COUNTY

Div. 1 Page 603

Div. 1 East Page 608

Gloucestershire Co.
N. Berkshire
Oxfordshire Sen.
Reading
Wiltshire

Premier Div. Page 625

Div. 1E & 1W

Division 2 Page 645

Div. 3

Division 1 Page 707

Devon Co.
Gloucestershire Co.
Somerset Sen.
South Western
Wiltshire Co.

HAMPSHIRE LEAGUE	DORSET COMB.
Division 1 Page 687	Page 691
Div. 2	Dorset

Eastern Division Page 545

		MIDLAND ALLIANCE

Page 733

ICIS	Express & Star	Everards Brewery
MIDLAND COMB.	**WEST MIDLANDS**	**LEICS. SENIOR**
Premier Div. Page 747	Premier Div. Page 755	Premier Div. Page 765
Div. 1,2,3	Div. 1N & 1S	Div. 1

Jewson	Eagle Bitter
EASTERN COUNTIES	**UNITED COUNTIES**
Premier Div. Page 569	Premier Div. Page 653
Division 1 Page 583	Division 1 Page 667

Anglian Comb.
Cambridgeshire
Essex & Suffolk
Border
Suffolk & Ipswich

Bedford & Dist.
Cen. Northants
Comb.
E. Northants
Huntingdonshire Co.
Peterborough &
Dist.

Dr MARTENS LEAGUE

Chairman: D S R Gillard

Secretary: D J Strudwick

PO Box 90, Worcester WR3 8RX   Tel: 01905 757509

KETTERING'S CORONATION

Just as Queen Elizabeth II began to celebrate her Golden Jubilee, Kettering Town were crowned Champions of the Dr Martens League Premier Division; the town of Hastings won the battle for the Eastern Division; Halesowen Town became Kings of the Western Division and Dorchester Town reigned over everyone in the League's Challenge Cup.

The race for the Premier Division crown proved to be one of the most exciting in the history of the Championship. And, with just two wins from their first six games, Kettering Town seemed unlikely candidates to collect the crown jewels.

Folkestone Invicta, Havant & Waterlooville and Weymouth flirted with the top of the table in the early weeks of the campaign before the Hampshire side took command for a six-week spell. Crawley Town then took the reins for a fifteen-week period before abdicating top spot in favour of Tamworth on 16th February. With the exception of one week, Tamworth then led the Division for the next twelve weeks before vacating the throne on the final day of the season in one of the most climactic days in the history of the competition.

With one game left to play, Tamworth led Kettering Town by virtue of having a goal difference superior by two. Both clubs were locked on 84 points and had even scored the same number of goals, so there was a real possibility that a play-off would be required to separate the teams and to decide the Championship. Arrangements were put in place for a match to take place at Filbert Street, Leicester the evening before the FA Cup Final. The final day's fixtures were not for the faint hearted. Both teams had to win their final match and, incredibly, still had to hope their rival had not won, and in Tamworth's case they had to hope the Poppies could not win by a margin of at least two goals greater.

Who knows what really happens in the minds and bodies of sportsmen when the chips are down to this extent? What we do know is, however, experience is a good tool to have in your kit bag. So perhaps it was experience that saw the ex-Football Conference team regain its former status with a nerveless 2-1 victory at Tiverton Town, while the Lambs, who have never been in such a position before, drew 3-3 at Folkestone Invicta to allow the gold medal to slip from their grasp at the final fence. As if to rub salt in Tamworth's wounds, Folkestone's keeper Dave Wietecha saved a penalty! Football can be a cruel game.

THE EASTERN DIVISION

In fact, football is often a cruel game. A manager's ability does not always reap the benefits it deserves. But if grit and determination, coupled with skill and a vast knowledge of the game guaranteed success, you could wager a king's ransom on George Wakeling. Having taken Hastings Town very close to promotion last season, Mr Wakeling's charges this year were never out of the Eastern Division's top three throughout the whole season.

George was an astute defender in his playing days. It is no surprise to me, therefore, that his team conceded less than a goal per game in its quest for the title. Not that Hastings relied on defence. In their 42 League sorties, the team from the Pilot Field scored 85 goals and won 29 of their League matches.

Dorchester Town's manager, Mark Morris, was also an accomplished defender. Perhaps it is no coincidence, there-

fore, that his team also complied a miserly record in the 'Goals Against' column - 36 against in 42 fixtures. But despite this fine record the Magpies slipped up on the run-in and allowed Grantham Town to take the silver medals.

Not that Grantham Town did not deserve their success. The Gingerbreads were third last year and were always a good bet to be in the frame this time around. Manager John Wilkinson's team contained a mixture of effervescent youth and vast experience. The blend proved to be golden. Grantham equalled Hastings' tally of 29 victories during the season and amassed 99 League goals. The Gingerbreads not only regained the Premier Division status they lost two seasons ago, they won the Merit Cup for having bagged the most goals in the League season.

At a glance the League could suggest that these three clubs had everything their own way, but that was not the case. Histon and Stamford are clearly emerging clubs. Fisher Athletic (London) showed enough spirit to suggest they are like the proverbial 'resting' actor before regaining centre stage. And Eastbourne Borough were undefeated at home against the three top clubs. Only Dorchester Town returned home from Sussex with anything at all, a 1-1 draw. Among others, Garry Wilson and his young Eastbourne consorts are clearly one of the teams to watch.

THE WESTERN DIVISION

After several seasons in the top flight Halesowen returned to a Regional First Division at the end of last season. And following their relegation the club also returned to their traditional royal blue and white strip. (I bet the loyalists amongst the Recreation Ground faithfuls (in particular HR, who I am sure still watches every Halesowen match) were relieved to see tradition return.) The new regalia coincided with an upturn in fortunes and the Yeltz have returned to the Premier Division after one season.

Following a nervous start, Halesowen quickly lifted themselves into the pack of early contenders. Solihull Borough, Evesham United, Chippenham Town and Clevedon Town were all amongst the early pacesetters. Atherstone United and newcomers Stourport Swifts also courted the top places.

Solihull Borough's challenge finally faded when they lost 4-1 at Halesowen on Easter Monday. Having moved to the top of the table on 1st December the Yeltz were, by now, in irrepressible form. Even a few heart-stopping moments in the final few fixtures, when they dropped valuable points to Cinderford Town and Gloucester City, failed to prevent them taking the Championship ahead of Chippenham Town. Manager Brendan Phillips once again appears in the Honours List. The prize money this manager has won for his clubs, down the years, must by now read like the Civil List. Certainly this year's success may, I hope, have helped ameliorate a personal loss for Brendan.

The Freshmen from Chippenham can be proud of their magnificent season, as the men from Wiltshire were amongst the leaders throughout the campaign. They took four points off winners Halesowen and concluded their season with a 4-0 win over Swindon Town in the Wiltshire County Cup Final.

In congratulating all the winners, it must be acknowledged teams do finish at the bottom of the table. So in bidding farewell to Kettering Town, who move on to the Football Conference, the League welcomes back Dover Athletic into the Premier Division.

The four clubs to be promoted from the Regional Divisions will move up at the expense of Newport IOW, King's Lynn, Merthyr Tydfil and Salisbury City, four significant and long serving members of the League for whom we hope more stately days will soon return.

Only three clubs qualified for promotion to the Regional Divisions from the feeder leagues this year. So following the loss of Bloxwich Town during the season, and the loss of Bilston Town soon after the end of the campaign, only Wisbech Town are scheduled to be relegated. The Directors send the Fenmen their best wishes for a speedy return and extend a courteous, but hopefully temporary, royal wave of farewell. These three clubs will be replaced in next season's complement by Bromsgrove Rovers, Fleet Town and Taunton Town. All have been in the League before, so the League is pleased to extend a metaphoric fanfare to our old friends.

THE LEAGUE CHALLENGE CUP

The League's Cup Competition threw up its usual quota of strange results during the season. For example, thirteen Premier Division clubs lost their place in the tournament in the First Round, and only four of those lost to Premier colleagues. Realistically, it is accepted that many clubs use the competition to play 'squad' players but there can be no excuse for nine Premier outfits losing, some quite resoundingly, to Regional Division clubs, at this stage of the competition. I can only imagine there was a hasty review of what constituted a 'squad' player at some clubs in several areas of the League.

However, Ashford Town, Dorchester Town, King's Lynn and Solihull Borough reached the semi-final stage to share the not inconsiderable prize money and Dorchester Town and King's Lynn emerged from the semi-finals to contest a competitive final tie.

A Phil Andrews goal for Dorchester and three male streakers lifted the clouds on a cold and dull Norfolk evening. The second-leg was not so close. The Linnets conceded further goals in the thirteenth minute (Phil Andrews) and in the 25th minute (Daniel O'Hagan) without making a great deal of impact on the Magpies' defence. When Justin Keeler scored Dorchester's third goal on the night, to make it 4-0 on aggregate, the Dorset side were home and dry in really majestic style.

WHAT LIES IN THE FUTURE?

For 108 years the Southern Football League has been the prominent player to organise and administer a football league, without boundaries, and throughout the South of England. Quickly brushing aside old history that refers to the number of clubs who have moved from The Southern Football League into The Football League and the fact the League can boast a winner of the FA Cup, The FA Trophy and the FA Vase, The Southern Football League is still the best supported League beneath The Football Conference. In 22 years the League has never failed to honour its responsibility to promote a club to The Football Conference. Indeed, the last four clubs to win promotion to The Football League (Cheltenham Town, Kidderminster Harriers, Rushden & Diamonds and now Boston United), were all promoted to The Football Conference from The Southern Football League.

The strength of The Southern Football League is reflected even further in yet another issue that arose at the end of last season. Former members Burton Albion (who finished runners-up for the last two seasons) and Gravesend & Northfleet (whose best position in recent seasons in the SFL was eleventh) have both won promotion to The Football Conference from their new leagues, the Northern Premier and the Isthmian respectively.

And talking of former members, the two clubs that contested The Football League Division Three Play-Off final at The Millennium Stadium in Cardiff this season (Cheltenham Town and Rushden & Diamonds) were both members of The Southern Football League within the last six years!

It is little wonder the Directors of The Southern Football League wish to be party to driving forward the ambitions of its member clubs rather than to allow them to stagnate indefinitely in the present archaic structure. Having said all that, the Board has been brave enough not to impose its opinions on its member clubs. It has chosen instead, not to advise or instruct its member clubs on what the Board perceives would be the best option. Instead, the League's Board has stood aside to allow the clubs to choose the route of their own future.

SPONSORSHIPS AND THE FOOTBALL ASSOCIATION

Well, it can be easily seen it has been another busy and successful year in the Dr Martens Football League. But success has not, and cannot, be achieved at this level of the game without a great deal of help. Through the R Griggs Group Limited, Dr Martens have again afforded the League magnificent sponsorship support. The financial assistance that enables over £90,000 to be channelled back to clubs is plain for all to see. The much less visible back-up provided by Max and Steven Griggs, Mark Darnell, Dave Joyce and Sue Hughes has been equally as important. The Board thanks you all for your help.

The reliable ICIS Sportswear Limited will once again sponsor the League's Bench Kit and have agreed to take on board a 'safe hands' award designed to benefit the goalkeepers who concede fewest goals each month. Thanks again ICIS Limited.

The Football Association has once again been superb with its assistance to the Competition. This year the League has received a £20,000 administration grant, £1,500 towards the cost of running the Match Officials Assessment Scheme and a further £1,500 worth of funding to help with new IT equipment. Thank you Soho Square.

Taken from the Directors' Report on the League's activities for the 2001-02 season by Dennis Strudwick, Treasurer and Company/League Secretary

DR MARTENS LEAGUE CLUBCALL
09068 12 11 51

25 in 25

A review of the progress made by the **Southern League** and its member clubs during the twenty-five year life span of the F.A. Non-League Club Directory (1978 - 2002) will be available in the next year. It will be one of a series of 25 and will contain features, statistics and photos in at least 160 pages dedicated purely to the Southern League members.

Further details can be found on page 17 so make sure of your copy of this exciting limited edition.

PREMIER DIVISION FINAL LEAGUE TABLE 2001-02

		P	HOME			AWAY			TOTAL						
			W	D	L	W	D	L	W	D	L	F	A	GD	Pts
1	Kettering Town	42	12	4	5	15	2	4	27	6	9	80	41	39	87
2	Tamworth	42	16	5	0	8	8	5	24	13	5	81	41	40	85
3	Havant & Waterlooville	42	14	4	3	8	5	8	22	9	11	74	50	24	75
4	Crawley Town	42	12	3	6	9	7	5	21	10	11	67	48	19	73
5	Newport County	42	10	6	5	9	3	9	19	9	14	61	48	13	66
6	Tiverton Town	42	10	4	7	7	6	8	17	10	15	70	63	7	61
7	Moor Green	42	10	6	5	8	1	12	18	7	17	64	62	2	61
8	Worcester City	42	9	7	5	7	5	9	16	12	14	65	54	11	60
9	Stafford Rangers	42	13	2	6	4	7	10	17	9	16	70	62	8	60
10	Ilkeston Town	42	8	8	5	6	8	7	14	16	12	58	61	-3	58
11	Weymouth	42	9	4	8	6	7	8	15	11	16	59	67	-8	56
12	Hinckley United	42	10	5	6	4	8	9	14	13	15	64	62	2	55
13	Folkestone Invicta	42	10	5	6	4	7	10	14	12	16	51	61	-10	54
14	Cambridge City	42	7	7	7	5	9	7	12	16	14	60	70	-10	52
15	Welling United	42	8	7	6	5	5	11	13	12	17	69	66	3	51
16	Hednesford Town	42	9	4	8	6	2	13	15	6	21	59	70	-11	51
17	Bath City	42	9	3	9	4	8	9	13	11	18	56	65	-9	50
18	Chelmsford City	42	8	6	7	5	5	11	13	11	18	63	75	-12	50
19	Newport IoW	42	6	7	8	6	5	10	12	12	18	38	61	-23	48
20	King's Lynn	42	6	8	7	5	5	11	11	13	18	44	57	-13	46
21	Merthyr Tydfil	42	8	7	6	4	1	16	12	8	22	53	71	-18	44
22	Salisbury City	42	4	5	12	2	3	16	6	8	28	36	87	-51	26

PREMIER DIVISION RESULTS CHART 2001-02

	1	2	3	4	5	6	7	8	9	10	11	12	13	14	15	16	17	18	19	20	21	22
1 Bath City	X	1-1 562	1-1 828	1-2 612	2-0 899	2-5 743	3-4 413	1-2 622	1-1 620	0-1 899	0-1 650	4-2 629	0-2 579	2-1 708	0-1 331	1-0 697	4-3 639	1-2 787	4-2 958	2-1 496	2-1 710	4-0 718
2 Cambridge City	1-3 433	X	1-1 767	0-1 349	0-0 467	2-1 665	2-1 440	3-2 309	1-1 293	2-1 764	2-1 758	2-2 316	0-1 321	1-2 477	2-0 536	1-3 273	1-1 617	1-1 617	1-3 439	2-0 276	2-2 649	0-2 416
3 Chelmsford City	1-3 609	0-3 567	X	2-2 788	2-1 627	0-3 520	1-1 585	6-1 619	2-0 517	0-2 707	2-2 454	2-1 484	0-2 462	3-1 602	2-0 855	3-2 454	0-0 602	1-1 491	2-2 705	2-4 573	3-2 380	2-1 584
4 Crawley Town	3-0 762	4-3 1165	3-3 1050	X	1-1 856	3-0 1260	4-1 814	1-0 949	2-0 1002	0-2 2133	1-0 774	2-1 1332	1-2 1021	0-1 1146	2-0 380	4-0 637	1-2 1028	1-2 1830	3-0 867	2-4 1777	0-0 1100	1-0 1317
5 Folkestone Invicta	1-1 341	2-1 268	2-1 358	2-1 309	X	1-1 346	2-1 452	2-1 464	0-2 340	2-3 284	1-2 382	1-2 367	2-2 333	3-1 436	2-1 458	2-0 338	2-1 339	3-3 1277	0-3 281	1-0 504	1-3 424	1-3 379
6 Havant & Waterlooville	3-0 586	4-1 613	4-1 394	2-0 694	2-2 607	X	2-1 429	5-0 575	2-2 467	1-3 689	0-0 475	4-0 443	3-1 599	1-3 726	1-2 601	2-0 505	2-1 584	0-2 589	3-3 505	1-0 549	3-2 594	1-0 513
7 Hednesford Town	1-0 639	1-1 609	1-2 627	0-0 607	3-1 530	2-1 624	X	4-0 444	3-2 650	0-2 920	0-2 731	3-0 565	1-2 689	0-2 620	1-4 455	6-0 650	3-3 1319	1-2 931	3-4 777	1-1 601	2-4 556	0-3 767
8 Hinckley United	2-2 313	2-2 402	2-0 455	0-1 577	1-2 320	2-4 327	4-0 444	X	2-2 324	2-1 966	0-0 389	1-0 433	3-1 240	0-2 417	1-2 483	2-1 308	3-0 415	1-0 1102	1-0 471	1-0 378	3-2 327	0-0 326
9 Ilkeston Town	3-3 577	1-1 452	3-3 510	1-0 563	2-1 642	2-0 401	2-0 562	1-1 526	X	0-2 842	3-1 465	1-0 521	2-1 559	0-1 496	2-1 577	0-1 547	2-2 702	1-1 787	0-2 527	3-2 497	1-2 546	1-2 521
10 Kettering Town	1-1 1418	4-2 1957	4-2 1461	1-3 1545	2-1 1394	3-1 1354	3-1 1455	2-1 1281	1-2 1456	X	3-0 1842	1-2 1212	2-1 1458	1-2 1324	1-2 1666	4-0 1295	1-0 1214	1-2 1395	1-1 1441	1-1 1175	4-1 2420	4-1 1571
11 King's Lynn	1-1 647	1-1 818	3-0 684	2-2 861	0-2 885	1-1 754	1-0 597	1-1 646	0-1 1145	0-3 1192	X	0-1 870	1-0 634	4-2 1023	1-1 476	3-2 683	2-0 749	2-0 874	0-1 538	1-2 439	0-0 777	1-2 770
12 Merthyr Tydfil	3-1 736	3-1 511	3-1 481	2-2 456	1-0 409	3-1 523	3-1 561	2-2 501	2-3 405	1-0 725	0-1 870	X	1-2 438	1-1 848	1-4 353	3-2 501	2-0 325	1-1 1014	1-2 564	4-4 434	1-2 506	0-0 498
13 Moor Green	0-0 359	1-2 347	3-1 317	3-1 367	2-0 292	2-1 350	1-4 447	2-1 253	1-1 348	0-2 586	4-0 267	1-0 309	X	1-2 324	1-4 651	1-1 277	1-1 491	3-2 1010	3-4 339	2-1 234	7-1 332	3-1 368
14 Newport County	1-0 902	2-2 669	0-1 804	1-1 653	4-1 526	2-0 525	0-1 722	0-1 709	3-0 610	0-2 722	2-1 655	3-0 1059	2-1 324	X	0-4 443	0-0 810	2-2 774	0-4 883	3-0 807	1-1 661	1-2 716	0-2 752
15 Newport IoW	2-1 683	1-1 354	0-3 423	1-2 356	1-1 345	0-1 561	0-1 905	1-1 502	2-1 487	0-2 650	0-0 636	2-3 463	2-1 702	0-4 443	X	0-0 557	1-0 466	0-4 524	0-3 555	1-1 518	0-0 433	1-1 315
16 Salisbury City	0-1 455	1-1 393	1-3 379	0-3 481	2-0 481	2-0 340	1-0 300	1-1 375	1-1 397	1-2 539	0-3 324	1-2 439	5-0 370	0-2 460	0-0 557	X	1-4 382	1-2 444	1-2 417	1-0 199	2-3 433	1-1 886
17 Stafford Rangers	2-0 483	2-2 767	1-0 598	0-0 535	1-2 696	0-2 558	3-0 1381	4-2 576	1-1 725	2-3 679	3-2 599	2-0 694	3-4 330	2-0 502	1-0 466	3-0 698	X	0-1 1058	6-2 640	3-2 587	2-1 779	1-2 1017
18 Tamworth	1-1 689	2-2 753	1-0 1237	2-0 642	1-1 955	1-1 582	3-0 623	2-1 663	1-1 752	1-0 803	4-1 852	2-0 1111	2-0 638	2-0 812	0-4 524	5-1 2240	0-1 1058	X	3-2 826	1-0 975	3-0 1165	0-2 1317
19 Tiverton Town	3-1 860	5-0 734	0-1 691	0-1 726	2-0 903	0-1 645	1-1 703	1-1 722	3-2 783	3-2 1996	1-1 743	1-3 499	1-1 738	2-1 642	0-3 555	2-1 528	3-3 1213	3-2 826	X	X 748	0-1 1083	1-3 1040
20 Welling United	4-0 518	4-4 465	2-4 654	2-3 675	2-4 602	1-2 443	4-1 500	3-2 501	1-0 442	1-1 608	0-1 494	1-0 512	0-0 417	0-0 649	1-1 518	5-1 516	3-2 608	3-3 848	X 748	X	1-1 570	1-3 803
21 Weymouth	0-0 930	4-2 724	1-2 883	1-2 1058	1-1 702	0-1 741	0-4 712	4-3 673	3-1 767	1-1 1005	2-1 778	4-1 701	0-1 803	0-1 804	1-0 940	2-1 701	0-1 630	X 729	4-2 1303	1-1 705	X	1-2 903
22 Worcester City	0-1 1224	1-2 1054	1-1 811	3-0 876	1-1 1033	0-0 1004	0-1 803	1-1 967	2-2 938	1-1 1152	3-1 941	1-0 769	3-2 837	2-0 1047	1-1 886	6-0 886	1-2 1017	0-2 1317	3-3 1040	2-1 803	3-3 1011	X

DR MARTENS CHALLENGE CUP 2001-02

PRELIMINARY ROUND

Sittingbourne	v	Chatham Town	2p3, 0-0
Wisbech Town	v	Spalding United	1-2

FIRST ROUND

Dorchester Town	v	Bashley	4*3	Weymouth	v	Salisbury City	4-0
Newport County	v	Bath City	1-3	Cinderford Town	v	Gloucester City	3-0
Merthyr Tydfil	v	Swindon Supermarine	3-0	Clevedon Town	v	Tiverton Town	5-2
Mangotsfield United	v	Chippenham Town	3*2	Cirencester Town	v	Weston Super Mare	2-1
Hastings Town	v	Dartford	3*1	Erith & Belvedere	v	Folkestone Invicta	1-2
Tonbridge Angels	v	Welling United	2-1	Eastbourne Borough	v	Fisher Athletic	3*1
Crawley Town	v	Chatham Town	3-1	Burnham	v	St Leonards	4-2
Ashford Town	v	Chelmsford City	1*0	Havant & W'ville	v	Newport IoW	2-0
Grantham Town	v	Kings Lynn	1-2	Kettering Town	v	Corby Town	3-1
Spalding United	v	Histon	1-7	Rothwell Town	v	Racing Club Warwick	1*0
Stafford Rangers	v	Bloxwich United	1p4, 1-1	Hinckley United	v	Atherstone United	1-4
Stamford AFC	v	Cambridge City	1-0	Gresley Rovers	v	Ilkeston Town	1-0
Hednesford Town	v	Evesham United	1-3	Solihull Borough	v	Sutton Coldfield Tn	1-0
Bilston Town	v	Halesowen Town	1-0	Rugby United	v	Banbury United	1-2
Tamworth	v	Bedworth United	1-4	Worcester City	v	Rocester	2-0
Stourport Swifts	v	Redditch United	4-5	Moor Green	v	Shepshed Dynamo	5-4

SECOND ROUND

Dorchester Town	v	Weymouth	3-2	Bath City	v	Cinderford Town	3-1
Merthyr Tydfil	v	Clevedon Town	2-0	Mangotsfield United	v	Cirencester Town	3-1
Hastings Town	v	Folkestone Invicta	5-0	Tonbridge Angels	v	Eastbourne Borough	1-2
Crawley Town	v	Burnham	6-0	Ashford Town	v	Havant & W'ville	2-1
King's Lynn	v	Kettering Town	6-1	Histon	v	Rothwell Town	1-3
Bloxwich United	v	Atherstone United	**	Stamford AFC	v	Gresley Rovers	0-1
Evesham United	v	Solihull Borough	1-2	Bilston Town	v	Banbury United	2-1
Bedworth United	v	Worcester City	4-0	Redditch United	v	Moor Green	1-4

** Bloxwich United withdrew, Atherstone United bye

THIRD ROUND

Bath City	v	Dorchester Town	0-2	Merthyr Tydfil	v	Mangotsfield United	3-0
Hastings Town	v	Eastbourne Borough	2-3	Crawley Town	v	Ashford Town	1p4, 2-2
King's Lynn	v	Rothwell Town	2-1	Atherstone United	v	Gresley Rovers	2-1
Solihull Borough	v	Bilston Town	4-0	Bedworth United	v	Moor Green	4*3

FOURTH ROUND

Dorchester Town	v	Merthyr Tydfil	3-0	Eastbourne Borough	v	Ashford Town	1-0
Atherstone United	v	King's Lynn	0-2	Solihull Borough	v	Bedworth United	3-2

SEMI-FINALS

Dorchester Town	v	Eastbourne Borough	2-1	King's Lynn	v	Solihull Borough	2-1

FINAL

King's Lynn	v	Dorchester Town	0-1, 0-3

PREMIER DIVISION LEADING GOALSCORERS 2001-02

29	Paul Kiely	Stafford Rangers	19	Darren Roberts	Tamworth
28	James Taylor	Havant & Waterlooville	18	Gary Abbott	Welling United
25	David Laws	Weymouth	18	Glen Kirkwood	Ilkeston Town
22	Nathan Lamey	Moor Green	18	Adam Webster	Worcester City
20	Ryan King	Salisbury City	17	Jamie O'Rourke	Havant & Waterlooville
20	Lee Phillips	Weymouth	15	Daniel Carroll	Crawley Town
20	Dale Watkins	Kettering Town	15	Timothy Hambley	Havant & Waterlooville
19	Adrian Foster	Bath City	15	Anthony Hemmings	Tamworth

SOUTHERN LEAGUE - PREMIER DIVISION - LAST TEN YEARS

	92-93	93-94	94-95	95-96	96-97	97-98	98-99	99-00	00-01	01-02
Ashford Town	-	-	-	-	19	21r	-	-	-	-
Atherstone United	15	4	15	17	11	9	16	22r	-	-
Baldock Town	-	-	-	18	20r	-	-	-	-	-
Bashley	9	21r	-	-	-	-	-	-	-	-
Bath City	-	-	-	-	-	6	4	4	15	17
Boston United	-	-	-	-	-	xfer from NPL	2	1p	-	-
Bromsgrove Rovers	-	-	-	-	-	19	22r	-	-	-
Burton Albion	8	11	3	16	6	3	13	2	2	-
Cambridge City	14	17	9	19	18	13	20	14	16	14
Chelmsford City	12	6	15	12	22r	-	-	-	-	18
Cheltenham Town	2	2	2	3	2p	-	-	-	-	-
Clevedon Town	-	-	-	-	-	-	-	8	19r	-
Corby Town	3	9	22r	-	-	-	-	-	-	-
Crawley Town	=6	5	11	9	17	10	11	12	11	4
Dorchester Town	18	18	6	13	15	4	18	18	21r	-
Dover Athletic	1p	-	-	-	-	-	-	-	-	-
Farnborough Town	-	1p	-	-	-	-	-	-	-	-
Fisher Athletic	-	-	-	-	-	-	-	-	20r	-
Folkestone Invicta	-	-	-	-	-	-	-	-	17	13
Forest Green Rovers	-	-	-	-	-	-	1p	-	-	-
Gloucester City	13	10	4	4	3	11	6	20r	-	-
Gravesend & Northfleet	-	-	14	11	14	to Isthmian Lge		-	-	-
Grantham Town	-	-	-	-	-	-	17	19r	-	-
Gresley Rovers	-	14	8	5	1	17	21r	-	-	-
Halesowen Town	10	3	13	2	4	5	8	11	22r	-
Hastings Town	16	12	12	8	16	14	5r	-	-	-
Havant & Waterlooville						**	-	13	6	3
Hednesford Town	4	13	1p	-	-	-	-	-	-	16
Hinckley United	-	-	-	-	-	-	-	-	-	12
Ilkeston Town	-	-	-	20r	-	-	3	9	14	10
Kettering Town	-	-	-	-	-	-	-	-	-	1p
King's Lynn	-	-	-	-	5	8	10	5	3	20r
Leek Town	-	-	7	-	-	-	-	-	-	-
Margate	-	-	-	-	-	-	-	3	1p	-
Merthyr Tydfil	-	-	-	7	9	2	15	17	18	21r
Moor Green	19	19r	-	-	-	-	-	-	9	7
Newport AFC (County from 99-00)	-	-	-	14	21r	-	-	7	10	5
Newport I.o.W.	-	-	-	-	-	-	-	-	-	19r
Nuneaton Borough	-	22r	-	-	7	12	1p	-	-	-
Rothwell Town	-	-	-	-	-	16	19	21r	-	-
Rushden & Diamonds	-	-	5	1p	-	-	-	-	-	-
St Leonards	-	-	-	-	-	22r	-	-	-	-
Salisbury City	-	-	-	15	12	18	12	16	13	22r
Sittingbourne	-	8	20r	-	8	20r	-	-	-	-
Solihull Borough	=6	6	19r	-	-	-	-	-	-	-
Stafford Rangers	-	-	-	21r	-	-	-	-	7	9
Sudbury Town	-	-	18	10	11	to Eastern Lge.		-	-	-
Trowbridge Town	5	7	21r	-	-	-	-	-	-	-
Tamworth	-	-	-	-	-	15	9	6	12	2
Tiverton Town	-	-	-	-	-	-	-	-	-	6
V.S. Rugby	20r	-	17	22r	-	-	-	-	-	-
Waterlooville	11	20r	-	-	-	-	**	-	-	-
Welling	-	-	-	-	-	-	-	-	4	15
Weymouth	21r	-	-	-	-	-	14	10	5	11
Worcester City	17	15	10	6	10	7	7	15	8	8

BATH CITY

CLUB OFFICIALS

Chairman: Stephen Hall
Directors: G.Todd,P.Weaver,M.Hughes.
P.Williams and A Pierce

Secretary: Quentin Edwards c/o the club,
01225 423087 (B) & 07785 795532 (M)

Commercial Director: G.Todd
Safety Officer: J Watt
Press Officer:Q.Edwards

FOOTBALL MANAGEMENT TEAM

Manager: Alan Pridham
Assistant Manager: Gary Smart
Physios: Dave Lukins

FACT FILE

Founded: 1889
Nicknames: The City or The Romans
Midweek home matchday: Tuesday
Colours: Black & white stripes/black/b & w
Change: All yellow
Youth League: South West Counties
Ladies Team: Yes
Unofficial Club Website:www.bathcityfc,com
2001-02
Captain: Gary Thorne
Top scorer: Adrian Foster 21
P.o.Y.: Gary Thorne

Kick-off 3pm
Tuesday
1st January

Newport
Isle of Wight

Season 2001/2002 Issue 15 £1.50

Pages: 48   Price £1.50

Editor: Chris Stillman
Tel: 01761 433528

GROUND Twerton Park, Twerton, Bath Avon BA2 1DB. Tel: 01225 423087/313247 Fax: 01225481391 Email Address: ofice@bathcityfc .freeserve,co,uk:
Directions: Twerton Park is situated on the A4/A36 Lower Bristol Road - on theBristol side of Bath City Centre (Approx 2.5 miles). The area is serviced byJ18 on the M4. From the centre of Bath the bus route is No.5 - Twerton HighStreet
Capacity: 8,840   Seated: 1,017   Covered Terracing: 4,800
Clubhouse: Several bars open all week and full service with menu on match-days catering
for up to 250 people   Club Shop: Contact MrM.Brush

PREVIOUS   **Grounds:** The Belvoir Ground, Lambridge 1889-1932
Leagues: Southern League, Vauxhall Conference

CLUB RECORDS   **Attendance:** 18,020 v Brighton & Hove Albion, FA Cup.
Defeat: 9-0 Yeovil Town 46-47   **Victory:** 8-0 v Boston United 98-99
Career goalscorer: Paul Randall.   **Career appearances:** David Mogg (530)
Transfer fee paid: £15,000 for Micky Tanner from Bristol City
Transfer fee received: £80,000 for Jason Dodd from Southampton

BEST SEASON   FA Cup: Third Round 63-64, 0-3 v Bolton W. (A) after 1-1: 93-94   FA Trophy: 4th Round, 89-90
HONOURS   Southern League Champions 59-60, 77-78; R-up 29-33, 61-62, 89-90; Southern League Cup 78-79;
Somerset Premier Cup 51-52, 52-53, 57-58, 59-60, 65-66, 69-70, 77-78, 80-81, 81-82, 83-84, 84-85, 85-86, 88-89, 89-90, 93-
94, 94-95;Anglo-Italian Cup R-up 76-77, 77-78
Players progressing: Alan Skirton (Arsenal),Tony Book (Plymouth A.), Kenny Allen (Bournemouth), Peter Rogers (Exeter C.), R Bourne (Torquay),
Martyn Rogers (Exeter City)Dave Wiffil (Manchester C.), , Brian Wade (Swindon Town), Jeff Meacham (Bristol R.), Martin Hirst (BristolC.), Paul
Bodin (Swindon), Graham Withey (Coventry), Jason Dodd (Southampton), Paul Adcock (Torquay)

Back row,left to right: Lee Vickerman, Jamie Gosling, Graham Maclean, Clinton Green, Gary Thorne, Paul Donnelly, Jamie Mills, Kark Keen, Jamie Crandon, Marco Milciche. **Middle row:** Terry Hardwell (physio), Dave Burns (Coach), Ian Harvey, Nigel Gillard, Mark Hervin, Paul Milsom, Liam Bull, Colin Towler, Brad Thomas, James Zabek, Gary Powell, Andy Eisentrager (Coach) . **Front row:** John Forster, Roy Pitman, Mike Hughes, Geoff Todd, Stephen Hall, Frank Entwistle, Alan Pridham, Andrew Pierce, Phil Weaver and Quentin Edwards.

SOUTHERN LEAGUE PREMIER DIVISION

Date	Comp.	Opponents	Att.	Score	Goalscorers
18.08	DM P	CHELMSFORD CITY	828	1 - 1	Dobinson 60[og]
21.08	DM P	Weymouth	930	0 - 0	
25.08	DM P	Moor Green	359	0 - 0	
27.08	DM P	HAVANT & WATERLOOVILLE	743	2 - 5	Foster 72, Wyatt 90
01.09	DM P	CAMBRIDGE CITY	563	1 - 1	Bartlett 86
03.09	DM P	Newport County	902	0 - 1	
08.09	DM P	ILKESTON TOWN	620	1 - 1	Zabek 53
11.09	DM P	Crawley Town	762	0 - 3	
15.09	DM P	Tamworth	689	1 - 1	Foster 20
18.09	DM P	WEYMOUTH	710	2 - 1	Gosling 23, Foster 35
22.09	DM P	Kettering Town	1418	0 - 0	
29.09	FA Cup Q2	BIDEFORD	765	1 - 3	Powell 42
06.10	DM P	HEDNESFORD TOWN	413	3 - 4	Williams 12, Foster 38 66
09.10	DM P	NEWPORT COUNTY	708	2 - 1	Foster 26, Thomas 63
13.10	DM P	MOOR GREEN	579	0 - 2	
20.10	DM P	Cambridge City	433	3 - 1	Wooding 11[og], Milsom 18, Gosling 42[p]
23.10	DM P	CRAWLEY TOWN	612	1 - 2	Thomas 58
03.11	FA Trophy 1	NEWPORT COUNTY	877	2 - 3	Foster 21, Gosling 86[p]
06.11	DM P	Hinckley United	313	2 - 2	Milsom 13, Thorne 90[p]
10.11	DM P	MERTHYR TYDFIL	629	4 - 2	Milsom 5, Foster 37 80, Gosling 42
12.11	Lge Cup 1	Newport County	333	3 - 1	Foster 7 16 40
17.11	DM P	Salisbury City	455	1 - 0	Milsom 88
24.11	DM P	KING'S LYNN	650	0 - 1	
26.11	Som. PC 2	Bristol City	332	1 - 0	Harvey 101
08.12	DM P	KETTERING TOWN	899	0 - 1	
11.12	Lge Cup 2	CINDERFORD TOWN	201	3 - 1	Zabek 23, Drysdale 27 37
15.12	DM P	Ilkeston Town	577	3 - 3	Thorne 19, Thomas 33, Milsom 48
26.12	DM P	Havant & Waterlooville	586	0 - 3	
29.12	DM P	Welling United	518	0 - 4	
05.01	DM P	HINCKLEY UNITED	622	1 - 2	Hopkins 89[p]
12.01	DM P	Chelmsford City	609	3 - 1	Gosling 26, Collier 87, Williams 90
19.01	DM P	TAMWORTH	787	1 - 2	Davis 49
22.01	Lge Cup 3	DORCHESTER TOWN	262	0 - 2	
02.02	DM P	Stafford Rangers	483	1 - 2	Williams 53
05.02	DM P	NEWPORT IOW	498	0 - 1	
09.02	DM P	Folkestone Invicta	341	1 - 1	Milsom 44
12.02	DM P	WELLING UNITED	496	2 - 1	Milsom 68, Cleverley 86
16.02	DM P	Hednesford Town	639	0 - 1	
19.02	Som. PC QF	MANGOTSFIELD UNITED	243	3 - 2	Drysdale 45, McLean 60, Foster 65
02.03	DM P	TIVERTON TOWN	958	4 - 2	Gilroy 20, Milsom 21, Foster 25, Thorne 35
09.03	DM P	Merthyr Tydfil	736	1 - 3	Foster 90
16.03	DM P	STAFFORD RANGERS	639	4 - 3	Harvey 39, Gilroy 60[p], Thorne 86, Foster 90
23.03	DM P	King's Lynn	647	1 - 1	Foster 31
30.03	DM P	WORCESTER CITY	718	4 - 0	Drysdale 35[p], Cleverley 55, Thorne 57, Foster 90
01.04	DM P	Tiverton Town	860	1 - 3	Drysdale 65[p]
06.04	DM P	SALISBURY CITY	697	1 - 0	Emms 34[og]
09.04	Som. PC SF	Clevedon Town	287	0 - 1	
13.04	DM P	Newport IOW	683	1 - 2	Harvey 66
20.04	DM P	FOLKESTONE INVICTA	899	2 - 0	Foster 55, Cleverley 75
27.04	DM P	Worcester City	1224	1 - 0	Foster 21

PLAYING SQUAD

Goalkeepers: Mark Hervin (Clevedon T), Ray Johnston (Bishops Sutton)
Defenders: Andy Williams (Swindon T), Gary Kemp (Newport Co), Andy Minturn (Cirencester), Gary Thorne (Newport Co), Jason Drysdale (Aberystwyth T), Chris Honor (Basingstoke), Mike Trought (Bristol R)
Midfield: Jamie Gosling (Team Bath), Jim Rollo (Merthyr Tydfil), Iain Harvey (Clevedon T), Joe Collins (Paulton R), Marco Micciche (Clevedon T), Gary Horgan (Cirencester), Wayne Cleverley (Swindon T)
Forwards: Frankie Bennett (Weston-S-M), Adrian Foster (Forest Green), Jamie Crandon (Paulton R), Neal Bartlett (Army), Paul Milsom (Clevedon T)

CAMBRIDGE CITY

Welcome to Milton Road home of

Cambridge City Football Club
Formed in 1908 - 94th season   *2002/3 Season*

CLUB OFFICIALS
Chairman: Denis Rolph
President: Sir Neil Westbrook, CBE MA FRICS
Secretary: Stuart Hamilton
1 Parsonage Close, Highfield
Caldicote,Cambridge
Tel No: 01954 212602
email: stuartcambridgecityfc.com
Press Officer: Secretary

FACT FILE
Formed: 1908
Nickname: Lilywhites
Sponsors: Lancer UK
Colours:White /black/ white. Change All Sky
Midweek matchday: Tuesday
Reserves' League: Eastern Counties
Website: www.cambridgecityfc.com

2001-02
Captain: darren Collins
P.o.Y.: Adam Wilde
Top Scorer: Kevin Wilkin 15

FOOTBALL MANAGEMENT TEAM
Manager: David Batch
Asst. Manager: Andy Kirkup
Physio: Damion Doyle

Dr Martens League - Premier Division

City v Halesowen Town
Vol 6   *Issue 05*   Saturday 14 September - Kick off 3pm   £1.50

Main Club Sponsors
LANCER

GROUND	City Ground, Milton Road, Cambridge CB4 1UY Tel: 01223 357973
Directions:	Fifty yards on left from start of A1309, Cambridge to Ely Rd. (Behind Westbrook Centre). Thirty minutes walk from Cambridge BR
Capacity:	5,000 Cover: 1,400 Seats:533 Floodlights: Yes
Clubhouse:	11am-11pm Mon-Sat, 12-3 & 7pm-10.30 Sun. Bingo, Dances, Pool, Darts
Club Shop:	Sells programmes, club history, badges, scarves, pennants, replica shirts Contact Neil Harvey (01223 235991)

Pages: 48   Price: £1.50
Editor: Secretary
Local Press: Cambridge Evening News
Local Radio: BBC Radio Cambridge

PREVIOUS   **Leagues:** Bury & Dist. 08-13 19-20, East Anglian 08-10, Southern Olympian 11-14, Southern Amateur 1913-35, Spartan 35-50, Athenian 50-58   **Name:** Cambridge Town 1908-51

CLUB RECORDS   **Attendance:** 12,058 v Leytonstone, FA Amateur Cup 1st Rd, 1949-50
Scorer: Gary Grogan   **Appearances:** Mal Keenan
Fee Paid: £8,000 for Paul Coe (Rushden & Diamonds)   **Fee Received:**£100,000 from Millwall for Neil Harris 1998

BEST SEASON   **FA Amateur Cup:** Semi Final 27-28   **FA Trophy:** 2nd Rd. 86-87 87-88
FA Cup: 1st Rd; v Ashford 66, v Swindon 46, v Walthamstow Ave. 48, v Hereford 93, v Wigan Ath. 99

HONOURS   Southern Lg 62-63 (R-up 70-71, Southern Div 85-86, Div 1 R-up 69-70, Champ Cup62-63; E Anglian Cup (9); Eastern Prof Floodlit Lg 65-66 72-73, Cambs Prof Cup(6); Cambs Invitation Cup (7); Spartan Lg 47-48 48-49 (R-up 49-50); EasternDiv Champs 45-46); Southern Amat Lg 20-21 27-28 28-29 30-31 31-32; Bury & Dist.Lg (4); E Anglian Lg (6); AFA Snr Cup 30-31 46-47 47-48(shared) 48-49 49-50;AFA Invitation Cup 50-51; Hunts Prem Cup 62-63 64-65; Suffolk Sen Cup 09-10; Addenbrookes Hosp Cup 87-88; The Munns Youth Cup 82-83 83-84 84-85; ChilternYouth Lge Cup R-up 75-76; South Mids Lg Youth Trophy 82-83; Robinson Cup 87-8889-90; Jim Digney 89-90; Essex & Herts Youth Lg 89-90 Southern Lg Cup R-up 98-9

Players progressing: K Wright (West Ham 46), A Gallego(Norwich 47), A Stokes (Watford 61), D Weddle (Middlesbrough 61), D Hicksen(Bury 62), B Harvey (Blackpool 62), R Whitehead (Darlington 62), G Cummins(Hull 62), R Pearce (Peterborough 63), A Banks (Exeter 63), T Carroll (Ipswich66), Dominic Genovese (Peterborough 88), Roy Jones (Swindon), Winston Dubose(Oldham), K Wilkin (Northampton Tn 91), S Flack (Cardiff City 95), D Hedcock(Sheffield Wed 96), Neil Harris (Millwall 1998), Tesfaye Bramble, Shane Wardley (Southend United)

Back row left to right: Martin Fox, Kevin Wilkin, Matt Nurse, Andy Taylor and Tim Wooding
Front row: John O'Flynn, Matt Hann, Steve Wenlock (Captain), Adam Wilde, Chris Tovey (Player Manager) and Jon Challinor.

SOUTHERN LEAGUE PREMIER DIVISION

Date	Comp.	Opponents	Att.	Score	Goalscorers
18.08	DM P	MOOR GREEN	321	0 - 1	
20.08	DM P	Chelmsford City	567	3 - 0	Chillingworth 31, Fox 82[p], Wilde 89
25.08	DM P	Hinckley United	402	2 - 2	Chillingworth 22 72
27.08	DM P	KETTERING TOWN	764	2 - 1	Wilkin 37, O'Flynn 86
01.09	DM P	Bath City	563	1 - 1	Wilkin 34
03.09	DM P	FOLKESTONE INVICTA	467	0 - 0	
08.09	DM P	MERTHYR TYDFIL	316	2 - 2	Wilkin 17, Wilde 25
11.09	DM P	Welling United	465	4 - 4	Challinor 15, Chillingsworth 34, Wilkin 82 85
15.09	DM P	Weymouth	724	2 - 4	Wilkin 59, Chillingsworth 71
17.09	DM P	CRAWLEY TOWN	349	0 - 1	
22.09	DM P	Newport County	669	2 - 2	Chillingsworth 42 78
29.09	FA Cup Q2	Dunstable Town	225	3 - 2	Wenlock 16, Taylor 85 87
05.10	DM P	CHELMSFORD CITY	767	1 - 1	Holden 80 F
09.10	DM P	Folkestone Invicta	268	0 - 1	
13.10	FA Cup Q3	Chesham United	436	1 - 0	O'Flynn 83
20.10	DM P	BATH CITY	433	1 - 3	Nacca 37
22.10	DM P	WELLING UNITED	276	2 - 0	Fox 2[p], King 65
27.10	FA Cup Q4	Hucknall Town	593	1 - 1	O'Flynn 11
29.10	FA Cup Q4 R	HUCKNALL TOWN	598	3 - 1	Wilkin 3 34, Pope 84
03.11	FA Trophy 1	GLOUCESTER CITY	289	4 - 1	Wilkins 35, Challinor 44, Fox 69, Pope 72
10.11	DM P	Worcester City	1054	2 - 1	Wilkin 15, Wilde 76
13.11	Lge Cup 1	Stamford	134	0 - 1	
17.11	FA Cup 1	Exeter City	2849	0 - 3	
24.11	DM P	WEYMOUTH	649	2 - 2	Wilkin 68, Holden 73
01.12	FA Trophy 2	Banbury United	486	2 - 0	Hann 50, Wilkin 76
08.12	DM P	Tamworth	753	2 - 2	Hann 10, Wilkin 39
15.12	DM P	Newport IOW	354	0 - 1	
22.12	Cambs IC P	NEWMARKET TOWN	113	7 - 1	Fox 31, Hann 44, Wilde 62, Wilkin 65 82, Wignall 68, Nightingale 90
26.12	DM P	Kettering Town	1957	2 - 1	Wilkin 12, Essendoh 45
29.12	DM P	Havant & Waterlooville	613	1 - 4	Wilde 5
08.01	Cambs IC QF	COTTENHAM UNITED	185	3 - 0	Wilkin 53, Nightingale 63 89
12.01	FA Trophy 3	HENDON	404	1 - 1	Wooding 83
19.01	DM P	KING'S LYNN	758	2 - 1	Fox 23, Gutzmore 76
26.01	DM P	Merthyr Tydfil	511	3 - 1	Essandoh 27, Nightingale 69 85
02.02	FA Trophy 3 R	Hendon	281	0 - 2	St Albans City
09.02	DM P	Tiverton Town	734	0 - 5	
12.02	DM P	HINCKLEY UNITED	309	3 - 2	Essandoh 42, Fox 55[p], Challinor 74
16.02	DM P	WORCESTER CITY	416	0 - 2	
02.03	DM P	Crawley Town	1165	3 - 4	Wilkin 15 53, Beale 51
05.03	DM P	ILKESTON TOWN	293	1 - 1	Gutzmore 80
09.03	DM P	Salisbury City	393	1 - 1	Wilde 50
12.03	Cambs IC SF	Ely City	131	0 - 2	
16.03	DM P	TIVERTON TOWN	437	1 - 3	Wilde 49
19.03	DM P	NEWPORT COUNTY	477	1 - 2	Beale 1
23.03	DM P	Moor Green	347	2 - 1	Fox 55[p], Holden 59
26.03	DM P	SALISBURY CITY	273	1 - 3	Wooding 89
30.03	DM P	NEWPORT IOW	331	2 - 0	Wilde 24 79
01.04	DM P	King's Lynn	818	1 - 1	Wilde 62
06.04	DM P	Hednesford Town	609	1 - 1	Skelly 10
09.04	DM P	STAFFORD RANGERS	265	1 - 1	Wilde 79
13.04	DM P	TAMWORTH	617	1 - 1	Essandoh 14
15.04	DM P	Ilkeston Town	452	1 - 1	Wilkin 89
20.04	DM P	Stafford Rangers	767	0 - 3	
23.04	DM P	HEDNESFORD TOWN	440	2 - 1	Hann 65, Nightingale 80
27.04	DM P	HAVANT & WATERLOOVILLE	660	2 - 1	Wilde 14, Holden 16

PLAYING SQUAD

Goalkeepers: Martin Davies (Llanelli), Nicky Rust (Braintree T), Matt Nurse (Leicester C)
Defenders: Tim Wooding (Boston Utd), Russell Flitton (Mildenhall), Richard Skelly (Chelmsford C), Jack Wignall (Dagenham & Red), Colin Vowden (Dover Ath), Steve Holden (Stevenage B), Andy Pincher (Chelmsford C)
Midfield: Adam Wilde (Cambridge Utd), Che Wilson (Bristol R), Billy Beall (Leyton Orient), Louis Evans (King's Lynn), Matty Clements (King's Lynn)
Forwards: Rob Nightingale (Youth), Leon Gutzmore (Braintree T), Darren Collins (Kettering), Kevin Wilkin (Nuneaton B)

CHELMSFORD CITY

CLUB OFFICIALS

Chairman: **Peter Stroud**
Tel: 01245 471917(H) 07900 228800M)

Secretary: **David Selby**
34 Paddock Drive,Chelmsford CM1 6SS
Tel 01245 464922

FACT FILE
Formed: 1938
Nickname: City or 'The Clarets'
Sponsors:Countryside Properties Plc
Colours: Claret with white trim/white/claret
Change colours: All white with claret trim
Midweek matches : Monday
Club Website: www.chelmsfordcityfc.com

FOOTBALL MANAGEMENT TEAM

Manager: Paul Parker

2000-01
Captain: Brett Girling
Top Scorer: Steve Portway 43
P.o.Y: Gary Bennett

GROUND

Ground Share with Billericay Town
New Lodge, Blunts Wall Road, Billericay CM12 9SA Tel: 01277 652188

Directions: From Shenfield (A129) right at 1st lights then 2nd right. FromBasildon (A129) over 1st lights in town, then left at next lights and 2nd right. Half mile from Billericay (GER) station (London Liverpool St. - Southend line). Ground 5 mins walk from buses 222, 251, 357, 255, 551
Capacity: 3,500   Seats: 424   Cover: 600   Floodlights: Yes
Clubhouse: Open eves 8-11pm (except Mon),1pm-11pm Sat & w/e lunch noon-2.30pm.
Club Shop: Sells progs, badges, scarves, mugs etc. Contact Helen Williams via club

Pages: 52   Price: £1.50
Editor: Trevor Smith (01473 824782)

Local Press: Essex Chronicle,
Chelmsford Weekly News,
East Anglian Daily Times, Evening Gazette
Local Radio: Essex Radio/Breeze AM,
BBC Essex, Chelner FM

PREVIOUS   **Leagues:** None   **Grounds:** New Whittle Street 38-97, Maldon Town 97-98
                 Name: None (Brentwood Town were incorporated in 1970)
CLUB RECORDS   **Attendance:** 16,807 v Colchester, Southern League 10/9/49
                 Goalscorer: Tony Butcher, 287 (1957-71)   **Appearances:** Derek Tiffin, 550 (1950-63)
                 Win: 10-1 v Bashley (H) Dr Martens Leagu 26/4/2000
                 Defeat: 2-10 v Barking (A), FA Trophy, 11/11/78
                 Fee Paid: £10,000 for Tony Rogers (Dover Athletic, 1992)   **Fee Received:** £50,000 for David Morrison (Peterborough 94)
BEST SEASON   **FA Cup:** 4th Rd, 1938-39 (v Birmingham City). 1st Rd 26 times
                 FA Trophy: Semi-final 69-70 v Telford Utd
HONOURS   Southern Lg 45-46 67-68 71-72 (R-up 48-49 60-61 63-64 65-66); Southern Div 88-89, R-up 97-98, Lg Cup 45-46 59-60 (R-up 60-61); Merit Cup 71-72; Southern Lg War-Time (East) 39-40); Essex Prof Cup 5; Essex Snr Cup 85-86 88-89 92-93;
        Non-League Champs Chall Cup 71-72; E Anglian Cup 48-49; Eastern Co's Lg(3) 46-49(Lg Cup 59-60); Eastern F'lit Comp 6,
   (Cup 72-73 74-75); Metropolitan Lg 67-68, Lg Prof Cup 67-68, Autumn Shield 70-71; Essex Snr Lg Cup 84-85; Harry Fisher Mem. Tphy 88-89
Players progressing: G Merton (Watford 48), G Adams (Orient 49), W O'Neill(Burnley 49), B Farley/S McClellan/L Dicker/P Collins (Spurs 49/49/51/68), O Hold (Everton 50), R Marden (Arsenal 50), C McCormack (Barnsley 50), D Sexton(Luton 51), W Bellet & R Mason & A Nicholas (Orient 61 & 63 & 65), R Gladwin(Norwich 66), B King (Millwall 67), J O'Mara (Bradford City 74), N Spink (Aston77), M Dziadulewicz (Wimbledon 79), M Cawston (Southend 84), P Coleman (Exeter84), J Keeley & A Owers (Brighton 86 & 87), I Brown (Bristol C 93), D Morrison (Peterborough 94)

Back ,left to right: Nicky Gyuory, Ian Wiles, Richard Hurst, Mick Riutherford and Gary Cross
Front row: Ansah Owusa, Steve Saunders, Brian Statham, Junior Samuels, Sam Keevel , Phil Gray.

SOUTHERN LEAGUE PREMIER DIVISION

Date	Comp.	Opponents	Att.	Score	Goalscorers
18.08	DM P	Bath City	828	1 - 1	Lewis 90
20.08	DM P	CAMBRIDGE CITY	567	0 - 3	
25.08	DM P	TAMWORTH	491	1 - 1	Samuels 16
27.08	DM P	Crawley Town	1050	3 - 3	Hockton 66, McCarthy 81, Dobinson 87
01.09	DM P	Hinckley United	455	0 - 2	
03.09	DM P	KING'S LYNN	454	2 - 2	Hockton 31[p] 73[p]
08.09	DM P	NEWPORT COUNTY	602	3 - 1	McCarthy 25, Dobinson 36 43
11.09	DM P	Newport IOW	423	3 - 0	Williamson 33, Dobinson 62, Hockton 75
15.09	DM P	Hednesford Town	627	2 - 1	Bishop 2, Cambridge 59
17.09	DM P	FOLKESTONE INVICTA	627	2 - 1	Hockton 5, Lee 54
22.09	DM P	TIVERTON TOWN	705	2 - 2	Cambridge 1, Hockton 24
29.09	FA Cup Q2	Braintree Town	1093	1 - 0	Dobinson 17
05.10	DM P	Cambridge City	767	1 - 1	Samuels 50
09.10	DM P	King's Lynn	684	0 - 3	
14.10	FA Cup Q3	HARLOW TOWN	835	1 - 1	Lee 90
17.10	FA Cup Q3 R	Harlow Town	636	0 - 3	
20.10	DM P	ILKESTON TOWN	517	6 - 1	Hockton 44 53 77, Lee 57, Bishop 59, Cambridge 73
22.10	DM P	NEWPORT IOW	536	3 - 0	Hockton 4 39[p], Cross 53
27.10	DM P	Moor Green	317	1 - 3	Lee 87
03.11	FA Trophy 1	Gravesend & Northfleet	829	0 - 2	
10.11	DM P	SALISBURY CITY	454	3 - 2	Lee 9 50, Adams 17
13.11	Lge Cup 1	Ashford Town	179	0 - 1	
17.11	DM P	Weymouth	883	1 - 2	Samuels 25
24.11	DM P	CRAWLEY TOWN	788	2 - 2	Williamson 56, Wall 61
26.11	Essex SC 3	HORNCHURCH	169	6 - 0	Skelly 40, Williamson 45 67, Samuels 68, Bower 77[og], Cross 88
08.12	DM P	Salisbury City	379	3 - 1	Skelly 7, Cambridge 27, Hockton 77
15.12	DM P	STAFFORD RANGERS	602	0 - 0	
26.12	DM P	Folkestone Invicta	358	1 - 2	Wall 85
29.12	DM P	Kettering Town	1461	2 - 4	Gough 27, Cambridge 79
05.01	DM P	Merthyr Tydfil	481	1 - 3	Cross 66
12.01	DM P	BATH CITY	609	1 - 3	Hockton 75
15.01	Essex SC 4	Concord Rangers	118	2 - 0	Hockton 40, Cambridge 85
19.01	DM P	Stafford Rangers	598	1 - 2	Gough 47
28.01	DM P	WEYMOUTH	380	2 - 1	Gough 47, Girling 62
02.02	DM P	HEDNESFORD TOWN	535	1 - 1	Cambridge 50
11.02	Essex SC QF	LEYTON	177	3 - 0	Williamson 32, Tovey 49, Samuels 58
16.02	DM P	Welling United	654	4 - 2	Cambridge 36, Wiles 69, Dobinson 89, Hockton 90
23.02	DM P	MERTHYR TYDFIL	484	2 - 1	Cambridge 57, Samuels 83
09.03	DM P	Worcester City	811	1 - 1	Hockton 57
12.03	DM P	Havant & Waterlooville	394	1 - 4	Cross 86
16.03	DM P	Ilkeston Town	510	3 - 3	Dobinson 41, Wiles 55, Lewis 67
20.03	Essex SC SF	CANVEY ISLAND	307	2 - 3	Cambridge 19 57
23.03	DM P	HAVANT & WATERLOOVILLE	520	0 - 3	
25.03	DM P	MOOR GREEN	462	0 - 2	
30.03	DM P	Tamworth	1237	0 - 1	
01.04	DM P	KETTERING TOWN	707	0 - 2	
06.04	DM P	WORCESTER CITY	584	2 - 1	Lee 13, Samuels 86
13.04	DM P	Tiverton Town	691	1 - 0	Cambridge 8
20.04	DM P	HINCKLEY UNITED	619	0 - 2	
22.04	DM P	WELLING UNITED	573	1 - 2	Cambridge 62[p]
27.04	DM P	Newport County	804	0 - 3	

PLAYING SQUAD

Goalkeepers: Richard Hurst (St Albans C)

Defenders: Brian Statham (Chesham Utd), Nick Gyoury (Enfield), Simon Clarke (Hendon), Garry Cross (Slough T), Ian Wiles (Heybridge Swifts), Ian Cousins (Burnham Ramblers)

Midfield: Russell Williamson (Southend), Keith Sharman (Crawley T), Sam Keevill (Slough)

Forwards: Kris Lee (Heybridge Swifts), Tony Samuels (Boreham Wood), Phil Gray (Oxford Utd)

CHIPPENHAM TOWN

CLUB OFFICIALS
President: Doug Webb
Chairman: Malcolm Lyus
Vice-Chairman: T.B.A.
Treasurer: Richard Terrell
Press Officer: Chris Blake
Commercial Manager: Sue Evans
Secretary: Chris Blake, 28 Sadlers Mead,
Chippenham, Wilts SN15 3PB
Tel: 01249 658212

FOOTBALL MANAGEMENT TEAM

Manager: Tommy Saunders
Physio: Barnes Sports Clinic

FACT FILE
Formed: 1873
Nickname: The Bluebirds
Club Sponsors: D.L.Windows, Costcutters,
Shoestrings, Crane Merchandising Systems,
Club colours: All Navy blue
Change colours:All white or All yellow
Midweek matches: Wednesday
email: chris.banks@westbrake.com

2001-02
Captain: Grantley Dicks
P.o.Y.: Shane Andrews
Leading Scorer: Matt Rawlins 22

GROUND
Hardenhuish Park, Bristol Road, Chippenham
Tel: 01249 650400
Website: www.chippenhamtownfc.co.uk

Pages: 32   Price: £1.00
Editors: Will Hulbert & Chris Blake

Local Press: Chippenham News,
Wilts Gazette, Wiltshire Chronicle

Directions: M4 jct 17, A350 into Chippenham, follow signs for Trowbridge/Bath until r'about, left onto A420 into town, ground 800yds on left 15 mins walk from railway station on main A420 Bristol Road
Capacity: 4,000   Seats: 300   Cover: 1,000   Floodlights: Yes
Clubhouse: Yes, open matchdays. Food available   **Club Shop:** Yes

PREVIOUS   **Leagues:** Hellenic, Wiltshire Senior, Wiltshire Premier, Western League
    Grounds: Westmead, Lowden, Little George Lane, Malmesbury Rd

RECORD   **Gate:** 4,800 v Chippenham Utd, Western League 1951
    Goalscorer: Dave Ferris   **Appearances:** Ian Monnery

BEST SEASON FA Cup: 1st Rd 51-52   **FA Vase:** Finalists 99-00
HONOURS   F.A. Vase R-up 99-00, Western Lg 51-52 R-up 00-01, Div 1 80-81, Div 2 52-53 (Res) 80-81. Wilts Senior Cup; Wilts Senior League; Les Phillips Cup (Western Lg Cup) 99-00 00-01, Wilts Premier Shield 2001-02. Dr Martens Division 1 Western Division: Runners-Up 2001-02

Back row, left to right: Mark Badman, Tom Gould, Dave Godley, Paul Thompson, Adie Mings, Mark Robinson and Matt Rawlings. Middle row: John Lock (Physio), Steve King, Giles Harris, Simon Charity, Steve Brown, Mark Harrington, Wayne Thorne, Paul Hunt, Andy Pitman, Paul Trace (Kit) aned Tony Godwin (Kit). Front Row: Juliano. Steve Tweddle, Gareth Davies, Tommy Saunders, Shane Andrews, Colin Towler, Nolan Pierre .
Photo: Sunday Independant

SOUTHERN LEAGUE PREMIER DIVISION

Date	Comp.	Opponents		Att.	Score	Goalscorers
18.08	DM West	Bilston Town	258	2 - 1		Hunt 6, Rawlins 75
22.08	DM West	CINDERFORD TOWN	619	0 - 0		
25.08	DM West	HALESOWEN TOWN	592	2 - 2		Tweddle 15[p] 65
27.08	DM West	Swindon Supermarine	570	3 - 0		Tweddle 24 46, Brown 80
01.09	FA Cup P	Shepton Mallet Town	271	1 - 1		Bright 20
05.09	FA Cup P R	SHEPTON MALLET TOWN	247	3 - 0		Own-Goal Dix Rawlins ??
08.09	DM West	Solihull Borough	279	1 - 0		Tweddle 72
12.09	DM West	MANGOTSFIELD UNITED	525	3 - 0		Rudge 29, Charity 62, Brown 69
15.09	FA Cup Q1	FROME TOWN	625	3 - 0		Bright 15, Rawlins 55, Mings 66
22.09	DM West	EVESHAM UNITED	578	1 - 2		Rawkins 60
25.09	DM West	Clevedon Town	410	2 - 3		Harrington 11, Andrews 61
29.09	FA Cup Q2	St Blazey	401	1 - 3		Rawlins 17
06.10	DM West	RACING CLUB WARWICK	302	1 - 1		Charity 11
09.10	DM West	Cinderford Town	227	1 - 0		Rudge 85
13.10	DM West	SHEPSHED DYNAMO	466	4 - 0		Bent 45 71, Brown 53, Charity 90
16.10	DM West	Weston-super-Mare	271	1 - 3		Mings 13
20.10	DM West	Bloxwich United	146	4 - 1		Bent 1, Charity 7 44, Bright 86
24.10	DM West	REDDITCH UNITED	420	4 - 0		Rawlins 23 26 65, Bent 89
27.10	DM West	Gresley Rovers	394	2 - 2		Brown 53, Rawlins 75
03.11	FA Trophy 1	WALTON & HERSHAM	545	1 - 4		Rawlins 58
06.11	Wilts PS 1	Amesbury Town	140	3 - 0		Bent 37, Bright 64, Rawlins 89
10.11	DM West	BEDWORTH UNITED	425	2 - 1		Bent 5, Tweddle 60
13.11	Lge Cup 1	Mangotsfield United	328	2 - 3		Tweddle 60[p], Bright 86
17.11	DM West	BILSTON TOWN	421	2 - 0		Bent 10, Rawlins 12
24.11	DM West	Redditch United	307	3 - 1		Bent 45 47, Tweddle 63
08.12	DM West	Evesham United	221	6 - 0		Tweddle 28 47, Rawlins 34 79, Bent 52, Woods 89
15.12	DM West	CIRENCESTER TOWN	582	3 - 0		Rudge 1, Tweddle 6, Dicks 18
22.12	DM West	Halesowen Town	912	1 - 0		Rawlins 70
26.12	DM West	SWINDON SUPERMARINE	864	1 - 1		Bent 64
29.12	DM West	STOURPORT SWIFTS	500	1 - 0		Rawlins 53
09.01	Wilts PS QF	MELKSHAM TOWN	402	5 - 0		Tweddle 19[p] 56[p], Charity 53, Brown 64, Skidmore 90
12.01	DM West	CLEVEDON TOWN	1106	4 - 0		Rudge 44, Brown 45 54, Rawkins 50
19.01	DM West	Bedworth United	217	2 - 1		Brown 60, Andrews 73
29.01	DM West	Gloucester City	318	1 - 1		Tweddle 77
02.02	DM West	SUTTON COLDFIELD TOWN	420	1 - 1		Rawlins 27
09.02	DM West	Stourport Swifts	205	0 - 0		
16.02	DM West	Sutton Coldfield Town	224	2 - 1		Brown 63, Tweddle 65
23.02	DM West	GRESLEY ROVERS	553	0 - 1		
02.03	DM West	Racing Club Warwick	152	4 - 0		Brown 18, Bent 46 56, Rawlins 62
06.03	Wilts PS SF	Westbury United	n.k	1 - 0		Bent 65
09.03	DM West	ATHERSTONE UNITED	466	2 - 0		Rawlins 31, Rudge 66
16.03	DM West	WESTON-SUPER-MARE	914	1 - 1		Tweddle 17
20.03	DM West	SOLIHULL BOROUGH	542	3 - 1		Davies 30, Rudge 45, Bent 84
26.03	DM West	Rocester	104	2 - 0		Harrington 68, Tweddle 82
30.03	DM West	Mangotsfield United	537	0 - 1		
01.04	DM West	GLOUCESTER CITY	842	1 - 0		Bent 78
06.04	DM West	ROCESTER	706	4 - 0		Davies 31, Andrews 34, Dicks 51, Bent 78
13.04	DM West	Atherstone United	303	3 - 1		Charity 2, Brown 53, Bent 56
18.04	DM West	Cirencester Town	443	3 - 1		Mings 20, Brown 75, Charity 85
21.04	Wilts PS F	SWINDON TOWN	1204	4 - 0		Rudge 14, Rawlins 51, Brown 59, Bent 76
27.04	DM West	Shepshed Dynamo	292	2 - 1		Rawlins 10, Fraser 85

PLAYING SQUAD

Goalkeepers: Paul Thompson (Devizes), Ian Jones (Mangotsfield)
Defenders: Andy Pitman (Afan Lido), Colin Towler (Bath), Gareth Davies (Swindon), Grantley Dicks (Gloucester), Shane Andrews (Clevedon), Tom Gould (Team Bath), Mark Robinson (Swindon), Murray Fishlock (Woking)
Midfield: Andy Catley (Weston-S-M), Mark Badman (Bath), Mark Harrington (Bath), Wayne Thorne (Clevedon), Simon Charity (Paulton R), Will Halliwell (Southampton), Giles Harris (Clevedon)
Forwards: Steve Tweddle (Melksham), Matt Rawlins (Gloucester), Martin Paul (Newport Co), Adie Mings (Basingtoke)

CRAWLEY TOWN

THE OFFICIAL MATCHDAY PROGRAMME OF CRAWLEY TOWN

Red Devils

CLUB OFFICIALS
Chairperson: **Ms Jo Gomm**
Vice Chairman: **Dave Brown**
President: **Les Turnbull**
Secretary: **Dave Haining**
20 Irving Walk, Tilgate, Crawley RH10 5BQ
Tel: 01293 535683
Chief Executive: **John Duly**
Managing Director: **Steve Duly**

FOOTBALL MANAGEMENT TEAM
Football Team Manager: Billy Smith
Coaches: Brian Owen & Ron Wilson
Asst Man: J Broughton Physio: R Massimo

FACT FILE
Formed: 1896
Nickname: The Reds
Sponsors: Providian Bank
Colours: All red Change:All blue
Midweek matchday: Tuesday
Reserves' League: Suburban
Website: www.crawley-town-fc.co.uk

200102
Captain: Luke Anderson
P.o.Y.:Danny Carroll
Top Scorer: Danny Carroll 15

Crawley Town
versus
Newport County
SATURDAY 7th SEPTEMBER 2002 - KICK-OFF 3.00PM

£1.50

GROUND   Broadfield Stadium, Brighton Road, Crawley RH11 9RX Tel: 01293 410000

Directions: M23 exit 11, 2nd exit off roundabout, A23, towards Crawley.
Turn left at next r/about into ground

Capacity: 4,996   Cover: 4,200   Seats: 1,080   Floodlights: Yes

Clubhouse: Mon-Fri: Evenings 7-11 Sat: 12-11 Sun 12-8
Club Shop: Programmes, metal badges, hats, scarves, mugs, replica kits and other items

Pages: 36 Price: £1.50
Editors: Jim Green & Steve Duly
Tel: 01293 410000
Local Press: Crawley Observer, Crawley News,
The Argus Local Radio: Radio Mercury, BBC
Southern Counties

PREVIOUS   **Leagues:** Sussex County 1951-56; Metropolitan 56-63   **Grounds:** Malthouse Farm 1896-1914 38-40; Victoria Hall + Rectory
Fields 18-38;Yetmans Field 45-49, Town Mead 49-53 54-97, Ifield Rec Grd 53-54

CLUB RECORDS **Attendance:** 4,104 v Barnet, FA Cup 2nd Rd 4/12/93
Goalscorer: Phil Basey 108 (68-72)   **Appearances:** John Maggs 652 (63-73 75-79)
Win: 10-0 v Chichester United, Sussex Co. Lge Div 2 17-12-55 and v Crowborough A,Sussex Floodlit Cup 25-09-01
Defeat: 0-10 v Arundel (A), Sussex County Lge 09-02-52
Fee Paid: £5,000 for David Thompson (Wokingham, May 92)
Fee Received: £75,000 for Jay Lovett from Brentford ,2000.

BEST SEASON **FA Trophy:** 3rd Rd 98-99
FA Cup: 3rd Rd Proper 91-92, 0-5 v Brighton & HA (A)   League Clubs defeated: Northampton Town 91-92
HONOURS Sussex Snr Cup (2) 89-91 (R-up 58-59 95-96); Sussex I'mediate Cup 26-27,01-02Sussex Prof. Cup 69-70; Southern Lg S Div.R-up
83-84; Merit Cup 70-71;Sussex Floodlit Cup (3) 90-93; Sussex Lg Div 2 R-up 55-56; Gilbert RiceF'lit Cup 79-80 83-84; Southern Co's Comb.
Floodlit Cup 85-86; Met Lg Chal. Cup 58-59; Mid-Sussex Snr 02-03; Montgomery Cup 25-26 Sussex Floodlit Cup 98-99 Southern Lg Cup R-up:20
00-01Suburban League Southern Division Champions 2001-02

Players progressing: Ray Keeley, Graham Brown (Mansfield 68), Andy Ansah (Brentford 87), Craig Whitington (Scarborough 93),Ben Abbey
(Oxford United 99), John Mackie (Reading 99), Jay Lovett (Brentford 2000)

Back Row l to r: John Timlin, Matt Hodge, Danny Glover, Connor McCurdy, Scott Kirkwood, Stewart Holmes, Neil Le Bihan, Dave Stevens.
Middle: Steve Duly (Managing Director), Larry Rushin (Reserve Team Asst. Manager), Jason McCoy, Ben Judge, Kevin Hemsley, Marc Pullan,
Andy Little, Matt Ottley, Ellis Hooper, Danny Hockton, Nic McDonnell, Francis Vines (Reserve Team Manager), Pam Harrison (Asst. Sports
Therapist), John Duly (Chief Executive) **Front:** Ron Wilson (Goalkeeping Coach), Brian Owen (Coach), Mo Harkin, Ian Payne, Warren Bagnall,
Bill Smith (1st Team Manager), Peter Fear, Lee Doherty, Nigel Brake, John Broughton (1st Team Asst. Manager), Jimmy Bolton (Coach).

Date	Comp.	Opponents	Att.	Score	Goalscorers
18.08	DM P	HEDNESFORD TOWN	814	4 - 1	Harlow 10, Waugh 19, Holmes 62, Carroll 70
21.08	DM P	Folkestone Invicta	309	1 - 2	Collins 74
25.08	DM P	Kettering Town	1545	3 - 1	Payne 17[p], Carroll 61 85
27.08	DM P	CHELMSFORD CITY	1050	3 - 3	Sharman 20 45, Waugh 90
01.09	DM P	Tiverton Town	726	2 - 1	Carroll 20, Waugh 90
04.09	DM P	NEWPORT IOW	855	2 - 0	Dack 22, Payne 84[p]
08.09	DM P	Tamworth	642	0 - 2	
11.09	DM P	BATH CITY	762	3 - 0	Brake 29, Harlow 65, Waugh 67
15.09	DM P	STAFFORD RANGERS	1028	1 - 2	Bagnall 65
17.09	DM P	Cambridge City	349	1 - 0	Holden 72[og]
22.09	DM P	Moor Green	367	1 - 3	Dack 77
25.09	Sussex FC 1	Crowborough Athletic	220	10 - 0	Restarick 3, Bagnall 2, Harlow 3, Carroll, Collins.
29.09	FA Cup Q2	Fareham Town	410	1 - 1	Restarick 76
02.10	FA Cup Q2 R	FAREHAM TOWN	617	4 - 0	Restarick 28, Carroll 60, Bagnall 79, Harlow 88
06.10	DM P	KING'S LYNN	774	1 - 0	Harlow 60[p]
09.10	DM P	Newport IOW	356	2 - 1	Restarick 30 84
13.10	FA Cup Q3	Weymouth	831	1 - 3	Restarick 4
20.10	DM P	WEYMOUTH	1100	0 - 0	
23.10	DM P	Bath City	612	2 - 1	Carroll 1, Bagnall 12
27.10	DM P	ILKESTON TOWN	1002	2 - 0	Collins 76, Bagnall 83
30.10	Sussex FC2	NEWHAVEN	380	3 - 0	
03.11	FA Trophy 1	NEWPORT IOW	848	0 - 1	
10.11	DM P	Stafford Rangers	535	0 - 0	
13.11	Lge Cup 1	CHATHAM TOWN	386	3 - 1	Collins 59 85 90
17.11	DM P	HAVANT & WATERLOOVILLE	1260	3 - 0	Collins 2, Banall 18, Restarick 75
21.11	Sussex SC 2	Ringmer	204	1 - 0	Collins 24
24.11	DM P	Chelmsford City	788	2 - 2	Judge 22, Collins 23
01.12	DM P	WORCESTER CITY	1317	1 - 0	Carroll 1
15.12	DM P	Hednesford Town	607	0 - 0	
22.12	DM P	KETTERING TOWN	2133	0 - 2	
26.12	DM P	Welling United	675	3 - 2	Hone 64[og], Carroll 72 77
29.12	DM P	MERTHYR TYDFIL	1332	2 - 1	Thomas 71[og], Carroll 85
05.01	DM P	Weymouth	1058	2 - 1	Sharman 43, Abbey 80
08.01	Lge Cup 2	BURNHAM	415	6 - 0	Doherty 8, Carroll 45, Collins 46 65 67 70
12.01	DM P	Hinckley United	577	1 - 0	Carroll 70
15.01	Sussex SC 3	RYE & IDEN UNITED	341	4 - 0	Abbey 25, Waugh 39 46 75
19.01	DM P	WELLING UNITED	1777	2 - 4	Restarick 21 78
22.01	Lge Cup 3	ASHFORD TOWN	332	2 - 2	Bagnall 46, Waugh 87 Lost 1-4 after pens.
29.01	Sussex FC QF	RINGMER	256	2 - 0	Own-Goal 4, Collins 57
02.02	DM P	Ilkeston Town	563	0 - 0	
16.02	DM P	Merthyr Tydfil	456	2 - 2	Nabil 58, Payne 72[p]
19.02	DM P	FOLKESTONE INVICTA	856	1 - 1	Dack 55
23.02	DM P	NEWPORT COUNTY	1146	0 - 1	
02.03	DM P	CAMBRIDGE CITY	1165	4 - 3	Carroll 23 90, Payne 45[p], Judge 87
04.03	Sussex SC QF	Hastings Town	371	0 - 2	
09.03	DM P	Havant & Waterlooville	694	0 - 2	
16.03	DM P	TAMWORTH	1830	1 - 2	Judge 42
23.03	DM P	Worcester City	876	0 - 3	
30.03	DM P	TIVERTON TOWN	867	3 - 0	Collins 14 37, Stevens 87
01.04	DM P	Salisbury City	481	3 - 0	Cook 47[og], Abbey 55 66
06.04	DM P	HINCKLEY UNITED	949	1 - 0	Carroll 90
09.04	DM P	SALISBURY CITY	637	4 - 0	Doherty 58, Stevens 68 82 90
13.04	DM P	Newport County	653	1 - 1	Stevens 45
17.04	Sussex FC SF	HORSHAM YMCA	278	2 - 0	Collins 75, Payne 84[p] @ Horsham
20.04	DM P	MOOR GREEN	1021	1 - 2	Carroll 80
27.04	DM P	King's Lynn	861	2 - 2	Abbey 73, Holmes 85
29.04	Sussex FC F	Horsham	n.k	0 - 0	Lost 4-5 after pens @ Lancing

Goalkeepers: Andy Little (Banstead Ath)

Defenders: Ian Payne (Vancouver 86ers), John Ugbah (Welling Utd), Lee Doherty (Grays), Marc Pullan (Peacehaven), Stewart Holmes (Saltdean Utd), Ben Judge (Croydon)

Midfield: David Harlow (Sutton Utd), Jimmy Dack (Farnborough), Neil Le Bihan (Dover), Peter Fear (Kettering), Nigel Brake (Redhill)

Forwards: Danny Hockton (Chelmsford), Dave Stevens (Dulwich Hamlet), Marurice Harkin (Nuneaton), Robbie Collins (Redhill), Warren Bagnall (Lewes)

PLAYING SQUAD

Match Facts 2001-02

DOVER ATHLETIC

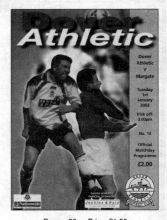

CLUB OFFICIALS
Chairman: Jim Gleeson
Directors: J.Spencer and C Harman
Secretary: D.Hmmon
c/o club 01304 822373
Commercial Manager & Press Officer:
Dave Scoggins Tel: 01304 240041

FOOTBALL MANAGEMENT TEAM
Manager: Gary Bellamy
Assistant Manager: Clive Walker
Reserve Team Manager: Steve Nolan
Physiotherapist: Shaun Roper
Club Doctor: Dr. S F Hodnett

FACT FILE

Founded: 1983
Nickname: The 'Whites'
Club Sponsors: Jenkins & Pain
Club colours:
White shirts Black shorts, white socks
Change colours:
Yellow shirts yellow shorts, yellow socks
Reserve team's league: Kent League Div. 1
Midweek home matchday: Tuesday
email: dover.athletic@virgin.net

GROUND   Crabble Athletic Ground, Lewisham Road, River, Dover, Kent. CT17 0JB
Telephone No : 01304 822373 Fax: 01304 821383
Directions: Follow the A2 from Canterbury until you pass the Forte Posthouse on your left and approach a r-about with McDonalds & petrol station on your left. Turn right signed 'Town Centre' & follow down the hill.
Capacity: 6,500   Covered Terracing: 4,900   Seats: 1,000   Floodlights: Yes

Pages: 38   Price: £1.50
Editor: Chris Collins
Tel: 01304 822373
email: dover.athletic@virgin.net

Clubhouse: Social Club open 7 days a week. Meals available.
Steward: Gavin Hughes 01304 822306.
Club Shop: At the ground. Open matchdays for general souvenirs. Contact 01304 822373

Local Press: Dover Express; Dover Mercury
Local Radio: Radio Kent; Invicta FM
Neptune Radio

PREVIOUS   **Leagues:** Kent League, Southern League, Conference
                   Grounds: None   **Names:** Dover FC
CLUB RECORDS   **Attendance:** 4,035 v Bromsgrove Rovers, Southern League April 92
                   Win: 7-0 v Weymouth 03.04.1990   **Defeat:** 1-7 v Poole Town
                   Career Goalscorer: Lennie Lee 160   **Career Appearances:** Jason Bartlett 539
                   Transfer Fees Paid: £50,000 for David Leworthy (Farnborough Town) Aug. 93
                                           Received: £50,000 for Ricky Reina (Brentford) '97
BEST SEASON   **FA Cup:** Fourth Qualifying Round x 8
                   (as Dover FC) 2nd Round 75-76 1-4 v Southend Utd. (A) League club defeated Colchester Utd.
                   FA Trophy: Semi-Final 97-98   **FA Amateur Cup:** Did not compete
                   League: 6th Conference 99-00
HONOURS   Southern League - Premier Division 89-90, 92-93; Southern Division 87-88; Championship Match 1990, 1993;
                   Premier Inter League Cup 90-91; Challenge Cup 91-92.   Kent Senior Cup 90-91, R-up 93-94, 96-97
Players progressing: Ricky Reina (Brentford) 1997

Back Row: Roy Godden, Nicky Dent, Matt Carruthers, Simon Glover, Tommy Tyne and Dave Bathgate. **Middle Row:** Robin Hastie (Kit Manager), Kristian James, Steve Norman, Nicky Humphries, Paul Hyde (Assistant Manager) Andy Arnott, Jamie Day and Ieuan Phillips (Physio).
Front Row: Mark Lovell, Lee Spiller, Tony Browne, Clive Walker (Manager), Danny Chapman, Darren Davies and Eann Readings

SOUTHERN LEAGUE PREMIER DIVISION

Date	Comp.	Opponents	Att.	Score	Goalscorers
18/08	Conf.	TELFORD UNITED	1001	0 - 1	
21/08	Conf.	Barnet	1377	0 - 2	
25/08	Conf.	Nuneaton Borough	1269	0 - 3	
27/08	Conf.	FOREST GREEN ROVERS	732	1 - 2	Scott 75
01/09	Conf.	Doncaster Rovers	2044	1 - 2	Scott 34
03/09	Conf.	HAYES	817	3 - 2	Scott 2 7, Tyne 86
08/09	Conf.	Hereford United	1541	0 - 3	
10/09	Conf.	BOSTON UNITED	882	3 - 2	Scott 24[p] 74, Tyne 90
15/09	Conf.	STALYBRIDGE CELTIC	1008	1 - 0	Scott 31[p]
18/09	Conf.	Farnborough Town	713	0 - 1	
22/09	Conf.	YEOVIL TOWN	1015	1 - 2	Elliott 43
29/09	Conf.	Morecambe	1365	1 - 2	Elliott 45
02/10	Conf.	Woking	1546	0 - 4	
06/10	Conf.	NORTHWICH VICTORIA	657	2 - 1	Scott 39 Allen 75
08/10	Conf.	DAGENHAM & REDBRIDGE	907	0 - 1	
13/10	Conf.	Scarborough	870	1 - 1	Scott 2
20/10	Conf.	Southport	863	2 - 0	Carruthers 26 Strouts 75
27/10	FA Cup Q4	HEREFORD UNITED	1221	0 - 1	
03/11	Conf.	STEVENAGE BOROUGH	1319	0 - 1	
10/11	Conf.	Leigh RMI	325	2 - 1	Strouts 22, Scott 53
17/11	Conf.	NUNEATON BOROUGH	1007	1 - 2	Scott 90
24/11	Conf.	CHESTER CITY	905	1 - 0	Tyne 62
01/12	Conf.	Telford United	974	3 - 4	Leberi 16 Scott 68,90
08/12	Conf.	SOUTHPORT	861	0 - 1	
15/12	Conf.	BARNET	1004	2 - 2	Strouts 65, Leberl 72
26/12	Conf.	Margate	3676	1 - 0	Aggrey 59
05/01	Conf.	Hayes	655	1 - 2	Day 6
12/01	FA Trophy 3	Stevenage Borough	1316	1 - 5	Norman 76
19/01	Conf.	DONCASTER ROVERS	1157	0 - 1	
29/01	Kent SC QF	Ashford Town	320	1 - 5	Frost 47
09/02	Conf.	Northwich Victoria	811	1 - 2	Kelly 64
16/02	Conf.	SCARBOROUGH	1005	0 - 2	
20/02	Conf.	Forest Green Rovers	509	1 - 2	Ramsay 32
23/02	Conf.	Dagenham & Redbridge	1510	0 - 1	
02/03	Conf.	FARNBOROUGH TOWN	1010	2 - 1	Kelly 74[og], Strouts 90
09/03	Conf.	Boston United	2042	2 - 4	Le Bihan 30, Strouts 39
16/03	Conf.	HEREFORD UNITED	952	0 - 1	
23/03	Conf.	Stalybridge Celtic	658	2 - 0	Seabury 40[p], Allen 84
25/03	Conf.	MARGATE	2325	0 - 0	
01/04	Conf.	Stevenage Borough	1604	3 - 1	Kelly 12, Carruthers 27, Le Bihan 63
06/04	Conf.	LEIGH RMI	907	0 - 0	
08/04	Conf.	WOKING	1121	2 - 2	Scott 20, Bathgate 84
13/04	Conf.	Chester City	1660	0 - 3	
20/04	Conf.	MORECAMBE	953	1 - 1	Seabury 54
27/04	Conf.	Yeovil Town	2852	0 - 2	

Goalkeepers: Paul Hyde (Leyton Orient)
Defenders: Tony Browne (Folkestone), Nick Humphries (Tonbridge), Steve Norman (St Leonards),
Andy Arnott (Stevenage), Kevin Seabury (Shrewsbury), Dean Readings (Youth), Craig Cloke (Youth)
Midfield: Jamie Day (Bournemouth), Darren Davies (Morton), Danny Chapman (Folkestone),
Lee Spiller (Chesham), Kristian James (Port Talbot), Simon Glover (Welling) , David Bathgate (Youth)
Forwards: Matt Carruthers (Folkestone), Tommy Tyne (Millwall), Roy Godden (St Leonards),
Nicky Dent (Folkestone)

FOLKESTONE INVICTA

CLUB OFFICIALS

Chairman: **Bob Dix**
President: **Bill Hewson**
Secretary: **Frank Clarke**
c/o Football club

FOOTBALL MANAGEMENT TEAM

Manager: Neil Cugley
Asst Manager: Dave Williams
Physio: Frank Clarke

FACT FILE
Founded: 1936
Sponsors: Eurotunnel (Le Shuttle)
& Silver Spring
Colours: Amber & black stripes/black/amber
Change Colours:white/blue/white
Midweek matchday: Tuesday
Reserves League: Winstonlead Kent Div 1
Club Website: www.folkestoneinvicta.co.uk

2001-02
Captain:D.G.Chapman
Leading Scorer: J.Dryden 17
P.O.Y. J.Dryden

TAMWORTH
Dr Martens League Premier Division
Saturday, April 27th, 2002 – Kick off 3.00pm

GROUND   The New Pavilion, Cheriton Road, Folkestine, Kent CT20 5JU
Tel: 01303 257461

Directions: On the A20 behind Safeway foodstore, midway between Folkestone Central &
West BR stations

Capacity: 6,500   Seats: 900   Cover: 3,500   Floodlights: Yes

Clubhouse: Yes, Stripes Club & Invicta Club
Club Shop: Yes (01303 257266)

Pages: 60   Price: £1.25
Editor: Richard Morrell (01303 276517)

Local Press: Folkestone Herald
Local Radio: Neptune Radio, Radio Light

PREVIOUS   **Ground:** South Rd, Hythe (pre-1991). Kent County Lg matches were played on council pitches
Leagues: Kent County (pre-1991-98)   **Name:**

CLUB RECORDS **Attendance:** 2,332 v West Ham Utd Friendly Nov 96
Ground Record: 7,881 Folkestone Town v Margate, Kent Snr.Cup 1958
Win: 9-0 v Crockenhill WHL Div 1   **Defeat:** 0-7 v Crockenhill WHL Div 1

BEST SEASON   **FA Vase:** Last sixteen 97-98
FA Cup: 2nd Qual Rd 95-96   Leagues Clubs Defeated: None

HONOURS   (since joining Winstonlead Kent League) Kent Lge R-up 97-98, Kent Senior Trophy R-Up 93-94, 94-95,98-99,99-00
Dr.Martens League ,Eastern Division Runners-up: 99-00 Promotion to Dr.Martens Premier Division 1999-2000

Folkestone Invicta FC 2002/3 - **Back row,** from left: Steve Hogg, Michael Everitt, Allan Tait, Steve Hafner, Steve Restarick.
Middle row: Neil Pilcher (boardroom hospitality), Dave Williams (assistant manager), Mark Towse, Tony Henry, Dave Wietecha, Paul
Egan, Jimmy Dryden, Lee Dyson, Brian Merryman (director), Bob Dix (chairman). **Front row:** Dayne Southern (kit manager), Andy
Morris, Paul Chambers, Scott Daniels, Neil Cugley (manager), Dan Larkin, Martin Chandler, Scott Lindsey, Frank Clarke (associate direc-
tor, physio, secretary and groundsman).   **Photo** courtesy of the Folkestone Herald

SOUTHERN LEAGUE PREMIER DIVISION

Date	Comp.	Opponents	Att.	Score	Goalscorers
18.08	DM P	Tiverton Town	903	0 - 2	
21.08	DM P	CRAWLEY TOWN	309	2 - 1	Chandler 4, Hogg 64
25.08	DM P	SALISBURY CITY	338	2 - 0	Dryden 43, Hogg 61
27.08	DM P	Welling United	602	4 - 2	Daniels 12, Virgo 30[p] 86[p], Hogg 73
01.09	DM P	HEDNESFORD TOWN	452	1 - 0	Curtis 46[og]
03.09	DM P	Cambridge City	467	0 - 0	
08.09	DM P	HINCKLEY UNITED	464	1 - 3	Dent 67
11.09	DM P	Havant & Waterlooville	607	2 - 2	Dent 57, Daniels 63
15.09	DM P	WORCESTER CITY	379	2 - 1	Chandler 53, Virgo 75[p]
17.09	DM P	Chelmsford City	627	1 - 2	Dryden 13
22.09	DM P	Ilkeston Town	642	1 - 2	Brown 45
29.09	FA Cup Q2	Molesey	316	3 - 1	A Hogg 34, Dent 46, Dryden 89
06.10	DM P	KETTERING TOWN	284	2 - 3	Brown 54, Dent 80
09.10	DM P	CAMBRIDGE CITY	268	1 - 0	Reina 57
13.10	FA Cup Q3	Horsham	549	2 - 1	Dryden 29 90
20.10	DM P	Stafford Rangers	696	2 - 1	Browne 15, Daniels 57
27.10	FA Cup Q4	WELLING UNITED	724	1 - 1	Dryden 10
30.10	FA Cup Q4 R	Welling United	1026	1 - 5	Hogg 28
03.11	FA Trophy 1	TIVERTON TOWN	365	0 - 1	
10.11	DM P	MOOR GREEN	333	1 - 0	Dryden 90
13.11	Lge Cup 1	Erith & Belvedere	84	2 - 1	Dent 42, Chandler 83
17.11	DM P	King's Lynn	885	2 - 0	Azzapardi 4, Dent 29
24.11	DM P	NEWPORT IOW	380	2 - 2	Dryden 29, Dent 56
27.11	DM P	HAVANT & WATERLOOVILLE	346	1 - 1	Dryden 59
08.12	DM P	Moor Green	292	0 - 2	
11.12	Lge Cup 2	Hastings Town	215	0 - 5	
15.12	DM P	TIVERTON TOWN	281	0 - 3	
18.12	Kent SC 1	TONBRIDGE ANGELS	178	2 - 1	Dryden 39 43
22.12	DM P	Salisbury City	300	0 - 2	
26.12	DM P	CHELMSFORD CITY	358	2 - 1	Morris 17, Chandler 84
29.12	DM P	Newport IOW	345	1 - 1	D G Chapman 63
05.01	DM P	KING'S LYNN	382	1 - 2	Henry 2
19.01	DM P	WEYMOUTH	424	1 - 3	Daniels 7
26.01	DM P	Worcester City	1033	1 - 1	Bower 32
02.02	DM P	MERTHYR TYDFIL	367	1 - 0	McRobert 40
09.02	DM P	BATH CITY	341	1 - 1	Morris 24
16.02	DM P	Tamworth	955	1 - 1	Dent 54
19.02	DM P	Crawley Town	856	1 - 1	Chandler 44
23.02	DM P	STAFFORD RANGERS	339	2 - 1	Dent 16, Henry 53
02.03	DM P	Hednesford Town	530	1 - 3	Dent 69
09.03	DM P	Weymouth	702	1 - 1	Virgo 24[p]
16.03	DM P	Hinckley United	320	2 - 1	Chandler 88, Dryden 90
19.03	Kent SC QF	MARGATE	314	1 - 2	Dryden 70
23.03	DM P	NEWPORT COUNTY	434	3 - 1	Chandler 28, Dryden 71, Dent 90[p]
30.03	DM P	Kettering Town	1394	1 - 2	Dryden 49
01.04	DM P	WELLING UNITED	504	0 - 0	
06.04	DM P	Merthyr Tydfil	409	0 - 1	
13.04	DM P	ILKESTON TOWN	340	0 - 2	
15.04	DM P	Newport County	526	1 - 4	Towse 8
20.04	DM P	Bath City	899	0 - 2	
27.04	DM P	TAMWORTH	1277	3 - 3	Virgo 5[p], Morris 25, Dryden 53

PLAYING SQUAD

Goalkeepers: Dave Wietecha (Tonbridge)

Defenders: Andy Larkin (Hastings), Andy Morris (Ashford T), Dan Larkin (Chatham), James Virgo (Dover), Mark Towse (Hythe Utd), Peter McCann (Erith), Scott Daniels (Dover), Anthony Henry (Lincoln)

Midfield: Martin Chandler (West Ham), Darren Winfield (Youth), Steve Hogg (St Leonards)

Forwards: Allan Tait (Deal), Ricky Reina (Ramsgate), James Dryden (Youth), Jon Ayling (Youth)

GRANTHAM TOWN

DR MARTEN'S LEAGUE – Eastern Division

Welcome to the home of...

GRANTHAM TOWN FC

2001-2002 Official Matchday Programme - £1.30

CRYSTAL   Journal *Follow Town every Friday*

PROGRAMME SPONSOR: FERSINA LINCOLNSHIRE

CLUB OFFICIALS

Chairman: **Barry Palmer**
President: **Michael Bird**

Secretary: **Pat Nixon**
72 Huntingtower Road, Grantham,
Lincs NG31 7AU
Tel: 01476 419391 FAX: 01476 419392

FOOTBALL MANAGEMENT TEAM
Manager:John Wilkinson
Asst Mgr:Tony Simmons
Physio: Nigel Marshall

FACT FILE
Formed: 1874
Nickname: Gingerbreads
Sponsors: Crystal Motors
Colours: White & Blac/black/black
Change: Orange
Midweek matchday: Tuesday
Reserve League: Central Conference
Club Website: www..granthamtownfc.co.uk
www.cheiroa.domon.co.uk/gtfc
2000-01
Captain: Adrian Sped
P.o.Y.: Dave Gilbert
Top scorer: Gary Bull

Programme: 38 pages £1.50

Local Press: Grantham Journal, Nottingham
Evening Post, Melton & GranthamTrader,
Grantham Citizen, Lincolnshire Echo
Local Radio: Radio Lincolnshire, Lincs FM

GROUND   South Kesteven Sports Stadium, Trent Road, Grantham, Lincs Tel: 01476 402224
Directions: Midway between A1 and A52 on edge of Earlesfield Industrial Estate; from A1
take A607 to Earlsfield Ind. Est and continue into Trent Rd
Capacity: 7,500   Cover: 1,950   Seats: 750   Floodlights: Yes

Clubhouse: (01476 402225) Open evenings and weekends. Bar, darts, pool etc.Frequent live
entertainment. Available for functions **Club Shop:** Programmes and a wide range of souvenirs. Contact club number.

PREVIOUS   **Leagues:** Mid Amat All, Central All. 11-25 59-61, Midland Co's 25-59 61-72,Southern Lge 72-79, Northern Prem. 79-85
                     Names: Grantham FC, pre-80. Grounds: London Rd up to 90

CLUB RECORDS Attendance: 3,695 v Southport. F.A.Trophy Quarter Final 97-98
                     Win: 13-0 vRufford Colliery (H), FA Cup Preliminary Rd 15/9/34   **Career Goalscorer:** Jack McCartney 416
                     Defeat: 0-16 v Notts County Rovers (A), Midland Amateur All. 22/10/1892   **Career Appearances:** Chris Gardiner 664
                     Transfer fee paid:undisclosed for Mario Ziccari   **Transfer fee received:** £20,000 for Gary Crosby (Notts Forest 87)

BEST SEASON   **FA Cup:** 3rd Rd 1883-84 86-87 1973-74. Comp Proper on 23 occasions
                     FA Trophy: Quarter Final 1971-72, 97-98

HONOURS   Southern Lg R-up 73-74 (Div 1 Nth) 72-73 78-79, Merit Cup 72-73), Southern Lg Mid Div Champions 97-98. Eastern Division
R-up. 2001-02 Midland Co's Lg(3) 63-64 70-72 (R-up 37-38 64-65 69-70, Lg Cup 68-69 70-71), Midland Amtr Lg10-11 (Lg Cup R-up 10-11),
Central All. 24-25 (Southern Div R-up 59-60), Lincs Snr Cup 1884-851936-37 (R-up(5) 34-36 39-40 45-47), Lincs Co. `A' Cup(3) 53-54 60-62 (R-
up 49-50 52-53 57-58), Lincs Co. Snr Cup 71-72 82-83 (R-up 80-81)

Players progressing: E Morris (Halifax 50), P Thompson/R Cooke (Peterborough 64/80), J Rayner (Notts County 64), D Dall (Scunthorpe 79),
          N Jarvis/H Wood (Scunthorpe 80), D White (Bristol Rvrs 86), T Curran (Grimsby 87), G Crosby (Nottm Forest 87),
          A Kennedy (Wrexham 87), R Wilson (Lincoln 87)

Back row left to right: Ian Wilkins, Seamus Lawless, Mario Ziccardi, Rick Wright, Danny George and Dave Gilbert.
Middle row: Peter Day (Finance Director), Paul Teare (Youth Developement Director), Matt Carvell, Migg Hogg (Coach), John Wilkinson
(Manager), Tony Simmons (Asst. man.), Nigel Marshall (Physio), Mark Foster, Chris Hall, George Freeston and Pat Nixon (Secretary).
Front row: Tim Harrison (Director), Dave Taylor, Darren Dye, Brendon McDaid, Stuart Wilson, Adrian Speed, Gary Bull, Rick Ranshaw,
Lee Marshall, Ken Healey (Commercial Director) and Barry Palmer (Chairman)   **Photo:** Dean Fardell

SOUTHERN LEAGUE PREMIER DIVISION

Date	Comp.	Opponents	Att.	Score	Goalscorers
01.08	Lincs SC 1	Gainsborough Trinity	n.k	0 - 0	Lost 4-2 after pens.
18.08	DM East	TONBRIDGE ANGELS	354	1 - 0	Marshall 54
21.08	DM East	Wisbech Town	352	6 - 0	Flanz 4[og], Neal 11, McDaid 15, Marshall 33 61, Bull 48
25.08	DM East	Burnham	142	2 - 1	Speed 89, George 90
27.08	DM East	SPALDING UNITED	475	1 - 1	Bull 6
01.09	FA Cup P	GLAPWELL	278	3 - 2	Hawley 71, Simmons 80, Marshall 82
08.09	DM East	DARTFORD	343	0 - 1	
11.09	DM East	Rugby United	237	1 - 2	Neil 65
15.09	FA Cup Q1	Stamford	456	3 - 0	Hawley 18, McDaid 23 65
22.09	DM East	Dorchester Town	597	0 - 1	
25.09	DM East	HISTON	258	1 - 1	Dye 31
29.09	FA Cup Q2	ILKESTON TOWN	568	2 - 1	Hawley 79, Ranshaw 90
06.10	DM East	BANBURY UNITED	219	4 - 1	Ranshaw 4 27 29, Speed 17
09.10	DM East	WISBECH TOWN	296	2 - 0	Bull 16, McDaid 84
13.10	FA Cup Q3	Billericay Town	642	1 - 2	Bull 45[p]
20.10	DM East	EASTBOURNE BOROUGH	344	2 - 0	Speed 65 68
23.10	DM East	RUGBY UNITED	348	6 - 0	McDaid 2, Speed 9, Ranshaw 13 73, Wilson 33 77
27.10	DM East	Hastings Town	484	3 - 1	Burt 35[og] 55[og], Marshall 72
30.10	DM East	Fisher Athletic	131	1 - 0	McDaid 41
03.11	FA Trophy 1	STAMFORD	409	1 - 0	Dye 70
10.11	DM East	ASHFORD TOWN	301	4 - 1	Speed 23, Bull 41, McDaid 57, Wilson 59
13.11	Lge Cup 1	KING'S LYNN	248	1 - 2	McDaid 82
17.11	DM East	Tonbridge Angels	326	2 - 1	Bull 32 53
20.11	DM East	Stamford	320	5 - 2	Bull 2[p] 64, Dye 42, Gilbert 84, Ranshaw 90
24.11	DM East	FISHER ATHLETIC	405	2 - 1	Gilbert 14, Speed 78
27.11	DM East	Histon	261	2 - 2	McDaid 29, Wilson 77
01.12	FA Trophy 2	FRICKLEY ATHLETIC	410	5 - 1	Wilson 26 48, Ranshaw 33, Bull 55[p], Taylor 90
08.12	DM East	Erith & Belvedere	128	3 - 0	Marshall 60, Wilson 66, McDaid 90
15.12	DM East	ST LEONARDS	348	3 - 1	Wilson 36, Speed 42, Taylor 87
29.12	DM East	Corby Town	187	1 - 0	Dye 64
05.01	DM East	Chatham Town	214	3 - 5	Bull 5 28, Ranshaw 64
12.01	FA Trophy 3	MOOR GREEN	525	2 - 1	McDaid 3, Gilbert 85
19.01	DM East	HASTINGS TOWN	635	1 - 1	Bull 47[p]
22.01	DM East	Spalding United	278	4 - 2	Bull 30[p] 40, McDaid 47, Speed 61
02.02	FA Trophy 4	CANVEY ISLAND	1222	1 - 4	Taylor 33
05.02	DM East	BURNHAM	340	3 - 2	Ranshaw 60, Wilkin 85, Bull 90[p]
09.02	DM East	Eastbourne Borough	486	0 - 4	
16.02	DM East	Bashley	201	1 - 2	Bull 16[p]
19.02	DM East	STAMFORD	376	1 - 1	Speed 18
02.03	DM East	DORCHESTER TOWN	430	1 - 0	McDaid 49
09.03	DM East	St Leonards	247	4 - 0	McDaid 46, Bull 51 57 84
12.03	DM East	SITTINGBOURNE	363	0 - 0	
16.03	DM East	Ashford Town	316	3 - 0	Wilson 23, Ranshaw 47 51
20.03	Lincs SC SF	Lincoln City	n.k	2 - 1	Bull 80, Neil 83
23.03	DM East	CHATHAM TOWN	414	6 - 1	Gilbert 26, Bull 38[p] 47[p] 73, Wilson 40, Taylor 89
26.03	DM East	Sittingbourne	197	1 - 2	McDaid 39
30.03	DM East	CORBY TOWN	406	3 - 0	Ranshaw 19 46, Gilbert 29
01.04	DM East	Rothwell Town	326	3 - 1	Ranshaw 23, Taylor 60 62
06.04	DM East	ERITH & BELVEDERE	411	4 - 2	Taylor 19 57, Bull 26 36
13.04	DM East	Dartford	283	4 - 2	Speed 25, Taylor 48, Kevin 54[og], Wilson 82
16.04	DM East	ROTHWELL TOWN	442	1 - 0	McDaid 70
20.04	DM East	BASHLEY	622	3 - 1	Ranshaw 65, Gilbert 70[p], McDaid 81
27.04	DM East	Banbury United	578	1 - 0	Ranshaw 70

Match Facts 2001-02

PLAYING SQUAD

Goalkeepers: Mario Ziccardi (Lincoln Utd)

Defenders: Adrian Speed (Holbeach), Danny George (Hinckley Utd), Darren Dye (Lincoln Utd), Ian Wilkins (Spalding), Jim Neil (Gainsborough), Matt Carvell (Gresley R), Rick Wright (Lincoln Utd), Steve Wrnlock (Cambridge C)

Midfield: Brendan McDaid (Lincoln Utd), Chris Shaw (Youth), Dave Gilbert (Spalding), Jason Minett (King's Lynn), Lee Marshall (Scunthorpe), Wayne Hallcro (King's Lynn)

Forwards: Gary Bull (Scunthorpe), Stuart Wilson (Shepshed), Rick Ranshaw (Lincoln Utd), Jamie Clarke (King's Lynn), Jon Hawley (Lincoln)

HALESOWEN TOWN

CLUB OFFICIALS
Chairman:NigelPitt
President: **Laurence Wood**
Vice Chairman: **Paul Floud**
Secretary: **Stewart Tildesley**
83 Bloomfield Street, Halesowen B63 3RF
Tel: 0121 5508443(H) 07710 434708(M)
Commercial Manager & Press
Officer:**Brendan Phillips**

FACT FILE
Formed: 1873
Nickname: Yeltz
Sponsors: T.B.A.
Newsline: 09066 555818
Colours: Blue with white trim
Change colours: White & Black
Midweek home matchday:Tuesday
Reserve's League: None

FOOTBALL MANAGEMENT TEAM

Manager: Brendan Phillips
P.o.Y.: Neil Smith
Physio: Jeff Jones

2001-02
Captain: Lee Collins
P.o.Y.: Neil Smith
Top Scorers: Leroy May 18

GROUND The Grove, Old Hawne Lane, Halesowen, West Midlands B63 3TB
FAX No: 01902 714221 Tel No: 0121 550 2179

Directions: M5 jct 3, A456 (signed Kidderminster) to 1st island turn right (signed A459 Dudley), left at next island (signed A458 Stourbridge), at next island take 3rd left into Grammar School Lane, then Old Hawne Lane - ground 400 yds on left

Capacity: 5,000 **Cover:** 1,518 **Seats:** 518 **Floodlights:** Yes
Clubhouse: (0121 602 2210) 12-2.30 & 7-11 (10.30 Sun) pm daily.Cold snacks served.
Club Shop: Sells replica strips, T-shirts, waterproof tops, coats, scarves, programmes, badges etc

Pages: 44 Price: £1.50p Editor: R Pepper
Local Press: Sports Argus, Express & Star, Birmingham Mail, Halesowen News, Stourbridge & Halesowen Chronicle
Local Radio: BBC West Midlands, B.R.M.B., Beacon

PREVIOUS **Leagues:** West Mids 1892-1905 06-11 46-86, Birmingham Comb. 11-39

CLUB RECORDS **Attendance:** 5,000 v Hendon F.A. Cup 1st Rd Proper 1954, (18,234 v Southall,1986 FA Vase Final at Wembley)
Goalscorer: Paul Joinson 369 **Appearances:** Paul Joinson 608
Win: 13-1 v Coventry Amateurs, Birmingham Senior Cup, 1956
Defeat: 0-8 v Bilston, West Midlands League, 7/4/62
Fee Paid: £7,250 for Stuart Evans (Gresley 1996)
Fee Received: £40,000 for Jim Rodwell (Rushden & Diamonds 96)

BEST SEASON **FA Vase:** Winners 84-85, 85-86 R-up 82-83 **FA Trophy:** 3rd Round Proper 94-95
FA Cup: 1st Rd 9 times: 54-55 then each season from 84-85 to 91-92

HONOURS Southern Lg Premier Div R-up 96, Southern Lg Midland Div 89-90, Western Division 01-02 W Mids Lg(5) 46-47 82-85 85-86 (R-up 64-65, Lg Cup 82-83 84-85),B'ham Snr Cup 83-84,97-98 (R-up 51-52 67-68), Staffs Snr Cup 88-89 (R-up 83-84), FA Vase (2) 84-86 (R-up 82-3) Worcs Snr Cup 51-52 61-62 (R-up 87-88), Midland Comb. Res Div 89-90

Players progressing: Arthur Proudler (Aston Villa), Cyril Spiers (Aston Villa), Billy Morris (Wolves), Dean Spink (Aston Villa), Stuart Cash (Nottm Forest), Andrew Pearce, Tim Clarke & Sean Flynn (Coventry), Dean Stokes (Port Vale), Frank Bennett (Southampton), Julian Alsop (Bristol Rovers)

Back row left to right: Colin Brookes (General Manager), Ryan Robinson-Little (Kit Manager), Tim Clarke, Andy Spencer, John Newall, Jason Burnham, Neil Smith, Ross Collins, Gary Smith, Andy Jones, Dennis Bailey, Mark Garvey and Jeff Jones (Physio).
Front row: Alex Cowley, Kelvin Phillips, Stuart Skidmore, Mark Taylor, Richard Colwell, Brendan Phillips (Manager), Lee Collins (Captain), Nigel Pitt (Chairman), Leslie Hines, Leroy May, Karl Brennan and Stuart How.

SOUTHERN LEAGUE PREMIER DIVISION

Date	Comp.	Opponents	Att.	Score	Goalscorers
18.08	DM West	GRESLEY ROVERS	479	3 - 0	Giddings 6 35 51
21.08	DM West	Sutton Coldfield Town	112	0 - 2	
25.08	DM West	Chippenham Town	592	2 - 2	Hunt 3[og], Hines 90[p]
27.08	DM West	REDDITCH UNITED	478	2 - 1	N Smith 4, May 45
01.09	FA Cup P	CHASETOWN	357	2 - 0	Hall 87, G Smith 90
08.09	DM West	Swindon Supermarine	203	1 - 0	May 82
11.09	DM West	ROCESTER	353	4 - 0	Hines 44, Anthony 48[og], R Collins 71, Giddings 86
15.09	FA Cup Q1	STAVELEY MINERS WELFARE	358	2 - 0	May 12, Giddings 83
22.09	DM West	Weston-super-Mare	233	0 - 0	
25.09	DM West	STOURPORT SWIFTS	501	3 - 0	Jones 2 87, Giddngs 83
29.09	FA Cup Q2	Moor Green	561	2 - 0	Jones 20, Hall 78
06.10	DM West	CLEVEDON TOWN	453	2 - 0	Jones 82, Giddings 84
09.10	DM West	SUTTON COLDFIELD TOWN	432	2 - 0	Hines 53[p], Hall 61
13.10	FA Cup Q3	CANVEY ISLAND	823	0 - 2	
20.10	DM West	CINDERFORD TOWN	472	1 - 2	L Collins 89
23.10	DM West	Rocester	176	1 - 1	May 53
27.10	DM West	ATHERSTONE UNITED	576	1 - 0	Jones 40
03.11	FA Trophy 1	Barrow	1126	1 - 2	Giddings 10
10.11	DM West	Cirencester Town	182	1 - 0	R Collins 77
13.11	Lge Cup 1	Bilston Town	207	0 - 1	
17.11	DM West	MANGOTSFIELD UNITED	506	1 - 1	Crawford 75
20.11	Birm SC 2	HEDNESFORD TOWN	205	2 - 0	Skidmore 18, Jones 85
24.11	DM West	Racing Club Warwick	250	0 - 0	
27.11	DM West	Stourport Swifts	258	3 - 2	Burnham 68[p] 76[p], G Smith 90
01.12	DM West	Shepshed Dynamo	240	2 - 1	Burnham 21[p], Smith 77
08.12	DM West	SHEPSHED DYNAMO	536	6 - 0	Burnham 39[p], May 55, Ross 69, Hall 87 88, G Smith 89
15.12	DM West	Gresley Rovers	496	3 - 0	Spencer 34, Hall 59, Hines 77
18.12	Worcs SC QF	Evesham United	115	1 - 1	R Collins 59
22.12	DM West	CHIPPENHAM TOWN	912	0 - 1	
26.12	DM West	Redditch United	428	3 - 1	L Collins 72, May 81, Spencer 89
29.12	DM West	Atherstone United	357	5 - 2	Bailey 2, Spencer 33 90, Smith 45, Hart 66[og]
12.01	DM West	BILSTON TOWN	619	3 - 0	Spencer 60, Burnham 64[p], Bailey 89
15.01	Birm SC 3	BIRMINGHAM CITY	532	0 - 3	
19.01	DM West	Gloucester City	476	2 - 0	Skidmore 19, Ross 69
29.01	Worcs SC QF R	EVESHAM UNITED	201	1 - 0	Burnham 45[p]
09.02	DM West	Clevedon Town	361	2 - 0	Burnham 89[p], Bailey 90
16.02	DM West	Evesham United	288	3 - 0	Smith 19, May 39, Spencer 64
19.02	DM West	CIRENCESTER TOWN	403	1 - 0	Spencer 21
23.02	Worcs SC SF	MOOR GREEN	n.k	1 - 1	Jones 12
02.03	DM West	Solihull Borough	462	1 - 1	May 38
09.03	DM West	Bedworth United	303	3 - 0	May 25 90, Jones 62
12.03	Worcs SC SF R	Moor Green	308	0 - 3	
16.03	DM West	SWINDON SUPERMARINE	602	5 - 1	Hines 21 45, Spencer 26, May 53, Burnham 58[p]
19.03	DM West	WESTON-SUPER-MARE	469	2 - 2	Spencer 89, Smith 90
23.03	DM West	RACING CLUB WARWICK	527	6 - 0	May 4 72, Jones 46 64 77, Cowley 90
26.03	DM West	EVESHAM UNITED	503	3 - 0	May 27 37 44
30.03	DM West	Bilston Town	361	2 - 1	May 24, Taylor 30
01.04	DM West	SOLIHULL BOROUGH	856	4 - 1	Spencer 14 56, Skidmore 59, May 74
06.04	DM West	Cinderford Town	363	0 - 0	
13.04	DM West	GLOUCESTER CITY	738	0 - 0	
20.04	DM West	Mangotsfield United	403	2 - 1	Taylor 65, Jones 82
27.04	DM West	BEDWORTH UNITED	731	0 - 1	

PLAYING SQUAD

Goalkeepers: Tim Clarke (Kidderminster)
Defenders: Dominic Reece (Woking), Jason Burnham (Rugby Utd), Lee Collins (Stoke), Sean James (Harrow B), Ross Collins (Youth), Richard Colwell (Halesowen Harriers)
Midfield: Aengus Martin (Solihull), Jimmy Quiggan (Hereford), Karl Brennan (Hinckley Utd), Les Hines (Kidderminster), Mark Taylor (Nuneaton), Neil Smith (Stafford R), Stuart Skidmore (Causeway Utd)
Forwards: Andy Jones (Halesowen Harriers), Andy Spencer (Boldmere), Leroy May (Enfield), Richard Leadbeater (Nuneaton), Rob Elmes (Hereford)

HASTINGS UNITED

CLUB OFFICIALS

Chairman: Nigel Jones
President: Mick Maplesden
Vice Chairman: T.B.A.
Secretary : R A Cosens
22 Baldslow Road, Hastings TN34 2EZ
01424 427867 (H) 01424 444635 (B)
0771 2634288 (M)

FOOTBALL MANAGEMENT TEAM
Team Managers: George Wakeling
Asst Manager:Mark Leaney
Physio: T.B.A.

FACT FILE
Formed: 1894
Nickname: The Arrows
Sponsors: Real Pine
Colours: Claret & Blue
Change colours:Blue/Yellow
Midweek matchday: Tuesday
Reserves' League: Bass Kent Div 1
Newsline: 09066 555 879
00-01- Captain: Tony Burt
P.o.Y.:Adam Flagan
Top scorer:Chris Honey & Paul Jones 15

Pages: 76   Price: £1
Editor: David Bealey Tel: (01797 253310)
Local Press:Hastings Observer,Evening Argus
Local Radio: BBC Southern Counties
Southern Sound, Arrow FM
Website:www.hastingstownnfc.the-bench.co.uk

GROUND   The Pilot Field, Elphinstone Road, Hastings TN34 2AX Tel: 01424 444635

Directions: From A21 turn left at 3rd mini-r'bout into St Helens Rd, left after 1 mile into St Helens Park Rd, this leads into Downs Rd, at end of Downs Rd (T-junction) turn left, ground 200yds on right. From town centre take Queens Road (A2101). Right at roundabout into Elphinstone Road - ground 1 mile on right.
1 1/2 miles from Hastings BR station - infrequent bus service fromtown centre to ground

Capacity: 4,050   Cover: 1,750   Seats: 800   Floodlights: Yes

Clubhouse: Open matchdays and every evening
Club Shop: Sells replica kits, scarves, programmes, pens, key-rings, badges etc

PREVIOUS   **Leagues:** South Eastern 04-05, Southern 05-10, Sussex County 21-27 52-85,Southern Amateur 27-46, Corinthian 46-48
Name: Hastings & St Leonards Amateurs   **Ground:** Bulverhythe Rec Gd (pre 76)

CLUB RECORDS Attendance: 4,888 v Notts Forest, friendly 23/6/96. Competitive: 1,774 v DoverAthletic, Southern Lge Prem. Div. 12/4/93
Goalscorer: (Season) Terry White (33) 99-00
Transfer Fee Paid: £8,000 for Nicky Dent from Ashford   **Received:** £50,000 for Paul Smith from Notts Forest

BEST SEASON   FA Cup: 4th Qual. Rd 85-86, 2-3 v Farnborough Town (A)   **FA Trophy:** 3rd Rd 1998-99
FA Amateur Cup: 3rd Rd. 38-39   **FA Vase:** 5th Rd. rep. 90-91

HONOURS   Southern Lg Cup 94-95, Southern Div 91-92, Div 2 R-up 08-09, Div 2(B) 09-10; Sussex Co Lg R-up 21-22 25-26, Lg Cup 80-81, Div 2 79-80 (R-up 59-60), Div 2Cup 79-80; Sussex Sen Cup 35-36 37-38 95-96 97-98; AFA Snr Cup 37-38; Gilbert Rice F/lit Cup 89-90

Players progressing: Peter Heritage (Gillingham), Paul Smith (Nottm Forest)

Back row, left to right:Town celebrate with The Dr Martens Eastern Division Shield. George Wakeling (Manager), Tom Osbourne, Adam Flanagan, Dave King, Stuart Playford, Steve Ferguson, Paul Ruddy and Terry White (Coach). **Front row:** Graham Webb, Steve Webb, Paul Jones, Stuart Miles, Tony Burt (captain), Duncan McAuthur and Danny Simmonds

SOUTHERN LEAGUE PREMIER DIVISION

Date	Comp.	Opponents	Att.	Score	Goalscorers
18.08	DM East	WISBECH TOWN	356	2 - 1	Burt 84, Honey 89
21.08	DM East	Tonbridge Angels	432	5 - 1	Honey 44, Burt 47 78, Ferguson 70, Simmonds 72
25.08	DM East	Rugby United	273	0 - 0	
27.08	DM East	EASTBOURNE BOROUGH	551	1 - 0	Jones 88
01.09	FA Cup P	RINGMER	348	3 - 0	McArthur 4, Ruddy 69, Jones 88
08.09	DM East	Rothwell Town	163	4 - 2	Burt 19, Jones 61 73, McArthur 68
11.09	DM East	BASHLEY	368	2 - 0	McRobert 17, McArthur 26
15.09	FA Cup Q1	CHICHESTER CITY UNITED	377	3 - 0	Simmonds 56, Ferguson 80, Honey 84
22.09	DM East	Banbury United	255	3 - 2	Simmonds 45, McRobert 52, Honey 89
25.09	DM East	FISHER ATHLETIC	528	2 - 1	Jones 2, Simmonds 5[p]
29.09	FA Cup Q2	NEWPORT IOW	516	0 - 2	
05.10	DM East	DORCHESTER TOWN	418	0 - 0	
09.10	DM East	TONBRIDGE ANGELS	438	3 - 0	Jones 13, Burt 69, Simmonds 75[p]
20.10	DM East	CORBY TOWN	445	1 - 2	Yates 4
23.10	DM East	Bashley	152	0 - 0	
27.10	DM East	GRANTHAM TOWN	484	1 - 3	Jones 52
30.10	DM East	Ashford Town	380	2 - 0	Simmonds 41, Burt 53
03.11	FA Trophy 1	Enfield	126	1 - 2	Yates 90
10.11	DM East	Chatham Town	204	2 - 1	Myall 27, Simmonds 69
13.11	Lge Cup 1	DARTFORD	185	3 - 1	Simmonds 39[p], Yates 94 119
17.11	DM East	ROTHWELL TOWN	339	3 - 0	Playford 49, Simmons 71, Honey 88
20.11	Sussex SC 2	LANCING	154	8 - 0	
24.11	DM East	ERITH & BELVEDERE	361	3 - 2	Flanaghan 17, Langrey 71 90
08.12	DM East	Corby Town	80	5 - 0	Myall 7 44, Flanagan 24 50, Zahana 27
11.12	Lge Cup 2	FOLKESTONE INVICTA	215	5 - 0	Zahana 4, Honey 37 57, Yates 48 77
22.12	DM East	RUGBY UNITED	405	4 - 1	Myall 5 14, Jones 7 36
26.12	DM East	Eastbourne Borough	776	0 - 3	
29.12	DM East	Burnham	136	2 - 1	Flanagan 6, McArthur 42
05.01	DM East	STAMFORD	476	1 - 0	McArthur 74
12.01	DM East	Dorchester Town	605	1 - 1	Jones 26
19.01	DM East	Grantham Town	635	1 - 1	Myall 78[p]
22.01	Lge Cup 3	EASTBOURNE BOROUGH	309	2 - 3	Flanagan 36, Eldridge 39
29.01	Sussex SC 3	Arundel	93	6 - 1	Jones 23 44 55, Yates 33, McArthur 38, Zahna-Oni 53
02.02	DM East	Stamford	164	1 - 1	Yates 9
05.02	DM East	ST LEONARDS	684	0 - 1	
16.02	DM East	Sittingbourne	292	3 - 0	Flanagan 4, Osborne 30, Honey 72
19.02	DM East	DARTFORD	364	1 - 0	Myall 67
23.02	DM East	BURNHAM	374	1 - 0	Flanagan 36
02.03	DM East	Fisher Athletic	149	3 - 2	McArthur 14, Flanagan 31, Farley 61[og]
04.03	Sussex SC QF	CRAWLEY TOWN	371	2 - 0	Flanagan 94, Myall 98
09.03	DM East	Spalding United	111	1 - 0	Ruddy 1
12.03	Sussex SC SF	LEWES	420	1 - 2	Flanagan 51 Eastbourne Borough
16.03	DM East	HISTON	477	2 - 0	Flanagan 21, Hegley 55
19.03	DM East	Erith & Belvedere	191	3 - 2	Honey 5 66, Zahna-Oni 13
23.03	DM East	SPALDING UNITED	474	3 - 2	Honey 1, Jones 87, McArthur 90[p]
26.03	DM East	BANBURY UNITED	488	4 - 0	Ruddy 16, Honey 39, McArthur 45, Restarick 75
30.03	DM East	SITTINGBOURNE	626	0 - 0	
01.04	DM East	St Leonards	915	4 - 0	Jones 31, Simmonds 57[p], Honey 73, Myall 74
06.04	DM East	Histon	261	2 - 1	Simmonds 50, Playford 71
13.04	DM East	CHATHAM TOWN	574	2 - 0	Harvey 36, Restarick 85
16.04	DM East	Dartford	370	1 - 3	Zahna-Oni 89
20.04	DM East	Wisbech Town	374	4 - 2	Ruddy 3, Flanagan 28, Zahna-Oni 29, Honey 46
24.04	Hast. SC F	ST LEONARDS TOWN	n.k	3 - 2	Cornwall 12, Neal 87, Hegley ??
27.04	DM East	ASHFORD TOWN	743	2 - 2	Burt 10, Zahna-Oni 18

493

HAVANT & WATERLOOVILLE

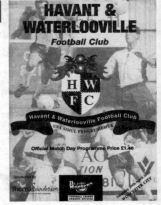

HAVANT & WATERLOOVILLE
Football Club

Official Match Day Programme Price £1.60

CLUB OFFICIALS

Chairman: Derek Pope

President: Arthur Saitch, Maurie Hibberd

Vice Chairman: Peter Dermott

Directors: Trevor Brock, Ray Jones, John Carter, Peter Faulkner, Sandy Peters

Secretary: Trevor Brock, 2 Betula Close, Waterlooville, Hampshire. PO7 8EJ
Tel:02392 267276

FOOTBALL MANAGEMENT TEAM

Joint Managers: Mick Jenkins & Liam Daish

Physio: Phil Ashwell

FACT FILE

Formed: 1998
Nickname: Hawks
Sponsors: Thomas Sanderson
Colours: All White
Change colours: Gold & Blue
Midweek matchday: Tuesday
Reserves' League:Capital

2000-01
Top Scorer: James Taylor 25
Captain:Tim Hambley
P.o.Y.: Gareth Hall

Pages: 32   Price: £1.60
Editor: Adrian Gardiner

Local Press: News (Portsmouth)
Radio:Radio Solent,Power FM,The Quay

GROUND   Westleigh Park, Martin Road, West Leigh, Havant PO9 5TH Tel: 02392 787822

Directions: Take B2149 to Havant off the A27 (B2149 Petersfield Rd if coming out of Havant). 2nd turning off dual carriageway into Bartons Road then 1st right into Martins Road. 1 mile from Havant station

Capacity: 4,500   Cover: 2,500   Seats: 560   Floodlights: Yes

Clubhouse: Open every day, lunchtime and evening. 2 bars, function suites. Hot & cold food available   Club Shop: Sells various souvenirs & progs

PREVIOUS   (Havant) **Leagues:** Portsmouth 58-71; Hants 71-86; Wessex 86-91. **Names:** Leigh Park; Havant & Leigh Park; Havant Town
        Grounds: Front Lawn 1958-83   (Waterlooville) **Leagues:** Waterlooville & District, Portsmouth 38-53, Hants1953-71.
                Grounds: Convent Ground 10-30, Rowlands Avenue Recreation Ground 30-63, Jubliee Park 63-98

CLUB RECORDS   Attendance: 3,500 v Wisbech Town, FA Vase QF 85-86
(Havant)   **Win:** 10-0 x3; v Sholing Sports (H), FA Vase 4th Rd 85-86, v Portsmouth R.N. (H), Wessex League 90-91;
        & v Poole Town, Southern Lge SouthernDiv. 94-95.   **Defeat:** 1-7 v Camberley Town (H), FA Vase 3rd Rd 88-89
        Career Goalscorer: Tony Plumbley 348   **Career Appearances:** Tony Plumbley 510
        Fee paid: £5,750 for John Wilson (Bashley, 90)   **Fee Received:** £60,000 forGary McDonald from Peterboro' U 0 0-01
        Fee paid: £7,000 for Steve Tate (Havant Town, 93)   **Received:** £6,000 for Dave Boyce (Gravesend & Northfleet, 93)

BEST SEASON   (Havant) FA Cup: 1st Rd Proper (H) 1-2 2000-01 **FA Vase:** Qtr Final 85-86 **F.A.Trophy:** 3rd Rd 98-99
        (Waterlooville)   **FA Trophy:** 3rd Rd 98-99 (lost 0-1 at Worcester City)   **FA Amateur Cup:** 1st Rd 59-60
        FA Cup: 1st Rd 2nd replay 83-84, 0-2 v Northampton T. (A) after two 1-1 draws

HONOURS   (Havant): FA Sunday Cup 68-69, Wessex Lg 90-91 R-up 88-89, Hampshire Lg Div 372-73 Div 4 71-72, Hampshire Sen. Cup 93-94,94-95 R-up 91-92 Hants.I'mediate Cup, Hampshire Junior Cup, Russell Cotes Cup 91-92, Portsmouth Sen. Cup 83-84 84-85 91-92, Gosport War Memorial Cup 74-75 91-92 92-93 94-95,Southern Counties F'lit Cup R-up 91-92, 00-01, Hampshire F'lit Cup 85-86, Portsmouth Lg.
        (Waterlooville): Southern Lg Div 1 Sth 71-72 Lg Cup 86-87, R-up 82-83, Hants Lg R-up 69-70 Div 2 59-60 64-65, Div 3 East R-up 53-54, Hants Sen. Cup 69-7072-73 84-85 R-up 75-76 90-91,00-01, Russell Cotes Cup 88-89, Portsmouth Lg 49-50 50-51 51-52 Div 2 46-47, Div 3 38-39, Portsmouth Sen. Cup 68-69, Portsmouth Victory Cup 59-60 69-70,00-01
        (H&W): Southern Lg.Southern 98-99, Capitol Lg R-up: 00-01 Hampshire Senior Cup Winners 00-01 R-up: 01-02

Back row left to right: Liam Daish, Shaun Gale, Garerth Hall, James Taylor, Paul Nicholas and Jamie O'Rourke.
Front row: Neil Champion, Gary Connolly, Tim Hambley (Captain), Chris Ferrett and Neil Davis. **Photo:** Eric Marsh

494

Date	Comp.	Opponents	Att.	Score	Goalscorers
18.08	DM P	Tamworth	582	1 - 1	Taylor 70
22.08	DM P	TIVERTON TOWN	505	3 - 3	Wood 1, Hambley 44[p], Taylor 52
25.08	DM P	MERTHYR TYDFIL	443	4 - 0	Daish 14 79, Taylor 21 26
27.08	DM P	Bath City	743	5 - 2	Taylor 1 55, O'Rourke 49, Hambley 57[p] 77[p]
01.09	DM P	STAFFORD RANGERS	584	2 - 1	Daish 48, Hall 89
04.09	DM P	Welling United	443	2 - 1	Taylor 61, Hambley 85
08.09	DM P	Worcester City	1004	0 - 0	
11.09	DM P	FOLKESTONE INVICTA	607	2 - 2	O'Rourke 28 83
15.09	DM P	KING'S LYNN	475	0 - 0	
19.09	DM P	Tiverton Town	645	1 - 0	O'Rourke 52
22.09	DM P	HINCKLEY UNITED	575	5 - 0	Taylor 6 62 67, O'Rourke 59 76
25.09	Hants RCC 2	TOTTON	60	2 - 1	
29.09	FA Cup Q2	Thame United	287	4 - 3	Daish 23, Hambley 47[p], Williams 54[og], O'Rourke 69
06.10	DM P	Weymouth	741	1 - 0	Hambley 76
09.10	DM P	WELLING UNITED	549	1 - 0	O'Rourke 70
13.10	FA Cup Q3	Croydon	168	1 - 0	Hambley 85
20.10	DM P	Hednesford Town	624	1 - 2	O'Rourke 11
23.10	Hants SC 2	MONEYFIELDS	258	9 - 0	Leworthy 2, O'Rourke, Davis, Miller, **Taylor 4**
27.10	FA Cup Q4	BARNET	1143	1 - 1	Connelly 50
03.11	FA Trophy 1	GRAYS ATHLETIC	411	2 - 3	Ferrett 21, Hall 90
06.11	FA Cup Q4 R	Barnet	1414	0 - 3	
10.11	DM P	KETTERING TOWN	689	1 - 3	Hambley 44
13.11	Lge Cup 1	NEWPORT IOW	237	2 - 0	Gale 66, Hambley 68
17.11	DM P	Crawley Town	1260	0 - 3	
24.11	DM P	SALISBURY CITY	505	2 - 0	Daish 8, Taylor 9
27.11	DM P	Folkestone Invicta	346	1 - 1	O'Rourke 10
08.12	DM P	Stafford Rangers	558	2 - 0	Hambley 67 87
11.12	Lge Cup 2	Ashford Town	159	1 - 2	Taylor 50[p]
15.12	DM P	TAMWORTH	589	0 - 2	
18.12	Hants SC 3	CHRISTCHURCH	101	5 - 1	Daish 34 66, Taylor 55, Hambley 64, Blake 86
22.12	DM P	Merthyr Tydfil	523	1 - 1	Daish 9
26.12	DM P	BATH CITY	586	3 - 0	O'Rourke 28 76, Barnett 86
29.12	DM P	CAMBRIDGE CITY	613	4 - 1	Daish 37, Taylor 57 70, Hambley 90
08.01	DM P	Moor Green	350	1 - 2	Taylor 57
15.01	Hants SC QF	BASHLEY	205	5 - 1	Hambley 13[p] 73, Wilkinson 37, Taylor 58, Hall 81
19.01	DM P	Hinckley United	327	4 - 2	Taylor 37, Wilkinson 58, O'Rourke 60 74
16.02	Hants RCC QF	Winchester City	241	2 - 0	Champion 26, O'Rourke 57
19.02	DM P	Salisbury City	340	0 - 2	
23.02	DM P	ILKESTON TOWN	467	2 - 2	Taylor 66[p] 85[p]
27.02	DM P	NEWPORT IOW	458	2 - 1	Wood 8, Daish 70
02.03	DM P	Kettering Town	1354	1 - 3	Wood 43
05.03	Hants SC SF(1)	GOSPORT BOROUGH	272	2 - 1	Taylor 17, Scannell 40[og]
09.03	DM P	CRAWLEY TOWN	694	2 - 0	Taylor 9, Judge 28[og]
12.03	DM P	CHELMSFORD CITY	394	4 - 1	Taylor 16 48, O'Rourke 36, Hambley 74[p]
16.03	DM P	WEYMOUTH	594	3 - 2	Taylor 44 68 78
19.03	Hants SC SF(2)	Gosport Borough	359	1 - 1	Wood 89
23.03	DM P	Chelmsford City	520	3 - 0	O'Rourke 33, Davis 44, Hambley 89
26.03	Hants RCC SF	BOURNEMOUTH	69	0 - 3	
30.03	DM P	NEWPORT COUNTY	726	1 - 3	O'Rourke 28
01.04	DM P	Newport IOW	561	1 - 0	O'Rourke 54
06.04	DM P	MOOR GREEN	599	3 - 1	Hambley 18 55[p], Taylor 49
08.04	DM P	Ilkeston Town	401	0 - 2	
13.04	DM P	King's Lynn	754	1 - 1	Gale 57
16.04	DM P	HEDNESFORD TOWN	429	2 - 1	O'Rourke 28, Connolly 49
20.04	DM P	WORCESTER CITY	513	1 - 0	Taylor 20
22.04	DM P	Newport County	525	0 - 2	
27.04	DM P	Cambridge City	660	1 - 2	Taylor 45
01.05	Hants SC F	ALDERSHOT TOWN	3523	1 - 3	Champion @ Southampton

PLAYING SQUAD

Goalkeepers: Aaron Kerr (Wolves), Alan Knight (Portsmouth), Paul Nicholls (Chelsea)
Defenders: Alec Masson (Wolves), Ben Price (Portsmouth), Chris Ferrett (Dorchester), Gareth Hall (Swindon), Gary Connolly (Portsmouth), Karl Miller (Youth team), Shaun Gale (Exeter City), Liam Daish (Coventry)
Midfielders: Bobby Howe (Swindon), Dean Blake (Bogner Regis T), James Ford (AFC Bournemouth), Neil Davis (Southampton), Tim Hambley (Fisher Athletic), Neil Champion (Aldershot)
Forwards: James Taylor (Bashley), David Leworthy (Kingstonian), Jamie O'Rourke (Cowes Sports), Lee Disney (Youth Team), Paul Wood (Happy Valley-Hong Kong), Phil Barnett (Portsmouth), Warren Haighton (Woking)

HEDNESFORD TOWN

CLUB OFFICIALS
Directors: John Baldwin, Steve Price & Carole Price
President: Nigel Tinsley
Chairman: Steve Price
General Manager: David Degg
Football Secretary: Sue Thomas c/o club
Club Secretary: Sue Thomas
Press Officer: Neil Holde
Community Officer & Youth Development: James Thomas

FOOTBALL MANAGEMEN TE AM

Manager: Ian Painter

FACT FILE
Founded: 1880
Nickname: The Pitmen
Club Sponsors: Extra Personnel
Club colours: White/black/black
Change colours: Red/white/white
Midweek home matchday: Monday
Reserves' league: Central Conference,
Web site: www.hednesfordtownfc.co.uk
Hotline Number: 09066 555880
Season 2000-01
Leading Scorer:
P.o.Y.:
Captain:

GROUND Keys Park, Hednesford, Cannock, Staffordshire WS12 5DW
Tel: 01543 422870, Fax: 01543 428180, Hotline: 0930 555880
SIMPLE DIRECTIONS: M6 J11 to Cannock, through traffic lights to island , 3rd exit, next island, 2nd exit onto Lichfield Rd. Next island 1st exit, next island straight on, next island 3rd exit, continue to mini-island. Keys Park is straight on (signposted from 2nd island.)
CAPACITY: 6,000 **SEATED:** 1,000 **COVERED TERRACING:** 1,000
CLUB SHOP: Open throughout the week
SOCIAL FACILITIES: Strikers Bar - Open matchdays and every evening 7-11 except Sunday. No food available. Chase Suite holds functions

Pages: 32 Price: £1.50
Editor: James Thomas
Local Press: Express & Star; Sporting Star; Chase Post; Cannock Mercury; Birmingham Evening Mail; Sports Argus; The Chronicle
Local Radio: Radio WM; BRMB; WABC; Beacon; Signal; BBC Radio Stoke

PREVIOUS **Leagues:** Walsall & District; Birmingham Combination 08-15, 45-53; West Midlands 19-39, 53-72, 74-84; Midland Counties 72-74; Southern League 84-95; Conference 95-01.
Grounds: The Tins (behind Anglesey Hotel) until 1904, Cross Keys until 1995.
HONOURS Welsh Cup R-up 91-92; Southern League - Prem. Div. 94-95; Midland Div. R-up 91-92, Lge. Cup R-up 86-87; West Midlands. Lge 77-78, R-up 83-84; Lge. Cup 83-84; Birmingham Comb. 09-10 50-51, R-up 12-13 52-53; Staffs Senior Cup 69-70, 73-74; R-up 92-93; Birmingham Sen. Cup 35-36; R-up 93-94. **Names:** None
CLUB RECORDS **Attendance:** 10,000 v Walsall F.A.Cup 1919-20
Win: 12-1 v Birmingham City, B'ham Wartime Lge Cup 40-41, 12-1 v Redditch United, B'ham Comb. 52-53
Defeat: 0-15 v Burton, B'ham Comb. 52-53
Career goalscorer: Tosh Griffiths, Joe O'Connor (post-war) **Career appearances:** Kevin Foster
Transfer fee paid: £12,000, for Steve Burr (Macclesfield Town 1991)
Transfer fee received: £50,000, for Dave Hanson (Leyton Orient)
BEST SEASON **FA Cup:** Fourth Round 1996-97 2-3 v Middlesbrough (A)
League clubs defeated: Blackpool 96-97, York City 96-97, Hull City 97-98, Barnet 98-99
FA Trophy: 1997-98, 3rd Round 1-2 v Grantham Town (A) **League:** 3rd, Conference 95-96
Players Progressing (Post War): Brian Horton (Port Vale 70), Vernon Allatt (Halifax T. 79); Chris Brindley (Wolverhampton W. 86), Scott Cooksey (Shrewsbury T. 98), Dave Hanson (Leyton Orient), Paul Ware (Macclesfield T.), Keith Russell (Blackpool 97)

Back row left to right: Chris Salt , Stuart Lake, Adam Shakespeare, Adam Jenkins, Mark Gayle, Chris Wood, Craig Hopkins, Scott Bonsall and Lennie Curtis. **Middle Row:** Don Drakeley (Physio), Spencer Lloyd, Val Owen, Paul Bagshaw, Neil Davis, Richard Lucas,Robbie Meacham, Leon Brown and James Thomas. **Front row:** Graham Lancashire, Dean Craven, Wayne Simpson, Paul Raymor (Manager), Gavan Walker (Assistant Manager), Mark Haran, Thomas Griffiths, Jonathan Pickess and Stewart Airdrie.

Date	Comp.	Opponents	Att.	Score	Goalscorers
18.08	DM P	Crawley Town	814	1 - 4	Lucas 17
20.08	DM P	TAMWORTH	931	1 - 2	Francis 78
25.08	DM P	KING'S LYNN	732	0 - 2	
27.08	DM P	Stafford Rangers	1381	0 - 3	
01.09	DM P	Folkestone Invicta	452	0 - 1	
03.09	DM P	ILKESTON TOWN	650	3 - 2	Lancashire 20, Francis 80, Lake 85
08.09	DM P	SALISBURY CITY	650	6 - 0	Bagshaw 10, Lancashire 29 41, Francis 34, Meecham 44, Haran 73
11.09	DM P	Hinckley United	444	0 - 4	
15.09	DM P	CHELMSFORD CITY	627	1 - 2	Lancashire 30
18.09	DM P	Tamworth	623	0 - 3	
22.09	DM P	WEYMOUTH	536	2 - 4	Airdrie 35, Lancashire 54
29.09	FA Cup Q2	STAFFORD TOWN	401	4 - 3	Davis 32, Francis 61 72, Pickess 90
06.10	DM P	Bath City	413	4 - 3	Davis 43 46 58 90
08.10	DM P	Ilkeston Town	562	0 - 2	
13.10	FA Cup Q3	Bedford Town	736	0 - 2	
20.10	DM P	HAVANT & WATERLOOVILLE	624	2 - 1	Lancashire 27, Davis 30
22.10	DM P	HINCKLEY UNITED	698	2 - 1	Lancashire 16, Airdrie 54
27.10	DM P	Salisbury City	300	0 - 1	
03.11	FA Trophy 1	RACING CLUB WARWICK	405	5 - 0	Lake 33, Francis 55, Lancashire 57, Brown 84, Shakespeare 86
10.11	DM P	NEWPORT IOW	601	1 - 2	Lancashire 74
12.11	Lge Cup 1	EVESHAM UNITED	191	1 - 3	Dyson 83[p]
20.11	Birm SC 2	Halesowen Town	205	0 - 2	
24.11	DM P	MERTHYR TYDFIL	565	3 - 0	Trainer 12 77, Charie 18
27.11	Staffs SC 2	Chasetown	152	2 - 2	Trainor 65, Brown 77
08.12	DM P	Tiverton Town	703	0 - 2	
10.12	FA Trophy 2	GATESHEAD	252	2 - 1	Lake 7 51
15.12	DM P	Crawley Town	607	0 - 0	
19.12	Staffs SC 2 R	CHASETOWN	n.k	6 - 1	Francis ?? Brown ?? Lancashire Shakespeare ??
29.12	DM P	Moor Green	447	4 - 1	Davis 12 79, Lancashire 50 64
12.01	FA Trophy 3	Scarborough	951	0 - 2	
19.01	DM P	WORCESTER CITY	767	0 - 3	
02.02	DM P	Chelmsford City	535	1 - 1	Polston 65
09.02	DM P	WELLING UNITED	601	1 - 1	Davis 40
12.02	DM P	Kettering Town	1455	1 - 1	Davis 73
16.02	DM P	BATH CITY	639	1 - 0	Davis 10
18.02	Staffs SC QF	RUSHALL OLYMPIC	195	1 - 1	Ajetunndai 26
23.02	DM P	Welling United	500	1 - 4	Lucas 50[p]
25.02	DM P	Worcester City	803	1 - 0	Craven 45
02.03	DM P	FOLKESTONE INVICTA	530	3 - 1	Lake 37, Davis 59, Airdrie 73
04.03	DM P	STAFFORD RANGERS	1319	3 - 3	Airdrie 29 78, Davis 72
07.03	Staffs SC QF R	Rushall Olympic	128	0 - 1	
09.03	DM P	King's Lynn	597	0 - 1	
11.03	DM P	KETTERING TOWN	920	1 - 2	Barrow 23
16.03	DM P	Merthyr Tydfil	561	1 - 3	Lake 82
23.03	DM P	Weymouth	712	4 - 0	Rae 38, Lake 60, Lucas 70, Airdrie 72
25.03	DM P	NEWPORT COUNTY	620	3 - 2	Lake 6, Brownrigg 21, Davis 45
30.03	DM P	MOOR GREEN	689	1 - 2	Barrow 72
01.04	DM P	Newport County	722	1 - 0	Airdrie 24
06.04	DM P	CAMBRIDGE CITY	609	1 - 1	Davis 11
16.04	DM P	Havant & Waterlooville	429	1 - 2	Francis 90
20.04	DM P	TIVERTON TOWN	777	2 - 1	Airdrie 10 90
23.04	DM P	Cambridge City	440	1 - 2	Lake 38
27.04	DM P	Newport IOW	905	1 - 0	Rae 54

Match Facts 2001-02

PLAYING SQUAD

Goalkeepers: Adam Jenkins (Youth Team), Mark Gayle (Chesterfield)
Defenders: Adam Shakespeare (Hereford), Ashley Williams (Youth Team), Chris Brindley (Stafford Rangers), Chris Salt (Youth Team), Darren Simkin (Stafford Rangers), James Dyson (Birmingham), Les Robinson (Mansfield), Matt Gardiner (Hereford), Richard Lucas (Boston United), Stuart Ryder (Stafford Rangers), Tom Griffiths (Youth Team), Wayne Simpson (Nuneaton)
Midfielders: Carl Adams (Bedford Town), Derek Rae (Elgin), Mark Jones (Raith), Robbie Meacham (Youth Team), Shaun Wray (Stafford), Spencer Lloyd (Youth Team), Stuart Lake (Walsall), Wayne Thomas (Shrewsbury), Paul Ware (Rochdale)
Forwards: Stewart Airdrie (Guiseley), Adewale Ajet (Hamilton Acedemical), Damien Charie (Youth Team), Graham Lancashire (Rochdale), Kevin Francis (Hull), Steve Piearce (Hereford)

HINCKLEY UNITED

HINCKLEY UNITED FOOTBALL CLUB

Sponsored by **Transco**

CLUB OFFICIALS

Chairman: **Kevin Downes**
Vice Chairman: **Rob Mayne**
Secretary: **Ray Baggott**
37 Laneside Drive, Hinckley, Leics.
LE10 1TG (01455 447278)
Press Officer: **Andy Gibbs** (01455 617828)

FOOTBALL MANAGEMENT TEAM
Manager: Dean Thomas
Coach:Charlie Palmer
Physio: Julie Hayton

FACT FILE
Formed: 1997
Sponsors: Transco
Colours: Red & blue stripes/blue/red
Change colours: Amber & black
stripes/black/amber
Midweek matchday: Tuesday
Reserves' League: Mid Comb Res Div
Unofficial Website:
www.hinckleyunitedfc.co.uk
2001.02
Top scorer: Jamie Lenton 18
Captain: Morton Titterton
P.o.Y.: Stuart Storer

SATURDAY 27TH APRIL 2002
HINCKLEY UNITED
versus
WELLING UNITED
DR MARTENS LEAGUE PREMIER DIVISION

2001-2002 SEASON   "THE KNITTERS" OFFICIAL PROGRAMME £1

GROUND Middlefield Lane, Hinckley, Leics. LE10 0RB 01455 613553/615012
Directions: From M69 junction 1 take A5 north to Dodwells Island, then A47(sign Leicester).
At 3rd r/about turn right (Stoke Road) then first left(Tudor Road), until crossroads. Turn left
(Middlefield Lane), ground at end oflane on left
Capacity: 5,000   Cover: 1,300   Seats: 320   Floodlights: Yes
Clubhouse: Social club with lounge, games room and concert hall
Club Shop: Sells programmes, books, vidoes, badges, mugs , replica shirts,scarves, hats,etc.

Pages: 60   Price: £1   Editor: Alan Mason
Local Radio: BBC Radio Leicester
Local Press: Heartland Evening News,
Hinckley Times, Leicester Mercury,Hinckley
Coventry Evening Telegraph

PREVIOUS   **Names:** Hinckley Athletic (1889) & Hinckley Town (prev. Westfield Rovers 58-66) merged in 1997
Grounds: Westfield Playing Field 58-60; Coventry Rd Rec Grd 60-68; Leicester Rd68-97
Leagues: Town: S Leicester & Nuneaton Amat, Leics Snr 72-86, Central Mids 86-88, West Mids 88-90
Athletic: Leics. & Northants; Leics. Sen.; Birmingham Comb. 14-39 47-54; West Midlands (Regional) 54-59 64-94; Southern 63-64
CLUB RECORDS Attendance: Town: 2,000 v Real Sociedad 86. **Athletic:** 5,410 v Nuneaton Boro 49 **United:** 2,661 v Cheltenham Town
(F.A.Cup 2nd Rd. (H) 2001-02
Win: 9-1 vRocester (Away) 28.8.2000   **Defeat:** 0-6 v Redditch United (a) 7.11.1988
Career Goalscorer: Jamie Lenton 54 **Career Appearances:** Morton Titterton 213
Fee paid: **Fee received:**
BEST SEASON   FA Trophy: United: 4th Rd 2-3 v Yeovil Town 98-99
FA Cup: 2nd Round Proper v Cheltenham Town (Home) 0-2. 2001-02
HONOURS   Dr. Martens (Southern) Western Division Champions 2000-2001, Westerby Challenge Cup Winners 2000-2001,2001-02
Players progressing: Athletic: John Allen (Port Vale), Keith Scott (Swindon via Wycombe W.), Gary Pick (Hereford), Mike Love (Wigan)

Back row left to right: Dean Thomas (Manager), Julie Hayton (Physio), Neil Cartwright, Jamie Williams, Justin Jenkins, Morton Titterton, Tim Wilkes, Guy Hadland, Niki Preston (Partly hidden), Farhad Afabdiyev, Leon Blake and Scott Eustace. **Middle row:** Scott Huckerby and Andy Lucas. **Front row:** Andy Penny, Stuart Storer, Jamie Lenton and Phil Stant.

Date	Comp.	Opponents	Att.	Score	Goalscorers
18.08	DM P	Welling United	501	2 - 3	Titterton 21, Lenton 77
21.08	DM P	KING'S LYNN	389	0 - 0	
25.08	DM P	CAMBRIDGE CITY	402	2 - 2	Titterton 58, Lucas 70
27.08	DM P	Worcester City	967	3 - 4	Lenton 30, Hunter 42, Titterton 65
01.09	DM P	CHELMSFORD CITY	455	2 - 0	Lenton 53[p] 78
04.09	DM P	Stafford Rangers	593	2 - 4	Hunter 69 88
08.09	DM P	Folkestone Invicta	464	3 - 1	Lucas 12, Titterton 88, Hunter 90
11.09	DM P	HEDNESFORD TOWN	444	4 - 0	Lenton 39 90[p], Titterton 73, Hunter 86
15.09	DM P	NEWPORT IOW	455	1 - 2	Penny 24
18.09	DM P	King's Lynn	646	1 - 1	Hunter 82
22.09	DM P	Havant & Waterlooville	575	0 - 5	
29.09	FA Cup Q2	Bilston Town	310	3 - 1	Penney 60, Lucas 81 87
06.10	DM P	MOOR GREEN	240	3 - 1	Lucas 45, Rowlands 65, Lenton 85[p]
09.10	DM P	STAFFORD RANGERS	415	3 - 0	Wilkes 13, Gordon 14, Rowland 48
13.10	FA Cup Q3	Histon	284	3 - 3	Penny 63, Gordon 65, Lenton 70
16.10	FA Cup Q3 R	HISTON	360	2 - 0	Titterton 73, Lucas 78
20.10	DM P	Merthyr Tydfil	501	2 - 2	Wilkes 3, Titterton 49
22.10	DM P	Hednesford Town	698	1 - 2	Wilkes 11
27.10	FA Cup Q4	Weymouth	1258	2 - 1	Lucas 72, Lenton 90
03.11	FA Trophy 1	EASTWOOD TOWN	365	2 - 1	Hunter 9, Brennan 31
06.11	DM P	BATH CITY	313	2 - 2	Hamilton 55, Penney 63
10.11	DM P	Newport County	709	2 - 0	Lenton 61, Lucas 72
13.11	Lge Cup 1	ATHERSTONE UNITED	204	1 - 4	White 79
17.11	FA Cup 1	Grays Athletic	1133	2 - 1	Hunter 49, Lenton 67
24.11	DM P	Kettering Town	1281	1 - 2	Hunter 49
01.12	FA Trophy 2	Lancaster City	289	1 - 2	Gordon 64
08.12	FA Cup 2	CHELTENHAM TOWN	2661	0 - 2	
15.12	DM P	SALISBURY CITY	308	2 - 1	Cartwright 24, Huckerby 41
18.12	DM P	ILKESTON TOWN	324	2 - 2	Huckerby 36, Lenton 70
29.12	DM P	TIVERTON TOWN	471	3 - 4	Huckerby 3, Williams 8, Titterton 76
05.01	DM P	Bath City	622	2 - 1	Lucas 76, Rowlands 84
08.01	Leics CC QF	SHEPSHED DYNAMO	163	4 - 1	O'Toole 3 11 78, Lucas 72
12.01	DM P	CRAWLEY TOWN	577	0 - 1	
15.01	DM P	Tamworth	663	1 - 2	O'Toole 50
19.01	DM P	HAVANT & WATERLOOVILLE	327	2 - 4	Lenton 25, Hadland 90
26.01	DM P	Weymouth	673	1 - 1	Huckerby 90
09.02	DM P	NEWPORT COUNTY	417	0 - 2	
12.02	DM P	Cambridge City	309	2 - 3	Huckerby 81, Lenton 85[p]
16.02	DM P	Salisbury City	375	1 - 1	Hunter 79
23.02	DM P	WORCESTER CITY	326	0 - 0	
26.02	DM P	Moor Green	253	1 - 1	Huckerby 48
02.03	DM P	WEYMOUTH	327	3 - 2	Huckerby 6, Williams 68, Titterton 73
09.03	DM P	Tiverton Town	722	1 - 1	Penney 83
12.03	Leics CC SF	DOWNES SPORTS	170	4 - 1	Hunter 4, Eustace 33, Lenton 72[p], Huckerby 85 @ Holmes Park
16.03	DM P	FOLKESTONE INVICTA	320	1 - 2	Lenton 70[p]
23.03	DM P	KETTERING TOWN	966	2 - 1	Hunter 12, Lenton 75[p]
30.03	DM P	Ilkeston Town	526	1 - 1	Stant 3
01.04	DM P	TAMWORTH	1102	1 - 0	Huckerby 86
06.04	DM P	Crawley Town	949	0 - 1	
13.04	DM P	MERTHYR TYDFIL	433	1 - 0	Stant 2
16.04	DM P	Newport IOW	502	0 - 0	
20.04	DM P	Chelmsford City	619	2 - 0	Hadland 74, Lucas 88
22.04	Leics CC F	Oadby Town	n.k	3 - 1	Titterton 4, Stant 67, Blake 85 @ Leicester City
27.04	DM P	WELLING UNITED	378	1 - 0	Huckerby 16

PLAYING SQUAD

Goalkeepers: Chris Taylor (Bedford Town), Farhad Afandiyev

Defenders: Andy Penny (Solihull Borough), Beven Browne (Cambridge City), Craig Smith (Belper Town), Guy Hadland (Aston Villa), Jamie March (Kings Lynn), Martin Fox (Cambridge), Neil Cartwright (Youth Team), Nick Preston (Youth Team), Scott Eustace (Stevenage), Simon Dakin (Kings Lynn)

Midfielders: Dave Crowley (Nuneaton), Gavin O,Toole (Aberystwyth), Jamie Lenton (VS Rugby), Jamie Williams (Nuneaton), Leon Blake (Stourbridge), Leon Doughty (Atherstone United), Moreton Titterton (Bedford), Stuart Storer (Chesham), Tim Wilkes (Grantham)

Forwards: Paul Hunter (Moor Green), Andy Lucas (Shepshed Dynamo), Jermaine Gordon (Downes Sports), Richard Mitchell (Kidsgrove)

ILKESTON TOWN

CLUB OFFICIALS
Chairman: **Paul Millership**
President: **Robert Lindsay**
Secretary: **Robert Easton,**15 Regina
Crescent,Ravenshead,Notts.NG15 9AE
Tel: 01623 793927(H) 07831 303031(M)
Commercial Management:
J Sports Promotions Ltd

FACT FILE

Re Formed: 1945
Nickname: The Robins
Sponsors: Ron Brooks Ilkeston Toyota
Colours: Red/whitek/red
Change colours:White/Black/White
Midweek matchday:Wednesday
Res' League: Midland RegionalAlliance

FOOTBALL MANAGEMENT TEAM

Manager: John McGinlay
Asst Manager: Andy Mason

GROUND   New Manor Ground, Awsworth Rd, Ilkeston Tel: 0115 932 4094

Directions: M42 to M1 junc 23A, continue on M1 to junc 26, exit left onto A610 towards
Ripley, take 1st exit signed Awsworth and Ilkeston (A6096), follow bypass signed Ilkeston
A6096. Turn right after 1/2 mile signed Cotmanhay. Ground 200 yards on left
Capacity: 3,500   Seats: 270   Cover: 1,100   Floodlights: Yes

Pages: 32   Price: £1
Editors: Mic Capill, J Shiels, D Payne

Clubhouse: Open Wed-Fri 7-11pm, Sat-Sun noon-3 & 7-11pm, and Mon or Tue if there is a
match. Snacks behind bar. Large tea bar open matchdays 2-5pm (6.30-9pm for night games)
Club Shop: Sells wide range of souvenirs & programmes + `Team Talk'.
Contact Manager (0115 9305 622) or club secretary

PREVIOUS   **Leagues:** Midland 1894-1902 25-58 61-71; Notts & Derby Senior 1945-47; CentralAlliance 47-61; Midland
Counties 1961-71 73-82; Southern League 1971-73; Northern Co.East 1982-86; Central Midlands 86-90; West Midlands (Regional) 90-94.
Ground: Manor Ground, Manor Rd (1945-92)

CLUB RECORDS **Attendance:** 2,504 v Boston United FA Cup 1st Rd 15/11/97
Win: 14-2 v Codnor M.W 46-47: 13-0 v Swanwick OB 46-47
Defeat: 1-11 v Grantham T. 47-48: 0-10 v VS Rugby 85-86
Career Goalscorer: Jackie Ward 141. **Career Appearances:** Terry Swincoe 377
Season Goalscorer: Barry Jepson 62, 1952-53
Transfer fee paid: £7,500 Justin O'Reilly (Southport 1998) **Fee received:** £25,000 for Francis Green (Peterborough Utd)

BEST SEASON **FA Cup:** 2nd Round - 1997-98 1-1, 1-2 v Scunthorpe Utd, 1999-00 0-3 (A) after 1-1 (H) v Rushden & Diamonds
FA Vase: 4th Round 88-89 1-2 v Tamworth
FA Trophy: 3rd Round 82-83 1-5 v Enfield, 94-95 2-2, 1-2 v Kidderminster H

HONOURS Southern Lge, Midland Div 94-95, (R-up 97-98); West Mids (Regional) Lg 93-94, Div 1 91-92, Lg Cup 91-92;
Central Mids Lg Cup 87-88; Midland Lg 67-68 (R-up 1898-99); Midland Co Lg 67-68;
Central Alliance 51-52 52-53 53-54 54-55(R-up 47-48 55-56)

SOUTHERN LEAGUE PREMIER DIVISION

Date	Comp.	Opponents	Att.	Score	Goalscorers
18.08	DM P	Salisbury City	397	1 - 1	Holmes 35
20.08	DM P	STAFFORD RANGERS	702	2 - 2	Williams 30, Knapper 61[p]
25.08	DM P	WORCESTER CITY	521	1 - 2	Holmes 39
27.08	DM P	King's Lynn	1145	1 - 0	Williams 87
01.09	DM P	WELLING UNITED	497	3 - 2	Hemmings 8, Holmes 14 62
03.09	DM P	Hednesford Town	650	2 - 3	Holmes 43, Hemmings 60
08.09	DM P	Bath City	620	1 - 1	Hemmings 78
10.09	DM P	TAMWORTH	787	2 - 1	Hemmings 56, Wright 84
15.09	DM P	MERTHYR TYDFIL	521	1 - 0	Knapper 57[p]
18.09	DM P	Stafford Rangers	725	2 - 1	Timons 18, Kirkwood 35
22.09	DM P	FOLKESTONE INVICTA	642	2 - 1	Kirkwood 1 54
29.09	FA Cup Q2	Grantham Town	568	1 - 2	Kirkwood 7
05.10	DM P	Worcester City	938	2 - 2	Kirkwood 22, Wright 42
08.10	DM P	HEDNESFORD TOWN	562	2 - 0	McKenzie 82, Kirkwood 88
20.10	DM P	Chelmsford City	517	1 - 6	Holmes 20
27.10	DM P	Crawley Town	1002	0 - 2	
30.10	DM P	Tamworth	752	1 - 1	Hemmings 87
03.11	FA Trophy 1	GAINSBOROUGH TRINITY	468	1 - 0	Knapper 53
10.11	DM P	WEYMOUTH	546	2 - 2	Kirkwood 30, Hemmings 60
14.11	Lge Cup 1	Gresley Rovers	n.k	0 - 1	
17.11	DM P	Merthyr Tydfil	405	3 - 2	Robinson 48, Kirkwood 87 88
24.11	DM P	MOOR GREEN	559	2 - 1	Hemmings 8, Kirkwood 61
27.11	Derbys SC 3	Staveley Miners Welfare	91	5 - 1	Kirkwood 19 43 68, Knapper 40[p], Wright 88
01.12	FA Trophy 2	Hyde United	355	4 - 0	Abbott 22, Holmes 72 90, Hemmings 80
11.12	Derbys SC QF	Long Eaton United	180	4 - 0	Kirkwood 30, Robinson 74 84, Holmes 85
15.12	DM P	BATH CITY	577	3 - 3	Knapper 22[p], Nwadikwe 28, Hemmings 36
18.12	DM P	Hinckley United	324	2 - 2	Kirkwood 2, Holmes 22
22.12	DM P	Tiverton Town	783	2 - 3	Holmes 32, Hemmings 82
29.12	DM P	SALISBURY CITY	547	0 - 1	
05.01	DM P	Welling United	442	0 - 1	
12.01	FA Trophy 3	TELFORD UNITED	792	0 - 2	
02.02	DM P	CRAWLEY TOWN	563	0 - 0	
16.02	DM P	TIVERTON TOWN	527	0 - 2	
18.02	Derbys SC SF	GRESLEY ROVERS	244	1 - 1	Wright 37 4 5
23.02	DM P	Havant & Waterlooville	467	2 - 2	Kirkwood 41, Holmes 44
02.03	DM P	Newport County	610	0 - 3	
05.03	DM P	Cambridge City	293	1 - 1	Kirkwood 90
09.03	DM P	KETTERING TOWN	842	0 - 2	
16.03	DM P	CHELMSFORD CITY	510	3 - 3	Kirkwood 28 45, Wright 76
19.03	DM P	Kettering Town	1456	2 - 1	Challinor 53, Robinson 78
23.03	DM P	Newport IOW	487	1 - 2	Knapper 73
25.03	DM P	KING'S LYNN	465	3 - 1	Kirkwood 14, Kennerdale 26, Robinson 74
30.03	DM P	HINCKLEY UNITED	526	1 - 1	Timmons 63
01.04	DM P	Moor Green	348	1 - 1	Kirkwood 87
06.04	DM P	NEWPORT COUNTY	496	0 - 1	
08.04	DM P	HAVANT & WATERLOOVILLE	401	2 - 0	Kennerdale 45, Kirkwood 79
13.04	DM P	Folkestone Invicta	340	2 - 0	Holmes 14, Robinson 35
15.04	DM P	CAMBRIDGE CITY	452	1 - 1	Holmes 71[p]
20.04	DM P	NEWPORT IOW	483	0 - 0	
27.04	DM P	Weymouth	767	1 - 0	Fairbrother 86

PLAYING SQUAD

Goalkeepers: Mark Smith (Scarborough)

Defenders: Barry Woolley (Gresley Rovers), Gavin Stone (Bilston Town), Matt McKenzie (Grimsby T), Simon Coleman (Rochdale)

Midfielders: Ian Robinson (Hednesford Town), Anton Foster (Youth Team), Emeka Nwadike (Kings Lynn), Mark Walters (Bristol Rovers), Paul Bagshaw (Emley), Ryan Ford (Notts County), Scott Dundas (Stafford Rangers), Steve Coates (Gresely Rovers), Steve Lenagh (Kettering Town)

Forwards: Carl Wright (Ipswich Town), David Hardy (Youth Team), David Holmes (Burton Albion), John McGinlay (Gresely Rovers), Leon Kelly (Cambridge United), Paul Kiely (Stafford Rangers), Tom Williams (Ripley T)

MOOR GREEN

CLUB OFFICIALS
Chairman: Ian Childs
Vice-Chairman: John Bassford

Secretary: Nigel Collins
7 The Morelands, West Heath,
Birmingham B31 3HA
Tel: 0121476 4944 (H) 0121 777 8961 (W)
07753 900133 (M)
Email: nigelcollins@lineone.net
Press Officer: Peter Clynes 0121 745 3262
Commercial Man.: Commercial Dept.0121 777 8961

FOOTBALL MANAGEMENT TEAM
Manager: Bob Faulkner
Coaches: Doug Griffiths & Mark Harrison
Physio: Steve Shipway

FACT FILE
Formed: 1901
Nickname: The Moors
Sponsors:Alexander Forbes Insurance
Colours: Navy Blue with sky blue band
Change colours: Jade & lime
Midweek matchday: Tuesday
Reserve League: No reserve team
Website:www.moorgreenfc.co.uk

GROUND	`The Moorlands', Sherwood Rd., Hall Green. B28 OEX
	Tel: 0121 777 8961 or 0121 624 2727
Directions:	Off Highfield Rd, which is off A34 (B'ham to Stratford)
	Hall Green & Yardley (BR) half mile
	Capacity: 3,250 Cover: 1,200 Seats: 250 Floodlights: Yes
Clubhouse:	Two bars, dance floor. Open nightly & weekend lunch
Club Shop:	Selling scarves, mugs, stickers, programmes etc

Programme: Pages: 40 Price: £1.50
Editor:Martin North(0121 603 7357)
Local Press: Solihull News, Solihull Times,
Birmingham Post & Mail, Express &Star
Local Radio: Radio WM, BRMB

PREVIOUS **Leagues:** (friendlies only 1901-21) Birmingham & Dist. A.F.A. 1908-36; Central Amateur 36-39; Birmingham Comb 45-54; West Mids 54-65; Midland Comb 65-83
Grounds: Moor Green Lane 1901-02; numerous 02-22; Windermere Road 1910-30

CLUB RECORDS **Attendance:** 5,000 v Romford, FA Amtr Cup 51
Career Goalscorer: Phil Davies 221   **Career Appearances:** Michael Hawkins 800
Transfer fee paid: £1,000 for Adrian O'Dowd (Alvechurch)
Transfer fee received: £90,000 for Ian Taylor (Port Vale)

BEST SEASON **FA Cup:** 1st Rd Proper 79-80 (lost 2-3 Stafford Rgs)
FA Trophy: 1st Rd Prop 90-91, 0-3 v Burton Albion; 96-97, 3-5 v AshtonUnited

HONOURS Southern Lg Mid Div R-up 87-88, Mids Comb 80-81 (R-up(4) 74-76 79-80 82-83, Div 185-86, Presidents Cup(2) 66-68 78-79), Mids Comb Chall Cup 80-81 (R-up 69-7082-83), Lord Mayor of B'ham Charity Cup 90-91, Mids F'lit Cup(2) 90-92, Tony Allden Tphy 81- 82, B'ham Snr Cup 57-58, Worcs Snr Cup 2000-01 R-up 86-87, 01-02 B'ham Jnr Cup66-67, Worcs Jnr Cup 85-86, Solihull Charity Cup 85-86, Smedley Crook Mem.Cup 87-88, Cent Amat Lg 36-37 37-38 38-39, Verviers (Belg) Tphy 32-33 36-37,AFA Chall Cup 38-39, AFA Snr Cup 26-27 35-36, Mids F'lit Yth Lg Cup R-up 87-88,B'ham County Yth Lg Cup R-up 83-84. Birmingham Senior Cup: 2000-01

Players progressing: H Smith/R Jefferies (Aston Villa 47/50), F Pidcock(Walsall 53), P Woodward/B Mack (W B Abion 54), S Cooper (Birmingham City 83),K Barnes (Manchester City), P Brogan (Mansfield Town), I Taylor (Pt Vale 92), S Talbot (Pt Vale 94), D Busst (Coventry 92)

SOUTHERN LEAGUE PREMIER DIVISION

Date	Comp.	Opponents	Att.	Score	Goalscorers
07.08	Birm SC (00-01) F	TAMWORTH	n.k	3 - 1	Stanley 55, Martin 92, Lamey 116
18.08	DM P	Cambridge City	321	1 - 0	Stanley 50[p]
21.08	DM P	MERTHYR TYDFIL	309	1 - 0	Martin 4
25.08	DM P	BATH CITY	359	0 - 0	
27.08	DM P	Tamworth	638	0 - 2	
01.09	DM P	SALISBURY CITY	277	1 - 1	Lamey 90
03.09	DM P	Worcester City	837	2 - 3	Lamey 65, Stanley 84[p]
08.09	DM P	WELLING UNITED	234	2 - 1	Lamey 20 81
11.09	DM P	King's Lynn	634	0 - 1	
15.09	DM P	TIVERTON TOWN	339	1 - 1	Petty 53
18.09	DM P	Merthyr Tydfil	438	2 - 1	Martin 32, Myers 90
22.09	DM P	CRAWLEY TOWN	367	3 - 1	Lamey 2, Martin 59, Softley 87
29.09	FA Cup Q2	HALESOWEN TOWN	561	0 - 2	
02.10	DM P	WORCESTER CITY	368	3 - 1	Lamey 36, Gayle 53, Crisp 69
06.10	DM P	Hinckley United	240	1 - 3	Crisp 11
13.10	DM P	Bath City	579	2 - 0	Petty 13, Martin 90
20.10	DM P	Newport County	702	1 - 2	Lamey 10
23.10	DM P	KING'S LYNN	237	4 - 0	Lamey 21, Myers 45, Martin 69, Softley 71
27.10	DM P	CHELMSFORD CITY	317	3 - 1	Martin 47, Scheppel 54, Myers 55
03.11	FA Trophy 1	BAMBER BRIDGE	325	3 - 0	Crisp 20, Lamey 78, Stanley 86
10.11	DM P	Folkestone Invicta	333	0 - 1	
13.11	Lge Cup 1	SHEPSHED DYNAMO	147	5 - 4	Brighton 7, Gayle 29 30, Martin 34, Stanley 70
20.11	Birm SC 2	DARLASTON TOWN	122	4 - 0	Gayle 12, Softley 47, Petty 52, Myers 88
24.11	DM P	Ilkeston Town	559	1 - 2	Perry 87
01.12	FA Trophy 2	TRAFFORD	347	2 - 1	Crisp 50, Peer 89[p]
03.12	Worcs SC QF	Worcester City	302	3 - 2	Gayle 16, Stanley 18 61
08.12	DM P	FOLKESTONE INVICTA	292	2 - 0	Softley 11, Gayle 56
11.12	Lge Cup 2	Redditch United	140	4 - 1	Myers 30, Lamey 34 59 88
15.12	DM P	Weymouth	803	1 - 0	Myers 67
26.12	DM P	TAMWORTH	1010	3 - 2	Gayle 15 50, Myers 43
29.12	DM P	HEDNESFORD TOWN	447	1 - 4	Lamey 77
08.01	DM P	HAVANT & WATERLOOVILLE	350	2 - 1	Lamey 31, Stanley 59
12.01	FA Trophy 3	Grantham Town	525	1 - 2	Martin 81
15.01	Lge Cup 3	Bedworth United	150	3 - 4	Gayle 8, Hunter 82, Lamey 84
19.01	DM P	Tiverton Town	738	0 - 2	
22.01	Birm SC 3	WALSALL	198	3 - 2	Lamey 59 77 81
09.02	DM P	Kettering Town	1458	1 - 2	Lamey 35
12.02	Birm SC QF	BURTON ALBION	305	3 - 1	Lamey 12 45[p], Myers 26
16.02	DM P	WEYMOUTH	332	7 - 1	Gayle 3 56, Myers 13, Lamey 45 71 87 90
23.02	Worcs SC SF	Halesowen Town	n.k	1 - 1	Martin 68
26.02	DM P	HINCKLEY UNITED	253	1 - 1	Softley 53
02.03	DM P	Salisbury City	330	0 - 5	
05.03	Birm SC SF	NUNEATON BOROUGH	244	0 - 4	
09.03	DM P	Newport IOW	370	1 - 2	Crisp 45
12.03	Worcs SC SF R	HALESOWEN TOWN	308	3 - 0	Lamey 9 73, Scheppel 85
16.03	DM P	NEWPORT IOW	353	1 - 4	Stanley 20
19.03	DM P	Stafford Rangers	498	4 - 3	Lamey 6 13, Scheppel 57, Martin 70
23.03	DM P	CAMBRIDGE CITY	347	1 - 2	Stanley 45
25.03	DM P	Chelmsford City	462	2 - 0	Gayle 30, Martin 36
30.03	DM P	Hednesford Town	689	2 - 1	Stanley 16, Martin 89
01.04	DM P	ILKESTON TOWN	348	1 - 1	Gayle 4
04.04	Worcs SC F(1)	KIDDERMINSTER HARRIERS	339	0 - 2	
06.04	DM P	Havant & Waterlooville	599	1 - 3	Myers 64
09.04	DM P	NEWPORT COUNTY	324	1 - 2	Blake 89
13.04	DM P	KETTERING TOWN	586	0 - 2	
16.04	DM P	Welling United	417	1 - 1	Blake 51
20.04	DM P	Crawley Town	1021	2 - 1	Lamey 20, Myers 61
24.04	Worcs SC F(2)	Kidderminster Harriers	539	1 - 0	Scheppel 20
27.04	DM P	STAFFORD RANGERS	491	1 - 1	Gayle 56

Match Facts 2001-02

PLAYING SQUAD

Goalkeepers: Adam Rachel (Blackpool)

Defenders: Chris Gillard (Port Vale), Denis Mulholland (Bromsgrove R), Guy Sanders (Bedworth Utd), Richard Robinson (GMP Sports)

Midfielders: Danny Scheppel (Worcester), Dean Peer (Shrewsbury), Jai Stanley (Bedworth Utd), Jamie Petty (Solihull Borough), Martin Myers (Redditch Utd), Josh Walker (Shrewsbury T.), Mark Crisp (Cheltenham), Nicky Carter (Bloxwich Utd)

Forwards: Jae Martin (Woking), John Gayle (Torquay Utd), Nathan Lamey (Hitchin T), Wes Joyce (Malvern T)

NEWPORT COUNTY A.F.C.

CLUB OFFICIALS

Chairman: Wallace Brown
Secretary: Mike Everett
43 Downing Street, Newport. NP19 0JL
Tel: 01633 669572

Club Website: www.newport-county.co.uk

Club's Email : hq.newportcounty@virgin.net

FACT FILE
Formed: 1989
Nickname: The Exiles
Sponsors: Acorn Recruitment
Colours: Amber shirts and black shorts
Change colours: Blue & Black Stripes/Black
Midweek matchday: Monday.
Youth League: South West Counties Youth

FOOTBALL MANAGEMENT TEAM
Manager: Tim Harris
Physio: John Fitzgerald
, Kit Manager: Tony Gilbert

2001-02
Captain: Darren Robison
Top scorer: Martin Paul 16
P.o.Y.: Pat Mountain

GROUND   Club Headquarters: Newport Stadium, Spytty Park,Langland Way, Newport,
South Wales   FAX 01633 666107   Tel: 01633 662262
Directions: From Severn Bridge on M4 take 1st exit signed Newport (jct 24), 1st left at r'bout
follow signs for industrial area, left at r'bout after 2 1/2miles, over 2 r'bouts, next left
for ground. Ample free parking available at ground
Capacity:4,300   Cover: 1,236   Seats: 1,236   Floodlights: Yes
Clubhouse: Small bar at ground with hot and cold snacks also available.
Club Shop: Open matchdays, sells a wide selection of souvenirs & programmes

Pages: 40   Price: £1.50
Editor: Wallace Brown (01633 265500)

Local Press:
South Wales Argus, South Wales Echo
Local Radio: Red Dragon, Real Radio

PREVIOUS   **Leagues:** Hellenic 89-90   **Grounds:** London Road, Moreton-in-Marsh 89-90; Somerton Park, Newport 90-92;
Gloucester City FC 92-94 (exile period due to dispute with FAW re League of Wales).
Names: Newport AFC were formed after the demise of Newport County in1988-89, name change 1999.

CLUB RECORDS Attendance: 3,721 v Blackpool. F.A.Cup , First Round Replay 2001-02
Win: 9-0 v Pontlottyn Blast Furnace (A), Welsh Cup First Round 1/9/90
Defeat: 1-6 v Stafford Rangers (A) BHL 6/1/96
Career Goalscorer: Chris Lilygreen 93   **Career Appearances:** Mark Price 275 (222 Lg + 53 cup)
Transfer fee paid:£5,000 for Shaun Chapple from Forest Green Rovers £1,000 from RedditchU for Paul Burton
Transfer fee received: E5,000 from Merthyr Tydfil for Craig Lima
BEST SEASON   FA Cup: First Round 2001-02   **FA Trophy:** 3rd Rd 99-00, 00-01   **FA Vase:** N/A
HONOURS   Hellenic Lge Prem Div 89-90 (Lge Cup 89-90); Glos Sen Cup Winners 93-94;Southern Lg. Mid Div Champions 94-95, R-up
98-99 Merit Cup Jnt Win 94-95, 98-99 Gwent FA Sen.Cup Winners 96-97,97-98,98-99,99-00 ,00-01,01-02Herefordshire Senior Cup. 98-99

Back row left to right: Tony Gilbert (Kit Manager), Nathan Davies, Steve Benton, Lewis Sommers, Matthew Rose, Lee Stanton, Martin Paul and Ray Brown (Asst Kit Manager).**Middle row:** Graham Jones (Club Doctor), Stuart James, Jeff Eckhart, Dean Lewis, Pat Mountain, Matt Taylor, Richard French, Billy Clark, Jason Perry and John Fitzgerald (Physio). **Front row:** Scott Walker, Steve Cowe, Ryan Souter, Tim Harris (Manager), Darren Robinson (Captain), Chris Hyde, (Assistant Manager)., Garry Shepherd, Scott Griffin and Darren Ryan.
Kneeling: Ryan Dorrian, Rhys Edwards (Left) and Jamie Hammonds and Raith Plant (right).

SOUTHERN LEAGUE PREMIER DIVISION

Date	Comp.	Opponents	Att.	Score	Goalscorers	
18.08	DM P	King's Lynn	1023	2 - 4	Shepherd 65 72	
20.08	DM P	SALISBURY CITY	810	0 - 0		
25.08	DM P	STAFFORD RANGERS	774	2 - 2	Walker 10, Eckhardt 85	
27.08	DM P	Merthyr Tydfil	848	1 - 1	James 47	
01.09	DM P	Kettering Town	1324	2 - 1	Walker 10, Souter 45	
03.09	DM P	BATH CITY	902	1 - 0	Paul 33	
08.09	DM P	Chelmsford City	602	1 - 3	Eckhardt 65	
11.09	DM P	Weymouth	804	1 - 2	Griffin 8	
15.09	DM P	WELLING UNITED	661	2 - 1	Shepherd 16, Souter 70	
18.09	DM P	Salisbury City	460	2 - 0	Rose 10, Eckhardt 29	
22.09	DM P	CAMBRIDGE CITY	669	2 - 2	Shepherd 26[p], Walker 75	
29.09	FA Cup Q2	Swindon Supermarine	577	1 - 1	Eckhardt 59	
01.10	FA Cup Q2 R	SWINDON SUPERMARINE	455	3 - 1	Shepherd 17, Paul 38 44	
06.10	DM P	Tamworth	812	0 - 2		
09.10	DM P	Bath City	708	1 - 2	Plant 87	
13.10	FA Cup Q3	Andover	648	4 - 0	Plant 38 44, Clark 45, Ryan 66	
16.10	FAW Prem B	Carmarthen Town	622	1 - 0	Ryan 20	
20.10	DM P	MOOR GREEN	702	2 - 1	Paul 45[p], Cowe 80	
22.10	DM P	WEYMOUTH	716	1 - 2	Paul 73[p]	
27.10	FA Cup Q4	Woking	2119	0 - 0		
29.10	FA Cup Q4 R	WOKING	1431	3 - 1	Ryan 11, Paul 65 79	
31.10	Gwent SC 1	Albion Rovers	250	5 - 3	Cowe 63 92, Souter 69[p], Thomas 83, Stephenson 112	
03.11	FA Trophy 1	Bath City	877	3 - 2	Paul 23, Ryan 43, Shepherd 83	
05.11	FAW Prem B	RHYL	519	0 - 0		
10.11	DM P	HINCKLEY UNITED	709	0 - 2		
12.11	Lge Cup 1	BATH CITY	333	1 - 3	Jones 71	
17.11	FA Cup 1	Blackpool	5005	2 - 2	Hughes 20[og], Clark 40	
19.11	FAW Prem B	CARMARTHEN TOWN	810	0 - 0		
24.11	DM P	TIVERTON TOWN	807	1 - 1	Rose 22	
28.11	FA Cup 1 R	BLACKPOOL	3721	1 - 4	Rose 24	
06.12	FA Trophy 2	Walton & Hersham	136	3 - 2	Paul 45, Whelan 46[og], Cowe 88	
08.12	DM P	Worcester City	1047	0 - 0		
11.12	FAW Prem B	Cwmbran Town	248	3 - 2	Clarke 9, Rose 28, Eckhardt 74	Barry Town
15.12	DM P	KING'S LYNN	655	2 - 1	Shephard 3, Paul 89[p]	
17.12	FAW Prem B	CWMBRAN TOWN	509	2 - 0	Cowe 45, Paul 74	
26.12	DM P	MERTHYR TYDFIL	1059	3 - 0	Carter 21, Cowe 54, Paul 90[p]	
29.12	DM P	TAMWORTH	883	2 - 1	Shephard 45 70	
08.01	FAW Prem B	Rhyl	93	2 - 1	Summers 41, Carter 50	
12.01	FA Trophy 3	Hampton & Richmond Borough	505	0 - 2		
15.01	FAW Prem QF	SWANSEA CITY	848	0 - 3		
19.01	DM P	NEWPORT IOW	651	0 - 0		
30.01	DM P	Tiverton Town	642	0 - 2		
09.02	DM P	Hinckley United	417	2 - 0	Walker 20, Rose 90	
16.02	DM P	KETTERING TOWN	722	1 - 2	Walker 45	
19.02	DM P	Stafford Rangers	502	1 - 2	Rose 11	
23.02	DM P	Crawley Town	1146	1 - 0	Paul 14	
02.03	DM P	ILKESTON TOWN	610	3 - 0	Rose 11, Cowe 27, Timmons 45[og]	
05.03	DM P	Newport IOW	443	4 - 0	Walker 46 72, Phillips 61, Ryan 90	
14.03	Gwent SC QF	Tredegar Town	150	1 - 0	Thomas 16	
16.03	DM P	WORCESTER CITY	752	0 - 2		
19.03	DM P	Cambridge City	477	2 - 1	Walker 62[p], Rose 85	
23.03	DM P	Folkestone Invicta	434	1 - 3	Rose 23	
25.03	DM P	Hednesford Town	620	2 - 3	Paul 82, Eckhardt 89	
30.03	DM P	Havant & Waterlooville	726	3 - 1	Paul 7 44, Walker 44	
01.04	DM P	HEDNESFORD TOWN	722	0 - 1		
06.04	DM P	Ilkeston Town	496	1 - 0	Fairbrother 4[og]	
09.04	DM P	Moor Green	324	2 - 1	Clark 19, Cowe 61	
13.04	DM P	CRAWLEY TOWN	653	1 - 1	Stevenson 20	
15.04	DM P	FOLKESTONE INVICTA	526	4 - 1	Rose 34, Towse 60[og], Paul 76, Walker 89	
18.04	Gwent SC SF	Chepstow Town	150	3 - 1	Edwards 52, Thomas 55, Fowler 78	
20.04	DM P	Welling United	649	0 - 0		
22.04	DM P	HAVANT & WATERLOOVILLE	525	2 - 0	Phillips 21 61	
27.04	DM P	CHELMSFORD CITY	804	3 - 0	Paul 11, Stevenson 28, Phillips 76	
07.05	Gwent SC F	RTB EBBW VALE	n.k	4 - 1	Phillips, French, Currie, Edwards	Caldicot Town

Goalkeepers:	Pat Mountain (Gloucester City), Jon Hallworth (Cardiff City)	
Defenders:	Andrew Thomas (Youth Team), Billy Clark (Forest Green Rovers), Gary Thorne (Newport C),	
	Jason Perry (Hull C), Jeff Eckhardt (Cardiff C), Lee Stanton (Cinderford T), Steve Benton (Cheltenham)	
Midfielders:	Darren Robinson, Matthew Rose (Gloucester C), Nathan Davies (Youth Team), Scott Walker (Bath C),	
	Darren Ryan (Merthyr Tydfil), Michael Fowler (Woking), Ryan Souter (Salisbury), Stuart James (Bath C)	
Forwards:	Garry Sheppard (Merthyr Tydfil), Neil Davis (Hednesford T), Steve Cowe (Swindon T),	
	Mark Dickenson (Trostre Spurs), Raith Plant	

PLAYING SQUAD

STAFFORD RANGERS

CLUB OFFICIALS

Chairman: J.Downing
Vice-Chairman: C.Went
Secretary: Peter Wall
c/o Stafford Rangers FC
Tel: 01785 602430

FOOTBALL MANAGEMENT TEAM
Manager: Phil Robinson
Coach: T.B.A.
Physio: T.B.A.

FACT FILE
Formed: 1876
Nickname: The Boro
Colours: Black & White stripes/black/black
Change: All Red
Midweek matchday: Tuesday
Reserves' League: T.B.A.

2001-02
Captain: Scott Dundas
P.o.Y.: Paul Kiely
TopScorer: Paul Kiely

£1.50

MAIN SPONSOR - FULWOOD ROOFING SUPPLIES

STAFFORD RANGERS v WORCESTER CITY
Official Matchday Magazine of Stafford Rangers FC

Pages: 40   Price: £1.50
Editor: Peter Wall Tel. 01785 602430
Local Press: Staffordshire Newsletter,
Express & Star, Evening Sentinel
Local Radio:
Radio Stoke, Beacon Radio, Signal Radio

GROUND Marston Road Stafford ST16 3BX Tel: 01785 602430 Fax : 01785 602431
Club Website: www.staffordrangers.co.uk

Directions: From M6 junction 14, A34 (Stone) to roundabout, straight over into Beaconside, take third right into Common Road, ground one mile ahead. From Town Centre, follow signs for B5066 (Sandon) turn left by new housing estate. Two miles from railway station

Capacity 3,000   Cover 1,500   Seats: 426   Floodlights: Yes

Clubhouse: Yes - Open every evening
Club Shop: Two shops, one old programmes and one souvenirs

PREVIOUS **Leagues:** Shropshire 1891-93, Birm 1893-96, 21-40, N Staffs 1896-1900, Cheshire 00-01, Birm Comb 00-12, 46-52, Cheshire Co. 52-69, N.P.L. 69-79, 83-85, Alliance Prem 79-83, GMVC 85-95
Grounds: Lammascotes, Stone Rd, Newtown, Doxey (until 1896)

CLUB RECORDS **Attendance:** 8,536 v Rotherham Utd FA Cup 3rd Rd 75
Win: 11-0 v Dudley Town FA Cup 6.9.58   **Defeat:** 0-12 v Burton Town Birmingham Lge 13.12.30
Career Goalscorer: M Cullerton 176   **Career Appearances:** Jim Sargent
Transfer fee paid: £13,000 for S Butterworth from VS Rugby 90
Transfer fee received: £100,000 for Stan Collymore from Crystal Palace 1990

BEST SEASON **FA Trophy:** Winners 1971-72 & 78-79. R-up 75-76
FA Cup: 4th Rd 74-75, 1-2 v Peterborough Utd. (H)   League clubs defeated: Halifax, Stockport, Rotherham

HONOURS Birm Comb Champ 12-13; Birm Lge Champ 25-26; N.P.L. Champ 71-72, 84-85, Champ Shield 84-85; FA Trophy 71-72, 78-79, R-up 75-76; Bob Lord Trophy 85-86; Wednesday Charity Cup 20-21; Mid F/light Cup 70-71; Jim Thompson Shield 86-87; Staffs Sen Cup 54-55 56-57 62-63 71-72 77-78 86-87 91-92 Dr.Martens Western Division 99-00

Players progressing: M Aleksic (Plymouth), J Arnold (Blackburn), R Williams/MCullerton/T Bailey (Port Vale), K Barnes (Man City), A Lee (Tranmere), ECameron (Exeter), W Blunt (Wolves), G Bullock (Barnsley), K Mottershead(Doncaster), McIlvenny (WBA), S Collymore (C Palace), P Devlin (Notts Co.),R Price (Birmingham C.)

Paul Kiely
Leading Goalscorer and Player of the Year
in action against Guiseley last season.
Photo: Chris Elsey

Date	Comp.	Opponents	Att.	Score	Goalscorers
18.08	DM P	NEWPORT IOW	652	1 - 0	Eccleston 15
20.08	DM P	Ilkeston Town	702	2 - 2	Kiely 70, Lovatt 74
25.08	DM P	Newport County	774	2 - 2	Kiely 38, Ecclestone 40
27.08	DM P	HEDNESFORD TOWN	1381	3 - 0	Dundas 32, O'Connor 57 80
01.09	DM P	Havant & Waterlooville	584	1 - 2	Dundas 46[p]
04.09	DM P	HINCKLEY UNITED	593	4 - 2	Kiely 14 17 50, O'Connor 28
08.09	DM P	WEYMOUTH	779	2 - 1	Simpkin 17, Kiely 82
11.09	DM P	Kettering Town	1214	0 - 1	
15.09	DM P	Crawley Town	1028	2 - 1	Kiely 63 82
18.09	DM P	ILKESTON TOWN	725	1 - 2	Kiely 45
22.09	DM P	SALISBURY CITY	698	3 - 0	Francis 50, O'Connor 62, Wray 74
29.09	FA Cup Q2	Newcastle Town	580	1 - 0	O'Connor 42
06.10	DM P	Tiverton Town	608	3 - 3	Kiely 21[p], Eccleston 36, Brindley 61
09.10	DM P	Hinckley United	415	0 - 3	
13.10	FA Cup Q3	St Margaretsbury	346	3 - 0	Simkin 45, Kiely 60, Francis 81
20.10	DM P	FOLKESTONE INVICTA	696	1 - 2	Kiely 4
23.10	DM P	KETTERING TOWN	679	2 - 3	Kiely 51, Brindley 74
27.10	FA Cup Q4	Canvey Island	561	1 - 5	Kiely 56
03.11	FA Trophy 1	Guiseley	337	0 - 0	
06.11	FA Trophy 1 R	GUISELEY	442	4 - 2	Eccleston 2 89, Read 55, Dundas 84
10.11	DM P	CRAWLEY TOWN	535	0 - 0	
13.11	Lge Cup 1	BLOXWICH UNITED	231	1 - 1	Francis 112 Lost 1-4 after pens.
17.11	DM P	Newport IOW	466	0 - 1	
20.11	Staffs SC 2	KIDSGROVE ATHLETIC	199	15 - 0	Kiely 4, Dundas 3, Francis 6, Wood 2
24.11	DM P	Welling United	500	2 - 3	Kiely 27, Simkin 38
01.12	FA Trophy 2	VAUXHALL MOTORS	555	0 - 3	
08.12	DM P	HAVANT & WATERLOOVILLE	558	0 - 2	
11.12	DM P	Merthyr Tydfil	325	0 - 2	
15.12	DM P	Chelmsford City	602	0 - 0	
29.12	DM P	King's Lynn	749	0 - 2	
15.01	Staffs SC QF	ROCESTER	326	4 - 1	Simkin 31, Kiely 35 40 58
19.01	DM P	CHELMSFORD CITY	598	2 - 1	Kiely 84[p], Brindley 90
02.02	DM P	BATH CITY	483	2 - 1	Kiely 45, Wray 67
09.02	DM P	MERTHYR TYDFIL	694	1 - 0	Kiely 5
12.02	DM P	Tamworth	1213	0 - 1	
19.02	DM P	NEWPORT COUNTY	502	2 - 1	Kiely 9 40
23.02	DM P	Folkestone Invicta	339	1 - 2	Lovatt 63
02.03	DM P	WELLING UNITED	587	2 - 1	Heath 5, Kiely 80
04.03	DM P	Hednesford Town	1319	3 - 3	Eccleston 74, Kiely 80, Simkin 90
09.03	DM P	TAMWORTH	1058	0 - 1	
12.03	DM P	WORCESTER CITY	515	1 - 1	Kiely 74
16.03	DM P	Bath City	639	3 - 4	Shaw 30, Dundas 55, Kiely 63
19.03	DM P	MOOR GREEN	498	3 - 4	Wray 28, Shaw 59, Dundas 71[p]
23.03	DM P	Salisbury City	382	4 - 1	Dundas 26 36 57, Cooper 44[og]
30.03	DM P	KING'S LYNN	599	3 - 2	Heath 19 43, Kiely 55
01.04	DM P	Worcester City	1017	2 - 1	Kiely 17, Eccleston 84
06.04	DM P	TIVERTON TOWN	648	6 - 2	Dundas 11, Berks 23, Kiely 27 35, Shaw 63, Heath 90
09.04	DM P	Cambridge City	265	1 - 1	Berks 21
13.04	DM P	Weymouth	630	1 - 0	Heath 28
15.04	Staffs SC SF	Newcastle Town	303	0 - 1	
20.04	DM P	CAMBRIDGE CITY	767	3 - 0	Berks 9, Kiely 22 68
27.04	DM P	Moor Green	491	1 - 1	Kiely 51

PLAYING SQUAD

Goalkeepers: Ryan Price (Telford Utd)

Defenders: Darren Boughey (Stoke C), Andrew Brookes (Youth Team), Lee Barrow (Hednesford T), Wayne Daniel (Boldmere St Michaels), Karl Ward (Youth Team), Alex Gibson (Port Vale), Jon Howard (Tamworth), Richard Beale (Redditch Utd)

Midfielders: Craig Lovatt (Leek T), David Berks (Aston Villa), Phil Robinson (Hereford Utd), Daryl Wilkes (Kidsgrove Ath), Ian Reed (Worcester C), Robert Heath (Stoke C)

Forwards: Tony Eccleston (Hednesford T), Chris Rowell (Hereford Utd), Dennis Bailey (Halesowen T), Robin Gibson (Wrexham), Andy Bott (Newcastle T), Danny Davidson (Hereford Utd), Joe O'Conor (Kingstonian)

TAMWORTH

CLUB OFFICIALS

Chairman: Bob Andrews
Vice-Chairman:
President: Len Gendle

Secretary: Russell Moore,
97 Honeybourne,Belgrave,Tamworth,Staffs
B77 2JG Tel Nos: 01827 706538 (H) 01827
65798 (W)
Press Officer: Dave Clayton
Commercial Manager: Russell Moore

FOOTBALL MANAGEMENT TEAM
Manager: Darron Gee
Asst Man.:Dave Norton
Physio: Peter Denham

FACT FILE
Formed: 1933
Sponsors: Bloor Homes
Nickname: Lambs or Town
Colours: All Red
Change colours: White,black,black
Midweek home matchday: Tuesday
Reserves' League: Central Conference

2001-02
Captain: Darren Crocutt
P.o.Y.: Darren Acton
Top scorer: Darren Roberts 23

Tamworth v Merthyr Tydfil
Pages: 28 Price: £1.50
Editor: Dave Clayton
Press: Tamworth Herald,Tamworth Times
Radio:Centre FM,Captal Gold/Radio WM
Club Website: www.thelambs.co.uk
Club's email address: rod@tamworthfc.co.uk

GROUND The Lamb Ground, Kettlebrook, Tamworth, Staffs B77 1AA
Tel: 01827 65798 FAX:0182762236
Directions: Follow the signs for Town Centre/Snowdome, then forKettlebrook.
The entrance to the ground &car parks is in Kettlebrook Road, 50yards
from the traffic island by the railway viaduct (B5000)
Capacity: 4,100 Cover: 1,191 Seats: 518 Floodlights: Yes
Clubhouse: Club on ground - open matchdays, training nights and tote night only
Clubshop: Yes

PREVIOUS **Leagues:** Birmingham Combination 33-54, West Midlands (initially Birmingham Lg) 54-72 84-88, Southern 72-79 83-84,
Northern Premier 79-83 **Grounds:** Jolly Sailor Ground 33-34

CLUB RECORDS **Attendance:** 4,920 v Atherstone Tn, Birm Comb 48 **Career Goalscorer:** Graham Jessop 195
Win: 14-4 v Holbrook Institute (H), Bass Vase 34 **Season Goalscorer:** Percy Vials 64 (36-37)
Defeat: 0-11 v Solihull (A), Birmingham Comb. 40 **Career Appearances:** Dave Seedhouse 869
Transfer Fee paid: £7,500 for Tony Hemmings (Ilkeston Town) Dec 2001
Transfer Fee received: £7,500 for Martin Myers (Telford Utd, 90)

BEST SEASON **FA Cup:** 2nd Rd 69-70 (0-6 at Gillingham) **FA Trophy:** Quarter Final **FA Vase:** Winners 88-89

HONOURS FA Vase 88-89, West Mids Lg 63-64 65-66 71-72 87-88 (R-up(2) 67-69, Div 2 55-56, Lg Cup(5) 64-66 71-72 85-86 87-88 (R-up 70-71)), Birmingham Snr Cup 60-61 65-66 68-69 (R-up 36-37 63-64), Staffs Snr Cup 58-59 63-64 65-66 01-02 (R-up 55-56 66-67 70-71), Midland F'lit Cup R-up 71-72 72-73, Camkin Cup 71-72 (R-up 70-71). Dr Martens Lg.Midland Division Winners 96-97

Players progressing: P Hilton (WBA 49), A Godridge (Swansea 50), W Ealing (Doncaster), Higgins (Fulham), P Weir (Cardiff), S Fox (Wrexham), S Cartwright (Colchester 88), S Ryder (Walsall), D Williams (Brentford)

Back row left to right: Mark Hallam, Mark Turner, Ron Gould, Gavin Saxby, Darren Acton, Jon Howard and David Foy.
Middle row: Pete Denham, Ian McKenna, Richard Follett, Nick & Dave Hayward, Scott Richards, Rob Warner, David Norton and Buster Belford.
Front row: Paul Hatton, Rob Mutchell, Degsy Bond,Gary Mills,Darren Gee, Lee Wilson and Darren Grocutt.

Date	Comp.	Opponents	Att.	Score	Goalscorers
18.08	DM P	HAVANT & WATERLOOVILLE	582	1 - 1	Turner 43
20.08	DM P	Hednesford Town	931	2 - 1	Hallam 9, Roberts 72
25.08	DM P	Chelmsford City	491	1 - 1	Mutchell 40
27.08	DM P	MOOR GREEN	638	2 - 0	Turner 2 49
01.09	DM P	Weymouth	729	1 - 2	Turner 25
04.09	DM P	KETTERING TOWN	803	1 - 0	Rickards 27
08.09	DM P	CRAWLEY TOWN	642	2 - 0	Foy 1, Hatton 74
10.09	DM P	Ilkeston Town	787	1 - 2	Hallam 22
15.09	DM P	BATH CITY	689	1 - 1	Hallam 11
18.09	DM P	HEDNESFORD TOWN	623	3 - 0	Wilson 49, Hallam 53, Mutchell 76
22.09	DM P	Newport IOW	524	4 - 0	Wilson 11, Hallam 13, Rickards 54, Roberts 81
25.09	Staffs SC 2	Pelsall Villa	225	2 - 2	Anger 30, Roberts 85
29.09	FA Cup Q2	Bromsgrove Rovers	873	2 - 2	Hallam 28 78
02.10	FA Cup Q2 R	BROMSGROVE ROVERS	724	1 - 0	Wilson 115
06.10	DM P	NEWPORT COUNTY	812	2 - 0	Roberts 8, Colley 82
09.10	DM P	Kettering Town	1395	1 - 1	Bailey 9
13.10	FA Cup Q3	WROXHAM	804	3 - 1	Gould 26, Rickards 57, Hallam 81
20.10	DM P	NEWPORT IOW	685	5 - 1	Roberts 14 25, Turner 27, Bailey 75, Hatton 89
27.10	FA Cup Q4	CIRENCESTER TOWN	1210	2 - 1	Gould 26, Colley 84
30.10	DM P	ILKESTON TOWN	752	1 - 1	Colley 55
03.11	FA Trophy 1	Leek Town	500	1 - 0	Warner 36
10.11	DM P	King's Lynn	874	1 - 1	Hallam 73
13.11	Lge Cup 1	BEDWORTH UNITED	410	1 - 4	Robinson 60[og]
17.11	FA Cup 1	ROCHDALE	3119	1 - 1	Wilson 43
20.11	Birm SC 2	BOLDMERE ST MICHAELS	232	2 - 3	Kearns 1, Roberts 36
24.11	DM P	WORCESTER CITY	826	3 - 2	McHugh 46, Hallam 73, Grocutt 76
27.11	FA Cup 1 R	Rochdale	2709	0 - 1	
04.12	FA Trophy 2	Sutton Coldfield Town	311	3 - 0	Colley 27, Turner 72, Foy 90
08.12	DM P	CAMBRIDGE CITY	753	2 - 2	Gould 17, Rickards 53
11.12	Staffs SC 2 R	PELSALL VILLA	210	8 - 0	Follett, Gould, Rickards, Colley 2, Mutchell, Mills 2
15.12	DM P	Havant & Waterlooville	589	2 - 0	Daish 10[og], Turner 70
26.12	DM P	Moor Green	1010	2 - 3	Roberts 21, Hallam 87
29.12	DM P	Newport County	883	1 - 2	Gould 90
05.01	DM P	Salisbury City	444	2 - 1	Grocutt 19, Roberts 65
12.01	FA Trophy 3	Worksop Town	904	3 - 4	Colley 14, Roberts 42 89
15.01	DM P	HINCKLEY UNITED	663	2 - 1	Roberts 23, Grocutt 77
19.01	DM P	Bath City	787	2 - 1	Turner 5, Colley 18
30.01	Staffs SC QF	BLOXWICH UNITED	n.k	99 - -1	
02.02	DM P	TIVERTON TOWN	826	3 - 2	Colley 12, Roberts 16[p] 57
09.02	DM P	Worcester City	1317	2 - 0	Hemming 54, Foy 56
12.02	DM P	STAFFORD RANGERS	1213	1 - 0	Rickards 88
16.02	DM P	FOLKESTONE INVICTA	955	1 - 1	Roberts 10
19.02	DM P	Tiverton Town	848	2 - 2	Hallam 65 87
23.02	DM P	KING'S LYNN	852	4 - 1	Hemmings 34 43, Roberts 83, Turner 88
02.03	DM P	Merthyr Tydfil	1014	1 - 1	Roberts 83
09.03	DM P	Stafford Rangers	1058	1 - 0	Hemmings 49
16.03	DM P	Crawley Town	1830	2 - 1	Roberts 12 49[p]
19.03	DM P	WELLING UNITED	975	1 - 0	Colley 77
23.03	DM P	MERTHYR TYDFIL	1111	2 - 0	Follett 70, Roberts 90
26.03	Staffs SC SF	RUSHALL OLYMPIC	362	4 - 2	Hallam 4 80, Gall 63, Rickards 74
30.03	DM P	CHELMSFORD CITY	1237	1 - 0	Hemmings 20
01.04	DM P	Hinckley United	1102	0 - 1	
06.04	DM P	WEYMOUTH	1165	3 - 0	Hemmings 25, Hallam 41, Rickards 90
09.04	DM P	Welling United	504	3 - 3	Grocutt 21, Gould 27, Hallam 34
13.04	DM P	Cambridge City	617	1 - 1	Hallam 35
20.04	DM P	SALISBURY CITY	2240	5 - 1	Turner 49, Gould 54, Grocutt 58, Hallam 72, Roberts 80
27.04	DM P	Folkestone Invicta	1277	3 - 3	Roberts 31 78, Walsh 55
02.05	Staffs SC F(1)	NEWCASTLE TOWN	582	3 - 1	Hallam 45, Grocutt 69, Roberts 76
07.05	Staffs SC F(2)	Newcastle Town	371	0 - 0	

Match Facts 2001-02

PLAYING SQUAD

Goalkeepers: Darren Acton (Kidderminster), Chris Gibson (Cadbury Ath)

Defenders: Darren Grocutt (Burton Alb.), David Haywood (Sutton Coldfield T), David Robinson (Kings Lynn), Frazer McHugh (Bromsgrove), Paul Hatton (Hednesford T), Rob Mutchell (Kettering T.), Rob Warner (Hereford), Steve Walsh (Barrow T)

Midfielders: Dave Norton (Gainsborough), Nick Colley (Telford), Mark Cooper (Forest Green R.), Richard Follett (R.C. Warwick), Andy Turner (Yeovil), Brian McGorry (Chester), Mark Turner (Kings Lynn), Tony Hemmings (Ilkeston)

Forwards: Mark Hallam (Forest Green R.), Lee Wilson (Spalding Utd), Mark Sale (Doncaster Rov.), Ian McKenna (Youth Team), Luke Rowlett (Rushden &Diamonds), Scott Ricketts (Derby C)

TIVERTON TOWN

TIVERTON TOWN
v WORCESTER CITY
Wednesday 21st August 2002 Kick off 7.45pm

PREMIER LEAGUE
£1.50

CLUB OFFICIALS
President: Dr Gavin Haig F.R.C.S.
Chairman: Dave Wright
Vice-Chairman: Pete Buxton
Football Secretary: Ramsay Findlay
35 Park Road, Tiverton, Devon EX16 6AY
Tel: 01884 256341
Treasurer: Kimm Smith
General Secretary: Tony Floyde

FOOTBALL MANAGEMENT TEAM
Manager: Martyn Rogers
Assistant Manager: Martin Grimshaw
Physio: Dai Morgan
Assistant Physio: Mike Perry

FACT FILE

Formed: 1920   Nickname: Tivvy
Colours: All Yellow
Change colours: All white
Midweek matches: Wednesday
Reserves' League: None
2001-02
Top Goalscorer: Kevin Nancekivell 20
Captain: Nicky Marker
P.o.Y.: Phil Everett

GROUND: Ladysmead, Bolham Road, Tiverton, Devon EX16 8SG   Tel: 01884 252397
Website: www.tiverton-town-fc.co.uk

Directions: M5 Jct 27, west towards Tiverton on A361, continue to end of dual carriageway
and turn left at r'about; ground entrance 300yds on right alongside BP petrol station

Pages: 56   Price: £1.50 (with colour)
Editor/ Press Officer: John Fournier
Tel: 01884 32654 & 07980 543634M

Capacity: 3,500   Seats: 400   Cover: 2,100   Floodlights: Yes

Clubhouse: Lunctimes, evenings. All day Sat during season. 3 bars. Food(burgers, chips etc)
Club Shop: Yes

HONOURS   FA Vase 97-98 98-99; Western Lg 93-94 94-95 96-97 97-98 (R-up 92-93 95-96 98-99);
Les Phillips Cup 92-93 94-95 95-96 96-97 97-98; Amateur Trophy 77-78 78-79, Div 1 R-up 88-89;
Devon St Lukes Cup 90-91 91-92 92-93 94-95 96-97 (R-up 89-90); Devon & Exeter Lg 51-52 66-67 70-71 84-85;
Devon Snr Cup 55-56 65-66; East Devon Snr Cup 35-36 37-38 52-53 55-56 60-61 62-63 66-67;
North Devon Charity Cup 72-73 86-87. Devon St Luke's Bowl 99-00; Dr. Martens Western Div. R-up 2000-01

PREVIOUS   **League:** Devon & Exeter; Western League   **Ground:** The Elms, Blundell Road 1920-39

BEST SEASON **FA Vase:** Winners 97-98 98-99, R-up 92-93
FA Cup: 1st Rnd 90-91 91-92 94-95 97-98

RECORD   **Attendance:** 3,000 v Leyton Orient, FA Cup First Round Proper 1994-95
Career Goalscorer: Phil Everett
Record Win: (DML) 7-1 v Cirenbcester 2001   **Record Defeat:** (DML) 2-6 v Stafford Rangers (A) 2001-02
Players progressing: Jason Smith (Coventry City 93 & Swansea City 98), Mark Saunders (1995) & Kevin Nancekivell (00) Plymouth Argyle

Back row, left to right: Martyn Grimshaw (Assistant Manager), David Steele, Antony Lynch, Steve Peters, Jon Vaughan, Nathan Rudge, Paul
Edwards, Phil Everett, Rob Cousins, Marcus Grose and Alan Morgan (Physio). **Front row :** Kevin Nancekivell, Luke Vinnicombe, Scott Rogers,
Steve Winter, Martyn Rogers (Manager), Jason Rees, Danny Haines, Richard Pears and James Mudge.

Date	Comp.	Opponents	Att.	Score	Goalscorers
18.08	DM P	FOLKESTONE INVICTA	903	2 - 0	Everett 13, Lynch 76
22.08	DM P	Havant & Waterlooville	505	3 - 3	Ovens 45, Lynch 49, Pears 87
25.08	DM P	Newport IOW	555	0 - 3	
27.08	DM P	WEYMOUTH	1083	0 - 1	
01.09	DM P	CRAWLEY TOWN	726	1 - 2	Nancekivell 37[p]
04.09	DM P	Merthyr Tydfil	564	2 - 1	Winter 54, Lynch 90
08.09	DM P	KING'S LYNN	743	1 - 1	Lynch 82
11.09	DM P	Salisbury City	417	3 - 0	Nancekivell 46, Ovens 53 80
15.09	DM P	Moor Green	339	1 - 1	Marker 71
19.09	DM P	HAVANT & WATERLOOVILLE	645	0 - 1	
22.09	DM P	Chelmsford City	705	2 - 2	Ovens 17, Chenoweth 88
29.09	FA Cup Q2	Salisbury City	586	3 - 3	Nancekivell 49 80[p], Ovens 53
03.10	FA Cup Q2 R	SALISBURY CITY	779	3 - 1	Pears 49 78, Nancekivell 81[p]
06.10	DM P	STAFFORD RANGERS	608	3 - 3	Pears 3, Rogers 5, Lynch 11
10.10	DM P	MERTHYR TYDFIL	499	1 - 3	Everett 90
13.10	FA Cup Q3	OXFORD CITY	676	3 - 1	Everett 5, Winter 51, Lynch 90
20.10	DM P	Worcester City	1040	2 - 4	Leonard 28, Nancekivell 46
24.10	DM P	SALISBURY CITY	528	1 - 0	Everett 36
27.10	FA Cup Q4	Billericay Town	926	2 - 1	Rogers 52, Pears 63
03.11	FA Trophy 1	Folkestone Invicta	365	1 - 0	Nancekivell 28
07.11	Devon SLCB QF	EXMOUTH TOWN	413	7 - 0	Mudge 9 28 66 77, Everett 19, Lynch 34, Nancekivell 41
10.11	DM P	Welling United	478	1 - 1	Winter 7
13.11	Lge Cup 1	Clevedon Town	322	2 - 5	Lynch 41, Mudge 90
17.11	FA Cup 1	Cardiff City	6638	1 - 3	Nancekivell 82
24.11	DM P	Newport County	807	1 - 1	Everett 80
01.12	FA Trophy 2	CROYDON	740	6 - 0	Rogers 6, Gross 14, Nancekivell 25 28 62, Mudge 30
08.12	DM P	HEDNESFORD TOWN	703	2 - 0	Everett 65, Mudge 69
15.12	DM P	Folkestone Invicta	281	3 - 0	Rogers 22, Nancekivell 46, Chenoweth 75
19.12	DM P	WORCESTER CITY	571	2 - 0	Everett 76 78
22.12	DM P	ILKESTON TOWN	783	3 - 2	Steele 70, Mudge 76, Winter 88
26.12	DM P	Weymouth	1303	1 - 2	Pears 83
29.12	DM P	Hinckley United	471	4 - 3	Marker 40, Mudge 78 90, Pears 85
05.01	DM P	NEWPORT IOW	822	2 - 1	Nancekivell 87, Lynch 89
12.01	FA Trophy 3	YEOVIL TOWN	2320	1 - 3	Lockwood 83[og]
19.01	DM P	MOOR GREEN	738	2 - 0	Steele 76, Nancekivell 78[p]
30.01	DM P	NEWPORT COUNTY	642	2 - 0	Lynch 85, Ovens 90
02.02	DM P	Tamworth	826	2 - 3	Everett 54, Peters 78
09.02	DM P	CAMBRIDGE CITY	734	5 - 0	Everett 26, Chenoweth 28 78, Nancekivell 31, Mudge 89
16.02	DM P	Ilkeston Town	527	2 - 0	Nancekivell 50, Everett 73
19.02	DM P	TAMWORTH	848	2 - 2	Nancekivell 3, Chenoweth 38
23.02	DM P	Kettering Town	1441	0 - 0	
02.03	DM P	Bath City	958	2 - 4	Ovens 60, Everett 75
09.03	DM P	HINCKLEY UNITED	722	1 - 1	Ovens 4
16.03	DM P	Cambridge City	437	3 - 1	Lynch 6 20, Nancekivell 58
23.03	DM P	WELLING UNITED	730	0 - 2	
26.03	Devon SLCB SF	EXETER CITY	712	1 - 2	Mudge 45
30.03	DM P	Crawley Town	867	0 - 3	
01.04	DM P	BATH CITY	860	3 - 1	Ovens 10 52 76
06.04	DM P	Stafford Rangers	648	2 - 6	Mudge 71, Lynch 73
09.04	DM P	King's Lynn	548	1 - 0	Chenoweth 45
13.04	DM P	CHELMSFORD CITY	691	0 - 1	
20.04	DM P	Hednesford Town	777	1 - 2	Lynch 63
27.04	DM P	KETTERING TOWN	1996	1 - 2	Chenoweth 25

Match Facts 2001-02

PLAYING SQUAD

Goalkeepers: Paul Edwards (Bideford)

Defenders: Neil Saunders (Bath), David Steele (Willand Rovers), Marcus Gross (Exeter), Rob Cousins (Forest Green), Steve Peters (Clevedon), Danny Haines (Merthyr Tydfil), Luke Vinnicombe (Clevedon T), Nicky Marker (Cheltenham T), Russell Gee (Exeter), Stuart Smith (Chard T)

Midfielders: Scott Rodgers (Bristol C), John Wilkinson (Exeter C), Nathan Rudge (Chippenham T), Steve Lester (Gloucester), Steve Winter (Basingstoke), Jason Rees (Torquay Utd), Kevin Nancekivell (Plymouth A), Paul Chenoweth (Gloucester C), Steve Ovens (Witney T)

Forwards: Anthony Lynch (Taunton T), Phil Everett (Dawlish), James Mudge (Exeter), Richard Pears (Clyst Rovers)

WELLING UNITED

MATCHDAY MAGAZINE £1.50

WELLING UNITED

WINGS

COOMES

40 Years 1963-2003

SEASON 2002-2003

BOOKMAKERS

CLUB OFFICIALS

President	E Brackstone
Chairman	Paul Websdale
Vice Chairman	Steven Pain
General Manager	Graham Hobbins
Club Secretary	Barrie Hobbins
	c/o the club

Tel: 0208 301 1196 Fax:0208 301 5676

Press Officer	Paul Carter
	c/o the club

FOOTBALL MANAGEMENT TEAM

Manager:Bill Williams
Coach: Nigel Donn
Physio: Peter Green

FACT FILE

Founded:	1963
Nickname:	The Wings
Club Sponsors:	E.Coomes, Bookmakers
Club colours:	Red/red/white
Change colours:	All white
Midweek home matchday:	Tuesday
Welling Wingsline:	09068 80 06 54

2001-02

Leading goalscorer:	Gary Abbott 31
Player of the Year:	Anthony Riviere
Captain:	Kevan Seabury

GROUND Park View Road Ground, Welling, Kent DA16 1SY
Tel: 0208 301 1196 Fax: 0208 301 5676

DIRECTIONS: M25, then A2 towards London. Take Welling turn-off, ground 1 mile.
By rail to Welling station (BR) - ground 3/4 mile.
CAPACITY: 4,000 **SEATED:** 1,070 **CLUBHOUSE:** Open on match days
CLUB SHOP: Sells programmes (League & non-League), scarves, mugs, caps, hats,
badges, replica kits etc. Manager Peter Mason.

Pages: 40 Price: £1.50
Editor: Barrie Hobbins

Local Press: Kentish Times;
Bexleyheath & Welling Mercury
Local Radio: Radio Kent;
Radio Invicta; R.T.M.

PREVIOUS	**Leagues:** Eltham & Dist. Lge 1963-71, London Spartan Lge 1971-77, Athenian Lge 1977-79, Southern Lge 1979-86, 2001
	Conference 86-2000 **Grounds:** Butterfly Lane, Eltham - 1963-78
RECORDS	**Attendance:** 4,100 v Gillingham, FA Cup
	Win: 7-1 v Dorking 1985-86 **Defeat:** 0-7 v Welwyn garden City 1972-73
	Career Goalscorer: John Bartley - 533 **Career Appearances:** Nigel Ransom - 1,066 & Ray Burgess - 1,044
	Transfer fee paid: £30,000 for Gary Abbott from Enfield
	Transfer fee received: £95,000 from Birmingham City for Steve Finnan.1995
BEST SEASON	**FA Cup:** Third Round 1988-89 0-1 v Blackburn Rovers League clubs defeated: Gillingham
	FA Trophy: Quarter Final 1988-89 0-1 v Macclesfield
HONOURS	London Spartan League 1978; Southern League Premier Division 1985/86; Kent Senior Cup 1985/86 98-99; London
	Senior Cup 1989/90; London Challenge Cup 1991/92, Runners-up 1993/94.

PLAYERS PROGRESSING: Paul Barron(Plymouth A), Andy Townsend (Southampton), Ian Thompson (AFC Bournemouth), John Bartley (Millwall), Dave Smith (Gillingham), Murray Jones (C. Palace), Kevin Shoemake (Peterborough), Tony Agana (Watford,), Duncan Horton (Barnet), Mark Hone (Southend), Steve Finnan & Steve Barnes (Birmingham City),Dean Standen (Luton Town)

L-R - Back Row: Kevin Seabury, Ray Aboagye, Paul Lorraine, Luke Morrish, Steve Sodje. **Middle:** Peter Green (physio), Dean Standers, Raphael Nade, James Simpson, Anthony Hogg, Russell Edwards, Glen Knight, John Farley, Ray Burgess (asst. manager). **Front:** Dave Powell, Anthony Riviere, Mark Hone, Bill Williams (manager), Gary Abbott, Billy Burgess, Paul Jones.

Match Facts 2001-02

Date	Comp.	Opponents	Att.	Score	Goalscorers
18.08	DM P	HINCKLEY UNITED	501	3 - 2	Overton 10, Powell 20, Glover 41
21.08	DM P	Newport IOW	518	1 - 1	Abbott 21
25.08	DM P	Weymouth	705	1 - 1	Standen 75
27.08	DM P	FOLKESTONE INVICTA	602	2 - 4	Riviere 39, Powell 42
01.09	DM P	Ilkeston Town	497	2 - 3	Standen 1, Fleming 58
04.09	DM P	HAVANT & WATERLOOVILLE	443	1 - 2	Lorraine 63
08.09	DM P	Moor Green	234	1 - 2	Overton 75[p]
11.09	DM P	CAMBRIDGE CITY	465	4 - 4	Overton 31, Abbott 62 64 88[p]
15.09	DM P	Newport County	661	1 - 2	Riviere 21
18.09	DM P	NEWPORT IOW	331	3 - 0	Abbott 18 41, Edwards 72
22.09	DM P	MERTHYR TYDFIL	512	1 - 0	Standen 55
29.09	FA Cup Q2	EGHAM TOWN	373	1 - 0	Abbott 51
06.10	DM P	Salisbury City	199	1 - 0	Abbott 5
09.10	DM P	Havant & Waterlooville	549	0 - 1	
13.10	FA Cup Q3	NEWPORT IOW	424	3 - 0	Riviere 11, Flemming 65, Abbott 67
20.10	DM P	KETTERING TOWN	608	1 - 1	Powell 20
22.10	DM P	Cambridge City	276	0 - 2	
27.10	FA Cup Q4	Folkestone Invicta	724	1 - 1	Abbott 31
30.10	FA Cup Q4 R	FOLKESTONE INVICTA	1026	5 - 1	Powell 35 47 72, Overton 39, Edwards 53
06.11	Kent SC 1	ERITH & BELVEDERE	204	1 - 1	Miles 91 Won 4-3 after pens.
10.11	DM P	TIVERTON TOWN	478	1 - 1	Rutherford 14
13.11	Lge Cup 1	Tonbridge Angels	234	1 - 2	Saunders 43
17.11	FA Cup 1	Reading	5338	0 - 1	
24.11	DM P	STAFFORD RANGERS	500	3 - 2	Abbott 33 54, Powell 81
01.12	FA Trophy 2	ERITH & BELVEDERE	400	8 - 1	Abbott 28 42 56 58 83, Watts 36, Powell 38, Standen 43
08.12	DM P	Merthyr Tydfil	434	4 - 4	Standen 1 60, Flemming 38, Riviere 88
15.12	DM P	WORCESTER CITY	464	1 - 3	Rutherford 35
26.12	DM P	CRAWLEY TOWN	675	2 - 3	Abbott 18, Samuels 70
29.12	DM P	BATH CITY	518	4 - 0	Abbott 38 81, Samuels 88, Johnson 90
05.01	DM P	ILKESTON TOWN	442	1 - 0	Brown 18
12.01	FA Trophy 3	Grays Athletic	378	4 - 2	Abbott 5 41 76 90[p]
15.01	London SC 4	METROPOLITAN POLICE	122	3 - 1	Barnes 17, Powell 60 82
19.01	DM P	Crawley Town	1777	4 - 2	Abbott 25, Tyne 35, Edwards 40, Riviere 74
29.01	DM P	Kettering Town	1175	1 - 3	Rutherford 84
02.02	FA Trophy 4	Woking	1815	2 - 4	Abbott 61, Standen 77
09.02	DM P	Hednesford Town	601	1 - 1	Hogg 50
12.02	DM P	Bath City	496	1 - 2	Edwards 31
16.02	DM P	CHELMSFORD CITY	654	2 - 4	Standen 11 54
19.02	London SC QF	Uxbridge	n.k	2 - 5	
23.02	DM P	HEDNESFORD TOWN	500	4 - 1	Abbott 10 81, Tyne 41 84
02.03	DM P	Stafford Rangers	587	1 - 2	Riviere 61
05.03	Kent SC QF	Fisher Athletic	121	2 - 3	D Powell 38, Brown 58
16.03	DM P	SALISBURY CITY	516	5 - 1	Standen 45, Rutherford 65, Abbott 76, Powell 80, Lindsey 88
19.03	DM P	Tamworth	975	0 - 1	
23.03	DM P	Tiverton Town	730	2 - 0	Abbott 47, Johnson 80
27.03	DM P	King's Lynn	439	2 - 1	Tyne 4, Abbott 10
30.03	DM P	WEYMOUTH	570	1 - 1	Tyne 5
01.04	DM P	Folkestone Invicta	504	0 - 0	
06.04	DM P	KING'S LYNN	494	0 - 1	
09.04	DM P	TAMWORTH	504	3 - 3	Tyne 16, Bryan 28, Standen 78
13.04	DM P	Worcester City	803	1 - 2	Standen 46
16.04	DM P	MOOR GREEN	417	1 - 1	Powell 13
20.04	DM P	NEWPORT COUNTY	649	0 - 0	
22.04	DM P	Chelmsford City	573	2 - 1	Statham 25[og], Brown 90
27.04	DM P	Hinckley United	378	0 - 1	

PLAYING SQUAD

Goalkeepers: Glenn Knight (Boreham Wood)
Defenders: Danny Twin (Youth Team), Chris Currie (Gravesend), Kevin Seabury (Dover Ath.), Russell Edwards (Dulwich), Luke Morrish (Dartford), Mark Hone (Kettering Town), Paul Lorraine (Youth Team)
Midfielders: Anthony Hogg (Folkestone Invicta), Danny Hogarth (Youth Team), Luke Anderson (Crawley T), Anthony Riviere (Faversham T), Dean Standen (Luton), Steve Barnes (Chesham)
Forwards: Gary Abbott (Aldershot), Dave Powell (Crawley), Raphael Nade (Hampton and Richmond Borough), Paul Jones (Hastings Utd), Derek Bryan (Gravesend & Northfleet), Tony Boot (Windsor & Eton)

WEYMOUTH

CLUB OFFICIALS	FACT FILE
Chairman: Terry Bennett	Formed: 1890
Vice Chairmen:	Nickname: The Terras
Mike Archer & Dave Higson	Sponsors: Park Engineering
President: Bob Lucas	Colours: Claret & sky/claret & sky
Secretary: Terry Northover	Change colours: Yellow
2 Stoke Rd, Weymouth, Dorset DT4 9JF	Midweek matchday: Tuesday
Tel: 01305 771480	Reserves' League: Wessex Comb

FOOTBALL MANAGEMENT TEAM
Manager: Geoff Butler
Coach:Ricky Haysom
Physio:Malcolm Coe

2001-02
Captain: AlexBrowne
Top scorer: Lee Phillips

GROUND Wessex Stadium, Radipole Lane, Weymouth, Dorset DT4 9XJ Tel: 01305 785558

Directions: Arriving from Dorchester on A354, turn right following signs to Granby Industrial Estate at Safeway r'bout - ground on right as you enter estate
Capacity: 6,600   Cover: all sides   Seats : 800   Floodlights : Yes
Clubhouse: Matchdays & functions. Hot & cold food available
Club Shop: Matchdays only. Progs & souvenirs.
During week contact Amanda (01305 815752)

Saturday 27th April, 2002
ILKESTON TOWN
Official Matchday Magazine £1.50

Pages: 36 Price: £1.50
Editor:James Murphy 01305 815656 Tel & Fax

Lcal Press: Dorset Evening Echo
Local Radio: Wessex FM

PREVIOUS   **Leagues:** Dorset Lge, Western 1907-23 28-49, Southern 23-28 49-79, Alliance Premier 79-89
Ground: Recreation Ground (until 1987)

CLUB RECORDS **Attendance:** 4,995 v Manchester Utd, ground opening, 21/10/87
Career Goalscorer: W Farmer, Haynes. 275   **Career Appearances:** Tony Hobson 1,076
Transfer fee paid: £15,000 for Shaun Teale (Northwich)   **Transfer fee received:** £100,000 for Peter Guthrie (Spurs, 1988)

BEST SEASON   **FA Cup:** Fourth Round 61-62, 0-2 v Preston N.E. (A). 1st rd on 29 occasions
League clubs defeated: Merthyr Town 24-25, Aldershot 49-50, Shrewsbury T. 56-57,Newport County 61-62, Cardiff C. 82-83
FA Amateur Cup: First Round 1900   **FA Trophy:** Fifth Round 2000-2001
HONOURS   All Prem Lg R-up 79-80 (Lg Cup 81-82); Prem Inter Lg Cup R-up 87-88 (QF 90-91);Sth Lg 64-65 65-66 (R-up 54-55 77-78), Lg Cup 72-73 (R-up 5), Sthn Div R-up 91-92; Wstn Lg 22-23, Div 2 33-34 36-37, (R-up 35-36 47-48); Dorset Sen. Cup (27);Mark Frowde Cup (13)

Players progressing: A Smith (Accrington 61), G Bond/T Spratt/A Donnelly/M Cave(Torquay 61/65/67/68), P Leggett (Swindon 62), R Fogg (Aldershot 63), B Hutchinson (Lincoln 65), A Wool (Reading 71), A Beer (Exeter 74), B Iles(Chelsea 78), G Roberts (Spurs 80), T Gulliver/R Hill/N Townsend/P Morrell/JSmeulders (Bournemouth 66/67/79/83/84), T Agana (Watford), A Townsend/D Hughes(Southampton), S Claridge (C Palace), B McGorry/S Teale (Bournemouth), T Pounder/R Evans (Bristol Rvrs), R Pethick (Portsmouth 93)

Back row,left to right: Dave Kiteley (Reserve Team Manager), Geoff Butler (Manager), John Waldock, Carl Mutch, Michael Dean, Michael Cooper, Simon Browne, Jason Matthews, John Bagnal, Lee Bradford, Michael Walker, Scott Daniels, Michael Sajic, Pete Dennis (Kit Manager) and Malcolm Coe (Physio).**Front row :** Lee Phillips, Lance Spencer, Ian Hutchinsonm, Mark Robinson, Alex Browne (captain), David Laws,Danny Bews, Mark Rawlinson and Mark Kenway.   **Photo:** Sunday Independant

Match Facts 2001-02

Date	Comp.	Opponents	Att.	Score	Goalscorers
18.08	DM P	Worcester City	1011	3 - 3	Brown 29 35, Dean 75
21.08	DM P	BATH CITY	930	0 - 0	
25.08	DM P	WELLING UNITED	705	1 - 1	Phillips 25
27.08	DM P	Tiverton Town	1083	1 - 0	Phillips 58
01.09	DM P	TAMWORTH	729	2 - 1	Robinson 24, Phillips 83
04.09	DM P	Salisbury City	545	3 - 2	Laws 45, Rawlinson 54, Phillips 86
08.09	DM P	Stafford Rangers	779	1 - 2	Laws 58
11.09	DM P	NEWPORT COUNTY	804	2 - 1	Phillips 13, Rawlinson 45
15.09	DM P	CAMBRIDGE CITY	724	4 - 2	Laws 62 72 75, Phillips 89
18.09	DM P	Bath City	710	1 - 2	Laws 76
22.09	DM P	Hednesford Town	536	4 - 2	D Rowbotham 66, Phillips 76 81[p], Browne 85
29.09	FA Cup Q2	Highworth Town	305	3 - 0	S Browne 24[p], Rowbotham 33, Hutchinson 53
06.10	DM P	HAVANT & WATERLOOVILLE	741	0 - 1	
09.10	DM P	SALISBURY CITY	701	2 - 1	Browne 11, Laws 87
13.10	FA Cup Q3	CRAWLEY TOWN	831	3 - 1	Browne 45, Phillips 49, Laws 90
20.10	DM P	Crawley Town	1100	0 - 0	
22.10	DM P	Newport County	716	2 - 1	Laws 43 60
27.10	FA Cup Q4	HINCKLEY UNITED	1258	1 - 2	Browne 76[p]
03.11	DM P	KING'S LYNN	778	2 - 1	Rawlinson 79, Phillips 81
10.11	DM P	Ilkeston Town	546	2 - 2	Laws 12, Browne 63
13.11	Lge Cup 1	SALISBURY CITY	399	4 - 0	Laws 19 44, Phillips 81, Hutchinson 88
17.11	DM P	CHELMSFORD CITY	883	2 - 1	Robinson 57, Laws 90
24.11	DM P	Cambridge City	649	2 - 2	Hutchinson 61, Laws 71
27.11	Dorset SC 3	WEYMOUTH SPORTS	228	5 - 0	Hutchinson 7 58, Phillips 77, Laws 74 89
01.12	FA Trophy 2	Chesham United	416	0 - 4	
04.12	Lge Cup 2	Dorchester Town	903	2 - 3	Laws 24, Browne 84[p]
08.12	DM P	King's Lynn	777	0 - 0	
15.12	DM P	MOOR GREEN	803	0 - 1	
26.12	DM P	TIVERTON TOWN	1303	2 - 1	Rowbotham 45, Phillips 75
29.12	DM P	Worcester City	903	1 - 2	Cross 29
05.01	DM P	CRAWLEY TOWN	1058	1 - 2	Sharman 7[og]
08.01	Dorset SC QF	ALLENDALE	172	8 - 2	Rowbotham, Underhay 2, Phillips 3, Rawlinson, Laws
19.01	DM P	Folkestone Invicta	424	3 - 1	Phillips 7 20 60
26.01	DM P	HINCKLEY UNITED	673	1 - 1	Browne 85[p]
28.01	DM P	Chelmsford City	380	1 - 2	Phillips 51
02.02	DM P	KETTERING TOWN	1005	3 - 1	Hutchinson 26, Phillips 49, Dean 69
16.02	DM P	Moor Green	332	1 - 7	S Browne 50[p]
23.02	DM P	NEWPORT IOW	940	0 - 2	
02.03	DM P	Hinckley United	327	2 - 3	Hutchinson 20, Laws 87
06.03	Dorset SC SF	Wimborne Town	226	4 - 1	Underhay 3, Parker 7, Robinson 19, D Rowbotham 65 @ Dorchester Town
09.03	DM P	FOLKESTONE INVICTA	702	1 - 1	Parker 9
12.03	DM P	Merthyr Tydfil	506	1 - 0	Rowbotham 81
16.03	DM P	Havant & Waterlooville	594	2 - 3	Parker 16 34
23.03	DM P	HEDNESFORD TOWN	712	0 - 4	
30.03	DM P	Welling United	570	1 - 1	Rawlinson 81
01.04	DM P	MERTHYR TYDFIL	701	4 - 1	Rawlinson 26, Robinson 63, Browne 71, Parker 81
06.04	DM P	Tamworth	1165	0 - 3	
09.04	DM P	Newport IOW	433	0 - 0	
13.04	DM P	STAFFORD RANGERS	630	0 - 1	
16.04	Dorset SC F	Dorchester Town	632	1 - 1	Rawlinson 71[p] Won 4-3 after pens.
20.04	DM P	Kettering Town	2420	1 - 4	Rawlinson 70[p]
27.04	DM P	ILKESTON TOWN	767	0 - 1	

PLAYING SQUAD

Goalkeepers: Jason Matthews (Clevedon)

Defenders: Alex Browne (Youth Team), Lee Bradford (Newport IOW), Simon Browne (Salisbury), John Waldock (Sunderland), Mark Kenway (Portland Utd), Steve Tully (Torquay)

Midfielders: Ian Hutchinson (Halifax), Martin Barlow (Exeter), Mark Rawlinson (Exeter), Michael Dean (AFC Bournemouth)

Forwards: Darren Rowbotham (Exeter), Lee Phillips (Plymouth Argyle), Mark Robinson (Gravesend), David Laws (Bishop Auckland), Mark Fitch (Portland Utd), Martin Underhay (Wimborne T)

WORCESTER CITY

CLUB OFFICIALS

Chairman: Dr Michael Sorensen
Vice Chairman: Laurie Brown

Secretary: Steve Bond
4 Ferry Close, Worcester, Worcs WR2 5PQ
Tel: 01905 423120/23003

FOOTBALL MANAGEMENT TEAM

Manager: John Barton
Assistant Manager: Mick Tuohy
Physio: Archie Richards

FACT FILE
Formed: 1902
Nickname: The City
Sponsors: Petrochem Carless
Newsline: 0930 555 810
Colours:White/blue/white
Change colours: Blue/white/blue
Midweek matchday: Monday
Reserve Lge: Midland Comb Reserves
2001-002
Captain: Carl Heeley
P.o.Y: Carl Heeley
Top Scorer: Mark Owen

Pages: 32   Price: £1.50
Editor: Julian Pugh (01905 723234)
Local Press: Berrows Journal,
Worcester Evening News
Local Radio: Radio Wyvern,
BBC Hereford & Worcester

GROUND St George's Lane, Barbourne, Worcester WR1 1QT Tel: 01905 23003 Fax: 26668

Directions: M5 jct 6 (Worcester North), follow signs to Worcester, right at first lights, St Georges Lane is 3rd left. 1 mile from Foregate Street (BR)station
Capacity: 4,004   Cover: 2,000   Seats: 1,125   Floodlights: Yes

Clubhouse: Open every evening and Saturday and Sunday daytime. Cold snacks available
Two shops: Outside ground (souvenirs). Inside ground (programmes) Contact club for details.

PREVIOUS   **Leagues:** West Mids (Birmingham) 1902-38, Southern 38-79, Alliance Premier 79-85
Names: Berwick Rangers   **Grounds:** Severn Terrace, Thorneloe, Flagge Meadow

CLUB RECORDS **Attendance:** 17,042 v Sheff Utd (lost 0-2), FA Cup 4th Rd 24/1/59
Win: 18-1 v Bilston, Birmingham League 21/11/31   **Defeat:** 0-10 v Wellington, Birmingham League 29/8/20
Career Goalscorer: John Inglis 189 (1970-77)   **Career Appearances:** Bobby McEwan 596 (1959-75)
Transfer fee paid: £8,500 for Jim Williams (Telford United, 1981)
Transfer fee received: £27,000 for John Barton (Everton, 1979)

BEST SEASON **FA Cup:** 4th Rd 58-59. 1st Rd (12)
FA Trophy: QF 69-70 73-74 80-81 81-82   **Welsh Cup:** Semi-Final 78-79
HONOURS Southern Lg 78-79, Div 1 67-68, Div 1 Nth 76-77, Lg Cup R-up 45-46 59-60, Chal.Cup 39-40, Champs Cup 78-79; West Mids (B'ham) Lg(4) 13-14 24-25 28-30 (R-up (3) 31-34); Worcs Snr Cup (26) 07-14 28-30 32-33 45-46(jt) 48-49 55-59 60-61 62-63 64-65 69-70 77-78 79-80 81-82 83-84 87-88 96-97; B'ham Snr Cup 75-76; Staffs Snr Cup 76-77; Inter Lg Champs Cup 78-79
Players progressing: A Awford (Portsmouth 91), P King/K Ball (Cardiff C.60/65), JWilliams/M Gayle (Walsall 79/91), J Fairbrother (Peterborough 65), DTennant (Lincoln 66), R Davies (Derby 71), N Merrick (Bournemouth 74), J Barton(Everton 79), A Preece (Wrexham 90), D Lyttle (Swansea 92) M.Griffiths (Torquay United 99)

Back Row: John Morris (Scout), Jon Holloway, Stewart Hadley, Carl Heeley, Marc Burrow, Mark Shail, Leon Jackson, Adam Webster, Rat Woods (Youth Development Officer). **Middle Row:** Martin Obrey (Assistant Physiotherapist), Archie Richards (Physiotherapist), Michael Blackwoood, Duncan Willetts, Danny McDonnell, Paul Wyatt, Darren Middleton, Paul Carty, Graham Selby (Head of Scouting), Mick Tuohy (First Team Coach). **Front Row:** Pat Lyons, Mark Owen, John Snape, John Barton (Manager), David Foy, Duncan Jones, Allan Davies.

Photo by Paul France

SOUTHERN LEAGUE DIVISION

Date	Comp.	Opponents	Att.	Score	Goalscorers
11.08	DML Shield	Margate	n.k	1 - 1	Owen 30 3 5
18.08	DM P	WEYMOUTH	1011	3 - 3	Owen 44[p] 88 90[p]
21.08	DM P	Kettering Town	1571	1 - 4	Owen 90
25.08	DM P	Ilkeston Town	521	2 - 1	Stant 8, Heeley 24
27.08	DM P	HINCKLEY UNITED	967	4 - 3	Owen 43 57[p], Burrow 88, Middleton 90
01.09	DM P	Newport IOW	490	1 - 1	Owen 53
03.09	DM P	MOOR GREEN	837	3 - 2	Owen 33 45[p] 76
08.09	DM P	HAVANT & WATERLOOVILLE	1004	0 - 0	
11.09	DM P	Merthyr Tydfil	498	0 - 0	
15.09	DM P	Folkestone Invicta	379	1 - 2	Owen 60[p]
17.09	DM P	KETTERING TOWN	1152	1 - 1	Cotterill 42
22.09	DM P	KING'S LYNN	941	3 - 1	Stant 30, Owen 61[p], Middleton 66
29.09	FA Cup Q2	Barnstaple Town	320	5 - 0	Owen 16 58 84, Middleton 37, Stant 71
02.10	DM P	Moor Green	368	1 - 3	Shepherd 67
05.10	DM P	ILKESTON TOWN	938	2 - 2	Owen 85[p] 87[p]
13.10	FA Cup Q3	St Blazey	596	3 - 2	Stant 19, Shepherd 50 52
20.10	DM P	TIVERTON TOWN	1040	4 - 2	Middleton 1, Stant 38 39 84
27.10	FA Cup Q4	Belper Town	1228	2 - 2	Heeley 24, Middleton 51
29.10	FA Cup Q4 R	BELPER TOWN	2377	3 - 1	Heeley 16, Middleton 80 84
03.11	FA Trophy 1	MANGOTSFIELD UNITED	862	1 - 1	Hyde 67
06.11	FA Trophy 1 R	Mangotsfield United	317	1 - 2	Stant 40[p]
10.11	DM P	CAMBRIDGE CITY	1054	1 - 2	Shepherd 4
12.11	Lge Cup 1	ROCESTER	249	2 - 0	Holloway 7, Bullock 53[p]
17.11	FA Cup 1	RUSHDEN & DIAMONDS	3313	0 - 1	
24.11	DM P	Tamworth	826	2 - 3	Stant 26 28
26.11	DM P	MERTHYR TYDFIL	769	1 - 0	Heeley 50
01.12	DM P	Crawley Town	1317	0 - 1	
03.12	Worcs SC QF	MOOR GREEN	302	2 - 3	Stant 23 84[p]
08.12	DM P	NEWPORT COUNTY	1047	0 - 0	
11.12	Lge Cup 2	Bedworth United	116	0 - 4	
15.12	DM P	Welling United	464	3 - 1	Shepherd 19 45 79
19.12	DM P	Tiverton Town	571	0 - 2	
22.12	DM P	NEWPORT IOW	823	4 - 0	Holloway 26, Jackson 45, Hadley 63, Shepherd 89
29.12	DM P	Weymouth	903	2 - 1	Bullock 68, Hadley 90
12.01	DM P	SALISBURY CITY	886	6 - 0	Hadley 14, Bullock 21 85 90[p], Burrow 43, Ellis 88
19.01	DM P	Hednesford Town	767	3 - 0	Webster 53, Bullock 70, Hyde 85
26.01	DM P	FOLKESTONE INVICTA	1033	1 - 1	Heeley 44
02.02	DM P	Salisbury City	315	1 - 1	Shepherd 90
09.02	DM P	TAMWORTH	1317	0 - 2	
16.02	DM P	Cambridge City	416	2 - 0	Webster 43, Dukes 88[p]
23.02	DM P	Hinckley United	326	0 - 0	
25.02	DM P	HEDNESFORD TOWN	803	0 - 1	
02.03	DM P	King's Lynn	770	2 - 1	Middleton 13, Shail 23
09.03	DM P	CHELMSFORD CITY	811	1 - 1	Middleton 51
12.03	DM P	Stafford Rangers	515	1 - 1	Carty 88
16.03	DM P	Newport County	752	2 - 0	Eckhardt 46[og], Webster 62
23.03	DM P	CRAWLEY TOWN	876	3 - 0	Webster 30 89, Heeley 33
30.03	DM P	Bath City	718	0 - 4	
01.04	DM P	STAFFORD RANGERS	1017	1 - 2	Jukes 69
06.04	DM P	Chelmsford City	584	1 - 2	Webster 29
13.04	DM P	WELLING UNITED	803	2 - 1	Webster 39 76
20.04	DM P	Havant & Waterlooville	513	0 - 1	
27.04	DM P	BATH CITY	1224	0 - 1	

PLAYING SQUAD

Goalkeepers: Danny McDonnell (Halesowen), Paul Wyatt (Rushden and Diamonds)
Defenders: Carl Heeley (Sutton Coldfield), Allan Davies (Burton Albion), Mark Shail (Kidderminster), Nathan Jukes (Dorchester), David Foy (Tamworth), Marc Burrow (Bromsgrove), Martin Weir (Kidderminster)
Midfielders: Ian Cottrill (Nuneaton), Jamie Hyde (Youth Team), Jon Holloway (Bath City), Pat Lyons (Burton Albion), Ray Woods (Bilston T), Dwaine McFarlane (WBA), John Snape (Hereford), Leon Jackson (Bilston T), Paul Carty (Hednesford)
Forwards: Mark Owen (Willenhall T), Darren Middleton (Forest Green), Stewart Hadley (Kidderminster), Adam Webster (Bedworth)

KING'S LYNN

Date	Comp.	Opponents	Att.	Score	Goalscorers
18.08	DM P	NEWPORT COUNTY	1023	4 - 2	March 5, Deakin 42, Hayes 45[p], Hudson 59
21.08	DM P	Hinckley United	389	0 - 0	
25.08	DM P	Hednesford Town	732	2 - 0	Hudson 1, Evans 90
27.08	DM P	ILKESTON TOWN	1145	0 - 1	
01.09	DM P	MERTHYR TYDFIL	870	0 - 1	
03.09	DM P	Chelmsford City	454	2 - 2	Hudson 4, Hayes 59[p]
08.09	DM P	Tiverton Town	743	1 - 1	Rowland 77
11.09	DM P	MOOR GREEN	634	1 - 0	Minett 49
15.09	DM P	Havant & Waterlooville	475	0 - 0	
18.09	DM P	HINCKLEY UNITED	646	1 - 1	Whitney 70
22.09	DM P	Worcester City	941	1 - 3	Clarke 79
29.09	FA Cup Q2	HARROW BOROUGH	916	1 - 0	Robinson 34
06.10	DM P	Crawley Town	774	0 - 1	
09.10	DM P	CHELMSFORD CITY	684	3 - 0	Jones 59, Robinson 64, Hudson 69
13.10	FA Cup Q3	CLACTON TOWN	1137	3 - 2	Fuff 39, Clarke 77, Hayes 90
20.10	DM P	Salisbury City	324	3 - 0	Robinson 45, Jones 56, Clark 73
23.10	DM P	Moor Green	237	0 - 4	
27.10	FA Cup Q4	FARNBOROUGH TOWN	1758	0 - 4	
03.11	DM P	Weymouth	778	1 - 2	Rowe 45
10.11	DM P	TAMWORTH	874	1 - 1	Rowe 89
13.11	Lge Cup 1	Grantham Town	248	2 - 1	Bloomfield 34, Evans 37
17.11	DM P	FOLKESTONE INVICTA	885	0 - 2	
24.11	DM P	Bath City	650	1 - 0	Bloomfield 55
01.12	FA Trophy 2	ASHTON UNITED	814	4 - 1	Clark 38 79, Bloomfield 39, White 70
08.12	DM P	WEYMOUTH	777	0 - 0	
11.12	Lge Cup 2	KETTERING TOWN	472	6 - 1	Hudson 25 45, C Clark 35, J Clark 61, Bloomfield 81, Hayes 89[p]
15.12	DM P	Newport County	655	1 - 2	Bloomfield 63
29.12	DM P	STAFFORD RANGERS	749	2 - 0	Hayes 79[p], Bloomfield 89
05.01	DM P	Folkestone Invicta	382	2 - 1	Bloomfield 45, Dakin 65
12.01	FA Trophy 3	Morecambe	939	0 - 2	
19.01	DM P	Cambridge City	758	1 - 2	Watts 39
09.02	DM P	SALISBURY CITY	683	2 - 1	Clements 63, Watts 80
12.02	Lge Cup 3	ROTHWELL TOWN	464	2 - 1	Clements 55, Hayes 90[p]
16.02	DM P	NEWPORT IOW	650	1 - 1	March 62
23.02	DM P	Tamworth	852	1 - 4	Hayes 75
02.03	DM P	WORCESTER CITY	770	1 - 2	Rowe 5
04.03	Lge Cup QF	Atherstone United	134	2 - 0	Vince 67 79
09.03	DM P	HEDNESFORD TOWN	597	1 - 0	Clements 52
12.03	Lge Cup SF	SOLIHULL BOROUGH	548	2 - 1	Clements 60 85
16.03	DM P	Kettering Town	1842	0 - 3	
23.03	DM P	BATH CITY	647	1 - 1	Watts 29
25.03	DM P	Ilkeston Town	465	1 - 3	Robinson 80
27.03	DM P	WELLING UNITED	439	1 - 2	Anderson 83
30.03	DM P	Stafford Rangers	599	2 - 3	Raynor 42, Stanhope 59
01.04	DM P	CAMBRIDGE CITY	818	1 - 1	Stanhope 45
06.04	DM P	Welling United	494	1 - 0	Watts 43
09.04	DM P	TIVERTON TOWN	548	0 - 1	
13.04	DM P	HAVANT & WATERLOOVILLE	754	1 - 1	Gale 35[og]
16.04	DM P	KETTERING TOWN	1192	0 - 3	
18.04	Lge Cup F(1)	DORCHESTER TOWN	535	0 - 1	
20.04	DM P	Merthyr Tydfil	374	1 - 3	Staff 64
23.04	DM P	Newport IOW	636	0 - 0	
25.04	Lge Cup F(2)	Dorchester Town	592	0 - 3	
27.04	DM P	CRAWLEY TOWN	861	2 - 2	Anderson 74, Clarke 88

MERTHYR TYDFIL

Date	Comp.	Opponents	Att.	Score	Goalscorers
18.08	DM P	KETTERING TOWN	725	0 - 2	
21.08	DM P	Moor Green	309	0 - 1	
25.08	DM P	Havant & Waterlooville	443	0 - 4	
27.08	DM P	NEWPORT COUNTY	848	1 - 1	Thomas 30[p]
01.09	DM P	King's Lynn	870	1 - 0	Mainwaring 90
04.09	DM P	TIVERTON TOWN	564	1 - 2	Eaton 33
08.09	DM P	Cambridge City	316	2 - 2	Eaton 65, Sharp 78
11.09	DM P	WORCESTER CITY	498	0 - 0	
15.09	DM P	Ilkeston Town	521	0 - 1	
18.09	DM P	MOOR GREEN	438	1 - 2	Ryan 28
22.09	DM P	Welling United	512	0 - 1	
29.09	FA Cup Q2	BRIDGWATER TOWN	385	4 - 1	Rice 15[og], Haines 17, Carter 75, Staton 85
07.10	DM P	NEWPORT IOW	476	3 - 1	Haines 31 54, Dodds 90
10.10	DM P	Tiverton Town	499	3 - 1	Marker 11[og], Knox 32 51
13.10	FA Cup Q3	MANGOTSFIELD UNITED	476	3 - 3	Staton 36[p], Carter 64, Lima 71
16.10	FA Cup Q3 R	Mangotsfield United	769	1 - 4	Savage 22
20.10	DM P	HINCKLEY UNITED	501	2 - 2	Rollo 2, Savage 75
03.11	FA Trophy 1	Tonbridge Angels	427	3 - 3	M Davies 40 59, Lima 65
06.11	FA Trophy 1 R	TONBRIDGE ANGELS	302	3 - 2	Davis 3 72, Rollo 90
10.11	DM P	Bath City	629	2 - 4	Powell 53[og], Dodds 69
13.11	Lge Cup 1	SWINDON SUPERMARINE	302	3 - 0	Dodds 24 77, Mumford 72
17.11	DM P	ILKESTON TOWN	405	2 - 3	Knox 65[p] 70
24.11	DM P	Hednesford Town	565	0 - 3	
26.11	DM P	Worcester City	769	0 - 1	
01.12	FA Trophy 2	Fisher Athletic	165	1 - 5	Beddard 88
04.12	Lge Cup 2	CLEVEDON TOWN	149	2 - 0	Knox 15, Haines 76
08.12	DM P	WELLING UNITED	434	4 - 4	Haines 8 76, Watts 62[og], Savage 90
11.12	DM P	STAFFORD RANGERS	325	2 - 0	Dodds 27, Knox 81
15.12	DM P	Kettering Town	1212	0 - 3	
22.12	DM P	HAVANT & WATERLOOVILLE	523	1 - 1	Elliott 58
26.12	DM P	Newport County	1059	0 - 3	
29.12	DM P	Crawley Town	1332	1 - 2	Hunt 32
05.01	DM P	CHELMSFORD CITY	481	3 - 1	Hunt 24 84[p], Mainwaring 89
12.01	DM P	Newport IOW	463	3 - 2	Hunt 12 77, Lima 55
26.01	DM P	CAMBRIDGE CITY	511	1 - 3	Beddard 76
29.01	Lge Cup 3	MANGOTSFIELD UNITED	151	3 - 0	Dodds 2, Savage 28, Rollo 73
02.02	DM P	Folkestone Invicta	367	0 - 1	
09.02	DM P	Stafford Rangers	694	0 - 1	
12.02	Lge Cup QF	Dorchester Town	230	0 - 3	
16.02	DM P	CRAWLEY TOWN	456	2 - 2	Mainwaring 12, Savage 51
23.02	DM P	Chelmsford City	484	1 - 2	Hunt 12
02.03	DM P	TAMWORTH	1014	1 - 1	Harries 68
09.03	DM P	BATH CITY	736	3 - 1	Burrows 31, Harries 57, Edwards 89
12.03	DM P	WEYMOUTH	506	0 - 1	
16.03	DM P	HEDNESFORD TOWN	561	3 - 1	Harries 27, Edwards 40, Hapgood 61
23.03	DM P	Tamworth	1111	0 - 2	
30.03	DM P	SALISBURY CITY	501	3 - 2	Hunt 55, Staton 80, Beddard 90
01.04	DM P	Weymouth	701	1 - 4	Hunt 5
06.04	DM P	FOLKESTONE INVICTA	409	1 - 0	Hunt 83[p]
13.04	DM P	Hinckley United	433	0 - 1	
20.04	DM P	KING'S LYNN	374	3 - 1	McNeil 34[og], Thomas 77, Mainwaring 90
27.04	DM P	Salisbury City	439	2 - 1	Mainwaring 63 81

NEWPORT I.O.W.

Date	Comp.	Opponents	Att.	Score	Goalscorers
18.08	DM P	Stafford Rangers	652	0 - 1	
21.08	DM P	WELLING UNITED	518	1 - 1	Tate 20
25.08	DM P	TIVERTON TOWN	555	3 - 0	Whittingham 47 85, Tatterton 62[og]
27.08	DM P	Salisbury City	481	1 - 1	Gibbons 7
01.09	DM P	WORCESTER CITY	490	1 - 1	Leigh 88
04.09	DM P	Crawley Town	855	0 - 2	
08.09	DM P	KETTERING TOWN	650	0 - 2	
11.09	DM P	CHELMSFORD CITY	423	0 - 3	
15.09	DM P	Hinckley United	455	2 - 1	Holbrook 12[p], Wakefield 58
18.09	DM P	Welling United	331	0 - 3	
22.09	DM P	TAMWORTH	524	0 - 4	
29.09	FA Cup Q2	Hastings Town	516	2 - 0	Gibbons 30, Rew 45
07.10	DM P	Merthyr Tydfil	476	1 - 3	Gibbons 59
09.10	DM P	CRAWLEY TOWN	356	1 - 2	Gibbons 47
13.10	FA Cup Q3	Welling United	424	0 - 3	
20.10	DM P	Tamworth	685	1 - 5	Leigh 55
22.10	DM P	Chelmsford City	536	0 - 3	
27.10	Hants SC 2	Andover New Street	n.k	9 - 0	
03.11	FA Trophy 1	Crawley Town	848	1 - 0	Gibbons 36
10.11	DM P	Hednesford Town	601	2 - 1	Wakefield 84, Thompson 89
13.11	Lge Cup 1	Havant & Waterlooville	237	0 - 2	
17.11	DM P	STAFFORD RANGERS	466	1 - 0	Gibbons 90
24.11	DM P	Folkestone Invicta	380	2 - 2	Wakefield 44 89
27.11	Hants SC 3	ESSO FAWLEY	117	5 - 0	Thompson 22 90, Barsdell 26, Tate 37, Holbrook 81
01.12	FA Trophy 2	Carshalton Athletic	266	0 - 1	
15.12	DM P	CAMBRIDGE CITY	354	1 - 0	Gibbons 38
22.12	DM P	Worcester City	823	0 - 4	
26.12	DM P	SALISBURY CITY	557	0 - 0	
29.12	DM P	FOLKESTONE INVICTA	345	1 - 1	Holbrook 85
05.01	DM P	Tiverton Town	822	1 - 2	Gibbons 90
12.01	DM P	MERTHYR TYDFIL	463	2 - 3	Arscott 30, Collins 72
19.01	DM P	Newport County	651	0 - 0	
29.01	Hants SC QF	Andover	158	2 - 1	Barsdell 58, Gibbons 71
05.02	DM P	Bath City	498	1 - 0	Moss 56
16.02	DM P	King's Lynn	650	1 - 1	Arscott 89
23.02	DM P	Weymouth	940	2 - 0	Moss 11, Leigh 60
27.02	DM P	Havant & Waterlooville	458	1 - 2	Thompson 90
02.03	IOW SC QF	SHANKLIN	179	5 - 0	Barsdell 11 16 41, Thomas 40 63
05.03	DM P	NEWPORT COUNTY	443	0 - 4	
09.03	DM P	MOOR GREEN	370	2 - 1	Laws 50 90
12.03	Hants SC SF(1)	Aldershot Town	782	0 - 2	
16.03	DM P	Moor Green	353	4 - 1	Laws 46 62 69, Leigh 60
23.03	DM P	ILKESTON TOWN	487	2 - 1	Leigh 11, Laws 63
26.03	Hants SC SF(2)	ALDERSHOT TOWN	441	0 - 2	
30.03	DM P	Cambridge City	331	0 - 2	
01.04	DM P	HAVANT & WATERLOOVILLE	561	0 - 1	
06.04	DM P	Kettering Town	1666	2 - 1	Laws 58 60
09.04	DM P	WEYMOUTH	433	0 - 0	
13.04	DM P	BATH CITY	683	2 - 1	Laws 73, Leigh 75
16.04	DM P	HINCKLEY UNITED	502	0 - 0	
18.04	IOW SC SF	RED STAR SPARTANS	129	3 - 0	Pitcher 50, Perry 83, Bridges 86
20.04	DM P	Ilkeston Town	483	0 - 0	
23.04	DM P	KING'S LYNN	636	0 - 0	
27.04	DM P	HEDNESFORD TOWN	905	0 - 1	
18.05	IOW SC F	COWES SPORTS	270	1 - 2	Barsdell 48

SALISBURY CITY

Date	Comp.	Opponents	Att.	Score	Goalscorers
18.08	DM P	ILKESTON TOWN	397	1 - 1	Sales 58
20.08	DM P	Newport County	810	0 - 0	
25.08	DM P	Folkestone Invicta	338	0 - 2	
27.08	DM P	NEWPORT IOW	481	1 - 1	Sales 20
01.09	DM P	Moor Green	277	1 - 1	Speakman 4
04.09	DM P	WEYMOUTH	545	2 - 3	Blackham 47, Speakman 81
08.09	DM P	Hednesford Town	650	0 - 6	
11.09	DM P	TIVERTON TOWN	417	0 - 3	
15.09	DM P	Kettering Town	1295	0 - 4	
18.09	DM P	NEWPORT COUNTY	460	0 - 2	
22.09	DM P	Stafford Rangers	698	0 - 3	
29.09	FA Cup Q2	TIVERTON TOWN	586	3 - 3	Shepherd 39, Bowers 42, Emms 90
03.10	FA Cup Q2 R	Tiverton Town	779	1 - 3	Mathie 32
06.10	DM P	WELLING UNITED	199	0 - 1	
09.10	DM P	Weymouth	701	1 - 2	Crook 90
20.10	DM P	KING'S LYNN	324	0 - 3	
24.10	DM P	Tiverton Town	528	0 - 1	
27.10	DM P	HEDNESFORD TOWN	300	1 - 0	Underhay 27[p]
31.10	Wilts PS 1	Swindon Supermarine	156	1 - 2	
03.11	FA Trophy 1	Tooting & Mitcham United	261	0 - 3	
10.11	DM P	Chelmsford City	454	2 - 3	Davies 31, Crook 41
13.11	Lge Cup 1	Weymouth	399	0 - 4	
17.11	DM P	BATH CITY	455	0 - 1	
24.11	DM P	Havant & Waterlooville	505	0 - 2	
08.12	DM P	CHELMSFORD CITY	379	1 - 3	King 67 F
15.12	DM P	Hinckley United	308	1 - 2	King 26
22.12	DM P	FOLKESTONE INVICTA	300	2 - 0	King 12, Turk 88
26.12	DM P	Newport IOW	557	0 - 0	
29.12	DM P	Ilkeston Town	547	1 - 0	King 85
05.01	DM P	TAMWORTH	444	1 - 2	King 87[p]
12.01	DM P	Worcester City	886	0 - 6	
19.01	DM P	KETTERING TOWN	539	1 - 2	King 4
02.02	DM P	WORCESTER CITY	315	1 - 1	Davies 74
09.02	DM P	King's Lynn	683	1 - 2	King 45[p]
16.02	DM P	HINCKLEY UNITED	375	1 - 1	Cooper 5
19.02	DM P	HAVANT & WATERLOOVILLE	340	2 - 0	Turk 40, King 65
02.03	DM P	MOOR GREEN	330	5 - 0	Bowers 16, King 44 84[p], Wallace 79, Griffin 90
09.03	DM P	CAMBRIDGE CITY	393	1 - 1	King 51
16.03	DM P	Welling United	516	1 - 5	Emms 89
23.03	DM P	STAFFORD RANGERS	382	1 - 4	King 90
26.03	DM P	Cambridge City	273	3 - 1	King 29, Richardson 27, Crook 85
30.03	DM P	Merthyr Tydfil	501	2 - 3	King 9 38
01.04	DM P	CRAWLEY TOWN	481	0 - 3	
06.04	DM P	Bath City	697	0 - 1	
09.04	DM P	Crawley Town	637	0 - 4	
20.04	DM P	Tamworth	2240	1 - 5	Turk 15
27.04	DM P	MERTHYR TYDFIL	439	1 - 2	Turk 88

WESTERN DIVISION FINAL LEAGUE TABLE 2001-02

		P	W	D	L	W	D	L	W	D	L	F	A	GD	Pts
1	Halesowen Town	40	14	3	3	13	6	1	27	9	4	85	24	61	90
2	Chippenham Town	40	12	6	2	14	3	3	26	9	5	81	28	53	87
3	Weston super Mare	40	13	3	4	9	7	4	22	10	8	70	38	32	76
4	Solihull Borough	40	7	9	4	13	2	5	20	11	9	75	42	33	71
5	Gresley Rovers	40	10	5	5	9	4	7	19	9	12	59	50	9	66
6	Sutton Coldfield Tn	40	12	3	5	5	8	7	17	11	12	53	46	7	62
7	Mangotsfield Utd	40	8	5	7	9	5	6	17	10	13	74	54	20	61
8	Stourport Swifts	40	12	3	5	6	3	11	18	6	16	59	59	0	60
9	Atherstone Unitd	40	9	5	6	7	3	10	16	8	16	61	59	2	56
10	Clevedon Town	40	8	4	8	7	7	6	15	11	14	57	58	-1	56
11	Bedworth United	40	8	3	9	8	4	8	16	7	17	59	63	-4	55
12	Evesham United	40	8	2	10	8	5	7	16	7	17	54	70	-16	55
13	Cirencester Town	40	9	2	9	8	1	11	17	3	20	64	69	-5	54
14	Gloucester City	40	8	5	7	6	5	9	14	10	16	48	63	-15	52
15	Cinderford Town	40	10	2	8	4	7	9	14	9	17	54	67	-13	51
16	Shepshed Dynamo	40	4	6	10	6	4	10	10	10	20	64	84	-20	40
17	Bilston Town	40	8	2	10	3	5	12	11	7	22	50	72	-22	40
18	Redditch United	40	7	5	8	4	1	15	11	6	23	47	77	-30	39
19	Swindon Supermarine	40	6	3	11	5	1	14	11	4	25	52	76	-24	37
20	Racing Club Warwick	40	7	6	7	1	5	14	8	11	21	38	63	-25	35
21	Rocester	40	2	8	10	3	4	13	5	12	23	33	75	-42	27

Records for Bloxwich United FC have been deleted

WESTERN DIVISION RESULTS CHART 2001-02

		1	2	3	4	5	6	7	8	9	10	11	12	13	14	15	16	17	18	19	20	21
1	Atherstone U	X	3-1	4-0	1-3	5-1	4-1	2-2	0-1	1-0	0-0	2-5	1-1	1-0	1-2	2-0	1-1	1-2	2-1	0-0	5-0	0-2
2	Bedworth U	2-1	X	0-3	1-2	1-3	2-1	1-1	3-0	4-1	0-2	0-3	1-4	1-1	3-1	1-0	0-4	0-2	1-1	2-0	4-2	2-3
3	Bilston Town	1-3	0-1	X	1-2	4-0	3-1	0-1	3-1	5-1	0-2	1-2	2-6	3-1	3-2	0-1	3-0	0-6	1-0	0-0	1-2	1-1
4	Chippenham	2-0	2-1	2-0	X	0-0	3-0	4-0	1-2	1-0	0-1	2-2	3-0	1-1	4-0	4-0	4-0	3-1	1-0	1-1	1-1	1-1
5	Cinderford T	4-1	2-4	2-0	0-1	X	1-1	2-1	4-0	2-1	3-5	0-0	1-4	1-0	4-1	2-1	0-2	0-0	1-1	0-0	0-1	0-1
6	Cirencester T	1-0	3-0	1-2	1-3	1-1	X	1-2	2-1	1-1	2-1	0-1	0-4	5-1	2-3	1-2	3-2	4-1	4-0	0-1	0-1	3-4
7	Clevedon T	0-3	0-1	3-2	3-2	4-1	1-2	X	0-0	1-3	1-2	0-2	0-0	2-1	6-0	2-2	2-5	1-3	2-0	2-2	2-1	1-0
8	Evesham U	1-1	3-2	3-1	0-6	0-2	0-3	2-3	X	3-0	1-4	0-3	2-1	1-0	2-0	2-2	1-2	2-4	1-2	1-0	2-1	1-2
9	Gloucester C	4-1	1-7	5-1	1-1	4-2	0-1	1-1	0-2	X	2-1	0-2	1-2	3-2	2-1	2-2	1-5	1-1	2-0	1-1	1-0	0-2
10	Gresley Rvrs	0-1	1-2	2-0	2-2	0-0	4-2	1-1	1-0	2-0	X	0-3	2-3	3-2	1-0	2-1	2-1	0-5	6-2	2-2	2-0	0-0
11	Halesowen T	1-0	0-1	3-0	0-1	1-2	1-0	2-0	3-0	0-0	3-0	X	1-1	6-0	2-1	4-0	6-0	4-1	3-0	2-0	5-1	2-2
12	Mangotsfield	3-1	1-1	0-0	1-0	2-0	4-1	0-0	1-3	1-1	1-2	1-2	X	3-3	2-0	4-0	6-2	0-3	0-3	0-1	3-2	1-3
13	RC Warwick	5-1	0-0	0-1	0-4	0-1	1-3	0-2	1-0	0-0	2-0	0-0	0-3	X	2-0	1-0	2-2	2-0	0-1	1-4	3-1	1-1
14	Redditch U	1-3	2-1	2-1	1-3	1-0	4-0	1-1	2-2	0-0	0-1	1-3	1-0	0-0	X	5-1	0-5	0-1	1-2	1-0	1-2	1-2
15	Rocester	0-4	1-2	1-1	0-2	1-1	0-1	0-2	0-1	0-1	1-0	1-1	2-2	0-0	2-0	X	1-1	1-1	1-2	1-3	0-3	2-2
16	Shepshed D	1-2	1-3	1-1	1-2	5-2	0-1	1-3	1-1	0-2	2-2	1-2	1-2	0-3	3-2	2-2	X	0-3	1-1	0-0	3-0	3-1
17	Solihull Boro	1-1	2-0	1-0	0-1	2-2	3-1	0-0	2-3	4-0	0-1	1-1	2-0	2-1	1-1	1-2	1-1	X	1-1	0-0	4-1	1-0
18	Stourport S	1-1	1-1	5-2	0-0	4-2	2-0	2-1	2-3	2-1	2-0	2-3	1-4	1-0	3-4	4-0	2-0	2-0	X	0-1	3-1	1-0
19	Sutton C Tn	6-0	1-1	2-1	1-2	1-1	5-1	1-0	1-1	0-1	3-1	2-0	2-1	2-1	2-1	2-1	3-2	0-4	0-1	X	1-0	0-3
20	Swindon S.	0-1	2-0	1-1	0-3	1-3	1-3	1-2	2-3	1-2	0-2	0-1	2-2	4-0	1-2	1-0	6-2	2-3	3-1	3-1	X	1-1
21	Weston S M	2-0	2-1	1-0	3-1	4-1	0-2	4-1	0-1	0-0	0-0	1-0	1-0	3-1	3-1	5-0	1-2	4-1	1-2	2-0	X

WESTERN DIVISION LEADING GOALSCORERS 2001-02

32	Derek Hall	Solihull Borough	17	Karl Bayliss	Gloucester City
22	Christopher Partridge	Bedworth	16	James Bent	Chippenham Town
21	Jody Bevan	Weston super Mare	16	James Cox	Weston super Mare
21	Christopher Smith	Solihull Borough	16	Matthew Rawlins	Chippenham Town
18	Darren Edwards	Mangotsfield United	15	Paul Danks	Redditch United
18	Kirk Master	Shepshed Dynamo	15	David Seal	Mangotsfield United
18	Leroy May	Halesown Town			

ATHERSTONE UNITED

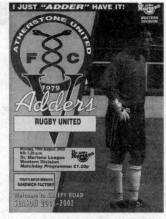

CLUB OFFICIALS

Chairman: Ku Akeredolu
President: Keith Allen
Secretary: Ian Chetwynd, 17 Crossway
Cottage, Nuneaton Road, Fillongley, Warwicks
CV7 8DL Mobile No: 0776 610 4452
Commercial Manager: T Jago

FOOTBALL MANAGEMENT TEAM

Manager: Kenny Willis
Asst Manager: Mick Bayley
Physio: Maurice Ayre

FACT FILE

Formed: 1979
Nickname: The Adders
Club Sponsors: T.B.A.
Colours: Red & white stripes/red/red
Change colours: Yellow & blue/blue/yellow
Midweek home matchday: Monday 7.30pm
Reserve's Lge: Midland Comb. Reserve Div.
Club Website: www.atherstoneunited.co.uk

2001-02
Captain: Dale Belford

Pages: 28   Price: £1
Editor: Brian Stephenson 01827 735441

Local Press: Tamworth Herald,
Evening News, Atherstone Herald,
Coventry Telegraph.
Local Radio: Mercia Sound, CWR

GROUND
Sheepy Road, Atherstone, Warwickshire. CV9 1HG
Tel: 01827 717829

Directions: Half mile north of town centre on B4116 Twycross/Ashby road.

Capacity: 3,500   Cover: 1,000   Seats: 373   Floodlights: Yes

Clubhouse: Open during normal licensing hours, all usual facilities.
Club Shop: Programmes, magazines, souvenirs etc. Contact: Sreve Clark 01827 712812

PREVIOUS   **Leagues:** West Midlands 1979-87

CLUB RECORDS **Attendance:** 2,873 v V.S. Rugby, F.A. Cup 1st Round Proper 1987-88
Win: 12-2 vTipton Town (H), West Midlands (Regional) League Premier Division 86-87
Defeat: 1-7 v Rushden & Diamonds, Beazer League Premier Division 94-95
Goalscorer: Alan Bourton   **Appearances:** Lee Spencer
Fee Paid: £4,500 to Gloucester City for Gary Bradder, 1989
Fee Received: £40,000 for Andy Rammell from Manchester United, September 1989

HONOURS   Southern Lge Midland Div 88-89; West Midlands Lge 81-82 86-87 (Lge Cup 81-82, Premier Div Cup 86-87, Div 2 Cup (Res.)
86-87); Walsall Senior Cup 83-84; Midland Combination Reserve Division 87-88; Birmingham Senior Cup R-up 89-90

BEST SEASON **FA Cup:** 2nd Rd Proper 1990-91, 0-1 v Crewe Alexandra (A)
FA Trophy: 1st Round 88-89 91-92.

Players progressing: Andy Rammell (Manchester United)

Back Row: Kenny Willis (Manager), Leon Leeson, Todd Perry, Danny Martin, Dale Belford, Peter Barry, Andy
Rutherford, Tommy Lenton, Maurice Ayre (Physio). **Front Row:** Kevin Charley, Ross Genner, Dale Turner, Scott
Blair, Chris Tullin, Romi Cammock, Roy Dunkley, Stuart Macmillan.

BEDWORTH UNITED

CLUB OFFICIALS
Chairman: **Peter Randle**
Vice Chairman: **Wayne Harris**
Secretary: **Graham J Bloxham**
43 Mount Pleasant Road, Bedworth,
Warwicks CV12 8EX
Mobile: 07748 640613
Press Officer: **Jamie Home**

FOOTBALL MANAGEMENT TEAM
Managers: Ian Drewitt
Assistant Manager:Marcus Law
Club Doctor: Philip Earl
Physio: John Roberts

FACT FILE
Formed: 1896   Nickname: Greenbacks
Sponsors: Worthington
Colours: Green & white/Green/Green.
Change colours: Yellow & green
Midweek matchday: Tuesday
Res: Mid Comb .Youth Lg:MidFloodlit
Club website:www.bedworthunited.fwsi.com

2001.02
Captain: Guy Sanders
Top Scorer: Chris Partridge
P..o.Y.: Braig Whitmore

Pages: 60   Price: £1.20
Editor: Ron Kemp 02476 318014

Local Press: Heartland Evening News, Weekly Tribune, Bedworth Echo, Coventry Evening Telegraph
Local Radio: Mercia Sound, BBC CWR

GROUND The Oval, Miners Welfare Park, Coventry Road, Bedworth CV12 8NN
Tel: 02476 314302   **Email Address:** ronald@dkemp.3freeservice.co.uk
Directions: M6 jct 3, into Bedworth on B4113 Coventry to Bedworth road, ground200yds past past Bedworth Leisure Centre on this road. Coaches should park atthis Leisure Centre.
Buses from Coventry and Nuneaton pass ground
Capacity: 7,000   Cover: 300   Seats: 300   Floodlights: Yes
Clubhouse: Social club open every day 7.30-11pm & w/e noon-3pm. Hot and cold bar food
Club Shop: Selling a wide range of souvenirs & programmes.
        Contact : Ron Kemp   01203 318014

PREVIOUS   **Leagues:** Birmingham Comb. 47-54; West Mids (at first Birmingham) Lg 54-72
        Name: Bedworth Town 47-68   **Ground:** British Queen Ground 11-39

CLUB RECORDS Attendance: 5,127 v Nuneaton Borough, Southern Lg Midland Division 23/2/82
        Win: 11-0   **Defeat:** 1-10
        Career Goalscorer: Peter Spacey (1949-69)   **Career Appearances:** Peter Spacey
        Transfer fee paid: £1,750 for Colin Taylor (Hinckley Town, 1991-92)
        Transfer fee received: £30,000 for Richard Landon (Plymouth Argyle, January 1994)

BEST SEASON   FA Trophy: Second Round 80-81   **FA Cup:** 4th Qualifying Rd 1983/89/90

HONOURS   Birmingham Comb.(2) 48-50, Birmingham Snr Cup(3) 78-79 80-82, Midland Floodlit Cup 81-82 92-93

Players progressing: Phil Huffer (Derby County 1953), Geoff Coleman(Northampton Town 1955), Ian Hathaway (Mansfield Town 1989), Richard Landon(Plymouth Argyle 1994),Robert Oddy (Coventry City 2002), Dan Pitham (Burnley 2002), Inderpaul Khela , Ashley Pringle and Phil Garner (all Kidderminster Harriers)

Back row left to right: James Richardson, Ben Steane, Guy Sanders, Craig Whitmore, Adam Cooper, Mark Jones, Ross Harrison, Martin Crowley, Scott McGreggor and Philip Earl (Club Doctor)
Front row: Paul John, Robert Oddy, Chris Goodman, Chris Partridge, Spencer Parsons, Dave Aston and Darren Beckett.

BROMSGROVE ROVERS

CLUB OFFICIALS

Chairman: Tom Herbert
President: Charles W Poole
Secretary: Brian Hewings c/o Club
Commercial Managers: Helen Herbert &
Terry Smith

FOOTBALL MANAGEMENT TEAM
Manager:Gary Hackett & Jon Ford
Coach Steve Ingram
Physios: Lee O'Neil & Wes Mole

FACT FILE
Formed: 1885
Sponsors: All Saints Masterfit (Bromsgrove).
Nickname: Rovers or Greens
Colours: Green & White stripes/green/white
Change colours: Red/black/black
Midweek matchday: Tuesday
Reserves' league: Central Conference.
Newsline: 0891 88 44 96

2001-02
Captain & P.o.Y.:Morgan Brooker
Top Scorer: Sam Bowen

BROMSGROVE ROVERS FOOTBALL CLUB
Dr. Martens Western Division

ROVERS
versus
CLEVEDON TOWN

OLD ROVER

Main Sponsor

BANKS'S

Match Sponsor Bromsgrove Rovers Supporters Society Ltd

PROGRAMME £1.00

GROUND: Victoria Ground, Birmingham Road, Bromsgrove, Worcs, B61 0DR
Tel: 01527 876949
Directions: Ground is situated on the north side of Bromsgrove on the Birmingham Road, off the A38 Bromsgrove by pass. The M5 and M42 join theA38 to the north of the town making it easy to get to the ground without havingto go into town. The 144 Midland Red bus runs from New Street StationBirmingham and passes the ground.
Capacity: 4,893   Seated: 394   Covered Terracing: 1,344
Clubhouse: Victoria Club (01527 878260) - Serves hot & cold food. Big screenTV, pool table & darts. Open matchdays and week-day evenings.
Club Shop: Selling replica clothing & souvenirs. Contact Doug Bratt (01527 874997).

Pages: 40   Price: £1.00
Editor: Phil Baker
Tel No: 01527 870861

PREVIOUS **Leagues:** Birmingham Lge 1898-08 53-65, Birmingham Comb. 1908-53, West Midlands 65-72, Southern Lge - Northern Div. 73-79, Midland Div. 79-86, Premier Div. 86-92, GMVC 92-97, Southern 97-01, Midland Alliance 01-02
Grounds: Old Station Road 1885-87, Recreation Ground 87-88, Churchfields 88-97,Well Lane 1897-1910.

CLUB RECORDS Attendance: 7,389 v Worcester City - 1957
Career - Goalscorer: Chris Hanks 238, 83-94   **Appearances:** Shaun O'Meara 763, 75-94
Win: 11-0 - v Hinckley Ath. 1970, v Halesowen Town `A' 1939     **Defeat:** 0-12 v Aston Villa `A' 1939
Fee paid: £3,000 for Recky Carter (Solihull B.) 93-94   **Fee received:** Undisclosed for Scott Cooksey (Peterborough) Dec. 93

HONOURS   Vauxhall Conference R-up 92-93, Lge Cup 94-95 95-96; Southern Lge Prem 91-92, R-up 86-87, Cup 92-93, R-up 86-87, Midland Div 85-86, Merit Cup 85-86, Cup 85-86, R-up 73-74 87-88; Bill Dellow Cup 85-86; Worcester Sen Cup (8), R-up (10); Birmingham Sen Cup 46-47, R-up 47-48 88-89; W Mid Lge Cup 67-70, Cup 67-68 70-71; Birminham Lge 59-60, R-up 04-05 56-57 60-61; Birmingham Comb 46-47, R-up 49-50 50-51; Hereford Charity Chall Cup 46-47, R-up 47-48.

Players progressing: M McKenna (Northampton 46),R Hartle (Bolton 52), A McLean (Bury 53), A Smith (A.Villa 54), M Deakin (CPalace 54), B Puster (Leicester 58), Tom Smith (Sheff Utd 1978), MalcolmGoodman (Halifax 1979), Steve Smith (Walsall 1980), Gary Hackett (Shrewsbury 1983), Bill McGarry, Martyn O'Connor (C Palace 1992), Scott Cooksey (Peterborough 1993), Steve Taylor (Crystal Palace 1995).

L-R - Back row: Pete O'Connell (Director), Steve Frost, Steve Pope, Brian Hewings (Football Secretary), Mark Clifton, James Dyson, Mark Crisp, Chris Taylor (now left the club), Matt Southwick, Neil Cartwright, Ross Collins (on loan from Halesowen Town), Steve Taylor (now Stourbridge FC), Phil Baker (Club/Company Secretary), Scott Laydon, Lee O'Neill (Physiotherapist).
Front row: Gary Hackett (Co-Manager), Stewart Brighton (Team Captain), Kevin Banner, Ashley Read, Paul Danks, Tom Herbert (Chairman), Mark Benbow, Les Palmer, Grant Beckett, Richard Burgess, Jon Ford (Co-Manager)
Missing: Matt Lowe, Paul Lloyd, Leon Broadhurst, Steve Thomas, Tony Partridge (Director), Wes Mole (Director), Steve Ingram (Coach).

CINDERFORD TOWN

CLUB OFFICIALS

Chairman: Ashley Saunders
President: S Watkins
Vice Chairman: Ray Reed

Secretary: Chris Warren
9c Tusculum Way, Mitcheldean,
Glos GL17 0HZ
01594543065 (H) 01594 542421 x 2360 (B)
Press Officer: Andy Little

FACT FILE

Formed: 1922 Nickname: Town
Sponsors: T.B.A.
Colours: Black & white stripes/black/black
Change colours: All Red
Midweek matchday: Tuesday
Reserves' League: No reserve team

FOOTBALL MANAGEMENT TEAM

Manager: Tony Hopkins
Asst. Manager:T.B.A.
Physio: Keith Marfell

OFFICIAL PROGRAMME · SEASON 2001 - 2002
CINDERFORD TOWN
AFC

FOOTBALL LEAGUE
WESTERN DIVISION

6th April 2002
HALESOWEN TOWN

£1

GROUND   The Causeway, Hilldene, Cinderford, Glos. Tel: 01594 827147 or 822039

Directions: From Gloucester take A40 to Ross-on-Wye, then A48 - Chepstow. In 8miles turn right at Elton garage onto A4151 signed Cinderford, thru Littledean, up steep hill, right at crossroads, second left into Latimer Rd. Ground 5 minswalk from town centre

Capacity: 2,500   Cover: 1,000   Seats: 250   Floodlights: Yes

Clubhouse: Open every day. 2 bars, kitchen, 2 skittle alleys, darts, dancehall,committee room
Club Shop: Souvenirs, club badges (£˜3.00), ties, mugs , scarves and pennants .

Pages: 50   Price: £1.00
Editor: Dave Roberts
Tel: 01594 824365

PREVIOUS   **Leagues:** Glos Northern Snr 22-39 60-62, Western 46-59, Warwickshire Comb 63-64,West Midlands 65-69, Gloucestershire County 70-73 85-89, Midland Comb. 74-84,Hellenic 90-95

              Names: None   **Grounds:** Mousel Lane, Royal Oak

CLUB RECORDS   **Attendance:** 4,850 v Minehead, Western League, 1955-56

                    Win: 13-0 v Cam Mills 38-39   **Defeat:** 0-10 v Sutton Coldfield 78-79

                    Career Appearances: Russell Bowles 528   **Career Goalscorer:** Unknown

BEST SEASON   **FA Cup:** 2nd Rd v Gravesend 95-96   **FA Trophy:** 2nd Qual Rd

                    FA Vase: 2nd Rd 91-92   **FA Amateur Cup:** 3rd Qual Rd 52

HONOURS   Hellenic Lg Premier Champions 94-95, Premier Lg.Cup 94-95, Floodlit Cup 93-94,Div 1 90-91; Glos Northern Snr Lg Div 1 38-39 60-61, R-up (6); Nth Glos Lg Div1 38-39 60-61; Glos Snr Amtr Cup (Nth) (6), R-up (3); Western Lg Div 2 56-57; Warwickshire Comb. 63-64; W Mids Lg Prem Div Cup 68-69; Glos Jnr Cup (Nth) 80-81; Midland Comb. 81-82; Glos Co. Lg R-up 69-70 71-72 73-74; Glos FA Trophy R-up 92-93; Hungerford Cup 94-95, Glos.Sen Cup Finalists 00-01

L-R - Back Row: Jason Donovan (coach), Tommy Callinan (asst. manager), Leigh Hall, Clayton Hook, Jayson Hoskins, Andy Fisher, Chris Bale, Damien Edwards, Simon Truman, Tom Phillips, Keith Marfell (physio).
Front: Lee Brown, Daryl Addis, Scott Griffin, Lee Relish, Tony Hopkins (manager), Jamie Hammonds, Richard Pugh.

CIRENCESTER TOWN

CLUB OFFICIALS

Chairman: Stephen Abbley
17 Dianmer Close, Hook, Swindon. SN4 8ER.
Tel: 01743853293 (H) 01793 884900 (B)
Secretary: Jim Saunders,16 Arnold Way
Cirencester, Glos. GL7 1TA
Tel: 01285 659002 (H)
Commercial Manager: Stephen Abbley
Press Officer: Jim Saunders

FOOTBALL MANAGEMENT TEAM

Manager: Brian Hughes
Physio: T.B.A.

FACT FILE

Founded: 1889Nickname: Centurians
Sponsors: P.H.H./Cheltenham Windows
Colours: Red & black/ black/ red
Change colours: All Blue
Midweek Matchday: Tuesday
Reserves' League: Cirencester & District
2001-2002
P.o.Y.: Kevin Sawyer
Captain & P.o.Y.: Giles Harris

GROUND Corinium Stadium,Kingshill Lane, Cirencester Tel: 01285654543

Directions: Leave by-pass at Burford Road roundabout to the left. Then right at lights,laft at junction first left and ground is 250 yards on right.
Capacity: 4,500   Seats: 550   Cover: 550   Floodlights: Yes

Clubhouse: Open Tuesday - Friday evenings & Saturday. Snacks are available onmatch-days.   Club Shop: None

Pages: ??   Price: £1
Editor: Anna Corkoran Tel. 01258 654543

Local Press:
Standard, Western Daily Press
Local Radio:
BBC Radio Gloucester, Severn Sound

PREVIOUS   **Leagues:** Hellenic League Names: None. Grounds: Smithfield Stadium

CLUB RECORDS **Attendance:** 2,600 v Fareham 1969
Win: Unknown **Defeat:** Unknown
Career Goalscorer: Unknown **Career Appearances:** Unknown
Transfer fee paid: None **Transfer fee received:** None

BEST SEASON **FA Trophy:** 1st Qual. Round 1996-97 (1st season in comp.)
FA Vase: Never past the 1st Round   **FA Cup:** 4th Qualifying Round, 2001-02

HONOURS Gloucestershire Senior Amateur Cup 89-90; Hellenic League Div One Challenge Cup 90-91; Hellenic League Prem Div 95-96, League Cup 95-96; Gloucestershire County Cup 95-96

Players progressing: None

Gary Horgan (No.8) scores from this free kick against Tamworth in last season's FA Cup.   **Photo**: Paul Barber

CLEVEDON TOWN

CLUB OFFICIALS
Chairman: John Croft
Directors: R.J.Ayers, B.W.Bradshaw, S.T.Haas,
T Walsh and G,Thomas
Secretary: Mike Williams
34 Robinia Walk, Whitchurch,
Bristol BS14 0SHTel: 01275 833835
Commercial Manager: Gary Bradshaw
(M) 07768 270718

FOOTBALL MANAGEMENT TEAM
Manager: Steve Fey
Coach: David Mogg Physio: Steve Tregale
Youth Team Manager: Chris Parmer

FACT FILE
Formed: 1880
Nickname: The Seasiders
Sponsors: Bradshaw Group
Colours: Blue & white stripes/blue/blue
Change colours: All yellow or all green
Midweek Matches: Tuesday
Youth Team: Som Youth Floodlit, SWCo
Web-site: www.clevedontownafc.co.uk
2001-02
CaptainLee Jefferies
P.o.Y.: Olly Price

GROUND Ha nd Stadium, Davis Lane, Clevedon email: info@handstadium.co.uk
Fax: 01275 871601 Tel: 01275 871600(ground) 01275 341913 (office)

Directions: M5 Jct 20 - follow signs for Hand Stadium; first left into Central Way (at island just after motorway), 1st left at mini-r'bout into Kenn Rd, 2nd left Davis Lane; ground half mile on right. Or from Bristol(B3130) left into Court Lane (opposite Clevedon Court), turn right after 1mile, ground on left. Nearest BR station: Nailsea & Backwell. Buses from Bristol
Capacity: 3,650 Seats: 300 Cover: 1,600 Floodlights: Yes
Clubhouse: Open every day and evening. Separate function suite & lounge bar.Hot food available. Matchday refreshment bar within ground sells confectionary, teas & hot food
Club Shop: Sells all types of souvenirs, programmes and replica kit. Exchanges welcome.
Contact Stev Small **Supporters Club Chairman:** Russell Coneybeare

Pages: 34 Price:£1.30
Editor: Russell Isaac (01275 343000)

Local Radio: Radio Bristol, Star 107.7 FM
Local Press: Clevedon Mercury
Evening Post, Western Daily Press

PREVIOUS **Leagues:** Weston & District, Somerset Senior, Bristol Charity, Bristol & District, Bristol Suburban, Western 74-93
Grounds: Dial Hill ('till early 1890's); Teignmouth Road ('till 1991)
Names: Clevedon FC, Ashtonians (clubs merged in 1974)

CLUB RECORDS **Attendance:** 1,600 v Bristol City, Friendly. 27/7/98 Ground Record: Bristol Rovers v Ipswich Town 24/7/02
(At Teignmouth Road: 2,300 v Billingham Synthonia, FA Amateur Cup, 52-53)
Win: 18-0 v Dawlish Town (H), Western League Premier Division 24/4/93
Defeat: 13-3 v Yate YMCA (A), Bristol Comb 67-68

BEST SEASON **FA Cup:** 3rd Qual. Rd 2nd replay 92-93 v Newport AFC, 2-4 after two 1-1
FA Amateur Cup: 3rd Round Proper, 52-53 **FA Vase:** 6th Round 87-88, v Sudbury Town (A) **FA Trophy:** 2nd Round 98-99

HONOURS Southern League, Midland Division 98-99, Western League 92-93 (R-up 91-92), League Cup (R-up 92-93), Bristol Charity League 37-38,40-41, Somerset Senior Cup 01-02 04-05 28-29 , 00-01,01-02 Somerset Snr League 36-37, Div 1(Res). 92-93, Bristol & suburbanLeague 25-26,27-28,28-29, Weston & District League: 39-40,43-44,44-45, Somerset Premier Cup;86-87,98-99, 00-01,01-02 Somerset Junior Cup 1897-98,Somerset Medal Competition: 87-88, Clevedon Charity Cup 26-27,30-31.
Players Progressing: Jason Eaton (Bristol City) and Jonathon Gould (Halifax Town)

Back row left to right: Steve Fey (Manager), Gary Smart (Assistant Manager), Keith Knight, Karl Bayliss, Tony Cook, Jason Matthews, Oliver Price, Lee Barlass, Steve Peters and Steve Robbins. **Front row:** Steve Lester, Mark Badman, Bradley Thomas, Tommy Callinhan, Lee Jeffries, Darren Keeling , Mark Palmer, Wayne Thorne and Mark Clode.

EVESHAM UNITED

CLUB OFFICIALS
Chairman: **Jim Cockerton**
Vice Chairman: **Steve Lane**
President: **M E H Davis**
Treasurer: **Dave Wright**
Secretary/Press Officer: **Mike J Peplow**
68 Woodstock Rd, St Johns,
Worcester WR2 5NF
Tel: 01905 425993

FOOTBALL MANAGEMENT TEAM

Manager: Phil Mullen
Asst Manager: Paul Davies
Physio:Phil Greenway

FACT FILE

Nickname: The Robins
Sponsors; Dane Valley
Colours: Red & white/black/black
Change Colours: All blue
Formed: 1945
Midweek matches: Tuesday
Reserves' League: No reserve team
2001-02 Captain:Steve Taylor
P.o.Y: Phil Preedy
Top Scorer: Phil Preedy

Pages: 58   Price: £1
Editor: Mike Peplow (01905 425993)
Local Press: Evesham Journal,
Worcester Evening News, Gloucester Echo
Local Radio: Classic Gold
BBC Hereford & Worcester, FM102 The Bear

GROUND   Common Road, Evesham, Worcestershire WR11 4PU Tel: 01386 442303

Directions: From Evesham High Street turn into Oat St, and join one-way system,turn right between Willmotts factory called Conduit Hill into Common Rd, ground 200yds down on right just before railway bridge. 5 minutes walk from Evesham BR station
Capacity: 2,000   Seats: 350   Cover: 600   Floodlights: Yes
Clubhouse: Open matchdays and training nights.
        Cold food available in club, and hot food from tea hut on matchdays
Club Shop: Contact John Hawkins c/o the club

PREVIOUS   Leagues: Worcester, Birmingham Combination, Midland Combination 51-55 65-92, West Midlands Regional 55-62
        Name: Evesham Town   **Ground:** The Crown Meadow (pre-1968)

CLUB RECORDS Attendance: 2,338 v West Bromwich A., friendly 18/7/92
        Win: 11-3 v West Heath United   **Defeat:**1-8 v Ilkeston Town
        Career Goalscorer: Sid Brain   **Career Appearances:** Rob Candy
        Transfer fee paid: £1,500; to Hayes for Colin Day, 1992
        Transfer fee received: £5,000 for Simon Brain (to Cheltenham Town)

BEST SEASON   FA Vase: Quarter Finals 1991-92   FA Amateur Cup: Runners-up 1923-24
        FA Trophy: 3rd Qual Rd 96-97   FA Cup: 2nd Qual Rd 96-97

HONOURS   FA Amateur Cup R-up 23-24, Worcestershire Snr Urn(2) 76-78 (R-up 90-91), Midland Comb.(6) 52-53 54-55 65-66 67-69 91-92
        (Chal. Cup 53-54 87-88 91-92 (R-up(5) 54-55 71-72 83-84 88-90)), Worcestershire Comb. 52-53 54-55; B'gham Combination
        R-up 30-31, Evesham Hosp. Cup 89-90, Tony Allden Mem. Cup 1973 19881992

Players progressing: Billy Tucker, Gary Stevens (Cardiff 77), Kevin Rose(Lincoln 78), Andy Preece (Northampton 86),
        Simon Brain (Hereford, via Cheltenham Town), Billy Turley (Northampton Tn)

Back: Phil Mullen (manager), Paul Davies (asst manager), Steve Lutz, Adam Blake, Jay Powell, Darren Steadman, Craig Ladek, Damion Quailey, Leroy May, Shaun Pratt, Scott Mullen, Paul West (coach) and physio Phil Greenway. **Middle:** Phil Preedy, Nathan Jukes, Darren Bullock, Mark Wolsey, Grant Pinkney, Matt Pendleton, Andy Smith and Danny James. **Front:** Russell Parmenter, Kays Sibanda, Luke Tovey, Pete Sollis and James Brown.   **Picture** courtesy of The Journal Series, Evesham.

GLOUCESTER CITY

Tigers' Review
Gloucester City FC

Dr Martens League
Western Division
ATHERSTONE UNITED
City Stadium, Meadow Park
Saturday 20 April 2002 3.00pm
Official Matchday Programme
£1.00

CLUB OFFICIALS

Chairman: Colin Gardner
President: R F Etheridge
Secretary: Jason Mills
25 Hewlett Road, Cheltenham,
Gloucestershire GL52 6AD
Tel/Fax: 01242 700496
Mob: 07768 750590

Club Email: mills.jason@virgin.net
Press Officer: c/o Secretary

FOOTBALL MANAGEMENT TEAM
Manager: Chris Burns
Assistant Manager: Brian Godfrey
Coach:Mike Cook
Physio: Adrian Tandy

FACT FILE

Formed: 1889
Nickname: The Tigers
Sponsors: Keyway
Colours: Yellow & black/black/black
Change colours: All Red
Midweek games: Tuesday

2001-02
Captain: Nat Griffiths
Top Goalscorer: Karl Bayliss (17)
Joint Ps.o.Y.:
Matt Bath & Dave Wilkinson

Pages: 44 Price: £1.00
Editor: Mike Dunstan Tel: 01242 250087

Local Press: Gloucester Citizen,
Western Daily Press
Local Radio: Severn Sound,
BBC Radio Gloucestershire

GROUND Meadow Park, Sudmeadow Road, Hempsted, Gloucester GL2 6HS
Tel: 01452 421400
Directions: From North: A40 then then A4301 towards City Centre & Historic Docks, right into Severn Road over swingbridge, right into Llanthony Road/Hempsted Lane, 2nd right into Sudmeadow Road, ground 50yds on left
Capacity: 3,500   Cover:2,500   Seats: 560   Floodlights: Yes
Clubhouse: Meadow Park Sports & Social Club in ground. Normal licensing hours.
Club Shop: Yes

PREVIOUS **Leagues:** Bristol & Dist. (now Western) 1893-96, Gloucester & Dist. 97-1907, NorthGlos. 07-10, Glos. North Senior 20-34, Birmingham Comb. 1935-39
Grounds: Longlevens 1935-65, Horton Road 65-86   **Name:** Gloucester Y.M.C.A

CLUB RECORDS **Attendance:** 4,000 v Dagenham & Redbridge, FA Trophy S-F 2nd Leg, 12.4.97
Win: 10-0 v Sudbury Town (H), FA Cup 3rd Rd Q., 17.10.98
Defeat: 1-12 v Gillingham 9.11.46
Goalscorer: Reg Weaver, 250   **Appearances:** Stan Myers & Frank Tredgett in 1950s
Fee Paid: £25,000 for S Fergusson (Worcester City), and D Holmes (Gresley R.)
Fee Received: £25,000 Ian Hedges (AFC Bournemouth, 1990)

BEST SEASON FA Cup: 2nd Rd 89-90   FA Trophy: Semi-Final 1996-97

HONOURS Southern Lg R-up 90-91, Lg Cup 55-56 R-up 81-82, Midland Div 88-89), Glos NthSen Lg 33-34,
Glos Sen. Cup 37-38 49-58 65-66 68-69 70-71 74-75 78-79 79-80 81-82 82-83 83-84 90-91 92-93; Sen Amat Cup (Nth) 31-32)

Players progressing: Numerous including - William Teague (61) & Rod Thomas (64) to Swindon, John Layton (Hereford 74), Ian Main (Exeter 78), Mike Bruton (Newport 79), Mel Gwinnett (Bradford C. 84), Steve Talboys (Wimbledon 91)

Back row left to right
Steve Jenkins,
David Wilkinson,
Matthew Taylor,
Gavin Rea
and Andy Hoskins.
Middle row:
Ade Tandy (Physio),
Luke Prince,
Mark Temple,
Will Steadman,
Nick Delves,
Tom Webb
and Brian Godfrey (Asst.Manager)
Front row:
Craig Temple,
Mark Hardcastle,
Neil Griffiths
Chris Burns (Player Manager),
Gary Marshall,
Dominic Dunton
and Lee Smith.

GRESLEY ROVERS

CLUB OFFICIALS
Chairman: Mark Evans
President: Gordon Duggins
Vice Chairman: George Sutton
Secretary / Press Officer: Neil Betteridge,
34 Thorpe Downs Road, Church Gresley,
Swadlincote, Derbys DE11 9FB
Tel: 01283 226229
Commercial Director: Mark Evans

FOOTBALL MANAGEMENT TEAM

Manager: Jon Newsome
Asst Manager: Alan Titterton
Physio: Gary Harrison

FACT FILE
Formed: 1882
Nickname: The Moatmen
Sponsors:
Colours: Red/white/red
Change colours: White/black/white
Midweek matchday: Tuesday
Reserves' League: Midland Comb (Res. Div.)
2001-02
Captain:Stuart Evans
P.o.Y.: Barrie Woolley
Top scorer: Chris Parkins 14

GROUND   Moat Ground, Moat Street, Church Gresley, Swadlincote, Derbys., DE11 9RE.
Tel: 01283 216315   Club Website: www.gresleyrovers.co.uk

Directions: To A444 via either the A5, A38, A5121 or M42 , Junction 11. On reaching A444 head for Castle Gresley. Take exit at large island to Church Gresley, at next island 2nd exit (Church St), then 2nd left (School St) then 1st left into Moat St. 5 miles Burton-on-Trent (BR). Buses from Swadlincote and Burton

Capacity: 2,000   **Cover:** 1,200   **Seats:** 400   **Floodlights:** Yes
Clubhouse: Inside ground, open Mon & Thurs evenings & matchdays
Club Shop: Sells merchandise, programmes, metal badges etc.

Pages: 32   Price: £1.00

Local Press: Derby Evening Telegraph, Burton Mail, Burton Trader, SwadlincoteTimes
Local Radio: BBC Radio Derby .

PREVIOUS   **Leagues:** Burton Lge 1892-95 97-01 09-10 43-45, Derbyshire Sen 1895-97 02-03,Leics Sen 1890-91 98-99 08-09 10-12 15-16 35-42 45-49, Notts 01-02, Midland 03-06, Central All 11-15 19-25 49-53 59-67, Birmingham Comb 25-33 53-54, Birmingham (now West Mids) 54-59 75-92, Central Comb 33-35, East Mids 67-75
Grounds: Mushroom Lane, Albert Village 1882-95, Church Str., Church, Gresley. 1895-1909

CLUB RECORDS **Attendance:** 3,950 v Burton Albion, Birmingham (now West Mids) Lg Division One 57-58
Win: 23-0 v Holy Cross Priory, Leics Jun Cup 1889-90   **Defeat:** 1-15 v Burton Crusaders 1886-87
Career Goalscorer: Gordon Duggins 306   **Career Appearances:** Dennis King 579
Transfer fee received: £30,000 for Justin O'Reilly (Port Vale 1996)
Transfer fee paid: £2,500 for David Robinson (Ilkeston Town 97)

BEST SEASON **FA Vase:** Runners-up 90-91, (SF 92-93)   **FA Trophy:** Qtr Finals 95-96
FA Cup: 1st Rd Proper: 30-31 (1-3 at York City), 94-95 (1-7 at Crewe Alex.)   League clubs defeated: None

HONOURS   Southern Lge Champ 96-97; FA Vase R-up 90-91; West Mids Lg 90-91 91-92 (R-up 85-86 88-89); Lg Cup 88-89 R-Up. 86-87 91-92; Southern Lg Mid Div R-up 92-93; Derbys Snr Cup (7), (R-Up (3); Leics Snr Cup 1898-99 46-47 (R-Up 1899-90 45-46); Leics Sen Lg 00-01 46-47 47-48 R-Up (7); Coalville Charity Cup 46-47; Derby Senior Cup (S) (2) R-Up 00-01 01-02 Bass Vase (6); Cent All 64-65 66-67 R-Up(3) (Lg Cup 52-53); East Mids Reg Lg (2) R-Up (2); Dr.Martens (S Lge) Cup Fin 93-94

Players progressing: Phil Gee (Derby County 85), Mark Blount (Sheffield Utd 94), Colin Loss (Bristol City 94), Justin O'Reilly (Port Vale 96)

L-R - Back Row: Paul Tomlinson, Andy Cheetham, Andy Bourne, Brad Clarke, James Lindley, Ian Bluck, Michael Crawford, Mark Peters
Front Row: Gary White, Jamie Barrett, Chris Parkins, Carl Timms, Richard Wardle, Earl Alexander, Chris Gray

MANGOTSFIELD UNITED

THE FIELD REVIEW
MANGOTSFIELD UNITED
FOOTBALL CLUB Ltd.
FOUNDED 1951
AFFILIATED TO GLOUCESTERSHIRE F.A. AND SOMERSET & AVON F.A.

FLO GAS

Western Division Season 2001/2002

SATURDAY 20th APRIL 2002   HALESOWEN TOWN

Official Programme £1

CLUB OFFICIALS

President: Richard Davis
Chairman: Roger Pullin
Vice Chairman: Len Street
Secretary & Press Off: Roger Gray
105 Chiltern Close, Warmley, Bristol
BS15 5UW Tel: 0117 961 6523
(Mobile) 07768 467851

FOOTBALL MANAGEMENT TEAM

Manager: Andy Black
Assistant Manager: Shaun Penny
Physio:Tammy Mullin

FACT FILE

Founded: 1950   Nickname: The Field
Sponsors: Flo Cas
Colours: Sky & maroon/maroon/sky
Change colours: Yellow/navy/yellow
Midweek matchday: Tuesday 7.45
Reserve League: Somerset County

2001-02
Captain: Lee Barlass
P.o.TY .& Top Scorer: David Seal 30

GROUND   Cossham Street, Mangotsfield, Bristol BS17 3EW Tel: 0117 956 0119

Directions: M4 jct 19, M32 jct 1; A4174 marked Downend, through lights, over double mini-r'bout to Mangotsfield, left by village church onto B4465 signposted Pucklechurch, ground quarter mile on right. From central Bristol take A432 thru Fishponds, Staple Hill, to Mangotsfield and turn right by village church onto B4465. From Bath/Keynsham follow A4175, right at island at Willsbridge onto A431, then rejoin A4175 at next island (Cherry Garden Hill) to Bridge Yate, straight over double mini-r'bout and take 1st left, right into Carsons Rd after 1 mile and follow to Mangotsfield village & turn right by church onto B4465

Capacity: 2,500   Seats: 300   Cover: 800   Floodlights: Yes   Club Shop: Yes

Pages: 32   Price: £1.00
Editor: Bob Smale (0117 9401926)

Clubhouse: Open 11-11. Snacks - hot food on matchdays. Lounge bar for functions etc

PREVIOUS   **Leagues:** Bristol & District 50-67; Avon Premier Combination 67-72; Western League 72-00
RECORD   **Attendance:** 2,386 v Bath City, FA Cup 77-78
                 Goalscorer: John Hill   **Appearances:** John Hill 600+
                 Win: 14-0 v Dawlish (a) 1993 Western League   **Defeat:** 3-13 v Bristol City United (Bristol & District Div 1)
                 & 17-0 v Hanham Sports (Bristol & District League `Div 6)

HONOURS   Western Lg 90-91r-up 99-00, Lg Cup 73-74 r-up 86-87, Div 1 r-up 82-83; Somerset Prem. Cup 87-88, r-up 88-89 95-96;
                 Glos Snr Cup 68-69 75-76; Glos FA Trophy 84-85 86-87 90-91 94-95 96-97; Hungerford Invitation Cup 74-75;
                 Rothmans Nat. Cup r-up 77-78; Hanham Invit. Charity Cup 84-85 85-86;
                 Youth honours: Glos Yth Shield 81-82 84-85 (R-up 82-83); Somerset Floodlit Yth Lg 81-82 82-83 83-84 84-85 87-88 98-99;
                 Somerset Yth Shield 76-77
                 Reserve honours Somerset Snr Lg (Res.) Div 1 98-99 Div 2 97-98 75-76, Div 3 74-75; Somerset Comb. Cup 74-75

BEST SEASON **FA Vase:** Semi Final 95-96   **FA Cup:** 4th Qualifying Rd Replay v Lewes 0-0 (H) 0-2 (A) 2001-02
Players progress ing: G Megson, S White, G Penrice, P Purnell, N Tanner, M Hooper

Back row,left to right: Andy Black (Manager), Jon Crowley, Darren Edmunds, Scott Hendy,Rob Clarke, Lee Barluss, Dale Esler, Nick Brooks, Gareth Loyden, Tammy Mullen (Physio) , Shaun Penny (Assistant Manager). **Front row:** Lee Gritson, Ricky Gingell, Adam Sims, Dean Pendry, Leon Cousins, Mark Summers and Mike Davis   Photo: Sunday Independant

MERTHYR TYDFIL

CLUB OFFICIALS

Chairman: Wyn Holloway
Vice Chairman: Paul Sugrue
Football Sec: Anthony Hughes
Press Off. Robert Davies

FACT FILE

Formed: 19445
Nickname: The Martyrs
Sponsors:T.B.A.
Colours: White & black/black/black
Change colours: Royal Blue/white
Midweek home matchday: Tuesday
Reserves' League: None
Club Website: www.themartyrs.com

FOOTBALL MANAGEMENT TEAM

Manager: Andy Beattie
Assistant Manager: John Relish

2001-02
Top scorer:Paul Hunt 9
Captain: Neil Thomas
P.o.Y.: Danny Haines

FA CUP
First Qualifying Round
SATURDAY 14th September 2002
3PM KICK OFF

GROUND Penndarren Park, Merthyr Tydfil, Mid Glamorgan Tel: 01685 384102
Email Address: pughy@tinyonline.co.uk

Directions: (South) A470 Express Way to Merthyr Centre to Pontmorlais (traffic lights) turn left then first right, first right at Catholic Church and right again into Park Terrace . (North) Heads of theValley road to Town Centre, to Pontmorlais(traffic lights) turn right, then as above
Capacity: 10,000 Seats: 1,500 Cover: 5,000 Floodlights: Yes
Clubhouse: Open Mon. to Sun. 6.30 - 11.00pm. 2 club cafes open on matchdays for hot food
Club Shop: Sells replica kits, club souvenirs & programmes.
Contact Mel Jenkins01443 692336

Pages: 36 Price: £1.20
Editors: Tel: 01685 359921 or 01685 386388
Robert Davies and Mike Donovan

Local Press: Merthyr Express
Local Radio: Valleys Radio

PREVIOUS **Leagues:** Southern League 46 -89 (Southern League 46-59, 1st Division 59-61, 64-71, !st Div. North 72-79, Premier Div. 61-64, 71-72, 88-89, Midland Div. 79-88), G M Conference 89-95.
Names: None **Grounds:** None

CLUB RECORDS **Attendance:** 21,000 v Reading FA Cup 2nd Rnd 1949/50
Win: 11-0 v Rushden 1987 **Defeat:** 9-2 v Altrincham 1993
Transfer fee paid: £10,000 to Cardiff City for Robbie James 1992
Transfer fee received: £12,000 for Ray Pratt from Exeter City 1981

BEST SEASON **Welsh FA Cup:** Winners 48-49 50-51 86-87
FA Trophy: 3rd Rd v Northwich Vic 95-96 **FA Cup:** 2nd Round on six occasions. League clubs defeated: Bristol Rovers

HONOURS Welsh FA Cup 48-49, 50-51, 86-87; Southern League 47-48, 49-50, 50-51, 51-52, 53-54; Southern League (Midland) 87-88; Southern League (Premier) 88-89;Southern League Cup 47-48, 50-51

Players Progressing : Syd Howarth (Aston Villa), Cyril Beech, Gilbert Beech,Bill Hullet, Ken Tucker (Cardiff City), Nick Deacy (Hereford United), Gordon Davies (Fulham), Ray Pratt (Exeter City), Peter Jones, Paul Giles (Newport County)

RACING CLUB WARWICK

RACING CLUB WARWICK F.C.
V
SHEPSHED DYNAMO

DR MARTENS LEAGUE WESTERN DIVISION
TUESDAY SEPTEMBER 10th 2002
KICK OFF 7:45
OFFICIAL MATCHDAY PROGRAMME £1.00

CLUB OFFICIALS

Chairman: **Jim Wright**

Secretary: **Pat Murphy**
Tel: 01926 612675

FOOTBALL MANAGEMENT

Manager:Billy Hollywood

FACT FILE

Formed: 1919
Nickname: Racers
Colours: Gold & black
Change colours: Red&white/red/red
Midweek matchday: Tuesday
Youth's League: Mid F/Lit Yth Lge

2001-02
Captain: M.Hodson
P.o.Y.: C.Wells
Top scorer: C.Hughes 9

GROUND   Townsend Meadow, Hampton Road, Warwick CV34 6JP
Tel: 01926 495786

Directions: On the B4189 Warwick to Redditch road (via Henley in Arden) next to owners' & trainers' car park of Warwick Racecourse. From M40 jct 15 (1 1/2 miles) take A429 into Warwick, left into Shakespeare Ave., straight over island, right at T-junction into Hampton Rd, ground 300yds on left. 2 milesfrom Warwick BR station
Capacity: 1,000   Cover: 200   Seats: 250   Floodlights: Yes
Clubhouse: 01926 495786 Open every evening & Sat &Sun lunchtimes
Club Shop: Scarves, mugs, badges, programmes - contact Secretary

Pages: 20 Price: £1.00
Editor: Phil Street
Local Press: Warwick Advertiser, Leamington Courier, Coventry EveningTelegraph
Local Radio:C.W.R. BBC Radio Coventry, Bear Radio

PREVIOUS   **Leagues:** Birmingham & West Mids All., Warwickshire Comb., West Midlands (Regional) 67-72, Midland Comb. 72-89
    Names: Saltisford Rovers 1919-68   **Grounds:** Coventry Road

CLUB RECORDS   **Attendance:** 1,000 v Halesowen Town, FA Cup 1987
    Transfer fee paid: £1,000 for Dave Whetton (Bedworth United)   **Win:** 9-1 v Knowle
    Transfer fee received: £5,000 for Ben Foster (Stoke City)   **Defeat:** 0-7v Redditch United
    Career Goalscorer: Steve Edgington 200   **Career Appearances:** Steve Cooper 600

BEST SEASON   **FA Vase:** 4th Round 77-78   **FA Cup:** 3rd Qual Rd 92-93   **FA Trophy:**

HONOURS   Midland Combination 87-88 (R-up 88-89); Warwick Lg 33-34 34-35 35-36; Birmingham & West Mids Alliance 48-49; Birmingham & Dist Alliance Senior Cup 49-50; Leamington & Dist Lg 37-38 45-46 46-47 47-48; Leamington Hospital Cup 37-38 46-47; Warwick Cinderella Cup 35-36 36-37 37-38 38-39 46-47; T G John Cup 36-37; Leamington Junior Cup 38-39 46-47

Players progressing: Ben Foster (Stoke City,April 2001)

Back row left to right: Craig Hayward, Keith Marlow, Mark Hodson, Neil Stephenson, Adam Kinder, Luke Yates and Darren Massingham.
Front row: Kim Green, Colin Wells, Justin Wiseman, David Jackson, Paul Eden, Paul Guzzard and Jamie McWilliams.

REDDITCH UNITED

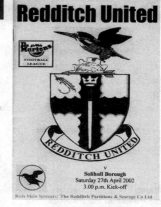

Redditch United

CLUB OFFICIALS

Chairman: Neil Paget
President: Major Jim Gillespie MBE
Secretary: Alan Wolfe,18 Packwood
Close,Webheath, Redditch,Worcs. B97
5SJ)Tel No: 01527 543044 (H)
Commercial Manager: Pat Cremin
Press Off: Neil Paget Tel:01527 543999

FOOTBALL MANAGEMENT TEAM

Manager: Rod Brown
Assistant Manager: Gary Whild
Coach: Kim Casey Physio: Peter James

FACT FILE

Formed: 1891

Nickname: The Reds

Colours: Red with Blue collar & cuffs

Change colours: Blue with red collar & cuffs

Midweek matchday: Tuesday

Reserves' League: Midland Comb. Res Div

2001-02

Captain:

P.o.Y:

Top scorers:

v
Solihull Borough
Saturday 27th April 2002
3.00 p.m. Kick-off

Reds Main Sponsors: The Redditch Partitions & Storage Co Ltd

GROUND Valley Stadium, Bromsgrove Road, Redditch B97 4RN Tel: 01527 67450
Directions: Access 7 on town centre ring-road takes you into Bromsgrove Road (via Unicorn
Hill) - ground entrance 400yds past traffic lights on right.Arriving from Bromsgrove take first
exit off dual carriageway. Ground 400 ydsfrom Redditch BR station and town centre
Capacity: 5,000   **Cover:** 2,000   **Seats:** 400   **Floodlights:** Yes
Clubhouse: Large clubroom and lounge boardroom. Open matchdays and for private hire.
Food available on matchdays; steaks hot dogs, burgers, chips, bovril etc
Club Shop: Not at Present

Prog: Pages: 50 Price: £1.00
Editor: Michael Swanborough
Local Press: Redditch Advertiser, Birmingham
Evening Mail, Redditch Standard
Local Radio: BBC Hereford & Worcester
The Bear Radio FM102

PREVIOUS   **Leagues:** B'ham Comb. 05-21 29-39 46-53, West Midlands 21-29 53-72, Southern 72-79, 81- Alliance Premier (Conf) 79-80
Name: Redditch Town   **Ground:** HDA Spts Ground, Millsborough Rd

CLUB RECORDS **Attendance:** 5,500 v Bromsgrove, league match 54-55
Transfer fee paid: £3,000 for Paul Joinson from Halesowen Town
Transfer fee received: £42,000 for David Farrell (Aston Villa, 1991)

BEST SEASON **FA Cup:** 1st Rd replay 71-72, 0-4 v Peterborough U (A) after 1-1 draw. Also 1st Rd 71-72
FA Trophy: 4th Round 1998-99 0-2 v Boston United

HONOURS   Southern Lg Div 1 Nth 75-76 (Midland Div R-up 85-86) S.Lg Cup R-up 97-98 West Mids (B'ham) Lg Southern Sect. 54-55,
Birmingham Comb. 13-14 32-33 52-53 (R-up 06-07 14-15 51-52), Staffs Snr Cup 90-91, Birmingham Snr Cup 24-25 31-32 38-39 76-77, Worcs
Snr Cup 894-95 1930-31 74-75 76-77 (R-up 1888-89 1929-30 52-53 73-74), Worcs Jnr Cup 90-91

Players progressing: Hugh Evans (Birmingham 1947), Trevor Lewes (Coventry1957), David Gilbert (Chesterfield 1960), Mike Tuohy (Southend Utd
1979), NeilSmith (Liverpool), David Farrell (Aston Villa 1992), Neil Davis (Aston Villa 1991)

Left to right

Back row:
Paul Jones,
Gavin Barrett,
Steve Frost,
Harvey Willetts,
Mark Crighton,
Neil Began.

Front row:
Mark Swain,
Andy Bradley,
Paul Danks,
Richard Field,
Scott Colcombe.

ROCESTER

CLUB OFFICIALS

Chairman: Alf.Hawksworth

Secretary: Gilbert Egerton
23 Eaton Rd, Rocester, Uttoxeter,
Staffs ST145LL.
Tel: 01889 590101

FOOTBALL MANAGEMENT TEAM

Manager: Warren Campbell

FACT FILE

Founded: 1876 Nickname: Romans
Sponsors:
Colours: Amber & black/black/black
Change colours: All blue
Reserves' Lge: North Staffs (North)
Midweek matchday: Tuesday

2001-02
Captain : Richard Owen
Top Scorer: Emeka Ejiofor
P.o.Y.: Andy Bostock

ROCESTER FOOTBALL CLUB

Joint Main Sponsors
M J BARRETT KEYSTONE COMPUTER GROUP

DR. MARTEN'S LEAGUE WESTERN DIVISION
Saturday, 17th November, 2001
ROCESTER - v - ATHERSTONE UTD
K.O. 3.00 p.m.
League

MATCHDAY PROGRAMME
SEASON 2001/2002

GROUND Hillsfield, Mill Street, Rocester, Uttoxeter, Staffs Tel: 01889 590463
Email Address: rocester@floodlight org.uk
Directions: From A50 r'bout adjoining Little Chef at Uttoxeter take B5030 to Rocester & Alton Towers, right into Rocester village after 3miles over narrow bridge, in village centre bear right at sharp left-hand bend into Mill St., ground 500yds on left just past former cotton mill.

32 pages £1.00
Editor: Barry Brosnan
Tel: 01889 567795

Capacity: 4,000 Seats: 230 Cover: 500 Floodlights: Yes

Clubhouse: On matchdays (normal licensing hours). Hot drinks & snacks.
Club Shop: Yes

PREVIOUS **Leagues:** Ashbourne; Leek & Moorland; Cheadle & Dist; Uttoxeter Amateur; Stafford 53-57; Staffordshire County North 57-84; Staffordshire Senior 84-87; West Midlands 87-94; Midland alliance 94-99.
Ground: Mill Street, Rocester (1876-1986),Hillsfield ,Mill St. 1987-2002

BEST SEASON **FA Cup:** 3rd Qual. Round 97-98, 1-2 v Bromsgrove Rovers (A) **FA Vase:** 5th Round 86-87, 1-3 v Garforth Town (H) aet.

RECORDS **Attendance:** 1,026 v Halesowen T., FA Vase 4th Rd Jan.'87 (at Leek Town) Won 3-1 a.e.t.
Goalscorer: Mick Collins **Appearances:** Peter Swanwick.(A goalkeeper who played for 20 years -1962-82)
Fee Paid: £1,000 for Paul Ede from Burton Albion, Sept.1989.
Fee Received: £12,000 for Mark Sale from Birmingham City 1994
Win: 14-0 (twice) **Defeat:** 0-9

HONOURS West Mids Lg R-up 89-90 (Div 1 87-88, Div 1 Cup 87-88), Staffs Senior Lg (2) 85-87, Staffordshire FA Vase 85-86 87-88; Midland Alliance 98-99

Players progressing: Bert Carpenter (Manchester Utd), Joe Carpenter (Brighton), George Shepherd (Derby), Mark Sale (Birmingham, Torquay),Tony Hemmings (Wycombe via Northwich)

RUGBY UNITED

SEASON 2001/2002 £1.50

rugby united football club

OFFICIAL MATCHDAY MAGAZINE

the valley

26th December
2001
Kick-off 3.00pm
Dr Martens
Eastern Division

Rugby United
-v-
Erith & Belvedere

CLUB OFFICIALS
Chairman: Brian Melvin
Secretary: Doug Wilkins,
298 Rocky Lane, Great Barr,
Birmingham B42 1NQ
Tel: 0121 681 1544 (H 0121 686 4068 (F)
Press Officer: Alan Turner
Tel: 01788 567181
Commercial Manager:Lisa Melvin

FOOTBALL MANAGEMENT TEAM
Manager:Tony Dobson
Asst Manager: Steve Shay
Physio: Bob Gardner

FACT FILE
Formed: 1956   Nickname: The Valley
Sponsors: Rugby Telegraph & Melbros Ltd
Colours: Navy & sky/navy/navy
Change colours: All Red
Midweek matchday: Tuesday
Club Newsline: 0930 555971
Reserves' League: Midland Combination
2001-02
Top scorer: Robbie Beard 14
Captain: Craig Herbert
P.o.Y.: Craig Herbert

GROUND: Butlin Road, Rugby, Warks. CV21 3ST   Tel: 01788 844806 www.rugbyutd.co.uk
Directions: The ground is situated off Clifton (B5414) on the north side of Rugby. 1 mile walk
from the station   Club Call Line: 09066 555971
Capacity: 6,000   Cover: 1,000   Seats: 240   Floodlights: Yes

Pages: 36   Price: £1.50
Editor: Secretary Tel: 0121 240 4521
Local Press: Rugby Advertiser, Coventry
Evening Telegraph, Rugby Observer
Local Radio: Mercia Sound, CWR

Clubhouse: Open every night and weekend lunchtimes. Entertainment Saturday nights.
Excellent facilities include Long Alley Skittles, darts and pool
Club Shop: Yes

PREVIOUS   **Name:** Valley Sports, Valley Sports Rugby
                  Leagues: Rugby & District 1956-63, Coventry & Partnership, North Warks 63-69, United Counties 69-75, West Midlands 75-83

CLUB RECORDS Attendance: 3,961 v Northampton FA Cup 1984
                  Win: 10-0 v Ilkeston Tn FA Trophy 4/9/85   **Defeat:** 1-11 v Ilkeston Town (A) 18.4.98
                  Career Goalscorer: Danny Conway, 124   **Career Appearances:** Danny Conway, 374
                  Transfer fee paid: £3,500 R Smith, I Crawley, G Bradder **Transfer fee received:** £15,000 T Angus (Northampton)

BEST SEASON   **FA Cup:** 2nd round 87-88, plus 1st Rd 84-85 85-86 86-87 94-95 League clubs defeated: None
                  FA Trophy: **FA Vase:** Winners 82-83

HONOURS   Southern Lg Midland Div 86-87 (R-up 94-95, Lg Cup 89-90), FA Vase 82-83,Mid Floodlit Cup 84-85 89-90 98 -00(R-up 86-87),
                  Birmingham Snr Cup 88-89 91-92, Utd Co's Lg Div 3 Cup 69-70.
                  All-time record FA Trophy win: 10-0 away to IlkestonTown, Preliminary Rd 85-86

Players progressing: S Storer (Birmingham 1985), S Bicknell (Leicester), S Norris (Scarborough), T Angus (Northampton Town),
                          Ashley Walker (Peterborough), Ian King (Stoke City)

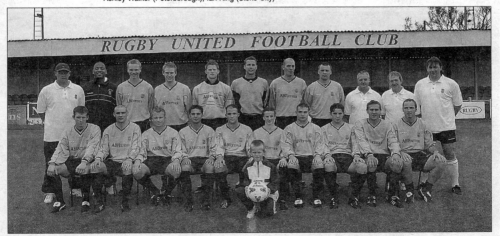

L-R - Back Row: Tony Dobson (manager), Jermaine Gordon, Lee Tatton, Andy Commander, Dean Thomas, Jason Pearcey, Ben Milner, Craig
Herbert, Steve Townsend (assistant), Bob Gardner (physio), Steve Shea (asst. manager). Front: Nathan Thompson, Jamie Williams, Paul O'Brien,
Karl Brennan, Dave Pearson, Neil Melvin, Danny Hall, Ryan Nash, Rory Squire, Gary Redgate. (Mascot: Jack Dobson).

SHEPSHED DYNAMO

CLUB OFFICIALS

Chairman: Michael Voce
President: Gilbert Kinch
Secretary: Peter Bull
17 Welland Rd, Barrow-on-Soar,
Leicestershire LE12 8NA
Tel: 01509 413338
Press Officer: John Brindley
Tel: 07971 339105

FOOTBALL MANAGEMENT TEAM

Manager: Dave Williams
Coach: Frank Benjamin
Physio: Alan Cook

FACT FILE
Re-formed: 1994
Nickname: Dynamo
Sponsors: Coalville Paints
Colours: Black & white stripes/black/black
Change colours: All Purple
Midweek matchday: Tuesday
Reserves' League: Midland Comb.

Local Press: Loughborough Echo,
Leicester Mercury, Coalville Times
Local Radio: Radio Leicester, Oak FM

Season 2002/03
Shepshed Dynamo F.C.
Versus
Cirencester Town
Saturday 7th September, 2002
Dr Martens League – Western Division
Today's Match Ball Sponsors:
Manpower
Official Matchday Programme: £1.20

GROUND
The Dovecote, Butthole Lane, Shepshed, Leicestershire
Tel: 01509 650992

Directions: M1 junction 23, A512 towards Ashby, right at first lights, right at garage in Forest Street, right into Butthole Lane opposite Black Swan. Five miles from Loughborough (BR)

Capacity: 5,000   Cover: 1,500   Seats: 209   Floodlights: Yes

Clubhouse: Takes 120 in main room, 50 in others
Club Shop: Yes (Steve Straw & Alan Gibson)

Programme
Pages: 40   Price: £1.20
Editor: Andy Reid 0116 2608295
email: andy.macmillan@ntlworld.com

PREVIOUS   **Leagues:** Leicestershire Senior 07-16 19-27 46-50 51-81, Midland Counties 81-82, Northern Counties (East) 82-83,
Southern 83-88, Northern Premier 88-93, Midland Combination 93-94, Midland Alliance 94-96
Names: Shepshed Albion 1890-1975 91-94, Shepshed Charterhouse 75-91
Grounds: Ashby Road (pre-1897), Little Haw Farm

CLUB RECORDS   **Attendance:** 2,500 v Leicester C. (friendly) 96-97
Win: 10-0 v Bloxwixh T. (H), Mid. Comb. 93-94   **Defeat:** 0-7 v Hyde Utd. (A) NPL 90-91
Career Goalscorer: Jeff Lissaman 104 (81-86)   **Career Appearances:** Austin Straker 300
Transfer fee paid: £2,000 for Doug Newton (Charterhouse)
Transfer fee received: £10,000 for John Deakin from Birmingham City (Charterhouse)

BEST SEASON   **FA Vase:** Semi-Finalists 78-79   **FA Trophy:** 3rd Rd Replay v Emley 98-99
FA Cup: 1st Rd   82-83, 1-5 v Preston North End (A), 96-97 v Carlisle United (a) 0-6

HONOURS   Southern Lge Midland Div. R-up 83-84, N.C.E. Lge 82-83, Lge Cup 82-83; Midland Counties Lge 81-82, Lge Cup 81- 82;
Leicestershire Senior Lge 10-11 20-21 78-79 79-80 80-81, R-up 21-22, Div 2 53-54 65-66 77-78, Div 2 Cup 77-78;
Leicestershire Senior Cup (7); Loughborough Charity Cup 92-93 01-02; Midland Alliance Winners 95-96

Players progressing: Neil Grewcock (Burnley 84), Gordon Tucker (Huddersfield 87), Devon White (Bristol R. 87), John Deakin (Birmingham City)

Back row: Frank Benjamin (coach), Tommy Goodwin, Jordan King, Andy davies, Michael Voce (chairman), Peter Bull (secretary), Dave Wheatley (general manager), Adam Stevens, Adrian Greatrex, Scott Mackay, Dave Williams (manager).
Front: Sukhjit Heer, Alex Peck, Lee Quincey, Jamie Newbold, Tim Warner, Kirk Master, Andy Peake, Carl Slater, Keith Morris.

SOLIHULL BOROUGH

CLUB OFFICIALS

Chief Executive: John Hewitson
President: Joe McGorian
General Manager: Trevor Stevens
Secretary: Joe Murphy, 2 Wilford Grove,Solihull B913FP Tel NBo: 0121 7090545 Mobile: 07811 337345
Club Fax: 0121 711 4045
Press Officer: Richard Crawshaw
Tel: 01564 702746 or 07712 791202(m)

FOOTBALL MANAGEMENT TEA
Manager: Dave Busst
Assistant Manager: Paul Holleran
Physio: Graham Jones F.A.Dep.lst
Res.Managers: Guy Russell & Dave Fearon

FACT FILE
Formed: 1953
Nickname: Boro
Sponsors: Carling Black Label
Colours: Red/white/red
Change colours: White/black/white
Midweek matchday: Monday
Reserves League: Midland Comb.Res Div

2001-02
Captain: Matt Smith,
P.o.Y.: Derek Hall
Top scorer:Derek Hall 32

Pages: 44 Price: £1.50
Editor: Jore Murphy(07811 337345))
Local Press: Solihull Times, Solihull News, Sunday Mercury, Sports Argus
Local Radio: Radio WM, BRMB
Club Website: www.sbfc 2000,co,uk

Ground: Damson Park, Damson Parkway,Solihull,W.Mids B91 2PP(0121 705 6770)
Directions: Leave M42 at Jnct 6. A45 for 2 miles towards B'ham.Past Honda Garage and opp Forte Posthouse Hotel, left at filter to traffic lights into Damson Parkway.(Signpost Landrover/Damsonwwod) Go round roundabout, down other side of dual crriageway for 100 jds .Ground on left. From Coventry use A45 to Posthouse. Solihull,A41 into Hampton Lane and Yew Tree LaneLane.
Capacity: 9,500   Cover: 2,000   Seats: 400   Floodlights: Yes
Clubhouse: Country Club facilities and all type of functions can be booked.(0121 705 6770)

PREVIOUS   **Leagues:** Mercian; Midland Combination 69-91
Name: Lincoln FC   **Grounds:** Widney Stadium, Solihull 65-88,Moor Green 88-98,Redditch 98-00
CLUB RECORDS Attendance (at new ground): 721 v Chester City F.A.Trophy , 4th Rd replay 2001-02..
Win: 9-1 v Alfreton Town FA Trophy 1st Rd 97-98
Defeat: 1-6 v Tiverton Town (A) Southern League (Western) 99-00
Career Goalscorer: Joe Dowling 138   **Career Appearances:** Darrel Houghton 360
Transfer fee paid: £15,000 for Recky Carter, from Kettering Town
Transfer fee received: £30,000 from Coventry City for Andy Williams
BEST SEASON   **FA Cup:** 1st Rd 97-98; 1-1,3-3 (2-4pen) v Darlington and 92-93, 2-2,2-3 v V.S.Rugby
FA Vase: 5th Rd 74-75   **FA Trophy:** 4th Rd Prop 97-98 and 2001-02

HONOURS   Southern Lg Midland Div 91-92; Midland Comb. R-up 84-8590-91, Chall Cup R-up 73-74 90-91, Presidents Cup R-up 69-70; Lord Mayor of Birmingham Charity Cup 91-92 92-93 94-95 96-97; Worcs Sen. Cup R-up 92-93 96-97 97-98; 99-00Birmingham Sen. Cup 94-95

Players Progressing: Kevin Ashley (Birmingham C.), Andy Williams (Coventry C.), Geoff Scott . Danny Conway ,Nicky Cross and Alan Smith (LeicesterC.), Dean Spink (Aston Villa), John Frain (Northampton T.), Jamie Campbell (Walsall) and John Gayle (Birmingham City)

Back row left to right: Martin Hier, Craig Dutton, Matt Smith, Derek Hall, Nick Amos, Mike Payne, Richard Anstiss, Lee Saunders, Gary Knight, Simon Hollis, Andy Lovelock and Graham Jones (Physio). **Front row:** Chris Smith, Ian Cooper, Richard Beale, Paul Hoilleran (Assistant Manager), David Busst (Manager), Peter Sutton, Jamie Campbell and Brett Healy.

STOURPORT SWIFTS

CLUB OFFICIALS

Chairman: Chris Reynolds

President: Roy Crowe

General Manager: John McDonald

Secretary: Nigel Green
Anchor Inn, Main Road,
Wyre Piddle,Worcs. WR10 2JB
Tel No: 01386 552799
Email: n.green32@btinternet.com.

Matchday Contact: John McDonald

Tel: 01299 82088

FACT FILE
Founded: 1882.
Nickname: Swifts
Sponsors: Reynolds of Rushock
Colours: All Yellow
Change colours: White/black/black
Midweek matchday: Tuesday

Programme: 40 pages £1.50
Editor: Malcolm Cowell c/o Club
Tel NO: 01299 250800 (W)

FOOTBALL MANAGEMENT TEAM
Manager: Tim Langford
Assistant Manager: Jan Mulders
Coach: John Powell   Physio: MalcolmCowell

GROUND	Walshes Meadow, Harold Davis Drive, Stourport-on-Severn. Tel: 01299 825188. Club Website: http://www.fly.to/swifts
Directions:	Follow one-way system through Stourport sign posted Sports Centre.Go over River Severn Bridge, turn left into Harold Davies Drive. Ground is at rear of Sports Centre. Nearest rail station is Kidderminster.
Capacity:	2,000 Seats: 250 Cover: 150 Floodlights: Yes
Clubhouse:	Open matchdays. Hot snacks available. Licensed bar.
Club Shop:	No
PREVIOUS	**Leagues:** Kidderminster/ Worcester/ West Midland Regional, Midland Football Alliance 1998-2001 **Grounds:** Bewdley Rd; Moor Hall Park; Feathers Farm; Olive Grove; Hawthorns.
RECORDS	**Attendancee:** 4,000 v Birmingham, charity match. **Goalscorer:** Gary Crowther **Appearances:** Ian Johnson **Win:** 10-0 **Defeat:** 1-7

BEST SEASON FA Cup: 3rd Q Rd 2001-02   **F.A.Vase:** 6th Rd 20001

HONOURS	West Mids Prem Div R-Up 94-95 96-97 97-98, Lg Div 1 R-up 87-88, Prem Div Cup 92-93, Div 2 Cup R-up 82-83; Worcs Snr Urn 92-93 93-94 94-95 97-98 Worcs Infirmary Cup 94-95 95-96 97-98; MFA 2000-01

Back Row L-R: Mark Dearlove, Lee Booth, Matt Southwick, Ross Knight, Rob Clarke, Jan Mulders, Tim Nicholls, Simon Marsh, Brendan Hackett (Player/coach). **Front L-R:** Paul Moutford, Lea Shaw (capt), Rod Brown (Manager), Alex Cowley, Adrian Cooper.

SUTTON COLDFIELD TOWN

CLUB OFFICIALS

Chairman: Tom Keogh

Secretary: Alan Fleming, 28 Manor Road,Streetly, West Midlands B75 5PY
Tel :07970 573638 (H) 0121 354 2997 (W)

FOOTBALL MANAGEMENT TEAM
Manager: Chris Keogh
Asst Man: Brian Kenning
Physio: Ed Judge

FACT FILE
Formed: 1897 Nickname: Royals
Colours: Blue & White/Blue/Blue
Change colours: White/ Red/White
Midweek matchday: Tuesday
Feeder Team: Sutton Town(Mid Comb)
2001-2002
Captain:Tim Steele
P.o.Y.: Justin Bray
Top Goalscorer: Leon Mitchell 11

GROUND Central Ground, Coles Lane, Sutton Coldfield B72 1NL Fax/Tel: 0121 354 2997 or 0121 355 5475 **Email Address:** alan.fleming1@btinternet,com
Directions: A5127 into Sutton, right at Odeon cinema (Holland Rd), then first right into Coles Lane - ground 150 yds on left. 10 mins walk from SuttonColdfield (BR), bus 104 from Birmingham
Capacity: 4,500   Cover: 500   Seats: 200   Floodlights: Yes
Clubhouse: Brick built lounge & concert room, fully carpeted and extensively decorated
Open daily, food available
Club Shop: Selling metal badges, scarves, hats, pens, rosettes, progs
Contact : Bill Portman

Pages: 28   Price: £1.20
Editor: Peter Young
Local Press:
Sutton Coldfield News, Sutton Observer
Local Radio: BRMB, Radio WM

PREVIOUS   **Leagues:** Central Birmingham, Walsall Sen., Staffs Co., BirminghamComb. 50-54, West Mids (Regional) 54-65 79-82, Midlands Comb. 65-79   **Name:** Sutton Coldfield FC 1879-1921
Grounds: Meadow Plat 1879-89/ Coles Lane (site of current ambulance station) 90-1919

CLUB RECORDS   **Attendance:** 2,029 v Doncaster Rovers, F.A. Cup 80-81 (Receipts £2,727)
Career Goalscorer: Eddie Hewitt 288   **Career Appearances:** Andy Ling 550
Fee paid: £1,500 twice in 1991, for Lance Morrison (Gloucester) , Micky Clarke(Burton A.) and Steve Farmer (Atherstone U)
Fee received: £25,000 for Barry Cowdrill (WBA 1979)

BEST SEASON   **FA Cup:** 1st Rd 80-81, 0-1 v Doncaster R (H), 92-93, 1-2 v BoltonWanderers (A)
FA Trophy: 1st Round replay 1989-90   **FA Amateur Cup:** 2nd Round 1970-71

HONOURS   Southern Lg Midland Div R-up 82-83, West Mids Lg 79-80 (Lg Cup 80-81 81-82), Midland Comb.(2) 77-79 (R-up(2) 69-71, Lg Cup 69-70), Walsall Senior Lg 46-47, Walsall Sen. Cup(3) 77-80 (R-up 80-81), Staffs Sen. Cup R-up 89-90, Lord Mayor of Birmingham Charity Cup 95-96, R-up 93-94, Worcs Sen. Cup SF 88-89, Walsall Challenge Cup R-up 46-47 47-48, Sutton Charity Cup 46-47 65-66 71-72 86-87 89-90 90-91, Express & Star Cup 44-45 Dr Martens Cup 98-99
Players progressing: Arthur Corbett (Walsall 49), Paul Cooper (Manchester C.), Noel Blake (Leeds), Steve Cooper (Barnsley), Peter Latchford (WBA), Mark Smith (Wolves), John Barton (Everton), Barry Cowdrill (WBA 79),Colin Dryhurst (Halifax 79), Dale Belford (Notts Co. 87), Ellis Laight (Torquay 92)

Back Row,left to right: R. Richardson (Coach),K. Murragh, C.Ferguson, D. Massingham, M.Gray, S.Farmer, E. Ejiofor, D.Baker, J. Bray, B. Burns, W. Dyer, K. Jones, D.Shaw and E.Judge (physio) **Front Row:** K.Thompson, L.B ailey, D. Burrows, A. Ling, C. Keogh (Manager), B. Kenning (Assistant Manager),S. Tucker, M. Smioz, M. Gardiner, S. Randall and A. Hughes

SWINDON SUPERMARINE

CLUB OFFICIALS

Chairman: Steve Moore
President: Cliff Puffett
Secretary: Judi Moore,
Chardon Rise, Bell Lane,
Liddington,Swindon, SN4 0HH
Tel: 01793 828778
Press Officer: Leigh Moore
01793 790685

FOOTBALL MANAGEMENT TEAM
Manager: John Murphy
Coach: Adie Brittain
Physio: Wayne Roberts

FACT FILE
Founded: 1992
Nickname: 'Marine'
Sponsors: Fuelforce
Colours: Blue & white hoops/blue/blue
Change colours: Red & White/Red/Red
Midweek Matchday: Wednesday

2001-02
Top scorer: Steve Bennett
P.o.Y. & Captain: Steve ~Bennett

GROUND	Hunts Copse, South Marston, Swindon
	Tel: 01793 828778. E-mail: supermarinefc@aol.com.
Directions:	On A361 Swindon/Highworth road, adjoining South Marston Ind. Estate.
	Six miles from Swindon (BR) - buses in direction of Highworth, Fairford &
	Lechdale. If lost ask for Honda.
Capacity:	3,000 Seats: 300 Cover: 300 Floodlights: Yes
Club Shop:	Opening this season - contact Andy Garrett **Clubhouse:** Yes

Pages: 40   Price: £1.00
Editor: Keith Yeomans
Tel: 07721 885728 01793 487461
email: supermarinefc@aol.com

PREVIOUS	**Leagues:** Wiltshire Lge., Hellenic League to 2001
	Names: Vickers Armstrong 46-81,Supermarine 82-91 (merged 1992),
	Penhill Youth Centre 70-84, Swindon Athletic 84-89 (merged)
	Ground: Supermarine: Vickers Airfield (until mid-1960s);
	Swindon Ath.: Merton 70-84; `Southbrook', Pinehurst Road 84-92
RECORD	**Attendance:** 1,550 v Aston Villa
HONOURS:	Hellenic Lge - Premier Div. 97-98, 00-01, R-up 95-96 98-99; Div. One 85-86 86-87; Reserve Section 96-97; Lge Cup 96-97,99-00;
	Floodlit Cup 97-98.,99-00, 00-01. Wiltshire Senior Cup 82-83, 86-87, 89-90. Wilts Premier Shield 96-97.Wilts Youth Cup 01-02,
	Hellenic Challenge Cup 96-97, 99/00.

Swindon Supermarine 2002-03
L-R - Back Row: Tom Jones, Gary Smart, Steve Benbow, Liam Bull, Peter Macklin, Gary Swann.
Middle: Laura Chamberlain (club masseur), Nick Beaverstock, Darren McCluskey, Steve Winchcombe,
Steve Davies, Paul Donnelly, Ian Howell, Tariq Hussain.
Front: Richard Knox, Bryan Smith, Steve Bennett (capt.), Leigh White, Tate Hulbert, Marc Richards, Steve Dixey.

TAUNTON TOWN

Taunton Town Football Club

Somerset FA

Home of the Peacocks
2002-03

Pages: 32   Price: £1
Editor: Les Gill
Newsline: 0930 555 849
Local Radio: Orchard FM, Radio Bristol
Local Press: Somerset County Gazette

CLUB OFFICIALS
Chairman: T F Harris
Secretary: Joan Ellis
c/o the club
Tel: 01823 333833 (H)
Press Officer: Les Gill

FACT FILE
Formed: 1947
Nickname: Peacocks
Club Sponsors: T.G.Roofing
Colours: Sky blue & claret/claret/sky blue
Change colours: Yellow/sky blue/yellow
Midweek matches: Tuesdays
Reserves ' League: None

FOOTBALL MANAGEMENT TEAM
Manager: Russell Musker
Asst. Man: Tom Kelly
Physio: Kevin Matthews

2001-02
Captain:
P.o.Y.:
Top Scorer:

Ground: Wordsworth Drive, Taunton, Somerset TA1 2HG Tel: 01823 278191
Directions: Leave M5 Jct 25, follow signs to town centre, at 2nd set of lights turn left into Wordsworth Drive; ground on left. 25 mins walk from Taunton (BR); turn left out of station and follow road right through town centre bearing left into East Reach. Follow road down and turn right into Wordsworth Drive shortly after Victoria pub
Capacity: 4,000   **Seats:**400   **Cover:** 1,000   **Floodlights:** Yes
Clubhouse: Social club to accommodate 300, full bar facilities.
         Separate bar & hall for private functions
Club Shop: Yes

PREVIOUS   **Leagues:** Western 54-77; Southern 77-83, Western 83-2002
                Grounds: Several prior to 1953

CLUB RECORDS   **Attendance:** 3,284 v Tiverton Town, **FA Vase:** Winners 00-01
                Appearances: Tony Payne   **Scorer** (in a season) : Reg Oram 67
                Win: 12-0 v Dawlish Town (A), FA Cup Prel. Rd, 28/8/93
                Defeat: 0-8 v Cheltenham Town (A), FA Cup 2nd Qual. Rd, 28/9/91

BEST SEASON   **FA Cup:** 1st Rd Proper 81-82, 1-2 v Swindon T. (A)
                FA Trophy: 1st Rd Proper 80-81, 1-5 v Hendon at Q.P.R
                FA Vase: Winners 00-01, R-up 93-94, S-F 97-98 98-99

HONOURS   FA Vase Winners 00-01 R-up 93-94, Western Lge Champions 68-69 89-90,95-6,98-9,99-00, 00-01 (R-up 93-94 97-98, Les Phillips R-up 93-94 97-98, Alan Young Cup 73-74 75-76 (jt with Falmouth), Charity Chall. Cup 49-50, 50-51), Somerset Snr Lg 52-53, Som Prem.Cup R-up 82-83 89-90 92-93 98-99

Players progressing: Charlie Rutter (Cardiff), Stuart Brace (Southend), Steve Winter (Torquay) Kevin Maloy (Exeter C.)

Back row,left to right: Barry Wilson (Trainer), Danny Bance, Tom Stocco, Luke Dawkins, Gary Fisher, Alan Pike, Marcus Vaughan, Steve Jenkins, Chris Slough, Mark Gammon, Danny Harris, Pau Keates (Physio). **Front row:** Ian Bastow, Peter Howe, Robbie Herrera, Tom Kelly (Player/Assistant Manager), Chris Myers, Russell Musker (Manager), Ellis Laight, Matt Byrne and Peter Knox.   **Photo:** Sunday Independant

WESTON-super-MARE

WESTON-SUPER-MARE FOOTBALL CLUB
DR. MARTENS SOUTHERN LEAGUE WESTERN DIVISION

the Seagulls · Official Club Magazine

CLUB OFFICIALS

President: **D A Usher**

Chairman: **Paul T Bliss**

Secretary/Press Officer: **Stuart Marshall**
c/o Weston Super Mare FC
Tel: 01934 621618

FOOTBALL MANAGEMENT TEAM
Manager: Frank Gregan
AssistantManager: David Mehew
Player-Coach: Andy Mason
Physio: Bob Baird

FACT FILE

Formed: 1899
Nickname: Seagulls
Sponsors:
Colours: White/blue/blue
Change colours: All yellow
Midweek matches: Tuesday
Reserves' League: Somerset Senior
2001-02
P.o.Y.: Mike Kilgour
Top Scorer: Jody Bevan 26

GROUND   Woodspring Park, Winterstoke Road, Weston-super-Mare BS23 3YG
Tel: 01934 635665 Directions: M5 Jct 21. A370 along dual carriageway to 4th roundabout. First
left and immediately right at small roundabout, club on right. FromSouth: M5 Jct 22, follow
Weston signs for approx 7 miles, right at first r'bout(by Hospital), left at next r'bout, ground 1
mile on left. Twenty minutes walk fromWeston-super-Mare (BR)
Capacity: 3,000   Seats: 278   Cover: 1,300   Floodlights: Yes
Clubhouse: Mon-Fri 7-11pm, Sat 12-11pm, Sun 12-3 & 7-11pm.
            2 skittle alleys, 2bars. Bar meals and hot meals everyday
Club Shop: Selling a wide range of souvenirs & programmes.Contact Alan White at the club.

Pages: 32   Price: £1
Editors: Stuart Marshall & Phil Sheridan
Tel. 01934 621618
Local Press:
Bristol Evening Post, Western Daily Press
Local Radio: Somerset Sound, Radio Bristol
Star 107.7

PREVIOUS   **League:** Western 1900-92 (Not continuous)   **Name:** Borough of Weston-super-Mare
                  Grounds: The Great Ground, Locking Road 48-55, Langford Road 55-83

CLUB RECORDS Attendance: 2,623 v Woking, FA Cup First Round Proper replay 23/11/93
                At Langford Road: 2,500 v Bridgwater Town, FA Cup First Round Proper replay 1961-62
                Win: 11-0 v Paulton Rovers   **Defeat:** 1-12 v Yeovil Town Reserves
                Career Goalscorer: Matthew Lazenby, 180   **Career Appearances:** Harry Thomas, 740
                Transfer fee received: £20,000 Stuart Jones fromSheffield Wednesday 98   **Transfer fee paid:** None

BEST SEASON   FA Cup: 1st Rd Proper replay 61-62, 0-1 v Bridgwater Town after 0-0; 94-95, 0-1 v Woking (A) after 2-2
                FA Trophy: 14th Round 98-99   **FA Vase:** Have not entered

HONOURS   Somerset Snr Cup 23-24 26-27; Western Lg Champions 91-92 (R-up 76-77), Lg Cup 76-77 (R-up 89-90), Merit Cup 76-77 77-
78; Somerset Snr Lg (Reserves) Div 1 87-88 (R-up 90-91), Div 2 R-up 85-86, Div 3 84-85 Div 3 2000-01, Div 201-02.
Players progressing: Shaun Rouse (Carlisle United 94), Ian Maine, John Palmer(Bristol City),Wayne Brown(Chester City 97), Stuart Jones
(Sheffield Wed 98), Ryan Souter (Bury 99)

Back row left to right: Dave Lukins, Leigh White, Alan Bird, Jody Bevan, Justin Pritchard, Steve Weaver, Mike Kilgour,
Marc Richards, Dave Hunt and Andy Smith. **Front row**: Jimmy Cox, Andy Catley, Ryan King, Dave Butler, Norman Parselle,
Dave Watts and Aaron Blakemore.

EASTERN DIVISION FINAL LEAGUE TABLE 2001-02

		P	W	D	L	W	D	L	W	D	L	F	A	GD	Pts
1	Hastings Town	42	15	3	3	14	5	2	29	8	5	85	38	47	95
2	Grantham Town	42	15	5	1	14	1	6	29	6	7	99	43	56	93
3	Dorchester Town	42	16	4	1	10	6	5	26	10	6	81	36	45	88
4	Histon	42	15	2	4	8	6	7	23	8	11	83	49	34	77
5	Stamford	42	15	2	4	9	2	10	24	4	14	76	61	15	76
6	Fisher Athletic (Lon)	42	13	4	4	7	6	8	20	10	12	83	56	27	70
7	Eastbourne Borough	42	11	5	5	10	1	10	21	6	15	63	46	17	69
8	Dartford	42	11	2	8	7	3	11	18	5	19	62	66	-4	59
9	Erith & Belvedere	42	8	1	12	10	2	9	18	3	21	75	79	-4	57
10	Bashley	42	10	7	4	5	4	12	15	11	16	71	64	7	56
11	Burnham	42	8	3	10	7	7	7	15	10	17	52	54	-2	55
12	Rugby United	42	10	4	7	6	2	13	16	6	20	56	67	-11	54
13	Rothwell Town	42	9	3	9	5	5	11	14	8	20	45	66	-21	50
14	Ashford Town	42	7	3	11	7	3	11	14	6	22	58	78	-20	48
15	Banbury United*	42	12	2	7	1	7	13	13	9	20	53	66	-13	47
16	Chatham Town	42	7	6	8	6	2	13	13	8	21	56	87	-31	47
17	Sittingbourne	42	9	0	12	5	4	12	14	4	24	46	69	-23	46
18	Spalding United	42	8	4	9	5	2	14	13	6	23	72	84	-12	45
19	Tonbridge Angels	42	10	3	8	3	3	15	13	6	23	65	80	-15	45
20	St Leonards	42	7	2	12	7	1	13	14	3	25	52	88	-36	45
21	Corby Town	42	4	9	8	6	4	11	10	13	19	54	82	-28	43
22	Wisbech Town	42	6	5	10	5	3	13	11	8	23	56	84	-28	41

* point deducted

EASTERN DIVISION RESULTS CHART 2001-02

		1	2	3	4	5	6	7	8	9	10	11	12	13	14	15	16	17	18	19	20	21	22
1	Ashford T	X	3-0	0-0	1-1	0-1	1-4	0-1	0-2	0-1	3-2	3-2	0-3	0-2	1-1	1-2	2-1	6-1	0-3	0-1	2-3	3-2	1-0
2	Banbury U	2-1	X	4-1	2-2	2-1	1-1	4-1	0-1	3-1	0-3	2-0	0-1	2-3	1-0	1-0	0-1	1-3	3-0	2-1	1-0	0-2	3-0
3	Bashley	2-3	3-1	X	2-1	4-1	4-2	2-0	1-1	0-2	1-2	2-1	2-1	0-0	2-1	1-0	2-1	0-1	1-3	1-0	0-0	3-3	8-0
4	Burnham	0-0	0-1	1-0	X	1-1	3-0	0-1	1-3	0-1	1-5	0-0	1-2	1-2	0-6	0-1	2-0	2-0	2-1	2-0	0-1	3-1	3-2
5	Chatham T	2-5	3-3	2-4	1-1	X	1-1	1-2	2-2	0-3	2-3	1-1	5-3	1-2	0-4	1-2	1-0	0-0	3-1	1-0	2-1	2-1	4-2
6	Corby T	1-1	1-1	1-1	0-0	2-3	X	3-2	2-4	1-0	0-5	0-2	0-1	0-5	2-1	1-1	2-2	1-1	1-5	2-2	2-0	0-0	1-3
7	Dartford	3-1	1-1	1-0	5-4	2-0	2-0	X	0-1	1-2	4-0	1-1	2-4	3-1	0-2	2-1	3-1	0-3	1-3	2-6	1-3	3-2	2-1
8	Dorchester	6-1	2-0	1-1	2-0	3-1	3-0	2-0	X	2-1	1-0	1-0	1-1	4-0	3-1	2-2	0-1	2-1	1-0	5-4	4-0	1-1	3-1
9	Eastbourne	1-2	2-1	3-2	0-2	0-2	2-2	1-0	1-1	X	2-2	3-3	4-0	3-0	0-3	1-0	2-3	3-0	2-0	2-0	0-0	2-0	0-3
10	Erith & Bel.	2-1	1-1	1-0	0-1	2-0	3-2	2-5	0-1	0-3	X	3-4	0-3	2-3	2-1	0-3	2-3	1-2	2-1	5-2	1-2	3-1	0-1
11	Fisher Ath	5-2	2-2	1-1	0-3	5-0	3-0	0-0	2-2	2-0	2-1	X	0-1	2-3	2-3	2-1	2-1	3-2	6-1	4-1	5-3	2-1	2-0
12	Grantham	4-1	4-1	3-1	3-2	6-1	3-0	0-1	1-0	2-0	4-2	2-1	X	1-1	1-1	1-0	6-0	0-0	1-1	3-1	1-1	1-0	2-0
13	Hastings	2-2	4-0	2-0	1-0	2-0	1-2	1-0	0-0	1-0	3-2	2-1	1-3	X	2-0	3-0	4-1	0-0	3-2	0-1	1-0	3-0	2-1
14	Histon	1-0	2-1	3-1	1-2	2-0	3-1	3-1	2-0	1-0	5-2	0-1	2-2	1-2	X	1-4	2-1	3-0	1-2	1-0	4-2	4-2	4-2
15	Rothwell	0-2	2-2	1-2	1-0	1-1	0-1	1-0	1-0	0-1	0-1	1-4	1-3	2-4	1-3	X	0-1	2-0	1-0	1-0	4-2	3-2	0-0
16	Rugby U	4-0	1-1	4-1	0-1	1-2	0-3	0-0	2-1	1-0	0-2	3-0	2-1	0-0	1-2	0-0	X	2-0	3-2	2-0	0-1	0-2	3-2
17	Sittingb'rne	0-1	4-1	2-1	1-2	3-0	2-1	0-2	0-2	0-2	1-3	0-4	2-1	0-3	1-0	3-1	2-0	X	2-3	2-0	0-2	1-2	1-2
18	Spalding	3-2	1-0	2-3	1-1	1-2	2-1	1-1	1-3	2-2	2-3	0-1	2-4	0-1	1-1	5-0	1-3	2-0	X	4-3	1-3	3-0	3-1
19	St Leonards	2-1	2-1	2-5	0-3	1-2	1-3	2-4	0-3	3-1	2-0	0-0	0-4	0-4	1-4	0-0	3-1	2-1	1-5	X	1-3	1-0	0-3
20	Tonbridge	1-3	1-0	2-1	2-0	3-2	2-1	2-1	3-2	1-2	2-1	2-5	1-1	1-0	7-0	2-1	3-0	2-1	1-3	X	1-2	4-0	1-3
21	Tonbridge	4-0	2-1	4-0	2-2	2-1	3-4	2-0	1-4	0-3	2-2	1-3	1-2	1-5	2-2	2-0	3-1	3-2	3-1	1-2	4-0	X	0-1
22	Wisbech T	0-2	2-0	0-3	1-1	3-0	2-2	2-1	1-1	0-1	1-2	1-1	0-6	2-4	1-1	1-4	3-2	1-2	6-1	1-2	1-3	3-1	X

EASTERN DIVISION LEADING GOALSCORERS 2001-02

29	Darren Adams	Erith & Belvedere	21	Neil Kennedy	Histon
26	Lee Stephenson	Spalding United	19	David Hassett	Ashford Town
25	Justin Keeler	Dorchester Town	19	Carl Holmes	Stamford
25	Daniel O'Hagan	Dorchester Town	17	Peter Munns	Histon
23	Matthew Allen	Eastbourne Borough	16	Matthew Groves	Dorchester Town
22	Gary Bull	Grantham Town	16	Malcolm Ndekwe	Stamford
21	Simon Austin	Chatham Town	16	Richard Ranshaw	Grantham Town
21	Leroy Huggins	Fisher Athletic			

ASHFORD TOWN

CLUB OFFICIALS

Chairman: Tim Thorogood
President: Ashley M Batt
Secretary/Press Officer: Alan Lancaster
128 Kingsnorth Rd, Ashford, Kent
TN23 2HY Tel: 01233 621325
Commercial Director: Ernie Warron
Tel: 01233 634125

FACT FILE
Formed: 1930
Nickname: Nuts & Bolts
Colours: Green/navy/green
Change colours: White&green/green/white
Midweek home matchday: Tuesday
Reserves' League: Go Travel Kent Lge

FOOTBALL MANAGEMENT TEAM
Manager: Tim Thorogood
Asst Manager: Fary Anderson
Coach: Tim Thorogood
Physio: George Sargeant

2001-02
Leading goalscorer:Dave Hassett 20
Captains: Peter Mortley & Stuart White

GROUND The Homelands, Ashford Road, Kingsnorth, Ashford, Kent TN26 1NJ
Tel: 01233 611838
Directions: M20 jct 10, follow A2070 signs towards Brenzett & Lydd airport, dual carriageway
to junction of old A2070, ground 1 mile on left thro' village of Kingsnorth. 4 miles south of Ashford
Capacity: 3,200   Cover: 1,250   Seats: 500   Floodlights: Yes
Clubhouse: Open matchdays and for special functions. Licensed bar, function room. Limited
food - sandwiches & simple snacks.
Club Shop: Sells old progs, pennants, scarves, badges etc. Contact Alan Bird(01233 662680)

Pages: 32 Price: £1.00
Editor: Dereek West

Local Press: Kentish Express
Local Radio: Radio Kent, Invicta Radio

PREVIOUS **Names:** Ashford United, Ashford Railway, Ashford F.C.
Leagues: Kent 30-59. Ground: Essella Park, Essella Rd 30-87

CLUB RECORDS **Attendance:** 6,525 (at Essella Park, previous ground), v Crystal Palace, FA Cup 1st Rd 1959.
3,363 (at current ground), v Fulham FA Cup 1st Round 1994.
Goalscorer: Dave Arter 197. **Appearances:** Peter McRobert 765
Win: 10-1 v Bury Town, February 1964. **Defeat:** 0-8 v Crawley Town, November1964
Fee Paid: £7,000 for J Ross & D Arter (Sittingbourne, March 94)
Fee Received: £25,000 for Jeff Ross & Dave Arter (Hythe Tn, 90). Individually: £20,000 for Lee McRobert (Sittingbourne, 93)

BEST SEASON **FA Trophy:** Semi Final 72-73, 96-97 2nd Rd
FA Cup: 2nd Rd 61-62, 0-3 v QPR (H), 66-67, 0-5 v Swindon (A). 1st Rd 7 times.   League clubs defeated: None.
HONOURS FA Trophy SF 72-73; Southern Lg Southern Div R-up 86-87 95-96; Kent Lg 48-49(R-up 31-32), Lg Cup 38-39; Kent Senior Cup
58-59 62-63 92-93 95-96
Players progressing: Ollie Norris (Rochdale 61), HowardMoore (Coventry 66), Tony Godden (WBA 75), Lee McRobert (Millwall 94)

Left to Right

Back row:
Simon Elliott,
Ian Gibbs,
Jamie Gardner,
John Whitehouse,
Martin Anderson
and Stuart White.

Front row:
Aaron O'Leary,
Sammy Saunders,
Ian Ross,
Dave Hasset
and Lee McRobert

Photo: Alan Coomes

BANBURY UNITED

CLUB OFFICIALS
Chairman: Paul Saunders
Vice Chairman: Brian Kay
President: David Jesson
Commercial Mgr: T.B.A.
Press Officer: Dale Bennett
Secretary: B Worsley, c/o Sol Systems, Unit 4
Mallorie Hse, Beaumont Rd,Banbury, OX16 7RH
Tel: 01295 265638 (H), 01295 255536 (B)
Email: bworsley@solsystems.freeserve.co.uk

FOOTBALL MANAGEMENT TEAM
Manager: Kevin Brock
Assistant Manager: Brian Robinson
Physio:Wally Hastie

FACT FILE
Founded: 1933 Reformed: 1965
Nickname: Puritans
Sponsors: Alex Lawrie Factors.
Colours: Red & gold/red/red
Change colours: White /white/white
Midweek matches: Tuesday
Reserves' Lge: Hellenic Res Div 1

2001-02
Captain: Jonathon Corbett
P.o.Y.: Jonathon Corbett
Top Goalscorer: Matthew Gooderick 24

GROUND Spencer Stadium, off Station Rd, Banbury, Oxon .
Tel: 01295 263354

Directions: M40 jct 11, follow signs for Banbury then BR station, turn right down narrow
lane before entering station forecourt; eastern end of town
Capacity: 6,500   Seats: 250   Cover: 500   Floodlights: Yes
Clubhouse: Open match days & week-ends. Mid-week on hire.
Hot food available during after matches
Club Shop: Yes

Pages: 40   Price: £1.00
Editor: Kevin Hicklin

Club Website: www.banburyunited.co.uk
Unofficial sites:
www..banbury-united.cityslide.com
www.expage.com.bufc

HONOURS   Oxon Snr Cup 78-79 87-88 (R-up7); Birmingham Comb. R-up 47-48; Oxon Prof. Cup 52-53(jt) 70-71(jt) 72-73 77-78 79-80(jt);
Hellenic premier Winners 99-00 Hellenic Lg.Cup R-Up 91-92; Birmingham Snr Cup R-Up 48-49 59-60 (S.F.46-47); Oxon Snr Lg. 34-35 39-4047-
48 (res); Oxon Hosp. Cup 46-47 (R-up 45-46); Oxon Benev. Cup R-up 77-78 80-8182-83; Daventry Charity Cup 88-90; Smiths Mem. Cup 68-70
(R-up 66-68); Hitchin Centenary Cup 68-69 (R-up 67-68); Leamington Charity Cup 51-52; Bucks Charity Cup 00-01
Warks Comb. R-up 57-58 60-61, Presidents Cup R-up 60-61; Midland Floodlit Cup 67-68; Wallspan Comb. 85-86
PREVIOUS   **Leagues:** Banbury Jnr 33-34; Oxon Snr 34-35; Birmingham Comb. 35-54; W.Mids 54-66; Southern 66-90
Name: Banbury Spencer
BEST SEASON   FA Cup: 1st Rd replay 73-74 (Also 1st Rd 47-48 61-62 72-73)
FA Trophy: 3rd Rd 70-71 73-74
RECORDS   **Attendance:** 7,160 v Oxford City, FA Cup 3rd Qual.Rd, 30/10/48
Goalscorer: Dick Pike (1935-48), Tony Jacques (65-76) - both 222
Appearances: Ian Bowyer (557) Fee Paid : £2,000 for Phil Emsden (Oxford Utd, Jan 1980)
Fee Received: £20,000 Kevin Wilson (Derby, December 1979)
Win: 12-0 v RNAS Culham, Oxon Snr Cup 45-46
Defeat: 2-11 v West Bromwich Albion `A', Birmingham Comb. 38-39
Players progressing: Ollie Kearns (Reading), Kevin Wilson & Richard Pratley(Derby), Mick Kearns & Terry Muckleberg (Oxford),
Martin Singleton (Coventry)

Back row left to right: Brian Robinson (Assistant Manager), Wally Hastie (Physio), Jason Allen, Ben Milner. Simon Tricker, Jody McKay, Andrew
Wallbridge, Terry Muckelberg, Jimmy Simpson, Russ Hayes (Physio)
Front row: George Redknap, Ady Fuller, Jon Corbett, Matty Travers, Kieran Sullivan, Liam O'Neill and Matty Gooderick

BASHLEY

CLUB OFFICIALS

Chairman: Ray Pinney
President: Trevor Adams
Vice Chairman: Derick Binns
Secretary: Pete Plowman,
c/o Bashley F.C.
Mobile:07944 629383

FOOTBALL MANAGEMENT TEAM

Manager: Barry Blanckley
Assistant Manager: Fraser Quirk
Reserves Manager: Chris Collinge

FACT FILE
Formed: 1947
Nickname: The Bash
Sponsors: Spaceage
Colours: Yellow & black
Change colours: Blue & white
Midweek matchday: Tuesday
Reserves' League: Wessex Comb

Programme
Pages: 36 Price: £1
Local Press: Bournemouth Echo,
Southern Pink, New Milton Advertiser
Local Radio: 2CR,Solent, Ocean Sound

GROUND   Recreation Ground, BashleyRd., New Milton,Hampshire BH25 5RY.
Tel: 01425 620280 FAX: 01425 638376

Directions: A35 Lyndhurst towards Christchurch, turn left down B3058 towards New Milton,
ground on left in Bashley village. Half hour walk from New Milton (BR) station

Capacity: 4,250   Cover: 1,200   Seats: 300   Floodlights: Yes

Clubhouse: Usual licensing hours. Snacks available   **Club Shop:** Open matchdays

PREVIOUS   **Leagues:** Bournemouth 50-83; Hants 83-86; Wessex 86-89

CLUB RECORDS **Attendance:** 3,500 v Emley, F.A. Vase S.F. 1st Leg 87-88
Win: 21-1 v Co-operative (A), Bournemouth Lge, 64   **Defeat:** 2-20 v Air Speed(A), Bournemouth Lge, 57
Career Goalscorer: Colin Cummings   **Career Appearances:** John Bone
Transfer fee paid: £7,500 for J Stagg from Andover   **Transfer fee received:** £7,500 for Darren Powell from Weymouth 95

BEST SEASON   **FA Cup:** 2nd Rd Proper 1994-95, 0-1 v Swansea City
FA Vase: Semi Final 87-88, Qtr Final 88-89 FA Trophy: 2nd Round 91-92

HONOURS   Southern Lg Southern Division 89-90 (Lg Cup SF 89-90), Wessex Lg 86-87 87-88 88-89, Hants Lg Div 3 84-85,
Hants Lg Combination 88-89, Russell Cotes Cup 88-89 90-91 92-93

Players Progressing : Wayne Brown (Bristol C 1994), David Billington Peterborough 1996), Ryan Young (Plymouth 1997), Dean Higgins (Torquay 1998), Danny Smith (Bournemouith 1998), Craig Davies (Cardiff City 1998), Tony Wallis (Cardiff C 1999), Wade Elliott (AFC Bouremouth 2000)

Back Row, Left To Right: Glen Botterill (Reserve Physio), John Clare (1st Team Physio), Lee Harvey, Paul Wilson, Derek Brown, Gary Williams (Reserve Manager), James Heeps, Andy Lomas (Assistant Manager), Steve Jackman, Eddie Lawley, Paul Turner, Kevin Slinn, Steve Gee (Reserve Team Assistant), Kenny Mist (Chief Scout) **Front Row:** Grant Haley, Carl Adams, Josh Sozzo, Paul Covington, Roger Ashby (Manager), Ian Edge, Rob Miller, Mark Paul, Steve Berry.

BURNHAM

CLUB OFFICIALS

Chairman: Malcolm Higton
Vice Chairman: Mark Green
Press Officer: Secretary
Secretary: Alan King
41 Underwood Road, High Wycombe,
Bucks HP13 6YD (01494523920 (H)
078999 41414(M)

FOOTBALL MANAGEMENT TEAM

Manager: Jim Greenwood
Assistant Manager:Jackie Stuart
Coach:Steve Mellor
Physio: Sally Carey

FACT FILE

Founded: 1878
Sponsors: PKGraphics
Colours: Blue & white/blue/white
Change colours: Yellow/yellow/black
Midweek matchday: Tuesday 7.30
Reserve Team's Lge: Suburban

2001-02
Captain: Paul Brett
P.o.Y.: Paul Brett
Top Scorer: Micky Durkin 19

32 pages   Editor: Cliff Sparkes
Local Press:
Slough Observer, South Bucks Express,
Maidenhead Advertiser, Buckingham Advertiser
Local Radio:
Star FM, BBC Thames Valley, Swan F.M.

Ground: The Gore, Wymers Wood Road, Burnham, Slough SL1 8JG
Tel: 01628 602467/602697

Directions: North west of village centre, 2 miles from Burnham BR station, 2miles from M4 junction 7, 5 miles from M40 junction 2, 100yds north of Gorecrossroads - fork right into Wymers Wood Rd and ground is immediately on right

Capacity: 2,500   Cover: 250   Seats: 250   Floodlights: Yes

Clubhouse: Open every evening and w/e lunch.
Darts and pool, two bars, usual matchday food   **Club Shop:** Yes

HONOURS Athenian Lg R-up(2) 78-80, Hellenic Lg 75-76 98-99 (Div 1 R-up 72-73, Lg Cup 75-76 98-99, Div 1 Cup 71-72), London Spartan Lg 84-85 (Lg Cup 84-85), Reading Comb. Lg Cup 70-71 (All Champions Cup 70-71), Wycombe Comb. R-up (4) 65-67 68-70

PREVIOUS **Leagues:** Sth Bucks & East Berks; Maidenhead Intermediate; Windsor,Slough & Dist; Gt Western Comb. 48-64; Wycombe Comb. 64-70; Reading Comb. 70-71; Hellenic 71-77; Athenian 77-84; London Spartan 84-85; Southern 85-95; Hellenic 95-99
Name: Burnham & Hillingdon 1985-87   **Ground:** Baldwin Meadow (until 20's)

BEST SEASON **FA Cup:** 3rd Qualifying Rd   **FA Vase:** Semi-Final 82-83, Q-F 77-78.
FA Trophy: 4th Round Replay 99-00

RECORD **Attendance:** 2,380 v Halesowen Town, FA Vase 2/4/83
Scorer: Fraser Hughes 65, 69-70   **Win:** 18-0 v High Duty Alloys, 70-71
Defeat: 1-10 v Ernest Turners Sports, 63-64

Players progressing: D Hancock (Reading), R Rafferty (Grimsby Town), D Payne(Barnet)

Back row, left to right: Steve Mellor (coach), Jackie Stuart (Assistant Manager), Paul Brett (Captain), Danny Honey, Terry Mitchell, Andrew Dugdale, John Mitchell and Jon Norris.
Front row: Tony Thompson, Steve Bunce, Matty Potter, Steve Lockhart, Grant Eaton, Craig O'Connor, Micky Durkin and FrankMcCormack.

CHATHAM TOWN

CLUB OFFICIALS

Chairman: Frank Skinner

Secretary: Brian Burcombe
4 Hallwood Close, Parkwood, Rainham,
Kent ME8 9NT
Tel: 01634 363419

FOOTBALL MANAGEMENT TEAM
Manager: Peter Coupland
Asst Manager: Phil Miles

FACT FILE
Founded: 1882
Nickname: Chats
Sponsors: Topps Scaffolding
Colours: Red & black/black/black
Change Colours: Yellow & green
Midweek matchday: Tuesday

2001-02
Captain: Phil Miles
P.o.Y.: Simon Austin
Top Scorer: Simon Austin

GROUND   Maidstone Road Sports Ground, Maidstone Road, Chatham, Kent
Tel: 01634 812194

Directions: M2, A229 Chatham turn-off, follow signs to Chatham, ground one and a half
miles on right opposite garage. 1 mile from Chatham (BR).
Capacity: 5,000   Seats: 500   Cover: 1,000   Floodlights: Yes

56 pages   Price: £1.00
Editor: Tony Smith

Clubhouse: Matchdays and functions

PREVIOUS   **Names:** Chatham FC; Medway FC (1970s)
Leagues: Southern (several spells); Aetolian 59-64; Metropolitan 64-68;Kent (Sev. spells),
Ground: Great Lines, Chatham 1882-90

RECORD   **Gate:** 5,000 v Gillingham, 1980

BEST SEASON   **FA Cup:** QF 1888-89 (incl 2-0 v Nottm Forest 2-0)   **FA Trophy:** 3rd Rd 70-71

HONOURS   Kent Lg (9) 1894-95 03-05 24-25 26-27 71-72 73-74 76-77 79-80 00-01
(R-up 02-03 23-24 25-26 70-71 74-75 80-81, Lg Cup 71-72 76-77 (R-up(3)),
Thames & Medway Comb.(5) 1896-97 04-06 19-20 23-24, Kent Snr Cup 1888-89 1904-05 10-11 18-19, Kent Snr Shield 19-20

Back row, left to right: Peter Coupland, Garry Tilley, Kevin Fewell, Chris Cooke, Cliff Hearn, Lee Riley, Mark Freeman, Simon Austin,
Andy Larkin and Phil Miles.
Front row: Joe Dowley, Steve Best, Dave Monteith, Lee Bremner, Shawn Mitchell, Matt Hoggins and Jon Neal.
Photo: Alan Coomes

CORBY TOWN

THE STEELMAN
THE OFFICIAL MATCHDAY PROGRAMME OF
CORBY TOWN FOOTBALL CLUB
SEASON 2001/2002 - £1

CLUB OFFICIALS
Chairman: James Kane C.B.E.
President: Vacant
Secretary: Gerry Lucas, 8 Richmond
Avenue, Kettering, Northants NN15 5JG
Tel: 01536 513507 (H) 07932 633343 (M)

FOOTBALL MANAGEMENT TEAM
Manager: Wayne Spencer
Assistant Manager: T.B.A.
Physio: Rob Earley

FACT FILE
Formed: 1948
Nickname: The Steelmen
Sponsor:Corus
Colours: White/black/black
Change colours: White& Red,white,white
Midweek matchday: Wednesday
Reserves' League: United Counties Res Div

Season 2001-002
Captain:Gary Kennedy
P.O.Y.: Gary Kennedyr
Top Goalscorer: Wayne Spencer 15

WRS
McCulloch

corus

GROUND Rockingham Triangle Stadium, Rockingham Road, Corby NN17 2AE
Tel: 01536 406640
Directions: On northern outskirts of town at junction of A6003 and A6116,opposite entrance
to Rockingham Castle grounds. One and a half miles from Corby (BR)
Capacity: 3,000 Cover: 1,150 Seats: 960 Floodlights: Yes
Clubhouse: Trackside Bar open matchdays and during the week for hot food etc.
Club Shop: Sells badges, progs etc.(Before & half time) C .Woolmer Tel: 01536 260900

Pages: 32 Price: £1
Editor: David.Tilley
Local Press: Northampton Evening Telegraph
Local Radio: BBC Radio Northampton,
Hereward, Connect F.M.
Cllub's Email : corbytownfc@ talk21.com

PREVIOUS **Leagues:** United Counties 35-52, Midland 52-58
CLUB RECORDS **Attendance:** 2,240 v Watford, pre-season friendly 86-87
At Old Ground; 10,239 v Peterborough Utd, FA Cup 3rd Qual. Rd 52-53
Win: 14-0 v Gainsborough Trinity, 56-57 **Defeat:** 0-10 v Paget Rangers, 95-96
Career Goalscorer: David Hofbauer 141 (84-95) **Career Appearances:** Derek Walker600 (78-92)
Transfer fee paid: £2,700 for Elwyn Roberts (Barnet, 81) **Transfer fee received:** £20,000 for Matt Murphy (Oxford U. 93)

BEST SEASON FA Cup: 3rd Rd 65-66 (lost to Plymouth). 1st Rd on five occasions; 54-55 63-6667-68
League clubs defeated: Luton Town 65-66 **FA Trophy:** 3rd Rd, 1986-87

HONOURS UCL 50-51 51-52 (R-up 37-38), Midland Lg R-up 52-53, Southern Lg Midland Div R-up 90-91 (Merit Cup 63-64 90-91),
Northants Snr Cup 6; Maunsell Cup 83-84, Daventry Charity Cup 94-95, Midland Floodlit Cup 74-75, Evans Halshaw F'lit Cup
91-92, Anglia Floodlit Trophy 68-69 72-73, Chelmsford Invitation Cup 63-64 64-65 65-66 (joint), Kettering & Dist Samaritan Cup
60-61(joint) 68-69, Wellingborough Charity Cup 50-51, Desborough Nursing Cup 48-49 50-51 (joint), Bob Cumning Cup 6

Players progressing: A McCabe (Chesterfield 55), L Chalmers (Leicester C. 56), K Brown (Nottm Forest 56), P Kearns (Aldershot 62),
N Dean (Southampton 63), H Curran (Millwall 64), D McNeil/A McGowan/G Reilly (Northampton69/75/76), P Chard (Peterborough 79), T Morley
(West Ham), J Flower (SheffieldUtd), M Murphy (Oxford Utd 93), C McKenzie (Hereford 94)

Back row left to right: Wayne Spencer, Jamie Hawthorn, Vinny Byfield, Des Elliott, Mark Wood, Stewart Marshall, C.Vallance and
Michael McConnell. **Front row:** David Barrett, Craig Connell, Sean Brennan, Ian Walker, Gary Kennedy, Ged Gribbon and Alan Campbell.

DARTFORD

CLUB OFFICIALS

Chairman: **David Skinner**
Vice Chairman: **Norman Grimes**
Secretary: **Peter Martin**
10 Pembroke Place,Sutton-at-Hone,
Dartford, Kent DA4 9GN
(01322 864038)
Com.Man.: **Steve Irving** 07961 303704

FOOTBALL MANAGEMENT TEAM

Manager: Tommy Sampson
Ass Man:Martin Farnie Physio:Dave Phillips
Coach: Paul Sawyer

FACT FILE

Formed: 1888
Nickname: The Darts
Colours: White & black/black/black
Change colours: All Red
Midweek home matchday: Tuesday
Res League:Go Travel Kent Div 1
Website: www.dartfordfootballclub.co.uk

2001-02

Captain: Luke Morrish
P.o.Y.: Danny Evans

Pages: 40 Price: £1

Editor: Mike Brett-Smith Tel: 01322 277243

Press: Dartford Times, Dartford Messenger
Local Radio: Radio Kent.

GROUND Gravesend & Northfleet FootballClub
Directions: From Dartford Town Centre: Take A226 to Gravesend/Swanscombe for 4 miles
until Swansccombe. At bottom of Galley Hill through lights and ground is immediately on left.
From A2 coastbound: Take Bluewater/Greenhithe exit (B255) and at second roundabout,
with McDonalds onright) turn right towards Swanscombe junction with A226 . Then as above.
British Rail: Northfleet Station two minutes from ground
Dartford F.C. Email Address: peter@martinpe.freeserve.co.uk

PREVIOUS
Leagues: Kent (6) 1894-96 1897-8 1899-02 09-14 21-26 93-96 Southern Lg 1896-98, 99-1900, 26-81, 82-84, 86-92; GMVC 81-82, 84-86
Grounds: The Brent/ Westgate House, Potters Meadow, Engleys Meadow, Summers Meadow, Watling St, Cray Wanderers, Erith & Belverdere, and & Purfleet

CLUB RECORDS **Attendance:** 11,004 v Leyton Orient FA Cup 48
Career Appearances: Steve Robinson 653
Win: 11-1 v Faversham Tn Kent Snr Cup 65   **Defeat:** 0-10 v Guildford City SouthernLge 46
Transfer fee paid: £6,000 for John Bartley (Chelmsford 88) **Received:** £25,000 forAndy Hessenthaler (Redbridge Forest)

BEST SEASON **FA Trophy:** Runners-up 74   **FA Vase:** 2nd Qual Rd 95/96
FA Cup: 3rd Rd Prop 35-36 & 36-37   League clubs defeated: Cardiff (1935), Exeter(1961), Aldershot (1968)

HONOURS Southern Lg 1930-31, 31-32, 73-74, 83-84, R-up 87-88, 88-89, Eastern Div 30-31,31-32, Southern Div 80-81, Southern Lg Div 2 1896-97, Lg Cup 76-77, 87-88, 88-89, Championship Shield 83-84, 87-88, 88-89; Kent Lg 1995-96, Lg Cup 24-25,Kent Snr Cup 29-30, 34-35, 38-39, 69-70, Snr Trophy 95-96, Inter Lg Chall 1974;FA Trophy R-up 1974

Players progressing: Idris Hopkins (Brentford 32), Fred Dall(West Ham 36), Riley Cullum/Fred Alexander/Ted Croker (Charlton 47/48/48) Frank Coombs (Bristol C 49), James Kelly (Gillingham 51), Tom Ritchie (Grimsby 58), Dave Underwood (Watford 60), Derek Hales (Luton 72), Andy Hessenthaler (Watfordvia Redbridge F),Jimmy Bullard (West Ham United)

L-R - Back Row: Dave Phillips (club physio), Paul Bates, Danny Whelan, Shaun Loft, Joe Kevin, Craig Tucker, Adam Morrish, Terry Ratchford, Steve Marriner, Graham Robertson, Alan Tutton. **Middle:** Phil Eagle, Matt Smith, Paul McCarthy (club captain), Martin Farnie (asst. manager), Tommy Sampson (manager), Paul Sawyer (coach), Danny Evans, Matt Fagan, Tommy Martin. **Front:** Steve taylor, Terry McCainn, Rob Browning, Richard Everitt, Chris Jones, Wayne Grizzle, Richard Usherwood.

DORCHESTER TOWN

CLUB OFFICIALS
Chairman: **E,C,G,Belt**
President: **A.E.Miller**
Vice Chairman: **K Miller**
Comm Mgr: **Brian Benjafield**
Secretary: **David Martin**
21 Diggory Crescent, Dorchester
01305 262345
General Manager: **Keith Kellaway**

FOOTBALL MANAGEMENT TEAM

Manager: Mark Morris
Physio: Geoff Dine

FACT FILE
Formed: 1880
Nickname: The Magpies
Sponsors:A.J.Dennis & Son
Colours: Black & white stripes/black/black
Change colours: All red
Midweek games: Tuesdays (7.45)
Newsline (Magpies Hotline): 0839 664412
Reserves' League: Dorset Comb

2001-02
Captain: Matt Lonnon
P.o.Y.:Mark Jermyn
Top Scorers:J.Keeler D O'Hagan 25 each

The Magpies v Banbury United
Saturday 2nd February : KO 3.00pm
Servicemaster
Mr C. Clifford

A. J. Dennis & Sons Ltd.
Official Matchday Programme   £1.50

GROUND   Avenue Stadium, Weymouth Avenue, Dorchester DT1 2RY Tel: 01305 262451

Directions: Situated at the junction of the town bypass (A35) and the Weymouth road (A354)
Nearest station: Dorchester South
Capacity: 5,009   Cover: 2,846   Seats: 697   Floodlights: Yes

Clubhouse: Dorchester Lounge Club - access via main entrance to stadium.
Cold food and snacks
Club Shop: Sells replica shirts, badges, mugs, etc

Pages: 32   Price: £1.50
Editor: Melvin Cross (01305 848365)

Local Press: Dorset Evening Echo,
Western Gazette, Western Daily Press
Local Radio: Radio Solent, Wessex FM

PREVIOUS   **Leagues:** Dorset; Western 1947-72
Grounds: Council Recreation Ground, Weymouth Avenue 1880-1929; The Avenue Ground, Weymouth Avenue 29-90

CLUB RECORDS   **Attendance:** 4,000 v Chelsea, official ground opening 1990. Competitive: 4, 159 v Weymouth, Southern Lge Prem Div , 99
Goalscorer: Dennis Cheney 61 (in one season)   **Appearances:** Derek (Dinkie) Curtis 458 50-66
Win: 7-0 v Canterbury (A), Southern Lge Southern Div 86-87
Defeat: 0-13 v Welton Rovers Western Lge 66
Fee Paid: £12,000 for Chris Townsend (Gloucester City, 1990)
Fee Received: £35,000 for Trevor Senior (Portsmouth, 1981)

BEST SEASON   **FA Trophy:** 3rd Rd replay 71-72, 96-97
FA Cup: 2nd Rd Replay 81-82, 1-2 v A.F.C. Bournemouth after 1-1. 2nd Rd 54-55 57-58; 1st Rd8 times

HONOURS   Southern Lg 85-85, R-up 79-80 Div 1 Sth R-up 77-78, Lg Cup 86-87 R-up 91-92; Western Lg 54-55 R-up 60-61, Div 2 R-up
49-50, Lge Cup 54-54; Dorset Snr Cup 50-51 60-61 67-68 68-69 71-72 93-94 94-95; Dorset Lg 37-38

Players progressing: Len Drake (Bristol Rov. 57), David Noake (Luton 59), Mike Turner (Swindon 61), Trevor Senior (Portsmouth 81), David West
(Liverpool 83), Mike Squire (Torquay 84), Jeremy Judd (Torquay 84),Tony White (Bournem'th 85), Graham Roberts (Spurs, Chelsea, Rangers,
England) who progressed via Weymouth. Darren Garner (Rotherham U, 95), Craig Taylor (Swindon),Syfyan Ghazghazi (Club African De Tunis 98)

Back row,left to right: Mark Morris (Manager),Mark Jermyn, Mike White, Martin Shepherd, Matty Holmes, Oliver Cherrett, Carl Poore,
David Elm, Matt Lonnon, Mark Ormorod, Derek Taylor (Kit Manager) and Brian Benjafield. **Front row:** Jamie Brown, Matt Groves, Andy
Harris, Simon Radcliffe, Phil Andrews, Marcus Oldbury, Justin Keeler and Geoff Dine (Physio).   **Photo:** Peter Barnes

EASTBOURNE BOROUGH

CLUB OFFICIALS

Chairman: Len Smith
President: J Stonestreet
Secretary: Mrs Myra Stephens,
7b Erica Close, Langney, Eastbourne,
East Sussex BN23 6HY
Tel/Fax: 01323 766050 0771 8027981 (M)

FOOTBALL MANAGEMENT TEAM

Manager: Garry Wilson
Coach: Nick Greenwood
Physio: Ray Tuppen

FACT FILE

Founded: 1966 Nickname: Sports
Sponsors: 1st Class Window Systems Ltd.
Colours: Red & Black
Change: White/red/white
Midweek Matchday: Tuesday
Reserve League:Sussex Co.Prem Res.
2000-01 Capt: Daren Pearce
Top Scorer: Matt Allen 2
Ps.o.Y.: Ben Austin &Daren Pearce

76 Pages   Price: £1.20
Programme Editor: Mike Spooner
Tel./Fax: 01323 461003(W)
01323 471071(H)
Website: www.eastbourne borough fc.co.uk
Local Press: Eastbourne Gazette & Herald

GROUND   Langney Sports Club, Priory Lane, Eastbourne, East Sussex Tel: 01323 766265
Email Address: head@stoucrosse-sussex.sch.uk

Capacity: 2,500   Seats: 300   Cover: 2,500   Floodlights: Yes

Directions: A22 to Polegate, A27 to Stone Cross, right onto B32104 to Langney Shopping
Centre, then left and first right past crematorium.
One mile from Pevensey & Westham(BR). Buses from Eastbourne

Clubhouse: Open every evening & lunchtime with adjoining sports hall, boardroom and
matchday tea bar   **Club Shop:** Yes

HONOURS   Unijet Sussex County League Champions 99-00, Sussex Co. Lg R-up 91-92, Div 2 87-88, Lg Cup 89-90, Div 3 86-87,
Div 3 Cup 86-87, 5-aside 1990; Sussex I'mediate Cup 85-86, Eastbourne Chall. Cup 85-86 86-87 99-00 00-01 .Promotion to
Southern League (Dr Martens) Eastern Division 1999-20 Sussex Senior Cup : 2001-02

PREVIOUS   **League:** Eastbourne & Hastings, Unijet Sussex Oo League.**Name:** Langney Sports
Grounds: Princes Park, Wartling Rd, Eastbourne/ Adjacent pitch

ECORDS   **Attendance:** 1400 Sussex Senior Cup Final May 2000(Brighton & H v Hastings T)
Goalscorer: Nigel Hole 146 **Appearances:** Darren Baker 485
Win: 10-1 v Haywards Heath Town, Sussex County Lg Div. 1 11/4/92
Defeat: 0-8, v Sheppey United (A), FA Vase Prel. Rd 9/10/93
v Peacehaven & Telscombe (A), Sussex County Lg Div. 1 9/11/93

Back row left to right: Garry Wilson (Manager), Matt Smart, Andrew Ducille, David Adams, John Scarborough, Paul Stark, Ben Austin, Darren Baker, Stuart Tuck, Nick Greenwood (Coach) and Ray Tuppen (Physio).
Front row: Luke Denton, Matt Crabb, Matt Allen (mascot), Daren Pearce, John Westcott, Mark Goodwin and Paul Stevens.

ERITH & BELVEDERE

CLUB OFFICIALS
Chairman: **John McFadden**
President: **L O'Connell**
Vice Chairman: **Peter Bird**
Secretary: Miss **Kellie Discipline**
108 Chastilion Road, Dartford, Kent DA1
3LG Tel: -01322 275766
Press Off./Commecial Man.: Martin Tarrant
Tel: 01322 275766

FOOTBALL MANAGEMENT TEAM
Manager: Mike Acland 01322 225594
Asst Man ager: Dave Hough
Coach: Barry Fox
Physio: Rob Couldwell

FACT FILE
Formed: 1922
Nickname: Deres
Colours: Blue & white/blue/blue
Change colours: All red
Midweek home matchday:Tuesday
Reserves' League: Kent League Div 1

2001-02
Captain: Paul Roberts
P.o.Y.: Darren Adams
Top scorer: Darren Adams 28

GROUN D Park View Rd Ground, Welling, Kent DA16 1SY Tel: 0181 301 1196
Email Address; kelliedt@tinyworld,co.uk
Directions: As for Welling United F.C.:M25,then A2 towards London.Take Welling turn-off, ground one mile. By rail to Welling stationBR (BR) ground 3/4 mile.
Capacity: 1,500   Cover: 1,000   Seats: 500   Floodlights: Yes
Club Shop: Sells programmes, badges and pens
Clubhouse: Licensed social club open matchdays and weekends. Cold snacks available.
Separate canteen provides hot food on matchdays

Pages: 30   Price: £1.00p
Editor: Mike Tarrant Tel: 01322 275766

Local Press:
Kentish Times, Kentish Independent
Local Radio: Radio Kent, Radio Mellenium

OFFICIAL PROGRAMME £1.50

PREVIOUS   **Leagues:** Kent 22-29 31-39 78-82, London 29-31, Corinthian 45-63, Athenian 63-78
Names: Belvedere & District FC (Formed 1918, restructured 1922)

CLUB RECORDS **Attendance:** 5,573 v Crook Colliery Welfare Amt Cup 3rd Rd 1949
Win: 14-2 v Royal Marines, Kent Lge 18/11/33. (16-2 v RAF Friendly 4/9/41) **Defeat:** 0-15 v Ashford, Kent Lge 28/4/37
Career Appearances: Dennis Crawford 504, 56-71   **Career Goalscorer:** Colin Johnson284, 61-71

BEST SEASON   **FA Amateur Cup:** Runners-up 1923-24, 37-38 **FA Trophy:** Third Qualifying Round second replay 89-90
FA Vase: Third Round 76-77   **FA Cup:** 4th Qual Rd 1924-25 (Equiv to 1st Rd Prop). League clubs defeated: None

HONOURS   FA Amat Cup R-up 23-24 37-38; Athenian Lge Div 1 R-up 70-71 (Lge Cup 73-74), Memorial Shield 67-68; Corinthian Lge R-up
62-63, (Lge Cup 47-48 48-49 49-50); Kent Lge 81-82, (Lge Cup R-up 81-82); London Sen Cup 44-45 (R-up 38-39); KentAmat
Cup 6, (R-up 4); Kent F/lit Lge R-up 67-68; Kent Interm Cup R-up 90-91; Kent Jun Cup 67-68; Kent County Yth Lge 90-91;
Kent Yth Cup 87-88. Bromley Hosp Cup 38-39; Essex & Herts Border Comb Cup 73-74.

Players progressing: John Coshall (West Ham 28), Fred Ford 36/ Cyril Hammond 46/ KeithPeacock 62 (Charlton),
Tommy Ord (Chelsea 72), Sean Devine (Barnet 95)

Back row, left to right: Dominic Barclay, Tim Bealy, Chris Whitehouse, John Odlum, Glenn Billenness and Martin Driscoll
Front row: Scott Bennetts, Darren Adams, Jason Davy, Dean Morris and Darren Gowler.   **Photo:** Alan Coomes

FISHER ATHLETIC (LONDON)

CLUB OFFICIALS
Chair : Richrad Jones
Secretary: **John Leyden**,33 Carew
Close,Chafford100,Nr Grays,Essex
Tel No: 01375 481224
General Manager: **Elaine O'Keefe**

FOOTBALL MANAGEMENT TEAM
Manager: Bob Davies
Player-Coach: Tony Dolby
Physio: Joe Miller

FACT FILE

Formed: 1908
Nickname: The Fish
Sponsors:
Colours: Black & white stripes/black/black
Change colours: Blue/white/white
Midweek matchday: Tuesday
Reserves' League: Suburban Premier

FISHER ATHLETIC F.C.

WELCOME TO SURREY DOCKS STADIUM
HOME OF

FISHER ATHLETIC F.C.
v
ERITH & BELVEDERE

Tuesday 29th January 2002
K.O. 7.45 PM

£1.00

GROUND	The Surrey Docks Stadium, Salter Road, London SE16 5LH
	15 mins from Canada Water (tube)Tel: 0207 231 5144 Fax:0207 2520060
Directions:	8 minutes walk from Rotherhithe (tube).
	2 miles from London Bridge (main line). Buses 381,225
Capacity: 5,300	Cover: 4,283 Seats: 400 Floodlights: Yes
Clubhouse: None	Club Shop: None

Pages: 40   Price: £1.50
Editor: Teresa Watson
Local Press: Southwark News,
South London Press
Local Radio: Capital & Capital Gold

PREVIOUS **Leagues:** Parthenon, West Kent, Kent Amateur, London Spartan 76-82, Southern 82-87, GMV Conference 87-91
Names: Fisher Athletic 08-93, Fisher`93 93-96   **Ground:** London Road, Mitcham

CLUB RECORDS **Attendance:** 4,283 v Barnet, GMV Conference 4/5/91
Win: 7-0 v Lewes Sept 95, FA Cup   **Defeat:** 1-8 v Clevedon (away) 10.03.01
Career Goalscorer: Paul Shinners 205   **Career Appearances:** Dennis Sharp 720
Transfer fee paid: £2,500 for Ben Taylor (Sittingbourne)
Transfer fee received: £45,000 for Paul Gorman (Charlton 1991)

BEST SEASON **FA Cup:** 1st Rd 84-85 (0-1 at home to Bristol City), 88-89 (0-4 at BristolRovers)
FA Trophy: Third Round replay 87-88 **FA Vase:** Second Round replay 82-83   **FA Amateur Cup:**

HONOURS Southern Lg 86-87 (R-up 83-84, Southern Div 82-83, Lg Cp 84-85, Championship Cup 87-88, Merit Cup), London Spartan Lg
80-81 81-82 (R-up 78-79, Senior Div77-78, Div 2 R-up 76-77), Parthenon Lg 61-62 (Lg Cup 63-64 65-66), Kent AmateurLg 73-
74 74-75 (R-up 72-73),Kent Intermediate 97-98.98-99 London Senior Cup 84-85 87-88 88-89, LondonIntermediate Cup 59-60
(R-up 75-76), Kent Senior Cp 83-84, Kent Senior Trophy 81-82 82-83, Surrey Inter Cup 61-62,Southern Lg. Eastern Div 99-00

Players progressing: John Bumstead (Chelsea), Trevor Aylott (Bournemouth), Paul Shinners (Orient 84), Dave Regis (Notts Co. - via Barnet),
Paul Gorman(Charlton 91), Sean Devine (Barnet via Okonia Nicossia), George Barry (LeytonOrient),
Dean Martin (West Ham Utd), Jason Lee (Charlton), Ken Charlery (Barnet), Steve Watts (Leyton Orient)

Back row, left to right: Bill Jacobs (P.R.O.), John Leyden (Secretary), Joe Miller all standing and John Sampson, Colin Luckett, Steve Aris, Roddy Dumbuya, Leroy Huggins & Paul Manning. **Second row:** John McKenzie, John Mahoney, Mo Munden, John Mighty, John Farley, Sam Tydeman with Michael Scowen & Ben Cray standing. **Third row:** Ben Taylor, Steve Portway, Tostao Kwashi & Andy Kearns. **Front row:** Les Rowe (Club Captain), Bob Davies (Director of Football), Michael Roberts, Keith Stevens (Manager), Tony Dolby & Richard Jones (Chairman). Mascot: Alfie Powell.

FLEET TOWN

CLUB OFFICIALS
Chairman: Martn Griffiths
President: Tony Frost
Vice Chairman: Jon Goodyear
Secretary: John Goodyear
25 Velmead Road,Fleet,Hants GU52 7LJ
Email: goodyear.john@btinternet.com

FOOTBALL MANAGEMENT TEAM
Manager:Steve Beeks
Asst Man: Dave Skilton
Coach: Jesse Bone & Mervyn Grifiths
Physio: David Keir

FACT FILE
Founded: 1890 Re-Formed: 1947
Nickname: The Blues
Sponsors: Southern Coating Contractors Ltd.
Colours: Navy & sky/sky/navy & sky
Change: Red & Black
Midweek Matches: Tuesday
Reserves' League: Suburban(Wednesdays)

2001-02
Captain: Gary Stockwell
P.o.Y.: John Murphy
Top Scorer: Ian Mancey

GROUND:
Calthorpe Park, Crookham Road, Fleet, Hants
Tel: 01252 623804

PROGRAMME
20 Pages Price: £1.00
Editor: Stuart Reeves
Website: www.fleettownfc.co.uk

Directions: Leave the M3 at Junction 4A. Follow signs to Fleet via A3013.
At 5th roundabout (a T-junction), turn left over railway bridge.
Carry on past `Oatsheaf' pub on the right - ground is 1/4 mile further on right.
Capacity: 2,000   Seats: 200   Cover: 250   Floodlights: Yes

Clubhouse: Yes. Hot & cold food served   **Club Shop:** Yes

PREVIOUS **Leagues:** Hampsire 61-77, Athenian, Combined Co's, Chiltonian, Wessex 89-95, Southern 95-00, Wessex 00-02
Names: None   **Grounds:** None

CLUB RECORDS **Win:** 15-0 Pertersfield 26.12.94   **Defeat:** 0-6 v Margate 1999
Attendance: 1,050 v Coventry City 1995 (Pre-Season Frirerndly)
Transfer fee paid: £3,000 to Aldershot Dec 99 for Mark Russell 1991
Career Goalscorer: Mark Frampton 428 **Appearances:** Mark Frampton250

BEST SEASON F.A.Cup: 2nd Q 97-98 F.A.Trophy: 2nd Rd 97-98 F.A.Vase: 3rd Rd 94-95

HONOURS Wessex Lg 94-95 Runners-Up 01-02, Lg Cup R-up 92-93, 01-02; Hants Lg Div 2 R-up 61-62 (Div 1 R-up 60-61),
Aldershot Snr Cup 92-93, 99-00; Simpsonair Challenge Shield 1993, Hants Yth Lg Div 3 92-93.

HISTON

CLUB OFFICIALS

Chairman: Gareth Baldwin
President: G P Muncey
Secretary: Mrs Baldwin,
5 Caxton Lane, Foxton,
Cambridge CB2 6SR (Tel: 01223 872246)
Press Officer: Streve Wells(01353 862367)
Email:stevenwells1@ composerve.co

FOOTBALL MANAGEMENT TEAM

Manager: Steve Fallon
Coach:Chris Tovey
Physio; Lee Petrucci

FACT FILE

Founded: 1904
Sponsors:Webster Building & Civil Engineers
Colours: Red and blackstripes/black/black
Change colours: Sky & Navy/navy/sky ?
Midweek Matches: Tuesday
Reserves League: Jewson Premier
Website: www.histonfootballclub.tripod.com

2000-01
Captain: Andrew Jeffrey
P.o.Y.: Neil Andrews
Top Scorer: Neil Kennedy (29)

SEASON
2001-2002

WEBSTER

48 pages   £1.00
Editor: Sreve Wells
Local Press : Cambridge Evening News
Local Radio: Q103, Star FM
BBC Radio Cambridgeshire

GROUND   Bridge Rd, Impington, Cambridge Tel: 01223 232301   Fax: 01223 237373
Club Website: http:: //histonfootballclub.tripod.com
EMAIL Address: gareth@corporate innovations.co.uk

Directions: Leave A14 northern Cambridge bypass on B1049 (signposted Histon and
Cottenham). Ground half a mile on right.
5 miles from Cambridge (BR). Bus No.104

Capacity: 3,250   Seats: 250   Cover: 250   Floodlights: Yes

Clubhouse: Bar/lounge open Tues-Sun eves, Sun lunch and matchdays.Snacks available

HONOURS   Eastern Co's Lg - Prem. Div. 99-00, Div 1 R-up 96-97, Cup 90-91;
Cambridge Invitation Cup 77-78 79-80 96-97,00-01 (R-up 50-51 52-53 53-54);
Spartan Lg Div 1 (East) 50-51; Cambs Chall Cup; Cambs Lg Section;
Kershaw Prem Lge 00-01R-up 97-98, Sen Lge A 96-97, Cup 96-97;00-01
Auto Trader Lge & Cup (U18) 96-97 Kershaw Champions Co Cup (U18) 98-99, Colts League (U17) Champions 98-99

PREVIOUS   **Leagues:** Cambridgeshire 04-48; Spartan 48-60; Delphian 60-63; Athenian 63-65; Eastern Counties 66-00
Name: Histon Institute 04-51

BEST SEASON   **FA Cup:** 4th Qual. Rd. 89-90   **FA Vase:** 4th Rd 96-97, 97-98   **F.A .Trophy:** 4th Round 2000-2001

RECORD   **Attendance:** 6,400 v King's Lynn, FA Cup 1956

Back row left to right: Gary Walker, Neil Coburn, Roscoe Hipperson, Paul Barber, Neil Kennedy, Andy Jeffery, James Saddington, Wayne Goddard, Louie Farrington and Steve Fallon (Manager). **Front row:** Bobby Broom (Assistant Manager) , Neil Andrews, Matty Haniver, Jamie Barker, Peter Hunns, Shaun Harrington and Adie Cambridge

KING'S LYNN

CLUB OFFICIALS

Chairman: Colin Nichols
President: Jim Chandler

Secretary: Nigel Link
58 Hall Lane, West Winch, Kings Lynn
PE33 0PP
Tel:01553 841089 (H)
07885 144039 (M)

FOOTBALL MANAGEMENT TEAM

Director of Football: Kevin Boon
Manager: Peter Morris
Physio: Dave Edgeley

FACT FILE

Formed: 1879
Nickname: The Linnets
Sponsors: Lynn News
Colours: Royal Blue with gold trim/Blue/Blue
& Gold hoops
Change colours: Purple & Navy
Midweek home matchday: Tuesday
Reserves League: Jewson Eastern Div 1

GROUND The Walks Stadium, Tennyson Road, King's Lynn PE30 5PB
Tel: 01553 760060

Directions: At mini r-about arriving from A10/A47 take Vancouver Avenue. Ground on left after a half mile. Quarter mile from King's Lynn (BR), half mile from bus station

Capacity: 8,200   Cover: 5,000   Seats: 1,200   Floodlights: Yes

Clubhouse: Normal licensing hours, with extension on matchdays
Club Shop: Sells metal badges and other merchandise

Pages: 24 Price: £1.20
Editor: Secretary
Local Press: Lynn News & Advertiser,
Eastern Daily Press
Local Radio: KLFM

PREVIOUS **Leagues:** Norfolk & Suffolk; Eastern Co.s 35-39 48-54; UCL 46-48; Midland Co.s54-58; NPL 80-83
Name: Lynn Town Ground: None

CLUB RECORDS **Attendance:** 12,937 v Exeter, FA Cup 1st Rd 50-51
Win: 17-0 v Beccles 29/30   **Defeat:** 0-11 v Aston Villa FA Cup 1905/6
Career Appearances: Mick Wright 1,152 (British Record) **Career Goalscorer:** Malcolm Lindsay 321
Transfer Fee Paid: Shaun Keeble Wisbech 98-99   **Transfer Fee Received:** Mark Paul , Southampton.98-99

BEST SEASON **FA Cup:** 3rd Rd 61-62 (0-4 at Everton). Competition Proper on 14 occasions; 05-06 37-38 49-50 51-52 58-63 64-65 68-69 71-72 73-74 84-85. Rd 2 97-98   League clubs defeated: Aldershot 59-60, Coventry 61-62, Halifax 68-69
FA Trophy: 2nd Rd 78-79   **FA Vase:** 5th Rd 94-95 (0-2 at Diss Town   **FA Amateur Cup:** R-up 1900-01

HONOURS FA Amateur Cup R-up 1900-01, Southern Lg R-up 84-85 (Div 1 R-up 63-64), NPLPresidents Cup 82-83, Eastern Co's Lg 53-54 (R-up 49-50 52-53 (Lg Cup 53-54),Norfolk & Suffolk Lg(8)(R-up(6)), E Anglian Lg R-up(2), Norfolk Snr Cup(19)(R-up(20), Norfolk Invitation Cup 94-95, Norfolk Premier Cup 68-69(jt) 73-74, EastAnglian Cup(4)(R-up(3), Eastern Prof Floodlit Lg 68-69, Southern Lg Midland R-up 95-96 ,U.C.L. Reserve Division, League & Cup 'double', 99-00. Southern League Cup. R-up: 2001-02
Players progressing: N Rowe (Derby 1949), B Taylor & P Ward (Bradford P. A. 54& 55), T Reynolds (Darlington 54), G Reed (Sunderland 55), P McCall (Bristol C55), J Neal (Swindon 57), T Dryburgh (Oldham 57), J Hunter (Barrow 59), JStevens (Swindon), G Catleugh (Watford), George Walters (Chesterfield 64), PMcNamee (Notts County 1966), W Biggins (Burnley), Jackie Gallagher(Peterborough 80), Andy Higgins (Rochdale 83), Neil Horwood (Grimsby 86),Darren Rolph (Barnsley 87), Mark Howard (Stockport 88), Andy Hunt, Malcolm Lindsay

Back row left to right: Jason Minett, Simon Dakin, Adie Hayes, Kristian Jones, Stevie Wilson, Dave Robinson (Captain), Simon Nobes, Craig Clark, Ross McNeil, Glen Fuff, Jamie Clarke and Chris Bacon. **Front row:** Dave Edgeley (Physio), Zeke Rowe, Lee Hudson, Tommy Wright (Player/Coach), Tony Spearing (Manager), Darren Bloodworth (Reserves Manager), Jamie March, Wayne Anderson and Richard Simper (Kitman)

NEWPORT I.W.

CLUB OFFICIALS
Chairman: Bill Manuel **Pres:** W Bunday
Director of Football: Tony Mount
Secretary: Chris Cheverton
40 Whitehead Crescent, Wootton Bridge,
I.o.W. PO33 4JF   Tel: 01983 883879
Office Manager: Pauline Crisp
Press Officer: Jim Baldwin
Tel: 01983 521836

FOOTBALL MANAGEMENT TEAM
Manager: Richie Reynolds
Assistant Manager: Bunny Warwick
Physio: Chris Cheverton

FACT FILE
Formed: 1888   Nickname: The Port
Colours: all Yellow with blue trim
Change colours: Sky blue with blue trim
Midweek matchday: Tuesday
Reserves' League: Wesex League
Clubcall: 09066 555 890

2001-02 Captain: John Price
P.o.Y. Players': Colin Matthews.
Leading goalscorer: Danny Gibbons &
David Laws 9

GROUND: St. George's Park, St George's Way, Newport, Isle of Wight, PO30 2QH.
Tel: 01983 525027.   Club Website: None
Directions: Roads from all ferry ports lead to Coppins Bridge R-abt at eastern end of town.
Take Sandown/Ventnor exit, go to small r-about, St George's way is 1st exit, ground on left 5
mins walk from Newport Bus station along Church Litten (past old ground) turn left then right
at r-about.
Capacity: 5,000   Cover: 1,000   Seats: 300   Floodlights: Yes   **Club Shop:**
Sells souvenirs & progs. Contact Roger Sanders 01983 825925
Clubhouse: Open every evening & weekend lunch times. 2 bars, full range of hot and cold
bar snacks. Cnack Bar inside ground

Pages: 28   Price: £1
Editor: Sheryl Penney (023 9221 0015)
Local Press:
Portsmouth Evening News,
I.o.W. County Press,
Southampton Evening Echo
Local Radio:
Solent, Isle of Wight Radio, Ocean Sound

PREVIOUS   **Leagues:** Isle of Wight 1896-1928; Hants 28-86; Wessex 86-90
Ground: Church Litten (previously Well's Field) 1888-1988

CLUB RECORDS **Attendance:** 2,270 v Portsmouth (Friendly) : 7th July 2001 and 2,217 FA Cup 1st Rd Nov 1994 v Aylesbury U.,
Win: 14-1, v Thornycroft Athletic (H),Hampshire Lge Div. One, 22.12.45
Defeat: 1-11 v Emsworth(A) Hampshire Div. Lge 1926-27   **Career Appearances:** Jeff Austin 540 (69-87)
Career Goalscorer: Roy Gilfillan 220 1951-57   **Record Goalscorer:** Frank Harrison 62 1929-30
Fee paid: £5,000 for Colin Matthews (Bognor Regis Town 00) **Fee received:** £2,250 for Mick Jenkins (Havant) 92-3
BEST SEASON   **FA Trophy:** 4th Rd 99-00   **FA Vase:** Fifth Round 91-92, 92-93
FA Cup: 2nd Rd 35-36 45-46. 1st Rd another 8 times - 52-53, 53-54, 54-55, 56-57, 57-58, 58-59, 94-95, 95-96
League clubs defeated: Clapton Orient 45-46

HONOURS   Dr. Martens Lge Eastern Div. 00-01, Wessex Lg R-up 89-90, Comb. 91-92, 99-00 (res 2.) League Cup 01-02 (res); Hants Lg
(11), R-up (7), Div 2 R-up   70-71, Hants Snr Cup (8); Russell Cotes Cup (3); Pickford Cup (4); Isle of Wight Snr (Gold) Cup (34); Hants F'lit Cup
76-77 77-78; Isle of Wight Lg (4) 07-09 23-24; Hants I'mediate Cup 31-32 96-97; Hants Comb. Cup 38-39

Players progressing: Gary Rowatt (Cambridge United)

Back row, left to right: Alex Perry, Jon Holmes, Neil Guile, Danny Gibbons, Danny Rofe and Robbie Harbutt.
Front row: Adam Laing, Simon Pilcher, Adam Barsdell, Leigh Cole and Dave Udy.   **Photo:** Alan Coomes

ROTHWELL TOWN

Rothwell Town
Football Club
Matchday Programme £1.00

CLUB OFFICIALS

Chairman: **Keith Johnson**
President: **Ken Cheney**
Secretary: **Roger Barratt**
18 Norton St., Rothwell, Northants NN14 2DE
Tel: 01536 507744
Press Officer : **Mark Southon**
Tel: 07870 551428

FOOTBALL MANAGEMENT TEAM
Manager: Nick Platnauer
Physio: Bob Bramah

FACT FILE

Founded: 1895
Nickname: The Bones
Sponsors:Springfir Country Homes
Colours: Blue with white trim/blue/blue
Change Colours: Red, black & white trim, black/red
Midweek matchday: Tuesday
Newsline: 0930 555 829
Reserves' League: Utd Counties Res Div

Pages: 48 Price: £1.00 Editor &
Media Relations Officer: Mark Southon
Tel: 07860 551428

Local Press: Northants Evening Telegraph,
Chronicle & Echo, Herald & Post
Local Radio: BBC Radio Northants, KCBC

GROUND Cecil Street, Rothwell, Northants NN14 2EZ Tel: 01536 710694
Directions: A14/A6 to Rothwell. At town centre r'about turn into BridgeStreet (right if northbound, left if southbound), take 3rd left into TreshamStreet, ground is at top on left.
3 miles from Kettering (BR); Rothwell is served by Kettering to Market Harborough buses
Capacity: 3,500 Seats: 264 Cover: 1,264 Floodlights: Yes
Clubhouse: Rowellian Social Club, open every evening and weekend lunchtimes.Crisps and rolls available on matchdays (hot food and drinks available in ground). `Top of the Town Ballroom', lounge seats 200
Club Shop: Sells various souvenirs incl. metal badges.

PREVIOUS **Leagues:** Northants 1896-1911 21-33, Kettering Amateur 11-21 33-48, Leics.Senior 48-50, United Counties 50-56 61-94, Central Alliance 56-61 **Grounds:** Harrington Rd, Castle Hill **Name:** Rothwell Town Swifts

CLUB RECORDS **Attendance:** 2,508 v Irthlingborough Diamonds, United Counties League 1971
Win: 17-0 v Stamford, FA Cup Preliminary Round replay 1927
Defeat: 1-10 v Coalville Town, Leicestershire Sen Lge 1949
Transfer fee paid: Undisclosed for Andy Wright (Aylesbury 1992)
Transfer fee received: Undisclosed for Matty Watts (Charlton 1990)

BEST SEASON **FA Cup:** Fourth Qualifying Round 99-00
FA Trophy: Second Round Proper 94-95 **FA Vase:** Fifth Round 92-93 (1-2 v Bridlington Town)

HONOURS Northants Lg1899-1900 (R-up 1895-96 96-97 97-98), Northants Snr Cup 1899-1900 23-24 59-60 88-89 95-96 01-02 (R-up 24-25 71-72 87-88), United Counties Lg 92-93 94-95 (R-up 69-70 70-71 87-88 89-90 90-91), KO Cup 55-56 70-71 71-72 91-92 92-93 (R-up 77-78 79-80 82-83), Div 2 52-53 53-54, Div 2Cup 52-53 53-54, Benevolent Cup 92-93 94-95 (R-up 89-90 90-91) Southern League Mid Div R-up 96-97

Players progressing: Lee Glover (Nottingham Forest) 1987, Matty Watts (CharltonAth.) 1990, Mathew Lawrence (Wycombe Wanderers) and Chris McKenzie (Leyton Orient)

Back Row: Kim Davis (asst. manager), Wayne Spencer (player-coach), Dean Foley, Richard Preston, Andy Greensmith, John Hughes, Carl Lake, Adam Sturgess, Richard Weale, Danny Liquorish (goalkeeping coach), Kenny Williams (kit manager).
Front Row: Jason Turner, Chris Smith, Danny Porter (captain), Simon Underwood, Ossie Mintus, Jamie Kearns, Nick Platnauer (manager), Ben Hill, Matty Curtis. **Picture** courtesy of Northamptonshire Evening Telegraph

SALISBURY CITY

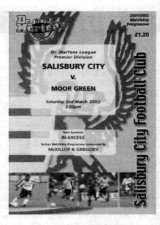

CLUB OFFICIALS
Chairman: P R McEnhill **Director:** R.Wike
Secretary: Douglas Ferraro, Flat 2, 13 Meadow Road, Salisbury, Wiltshire SP2 7BN Tel No: 07803 247874
Email douglasf71@aol.com
Press Off: Alec Hayter Tel: 01264 773765
Youth Development Off: Symon Pickett
Football in Community Off.: Andy Cook

FOOTBALL MANAGEMENT TEAM
Manager: Ken Cunningham-Brown
Asst. Manager: Mick Burford
Youth Coach: Simon Pickett
Physio: Conrad Parrott

ACT FILE
Formed: 1947
Nickname: The Whites
Sponsors: In-Excess
Colours: White/black/white
Change colours: All yellow
Midweek matchday: Tuesday
Reserve Team's League: Wessex Comb
Club Line: 'City Line' 0906 555 864
Website:www.salisbury-city-fc.com

2001-02
Capt: Mathew Davies
Top scorer: Ryan King
Fitness Therapist : Dawn Cornforth

Dr. Martens League
Premier Division

SALISBURY CITY
v.
MOOR GREEN

Saturday 2nd March 2002
3.00pm

IN-EXCESS

Todays Matchday Programme Sponsored by
McKILLOP & GREGORY

2001/2002
Matchday
Programme
£1.20

GROUND The Raymond McEnhill Stadium, Partridge Way, Old Sarum, Salisbury SP4 6PU Tel:01722 326454, Fax 01722 323100 Club Website: www.salisbury-city-fc.com
Directions: The Stadium is situated off A345 (Salisbury - Amesbury) road on the northern edge of the city 2 miles from the City centre. Continue on this road, turn right onto A338 signed Old Sarum Business Park, Partridge Way & ground on left (well signposted)
Capacity: 4,038   Cover:2,300   Seats: 462   Floodlights: Yes
Clubhouse: On ground, . Hot & cold snacks. Hospitality Boxes available for hire.
Club Shop: Sells replica shirts, memorabilia, programmes, scarves, metal badges, souvenirs.
Contact Lynn Tucker, Commercial Office (01722 326454)

Pages: 48   Price: £1.50
Editors: Dave Todd & Alec Hunter

Local Press: Salisbury Journal, Evening Echo & Sports Echo, Western DailyPress
Local Radio: Wiltshire Sound, Spire F.M

PREVIOUS **Leagues:** Western 47-68
Name: Salisbury FC, 47-92   **Ground:** Hudson Field 47-48, Victoria Park 48-97
CLUB RECORDS Attendance: 8,902 v Weymouth, Western League 48
New Ground: 2,570 v Hull City F.A. Cup 1998.   **Win:** 11-1 v R.A.F Colerne (H) Western League Div 2 1948
Defeat: 0-7 v Minehead, Southern League 1975
Career Goalscorer: Royston Watts 180 (59-65)   **Career Appearances:** Barry Fitch 713 (63-75)
Transfer fee paid: £5,750 for Peter Loveridge (Dorchester Town, 90)
Transfer fee received: £20,,000 for Adrian Randall (Forest Green Rovers)
BEST SEASON FA Trophy: 2nd Rd 96-97 (lost to Dorchester Town)
FA Amateur Cup: 2nd Rd 49-50 (lost to Dulwich Hamlet))   **FA Cup:** 2nd Rd 59-60 (lost to Newport County)
HONOURS   Southern Lg Southern Div Champ 94-95, R-up 85-86 92-93; Western Lg 57-58 60-61,R-up 58-59 59-60 61-62 66-67 67-68; Hants Senior Cup 61-62 63-64; Wilts PremierShield 56-57 59-60 61-62 66-67 67-68 70-71 77-78 78-79 95-96 98-99,00-01
Players progressing: Eric Fountain (Southampton 48), Cyril Smith (Arsenal 48),Tony Alexander (Fulham 65), John Evans (Stockport County 67), Graham Moxon (Exeter 75), Eric Welch (Chesterfield 76), Ian Thompson (Bournemouth 83),Trevor Wood (Port Vale 88), Denny Mundee (Bournemouth 88), Matthew Carmichael (Lincoln 90), Frank Monk (Southampton 47)George Marks 49), Joe Stocks (Millwall 64), (H)Jason Matthews (Exeter C)

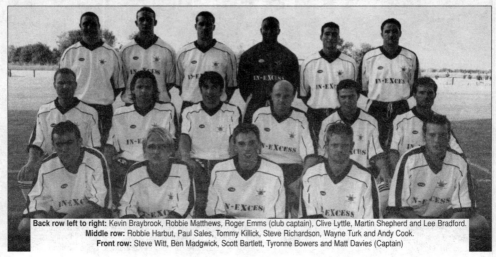

Back row left to right: Kevin Braybrook, Robbie Matthews, Roger Emms (club captain), Clive Lyttle, Martin Shepherd and Lee Bradford.
Middle row: Robbie Harbut, Paul Sales, Tommy Killick, Steve Richardson, Wayne Turk and Andy Cook.
Front row: Steve Witt, Ben Madgwick, Scott Bartlett, Tyronne Bowers and Matt Davies (Captain)

SITTINGBOURNE

CLUB OFFICIALS
Chairman: Andy Spice
President: E H Bennett (in memorium)
Secretary: John Pitts, 4 Silverdale Grove
Sittingbourne, Kent ME10 1UY (Tel No:
01795 476809 Fax 07092 112833)
email: John@sittingbournefc.co.uk
Commercial Manager: John Cooper

FOOTBALL MANAGEMENT TEAM
Manager:Mark Beeney
Assistant Manager/Coach: Steve Nolan
Physio: Gary Wisdom

FACT FILE
Formed: 1881   Nickname: Brickies
Sponsors: Medway Galvanising.
Colours: Red & black stripes/black/red
Change colours: All yellow
Midweek matchday: Tuesday
Reserves' league: Go Travel Kent

2001-02
Captain: Michael Everitt
P.o.Y.: Andrew Drury
Top Scorer: Bradley Spice (12)

£1

Pages: 44 Price: £1
Editor: John Pitts ,Secretary.
Local Press: East Kent Gazette, Kent Today,
Kent Messenger Extra, Sittingbourne &
Sheppy Adscene.
Local Radio: Invicta Supergold, BBC Radio
Kent, Invicta FM,Medway ,Mercury F.M.

GROUNDCentral Park, Eurolink, Sittingbourne, Kent ME10 3SB Tel: 01795 435077/420444
Fax: 01795 420444 Email Address: club@sittingbournefc.co.uk
Directions: Through Sittingbourne on main A2, club signposted clearly and regularly from both
east and west. 1 mile from Sittingbourne BR station.
Capacity: 8,000   Cover: 3,300   Seats: 2,000   Floodlights: 420 lux
Clubhouse: The Cabin (01795 435077)
Club Shop: Sells a wide selection of souvenirs etc. Open matchdays or contact Ann Morrison
(01795 664436)   Official Club Website: www.sittingbournefc.co.uk

PREVIOUS   **Leagues:** Kent 1894-1905 09-27 30-39 46-59 68-91, South Eastern 05-09, Southern 27-30 59-67
Grounds: SittingbourneRec. Ground 1881-90, Gore Court Cricket Ground 90-92, The Bull Ground1892-1990
Names: Sittingbourne United 1881-86

CLUB RECORDS Attendance: 5,951 v Tottenham Hotspur, friendly 26/1/93
Transfer fee paid: £20,000 to Ashford Town for Lee McRobert, 1993.
Transfer fee received: £210,000 from Millwall for Neil Emblen and Michael Harle, 1993

BEST SEASON   FA Cup: 2nd Rd 25-26 (0-7 at Swindon Town), 28-29 (1-2 at Walsall), plus 1st Rd26-27 30-31 62-63
FA Trophy: **FA Vase:**
HONOURS   Southern Lg Southern Div 92-93 95-96; Kent Lg 1897-98 1902-03 57-58 58-59 75-76 83-84 90-91 (Lg Cup 25-26 58-59 73-74
80-81, Div 2 Cup 54-55 57-58 83-84 86-8787-88); Kent Senior Cup 01-02 28-29 29-30 57-58; Kent Senior Shield 25-26 27-28
53-54; Kent Senior Trophy 89-90; Thames & Medway Cup 55-56 58-59; Thames & Medway Comb 02-03 07-08 11-12 24-25
25-26; Chatham Charity Cup 03-04 19-20;" Kent Midweek Lg(res) 91-92 (Lg Cup 90-91).
Players progressing: Jason Lillis (Walsall 93), Neil Emblen & Michael Harle 93, Steve Forbes 94, Lee McRobert 95 (Millwall)
Jimmy Case (Brighton 93), Lee Harper (Arsenal 94)

Back row left to right: Mark Beeney (Manager), Kieron Marsh, James Campbell, Gavin Hooper, Tyrone King, Bradley Spice and Corrie Griffin.
Front row: Sammy Okafor, Michael Everitt, Andrew Drury, Clint Gooding, Cliff Cunningham, John Guest and Paul Campbell.

SPALDING UNITED

CLUB OFFICIALS

Chairman: **Alan Mitchell**
President: **John Chappell**
Press Officer: **Ray Tucker**
Secretary: **Alan Clarke,** 68 Daniels
Crescen t, Long Sutton,Lincs.PE12 9DR
Tel No: 01406 362582

FOOTBALL MANAGEMENT TEAM

Manager: Nick Anderson
Asst Manager: Alex Irvine
Physio: Pauline Yarborough

FACT FILE

Founded: 1921
Nickname: Tulips
Sponsors:
Colours: Tangerine & black/black/tangerine
Change: Sky/white/sky
Midweek matchday: Tuesday
Reserve League: Utd Counties Res Div

GROUND   Sir Halley Stewart Playing Field, Winfrey Avenue, Spalding Tel: 01775 713328

Directions: Town centre off A16, adjacent to bus station. 250 yds from Spalding(BR) station

Capacity: 7,000   Seats: 350   Cover: 2,500   Floodlights: Yes

Clubhouse: Open matchdays, and events   Club Shop: Yes

36 Pages   Price: 50p
Editor: Graham Walmsley

Local Press : Lincs Free Press, Spalding
Guardian, Peterborough EveningTelegraph

HONOURS	Utd Counties Lg 54-55 74-75 87-88 98-99 R-up 50-51 51-52 52-53 72-73 75-76 96-97; KO Cup 54-55 94-95; Northern Co's East Lg 83-84; Lincs Snr Cup 52-53; Hinchingbroke Cup: 98-99 Lincs Snr `A' Cup 87-88, 98-99 R-up 97-98; Snr `B' Cup 50-51; Evans Halshaw F'lit Cup 89-90
PREVIOUS	**Leagues:** Peterborough; Utd Co's 31-55 68-78 86-88 91-99; Eastern Co's 55-60; Central Alliance 60-61; Midland Co's 61-68; Northern Co's East 82-86; Southern 88-91
BEST SEASON	**FA Cup:** 1st Round 57-58, 1-3 v Durham City (A), 64-65, 3-5 v Newport Co. (A) **FA Trophy:** 3rd Rd 99-00 **FA Vase:** Quarter-Finals 89-90, 1-3 v Guiseley
RECORD	**Attendance:** 6,972 v Peterborough, FA Cup 1952

Players progressing: Carl Shutt (Sheffield Wed.)

ST. LEONARDS

CLUB OFFICIALS
Chairman: John Cornelius
Patron: Leon Shepherdson
President: Mrs K Shepperdson
Vice-Chairman: Danny Bossum
Secretary: Tony Leppard c/o The Club
Business Manager: Dale Seymour
Tel: 01424 434755 or 07976626716
Press Officer: Roy Russell 01424846008

FOOTBALL MANAGEMENT TEAM

Manager:Glyn White
Physio: Rob Greig

FACT FILE

Formed: 1971
Nickname: Saints Sponsors:
Shirt Sponsor: Hastings Direct (Insurance)
Clubcall Line: T.B.A.
Colours: Blue/white/blue
Change colours: White/black/white
Midweek Matchday: Monday
Reserves' League: Sussec County

Pages: 60 Price: £1
Editor:T.B.A.
Local Press: Hastings Observer, Eve Argus
Local Radio: Arrow FM, BBC Southern
Counties Radio, Southern FM
Club Call Line: 09068 800 680

Club Website : www.freezone.co.uk/stlfc

GROUND The Firs, Elphinstone Rd, Hastings, East Sussex Tel: 01424 434755 Matchday Office 01424 716362 **Directions:** From M25 & London approach Hastings on the A21. immediately afterthe junct with the A28 on the northern borough boundary, turn right into Junction Rd. At T junct with B2093 turn right onto The Ridge. After 2 miles turn right, opposite the cemetary, into Elphinstone Rd, grd 600yards down hill on left. Nearest station; Ore (Connex South East), 1 mile uphill (no bus or taxi). Hastings (Connex South East) 1.5 miles. Bus service from town centre to ground

Capacity: 3,768 (Day), 3,015 (Even)   Seats: 251   Cover: 1,000   Floodlights: Yes
Clubhouse: Licensed bar open normal pub hours. Hot food matchdays. Hot food from opening on match days.Hot food and other refreshments available from tea bar during matches.
Club Shop: Yes, selling leisure & sports wear, souvenirs & publications, open matchdays

PREVIOUS   **Leagues:** Eastbourne & Hastings 71-82, Southern Counties Comb 82-88, Sussex County 88-96
Grounds: Council pitches 71-73, Pannel Lane, Pett 73-93   **Names:** Stamco (71-96), St Leonards Stamcroft 96-98

CLUB RECORDS **Attendance:** at new ground1,798 v Tiverton Town, FA Vase 4th Rd. 15/01/95
at old ground: 527v Hastings Town, Sussex Senior Cup 2nd Rd 5/12/92
Win: 10-1 v Portfield(H), Sussex County League Div One 4/12/93   **Defeat:** 2-10 v Rothwell Town (a0 Dr Martens) 19.10.00
Career appearances: Keith Miles 292 (1995-2001)   **Career Goalscorer:** Keith Miles (134) 1995-2001)
Transfer fee paid: None   **Transfer fee received:** £8,000 for Jon Magee (Margate)

BEST SEASON: **FA Cup:** 3rd Qual Rd 96-97 97-98   **FA Vase:** 5th Rd 94-95   **FA Trophy:** 3rd Rd 96-97

HONOURS   Sussex Sen Cup 96-97; Sussex RUR Charity Cup R-up 94-95; Hastings Snr Cup 89-90 95-96 96-97, R-up 92-93 97-98;
Dr Martens Lge Southern Div R-up 96-97, Merit Cup 96-97; Sussex County Div 1 R-up 94-95 95-96, Div 2 R-up 92-93,
Cup R-up 89-90 90-91, Div Three R-up 88-89, Cup R-up 88-89 Kent Midweek Lg.Cup Winners 98-99

Player progressing: Sasha Ilic (Charlton Ath 97)

Back row, left to right: Andy Hargreaves (Team Attendant), Des Boateng, Terry White, Roy Godden, Dave Fisher, Phil Henderson, John Odlum, Richard Callaway, Danny Moody, Glyn White (Manager) and Kevin Burgess (Coach).
Front row: Dominic Barclay, Gavin Ramsden, Andy Johnson, Steve Smith, Jimmy Elford, Peter McCann and Richard Devine.

STAMFORD

STAMFORD AFC
PROGRAMME

Southern League Football (Eastern Division)

At the Newflame Stadium
SEASON 2001 – 2002

CLUB OFFICIALS

Chairman: **Ken Joynson**
Vice-Chairman: **Richard Jacobs**
Secretary: **Jeremy Biggs**
`The Essendine', Essendine, Stamford,
Lincs., PE9 4LD Tel: 01780 763048
Press Officer: **As Secretary**

FOOTBALL MANAGEMENT TEAM

Manager:Billy Jeffrey
Assistant: Nick Ashby
Physio: Pete Foskett

FACT FILE

Founded: 1896   Nickname: Daniels
Sponsors: Silvelink Restaurant/Newflame
Colours: Red
Change Colours: Yellow & green
Midweek matchday: Tuesday
2001-01
Captain: Darren Clyde
P.o.Y.: Andy Peaks
Top Scorer: Carl Holmes 20

GROUND   Newflame Stadium, Kettering Road,, Stamford, Lincs
Tel: 01780 763079 (Clubhouse) 01780 766027 (Pressbox)

Directions: Off A43 Kettering Rd, 1 mile east of A1. 200 yds from station
Capacity: 5,000   Seats: 250   Cover: 1,250   Floodlights: Yes
Clubhouse: Open matchdays, Sunday lunchtimes.
      Food available matchdays - hot and cold
Club Shop: Wide range of Lge + non-Lge progs & club souvenirs.

Pages : 44   Price:£1,00
Editor: Robin Peel
Local Newspapers: Stamford Mercury,
Peterborough Evening Telegraph,
Herald &Post
Local Radio:Rutland Radio,LincsFM
Radio Lincolnshire & Radio Cambridgeshire

PREVIOUS   **Leagues:** Peterborough; Northants (UCL) 08-55; Central Alliance 55-61; Midland Co's 61-72; UCL 72-98
      Grounds: None   **Names:** None

CLUB RECORDS **Attendance:** 4,200 v Kettering, FA Cup 3rd Qual Rd 53
      Win: 13-0 v Peterborough Reserves, Northants Lge 29-30   **Defeat:** 0-17 v Rothwell,FA Cup 27-28
      Appearances: Dick Kwiatkowski 462   **Goalscorer:** Bert Knighten 248

BEST SEASON **FA Cup:** 12-13 5th Qual. Round
      FA Vase: Winners 79-80, R-up 75-76 83-84   **FA Trophy:** 00-01 (1st season) 2nd Round
HONOURS   FA Vase 79-80 (R-up 75-76 83-84); Utd Co's Lg 75-76 77-78 79-80 80-81 81-82 96-97 97-98 (KO Cup 51-52 75-76 79-80 81-
82 85-86); Northants Lg 11-12; Lincs Snr`A' Cup 78-79 82-83 97-98, 00-01; Lincs Snr `B' Cup 51-52 53-54; William Scarber
Mem. Cup 70-71 82-83 85-86 88-89 93-94 94-95; Stamford Chal. Cup 89-90; Lincs Jnr Cup 48-49 Hinchbrooke Cup 1906-07, 07-08, 97-98
Players progressing: A Birchenall (Chelsea), R Chester(Aston Villa), T Tye (Chelsea), G Fell (Brighton), C Chapman (Wolves), S Collins
(Peterborough), K Alexander (Grimsby), A Tillson (Grimsby), B Stubbs (Notts Co.), D Genovese (Peterborough), J Johnson, C MacCarney (Notts
Co), B McNamara (Northampton), D Norris (Bolton), M.Clifford (Boston United)

Back row left to right: Andy Drummond (Reserves Manager), Malcolm Ndekwe, Carl Holmes, Matt Green, Darron Clyde (captain), Steve
Corry, Adam Hancock, Nick Ashby (Assistant Manager), Dennis Rhule ansd Billy Jeffrey (Manager).
Front row: Pete Foskett (Physio), Paul Sherlock, Richard Bailey, Kevin Ainslie, Andy Peaks, Warren Donald and David Staff.

TONBRIDGE ANGELS

OFFICIAL MATCH DAY MAGAZINE OF

CLUB OFFICIALS

Chairman: **Howard Luft**
Vice Chairman: **Maurice Brown**
Secretary: **Charlie Cole**
30 Faraday Ride,Tonbridge TN10 4RL
Tel No: 01732 354985
Press Officer:T.B.A.
Commercial Manager:Andrew Gidley

FOOTBALL MANAGEMENT TEAM

Manager: Alan Walker
Physio: Chris Dunk

FACT FILE

Founded: 1948
Nickname: The Angels
Sponsors: Brewers
Colours: Royal Blue with white trim
Change Colours: Yelow/Black/Yellow
Midweek matchday: Tuesday
Reserves League: Suburban
2000-2001
Top Scorer: Brendon Cass
P.o.Y. Nick Humphrey
Captain: Alan Tutton

Pages: 38 Price: £1
Editor:Maurice Brown c/o Club

Local Press: Kent Messenger, Courier,
Sevenoaks Leader
Local Radio: Mercury, Radio Kent, K,F.M.

GROUND	Longmead Stadium, Darenth Avenue, Tonbridge, Kent TN10 3JW Tel: 01732 352417
Directions:	From Tonbridge BR station, through High Street, north up Shipbourne Rd (A227 Gravesend road) to 2nd mini-r'bout (`The Pinnacles' pub), left into Darenth Avenue, ground at bottom of Avenue, far side of car park
Capacity:	5,000 Seats: 202 Cover: 400 Floodlights: Yes
Clubhouse:	Open Mon-Sat evenings and Sunday lunchtimes. Hot food on matchdays from burger bar
Club Shop:	Yes, progs, replica kits etc, contact Lorraine Parks (01732 350865)

PREVIOUS   **Leagues:** Southern 48-89, Kent 89-93
Ground: The Angel 48-80   **Names:** TonbridgeAngels, Tonbridge F.C., Tonbridge A.F.C

CLUB RECORDS Attendance: 1,463 v Yeovil Town, FA Cup 4th Qualifying Round 26/10/91.
At theAngel Ground: 8,236 v Aldershot, FA Cup 1st Round 1951
Win: 11-1 v WorthingFA Cup 1951   **Defeat:** 2-11 v Folkstone, Kent Sen Cup 1949
Career Goalscorer: Unknown   **Career Appearances:** Mark Gillham, 520 to date
Transfer fee paid: **Transfer fee received:** £7,500 for Paul Emblen (Charlton Ath 97)

BEST SEASON FA Cup: First Round (proper) 50-51 51-52 52-53 67-68 72-73
FA Trophy: **FA Vase:**

HONOURS   Kent League 94-95 (League Cup (2)), Southern League Cup Runners-up (2) (SF(1)), Kent Senior Cup 64-65 74-75 (Runners-up (2)), Kent Senior Shield 51-5255-56 57-58 58-59 63-64

Players progressing: R Saunders, M McMcDonald, T Burns, I Seymour, G Moseley, TMorgan, Neil Emblen, Paul Emblen.

Back row left to right: C.Blewden,C.Coneally, M. Vercess, B.Cass, M.Morgan, D.Hunt, J.Radford, S.Ball, R.Royston, N.Humphrey, and R.Cott. **Front row:** N.Donn, C. Dunk, J.Allman, D. Tingley, K.Wilson, A.Tutton (captain), R.Briggs and J.Dixon.

Welcome to Ram Meadow

Home of

BURY TOWN F.C

1995 L...

Cecil & Larter OFFICIAL CLUB SPONSOR

JEWSON
FOOTBALL LEAGUE

OFFICIAL MATCH DAY PROGRAMM

RY TOWN F.C. BURY TOWN F.C. BURY TOWN F.C. BURY TOWN F.C. BURY TOWN F.C. BURY TOW

Programme printed by MIROPRESS

80p

The Seasider

Official Match Day Programme
Season 2001-2002

£1

Felixstowe & Walton United F.C.

Members of the Jewson Eastern Counties League

East Anglian Cup - Group 8 Final
Tuesday 16th April 2002 - K.O. 7.45pm
MCP plc   Great Wakering Rovers F.C.   MCP plc

OFFICIAL PROGRAMME £1

LOWESTOFT TOWN FOOTBALL CLUB

2001/2002 Season

Saturday 7th December 2001
Kick off: 3pm
Jewson League Premier Division
Lowestoft Town V Harwich & Parkeston

CLUB MAIN SPONSOR

TODAY'S MATCH SPONSOR

Match Ball Sponsor
Fanzie
'There's only one F in Lowestoft'

www.lowestofttownfc.co.uk

WINNERS
JEWSON LEAGUE
CUP & SUFFOLK
PREMIER CUP 2001

JEWSON FOOTBALL LEAGUE - *PREMIER DIVISION*
Official Matchday Programme - 50p   SEASON 2001 / 2002

Woodbridge Town

Football

Club

The Woodpeckers

WELCOME
TO
NOTCUTTS
PARK

Founded 1885

www.woodbridgetownfc.com

Brafe Engineering
01394 380000

Neil Davies Ltd
01728 724400

Main Sponsors of Woodbridge Town Football Club

JEWSON EASTERN COUNTIES LEAGUE

Feeder to: Dr Martens League
Founded 1935

Hon. Patron: Derek Needham   **President:** Roger Pauley
Secretary: Colin Lamb, 3 Land Close, Clacton-on-Sea, Essex CO16 8UJ
Tel: 01255 436398
www.jewsonleague.co.uk

The League produced one of non-League football's greatest `fairy stories' as Tiptree United overcame the underdog tag and actually reached the F.A. Vase Final by beating their own champions and red hot favourites, AFC Sudbury in their two legged semi-final (2-0 at Sudbury and 0-0 at home).

In the League AFC Sudbury retained the title with a seven point margin over Wroxham, who also enjoyed a good run in the Vase, while Lowestoft Town could also look back on their season with satisfaction as they along with the two leaders scored more than 100 goals. Others, who made their presence well felt were Clacton Town, Gorleston and Stowmarket Town.

The bottom two places in the table were occupied by Swaffham Town and Felixstowe & Walton United with both slightly out of their depths but not disgraced, although the former did concede more than 100 goals.

Division One champions were Norwich United by a narrow three point margin over Histon's Reserves, but it was sad to see March Town United prop up the table with only thirteen points.

In the domestic parochial competitions the League Cup saw Clacton Town with an extra time goal success over Dereham Town take the honours at Diss, while Tiptree United's consolation result was in doubt until Whitby Bay scored in extra time, but the quite staggering achievement of Tiptree United will be treasured by all involved, and will go down in the League's folklore as one of its greatest moments.

PREMIER DIVISION FINAL LEAGUE TABLE 2001-02

	P	W	D	L	F	A	Pts
AFC Sudbury	42	32	4	6	139	54	100
Wroxham	42	29	6	7	114	46	93
Lowestoft Town	42	24	8	10	106	55	80
Clacton Town	42	20	16	6	83	41	76
Gorleston	42	21	8	13	77	69	71
Stowmarket Town	42	20	10	12	75	64	70
Bury Town	42	19	7	16	70	53	64
Woodbridge Town	42	16	14	12	62	61	62
Ely City	42	19	5	18	71	73	62
Maldon Town	42	17	10	15	78	78	61
Mildenhall Town	42	18	7	17	68	68	61
Dereham Town	42	16	7	19	59	64	55
Soham Town Rangers *	42	16	8	18	68	80	55
Fakenham Town	42	13	13	16	59	66	52
Tiptree United	42	13	10	19	53	69	49
Diss Town	42	14	7	21	66	84	49
Great Yarmouth Town	42	13	9	20	41	65	48
Harwich & Parkeston	42	13	5	24	46	81	44
Newmarket Town	42	10	13	19	65	89	43
Ipswich Wanderers	42	11	8	23	53	69	41
Felixstowe & Walton U	42	7	9	26	38	88	30
Swaffham Town	42	7	4	31	39	113	25

* points adjustment

PREMIER DIVISION RESULTS CHART 2001-02

		1	2	3	4	5	6	7	8	9	10	11	12	13	14	15	16	17	18	19	20	21	22
1	Bury Town	X	2-3	2-0	2-0	0-1	1-1	1-1	1-2	2-0	0-1	2-0	0-2	0-1	4-2	4-0	4-1	2-2	2-3	1-2	0-2	1-1	1-0
2	Clacton T	0-0	X	0-0	0-0	3-1	2-1	0-0	3-0	1-1	1-0	1-0	3-3	3-0	5-0	3-3	1-1	1-1	2-3	4-1	0-0	0-2	4-0
3	Dereham T	0-1	0-2	X	6-0	2-1	1-1	2-0	0-2	3-1	0-1	2-1	3-1	0-1	0-2	0-3	2-1	1-1	0-1	4-1	2-2	1-1	1-2
4	Diss Town	3-1	1-2	5-4	X	5-2	3-2	1-0	2-1	0-1	3-2	2-0	0-5	1-1	4-2	1-4	0-3	2-5	2-2	5-0	1-2	0-2	1-4
5	Ely City	3-0	1-1	2-3	2-1	X	0-1	2-0	0-2	1-2	2-1	1-0	3-1	1-1	2-3	2-2	4-0	2-2	0-5	2-3	0-1	2-0	2-1
6	Fakenham	2-2	1-3	3-0	3-2	1-1	X	4-0	4-3	1-1	0-3	2-0	0-2	2-2	1-1	4-3	2-2	3-0	2-7	2-0	1-1	0-2	0-2
7	Felix & W	0-2	1-3	1-2	2-2	0-2	0-0	X	1-1	0-0	0-1	1-3	1-5	4-1	0-3	0-1	0-2	0-1	1-5	1-1	2-1	0-3	1-5
8	Gorleston	2-2	1-1	3-0	3-1	4-1	2-0	2-0	X	2-1	0-1	1-1	4-1	4-2	2-2	3-2	2-1	3-2	1-3	1-0	1-1	1-0	4-1
9	Yarmouth	1-2	1-0	0-2	1-0	1-0	1-0	0-2	1-1	X	0-0	0-0	0-4	1-2	1-1	2-1	0-2	2-1	3-0	2-1	2-1	1-1	1-2
10	Harwich	0-5	0-6	1-2	1-1	1-3	1-0	1-1	0-3		X	0-1	3-2	0-2	1-2	2-4	2-6	5-0	2-0	1-1	0-2		
11	Ipswich W	1-3	0-1	1-5	1-3	4-2	1-0	1-1	1-3	2-2	2-5	X	2-0	6-0	0-1	1-1	2-4	1-3	0-1	0-1	2-2		
12	Lowestoft	1-0	0-0	1-2	0-2	4-0	2-2	2-3	4-1	4-0	4-1	2-1	X	5-5	4-1	3-0	5-1	1-1	3-2	6-1	4-1	1-2	3-0
13	Maldon Tn	0-3	0-3	4-1	2-2	2-1	1-2	4-2	5-1	3-2	3-0	6-2	0-1	X	1-0	0-0	6-0	1-0	5-0	2-1	2-0	3-1	
14	Mildenhall	2-0	2-2	1-1	2-2	0-3	2-3	1-2	2-0	2-0	3-1	3-1	1-2	1-2	X	6-2	1-2	1-0	0-0	2-1	2-1	2-1	1-2
15	Newmarket	0-4	1-1	0-0	2-3	0-1	1-2	0-1	4-0	6-0	0-2	3-3	5-5	1-0	3-0	X	3-2	0-4	2-2	2-3	1-1	0-5	
16	Soham T	2-3	1-0	2-0	3-1	0-3	1-1	1-2	3-2	2-3	0-2	2-0	0-2	3-0	2-0	1-1	X	0-3	0-5	3-1	1-1	3-3	0-2
17	Stowm'ket	1-4	0-4	0-3	2-1	3-0	2-0	4-1	5-1	0-0	4-0	1-1	2-1	3-0	1-1	0-4		X	2-3	1-0	2-1	1-0	1-3
18	Sudbury	1-2	7-2	1-0	3-0	3-3	3-0	4-0	3-2	5-1	2-1	2-6	3-0	4-0	6-0	7-3	4-2		X	4-3	5-0	7-3	1-2
19	Swaffham	1-2	0-5	3-1	0-4	0-2	1-2	3-1	1-4	1-0	0-3	1-2	1-1	0-3	0-4	0-2	0-2	2-3	X	1-1	1-2	1-4	
20	Tiptree U	2-1	1-1	2-0	2-0	1-2	1-0	2-2	2-3	4-0	1-0	1-2	0-3	2-2	1-2	2-0	1-2	0-2	0-3	4-1	X	2-2	1-4
21	Woodbridge	3-1	0-3	0-3	1-0	1-6	1-0	2-1	1-0	1-0	0-0	1-1	0-0	2-2	5-1	3-3	2-2	0-0	6-2	0-1		X	0-0
22	Wroxham	3-0	4-3	6-0	5-0	6-1	3-1	6-1	4-2	5-1	2-0	1-0	2-2	4-0	1-3	4-0	4-1	1-1	1-1	3-0	3-0	2-2	X

DIVISION ONE FINAL LEAGUE TABLE 2001-02

	P	W	D	L	F	A	Pts		P	W	D	L	F	A	Pts
Norwich United	36	25	7	4	83	22	82	Cornard United	36	14	3	19	60	73	45
Histon Res.	36	25	4	7	99	34	79	Whitton United	36	12	6	18	49	58	42
Haverhill Rovers	36	23	7	6	85	31	76	Halstead Town	36	11	8	17	53	68	41
Leiston	36	24	4	8	74	36	76	Hadleigh United	36	11	8	17	51	72	41
Needham Market	36	22	5	9	79	42	71	Downham Town	36	11	5	20	60	82	38
King's Lynn Res.	36	19	8	9	84	44	65	Warboys Town	36	9	7	20	38	75	34
Stanway Rovers	36	18	5	13	72	52	59	Brightlingsea United	36	9	4	23	49	105	31
Somersham Town	36	15	8	13	51	60	53	Thetford Town	36	7	6	23	37	97	27
Wisbech Town Res.	36	15	5	16	58	64	50	March Town United	36	3	5	28	45	124	14
Cambridge City Res.	36	13	7	16	79	67	46								

DIVISION ONE RESULTS CHART 2001-02

		1	2	3	4	5	6	7	8	9	10	11	12	13	14	15	16	17	18	19
1	Brightlingsea United	X	3-2	1-3	2-1	2-5	3-0	0-5	1-4	4-3	1-2	1-1	0-1	0-2	0-1	1-4	3-1	3-2	0-0	4-3
2	Cambridge City Res.	2-2	X	2-0	4-0	3-0	1-1	1-4	1-0	1-2	1-2	6-1	3-3	3-3	0-1	4-0	4-0	3-0	1-1	7-0
3	Cornard United	7-2	0-5	X	2-3	2-0	0-2	1-4	0-3	2-0	0-1	7-0	1-2	3-2	0-1	3-0	0-2	4-2	2-4	2-1
4	Downham Town	6-0	1-5	3-3	X	3-5	1-3	1-2	2-0	2-2	0-2	2-4	3-4	0-3	2-2	0-3	2-3	2-1	2-1	1-3
5	Hadleigh United	3-0	2-1	2-2	1-0	X	1-3	2-0	0-5	3-2	1-2	4-3	0-0	0-3	2-2	1-3	0-5	3-0	1-1	
6	Halstead Town	5-0	6-2	1-3	0-1	1-1	X	1-1	0-0	0-6	0-6	4-2	1-0	1-3	1-2	0-1	4-0	1-2	1-1	3-2
7	Haverhill Rovers	5-4	6-0	2-0	5-2	3-0	3-1	X	1-3	2-2	0-1	3-2	2-0	0-0	0-0	1-0	1-1	3-0	4-0	0-1
8	Histon Res.	4-0	1-1	3-0	4-1	6-2	2-1	0-1	X	2-0	1-2	6-4	2-2	0-1	7-1	7-2	3-2	5-1	2-0	2-0
9	King's Lynn Res.	4-0	5-2	5-0	5-1	2-0	3-1	0-3	0-0	X	3-0	4-0	2-2	0-3	5-1	1-2	4-0	1-0	1-1	1-0
10	Leiston	3-0	3-2	6-0	2-2	2-1	5-0	0-3	0-2	2-2	X	6-1	1-0	1-2	1-0	3-2	1-2	2-2	2-1	2-1
11	March Town United	2-3	2-2	4-1	1-2	1-1	3-5	0-0	3-5	1-2	0-4	X	0-1	0-3	0-2	0-7	1-3	1-2	0-4	1-3
12	Needham Market	3-1	0-2	1-2	2-1	1-4	2-0	1-2	2-1	1-0	5-0	X	3-1	7-1	6-0	3-0	2-1	2-1	3-1	
13	Norwich United	3-0	5-1	0-2	3-0	3-0	2-0	1-1	2-1	1-2	2-0	11-0	2-0	X	1-1	2-0	5-1	3-0	1-0	1-0
14	Somersham Town	5-1	3-1	1-1	1-2	1-2	2-1	0-1	0-4	3-1	0-0	2-0	1-4	0-5	X	1-1	7-3	0-1	2-1	3-2
15	Stanway Rovers	3-4	3-1	0-2	1-2	2-0	3-0	2-1	1-0	2-1	4-1	2-2	0-0	1-0	X	10-0	2-0	0-1	2-2	
16	Thetford Town	1-1	2-3	4-1	2-0	1-1	0-1	0-8	0-1	0-4	0-3	0-2	2-2	1-1	1-3	X	2-2	0-4	0-1	
17	Warboys Town	3-1	1-0	1-3	1-1	0-0	1-1	0-3	0-4	0-5	0-3	1-1	1-2	0-2	1-1	1-4	2-0	X	1-0	2-0
18	Whitton United	3-0	1-0	2-1	0-4	1-0	2-2	1-3	0-3	1-1	1-2	5-2	0-6	0-1	0-1	0-3	3-0	5-0	X	2-1
19	Wisbech Town Res.	3-1	3-2	1-0	0-4	4-3	1-3	2-2	1-5	2-2	0-1	3-1	1-2	0-0	2-0	1-0	2-0	5-1	4-2	X

MILLENNIUM CUP

FIRST ROUND

Bury Town	v	Great Yarmouth T	2*4	Downham Town	v	King's Lynn Res.	0-1
Halstead Town	v	Mildenhall Town	0-1	March Town United	v	Warboys Town	4-3
Needham Market	v	Leiston	3-1	Stowmarket Town	v	Wisbech Town Res.	2-1
Tiptree United	v	Harwich & Parkeston	7-1	Whitton United	v	Gorleston	1-2

QUARTER-FINALS

March	v	Great Yarmouth T	0-4	Mildenhall Town	v	Gorleston	2-3
Stowmarket Town	v	King's Lynn Res.	1-4	Tiptree United	v	Needham Market	3-0

SEMI-FINALS

Great Yarmouth Tn	v	King's Lynn Res.	2-1	Tiptree United	v	Gorleston	2-1

FINAL

Great Yarmouth Town v Tiptree Utd 0-3 at Woodbridge Town

LEAGUE CUP 2001-02

PRELIMINARY ROUND

Dereham Town	v	Warboys Town	5-0	Fakenham Town	v	Great Yarmouth Tn	3-1
Felixstowe & Walton U	v	Brightlingsea United	2-0	Harwich & Parkeston	v	Histon Res.	1-2
Haverhill Rovers	v	Woodbridge Town	2-1	Ipswich Wanderers	v	Somersham Town	4-0
Needham Market	v	Leiston	0-2	Soham Town Rangers	v	Downham	5-1
Tiptree United	v	Bury Town	5-0				

FIRST ROUND

Cambridge City Res.	v	Leiston	4-1	Cornard United	v	Dereham Town	0*1
Ely City	v	Swaffham Town	3-0	Felixstowe & Walton U	v	March Town United	3-1
Haverhill	v	Soham Town Rngrs	0-6	Ipswich Wanderers	v	Halstead Town	2-0
King's Lynn Res.	v	Lowestoft Town	0-6	Maldon Town	v	Clacton Town	0-5, 3*3
Mildenhall Town	v	Wroxham	0-2	Newmarket Town	v	Histon Res.	2-0
Norwich United	v	Stowmarket Town	1-0	Thetford Town	v	Diss Town	1-2
Tiptree United	v	Sudbury	0-1	Stanway Rovers	v	Fakenham Town	0-3
Whitton United	v	Hadleigh United	4-0	Wisbech Town Res.	v	Gorleston	2-1
(Whitton expelled)							

SECOND ROUND

Ely Cty	v	Newmarket Town	4-1	Fakenham Town	v	Dereham Town	0-3
Felixstowe & Walton U	v	Clacton Town	1-2	Hadleigh United	v	Lowestoft Town	1-8
Ipswich Wanderers	v	Diss Town	4*3	Norwich United	v	Sudbury	3-2
Soham Town Rangers	v	Wisbech Town Res.	3-1	Wroxham	v	Cambridge City Res.	1-0

QUARTER-FINALS

Dereham Town	v	Ely City	2-0	Lowestoft Town	v	Ipswich Wanderers	1-5
Soham	v	Norwich United	2-4	Wroxham	v	Clacton Town	0-2

SEMI-FINALS

Dereham Town	v	Ipswich Wanderers	1-0				
Norwich United	v	Clacton Town	0-3, 1*1				

FINAL

Dereham Town	v	Clacton Town	0*1	at Diss Town

DIVISION ONE CUP

PRELIMINARY ROUND NORTH (Two legs)

Norwich United	v	Downham Town	1-1, 3-1	Wisbech Town Res.	v	Histon Res.	0-5, 1-2

PRELIMINARY ROUND SOUTH (Two legs)

Whitton United	v	Haverhill Rovers	1-0, 2-3	(Haverhill Rovers win on away goals)

FIRST ROUND NORTH (Two legs)

Cambridge City Res.	v	Thetford Town	3-1, 1-2	Norwich United	v	March Town U	1-3, 3-3
Somersham Town	v	Histon Res.	1-6, 1-6	Warboys Town	v	King's Lynn Rs	0-6, 1-5

FIRST ROUND SOUTH (Two legs)

Brightlingsea United	v	Stanway Rvrs	3-6, 1-1	Cornard United	v	Haverhill Rovers	1-0, 1-2
Halstead	v	Leiston	1-2, 0-1	Needham Market	v	Hadleigh United	0-1, 4-0
(Haverhill Rovers win on away goals)							

QUARTER-FINALS (Two legs)

Cambridge City Res.	King's Lynn Res.		2-0, 2-2	Leiston	v	Needham Mkt	0-1, 3-1
March	v	Haverhill	0-5, 0-0	Stanway Rovers	v	Histon Res.	0-4, 4-1

SEMI-FINALS (Two legs)

Cambridge City Res.	v	Histon Res.	0-1, 2-0	Haverhill	v	Leiston	0-1, 1-1
(Cambridge City Res. expelled)							

FINAL

Leiston	v	Histon Res.	3-2	at Needham Market

BURY TOWN

Secretary: Mrs Wendy Turner, 64 Winthrop Rd., Bury-St-Edmunds, Suffolk. IP333UF
Tel Nos: 01284 753688 (H) 01284 762021 (W)   **Club Website:** www.burytownfc.co.uk
Ground: Ram Meadow, Cotton Lane, Bury St Edmunds, Suffolk IP33 1XP Tel: 01284 754721
Directions: Leave A14 at sign to Central Bury St Edmunds, follow signs to town centre at exit
r'bout, at next r'bout 1st exit into Northgate St, L. at `T' junct (lights) into Mustow St, left immediately
into Cotton Lane - ground 350 yds on right, through `Pay & Display' car park. 10 mins from station
Capacity: 3,500   **Cover:** 1,500   **Seats:** 300   **Floodlights:** Yes
Clubhouse: Members'/Public Bars open at matchdays   **Club Shop:** Yes

HONOURS   Eastern Counties Lg 63-64, R-up 37-38, Lg Cup 61-62 63-64; Metropolitan Lg
                65-66, R-up 67-68 70-71, Lg Cup 67-68, Professional Cup 65-66;
                Suffolk Premier Cup (9); Suffolk Senior Cup 36-37 37-38 38-39 44-45 84-85
PREVIOUS   **Leagues:** Norfolk & Suffolk; Essex & Suffolk Border; Eastern Co's 35-64 76-87;
Metropolitan 64-71 **Names:** Bury St Edmunds 1895-1902; Bury Utd 02-06, Bury Town(1995) Ltd.
BEST SEASON   **FA Cup:** 1st Rd replay 68-69, 0-3 v AFC Bournemouth (A) after 0-0
                FA Vase: Qtr Finals 88-89   **FA Trophy:** 2nd Rd 70-71
CLUB RECORDS Attendance: 2,500 v Enfield, FA Cup 3rd Qual. Rd 1986 **Goalscorer:** Doug
Tooley 58 **Appearances:** Doug Tooley **TransferFee Paid:** £1,500 for Mel Springett (Chelmsford
1990) **Fee Received:** £5,500 forSimon Milton (Ipswich) .**Players progressing:** D Lewis
(Gillingham), L Carberry T.Pearce+S.Milton(Ipswich), T Bly (NorwichCity) + G Stevens (Brighton),

FACT FILE
Formed: 1872
Nickname: The Blues
Colours: All blue
Change colours: Red/black/yellow
Midweek matchday: Tuesday
Programme: 40 pages 80p
Editor: Mrs Wendy Turner

CLUB PERSONNEL
Chairman: Russell Ward
Vice Chairman: Robin Calton
President: Cyril Elsey
Manager: Richard Wilkins
Asst Manager: Trevor Collins
Physio: Darren Gibbs

2001-02
Captain: Trevor Collins
P.o.Y.:Andy Eadie
Top scorer: Ian Stringfellow 22

CLACTON TOWN

Secretary: Mrs Linda Pigeon c/o Club Tel: 01255 476133 email: secretary@clacton-town.com

Ground: The Rush Green Bowl, Rushgreen Road, Clacton-on-Sea, Essex CO16 7BQ
                Tel/Fax: 01255 432590 email: supporters@clacton-town.com
Directions: A133 to Clacton, at r'bout right into St Johns Rd, 4th left CloesLane, 3rd right
Rushgreen Rd, ground approximately half mile on right. From B1027 take main Jaywick turn
off (Jaywick Lane), then 2nd left after about half a mile into Rushgreen Rd. Ground 400 yds.
2 miles from Clacton (BR), buses 3, 5or 5a to Coopers Lane/Rushgreen Rd
Capacity: 3,000   **Seats:** 200   **Cover:** Yes   **Floodlights:** Yes   Club Shop: Yes
Clubhouse: Licensed club. Open 7-11pm Mon-Fri, all day Sat & Sun.
                Hot & cold food available at all times.

HONOURS   Southern Lg Div 1 59-60; Eastern Co's Lg R-up 36-37 53-54 64-65 74-75
                (Lg Cup 73-74), Div 1 98-99 (Lg Cup 98-99); Eastern F/lit Cup 95-96;
                East Anglian Cup 53-54,99-00; WorthingtonEvans Cup 56-57 67-68 74-75.
PREVIOUS   **Leagues:** Eastern Co's 35-37 38-58; Southern 58-64
                Grounds: Clacton Stadium, Old Road 06-87; Gisburnd Av (temp)
RECORD   **Attendance:** 3,505 v Romford, FA Cup 1st Qual. Rd 1952 (at Old Road)
BEST SEASON   **FA Vase:** 4th Rd 74-75,99-00 ,**FA Cup:** 1st Rd,1-3 v Southend U. (H) 60-61
Players progressing: Vivian Woodward (Spurs), Mick Everitt (Arsenal), Christian McLean (Bristol R.)

FACT FILE
Founded: 1892
Nickname: Seasiders
Colours: White/white/royal blue
Change colours: yellow/yellow/royal blue
Midweek Matches: Tuesday
Programme: 40 pages, £1
Editor: Jon Gooding (01473 420731)
Local Press: Clacton Gazette
web site: www.clacton-town.com
CLUB PERSONNEL
Owner: Jeff Dewing
Chairman: Mick Brpoadbent
Commercial Manager: Michelle Stanley
Tel:01255822169
Team Manager: Richie Powling

2000-01
Captain: Steve Howe
P.o.Y.: Shane Bailey
Top Goalscorer: Mitchell Springette 14

DEREHAM TOWN

Secretary: Terry Cator, 4 Yarrow Road, Dereham, Norfolk, NR20 3BH Tel: 01362
                694082(H) 01362 690460(W)

Fixtures Sec: David West Tel: 01362 693006 (H) 01362 692433 (B)

Ground: Aldiss Park, Norwich Road, Dereham, Norfolk NR20 3AL
                Tel/Fax: 01362 690460
Capacity: 3,000   Seats: 50   Cover: 500   Club Shop: (01362 690460)

HONOURS   Anglian Combination 97-98, Jewson Eastern Div 1 R-up 2001-02

PREVIOUS   **Leagues:** Dereham & Dist., East Anglian, Anglian Combination >98
                Names: Dereham, Dereham Hobbies
                Grounds: Recreation Ground 1890-1998

RECORD   **Defeat:** 0-13, v Gorleston, Norfolk Sen. Cup 9.1.1926

FACT FILE
Formed: 1890
Nickname: The Magpies
Colours: Black & white/black/white
Change colours: all Red
Midweek matchday; Tuesday
Programme - 20 pages 50p
Editor: Barnes Print
Tel: 01362 860781 Fax: 01362 860977
Website: www.derehamtownfc.com

CLUB PERSONNEL
Chairman: Tim Warner Tel: 01362 692419 (H)
Managers: Paul Jarvis & Steve Rushbrook

2001-02
Captain: Matthew Henman
P.o.Y.: Ollie Christie
Top Scorer: Graham Barrett 10

DISS TOWN

Secretary: Pam Lattimore, 7 Station Road, Pulham St. Mary, Diss, Norfolk, IP21 4QT.
01379 608905 Tel/Fax - 07711 470858M

Ground: Brewers Green Lane, Diss Tel: 01379 651223

Directions: Just off B1066 Diss-Thetford road, near Roydon School. 1 1/2 miles from Diss (BR)
Capacity: 2,500   **Seats:** 280   **Cover:** Yes   **Floodlights:** Yes
Club Shop: Yes, incl. pennants
Clubhouse: Open evenings (except Sunday), Sat/Sun lunchtimes, and matchdays
HONOURS   FA Vase 94-95; Eastern Co's Lg Div 1 91-92, Anglian Comb. 76-77 78-79(R-
                  up 74-75, Div 1 67-68 73-74, Lg Cup 67-68 79-80 81-82), Norfolk & Suffolk
                  Lg R-up 55-56 (Applegate Cup 56-57 57-58(joint)(R-up 55-56)), Norfolk Snr
                  Cup 74-75 95-96, Norfolk Jnr Cup 1891-92, Jewson Prem Lge R-up 95-96
                  R-up Millennium Trophy 2001

PREVIOUS   **Leagues:** Norwich & District; Norfolk & Suffolk 35-64; AnglianComb. 64-82
                  Ground: Roydon Road 1886-1982
BEST SEASON   **FA Vase:** Winners 94-95, QF 91-92
RECORDS   **Attendance:** 1,731 v Atherton LR, FA Vase SF 1st leg 19/3/94

Players progressing A Thurlow (Man City), M Cawston (Norwich), T Whymark(Ipswich),
                    C Stafford, P Gibbs (Colchester)

FACT FILE

Founded: 1888
Nickname: Tangerines
Sponsors: Apple Garages
Colours: Tangerine/navy/tangerine
Change colours: Sky blue/navy/navy
Midweek Matches: Tuesday
Reserve's League: Anglian Combination
Programme: 16 pages, 80p
Editor: Gary Enderby (01379 608767)

CLUB PERSONNEL

Chairman: Des Tebble
President: Roger Weeks
Treasurer: Tony Collins
Managers: Robert Fleck
Physio: Adrianna Brookman

ELY CITY

Secretary: Derek Oakey, 11 Frederick Talbot Close, Soham, Nr. Ely Cambs, CB7 5EY
Tel Nos: 01353 722141 (H)   01353 722179 (W)   **Email Address:** derk.oakey@tesco.net

Ground: Unwin Sports Ground, Downham Road (01353 662035)

Directions: A10 Ely by-pass turn off for Downham. 3 miles (approx) from Ely(BR)

Capacity: 1,500   **Seats:** 150   **Cover:** 350   **Floodlights:** Yes   **Shop:** No

Clubhouse: Open matchdays, refreshments available

Club Shop: Metal Badges: Yes
HONOURS   Cambs Snr Cup 47-48, Eastern Co's Lg R-up 69-70 (Lg Cup 79-80)
                   Jewson Eastern Div 1 Winners 1996-97,R-up 1999-00,Cup Winners 99-00

PREVIOUS   **Leagues:** Peterborough; Central Alliance 58-60
                   Grounds: Paradise Ground (1890 1986)

BEST SEASON   **FA Cup:** 1st Rd 56-56 (2-6 v Torquay)
RECORD   **Gate:** 260 v Soham, Eastern Co's Lg Div 1, 12/4/93
                   At old ground: 4,260 v Torquay, FA Cup 56-57

FACT FILE

Founded: 1885
Nickname: Robins
Colours: All red with white trim
Change colours: Jade/black/jade
Midweek Matches: Tuesday
Programme: 24 pages- 50p
Editor: Derek Oakley
Local Press: Ely Standard (01353 667831)
Club Website: elycityfc.com

CLUB PERSONNEL

Chairman: Brian Jordan
Manager: Steven Taylor

FAKENHAM TOWN

Secretary: Edric Linnell, 40 Warren Avenue, Fakenham, Norfolk NR21 8NP Tel: 01328 855445

Ground: Clipbush Lane, Fakenham NR21 8SW   Tel/Fax: 01328 856222

Directions: Corner of A148 & Clipbush Lane
Capacity: 3,000   **Seats:** 264   **Cover:** 500   **Floodlights:** Yes

Clubhouse: Bar, TV. Refreshments available Tel: 01328 855859
Club Shop: Yes
HONOURS   Norfolk Snr Cup 70-71 72-73 73-74 91-92 93-94 94-95;,98-99 Eastern Co's
Premier Division R-up: 98-99, Lg Div1, R-up 91-92; Anglian Comb. Cup 78-79
PREVIOUS   **Leagues:** N Norfolk 1884-1910; Norwich & Dist 10-35; Norfolk & Suffolk 35-
                 64; Anglian Comb 64-87
                 Grounds: Hempton Green 1884-89; Star Meadow 89-1907;
                 Barons Hall Lawn 1907-96

BEST SEASON **FA Vase:** 98-99 3rd Rd   **FA Cup:**
RECORD   **Gate:** 1100 v Watford-official opening of new ground

Players progressing Nolan Keeley (Scunthorpe)

FACT FILE

Founded: 1884
Nickname: Ghosts
Sponsors:Warner Paperbacks
Colours: Amber & black/black/amber
Change colours: Red & Black,red,red
Midweek Matchday: Tuesday
Reserves' League: Anglian Comb
Programme: 32 pages, 50p
Editor: John Cushion
Tel: 01328 862548
Local Press : Dereham & Fakenham Times

CLUB PERSONNEL

Chairman: Tony Fisher
President: G Middleditch
Press Officer: J Cushion
Commercial Manager: T.Vertigan
Managers: Neil Jarvis/Stuart Woodhouse

GORLESTON

Secretary: Arthur Ottley,60 Peterhouse Avenue,Gorleston, Great Yarmouth, Norfolk NR31 7PZ
Tel Nos: 01493 603353 (H) 01263 738335 (W) 07774 205949 (M)
Ground: Emerald Park, Woodfarm Lane, Gorleston, Great Yarmouth Tel: 01493 602802

Directions: On Magdalen Estate - follow signs to Crematorium, turn left and follow road to ground.
Five and a half miles from Great Yarmouth Vauxhall (BR)
Capacity: 5,000   Seats: 2000   Cover: 4,000   Floodlights: Yes
Clubhouse: Bar, colour TV, snacks. Matchday Tea, coffee,cold drinks, burgers,
hotdogs, rolls   **Club Shop:** No

HONOURS	Eastern Co's Lg 52-53 72-73 79-80 80-81; Lge Cup 55-56; Norfolk Snr Cup x 13, R-up x 25; Anglian Comb. 68-69, Norfolk & Suffolk Lg x 7; E Anglian Cup (3);Jewson Lge Div 1 95-96
PREVIOUS	**Leagues:** Gt Yarmouth & Dist; Norfolk & Suffolk; Anglian Comb
BEST SEASON	**FA Cup:** 1st Rd. 51-52, 57-58 **FA Vase:**
RECORD	**Attendance:** 4,473 v Orient, FA Cup 1st Rd 29/11/51

Players progressing: J Joblins (Norwich), M Bailey (Wolves), D Stringer(Norwich), R Carter (Aston Villa), D Carter (Man City), A Brown (Charlton), S Morgan (Cambridge), P Gibbs (Colchester)

FACT FILE

Founded: 1884
Nickname: Greens
Colours: Green & White/whitw/white
Change colours: All blue
Midweek Matchday: Tuesday
Programme: 56/60 pages £1.00
Editor:Simon Barnes Printing

CLUB PERSONNEL

Chairman & President: Jimmy Jones

Managers: Alan Smith

GREAT YARMOUTH TOWN

Secretary: Brian Smith, The Bungalow, Humberstone Farm, Cobholm, Great Yarmouth, Norfolk
NR31 0AZ. Tel & Fax: 01493 656099
Ground: Wellesey Recreation Ground, Wellesey Road (01493 843373)

Directions: Just off Marine Parade, 200yds north of Britannia Pier.1/2 m from Vauxhall BR(BR)
Capacity: 3,600   Seats: 500   Cover: 2,100   Floodlights: Yes   Club Shop: Yes

Clubhouse: (01493 843373). Committee Room, Sky TV, darts, pool. Hot & cold food

HONOURS	Eastern Co's Lg 68-69 (R-up 56-57 67-68 77-78 78-79), Lg Cup 37-38 74-75 80-81; East Anglian Cup(3); Norfolk Senior Cup x 12, R-up x 22; Norfolk Premier Cupx 2 jt; Norfolk & Suffolk Lg 13-14 26-27 27-28; Anglian Comb. Cup 65-66(res); E Anglian Lg 56-57(res)
PREVIOUS	**Leagues:** Norfolk & Suffolk
BEST SEASON	**FA Cup:** 2nd Rd 52-53, 1st Rd 47-48 **FA Vase:** Semi-Final 82-83
RECORD	**Attendance:** 8,944 v Crystal Palace, FA Cup 1st Rd 52-53
	Appearances: Mark Vincent 538 (1984-2001)
	Scorer: Gordon South 298 (1927-47) **Win:** 14-0, 2.2.10

Players progressing: R Hollis (Norwich), M Blyth & N Keeley (Scunthorpe), S Davy (West Ham),
K Ready (Aston Villa), G Butcher (Blackburn)

FACT FILE

Founded: 1897
Nickname: Bloaters
Colours: Amber & black stripes/black/black
Change colours: All blue
Midweek Matches: Tuesday
Programme: 40 pages, #1.00
Editor: Jon Gooding, 67 Ramsgate Drive,
Ipswich. IP3 9DD

CLUB PERSONNEL

Chairman: Arthur Fiske

Manager: Paul Tong

2001-02

Captain: Lee Humphreys
Top Scorer: Robert George 11
P.o.Y.: Alan Darby

HARWICH & PARKESTON

Secretary:	Andy Schooler, 21 The Vineway, Harwich, Essex CO12 4AX 01255 504590 (H) 01255 509700 (B) 01255 509718 (Bus. Fax)
Ground:	Royal Oak, Main Road, Dovercourt, Harwich CO12 4AA Tel: 01255 503649
Directions:	On main road into Dovercourt. 600 yds from Dovercourt (BR) FLoodlights: Yes Capacity: 5,000 Seats: 350 Cover: 1,000
Clubhouse :	Open every day. Dances, bingo, darts, pool, function room Club Shop: No
HONOURS	FA Amateur Cup R-up 1898-99 52-53; Eastern Counties Lg 35-36 (jnt) (Lg Cup 35-36 36-37 96-97); Essex County Lg 37-38; Athenian Lg Div 1 R-up 65-66 (Div 2 64-65, Lg Cup 64-65); Essex Sen. Cup 1898-99 36-37; Essex Sen. Trophy 89-90; AFA Senior Cup 35-36 36-37; Worthington Evans Cup 80-81
PREVIOUS	**Leagues:** Eastern Co's 35-37 38-64; Essex County 37-38; Athenian 64-73 83-84; Isthmian 73-83 **Ground:** Phoenix Field, Seafront
BEST SEASON	**FA Vase:** Q-F 90-91 **FA Cup:** FA Amateur Cup: R-up 1898-99, 52-53
RECORD	**Attendance:** 5,649 v Romford, FA Amat Cup 4th Rd 1938

Players progressing: I Gillespie (C Palace), G Waites, K Sanderson, I Brown(Bristol City 91)

FACT FILE

Founded: 1875
Nickname: Shrimpers
Colours: White & black/black/black
Change colours: All Red
Midweek Matches: Tuesday
Reserve Lge: Essex & Suffolk Border Lge
Prem. Div
Programme: 28 pages, 50p
Editor: Carl Allen
01255 552510
Website: mysite.freeserve.com/the shrimpers

CLUB PERSONNEL

Chairman:Tony Armstrong
President:Terry Rowlands
Press Officer: Carl Allan
Managers:Nigel Box & Adrian Gray

Dereham Town.
Back Row (l-r):
Matthew
Henman,
Matthew
Gorham,
Bob Stevens,
John Fox,
Billy Handel,
Chris Pert.
Front Row:
Graham Barrett,
Mark Adams,
Neil Maguire,
Stuart King,
Martin Pert.
Photo:
Arthur Evans

Maldon Town, 4-2 winners away to Buckingham Town in a Preliminary Round FA Cup tie replay. Back Row (l-r): Colin Wallington (Manager), Craig Hutley, Terry Warwick, Paul Yun An, Jon Cardy, James Keeble, Laurie Sturrock, Ian Hutley (Goalkeeping Coach). Front Row: Danny Brookes, Scott Witney, Adrian Harris, Craig Newman, Paul Delaney, Mark Emerson, Rob Walker. Photo: Arthur Evans

Great Yarmouth Town receiving a cheque for Good Behaviour Award. Back Row (l-r): Kevin Antcliffe (Jewson League), Paul Tong (Manager), Josh Barzey, Michael Merrick, Nick Banham, Mark Vincent, Jody Harrison, Paul Symonds, Chad Pillar, Danny Brown, Richard Daniels, Arthur Fisk (Chairman), Terry Reeves (Physio). Front Row: Derek Bevan (Coach), Darren Lamb, Scott McKinney, Robert George, Lee Humphreys, Lee Henwood, Lee Brown

HISTON RESERVES

FACT FILE

Secretary:	Mick W Collis, 22 Haddows Close, Longstanton, Cambridge CB4 5DJ Tel: 01954 201083 (H)
Ground	Bridge Rd, Impington, Cambridge Tel: 01223 232301 Fax: 01223 237373 **Club Website:** Website: www.histonfootballclub.tripod.com **EMAIL Address:** gareth@corporate innovations.co.uk
Directions:	Leave A14 northern Cambridge bypass on B1049 (signposted Histon and Cottenham). Ground half a mile on right. 5 miles from Cambridge (BR). Bus No.104
Capacity: 3,250	Seats: 250 Cover: 250 Floodlights: Yes
Clubhouse:	Bar/lounge open Tues-Sun eves, Sun lunch and matchdays.Snacks available
HONOURS	Eastern Co's Lg Div 1 R-up 01-02, Div.1 Lge Cup R-up 01-02.

Founded: 1904
Colours: Red & black stripes/black/red & black
Change colours: Sky & navy/navy/sky & navy
Midweek matches: Wednesday

CLUB PERSONNEL

Chairman: Gareth Baldwin
President: G P Muncey
Manager: Nacer Relizani

IPSWICH WANDERERS

FACT FILE

Secretary:	Martin Head, 246 Sidelate Lane, Ipswich, Suffolk. IP4 3DH Tel: 01473 414390 Email address: headmartin@hotmail,com
Ground:	Humberdoucey Lane, Ipswich, Suffolk Tel: 01473 728581
Directions:	Take Woodbridge Road out of Ipswich,then left fork into Playford Road.Take first left into Humberdoucy Lane Ground 300yds on right
	Capacity: 2,000 Seats: 50 Cover: Yes Floodlights: Yes
Clubhouse:	Bar,Tea, coffee, cold drinks, confectionary, burgers, hotdogs,sandwiches, rolls
HONOURS	Eastern Lge Div 1 97-98
BEST SEASON	**FA Cup:** 2nd Q Rd 2000-01 **FA Vase:** 2nd Q Rd 2000-01
PREVIOUS	**Leagues:** Little David SundayNames: Loadwell Ipswich
RECORD	**Attendance:** 335 v Woodbridge, ECL Div 1 4/4/94

Founded: 1983
Nickname: Wanderers
Sponsors: N.T.L.
Colours: All Blue
Change colours: Red & black/black/red & black
Midweek Matches: Tuesday
Programme: Yes
Editor: Alan Haste (01473 711877)
Local Press: East Anglian Daily Times,
Evening Star

CLUB PERSONNEL

Chairman: A.Haste
President: P.Emmerson
Manager: Alan Dilloway

LOWESTOFT TOWN

FACT FILE
Founded: 1885
Nickname: Blues
Sponsors: CWA Group
Colours: Royal Blue/white/blue
Change colours: All red
Midweek Matches: Tuesday
Reserves' Lge: Anglian Combination
Programme:44 pages £1.00
Editor: Shaun Cole
Website: www.lowestofttownfc.co.uk

CLUB PERSONNEL
Chairman: Shaun Cole
President: Roy Harper
Manager: Michael Chapman

2001-02
Captain: Ian Smith
Top Scorer: Gary McGee 35

Secretary:	Terry Lynes, 31 Avondale Road Lowestoft, Suffolk NR32 2HU
	Tel: 01502 564034 (H) 07930 872947(M) Email: terry@ltfcblues.freeserve.co.uk
Ground:	Crown Meadow, Love Rd, Lowestoft Tel: 01502 573818
Directions:	Just off A12, 10 mins from Lowestoft (BR)
Capacity: 3,000	Seats: 466 Cover: 500 Floodlights: Yes
Clubhouse:	Pub hours, Snacks available **Club Shop:** Yes (incl metal badges)

HONOURS Eastern Co's Lg(8) 35-36(jnt) 37-38 62-63 64-65 67-68 69-71 77-78, Lg Cup(8) 38-39 54-55 65-67 68-69 75-76 83-84; 00-01Norf. & Suffolk Lg(8) 1897-99 1900-04 28-29 30-31; Suffolk Prem. Cup(7) 66-67 71-72 74-75 78-80; 99-00,00-01Suffolk Snr Cup(10) 02-   03 22-24 25-26 31-32 35-36 46-49 55-56; E Anglian Cup(10); Anglian Comb. (Res.) 77-78 79-80 (Lg Cup 76-77); E Anglian Lg (Res.) 57-58 63-64

PREVIOUS	**League:** Norfolk & Suffolk 1897-1935
BEST SEASON	**FA Cup:** 1st Rd 26-27 38-39 66-67, 67-68, 77-78
RECORDS	**Attendance:** 5,000 v Watford, FA Cup 1st Rd 67
	Goalscorer: M Tooley 383 **Appearances:** C Peck 629
	Win: 19-0 v Thetford Town (H), Eastern Counties League

Players progressing: Eddie Spearitt (Ipswich 1965), Nigel Cassidy (Norwich1967), Richard Money (Scunthorpe 1973), Graham Franklin (Southend 1977)

Felixstowe & Walton United

Soham Town Rangers lost 3-4 away to Burnham in the FA Cup First Qualifying Round. Back Row (l-r): Neal Docking, Mark Atkins, Dave Thompson, Ian Magnus, Andrew Metcalfe, Jason Hohonis, Michael Simpson. Front Row: Mark Kingston, Aaron Rutter, Adi Bullett, Kori Davis, Andy Coleman. Photo: Arthur Evans

Cornard United celebrate with the Harwich Senior Charity Cup after defeating Clacton Town 2-1 by a Golden Goal from Robert Ford.

MALDON TOWN

FACT FILE

Secretary: Phil Robinson, 9 Lyndhurst Drive, Bicknacre, Essex CN3 4XL
Tel No: 01245 222633 (H) & 01206 753498 (W)
Email Address: angelina1@btinternet.com

Founded: 1946 Nickname: 'The Town'

Colours: Blue & white hoops/blue/blue

Ground: Wallace Binder Ground, Park Drive, Maldon CM9 5XX (01621 853762)

Change colours: Red & black
hoops/black/black

Capacity: 2,500   Seats: 250   Cover: 500   Floodlights: Yes

Midweek Matchday: Tuesday

Programme:24 pages £1.00

HONOURS   Essex Snr Lg 84-85 (Sportsmanship Award 87-88,88-89,94-95, Res
Shield 93-94), Res Cup:94-95, Essex & Suffolk Border Lg 55-56 (Cup 64-65),Essex
Intermediate Cup 51-52, Tolleshunt D'Arcy Cup 93-94,99-00

Editor: Alan Drewer

Club Website: http://www.maldontownfc.co.uk

PREVIOUS   **Leagues:** Mid Essex, N. Essex, Essex & Suffolk Border, Essex Senior
Ground: Fambridge Road (pre-1994)

CLUB PERSONNEL

BEST SEASON   **FA Cup:** 2000-01   **FA Vase:** 2000-01

Chairman: Bob Large

Manager: Colin Wallington

RECORDS   **Attendance:** 33 v Millwall July 2000

MILDENHALL TOWN

FACT FILE

Secretary: Karen Goodwin, 33 Kelsey Creacent,Cherry Hinton, Cambridge,
Cambs.CB1 9XT Tel Nos: 01223 515330 (H) 0786 781 0944 (M)

Founded: 1890
Nickname: The Hall
Colours: Amber/black/black

Ground: Recreation Way, Mildenhall, Suffolk (01638 713449)

Change colours:White/sky blue/white
Midweek Matchday: Tuesday

Directions: Next to swimming pool/carpark, quarter of a mile from town centre

Programme: £1.00
Editor: Frank Marshall (01638 720616)
Local Press : Bury Free Press,

Capacity: 2,000   Seats: 50

Newmarket Journal,
Cambridge Evening News,East Anglian Daily

Clubhouse: Open matchdays & functions. Light refreshments available

Times,Green 'Un

HONOURS   Suffolk Junior Cup 1899-1900

CLUB PERSONNEL
Chairman: Brian Brigden

PREVIOUS   **Leagues:** Bury & District; Cambs Lg 2B, 1B & Premier

Vice Chairman: frank Marshall
Fixture Secretary: Colin Marchant

RECORD   **Attendance:** 350 v Norwich City, friendly 22/7/89

Tel: 01842 812123
Managers: Steve O'Donoghue

NEWMARKET TOWN

Fixture Secretary: Elaine Jeakins, 140 New Cheveley Road,Newmarket CB88BY
Tel Nos: 01638 602525 (H) 01638 750201 (W) 07801 815682 (M)

FACT FILE

Ground: Cricketfield Road, off New Cheveley Road, Newmarket (01638 663637)

Founded: 1877

Directions: 400 yds Newmarket (BR) - turn right into Green Rd, right at cross roads New
Cheveley Rd, ground at top on left

Nickname: Jockeys
Colours: Yellow & navy/navy/yellow

Capacity: 1,750   Seats: 144   Cover: 150   Floodlights: Yes

Change Colours: All Red

Clubhouse: Matchdays only. Refreshments available

Midweek Matches: Tuesday
Programme:£1.00

HONOURS   Suffolk Snr Cup 34-35 93-94; Cambs Invitation Cup 58-59; Cambs Chall.
Cup 21-22 26-27; Cambs Snr Lg, 19-20; Ipswich Snr Lg 30-31 31-32 32-33
33-34; Peterborough Lg 57-58; Suffolk Premier Cup 93-94 94-95 96-97

Editor: Tony Pringle (01638 669438)

CLUB PERSONNEL
Chairman: Alan Collen

PREVIOUS   **League:** Bury Snr; Ipswich Snr; Essex & Suffolk Border; Utd Co's 34-37;
Eastern Co's 37-52

President: M J Nicholas
Manager: Chris Nunn

BEST SEASON   **FA Cup:** 4th Qual. Rd 92-93, 0-2 v Hayes (H)
FA Vase: 4th Round 91-92

2000-01
Captain Darren Coe

RECORD   **Attendance:** 2,701 v Abbey Utd (now Cambridge Utd),
FA Cup 1st Qual.Rd 1/10/49

P.O.Y.: Andy Oxborough
Top Scorer: Paul Shaw 19

Players progressing: Mick Lambert (Ipswich), M Wright (Northampton), G Tweed(Coventry), R
Fuller (Charlton), Colin Vowden (Camb.Utd.)

NORWICH UNITED

Secretary: Keith Cutmore,42 Desmond Drive,Old Catton, Norwich NR6 7JN
Tel. No.: 01603 407148 (H) 07946033588 (M)

Ground: Plantation Road, Blofield, Norwich, Norfolk NR13 4PL
Tel: 01603 716963
Website:www.norwichunited.fsnet.co.uk

Directions: Half a mile from Blofield village - coming from Norwich on Yarmouth Rd turn
left in Blofield at Kings Head pub & follow to Plantation Rd (grd on right after
bridge over bypass). 1/2 hour Brundall BR (Norwich-Yarmouth line)
Capacity: 3,000 **Seats:** 100 **Cover:** 1,000 **Floodlights:** Yes
Clubhouse: Matchday food & drink: Tea, coffee, cold drinks, hotdogs, burgers, soup, sandwiches, rolls
Club Shop: Yes incl. metal badges & pennants

HONOURS Eastern Co's Lg Div 1 90-91 01-02, R-up 89-89, Lg Cup 91-92,
Anglian Combination 88-89. Jewson League Div 1 2001-02
PREVIOUS **Ground:** Gothic Club, Heartsease Lane, Norwich (until end of 90-91)
RECORD **Attendance:** 401 v Wroxham, League match, 2/10/91
Goalscorer: M Money **Appearances:** Tim Sayer

FACT FILE
Founded: 1903
Nickname: Planters
Colours: Yellow/blue/blue
Change colours: All red.
Midweek Matches: Tuesday
Programme: 24 pages, 50p
Editor:Barnes Print
Local Press : Eastern Counties Newspapers

CLUB PERSONNEL
Chairman: John Hilditch, Pres Michael Miles
Vice-Chairman: Peter Bowyer
Managers: Paul Franklin & Donny Pye
Physio: Martyn Parker

2001-02
Captain :Brian Payne
P.o.Y.: Greg Murphy
Top Scorer:Jamie Hunton

SOHAM TOWN RANGERS

Secretary: Peter Luck, Flat 5 17-21 Churchgate Street,Soham,Ely,Cambs. CB7 5DS
Tel No: 01353 727765 (H) 0775 951 3898

Ground: Julius Martin Lane, Soham, Ely , Cambs.CB7 5DE Tel: 01353 720732

Directions: A142 between Newmarket and Ely, at roundabout at northern end of by-pass
turn left towards town centre and then right at the corner shop into Julius
Martina Lane. Ground is on left
Capacity: 2,000 **Seats:** 250 **Cover:** 1,000 **Floodlights:** Yes **Shop:** Yes

Clubhouse: Function Room, Lounge Bar, Stud Bar, Public Bar.Available for private hire
Clubhouse Manager: M.Howe **Club Shop:** Yes
HONOURS Eastern Co's Lg Div 1 R-up 92-93; Peterborough & District League (3),
Milleniuim Cup 2000-01, Cambs Invitation Cup 1990-91, 97-98, 98-99
PREVIOUS **Leagues:** Peterborough & Dist
Ground: Soham Rangers: Brook Street 1919-47
Names: Soham Town and Soham Rangers merged in 1947
RECORD **Attendance:** 3,000 v Pegasus, FA Amateur Cup 1963
BEST SEASONS **F.A.Cup:** 3rd Q v Kings Lynn (A) 70-71
F.A.Vase: 4th Round v Aldershot Town (A) 93-94

FACT FILE
Founded: 1947
Nickname: Town or Rangers
Main Sponsor: C.J.Murfitt
Colours: Green & white/ black/green
Change colours: Blue/black/ black
Midweek Matchday: Tuesday
Reserves ' League: Cambs Senior. A
Programme: £1.00 Editor : 01473 420731
Local Press : Ely Standard, Newmarket
Journal, Cambridge Evening News

CLUB PERSONNEL
Chairman: C.J.Murfitt Pres: Vinnie Jones
Manager R Goodjohn Coach: K. Murray
Physio: M. Drury

2001-02
Leading goalscorer: Neal Docking 36
Captain: Kori Davis
P.o.Y.: N.Docking & P Hinde

STOWMARKET TOWN

Secretary: Mrs Bev Mead, 1Hollytree Cottage, Mendlesham Road,Cotton,Stowmarket
IP14 4NV (Tel No: 01449 612533)
Ground: Green Meadows Stadium, Bury Road, Stowmarket
Tel: 01449 612533
Directions: About 800 yds from Stowmarket BR station - turn right at 1st lights and head
out of town over r'bout into Bury Road - ground on right
Capacity: 2,000 Seats: 200 Cover: 450 Floodlights: Yes
Clubhouse: Bar open 6.30pm onwards Mon-Fri, weekends 12.0pm onwards.
Matchday food available Club Shop: Yes, incl. metal badges.
HONOURS Eastern Co's Lg R-up 91-92, Suffolk Premier Cup(4), Suffolk Snr Cup(10)
Suffolk Jnr Cup., Churchman Cup: 99-00.
PREVIOUS **Leagues:** Ipswich & Dist.; Essex & Suffolk Border 25-52
Grounds: The Cricket Meadow, 1883-1984
Names: Stowupland Corinthians; Stowmarket Corinthians; Stowmarket FC
BEST SEASON **FA Cup:** 2nd Q Rd 1992 **FA Vase:** 4th Rd 1983-84
RECORD **Attendance:** 1,200 v Ipswich Town, friendly July 1994
At Cricket Meadow: 3,800 v Romford, FA Amtr Cup 1st Rd 15/12/51

Players progressing: Craig Oldfield (Colchester), Les Tibbott, Ted Phillips & Brian Klug (Ipswich)

FACT FILE
Founded: 1883
Nickname: Stow
Colours: Gold & black/black/black
Change colours: All Red
Midweek Matches: Wednesday
Reserves' Lge: Essex & Suffolk Border
Programme: 20 pages,60p
Ed: Jonathon Gooding (01473 420731)
Local Press: East Anglian, Bury Free Press

CLUB PERSONNEL
Chairman: Derek Barnard
President: John Bultitude
Fixture Sec: Christine Gillingham
Tel: 01449 674507(H) 07880 732416(M)
Manager: Mel Aldis
Coach: Mark Barnard
Physio: John Chandler

Dereham Town's Oliver Christie (right) challenges Sidley United's Owen Ball in the FA Vase. Photo: Roger Turner

Ross Standen, Lewes goalkeeper, takes a tumble in a crowded goalmouth during their FA Vase Sixth Round tie with AFC Sudbury. Photo: Roger Turner

Tiptree United, prior to their 2-1 victory over Burgess Hill in the FA Vase Quarter Finals. Back Row (l-r): Chris Powell, Wayne Houghton, Andy Brady, Steve Parnell, Dave Snelling, Adam Gillespie, Dave Mackrory, Steve Daly, Alex Snow, Jason Haygreen, Phil Battell, Alan Bailey (Asst Mngr). Front Row: Ian Fish, Kevin Ford, Steve Wareham, Matthew Farlie (Mascot), Dave Barefield, Dave Lodge, Russell Jackson. Photo: Arthur Evans

AFC SUDBURY

FACT FILE

Founded: 1st June,1999
Colours: Yellow/blue/yellow
Change Colours: All Red
Midweek Matchday: Tuesday
Programme: 48 + pages £1
Editor:Peter Scott (01787 379123)
Local Press : Suffolk Free Press,
East Anglian Daily Times

Ground: Kingsmarsh Stadium, Brundon Lane, Sudbury, Suffolk CO10 1WQ (01787 376213)
Directions: From Sudbury centre follow Halstead/Chelmsford signs for about 1mile. 1st right
after railway bridge at foot of steep hill, and 1st right after sharp left hand bend
Capacity: 2,500 **Seats:** 200 **Cover:** 150 **Floodlights:** Yes
Clubhouse: Matchdays/ training nights **Shop:** Yes Contact: Darren Witt (M) 0402 159375)

HONOURS WANDERERS - Eastern Co's Lg Div 1 92-93, Ess. & Suff. Border Lg(2) 89-91
(R-up 88-89), Suffolk Snr Cup 90-91**TOWN:**Southern Lge -Lge Cup 93-94, R-up 97,Championship
93-94, Southern Div (Post War)R-up 93-94; Eastern Counties Lg x 7, R-up x 6, Lg Cup x 6, Suffolk
Prem.Cup x 13, R-up x 8, Suffolk Sen. Cup(2); E. Anglian Cup 85-86 91-92, R-up 83-84 95-96;
Essex Suff Border Lg x 5; E.S.B.L.Cup 49-50, R-up 46-47; East F'lit Group -94 & 95
A.F.C.: Eastern League Champiuons 2001-02 Suffolk County Premier Cup Winners 2001-02

PREVIOUS Names: Sudbury Town (1885) & Sudbury Wanderers (1958) merged 1999
Leagues: Wanderers- Essex & Suffolk Border. Town Suffolk & Ipswich;
Essex & Suffolk Border; Eastern Co 55-90; Southern Int-97 Eastern Co. 98-99
BEST SEASON FA Vase: Semi-Final v Tiptree United . Lost 0-2,0-0 2201-02
(as A.F.C.) **FA Cup:** 1st Round Proper, 00-01 (1-6 v Darlington)
TOWN **FA Vase:** Runners-up 88-89 **FA Trophy:** 3rd Rd.Proper 95-96
FA Cup: 2nd Rd Proper 96-97, 1-3 v Brentford. Played at Colchester Utd. F.C.

CLUB PERSONNEL

Joint Chairman: Nick F Smith & Phil Turner

Secretary: David Webb
6 Melford Road, Sudbury, Suffolk CO10 1LS
Tel: 01787 372352 (H) 01787 886000 x6223 (B)

Manager: Keith Martin

TIPTREE UNITED

FACT FILE

Founded: 1933
Nickname:The Jam -Makers
Sponsors: Tiptree Building Supplies
Colours: Red& blackstripes/black/black
Change colours: Yellow/blue/white
Midweek Matchday: Tuesday
Reserves: Essex & Suffolk Border Lg Div 1
Programme: 32 pages, 50p Editor: Secretary
Local Press : Colchester Evening Gazette,
Essex County Standard'
* Voted Eastern' Programme of the Year'
Website: www.tiptreeunited.com

Secretary: John Wisbey, 103 Peace Road, Stanway, Colchester, Essex
Tel Nos: 01206 564222 (H) 0403 585814 (M)
Email: john.wisbey@talk21.com
Ground: Chapel Road, Tiptree, Essex Tel: 01621 815213
Directions: Enter town on B1023 - Chapel Road is left at second crossroads,
ground 200yds on left. 3 miles from Kelverdon (BR).
Served by Eastern NationalColchester to Maldon bus

Capacity: 2,500 **Seats:** 150 **Cover:** 300 **Floodlights:** Yes

Clubhouse: Open daily 7-11pm (all day Fri & Sat) & 12-2.30, 7-10.30 Sun.
Large bar, two snooker tables, pool, darts, netball, badminton, pigeon club,
bingo. Dance hall seats 180, small hall seats 60. **Club Shop:** No

HONOURS Essex Snr Tphy 80-81, Eastern Co's Lg 81-82 (Lg Cup 81-82 84-85),
Essex Snr Lg R-up 75-76 77-78, Harwich Charity Cup (4),
Jewson Eastern Div 1 Champions 99-00

PREVIOUS Leagues: Essex & Suffolk Border; Essex Snr 78-84

RECORD Attendance: 1,210 v Spurs, floodlight inauguration Dec 1990

CLUB PERSONNEL

Chairman: T.B.A.
President: Peter Fidge
Manager: Neil Farley

WISBECH TOWN

FACT FILE
Founded: 1920 Nickname: Fenmen
Newsline: 09066 555865
Colours: All Red
Change colours: Yellow/Green/Yellow
Midweek Matchday: Tuesday
Programme: Pages: 44 Price: £1
Editor: Gordon Smith Tel: 01945 581767

Secretary: Mrs Dorothy Hill, 19 Mansell Road, Wisbech ,Cambs. PE13 2SP Tel: 01945 581767

Ground: Fenland Park, Lerowe Road, Wisbech, Cambs Tel: 01945 584176
Directions: Follow A47 bypass to the West Walton turn off roundabout where there is a Little
Chef, turn left for Wisbech, Lerowe Road is first left after 30mph sign. Entering town from north
along A1101 cross Freedom Bridge, atroundabout go straight over sign Walsoken/West Walton
Capacity: 3,800 **Seats:** 284 **Cover:** 1,000 **Floodlights:** Yes
Clubhouse: Open every evening. Matchday food & drink - Tea, coffee, cold drinks, confectionary,
burgers, hotdogs, soup, sandwiches, rolls Club Shop (open matchdays): Contact Secretary

PREVIOUS Leagues: Peterborough 1920-35; Utd Co's 35-50; Eastern Co's 50-52 70-97;
Midland 52-58; Southern 58-70, 97-02
CLUB RECORDS Attendance: 8,004 v Peterborough United, Midland League 25/8/57
Goalscorer: Bert Titmarsh 246 (31-37) **Appearances:** Jamie Brighty (731)
BEST SEASON FA Cup: 2nd Rd 57-58, 97-98 League clubs defeated: Colchester
FA Trophy: 3rd Qual Rd. 97-98 **FA Vase:** Semi-Finals 84-85, 85-86

HONOURS Southern Lg Div 1 61-62; Utd Co's Lg (3) 46--47-48 49-50+ 61-62 (res) (R-up
48-49, Lg Cup 35-36 (R-up 46-47); Midland Lg R-up 57-58; Eastern Co's Lg 71-72 76-77 90-91,
R-up 70-71 73-74 83-84 92-93 96-97, Lg Cup x4, R-up x3; Cambs Invit Cup x8; E Anglian Cup 87-
88 (R-up 40-41 48-49); Peterborough Lg x5; Peterborough Snr Cup 32-33 76-77 89-90 97-98

CLUB PERSONNEL
Chairman: Barry Carter
Vice Chairman: George Campion
President: J W A Chilvers
Press Off.: Colin Garwood (01945 588435)
Manager: Ian Benjamin
Assistant Manager: Roy McManus
Res. Manager: Jackie Gallagher
Assistant Gary Shailes
2001-02
Captain& P.o.Y.: Ian Pledger
P.o.Y.: Duncan Roberts
Top scorer: Andy Furnell 12

WOODBRIDGE TOWN

Secretary: Eric Smy,10 Peterhouse Crescent,Woodbridge, Suffolk IP12 4HT
Tel No: 01394 384213

Ground: Notcutts Park, Seckford Hall Road, Woodbridge, Suffolk IP12 4DA Tel: 01394 385308

Directions: Turning into Woodbridge off last rounda'bout from Lowestoft, or first roundabout from Ipswich. Take first turning left and first left again. Drive to ground at end of road on left.

Capacity: 3,000   **Seats:** 50   **Cover:** 200   **Floodlights:** Yes
Clubhouse: Visitors bar, lounge bar, function hall.Matchday Tea, coffee, cold drinks, hotdogs,
soup, burgers, sandwiches, rolls.
HONOURS   Suffolk Sen Cup(4), Jun Cup (4); Eastern Co Lg Cup 93-94 97-98, Lge Div 1
R-up 93-94; Ipswich Sen Lge (2)

PREVIOUS   **Leagues:** Suffolk & Ipswich Ground: Kingston PF
BEST SEASON   **FA Cup:** 3rd Rd Q 97-98 & 00-01   **FA Vase:** 6th Round 98-99

RECORD   **Attendance:** 3,000 v Arsenal, floodlight opener 2/10/90

FACT FILE
Founded: 1885
Nickname: The Woodpeckers
Sponsors: John Grose
Colours: Black & white stripes/black/black
Change colours: All blue
Midweek Matchday: Tuesday
Reserves League: Essex & Suffolk Border
Programme: 20-24 pages ,50p
Editor: D Crowley
Local Press : East Anglian Daily Times
CLUB PERSONNEL
Chairman: Keith Dixon
President:Andrew Dalby
Football Sec: David Crowley (01394 384853)
Commercial Manager: Richard Snelham
Manager: David Hubbick
2001-02
Captain: Carl David
Top Scorer:Andy Coote 21
Ps.o.Y.: Ian Williams & Mark Bailey

WROXHAM

Secretary : Chris Green, 24 Keys Drive, Wroxham, Norfolk NR12 8S Tel: 01603 783936 (H)
079412385 (M) Email Address: secretary@wroxhamfc.com
Ground: Trafford Park, Skinners Lane, Wroxham, Norfolk Tel: 01603 783538
Directions: Arriving from Norwich turn left at former Castle PH and keep left to ground. One and a half miles from Wroxham + Hoveton (BR). Buses 722, 724 and717
Capacity: 2,500   Seats: 50   Cover: 250   Floodlights: Yes
Clubhouse: Bar, pool, darts etc. Drinks, hot & cold food   Club Shop: No

HONOURS Eastern Co's Lg 91-92 92-93 93-94 96-97 97-98, 98-99, R-up 94-95,99-00,01-02
Lg.Cup 92-93,99-00R-up 90-91), Div 1 88-89; Norfolk Snr Cup 92-93 96-97 97-98;99-00,01-2
Anglian Comb(6) (LgCup(7); Reserves did the double in 94-95.Jewson Res K.O. Cup 00-01
PREVIOUS   **Leagues:** Norwich City; East Anglian; Norwich & Dist.; Anglian Comb. 64-88
Grounds: Norwich Road; The Avenue; Keys Hill (all pre-1947)
BEST SEASON   **FA Vase:** Quarter Final v Durham City 2001-02
RECORDS   **Attendance:** 1,011 v Wisbech Town, E. Counties Lge Prem. Div. 16/3/93
Goalscorer: Matthew Metcalf. Appearances: Stu Larter
Win: 15-2 v Thetford Town (H), E. Counties Lge Prem. Div. 17/1/92
Defeat: 1-24 v Blofield (A), Norwich & District League, early 1960s
Players progressing: Matthew Metcalf (Brentford) 93, Paul Warne (Wigan Athletic) 97

FACT FILE
Founded: 1892
Nickname: Yachtsmen
Colours: All Blue
Change colours: All Red
Midweek Matchday: Tuesday
Reserves ' League: Anglian Comb Prem Div
Programme: 20 pages
Editor: Matt Carpenter
Local Press : North Norfolk
Eastern Football (Norwich 628311)
Web-site:www.wroxhamfc.com

CLUB PERSONNEL
Chairman: Ray Bayles President: L King
Press Officer: Secretary
Joint Managers: Peter Smith & Marty Hubble
Physio: P.Terrington

2001-02
P.o.Y. : Shaun Howes
Top Scorer: Russell Stock

BRIGHTLINGSEA UNITED

Secretary: Michael Cole, The Sun, New Street, Brightlingsea, Essex, CO7 0DJ.
Tel Nos: 01206 302179H   07966 388458W
Ground: North Road, Brightlingsea, Essex (01206 304199)
Directions: B1027 Colchester - Clacton, B1029 from Thorrington Cross - follow Church Road into town, left into Spring Road, left into Church Road. Nearest station - Colchester - then bus 78 to Brightlingsea
Capacity: 2,000   Seats: 50   Cover: 250   Floodlights: Yes   Club Shop: Yes
Clubhouse: Open matchadays & every evening, except Sunday. Matchday tea, coffee and snacks
HONOURS   Essex Snr Lg 88-89 89-90 (Harry Fisher Mem. Tphy 89-90 (R-up 88-89), Lg Cup R-up 78-79), Eastern Co's Lg Div 1 R-up 90-91, Essex & Suffolk Border Lg Prem. Div Cup 71-72, Harwich Charity Cup 87-88, Worthington Evans Cup 76-77 77-78 78-79
PREVIOUS   Leagues: Tendring Hundred, Essex & Suffolk Border, Essex Senior 1972-90
RECORD   Gate: 1,200 v Colchester, friendly 68-69

FACT FILE
Founded: 1887   Nickname: Oystermen
Colours: Red & white,red,red
Change colours: Yellow & Navy, navy,navy
Midweek Matches: Tuesday
Programme: 24 pages, 30p
Editor: Kim Lay (01206 305797)
Local Press: Essex County Standard,
Evening Gazette

CLUB PERSONNEL
Chairman: Michael Cole
Manager: Ken Ballard

CAMBRIDGE CITY RESERVES

Secretary: Stuart Hamilton, 55 Crowhill, Godmanchester, Huntingdon, Cambs
             Tel: 01480 382675

Ground: City Ground, Milton Road, Cambridge CB4 1UY Tel: 01223 357973
Directions: 50 yards on left from start of A1309, Cambridge to Ely Rd.
             30 minswalk from Cambridge BR
             Capacity: 5,000   Cover: 1,400   Seats:423   Floodlights: Yes

Clubhouse: 11am-11pm Mon-Sat, 12-3 & 7pm-10.30 Sun. Bingo, Dances, Pool, Darts

Club Shop: Sells programmes, club history, badges, scarves, pennants, replica shirts etc.
             Contact Neil Harvey (01223 235991)

FACT FILE
Colours: White & black halves/black/white &
black hoops
Change colours: Green & Yellow
halves,green,green& yellow hoops
Midweek matchday: Monday
Programme Editor: Secretary

CLUB PERSONNEL
Chairman: Dennis Rolph
Fixtures Sec.: Andy Dewey
50 Doggett Rd., Cherry Hinton, Cambridge
01223 245694 (H) 01223 555410 (Bus. Fax)
Manager:Jeremy George
Tel; 01954 782484

CORNARD UNITED

Secretary: Chris Symes, 22 Greenacres, Mile End, Colchester, Essex CO4 (01206 851627)
Ground: Blackhouse Lane Sportsfield, Great Cornard, Suffolk (01787 376719)
Directions: Left off r'bout on A134 coming from Ipswich/Colchester intoSudbury, follow signs for Country Park - ground is immediately opposite along Blackhouse Lane
Capacity: 2,000   Seats: 250   Cover: 500   Floodlights: Yes   Club Shop: No
Clubhouse: Open matchdays & Sunday lunchtimes. Matchday Tea, coffee, colddrinks, & snacks
HONOURS   Eastern Co's Lg Div 1 89-90 (Lg Cup R-up 92-93), Essex & Suffolk BorderLg 88-89 (Lg Cup 88-89), Suffolk Snr Cup 89-90, Suffolk Jnr Cup R-up 84-85, Harwich Senior Charity Cup 2001-02, Eastern Floodlight League Cup 2001-02
PREVIOUS   Leagues: Sudbury S/day 64-65; Bury St Edmunds & Dist 65-72; Colchester71-78; Essex Suffolk Bord 78-89. Grounds: Cornard Rec 64-71; Great CornardUpper School 71-85
RECORDS: Appearances: Keith Featherstone **Goalscorer :** Andy Smiles
Attendance: 400 v Colchester Utd 1997 **Win:** 18-2 v St Peters House, Colchester Lge 14/9/72
Defeat: 4-10 v Finningham, Bury Lge 7/2/68

FACT FILE
Founded: 1964   Nickname: Ards
Sponsors: Pizza Town
Colours: Blue & white/white/blue
Change colours: Yellow
Midweek Matches: Tuesday
Reserve League: Essex & Suffolk Border
Prog:16 pages Ed:Neil Cheese(01787311368)
Local Press : Suffolk Free Press,
East Anglian Daily Times
CLUB PERSONNEL
Chairman: Chris Symes Vice-Chair: Mike
FordManager: Chris Symes
Assistant.Managaer: Mike Ford
Asst Man.: Jason Stalker   Physio: Mike Ford

DOWNHAM TOWN

Secretary: F. Thorne, 6 Maple Rd., Downham Market, Norfolk, PE38 9PY. (01366 382563)

Ground: Memorial Field, Lynn Road, Downham Market, Norfolk (01366 388424)

Directions: One and a quarter miles from Downham Market (BR) - continue to townclock, turn left and ground is three quarters of a mile down Lynn Road
Capacity: 1,000   Seats: 60   Cover: Yes   Floodlights: Yes
Clubhouse: Bar open matchdays, refreshments & snacks available

HONOURS   Peterborough Lg (5) 62-63 73-74 78-79 86-88;
            Norfolk Senior Cup 63-64 65-66 (R-up(3) 66-69)

PREVIOUS   Leagues: Peterborough

RECORD   Attendance: 325 v Wells Town Norfolk Senior Cup, 1998-99

FACT FILE
Founded: 1881
Nickname: Town
Sponsor: Lynwere Engineering
Colours: Red/white/red
Change colours: Sky/Navy/sky
Midweek Matches: Tuesday
Programme: Yes, with entry
Editor: Chairman

CLUB PERSONNEL
Chairman: John Fysh
President: Louis Barker
Manager: Steve Tyres

583

FELIXSTOWE & WALTON UNITED

Secretary: Chris Ryan,43 Brook Lane,Felixstowe,Suffolk IP11 7LG (01394 275873)
Ground: Dellwood Avenue, Felixstowe IP11 9HT Tel: 01394 282917
Email Address: felixstowe@btinternet.com
Website: http://www.felixstowe,btinternet.co.uk
Directions: A14 to Felixstowe. Turn right at 3rd r'bout then 1st left - ground100 yds on left. 5 mins walk from Felixstowe (BR) and town centre
Capacity: 2,000 **Seats:** 200 **Cover:** 200 **Floodlights:** Yes
Clubhouse: Bar, snack bar, TV, **Club Shop:** Yes, including enamel badges
HONOURS Suffolk Senior Cup 66-67, 74-75 and 98-99 (as Walton United)
PREVIOUS **Leagues:** Essex & Suffolk Border; Ipswich & District
Names: Felixstowe Port & Town, Felixstowe Town, Felixstowe United
Merged with Walton United in 2000
Grounds: Tennis Club,Ferry Road.
RECORD **Attendance:** 1,500 v Ipswich Town, floodlight inauguration 25/1/91

FACT FILE
Founded: 1890   Nickname: Seasiders
Colours: Red & white stripes/black/red
Change: Yellow & Blue/yellow/yellow
Midweek Matches: Tuesday
Programme: 48 pages, £1.00
Editor: Phil Griffiths Tel: 01394 277156
Local Press: East Anglia Daily Times
CLUB PERSONNEL
President: Dave Ashford
Chairman: Tony Barnes
Fixture Sec: Chris Ryan (01394 275873)
Manager: Paul Adams (01473 404559)
2001-02
Captain: Nicky Barker
Top Scorer & P.o.Y.: Robbie Fuller 18

GODMANCHESTER ROVERS

Secretary: June Coxhead, 28 Dovehouse Close, Godmanchester, Cambs PE29 2DY
(T: 01480 383357 F: 01480 395137)

Ground: Bearscroft Lane, Godmanchester, Cambs.

Directions: From A14 turn off for Godmanchester. Take A1198 towards Wood Green Animal Shelter, half mile from A14 on left down Bearscroft Lane

Capacity **Cover:** 150

Floodlights: Yes
Club shop: No

Previous League: Cambridgeshire Lge. >2002

FACT FILE
Founded: 1911   Nickname: Goddy/Rovers
Sponsors: Terry Allgood, Sainsbury, Amec
Colours: Sky blue/navy/navy
Change: Green/black/black
Midweek Matches: Tuesday
Programme: 16-20 pages, £1.00
Editor: Tim Holmes, 23 Post St,
Godmanchester, Cambs
CLUB PERSONNEL
President: Jack Hills
Chairman: Keith Gabb
Manager: Eric Cheesewright
Assistant Managers:
Daryl Potter, Neil Morean, Paul Allgood
Physio: Sandra Holmes
General Manager: Roger Coxhead

HADLEIGH UNITED

Secretary: Peter Hutchings, 3 Mowlands, Capel St Mary, Ipswich. IP9 2XB Tel: 01473 311093

Ground: Millfield, Tinkers Lane, Duke Street, Hadleigh, Suffolk Tel: 01473 822165

Directions: Turn off A12 approx halfway between Ipswich & Colchester. Take B1070 & follow signs to Hadleigh. Duke Street is off the High Street - turn left by Library
Capacity: 3,000 **Seats:** 250 **Cover:** 500 **Floodlights:** Yes
Clubhouse: Open matchdays. **Website:** hadleigh-utd.co.uk

HONOURS Ipswich & Dist./Suffolk & Ipswich Lg 53-54 56-57 73-74 76-77 78-79
(Mick McNeil) Lg Cup 76-77 80-81 81-82 86-87;
Suffolk Senior Cup 68-69 71-72 82-83. Eastern Co.Lg Champions 93-94
PREVIOUS **Leagues:** Suffolk & Ipswich (prev. Ipswich & D.)(pre-1991)
Grounds: Grays Meadow, Ipswich Road
RECORDS - Gate: 518 v Halstead Town, FA Vase Replay 17.1.95 **Win:** 8-1 v Chatteris(A) 17/1/95
Defeat: 0-7 v Harwich & Parkston (H) 12/10/96, & Wisbech (H) 26/4/97

FACT FILE
Founded: 1892
Nickname: Brettsiders
Sponsors: T.B.A.
Colours: White & navy/navy/navy
Change colours: All yellow
Midweek Matches: Tuesday
Reserves' Lge: Essex & Suff. Border
Programme: 12 pages, 50p
Editor: Peter Hutchings (01473 311093)
CLUB PERSONNEL
President: K.Grimsey
Chairman: Rolf Beggerow
Manager: Louis Newman

HALSTEAD TOWN

Secretary: Stephen Webber, 12 Ravens Ave, Halstead, Essex CO9 1NZ
Tel: 01787 476959 (H) 01284 767278 (B)
Ground: Rosemary Lane, Broton Ind Est, Halstead, Essex CO9 2HR Tel: 01787 472082
Directions: A131 Chelmsford to Braintree - follow signs to Halstead. In Halstead, 1st left after Police Station, then 1st right, and first left to ground
Capacity: 2,000 **Seats:** 312 **Cover:** 400 **Floodlights:** Yes
Clubhouse: Open evenings and matchdays
HONOURS Eastern Co's Lg 94-95 95-96, R-up 93-94 (Div 1 R-up 89-90), Cup 95-96;
Essex Senior Trophy 94-95 96-97; Knight Floodlit Cup R-up 90-91; Essex &Suffolk
Border Lg 57-59 77-78 94-95 (res), (R-up 49-50 54-55 60-61), Div 1 (res) 94-95); Essex Snr Lg Cup
R-up 79-80; Essex Jnr Cup 01-02 46-47 (R-up 00-01)
Previous Leagues: Nth Essex; Halstead & Dist.; Haverhill; Essex & Suffolk Border; Essex Snr 80-88
RECORD **Attendance:** 4,000 v Walthamstow Avenue, Essex Senior Cup 1949
Players progressing Steve Allen (Wimbledon Physio)

FACT FILE
Founded: 1879   Nickname 'The Town'
Colours: White /black/black
Change colours:Red/white/red
Midweek Matches: Tuesday
Page 24 Programme: 50p
Editor: Paul Downes Tel: 01787 477320 (H)
Local Press : Halstead Gazette
CLUB PERSONNEL
Chairman: Mick Coe
Vice-Chairman:Ralph Wilkin
President: Philip Partridge
Fixture sec.:Steve Webber
Manager: Paul Grimsey
Physio: B Dunster

HAVERHILL ROVERS

Secretary: Chris Rice, 23 Ovington Place, Haverhill, Suffolk. CB9 0BA
Tel: 01440 712396 (H) 07880 966423 (M)

Ground: Hamlet Croft, Haverhill, Suffolk Tel: 01440 702137

Directions: Centre of Haverhill

Capacity: 3,000   Seats: 200   Cover: 200   Floodlights: Yes
Clubhouse: Open matchdays and functions. Snacks available

HONOURS Eastern Co's Lg 78-79 Lg Cup 64-65; Essex & Suffolk Border Lg 62-63 63-64;
East Anglian Cup 90-91; Suffolk Sen Cup 96-97

PREVIOUS **League:** Essex & Suffolk Border

RECORD **Attendance:** 1,537 v Warrington Town, FA Vase QF 86-87

Players progressing: R Wilkins (Colchester)

FACT FILE
Founded: 1886   Nickname: Rovers
Colours: All red
Change colours:All yellow
Midweek Matches: Tuesday
Programme: 24 pages,50p
Editor: Ray Esdale (01440 704670)
Local Press : Haverhill Echo,Cambridge
Evening News
CLUB PERSONNEL
Chairman: Terry McGerty
President: N Haylock
Press Officer: Ray Esdale
Manager: Paul Goodman
Physio: Nel Franklin

KING'S LYNN RESERVES

Secretary: Ken Rout, Mandlyn, Fen Lane, Ashwicken, King's Lynn, Norfolk PE32 1AW
Tel: 01553 630532 (H) 01553 764494 (B) 07850 395422 (M)
email: anglian.access@btinternet.com (office hours)

GROUND The Walks Stadium, Tennyson Road, King's Lynn PE30 5PB
Tel: 01553 760060

Directions: At mini r-about arriving from A10/A47 take Vancouver Avenue. Ground on left
after a half mile. Quarter mile from King's Lynn (BR), half mile from bus station
Capacity: 8,200   Cover: 5,000   Seats: 1,200   Floodlights: Yes

Clubhouse: Normal licensing hours, with extension on matchdays
Club Shop: Sells metal badges and other merchandise

FACT FILE
Colours: Blue & gold stripes/blue/blue & gold
Change colours: All purple and navy
Midweek matches: Tuesday

CLUB PERSONNEL
Manager: Darren Bloodworth

LEISTON

Chairman: Barry Spall, 'Loucarand', 5 Queen Elizabeth Close, Leiston, Suffolk IP16 4XB
Tel: 01728 831950 (H & B)

Secretary: Mark Pattinson, 'Fernhouse', 40 Eastward Ho, Leiston, Suffolk IP16 4XB
Tel: 01728 635016 (H) 01473 608230 (B) 01473 608607 (Bus. Fax)
email: mark.L.pattinson@bt.com

Ground: LTAA, Victory Road, Leiston, Suffolk IP16 4LD
Tel: 01728 830308

FACT FILE
Colours: Blue & whaite/blue/red
Change colours: Amber & red/red/red
Midweek matches: Wednesday
Programme: Yes
Editor: David Rees
Tel: 01728 833549

Manager: Mark Hood
Tel: 01502 501963

LONG MELFORD

Ground: Stoneylands, New Road, Long Melford, Suffolk. Tel: 01787 312187

Previous Leagues: Essex & Suffolk Border Lge. >2002

MARCH TOWN UNITED

Secretary: R S Bennett, 47 Ellingham Ave, March, Cambs PE15 9TE (01354 653271)

Ground: GER Sports Ground, Robin Goodfellows Lane, March (01354 653073)

Directions: 5 mins from town centre, 10 mins from BR station

Capacity: 4,000   **Seats:** 500   **Cover:** 2,000   **Floodlights:** Yes

Clubhouse: On ground, seating 150. Light refreshments available

HONOURS	Eastern Co's Lg 87-88 (Lg Cup 60-61), Utd Co's Lg 53-64, Cambs Invitation Cup 54-55, East Anglian Cup 53-54 (jt withBarking)
PREVIOUS	**Leagues:** Peterborough; Isle of Ely; Utd Co's 48-54
	Ground: The Avenue (prior to 1946)
BEST SEASON	FA Cup 1st Rd53-54 77-78,
RECORD	**Gate:** 7,500 v King's Lynn, FA Cup 1956

FACT FILE
Founded: 1885
Nickname: Hares
Club colours: Orange & black/black/black
Change colours: Yellow/blue/blue
Midweek Matches: Tuesday
Programme: 30p
Editor: R Bennett
Local Press : Cambs Times, Fenland Advertiser, Peterborough Evening Telegraph

CLUB PERSONNEL
Chairman: Gary Wesley
President: D Wilkinson

NEEDHAM MARKET

Secretary: D Bloomfield, 33 Quinton Road, Needham Market, Suffolk IP6 8DA
Tel: 01449 720693

Fixture Secrtary: P Collier, 9 The Knoll, Framlingham, Woodbridge IP13 9DH
Tel: 01728 724108

Ground: Bloomfields, Quinton Road, Needham Market, Suffolk
Tel: 01449 721000

Directions: Quinton Road is off Barretts Lane which in turn is off Needham Market High Street

Capacity: 1,000   **Seats:** 250   **Cover:** 250   **Floodlights:** Yes   **Club Shop:** No

PREVIOUS	**Leagues:** Ipswich & District; Suffolk & Ipswich >96	
	Grounds: Youngs Meadow; Crowley Park >96	**Names:** None
HONOURS	Suffolk & Ipswich Lge 95-96	

FACT FILE
Founded: 1927
Nickname: N/A
Colours: All Green
Change Colours: All white
Midweek Matchday: Tuesday
Programme Editor: Ian Verneau
Tel No: 01473 413957

CLUB PERSONNEL
Chairman: A.Sparkes
Managers: Colin Macrow & Colin Sinclair
2001-02
Leading goalscorer: Mark Wake 18
Captain: Dean Folkard
P.O.Y.: Mat Fenn

SOMERSHAM TOWN

Secretary: Matthew Dunster, 29 Windsor Gardens,Somersham,Huntingdon, Cambs. PE17 3DY
Tel No: 01487 740786

Ground: West End Ground, St Ives Road, Somersham, Cambs (01487 843384)

Directions: On A604 St Ives to Somersham on right as you enter town

Capacity: 1,500   **Seats:** None   **Cover:** 200   **Floodlights:** Yes

Clubhouse: Open Friday, Sat/Sun lunchtimes

HONOURS	Hunts Snr Cup 72-73 94-95, Peterboro Snr Cup 84-85, Hinchingbrooke Cup 53-54, Cambs Lg Premier B Div 94-95 (reserves)
PREVIOUS	**League:** Peterborough & District
RECORDS	**Attendance:** 538 v Norwich City, floodlights inauguration 91
	Goalscorer & Appearances: Terry Butcher

Local Press : Hunts Post, Cambs News, Citizen Express, St Ives Weekly

FACT FILE
Founded: 1893   Nickname: Westenders
Sponsors: Rapidtech (UK) Ltd
Colours: All old gold with black trim
Change colours: red&blue stripes/ blue/ red
Midweek Matchday: Tuesday
Reserve League: Kershaw Senior A
Programme: 76 pages, 50p
Editor: Tim Egan

CLUB PERSONNEL
Chairman: Alan Bailey
Vice-Chairman: Norman Burkett
President: Jack Marjason
Manager: Norman Hudson
Coach: Bob Barnett   Physio: Alan Magnus

STANWAY ROVERS

Secretary: Alan Brierley, 19 Barley Way, Stanway, Colchester CO3 5YD (01206 521606 + Fax)

Ground: `Hawthorns', New Farm Road, Stanway, Colchester, Essex (01206 578187)

Directions: Take turn off marked Stanway off A12. Turn right(from London)or left from Ipsw ch+ go over flyover to Tollgate r'bout, 1st rt into Villa Rd, after 25 yds turn left into Chaple Rd, 200 yds on left into New Farm Rd, ground 400 yds on left.Nearest BR station is Colchester North

Capacity: 1,500   **Seats:** None   **Cover:** 250   **Floodlights:** Yes   Shop: No

Clubhouse: 6.45-11pm eves, 12-11pm Sats. Rolls, soup, tea, coffee etc available matchdays

Club Shop: Pennants & ties (Club website:lineone.net/ m alan brierley

HONOURS Esx Intermediate Cup R-up 89-90 90-91, Esx & Suffolk Border Lg R-up 91-2 (Div 1 86-87, Div 2 81-81 85-86), Esx Jnr Cup R-up 74-75

PREVIOUS	**Leagues:** Colchester & E Essex; Essex & Suffolk. Border (pre-1992)
	Ground: Stanway Secondary School, Winstree Road (20 years)
RECORD	**Gate:** 166 v Sudbury Town FA Vase 4/10/97 **Win:** 8-1 v Swaffham Town
	(H), E. Counties Lge Div. 1 26/3/94 **Defeat:** 0-10 v Sudbury Townt (A), E.C.L. Cup

FACT FILE
Founded: 1955   Nickname: Rovers
Sponsors: David Martin Eastate Agents
Colours: Gold& black stripes/black/black
Change : Red & blue halves/ blue/yellow
Midweek matchday: Wednesday
Reserves' Lge: Essex & Suff. Border
Programme: 12 pages, 50p
Editor: Alan Brierleylocal Press:
Essex Co. Standard, Evening Gazette

CLUB PERSONNEL
Chairman: Peter Cracknell
President: Richard Deguille
Manager:Steve Ball
Physio: Stuart Bevis

SWAFFHAM TOWN

Secretary: D.R.Ward, 14 Mount Close,Swaffham. PE37 7BX
Tel: 01760 722516 (H) 01760 720130 (Fax) 07771 960863 (M)
Email Address: pepward@aol,com

Ground: Shoemakers Lane, Swaffham, Norfolk (01760 722700)
Capacity: 2,000   Seats: 50 Cover: 250   Floodlights: Yes

Clubhouse: Open Tuesday, Thursday, Saturday plus functions

HONOURS Norfolk Snr Cup (2), Anglian Comb. 89-90 (Div 1 88-89)
Jewson Divison 1 Champions 00-01

PREVIOUS **Leagues:** Dereham, Anglian Combination

RECORD **Attendance:** 250 v Downham Town, Eastern Co's League Cup 3/9/91

2001-02 Captain : JohnHiggs   Top Scorer: Thomas Marenghi 24
Ps.o.Y: S.tuart Seales & Scott Voutt

FACT FILE
Founded: 1892
Nickname: Pedlars
Midweek Matchay: Tuesday
Colours: Black & white stripes/black/black
Change: Yellow/Blue/Blue
Programme: 36 pages, Free
Editor: Simon Barnes

CLUB PERSONNEL
Chairman:Les Elmer
President: Stewart Collins
Manager: Robin Sainty

THETFORD TOWN

Secretary: R.Richards, 60 Nunnery Drive, Thetford, Norfolk IP243EN Tel Nos: 01842
764282 (H) 01284 701121 (W) Email Address: omwgh@lineone.net

Ground: Mundford Road, Thetford, Norfolk Tel: 01842 766120

Directions: Off bypass (A11) at A143 junction - ground 800yds next to sports ground

Capacity: 2,000   Seats: 400   Floodlights: Yes

Clubhouse: Bar, teas, refreshments, light meals & snacks   **Club Shop:** No

HONOURS Eastern Co's Lg R-up 89-90, Norfolk & Suffolk Lg 54-55;
Norfolk Senior Cup 47-48 90-91

PREVIOUS **Leagues:** Norfolk & Suffolk   **Grounds**: None

RECORD **Attendance:** 394 v Diss Town, Norfolk Snr Cup 91

Players progressing: Dick Scott (Norwich C.), Kevin Seggie (Leeds U.),Simon Milton (Ipswich T.)

Local Press: Thetford & Watton Times, Bury Free Press

2001-02 **Capt:** Peter Smith **P.o.Y.:** Paul Mlczek **Top Scorer:** Lawrence Breen

FACT FILE
Founded: 1883
Sponsors: Thetford Garden Centre
Colours: Claret & blue/claret/claret
Change: Yellow & blue
Midweek Matches: Wednesday
Reserves League: Anglian Comb
Programme: 50p
Editor: Denise Jones (01842 761876)
Club Website: thetford townfc.fsnet.co.uk

CLUB PERSONNEL
Chairman: Peter Jones
Vice-Chairman: Mike Bailey
Press Officer: Paul Stevenson
Manager: Steve Livingstone

WARBOYS TOWN

Secretary: Martin England, 39 High Street, Warboys, Huntingdon, Cambs PE28 2TA
Tel: 01487 822503

Ground: Sports Field, Forge Way, off High Street, Warboys, Cambs Tel: 01487 823483

Directions: Access through Forge Way, half way along south side of High Street

Capacity: 2,000   Seats: 50   Cover: 200   Floodlights: Yes

Clubhouse: Bar, lounge, function hall. Open every eve. & Sun. lunch. Entertainment, drinks & snacks

HONOURS Utd Co's Lg Div 2 R-up 54-55, P'boro Lg R-up(2) 59-60 61-62, P'boro SnrCup
63-64, Hunts Snr Cup 26-27 28-29 31-32 32-33,94-95. (R-up 92-93,95-96), Hunts Scott Gatty Cup
30-31. Reserves: Hunts Benevolent Cup 57-58, Hunts Junior Cup 24-25 27-28 52-53, Hunts Lower
Junior Cup 75-76 77-78. Eastern League Div 1 R-up: 95-96, Lg.Cup R-up: 97-98

PREVIOUS **Leagues:** Peterborough & Dist 46-48 56-88; Utd Co's 50-56; Huntingdonshire 48-50

RECORD **Attendance:** 500 v Ramsey Town, Hunts Senior Cup Semi Final

Players progressing: Alec Chamberlain (Ipswich and Watford)

FACT FILE
Founded: 1885
Nickname: Witches
Colours: Red /black/red
Change colours: White/red/white
Midweek Matches: Tuesday
Programme: 12 pages,50p
Editor: Martin England
Local Press : Hunts Post (01480 411481)

CLUB PERSONNEL
Chairman: Roger Pauley
Manager: Ian Jones

WHITTON UNITED

Secretary: David Gould, 7 Karen Close, Ipswich, Suffolk IP1 4LP   Tel: 01473 253838

Ground: King George V Playing Field, Old Norwich Road, Ipswich, Suffolk. Tel: 01473 464030

Directions: Turn off A14, junction A1156 approx 3 miles west of A12/A14junction

Capacity: 600   Seats: No   Cover: 100   Floodlights: Yes

Club Shop: No

Clubhouse: Licensed Bar. Hot & Cold Food available

HONOURS Suffolk Senior Cup 58-59 62-63 92-93; Suffolk & Ipswich Lge 46-47 47-48
65-66 67-68 91-92 92-93, Jewson Fairplay Trophy 96-97, 97-98

PREVIOUS **Leagues:** Suffolk & Ipswich   Grounds: Old Norwich Rd, Ipswich

RECORD **Attendance:** 528 v Ipswich Town 29/11/95
League 244 v Ipswich Wanderers13/1/96

FACT FILE
Formed: 1926   Nickname: None
Sponsors: Speedyhire
Colours: Green & white/white/green
Change colours: All red
Midweek Matches: Wednesday
Youth's League: U18 Eastern Jun Alliance
Programme: 24pages- 50p
Editor/ Press Officer:Mark Woodward

CLUB PERSONNEL
Chairman: John Watkins
President: Russell Woodward
Fixture Sec: Alan Elliott (01473 461931)
Manager: Paul Smythe

WISBECH TOWN
Football Club
Season 2001/02

Main Club Sponsor
Ace Frames Ltd.
Dr. Martens
JEWSON FOOTBALL LEAGUE

Welcome To The Bridge

SEASON
2001-2002

WEBSTER

Dr. Martens

JEWSON

Jewson League
Division One

HISTON RESERVES
v
KINGS LYNN RESERVES

Saturday 27th April 2002
Kick off 3pm

Vol No 1
Issue No 23   £1.00

Harwich
&
Parkeston
Football Club

Members of the Jewson League

with CO-OP Fiveways

2001 - 2002
Season

Programme 50p

BLOATERS BULLETIN £1
Wirral Jewson League
Programme of the Year 2000-2001

Gt Yarmouth Town FC

JEWSON (Eastern Counties) LEAGUE
Season 2001-2002

Jewson Premier
AFC SUDBURY
Tuesday 30th April 2002
KO 7.45pm

Welcome To Wellesley Road

CLUB SPONSORS
Richmond Farms   Hippodrome Circus
Gt Yarmouth Ceilings   Lovewell-Blake

CHERRY RED RECORDS
HELLENIC FOOTBALL LEAGUE

Patron: Sir Henry Cooper OBE, KSG. (2001)
Chairman: Michael Broadley

Secretary: Brian King, 83 Queens Road, Carterton, Oxon OX18 3YF
Tel/Fax: 01993 212738 **E-mail:** king.brian@ukgateway.net

A couple of weeks after the end of season the Hellenic League lost its founder and President Norman Matthews, aged 78. There is little that can be said to impact the loss we have suffered with Norman's death. Those who knew Norman and were present at when he received the Football Association's "meritorious service medal" in early April will have been shocked, as I was, to see how poorly he looked. Nonetheless, in his usual spirit Norman entertained those present with a history lesson on the formation of the league. His passing was a sad day for all in football.

North Leigh Football Club was installed as Premier Division Champions on 30th April after beating Shortwood United 3-1, they joined the Hellenic League in 1992 from junior football and have made steady progress through that time being promoted to the Premier Division in 1993. This was the club's first top three finish since promotion.

The Premier Division was very competitive with five different clubs topping the table at various times during the season. Didcot Town made the early pace with seven wins and two draws to top the table for the first seven weeks of the season. Yate Town who finished third for the second season running had a purple patch with eleven straight wins during late October to mid January but faded during the final run-in.

Gloucester United played quality football and were always in contention until the crunch match at North Leigh on 20th April that resulted in a draw. North Leigh manager Mark Gee said after that result: "this draw puts Gloucester in pole position and I expect them to be champions". These comments struck home with the North Leigh players as they collected maximum points from there last four matches whilst Gloucester United, with ground share problems with their landlords, managed only four out of twelve points to finish second to North Leigh. After winning the title Mark Gee commented: "when we drew with Gloucester a couple of weeks ago it took the pressure off us as we then had to rely on them slipping up. It was a hard run in but we gave very little away and it's a great feeling to be the Premier Division Champions, it's the biggest achievement in my football career". Club chairman Peter King said: " words cannot describe how I feel at the moment after this marvellous achievement for this village club in winning the Premier Division Championship. It is my proudest moment after some 35 years involvement at North Leigh".

HONOURS LIST 2001-02

PREMIER DIVISION		RESERVE DIVISION TWO EAST	
Winners	Runners-Up	Winners	Runners-Up
North Leigh	Gloucester United	Finchampstead	Eton Wick
DIVISION ONE WEST		**LEAGUE CUP**	
Hook Norton	Pewsey Vale	Gloucester United	North Leigh
DIVISION ONE EAST		**SUPPLEMENTARY CUP**	
Finchampstead	Aston Clinton	Purton	Old Woodstock Town
RESERVE DIVISION ONE		**BRIAN WELLS MEMORIAL TROPHY**	
Carterton Town	Swindon Supermarine	Pewsey Vale	Hook Norton
RESERVE DIVISION TWO WEST		**RESERVE DIVISIONS CUP**	
Brackley Town	Kidlington	Didcot Town	Binfield

FINAL LEAGUE TABLES 2001-02
PREMIER DIVISION

	P	W	D	L	F	A	Pts		P	W	D	L	F	A	Pts
North Leigh	42	30	8	4	97	36	98	Wantage Town	42	15	10	17	67	65	55
Gloucester United	42	29	6	7	106	48	93	Pegasus Juniors	42	16	5	21	65	92	53
Yate Town	42	24	13	5	105	39	85	Southall Town	42	14	9	19	55	66	51
Abingdon United	42	24	8	10	86	51	80	Highworth Town	42	14	7	21	66	77	49
Didcot Town	42	24	6	12	93	56	78	Henley Town	42	12	10	20	51	65	46
Fairford Town	42	21	10	11	72	42	73	Cirencester Acad.	42	11	11	20	61	71	44
Brackley Town	42	20	9	13	70	55	69	Almondsbury Town	42	12	6	24	53	84	42
Tuffley Rovers	42	19	11	12	53	61	68	Wootton Bassett	42	11	9	22	39	75	42
Shortwood United	42	20	7	15	67	66	67	Bicester Town	42	9	6	27	58	97	33
Bishops Cleeve	42	19	8	15	79	51	65	Harrow Hill	42	7	2	33	31	104	23
Carterton Town	42	18	10	14	71	48	64	Cheltenham Saras	42	3	9	30	30	126	18

DIVISION ONE (WEST)

	P	W	D	L	F	A	Pts
Hook Norton	32	22	8	2	69	21	74
Pewsey Vale	32	20	5	7	80	39	65
Ardley United	32	18	8	6	83	51	62
Purton	32	18	4	10	63	52	58
Ross Town	32	15	10	7	56	41	55
Winterbourne United	32	15	9	8	73	41	54
Middle Barton	32	13	8	11	62	64	47
Old Woodstock Town	32	11	10	11	47	38	43
Shrivenham	32	12	6	14	57	63	42
Kidlington	32	11	8	13	36	38	41
Chipping Norton Town	32	10	7	15	49	68	37
Malmesbury Victoria	32	8	11	13	49	53	35
Easington Sports	32	9	8	15	37	54	35
Clanfield	32	7	9	16	40	61	30
Cirencester United	32	8	4	20	36	69	28
Headington Amateurs	32	6	7	19	40	79	25
Letcombe	32	3	10	19	42	87	19

DIVISION ONE (EAST)

	P	W	D	L	F	A	Pts
Finchampstead	32	20	6	6	73	40	66
Aston Clinton	32	19	7	6	76	37	64
RS Basingstoke	32	16	7	9	64	53	55
Martin Baker Sports	32	15	8	9	68	43	53
Englefield Green	32	16	4	12	64	51	52
Milton United	32	12	13	7	50	37	49
Bisley Sports	32	14	5	13	53	53	47
Prestwood	32	13	6	13	58	58	45
Penn & Tylers Green	32	12	8	12	56	50	44
Eton Wick	32	12	6	14	53	59	42
Quarry Nomads	32	12	6	14	54	74	42
Drayton Wdrs	32	11	4	17	56	86	37
Peppard	32	8	11	13	39	46	35
Binfield	32	9	7	16	44	53	34
Rayners Lane	32	8	10	14	55	66	34
Hounslow Borough	32	5	11	16	47	76	26
Chalfont Wasps *	32	6	9	17	44	72	24

PREMIER DIVISION RESULTS CHART 2001-02

		1	2	3	4	5	6	7	8	9	10	11	12	13	14	15	16	17	18	19	20	21	22
1	Abingdon	X	2-2	8-1	1-1	1-0	1-2	1-0	1-0	0-1	3-3	3-1	5-1	1-0	1-1	1-0	6-0	4-0	2-4	1-0	0-1	0-0	2-1
2	Almonds'y	5-1	X	4-1	2-5	0-2	1-2	1-0	2-0	1-1	0-1	2-0	3-1	0-0	2-3	3-4	0-3	2-2	2-3	0-2	0-2	1-5
3	Bicester	0-1	2-2	X	3-2	1-0	0-3	0-1	1-2	1-2	1-2	2-4	4-2	2-2	1-1	1-3	1-2	0-1	1-2	3-1	0-1	1-2
4	Bishops C	2-1	1-0	4-0	X	4-1	4-0	6-1	0-2	0-2	0-2	1-3	2-0	3-1	1-1	2-1	0-1	2-0	0-1	3-1	2-2	1-2
5	Brackley T	1-2	2-0	2-2	2-1	X	1-0	3-0	0-2	0-2	2-0	0-0	6-0	1-0	0-2	2-1	1-0	1-1	1-1	5-0	3-5	3-1	1-1
6	Carterton T	1-2	2-1	4-0	0-0	0-0	X	5-0	3-1	2-2	2-3	3-2	1-0	4-0	0-3	0-1	1-1	4-0	0-1	2-2	0-0	0-0
7	Chelt'ham	2-5	1-3	2-2	1-1	0-3	1-5	X	2-2	0-5	1-3	0-6	0-2	2-2	2-1	1-1	0-3	0-1	1-1	1-3	0-2	0-6
8	Cirencester	0-1	2-1	3-0	1-2	2-2	1-1	1-1	X	2-1	1-3	1-2	4-1	2-3	0-0	1-1	3-4	0-1	1-1	1-1	3-0	1-1
9	Didcot Tn	2-4	5-1	4-5	1-3	2-1	1-1	2-0	4-3	X	2-0	4-0	2-1	6-2	0-2	6-0	1-0	2-1	3-3	3-0	3-0	0-0
10	Fairford T	2-2	0-1	7-1	1-3	0-1	1-2	8-0	2-1	0-1	X	3-1	3-1	0-0	2-2	5-1	1-1	2-0	1-0	0-0	0-0	2-0	1-1
11	Gloucester	1-2	5-0	5-4	3-1	6-1	3-0	6-0	3-1	1-0	2-1	X	3-0	3-0	4-1	1-3	3-0	5-2	3-0	1-2	4-2	1-1	1-0
12	Harrow Hill	0-1	1-0	1-0	0-3	0-2	1-0	3-1	0-2	0-0	0-3	1-2	X	0-1	2-1	0-3	2-1	1-2	0-0	1-4	0-0	0-1	0-5
13	Henley T	2-0	3-0	1-3	2-2	1-1	0-3	5-0	3-1	1-1	0-0	1-4	4-0	X	1-0	0-2	4-1	0-3	0-0	0-1	0-2	1-1	1-1
14	Highworth	1-4	4-0	2-4	1-0	5-0	1-2	6-0	1-5	2-1	0-1	1-2	5-2	2-1	1-2	X	0-5	1-1	3-1	1-1	0-1	2-0	2-3	1-1
15	North L	1-1	4-1	3-0	2-1	4-4	3-1	2-0	2-1	1-1	2-0	0-0	1-1	1-0	6-2	X	9-3	3-1	1-0	0-3	5-1	6-0	2-2
16	Pegasus J	2-1	0-1	1-0	0-3	0-6	0-2	2-1	3-1	0-3	4-1	1-2	4-2	4-1	0-0	2-0	X	1-3	1-2	0-2	2-1	4-0	4-4
17	Shortwood	2-1	2-2	2-2	0-5	4-0	2-1	1-0	3-1	4-5	1-2	1-1	3-2	2-0	1-5	0-0	X	0-2	3-1	3-0	2-1	0-5
18	Southall T	1-3	2-1	3-2	2-2	0-1	2-6	6-0	1-1	1-3	1-2	0-0	1-0	1-4	3-4	0-1	0-1	2-1	X	1-1	1-2	4-0	2-2
19	Tuffley R	0-4	0-0	1-0	1-0	1-0	0-0	3-4	2-1	2-6	0-2	2-2	5-3	2-2	2-1	0-1	1-0	1-0	0-1	X	1-1	1-1	0-6
20	Wantage T	3-4	1-2	1-3	2-1	0-2	1-0	2-2	1-0	0-0	1-1	9-1	3-0	1-0	2-4	1-1	4-0	0-1	X	3-1	1-4
21	Wootton B	2-2	0-2	1-0	1-1	1-3	0-3	2-1	2-0	4-2	0-2	0-1	2-1	0-1	0-3	2-1	0-1	0-2	2-2	0-4	X	0-2
22	Yate Town	2-0	4-1	2-0	3-1	2-3	2-1	1-1	4-0	6-2	0-0	1-4	4-0	4-0	2-1	0-1	3-3	3-0	2-0	5-0	1-0	3-1	X

North Leigh, Hellenic
League Champions.
Back Row (l-r):
Matty Gorman, Nick
Hughes, Justin
Timms, Stuart Huxley,
Peter Hutter, Andy
McCabe, Kevin Alder,
Mark Lewis.
Front Row:
Joe Burnell, Jamie
Jackson, Craig
Pearman, Darren
Maisey, Sean Bott.
Photo: Arthur Evans

LEAGUE CUP 2001-02

PRELIMINARY ROUND

Almondsbury Town	2 v 0	Cirencester Utd
Bicester Town	5 * 3	Prestwood
Binfield	1 v 3	Englefield Green Rvrs
rematch: Binfield	1 v 4	Englefield Green
Chelt. Saracens	1 * 2	Old Woodstock
Chipping Norton	0 v 2	Fairford Town
Cirencester Academy	5 v 0	Clanfield
Drayton Wanderers	0 v 2	Quarry Nomads
Easington Sports	0 v 1	Pewsey Vale
Eton Wick	4 v 3	Wantage Town
Harrow Hil	0 v 1	Malmesbury Victoria
Headington Amateurs	0 v 5	Yate Town
Henley Town	4 v 0	Aston Clinton
Hounslow B.	1 v 3	Penn & Tylers Green
Letcombe	0 v 2	Finchampstead
Martin Baker Sports	3 v 1	Bisley Sports
Middle Barton	1 * 2	Pegasus Juniors
Milton United	0 v 1	Kidlington
North Leigh	3 v 0	Purton
Peppard	2 * 2	Ardley United
Replay: Ardley United	5 v 0	Peppard
Rayners Lane	4 v 0	Chalfont Wasps
Shrivenham	1 v 3	Bishops Cleeve
Southall Town	6 v 0	RS Basingstoke
Winterbourne United	4 v 2	Tuffley Rovers
(Winterbourne United expelled)		
Witney Academy	1 * 2	Ross Town
Wootton Bassett Town	3 v 1	Hook Norton

FIRST ROUND

Almondsbury Tn	2 * 2	Old Woodstock
Replay: Old Woodstock	2 v 3	Almondsbury Town
Bicester Town	1 * 3	Henley Town
Englefield Green	1 v 2	Southall Town
Eton Wick	3 * 3	Kidlington
Replay: Kidlington	2 v 3	Eton Wick
Fairford Town	2 v 0	Shortwood United
Finchampstead	0 * 0	Didcot Town
Replay: Didcot Town	4p,2*2,2p	Finchampstead
Highworth Town	1 v 3	Carterton Town

First Round cont.

Malmesbury Victoria	0 v 1	Gloucester Utd
Martin Baker Sports	4 v 3	Ardley United
North Leigh	5 v 2	Cirencester Academy
Pegasus Juniors	7 * 4	Bishops Cleeve
Penn & Tylers Green	4 v 1	Quarry Nomads
Rayners Lane	1 * 1	Abingdon United
Replay: Abingdon Utd	3 v 0	Rayners Lane
Ross Town	2 v 0	Pewsey Vale
Wootton Bassett Town	3 v 1	Tuffley Rovers
Yate Town	2 v 0	Brackley Town

SECOND ROUND

Carterton Town	2 v 0	Ross Town
Eton Wick	1 * 1	Penn & Tylers Green
(Penn & Tylers Green expelled)		
Henley Town	1 v 4	Abingdon United
Martin Bake	3 v 4	Almondsbury Town
North Leigh	1 * 1	Didcot Town
Replay: Didcot Town	1 v 2	North Leigh 2
Pegasus Juniors	1 v 2	Gloucester United
Southall Town	2 v 3	Fairford Town
Wootton Bassett Town	2 v 9	Yate Town

QUARTER-FINALS

Carterton Town	1 * 2	Yate Town
Eton Wick	0 v 4	North Leigh
Fairford Town	3 * 3	Almondsbury Town
Replay: Almondsbury T	0 v 4	Fairford Tn
Gloucester United	1 v 0	Abingdon United

SEMI-FINALS
(played over two legs)

Gloucester United	5 v 1	Fairford Town
Fairford Town	1 v 0	Gloucester United
North Leigh	4 v 0	Yate Town
Yate Town	2 v 0	North Leigh

FINAL
at Carterton Town

North Leigh	1 * 2	Gloucester United

SUPPLEMENTARY CUP 2001-02

PRELIMINARY ROUND

Bisley Sports	5 v 1	Chalfont Wasps
Drayton Wanderers	1 v 0	Letcombe
Harrow Hil	0 v 4	Hook Norton
Pewsey Vale	4 * 1	Cirencester Acad.
Purton	3 * 1	Easington Sports
Quarry Nomads	3 v 5	RS Basingstoke
Shrivenham	1 * 0	Cheltenham Saras
Wantage Town	6 v 0	Milton United

(Wantage Town expelled)

Witney Academy	1 v 4	Highworth Town

FIRST ROUND

Ardley United	5 v 3	RS Basingstoke
Aston Clinton	4 v 0	Englefield Green
Bishops Cleeve	5 v 1	Pewsey Vale
Chipping Norton	2 v 4	Old Woodstock Tn
Clanfield	2 v 5	Hook Norton
Drayton Wanderers	2 v 3	Brackley Town
Highworth Town	9 v 0	Headington
Hounslow Borough	1 v 7	Peppard
Kidlington	2 v 0	Binfield
Milton United	1 * 1	Bicester Town
Replay: Bicester Town	0 v 3	Milton United
Prestwood	0 v 4	Finchampstead
Purton	2 v 1	Shrivenham
Rayners Lane	0 * 1	Bisley Sports
Shortwood United	2 v 1	Cirencester Utd
Tuffley Rovers	1 v 2	Malmesbury Vics
Winterbourne United	0 v 2	Middle Barton

SECOND ROUND

Aston Clinton	1 v 0	Shortwood United
Bisley Sports	0 v 4	Highworth Town
Finchampstead	1 v 0	Brackley Town
Kidlington	2 v 1	Hook Norton
Milton United	2 v 3	Middle Barton
Old Woodstock Town	3 v 1	Malmesbury
Peppard	1 v 5	Ardley United
Purton	1 v 0	Bishops Cleeve

QUARTER-FINALS

Highworth Town	2 v 0	Middle Barton
Kidlington	3 v 5	Finchampstead
Old Woodstock Town	2 v 1	Ardley Utd
Purton	2 v 1	Aston Clinton

SEMI-FINALS

(played over two legs)

Finchampstead	0 v 1	Purton
Purton 3p,2*3,1p		Finchampstead
Old Woodstock Tn	1 v 1	Highworth Town 1
Highworth	0 v 2	Old Woodstock Town

FINAL

at Abingdon United

Purton	3 v 1	Old Woodstock Town

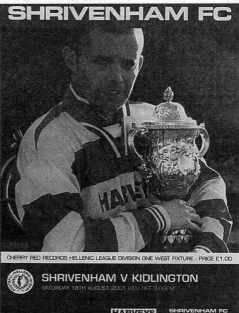

ABINGDON UNITED

Secretary: John Blackmore,91 Gainsborough Green, Abingdon, Oxon OX14 5JL(01235 202124)
Ground: Northcourt Road, Abingdon OX14 1PL Tel: 01235 203203
      Capacity: 2,000   Seats: 52   Cover: 120   Floodlights: Yes

Directions: From north (Oxford) leave A34 at Abingdon north sign and Northcourt Rd is 1st major turning after r'bout. From South, East or West leave Abingdonon A4183 and turn left into Northcourt Rd after 1 mile. 2 miles from Redley (BR)
Clubhouse: Two bars, food available. Open normal pub hours every day

HONOURS	N Berks Lg 53-54 (Lg Cup R-up 53-54), Charity Shield 52-53; Hellenic Lge - Prem Div R-up 96-97, Div 1 R-up 76-77 81-82, Res. Div 97-98, F/Lit Cup 96-97, Lg Cup R-up 89-90, Div 1 Cup 65-66 81-82 R-up 66-67, Reserve Cup 98-99 R-up 93-94; Berks & Bucks Senior Cup R-up 83-84, Senior Trophy 97-98 R-up 93-94 96-97
PREVIOUS	**League**: North Berks **Grounds**: None
RECORD	**Gate:** 1,500 v Oxford Utd 1994 **Appearances:** D Webb

FACT FILE
Founded: 1946
Nickname: The U's
Colours: All yellow
Change colours: All Blue
Midweek matchday: Tuesday
Reserves' Lge: Suburban
Programme: 50p
Editor: W Fletcher, ACJI (01235 203203)
Website: abingdonunitedfc.co.uk
2001-02:
Captain: Richard Pierson
Top Scorer: Kai Ridley 20
CLUB PERSONNEL
Chairman: Derek Turner
General manager: John Blackmore
Manager: Ray Hayward
Coach: Mark O'Hara
Physio: JamesFoote & Chris Janes
Press Officer: Bill Fletcher (01235 203203)

ALMONDSBURY TOWN

FACT FILE

Secretary: Roger Perry, 61 Brookbridge House, Standfast Road, Henbury, Bristol BS10 7HW
      Tel No: 0117 959 0309

Ground: Oakland Park, Gloucester Rd., Almondsbury, Bristol BS12 4AGTel: 01454 612220

Directions: Adjacent to M5 junction 16 - follow A38 Thornbury - ground first left. 4 miles from Bristol Parkway (BR). County bus services to Thornbury,Stroud and Gloucester
      Capacity: 2,000   Seats: None   Cover: No   Floodlights: Yes
Clubhouse: 7 days, all sports, refreshments, function room, entertainment,skittles

HONOURS	Glos Co. Lg(4) 76-78 79-81 (R-up 75-7681-82), GFA Chal. Tphy 78-79 (R-up 80-81), Avon Prem. Comb. 74-75, Glos SnrAmtr Cup 87-88, Hellenic Lg 83-84 (R-up 82-83, Lg Cup(2) 83-85)
PREVIOUS	**Leagues:** Bristol Weslyan; Bristol Suburban; Bristol Premier Comb.; GlosCo **Ground:** Almondsbury Rec. (until 1986)
BEST SEASON	**FA Vase:**R-up 78-79, SF 77-78
RECORD	**Gate:** 2,100,Hellenic Cup Final replay 89-90 (Newport AFC v Abingdon U)

Founded: 1897
Nickname: Almonds
Colours: Royal blue/navy/navy
Change colours: Tangerine/black/black
Midweek Matchday: Tuesday
Programme: 20 pages 25p
Editor: Roger Perry
Tel: 0117 959 0309
Top Scorer 00-01: Ali El Morissy

CLUB PERSONNEL
Chairman: Brian Tufton
President: Peter Howarth
Manager: Shaun Honor
Coach: Micky Jefferies & Shaun Heyes
Physio: Peter Allen & Brian North

BICESTER TOWN

FACT FILE
Founded: 1876
Nickname: Foxhunters
Colours: Red & black/black/red or white
Change: Green & yellow/green/green
Club's Email:philip@bassett38,freeserve,co.uk
Midweek Matchday: Tuesday
Reserves' league: Hellenic Lge Res. Div.
Programme: With entry
Editor:Phil Allen (01869 252125)

Secretary:	Duncan Currie Tel No: 01869 327308 (H)
Ground:	Sports Ground, Oxford Rd, BicesterTel: 01869 241036 (office& fax) Capacity: 2,000 Seats: 250 Cover: 550 Floodlights: Yes
Directions:	From Oxford; past Tescos on outskirts of Bicester - ground on right From Aylesbury; turn left at first island on outskirts of Bicester ontobypass, right at next island, pass Tescos & ground on right
Clubhouse:	One bar
HONOURS	Hellenic Lg 60-1 77-78 (Lg Cup 90-91 (R-up 92-93), Div 1 76-77)
PREVIOUS	**League**: Oxon Senior **Name:** Slade Banbury Road (pre-1923)
RECORD	**Attendance:** 955 v Portsmouth, floodlight inauguration 1/2/94

CLUB PERSONNEL
Chairman: David Simpson
Vice Chairman: Ray Honour
President: Michael Kinane
Fixture Secretary: Phil Allen
Press Officer: David Simpson
Manager: Barry Grant
Coach: Kevin Leach
Physio: Ray Huntley

BISHOPS CLEEVE

FACT FILE

Secretary:	Phil Tustain, 36 Hardy Road, Bishops Cleeve, Cheltenham GL52 4BN
	Tel: 01242 697281 (H) 01242 673333 x 2287 (B)
Ground:	Kayte Lane, Bishops Cleeve, Cheltenham Stand : 50 Floodlights: Yes
Directions:	North of Cheltenham on the A534, pass Racecourse then turn right at traffic lights and then left into Kayte Lane, ground half a mile on the left.
Clubhouse:	Full facilities, bar, dance area
HONOURS	Hellenic Lg Cup R-up 90-91, Helleneic Div 1West R-up: 2001-02
PREVIOUS	**Leagues:** Cheltenham, Nth Glos
	Grounds: The Skiller (pre-1913), Village Field (pre-1950)
RECORD	**Attendance:** 1,000 v Newport AFC

Founded: 1892
Nickname: Skinners
Colours: Green&black/black/black
Change colours: Yellow/blue/green
Midweek Matchday: Wednesday

CLUB PERSONNEL

President: John Davies
Chairman: David Walker
Manager: Paul Collicutt
Press Officer:Will Pember
Tel: 01242 673800
Programme Editor: John Banfield

Coach:John Banfield
Physio: Will Pember

BRACKLEY TOWN

FACT FILE

Secretary/Press Officer: Pat Ashby, 2 Barrington Court, Ward Road, Brackley, NN13 7LE
Tel: 01327 262955(H) 01280 840900(O) 07930 143504(M)
Ground: St James Park, Churchill Way, Brackley, Northants NN13 7EJ.   Tel: 01280 704077
Office: 01280 703652:   Club Website: www.the-saints.co.uk   Club Email: btfc1890@aol.com

Directions:	Churchill Way, east off A43, south end of town
	Capacity: 3,500 Cover: 150 Seats: 300 Floodlights: Yes
Clubhouse:	Fully licensed. Lounge & main hall. Food available. Open all week.
Club Shop:	Yes, selling club merchandise,programmes and badges etc.
PREVIOUS	**Leagues:** Banbury & District; North Bucks; Hellenic 77-83; United Counties 83-94; Hellenic 94-97,Southern 97-99 **Names:** None
	Ground: Banbury Road, Manor Road, Buckingham Road (up to 1974)
	CLUB RECORDS Attendance: 720 v Kettering, Northants Senior Cup 1989
	Fee Received: £2,000 for Phil Mason from Oxford City 98
BEST SEASON	**FA Trophy:** 1st Qual Rd 97-98
	FA Cup: 2nd Qual Rd 97-98 League clubs defeated: **HONOURS**

United Counties R-up 88-89 (Div 1 83-84); Northants Snr Cup R-up 88-89;
Buckingham Charity Cup (3); Hellenic Lg Prem 96-97, Div 1 Cup 82-83. **Players progressing:**
Jon Blencowe (Leicester)   **Transfer Fee Paid:** None

Formed: 1890   Nickname: Saints
Colours:Red /white/white
Change colours: All Orange
Midweek matchday: Tuesday or Wednesday
Programme: Price: £1
Editor: Brian Martin(01280 706619)
Local Press: Brackley Advertiser,
Banbury Guardian, Herald & Post
Milton Keynes Citizen - Local Radio: Fox FM

CLUB PERSONNEL

Managing Director: Mike Bosher
Chairman: Keiran Flanigan
Com. Man: Ray Styles: 0772 040587
President: Clive Lomax
Press Officer: Brian Martin
Manager: Tim Fowler Asst.Man: Pete Salt
Leading goalscorer: Frankie Dorrian 27
Captain: Jason Allen
P.o.Y.: Neil King

CARTERTON TOWN

FACT FILE

Secretary:	CathrynTaylor, 23 Mirfield Road,Witney, Oxon. OX28 5BD (01993 840628)
Ground:	Kilkenny Lane, Carterton, Oxfordshire (01993 842410)
Directions:	Enter Swinbrook Rd which off the Burford-Carterton road, proceed into Kilkenny Lane (one track road), ground car park 200yds on left before sharp corner. Hourly buses to Carterton from Oxford
	Capacity: 1,500 Seats: 75 Cover: 100 Floodlights: Yes
Clubhouse:	Lounge & fully licensed bar open every day 7.00-11pm, Sat & Sun: noon-11pm Sat 4-6pm. Snacks & meals available
HONOURS	Oxon Junior Shield 85-86; Oxon Snr Cup R-up 90-91 96-97 98-99 Witney & Dist.Lg 65-66 (Div 1 84-85 76-77); Hellenic Lg Div 1 89-90 93-94 (Reserve Div 1989-90 (R-up 93-94)); Oxon Intermediate Cup R-up 93-94(res.)Hellen Supplementary Cup 99-00, Hellenic League Challenge Cup 2000-01, Reserves Diovision 1. 2001-02
PREVIOUS	**Leagues:** Witney & District
RECORD	**Gate:** 600 v Oxford Utd, Oxon Snr Cup 93-94
	Goalscorer: Phil Rodney

Founded: 1922
Reformed: 1946/1983
Colours: Black & white/black/black
Change colours: Yellow&blue/blue/blue
Midweek matches: Tuesday
Programme: 20 pages 50p
Editor: Rosie Tomasiello (01993 840214)
Website: www.cartertontownfc.co.uk

CLUB PERSONNEL

President: G Fox
Chairman: Robert Taylor
Match Secretary: Glynn Yates

Manager: Paul Berry
Physio: Andy Slater
Coach:Terry Merriman

Captain: Nathen Woodley
P.o.Y.: Nick Heritage
Top Scorer:Ricky King

CIRENCESTER FOOTBALL ACADEMY

FACT FILE

Secretary: Matt Sykes, 2 Stratton Brook, Gloucester Road, Cirencester GL7 2LD
Tel: 01285 653062 (H) 07768 758550 (M) 01285 643938 (F)
Email: msykes@omniwhittington.co.uk

Ground: Cirencester Town FC, Tetbury Road, Cirencester GL7 6PX
Tel: 01285 654783

Directions: From A419 head towards Cirencester town centre (follow signs for Cirencester Hospital). Turn left at Hospital roundabout, and the ground entrance is on the left at the next roundabout.

RECORD **Attendance:** 115 v Fairford Town, May 2001

Nickname: Academy
Colours: Green & white hoops/white/green
Change colours: Red & black/black/red
Midweek Matchday: Wednesday

CLUB PERSONNEL
Chairman: Alan Sykes
Tel: 01285 654783
Press Officer& Prog Ed:
Kirstine Fraser Tel: 01793 823046

Joint Managers:
John Freeth & David Hawkins
Physio: Steve Slattery

DIDCOT TOWN

FACT FILE

Secretary: Phil Hussey c/o Loop Meadow Stadium
Ground: Loop Meadow Stadium, Bowmont Water, Didcot, OX11 7GA.
Website: http://users.tinyoline.co.uk/stevetclare/DTFC1/
Capacity: 5,000   Seats: 250   Cover: 500   Floodlights: Yes

Directions: From Town Centre: Take station road (old ground) and turn right under bridge just before station into Cow Lane. Left by Ladygrove Pub into Tamar Way. Then first left at roundabout. From A34: leave at Milton interchange and take Didcot road for approximately one mile. At roundabout take perimeter road Cross three more roundabouts and turn right at third into Avon Way

Clubhouse: Every evening and 12 noon to close at weekends and national holidys.

HONOURS Hellenic Lg 53-54,Lg Cup 1965-66 66-67 92-9397-98 Div 1 76-77,Div1 Cup 76-7, Berks & Bucks Senior Trophy 2000-01

PREVIOUS **Leagues:** Hellenic 53-54; Metropolitan League 57-63
RECORD **Attendance:** 825 v Oxford United, 2001

Founded: 1907
Nickname: Railwaymen
Colours: All red & white
Change colours: Blue & yellow stripes
Midweek Matchday: Tuesday
Programme: 50p
Editor: Steve Clare & Andy Selby

CLUB PERSONNEL

President:
Chairman: John Bailey
Manager: Pete Cox
Ass.Managar: John Heapy
Player-Coach: Andy Cooper
Physio: Mark Roberts

FAIRFORD TOWN

FACT FILE

Secretary: William Beach, 33 Park Close, Fairford, GL7 4LF Tel: 01285 712136 (H)
Email address: ftfc00@hotmail.com
Ground: Cinder Lane, London Road, Fairford, Cirencester Tel: 01285 712071

Directions: Entering Fairford on A417 from Lechlade turn left down Cinder Lane150yds after 40mph sign. From Cirencester on same road, follow thru village andturn right down Cinder Lane 400yds afterRailway Inn.
Buses from Swindon,Lechlade and Cirencester
Capacity: 2,000   Seats: 100   Cover: 150   Floodlights: Yes
Clubhouse: Open each evening, weekend lunches & before and after all games
Club Shop: Yes
HONOURS Glos Challenge Trophy 79-80, 98-99 (R-up 82-83); Hellenic Lg R-up 78-79 79- 80 90-91 94-95, (Premier Div Cup 78-79, Div 1 71-72, Div 1 Cup 71-72); Glos Jnr Cup 62-63; Swindon & Dist Lg 64-65 68-69 ,Hellenic floodlit Trophy: 2001-02
PREVIOUS **Leagues:** Cirencester & District (pre-1946)/ Swindon & District 46-70
Grounds: None
RECORD **Attendance:** 1,525 v Coventry City, friendly July 2000
Goalscorer: Pat Toomey   **Win:** 9-0 v Moreton T   **Defeat:** 0-9 v Sharpness

Founded: 1891   Nickname: Town
Colours: Red/white/red
Change colours:All Blue
Midweek matchday: Wednesday
Reserves' League: Hellenic Reserve section
Programme: 20 pages with admission
Editor/Press Officer: President
Club Website: http://welcometo/ftfc

CLUB PERSONNEL
Chairman & Commercial Manager:
Stuart Pike Tel: 01285 712364
President: Michael Tanner
Manager: Mark Webb
Physio: Ian Watkins
2001-02
Captain: John Hathaway
P.o.Y.: Lee Clark
Top Scorer: Lee Stoddart 40

GLOUCESTER UNITED

FACT FILE

Secretary:	Dave Phillips, 14 Woodcock Close, Abbeydale, Gloucester GL4 4WT
	Tel: 01452 414766 (H/Fax) 07754 088063 (M - matchdays only)

Colours : All blue

Ground	City Stadium, Meadow Park, Sudmeadow Road, Hempsted, Gloucester GL2 5HS
	Tel: 01452 421400
	Floodlights: Yes

Change colours: Red/red/white

Midweek fixtures: Wednesday

Directions	From junction 11 of M5 take A40 towards City Centre, follow signs for Historic Docks. On approach to docks turn right over narrow bridge into Severn Road (signposted Hempsted). Turn right into Hempsted Lane and then second right into Sudreadow Road. Ground is 50 yards on the left.

CLUB PERSONNEL

Chairman: Richard Bull

Vice Chairman: Pat Casey

Press Officer: Dave Phillips

Record	**Attendance:** 120 v Shortwood Utd, 25.10.00
Honours:	Hellenic D1 West 99-00; Floodlite Cup R-up 99-00

Man: Douglas Foxwell   01452 538116

Coach: John Hamilton

Physio: Ricky Clutterbuck

HENLEY TOWN

FACT FILE

Secretary:	Tony Kingston, 50 Birdhill Avenue Reading Berks. RG2 7JU
	Tel: 01189 670196(H) 07712139502 (M); 01189 844496 (B);
	Fax: 01189 842201;E-mail: ad.kingston@ntlworld.com

Founded 1871

Nickname: The Lillywhites or Town

Colours: White & black/black/black

Change cols.: Yellow & Green /green/green

Ground:	The Triangle, Mill Lane ,Henley-on-Thames
	Tel: 01491 411083
Directions:	From Henley Town Centre take the A4155 Reading Road.
	Mill Lane is approx. 1 mile on the left past the Newtown Ind. Est. and
	immed. before the Garage and roundabout for Tesco.
	The ground is on the left, over the railway bridge.
	Henley-on-Thames Railway Station ten minutes walk.
	Buses 328 Reading or 329 Wycombe
	Seats: 60 **Cover:** 160 **Floodlights:** Yes

Midweek fixtures: Tuesday

Prog Ed: Raf Lobato (0118 9019326)

Web site: www.henleytown.co.uk

CLUB PERSONNEL

Chairman: Andrew Bryan

Press Officer: John Bailey (01491 573914)

Clubhouse:	Open evenings plus all day Sat,Sun
Record Gate:	2000+ v Reading, 1922
Recent Honours:	Hellenic Lge Div1East 00-01 Oxon Senio Cup (5)

Manager: Kevin Davies

Coach: Keith Stiles Physio: Richard Ellis

Youth Development: Jack Hollidge

HIGHWORTH TOWN

FACT FILE

Founded: 1894

Nickname: Worthians

Sponsors: One Stop

Secretary: Fraser Haines, 222 Windrush, Highworth, Swindon SN6 7EB (01793861109)

Ground: Elm Recreation Ground, Highworth. (01793 766263)

Colours: Red & black/black/red

Change colours: Blue/white/blue

Directions: Enter on A361 from Swindon, past Simpsons Garage, straight overisland, next sharp left into Green by Vet's Surgery - ground & car park 60ydson left next to Sports Hall

Midweek matchday: Tuesday

Reserves Lge: Hellenic Reserve Div

Capacity: 2,000	Seats: 50		Cover: 250	Floodlights: Yes	Club Shop: No

Programme: 16 pages, 60p

Editor: Mike Markham (01793 763462)

Clubhouse: Sat 12-2.30 & 4.30-11pm. Mon to Fri 7-11pm. Rolls & Hot food

CLUB PERSONNEL

President: Alan Vockins

HONOURS	Wilts Snr Cup 63-64 72-73 95-96 97-98(R-up 88-89), Hellenic Div 1 Cup 88-89,Arthur Shipway Cup 88-89 93-94, Swindon & District Lg 63-64 64-65 65-66 68-69 Hellenic Supplementary Cup Winners: 98-99, Hellenic Reserve Division Two Winners 98-99, Hellenic Premier Division R-Up 9-00

Chairman: Geoff Melcott

Match Secretary: Dave Evans (01793 763548)

Press Officer:Chairman

Manager: John Fisher

PREVIOUS	**Leagues:** Wilts; Swindon & Dist

Coach: Clive Maguire Physio:Alan Jenning

2001-02

RECORD	**Attendance:** 2,000 v QPR opening Floodlights
	Scorer: Kevin Higgs **Appearances:** Rod Haines
	Win: 12-0 v Beeches, Arthur Shipway Cup 1992
	Defeat: 2-8 v Milton United, Hellenic Lge Div. 1, 1987

Top Scorer:Warren Fuller

Captain: Dave Webb

P.O.Y.: Warren Fuller

Bicester Town, 2-0 victors at home to Brightlingsea United in the FA Vase Second Round. Back Row (l-r): Barry Grant, James Blackmore, Dave Griffiths, Chris Please, Steve Ayris, Richard Darvill, Chris Johnson, Alex Lynch, Matthew Cresswell, Paul Darch. Front Row: Micky Marshall, Paul Hammond, Stuart Fox, James Lisseter, Simon Fox, Dan Huntley. Photo: Arthur Evans

Carterton Town FC

Hook Norton. Back Row (l-r): Dave Risato (Manager), Steve Slaughter (Physio), Andrew Lester, Neil Donovan, Greg Shawyer, Darren Farley, Marcus Townsend, Mark Willis, John Evans, Arron Parkinson, Adrian White, Ryan Butler. Front Row: Garnet Thomas, Jake Tyrrell, James Pope, Karlton Stratford (Capt), Richard Knight, Russell Wilkins, Oliver Barlow, Lewis Travers

HOOK NORTON

FACT FILE

Secretary:	Dave Macfarlane, Byeways, East End, Hook Norton, Oxon, OX15 5LG
	Tel: 01608 737123(H) 07989 852632(M)
Ground:	The Bourne, Hook Norton OX15 5PB 01608 737132
Directions:	From Oxford – A44 to junction with A361 turn right, take 1st left to a 'T' junction, turn right & enter village, after 30 MPH turn left then 1st right into 'The Bourne', take 1st left into ground.
	Floodlights No
Previous League:	Oxford Senior League
Record Gate:	244 v Banbury United 12th Dec 1998
Honours:	Oxford Senior League Champions 2000-01
	Hellenic Lge Div.1 West Champions 01-02

Nickname: Hooky
Colours: All maroon with silver grey trim
Change colours: White with red trim/red/red
Midweek fixtures: Tuesday
Program Editor: Mark Willis 01608 664101
email: repro@kmslitho.co.uk

CLUB PERSONNEL

Chairman: Christopher Moores
Deputy Chairman: Michael Barlow
Press Officer: Laura Riley 01608 730108

Manager David Risato
Coach: Vinny Halsall & Gerry Duggan
Physio: Steve Slaughter & John Hughes

NORTH LEIGH

FACT FILE

Secretary:	Peter J Dix, 8 Windmill Close, North Leigh, Nr Witney, Oxon OX8 6RP
	Tel: 01993 881199
Match Secretary:	Keith Huxley, The Orchard, Cote, Bampton, Oxon. OX18 2EG
	Tel: 01993 851497 (H) 0118 913 3223 (B)
	email: keith_huxley@fwuk.fwc.com
Ground:	Eynsham Hall Park Sports Ground, North Leigh, nr Witney, Oxon OX8 6PW
	Tel: 0993 881427
Directions:	Ground is situated off A4095 Witney to Woodstock road 3 miles east of Witney. Entrance to ground is 300yds east of Main Park Entrance
Capacity: 2,000	**Seats:** 100 **Cover:** 200 **Floodlights:** Yes
Clubhouse: Bar open matches. Snacks available **Club Shop:** No	
PREVIOUS	**Leagues:** Witney & District 08-89
CLUB RECORDS	**Attendance:** 300 v Oxford United, Friendly August 1998
	Scorer: P Coles **Appearances:** P King

Founded: 1908
Nickname: None
Sponsors: Various
Colours: Yellow & red/red/yellow
Change colours: All claret & blue
Midweek matches: Tuesday
Programme: 20 pages, £1 with entry
Editor: Janice Carter

CLUB PERSONNEL

President: Mrs Christine Smith
Chairman: Peter King
Press Officer: Barry Norton
Tel: 01993 881777

Manager: Mark Gee
Asst Manager: David Ebsworth
Physio: Andrew Davidson

HONOURS Hellenic Lg Div 1 R-up 92-93 (Reserves Cup 93-94), Oxon Jnr Shield 56-57 83-84, Oxon Charity Cup 84-85 88-89, Witney & Dist. Lg(13) 50-57 84-90 LgCup (10) 47-48 51-52 53-55 56-57 81-82 85-89), Oxon Yth Cup 93-94 94-95,OxonYth u17 Lg & Cup 93-94. Oxford Sen. Cup R-Up 94-95. Marriott Cup 95-96; Oxon U-16 Youth Cup 98-99, Allied Counties Under 18 Youth (West Div)Winners

---

PEGASUS JUNIORS

FACT FILE

Secretary:	Brian James, 7 Loder Drive, Hereford HR1 1DS
	Tel: 01432 274982 (H) 01432 348131 (B) 077 900 92444(M)
Ground:	Leisure Centre, Holmer Road,Hereford
Directions:	A49 Ross Road over Greyfriars Bridge, Victoria Street to end of Edgar Street, then turn left to next mini roundabout and then right.Leisure Centre 500 yds on left.
Capacity:	1,000 Seatrs 50 Cover : Yes Floodlights: Yes
Clubhouse:	48 St Owens Street
HONOURS	Herefordshire Snr Amtr Cup 71-72; Worcs Senior Urn 85-86;
	Herefordshire Co. Chal. Cup (6) 81-83 84-85 87-88 89-90, 98-99, R-up 93-94;
	Hellenic Lg Div 1 84-85 98-99, R-up 93-94, Div 1 Cup R-up 93-94)
PREVIOUS	**Leagues:** Leisure Centre
RECORD	**Attendance:** 1,400 v Newport AFC 89-90

Founded: 1955
Colours: All red
Change colours: Blue
/blue/blue
Midweek Matchday: Tuesday/Wednesday
Programme: 50p
Editor: Kevin Bishop (01432 353805)

CLUB PERSONNEL

President: Mark Ellis
Chairman: Steve Knight
Press Officer: Chris Wells
Manager: Owain Meale
Assistant. Manager: Joe Wright
Physio: Dave Smith

2001-2002
Top Goalscoreer: Mak Davis 21

PEWSEY VALE

Secretary: Liz Montague, 39 Swan Meadow, Pewsey, Wilts, SN9 5HP
E-mail: montymadhouse@btinternet.com

Ground: Recreation Ground, Ball Rd, Pewsey Tel: 01672 562990

Directions: On entering Pewsey from A345, at the Market Place proceed to end of High Street and turn right into Ball Rd, entrance to ground on right opposite pub. BR to Pewsey station

Capacity   Unlimited   Cover: Yes   Floodlights: No

PREVIOUS **League:** Wiltshire County (pre-1993), Western League 93-01
Name: Pewsey Y.M. (until late 1940s)

HONOURS Wiltshire County League 92-93

FACT FILE

Colours: Black & White]/Black/Black
Change colours:
Navy & lime green/navy/lime green & navy
Midweek matchday: Tuesday

CLUB PERSONNEL

Chairman: Rob Thompson

Manager: Don Rogers

SHORTWOOD UNITED

Secretary: Mark Webb, 1 The Bungalow, Shortwood, Nailsworth, Stroud, Glos GL60SD
Tel: 01453 833204 (H)   0781 2842724 (M)

Ground: "Meadow Bank", Shortwood, Nailsworth, Gloucestershire (01453 833936)

Directions: In Nailsworth turn into Spring Hill then first left. Continue pastshop and and keep left past "Britannia" (signposted Shortwood) - continue toend for ground. 4 miles from Stroud (BR)

Capacity: 5,000   Seats: 50   Cover: 150   Floodlights: Yes   Club Shop: No

Clubhouse: Mon-Sat 7-11pm, Sun 12-2 & 7-10.30pm.. Hot food kitchen on matchdays

HONOURS Glos.Co.Lg 81-82 (R-up 80-81), Glos Tphy 83-84 91-92,94-95,(R-up 79-80), Hellenic Lg 84-85 91-92 (R-up 85-86 89-90 94-95, Div 1 R-up 83-84, Div 1Cup83-84), Prem Lge Cup R-up 95-96, Hungerford Merit Cup, Glos Snr AmCup 85-86,99-00 R-up 79-80), Stroud Charity Cup 91-92 92-93 94-95 00-01(R-up 95-96), Stroud Lg 27-28 (Div 2 26-27 64-65(res), Div 3 25-26 49-50(res) 62-63(res)), Glos Northern Snr Lg R-up (3)res)(Div 2 62-63 80-81(res) 90-91(res)), Arthur Shipway Cup 78-79 79-80, Supp'tary Cup R-up 98-99, Glos N. Sen 2 R-up 98-99

PREVIOUS **Leagues:** Stroud; Glos Northern Snr; Glos Co
Ground: Table Land, Wallow Green

RECORD **Attendance:** 1,000 v Forest Green Rovers, FA Vase 5th Rd 81-82
Goalscorer: Peter Grant   **Appearances:** Peter Grant
Win: 11-0   **Defeat:** 0-9   **Fee Received:** Paul Tester (Cheltenham, 80-81)

2001-02 Captain: Lee Driver-Dickenson   P.o.Y.: Craig Cole   Top Scorer: Craig Cole 29

FACT FILE
Founded: 1900
Nickname: The Wood
Sponsors: Ecotricity
Colours: Red & white,red,white
Change: Blue/Blue/Yellow
Midweek matchday: Tues or Wed
Reserves' League: Glos Northern Snr 1
Programme: 18 pages, 50p
Editor:Kenton Posthlethwaite

CLUB PERSONNEL
Chairman: Peter Webb
Vice C'men: W Stratford, W Lewis
President: R T Tanner
Press Officer: Keith Norbury
Tel: 01453 83 5094 (H) 07816205152 (M)

Manager: John Evans
Coach: Ryan Gannaway

SOUTHALL TOWN

FACT FILE

Secretary: George Twyman, 119 Dormers Wells Lane Southall Middlesex UB1 3JA
Tel & Fax: 0208 574 5047(H & B) Email: craig@craig brown.co.uk

Match Sec.: Eddie Mee, 11 Charles Hocking Hse, Bollo Bridge Rd, Acton London W3 8DA.
Tel: 0208 993 4477(H) 07940 287 985 (Bus)

Ground: Yeading FC. The Warren Beconsfield Road Hayes Middx
Tel 0208 848 7362

Capacity: 3,500   Cover: 1,000   Seats: 250   Floodlights: Yes

Directions: Leave M4 at junction 3, The Parkway onto Hayes by-pass. Continue to the second filter road and turn right onto A4020 Uxbridge Road, then take first turning on right into Springfield Road. Continue to end of road, turn left into Beconsfield Road, ground on right hand side at end of the road.the left hand side opposite the Church.

PREVIOUS **Leagues:** Isthmian League to 00.

RECORD **Attendance:** 45 v Finchampstead 00-01

2001-02 **Leading Goalscorer:** Steven Newing 16
P.o.Y.: Rory Smith   **Captain:** Leon Lewis

Nickname: The Town
Colours: Red & white stripes/black/black
Change colours: Yellow & blue/blue/blue
Midweek Matchday: Wednesday
Programme: £1
Editor: Craig Brown:0208861 6215
email: craig@craigbrown.co.uk

CLUB PERSONNEL
Chairman: Manjit S Lit

Press Officer: Manjit S Lit
Tel: 0208 893 5373 Fax: 0208 571 9410

Manager: Dennis Bainborough
Coach: Del Deanus
Physio: TBA

TUFFLEY ROVERS

Secretary: Graham Moody, 50 Giles Cox, Quedgeley, Gloucester GL2 4YL
Tel: 01452 724083 (H & Fax) 01452 522009 (B)

Ground: Glevum Park, Lower Tuffley Lane, Gloucester Tel: 01452 423402

Directions: Follow Gloucester city ring-rd to traffic lights signed M5 South & Bristol.
Turn right signed Hempsted & city centre, after 200yds turn right (McDonalds on corner) into Lower Tuffley Lane, ground 400yds on left
Capacity: Seats: 50 Cover: Yes Floodlights: Yes

Clubhouse: 800 yds from ground. Open before & after matches, and normal pub hours at other times. Snacks available. Club Shop: No

HONOURS Hellenic Lg Div 1 92-93 (Div 1 Cup 92-93, F'lit Cup 98-99), Glos Co. Lge 90-91, Glos SnrAmtr Cup 87-88, Stroud Lg 72-73,94-95, Glos Northern Sen. Lg. Div 1 87-88 98-99 (res) Div2 79-80.

PREVIOUS **Leagues:** Stroud; Glos Northern Senior; Glos County (pre-1991)
Grounds: Stroud Rd, Gloucester; Randwick Park, Tuffley

RECORD **Attendance:** 150 v Cinderford Town 94-95

FACT FILE

Founded: 1929
Nickname: Rovers
Club Sponsors: Albell Construction
Colours: Claret & blue/claret/claret
Change colours: White/blue/blue
Midweek Matchday: Tuesday
Reserve League: Glos.Northern Senior Lge
Programme: approx 10 pages with entry
Editor: Graham Moody

CLUB PERSONNEL

President: T.B.A.
Chairman: Tony Newport

Manager: Chris Gardner
Coach: Rob Whittington
Physio: Sean Tracey

WANTAGE TOWN

Secretary: Alan Parker, Little Orchard, Manor Road, Wantage, OX12 8DW
Tel: 01235 763842 (H & Fax)

Ground: Alfredian Park, Manor Road, Wantage, Oxon Tel: 01235 764781

Directions: Take Hungerford Road from Wantage (A338)
The ground is signposted on right opposite recreation ground
Capacity: 1,500 Seats: 50 Cover: 300 Floodlights: Yes

Clubhouse: Mon-Fri 7.30-11pm, Sat noon-2.30, 4-7pm Club Shop: No

HONOURS Hellenic Lg R-up 81-82, Div 1 80-81 (R-up 69-70 87-88 91-92 95-96), Div1 Cup R-up 91-92; Oxon Snr Cup 82-83; Berks & Bucks Intermediate Cup 54-55; Swindon & District Lg 07-08 33-34 52-53 55-56

PREVIOUS **Leagues:** Swindon & Dist. 1901-12 30-35 47-56; N Berks 12-22 38-40 46-47; Reading & D. 22-30 35-38
Ground: Challow Park (pre-1922)

RECORD **Attendance:** 500 v Newport AFC 89
Win: 11-1 v Amersham Town (A), Hellenic League 60-61
Defeat: 0-14 v Thame United (A), 20/1/62
Goalscorer: A Rolls

Players progressing: Roy Burton and Colin Duncan (both Oxford United)

FACT FILE

Founded: 1892
Nickname: Alfredians
Sponsors: Broadway Motors
Colours:Green &white/white/white
Change Colours: Blue & white/black/black
Programme: 28 pages, 50p
Editor: Tony Woodward (01367 241328)
Midweek Matchday:Tuesday

CLUB PERSONNEL

Chairman: Tony Woodward
President:John Hutchings
Match Secretary: Colin Blunsden
Tel: 01235 768605 (H)
1st Team Manager: Stuart Peace
Coach: Terry Delaney
Physio: Ian Howard

WOOTTON BASSETT TOWN

Secretary: Rod Carter, 14 Blackthorn Close, Wootton Bassett, Swindon SN4 7JE
Tel: 01793 851386 (H); 01793 494367 (B); 01793 494355 (F); 07946 034999 (M) Email: rod.carter@woolworths.co.uk

Ground: Gerard Buxton Sports Ground, Rylands Way, Wootton Bassett, Swindon 01793 853880

Directions: M4 jnct 16 to Wootton Bassett (A3102), left at 2nd r'bout (Prince of Wales pub on right), 2nd left into Longleaze (just after Mobil garage) and Rylands Way is 3rd right by shops, ground 100yds on right. From Calne/Devizes direction proceed thru town centre and turn right into Longleaze after Shell petrol station on right - Rylands Ave. is 3rd left. Coming from Malmesbury take last exit off r'bout by Prince of Wales pub and Longleaze is 2nd left

Capacity: 4,000 Seats: None Cover: 350 Floodlights: Yes Club Shop: No
Clubhouse: Open every matchday. Matchday refreshments - teas, coffees, soups & light snacks

PREVIOUS **Leagues:** Wilts (pre-1988) **Grounds:** None
RECORD **Gate:** 2,103 v Swindon T., friendly 7/91 **Win:** 11-2 **Defeat:** 0-9
Scorer: Brian (Toby) Ewing **Appearances:** Steve Thomas
HONOURS Hellenic Lg Div 1 Cup 89-90 93-94, Wilts Lg 87-88 (Div 2 84-85,Subsidiary Cup 78-79), Wilts Snr Cup R-up 02-03 03-04 87-88, Ghia Snr 83-84,Ghia Jnr Cup R-up 88-89, FA Amateur Cup QF 26-27

FACT FILE

Founded: 1882
Colours: Blue & yellow/blue/yellow
Change colours: Red/black/black
Midweek matchday: Tuesday
Reserve's League: Wiltshire
Programme: 12 pages, free
Editor: Roger Williamson Tel: 01793 850751

CLUB PERSONNEL

Chairman: Paul Harrison
President: Keith Lodge
Press Officer: Rod Carter (see Sec)

Manager: Peter Yeardley
Coach: Mike Byrne
Physio: TBA

YATE TOWN

Secretary: Terry Tansley, 1 Tyning Close, Yate, Bristol. BS37 5PN
Tel: 01454 324305
Ground: Lodge Road, Yate, Bristol BS37 7LE Tel: 01454 228103

Directions: M4 jct 18, A46 towards Stroud, then A432 to Yate. Turn right at top of railway bridge into North Road, first left past traffic lights. Five miles from Bristol Parkway BR main line station, half mile from Yate BR station. Buses 329, X68 and 328

Capacity: 2,000   Cover: 400   Seats: 236   Floodlights: Yes

Clubhouse: Open every night & weekend lunchtimes. Skittles, darts, pool, live entertainment

Club Shop: Selling programmes & usual souvenirs. Contact: Secretary

HONOURS Hellenic Lg(2) 87-89 (Div 1 R-up 84-85, Lg Skol Cup R-up 87-88), Glos Chal.Tphy 88-89,00-01 (R-up 78-79), Glos Snr Amtr Cup Sth 77-78 91-92(res) 92-93(res),Glos Snr Chal. Cup (Nth) R-up 89-90 92-93 94-95, Stroud Charity Cup R-up 74-75 81-82 84-85 (Sect. A Winners(6) 76-78 79-80 82-83 87-89), Berkeley Hosp. Prem.Cup(3) 73-75 80-81, S.W. Co's Sutton Vase 85-86 Dr.Martens Fairplay award 98-99, 99-00

BEST SEASON   FA Vase: Fifth Round 1991-92

CLUB RECORDS Win: 13-3 v Clevedon, Bristol Premier Comb 67-68

CareerGoalscorer: Kevin Thaws   **Career Appearances:** Gary Hewlett

Transfer fee - Paid: None   **Received:** £15,000 for Mike Davis (Bristol Rovers 93)

PREVIOUS   Leagues: Gloucestershire County 68-83, Hellenic 83-89, Southern Lge 89-00

FACT FILE
Formed: 1946
Nickname: The Bluebells
Colours: White/navy/navy
Change colours: All Red
Midweek matchday: Tuesday
Reserve Team's League: Bristol Suburban
Programme - Pages: 40 Price: £1
Editor: Terry Tansley c/o Club
Website:www.yatetownfc.co.uk

CLUB OFFICIALS

Chairman: Peter Jackson
President: Roger Hawkins
Press Officer: Secretary

Manager : Richard Thompson
Physio: Ken Dodd

Didcot Town.
Back Row (l-r): John Heapy (Asst Mngr), Mark Roberts (Physio), Andy Cooper, Andy Marriott, Paul Noble, Jamie Heapy, Geoff Simmonds, Fletcher Hoey (no relation to Kate!), Damien O'Glesby, Dwayne Strong, Peter Cox (Mngr). Front Row: Simon Kelly, Lee Fuller, Ross Tyler, Ian Concannon, Phil Thomas (Capt), Andrew Small (Mascot), David Bevan, Glyn Jones.
Photo: Arthur Evans

Gloucester United.
Back Row (l-r): Dave Phillips (Sec), Dougie Foxwell (Manager), Johnny Meadows, Adie Griffin, Tom King, Andy Pritchett (Capt), Colin Peacey, Richard Moore, John Hamilton. Front Row: Kevin Willetts, Kevin Lee, Steve Badhams, Julian Freeman, Edward Ward, Matthew Casey.
Photo: Arthur Evans

Above: Henley Town.
Back Row (l-r): Robbie Wright, Nicky Nash, Darren Russell, Stuart Gosby, Gary Kingston, Adam Markwell, Phillip Humphries, Simon Rowland. Front Row: Bernie Harris (Joint Mngr), Paul Lawrence, James Hollidge, Ollie Maskell, Jason Kingston (Mascot), Graham Jack (Capt), Liam Higgins, Kevin Davies (Joint Mngr).
Photo: Arthur Evans

SEASON 2001-02
ADMISSION £2.50
(Including Programme)

ADDERBURY PARK

Secretary Clive Boddy 5 Coppice Close Banbury Oxon OX16 9SW
Tel: 01295 255641 (H) 01295 225004 (B) 01295 225005 (F)

Ground: Adderbury Park Playing Fields, Round Close Road, Oxford.
Tel: 07788 867532

Directions: Take the A4260 from Oxford, enter village and turn left at village green into High Street, then into New Road, turn sharp left into Round Close Road. Ground entrance is 100 yards on left.

Previous League: Oxfoidshire Senior Lge.>2002

FACT FILE
Colours: Green & white hoops/white/green
Change: Red/black/black
Midweek matchday: Tuesday
Program Editor: James Easterbrooke
01295 810847 email: jimbo111@tinyworld.co.uk

CLUB PERSONNEL
Chairman: Pete Spicer
01295 265635 email: peejay@supanet.com
Press Officer: Joel Bloxham 01295 253355 email:
Topstriker69@aol.com

Manager: Jim Hay
Coach/Physio: Dennis Horrocks

ARDLEY UNITED

Secretary: Alan Mitchell, 24 Orchard Road,Ardley,Bicester,Oxon OX27 7PW
Tel: 01869 346854(H) 01865 846799(W) 01865 846333(FAX)

Ground: The Playing Fields, Ardley Road,Ardley (01869 346429)

Directions: M40 junc 10 take B430 towards Middleton Stoney on the right after1/2 mile. From Oxford take A430 through Weston-on-the-Green & Middleton Stoney on the left hand side.
Capacity: Cover: Seats: Floodlights

Clubhouse:

HONOURS Oxon Snr Lg R-up 92-93 (Pres. Cup R-up 90-91 91-92) Hellenic League Div One 96-97,97-98 Division One Cup 94-5,95-6,96-7,97-98

PREVIOUS **Leagues:** Oxon Snr (pre-1993)

RECORD **Attendance:** 91 v North Leigh (1999)

FACT FILE
Founded:
Colours: Sky/navy/sky
Change colours: Yellow/black/yellow
Midweek matchday: Tuesday
Programme Yes Ed: Barbara Gow

CLUB PERSONNEL
President: Ben Gow
Chairman: Norman Stacey
Secretary: Alan Mitchell
Tel: 01869 346854 (H)
Manager: Paul Spittle
Coach: Tony Blossom
Physio: Clive Wright

CHELTENHAM SARACENS

Secretary: Robert Attwood, 179 Arle Road, Cheltenham GL51 8LJ
Tel: 01242 515855 (H) 01242 241819 (B) 01242 222994 (Fax)

Ground: Petersfield Park, Tewkesbury Road, Cheltenham GL51 9DX(01242 584134)

Directions: Take A40 west out of Gloucester, follow A40 for 8 miles then takeA4136 to Longhope, pass by on the outskirts of Michealdean, up steep hill (Plump Hill), then second turn on the right signed Harrow Hill. At phone box on the left turn right into Larksfield Road, ground on right at top of hill. Reserves' Ground: Petersfield Park, Tewkesbury Road, Cheltenham (01242 584134) Directions: 1 mile from Cheltenham centre on A4019 Tewksbury Road (next to B &Q) - 1st left over railway bridge, 1st left and follow service road

Clubhouse: 2 mins away at 16-20 Swindon Rd, Cheltenham

HONOURS Glos Snr Cup 91-92 Glos Primary Cup 71-72, Winners Hellenic Div 1 99-00

PREVIOUS **League:** Cheltenham 1964-86

RECORD **Attendance:** 120 v Bishops Cleeve, 1.1.95

Players progressing: S Cotterill (Wimbledon) 88, K Knight (Reading) 89

FACT FILE
Founded: 1964 Nickname: Saras
Colours: Blue&yellow/blue/yellow
Change colours: Black, white stripe/black/black
Midweek Matchday: Wednesday
Reserves League: Hellenic Reserve section
Programme : 20 pages, 50p
Editor: Kevin Dix 01242 690405
Email: kevindix@blueyonder.co.uk
01-02 Top Scorer: Stewart Mitchinson 11

CLUB PERSONNEL
Chairman : Paul Passey (01452 856275)
Press Officer: Bob Attwood(01242 515855)
Manager: Ian Ford
Coach:Gerald Oldham Physio: Chris Hawkins

CHIPPING NORTON TOWN

Secretary: Bob Tanner, 36 Fox Close, Chipping Norton, Oxon. OX7 5BZ
Tel: 07881 712624

Match Secretary Terry Maycock, 31 Newlands, Witney, Oxon. OX28 3JL
Tel: 01993 778260

Ground: Walterbush Road, Chipping Norton, OX7 5DP
Tel: 01608 645311 or 01608 642562

Directions: From South – A361 to Chipping Norton, past school on right, take 1st left turning into Walterbush Road.
From North – drive through town and take A361 towards Burford by Kings Arms, past fire station on left, then take 1st right into Walterbush Road.
Floodlights: Yes

Record Gate: 1000 v Wolverhampton Wanderers 1981

FACT FILE
Re-formed 2001
Nickname: The Magpies
Colours: Black & white stripes/black/black & white
Change colours: Yellow/blue/yellow
Midweek fixtures: Tuesday

CLUB PERSONNEL
Chairman: Nigel Harrison
email: happyhaulier@btinternet.com
Tel: 01993 703319
Program Editor: Terry Maycock
Tel: 01993 778260
Manager: Alan Dore
Coach: TBA Physio: TBA

CIRENCESTER UNITED

Secretary/Press Officer: Gordon Varley, 95 Vaisey Rd, Cirencester, Glos GL7 2JW
Tel: 01285 657836 (H) 0973 631650 (M) 01367 718259 (B)
Ground: Four Acres P.F., Chesterton Lane, Cirencester Tel: 01285 885460
Directions: Follow by-pass towards Bristol, under footbridge, first left , ground 200yds on left hand side
Seats: None   Cover: No   Floodlights: No   Club Shop: No
Clubhouse: Training nights & matchdays. Rolls & sundries available
HONOURS Glos Snr Amtr Cup R-up 86-87 89-90; Cirencester Lg 72-73 74-75 (Div 2(3)71-73 74-75, Lg Cup 74-75, Res. Cup 74-75); Cheltenham Lg 76-77 83-84 (Div 275-76, Lg Cup 83-84 (R-up 86-87), Snr Charity Cup 86-87); Stroud Charity Cup86-87 (Section A 82-83 83-84); Arthur Shipway Cup 86-87 (R-up 87-88 92-93);Fairford Hospital Cup R-up(4) 83-85 90-91 92-93; Hellenic Res Div 95-96, Cup96-97
PREVIOUS   **Leagues:** Cirencester & Dist.(4 yrs); Cheltenham (8 yrs)
RECORDS   **Scorer:** M Day   **Appearances:** J.Stratford 310

FACT FILE
Founded: 1970   Nickname: Herd
Colours: Red & black/black/red
Change colours: All Blue
Midweek Matchday: Wednesday
Programme: 40 pages, 50p
Editor: N Warriner (01285 656187)

CLUB PERSONNEL
President:R.Trinder
Chairman: Paul King
Press Officer: As Secretary
Manager: Ivor Probert
Coach: P.Messenger
Physio: Brian Muir

CLANFIELD

Secretary: John Osborne, 70 Lancut Road, Witney, Oxon OX28 5AQ   Tel: 01993 771631
Ground: Radcot Road, Clanfield, Oxon   Tel: 01367 810314
Directions: Situated on the A4095, 8 miles west of Witney & 4 miles east of Faringdon, at the southern end of Clanfield. Buses from Witney - contact Thames Transit for details
Capacity: 2,000   Seats: No   Cover: 300   Floodlights: No
Clubhouse: Every evening & Sat/Sun lunch   Club Shop: No
HONOURS Oxon Jnr Shield 32-33, Oxon I'mediate Cup 67-68, Witney & Dist. Lg 66-67 (Div 1 65-66, Div 2 64-65), Hellenic Lg Div 1 69-70 (Premier Div Cup 72-73, Div1 Cup 69-70 85-86), Jim Newman Mem. Tphy 83-84 87-88, Faringdon Thursday Memorial Cup 69-70 71-72 96-97
PREVIOUS   **Leagues:** Nth Berks; Witney & Dist
RECORD   **Attendance:**102 v Witney Acadeny 2000 Top Goalscorer: D.Hamill(9)

FACT FILE
Founded: 1890
Nickname: Robins
Sponsors: Green King
Colours: All red
Change colours: Yellow & Black/black/black
Reserves' League: Hellenic Lge Res. section
Prog: 8 pages, with admission Ed: Secretary
CLUB PERSONNEL
President: B WallisChairman: J Osborne
Manager: Jason Court
Press Officer&Physio: Trevor Cuss
2001-02 Captain: Jason Court
Top Scorer: Neil Barrett 13
P.o.Y.: Steve Wright

EASINGTON SPORTS

Secretary: Matthew Wiggins, 26 Victoria Place, Banbury, OX16 3NN. Tel: 01295 256714
Ground: Addison Road, Banbury, Oxon, OX16 9DH (01295 257006)
Club Email: matt@wiggins1.freeserve.co.uk
Directions: From Oxford A423. After passing under flyover on the outskirts of Banbury take first turning left into Grange Road then third right into AddisonRd. Ground at top on left. One and a half miles from Banbury (BR)
Capacity: 1,000   Seats:0   Cover: 30Floodlights: No   Programme: Yes
Clubhouse: Changing rooms, showers, bar facilities and food
HONOURS   Oxon Snr Cup R-up, Oxon Intermediate League & Cup, Oxon Snr Lg
PREVIOUS   **Leagues:** Banbury Jnr; Oxon Snr; Warwick Combination
                Ground: Bodicote
RECORD   **Attendance:** 250 v Witney Town 68

FACT FILE
Founded: 1946
Colours: Red & white/black/red & white
Change colours: Blue/ white
Midweek Matchday: Wednesday
Reserves' League: Hellenic Res. section

CLUB PERSONNEL
Chairman: T.B.A.
President: Bob Cogbill
Manager/Coach: Andy Maguire
Physio: Bernie Jarvis
Press Officer: T.B.A.

HARROW HILL

Secretary/Match Sec: Robert Partridge, 20 Littledean Hill Road, Cinderford, Glos., GL14 2BE
Tel: 01594 825360 (H)   01594 825225 (B)
Club Email: geoff@tuffley33.freeserve.co.uk
Ground: Larksfield Road, Harrow Hill   Tel: 01594 543873
Directions: Take A40 west out of Gloucester, follow A40 for 8 miles then takeA4136 to Longhope, pass by on the outskirts of Michealdean, up steep hill(Plump Hill), then second turn on the right signed Harrow Hill. At phone box onthe left turn right into Larksfield Road, ground on right at top of hill
RECORD   **Attendance:** 350 v Cinderford Town 92
2001-02   Leading goalscorer: Bobby Clark 8
                Captain: Paul Frowen   P.o.Y.: Paul Frowen

FACT FILE
Founded: 1932
Nickname: Harry Hill
Colours: Claret & blue/sky/sky
Change Colours: Purple & green/black/black
Midweek Matchday: Wednesday

CLUB PERSONNEL
Chairman: Reg Taylor
Press Officer: Geoff Tuffley
10A Bilson, Cinderford, Glos., GL14 2LJ
Tel 01594 825655(H)   077524 75514 (M)
Manager: Neil Walding
Coach: Steve Boseley
Physio: Martin Burford

HEADINGTON AMATEURS

Secretary: Stephen Giles, 67 Lucerne Ave.,Bure Park,Bicester, Oxon.OX26 3EG
Tel No: 01869 246141   **Email Address:** steve.giles3@ btinternet.com
Ground: Barton Rec., Barton Village Road, Barton, Oxon Tel: 01865 760489
Directions: From Green Rd r'bout, Headington, (on A40) take Barton/Islip exit(1st exit coming from Witney, last coming from London), turn left into NorthWay, follow road for half mile - ground at bottom of hill on left Seats: None Cover: None   Floodlights: No   Club Shop: No
Clubhouse: Tues & Thurs 6-11, Sat matchdays 4.45-11. Rolls, chips,burgers, hot dogs, etc
HONOURS Oxon Snr League(4) 72-74 75-77 (R-up 71-72 74-75 77-78 81-82 84-85, Div1 68-69, Presidents Cup(2) 72-74 (R-up 71-72 77-78 84-85)), Oxon Charity Cup75-76 (Intermediate Cup 88-89), Hellenic League Div 1 R-up 87-88 (Res. Sect.92-93, Res. Cup 91-92)
PREVIOUS Leagues: Oxford City Junr 49-66; Oxford Sen 67-88 **Grounds:**Romanway,Cowley
RECORDS Attendance: 250 v Newport AFC 91 **Scorer:** Tony Penge **Appearances:**Kent Drackett **Win:** 6-0 v Carterton (H) 91 **Defeat:** 0-9 Highworth Town (a) 2002 RPM Records Cup
Player Progressing: James Light (Oxford United) 1970s

FACT FILE
Founded : 1949   Nickname: A's
Sponsors: Shaun Bradford Decorating & Construction
Colours: All red Change: Blue/blue/white
Midweek matchday: Tuesday
Programme: 8 pages, £1 with entry
Editor: Stan Hawkswood (01865 876485)
2001-02 Captain: Ben Wales P.o.Y.: Dale Thorne Top Scorer: Matthew Phillips 8
CLUB PERSONNEL
Pres: Shaun.Bradford Chairman: Donald Light
Press Officer: Donald Light
Manager: Phil Major
Coach/Physio: Graham McAnulf

KIDLINGTON

Secretary: David Platt, 57 Cherry Close,Kidlington, Oxon OX5 1HHJ (01865 370266 (H)
                    01865 244161(W) EMail Address: david@jplatt99.freeserve.co.uk
Ground: Yarnton Rd, Kidlington, Oxford Tel: 01865 375628   f loodlights: No
Clubhouse: Two bars open after matches
Directions: From Kidlington r'bout (junction of A4260 & A34) A423 north toKidlington; after
                   3rdlights take 2nd left (Yarnton Road), ground is 200yds onthe left ,just passes
                   the turning to Morton Avenue.
HONOURS   Oxon Snr Lg 53-54 (R-up 47-48), Hellenic Lg Cup 74-75 (R-up 68-69 73-7474-
                   75, Div 1 R-up 63-64 78-79), Oxon Intermediate Cup 52-53 84-85 (R-up 68-69
                   73-74 74-75), FA Vase 5th last sixteen 76-77
PREVIOUS   **League:** Oxon Snr 47-54
RECORD   **Attendance:** 2500 v Showbiz XI 1973
2000-01   **Captain:** Warren Jones **Top Scorer:** Luke Holden (11)
                   P.o.Ys.: Kevin Williams and Jon Twiss

FACT FILE
Founded: 1909
Colours: Green & black/black/green
Change colours: Red & white stripes/redk/red
Midweek Matchday:Tuesday/ Wednesday
Programme: 32pages £1.50
Editor: M A Canning

CLUB PERSONNEL
President: Gordon Norridge
Chairman: Geoff Talboys
Manager: Anton Vircavs
Coach: Martin Baker Physio: Michelle Hopcroft
General Manager: Karl Grossman

LETCOMBE

Secretary: Des Williams, 8 Larkdown, Wantage, Oxon. OX12 8HE
                   Tel: 01235 764130 (H)
Ground: Bassett Road, Letcombe Regis, Wantage, Oxon
Directions: B4507 Swindon road from Wantage, left for Letcombe Regis, follow road thru
Letcombe Regis; ground on right on far side of village
Unofficial Club Website: www.letcombefc.co.uk
                   Seats: No   Cover: No   Floodlights: No   Club Shop: No
Clubhouse: Open matchdays and functions only
HONOURS   Chiltonian Lg Div 1 90-91, North Berks Lg 89-90 (Lg Cup 87-88, WarMemorial
                   Cup 89-90,   A G Kingham Cup 89-90, Faringdon Mem Cup 97-8 98-99 99-00
PREVIOUS   **Leagues:** North Berks 60-90; Chiltonian 90-93
RECORDS   **Attendance:** 90 v Courage (Reading) 03.90
                   Scorer: R Taylor   **Appearances:** P Davies
2001-02 Captain: Sean McCulloch   Top Scorer Mark Rees 13   P.o.Y.: Mark ce la Coze

FACT FILE
Founded: 1960
Nickname: Brooksiders
Sponsors: T.B.A.
Colours: Purple/Navy/Purple
Change colours: Blue& Green/Green/Green
Midweek Matchday: Wednesday
Reserves' Lge: Hellenic Res. sect
Programme: £1.50p with entry
Editor: Russell Stock (01235 762387)

CLUB PERSONNEL
Pres Jim VennartChairman: Dennis Stock
Vice-Chairman: Russell Stock
Manager: Matty Goddard
Coach & Physio: Des Williams

MALMESBURY VICTORIA

Secretary: Sue Neale, 30 Gastons Road, Malmesbury, Wilts. SN16 0BE
                   Tel: 01666 823560   E-Mail: sue@paulneale.freeuk.com

Ground: Flying Monk Ground, Gloucester Road, Malmesbury
                   Tel: 01666 822141
Website: www.malmesbury-victoria.com
Directions: From A429 turning signposted Tetbury (by Nurdens Garden Centre),
go past school and take next left B4014 signposted Sherston. Go down hill to mini
roundabout, straight over roundabout. Go past Somerfield's super store, narrow right
turning into ground behind super store.
Previous   Leagues: Wiltshire Premier League
Honours   Wiltshire League Champions 99-00 Wiltshire Senior Cup 01-02

2001-02   **Capt:** Graham Jones **P.o.Y.:** Chris Mintern **Top Scorer:** Andy Sandell 14

FACT FILE
Nickname: The Vic's
Colours: Black & white stripes/black/black
Maroon, blue sleeves/blue/maroon
Midweek fixtures: Tuesday or Wednesday

CLUB PERSONNEL
Chairman: Brian Slade 01666 825705
Press Officer: Brian Slade 01666 823211
Programme Ed: Paul Neale 01666 823560
Manager: John Norris 01666 840450
Coach: Graham Learmonth

MIDDLE BARTON

FACT FILE

Founded: 1952
Midweek Matchday: Wednesday
Colours: Blue & white/blue/white
Change colours: Yellow/black/black
Programme: Yes, first season

Secretary: Julie Reed, 5 Hillside Road, Middle Barton, Oxon OX7 7EY
Tel: 01869 347388
Match Secretary: Jeane Beale, 3 Dorne Closer, Middle Barton, Oxon OX7 7HD
Tel: 01869 340753
Ground: Worton Road, Middle Barton, Oxon. Tel: 01869 347597

Directions: Middle Barton village is situated on the B4030, 5 miles east of Enstone. 200 metres passed the Fox PH turn left at cross roads, ground 200 metres on right.

Clubhouse: Open every evening

Previous League: Oxfordshire Senior League

Honours: Oxfordshire Sen. Lge R-up 98-99

CLUB PERSONNEL

President: Derrick Jarvis
Chairman: John Hanks
Press Officer: Phil Smith (01869 347471)
Manager/Coach: Tim Fowler
Physio: Lucy Waring

OLD WOODSTOCK TOWN

FACT FILE
Founded:
Midweek Matchday: Tuesday
Colours: Blue & red/blue/ red
Change colours: White/green/blue
Programme : Yes Ed: Mike Harris

Secretary: Ian F. Lenegan
c/o Workplace Systems plc.,Precedent Drive, Rooksley, Milton Keynes MK13 8PP
Tel:08362 42300(H), 01908 251301or 251311 (W) 01908 201287 (Fax)

Ground: New Road, Woodstock

Directions: A44 from Oxford into centre of Woodstock, turn right opposite The Crown into Hensington Road. After half a mile the road bends to the right, take the first turning right into New Road, ground half-way along on the left.

HONOURS Oxfordshire Sen. Lge 98-99

PREVIOUS **Leagues:** Oxfordshire Senior League

CLUB PERSONNEL
President: Ian F Lenegan
Chairman: Ted Saxton
Press Officer: Mick Harris (01865 376018)
Manager: Andrew Townsend
Coach:Trevor Stokes
Physio: Graham Bowerman

PURTON

Secretary: Alan Eastwood, 12 Hylder Close,Woodhall Park,Swindon,Wilts. SN2 2SL
Tel: 01793 729844 **Email Address:** eastwood@hylder.fsnet.co.uk
Ground: The Red House, Purton, Tel: 01793 770262 (Saturday afternoons only)

Directions: Purton is on B4041 Wootton Bassett to Cricklade Road. Ground nearvillage hall
Capacity   Seats:None   Cover: None   Floodlights: No
Clubhouse: Open after matches and before matches on Saturdays

HONOURS Wiltshire Lg Div One 48-49 85-86, Div2 83-84, Div3 86-87; Wilts Senior Cup (6) 38-39 48-49 50-51 54-55 87-88, 88-89,94-95 Wilts Yth Cup 77-78 85-86 88-89, Fairford Hosp. Cup (3) 87-89 93-94 Hellenic Lg. Div One 95-96, Hellenic Supplement Cup 2001-02
RECORD **Attendance :**508 v Dorcan 5.5.85
2000-01 **Captain :**Lee Marshall   **P.o.Y&Top Goalscorer:** Steve Tucker 32

FACT FILE
Founded: 1923
Nickname: The Reds
Sponsors: The Care Company
Colours: All red
Change colours: All purple
Midweek Matchday: Wednesday
Programme: 36 pages
Editor: Alan Eastwood (01793 729844)

CLUB PERSONNEL
President: Graham Price
Chairman: Tony Brown
Press Officer: Alan Eastwood
Manager: Alan Clark

ROSS TOWN

Secretary: Alan Bridges, Re-adel, Willowbrook,Greytree,Ross-On-Wye HR9 7JS.
Tel: 01989 564432 (H) 01594 542421 x 1276 (W)
Ground: Cinderford Town FC, Causeway Ground, Hilldene, Cinderford (01594822039)
Directions: From Gloucester take A40 to Ross-on-Wye, then A48 - Chepstow. In 10miles turn right at Elton garage onto A4151to Cinderford, thru Littledean, up steep hill, right at crossroads, and left into Latimer Rd.(F.C signposted).
Ground 5 mins walkfrom town centre
Capacity: 3,500   Cover: 1,000   Seats: 250   Floodlights: Yes
HONOURS Hereford Lge 94-95, Charity Shield 95-96; Hereford FA Charity Bowl 94-95; Worcester & Dist Lge 95-96, Baylis Cup 95-96; Hereford FA County Chall Cup 97-99 R-up 96; 98-99 Pershore Hospital Charity Cup R-up 95-96, Hellenic Lg Cup R-up: 99-00
PREVIOUS **Leagues:** Hereford Lg, Worcester & District League.
RECORD **Attendance:** 147 v Harrow Hill 26/3/97

FACT FILE
Founded:1993
Nickname: Riversiders
Colours: Red /black/black
Change colours:Green/Green/White
Midweek Matchday: Tuesday/Wednesday

CLUB PERSONNEL
Patron: Dave Sexton
Chairman: Geoff Jones
Director of Football and
Press Officer: Chris Parsons (01989 566712)
Manager: Martin Thomas
Coach: Chris Parsons
Physio: Sylvia Durham

SHRIVENHAM

Secretary: Matthew Hampson, 12 Grange Drive, Swindon, Wilts SN3 4LD
Tel: 01793 330983(H) 01793 423033 (B 07748 804593 M
E-mail: brad@currybeast.com

Match Secretary: Robb Forty, 40 Stallpitts, Shrivenham, Swindon, Wilts
Tel: 01793 783309(H) 01793 643744(B)

Ground: The Recreation Ground, Shrivenham SN6 8BJ
Tel: 01793 784453

Directions: 'Off Highworth Road, Shrivenham' Village is signposted off A420, six miles
east of Swindon, four miles west of Faringdon
Floodlights: No

Previous League: North Berks League
Record Gate 800 v Aston Villa X1 21st May 2000
Honours North Berks League Champions 00-01

FACT FILE
Colours: Blue & white hoops/blue/white.
Change colours: All Red & black
Midweek fixtures: Tuesdays

CLUB PERSONNEL

Chairman: Ian Richardson 01793 782033
Press Officer: Dan Prescott 07989 603948
Program Editor: Dan Prescott 07989 603948
Manager: Dave Clauson
Coach: Dave Clauson
Physio: P Mansfield

SLIMBRIDGE TOWN

Secretary: David Phillips, 14 Woodcock Close Abbeydale Gloucester GL4 4WT
Tel: 01452 414766 (T & F) 07754 088063 (Match Days Only)

Ground: Wisloe Road, Cambridge, Glos. GL2 7AF Tel: 01453 890361
Floodlights: No

Directions: From the A38 take the A 4135 to Dursley ground is 100 yards on left.

Previous League: Gloucestershire County Lge.

Record Gate: 110 v Pucklechurch 18th August 2001 (Glos County Lge)

FACT FILE

Colours: Blue/blue/white
Change: Red/black/red
Program Editor: Martin Tudor
Tel: 01453 549447
Midweek matchdays: Tuesday

CLUB PERSONNEL

Chairman: John Mack
Tel: 01453 543104
Manager: Doug Grey
Tel: 01453 544306
Coach: Alan Ward
Physio: Harry Brooks

WINTERBOURNE UNITED

Secretary: John Lloyd, 9 Stanford Close, Frampton Cotterell, Bristol. BS36 2DG
Tel: 01454 775841(H) 0117 9552048(B) E-mail john-lloyd@1-nil.co.uk

Ground Parkside Avenue, Winterbourne, Bristol BS36 1LX 01454 850059
Directions Leave Junction 1 of M32 turn left then left again at traffic lights, sign
posted Yate. Keep on road for two miles into Winterbourne After Ridings
High School turn right into Parkside Avenue, ground on right.
Floodlights No

Previous League: Gloucester County League
Honours: Gloucester County League Champions 00-01

FACT FILE
Nickname: The Bourne
Colours: White/red/red
Change colours: Red/white/white or red
Midweek fixtures: Tuesday or Thursday

CLUB PERSONNEL
Chairman: Robyn Maggs
Tel: 01454 887338
Press Officer: as Chairman
Program Editor: John Lloyd 01454 775841
Manager Stewart Jones
Coach: Richard Dunn
Physio: Ken Purnell

WITNEY UNITED

Secretary: Adrian Bircher 13 Colwell Drive Witney Oxon OX28 5NJ
Tel: 01993 200913 (H) 01865 393356 (B) 07779 326074 (M)

Ground: Marriotts Stadium, Downs Road, Witney OX8 5LY
Tel: 01993 702549

Directions: From West: A40 eastbound towards Oxford. At Minster Lovell r'about, take the
first exit towards Minster Lovell. After two miles turn right into Downs Road (signposted for
Witney Lakes Golf Club), ground half a mile on right.
From Witney town centre: head west down Welch Way, at r'about take 3rd exit
into Curbridge Road. At r'about, take 3rd exit into Deer Park Road, at traffic lights turn left into
Range Road, at end turn left ground is 400 yards on right.
Capacity: 3,500 Cover: 2,000 Seats: 280 Floodlights: Yes

FACT FILE
Formed 2002
Colours: Gold/black/black
Change: Green/white/green
Midweek matchday: Tuesday
Program Editor: Kieren Bushell
Tel: 07768 071102

CLUB PERSONNEL
Chairman: Philip Webb
Tel: 01993 844666
email: PAWebb01@aol.com

Manager: Ian Feaver
Coach/Physio: John Nolan

ASTON CLINTON

Secretary: John Roberts, 7 Garland Way, Aston Clinton, Bucks. HP22 5QW
Tel: 01296 630160 (H/Fax) email: john7gar@aol.com

Ground: Aston Clinton Park, London Road, Aston Clinton HP22 5HL
Tel 01296 630888
Floodlights: No

Directions: On the A41 London road opposite the Duck in Pub,
signposted "Aston Clinton Park".

PREVIOUS **League:** Chiltonian League to 99
RECORD **Attendance:** 74 v Penn & Tylers Green 00-01
00-01 **Leading Goalscorer:** Neil Roberts (13)

FACT FILE
Colours: Blue & white/blue/blue
Change colours: Red & white/white/red
Midweek fixtures: Tuesday

CLUB PERSONNEL
Chairman: John Roberts
01296 630160
Press Officer & Program Editor
Michael Dedman 01296 631093
Manager: guillermo Ganet
Coach: John Roberts

BINFIELD

Secretary: Vernon Bradshaw, 21 Audley Way Ascot Berks SL5 8EE
Tel: 01344 886144 (H); 01344 356651 (B)

Ground: Stubbs Lane Binfield   01344 860822

Directions From A329 Bracknell to Wokingham Road, turn by the Travel Lodge into
St. Marks Road, through the village into Terrace Road South & North,
then at T junction by All Saints' Church turn right & then left into Stubbs Hill.

Record Gate: 268 v Englefield 2001-02
Previous League: Chiltonian

FACT FILE
Colours: All reded.
Change colours:All Blue
Midweek fixtures: Tuesday
Nickname: Moles
CLUB PERSONNEL
Chairman: Bob Alloway
Press Officer: Glen Duggleby
Programme Editor: Rob Jones
Manager:T.B.A.
Coach: T.B.A.
01-02 Top scorer: Nicky Kellaway 19

BISLEY SPORTS

Secretary Michael Clement, 3 Lower Guilford Road, Knaphill, Woking, Surrey, GU21 2EE
Tel: 01483 475003 (H) 01483 736286 (B) E-mail: mclem0@aol.com
Ground: Burghfield Sports Grnd, Church Lane, Bisley GU24 9EB
Tel: 07796 094941
Directions: Exit M3 at Junction 3. Head southbound on A322 towards West End & Bisley.
Go over two roundabouts then turn left opposite the Hen & Chicken P. House
into Church Lane, ground is about 400 yards on left hand side.
Floodlights: No

FACT FILE
Colours:Shirts – Blue & black/black/black
Change colours: All red
Midweek fixtures: Tuesday
CLUB PERSONNEL
Chairman: Peter Lucas
email: sales@carfiles.co.uk Tel: 01276 671314
Press Officer: See Secretary
Program Editor: Bruce Henderson
Tel: 01483 472432
Manager: Andy Clement Tel: 01276 24374
Coaches: John Cook & Bruce Henderson

CHALFONT WASPS

Secretary: Bruce Keen, 25 Albion Crescent, Chalfont St Giles, Bucks. HP8 4ET
Tel: 01494 875129 (H) email: bruce.keen@tesco.net
Match Sec/Press Off. & Prog. Editor: Bob Isherwood 01494 871445 (H)
Ground: Crossleys, Bowstridge Lane, Chalfont. HP8 4QN Tel: 01494 875050
Directions On entering Chalfont St. Giles Village from A413 (Aylesbury - Uxbridge
Road), turn left into Bolostridge Lane immediately after the shops. After a quarter of a mile
turn right into Crossleys by a small green. Ground is directly ahead through the gates
Record Attendance: 50 v Harrow Hill Rovers 00-01
Previous League: Chiltonian
00-01 Leading Goalscorer: Gavin Groves (21)

FACT FILE
Colours: Yellow & black striped/black/black.
Change colours: All Green
Midweek fixtures: Tuesday
Nickname: The Stingers

CLUB PERSONNEL
Chairman: Steven Waddington
Manager: John Franks
Coach: Denis Higgs

DRAYTON WANDERERS

Web Site: http://website.lineone.net/~drayton_wanderers
Secretary: Tom Ash, 28 Stonecroft Ave., Iver, Bucks. SL0 9QF Tel: 01753 654413
Ground: Cowley Hall, Cowley Road Uxbridge 01895 258269
Directions: 1 1/2 miles south of Uxbridge town centre, follow signs to Heathrow
Airport, entrance to ground opposite the Grand Union Public House.
Record Attendance: 105 v Uxbridge 1995
Previous League: Chiltonian League
00-01 Leading Goalscorer: Ian Jones (24)

FACT FILE
Colours: Black & white stripes/black/black
Change cols: Red & yellow stripes/red/red
Midweek fixtures: Wednesday
Nickname: Wanderers
Program Editor:Mick Turtle 01895 446575

CLUB PERSONNEL
Chairman: Kevin Kelly Tel: 01895 824465
email: kevin.l.kelly@bt.com
Manager: Mick Turtle
Coach: Mick Stafford & Alan Carter

ENGLEFIELD GREEN ROVERS

Secretary   Jon West, 74 Lindsay Road, New Haw, Surrey KT15 3BE
Email Address: www.goode @ terry.com
Ground: Coopershill Lane Englefield Green   01784 43566

Directions: Leave M25 at junction 13, A30 by passing Egham, at top of Egham Hill turn right at traffic lights. After passing Village Green on the left take 2nd turning right at the north east of green. Ground on the right after half a mile.

Record Gate: 100 v Eton Wick, 1999

2000-01   **P.o.Y. & Top Scorer** Barney Jones **Captain :** Richards Banks

FACT FILE
Colours: All green & white
Change cols.: Red & white halves/white/white
Midweek fixtures: Tuesday
Nickname: The Rovers
CLUB PERSONNEL
Chairman: Terence David Goode
Manager:Gerry Kelly
Coach: Walter Reynolds
Physio,Press Off & Prog Ed: Peter Casey

ETON WICK

Secretary :   Barrie Shurville, 21 The Wheat Butts, Eton Wick, Berks., SL4 6JH.
& Press Officer& Programme Editor   01753 862969 (H)   07860262614 (B)
Ground: 01753 852749

Directions: From M4 junction 7 follow A4 to Maidenhead. At first roundabout (Sainsbury's) take B3026 towards Eton Wick. Ground is on the right after theparade of shops. From Eton take B3026 and ground is on the left after the Catholic church.
Record Gate   500 v Andover, 1993 FA Vase

Season 1999/2000: Member of the Chiltonian League

FACT FILE
Nickname: The Wick
Cols:Amber/black/black   Change:All white
Midweek fixtures: Tuesday
CLUB PERSONNEL
Chairman: Micky Foulkes 01753 733629
Man/Coach:Rob Curtis   01753 851877
Physio: Bobby White
2001-01 Leading goalscorer: Ricky Allen
Capt: & P.o.Y.: Mick McManus

FINCHAMPSTEAD

Secretary: David Hobbs,57 Welford Road, Woodley,Berkshire RG5 4QS
Tel : 01189 696195   Web Site: www.finchampsteadfc.co.uk
Match Sec.:   Michael Husk, 16 Sadlers Lane Winnersh Berks RG41 5AJ
01189 785949 (H)
Press Officer: Stephen King 01189 732890 E-mail: Stephen@kingsb.fsnet.co.uk
Ground: Finchhampstead Memorial Park, Thevillage,FinchampsteaRG114JR
Tel No: 01189732890
Directions: A321 from Wokingham, then fork right onto B3016. At the Greyhound pub turn right onto the B3348. The ground is 200 yards on the right.
Record Gate   425 v Sandhurst, 1958/ 9
Previous League: Chiltonian

FACT FILE
Nickname: Finch
Colours: Sky blue & white/black/black
Change colours: All red
Midweek fixtures: Wednesday
CLUB PERSONNEL
Chairman: Kieron Brown (01344 452007)
E-mail: aquaspec@globalnet.co.uk
Manager: Steven McClurg
Coach : Willie Graham
Top Scorer 2001-02: Danny Humphries 25

HOLYPORT

Secretary: Eddie Pearce 1 Australia Ave Maidenhead Berks SL6 7DJ
Tel: 01628 673554 (H) 01628 680680 (B) 01628682700 (F)
E-mail: EddieP@Maidenads.co.uk

Ground: Braywick Sports Centre, Braywick Road, Maidenhead, Berks.
Tel: 01628 627066   Floodlights: No
Directions: From M4 exit at junction 8/9 take Maidenhead Central road, at roundabout take 1st left, follow dual carriageway for 300 yards and turn right into complex, signed Maidenhead Rugby club. In sports park follow road to the end, main pitch is on the left with changing rooms in front of you.
Previous League: East Berks. Lge >2002

FACT FILE
Colours: Claret/green/yellow
Change: Blue/red/red
Midweek matchday: Wednesday

CLUB PERSONNEL
Program Editor: Mark Burton
Tel: 01494 436331
Chairman: Norman House
Tel: 01628 626882
Manager: Mark Burton

HOUNSLOW BOROUGH F.C.

Secretary: Stefano Poulos, 7 Fairways Isleworth Middlesex TW7 4NS
0208 560 9763 (H); 0208 5800591 (B); 0208 560 1295 (F)
07765305003 (M)   E-mail hounslowborough.f.c@lineone,net
Program Editor: Lee-John Tansey   07889 342865   E-mail: l.tansey@talk21.com
Ground: White Lodge Syon Lane Isleworth   0208 560 8829
Directions: From M25 onto M4 at junction 3 then follow signs to Central London. At Gillett Corner turn left into Syon Lane. Ground 100 metres on the left.
From A40 turn at Target Roundabout and follow A312 Hayes by pass to A4 then follow signs to Central London until Gillett Corner, turn left and ground on the left.
Record Gate 200 v Rayners Lane, 3rd January 2000
Season 1999/2000: Member of the Chiltonian League

FACT FILE
Colours: Blue & white quarters/blue/blue
Change cols.: Red & black quarters/red/red
Midweek fixtures: Tuesday
Web site: www.sportworldwide.com
CLUB PERSONNEL
Chairman: James Stefanopoulos
0208 667 1269
Manager:Jamie Rooke (07760213481)
Coach:Antony Yersley Physio: Rehana Iqbal
2000-01 Capt:Tony Yearsley, P.o.Y.:W.ayne
Tisson Top Scorer: Junior Hickson 27

MARTIN BAKER SPORTS

Secretary: Michael Hayselden, 53 Leven Way Hayes Middlesex UB3 2SS
Press Off. & Prog. Editor 0208 5732887 (H); 0208 8406992 (B)

Ground: Martins Field Tilehouse Lane Denham 01895 833077
Club Email: mick.hayselden@bt.com
Directions: A412 from the A40 London / Oxford Road. (Do not confuse the A40 with
the M40 which runs parallel). The entrance to the ground is approximately 150 yards on
the right between the houses.
Season 1999/2000: Member of the Chiltonian League
2000-01 Leading Goalscorer: Ray Bennett 17   Captain & P.O.Y: Paul Curd

FACT FILE
Colours: White & blue/blue/blue
Change colours: Green or gold/green or
black/green or black
Midweek fixtures: Tuesday
Nickname: Baker Boys
CLUB PERSONNEL
Chairman: John Curd
Manager: Ray Flegg 0956 980880
Coach & Physio: Ron Wise

MILTON UNITED

Secretary: Sue Walker, 122 High St, Sutton Courtney, Abingdon, OX14 4AX Tel: 01235 847158 (H)
Ground: The Sportsfield,Milton Hill, Potash Lane,Milton Heights,Oxon Tel:01235 832999
Directions: Exit A34 at Milton, 10 miles south of Oxford & 12 miles north of J 13, M4. A4130
towards Wantage, after 100m 1st left, then 1st right into Milton Hill. Entrance 200m on left.
Capacity: Seats: 50   Cover:Seats   Floodlights: Yes   Club Shop: No
Clubhouse: On ground, open matchdays
HONOURS Hellenic Lg 90-91 (Div 1 89-90 R-Up.94-95)), Nth Berks Lg(4) 85-86 87-89(R-up 84-
85 86-87, Lg Cup(3) 84-86 88-89, Div 2 80-81, Charity Shield(4) 84-86 87-89 (R-up 82-83), Nth
Berks War Mem. Cup(3) 83-85 87-88, Berks & Bucks Intermediate Cup 90-91
RECORD   Attendance: 500 v Almondsbury Picksons, Hellenic Lg 90-91
            Goalscorer: Nigel Mott

FACT FILE
Founded: 1926
Colours: Sky & claret/claret/sky & claret
Change colours: Orange/white/white
Midweek matchday: Tuesday
Programme Editor / Press Officer:
David Taylor (01235 816376)
CLUB PERSONNEL
Chairman: Ken Tull   President: John Cannon
Match Secretary: Sid Tindall (01491 835630)
Manager: Paul Biddle
Coach: Nigel Mott Physio: John Belcher

PENN & TYLERS GREEN

Secretary: Malcolm James, Woodlands, Forty Green Rd, Forty Green, Beaconsfield HP9 1XS
Tel: 01494 677311 (H) 0207 777 0602 (B) email: malcolm.d.james@chase.com

Ground: Elm Road, Penn, Bucks HP10 8LF Tel: 01494 815346
Directions: Entrance to ground is off the main Hazlemere to Beaconsfield road. From
Beaconsfield follow the road through Penn towards Hazlemere, pass the
pond on green & ground entrance is on the right before going downhill.

Record   Attendance: 125 v Chalfont Wasps 00-01
Previous   League: Chiltonian
00-01   Leading Goalscorer: Paul Gardner (12)

FACT FILE
Colours: Blue & white striped/blue/white
Change colours: All yellow
Midweek fixtures: Tuesday
Program Editor: Neil Bellamy 01494 812492

CLUB PERSONNEL
Chairman & Match Secretary:
Robert Dalling 01494 671424
Press Officer: Neil Bellamy

Manager: Richard Mikurenda

PEPPARD

Secretary: Chris Boyles, 14 Redwood Avenue Woodley Reading Berks RG5 4DR
0118 9699488 (H); 0118 9872473 (B); 0118 9628130 (F)
E-mail: peppardfc@dboyles.freeserve.co.uk

Ground: Bishopswood Sports Ground Horsepond Road Gallowstree Common
0118 9722675
Directions: On the Cane End to Peppard road which runs between the A4074
(Reading to Woodcote & Oxford) and the B481 (Reading to Nettlebed) roads

Club website: www.geocities.com@peppardfc

FACT FILE
Colours: All red
Change colours: Light blue/navy/navy
Midweek fixtures: Tuesday
Website: www.geocities.com@peppard
CLUB PERSONNEL
Chairman: Sean Gillett 0118 9463425
2001-02
Captain : Kevin Watkins
P.o.Y.: Lee Hilliard
Top Scorer: Carlus Paree (10)

PRESTWOOD

Secretary: Paul Mullen, 16 Maybush Gardens, Prestwood, Bucks HP 16 9EA
Tel No: 01494 864048   EMail: paul.mullen @the-fa,org

Ground: Prestwood Sports Centre   01494 865946

Directions: From the Chequers Public House in the Centre of Prestwood, take the
road signposted to Great Hampden. The ground is approximately half a mile on the left.

Season 1999/2000: Member of the Chiltonian League

FACT FILE
Colours: Claret / claret
Change colours: orange/ blck/orange
Midweek fixtures: Tuesday

CLUB PERSONNEL
Manager:Steven Simmons 01494 725217
Res. Manager: A Henney 01494 712544

QUARRY NOMADS

Secretary: Keith Dolton, 58 Pitts Road Headington Oxford OX3 8AZ 01865 450256 (H)
Match Sec.: Linda Dolton, 58 Pitts Road Headington Oxford OX3 8AZ 01865 450256 (H)

Ground: Margaret Road Headington   07860 408769
Directions: Exit M40 J 8, then A40 towards Oxford to Green Road r'about (McDonalds on left), straight over towards Headington.Take third left into Wharton Road, then at T junction turn left into Margaret Road. Ground on left.

Record Gate 267 v Witney Town, 1994
Previous League: Chiltonian
00-01 Leading Goalscorer: Paul Kimber (11)

FACT FILE
Web Site: www.qnfc.co.uk
Colours: Black & white/black/black
Change colours: All yellow or all red
Midweek fixtures: Tuesday
Prog. Editor: Andrew Molden 01865 433686
E-mail: ac.mold@hotmart.com

CLUB PERSONNEL
Chairman: Richard Lawrence 01865 873258
Press Officer: Paul Dolton 01865 768970
Manager: Darren Henderson & Andrew
Physio: Paul Dolton

R.S. BASINGSTOKE

Secretary: Jacqui Townley, 26 Millard Close, Basingstoke RG21 5TT
Tel: 01256 357992 (H) 07802 211156 (M) 01256 330902 (F)
email: j.townley@another.com

Ground: Whiteditch Playingfield, Sherborne Rd., Basingstoke RG21 5TP 01256 814618
Directions: From M3 junction 6 cross Black Dam r'about take 2nd exit into Oakridge Rd, after approx. 3/4 mile you pass school, then turn left into Sherborne Road. Ground approx. 200 metres on left.

Record Gate: 120 v Hartley Witney, 1994
Previous League: Chiltonian
00-01 Leading Goalscorer: Dale Bristow (22)

FACT FILE
Colours: Red & black/red & black/black
Change colours: All blue
Midweek fixtures: Wednesday

CLUB PERSONNEL
Chairman & Press Officer:
Mike Davis 01256 468873
Manager: Albert Fox
Asst. Man.: Kevin Haystaff
Physio: Chris Townley

RAYNERS LANE

Secretary: Tony Pratt, 4 Stirling Close Cowley Uxbridge Middx. UB8 2BA
01895 233853 (H)
Ground: 151 Rayners Lane, Rayners Lane, South Harrow0208 8669659
Directions: From A40 Polish War Memorial (First junction after Northolt Aerodrome) turn left into A4180 (West End Road), approx. 500m turn right into Station Approach, at lights turn right into Victoria Road Sainsbury's on the right). At next roundabout continue straight on to lights and take 2nd turning on left into Rayners Lane. Ground is approx. half a mile on left.
Record Gate 550 v Wealdstone, 1983 Season 2000/2001: Member of the Hellenic Lg
2001-02 Leading goalscorer: Danny Mills 11**Captain**: Steve Bird **P.o.Y.**: Steve Cott

FACT FILE
Nickname: The Lane
Colours: Yellow/green/yellow
Change colours: White/blue/white
Midweek fixtures: Tuesday
CLUB PERSONNEL
Chairman: Richard Mitchell 020 8422 6340
Press Off/Prog.Ed: Tom Lynn
0208 868 4671
Manager/Coach: Richard Hedge
020 8480843
Physio: Ron Fairhead

GO TRAVEL
KENT LEAGUE

FEEDER TO: DR MARTENS LEAGUE

President: D D Baker   **Chairman:** P C Wager   **Vice Chairman:** D Richmond
Hon. Secretary & Treasurer: A R Vinter, Bakery House, The Street, Chilham, Nr
Canterbury, Kent CT4 8BX   Tel: 01227 730457   Fax: 01227 738880

During the past season we have, as a League, lost two of the oldest connections in our President, Mr Doug Baker, who gave us almost a lifetime of service in many capacities, and Mr Ernie Bennett, President of the Kent County Football Association also passed away in 2002. He was a regular visitor to our grounds and made many friends. We shall miss them both.

On the playing front we have seen, in the Premier Division, one of the closest contests for a few years with the Championship being taken on goal difference on the final day of the season. During the season, VCD Athletic put together an extraordinary unbeaten run of games which saw them open a substantial lead, this after losing on the opening day. The title race then developed into a "three horse race" with Deal Town and Maidstone United coming into the frame.

The leaders faltered, lost at home to Deal and then dropped points elsewhere, which made the final weeks of the season a nail-biting affair. There were only three points between them with one game left to play. Deal, in third place, had the better goal difference and were due to play Maidstone on the final day whilst VCD needed a win at Cray Wanderers three days earlier to claim their first title. A last minute equaliser by Cray denied VCD. On the final day, at the Charles Sports Ground in front of an excellent crowd, Maidstone United were crowned Champions when they defeated Deal by three goals to one. The "Stones" completed the double when they defeated Whitstable Town, watched by 856 spectators, in the Premier Division Cup two weeks later.

In Division One, played in two sections, we had a "Play-Off" for the Championship between Dartford and Dover Athletic, the two section winners. The South Coast side won, after extra time, and they went on to complete their own double as they defeated Thamesmead Town in the Division One Cup by a single goal. Due to the small number of fixtures in the Division, a Floodlight Trophy was arranged for clubs who wished to enter and have more games. Chatham Town finally came out on top in the competition.

On the County scene, Thamesmead Town defeated Cray Wanderers in the Final of the Kent Senior Trophy and the Kent Intermediate Cup was won by Thamesmead's Reserves when they beat Margate in the final. Nationally, Whitstable Town was our last survivor in the AXA FA Cup before they lost to Erith & Belvedere and Thamesmead Town reached the Third Round of the FA Carlsberg Vase before losing to Bemerton Heath.

During the season, the Kent Football League has taken part in a National Fair Play Award scheme run by Ladbrokes, which has made discipline a very important part of our game. Our League winners were Tunbridge Wells with 24 points and, I understand, they finished eleventh in the National list, a very creditable performance. Beckenham Town won the Northern Section of Division One, whilst Dover Athletic were the winners of the Southern Section award.

We would like to thank Bass Brewers for the support over the last three years of sponsorship, which came to an end in June. A new sponsorship deal was agreed with Go Travel of Chislehurst and Petts Wood. The Roberts family did so much for Kent Football in the past as Winstonlead, one of the longest running sponsorships in football, and we look forward to their continued and much appreciated support.

Paul Rivers, Hon Press Officer

PREMIER DIVISION FINAL LEAGUE TABLE 2001-02

	P	W	D	L	F	A	Pts	GD		P	W	D	L	F	A	Pts	GD
Maidstone United	30	20	6	4	72	32	66	40	Beckenham Town	30	11	7	12	43	45	40	-2
VCD Athletic	30	20	6	4	67	31	66	36	Whitstable Town	30	9	9	12	43	51	36	-8
Deal Town	30	19	5	6	79	38	62	41	Lordswood	30	8	9	13	44	55	36	-11
Thamesmead T	30	17	6	7	59	39	57	20	Slade Green	30	11	2	17	35	47	35	-12
Cray Wanderers	30	15	6	9	56	44	51	12	Erith Town	30	10	3	17	42	60	33	-18
Ramsgate	30	13	5	12	57	50	44	7	Hythe Town	30	8	7	15	31	49	31	-18
Herne Bay	30	13	5	12	53	49	41	4	Greenwich Boro	30	5	4	21	31	70	19	-39
Tunbridge Wells	30	10	10	10	45	46	40	-1	Faversham Town	30	3	6	21	30	81	15	-51

DIVISION ONE FINAL LEAGUE TABLES 2001-02

NORTHERN SECTION	P	W	D	L	F	A	Pts	GD		SOUTHERN SECTION	P	W	D	L	F	A	Pts	GD
Dartford	20	13	4	3	51	26	43	25		Dover Athletic	20	16	3	1	76	18	53	58
Cray Wanderers	20	14	3	3	46	22	42	24		Ramsgate	20	11	2	7	52	25	35	27
VCD Athletic	20	12	5	3	50	29	41	21		Sittingbourne	20	10	4	6	43	33	34	10
Chatham Town	20	10	3	7	33	28	33	5		Deal Town	20	10	3	7	59	44	33	15
Thamesmead T	20	10	3	7	40	36	33	4		Ashford Town	20	8	6	6	43	29	30	14
Furness	20	8	3	9	45	40	27	5		Folkestone Invicta	20	8	4	8	40	37	28	3
Erith Town	20	7	4	9	38	45	25	-7		Herne Bay	20	7	6	7	42	39	27	3
Beckenham T	20	6	3	11	26	35	24	-9		Hastings Town	20	7	2	11	44	58	23	-14
Tunbridge Wells	20	6	2	12	35	45	20	-10		Margate	20	6	4	10	36	54	22	-18
Lordswood	20	3	5	12	32	46	14	-14		Whitstable Town	20	5	5	10	32	59	20	-27
Greenwich Boro	20	3	1	16	23	67	10	-44		Hythe Town	20	1	3	16	12	85	5	-73

DIVISION ONE CHAMPIONSHIP PLAY-OFF: Dartford v Dover Athletic 1-3 after extra time

PREMIER DIVISION RESULTS CHART 2001-02

		1	2	3	4	5	6	7	8	9	10	11	12	13	14	15	16
1	Beckenham Town	X	1-2	3-2	3-1	2-0	5-0	1-3	4-1	2-1	1-1	1-0	1-0	0-1	1-1	1-1	1-1
2	Cray Wanderers	3-1	X	0-1	4-0	1-2	2-1	2-0	3-2	2-2	1-2	1-0	1-1	1-2	2-1	2-2	3-1
3	Deal Town	4-2	4-4	X	1-2	4-0	5-2	2-1	5-0	7-0	1-3	2-1	4-0	1-0	2-0	0-4	2-2
4	Erith Town	2-1	1-2	2-3	X	2-0	4-1	1-4	1-1	1-5	0-2	1-1	1-3	1-0	3-6	1-3	2-0
5	Faversham Town	0-1	0-5	2-1	0-3	X	2-2	2-3	0-2	1-3	2-3	1-1	0-1	1-3	2-1	1-3	0-4
6	Greenwich Borough	1-0	2-2	0-3	0-1	2-2	X	0-3	0-2	2-3	0-4	2-3	1-0	2-1	1-2	0-3	1-4
7	Herne Bay	4-0	1-4	1-1	4-2	1-0	2-1	X	1-2	2-0	3-4	1-3	4-1	2-2	3-1	2-4	0-2
8	Hythe Town	2-2	2-0	0-0	0-1	3-3	0-1	0-0	X	1-1	0-1	0-2	5-0	0-2	3-2	0-3	3-2
9	Lordswood	4-0	1-3	0-4	3-1	2-2	0-0	1-1	0-2	X	2-1	1-3	0-2	2-2	3-3	2-3	1-1
10	Maidstone United	2-2	0-1	2-0	1-2	5-2	4-0	1-2	3-0	3-2	X	2-0	3-1	1-0	3-0	1-0	3-1
11	Ramsgate	0-1	1-2	2-5	2-2	4-0	1-3	3-2	3-0	1-4	3-3	X	3-2	3-3	3-0	2-1	3-2
12	Slade Green	2-1	3-0	0-1	1-0	4-2	1-2	2-0	0-0	0-1	0-4	0-1	X	2-3	1-2	1-1	4-1
13	Thamesmead Town	2-1	5-1	2-3	4-2	3-1	4-2	3-0	0-0	2-0	2-2	2-1	0-1	X	4-2	1-5	2-1
14	Tunbridge Wells	0-2	2-1	2-2	1-0	3-0	2-1	0-0	3-0	0-0	1-1	4-3	3-1	1-1	X	0-0	0-0
15	VCD Athletic	2-0	2-0	0-5	2-1	8-1	3-2	3-0	2-0	2-0	0-0	3-2	1-0	0-2	2-1	X	2-1
16	Whitstable Town	2-2	1-1	1-4	2-1	1-1	0-3	2-1	2-0	1-0	3-7	1-0	1-0	0-1	1-1	2-2	X

FLOODLIGHT TROPHY TABLE

	P	W	D	L	F	A	Pts			P	W	D	L	F	A	Pts
Chatham Town	18	13	2	3	46	19	41		Deal Town	18	5	5	8	39	41	20
Dover Athletic	18	11	4	3	47	23	37		Lordswood	18	6	2	10	28	35	20
Herne Bay	18	9	5	4	38	31	32		Tunbridge Wells	18	5	3	10	23	40	18
Ramsgate	18	9	2	7	39	25	29		Hastings Town	18	4	5	9	29	44	17
Ashford Town	18	7	2	9	31	29	23		Margate	18	5	1	12	21	54	16

PREMIER DIVISION CUP 2001-02

FIRST ROUND

Lordswood	v	Tunbridge Wells	3-2	Faversham Town	v	VCD Athletic	VCD W/O
Deal Town	v	Beckenham Town	3-4	Thamesmead Town	v	Maidstone United	0-1
Herne Bay	v	Whitstable Town	1-2	Slade Green	v	Greenwich Boro	1-4, 2-2
Cray Wanderers	v	Ramsgate	1-0	Erith Town	v	Hythe Town	2-3

SECOND ROUND

Lordswood	v	VCD Athletic	0-4	Beckenham Town	v	Maidstone United	0-1
Whitstable Town	v	Greenwich Borough	3-0	Cray Wanderers	v	Erith Town	2-1

SEMI-FINALS (Two Legs)

VCD Athletic	v	Maidstone United	0-1, 2-4	Whitstable Town	v	Cray Wanderers 2-1, 0-0

FINAL

Maidstone United	v	Whitstable Town	2-0

DIVISION ONE CUP 2001-02

FIRST ROUND

Sittingbourne	v	VCD Athletic	0-3, 1-4	Whitstable Town	v	Herne Bay	6-1, 1-0
Folkestone Invicta	v	Erith Town	2-1, 5-3	Chatham Town	v	Tunbridge Wells	3-1, 3-3
Ramsgate	v	Lordswood	2-4, 3-0	Furness	v	Hythe Town	9-3, 3-0

SECOND ROUND

Cray Wanderers	v	Greenwich Boro	1-0, 2-0	VCD Athletic	v	Deal Town	1-2, 4-1
Beckenham Town	v	Margate	1-2, 0-2	Whitstable Town	v	Dover Athletic	0-2, 2-4
Folkestone Invicta	v	Dartford	2-0, 1-2	Ashford Town	v	Thamesmead T	0-2, 1-0
Chatham Town	v	Hastings Town	0-0, 1-0	Ramsgate	v	Furness	6-1, 3-2

THIRD ROUND

Cray Wanderers	v	VCD Athletic	1-3	Margate	v	Dover Athletic	2-4
Folkestone Invicta	v	Thamesmead Tn	0-4, 4-4	Chatham Town	v	Ramsgate	0-2

SEMI-FINALS

VCD Athletic	v	Dover Athletic	1-2, 2-4	Thamesmead Town	v	Ramsgate	1-0, 3-3

FINAL

Dover Athletic	v	Thamesmead Town	1-0

GOALS OF THE MONTH

	Premier Division	First Division
September	Deal Town	Dover Athletic
	Greenwich Borough	
	Herne Bay	
	Whitstable Town	
	Ramsgate	
October	Cray Wanderers	Furness
	Deal Town	
November	VCD Athletic	Ramsgate
December	Deal Town	Dover Athletic
January	Maidstone United	Lordswood
February	Deal Town	Dover Athletic
March	Thamesmead Town	Deal Town
		Herne Bay
April	Maidstone United	VCD Athletic

MANAGER OF THE MONTH

September	Martin Ford	VCD Athletic
October	Ian Jenkins	Cray Wanderers
November	Terry Hill	Thamesmead T
December	Simon Bryant	Deal Town
January	Jim Ward	Maidstone Utd
February	Simon Bryant	Deal Town
March	Jim Ward	Maidstone Utd
April	Terry Hill	Thamesmead T

FAIR PLAY AWARDS

	Played	Pts	Ave
Premier Division			
Tunbridge Wells	30	24	0.800
Thamesmead Town	30	27	0.900
Lordswood	30	30	1.000
Faversham Town	30	32	1.067
Maidstone United	30	34	1.133
VCD Athletic	30	35	1.167
Erith Town	30	35	1.167
Deal Town	30	37	1.233
Ramsgate	30	40	1.333
Whitstable Town	30	42	1.400
Slade Green	30	42	1.400
Greenwich Borough	30	49	1.633
Beckenham Town	30	50	1.667
Herne Bay	30	57	1.900
Hythe Town	30	58	1.933
Cray Wanderers	30	67	2.233
Division One South			
Dover Athletic	20	15	0.750
Deal Town	20	16	0.800
Folkestone Invicta	20	16	0.800
Division One North			
Beckenham Town	20	9	0.450
Thamesmead Town	20	13	0.650

BECKENHAM TOWN

Secretary: Peter Palmer,36 Inglewood,Pixton Way, Selsdon, Surrey CR0 9LP
Tel: 020 86513363 Mobile 0374 728758

Ground: Eden Park Avenue, Beckenham, Kent   Tel: 0181 650 1066

Directions: M25, A21 to Bromley then follow signs to Beckenham. Ground 1 mile west of town off A214, 2 mins walk from Eden Park (BR) station - trains from London Bridge. Bus 264
Capacity: 4,000   Seats: 120   Cover: 120   Floodlights: Yes
Clubhouse: All day opening at weekends. Hot & cold food, teas, etc. Bar & dance area. Pool & fruit machines   Club Shop: Yes

HONOURS London Spartan Lg Cup R-up 77-78 78-79, Kent Snr Tphy R-up 81-82 93-94, Kent Lg Cup R-up 84-85 92-93 (Div 2 Cup R-up 90-91)

PREVIOUS **Leagues:** S. E. London Amtr 71-73; Metropolitan 73-75; London Spartan 75-82
Ground: Stanhope Grove, Beckenham (60 yrs)

RECORD **Gate:** 720 v Berkhamstead F.A.Cup 94-95
Scorer: Ricky Bennett   **Appearances:** Lee Fabian

FACT FILE
Reformed: 1971
Nickname: Reds
Colours:All Red
Change Colours:Yellow/blue/blue
Midweek matchday: Tuesday
Programme: 8 pages, 50p
Editor:Secretary

CLUB PERSONNEL
Chairman: John Weatherhead
Vice Chairman: B Hollaway
Manager: Kevin Sugrue
Asst Manager: J Moore

CRAY WANDERERS

Secretary: Dave Brown,16 Westhurst road, Chislehurst, Kent BR7 6HT (020 8467 2128)
Ground: Bromley F.C. Hayes Lane, Bromley, Kent BR2 9EF (0181 460 5291 or 0181 313 3992)
Directions: One mile from Bromley South (BR). Buses 316, 146 and 119 passground.
Junction 4 off M25, then A21 towards London
Capacity: 5,000   Cover: 2,500   Seats: 1,300   Floodlights: Yes
Clubhouse: Open pub hours (freehouse). Hot & cold food available   Club Shop: Yes

HONOURS London Lg(2) 56-58 (Lg Cup 54-55), Aetolian Lg 62-63 (Lg Cup 63-64), GtrLondon Lg 65-66 (Lg Cup(2) 64-66), Metropolitan Lg Cup 70-71 (Amtr Cup(2) 66-68), London Spartan Lg(2) 76-78, Kent Lg 01-02 80-81 (R-up 79-80 90-91, Lg Cup 83-84), Kent Snr Tphy 92-93, Kent Amtr Cup(4) 30-31 62-65
PREVIOUS **Leagues:** Kent 1894-1903 6-7 9-14 34-38; W Kent 03-06 07-09; London 20-34 51-59; Kent Amtr 38-39 46-51; S London All 43-46; Aetolian 59-64; GtrLondon 64-66; Metropolitan 66-71; London Metropolitan 71-75; London Spartan 75-78
Grounds: Star Lane; Tothills; Twysden; Fordcroft; Grassmeade, St Mary Cray
CLUB RECORDS Gate: 1,523 v Stamford, F.A. Vase QF 79-80
Goalscorer: Ken Collishaw, 272   **Appearances:** John Dorey c500, 61-72
Win: 15-0 v Sevenoaks, 1894-95   **Defeat:** 1-11 v Bromley, 20-21

FACT FILE
Founded: 1860
Nickname: Wands
Sponsors: Hillman Grant
Colours: Amber & black
Change Colours: White/black/black
Midweek matchday: Wednesday
Programme: 32 pages, 50p
Editor/Press Officer: Greg Mann
Tel: 0181 318 9604(H) 0171 500 4496B)
Websites: http://hometown.aq.com\cray
or wanderersfc/club.html

CLUB PERSONNEL
Chairman: Gary Hillman
President: Bill Faulkner
Team Manager: Ian jenkins
Asst.Manager: John Allwright
Reserve Team Manager: Sam Wright

DEAL TOWN

Secretary: Colin Adams,156 Mill Hill, Deal, Kent CT149JA (01304 372784)

Ground: Charles Sports Ground, St Leonards Road, Deal, Kent   Tel: 01304 375623
Directions: A258 through Walmer, left into Cornwall Road, continue intoHamilton Road, veer left into Mill Rd, follow round to right into Manor Road, right into St Leonards Road, ground 100 yards on right. 1 mile from both Walmerand Deal BR stations. Local buses stop near ground
Capacity: 2500   Seats: 180   Cover: 180   Floodlights: Yes
Clubhouse: Matchdays & functions. Bar. Tea bar with hot & cold food   Club Shop: Yes
HONOURS F.A.Vase Winners 99-00,   Kent Lg 53-54,99-00 (R-up 88-89,98-99) Lg Cup 57-58, 81-82 , 98-99 (R-up 94-95), Kent Snr Tphy 94-95 , 99-00 R-up 82-83 90-91, Gtr London Lg Cup 67-68, Aetolian Lg R-up 59-60

PREVIOUS **Leagues:** Kent 09-59; Aetolian 59-63; Southern 63-66; Gtr London 66-71

RECORDS **Gate:**(Competitive) 2,495 v Newcastle Town F.A.Vase, S-Final 2nd Leg. 26.3.00
Scorer: Joe Brayne 175
Appearances: Alan Barrow 544 (recent times)

Player progressing: Danny Wallace (Southampton)

FACT FILE
Founded:1908
Nickname: Town
Sponsors: Adamson Motors
Colours: Black & white hoops/white/white
Change: Yellow & Blue halves/blue/blue
Midweek matchday: Tuesday
Reserves' Lge: Bass Brewers Kent Div 1
Programme: 36/40 pages, £1.00
Editor: Colin Adams (01304 372784)

2001-02
Captain: Ian Hayes
P.o.Y.: Allan Tait
Top Scorer: Allan Tait 32

CLUB PERSONNEL
Chairman: Graham Johns
Vice-Chairman: David Saunders
Fixture Sec: Colin Adams (01304 372784)

Top:
Cray Wanderers FC
Photo:
Alan Coomes

Centre:
Greenwich Borough
Back Row (l-r):
Justin Roach,
Adrian Griffiths,
Jamie Muldowney,
Nathan Walkey,
Martin Roberts,
Martin Delany,
Sean Crayden.
Front Row:
Solomon Taiwo,
Paul Morrison,
Terry Cohen,
Steffan Moore,
Steve Cotter, Paul
Brown.
Photo:
Alan Coomes

Bottom:
Deal Town FC.
Back Row (l-r):
Dave Briggs
(Physio), Jamie
Marriott, Darren
Waring, Mick
Heather, John
Rigden, Craig
Tucker, Tom
Stephens, Darryl
Bartholomew,
Adam Galvin,
Jason Altree, Dave
Dadd (Mngrs Asst).
Front Row: Allan
Tait, Leon Ingram,
Andy Bowyer,
Simon Bryant
(Mngr), Ian Hayes,
Scott McRobert,
Mark Pollard,
Mascot Joe Bryant
(Manager's son)

ERITH TOWN

Secretary: Jim Davie, 6 Dashwood Close, Broomfield Road, Bexleyheath, Kent. DA6 7NU
Tel: 020 8306 7068

Ground: Erith Sports Stadium, Avenue Road, Erith, Kent DA8 3AJ (01322 350 271)
Directions: Off the A206 at Erith, into Victoria Road, then left at T junction into Avenue Road.
First right along driveway which leads to leisure car park, stadium on left.600 yards from Erith BR.
Capacity: 1,450   **Seats:** 1,006   **Cover:** 60**Floodlights:** Yes (156 lux)
Clubhouse: Use Leisure Facilities   **Shop:** No

PREVIOUS   Leagues: London Metropolitan Sunday 1959-91, London-Spartan 1991-96
Names: Woolwich Town 1959-89 and 1990-97 Woolwich Heathway 1989-90

CLUB RECORDS Appearances: Eric Nwaokobia 172 (9)
Victory: 7-2 v Canterbury City, Kent Sen. Trophy 20.12.00   **Defeat:** 0-8 v Deal
Goalscorer: Lee Putnam 29   **Goals in Season:** Dean Bowey 18 00-01
Attendance: 136 v Lewes F.A.Cup 1Q 99-00

HONOURS: Met Sunday Lge: Senior Section 1966, 1971, 1975.
London Spartan Lge: Intermediate Cup R-up 1994 & 1995. Div 1 R-up: 1995.
London F.A. Intermediate Cup R-up 1995. London F.A. Senior Cup R-up 2000

FACT FILE
Founded: 1959
Nickname: The Dockers
Colours: Yellow/black/black
Change Colours: White/red/red
Midweek matchday: Monday
Reserve League: Kent League
Programme: 40-52 pages £1.00 (Ian Birrell)

2001-02
Captain: Alan Hanlon
Top Scorer:Simon Williams 8
P.o.Y.: James Blyther

CLUB PERSONNEL
Chairman: Albert Putnam.   V. Chair: Phil Legg
President: Cyril Rebak
Manager: John Adams Coach: Jim Hardy
General Manager: Ian Birrell
Press Secretary: Matthew Panting

FAVERSHAM TOWN

Secretary: Ken Black, 181 Langley Way, West Wickham, Kent BR4 0DN
Tel Nos: 020 8325 0046 (H) 07932 770485 (M)
Ground: New Stadium, Salters Lane, Faversham, Kent (01795 532738)

Directions: On A2 (Canterbury road) just west of town
Capacity: 2,000   **Seats:** 350   **Cover:** 1,500   **Floodlights:** Yes
Clubhouse: Open matchdays (Sat/Sun/Tues) Wed/Thurs. Snacks sold

HONOURS Kent Lg 69-70 70-71 77-78 89-90, R-up 87-88, Lg Cup 70-71 90-91, R-up 82-83,
Kent Snr Tphy 76-77 77-78 (R-up 87-88 88-89),
Kent Amtr Cup 56-57 58-59 71-72 72-73 73-74

PREVIOUS   Leagues: Aetolian 59-64; Metropolitan 64-71; Athenian 71-76
Grounds: Ashford Rd 1901-46; Gordon Square 46-58

RECORD   Gate: 1,400 v Sheppey Utd, 1949
Scorer: Tony Rudd 43   **Appearances:** Bob Mason
Win: 8-0 v Greenwich B., Aug'89   **Defeat:** 0-9 v Sittingbourne, Jan '82

FACT FILE
Founded: 1901
Nickname: Town
Colours: White/blue/blue
Change Colours: All Blue
Midweek matchday: Wednesday
Reserves' League: Kent Lg Div 2
Programme: 16 pages, 40p
Editor: Andy Maxted

CLUB PERSONNEL
Chairman: John Glover
President: Cris Aisani
Commercial Mgr: Terry Whitehead
Manager: John Glover
Coach: Bob Mason

GREENWICH BOROUGH

Secretary: Sheila Crowhurst (Letters c/o club)
Tel Nos: 0207 3543509   07970 986537M
Ground: Harrow Meadow, Eltham Green Rd, Eltham, London SE9   Tel: 0208 8595788

Directions: South Circular (A205) to McDonalds, grd opposite.
1 mile from both Eltham and Kidbrooke BR stations
Capacity: 2,500   **Seats:** 5o   **Cover:** 50**Floodlights:** Yes
Clubhouse: Yes

HONOURS London Spartan Lg 79-80 (Lg Cup 82-83), Kent Lg 86-87 87-88 (Lg Cup 84-85
86-87), Kent Snr Tphy 84-85, FA Vase 5th Rd 89-90

PREVIOUS   Leagues: South London Alliance; Kent Amateur; London Spartan 77-84
Ground: Erith & Belvedere F.C. 1992-93
Name: London Borough of Greenwich

RECORD   Gate: 2,000 v Charlton, floodlight opening, 1978
Defeat : 0-8 v Faversham Town, August 1989

FACT FILE
Founded: 1928
Nickname: Boro
Colours: All Red
Change Colours: All white
Midweek matchday: Tuesday
Programme: 16 pages, 50p
Editor: Keith Harmer
Tel: 07930 618911 (M)

CLUB PERSONNEL
Chairman: T. Hassan
Manager: L. Hussein
Asst Manager: K. Crowhurst

Hythe Town. Photo: Folkestone & Hythe Herald

Above: Erith Town Back Row (l-r): P Sandhu, K Holt, B Hackett, B Edwards, P Reeves, D Websdale Front Row: I Summers, D Warner, A Hanlon (capt), S McAlpine, L Putnam

Riight: Maidstone United's Steve Marshall shields the ball from Ramsgate's Andy Weatherly Photo: Alan Coomes

HERNE BAY

Secretary: Simon Harris 72 Station Road, Herne Bay, Kent CT6 5QH
Email: roland@hernebay,co.uk

Ground: Winch's Field, Stanley Gardens, Herne Bay, Kent   Tel: 01227 374156

Directions: Leave new Thanet Way at Herne Bay/Canterbury exit. Follow signs toHerne Bay via Canterbury Road. After railway bridge (1/2 mile), take first left into SpencerRoad, then first left into Stanley Gardens, Ground on left **Clubhouse:** Open matchdays **Club Shop:** Yes
Capacity: 4,000   Seats: 200   Cover: 1,500   Floodlights: Yes

HONOURS Kent Lg 91-92 94-95 96-97 97-98, (R-up 92-93 00-01), Div 2 62-63 63-64, R-up92-93(res) 94-95(res), Lg Cup 96-97, R-up 78-79 97-98, Div 2 Cup 53-54; Kent Snr Tphy 78-79, 96-97; Kent Amtr Cup 57-58 (R-up 58-59 63-64 68-69 72-73); Aetolian LgDiv 2 62-63 63-64 (Lg Cup R-up 62-63), Div 2 Cup 62-63 63-64; Athenian Lg Div 2 70-71 (Lg Cup 66-67); Kent Amtr Lg Cup 53-54 54-55; Thames & Medway Comb. CupR-up 61-62; FA Cup 4th Qual. Rd 70-71 86-87.

PREVIOUS   **Leagues:** East Kent, Faversham & Dist, Canterbury & Dist, Kent Amateur, Kent 53-59, Aetolian 59-64, Athenian 64-74   **Ground:** Memorial Park 1886-1953

RECORDS   **Attendance:** 2,303 v Margate, FA Cup 4th Qual. Rd 70-71
Win: 19-3 v Hythe 1900
Defeat: 0-11 v RAF Manston, Kent Amateur Lge 1935
Fee received: £3,000 for Mark Munday (Gravesend) 1994

FACT FILE
Founded: 1886Nickname: The Bay
Colours: Blue & white halves
Change Colours: Red & black halves
Midweek matchday: Tuesday
Reserves' League: Kent Lge Div One
Programme: 36 pages, 70p
Editor/Press Off.: Doug Smith (01227742182)
Website: www.hernebayfc.co.uk

2001-02
Captain: Jon Warden
P.o.Y.: Scott Appleton
Top Scorer: Scott Appleton 17

CLUB PERSONNEL
Chairman: J Bathurst
Vice Chairman: W Dordoy
President: T.B.A.
Manager: Nick Denly
Asst. Manager: Gerry Allen
Physio: H.Roberts

HYTHE TOWN (2001)

Secretary: Martin R Giles, 21 Wych Elm Way, Hythe, Kent. CT21 6QE
Tel: 01303 265962 (H) 01303 267619 (B)
Email Address: infohythetownfc.co.uk

Ground: Reachfields Stadium, Fort Rd, Hythe, Kent.   Tel: 01303 264932 or 238256

Directions: On A259 west out of Hythe, turn left after light railway lights (Fort Road), entrance at end
Capacity: 3,000   Seats: 400   Cover: 2,400   Floodlights: Yes

Clubhouse: Bar open weekends/matchdays & training nights
Club Shop: No

HONOURS   None as Hythe United or Hythe Town (2001)

PREVIOUS   Leagues: Kent County and Southern
RECORD   Attendance: 2,147 v Yeading 1990 F.A.Vase Semi-Final
Names: Hythe Town and Hythe Town 1988 Ltd

FACT FILE
Founded: 1992
Sponsor: Autorite Finishers Ltd
Colours: All Red
Change Colours: All blue
Midweek Matchday: Tuesday
Programme: 60p
Website: www.huthetownfc.co.uk
Editor: Martin Whybrow

2001-02
Captain:Gary Miller
Top Scorers: Darren Light & Dan Jennings

CLUB PERSONNEL
Chairman: Paul Markland
President: Rt Hon Michael Howard QC
Press Officer: Richard Giles
Manager: David Linstrem
Physio: Dave Garlinge

LORDSWOOD

Secretary: Steve Lewis, Sunnybrook, Gorsewood Road, Hartley, Longfield, Kent DA3 7DF   Tel: 01474 708233 (H) 01233 822300 (B) 07775 541573 (M)
Email: s.lewis@claas.com

Ground: Lordswood Sports & Social Club   Tel: 01634 669138
North Dane Way, Walderslade, Chatham, Kent ME5 9XX

Directions:
Capacity: 600   Seats: 125   Cover: No   Floodlights: Yes

Clubhouse: Yes   **Club Shop:** No

HONOURS   None

PREVIOUS   **Leagues:** Kent County Lge

RECORD   **Attendance:** 650

FACT FILE
Founded: 1968
Nickname: Lords
Colours: Orange/black/black
Change Colours: Maroon
Midweek Matchday: Tuesday/Thursday
Reserve or Youth League: Both
Programme: Yes   Editor: T.B.A.
Website: www.lordswoodfc.co.uk

CLUB PERSONNEL
Chairman: J. O'Halloran
Vice Chairman: T.B.A.
Press Officer: T.B.A.
Manager: B.Zillwood

2001-02
Captain: Paul Piggott
P.o.Y.: Aaron Lacy
Top Scorer: P. Peterson 12

Slade Green FC before their FA Cup Extra Preliminary Round. Photo: Neil Thaler

Thamesmead Town. Back Row (l-r): Glen McTaggart, Wayne Barrett, Mark Penney, Curtis Williams, Paul Springett, Dean Kerley, Peter Deadman. Front Row: Dean Burns, Barry Stewart, Mark Simmons, Steve Northwood, Marcus Perona, Tommy Martin. Photo: Alan Coomes

VCD Athletic. Photo: Alan Coomes

MAIDSTONE UNITED

Secretary: Richard Yorke, 27 Churchill Way, Faversham, Kent ME13 7QX
Tel: 01795 534328

Ground: Ground share with Sittingbourne FC - Central Park Stadium, Eurolink
Industrial Park, Church Road, Sittingbourne ME10 3SB Tel: 01795 435077

Directions: Through Sittingbourne on main A2, club signposted clearly and regularly from
both east and west. 1 mile from Sittingbourne BR station.
Capacity: 8,000   Cover: 3,300   Seats: 2,000   Floodlights: 420 lux

FACT FILE
Founded: 1966
Reformed 1992
Colours: Gold/black/gold
Change Colours: All white
Midweek matchday: Tuesday
Programme: Yes
Editor: Steve Hemsley tel: 01892 514006

CLUB PERSONNEL
Chairman: Paul Bowden-Brown

RAMSGATE

Secretary: Martin Able, 164 Heath Lane, Dartford, Kent. DA1 2TW Tel No: 07958 993959 (H&M)
Ground: Southwood Stadium, Prices Avenue, Ramsgate, Kent   Tel: 01843 591662

Directions: From London on A229, A253 into Ramsgate - left into Netherhill atr'bout, right into
Ashburnham Rd, right into Southwood Rd. 15 mins walk from Ramsgate BR station; walk thru
Warre Recreation Ground, along St Lawrence HighStr., left at `White Horse', follow Southwood Rd
and turn right into PricesAvenue
Capacity: 5,000   Seats: 400   Cover: 600   Floodlights: Yes

Clubhouse: Open matchdays & private functions. Two bars, two pool tables,darts. Hot &
cold food on matchdays   Club Shop: No

HONOURS   Kent Lg 49-50 55-56 56-57 (Lg Cup 48-49 92-93 93-94 94-95) Kent I'mediate Cup
54-55, Kent Snr Cup 63-64, Thames & Medway Cup 60-61, KentSnr Shield 60-61,   Kent
Floodlit Tphy 69-70, Kent Snr Tphy(2) 87-89
PREVIOUS   **Leagues:** Southern 59-75
              Name: Ramsgate Athletic
RECORDS   **Gate:** 5,200 v Margate, 56-57
              Scorer: Mick Williamson
              Win: 9-1 v Crockenhill, Kent League Cup 22/1/94

FACT FILE
Founded: 1946
Nickname: Rams
Sponsors: Hoverspeed
Colours: Red & white stripes/red/red
Change Colours: Yellow & navy
stripes/navy/navy
Midweek matchday: Tuesday
Reserves' League: Kent Lge Div. Two
Programme: 28 pages
Editor: Steve Redford (01843 596138)

CLUB PERSONNEL
Chairman: Richard Lawson
Vice Chairman: C Payne
President: Tom Pendry
Commercial Manager: Martin Power
Tel: 01843 597703
Manager/Coach: Lennie Lee
Asst Manager: Dave Bostock
Physio: John Burroughs

SLADE GREEN

Secretary: Bruce Smith, 15 Gumping Rd, Orpington, Kent BR5 1RX Tel: 01689 858782

Ground: The Small Glen, Moat Lane, Slade Green, Erith, Kent Tel: 01322 351077

Directions: Off A206 between Erith & Dartford.
              400 yards from Slade Green BR station. Buses 89 & B13
Capacity: 3,000   Seats: 150   Cover: 400   Floodlights: Yes
Clubhouse: Yes; Hall, Directors Lounge & Canteen   Club Shop: No

HONOURS   Kent Snr Tphy 91-92 (R-up 80-81); Kent Lg Cup 82-83; Kent Amtr Lg 52-53 53-54
60-61 (Lg Cup 60-61); Kent Intermediate Cup 61-62; Kent Benevolent Cup46-47;
West Kent 60-61 65-66; Dartford Lg R-up 48-49 (Lg Cup 47-48 (R-up 46-47)); Erith Hospitals Cup
46-47 48-49; Gtr London Lg R-up 68-69; Plumstead Challenge Cup 48-49
PREVIOUS   Leagues: Dartford 46-52; Kent Amateur 52-62; Greater London 62-70
              Name: Slade Green Athletic 46-86
RECORDS   **Attendance:** 3,000 v Millwall, friendly 25/7/92
              Goalscorer: Colin Dwyer   **Appearances:** Colin Dwyer
Win: 14-0 v Island Social, Kent Amtr Lge 1953   **Defeat:** 1-9 v Whitstable Greater London 64-65
Players progressing : Roy Dwight (Nottm Forest), Alan Clark (Charlton) , Fred Lucas
(Charlton)Tommy Tute (Millwall Jan. 1999)

FACT FILE

Founded: 1946
Nickname: The Green
Sponsor: T.B.A.
Colours: All white
Change Colours: Yellow /black/yellow
Midweek matchday: Tuesday
Reserve League:
Programme: 44 pages, incl. with admission
Editor: Robert Smith (01322 287982)

CLUB PERSONNEL

Chairman: Brian Smith
President: William Dudley
Press Officer: Robert Smith (01322 287982)
Manager: Srteve Waite
Coach: Micky Orme
Physio: Alan Martin

THAMESMEAD TOWN

Secretary: Albert Panting,97 Sydney Road, Bexleyheath,Kent DA6 8HQ (0208303 1350 (H)
Ground: Bayliss Avenue, Thamesmead, London SE28 8NJ Tel: 0181 311 4211

Directions: By road: From Dartford tunnel A2 to London, exit Danson Interchange and follow
signs for Thamesmead and Abbey Wood. From Blackheath tunnel exit on south side and follow
signs to Woolwich, to Plumstead and then to Thamesmead
From Abbey Wood (BR) north east along Harrow Manor Way, into Crossway at 3rd r'bout, Bayliss
Av. is 3rd right (Bexley bus 272 stops in Crossway near Bayliss Av.

Capacity: 400   **Seats:** 125   **Cover:** 125   **Floodlights:** Yes   **Club Shop:** No

Clubhouse: Mon-Fri 6-11pm, Sat 12-11pm, Sun 12-3 & 7-10.30pm. Double bar,lounge, dancefloor, children's games room, video machines, hot & cold food.New members Bar

HONOURS   Spartan Lg Div 3 79-80 (Lg Cup 84-85 86-87; I'mediate champs 85-86);Kent
I'mediate Cup 83-84 94-95; 4 promotions & 9 trophies (inc London & Kent FA Cups)
in progress thru Spartan I'mediate Divs, 1980-87; Kent Lge Div 2 94-95, Div 2 Cup 94-95

PREVIOUS   **Leagues:** London Spartan 80-91
Ground: Meridian Sports Ground, Charlton

RECORDS   **Attendance:** 400 v Wimbledon, ground opening 1988
Appearances: Delroy D'Oyley   **Win** : 9-0 v Kent Police, Kent League 19/4/94

FACT FILE
Founded: 1970
Nickname: The Mead
Sponsors: Courage Brewery
Colours: Green& White/Green/Green
Change Colours: All blue
Midweek matchday: Tuesday
Reserves League: Winstonlead Kent D2
Programmes: Yes. 50p
Editor: Secretary

CLUB PERSONNEL
Chairman: Brian Morris
Vice Chairman: John Kelly
President: Albert Panting
Press Officer: Matthew Panting
Manager: Paul Blade
Physio: Allen Martin

TUNBRIDGE WELLS

Secretary: Mrs J.Rogers, 21 Bluebell Walks, Hunters Chase,Paddock Wood, Kent. Wadhurst,
East Sussex TN5 6PU   Email Address: ronrogers@skynew.net
Ground: Culverden Stadium, Culverden Down, Tunbridge Wells, Kent TN4 Tel: 01892 520517

Directions: Leaving town on main Tonbridge rd (A26), turn left into Culverden Down
ground half miie. 1 mile from Tunbridge Wells Central(BR).
Served by any Tunbridge Wells-Tonbridge bus - to St Johns
Capacity: 3,750   **Seats:** 250   **Cover:** 1,000   **Floodlights:** Yes
Clubhouse: Open matchdays and as required   **Club Shop:** No

HONOURS   Kent Lg 84-85 (R-up 68-69, Lg Cup 74-75 77-78 85-86 87-88)
Kent SnrTphy R-up 85-86 91-92
PREVIOUS   **Names:** None. predecessors: T . Wells FC 1886-1910 47-50 T. Wells Rgrs 03-
09 63-67; T. Wells Utd 51-62
Grounds: Down Lane 1906; Combley Park 06-10; Swiss Cottage 06-14;Down
Farm 19-39; St Johns 47-50; Eridge Road 50-67
RECORDS   **Attendance:** 967 v Maidstone United, FA Cup 1969
Goalscorer: John Wingate 151   **Appearances:** Tony Atkins 410
Win: 10-0 v Deal (H), May'86
Defeat: 1-11 v Deal Town (H), 20/2/93

FACT FILE
Founded: 1886 Reformed: 1967
Nickname: Wells
Colours: Red/Red/White
Change Colours: Blue/Blue/White
Midweek Matchday: Tuesday
Prog: 20 pages, 50p Editor: Secretary
Web: www.@team2.com/tunbridge wellsfc

CLUB PERSONNEL
Chairman: R.Rogers
Manager: Steve Clark

2001-02
Captain: Garry Valli
Top Scorer: Steve Gibbons 21

VICKERS CRAYFORD, DARTFORD ATHLETIC

Secretary: Brian Norris,Peelers Lodge ,21 St Edith's Road, Kemsing,Sevenoaks, Kent TN15 6PT.
Tel No: 01689 854302
Ground: Thamesmead Town FC, Bayliss Avenue, Thamesmead, London, SE28 8NJ
Tel: 0208 311 4211 (Temporary Groundshare)
Home Ground (Pending floodlights) Oakwood, Old Road, Crayford, Kent, DA1 4DN.
Home clubhouse: Lounge Bar every day and evening. Plus snack bar on matchdays.
Directions: From Abbey Wood (BR) north east along Harrow Manor Way, into Crossway at 3rd
r'bout, Bayliss Av. is 3rd right (Bexley bus 272 stops in Crossway near Bayliss Av. By road: From
Dartford tunnel A2 to London, exit Danson Interchange and follow signs for Thamesmead and
Abbey Wood. From Blackheath tunnel exit on south side and follow signs to Woolwich, to
Plumstead and then to Thamesmead.
Capacity: 400   **Seats:** 125   **Cover:** 125   **Floodlights:** Yes

PREVIOUS   **League:** Kent County. **Grounds:** Flamingo Park, Sidcup (pre 1994);
VCD Sports & Social Club,Old Road, Crayford
RECORD   **Victory:** 10-1 v Canterbury City 14.5.01 **Defeat:** 0-5 v Deal Town 20.4.02
HONOURS   Kent County Cup 61-62, 63-64, 94-95, R-Up: 84-85, 89-90. Kent County Lg
Div One 96-97 Kent County Premier 96-97. West Kent Cup 87-88.Kent Lge Cup R-up: Winners
99-00 ,Runners up 98-99. Kent Intermediate Shield (2) R-up(1), Erith Hosp Cup x4, R-Up x4; Kent
Sen, Tphy. R-up 00-01

FACT FILE
Founded: 1916
Nickname: The Vickers
Sponsors: MB Fire Protection
Colours: Green & white/green/green
Change Colours: Blue & white/blue/blue
Midweek matchday: Wednesday
Programme: 40 pages 50p

CLUB PERSONNEL
Chairman: Michael Bonello
Man:Martin Ford   Assist Man:Peter Burke
Coach:Roy Passey
Physio: Peter Burke

2001-02
Captain: Terry Barry
Top Scorer:Richard Dimmock
P.O.Y.: Terry Ratchford

WHITSTABLE TOWN

Secretary: George Corney, 46 Elizabeth Way, Herne Bay, Kent CT6 6ET (01227 363496)
Ground: Belmont Road, Belmont, Whitstable, Kent Tel: 01227 266012

Directions: From Thanet Way (A299), left at Tescos r'bout and down MillstroodRd - ground at bottom of road, 400yds from Whitstable (BR) station. Car park atGrimshall Rd entrance
Capacity: 2,000   **Cover:** 1,000   **Seats:** 500   **Floodlights:** Yes   **Club Shop:** Yes
Clubhouse: Social & recreation purposes, open all matchdays. Bar. Hot food &drinks at tea-bar

HONOURS Kent Lg Div 2 27-28 33-34 49-50 (Lg Cup 79-80 (R-up 89-90 91-92)), KentAmtr Lg East 60-61, Kent Amtr Cup 28-29, Kent Snr Tphy R-up 78-79 89-90 92-93,Gtr London Lg Cup R-up 65-66, Kent Amtr Cup 28-29, Kent Midweek Lg Cup 92-93

PREVIOUS **Leagues:** E. Kent 1897-1909; Kent 09-59; Aetolian 59-60; Kent Amtr 60-62 63-64; S E Anglian 62-63; Gtr London 64-67; Kent Premier 67-68 (also in New Brompton, Thanet & Faversham & Dist. Lges over the years)
Names: Whitstable Utd (pre-1886); Whitstable Swifts 93-95; WhitstableTown 95-1905; Whitstable FC 08-66

RECORDS Gate: 2,500 v Gravesend & Northfleet, FA Cup 3rd Qual. Rd,19/10/87
Goalscorer: Barry Godfrey   Appearances: Frank Cox 429 (1950-60)
Win: 18-0 v Greenstreet (H), Faversham & Dist. Lge 20-21
Defeat: 0-10 v Sittingbourne (A), FA Cup 1st Qual. Rd 62-63

FACT FILE
Founded: 1885
Nickname: Oystermen, Reds, Natives
Club Sponsors: D & J Tyres
Shirt Sponsor: McDonalds
Colours: Red & White//White/ Red
Change colours: Yellow/blue/yellow
Midweek matchday: Tuesday
Programme: 48 pages, 50p
Editor/Press Off: Bernie Thompson
Tel No: 01227 274138
CLUB PERSONNEL
Chairman: Joe Brownett
Vice Chairman: Trevor Rapley
President: George Gifford
Manager: Simon Kay/Doug Bosson
Asst Manager: John Crabbe
Physio: Tony Pattenden

BRITISH ENERGY KENT COUNTY
FOOTBALL LEAGUE

Founded: 1922

President: W C Manklow   **Chairman:** C T C Windiate

General Secretary: B H Bundock

Press Secretary: G Jenkins

Kings View, Shottenden Lane, Molash, Canterbury, Kent CT4 8EZ

Tel: 01233 740143 Email: geoff@kcfl2000.freeserve.co.uk

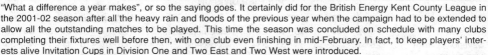

"What a difference a year makes", or so the saying goes. It certainly did for the British Energy Kent County League in the 2001-02 season after all the heavy rain and floods of the previous year when the campaign had to be extended to allow all the outstanding matches to be played. This time the season was concluded on schedule with many clubs completing their fixtures well before then, with one club even finishing in mid-February. In fact, to keep players' interests alive Invitation Cups in Division One and Two East and Two West were introduced.

Bearsted retained the League Championship by winning the Premier Division fourteen points ahead of runners-up Sevenoaks Town. The Champions suffered just one league defeat in the campaign, losing at home to Sevenoaks in mid-season, and became the first side to retain the title since the Premier Division, in the current competition format, commenced in 1992-93. To reward their efforts both on and off the field, Bearsted and Sevenoaks Town have been awarded Senior Status by the Kent County Football Association Ltd and will compete, together with fellow County League sides Crockenhill, Thames Poly and Milton Athletic, in next season's Kent Senior Trophy.

In Division One East Kennington, runners-up the previous campaign, had won the title before the end of March after a much fancied Tenterden Tigers' challenge fell away but they did eventually finish as runners-up. The Tenterden side did lift the Division's Invitation Cup after emphatically defeating Rye & Iden United by six goals to one in the final.

With just one defeat and leading Division One West for virtually the whole season, Old Roan clinched the Championship in April still with two matches remaining, and it only remained for no fewer than five sides to contest the runners-up spot during the closing weeks of the campaign, a position finally secured by Oakwood, following their promotion from Division Two a year earlier.

it was always a two-horse race in Division Two East with Dover Gate and Bliby, both in their debut season, contesting the top two positions for virtually the whole campaign with the Dover side, after just one defeat, eventually winning the title by a solitary point. Bliby were also runners-up in the Invitation Cup following a two-nil defeat by Lydd Town Reserves in the final.

Division Two West went to the wire with Bly Spartans, promoted last season, scoring the most goals with the best goal difference, but were pipped at the post for the Championship by Belvedere with both sides meeting in their final match of the season which ended in a draw, the point for Belvedere enough to secure the Championship by that singleton. Bly Spartans did, however, win the Invitation Cup, defeating Danson Furness Athletic following a penalty shoot out in the final.

With Halls already assured of the runners up position, Division Three West saw Farnborough Old Boys Guild and newcomers Samuel Montague Youth Club meet on the final day of the season in a 'winner takes all' confrontation where the victors would take the Championship. In a closely fought contest the Old Boys won by the odd goal in three, and the Youth Club had to be content with a creditable third position in the final table.

In Reserve Division One, Sevenoaks Town Reserves, hardly out of the top three all season, won the title by three points over rivals Bearsted Reserves. Having scored 82 goals in 22 League games played, Sevenoaks finished the campaign with the most superior goal difference in the entire League.

Reserve Division Two saw Holmesdale Reserves never off the top during this campaign and they had secured the title by early April. Eynsford Rovers eventually finished in second position ten points behind the champions.

In County Cup competitions the League had five clubs competing in the Lea-Ray Kent Senior Trophy, with Lydd Town and Milton Athletic defeating Greenwich Borough and Beckenham Town from the Bass Brewers Kent League in earlier rounds respectively. Milton Athletic progressed to the Semi-Finals of the competition where again they met Kent League opposition in Thamesmead Town, but unluckily went down by the only goal of the game to the competition's eventual winners.

The Kent Intermediate Challenge Shield was won by Stansfeld O&B Club who defeated fellow Kent County Leaguers Cray Valley (PM) by three goals to nil in the final played at Corinthian FC. These three goals were the first conceded by Cray Valley after four blank earlier rounds. Stansfeld O&B Club will now compete in next season's Kent Senior Trophy.

The League's domestic Cup competitions saw Stansfeld O&B Club defeat champions Bearsted following a penalty shoot-out in the final at Dr Martens League Ashford Town FC's ground. Another final requiring a penalty shoot-out to decide the winner was the Eastern Section Senior (Les Leckie) Cup at Hythe Town's ground with Milton Athletic eventually reigning supreme over New Romney. Hythe Town also hosted the Eastern Section Junior Cup final, which saw League newcomers Bliby overcome holders St Margaretsbury Reserves by five goals to nil. The final of the West Kent Challenge Shield was won by League debutants Cray Valley (PM) who defeated Otford United by four goals to two. The final of the Western Section Reserve Divisions Cup saw Greenways Reserves appearing for

the second season in succession, but were again defeated, this time by Reserve Division One Champions Sevenoaks Town Reserves by three goals to one.

The League's Representative team played a side selected from the Bass Brewers Essex Intermediate League at Bromley FC and convincingly recorded a six-nil victory. The annual match against the Rich City Sussex County League was again cancelled due to unfit ground conditions.

Finally, the British Energy Kent County Football League is honoured to accept an invitation from the Football Association to represent them and England in the third forthcoming UEFA Regions Cup, the qualifying round of which sees them travelling to Estonia in early September to compete against representative sides from San Marino, Czech Republic and the hosts. The finals of the competition will be played at a venue to be confirmed in June 2003.

Geoff Jenkins, Press Secretary

FINAL LEAGUE TABLES 2001-02
PREMIER DIVISION

	P	W	D	L	F	A	Pts		P	W	D	L	F	A	Pts
Bearsted	26	21	4	1	75	16	67	Sheerness East	26	10	5	11	38	38	35
Sevenoaks Town	26	16	5	5	83	33	53	Crockenhill	26	10	5	11	44	45	35
Milton Athletic	26	15	8	3	65	27	53	Snodland	26	8	5	13	38	72	29
Stansfeld O&BC	26	14	5	7	43	39	47	Lydd Town	26	9	1	16	40	60	28
New Romney	26	12	3	11	52	50	39	Greenways	26	7	4	15	36	52	25
Beauwater	26	11	4	11	48	48	37	Phoenix Sports	26	7	3	16	38	65	24
Wickham Park	26	11	3	12	60	60	36	Thames Poly	26	2	3	21	23	78	9

DIVISION ONE WEST

	P	W	D	L	F	A	Pts
Old Roan	24	18	5	1	69	16	59
Oakwood	24	15	3	6	49	31	48
Moonshot Athletic	24	13	5	6	43	30	44
AFC Blackheath	24	13	4	7	53	34	43
Cray Valley Ppr Mills	24	13	4	7	49	32	43
Rusthall	24	9	6	9	42	32	33
Aylesford Paper Mills	24	8	8	8	31	38	32
Eynsford	24	8	4	12	40	47	28
Fleetdown United	24	8	4	12	32	41	28
Holmesdale	24	6	5	13	38	60	23
Pembury	24	6	3	15	33	50	21
Otford United	24	4	6	14	24	63	18
Westerham	24	4	5	15	36	63	17

DIVISION ONE EAST

	P	W	D	L	F	A	Pts
Kennington	18	13	3	2	58	20	42
Tenterden Tigers	18	9	7	2	48	24	34
Snowdown Coll. W.	18	10	2	6	48	37	32
University of Kent	18	8	4	6	49	35	28
Bromley Green	18	8	3	7	49	37	27
Bettesanger Welf.	18	6	6	6	36	38	24
Norton Sports	18	7	2	9	33	47	23
St Margarets	18	6	4	8	29	52	22
Smarden	18	3	2	13	33	60	11
Rye & Iden Res.	18	3	1	14	28	61	10

PREMIER DIVISION RESULTS CHART 2001-02

		1	2	3	4	5	6	7	8	9	10	11	12	13	14
1	Bearsted	X	3-0	2-2	5-1	4-1	2-1	3-0	2-1	0-1	1-0	8-0	3-0	1-1	4-2
2	Beauwater	0-3	X	2-2	2-0	4-0	1-5	1-0	4-1	0-2	3-2	4-2	2-0	3-0	2-1
3	Crockenhill	1-2	2-1	X	0-4	3-0	0-0	0-2	3-1	0-5	3-0	2-2	4-0	3-0	3-0
4	Greenways	0-1	1-2	3-3	X	4-1	0-0	4-3	1-3	0-3	1-1	5-0	0-0	3-0	2-3
5	Lydd Town	1-4	0-1	3-0	2-1	X	2-3	1-2	4-2	0-0	0-1	1-2	2-4	2-0	7-3
6	Milton Athletic	1-2	1-1	6-1	3-0	3-2	X	5-0	3-0	3-3	2-1	2-2	0-0	10-0	1-0
7	New Romney	1-1	4-2	2-1	3-2	1-2	2-2	X	1-0	1-2	2-1	2-3	1-3	4-1	3-0
8	Phoenix Sports	1-6	2-1	3-0	2-0	0-2	2-3	2-1	X	0-4	1-3	3-1	2-3	0-0	2-2
9	Sevenoaks Town	0-4	5-5	0-4	5-0	7-0	1-2	5-1	7-1	X	5-0	7-1	2-1	5-0	2-3
10	Sheerness East	0-3	3-1	2-0	0-1	3-0	1-1	3-3	4-1	2-2	X	0-1	2-0	1-1	2-1
11	Snodland	0-2	3-2	0-3	2-0	2-3	0-3	2-1	1-1	0-5	2-0	X	1-1	4-0	1-3
12	Stansfeld O & BC	0-0	2-1	2-1	4-1	2-1	2-1	0-5	3-1	1-1	2-1	4-1	X	3-2	1-0
13	Thames Poly	0-2	2-1	1-2	0-2	0-1	1-2	2-3	1-2	2-3	0-3	7-2	0-5	X	1-6
14	Wickham Park	1-7	2-2	2-1	4-0	4-2	1-2	2-4	5-4	2-1	1-2	3-3	4-0	5-1	X

KENT COUNTY FOOTBALL LEAGUE OFFICIAL LEAGUE HANDBOOK
104 pages £5.00 including postage & packing

INTER-REGIONAL CHALLENGE CUP 2001-02

FIRST ROUND EAST

Betteshanger	v	Milton Ath	0-4	Bromley Green	v	Sheerness E.	2-3
Kennington	v	New Romney	2-6	Lydd Town	v	Smarden	6-0
Norton Sports	v	Tenterden Tigers	4p5, 1*1	University of Kent	v	St Margarets	3-0

FIRST ROUND WEST

Aylesford PM	v	Moonshot Ath	2-0	Beauwate	v	Eynsford	2-0
Pembury	v	Fleetdown Utd	1-3	Sevenoaks Town	v	Otford	2-0
Snodland	v	AFC Blackheath	0-5	Thames Poly	v	Oakwood	1-3
Whickham Park	v	Westerham	3-0				

SECOND ROUND EAST

Lydd Town	v	Milton Athletic	2-1	New Romney	v	Snowdown	5-2
Sheerness East	v	Univ. Kent	4-2	Tenterden	v	Rye & I. Res.	5-1

SECOND ROUND WEST

Aylesford PM	v	Greenways	5-0	Beauwater	v	Stansfeld O&B	1-2
Crockenhill	v	Blackheath	1-3	Fleetdown	v	Wickham Park	4-2
Holmesdale	v	Phoenix	2-0	Oakwood	v	Rusthall	6p5, 3*3
Old Roan	v	Bearsted	0-4	Sevenoaks	v	Cray Valley PM	0*1

THIRD ROUND WEST

Aylesford PM	v	Bearsted	0-2	AFC Blackheath	v	Oakwood	8-0
Cray Valley Paper Mills	v	Stansfeld O & B Club	2-3	Holmesdale	v	Fleetdown United	3-2

QUARTER-FINALS

AFC Blackheath	v	Sheerness East	2-0	Holmesdale	v	Tenterden Tigers	5p4, 1*1
Lydd Town	v	Bearsted	0p2, 1*1	New Romney	v	Stansfeld	0-1

SEMI-FINALS

Bearsted	v	Blackheath	4p3, 1*1	Holmesdale	v	Stansfeld	0-2

FINAL

Bearsted	v	Stansfeld O&B Club	4p5,1*1	at Ashford Town

LES LECKIE CUP 2001-02

FIRST ROUND

Betteshanger	v	Bromley Green	1-4	Lydd Town	v	Kennington	5-3
Norton Spts	v	New Romney	0-4	Rye Res.	v	Sheerness E.	2*6
Snowdown	v	Univ. Kent	2-4	St Margarets	v	Tenterden Tigers	2-3

QUARTER-FINALS

Bromley Green	v	Lydd Town	4-6	Milton Ath.	v	Sheerness E.	3-1
Smarden	v	Univ. Kent	1-5	Tenterden Tigers	v	New Romney	1-2

SEMI-FINALS

New Romney	v	Lydd Town	4-0	Univ. Kent	v	Milton Athletic	0-1

FINAL

New Romney	v	Milton Athletic	2p4, 2*2	at Hythe Town

WEST KENT CHALLENGE SHIELD 2001-02

QUARTER-FINALS

Bly Spartans	v	Tonbridge Invicta	1-3	Chipstead	v	NPI	6-0
Cray Valley Paper Mills	v	Old Roan	5-4	Rusthall	v	Otford United	4p5, 1*1

SEMI-FINALS

Chipstead	v	Otford United	3*5	Cray Valley Paper M	v	Tonbridge Invicta	5-0

FINAL

Otford United	v	Cray Valley Paper Mills	2-4	at Gravesend & Northfleet

BEARSTED
Secretary: Mrs Liz Owen, 21 Copsewood Way, Bearsted, Maidstone, Kent ME15 8PL(01622 737709)
Ground: Honey Lane, Otham, Maidstone. (0411 128034)
Founded: 1895
Colours: White/blue/blue
Change Colours: Yellow/blue/blue

BEAUWATER
Founded: 1927
Secretary: Robert Taylor, 24 Sun Lane, Gravesend, Kent DA12 5HG (01474 332208)
Ground: Beauwater Leisure Club, Nelson Road, Northfleet (01474 359222)
Colours: Purple/navy/purple
Change Colours: Red/Navy/Red

CROCKENHILL
Secretary: Mike Floate, Newlands Cottages, 71 Stones Cross Road, Crockenhill,Swanley, Kent BR8 8LX Tel No: 01322 668275
Ground: The Wested Meadow, Wested, Eynsford Road, Crockenhill, Kent. (01322 662097)
Founded: 1946
Colours: Red & white stripes/ black/ red
Change Colours: Blue & Black/ black/ black

GREENWAYS
Founded: 1965
Secretary: William Miller, 14 Cygnet Gardens, Northfleet, Kent DA11 7DN (01474 560913)
Ground: Beauwater Leisure Centre, Nelson Road, Northfleet, (01474 359222)
Colours: Green & white/green/green & white
Change Colours: Red & black/black/red & black

KENNINGTON
Founded: 1888
Secretary: Kevin Hayden, 36 Alec Pemble Close, Kennington, Ashford, Kent. TN24 9PF Tel No: 01233 627826
Ground: Kennington Cricket Club Club, Ulley Road, Kennington, Ashford, Kent
Colours: Yellow & sky blue/yellow/yellow
Change Colours: Red/blue/blue

LYDD TOWN
Founded: 1885
Secretary: Bruce Marchant, 14 Quested Road, Folkestone, Kent.Ct19 4BY Tel No: 01303 275403
Ground: The Lindsey Field, Dengemarsh Road, Lydd, Romney Marsh (01797 321904)
Colours: Red/green/green
ChangeColours:All Blue

MILTON ATHLETIC
Founded: 1926
Secretary: Paul Duffin, 18 Hales Road, Tunstall, Sittingbourne, Kent ME10 1SR (01795 471260)
Ground: UK Paper Sports Ground, Gore Court Road, Sittingbourne, Kent (01795 564213)
Colours: Blue & white/blue/white
Change Colours: Red & white /blue/white

NEW ROMNEY
Founded: 1895
Secretary: Daryl Masters, 44 Fernbank Cres, Folkestone, Kent CT19 5SFTel No: 01303 270941(H) 07900 086311 (M)
Ground: The Maud Pavilion, Station Road, New Romney, Kent (01797 364858)
Colours: Navy blue & yellow/ navy/yellow
Change Colours: Orange/blue/orange

OLD ROAN
Founded: 1905
Secretary: Brian Riley, 33 Buckler Gardens, Mottingham, London SE9 3BD (020 8857 0401)
Groud: John Roan PLaying Fields, Kidbrooke Park Road, Kldbrooke, London SE3 (020 8856 1915 or 020 8856 1012)
Colours: Blue & black stripes/ black/ black & blue.
Change Colours: Green & navy blue/navy/navy

SEVENOAKS TOWN
Founded: 1883
Secretary: Edwin Diplock, 23 Holly Bush Lane, Sevenoaks, Kent TN13 3TH (01732 454280)
Ground: Greatness Park, Seal Road, Sevenoaks (01732 741987)
Colours: Azure & black stripes/black/black
Change colours: Navy & scarlet quarters/navy/navy

SHEERNESS EAST
Founded: 1932
Secretary: Jonathan Longhurst, 34 Sunnyside Avenue, Minster Sheerness, Kent ME12 2EN (01795 870093)
Ground: Sheerness East Working Mens Club, 47 Queenborough Rd., Halfway, Sheerness (01795 662049)
Colours: Yellow/royal blue/royal blue
Change colours:Blue/black.blue

SNODLAND
Founded: 1940
Secretary: Terry Reeves, 136 Townsend Road, Snodland, Kent ME6 5RN (01634 240076)
Ground: Potyn's Field, Paddlesworth Road, Snodland, Kent. (01634 243961)
Colours: Yellow/ /red/black
Change colours:Sky & navy/navy/navy

STANSFELD OXFORD & BERMONDSEY CLUB
Founded: 1897
Secretary: Edward Ellis, 40 Tilbrook Road, Kidbrooke, London SE3 9QE (0208 319 0903)
Ground: F.K.G.Sports,Eltham Rd .,Lee Green S E 12
Colours: Yellow & blue/blue/yellow
Change Colours: All green

WICKHAM PARK
Founded: 1934
Secretary: Robbie Devlin,117 Hazlebank Road,London SE6 1LT Tel No: 07939 556737
Ground: Stanhope Recreation Ground, 103-105,Stanhope Grove,Beckenham Kent (020 8650 8154)
Colours: Mauve & white/white/white
Change Colours: Black & white stripes/black/black

KENT COUNTY LEAGUE DIVISION ONE WEST

A.F.C. BLACKHEATH
Secretary: Dave Wilson, 74 Shroffold Road, Bromley ,Ken BR1 5PF. Tel: 020 8698 1192
Ground: Slade Green F.C. Moat Lane , Slade Green Tel No: 01322 351077
Founded: 1983
Colours: Red & Black stripes/white/white
Change Colours: All white.

AYLESFORD PAPER MILLS
Founded: 1919
Secretary:Jeff Davis, 20 Penine Way, Maidstone, Kent
Tel No: 01622 717771
Ground: Cobdown Sports & Social Club, Ditton Corner, Station Road, Aylesford (01622 715552)
Colours: White with black trim/black/black
Change Colours: Red/black/black

BELVEDERE
Founded: 1923
Secretary: Paul Bell, 10 Abbotswood Road, Dulwich, London SE22 8DL Tel: 020 8693 6521 (H)
Ground: Belvedere Sports & Social Club, Woolwich Road, Belvedere. Tel: 01322 436724
Colours: Purple/navy/purple
Change: Green/blue/blue

BLY SPARTANS
Founded: 1982
Secretary: Tony Wheeler, 14 Lynnette Ave., Rochester, Kent ME2 3NH Tel: 01634 713404 (H) 07775 735543 (M)
Ground: Bly Spartans Sports Ground, Watling Sreet, Strood. Tel: 01634 710577
Colours: Maroon & sky blue/maroon/maroon
Change: Amber & black/black/amber & black

CRAY VALLEY (PM)
Founded: 1981
Secretary: Steve Chapman, 97 Yorkland Ave., Welling DA16 2LG
Tel: 020 8304 5387 (H) 01293 802208 (B)
Ground: Badgers Sports Ground, Middle Park Ave., London SE9
Tel: 020 8850 4273
Colours: Green/black/black
Change colours: white/white/green

EYNESFORD
Founded: 1895
Secretary: Robert Graham, 48 Goddington Lane, Orpington, Kent BR6 9DS Tel: 01689 821425
Ground: Westminster Fields, The Street, Horton Kirby.
Tel: 01322 865193
Colours: Black & white/black/black
Change Colours: Yellow & black/black/black

FLEETDOWN UNITED
Founded: 1971
Secretary: Brian Wakeman, 670 Princes Road, Dartford, Kent DA2 6JG (01322 228680)
Ground: Heath Lane, Dartford, Kent (01322 273848)
Colours: Tangerine/black/tangerine
Change colours: Blue &White/ blue/blue

HOLMESDALE
Founded 1956
Secretary: Mark Hayes, 12 Danson Way, Rainham, Kent. ME8 7EW (01634 327954)
Ground: Holmesdale Sports & Social Club, Oakley Road, Bromley Common (020 8462 4440)
Colours: Yellow & Green/ Green/ Green
Change Colours: Red/ Black/Black

MOONSHOT ATHLETIC
Founded: 1970
Secretary: Joseph Collymore, 37 Vaughan Williams Close, Deptford SE8 4AW (0208 691 2543)
Ground: Ten Em Bee Sports Ground, Bromley Road playing fields, Old Bromley Road, Downham, Kent (020 8313 9510)
Colours: Yellow/green/green
Change Colours: All burgandy

OAKWOOD
Founded: 1924
Peter Mannering, 24 Ellenswood Close, Otham, Maidstone, Kent ME15 8SQ Tel: 01622 862482
Ground: Honey Lane, Otham, Maidstone, Kent.
Colours: Red & white stripes/black/red
Change colours: Green & red/green/red

PEMBURY
Founded1908
Secretary: Michael Waterman, 26 The Coppice, Pembury, Tunbridge Wells Kent TN2 4EY (01892 824137)
Ground: Woodside Recreation Ground, Henwoods Mount, Pembury (07970 026628)
Colours: Black & White stripes/ black/black
Change Colours: All red

PHOENIX SPORTS
Founded: 1935
Secretary: Mrs Shirley Jarvis,31 Monkton Road,Welling,Kent Da16 3JU Tel No: 020 8854 5509
Ground: Phoenix Spts Club, Mayplace Rd East , Bexleyheath, Kent DA7 6JT (01322 526159)
Colours: Red & white/ black/black
Change Colours: Amber/black/black

RUSTHALL
Founded: 1899
Secretary: Michael Mace, 'The Roos', 28 Allan Close, Rusthall, Tunbridge Wells, Kent TN4 8PL (01892 540634)
Ground: Jockey Farm, Nellington Lane, Rusthall, Tunbridge Wells Tel : 01892 517224
Colours: Green & black/ green/ green
Change Colours: Red /black/black

THAMES POLYTECHNIC
Founded: 1888
Secretary: Mrs Sarah Manzi,46 Oldstaed Road,Bromley,Kent BR1 5RW Tel No: 020 8461 4212
Ground: Greenwich University Sports Ground, Kidbrooke Lane, Eltham, London SE9 (020 8850 0210)
Colours: Yellow /green/yellow
Change Colours: All blue
Previous league: Kent

KENT COUNTY LEAGUE
DIVISION ONE EAST

BETTESHANGER WELFARE
Secretary: David Fairclough, 55 Tormore Park, Deal, Kent CT14 9UR Tel: 01304 366883 (H) 07714 705582 (B)
Ground: Betteshanger Welfare Ground, Cavell Square, Mill Hill, Deal. Tel: 01304 372080
Colours: Red & white hoops/navy/red & white hoops
Change colours: Yellow & black/black/black

BLIBY
Founded: 1994
Secretary: Mrs Jacqui Barker, Frithfield, Aldington Frith, Ashford, Kent TN25 7HH Tel: 01233 720469 (H) 01233 720973 (B)
Ground: Sandyacres Sports & Social Club, Sandyhurst Lane, Ashford. Tel: 01233 627373
Colours: Navy & amber/navy/navy & amber
Change: Amber & navy/navy & amber/amber

BROMLEY GREEN
Founded: 1930
Secretary: Stanley Donald,12 Oast Meadow ,Willesborough, Ashford,Kent TN24 0AS Tel No: 01233 627916
Ground: The Swan Centre, Newtown Road, South Willesborough, Ashford, Kent
Colours: All Green. Change Colours: White/green/green

NORTON SPORTS
Founded: 1927
Secretary: Colin Page, 22 Haysel, Sittingbourne, Kent ME10 4QE (01795 426675)
Ground: Norton Pk, Provender Lane,Norton,Kent (01795 520088)
Colours: Sky Blue & white stripes/ black/ white
Change Colours: Red & black/black/white

SMARDEN
Founded: 1984
Secrtary: Brian Phillips, 4 Ashenden, Smarden, Ashford, Kent TN27 8RT Tel No: 01233 770743
Ground: The Minnis, Smarden, Nr Ashford, Kent
Colours: Blue & White/Blue/Blue.
Change Colours: Green & White/ Black/ Black

SNOWDOWN COLLIERY WELFARE
Founded: 1927
Secretary:Mrs Nicola Tong, 9 Ackholt Road, Aylesham, Canterbury, Kent CT3 3AF (0771 8525030))
Ground: Spinney Lane, Aylesham, Canterbury CT3 3AF (01304 840278)
Colours: Black & white stripes/black/black
Change Colours: Blue & black/white/white
Previous League: Kent

St MARGARETS
Founded: 1970 Re-formed:1993
Secretary: William Hay, 28 The Freedown, St Margarets at Cliffe, Nr Dover, Kent CT15 6BD (01304 852386)
Ground: The Alexandra Field, Kingsdown Road, St Margarets at Cliffe, Nr Dover
Colours: Red &blue/ red,white & blue/ red
Change Colours: White with red and blue trim/blue/red

TENTERDEN TIGERS
Founded: 1889
Secretary: Stephen Saxby, 46 Hopoes Grove,High Halden,Ashford, Kent TN26 3ND Tel No: 01233 850741
Ground: Recreation Ground, Recretaion Ground Rd., Tenterden (01580 762703)
Colours: Yellow/black/black
Change Colours: Blue & white/ blue/blue

UNIVERSITY OF KENT
Founded: 1967
Secretary: Aaron Campbell, Sports Federation, Sports Centre,University of Kent, Canterbury, Kent CT2 7NL Tel No: 01227 768027
Ground: The Playing Fields, University of Kent, off Giles Lane, Canterbury
Colours: Black & white stripes/black/black
Change Colours: Red & blackstripes/red/red

RICH CITY SUSSEX COUNTY LEAGUE
FEEDER TO: DR MARTENS LEAGUE
FOUNDED 1920

President: P H Strange   **Chairman:** Peter Bentley
Secretary: P Beard, 2 Van Gogh Place, Bersted, Bognor Regis PO22 9BG
Tel: 01243 822063 (H)   07966 457908 (M)   Fax: 01243 822063   www.scfl.org.uk

---

The season kicked-off in mid-August with the reigning League Champions, Sidley United, opening their campaign with a victory at Eastbourne United on Friday 10th. The following day Burgess Hill Town, runners-up in 2000-01, served notice that they had the desire to reclaim their title by hammering Peacehaven & Telscombe 5-0.

At the end of the first month of the new season Pagham led the way in Division One having already played eight games. Burgess Hill Town were only two points behind but had only played four. East Preston topped Division Two having only dropped two points in the opening day draw. Rye & Iden United were second, leading Oakwood on goal difference. The two new clubs in Division Three, Pease Pottage Village and Upper Beeding were neck and neck at the top, both with 100 percent records.

September began with F.A. Cup Preliminary Round ties, with a notable victory for Horsham YMCA, 4-0 at Walton Casuals.

On the second Saturday of the month it was F.A. Vase First Qualifying Round time and there were some noteworthy results for our sides against clubs from outside the county. Southwick won 2-1 at Merstham, Redhill won 1-0 at Whitstable Town and Wick beat Camberley Town 3-0.

Saturday 22nd saw a return to F.A. Vase action with the Second Qualifying Round, Selsey won 1-0 at Fareham Town, Hassocks beat Chipstead 3-0, Chichester City United won 3-1 at Horsham, Lancing beat Fleet Town by 3-2, Whitehawk won 1-0 over Lymington Town and Wick repeated that scoreline against Slade Green.

Hassocks rounded off their month with a 2-0 home win over Bromley in the F.A. Cup and Bosham surprisingly put six goals past Oving in the First Round of the SCFA Senior Cup.

Saturday 20th October saw Burgess Hill Town progress in the F.A. Vase with a handsome 4-0 home win over Egham Town, Chichester City United handed Barnstaple Town a hammering, winning 6-0 at home while Lancing were winning 2-0 at home to Ramsgate. In the RUR Cup Sidlesham defeated Shinewater Association 6-2.

Burgess Hill Town and Selsey were the only SCFL winners in the F.A. Vase Second Round on Saturday 11th November. The former winning 3-0 at Corinthian Casuals and the latter triumphing at home to Concorde Rangers.

In the F.A. Vase the two remaining SCFL sides were paired in the Third Round and Burgess Hill Town overcame Selsey by 4-0.

By the end of the year Burgess Hill Town had extended their lead at the top of Division One to a massive thirteen points, with Sidley United, Three Bridges and Selsey only parted by goal difference. Saltdean United already looked doomed to relegation but there was a fair scrap to avoid the other two places in the drop zone. Eastbourne United and Southwick were the occupants of those positions.

In the FA Vase Fourth Round, Burgess Hill were held to a 1-1 draw, at home, by Dorking but won the replay on penalties after another 1-1 draw. They marched on the FA Vase with a 4-0 win over Portleven in the Fifth Round, but Sussex involvement in the FA Vase finally came to an end at the beginning of March as both Burgess Hill Town and Lewes lost 2-1, to Tiptree United and Sudbury Town respectively, in the Sixth Round. The Hillians crowd was a massive 1,598.

Selsey met Arundel in the final of the SCFA RUR Charity Cup at Lancing and emerged 2-0 winners.

On Good Friday the League scheduled three Cup Finals in order that as many fans as possible could take in the games. The John O'Hara League Challenge Cup final saw Horsham YMCA lift the trophy with a 2-0 win over Ringmer. Rye & Iden United met Eastbourne Town in the Division Two Challenge Cup Final and also emerged 2-0 winners. In the Division Three Challenge Cup Final Crowborough Athletic defeated Haywards Heath Town 2-1.

By the end of March, Burgess Hill Town had gone 29 League games without defeat and were an incredible seventeen points clear at the top of the Division One table. Hailsham Town were in second place but had played six games more. At the foot, Saltdean United had just nine points and with only eight games remaining were already relegated.

There was a bit of a wobble in the Burgess Hull Town season as first they dropped two points with a 0-0 draw at neighbours Hassocks. Then they lost 1-0 to Horsham in the Semi-final of the floodlight Cup before finally losing their unbeaten record in a home match against Selsey.

Burgess Hill Town had gone 32 games, winning 25 and drawing six, scoring 88 and conceding just nineteen goals. Speculation had been rife that The Hillians would go the whole season without defeat but in the end their record did not match that of Lewes in 1964/65. In that season Lewes finished top but, for some reason, their final match with Littlehampton Town was not played. Their record was 31 games played, 27 wins, three draws, no defeats, 102 goals for and 22 goals against. That's enough history. Let's return to April 2002!

Steyning won the Vernon Wentworth Cup Final by beating Upper Beeding 2-0, Eastbourne Borough beat Chichester City United by 1-0 in the Final of the Reserve Section Cup and Burgess Hill Town finished off their season with the bitter taste of defeat at the hands of Ringmer, 2-0.

Having been challenging near the top for much of the season, Hailsham Town finally slipped to sixth place. Ringmer had made a late charge to claim the runners-up slot but the League title returned to Leylands Park as Burgess Hill Town won the Championship for the fifth time. Southwick, Eastborne United and Saltdean United all returned to Division Two football next season.

Moving in the opposite direction were Rye & Iden United, Shoreham and East Preston. Rye return to the top flight for the first time since 1979/80. Shoreham had spent just two seasons in Division Two and East Preston just one season. Bosham continued their yo-yo existence and dropped back to Divison Three after two seasons and Storrington return after four seasons.

New boys, Pease Pottage Village stormed through their first season in County League Football and, ground gradings permitting, should take the step up to Senior status for next season. Joining them in Divison Two will be close neighbours Steyning Town after five seasons in the wilderness of intermediate football.

St Francis and Lingfield occupied the last two places in the League and any chance of survival will depend on the ability of aspiring clubs to achieve the ground grading requirements of the Sussex County Football League.

FINAL LEAGUE TABLES 2001-02
DIVISION ONE

	P	W	D	L	F	A	Pts	GD
Burgess Hill Town	38	28	6	4	100	27	90	67
Ringmer	38	23	5	10	86	46	74	40
Chichester City U	38	21	4	13	72	66	67	6
Selsey	38	19	9	10	69	54	66	15
Sidley United	38	18	11	9	70	36	65	34
Hailsham Town	38	20	2	16	62	55	62	7
Three Bridges	38	18	7	13	82	61	61	21
Pagham	38	17	8	13	80	67	59	13
Arundel	38	17	6	15	51	64	57	-13
Horsham YMCA	38	16	6	16	74	58	54	16
Hassocks	38	15	8	15	57	65	53	-8
Peacehaven & Tels	38	15	7	16	58	63	52	-5
Whitehawk	38	14	9	15	69	55	51	14
Wick	38	15	3	20	56	64	48	-8
Redhill	38	12	5	21	65	83	41	-18
Littlehampton Town	38	11	7	20	64	84	40	-20
Sidlesham	38	11	7	20	56	77	40	-21
Southwick	38	10	9	19	44	76	39	-32
Eastbourne Utd	38	9	10	19	48	67	37	-19
Saltdean United	38	3	7	28	40	129	16	-89

DIVISION TWO

	P	W	D	L	F	A	Pts	GD
Rye & Iden United	34	26	3	5	102	33	81	69
Shoreham	34	22	7	5	74	32	73	42
East Preston	34	20	9	5	89	48	69	41
Eastbourne Town	34	20	5	9	84	39	65	45
East Grinstead T	34	18	10	6	70	40	64	30
Lancing	34	13	10	11	58	48	49	10
Broadbridge Hth	34	14	7	13	63	54	49	9
Westfield	34	14	6	14	65	57	48	8
Worthing United	34	13	9	12	65	63	48	2
Seaford	34	13	8	13	65	63	47	2
Crawley Down	34	12	9	13	58	50	45	8
Oakwood	34	12	8	14	45	55	44	-10
Wealden	34	13	4	17	55	68	43	-13
Mile Oak	34	11	4	19	42	70	37	-28
Oving	34	10	5	19	40	78	35	-38
Shinewater Assoc	34	9	6	19	51	91	33	-40
Storrington	34	3	6	25	31	74	15	-43
Bosham	34	3	4	27	31	125	13	-94

DIVISION THREE

	P	W	D	L	F	A	Pts	GD
Pease Pottage Vlge	30	22	6	2	88	35	72	53
Steyning Town	30	22	3	5	79	21	69	58
Forest	30	17	7	6	44	27	58	17
Crowborough Ath	30	17	3	10	38	48	54	20
Franklands Village	30	16	5	9	51	31	53	20
Haywards Hth Tn	30	14	5	11	46	48	47	-2
Newhaven	30	12	7	11	53	43	43	10
Upper Beeding	30	11	9	10	59	48	42	11
T.S.C.	30	9	8	13	61	58	35	3
Ifield	30	7	12	11	43	57	33	-14
Uckfield Town	30	8	9	13	36	61	33	-25
Hurstpierpoint	30	8	6	16	49	63	30	-14
Bexhill Town	30	8	4	18	32	65	28	-33
Ansty Rangers	30	7	5	18	48	75	26	-27
St Francis	30	7	4	19	43	83	25	-40
Lingfield	30	6	5	19	39	76	23	-37

DIVISION ONE RESULTS CHART 2001-02

		1	2	3	4	5	6	7	8	9	10	11	12	13	14	15	16	17	18	19	20
1	Arundel	X	1-4	1-2	2-0	0-2	2-1	3-1	2-2	1-1	1-3	2-0	3-2	4-2	1-0	0-1	0-2	2-1	1-4	3-1	2-0
2	Burgess Hill Town	2-0	X	2-0	1-0	2-1	2-3	2-1	2-1	2-1	3-1	3-1	0-2	12-0	0-2	4-2	1-1	4-2	3-0	5-1	2-0
3	Chichester City U	0-3	0-6	X	2-2	1-2	2-0	0-3	4-1	1-2	1-0	4-1	0-3	4-0	1-1	3-1	3-3	4-1	5-2	1-0	2-0
4	Eastbourne Utd	0-1	0-1	0-1	X	1-0	4-1	1-3	2-0	1-4	0-0	2-1	2-2	2-1	2-3	0-1	1-2	2-3	0-0	0-0	1-0
5	Hailsham Town	0-1	0-4	4-1	0-0	X	2-0	2-3	1-0	0-3	2-3	2-1	1-0	5-1	1-2	1-0	0-4	1-3	0-2	1-0	4-3
6	Hassocks	0-1	0-0	1-3	2-4	2-1	X	2-4	4-2	3-3	1-4	4-0	0-2	4-2	4-0	1-0	2-1	0-4	2-2	0-0	
7	Horsham YMCA	4-0	0-1	3-1	4-0	0-1	2-0	X	1-1	1-1	5-0	1-2	1-3	7-1	1-2	5-1	2-1	3-1	0-3	1-3	0-1
8	Littlehampton Tn	0-2	2-3	2-6	4-1	2-1	2-3	1-1	X	4-0	1-3	3-2	1-5	6-2	1-2	1-4	1-0	1-1	2-0	1-3	1-3
9	Pagham	2-2	2-2	4-0	0-0	1-3	0-2	3-2	2-0	X	3-0	5-1	3-2	1-2	1-5	2-1	1-1	1-0	4-2	4-5	4-0
10	Peacehaven & Tels	1-1	0-5	2-2	2-1	1-4	1-1	2-0	1-5	3-1	X	2-0	0-1	1-3	1-0	0-0	1-1	7-0	2-3	1-0	2-0
11	Redhill	3-1	0-4	4-3	4-4	2-3	2-1	1-3	2-2	0-2	1-0	X	2-4	5-0	1-1	3-1	1-4	1-1	2-2	0-1	1-3
12	Ringmer	4-0	2-2	0-1	4-1	3-1	1-1	3-1	1-2	5-0	2-1	2-1	X	4-0	1-4	0-1	3-1	2-0	0-0	1-2	2-0
13	Saltdean United	0-0	0-3	1-2	3-3	1-2	1-1	1-1	1-3	1-4	3-2	0-5	1-5	X	2-3	0-1	0-2	2-2	1-3	0-2	3-5
14	Selsey	1-0	0-2	1-4	4-2	2-1	0-3	1-1	2-0	2-1	0-0	4-2	1-1	4-0	X	1-3	3-0	1-1	2-1	2-1	2-3
15	Sidlesham	2-2	3-1	0-2	0-0	1-5	1-1	1-2	3-3	2-4	2-4	1-3	0-3	3-1	3-3	X	0-2	2-2	3-1	3-1	3-0
16	Sidley United	5-0	0-0	0-1	3-0	3-0	0-1	1-1	2-0	1-1	2-1	4-0	1-2	1-1	1-0	1-2	X	7-0	1-0	1-1	2-1
17	Southwick	4-1	1-4	0-1	0-5	2-3	0-3	0-2	1-2	2-0	2-3	2-3	1-1	0-0	2-0	1-1		X	0-0	0-2	1-0
18	Three Bridges	3-1	3-3	6-1	1-3	0-0	3-0	4-2	5-0	3-1	2-3	1-4	6-3	3-0	1-3	5-2	1-4	0-1	X	1-1	3-1
19	Whitehawk	0-1	0-1	1-2	2-0	0-2	7-0	4-1	3-3	3-2	0-1	0-3	2-0	10-1	4-4	4-2	2-2	0-0	1-2	X	0-0
20	Wick	4-2	0-2	3-1	5-1	0-3	0-1	3-1	3-1	1-4	4-2	1-0	1-3	3-1	1-1	4-0	1-2	1-2	0-2	1-0	X

DIVISION TWO RESULTS CHART 2001-02

		1	2	3	4	5	6	7	8	9	10	11	12	13	14	15	16	17	18
1	Bosham	X	1-2	1-5	0-3	2-5	1-8	1-3	3-2	3-2	0-6	1-4	1-2	1-4	3-5	0-4	1-5	0-5	1-3
2	Broadbridge Heath	3-1	X	1-2	1-4	2-3	0-1	1-2	4-0	0-0	4-0	1-1	2-1	2-1	1-3	2-1	2-1	1-1	1-2
3	Crawley Down	1-0	1-3	X	0-0	2-2	1-1	0-4	0-2	1-1	1-1	2-1	2-4	1-2	0-2	1-1	4-2	3-0	2-3
4	East Grinstead Town	5-0	1-1	1-1	X	0-1	3-2	3-1	2-3	1-1	3-0	2-3	4-1	2-0	0-2	1-0	4-0	3-2	2-2
5	East Preston	3-0	2-2	2-0	1-1	X	3-3	0-1	2-2	4-0	3-0	1-3	3-2	7-0	2-1	3-0	2-0	2-0	2-5
6	Eastbourne Town	5-0	2-1	0-1	0-1	2-1	X	3-1	4-1	5-0	4-0	2-1	2-1	7-3	4-2	3-0	3-4	2-2	2-0
7	Lancing	1-1	1-3	2-1	2-2	2-3	1-1	X	3-1	1-0	7-0	0-1	2-2	4-1	1-2	2-0	2-0	1-3	1-1
8	Mile Oak	2-2	2-0	2-3	2-3	1-4	0-3	0-1	X	5-0	1-0	0-4	2-1	1-1	0-0	3-2	1-0	2-0	0-2
9	Oakwood	3-1	1-1	0-0	0-1	2-4	2-1	1-1	1-0	X	3-2	2-4	3-1	3-1	0-3	2-0	0-2	4-0	4-2
10	Oving	1-1	1-2	1-0	1-1	0-5	0-4	2-1	3-0	1-1	X	0-4	3-0	2-1	1-2	2-0	1-2	0-6	2-0
11	Rye & Iden United	7-1	2-1	4-0	4-2	0-2	2-1	4-0	3-0	3-0	5-1	X	1-1	2-0	5-1	2-1	7-1	1-0	4-1
12	Seaford	2-0	3-3	1-0	1-2	2-5	1-0	2-2	6-2	1-3	4-3	2-5	X	6-2	0-0	2-0	0-0	3-1	1-1
13	Shinewater Association	9-1	3-4	1-8	0-2	4-4	2-0	1-1	1-0	1-4	1-1	0-2	3-2	X	2-0	0-1	0-4	0-0	0-5
14	Shoreham	5-0	5-0	1-1	1-1	4-0	1-0	1-1	1-0	1-1	1-0	1-0	8-1	X	2-1	2-2	2-0	2-0	
15	Storrington	2-0	0-3	1-6	0-4	0-0	0-3	2-2	2-3	0-1	1-2	0-4	0-1	1-1	0-3	X	1-3	1-1	2-3
16	Wealden	1-1	3-0	0-4	3-4	1-4	1-2	0-1	1-0	1-0	0-1	2-1	3-3	3-4	0-2	4-1	X	0-3	2-1
17	Westfield	4-0	0-4	2-1	2-0	3-3	2-4	2-1	6-0	1-0	2-1	1-4	2-1	1-0	2-4	2-3	1-3	X	2-2
18	Worthing United	3-2	1-0	1-3	2-2	1-1	0-0	3-2	1-2	2-0	3-0	3-3	0-3	1-2	2-3	3-3	4-1	1-6	X

LEADING SCORERS 2001-02
(League goals only)

DIVISION ONE

29	Peter Baker	Sidley United
24	Tony Holden	Ringmer
23	Steve Davies	Littlehampton Town
22	Patrick Massaro	Three Bridges
21	Jamie Laidlaw	Chichester City United
21	Steve Banks	Three Bridges
20	Roger Moore	Chichester City United

DIVISION TWO

30	Matt Huckett	East Preston
26	Paul Young	Broadbridge Heath
24	Gary Brockwell	Eastbourne Town

DIVISION THREE

26	Gareth Neathey	T.S.C.

TEAMS OF THE MONTH

MONTH	DIVISION ONE	DIVISION TWO	DIVISION THREE
August	Burgess Hill Town	Rye & Iden United	Pease Pottage Village
September	Hassocks	Shoreham	Franklands Village
October	Burgess Hill Town	Shoreham	Pease Pottage Village
November	Burgess Hill Town	Westfield	Crowborough Athletic
December	Burgess Hill Town	Shoreham	Steyning Town
January	Horsham YMCA	Eastbourne Town	Forest
February	Burgess Hill Town	Eastbourne Town	Steyning Town
March	Ringmer	East Grinstead Town	Newhaven
April/May	Sidlesham	East Preston	Pease Pottage Village

FAIR PLAY TABLE 2001-02
(League games only)

	games	yellow	red	total	ave.		games	yellow	red	total	ave.
Hassocks	38	16	0	16	0.42	Redhill	38	35	4	47	1.24
Horsham YMCA	38	17	1	20	0.53	Whitehawk	38	38	3	47	1.24
Burgess Hill Tn	38	22	0	22	0.58	Saltdean Utd	38	51	5	66	1.74
Littlehampton Tn	38	23	0	23	0.61	Southwick	38	56	3	68	1.79
Three Bridges	38	24	1	27	0.71	Peacehaven & T	38	52	6	70	1.84
Eastbourne Utd	38	19	4	31	0.82	Selsey	38	57	6	75	1.97
Arundel	38	28	2	34	0.89	Sidlesham	38	52	12	88	2.32
Pagham	38	29	2	35	0.92	Ringmer	38	66	8	90	2.37
Wick	38	34	1	37	0.97						
Chichester C Utd	38	32	2	38	1.00	Yellow card = 1 point					
Sidley United	38	37	1	40	1.05	Red card = 3 points					
Hailsham Town	38	38	2	44	1.16						

PAST RECORDS

LEAGUE DIVISION ONE

1981-82	Peacehaven & Tels
1982-83	Peacehaven & Tels
1983-84	Whitehawk
1984-85	Steyning Town
1985-86	Steyning Town
1986-87	Arundel
1987-88	Pagham
1988-89	Pagham
1989-90	Wick
1990-91	Littlehampton Town
1991-92	Peacehaven & Tels
1992-93	Peacehaven & Tels
1993-94	Wick
1994-95	Peacehaven & Tels
1995-96	Peacehaven & Tels
1996-97	Burgess Hill Town
1997-98	Burgess Hill Town
1998-99	Burgess Hill Town
1999-00	Langney Sports
2000-01	Sidley United
2001-02	Burgess Hill Town

LEAGUE DIVISION TWO

1981-82	Wick
1982-83	Horsham YMCA
1983-84	Portfield
1984-85	Shoreham
1985-86	Wick
1986-87	Pagham
1987-88	Langney Sports
1988-89	Seaford
1989-90	Bexhill Town
1990-91	Newhaven
1991-92	Portfield
1992-93	Crowborough Athletic
1993-94	Shoreham
1994-95	Mile Oak
1995-96	Saltdean United
1996-97	Littlehampton Town
1997-98	East Preston
1998-99	Sidley United
1999-00	Sidlesham
2000-01	Southwick
2001-02	Rye & Iden United

LEAGUE DIVISION THREE

1984-85	Oakwood
1985-86	Seaford Town
1986-87	Langney Sports
1987-88	Midway
1988-89	Saltdean
1989-90	Worthing United
1990-91	Ifield
1991-92	Hassocks
1992-93	Withdean
1993-94	Bosham
1994-95	Midhurst & Easebourne
1995-96	Ifield
1996-97	Sidlesham
1997-98	Lingfield
1998-99	Oving SC
1999-00	Bosham
2000-01	Rye United
2001-02	Pease Pottage Village

LEAGUE CHALLENGE CUP

1981-82	Horsham YMCA
1982-83	Whitehawk
1983-84	Steyning Town
1984-85	Littlehampton Town
1985-86	Steyning Town
1986-87	Arundel
1987-88	Wick
1988-89	Pagham
1989-90	Langney Sports
1990-91	Littlehampton Town
1991-92	Peacehaven & Tels
1992-93	Peacehaven & Tels
1993-94	Whitehawk
1994-95	Hailsham Town
1995-96	Shoreham
1996-97	Wick
1997-98	Burgess Hill Town
1998-99	Burgess Hill Town
1999-00	Saltdean United
2000-01	Sidley United
2001-02	Horsham YMCA

DIVISION TWO LEAGUE CUP

1981-82	Lancing
1982-83	Shoreham
1983-84	Haywards Heath
1984-85	Chichester City
1985-86	Pagham
1986-87	Selsey
1987-88	Chichester City
1988-89	Midhurst
1989-90	Oakwood
1990-91	Chichester City
1991-92	Redhill
1992-93	Lancing
1993-94	Shoreham
1994-95	Horsham YMCA
1995-96	Selsey
1996-97	Sidley United
1997-98	Three Bridges
1998-99	Sidley United
1999-00	Sidlesham
2000-01	Peacehaven & Tels
2001-02	Rye & Iden United

MERIT TABLE WINNERS

1981-82	Wick
1982-83	Peacehaven & Tels
1983-84	Portfield
1984-85	Steyning Town
1985-86	Wick
1986-87	Pagham
1987-88	Three Bridges
1988-89	Wick
1989-90	Wick
1990-91	Littlehampton Town
1991-92	Peacehaven & Tels
1992-93	Pagham
1993-94	Wick
1994-95	Wick
1995-96	Wick
1996-97	Wick
1997-98	Burgess Hill Town
1998-99	Horsham YMCA
1999-00	Arundel
2000-01	Redhill

Burgess Hill Town prior to their 1-2 defeat by Tiptree United in the FA Vase Quarter Finals. Back Row (l-r): Darin Killpatrick, Steve Harper, Andy Lutwyche, Sean Edwards (Player/Coach), Gary Callingham, Richard Carter, Tim Brown, Ashley Carr, Pat Gannon, Richard Waters, Daren Newman. Front Row: Des Guile, Adie Downey (capt.), Tommy Levitt, Paul Williams, Phil Churchill, Lee Isaac, Danny Bloor (Asst Mngr). Photo: Arthur Evans

Hassocks FC, who won an AXA FA Cup award for beating Bromley, are seen here before the previous round against Ash United. Photo: Eric Marsh

Southwick. Photo: Gordon Whittington

ARUNDEL

Secretary: Doug Feest, 142 Aldsworth Road, Worthing. BN12 4UU Tel: 01903 249276

Ground: Mill Road, Arundel, West Sussex.   Tel: 01903 882548

Directions: A27 from Worthing to Arundel over railway bridge to roundabout.
Second exit into Queen Street to town centre, turn right over bridge.
Car park leading to ground 100yards right
Capacity: 2,200   Seats: 100   Cover: 200   Floodlights: 206 lux

Clubhouse: 2 bars, kitchen, toilets, telephone, pool, darts, Sky TV. Normal pub hours. No food

HONOURS Sussex Co. Lg 57-58 58-59 86-87 (Lg Cup 86-87, Div 2 Cup 76-77, Res. Sect.
78-79, Res. Sect. Cup 78-79, Merit Table 80-81,Sussex Fives 1984 1987),
Sussex RUR Charity Cup 68-69 72-73 78-79 79-80, Sussex Jnr Cup 07-08,
West Sussex Lg (Res.) 70-71 (Malcolm Simmonds Cup 70-71)

PREVIOUS **League** : West Sussex 1896-1975   **Grounds:** Castle Park; Station Rd Ground

RECORD **Gate:** 2,200 v Chichester, League 67-68
Scorer: Paul J Bennett **Appearances:** 537, Paul Bennett (goalkeeper)
Win : 13-0 v Horsham YMCA (H), Sussex Co. Lge Div 1 21/12/85

Players progressing: John Templeman (Brighton & Hove Albion 1966)

FACT FILE
Founded: 1889
Nickname: Mulletts
Colours: Red & white halves/white/red
Change colours: Green/black/green
Midweek matchday: Tuesday
Reserves' Lge: Sussex Co. Res Div (West)
Programme: 8 pages, free Editor: P Wells
Local Press: Arun Herald

CLUB PERSONNEL
Chairman: Bob Marchant
Vice Chairman: S Brennan
Manager: Mike Rowland

BURGESS HILL TOWN

Secretary: Roger Puttick, 48 Maple Drive,Burgess Hill RH15 8AW Tel: 01444 243080
Email : bhtfcsocial@ aol.com

Ground: Leylands Park, Burgess Hill, West Sussex RH15 8AW Tel: 01444 242429
Capacity: 2,000   Seats: 100   Cover: Yes   Floodlights: Yes

Directions: Turn east from A273 London Road into Leylands Road, take 4th left (signposted)
Leyland Park. Nearest station Wivelsfield

Clubhouse: Bar & social facilities. Tea bar   **Club Shop:** Yes Club badges available

HONOURS Sussex County Lg 75-76 96-97, 97-98,98-99;01-02 Lg Cup 73-74 79-80 97-98 98-
99 (R-up 90-91), Div 2 74-75 (Cup 73-73), F/lit Cup 96-97, Res 76-77 77-78 91-92, Res. Sect.
East 77-78 82-83 84-85, Res. Cup 82-83 98-99; Yth Sect. West 91-92 East 95-96 96-97 97-98 98-
99 North 96-97 97-98; Sussex Fives 80; Mid-Sussex Lg 00-01 03-04 39-4046-47 56-57 (Div 2 03-
04 (res), Div 3 20-21 36-37, Div 4 (res) 56-57; Mid Sussex Snr Cup 94-95 96-97; 01-02
Montgomery Cup 39-40 56-57; Mowatt Cup 45-46; Sussex RUR Charity Cup 91-92; Sussex
I'mediate Cup 76-77; Sussex Yth Lge 96-97 97-98, Cup 91-92 97-98

BEST SEASON **FA Cup:** 4th Qual. Rd. 99-00, 1-4 v Hereford United
F.A.Vase: Quarter -Final v Tiptree United 2001-02
RECORD **Gate:**1,598 v Tiptree United F.A.Vase 6th Round

FACT FILE
Founded: 1882
Nickname: Hillians
Sponsors: Time 24
Colours: Yellow/black/yellow
Change colours: All red
Midweek matchday: Tuesday
Programme: Yes
Website: www.bhtfc.org.uk

CLUB PERSONNEL
Chairman: Ken Somerville
Patron: Jack Lake
Manager: Danny Bloor

2001-02
Captain: Adie Downey
Top Scorer: Phil Churchill 32
P.o.Y.:Pat Gannon

CHICHESTER CITY UNITED

Secretary: Peter Down, 14 Edith Cottages,Mill Road, West Ashling, Chichester PO18 8DG
Tel: 01243 574597 (H) email: peter.down1@byinternet.com

Ground: Church Road, Portfield, Chichester, West Sussex PO19 4HN Tel: 01243 779875
Capacity: 2,000   Seats: 20   Cover: 200   Floodlights: Yes

Directions: A27 from Arundel to Chichester, take road to signposted city centre then 1st left
(Church Rd) after supermarket r'bout. 1 mile from Chichester(BR)

Clubhouse: 2 bars, pool, snooker, seating for 100, dance floor, darts.
Teabar selling h & c food.

PREVIOUS **Names**: Chichester FC (pre-1948), Chichester City 48-00.
Amalgamated with Portfield in 2000

HONOURS Sussex Co. Lg Div 2 72-73 83-84 91-92 (Div 2 Cup 70-71 72-73, Res Sect
as Portfield Prem Lge 94-95, Cup 91-92), W Sussex Lg 46-47 48-49 (Malcolm Simmonds
Cup 46-47), Sussex Jnr Cup 45-46, Benevolent Cup 46-47
HONOURS Sussex Co. Lg(5) 59-61 67-68 72-73 79-80 Invit. Cup 47-48 54-55 56-57 63-64,
as Div 2 Cup 84-85 87-88 90-91, Sussex Snr Cup 25-26, Sussex RUR Charity Cup
Chichester City 60-61(jt with Brighton & HA) 63-64, Sussex I'mediate Cup 67-68

FACT FILE
Formed 2000
Chichester (1873)Portfield (1896)
Sponsors: McDonalds
Nickname: Lilywhites
Colours: Green& Blue/ Blue/ Blue
Change colours: All white
Midweek matchday: Tuesday
Programme Editor: T Wallis
Local Press: Chichester Observer

CLUB PERSONNEL

Chairman: Simon Kenny
Match Secretary:Phil Littlejohns
Tel: 01243 528007
Press Officer: T Wallis (01705 464438)
Manager: Adrian Girdler
Chief Coach: Kevin Holston
Physio: NickTaylor
Club Steward: Andy Smith(01243 775455)

EAST PRESTON

FACT FILE

Secretary:	Keith Freeman, 41 Ambersham Cres., East Preston, West Sussex BN161AJ
	Tel: 01903 771158
Ground:	Roundstone Recreation Ground, East Preston, West Sussex Tel: 01903 776026
	Capacity: Seats: None Cover: 40 Floodlights: Yes
Directions:	Less than a mile from Angmering (BR) station. A259 from Worthing to Roundstone Hotel (6 miles), turn south over railway crossing, left past Centurion garage, right into Roundstone Drive
Clubhouse:	Licensed bar open Mon-Fri evenings, Sat noon-11pm, Sun noon-11pm. Kitchen serves light refreshments on matchdays

Reformed: 1966
Nickname: None
Sponsors: Argyl insurance
Colours: White with black trim,black/white
Change: Black & yellow stripes/white/black
Reserves Lge: Sussex Co. Res. Div (Prem)
Programme: Yes
Editor: T.B.A.
Local Press: Littlehampton Gazette

HONOURS   Sussex Co. Lg Div 2 Champions 97-98Div 3 83-84, (R-up 90-91), Div 3 Cup 87-88 (R-up 89-90); West Sussex Lg 77-78 80-81 81-82 82-83 (Malcolm Simmonds Cup 80-81 82-83), Div2 Sth 81-82, Div 3 Sth 79-80, Div 5 Sth 82-83; Chichester Cup 87-88; BorehamTphy 77-78 90-91 (R-up 93-94); Vernon Wentworth Cup 80-81 89-90; 99-00 Worthing Lg 67-68 (Div 2 68-69 (res); Benevolent. Trophy 66-67 68-69; Worthing Charity Cup 68-69

PREVIOUS   **Leagues:** Worthing; W Sussex

CLUB PERSONNEL

President: Greg Stanley
Chairman:Mike Barnes
Manager: Vic Short
Asst Managers: Kevin Valentine & Simon Butler

HAILSHAM TOWN

FACT FILE

Secretary:	Derek York, 59 Anglesey Avenue, Horsebridge, Hailsham BN27 3BQ
/Press Officer	Tel: 01323 848024 (H)
Ground:	The Beaconsfield, Western Road, Hailsham, East Sussex
	Tel: 01323 840446
Directions:	A22 to Arlington Road, turn east, then left into South Road - left into Diplocks Way until Daltons. Four miles from Polegate (BR - Brighton-Eastbourne line); regular bus service from Eastbourne

Capacity: 2,000   Seats: None   Cover: 300   Floodlights: Yes
Clubhouse: Hot and cold snacks. Open every evening, matchdays and Sundays, teabar

Founded: 1885
Nickname: None
Colours: Yellow &Green/Green/gGreen
Change colours: All white
Midweek matchday: Tuesday
Programme: Yes
Editor: Secretary
Admission: ¨3.00

2001-02
Captain.: Kevin Isted
P.o.Y.: Martin Richardson
Top Scorer: Scott French 17

HONOURS   Sussex County Lg Div 2 R-up 80-81, Southern Co'sComb. 74-75, Sussex RUR Charity Cup, Sussex I'mediate Cup, Hastings Snr Cup,Sussex Jnr Cup, E Sussex Lg Cup, Hailsham Charity Cup, John O'Hara Cup 95-96

PREVIOUS   **League:** E Sussex, Southern Comb
BEST SEASON   **FA Vase:** 5th Rd 88-89
RECORD   **Gate:**1,350 v Hungerford, FA Vase Feb '89
    Goalscorer: H Stevens 51, 95-96   **Appearances:** P Comber 713

CLUB PERSONNEL
President: J.Whippy
Chairman: D.Griffiths
Manager: Brian Dennis

HASSOCKS

FACT FILE

Secretary:	Dave Knight, 21 Farnham Avenue, Hassocks, BN6 8NR
	Tel No: 01273 842023
Ground:	The Beacon, Brighton Rd, Hassocks Tel: 01273 846040
	Capacity: 1,500 Seats: None Cover: 100 Floodlights: Yes
Directions:	Off A273 Pyecombe Road to Burgess Hill, 300yds south of Stonepound cross roads (B2116) to Hurstpierpoint or Hassocks
Clubhouse:	Clubroom, bar, kitchen Club Shop: No

Founded: 1902
Nickname: The Robins
Sponsors: Icon
Colours: Red/white/red
Change colours: Blue/white/blue
Midweek Matchday: Tuesday/Wednesday
Programme: 24 pages, 50p
Editor: Dave Knight
Admission: £1.50
Local Press: Mid Sussex Times, Evening Argus

HONOURS   Sussex County Lg Div 3 91-92, Div 2 R-up 94-95, Res. Sect. East R-up 92-93; Southern Counties Comb. 76-77, Lg Cup R-up 79-80; Brighton Hove & Dist. Lg 71-72; Sussex Intermediate Cup 74-75 (R-up 80-81)

PREVIOUS   **Leagues:** Mid Sussex; Brighton Hove & Dist.; Southern Co's Comb
    Ground: Adastra Park, Hassocks (pre-1992)

RECORD   **Attendance:** 610 v Burgess Hill Town, Sussex County Lge 96-97

CLUB PERSONNEL
President: Maurice Boxall
Chairman: JimGoodrum (01273 842023)
Manager: Dave John

HORSHAM YMCA

Secretary: Bob Brading, 16 Hazelhurst Crescent, Horsham,.RM12 1XB
Tel No: 01403 250270 (H)
Ground: Gorings Mead, Horsham Tel: 01403 252689
Capacity: 1000   Seats: 150   Cover: 200   Floodlights: Yes

Directions: Approaching Horsham fron the East on A281 Brighton Road, the ground is on left & signposted opposite Gorings Mead

HONOURS Sussex Co Lge Div 2 65-66 82-83 R-up 94-95 (Lg Cup 81-82, Invitation Cup66-67 67-68, Div 2 Invit. Cup 59-60 61-62 94-95) Sussex RUR Cup Winners 2000-01

PREVIOUS **Leagues:** Horsham & Dist/Brighton & Hove/Mid Sussex
Grounds: Lyons Field, Kings Road

RECORD **Attendance:** 950 v Chelmsford City , FA Cup 2000

BEST SEASON: FA Cup: 4th Qual. Rd. 99-00 2-3 v Chelmsford City

FACT FILE
Founded: 1898
Nickname: YM's
Sponsors: Principal Copiers
Colours: White/black/white
Change colours: All Red
Midweek Matchday: Tuesday
Local Press: West Sussex County Times

CLUB PERSONNEL
Chairman:John Cashman
Manager: John Suter
Match Secretary: Robin Bishop
Tel: 01403 891622 Manager: John Suter
Physio: Robin Bishop

2001-02
Captain: Matt Ouffield
Ps.o.Y.: Stewart McCreadie & Jason Oumbrill
Top Scorer: Nick Flint 16

LITTLEHAMPTON TOWN

Secretary: John Savage, 66 Nelson Road, Worthing. BN12 6EN. (01903 502850)

Ground: The Sportsfield, St Flora's Road, Littlehampton (01903 713944)
Capacity: 4,000   Seats: 260   Cover: 260   Floodlights: Yes

Directions: 10 minutes walk from Littlehampton station (BR) - turn left alongTerminus Rd, continue through High Street and Church Rd to junction with St Flora's Rd (left)

Club Shop: No, but metal badges available
Clubhouse: Sportsman (Private Club). Separate board room & tea bar

HONOURS Sussex Co. Lg 58-59 (jt with Shoreham) 75-77, 84-85, 90-91, 96-97
Sussex Senior Cup 73-74

RECORD **Gate:** 4,000 v Northampton, FA Cup 1st Rd Proper 90-91

BEST SEASON **FA Vase** Semi-Final 90-91 v Gresley Rovers 1-3 (A), 1-2 (H)
FA Cup: 1st Round 90-91 v Northampton Town(H) 0-4

FACT FILE
Founded: 1894
Nickname: Marigolds
Colours: Gold/black/black
Change: All white
Midweek Matches: Tuesday
Programme:
Editor:
Local Press: Littlehampton Gazette
CLUB PERSONNEL
President: Ian Cunningham
Chairman:Andy Taylor
Manager: Neil Hider
2001-02
Captain: Darren Maynard
P.o.Y.: Steve Davies
Top Scorer: Steve Davies 24

PAGHAM

Secretary: David Bolland, 23 Tennyson Road, Bognor `Regis PO21 2SB
Tel No: 01243 829973
Ground: Nyetimber Lane, Pagham, West Sussex   Tel: 01243 266112
Capacity: 2,000   Seats: 200   Cover: 200   Floodlights: Yes

Directions: Turn off A27 Chichester by-pass (signposted A259 Pagham). Ground invillage of Nyetimber. Three miles from Bognor (BR). Buses 260 & 240

Clubhouse: Bar open matchdays and some evenings. Hot food, pool, darts,satellite TV. Tea bar
Club Shop: No

HONOURS Sussex Co. Lg R-up 80-81 87-88 88-89 92-93 (Div 2 78-79 86-87, Lg Cup88-89, Div 2 Cup 71-72 85-86, Res. Sect. West 80-81, Res Section Cup 77-78 80-81 87-88 88-89 90-91 96-97; Sussex F'lit Cup R-up 88-89; Sussex RUR Charity Cup88-89 (R-up 93-94); West Sussex Lg 65-66 68-69 69-70; Malcolm Simmonds Cup 67-68; Sussex I'mediate Cup 66-67
PREVIOUS **Leagues:** Chichester 1903-50; West Sussex 50-69   **Grounds:** None
RECORDS **Gate:** 1,200 v Bognor, 1971   **Scorer:** Mark Vickers/ R Deluca
Win: 10-1 v Seaford Town (A), Sussex County League Division Two, 1970
Defeat: 0-7 v Newport IOW (H), FA Amateur Cup, mid-1970s

FACT FILE
Founded: 1903
Nickname: Lions
Sponsors: City Sales Centre
Colours: White/black/red
Change colours: Yellow/green/green
Midweek Matchday: Tuesday
Reserve's League: Sussex Co. Res Premier
Programme: 12 pages, 50p
Editor: Rob Peach
Local Press: Bognor Observer

CLUB PERSONNEL
Chairman: Graham Peach
Vice-Chairman: Steve Newdick
President: A Peirce
Press Officer: John Rose(01243 545694)
Comm. Manager: Chairman
Manager: Paul Gilbert
Asst Manager: Kevin Hotson

Arundel's McLoughlin bursts through the Littlehampton defence.
Photo: D Nicholson

Horsham's Jamie Taylor and right Luke Gedling take on Lewes defender.
Photo: Clive Turner

Pagham under pressure from a Hassocks corner.
Photo: Graham Cotterill

PEACEHAVEN & TELSCOMBE

Secretary: Mrs Margaret Edwards, 2,Tuscan Court, The Esplanade, Telscombe Cliffs, East Sussex BN10 7HF   Tel: 01273 583022 (H) 07803 845329 (M)

Ground: Piddinghoe Avenue, Peacehaven, E. Sussex (01273 582471)
Directions: Arriving from Brighton on A259, cross r'bout and Piddinghoe Ave. is next left after 2nd set of lights - ground at end. From Newhaven Piddinghoe Ave. is first right after first set of lights. Three miles from Newhaven(BR). Peacehaven is served by Brighton to Newhaven and Eastbourne buses
Capacity: 3,000   Seats: None   Cover: 250   Floodlights: Yes
Clubhouse: Bar open evenings and weekends, pool darts, hot and cold food available. Tea bar

HONOURS Sussex Co. Lg 78-79 81-82 82-83 91-92 92-93 94-95 95-96 (R-up 77-78 80-81 90-91, Lg Cup 91-92 92-93, Div 2 R-up 75-76, Div2 Cup 75-76, Norman Wingate Tphy 82-83 91-92 92-93, Hayden Tphy 82-83 92-93, Div 2 Invitation Cup69-70, Sussex Snr Cup R-up 81-82 92-93, Sussex RUR Charity Cup 77-78 81-82 92-93 (R-up 80-81 89-90 90-91 94-95 95-96), Brighton Charity Cup 91-92 92-93 93-94, Vernon Wentworth 91-92 92-93

RECORD Attendance: 1,420 v Littlehampton, Lge 91

PREVIOUS Leagues: Lewes; Brighton

BEST SEASON FA Cup: 4th Qual. Rd 90-91   **FA Vase:** 6th Rd (Q-F) 95-96, 5th Rd 92-93

FACT FILE
Founded: 1923
Nickname: The Tye
Sponsors: Anchor Garage
Colours: All white and black
Change colours: Royal Blue
Midweek Matches: Tuesday
Programme: Yes
Editor: Secretary

CLUB PERSONNEL
Chairman: Jim Edwards
Match Sec: Fred Parris
Press Officer: Secretary
Manager: Peter Edwards

REDHILL

Secretary: Neil Hoad, 2b Earlswood Rd, Redhill, Surrey RH1 6HE   Tel: 01737 213847
Ground: Kiln Brow, Three Arch Road, Redhill, Surrey   Tel: 01737 762129
Email: michael@jbjovi.fsnet.co.uk

Directions: On left hand side of A23, two and a half miles south of Redhill
Capacity: 2,000   Seats: 150   Cover: 150   Floodlights: Yes
Club Shop: Sells usual range of souvenires. Contact Spencer Mitchell - 01737 780634
Clubhouse: Social club, bar, canteen, board room, club shop, tanoy, toilets
HONOURS Athenian 24-25 83-84 (Lg Cup 69-70 70-71), East &West Surrey Lg1902-3, Southern Sub Sen West Lg. 1902-03, Surrey Snr Cup 28-29 65-66, Gilbert Rice F'lit Cup 80-81, Sussex Co. Lg Div 2 Cup 91-92, Southern Co's Comb. Cup 90-91,98-99

PREVIOUS **Leagues:** E & W Surrey; Spartan 09-10; Southern Sub; London 21-23; Athenian 23-84; Spartan 84-88
Grounds: Memorial Sports Ground, London Road 1894-1986

BEST SEASON **FA Amtr Cup:** Semi-Final 25   **FA Cup:** 1st Round 57-58

RECORDS **Attendance:** 8,000 v Hastings United F.A.Cup 1956
Goalscorer: Steve Turner 119   **Appearances:** Brian Medlicott 766
Win : 12-1 v Southall (H) Athenian Lg. 1928-29
Defeat : 1-13 v Bromley (A) Athenian League 1945-46

FACT FILE
Founded: 1894   Nickname: Reds/Lobsters
Sponsors: Trident Microsystems Ltd.
Colours: All red   Change: White/black
Midweek matchday: Tuesday
Reserve League: Sussex Co.Lg
A4 size Programme: 72 pages 50p
National Winner Wirral Programme Survey
Editor: Michael Stewart
Website: http://redhillfc.tripod.com/
Local Press:Surrey Mirror/Redhill&Reigate Life

CLUB PERSONNEL
Chair: Nick Creasey   V.Chair: Alan Thurlbeck
President: Malcolm Chatfield
Press Officer: Michael Stewart
Man: Ian Dawes Assistant: : John Framks
Physio: Brian Watts
2001-02
Leading Goalscorer: Glen Barlow 23
Captain:Steve Roberts
P.o.Y.: Glen Barlow

RINGMER

Secretary: Gary Bullen, 13 Browns Parth, Uckfield, East sussex TN22 1LN
Tel Nos: 07769 936272 (M) 01825 769748 (H)

Ground: Caburn Ground, Anchor Field, Ringmer Tel: 01273 812738
Capacity: 1,000   Seats: 100   Cover: Yes   Floodlights: Yes

Directions: From Lewes road turn into Springett Avenue opposite Ringmer village green. Anchor Field first left. Three miles from Lewes (BR)

Clubhouse: 2 bars, function room, boardroom, tea bar
Club Shop: Club ties & metal badges

HONOURS Sussex Co. Lg 70-71, R-up: 01-02Div 2 68-69, Invit Cup 66-67; Res. Sect. East 79-80 80-81 (R-up 89-90), Yth Section 87-88, Yth SectionEast 87-88; Sussex Snr Cup 72-73 (R-up 80-81); Sussex Jnr Cup 25-26; Sussex Express Sen Charity Cup 94-95

PREVIOUS **League:** Brighton   **Grounds:** None   **Names:** None

BEST SEASON FA Cup 1st Rd Proper 70-71

RECORD **Gate:** 1,200 in FA Cup

FACT FILE
Founded: 1906
Nickname: The Blues
Colours: Sky & navy/navy/navy
Change colours: All yellow
Midweek Matchday: Tuesday
Programme: Yes
Editor: Martin BUrke (01797 230572)
Admission: £3.00
Local Press: Sussex Express

CLUB PERSONNEL
President: Sir G Christie
Chairman: Richard Soan
Manager: Glen Geard
Press Officer: Martin Burke(01797 230572)
Match Sec:John McWhirter (01323 847743)

2001-02
Captain: Glen Davies
P.o.Y.: Glen Davies
Top Scorer: Tony Holden 41

SELSEY

Secretary:	Denny Lee, 29 Malthouyse Cottages, West01243 605027
Ground:	High Street Ground, Selsey, Chichester, West Sussex Tel: 01243 603420
	Capacity: 2,250 Seats: 50 Cover: Yes Floodlights: Yes

Directions: Through Selsey High Street to fire station. Take turning into car park alongside the station. Entrance is in the far corner. Regular buses from Chichester

Clubhouse: Bar, hospitality room, lounge, toilets, kitchen

HONOURS Sussex Co. Lg R-up 89-90 (Div 2 63-64 75-76 (R-up 86-87), Div 2 Cup 86-87 (R-up 84-85), Div 2 Invitation Cup 63-64, Sussex 5-aside 88-89), Sussex SnrCup R-up 63-64, Sussex I'mediate Cup 58-59, Sussex Jnr Cup(Reserves) 76-77,West Sussex Lg 54-55 55-56 57-58 58-59 60-61 (Malcolm Simmonds Cup 55-56 56-57 57-58 58-59)

PREVIOUS **Leagues:** Chichester & Dist.; West Sussex

RECORD **Gate:** 750-800 v Chichester or Portfield, 50's

FACT FILE
Founded: 1903
Nickname: Blues
Sponsors: Ariel Cars
Colours: Blue/white/blue
Change colours:All red
Midweek Matchday: Tuesday
Programme Editor: Secretary
Match Secretary: Mandie Glew

CLUB PERSONNEL
President: Roy Glew
Chairman: Mike Hurst
Press Officer: Secretary
Manager:Danny Hinshelwood

SHOREHAM

Secretary:	Glenn Hilton, 2 Loneycourt, Wilmot Road,Shoreham by Sea, BN43 6JQ
	Tel No: 01273 705902(H) 01273 430775 (W)
Ground:	Middle Road, Shoreham-by-Sea, West Sussex Tel: 01273 454261
	Capacity: 1,500 Seats: 20 Cover: 1 stand Floodlights: Yes

Directions: Half mile from Shoreham-by-Sea (BR) - east across level crossing, up Dolphin Road, ground 150yds on right. Or, A27 to Shoreham. At Southlands Hospital turn left down Hammy Lane, left at end, ground opposite

Clubhouse: Seats 70. Bar, pool, darts, tea bar   **Club Shop:** No

HONOURS Sussex Co. Lg 51-53 77-78 (R-up 34-35, Div 2 61-62 76-77 84-85 93-94,Div 2 Cup 74-75 82-83, Invitation Cup 57-58), Sussex Snr Cup 01-02 05-06,Sussex F'lit Cup R-up 89-90, Sussex RUR Charity Cup 02-03 05-06, VernonWentworth Cup 86-87

PREVIOUS **League:** West Sussex   **Ground:** Buckingham Park (pre-1970)

RECORD **Gate:** 1,342 v Wimbledon (f/lt opening 86)

FACT FILE
Founded: 1892
Nickname: Musselmen
Sponsors: Len German Wholesalers
Colours:All royal blue
Change colours: All red
Midweek Matchday: Wednesday
Programme: Yes
Editor: Michael Wenham
Local Press: Shoreham Herald

CLUB PERSONNEL
President: Alf Bloom
Chairman: John Bell
Press Officer: Michael Wenham
Tel: 01273 596009
Manager: Roger Vrace

SIDLESHAM

Secretary:	Peter Turner, 64 Hawthorn Road, Bognor Regis PO21 2DD
	Tel: 01243 822860 (H)
Ground:	Sidlesham Recreation Ground, Sidlesham. Tel: 01243 641538

Directions: From the Chichester bypass take the B2145, signposted Hunston/Selsey Head towards Selsey. Upon entering Sidlesham the ground is on the right between houses

FACT FILE
Colours: Yellow & Green/green/yellow
Change colours: Red /white/red

CLUB PERSONNEL
Chairman: Alan Parker
"Farm View", Alandale Ave., Birdham,
Chichester PO20 7QN
Tel: 01243 513891 (H)
07887 507351 (M)
Vice Chairman: Roy Parker
Manager: Richard Towers
(01243 586887)

SIDLEY UNITED

Secretary: Mike Gardner, 24 Magpie Close, St Leonards on Sea, E Sussex TN38 8DY

Ground: Gullivers Sports Ground, Glovers Lane, Sidley, Bexhill-on-Sea
Tel: 01424 217078
Capacity: 1,500   Seats: None   Cover: 150   Floodlights: Yes

Directions: From Brighton on A259 to Bexhill bypass traffic lights, left intoLondon Road, continue into Sidley, right into Glovers Lane and 1st left into North Road.
One mile from Bexhill (BR)

Clubhouse: Large bar area & function room. Tea bar
Club Shop: No, but metal badges are available.

HONOURS Sussex Co. Lg Div 1 00-01 Jphn O'Hara League Cup: 00-01 01-02Div 2 58-59 64-65 98-99, Div. 2 Cup 98-99, Div 2 Invit. Cup 57-58; Sussex Intermediate Cup 47-48, Sussex Jnr Cup 24-25

PREVIOUS **Leagues:** East Sussex; Hastings & District
Grounds: None

RECORD **Attendance:** 1,300 in 1959

FACT FILE

Founded: 1906
Nickname: Blues
Sponsors: M.T.Drains
Colours: Navy & sky/navy/navy & sky
Change colours: Yellow & Black
Midweek Matchday: Tues/ Weds
Programme: Yes
Local Press: Bexhill Observer, Bexhill News

CLUB PERSONNEL
President: Tom Hyland
Chairman: Dickie Day
Joint Managers: Glen Sully & Peter Heritage

2001-02
Captain: Matt Duffield
Top Scorer:Nick Flint 16
P.o.Y.: Peter Baker

SOUTHWICK

Secretary: Gary Millis, 21 Grover Avenue, Lancing, West Sussex. BN15 9RG
Tel: 01903 761396 (H) 07801 477979 (M)

Ground: Old Barn Way, off Manor Hall Way, Southwick, Brighton BN43 4NT
Tel: 01273 701010

Directions: Five minutes walk from either Fishergate or Southwick BR stations.
By car A27 from Brighton take 1st left after `Southwick' sign to Leisure Centre.
Ground adjacent.

Capacity: 3,500   Seats: 220   Cover: 1,220   Floodlights: Yes
Clubhouse: Weekdays 12-3 & 6-11, all day Sat., normal hrs Sunday.
Members bar & boardroom with bar. Matchday snacks from tea bar.

HONOURS Isthmian Lg Div 2 Sth 85-86; Sus. Co. Lg 25-26 27-28 29-30 47-48 68-69 74-75, R-up x 9, Lg Cup 77-78 ,Div 1 Invit. Cup 65-66, Div 2 R-up 65-66; Combined Co's Lg R-up 84-85, Sus.Snr Cup x 10, Sus. RUR Charity Cup (10) 1896-97 08-09 10-11 24-26 27-30 37-38 76-77, W. Sus. Lg1896-97 97-98 1908-09 10-11, Sus. Jnr Cup 1891-92.

PREVIOUS **Leagues:** West Sussex 1896-1920; Sussex County 20-52 54-84; Metropolitan 52-54; Combined Co's 84-85; Isthmian 85-92.

BEST SEASON **FA Cup:** 1st Round 74-75, 0-5 v Bournemouth
FA Amtr Cup: 3rd Rd. 28-29 **FA Vase:** 3rd Rd. 79-80 85-86

RECORD **Attendance:** 3,200 v Showbiz side 1971
Players progressing: Charles & William Buttenshaw (Luton 1948)

FACT FILE
Founded: 1882
Nickname: Wickers
Sponsors: Taxi Link
Colours: Red & black stripes/black/red
Change Colours: All white
Midweek matchday: Tuesday
Reserve League: Sussex Co. Res Div
Programme: Yes
Editor/ Press Off.:
Paul Symes 01273 594142

CLUB PERSONNEL
Chairman: Barry Noonan
Vice-Chairman: John Shepherd
President: Dr D W Gordon.

Manager: Sammy Donnelly
Asst Manager: Fred Proto
Coach: Mick Fogden

Horsham YMCA, winners of the John O'Hara League Challenge Cup 2002 against Ringmer 2-0. Photo: D Nicholson

THREE BRIDGES

Secretary:	Martin Clarke, 18 Mannings Close, Pound Hill, Crawley RH10 3TX
	Tel: 01293 883726 (H), 07885 662940 (Mob)
Ground:	Jubilee Field, Jubilee Walk,Three Bridges, Crawley, West Sussex
	Tel: 01293 442000
	Capacity: 3,500 Seats: 120 Cover: 600 Floodlights: Yes
Directions:	From Three Bridges station, turn L. to Crawley. At 2nd T'light turn R. into
	Three Bridges road. Take 1st left (opp. Plough Inn) into Jubilee Walk.
Clubhouse:	Open every day 12 noon - 11pm (10.30pm Sunday) Carpeted lounge. Bar
	serving food, Players bar, Pool, Darts, Satelite big screen TV, Dance floor.
	Separate Tea Bar serving hot food on match days. Disabled toilet facilities.
Club Shop:	No
HONOURS	Sussex I'mediate Cup 84-85 Sussex Co. Lg R-up 85-86 87-88 88-89 Div 2
	54-55, R-up 68-69, 73-74, 79-80, 98-99, Invitation Cup 70-71, Div 2
	Invitation Cup 62-63, 73-74, Sussex RUR Charity Cup 82-83 R-up 85-86,
	87-88, 88-89. Co. Lge Div. 2 5-a-side 97-98, R-up 98-99
PREVIOUS	**League s:**Mid Sussex; E. Grinstead, Redhill&District 36-52 **Grounds:** None
	Names: Three Bridges 01-18, Three Bridges Worth 19-53, Three Bridges
	United 54-64.
RECORD	**Attendance:** 2,000 v Horsham, 1948

FACT FILE
Founded: 1901
Nickname: Bridges
Sponsors: Radio Mercury
Colours: Amber & black/black/black
Change colours: Blue & white/blue/white
Midweek Matchday: Tuesday
Programme: Yes
Editor: Andy West (01293 883163)
Local Press: Crawley Observer, Crawley News

CLUB PERSONNEL
Chairman: Alan Bell
Press Officer: Alf Blackler
Manager: Mickey Taylor
Asst. Manager: Chick Bain

2001-02
Leading goalscorer: Pat Massaro 27
Captain: Paul Leaver
P.O.Y.: Lee Butcher

WHITEHAWK

Secretary:	John Rosenblatt, 25 Arundel Street, Brighton BN2 5TH Tel: 01273 680322
Ground:	The Enclosed Ground, East Brighton Park Tel: 01273 609736
	Capacity: 3,000 Seats: None Cover: 500 Floodlights: Yes
Directions:	Follow Brighton seafront road towards Newhaven, turn inland (Arundel Road) oppo
	site Marina, 3rd right into Roedean Road, 1st left intoWilson Ave. 3 miles from
	Brighton (BR); take Newhaven, Eastbourne or Saltdean bus to Marina
Clubhouse:	Licensed bar, pool, darts. Board room. Tea bar Club Shop: No
Honours:	Sussex Co. Lg 61-62 63-64 83-84 (Div 2 67-68 80-81, Lg Cup 82-83 93-94,
	Invitation Cup 60-61 69-70, Div 2 Cup 80-81), Sussex Snr Cup 50-51 61-
	62,Sussex RUR Charity Cup 54-55 58-59 90-91, Sussex I'mediate Cup 49-50,
	Sussex Jnr Cup 48-49 51-52, Brighton Charity Cup 51-52 59-60 61-62 82-83
	87-88 88-89 89-90 90-91 97-98 98-99 99-00 Worthing Charity Cup 82-83
PREVIOUS	**League:** Brighton Hove & Dist**Grounds:** None
	Name: Whitehawk & Manor Farm Old Boys (until 1958)
BEST SEASON	FA Vase: 5th Round 93-94
RECORDS	**Gate:** 2,100 v Bognor Regis Town, FA Cup 4th Qualifying Rd replay 88-89
	Scorer: Billy Ford **Appearances:** Ken Powell 1,103

FACT FILE
Founded: 1945
Nickname: Hawks
Sponsors: Precision Metal Products
Colours: All red
Change colours: All blue
Midweek Matchday: Tuesday
Programme: £3.50 with admission
Editor: Fred Moore (01273 689433)
Local Press: Evening Argus

CLUB PERSONNEL
President: Ron Wiltshire
Chairman: Wally Sweetman
Match Sec: Fred Moore
Manager:Ian Chapman
Asst Manager: Glen Burvill

WICK

Secretary:	Paul Beard, 2 Van Gogh Place, North Bersted, Bognor Regis, W.Sussex PO22 9BG
	Tel: 01243 822063 (H)
Ground:	Crabtree Park, Coomes Way, Wick, Littlehampton, W. SussexTel: 01903 713535
	Capacity: 2,000 Seats: 50 Cover: 200 Floodlights: Yes
Directions:	A27 to Crossbush, left at traffic lights signed Littlehampton, after 1 mile cross
	level crossing, turn left into Coombes Way next to Locomotive PH - ground at
	end. One and a half miles from Littlehampton (BR)
Clubhouse:	First floor. Capacity 120. Tea bar Club Shp: No
HONOURS	Sussex Snr Cup 92-93; Sussex Co. Lg 89-90 93-94, Lg Cup 87-88 96-97 (R-up
	93-94 94-95), Div 2 81-82 85-86, Div 2 Cup R-up 81-82; Norman Wingate Tphy88-
	89 90-91, Res. Sect West 87-88 90-91 94-95; Sussex 5-aside R-up 85-86;Sussex
	RURCharity Cup 89-90 97-98;98-99 Gilbert Rice F'lit Cup R-up 80-81 81-82;
	Sussex Jnr Cup 59-60; Brighton Charity Cup 85-86; Sussex F'lit Cup R-Up 94-95
PREVIOUS	**League:** West Sussex **Grounds:** Southfields Rec
RECORD	**Attendance:** 900

FACT FILE
Founded: 1892
Nickname: Wickers
Sponsors: Swandean
Colours: Red & black/black/black
Change colours: All white
Midweek Matchdays: Tuesday
Reserve League: Sussex Co. Reserve Div
Programme: Yes
Editor:Secretary
Local Press: Littlehampton Gazette

CLUB PERSONNEL
Chairman: Barry Wadsworth
Vice-Chairman: T.B. A.
President: Jack Croft
Managers: Andy Baumfield & Steve Allen
Asst Manager: Ian Cole

Above left: Tony Blunt of Corinthian Casuals tries a spectacular diving header during their FA Vase tie away to Hailsham Town in the Second Qualifying Round.
Photo: Roger Turner

Above right: Horsham YM's Ellis Hooper (white), who has signed for Dr Martens Premier Division Crawley Town, is seen in action during the John O'Hara League Challenge Cup Final. Photo: Clive Turner

Centre left: Midfield action during the Pagham v Eastbourne United league match.
Photo: Graham Cotterill

Centre Right: Matt Duffield, Horsham YMCA Captain, scored the two goals against Ringmer FC in the John O'Hara League Challenge Cup Final. Matt holds the John O'Hara Cup in triuimph over his side's Cup victory. Photo: Clive Turner

Bottom: Brad Poole, Sidley United No 6, beats the Hassocks defence and heads towards goal in the FA Vase First Round. Photo: Roger Turner

BROADBRIDGE HEATH

Secretary: Richard Solman, 13 Monks Court, Monks Walk, Reigate, Surrey RH2 0SR
Tel: 01737 212335

Ground: Broadbridge Heath Sports Centre, Wickhurst Lane, Horsham   Tel: 01403 211311

Capacity: 1,300   Seats: 300   Cover: 300   Floodlights: Yes

Directions: Alongside A24, Horsham north/south bypass. From the A24 Horsham Bypass, at thelarge roundabout/underpass take the Broadbridge Heath Bypass towards Guildford and then at the first roundabout turn left into Wickhurst Lane.

Clubhouse: Bar. Kitchen serving meals,

HONOURS Sussex Yth Lg N. Div. 99-00, Southern Yth Lg S. Div. 00-01

PREVIOUS Leagues: Horsham, West Sussex, Southern Co's Comb

RECORD Attendance: 240

FACT FILE
Founded: 1919   Nickname: Bears
1st Team Sponsors: Identilam
Youth Sponsors: T.B.A.
Colours: All royal blue Change: All red or white
Midweek matches: Tuesday
Prog: Yes   Ed: Andy Crisp (01403 252273)
Admission: £2.50

CLUB PERSONNEL
Chairman: Keith Soane
President: G W Manketelow
Manager: Sam Chapman
2001-02
Leading goalscorer: Paul Young 34
Captain & P.o.Y.: Stuart McCall

CRAWLEY DOWN

Secretary: Bob Rashbrook, 3 Collier Row, Southgate, Crawley, West Sussex RH10 6ES
Tel 01293 411457 (H)

Ground: The Haven Sportsfield, Hophurst Lane, Crawley Down.
Tel: 01342 717140

Capacity: 1000   Seats: None   Cover: 50   Floodlights: No

Directions: From B2028, follow signpost for village to War Memorial, turn left into Hophurst Lane, ground 100 yards on left. From A22, Felbridge, left into Crawley Down   Road, ground 2 miles uphill on right.

HONOURS Sussex County Lge Div 3 R-Up 95-96
Sussex Intermediate Chall. Cup R-up 95-96

PREVIOUS League: Mid Sussex Football League

2001-02 Captain & P.o.Y.: Bob Chambers   **Top Scorers:** Nick Sullivan & DougCashman 20

FACT FILE
Colours: All red
Change: White/black/black
Programme:Yes
Website:
www.partners-solutions.co.uk/crawley down.info

CLUB PERSONNEL
Chairman: Brian Suckling
Vice-Chairman: Michael Martin
President: Tony Clements
Managers : Shaun Donnelly & Alan watson
Match Secretary: Andy hale
Physio: Mike Green

EAST GRINSTEAD TOWN

Secretar Martin Hill, The Flat,@A Saxbys Lane, Lingfield, Surrey RH7 6DN
Ground: East Court, East Grinstead   Tel: 01342 325885
Directions: A264 Tunbridge Wells road (Moat Road) until mini-r'bout at bottom of Blackwell Hollow, turn immediately right by club sign then 1st left, ground 200yds down lane past rifle club on right.

Capacity: 3,000   Seats: None   Cover: 400   Floodlights: Yes   Club Shop: No
Clubhouse: Open 1.30-10.30 matchdays, 6-11 midweek matches. Hot food available.

HONOURS Sussex RUR Charity Cup (R-up 74-75); Sussex Co. Lg Invitation Cup 51-52; Sussex Jnr Cup (jt) 07-08; Sussex Youth Cup 86-87; Southern Amtr Lg.Snr Div 3 31-32; Mid-Sussex Lg x 6, Lg Cup x 7; Brighton Lg x 3, Lg Cup x 3,Mid Sussex Junior Cup 2001-02
PREVIOUS Leagues: Mid-Sussex 00-15 35-37; Sussex Co. 20-32; Southern Amateur 32-35.
RECORD Attendance: 2,006 v Lancing, FA Amateur Cup 8/11/48
Appearances: Guy Hill in 19 seasons - 1977-94
2001-02 Captain & P.o.Y.: Dave Gilletley   **Top Scorer:** Dave Gilletley 16

FACT FILE
Founded: 1890   Nickname: Wasps
Sponsors: Rydon Group.
Colours: Gold/black/black
Change colours: All Blue
Midweek Matchday: Tuesday.
Reserves Lge: Sussex Co. Reserve Div East
Programme: 36 pages, 50p (Bruce Talbot)
Press Off.: Bruce Talbot 01293 543809
Local Press: East Grinstead Observer/East Grinstead Courier,SportsArgus
Website: www.egffc.co.uk

CLUB PERSONNEL
Chairman:Bruce Talbot Pres: Colin Dixon
Manager: Bobby Smith
Physio:Pam Presland

EASTBOURNE TOWN

Secretary: Viv Greenwood, 102 Latimer Rd., Eastbourne BN22 7DR (01323 460695)

Ground: The Saffrons, Compton Place Road, Eastbourne, East Sussex (01323723734)
Capacity: 3,000   Seats: 200   Cover: Yes   Floodlights: Yes

Directions: Turn south west off the A22 into Grove Road (opposite BR station), and the ground is 1/4 mile on the right

Clubhouse: Fully licensed bar. Board room. Tea bar

HONOURS Sussex County Lg. 76-77; Sussex Sen Cup x12 1889-91, 93-95, 98-1901, 02-03, 21-22, 31-35, 52-53; Sussex RUR Charity Cup 32-33, 47-48, 49-50; SouthernAmat. Lge. x2; AFA Sen. Cup 21-22, 24-25, R-up 22-23, 23-24; AFA Invitation Cup69-70, R-up 56-57, 68-69, 70-71

PREVIOUS Leagues: Southern Amtr 07-46; Corinthian 60-63; Athenian 63-76

RECORD Attendance: 7,378 v Hastings Utd. 1953

FACT FILE
Founded: 1882

Nickname: `Bourne'

Sponsor: Eastbourne Car Auctions

Colours: yellow/blue/yellow

Changes: Sky blueblack/black

Programme Editor: Chris Backhurst
Tel: 01323 505062

CLUB PERSONNEL
Chairman: Roger Addems
Manager: Dave Winterton

EASTBOURNE UNITED

FACT FILE
Founded: 1894   Nickname: The 'Us'
Colours: White/black/white
Change colours: All Sky Blue.
Midweek Matchday: Wednesday
Reserve Lge: Sussex County Res. Premier
Programme: 36 pages Editor:Kevin Townsend
Local Press: Eastbourne Gazette + Herald,
Evening Argus

Secretary: c/o Peter nashall, 3 Gilbert Road, Eastbourne BN 22 8JA
Tel No: 01323 644038(H)
Ground: The Oval, Channel View Rd, Eastbourne, East Sussex (011323-726989)
Capacity: 3,000   Seats: 160   Cover: 160   Floodlights: Yes
Directions: From A22 follow signs to eastbourne East/Seafront. Turn left onto seafront.
Turn left into Channel View Rd at Princess Park & ground 1st right. 2 miles from Eastbourne (BR)
Clubhouse: Bar, lounge, dancefloor, stage, tea bar, board room   **Club Shop:** Yes
HONOURS   Sussex Co. Lg 54-55, Div 2 R-Up 99-00 Sussex Snr Cup(5) 60-61 62-64 66-67 68-
69(R-up 89-90), Sussex RUR Charity Cup 55-56,Metropolitan Lg Cup 60-61,Athenian Lg Div 2 66-
67 (Div 1 R-up 68-69), Sussex I'mediate Cup 65-66 68-69
PREVIOUS   **Name:** Eastbourne Old Comrades   **Leagues:** Sussex Co. 21-28 35-56;
Metropolitan 56-64; Athenian 64-77; Isthmian 77-92   **Ground:** Lynchmere
RECORD   **Attendance:** 11,000 at Lynchmere
Players progressing: B Salvage, T Funnell, M French, L.Barnard

CLUB PERSONNEL
Chairman: Peter Snashall
Vice-Chairman: Kevin Townsend
President: Doug Sissons
Manager: Micky French
Asst Manager: Dave Shearing
Physio: Jo Henderson

LANCING

FACT FILE
Founded: 1941   Nickname: Lancers
Sponsors: Bacon & Co. Estate Agents
Colours: Yellow/blue/yellow
Change colours: All red
Midweek Matches: Wed Programme: Yes
Reserves League: Sussex Co Res. Prem.
Editor/Press Off.: Len Ralph (01903 763913)
2001-02 Captain: Martin Gray
Top Scorers Jamie Cole & Neil Richards 12
P.o.Y.: Glen Souter

Secretary: Brian Hill,17 Annweir Ave., Lancing, W. Sussex BN15 9NF
Tel: 01903 756165 (H&F) email: brian@whill20.fsnet.co.uk
Ground: Culver Road, Lancing, West Sussex Tel: 01903 764398
Web-site: www.lancingfc.co.uk
Directions: From A27 turn south at Lancing Manor r'about into Grinstead Lane, 3rd turning on
right North Farm Rd. Turn left then immed. right into Culver Rd. From railway station take 3rd turn-
ing on left heading north. Capacity: 2,400   Seats: 350   Cover: 350   Floodlights: Yes
Clubhouse: Open matchdays & training nights. Separate tea bar.   **Club Shop:** Yes
HONOURS Sussex Co. Lg R-up 49-50 64-65 (Div 2 57-58 69-70 (R-up 82-83), Div 2 Cup 81-82
92-93, Invitation Cup), Sussex RUR Charity Cup 65-66, Brighton Lg 46-47 47-48, Sussex
Intermediate Cup 46-47, Brighton Charity Cup 83-84 84-85 86-87.
PREVIOUS League: Brighton Hove & District   **Name:** Lancing Athletic
RECORDS Attendance: 2,591 v Tooting, FA Amateur Cup 22/11/47 At Culver Road: 2,340v
Worthing 25/10/52 **Career Appearances:** Dave Menzies 462 **Goals:** Paul Steele 113

CLUB PERSONNEL
Chairman: John Brown President: R G Steele
Match Sec: Don Stevens (01273 592653 (H)
Commercial Man.: Steve Talter(01903 851919)
Manager: Andy Gander Physio: Peter Towell

MILE OAK

FACT FILE
Founded: 1960
Nickname: The Oak
Colours: Tangerine/black/tangerine
Change colours: All blue
Midweek Matchday: Tuesday
Programme: Yes
Editor: C Tew (01273 416036)
Admission: £1.50
Local Press: Brighton Evening Argus,
Shoreham Herald

Secretary: Colin Brown, 19 The Crescent, Southwick, West Sussex BN42 4LB
Tel: 01273 591346
Ground: Mile Oak Recreation Ground, Graham Avenue, Mile Oak.Tel: 01273423854

Directions: From A27 take Mile Oak Road or Locks Hill & Valley Road to Chalky Road, ground
500yds on right along Graham Avenue which runs up valley fromcentre of Chalky Road
Capacity: Seats: None   Cover: Yes   Floodlights: Yes
Clubhouse: Mile Oak Pavillion; Hall and tea bar   **Club Shop:** No
HONOURS   Sussex Co.Lg.Div 2 Champions, Div 3 R-up 91-92 (Div 2 Cup R-up 92-93),
Southern Counties Combination 86-87, Brighton Hove & District Lg 80-81,
VernonWentworth Cup 85-86, Sussex Intermediate Cup R-up 88-89
PREVIOUS   **Leagues:** Southern Counties Combination; Brighton Hove & District
Ground: Victoria Rec., Portslade
RECORD   **Attendance:** 186

CLUB PERSONNEL
Chairman: L.Hamilton
President: D Bean
Manager: M.Cox

OAKWOOD

FACT FILE
Founded: 1966   Nickname: Oaks
Sponsors: Linden Plc
Colours: Red & black/black/black
Change colours: Blue& black/white/blue
Midweek Matchday: Tuesday
Reserves' Lge: Sussex Co. Reserve section
Programme: 24 pages
Editor: Scott Packer Local Press: Crawley
Observer, Crawley News

Secretary:S.A.Wildy, 45 Holmcroft, Southgate, Crawley, West Sussex (01293 409410)
Ground: Tinsley Lane, Three Bridges, Crawley, West Sussex   Tel: 01293 515742

Directions: From A23 to Gatwick, take 1st set of lights into Manor Royal, pass next lights, over
r'bout to warehouse marked Canon, turn right signposted Oakwood. Last clubhouse
down lane. Two miles north of Three Bridges (BR)
Capacity: 3,000   Seats: 20   Cover: Yes   Floodlights: Yes
Club Shop: Yes, incl. metal badges
Clubhouse: Large bar area, pool tables, multidart boards. Board room & tea bar
HONOURS   Sussex Snr Cup R-up 92-93, Sussex Co. Lg Div 2 R-up 89-90 (Div 2 Cup
89-90, Div 3 84-85), Southern Comb. Cup 83-84
PREVIOUS   **Leagues:** Crawley & Dist., Southern Co's Comb
Ground: Park pitches
RECORD   **Attendance:** 367   **Appearances:** Peter Brackpool

CLUB PERSONNEL
Chairman: Stuart Lovegrove
Press Officer & Match Sec: Scott Packer
Manager:Andy Maddox
Physios: Ms.S Widy & Frank Pushman

OVING

Secretary:	Nigel Strudwick,28 Lamorna Gardens,Chichester,West Sussex PO20 3RL Tel No: 01243 545665
Ground:	Highfield Lane, Oving, Nr Chichester, W Sussex. Tel: 01243 778900
Directions:	Into Oving past the Gribble Inn, follow road round to housing estate - Highfield Lane (left). Ground sign posted 50 yards on right.
	Capacity: 1,000 Cover: 100 Floodlights: No
Clubhouse:	No.Check with club officials re after match hospitality Metal Badges: Yes
HONOURS	W. Sussex Lge - Div 5 Cup 81-82, Div 5S 81-82, Div 4 Cup 82-83, Div 4S 82-83, Div 3S84-85. Div 2S 87-88, 91-92, Div 1 94-95, Prem. Div 95-96 96-97; Sussex Jun Cup: 86 91; Chichester char. Cup 90-91; Sussex Co. Inter. Cup R-up 98-99; Sussex Co. Div 3 98-99, Div 3 Cup R-up 98-99.Res West Div R-up 01-02
CLUB RECORDS	**Attendance:** 276 v Westfield, Sussex co. Lge Div. 3 8.5.99
Win:	10-0 v S B Sports (H) Sussex Co.linter. Cup 10.10.98 **Defeat:** 0-7 v Lancing (A) 15.12.01
PREVIOUS	**League:** West Sussex

FACT FILE
Formed: 1978-79   Nickname: "The Vikings"
Colours: Black & whitestripes/white/white
Change colours:Red& white/Black/Red
Reserves' Lge: Sussex Co. - Res. Sect. West
Programme: 32 pages 50p
Editor: Simon Jasinski (M) 07764 948622
(H) 01243374239 email: ovingfc.co.uk
CLUB PERSONNEL
Chairman: Alan Miller
Manager: Vijay Korgaoker
Asst. Manager: Andie Millard
Martch SecTamsin Mordle 07754773380(M)
2001-02
Captain: Brian Clarke
Top Scorer: Brian Clarke 7

PEASE POTTAGE VILLAGE

Secretary:	Mrs Sue Brooks, 115 Lark Rise, Langley Green, Crawley, W. Sussex RH11 7QG Tel: 01293 410657 (H) 01293 848100 (B) 07754 163029 (M) email: suebrooks57@aol.com
Ground:	Finches Field, Pease Pottage, Crawley, W. Sussex Tel: 01293 538651
Directions:	Off M23/A23 towards Brighton, turn off at Pease Pottage (turn off just past Crawley). Past service station to roundabout, take 3rd exit over bridge sharp left, follow signs to Finches Field. Approx. 300 yards past "Grapes" P.H., on the right.

FACT FILE
Colours:
Royal blue & white/royal/raoyal & white
Change: Yellow/blue/yellow

CLUB PERSONNEL

Chairman: Tony Read
29 Westpark Road, Handcross,
W. Sussex RH17 6DN
Tel: 01444 400059 (H) 01444 881565 (B)

Manager: Mick Butler

RYE-IDEN UNITED

Secretary:	Ged Say,18 Parkwwod Iden, nr Rye,East Sussex TN31 7XE Tel: 01797 280495 (H) 07776 101993 (M) email: ged@sayiden.fsnet.co.uk
Ground:	Sydney Allnut Pavilion, Rye Football & Cricket Salts, Fish Market Rd., Rye, East Sussex Tel: 01797 223855
Directions:	Outskirts of Rye on the A268, joins A259 opposite Skinners Rover garage. Fishmarket Road.
Previous	**League:** Sussex Co., Kent Co. >00
Honours:	Sussex Co. Lge Div. 3 Champions 01-02

FACT FILE
Founded: 1938
Colours: White, red & black/black/ red
Change colours: Burgundy/ black/burgundy

CLUB PERSONNEL
Chairman: J Sellman
Tel: 01797 224349 (H)

Manager: Alan Hood

SALTDEAN UNITED

Secretary:	Iain Fielding, 40 Rowan Way, Rottingdean, Brighton BN2 7FP Tel: 01273 304995
Ground:	Hill Park, Combe Vale, Saltdean, Brighton Tel: 01273 309898
	Capacity: 2,000 Seats: 50 Cover: Yes Floodlights: Yes
	Club Website: www.the-tigers.co.uk
Directions:	A259 coast road east from Brighton to Saltdean Lido, left into Arundel Drive West, and Saltdean Vale to bridle path at beginning of Combe Vale. Club 200yds along track
Club Shop:	Metal badges available
Clubhouse:	Licensed bar, lounge, juke box, video games, board room, tea bar.Pool table
HONOURS	Sussex Co. Lg Div 3 88-89, Div 2 95-96: John O'Hara Lg Cup Winners 2000
PREVIOUS	**League:** Brighton Hove & Dist Ground: None
RECORD	**Attendance:** 676

FACT FILE
Founded: 1966   Nickname: Tigers
Sponsors: FDM
Colours: Red & blackstripes/black/black
Change : Blue & whitestripes/blue/white
Programme: Yes Editor:Greg Hadfield
Local Press: Brighton Evening Argus & Sussex
Express
CLUB PERSONNEL
Chairman: Robin Hall
Vice Chairman:Mike Walker
President: Jim Bower
Press Officer: Iain Fielding
Manager: Steve Bean
Physio: Stan Pearce

Eastbourne Town. Photo: Gordon Whittington

Rye & Iden, Sussex County Div 2 Champions and League Cup winners Photo: Roger Turner

Westfield, Sussex County Div 2 Back Row (l-r) Mark Drinkwater, Ian Burt, John Lambert, Jamie Podmore, Nick Hall, Kevin Rose, Trevor Burgess. Front Row: Grant Murray, Tony Harris, Will Toal, Andrew Moore, Steve Ringwood, Duncan Jones. Photo: Roger Turner

SEAFORD TOWN

FACT FILE

Colours: Red & blue/blue/red
Change: Yellow & green/green/yellow

Secretary:	Chas Pulford,14 Rosemount Cloise, Bishopstone BN25 2TPO
	Tel: 01323 898286 (H) 01323 893040 (B) 07815 051128 (M)
	email: charles.pulford@btopenworld.com
Match Sec.:	Neil Vine, Flat 4, Miramar House West, 2 Grand Parade, Eastbourne BN21 3EH
	Tel: 07811 618361 (M)
Ground:	The Crouch, Seaford. Tel: 01323 892221
Directions:	A259 to Seaford. At mini r'about by station,
	turn LEFT (coming from Newhaven) or RIGHT (from Eastbourne).
	At end of Church St., across junction, then left at end. After 500 m turn left
	up Ashurst Rd. Bramber Rd. is at the top.

CLUB PERSONNEL

Chairman: Kevin Moore
Tel: 01323 897369 (H) 07760 173178 (M)

Manager: Duncan Kneller
Tel: 01323 892876 (H) 07760 175746 (M)

SHINEWATER ASSOCIATION

FACT FILE
Founded: 1990
Club Sponsors: T.B.A.
Colours: All Navy Blue
Change Colours: All Maroon
Programme: Free with entry
Programme Editor: Brian Dowling
Previous League: East Sussex

Secretary:	Brian Dowling, 79 Harebeating Drive, Hailsham BN27 1JE
	Tel: 01323 442488
Ground:	Shinewater Lane, Eastbourne. Tel: 01323 765880
	Capacity: 1,000 Seats: None Cover: 200 Floodlights: No
Directions:	A27, take B2104 to Eastbourne. At Stone Cross go under railway bridge, 1st
	right into Larkspur Drive, 1st left into Milfoil Drive, 3rd left into Shinewater Lane
Clubhouse:	Match days (01323 765880)
RECORD	**Attendance:** 302

CLUB PERSONNEL
Chairman: John Pinyoun
Managers: David Shearing

STEYNING TOWN

FACT FILE

Colours: All Red and white
Change: All sky blue & yellow

Secretary:	Mrs. Gina Barnes, 36 Shooting Field, Steyning W. Sussex BN44 3RQ
	Tel: 01903 815387 (H)
Ground:	The Shooting Field, Steyning, W. Sussex
	Tel: 01903 812228)
Directions:	Entering Steyning from the west. Take 1st left in the High St (Tanyard Lane)
	Follow into Shooting Field estate, ground is 4th turn on the left.
	Entering Steyning from the east. From the High St., turn right into Church
	St.. Turn left by Church into Shooting Field estate.
	NB Coaches MUST park in Church Street Car Park.

CLUB PERSONNEL
Chairman: Russell Matthews
Tel: 01903 813372 (H)

Manager: John Bolingbroke

WEALDEN

FACT FILE

Colours: Blue & white.
Change colours: Red & Black

Secretary:	Larry Hillman,26 Framelle Mount,Framfield,Uckfield TN22 5PT
	Tel: 01825 890764 (H) 07710 838843 (M)
	Email: larry@addagrip.co.uk
Ground:	Wealden Football Club, Old Eastbourne Road, Uckfield, East Sussex.
	Tel: 01825 890905
Directions:	Next to the Rajdutt Restaurant on the Old Eastbourne Road,
	south of Uckfield town centre.
Honours:	Sussex County Lge Div. 3 R-up 99-00

CLUB PERSONNEL
Chairman: Tom Parker

Manager: Gary Allen

Burgess Hill Town and Tiptree United take the field at the start of their FA Vase Quarter Final. A 'Sky' TV cameraman takes his film footage for viewers. Photo: Arthur Evans

Burgess Hill keeper saves a Dorking effort in their FA Vase replay. Their two games attracted over 1,000 fans. Photo: Eric Marsh

Yenni Odubade's well placed shot puts Eastbourne Town in front against Oakwood. They went on to win 5-0 Photo: Gordon Whittington

WESTFIELD

FACT FILE

Secretary: J. J. Archer, Gorse Cottage, Moor Lane, Westfield TN35 4QU
Tel: 01424 754516 (H) 01424 751030 (W)

Ground: Parish Field. Westfield Tel: 01424 751011

Directions: Take A21 towards Hastings, left onto A28, Westfield Lane - signposted to
Ashford. Approx. 2 miles to village, pitch on left on main road just past garage.

Colours: White & Green/green/green
Change Colours: Yellow & Green/ green/green

CLUB PERSONNEL

Chairman: G.A.Drinkwater
28 Churchfield, Westfield, Hastings TN35 4QN
Tel: 01424 754032 (H) 01424 751030 (B)

Manager: Shaun Hardy

WORTHING UNITED

Secretary: Malcolm Gamlen, 1 Westbourne Ave., Worthing, West Sussex BN14 8DE
Tel: 01903 263655

Ground: The Robert Albon Memorial Grd, Lyons Way, Worthing   Tel: 01903 234466
Capacity:1,000   Seats: 100   Cover: 500   Floodlights: No

Directions: From west past Hill Barn r'about to 2nd set of lights, turn left into Lyons Way.
From east 1st set of lights at end of Sompting bypass right into Lyons Way

Clubhouse: Bar (capacity 80), refreshment facilities (tea bar)   Metal badges: Yes

HONOURS As Wigmore Athletic prior to 1988. Sussex Co. Lg Challenge Cup 74-75
(Invitation Cup 59-60, Div 2 52-53, Div 2 Invitation Cup 59-60, Div 3 89-90,
Reserve Section West 92-93, Sussex Jnr Cup 49-50

PREVIOUS **Names:** Wigmore Athletic (founded 1948) merged with Southdown in 1988
Grounds: Harrison Road, Worthing

RECORD **Attendance:**180 v Northwood, FA Vase 3rd Rd 91-92

FACT FILE
Founded: 1988
Nickname: None
Sponsors: Tinsley Robor
Colours: Sky & white/navy/navy
Change : Green & white/white/green & white
Programme: Yes
Editor: D.Treacy (01903 690122)
Local Newspapers: Worthing Herald

CLUB PERSONNEL
President: Bob Albon
Chairman: Dennis Stoner
Press Officer: Secretary
Manager: Derrren Woods

BEXHILL TOWN
Secretary: Mrs Leigh Quinn, 37 Colebrook Road, Bexhill-on-Sea. TN39 3PX Tel: 01424 214197
Ground: The Polegrove, Brockley Rd, Bexhill-on-Sea, E. Sussex Tel: 01424220732 Directions: At Little Common r'bout take 3rd exit to Cooden Sea Rd, left into Cooden Drive for one and a half miles, Brockley Rd on the right. 3/4 mile from Bexhill Central (BR)
Colours: Green & white/white/white

BOSHAM
Chairman:Terry Longland Manager: Richard Mckenna
Secretary: Dick Doncaster, 61 Manor Way,Southbourne,Nr Emsworth PO10 8LY Tel: 0143 375184
Ground: Bosham Recreation Ground, Walton Lane, Bosham, W. Sussex Tel: 01243 574011
Directions: From Chichester take the A259 towards Portsmouth. On reaching Bosham turn left at the Swan P.H. roundabout. 1/2 mile to T junction, turn left & car park 50 yds on left.
Honours: Sussex County Lge Div. 3 99-00
Colours: Red/white/red Change Colours: White/black/white

CROWBOROUGH
Founded: 1894
Secretary: Phil Sharman, High Ridge, Green Lane, Crowborough TN6 2DF Tel: 01892 668176 (H)
Ground: Alderbrook Recreation Ground, Fermor Road, Crowborough Tel: 01892 661893
Directions: Turn east off A26 at Crowborough. Cross traffic lights, through High Street, right into Croft Rd, continue into Whitehill Rd and Fermor Rd, Alderbrook is 2nd right after mini-r'bout.
Clubhous Bar facilities & tea bar on matchdays Club Shop: No
Colours: Navy Blue/white/navy blue
Change colours: Yellow/green/yellow

FOREST
Secretary: Peter Farley,9 Owlbeech Way, Horsham, W.Sussex RH13 6AW. (01403 25256)
Ground: Roffey Sports & Social Club, Spooners Rd., Roffey. Tel: 01403 210221) Directions: Spooners Rd. is off the main Crawley road, 100 yds from the `Star'PH, towards Crawley
Colours: White/Navy Blue/ White

FRANKLANDS VILLAGE
Secretary: Mrs Linsey Worsfold, 151a Franklands Village, Haywards Heath. RH163RF. Tel: 01444 416475)
Ground: Hardy Memorial Playing Field, Franklands Village. Tel: 01444 440138) Directions: A272 (Haywards H. to Uckfield). Left at Princess Royal Hosp.r'about. 2nd left & ground at rear of social club
Colours: All Royal blue

HAYWARDS HEATH TOWN
Secretary: Steve Weller,52 Kents Road,Haywards Heath, Susex RH116 4HQ Tel No: 01444 457230
Ground: Hanbury Park Stadium, Haywards Heath Tel: 01444 412837 Directions: A272 to Haywards Heath town centre. At Sussex round-about, north on B2708 (Hazelgrove Road) take first right into New England Road, 4th right (Allen Road) leads to ground.
Colours: Blue & white stripes/blue/blue

HURSTPIERPOINT
Secretary: Rodney Wilson,12 St Mary's Road, Burgess Hill, RH15 8NU Tel: 01444 870356
Ground: Fairfield Rec. Ground, Cuckfield Road. (Tel: 01273 834783) Directions: At Hurstpierpoint crossroads, go north into Cuckfield Road (B2117) for 1km. Ground entrance between houses nos.158 & 160
Colours: Blue & white quarters/blue/blue

IFIELD
Secretary: Robert Anderson, 1 Old Orchards, Church Rd, Worth, Crawley. RH107QA. Tel: 01293 886215)
Ground: Ifield Sports Club, Ifield Green, Rusper Road. Tel: 01293 536569) Directions: From A23 Crawley by-pass going north, left at r'about signedCharlwood. Third left into Ifield Green, first right past Royal Oak (PH) into Rusper Rd
Colours: White/black/red

LINGFIELD
Secretary: Pamela Thomsett, 61 Drivers Mead. Lingfield,Surrey RH7 6EX Tel: 01342 832418 (H)
Ground: Sports Pavilion, Godstone Road, Lingfield, Surrey. Tel: 01342 834269
Directions: A22, 4 miles north of East Grinstead, to Mormon Temple roundabout, take exit Lingfield (B2028) Newchapel Road for 1 1/2 miles. Left at T junction into Godstone Road (B2029) and ground is 1/2 mile on left.
Colours: Red & yellow stripes/black/yellow Change:Blue & white stripes/white/ sky blue

MIDHURST & EASEBOURNE
Secretary: Ted Dummer, 14 Nine Acres, June Lane, Midhurst, W. Sussex GU29 9EP Tel: 01730 813887 (H) email: acs@harrisonren-wick.com
Ground: Rotherfield, Dodsley Lane, Easebourne, Midhurst, W. Sussex Tel: 01730 816557)
Directions: Ground one mile out of Midhurst on London Road (A286) opposite Texaco Garage. Ample car parking. Buses pass ground every hour
Colours: Royal blue/black/royal Change colours: All red

NEWHAVEN
Secretary: Peter Foote, 32 Valley Dene, Newhaven BN9 9NF Tel: 01273 513232
Ground: Fort Road Recreation Ground Tel: 01273 513940
Directions: A259, follow one-way system around town, left at Police Station into South Road, which becomes Fort Road.
Colours: Red & amber/red & amber/red

ST. FRANCIS RANGERS
Previous Names: Ansty Rangers & St. Francis
Secretary: Pat Bucknell, 79 Priory Way, Haywards Heath, W.Sussex RH16 3NS Tel: 01444 457726 (H)
Ground: The Princess RoyalHospital, Lewes Rd., Haywards Heath. Tel: Gd. 01444 474021 Social club: 01444 441881
Directions: Enter through main Hospital entrance on Lewes road, (A272 Haywards Heath). Follow signs to Sports Complex
Colours: Black & white/black/black

STORRINGTON
Secretary: Keith Dalmon, 4 End Cottages, Turnpike Road, Amberley. BN18 9LX Tel: 01798 831887 (H)
Ground: Recreation Ground, Storrington. Tel: 01903 745860
Directions: Turn west on A283 (off A24). Ground is opposite the pond to the west of the village.
Colours: All Blue Chanbge Colours : Yellow/black/yellow

UCKFIELD TOWN
Secretary: Jennie Hickman, 10 Wilson Grove, Uckfield, E.Sussex TN22 2BU (01825 762602)
Ground: Victoria Pleasure Grounds, Uckfield. Tel: 01825 769400)
Directions: Take Eastbourne road (old A22) south of Uckfield town cen-tre. Entrance to ground is 1/2 mile on the right (just after the Police sta-tion)
Colours: Red/black/black

UPPER BEEDING
Secretary: Mrs Anita Addison, Sheppens, Newham Lane, Steyning, W. Sussex BN44 3LR Tel: 01903 814077 (H) 01903 813109 (B)
Ground: Memorial Playing Field, High St., Upper Beeding BN44 3WN Tel: 01903 815930 **Directions:** From east/west A27 J A283 north to Upper Beeding. Ground opposite village hall in High St. From north/south A24 J A283 southbound. Turn left to Steyning/Upper Beeding.
Colours: Yellow & blue/blue/yellow & blue. Change: All royal blue.

THE EAGLE BITTER
UNITED COUNTIES LEAGUE
FEEDER TO: DR MARTENS LEAGUE

Chairman: Geoff Paul
Secretary: Roger Gamble, 8 Bostock Avenue, Northampton NN1 4LW   Tel: 01604 637766
Press Officer: Jeremy Biggs   Tel: 01780 763048

FORDS MOTOR TO SECOND CROWN

Ford Sports dominated the Eagle Bitter United Counties League season, winning the Premier Division by a record nineteen point margin, while the next nine clubs were covered by just fourteen points!

Back in August the title race looked wide open with at least half a dozen genuine contenders, while Fords had been hit by the loss of top marksman Lee Ross to Bloxwich. It took until November for Motormen boss Shane Geary to replace him, signing Andy Evans, the previous season's Premier top marksman, but now out of favour at Rounds. The signing proved to be a masterstroke with Evans firing hat tricks in his first two matches for Fords, and they quickly moved to the top of the table, never to be headed again.

After losing their opening match to Stotfold, Fords reeled off thirteen successive wins with Tyrone Kent and Ian Pearce doing well in unfamiliar attacking roles to support Jim Sugrue. Desborough and Bourne briefly held pole position but Wootton, who collected 26 points from their first ten matches, and the experienced Holbeach squad enjoyed lengthier spells at the head of the table before Fords came through to take up the pace.

By the turn of the year Fords had extended their unbeaten run to twenty games, and they led Holbeach by two points with three games in hand. A defeat by Desborough at the start of 2002 proved no more than a blip for the Motormen who responded with a seven match winning run to leave the pack struggling to stay in the hunt.

The pace slowed briefly in March as Fords lost at nearest challengers Holbeach and drew at reigning titleholders Boston and Vase heroes St Neots, but a win at Cogenhoe steadied the nerves and a return win over the Cooks at Royal Oak Way on 4th April sealed Ford's second title in three years. Manager Geary set his men a 100 point target to keep them focused through the last four games - they fell one short but still finished nineteen points clear of runners-up Holbeach.

All round strength earned Fords the title with their defensive record far and away the Premier's best. With goalkeeper Graham Bott, Gary Smith, Adrian Pestell and skipper Simon Williams in dominant form the mid season departure of Glen Gibb who emigrated to Australia was hardly noticed, as manager Geary and the club's longest serving player Martin Jennings performed well in wide positions while the higher grade experience of Chris Evans, Phil Murphy and Ian Pearce was always in evidence.

Holbeach stumbled in the closing weeks and needed a last match win over Yaxley to pip Cogenhoe to the runners-up medal on goal difference. The Keeble cousins Shaun and Nick were influential for the Tigers. Shaun topped the league scorecharts while Nick held the defence together as well as notching a double figure goal tally - indeed, Holbeach always posed a goal threat from all over the park with Darren Edey, Mark Melson and Ian Dunn all regularly on target.

Cogenhoe's new look side started poorly under Aidy Mann, but after just one win in eight games they found their form and made a good challenge as the season progressed. Darren Harmon finished second in the scorecharts and was again one of the league's class acts. Rounds made a name for themselves with the quality of their football, but their young side lacked the consistency to stay in the frame, finishing fourth ahead of Desborough whose very attack minded side produced good entertainment but again lacked consistency when it mattered.

St Neots kicked off the season with a massive squad and struggled to find the right blend early on, but their Vase progress boosted confidence. A consequence of their fine cup form was a fixture backlog and the Saints faded to finish sixth, just ahead of Wootton who failed to maintain their early season form and suffered a series of cup disappointments, losing three semi-finals. Reigning champions Boston Town had an exciting strike partnership in Jamie Graham and Liam Harrald, finishing as the top flight's third top scorers, but they too often came off second best against the league's leading lights.

Promoted pair Deeping and Daventry had satisfactory first top flight campaigns. Rangers snapped up some seasoned players and threatened to finish higher than tenth - their lowest position all season. Daventry had a difficult season with their promotion winning managers Adam May and Craig Robson leaving Elderstubbs during the season - but new boss Mark Shackleton brought stability and a respectable fifteenth place.

Wellingborough kicked off the season with a team of youngsters and found the going tough. Dave Evans and Mick Garrett both had spells at the helm before Tim Chamberlain was appointed manager and drafted in some experienced players. A host of new faces failed to gel, and the Doughboys just managed to reach a double figure points tally, finishing fourteen points adrift at the bottom.

Bugrooke managed a meagre 27 goals, and they too rang the managerial changes in mid season, replacing Scott Carlin with former Northampton Town coach Aidy Hill. The side took on a youthful look as personnel changes took place in numbers, but the results were much the same and the Badgers were left to fill the second relegation place. Kempston survived with three points to spare, but realistically that was an achievement after the Walnut Boys had to start out with an entire new look squad. Long Buckby only finished six points above the drop zone, but were never really in trouble this time round.

A busy summer of recruitment saw Newport Pagnell assemble a vastly experienced side and once they settled down they proved far too good for most of their Division One rivals. After going top of the section in October they stayed there and finished ten points clear of second placed Sileby, the only side to threaten the Swans' superiority.

Newport's strike pair of Anthony Clark and Darren Lynch contested the division's top scorer accolade and received valuable support from Paul Edgeworth as Newport plundered goals galore, their tally of 115 in 32 games enabling them to add the Baker Perkins Trophy for the highest scoring team to their silverware collection.

Sileby were the division's most improved side, climbing fourteen places on the previous season. They took four points off Newport and spent almost the whole season in the top three. Lack of floodlights at Fernie Fields prevented them from joining Newport in the top flight, but the season was nonetheless a memorable one.

Just six points separated third from eighth place in the division, with early season leaders Blisworth and Harrowby fading late on and Higham's consistency deserting them in the closing weeks. Whitworths and Thrapston finished strongly to claim fourth and fifth places respectively, but third place went to Woodford who were promoted to the Premier in only their fourth season in the league. New manager Phil Lines put together an exciting young side and the installation of floodlights and seating acquired from Northwich secured top flight status for the Byfield Road club.

Relegated pair Eynesbury and Potton struggled at the lower level, although Rovers found their goal touch late in the campaign to climb out of the bottom four. After going bottom of the table on the season's second Saturday, St Ives stayed there until their final match, when a point against Higham took them above Burton Park who had disastrously lost their last seventeen matches. Sadly, Sharnbrook failed to make the starting line, withdrawing in August after 33 years in the league.

UCL legend Roy Boon enjoyed an excellent first season in management as he steered Stotfold Reserves to the Reserve Division One crown, while Holbeach became the third successive club to win Reserve Division Two at the first attempt.

A lone David Broomes goal was sufficient to give Raunds the Knockout Cup with a 1-0 win over Yaxley in the final at Blackstone. Lower grade Sileby reached the semi-finals, while Potton produced the biggest upset in twenty years of open competition, beating Premier pacesetters Ford Sports 2-1 in a Second Round tie.

Wootton Reserves beat six higher grade sides to win the Reserve Knockout Cup, Yaxley being their final victims by a 2-1 score at Potton, an outstanding way for the Blue Cross second string to close their time in the league.

The Wootton senior side were our best FA Cup performers, beating Kingsbury and Harwich to reah the Second Qualifying Round where they lost 1-0 to Histon. Some compensation was £8,500 in prize money payments for their earlier victories.

St Neots disappointed on their league travels, but relished their away days in the FA Vase. They came out of the hat second in all six rounds, but overcame Stowmarket, Wembley, Romford, Melksham and Rushall before a last minute goal ended their run at Durham in Round Five. Generally it was an improved season for our clubs with Cogenhoe, Raunds, Stewarts & Lloyds and Stotfold all reaching Round Three.

County cups also proved successful with member clubs contesting finals in all five counties. St Neots went close to a Huntingdonshire double, beating Ely 5-1 in the Premier Cup final only to lose 3-0 to Eynesbury in a Senior Cup upset. Newport Pagnell won the Berks & Bucks Intermediate Cup with a 2-0 defeat of Forest Old Boys in the final, while Sileby pipped Rothwell Corinthians 2-1 to lift the Northants Junior Cup. Stotfold's quest for a Bedfordshire double saw the reserves beat 61FC Luton 4-1 to win the Intermediate Cup, but the Eagles lost by the same score to Biggleswade United in the Senior Cup. There were disappointing outcomes in the Lincolnshire finals, Holbeach going down 1-0 to Lincoln Moorlands in the Senior Cup 'A' final with Harrowby losing 3-2 to Sleaford in the Senior 'B' final. Yaxley's second string suffered two more reverses, losing in the finals of both Huntingdonshire competitions, the Scott-Garry and Benevolent Cups.

Other cup competitions saw Ford Sports win the Daventry Charity Cup for the first time, beating Bedworth 3-1 in the final, Desborough win the Desborough Charity Cup by beating Burton Park 7-0, while Yaxley's catalogue of final defeats was completed by a 2-0 loss to Barton Rovers in the Hinchingbrooke Cup.

Fair play awards went to Olney and Wellingborough Reserves, Ford Sports and Newport Pagnell added hospitality awards to their titles while, Shane Geary was an inevitable selection as manager of the year. Craig Evans became the first Lincolnshire official to win the Eric Evans Trophy awarded to the referee of the year, also winning a place on the new national list of contributory league referees along with Lincolnshire colleague Pete Stanton.

Jeremy Biggs, Press Officer

twentyfive in twentyfive twentyfive in twentyfive twentyfive in twentyfive twentyfive in twentyfive

25 in 25

A review of the progress made by the **United Counties League** and its member clubs during the twenty-five year life span of the F.A. Non-League Club Directory (1978 - 2002) will be available in the next year. It will be one of a series of 25 and will contain features, statistics and photos in at least 160 pages dedicated purely to the United Counties members.

Further details can be found on page 17 so make sure of your copy of this exciting limited edition

FINAL LEAGUE TABLES 2001-02

PREMIER DIVISION

		P	Home					Away					Total					Pts
			W	D	L	F	A	W	D	L	F	A	W	D	L	F	A	
1	Ford Sports Daventry	40	16	2	2	45	11	15	4	1	50	19	31	6	3	95	30	99
2	Holbeach United	40	15	2	3	63	21	10	3	7	47	31	25	5	10	110	52	80
3	Cogenhoe United	40	12	6	2	37	19	12	2	6	46	38	24	8	8	83	57	80
4	Raunds Town	40	12	5	3	49	24	9	6	5	46	30	21	11	8	95	54	74
5	Desborough Town	40	13	4	3	42	20	9	4	7	43	28	22	8	10	85	48	74
6	St Neots Town	40	15	2	3	50	22	8	2	10	30	25	23	4	13	80	47	73
7	Wootton Blue Cross	40	12	4	4	39	19	9	5	6	35	31	21	9	10	74	50	72
8	Boston Town	40	11	4	5	45	22	9	4	7	48	28	20	8	12	93	50	68
9	Stotfold	40	13	4	3	49	21	7	4	9	26	27	20	8	12	75	48	68
10	Deeping Rangers	40	13	2	5	46	29	7	4	9	33	27	20	6	14	79	56	66
11	Yaxley	40	9	4	7	44	33	7	7	6	29	24	16	11	13	73	57	59
12	Blackstone	40	8	3	9	27	31	8	2	10	30	37	16	5	19	57	68	53
13	Bourne Town	40	8	5	7	38	32	7	3	10	19	43	15	8	17	57	75	53
14	Stewarts & Lloyds Corby	40	9	2	9	39	36	5	5	10	22	36	14	7	19	61	72	49
15	Daventry Town	40	7	4	9	27	28	6	3	11	32	43	13	7	20	59	71	46
16	Buckingham Town	40	9	3	8	47	45	4	4	12	31	46	13	7	20	78	91	46
17	Northampton Spencer	40	8	4	8	29	25	4	0	16	23	38	12	4	24	52	63	40
18	Long Buckby	40	5	2	13	23	47	3	4	13	20	46	8	6	26	43	93	30
19	Kempston Rovers	40	7	2	11	29	41	1	1	18	16	60	8	3	29	45	101	27
20	Bugbrooke St Michaels	40	4	4	12	18	49	2	2	16	9	61	6	6	28	27	110	24
21	Wellingborough Town	40	3	1	16	14	75	0	0	20	15	82	3	1	36	29	157	10

DIVISION ONE

		P	W	D	L	F	A	W	D	L	F	A	W	D	L	F	A	Pts
1	Newport Pagnell Town	32	14	1	1	56	14	11	2	3	59	22	25	3	4	115	36	78
2	North'ton Sileby Rangers	32	11	4	1	53	9	9	4	3	37	17	20	8	4	90	26	68
3	Woodford United	32	13	1	2	40	13	5	4	7	21	27	18	5	9	61	40	59
4	Wellingboro Whitworths	32	9	4	3	31	23	7	5	4	26	24	16	9	7	57	47	57
5	Thrapston Town	32	10	3	3	45	21	6	5	5	32	31	16	8	8	77	52	56
6	Higham Town	32	7	5	4	32	21	9	3	4	34	23	16	8	8	66	44	56
7	Blisworth	32	7	5	4	28	14	8	3	5	22	17	15	8	9	50	31	53
8	Harrowby United	32	9	2	5	36	23	7	3	6	29	36	16	5	11	65	59	53
9	Irchester United	32	7	6	3	30	22	7	2	7	28	39	14	8	10	58	61	50
10	Olney Town	32	7	4	5	24	20	7	3	6	28	24	14	7	11	52	44	49
11	Cottingham	32	7	3	6	29	38	3	6	7	28	39	10	9	13	57	77	39
12	North'ton ON Chenecks	32	6	4	6	38	37	4	3	9	24	39	10	7	15	62	76	37
13	Eynesbury Rovers	32	7	3	6	32	24	2	3	11	11	35	9	6	17	43	59	33
14	Rothwell Corinthians	32	4	5	7	26	25	2	6	8	20	29	6	11	15	46	54	29
15	Potton United	32	4	1	11	19	49	1	2	13	19	58	5	3	24	38	107	18
16	St Ives Town	32	2	3	11	22	49	0	3	13	13	50	2	6	24	35	99	12
17	Burton Park Wanderers	32	2	4	10	20	42	0	1	15	13	51	2	5	25	33	93	11

RESERVE DIVISION ONE

	(Top Five)	P	W	D	L	F	A	W	D	L	F	A	W	D	L	F	A	Pts
1	Stotfold	38	16	3	0	55	9	10	4	5	40	21	26	7	5	95	30	85
2	Northampton Spencer	38	12	5	2	49	21	12	3	4	30	16	24	8	6	79	37	80
3	Deeping Rangers	38	13	4	2	44	20	10	2	7	34	31	23	6	9	78	51	75
4	Yaxley	38	15	4	0	60	11	7	4	8	30	28	22	8	8	90	39	74
5	St Neots Town	38	13	4	2	45	19	7	6	6	23	29	20	10	8	68	48	70

RESERVE DIVISION TWO

	(Top Five)	P	W	D	L	F	A	W	D	L	F	A	W	D	L	F	A	Pts
1	Holbeach United	34	16	1	0	65	20	13	1	3	50	18	29	2	3	115	38	89
2	Blisworth	34	12	0	5	49	23	13	3	1	52	16	25	3	6	101	39	78
3	Bourne Town	34	13	3	1	62	19	11	1	5	50	20	24	4	6	112	30	76
4	Olney Town	34	10	2	5	33	28	6	3	9	29	37	18	5	11	62	65	59
5	Wootton Blue Cross	34	9	4	4	43	20	8	3	6	31	25	17	7	10	74	45	58

PREMIER DIVISION RESULTS CHART 2001-02

		1	2	3	4	5	6	7	8	9	10	11	12	13	14	15	16	17	18	19	20	21
1	Blackstone	X	1-3	3-0	3-2	1-0	1-3	0-2	2-4	0-2	0-3	1-1	3-0	2-1	1-0	1-1	1-3	2-0	0-2	3-1	1-1	1-2
2	Boston	0-0	X	1-0	4-0	7-0	3-1	1-3	1-0	2-4	1-1	4-0	5-0	2-1	1-0	2-4	0-1	2-2	1-1	5-1	2-1	1-2
3	Bourne	2-2	2-1	X	3-1	0-0	1-2	3-1	0-2	2-1	0-2	0-2	3-2	1-1	2-0	3-5	3-1	2-2	0-1	8-1	2-2	1-3
4	Buckingham	3-2	3-2	7-0	X	4-0	3-4	0-5	4-2	1-2	1-3	2-4	1-1	3-1	3-2	3-3	2-2	0-3	2-5	2-1	1-2	2-1
5	Bugbrooke	0-1	0-0	1-1	1-0	X	1-3	5-2	2-5	1-6	1-5	1-6	2-0	0-0	0-4	0-5	0-3	1-4	1-1	1-0	0-2	0-1
6	Cogenhoe	1-0	1-0	3-0	1-1	2-1	X	2-0	1-1	2-2	1-2	0-5	4-2	4-0	1-0	1-1	1-0	3-0	2-0	5-2	1-1	1-1
7	Daventry	1-0	2-3	3-0	0-2	0-0	2-4	X	2-0	0-3	0-2	0-3	2-0	1-2	3-1	1-1	0-1	1-0	2-2	5-1	1-2	1-1
8	Deeping	4-0	0-1	1-3	4-3	1-2	6-1	3-2	X	3-2	0-3	3-1	3-0	2-1	3-1	1-0	2-0	1-2	2-1	3-2	2-2	2-2
9	Desborough	5-0	3-3	3-1	2-0	2-1	5-1	1-0	0-0	X	1-3	1-1	1-0	4-1	5-2	1-4	1-0	1-0	1-2	3-1	0-0	2-0
10	Ford Sports	4-2	1-1	4-0	2-1	1-0	2-1	3-1	2-0	0-1	X	1-0	7-0	3-1	1-0	2-0	3-1	4-0	1-2	1-0	3-0	0-0
11	Holbeach	4-1	2-1	6-0	5-1	6-1	1-2	4-0	1-2	0-0	3-2	X	3-2	2-0	1-2	3-0	0-0	3-1	3-1	8-0	6-4	2-1
12	Kempston	1-2	0-8	0-1	0-3	7-1	1-3	0-0	1-1	0-4	0-1	2-4	X	3-0	3-1	0-6	1-2	3-0	1-0	3-1	0-2	3-1
13	Long Buckby	0-4	0-4	2-2	1-3	2-1	3-1	0-3	0-3	1-4	0-1	1-3	1-0	X	2-1	0-2	1-6	2-2	0-1	6-1	1-3	0-2
14	N Spencer	0-3	0-0	0-1	4-1	1-0	0-2	1-1	3-0	5-1	1-2	3-2	1-0	0-0	X	1-3	0-5	0-1	2-0	5-0	1-2	1-1
15	Raunds	3-2	2-3	1-2	3-0	8-0	0-3	3-2	2-1	2-1	2-2	1-2	5-1	2-2	1-0	X	2-0	4-1	3-2	1-0	3-1	1-1
16	St Neot	3-2	0-3	2-0	4-1	5-1	1-4	3-1	1-0	1-0	1-1	1-1	4-0	6-1	3-2	1-2	X	2-1	2-0	6-0	2-1	2-1
17	S & Lloyds	0-1	3-4	0-1	3-3	4-0	2-2	3-2	2-1	3-1	2-3	1-3	1-3	3-2	2-1	1-0	X	2-1	2-0	5-0	0-3	1-3
18	Stotfold	4-0	5-1	1-2	1-1	4-0	2-3	0-1	1-1	3-1	1-1	4-2	4-1	2-1	2-1	3-1	1-1	X	4-1	3-0	2-1	
19	Wellingboro	0-4	0-10	2-1	1-5	0-1	1-6	1-3	0-6	0-6	0-6	0-5	3-2	1-3	1-2	1-1	0-3	3-0	0-4	X	0-3	0-4
20	Wootton	1-2	1-0	1-2	1-1	3-0	2-1	7-0	1-0	1-0	1-2	2-4	3-1	3-0	2-1	2-0	2-2	1-0	0-1	2-1	X	1-1
21	Yaxley	1-2	2-0	2-2	3-2	3-0	1-2	3-2	1-4	1-2	1-3	2-1	4-2	5-0	0-2	3-4	3-1	1-1	0-0	5-1	2-3	X

DIVISION ONE RESULTS CHART 2001-02

		1	2	3	4	5	6	7	8	9	10	11	12	13	14	15	16	17
1	Blisworth	X	3-1	6-0	1-1	1-0	0-2	1-1	1-1	0-0	1-3	0-2	8-0	0-0	3-1	2-1	1-0	0-1
2	Burton PW	2-2	X	4-4	2-0	0-1	0-5	1-4	1-6	2-4	1-5	0-1	0-0	0-1	4-0	1-4	2-2	0-3
3	Cottingham	1-0	5-1	X	3-2	2-3	1-6	4-3	1-7	2-1	0-5	2-4	1-1	3-2	2-0	1-1	0-1	1-1
4	Eynesbury	3-1	4-0	0-2	X	2-2	1-2	4-0	0-5	2-1	0-2	0-3	3-2	1-1	0-0	1-3	8-1	1-2
5	Harrowby	0-1	4-1	2-1	3-0	X	1-1	0-3	0-2	4-1	0-3	3-2	3-2	2-3	3-0	5-0	2-2	4-1
6	Higham	0-1	3-1	2-0	3-0	1-2	X	3-1	3-3	2-2	1-0	0-0	5-1	2-2	4-2	0-2	1-2	2-2
7	Irchester	0-1	3-2	0-0	3-0	1-1	2-0	X	4-3	3-1	2-3	1-4	4-2	3-1	2-2	1-1	0-0	1-1
8	Newport Pag	3-1	5-1	6-2	4-1	3-0	2-0	4-1	X	7-1	2-2	2-0	6-1	1-0	5-0	3-0	0-3	3-1
9	N. ON Chen.	1-2	4-1	3-3	0-0	5-2	1-3	2-3	2-4	X	2-2	0-4	3-1	3-1	4-3	3-3	3-2	2-3
10	N'ton Sileby	0-0	2-1	6-1	7-0	3-2	4-0	8-1	3-0	1-1	X	5-0	5-0	1-1	5-0	1-2	0-0	2-0
11	Olney	0-1	4-0	1-1	1-0	1-1	1-3	1-1	1-2	1-4	3-0	X	1-0	1-1	2-1	3-2	1-3	2-0
12	Potton	0-5	3-1	0-3	1-1	3-4	1-3	1-4	1-8	0-2	0-5	0-2	X	1-0	2-1	1-5	3-4	2-1
13	Rothwell Cor.	2-1	1-1	3-2	0-1	2-3	2-3	1-2	1-2	2-0	0-0	1-3	2-4	X	6-0	2-2	0-0	1-1
14	St Ives	2-4	2-0	1-6	1-2	2-6	1-1	1-3	0-7	1-2	2-4	1-1	2-1	2-2	X	1-4	1-3	2-3
15	Thrapston	3-0	3-1	2-2	2-1	5-0	2-3	2-0	2-3	6-2	0-0	2-2	5-2	5-3	4-0	X	0-2	2-0
16	Whitworths	0-2	2-0	1-1	2-1	4-0	0-0	0-1	0-5	3-1	3-2	3-2	5-2	2-1	2-2	2-2	X	2-1
17	Woodford	0-0	3-1	2-0	2-1	1-2	4-2	0-1	2-1	3-1	0-1	2-1	5-0	2-1	2-1	4-0	2-1	X

MONTHLY AWARDS

Month	Manager of the Month *Premier Division*	Manager of the Month *Division One*	Goalscorer of the Month
August	Jon Taylor (Wootton)	Graham Drury (Harrowby)	Martin Wormall (Harrowby)
September	Shane Geary (Ford Sports)	Simon Morrice (Blisworth)	Shaun Keeble (Holbeach)
October	Aidy Mann (Cogenhoe)	Nick Verity (Sileby)	Darren Harmon (Cogenhoe)
November	Chris Howell (St Neots)	Danni Janes (Newport Pagnell)	Graham Knight (Raunds)
December	Dick Creasy (Holbeach)	Danni Janes (Newport Pagnell)	Kevin Byrne (Desborough)
January	Paul Humphries (Yaxley)	Gary Petts (Thrapston)	Roy Anderson (Cogenhoe)
February	Chris Beckett (Deeping)	Steve Galbraith (Eynesbury)	Andy Evans (Ford Sports)
March	Derek Maddox (Desborough)	Mark Herring (Whitworths)	Martin Wormall (Harrowby)
April	Bob Don-Duncan (Boston)	Danni Janes (Newport Pagnell)	Jamie Graham (Boston)

Manager of the Year: Shane Geary (Ford Sports)

UNITED COUNTIES LEAGUE KNOCKOUT CUP 2001-02

PRELIMINARY ROUND

Blisworth	v	Harrowby	2-1	Kempston	v	Raunds	1-3
Long Buckby	v	Ford Sports	0-4	Wellingborough	v	Cogenhoe	0-3
Wootton	v	Newport Pagnell	3-0	Irchester	v	Bourne	1-4

FIRST ROUND

Burton PW	v	Sileby	0-5	Eynesbury	v	Potton	2-3
Rothwell Corinthians	v	Woodford	2*0	St Ives	v	Holbeach	0-6
Stewarts & Lloyds	v	St Neots	2-0	Stotfold	v	Olney	3-2
Yaxley	v	Cottingham	3-2	Boston	v	North'ton Spencer	2-3
Higham	v	Bugbrooke	1-3	Thrapston	v	Deeping	3-1
Blackstone	v	Bourne	0-3	Cogenhoe	v	Desborough	6-2
Daventry	v	Blisworth	5p3, 0*0	Wootton	v	Buckingham	5-2
ON Chenecks	v	Ford Sports	0-4	Whitworths	v	Raunds	0-5

SECOND ROUND

Stewarts & Lloyds	v	Stotfold	1-3	Thrapston	v	Sileby	0-2
Rothwell Corinthians	v	Bugbrooke	2-1	Cogenhoe	v	Yaxley	3p4, 1*1
Bourne	v	Raunds	0-3	Northampton Spncr	v	Wootton	1p4, 3*3
Potton	v	Ford Sports	2-1	Holbeach	v	Daventry	3*2

THIRD ROUND

Yaxley	v	Stotfold	1*0	Potton	v	Sileby	1-4
Wootton	v	Raunds	1-2	Holbeach	v	Rothwell Corinthians	3-1

SEMI-FINALS

Sileby	v	Yaxley	1*2	Holbeach	v	Raunds	1-3

FINAL

Raunds	v	Yaxley	1-0	at Blackstone. Referee: C Evans

UNITED COUNTIES LEAGUE LEADING SCORERS/APPEARANCES 2001-02

PREMIER DIVISION

Most Appearances		Leading Scorers		Holbeach United			
Blackstone				Steve Barnes	43	Shaun Keeble	40
Nathan Mitchell	41	Matt Farrington	7	Shaun Keeble	43		
Boston Town				**Kempston Rovers**			
Mick Brown	41	Liam Harrald	27	Linden Ingerson	40	Linden Ingerson	7
Bourne Town						Chris Nicholson	7
Darren Munton	42	Darren Munton	20	**Long Buckby**			
Buckingham Town				Shaun Tiernan	38	Scott McGuinness	5
Michael Cox	36	Abdul Abdi	13	**Northampton Spencer**			
Bugbrooke St Michaels				Simon McCarthy	40	Ben Foster	14
Scott Coleman	38	Kevin Eyre	7	**Raunds Town**			
Cogenhoe United				Scott Goodacre	46	Graham Knight	24
Aidy Mann	41	Darren Harmon	31	**St Neots Town**			
Darren Watts	41			Paul Bloss	41	Steve Kuhne	26
Daventry Town				**Stewarts & Lloyds**			
Lee Ault	39	Darren Towers	14	Paddy McCann	40	Dave Torrance	11
Deeping Rangers				**Stotfold**			
Martin Bradley	41	Simon Mead	20	Paul Stanley	40	Pete Saunders	19
Gianni Salerno	41			**Wellingborough Town**			
Desborough Town				Tom Francis	38	Joe Beard	6
Michael Chong	40	Kevin Byrne	24	**Wootton Blue Cross**			
		Michael Chong	24	Jon Hoggett	37	Darek Jozwiak	28
Ford Sports				**Yaxley**			
Simon Williams	42	Andy Evans	24	Matt Doyle	45	Simon Acton	13

BLACKSTONE

Secretary: Ian McGillivry, 20 New Rd, Ryhall, Stamford, Lincs PE9 4HL
Tel: 01780 762263 (H),**Ground:** Lincoln Road, Stamford Tel: 01780 757335

Directions: A6121 Stamford to Bourne road, 2nd left past MB works

Capacity: 1,000   Seats: 100   Cover: Yes   Floodlights: Yes

Clubhouse: Open evenings, lunchtimes & matchdays

HONOURS UCL Div 1 R-up 87-88 (Benevolent Cup R-up), Lincs Snr Cup `A' 92-93

PREVIOUS **Leagues:** Peterborough Works; Peterborough; Stamford & District
Names: Rutland Ironworks; Blackstone (until 1975)

RECORD **Gate:** 700 v Glinton
Win: 11-0 v Brackley, 22/1/94 (A Dunn 6 goals)
Scorer (in one game): A Dunn; 6 v Brackley Town, 22/1/94
Players progressing : Craig Goldsmith (Peterborough), Alan Neilson (Newcastle)

FACT FILE
Founded: 1920
Nickname: Stones
Sponsors: Ideal Shopfitters
Colours: Navy blue and white
Change Colours: Royal blue and white stripes
Midweek matchday: Tuesday
Programme: 32 pages with entry
Editor: Kevin Boor (01780 754584)
Local Press: Stamford Mercury, Herald & Post, Peterborough Evening Telegraph

CLUB PERSONNEL
President: Bill Sewell
Chairman: Darren Laughton
Manager: Mel Landin
Assistant Manager:Jim Shilling
Press Officer: Kevin Boor
Captain: Nathan Mitchell

BOSTON TOWN

Secretary: A Crick, Daisy Cottage, Shore Rd, Freiston, Boston, Lincs., PE22 0LN
Tel: 01205 760162. (H &Fax) 01205 313090 (W) 07718906053 (M)

Ground: Tattershall Road, Boston, Lincs Tel: 01205 365470

Directions: A52 Grantham-Sleaford, 2nd left into Brotherton Rd., Argyle St. to bridge, immediately over left into Tattersall road, ground 3/4 mile on left.
Capacity: 6,000   Seats: 450   Cover: 950   Floodlights: Yes   Club Shop: Yes
Clubhouse: Open evenings, except Sunday, matchdays & functions. Bar & Lounge. Darts & pool

HONOURS Midland Co's Lg 74-75 78-79 80-81 (Lg Cup 76-77); Lincs Snr `A' Cup (5)73-74 79-82 89-90 (Snr `B' Cup 65-66); Central Mids Lg 88-89; Central All 65-66; Lincs Lg 64-65; Und. Co. Lg. Prem Div 94-95, 00-01

PREVIOUS **Leagues:** Lincs 63-65; Central Alliance 65-66; Eastern Co's 66-68; Midland 68-82; Northern Co's East 82-87; Central Midlands 87-91 **Ground:** Mayflower Ground

BEST SEASONFA Cup: 1st Rd Proper 76-77, 1-3 v Barnsley (A)
FA Trophy: 2nd Round 79-80, 3-6 v Mossley (A) after 0-0
FA Vase: Semi-Finals 94-95, 0-2 (agg) v Taunton Town)

RECORD **Attendance:** 2,700 v Boston Utd, FA Cup 3rd Qual. Rd 1970
Goalscorer (in a season): Carl Smaller 48, 1994-95
Players progressing: Julian Joachim (Leicester City and Aston Villa) , Neil Mann (Hull City)

FACT FILE
Founded: 1963
Nickname: Poachers
Sponsors: Barclays Brokers, Graham Gill Carpets & Boston Snooker Centre
Colours: Sky Blue/ Royal Blue/Sky
Change: Yellow/white/yellow
Midweek Matchday: Tuesday
Reserves League: None 94-95
Programme: 40 pages, 50p(Ed-Sec)
Press Off:J.Rose 01205351501

CLUB PERSONNEL
Chairman: Mick Vines
Vice Chairman: J Rose
Treasurer: J Rose
Manager: Bob Don-Duncan
Ass.Manager: Vince Adams
Physio: Steve Greetham
2001-02 Leading goalscorer: Dave Scotney
Captain: Dean Elston
P.o.Y.: Matt Price

BOURNE TOWN

Secretary: Jim Ashton, Tulip Cottage, Fen Road,Dunsby, Bourne, Lincs. PE10 0UE
Tel No:0177888 440065
Ground: Abbey Lawn, Abbey Road, Bourne, Lincs Tel: 01778 422292

Directions: In market place take A151 Spalding Road, ground 500 yds on right.Public transport from Peterborough, Stamford and Grantham
Capacity: 3,000   Seats: 300   Cover: 750   Floodlights: Yes
Club Shop: Contact Sec.
Clubhouse: Small, open matchdays and specific events. Food, confectionary available

HONOURS Utd Co's Lg 68-69 69-70 71-72 90-91 (KO Cup 69-70, Benevolent Cup 90-91, Res Div 2 94-95), Lincs Snr `A' Cup 71-72 (R-up 92-93), Central Alliance Division 1 South 59-60, Lincs Intermediate Cup 85-86

PREVIOUS **Leagues:** Peterborough; UCL 47-56; Central All. 58-61; MidlandCos 61-63
Ground: Adjacent to cricket field after WW2 until 1947

RECORD **Attendance:** 3,000 v Chelmsford, FA Trophy 1970
Goalscorer: David Scotney
Players Progressing Peter Grummit (Nottm Forest), Shaun Cunnington (Wrexham), David Palmer (Wrexham)

FACT FILE
Founded: 1883   Nickname: Wakes
Sponsors:Sporting Lincs
Colours: Maroon & sky/sky/maroon
Change Colours: White & sky/white & sky/sky
Midweek matchday: Tuesday
Reserves' Lge: HSUCL Res Div 2
Programme: 30 pages, 75p
Editor: JimAshton (01778 440065)
Local Press: Stamford Mercury, Lincs Free Press, Peterborough EveningTelegraph, Bourne Local

CLUB PERSONNEL
Chairman: Don Mitchell
Vice-Chairman: Jim Ashton
President: Bob feetham
Press Officer: Jeff Hodson
Manager: Darren Munton
Assistant Manager: Pete Riches
Physio: John Handley

BUCKINGHAM TOWN

Secretary: Brian Maycock, 31 Westfield, Buckingham, Bucks Tel: 01280 815529

Ground: Ford Meadow, Ford Street, Buckingham Tel: 01280 816257
Capacity: 4,000   Cover: 420   Seats: 420   Floodlights: Yes

Directions: From town centre take Aylesbury (A413) road and turn right at Phillips Garage after 400yds. Public transport: train to Milton Keynes, then bus to Buckingham

Clubhouse: Open evenings 6.30-11 (12-11 Sat & Sun) Rolls etc available on matchdays. Bingo, dominoes, darts & pool. Concert room with stage for hire,capacity 150   **Club Shop:** Yes

HONOURS   Southern Lg Southern Div 90-91, Utd Co's Lg 83-84 85-86 (Div 1 R-up 75-76, Div 2 R-up 74-75, Lg Cup 83-84, Div 2 Cup R-up 74-75), Nth Bucks Lg 24-25 28-29 33-34 35-37 38-39 48-50(2) Aylesbury & Dist. Lg 02-03, Berks & Bucks Snr Cup 83-84, Berks & Bucks Jnr Cup 02-03 48-49 (R-up 38-39 72-73), Berks & Bucks Minor Cup 32-33, Buckingham Snr Charity Cup x11, r-up x 5

PREVIOUS   **Leagues:** Aylesbury & Dist; Nth Bucks; Hellenic 53-57; Sth Mids 57-74; Utd Co's 74-86; Southern Lge 86-97

BEST SEASON   **FA Cup:** 1st Round 1984-85   **FA Vase:** Quarter Finals 1990-91 & 92-93

RECORD   **Attendance:** 2,451 v Orient, FA Cup 1st Rd 84-85
Fee paid: £7,000 for Steve Jenkins (Wealdstone, 1992)
Fee received: £1,000 for Terry Shrieves (Kettering)

FACT FILE

Formed: 1883
Nickname: The Robins
Sponsors: Wipac
Colours: All red
Change colours: All blue
Midweek Matchday:
Reserves' League: No reserve team
Programme: Yes Editor: Carl Waine
Newsline: 0891 884 431
Local Press: Buckingham Advertiser,
MK Citizen, Herald & Post
Local Radio: Chiltern Radio,
Fox FM (102.6 fm), 3 Counties Radio

CLUB PERSONNEL
Chairman: Brian Maycock
Manager: Morrell Maison
Assistant Manager: Pete Riches

COGENHOE UNITED

Secretary: Mrs Sue Wright, 6 Brafield Road, Cogenhoe, Northants NN7 1ND
Tel: 01604 890737 (H), 01604 890277 (B), Fax: 01604 890641 email: sue@wrightandsmith.co.uk

Ground: Compton Park, Brafield Rd, Cogenhoe, Northants (01604 890521)
Directions: Turn off A428 at Brafield-on-the-Green, first turn right toCogenhoe or A45 to Billing Aquadrome. Carry on, take second Cogenhoe turn on left

Capacity: 5,000   Seats: 100   Cover: 200   Floodlights: Yes   Club Shop: No
Clubhouse: Tues-Fri 7-11, Sat 12-3 & 4-11, Sun 12-3 & 7-10.30 Snacks. Hot food on matchdays

HONOURS   UCL Div 1 R-up 86-87 (Res. Div 2 88-89), K.O. Cup 96-97; Daventry Charity Cup 91-92 95-96, (R-up 79-80); Central Northants Comb 80-81 82-83 83-84 (R-up 81-82, Prem Div Cup 82-83 (R-up 78-79), Div 1 up R-up 77-78, Charity Shield 82-83 83-84)

PREVIOUS   **League:** Central Northants Combination 1967-84
Ground: Cogenhoe Village PF 1967-84

RECORD   **Gate:** 1,000 v Eastenders XI, Charity match 8/7/90
Scorer & Appearances: Tony Smith
Win: 22-0 v Ravensthorpe, Cen. Northants Comb. Prem. Div KO Cup, 79-80
Defeat: 0-6 v Yardley United, Central Northants Comb. Div. 1, 76-77
Players progressing : Darren Bazeley (Watford 89), Darren Harmon (Notts Co. 89),Matt Murphy (Oxford Utd 93), Gary Leonard (Northampton 1978)

FACT FILE
Founded: 1967
Nickname: Cooks
Sponsors: Supertrucking
Colours: All royal blue
Change: Red & black stripes/black/red
Midweek matchday: Tuesday
Reserves' Lge: UCL Res. Div 1
Programme: 32 pages with Admission
Editor:Sue Wright
Local Press: Chronicle & Echo,
Northants Evening Telegraph
CLUB PERSONNEL
Chairman: Derek Wright
Vice Chairman: Bob Earl
President: Steve Brockwell
Comm. Man.: Robert Jones
Manager: Aidy Mann
Assistant Manager: Scott Carlin
Physio: Ian Blair

DAVENTRY TOWN

Secretary: Tim Kibblewhite,78 The Medway, Daventry, Northants.
Tel: 01327 703974 (H)

Ground: Elderstubbs Farm, Browns Road, Daventry, Northants
Tel: 01327 706286
Capacity: 2,000   Seats: 250   Cover: 250   Floodlights: Yes

Directions   Adjacent to A45 by-pass at top of Staverton Road Sports Complex
Clubhouse: Large bar/kitchen

HONOURS   UCL Div 1(2) 89-91 (Lg Cup R-up 92-93, Highest Aggregate Cup), Northants Junior Cup 36-37 60-61 91-92

PREVIOUS   **Leagues:** Northampton Town (pre-1987)/ Central Northants Combination 87-89

BEST SEASON   **FA Cup:** Prel. Rd 94-95
FA Vase: Preliminary Rd 91-92 94-95

RECORD   **Attendance:** 350 v Ford Sports 1991
Local Press :   Daventry Weekly Express, Herald & Post
Players Progressing: Martin Aldridge (Northampton)

FACT FILE

Founded: 1886
Sponsor: Campbell Estate Agents
Colours:White/black/black
Change colours:Claret & blue/claret/claret
Midweek Matchday: Tuesday
Reserves League: Central Northants Comb
Programme: 4 Pages Editor: Tony Perry

CLUB PERSONNEL

Chairman: Gary Roche
Vice Chairman: Grant Hughes
President: Paul Webster

Manager: Mark Shackleton
Assistant Manager.: Lee Ault
Physio: Tony Jackson

United Counties League Division One Champions 2001-02, Newport Pagnell Town, who capped the week they won the League by also winning the Berks & Bucks Intermediate Cup. Photo: Steve Ayre

United Counties League Cup Winners, Raunds Town. Photo: Gavin J Tutcher

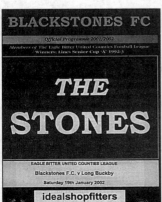

DEEPING RANGERS

Secretary: Haydon Whitham, 3 Everingham, Orton Brimbles, Peterborough PE2 5XP
Tel:01733 238539 (H) 07736 548500 M)

Ground: Deeping Sports Club, Outgang Road, Market Deeping, Lincs.
Tel: 01778 344701 Website: www.deepingrangers.co.uk
Capacity: 1,000 Seats: 180 Cover: 180 Floodlights: Ys

Directions: From Deeping town centre take the A15 towards Bourne. Turn right at
Towngate Tavern following signs to Industrial Estate & club is 1/4 mile on left.

Clubhouse: Bar and lounge. Changing rooms

HONOURS Peterborough & Dist. Lge Div 3 67, Div. 2 69, Div. 1 70, Prem. Div. R-up 95-96
98-99; Lincs Junior Cup 83-84 87-88 88-89, Lincs. Sen. B Cup 00-01, R-up
UCL Div 1 R-up 00-01, Fair Play Award 99-00, 00-01
Peterborough FA Senior Cup 91-92 96-97 Minor Cup 67,

PREVIOUS **League:** Peterborough & District

FACT FILE

Founded: 1966
Nickname: Rangers
Colours: Claret & blue
Change colours: White/claret/sky blue
Programme: Yes

CLUB PERSONNEL

President: Albert Lawrence
Chairman: Ed Bailey
Match Sec.:Robin Crowson
01778 348287(H) 07977 971796 (M)
Email: rwc@excite.co.uk

Manager: Chris Beckett
Asst. Manager: Dave Simpson

DESBOROUGH TOWN

Secretary: John Lee, 85 Breakleys Road, Desborough, Northants NN14 2PT
Tel: 01536 760002 Email Address: johnlee@froggerycottage.fsnet.co.uk

Ground: Waterworks Field, Braybrooke Rd, Desborough Tel: 01536 761350
Capacity: 8,000 Seats: 250 Cover: 500 Floodlights: Yes

Directions: Half a mile west of A6 following signs for Braybrooke
Clubhouse: Lounge & main hall, 2 bars, games room. Every eve. & w/e lunchtimes
Club Shop: No

HONOURS Utd Co's (Prev. Northants) Lg 00-01 01-02 06-07 20-21 23-24 24-25 27-28 48-49
66-67 (R-up 02-03 10-11 19-20 22-23 79-80, 98-99), Div 2 10-11, 28-9(Res),R-up
09-10 (Res) 26-27(Res) 51-52(Res), KO Cup 77-78 96-97 00-01; Northants Snr
Cup10-11. Desborough Charity Cup 2001-02
13-14 28-29 51-52; Desborough Charity Cup 97-98,98-99,99-00

PREVIOUS **Leagues:** None
RECORD **Attendance:** 8,000 v Kettering Town
Win: 10-1: v Huntingdon Utd (A) 1957 & v Stewarts & Lloyds (A) 1965, both UCL.
Defeat: 11-0 v Rushden Town (A) 1934
Fee received: £8,000 for Wakeley Gage, from Northampton Town
Players progressing: Wakeley Gage (Northampton), Jon Purdie & Campbell Chapman (Wolves),
Andy Tillson (Grimsby), Matt Murphy (Oxford United)

FACT FILE

Founded: 1896
Nickname: Ar Tarn
Colours: Blue & white stripes/blue/blue
Change Colours: All red
Previous Leagues: None
Midweek matchday: Tuesday
Programme: 40 pages with entry
Editor:John Lee
Local Press: Evening Telegraph,Northants
Post,Chronicle & Echo,& Harborough Mail
Website: www.artarn.co.uk

CLUB PERSONNEL

Chairman:Alan Panter
President: T.B.A.
Press Officer: John Lee
Manager: Kevin McGuire
Asst Manager: Dave McHuchison
Physio: Dave Marlow

FORD SPORTS

Secretary: Mick Fryatt, 2 Mayfield Drive, Daventry, Northants NN11 5QB
Tel Nos: 01327 876789 (H) 01327 305407 (W)

Ground: Royal Oak Way South, Daventry, Northants Tel: 01327 704914
Capacity: 1,000 Seats: Yes Cover: Yes Floodlights: Yes

Directions: Enter Daventry on A45 or A361 and follow signs for Royal Oak Way

Clubhouse: Yes

HONOURS UCL Premier Division 2001-02 ,Div 1 92-93, 95-96, Knockout Cup 97-98,
Benevolent Cup R-up 92-93; Daventry Charity Cup 201-02
Highest Agg. Goalscoring Trophy 92-93; Northants Sen Cup R-up 96-97

PREVIOUS **League:** Central Northants Comb

Player progressing: Martin Aldridge (Northampton)

FACT FILE

Founded: 1968
Nickname: Motormen
Sponsors: Ford Sports & Social Club
Colours: Blue & white/blue/blue
Change : Red & white/red/red
Reserves' Lge: UCL Res Div 2
Programme: 12 pages
Editor: John Hinton

CLUB PERSONNEL

Chairman: John Bailham
Manager: Shane Geary
Assistant Manager: Mick Bulliman
Physio: Dave Bull

HOLBEACH UNITED

Secretary: Paul Beeken, 36 West End, Holbeach, Lincs PE12 7HA Tel: 01406 425355 (H)
Email Address: secpaulathufc@aol
Ground: Carters Park, Park Road, Holbeach Tel: 01406 424761

Capacity:4,000   Seats: 200   Cover: 450   Floodlights: Yes

Directions: Second left at traffic lights in town centre, 220 yds down road on left.
From King's Lynn; sharp right at traffic lights

Clubhouse: Large bar, lounge & kitchen, open every night **Club Shop:** No

HONOURS   Utd Co's Lg 89-90 (KO Cup 64-65 89-90), Benevolent Cup, Evans Halshaw Cup
97-98; Lincs Snr Cup `A' 83-84 84-85 86-87 (Senior Cup `B' 57-58)

PREVIOUS   **Leagues:** Peterborough; Utd Co's 46-55; Eastern Co's 55-62; Midland Co's62-63

BEST SEASON **FA Cup:** 1st Rd Proper 82-83, 0-4 v Wrexham (at Peterborough)
FA Trophy: 2nd Qual. Round 69-70 71-72
FA Vase: 5th Round 88-89, 2-4 v Wisbech Town

RECORD   **Gate:** 4,094 v Wisbech 1954

Players progressing: Peter Rawcliffe (Lincoln)

FACT FILE
Founded: 1929 Nickname: Tigers
Sponsors: Ashwood Homes
Colours: Old gold & black stripes/black/black
Change Colours: All blue
Midweek matchday: Tuesday
Reserves' Lge: Peterborough
Prog: 44 pages, 50p Editor: David Ingle
Local Press : Lincs Free Press, Spalding
Guardian, Peterborough Evening Telegraph

CLUB PERSONNEL
Chairman: Chris Cooper
President: Francis Bissadike
Manager: Dick Creasey
Assistant Manager: Shaun Keeble

KEMPSTON ROVERS

Secretary: Alan Scott, 26 King William Rd, Kempston, Bedford MK42 7AT Tel: 01234 854875(H)
07813 088703 (M)   Email: arscott@archchemicals.com

Ground: Hillgrounds Leisure, Hillgrounds Rd, Kempston, Bedford Tel: 01234 852346.
Capacity: 2,000   Seats: 100   Cover: 250   Floodlights: Yes

Directions: M1 jct 13, A421 to Kempston, Hillgrounds Rd is off the B531 main Kempston-Bedford
road. Entrance to Hillgrounds Road is opposite Sainsburys onthe B531 - ground can be found just
over twi miles from Sainsburys entrance.British Rail to Bedford Thameslink/Midland then bus
No.103 from Bedford town centre stops outside ground
Club Shop: No, but old programmes available from clubhouse
Clubhouse: Open 7-11pm Tues - Sun. & we lunch 12-3pm. Sky TV, pool, hot pies & pasties.
HONOURS   United Counties Lge 73-74 (R-up 56-57 59-60), Div 1 57-58 85-86,
Div 2 55-56 (R-up 67-68), KO Cup 55-56 57-58 59-60 74-75 76-77.
Beds Senior Cup 08-09 37-38 76-77 91-92 (R-up 92-93)

PREVIOUS   **League:** South Midlands 27-53
Grounds: Bedford Rd 1900s-1973; Hillgrounds Road 74-86 (3 grounds in same road!)
BEST SEASON **FA Cup:**   **FA Vase:**
RECORD   **Attendance:** Unknown   **Scorer:** Doug Jack
Players progressing: Ernie Fenn (WBA), Matthew Woolgar (Luton 1994)

FACT FILE
Founded: 1884
Nickname: Walnut Boys
Club Sponsors: Audi Vindis Bedford
Colours: Red & white stripes/black/red
Change Colours: All yellow
Midweek matchday: Tuesday
Reserves's Lge: Bedford & Dist
Programme: 24 pages, 40p
Editor: Richard Coop (0378 629470)
Local Press: Bedfordshire Times,
Herald & Post, Beds on Sunday

CLUB PERSONNEL
President: H Gilbert
Chairman: Russell Shreeves
Vice-Chairman: Russell Shreeves
Press Officer : Secretary
Manager:Steve Fox
Asst Manager: Ian Simmons
Coach: Mel Fisher

LONG BUCKBY

Secretary: Dave Austin,8 Pytchley Drive, Long Buckby, Northampton NN6 7PL
Tel No: 01327 842788 (H) 07710723477(M) email: DJAUSTIN28@aol.com
Ground: Station Rd, Long Buckby Tel: 01327 842682
Capacity: 1,000   Seats: 200   Cover: 200   Floodlights: Yes

Directions: Daventry - Long Buckby rd. 400 yds from station (Northampton -Rugby line)

Clubhouse: Bar & concert room. Open matchdays

HONOURS   UCL KO Cup 84-85, UCL Div 2 70-71 71-72, Div 2 KO Cup 71-72, Div 3 69-
70; Northants Snr Cup R-up; Daventry Charity Cup 96-97

PREVIOUS   **Leagues:** Rugby & D.; Central Northants Comb. (pre-1968)
Name: Long Buckby Nomads 1936

BEST SEASON **FA Vase:** 2nd Rd 85-86
FA Cup: 1st Qualifying Rd 92-93

RECORD   **Gate:** 750 v Kettering, Northants Snr Cup Final 1984

Players progressing: Gary Mills (Nottm Forest), Vince Overson (Burnley),
Des Waldock (Northampton),Steve Norris (Scarborough)

FACT FILE
Nickname: Bucks
Sponsors: Northampton Elec Dist
Colours: All blue
Change colours: All red
Midweek matchday: Tuesday
Reserves' Lge: HSUCL Res Div 1
Programme: 8 pages
Editor: Rod Pryor (01604 845071)
Local Press : Chronicle & Echo,
Daventry Weekly News

CLUB PERSONNEL
President: Alister Bruce
Chairman: Ted Thresher
Manager: Steve Renshaw
Assistant Manager: Shaun Tiernan
Physio: Robert Stafferton

NEWPORT PAGNELL TOWN

Secretary: Denis Stoyles, 39 Ashfield, Stantonbury, Milton Keynes, MK14 6AU
Tel Nos: 01908 312862 (H) 07790 44980-5 (M)

Ground: Willen Road, Newport Pagnell Tel: 01908 611993

Capacity: 2,000   Seats: 100   Cover: 100   Floodlights: Yes

Directions: Adjacent to A422 Newport Pagnell by-pass

Clubhouse: Open every evening   Club Shop: No

HONOURS UCL Div 1 82-83,01-02 (R-up 91-92, Div 1 Cup 77-78),
Daventry Charity Cup R-up 93-9; .League Goalscoroing trophy 2001-02,
Berks & Bucks Intermediate Cup 2001-02

PREVIOUS Leagues: North Bucks 63-71; South Midlands 71-73

BEST FA Vase: 2nd Round 84-85

FACT FILE
Founded: 1963   Nickname: Swans
Sponsors: Brian Currie
Colours: White & green/green/green
Change colours: Red/green/green
Midweek Matchday: Tuesday
Reserves League: United Counties
Programme: 56 pages
Editor: Ernie Print (01908 612918)

CLUB PERSONNEL
Chairman: Gerry Ward
Vice Chairman: Ernie Print
President: Ken Inch
Manager:Danni Janes
Assistant Manager: Jason Rice

NORTHAMPTON SPENCER

Secretary: Nick Hillery, Cowntess Road, Northampton 01604 756580 (H) 07754 665724(M)

Ground: Kingsthorpe Mill, Studland Rd., Northampton NN3 1NF Tel: 01604 718898

Capacity: 2000   Seats: 100   Cover: 350   Floodlights: Yes

Directions: Turn off Kingsthorpe Road at traffic lights into Thornton Rd., 1st right into
Studland Rd. and ground is at the end.

Clubhouse: Open during normal licensing hours. Lounge and bar.   **Club Shop:** No

HONOURS: UCL 91-92, r-up 92-93, 97-98, Div. 1 84-85, KO Cup 88-89 93-94, r-up 87-88
96-97 97-98, Benevolent Cup 91-92; Northants Sen. Cup r-up 90-91 93-94.

PREVIOUS League: Northampton Town Lge 36-68
Name: Spencer School Old Boys
Grounds: Dallington Park 36-70, Duston High School 70-72

BEST SEASON FA Cup: 1st Qual. Rd 93-94, 96-97
FA Vase: 4th Round 87-88, 1-2 v Gresley Rovers

RECORDS Attendance: 800 v Nottm. Forest, dressing room opener 1993
Most Appearances: P.Jelley 6221984-2002

Players progressing: Paul Stratford (Northampton), Wakeley Gage (Northampton)

FACT FILE
Founded: 1936
Nickname: Millers
Sponsors:
Crisis Worldwide, International Couriers
Colours: Yellow/green/yellow
Change colours: All red
Midweek matchday: Tuesday
Reserves' League: UCL Res Div 1
Programme: 20 pages 50p
Editor: Andy Goldsmith (01604 412382)
Website: www.geocities.com/kirby42000

CLUB PERSONNEL
President: J Sampson
Joint Chairmen:
Graham Wrighting & Jim Connelly
Press Off.: Andy Goldsmith (01604 412382)
Manager: Bob Tansley
Assistant. Man.: Keith Bowen

RAUNDS TOWN

Secretary Mick Walden,5 Fernie Way,Wellingborough,Northants NN8 3LB (01933 279561)
Ground: Kiln Park, London Road, Raunds, Northants NN9 6EQ
Tel: 01933 623351, Matchdays 01933 460941
Directions: Take Raunds turning at roundabout on A45 and ground is first left
Nearest station; Wellingborough. Bus services local
Capacity: 3,000   Seats: 250   Cover: 600   Floodlights: Yes
Clubhouse: On ground, open every day
Club Shop: Open matchdays, selling shirts, books programmes, contact Malc York, c/o club
PREVIOUS Leagues: Rushden & Dist., Cen. Northants Comb., U.C.L., Southern Lge 96-00
Grounds: Greenhouse Field (until 1948), The Berristers (1948-91)
BEST SEASON FA Cup: 4th Qual Rd, 98-99 (0-2 v Enfield)
FA Vase: Semi-final v Arlesey Tn 94-5
FA Trophy: 3rd Rd v Weston-super-Mare 98-99 (2-2, 0-1)
HONOURS UCL Prem Champions 95-96, UCL Div 1 82-83 (R-up 91-92), KO Cup 90-91, 01-
02(R-up 83-84 93-94), Res Div 1 88-89 95-96 (R-up 86-87 87-88 89-90 90-91 91-92), Reserve KO
Cup 84-85 88-89 93-94; Northants Snr Cup 90-91; Hunts Premier Cup R-up 92-93; Daventry
Charity Cup R-up 83-84; Northants Jnr Cup 82-83 91-92 (res) 92-93 (res)
CLUB RECORDS Attendance: 1,500 v Crystal Palace, ground opening 23/7/91
Win: 9-0 v Potton 95, 11-2 v Brackley 93   **Defeat:** 0-6 v Baldock 83, vBuckingham 84-85
Career Goalscorer: Shaun Keeble 208   **Career Appearances:** Martin Lewis 355 (+29subs)

FACT FILE
Formed: 1946
Nickname: Shopmates
Colours: Red & black
Change Colours: Yellow
Midweek matchday: Tuesday
Reserves' League: UCL Reserve Div. One
Prog: Pages: Varies Price: 50p
Editor: Malc York 01933 311586
2001-02
Top Scorer: Graham Knight 24
P. of Y.: Scott Goodacre
Captain: StuartSmeathers

CLUB PERSONNEL
Chairman: George Hagan
President: Mahen Perera
Manager:Adam Sandy
Asst Manager: Dino Cirelli

Top:
Buckingham Town, losers 2-4 to Maldon in their FA Cup Preliminary Round replay. Back Row (l-r): Karl Yeomanson, Michael Cox, Jason Hagglewood, Darren Dykes, Matthew Primms, Abdul Abdi. Front Row: Dean Chapman, Aaron Brennan, Scott Ladley, Jon Mills, Graham Forbes
Photo: Arthur Evans

Centre:
Holbeach United Back Row (l-r): Matthew Warfield, Darren Eady, Ian Dunn, Martin Bunce, Nick Keeble, Matthew Heaton, Danny Hussey, Leigh Taylor. Front Row: Steve Barnes, Gavin Slator, Alan Ross, Shaun Keeble, Ben Beresford (mascot), Phil Barnes
Photo: Gordon Whittington

Bottom:
St Neots Town Back Row (l-r): Chris Howell (Manager), Ricky Dear, Scott Grant, Simon Claridge, Steve Young, Steve Kuhne, Vince Petty, Justin Hicks, Gerald Sylvester (Coach), Craig Lambert (Physio). Front Row: Michael McDonnell, Jason Meeds, Paul Bloss, Warren Brown, Trevor Smith, Nathan Buckland (Capt), Brett Fairholme, Andy Grieves, Andy Chapman.

ST. NEOTS TOWN

General Se: John Carroll **Co Sec:** Graham Moffitt **Fixture Sec:** Marion. Izzard (All c/o club)

Ground:	Rowley Park, Cambridge Rd, St Neots, Cambs Tel: 01480 470012
	Capacity: 3,000 Seats: 250 Cover: 850 Floodlights: Yes

Directions: Through the town centre, under the railway bridge, ground is first on the left

Capacity: 2,500 **Seating:** 160 **Covered Standing:** 300 **Floodlights :** Yes

Clubhouse: Yes with Conference,Banqueting and private functions all bookable

HONOURS Hunts Snr Cup(34), UCL 67-68 (KO Cup 67-68 68-69), Metropolitan Lg 49-50(Lg Cup 79-80), South Midlands Lg 32-33, Huntingdonshire Lg 90-91 92-92 92-93 94-95 Hunts.Prem Cup: 2001-02

PREVIOUS **Leagues:** South Midlands 27-36 46-49; United Counties 36-39 51-56 66-69 73-88; Metropolitan 49-51 60-66; Central Alliance 56-60; Eastern Counties 69-73; Huntingdonshire 90-94 **Name:** St Neots & District 1879-1957 **Ground:** Shortlands

BEST SEASON **FA Cup:** 1st Rd 66-67, 0-2 v Walsall (A)
FA Vase: 5th Rd 2001-02 **FA Trophy:** 2nd Qual. Rd 69-70 72-73

RECORD **Attendance:** 2,000 v Wisbech, 1966
Players progressing: Frank Atkins (Cambridge United), John Gregory (Aston Villa) and Matthew Oakey (Southampton)

FACT FILE
Founded: 1879 Nickname: Saints
Sponsors:Adam Kennedy, Midland Thermal, and Fleet Car Contracts
Club colours: Sky /navy/sky
Change colours:Yellow/Black/Yellow
Reserves' Lge: UCL Res Div 1
Programme: Yes Editor: Mike Birch
(Tel: 01480 395505)
'Saintly Text';Revolving Information screen.
Editor: Keith Moss
Web site: www.stneotsfc.com
CLUB PERSONNEL
Chairman: Bob Page Directors:John Carroll
Kenneth Harris and Neil Holmes
Commercial Man: Peter Hicks(01733 263656)
Team Manager: Chris Howell
Coaches: Gerald Sylvester,Barry Cavilla and
Mike Brooks Physio; Craig lambertr

STEWARTS & LLOYDS

Secretary:	Dave Foster, 29 Tettenhall Close, Corby, Northants NN198 9PJ
	Tel: 01536 746004(H) 01536 201234 Ext. 5292(W) 07818 264220(M)
	email: carol@carol77.fsnet.co.uk
Ground:	Recreation Ground, Occupation Road, Corby Tel: 01536 401497
	Capacity: 1,500 Seats: 100 Cover: 200 Floodlights: Yes
Directions:	The ground is situated on Occupation Rd at the rear of Stewart & Lloyds Leisure Club, next to old Corby Town F.C. ground

Clubhouse: Licensed bar **Club Shop:** No

HONOURS UCL R-up 85-86, Div 1(2) 73-75; UCL KO Cup, Prem 95-96, Div 1 Cup(2)73-75, Div 2 KO Cup(2) 75-77)

PREVIOUS **Leagues:** Kettering Amateur

BEST SEASON **FA Cup:** **FA Vase:**

RECORD **Goalscorer:** Joey Martin 46 (92-93)

Players progressing : Andy McGowan (Northampton), Willie Graham (Brentford)

FACT FILE
Formed: 1935
Nickname: None
Sponsor: Weldon
Colours: yellow & blue/blue/yellow
Change Colours:Sky blue/Navy blue/blue
Midweek matchday: Tuesday
Programme: 12 pages with admission
Editor/Press Officer: Dave Foster
CLUB PERSONNEL
Chairman: Peter Webb
Vice Chairmen: Gordon Hall, Harry Nelson
Manager: Elwyn Roberts
Asst Manager:Karl Binley
Physio: Roger White

STOTFOLD

Secretary: Bill Clegg, 12 Common Rd, Stotfold, Hitchin, Herts SG5 4BX Tel: 01462 730421
Club Email: football@stotfoldfc.freeserve.co.uk Website:www.stotfoldfc.freeserve.co.uk

Ground:	Roker Park, The Green, Stotfold, Hitchin, Herts Tel: 01462 730765
	Capacity: 5,000 Seats: 300 Cover: 300 Floodlights: Yes
Directions:	A507 from A1, right at lights, right at T-jct.
	A507 from Bedford via Shefford, left at lights, right at T-jct

Clubhouse: Clubroom, bar, refreshment bar, dressing rooms, physio room

HONOURS Utd Co's Lg R-up 93-94, KO Cup Winners 98-99 R-up 91-92, Res Div 1 87-88; Sth Mids Lg 80-81 (R-up 55-56 57-58 58-59 59-60 63-64 65-66 77-78), Div 1 53-54, Chal. Tphy 81-82; Beds Snr Cup 64-65 93-94; Beds Premier Cup 81-82; 98-99 Beds I'mediate Cup 58-59; Nth Beds Charity Cup 55-56 56-57 61-62 81-82 87-88 90-91 97-98;Beds Colts Lg 88-89; Southern Com Cup 94-95 95-96 96-97; Hinchingbrooke Cup R-up 97-98: Win. 99-00: R-up 00-01

PREVIOUS **Leagues:** Biggleswade & District/ North Herts/ South Midlands 51-84

BEST SEASON **FA Cup:** 00-01 **FA Vase:** 00-01

RECORD **Attendance:** 1,000 v Letchworth Town, FA Amtr Cup
Scorer: Roy Boon **Appearances:** Roy Boon/Dave Chellew

FACT FILE
Founded: 1904 Reformed: 1945
Nickname: Eagles Sponsors: Astron
Colours: Yellow/Blue/Yellow
Change Colours: All Sky blue
Midweek matchday: Tuesday
Reserves' League: UCL Reserve Division One
Programme: 22 pages with entry
Editor: Phil Pateman (01462 834581)
Local Press: Comet, Biggleswade Chronicle
CLUB PERSONNEL
Chairman: Phil Pateman
Vice Chairman: Graham Jarman
Pres: David Chellow Man: Ken Davidson
Asst Manager: Ken Baker
Press Officer: Bill Clegg
Physio: Dave Chivers
2001-02
Leading Goalscorer: P.Saunders
Captain: Ian Trott
P.o.Y.:Gareth Cottenden

WOODFORD UNITED

FACT FILE
Founded: 1946
Nickname: United
Sponsors: Huber + Suhner Uk Ltd
Colours: Red/black/white
Change Colours:White and sky blue
Reserves' League: Utd. Co. Res. Div 2
Programme: 16 pages
Editor: Andrew Worrall (01327 264716)

Secretary:	Pat Ashby, 2 Barrington Court, Ward Road, Brackley. NN13 7LE
	Tel Nos: 01327 262955 (H) 07930143504 (M) 01280 840900 (B)
Ground:	Byfield Road, Woodford Halse, Daventry, Northants. Tel: 01327 263734
	Capacity: 3,000 Seats: 120 Cover: 120 Floodlights: Yes
Directions	Off A 361 Daventry to Banbury Rd, on Woodford Road out of Byfield
Clubhouse:	Yes **Website:** www.wufc.net
PREVIOUS	Leagues: Central Northants Comb pre 70, UCL 70-78, Northants Comb
HONOURS	Northants Comb 66 67 90 92 95, KO Cup 66 90 93 95 98;
	United Counties Lge Div 2 74, KO Cup 74;

CLUB PERSONNEL
Chairman: Andrew Worrall
Vice-Chairman: R Adams
Manager: Phil Lines

WOOTON BLUE CROSS

FACT FILE
Founded: 1887
Nickname: Blue Cross
Sponsors: Vision Blinds
Colours: Blue & white/blue/blue
Change: All yellow
Reserves' League: United Counties Res. Div 1
Midweek matchday: Tuesday
Programme: 24 pages   Editor: Secretary
Local Press : Bedfordshire Times, Bedford
Herald, Beds Express, Beds on Sunday

Secretary:	Bryan Keens, 5 Stewart Court,Wootton,Des. MK43 9PH Tel : 012134 768214
Ground:	Weston Park, Bedford Road, Wootton Tel: 01234 767662
	Capacity: 2,000 Seats: 50 Cover: 250 Floodlights: Yes
Directions:	Four miles south of Bedford on main road through village at rear of Post Office
Clubhouse:	Main hall, bar, darts, pool, bingo. Open every evening and w/e lunchtimes
Club Shop: No	
HONOURS	Utd Co's Lg Div 2 67-68 69-70 (KO Cup 82-83, Div 2 Cup 64-65), South
	Midlands Lg 47-48 (R-up 49-50), Beds Sen. Cup 70-71, Hinchinbrooke Cup(5)
PREVIOUS	**Leagues:** Bedford & District; South Midlands 46-55
	Grounds: Recreation Ground, Fishers Field, Rose & Crown, Cockfield
BEST SEASON	**FA Vase:** 3rd Rd 74-75
	FA Cup: 2nd Qual. Rd 50-51 (3-4 v Hitchin (H))
RECORD	**Gate:** 838 v Luton, Beds Prem. Cup 1988

Players progressing: Tony Biggs (Arsenal)

CLUB PERSONNEL
President: J Clarke
Chairman: Trevor Templeman
Manager: Jon Taylor
Assistant Manager:Jim Burke
Coach: Ian Evason
Physio: Trevor Templeman
Press Officer: Secretary

YAXLEY

FACT FILE
Founded:
Sponsor: Reads Removals
Colours: All blue with white trim
Change colours: All tangerine or yellow
Programme: Yes
Editor:Malcolm Whaley

Secretary:	Alan Andrews, 3 Farringdon Close, Pterborough. PE1 4RQ
	Tel Nos: 01733 342897(H) 07939 841469(M) email: alan@yaxleyfc.com
Ground:	Leading Drove, off The Holme Road, Yaxley Tel: 01733 244928
	Capacity: 1,000+ Seats: 150 Cover: Yes Floodlights: Yes
Directions:	A1, then A15 at Norman Cross up to traffic lights. Turn right then immediately right
	again. Follow the road for approx. 1 mile, then turn right into Holme Rd..
	The ground is approx. 200 yards on left
HONOURS	UCL Div 1 96-97, Benevolent Cup 97-98; Hunts Senior Cup (5 times Inc 98-99)
	Peterborough League (2); Peterborough Senior Cup (2);
	West Anglia League;Scott-Gatty Cup
PREVIOUS	**Leagues:** Peterborough & District, Huntingdonshire, West Anglia

CLUB PERSONNEL
President: John Dowse
Chairman: Malcolm Whaley
Vice Chairman: Geoff Heathcote
Manager: Paul Humphries
Asst Manager: Jimmy Watson

BLISWORTH

Secretary:	Peter Edwards, 31 Windmill Ave, Blisworth, Northants NN7 3EQ
	Tel: 01604 858171 (H), 0585 369933 (B) 07885 369933 (M)
Ground:	Blisworth Playing Field, Courteenhall Road, Blisworth Tel: 01604 858024
	Capacity: 1,000 Seats: None Cover: None Floodlights: No
Directions:	Courteenhall Road off A43
Clubhouse:	Yes
HONOURS	Northants Junior Cup 88-99
PREVIOUS	**League:** Central Northants Combination 1978-87
	Player progressing: Dave Johnson (Northampton 83-84)

FACT FILE
Founded: 1890
Sponsors: Target Furniture, JB King Plant Hire
Colours: All red
Change colours: Yellow/black/yellow
Reserves' Lge: UCL Res. Div. 2
Programme: Yes   Editor: Liz Edwards
Tel: 01604 858171
CLUB PERSONNEL
Chairman: Pete Edwards President: L Piggott
Manager: Bob Earl
Asst Man:Gary Edwards, Coach:RichardlLarge
Physio: Elaine Johnson

BUGBROOKE ST MICHAELS

Secretary:	Roger Geary, 31 Kislingbury Rd, Bugbrooke, Northampton NN7 3QG
	Tel: 01604 831678
Ground:	Birds Close, Gayton Road, Bugbrooke Tel: 01604 830707
	Capacity: 2,500 Seats: 120 Cover: Yes Floodlights: Yes
Directions:	M1. Jct 16 Take a A45 to Northampton. At 1st roundabout follow signs to

Bugrooke. In villagefollow road straight through to club immediately past last house on left.

Clubhouse: Yes - normal licensing hours

HONOURS	Northants Junior Cup 89-90, Central Northants Comb. 68-69 69-70 70-71 71-72
	76-77 85-86, UCL Res Div 2 R-up 94-95 U.C.L. Div One Champions 98-99
PREVIOUS	**League** : Central Northants Combination 1952-87 **Ground:** School Close
RECORD	**Attendance:** 1,156 **Scorer:** Vince Thomas **Appearances:** Jimmy Nord

Players progressing: Kevin Slinn (Watford), Craig Adams (Northampton)

FACT FILE
Founded: 1929
Nickname: Badgers
Sponsors: Unusual Industries
Club colours: Black & white/black/black
Change colours: All Red
Reserves' Lge: UCL Res. Div. 1
Programme: Eight pages
Editor: Paul hancock
CLUB PERSONNEL
Chairman: Tom Treacy
President: John Curtis
Manager: Ade Hill
Assistant Manager:Mark Champlovier
Press Officer: Paul hancock

BURTON PARK WANDERERS

Secretary:	Roger Patrick,16 Church Stret, Burton Latimer, Northants.NN15 5LU
	Tel: 01536 724103 (H), 01536 725841 (W)
Ground:	Latimer Park, Polwell Lane, Burton Latimer Tel: 01536 725841
	Capacity: 1,000 Seats: 100 Cover: 150 Floodlights: No
Directions:	Entering Burton Latimer, turn off A6 Station Rd and right into Powell Lane;
	ground on the right
HONOURS	UCL Div 1 R-up, Benevolent Cup R-up
PREVIOUS	**League:** Kettering Amateur
RECORD	**Attendance:** 253 v Rothwell, May 1989

Players progressing : Shaun Wills (Peterborough), Laurie Dudfield (Leicester City)

FACT FILE
Founded: 1961   Nickname: The Wanderers
Sponsor: Prescott Motors
Colours: All Navy Blue
Change Colours: All red
Midweek matchday: Tuesday
Prog: 16 pages with entry   Ed: Michael Capps
Local Press : Northants Evening Telegraph,
Northants Post
CLUB PERSONNEL
Chairman: Roger Patrick
Vice Chairman: Stuart Coles
Manager: Roger Patrick
Assistant Manager: Hughie Duchan
Physio: Stuart Coles

COTTINGHAM

Secretary:	Lindsay Brownlie, 30 Bancroft Rd, Cottingham, Market Harborough LE168XA
	Tel: 01536 771009 (H) email: Lindsay Brownlie@Rigid.co.uk
Ground:	Berryfield Rd, Cottingham Tel: 01536 770051
	Capacity: 1,000 Seats: None Cover: Yes Floodlights: No
Directions:	One and a half miles from Corby on A427 turn right to Cottingham.At junction of

B670 turn left; Berryfield Road 200 yds on right

Clubhouse:	Bar & changing rooms
HONOURS	UCL Div 1 R-up 97-98; Northants Junior Cup
PREVIOUS	**Leagues:** Market Harborough; Kettering Amateur; East Midlands Alliance

FACT FILE
Founded:
Sponsors: B & J Decorators
Colours: Yellow/green/yellow
Change colours: Sky blue/navy/navy blue.
Reserves' Lge: UCL Res. Div. 2
Programme: No
CLUB PERSONNEL
Chairman: Mike Beadsworth
Vice Chairman: Brian Tilley
Manager: Graham Leech

EYNESBURY ROVERS

Secretary: Deryck Irons, 12 Hadleigh Close, Bedford MK41 8JW. Tel: 01234 268111
Email Address: patrick.erfc@btinternet.com
Ground: Hall Road, Eynesbury, St Neots Tel: 01480 477449
Capacity: 3,000 Seats: 200 Cover: 500 Floodlights: Yes
Directions: Two miles from A1, on South side of St Neots urban area, near Ernulf School
Clubhouse: Large bar, committee room.Available for private hire **Club Shop:** No

HONOURS UCL Div 1 76-77; Hunts Snr Cup 13-14 46-47 48-51 54-55 56-57 69-70 84-85
90-93 95-96,99-00,01-02; Hunts Premier Cup 50-51 90-91 95-96; Hinchingbrooke Cup (7) 46-
4748-52 57-58 66-67; Cambs Invitation Cup 61-62; E Anglian Cup R-up 90-91 91-92;Hunts Scott
Gatty Cup 35-36 56-57 84-85 89-90 (R-up 93-94 res); Hunts Jnr Cup 21-22 26-27
PREVIOUS **Leagues:** Sth Mids 34-39; UCL 46-52; Eastern Co's 52-63
BEST SEASON **FA Vase:** 3rd Rd 94-95 **FA Cup:** 4th Qual. Rd 54-55, 1-3 v Camb. Utd (A)
RECORD **Gate:** 5,000 v Fulham 1953 (Stanley Matthews guested for Eynesbury)
Players progressing: Chris Turner (Peterborough), Denis Emery (Peterborough)

FACT FILE
Founded: 1897 Nickname: Rovers
Sponsors: Classic Windows
Colours: Royal & white/royal/royal
Change Colours: Yellow/black/yellow
Midweek matchday: Tuesday
Reserves' League: Utd Counties Res. Div. 2
Prog: 32 pages, 50p Ed: Graham Mills
Website: www.eynesburyrovers.org.uk
CLUB PERSONNEL
Chairman: Brian Abraham
Vice Chairman:John Newland
Manager:Steve Galbraith
Ass.Man: Ken Churchill

HARROWBY UNITED

Secretary: Michael atter,6 Barrowby Road, Debdale, Lincs. NG32 1BD
Tel No: 01476 567426 (H) 07718 263386 (M)
Ground: Harrowby Playing Fields, Harrowby Lane, Grantham Tel: 01476 590822
Capacity: 1,500 Seats: 100 Cover: 150 Floodlights: Yes
Directions: From A1 take B6403, go past A52 roundabout, past Ancaster turn and take road
to Harrowby. Continue into Grantham, ground on right opposite Cherry Tree PH.
Clubhouse: Large bar open normal licensing hours

HONOURS Utd Co's Lg Div 1 91-92 (Benev. Cup R-up 91-92), Mids Regional All. 89-90 (Lg
Cup 89-90), Lincs Snr `B' Cup(2) 90-92
PREVIOUS **Leagues:** Grantham; Lincs; East Mids Regional Alliance (pre-1990)
BEST SEASON **FA Vase:** Preliminary Round 91-92
Players progressing: Richard Liburd (Middlesbrough), Kevin Pilkington (Mansfield Town)

FACT FILE
Founded: 1949
Nickname: Arrows
Sponsor: Crystal Grantham
Colours: Red & black hoops/black/red & black
Change : Yellow, blue and red.
Programme: 16 pages Ed: Paul Wilson
CLUB PERSONNEL
Chairman: Paul Wilson
Vice Chairman: Robert Wilson
Match Secretary: Mick Atter
Manager: Graham Drury
Asst Mgr: Steve Joseph Coach: Tony Cook
Physio: Nigel Burton
Groundsman: Malcolm Brothwell

HIGHAM TOWN

Secretary: Chris Ruff, 23 Queensway, Higham Ferrers, Northants. NN10 8BU Tel: 01933 358862
Ground: Recreation Ground, Vine Hill Drive, Higham Ferrers Tel: 01933 353751
Capacity: 1,000 Seats: Nil Cover: 100 Floodlights: No
Directions: From Kettering 1st right on A6 after junction to St Neots. From Bedford, 3rd left after
entering town on A6 from Rushden. Higham is served by London-Bedford-Corby United Counties
Coachlines, and their local services Northampton-Raunds and Bedford-Kettering
Clubhouse: During season 8.30-11pm Tues, Thurs, Fri, Sat after games & 12-1.30pm Sun.Light
refreshments available after Saturday games
HONOURSUCL Div 1 97-98, R-up 70-71 71-72 89-90 92-93 93-94 94-95 95-96 98-99;Northants
Lg 21-22 22-23(R-up 23-24 26-27); Northants Snr Cup 21-22 (R-up 30-31 32-33);
Maunsell Premier Cup 22-23 33-34 **PREVIOUS Leagues:** Wellingborough 20-21; Northants (now
UCL) 21-36; Rushden 46-50 **Ground:** Duchy Farm Field 20-24 **RECORD Attendance:** 5,700 v
Chesterfield, FACup final qualifying round replay 22-23 **Scorer:** Jon Ogden 157 (Lge)
Appearances : Brian Harbour 485 **Best Win:** 15-0 v Towcester T (H), UCL Div. 92/93

FACT FILE
Founded: 1895 Reformed: 1920 & 1946
Nickname: Lankies
Sponsors: Higham News
Colours: Sky & navy/navy/sky
Change colours:Green/black/black
Midweek matchday:: Tuesday
Reserves' Lge: UCL Reserve Div
Programme: 12 pages with admission
Editor: Secretary
CLUB PERSONNEL
President: Vijay Patel
Chairman: Richard Williams
Vice Chairman: Brian Kirk
Manager:Lee Howard
Physio: Keith Bates

IRCHESTER UNITED

Secretary: Glyn Cotter, 26 Denford Way, Wellingborough, Northants NN8 5UB
Tel: 01933 402514 (H) 07802 728736 (M)

Ground: Alfred Street, Irchester Tel: 01933 312877
Capacity: 1,000 Seats: None Cover:Yes Floodlights: No

Directions: Off Rushden Road to Wollaston Road, next to recreation ground

Clubhouse: Yes
HONOURS Northants LgDiv 2 30-31 31-32,Northants Jnr.Cup 29-30,33-34,48-49 75-6,
Rushden & Dis.t Lg 28-29 29-30,32-33,33-34 36-3746-47 50-51 51-52 56-57
BEST SEASON **FA Cup:** Prel. Rd 34-35
FA Vase: Preliminary Round 77-78
PREVIOUS **Leagues:** Rushden & District 1936-69

FACT FILE
Colours: Red & Blackstripes,black,black
Change colours:Black&White stripes,black,red
Reserves' Lge: UCL Res. Div. 2
Programme: No
CLUB PERSONNEL
Chairman: Geoff Cotter
Co Managers: Bob Reed/John Dower
Physio: Mick Howarth

NORTHAMPTON O.N. CHENECKS

Secretary: Dave Burrows, 14 Kingswell Road, Kingsthorpe, Northampton.
Tel Nos: 01604 713795 (H) 07802 979118 (M)

Ground: Old Northamptonians Sports Ground, Billing Road, Northampton Tel: 01604 34045

Capacity: 1,350   Seats: Yes   Cover: Yes   Floodlights: No

Directions: South ring road, exit A43 Kettering. Turn left at the lights, to the top of hill and the ground is 200 yds on right

Clubhouse: Yes

HONOURS UCL Div 1 77-78 79-80, Northants Jnr Cup R-up 93-94

PREVIOUS Leagues: N'pton Town (pre-1969)

FACT FILE
Founded: 1946
Colours: Red& Black stripes/black/black
Change colours: All red
Reserves' League: UCL Res Div 1
Midweek Matchday:
Prog.: 16 pages with entry
Editor: Eddie Slinn

CLUB PERSONNEL
Chairman: John Wilson
Vice Chairman: Eddie Slinn
President: Claude Hasdell
Manager: Peter Green
Asst Manager: Claude Hasdell
Physio: John Goodger

NORTHAMPTON SILEBY RANGERS
(formerly Northampton Vanaid)

Secretary: Tony Loveday, 28 Blueberry Rise, Ecton Brook, North'ton NN3 2AX (01604 406606)

Email Address: tony.loveday@talk21.com

Ground: Fernie Fields Sports Ground, Moulton, Northampton Tel: 01604 670366

Capacity: 700   Seats: 100   Cover: Yes   Floodlights: No

Directions: R'bout at Lumbertub pub take turn to Moulton, 1st right signposted

Clubhouse: Large bar with food

HONOURS UCL Div 1 93-94, Benevolent Cup R-up 93-94;
Northants Jnr Cup 93-94 96-97 97-98; Northampton Town Lg 88-89 89-90

PREVIOUS League: Northampton Town (pre-1993) **Name:** Northampton Vanaid >00
RECORD Attendance: 78

FACT FILE
Founded: 1968 Nickname: Sileby
Sponsors: Mr Removals
Colours: Red/Black/Black
Change colours: Black & white/stripes black/red
Reserves' League: UCL Res Div 1
Programme Editors: Tony & June Loveday
CLUB PERSONNEL
Chairman: Rob Clarke Vice Chairman: G,Law
President: N.Gibbs
Manager: Nick Verity Asst Man: T.Bonner
Physio: M.Arnold
Captain: Mark Pepperell

OLNEY TOWN

Secretary: Andrew Baldwin, 49 Midland Road, Olney, Bucks MK46 4BP
Tel: 01234 711071 (H) 07932 141623 (M) email: a.baldwin@cranfield.ac.uk
Club Website: www.olneytownfc.com

Ground: East Street, Olney , Bucks. Tel: 01234 712227
Capacity: 2,000   Seats: None   Cover: Yes   Floodlights: No

Clubhouse: Yes

Directions: Enter Olney on A509 from Wellingborough, 100yds on left enter East St, the ground is 200 yds on left

HONOURS UCL Div 1 72-73, Berks & Bucks I'mediate Cup 92-93

PREVIOUS Leagues: Nth Bucks, Rushden & District

FACT FILE
Founded: 1903
Sponsors: Cyclo Sports
Colours: Green&black/black/green
Change colours: Black&white/white/white
Programme: 8 pages - Editor: Michael Smith

CLUB PERSONNEL
Chairman: Malcom Thomas
President: Trevor Church
Manager: Russell Ward
Asst Manager: Pete Munting
Coach: Neil Bunker - Physio: Peter Munting

POTTON UNITED

Secretary: Derek Inskip, 16 Sheffield Close, Potton, Beds SG19 2NY Tel: 01767 260355
Ground: The Hollow, Biggleswade Road, Potton Tel: 01767 261100
Capacity: 2,000   Seats: 200   Cover: 250   Floodlights: Yes
Directions: Outskirts of Potton on Biggleswade Road (B1040). 3 1/2 miles from Sandy (BR).
United Counties buses from Biggleswade   **Clubhouse:** Yes
HONOURS Utd Co's Lg 86-87 88-89, KO Cup 72-73, Benevolent Cup 88-89; Beds Snr Cup(5)
47-49 63-64 75-76 77-78 (R-up 94-95 96-97); Wallspan Floodlit Cup 87-88; Hinchingbrooke Cup
51-52 84-85 89-90 91-92; Hunts Premier Cup 89-90 91-92 94-95(jt) 96-97; Beds I'mediate
Cup 43-44; Southern Comb. Cup 92-93; Nth Beds Charity Cup (12); East Anglian Cup 96-97; Jess
Pigott Trophy 96-97
PREVIOUS Leagues : Sth Mids 46-55; Central Alliance 56-61
BEST SEASON FA Cup: 3rd Qual. Round 74-75, 1-2 v Bedford Town
FA Trophy: 3rd Qual. Round 71-72 72-73   **FA Vase:** 5th Round 89-90, 1-2 v Billericay Town
RECORD Attendance: 470 v Hastings Town, FA Vase 1989

FACT FILE
Founded: 1943
Nickname: Royals
Colours: White/black/black
Change Colours: Blue
Midweek matchday: Tuesday
Reserves' Lge: UCL Res. Div. Two
Programme: 28 pages, 50p
Editor: Bev Strong
CLUB PERSONNEL
President: Peter Hutchinson
Chairman: Nigel Westhorp
Press Officer: Secretary
Manager: Richard Newman
Assistant Manager: Roy Johnson

Eynesbury Rovers celebrate winning the Hunts Senior Cup after defeating their higher grade opponents and local rivals St Neots Town 3-0 (aet) on May 6th 2002 at Warboys Town FC. Back Row (l-r): Steve Galbraith (manager), Tom Hobbs, Paul Childerley, Gareth Peck, David Fisk, Danny Workman, Dave Samal, Paul George, Waine Dickerson, Ken Churchill (Asst manager). Front Row: Daniel Bagnoli, Ross West, Barry Albone, Gavin Clark, Graham McMillan, Paul Carey (ex-Saint and hat-trick hero), Robert Dobson. Photo: Nik Cooke

Olney Town. Back Row (l-r): Peter Munting (Physio), Danny Munday, James Roffey, Russell Ward (manager), Damian Bird, Jason Cole, Danny Atkins, Stuart Keeping, Lee Bannister, James Gear, Neil Bunker (coach).
Front Row: Lee Cornish, Paul Adams, Mark Lancaster, Steve Foster, Chris Winton, Guy Stewart (capt), Tommy Collins. Photo: Gordon Whittington

United Counties League (Premier) Wootton Blue Cross had a superb start to the season and won the first 'Team of the Month' award, being presented here to manager Jon Taylor by League Vice-Chairman John Weeks. Photo: Gordon Whittington

ROTHWELL CORINTHIANS

Secretary: Mark Budworth, 5 Jackson way, Kettering, Northants. NN15 7DL
01536 521973 (H) 07730 416960(M) email: Mark Budworth@compuserve.com

Ground: Seargeant's Lawn, Desborough Road, Rothwell, Northants.
Tel: 01536 418688
Capacity: Unknown   Seats: 50   Cover: 200   Floodlights: Yes

Directions A6 towards Desborough, on right opposite Greening Road
Club House: Yes   **Club Shop:** No

HONOURS East Midlands Alliance (2)
PREVIOUS **League** East Midlands Alliance

FACT FILE
Founded: 1930's
Nickname: Corinthians
Sponsor: Springfir Estates
Colours: Red& white / black/black
Change colours: Blue 7 white/blue/blue
Programme: Yes Editor: Nick Garley
CLUB PERSONNEL
Chairman: Graham Dawson
Vice Chairmperson: May Clelland
President: Terry Smith
Manager: Colin Sinclair
Physio:John Dickson

ST. IVES TOWN

Secretary: Chris George, 16 Canberra Drive,St Ives. Terl Nos: 01480 382257 (H)
07775 854017 (M) E-mail: stivestownfc@hotmail.com
Ground: Westwood Road, St. Ives, Cambs.Tel: 01480 463207
Directions: From Huntingdon: A1123 thru Houghton, right at 2nd lighs intoRamsey Rd,
after quarter mile turn right opp. Fire Station into Westwood Road
From A604: Follow Huntingdon signs past 5 r'bouts, left into Ramsey Rd at
lights then follow as above.
Capacity: 5,000   Seats: 130 Cover: 300   Floodlights: Yes
Clubhouse: Bar and entertainment room. Normal licensing hours.
HONOURS Hunts Snr Cup 00-01 11-12 22-23 25-26 29-30 81-82 86-87 87-88,
Cambs League 22-23 23-24 24-25.
PREVIOUS **Leagues:** Cambs; Central Amtr; Hunts; P'boro. & D. (pre-1985).
Ground: Meadow Lane
RECORD **Gate:** 400 v Saffron Walden Town, FA Vase.

FACT FILE
Founded: 1887
Nickname: Saints
Colours: White & black/black/red
Change colours: Blue/black/black
Midweek matchday: Tuesday
Reserves' Lge: UCL Res Div 2
Programme editor: Alastair Robinson
Tel: 01480 460409 (H)
CLUB PERSONNEL
Chairman: Nevile Nania
Managers: Warren Everdale & Neil Morgan
Match Sec.:Peter Claridge,Tel Nos: 01480
466873 (H) 07889 161741 (M)

THRAPSTON TOWN

Secretary: Mark Brown, 3 Drayton Place, Irthlingborough, Northants. NN9 5TD
01933 388671 (H) 07885 640947 (M) email: mark @datsprint.co.uk

Ground: Chancery Lane, Thrapston, Northants Tel: 01832 732470
Capacity: 1,000   Seats: Yes   Cover: Yes   Floodlights: No

Directions: Chancery Lane off A605 in town centre
Clubhouse: Yes
HONOURS Northants Junior Cup 87-88, 98-99 Kettering Am Lg 70-71 72-73 73-74 77-78
UCL Div1 Runners -Up 99-00
PREVIOUS **League:** Kettering Amateur (pre-1978)

FACT FILE
Founded: 1960
Nickname: Venturas
Sponsor: IKEA
Colours: All Blue
Change colours: All Yellow
Programme: Yes   Editor: Barry Carter
CLUB PERSONNEL
President: Derek Barber
Chairman: Dave Harris
Vice Chairman: Barry Carter
Manager: Gary Petts
Asst Manager: Barry Carter
Physio: Zoe

WELLINGBOROUGH WHITWORTHS

Secretary: John Betts, 2 St Nary's Road, Bozeat, Wellingborough, Northants. NN29 7JU
Tel: 01933 664253 (H) 07967 221155 (M) email: johnsmbetts@aol.com
Ground: London Road, Wellingborough, Northants. Tel: 01933 227324
Capacity: 700   Seats: None Cover: Yes   Floodlights: No
Directions: Off London Road at Dog & Duck public house
Clubhouse: Yes
PREVIOUS **Leagues:** Rushden & Dist.; E. Mids All. (pre-1985)
HONOURS Rushden & District Lg 76-77; Northants Jun Cup 96

FACT FILE
Sponsor: Whitworth Brothers
Colours: All navy blue
Change colours: All purple
Reserves' Lge: UCL Res Div 2
Programme: No

CLUB PERSONNEL
Chairman: Bob Jarvis
Vice Chairman: Dave Woodley
President: Terry Faulkner
Manager: Mark Herring
Assistant Manager: Joe Smyth
Physio: Andrew King

Harrowby United. Photo: Gordon Whittington

Rothwell Corinthians. Photo: Gordon Whittington

Whitworths. Back Row (l-r): T Hewett, D Spaughton, R Hopkinson, J Daldy, S Grant, R Rice, S Goosey, M Cowper.
Front Row: S Atkinson, J Smyth, W Day, G Roberts, M Herring. Photo: Gordon Whittington

Lewes' Lee Newman (right) about to be challenged by Easbourne Borough's Darren Baker in the Sussex Senior Cup.
Photo: Roger Turner

Little Munden Sports FC, winners of the Hertfordshire Junior Cup for the first time after beating Hertford heath 3-0 in the Final.
Photo: Gordon Whittington

ISLE OF WIGHT F.A.

Chairman: K R Morris
Secretary: Andrew Justice, 12 The Mall, Binstead, Ryde, Isle of Wight PO33 3SF
Tel: 01983 565244

DIVISION ONE

	P	W	D	L	F	A	Pts
West Wight	22	15	4	3	53	17	45
Shanklin	22	15	2	5	79	26	47
East Cowes Vics	22	14	1	7	73	32	43
Binstead	22	13	3	6	56	35	42
W & B Sports	22	11	4	7	37	35	37
Red Star Spartans	22	11	3	8	60	43	36
Cowes Sports	22	10	2	10	51	36	32
Oakfield	22	9	4	9	46	37	31
Newport	22	9	3	10	46	39	**28
Brading Town	22	6	4	12	42	56	22
Brighstone	22	3	0	19	20	85	**7
Seaview	22	1	0	21	11	134	3

DIVISION TWO

	P	W	D	L	F	A	Pts
St. Helens BS	22	17	2	3	69	29	53
Carisbrooke	22	16	0	6	67	47	48
Ryde (WD) Utd	22	14	4	4	68	35	46
Niton	22	14	2	6	75	50	44
Sandown	22	12	1	9	65	43	37
GKN Westlands	22	8	3	11	41	46	37
Wakes	22	7	5	10	40	43	26
Northwood GB	22	6	6	10	46	58	24
Bembridge	22	7	3	12	59	70	24
Plessey	22	6	3	13	44	62	21
Medina	22	4	4	14	32	84	16
Yarmouth/Calbourne	22	2	5	15	33	72	11

DIVISION THREE

	P	W	D	L	F	A	Pts
Osborne Court	22	18	4	0	74	25	58
Brading Youth	22	13	5	4	57	30	44

COMBINATION ONE

	P	W	D	L	F	A	Pts
Oakfield	22	18	3	1	87	19	57
Shanklin	22	15	4	3	77	19	49

COMBINATION TWO

	P	W	D	L	F	A	Pts
Red Star Spartans	20	18	0	2	102	21	54
Wroxall	20	15	2	3	76	35	47

**2 Points deducted

ISLE OF WIGHT SENIOR (GOLD CUP) FINAL

Played 18th May, 2002 at Cowes Sports FC

NN deducted

Newport (IOW)   1 v 2   Cowes Sports
(A Barsdell)   (D Mew)
Attendance 270

---

25 in 25

A review of the progress made by the **Wessex League** and its member clubs during the twenty-five year life span of the F.A. Non-League Club Directory (1978 - 2002) will be available in the next year. It will be one of a series of 25 and will contain features, statistics and photos in at least 160 pages dedicated purely to the Wessex League members.

Further details can be found on page 17 so make sure of your copy of this exciting limited edition.

JEWSON WESSEX LEAGUE

FEEDER TO: Dr MARTENS FOOTBALL LEAGUE

President: Cyril Hurlock

Chairman: Norman Cook   **Vice Chairman:** Nick Spencer

Hon. Secretary: Tom Lindon, 63 Downs Road, South Wonston
Winchester, Hampshire SO21 3EW   Tel/Fax: 01962 884760

At the Annual Meeting Nick Spencer was elected as Chairman with Ray Barnes as Vice Chairman. With Portland United gaining membership through their promotion from the Dorset Combination League, the League anticipated a better season in terms of weather than the previous year.

Whilst the first match of the new campaign kicked off in August, we were soon into FA Cup matches, but Lymington & New Milton and AFC Newbury were surprisingly early casualties. However, there was FA Cup success in September for many of our clubs, Bournemouth claiming a massive win over Dorchester Town 3-1 with a gate of 241, whilst Blackfield & Langley, Downton, Whitchurch United, Bemerton Heath Harlequins, AFC Totton, Fleet Town and Cowes Sports all fell at the First Preliminary Round.

In the FA Vase on the 8th September AFC Newbury, Whitchurch United and Blackfield & Langley all lost and in the FA Cup First Qualifying Round Moneyfields, Thatcham Town, Bournemouth and B.A.T. all bid farewell until next season. The Second Qualifying Round of the FA Cup and Vase saw Bournemouth, Downton, Fareham Town, Eastleigh, Fleet Town and Gosport Borough all beaten. On the last Saturday of September Andover drew with Bashley, Brockenhurst turned Kingstonian over in front of 452 fans, Fareham drew with Crawley Town, Gosport Borough drew away to Lewes, Christchurch lost to Cirencester and finally, Eastleigh bowed out to Sutton United. Whilst all the cup competitions were going at full tilt, Malcolm constantly rearranged our league programme accordingly. It is interesting to note that AFC Totton were leaders of the First Division having played eleven matches, Andover were already five games behind due to cup success and Newport (IW) Reserves headed the Combination Division at the end of September. Should we ask the question as to whether there is too much Cup Football during the month?

October started with Cup Football once again, Andover beat Bashley, while Crawley ended Fareham Town's interest and finally Gosport Borough ended their challenge in the FA Cup losing to Lewes in what I recall to be considered controversial circumstances. The County Cup Competitions also started their First Round matches, together with our own League and Combination Cups, and Local Associaiton competitions. In the next round of the FA Cup Andover, watched by 642 paying customers, really gave the match away in a matter of a few minutes with silly mistakes, while Brockenhurst went out away to Cirencester in front of 272 fans. The FA Vase continued with great success for our remaining clubs, but BAT went out to Thatcham Town, who then were leaders of the First Division with Newport (IW) Reserves still leading the Combination.

In November AFC Totton, Andover, Christchurch, Lymington & New Milton and Portland United were all beaten, although three matches went to extra time. Fleet Town moved into pole position in the First Division and Weymouth Reserves took over the leadership of the Combination, a title they were to go on to win outright.

December was a poor month in terms of weather, and most of our remaining clubs - Cowes Sports, Moneyfields, Brockenhurst, Thatcham Town and Wimborne Town - bowed out of the FA Vase. Attendances were very good once again on Boxing Day, proof that people enjoy derby matches.

Having reached the Fourth Round of the FA Vase in January Bemerton Heath Harlequins lost to Great Wakering Rovers watched by 332 spectators.

By April Weymouth Reserves claimed the Combination Division title with some five matches to play, but the climax to the whole season came on the final day and the situation could not have been planned. Andover and Fleet Town played their final League match at Calthorpe Park, Andover only needing a draw to clinch their second championship, whilst Fleet required a draw to gain promotion. Watched by 623 spectators we ended up with two winners in effect, as both clubs achieved their objectives. At the other end of the table, Hamble ASSC, having occupied the relegation position since February, beat Wimborne Town, scoring the winning goal 40 seconds from the end of the match, thus condemning Swanage Town & Herston to relegation. Quite a fitting end to the League season.

The League Cup final paired Andover and Fleet Town together for the third time in a matter of weeks, and it is fair to say, perhaps, that this was not as an exciting match as the two league matches, but then cup finals can be like that. The final of the Combination Cup proved to be an excellent contest between Christchurch and Newport (IW). Lots of young players gave their all, and whilst Newport (IW) won the match we will remember the broken leg suffered by Danny Sheen of Christchurch. I am pleased to report that Danny is making a good recovery following surgery.

Concern needs to be expressed at the volume and amount of foul language used in football generally, and our league in particular. Reminders have been circulated with some success. Referees have the power to remove players who use such language, but understandably this is only applied (at times) when directed at an official personally, otherwise most matches would need to be abandoned when teams are reduced to less than seven players. Can clubs play a leading role in removing this cancer from our League and could sanctions not be introduced for use of such language during training sessions and matches?

The testing of floodlights proved to cause some clubs real problems, and whilst advance notice of the testing was given, some clubs appeared not to have been prepared. I am advised that individual bulbs lose some fifteen per cent of their efficiency each year - some consideration needs to be given to this aspect. Food for thought next time around!

Match programmes sent to the League for entry to the Best Programme Award have been poorly supported, and as some programmes are now professionally produced the committee has decided to end this particular award.

The League would like to thank long serving Secretaries Sheila Benfield, Pete Shires and Mick Geddes, who are standing down. It is hoped they will continue to serve their club in another capacity. Chairmen standing down are Ray Roberts of BAT, Terry Morris of Lymington & New Milton, and Gary Shaughnessy of Whitchurch United. On behalf of all concerned, please accept our thanks for your valuable contribution to our League in particular and football in general. Dixie Batt is not seeking re-election to the Management Committee after six years service, so thank you Dixie, and our loss is golf's gain? Our best wishes go with Fleet Town FC into the Southern Football League for a most successful season.

The League has had an excellent year. We have continued to operate in a professional manner and have seen some excellent football, and we have fulfilled our role of a supply league in promoting within the National League Structure. When the re-structuring does actually happen I feel we will be well placed to carry on the important role that we hold within the system.

The efforts in relation to charity have been particularly satisfying, as we have raised the sum of £4,127. Thank you for your contribution, it has been a most worthwhile effort. Well done to the winners of awards and prizes, and better luck next season to those who did not win this season. A special thanks to Steve Webber and Mike Warner for the continued support and interest of our valuable sponsor, Jewson. Thank you for your participation. See you next season.

ROLL OF HONOUR 2001-02

Jewson Wessex League
Champions   Andover FC
Runners Up   Fleet Town FC
Combination League
Champions   Weymouth FC
Runners Up   AFC Totton
League Cup
Winners   Andover FC
Finalists   Fleet Town FC
Combination Cup
Winners   Newport (IW) FC
Finalists   Christchurch FC
Russell Cotes Cup
Winners   Andover FC
Finalists   Bournemouth FC

Southern Counties FL Cup
Winners   Fleet Town FC
North Hants Senior Cup
Finalists   Andover FC
Isle of Wight Gold Cup
Winners   Cowes Sports FC
Finalists   Newport (IW) FC
Salisbury Hospital Cup
Winners   Bemerton Heath Harlequins FC
Fair Play Award
Winners   Whitchurch United FC
Longest FA Vase Run
Bemerton Heath Harlequins FC

DAILY ECHO CLUB OF THE MONTH AWARD

August	Bournemouth FC	January	Fleet Town FC
September	Thatcham Town FC	February	Lymington & New Milton FC
October	Thatcham Town FC	March	Fleet Town FC
November	Cowes Sports FC	April	AFC Totton
December	Andover FC		

FIRST DIVISION FINAL LEAGUE TABLE 2001-02

		P	W	D	L	F	A	W	D	L	F	A	Pts	GD
1	Andover	44	15	6	1	61	29	14	3	5	46	30	95	48
2	Fleet Town	44	16	5	1	56	21	13	2	7	48	29	94	54
3	AFC Totton	44	16	3	3	58	21	10	8	4	43	20	89	60
4	Gosport Borough	44	14	1	7	56	32	13	1	8	43	25	83	42
5	Brockenhurst	44	16	1	5	55	18	10	5	7	39	29	78	47
6	Lymington & New M	44	12	6	4	53	25	10	6	6	34	26	78	36
7	AFC Newbury	44	12	7	3	43	24	9	7	6	39	29	77	29
8	Wimborne Town	44	13	3	6	57	34	10	4	8	41	30	76	34
9	Moneyfields	44	8	10	4	32	26	13	3	6	40	28	76	18
10	Fareham Town	44	8	10	4	32	26	13	3	6	40	28	76	18
11	Bemerton Heath H	44	12	3	7	60	40	6	8	8	43	44	65	19
12	Thatcham Town	44	12	2	8	55	35	7	6	9	39	42	65	17
13	Eastleigh	44	9	5	8	46	36	9	4	9	45	35	63	20
14	Portland United	44	9	6	7	47	26	8	2	12	34	40	59	15
15	Christchurch	44	6	3	13	28	43	10	4	8	33	37	55	-19
16	Cowes Sports	44	11	3	8	36	29	4	6	12	30	44	54	-7
17	Blackfield & Langley	44	9	2	11	43	56	7	3	12	39	65	53	-39
18	Bournemouth	44	6	5	11	29	34	8	2	12	32	50	49	-23
19	B.A.T.	44	5	7	10	20	30	8	1	13	26	37	47	-21
20	Whitchurch United	44	3	3	16	15	48	2	2	18	12	68	20	-89
21	Downton	44	4	2	16	27	60	1	2	19	15	79	19	-97
22	Hamble ASSC	44	2	2	18	20	47	2	2	18	13	72	16	-86
23	Swanage Town & H	44	3	3	16	19	69	0	3	19	12	105	15	-143

COMBINATION DIVISION FINAL LEAGUE TABLE 2001-02

		P	W	D	L	F	A	W	D	L	F	A	Pts	GD
1	Weymouth Res	40	16	4	0	64	11	14	4	2	46	20	98	79
2	AFC Totton Res	40	14	4	2	75	25	11	5	4	44	32	84	62
3	Newport (IoW) Res	40	17	2	1	70	21	8	5	7	32	30	82	51
4	Gosport Borough Res	40	14	5	1	60	26	10	3	7	57	37	80	54
5	Sailsbury City Res	40	15	2	3	70	29	8	3	9	55	48	74	48
6	Bashley Res	40	13	4	3	73	34	9	3	8	63	41	73	61
7	Christchurch Res	40	11	4	5	64	35	9	7	4	49	26	70	52
8	Eastleigh Res	40	13	3	4	78	28	7	6	7	47	44	69	53
9	Lymington & NM Res	40	15	2	3	56	25	4	4	12	25	65	63	-9
10	Brockenhurst Res	40	12	3	5	47	17	6	5	9	35	36	62	29
11	Bemerton H H Res	40	10	2	8	55	38	7	1	12	31	42	54	6
12	B.A.T. Res	40	10	3	7	42	31	6	2	12	32	54	53	-11
13	Moneyfields Res	40	12	2	6	48	36	4	2	14	33	54	52	-9
14	Wimborne Town Res	40	9	3	8	51	41	6	0	14	40	59	48	-9
15	AFC Newbury Res	40	10	5	5	38	29	3	2	15	13	58	46	-36
16	Hamble ASSC Res	40	8	4	8	36	28	4	5	11	26	48	45	-14
17	Downton Res	40	6	4	10	24	35	3	2	15	14	79	33	-76
18	Horndean Res	40	6	5	9	39	54	2	3	15	22	65	32	-58
19	Whitchurch Utd Res	40	5	5	10	37	48	1	2	17	15	75	25	-71
20	Portsmouth RN Res	40	5	2	13	20	54	1	5	14	22	69	25	-81
21	Andover New St Res	40	4	2	14	33	76	2	1	17	20	98	21	-121

FIRST DIVISION RESULTS CHART 2000-01

	1	2	3	4	5	6	7	8	9	10	11	12	13	14	15	16	17	18	19	20	21	22	23
1	X	4-2	1-1	1-1	2-1	1-3	5-2	2-1	1-0	1-1	5-0	1-1	1-3	1-1	2-0	5-0	2-4	2-2	4-1	5-0	1-0	6-0	0-1
2	1-1	X	2-2	3-1	2-2	3-1	3-1	4-2	1-1	2-0	5-0	1-0	3-2	1-0	2-3	6-0	2-0	2-1	2-1	2-1	3-1	5-0	1-1
3	1-0	5-1	X	3-1	4-1	5-0	2-0	0-3	7-2	5-1	3-0	4-3	1-3	3-5	1-3	2-0	3-2	4-0	7-1	9-0	3-0	0-0	1-2
4	1-0	0-2	1-6	X	0-0	2-0	0-0	1-4	1-1	0-1	1-0	0-0	1-1	1-2	0-2	0-0	0-3	0-1	0-0	7-0	1-4	3-1	0-2
5	1-2	1-3	1-5	4-1	X	1-1	3-2	1-2	2-3	3-2	3-0	6-4	1-2	4-3	2-2	7-0	3-1	4-2	3-1	5-0	1-1	2-0	3-2
6	2-4	5-4	1-4	1-3	4-4	X	3-1	1-2	1-2	2-1	2-2	4-2	0-3	0-3	1-0	0-1	0-2	0-9	2-1	7-2	3-2	4-2	0-2
7	1-4	0-0	0-2	1-2	1-1	1-2	X	0-3	0-1	2-1	1-0	0-2	5-1	1-2	1-1	3-0	1-1	2-4	3-2	3-0	2-3	1-2	0-0
8	3-2	0-2	3-5	2-1	3-0	2-1	1-0	X	3-3	0-4	6-1	3-1	0-1	1-2	0-1	3-0	1-2	2-1	2-1	9-1	6-2	4-0	2-1
9	1-3	0-1	0-5	2-0	0-2	3-5	0-2	1-2	X	0-0	2-0	3-1	0-1	1-1	0-4	3-1	1-3	1-2	0-4	3-1	3-4	3-0	1-1
10	4-0	3-1	1-4	2-1	0-2	3-7	0-1	1-2	2-0	X	3-1	0-3	3-0	0-0	2-1	1-0	3-0	0-1	0-3	2-2	2-1	1-1	
11	1-1	0-2	1-7	1-2	2-2	0-3	1-3	1-3	1-2	2-1	X	0-3	0-3	0-1	0-6	4-3	1-3	1-4	1-2	7-1	0-6	3-0	0-2
12	2-2	1-7	0-4	0-2	2-3	7-0	0-1	3-0	3-0	3-1	2-0	X	1-2	1-4	1-1	5-1	1-1	2-1	5-1	1-1	1-2	4-1	1-1
13	1-1	0-0	2-2	2-0	1-1	3-1	1-1	0-3	2-1	1-1	4-1	1-0	X	3-5	0-0	4-0	4-1	1-1	3-0	0-2	0-0	2-2	
14	1-1	3-2	1-1	2-0	4-2	3-5	6-2	2-0	2-1	4-1	7-0	1-1	2-1	X	0-0	5-2	3-2	3-2	1-1	2-2	2-1	4-0	3-2
15	0-2	1-2	2-1	3-1	4-0	3-0	5-2	3-1	1-1	2-2	5-2	2-1	3-0	2-3	X	1-0	2-0	1-1	2-0	8-0	2-0	4-1	2-1
16	0-2	1-2	1-3	0-2	0-3	1-1	1-3	0-2	1-0	1-4	1-1	0-3	0-1	0-2	1-3	X	0-2	0-1	0-3	8-0	1-3	1-2	3-2
17	1-3	2-0	1-3	4-0	0-2	3-0	3-0	1-0	3-0	1-0	5-0	1-3	1-2	4-0	3-3	6-0	X	2-0	1-0	5-0	1-0	5-1	2-1
18	1-0	2-0	0-3	2-1	3-3	4-1	4-1	1-0	3-0	5-1	8-0	1-4	1-4	0-3	2-0	5-1	2-2	X	0-4	6-1	1-1	3-0	3-4
19	0-1	0-2	1-1	1-2	3-1	5-0	1-0	3-1	0-2	1-1	5-0	3-3	0-0	2-3	0-0	5-1	0-1	2-2	X	2-0	6-2	5-0	2-3
20	0-1	0-7	0-2	1-2	1-8	2-1	1-4	0-6	2-3	2-2	2-5	0-1	0-6	2-1	1-5	0-3	0-3	0-2	1-5	X	1-1	2-0	1-1
21	2-1	1-4	4-1	1-0	3-2	8-0	6-1	0-0	1-2	3-1	4-2	2-3	3-1	2-3	0-3	4-0	1-1	0-2	1-4	6-1	X	3-1	0-2
22	0-1	0-2	0-2	0-3	2-2	3-5	1-2	0-4	0-3	0-1	1-0	0-5	1-2	0-2	0-4	0-0	1-0	0-2	0-1	4-1	1-1	X	1-5
23	2-2	0-2	2-1	1-0	3-1	2-2	4-2	0-2	1-3	4-3	4-0	2-1	1-1	1-0	1-1	3-0	2-2	1-0	4-0	0-0	1-1	4-0	X

1	AFC Newbury	7	Bournemouth	13	Fareham Town
2	AFC Totton	8	Brockenhurst	14	Fleet Town
3	Andover	9	Christchurch	15	Gosport Borough
4	B.A.T.	10	Cowes Sports	16	Hamble Assc
5	Bemerton Hth Hqns	11	Downton	17	Lymington & N M
6	Blackfield & Langley	12	Eastleigh	18	Moneyfields

19	Portland United
20	Swanage Town & H
21	Thatcham Town
22	Whitchurch United
23	Wimborne Town

LEADING LEAGUE GOALSCORERS

FIRST DIVISION

36	Andy Forbes	Andover FC
36	Ian Mancey	Fleet Town FC
28	Sean Cook	Thatcham Town FC
27	Mark Frampton	Fleet Town FC
26	Neil Scammell	Gosport Borough FC
25	Patrick James	AFC Totton/Blackfield & L

LEAGUE CUP

11	Andy Forbes	Andover FC
6	Paul Odey	Andover FC
5	Gareth Barnes	Brockenhurst FC
5	Ian Mancey	Fleet Town FC

A.F.C. NEWBURY

Secretary: Mike Hall, 27 Sanden Close. Hungerford, Berks. RG17 0LA
Tel: 01488 685070 (H) 01635 566225 (W) 07714 953784 (M)
Email Address: mike.hall o @ talk21.com

Ground: Faraday Road, Newbury, Berks. Tel: 01635 523222

Directions: A34 to Robin Hood roundabout, then A4 towards Reading. Right at lights after 100 yards into Faraday Road. Ground at end of road.

Previous names: The club was formed in 1996 from the resources of Ecchinswell Football Club (1906), Shaw Boys and Belles Junior Football Club (established in 1972) and Wickham U17 Youth Team. The club operates from Faraday Road Stadium and this is the only link with Newbury Town F.C.

FACT FILE
Formed: 1996
Colours: Red/white/red
Change: Green/black/green
Reserves:Wessex Combination
Midweek Matches: Tuesday
Website (under construction)
www.@fcnewbury.com

CLUB PERSONNEL
Chairman: Steve Hartley Tel: 01488
683783(H) 0118 9304030 (W)

Manager: Andy Lyne

A.F.C. TOTTON

Secretary: Malcolm Tombs, 2Seymour Close,Calmore, Southampton SO40 2TW
Tel No: 023 8087 1790
GROUND: Testwood Park, Testwood Place, Totton, Southampton Tel:023 80868981
Directions: Five minutes walk from Totton station. Turn off at roundabout in Totton centre into Library Road.Then first left and second right into Testwood Place.

Capacity: 2,500   Seats: 200   Cover: 250   Floodlights: Yes   Club Shop: No

Clubhouse: Open for matches and training sessions. Burgers, sandwiches, tea,coffee, biscuits etc available

HONOURS :   Hampshire League 81-82, 84-85 Russell Cotes Cup 98-99

PREVIOUS :   **League:** Hants 1886-1986
Name: Totton FC until merger with Totton Athletic 1979
Grounds: Downs Park; Mayfield Park

RECORD: **Gate:** 600 v Windsor & Eton, F.A. Cup 4th Qual Rd 82-83

FACT FILE
Founded: 1886
Nickname: Stags
Colours: Blue with white trim/blue/blue
Change colours: Lime/Black/Black
Midweek Matches: Tuesday
Programme: 30 pages 50p

CLUB PERSONNEL
Chairman: John Dawson
Vice Chairman: R.Thurston
President: D Maton
Manager: Ian Robinson
Press Officer: P Chilcott (023 80860453)

ALTON TOWN

Secretary: Tony Hillman, 19a Beechwood Rd, Alton, Hants GU34 1RL
Tel: 01420 87103 (H)   07796 184095 (M)

Ground: Alton/Bass Sports Ground, Anstey Rd, Alton
Tel: 01420 82465
Capacity: 2,000   Covered Seating: 200   Floodlights: Yes

Directions: A31 from Winchester to Alton, through town and ground is on junction with Anstey Road and Anstey Lane.

Previous League: Hampshire League >2002

Senior Honours: Hampshire League Champions 2001-02

FACT FILE
Formed: 1991
Colours:White/black/black
Change colours: Red & black/white/white.
Midweek home matchday: Tuesday

CLUB PERSONNEL
Chairman: Jim McKell
Scotch Corner, Huntsmead, Alton,
Hants. GU34 2SF
Tel: 01420 82725 (H)   07740 099374 (M)

Manager: John Robson

ANDOVER

Secretary: Chris Jeremy, 23 Stubbs Court, Artists Way, Andover, Hants SP10 3QR
Tel: 01264 361973
Ground: Portway Stadium, West Portway Ind. Estate, Andover SP10 3LF Tel: 01264 391341
Directions: From the Andover By-pass A303 follow signs to Portway Ind. estate. On exiting the A303 turn right at r/about & over bridge, bear off left at next mini r/about and after 150yds turn right onto estate. Straight on until you enter Hopkinson Way, ground on left 4-500 yds
Capacity: 3,000   Cover: 250   Seats: 250   Floodlights: Yes
Clubhouse: Open matchdays & private function   Club Shop: No   Metal Badges: Yes

HONOURS Wessex Lg 00-01 R-up 94-95,97-98 Western Lg R-up 69-70 70-71; Hants Lg 13-14 24-25 33-34 44-45 48-49 50-51 61-62 (R-up 42-43); Northern Div 13-14, Div 2 R-up 37-38; Salisbury & Dist Lg (7) Hants Sen Cup (5); Russell Cotes Cup 23-24 31-32 37-38 44-45 52-53 58-59 60-61 61-62; Pickfords Cup 50-51; Hants Interm Cup 59-60 60-61; Hants Jun Cup 19-20 (R-up 1894-95 1910-11 12-13) N.Hants Cup 99-00 00-01

PREVIOUS   **Leagues:** Salisbury & D.; Hants 1896-98, 1899-1901, 02-62; Southern 1898-99,1971-93 98-99; Western 1962-71; Wessex Lge 93-98

BEST SEASON   **FA Cup:** 1st Rd 62-63, 0-1 v Gillingham
                    FA Trophy: 3rd Qual Rd 69-70, 70-71
                    FA Vase: 4th Rd 94-95, 1-3 v Falmouth Town (A)

FACT FILE

Founded: 1883
Nickname: The Lions
Colours: Red & black/black/red
Change cols: All Purple.
Midweek matchday: Tuesday
Reserve Team's League: None
Programme: 50 pages #1.00

CLUB PERSONNEL

Chairman: John Cunningham-Brown

President: R Coleman
Manager: Howard Goddard
Asst Manager:
Physio: Chris Burford
2000-01
Captain: Danny Barker
P.o.Y.: Vince Rusher
Top Goalscorer: Andrew Forbes 56

B.A.T. SPORTS

Secretary: Gill McClelland, 27 Saxon Road, Blackfield, Southampton SO45 1WY
Tel No: 023 8089 2314
Ground: BAT Sports Ground, Southern Gdns, off Ringwood Road, Totton SO 40 8RW
Tel: 023 8086243

Directions: Into centre of Totton, proceed up Ringwood Rd past small r'bout,2nd left into Southern Gardens. Half mile from Totton (BR), bus X2(Southampton-Bournemouth)

Capacity: 3,000   Seats: 150   Cover: 150   Floodlights: Yes

Clubhouse: Normal licensing hrs, all day for members' sports facilities. Hot & cold snacks

Best Season   **FA Vase:** 3rd Rd 99-00
Record Attendance   403 v AFC Bournemouth 3.05.02.

FACT FILE

Founded: 1925
Colours: All blue& yellow trim
Change: Red & black/red/red
Midweek Matches: Tuesday
Programme: 20 pages, 30p

CLUB PERSONNEL

Chairman: Mike Geddes
Manager: Andy Leader & Ray Collins

2001-02
Captain: Lee Hodder
P.o.Y.: Gareth Barfoot
Top Scorer: Dave Roberts 8

BEMERTON HEATH HARLEQUINS

Secretary: Andy Hardwick, 2 Ashley Rd, Salisbury, Wilts. SP2 7BZ Tel: 01722 333015 & mobile: 07931 284658

Ground: Western Way, Bemerton Heath, Salisbury, Wilts Tel: 01722 331925 (H) :
                 Club Office &FAX :01722 331218

Directions: Turn off A36 Salisbury-Bristol Rd at Skew Bridge (right turn if coming out of Salisbury), 1st left into Pembroke Rd for half mile, 2nd left along Western Way - ground quarter mile at end. 40 mins walk from Salisbury(BR) station.
              Bus 51 or 52 from city centre stops at junction of Pembroke Rd/Western Way
              Capacity : 2,100   Seats: 200   Cover: 350   Floodlights: Yes
              Clubhouse: Yes

HONOURS   Wilts Snr Cup 92-93. Wilts Lg(3) as Bemerton Athletic
PREVIOUS   **Names:** Bemerton Athletic, Moon FC & Bemerton Boys; all merged in 1989
               Leagues: Bem. Ath.: Salisbury & Wilts Comb.
                     Moon: Salisbury. & Andover Sunday   Bem.Boys: Mid Wilts
RECORD   **Attendance:** 1,118 v Aldershot Town FA Cup 1st Qual Rd Aug 94
              Appearances: Keith Richardson

FACT FILE

Founded: May 1989
Nickname: Quins
Colours: Black & white hoops/black/black & white hoops
Change colours: Yellow/white/white
Midweek Matches: Tuesday
Programme: 32 pages, 50p

CLUB PERSONNEL

Chairman: George Parker
President: Peter Say
Manager: Steve Slade
Coah:Andy Nash
Physio: Andy Nash

Bemerton Harlequins' Carl Jones slides the ball past Thamesmead's Micky Bradley in the FA Vase Third Round. Photo: Alan Coomes

Christchurch FC

Whitchurch United. Back Row (l-r): Graham Knight (Asst Mngr), Jason Dilham, Paul George, Neil Butler, Dave Smalley, Dean Robinson, Steve Morris, Ralph Soper-Dyer, Brian Drury (Manager). Front Row: Damian Hack, Paul Rolff, Mario Nurse, Marc Rees, Mick Loddon, Steve McNulty. Photo: Arthur Evans

BLACKFIELD & LANGLEY

Secretary: Doug Sangster, 3 Fir Tree Grove, Butts Ash Lane, Hythe, Hants SO45 3RA
Tel: 023 80844911 (H) 023 80313721 (B) Email: doug.sangster@tesco.net

Ground: Gang Warily Rec., Newlands Rd, Blackfield, Southampton, Hants SO45 1GA
Tel: 01703 893603

Directions: A326 from Totton. At Holbury mini roundabout take right fork signposted to Lepe and Fawley. After the 1st set of lights (170m) turn left into ground.

Previous League: Hampshire League

FACT FILE
Colours: Green & white/green/green
Change colours: Red & white/red/red
Midweek home matchday: Tuesday

CLUB PERSONNEL

Chairman: Ian Hore
5 Foxhayes Lane, Blackfield,
Southampton, Hants SO45 2QD
Tel: 023 8089 3325 (H)
023 8084 7659 (B)

2001-02
Leading goalscorer: Steve Wheatland 20
Captain: Simon Eagle
P.o.Y.: Jimmy Hooper

BOURNEMOUTH

Secretary: Mandy Vaughan, 33 Kings Park Road, Bournemouth BH7 7AE
Tel No. & Fax: 01202 258367

Ground: Victoria Park, Namu Rd., Winton, Bournemouth, Dorset Tel: 01202 515123

Directions: Any bus to Wimborne Road, Winton. 2 miles from Bournemouth Central(BR)

Capacity: 3,000 Seats: 250 Cover: 250 Floodlights: Yes Shop: No

Clubhouse: Open daily 7-11pm. Sandwiches & hot snacks available.

HONOURS Hants Lg 13-13 21-22, B'mouth Snr Cup 66-67 89-90, Texaco F'lit Cup R-up 91-92, Hants I'mediate Cup 49-50 69-70, Hants Yth Cup 54-55 57-58 67-68

PREVIOUS **Leagues:** Hampshire **Ground:** Dene Park 1888-90
Names: Bournemouth Rovers 1875-88; Bournemouth Dene Park 1888-90

RECORD **Scorer:** B Head
Fee Received: £1,500 for Chike Onourah (Wimborne 93-94)

FACT FILE
Founded: 1875
Nickname: Poppies
Sponsors:Bradbury Roofing
Colours: All Red
Change colours: All blue.
Midweek Matches: Tuesday
Reserves' League: Jewson Wessex Comb
Programme: 58 pages, 50p
Editor: Steve Maidment
Local Press: Evening Echo
CLUB PERSONNEL
Chairman:Robert Corbin
Vice Chairman: Frank Harvey
President: Ernie Simpkins
Comm. Manager:Steve Jones
Press Officer: Steve Maidment
Manager: Keith Williams
Asst Manager: Steve Sharkey
Coach: Pete Littlefield
Physio:John Edwards

BROCKENHURST

Secretary: Terry Simpson, Ramsbury House,Station Road, Sway,Lymington, Hampshire SO41 6BA (01590 682991)
Ground: Grigg Lane, Brockenhurst, Hants Tel: 01590 623544
Capacity: 2,000 **Seats:** 200 **Cover:** 300 **Floodlights:** Yes
Clubhouse: Every evening plus Tues, Fri, Sat & Sun lunchtimes

Directions: M27 Junc 1, A337 to Lyndhurst and A337 to Brockenhurst. Turn right at Carey's Manor Hotel into Grigg Lane. Ground is 200 yds on the right

HONOURS Hants Intermediate Cup 61-62; Bournemouth Senior Cup 60-61; Hampshire Lg 75-76, R-up 73-74 79-80, Div 2 70-71 R-up 60-61, Div 3 59-60.

PREVIOUS **League:** Hampshire Lge 24-26 47-86

RECORDS **FA Amateur Cup:** 2nd Round 73-4
Attendance: 1,104 v St Albans City F.A.Amateur Cup January 1974

2001-02 **Captain:** Jimmy Anderson **P.o.Y.:**No Award **Top Scorer:** Gareth Barnes 29

FACT FILE
Founded: 1898 Nickname: The Badgers
Sponsor: T.B.A.
Colours: Blue & white/blue/blue
Change colours: Green/black/green
Midweek Matches: Tuesday
Reserves League: Wessex Combination
Programme: 32 pages, £1.00
Editor/Press Officer: Dave Stansbridge
CLUB PERSONNEL
Chairman: Dave Stansbridge
President: Mike Kimber
Vice Chairman: Ray Colverson
Manager: Pete Moore Asst. Mgr: Dave Hukin
Reserves Manager: Andy Colverson
Physio: Dave Lane

CHRISTCHURCH

Secretary:	Mrs Dawn Page, 87 The Albany, Manor Road, Bournemouth BH1 3EJ
	Tel: 01202 551977
Ground:	Hurn Bridge Sports Club, Hurn Bridge, Avon Causeway, Christchurch
	Tel: 01202 473792
Directions:	A338 from Ringwood, turn off signed Hurn Airport on left. Before Airport use mini roundabout & take exit signed Sopley & ground is immed. on the right. 3 miles from Christchurch (BR)
Capacity:	2,000 Seats: 215 Cover: 265 Floodlights: Yes
Clubhouse:	Normal pub hours. Cooked food at lunchtimes
HONOURS	Hants Jnr Cup 1892-93 1911-12 20-21; Hants Int. Cup 86-87; Pickford Cup 91; Hants Lg Div 2 37-38 47-48 85-86 (Div 3 56-57); B'mouth Snr Cup (5) 56-57 59-60 67-70; B'mouth Page-Croft Cup 94-95
PREVIOUS	League: Hampshire Ground: Barrack Rd Recreation Grd (>1984)
RECORD	Appearances : John Haynes

Players progressing: Jody Craddock (Cambridge Utd 93), Dan West (Aston Villa 94)

FACT FILE
Founded: 1885
Nickname: Priory
Sponsors: Franklin Transport
Colours: All royal blue (white trim)
Change colours: All Red
Midweek Matches: Tuesday
Programme: 16 pages, 50p
Editor: Dennis Miller

CLUB PERSONNEL
Chairman: Majid Azzeddin
Vice Chairman: Ian Harley Pres: Joss Jenkins
Press Officer: Robin Osborne
Joint Managers: Nigel Cripps & Tony Brown
Physio: Kevin Jackson
2001-02
Captain: Steve Hillyer
P.o.Y.: Phil Langdown

COWES SPORTS

Secretary:	Bill Murray, 3 Firs Close, Cowes, Isle of Wight PO31 7NF
	Tel: 01983 294445
Ground:	Westwood Park, Reynolds Close, off Park Rd, Cowes, Isle of Wight PO31 7NT
	Tel: 01983 293793
Directions:	Take Park Rd out of Cowes . Reynolds Close is a right turn half mile up hill
	Capacity: 1695 Seats: Yes Cover: Stand Floodlights: Yes
	Clubhouse: Yes Club Shop: No
HONOURS	Hants. League 93-94, Isle of Wight Gold Cup 94-95 01-02,Wessex Lg.Cup 98-9
PREVIOUS	League: Hampshire (pre-1994)
BEST SEASON	FA Cup: 4th Qual. Rd replay 57-58, 1-4 v Trowbridge (A) after 2-2
	FA Vase: 5th Rd 99-00

FACT FILE
Founded:
Colours: Blue & white stripes,black,blue
Change colours: All Yellow
Midweek Fixtures: Tuesdays
Reserves' Lge: I.O.W. Saturday Lg.
Programme Editor: Roger Hendey

CLUB PERSONNEL
President: Ada Leigh
Chairman: Ian Lee
Manager: Derek Ohren

DOWNTON

Secretary:	Brian Ford, 11 Chantry Road, Wilton, Salisbury, Wilts.
	Tel No: 01722 743314
Ground:	Brian Whitehead Sports Ground, Wick Lane, Downton Tel: 01725 512162
Directions:	Travel south from Salisbury on A338 for about 7 miles. Turn right intoWick Lane, and the ground is a qtr mile on left
	Capacity: 1600 Seats: 250 Cover: Nil Floodlights: Yes
Clubhouse:	Bar with kitchen facilities Club Shop: No
HONOURS	Wilts Sen Cup 79-80 80-81, (R-up 55-56 91-92 94-95); Wilts Jun Cup 49-50; Bournemouth Sen Lge Cup 60 61 62 64 65 67 68, Sen Lge Cup 61-62 63-64 66-67, Cup 62-63 79-80; Wessex Lge Cup 95-96; Wessex Comb Cup (R-up 95-96); RussellCotes Cup 95-96; Hayward Cup 64-65
PREVIOUS	League: Bournemouth, Hants (pre-1993)

FACT FILE
Founded: 1905
Nickname: The Robins
Sponsor: Priority Mailing
Colours: Red/white/red
Change colours:Yellow/blue/yellow
Midweek Matchday: Tuesday
Programme: Yes
Editor:Paul Beaney

CLUB PERSONNEL
Chairman: James Blake
President: R Tanner
Manager: Mitch Blake
Asst.Manager: Steve Adlam
Coach: C Huxford
Physio: Pete Watts

EASTLEIGH

Secretary: Richard Vowles, 28 Franklyn Avenue, Sholing, Southampton, Hants SO19 8AP
Tel: 02380 447802
Ground: `Ten Acres', Stoneham Lane, North Stoneham, Eastleigh SO50 -9HT Tel: 02380 613361
Directions: M27, Jct 5, to r'bout - exit marked Stoneham Lane. Carry on to r'bout & come back
down Stoneham Lane, turning right opp. Concord Club. Ground 400 yds on left. Southampton
Parkway (BR) 3/4 mile. Bus 48 (S'hampton-Winchester) to Stoneham Church stop
Capacity: 2,300   Seats: 175   Cover: 210   Floodlights: Yes   Club Shop: No
Clubhouse: 11-11 Mon-Sat plus Sundays. Extensive function facilities. All catering undertaken

HONOURS   Wessex Lg Cup R-up 91-92, Hants Lg Div 2 69-70 (R-up 54-55 60-61 62-63
64-65(Res), Div 3(W) 50-51 53-54 70-71(Res), Comb.(Res) (3) R-up 96-Hants, Comb Cup (Res)
96-7,97-8 Midweek F'lit Cup 78-79, Soton Snr Lg(W) 49-50 (R-up 51-52(Res), Div 1 56- 57) 57-
58(Res)), Russell Cotes R-up 76-77 80-81 89-90,
PREVIOUS   **Leagues:** Southampton Jnr & Snr 46-59/ Hants 50-86
        Names: Swaythling Ath. 46-73; Swaythling 73-80
        Grounds: Southampton Common 46-47; Walnut Avenue, Swaythling 47-75
BEST SEASON   **FA Vase:** 4th Round 82-83,90-91, 94-95
RECORDS   **Gate:** 2,500 v Southampton, floodlight opener 30/9/75
        Scorer : Johnny Williams, 177   **Appearances** : Ian Knight, 611
Win: 12-1 v Hythe & Dibden (H) 11/12/48   **Defeat:** 0-11 v Austin Spts (A) 1/1/47

FACT FILE
Founded: 1946
Nickname: None
Sponsors: Southern Exhaust Services
Colours: White & Navy/Navy /White & Navy
Change colours: All red
Midweek matches: Wednesday
Programme: 32 pages with admission
Editor: Mark Pearce & Tommy Whale

CLUB PERSONNEL
Chairman: Roger Sherwood
President: Clive Wilson
Manager:Paul Doswell
Coach: David Hughes
Physio: Bert Wyatt

FAREHAM TOWN

Secretary: Malcolm Harper OBE, 20 Hampton Grove, Catisfield, Fareham, Hants PO15 5NL
    Tel: 01329 8413476 (H) 01329 844074 (Fax) 0410 689939 (M)
Ground: Cams Alders, Highfield Avenue, Fareham, Hants PO14 1JA Tel: 01329 231151
Directions: M27, J11, follow A27 towards Southampton. After passing Fareham station turn left at
traffic lights (2nd left) into Redlands Ave.. Turn right at Redlands Inn then left into Highfields Ave.
        Capacity: 5,500   Cover: 500   Seats: 450   Floodlights: Yes
Clubhouse: Open every evening except Sundays. Food available
Club Shop: Sells programmes, scarves & fanzines
HONOURS   Hants Lg (8) 59-60 62-67 72-73 74-75 (R-up 55-56 60-61 67-68 71-72 76-77 78-
79, Div 2 R-up 52-53, Eastern Div 24-25, Div 3 East 49-50), Hants Snr Cup 56-57
62-63 67-68 92-93, Russell Cotes Cup (6) 64-65 72-77, Gosport War Memorial
Cup, SW Co's Cup (2), Pickford Cup (2),
PREVIOUS   **Leagues:** Portsmouth 47-49, Hants 49-79, Southern 79-98
        Name: Fareham FC   **Ground:** Bath Lane
BEST SEASON   **FA Trophy:** Semi Final 86-87   **FA Amateur Cup:** 2nd Rd 63-64 66-67 73-74
        FA Vase: 1st Rd 98-9 **FA Cup:** 1st Rd replay 88-89, 2-3 v Torquay U. (H) after 2-2
RECORDS   **Attendance:** 2,650 v Wimbledon, FA Cup 1965.
        (at Southampton F.C.) 6,035 v Kidderminster H., FAT S-F 2nd leg 86-87
        Fee received: £43,000 for David Leworthy (Spurs)

FACT FILE
Formed: 1947
Nickname: The Town
Sponsors: Portsmouth Evening News
Colours: Red/white/red
Change colours: Whiteblack/black
Midweek matchday: Wednesday
Reserves' League: Hampshire Comb
Programme: 36 pages £1
Editor: Ian Tewson Tel. 01329 662624

CLUB PERSONNEL
Chairman: Bob Ralls
Director of Football: John Green
President: Ken Atkins
General Manager: Tony Adams (01705 615931)
Press Officer: M Willis
Manager: Jon Gittens
Physio: James McKay

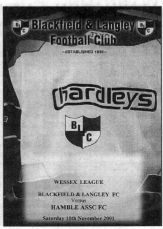

GOSPORT BOROUGH

Secretary: B V Cosgrave, 2 Cavanna Close, Rowner, Gosport PO13 0PE Tel: 01329314117
Ground: Privett Park, Privett Road, Gosport, Hants Tel: 01705 501042 (Office)
Directions: M27 Junct 11, A32 Fareham to Gosport. At Brockhurst r-about (about 3 miles) right into Military Rd passing thru H.M.S. Sultan, left into Privett Rd at next r-about, ground 300yds left signed `Privett Park Enclosure'. 2 miles from Portsmouth Harbour (BR) or Fareham (BR)
Capacity: 4,500   Cover: 500   Seats: 450   Floodlights: Yes   Club Shop: No
Clubhouse: Matchdays only - from 1.30 Sat., 6.30 Wed. Refreshment hut sells hot food & drinks
HONOURS Wessex Lg Cup 92-93, Southern Lg Div 1 South R-up 84-85, Hants Lg 45-46 76-77 77-78 (Div 3 (Res.) 70-71 75-76), Portsmouth Lg R-up 44-45, HantsSenior Cup 87-88, Russell Cotes Cup R-up 94-95, Hants Intermediate Cup 70-71, Portsmouth Senior Cup 61-62 69-70 70-71 94-95, South West Counties PrattenChallenge Cup 77-78
BEST SEASON   FA Trophy: 1st Rd 88-89   **FA Amateur Cup:** 3rd Rd 47-48 66-67
          FA Vase: 6th Rd rep 77-78   **FA Cup:** 4th Qual. Rd 80-81 (lost to Windsor & Eton)
PREVIOUS   Leagues: Portsmouth 44-45; Hants 45-78; Southern 78-92
          Name: Gosport Borough Athletic
RECORD   Attendance: 4,770 v Pegasus, FA Amtr Cup 1951
          Scorer: Richie Coulbert 192   **Appearances:** Tony Mahoney 764
          Win: 14-0 v Cunliffe-Owen, Hampshire Lg Div 1 45-46
          Defeat: 0-9 twice   v Newport, Hants Lg Div 1 47-48.
                        v Gloucester (A), SouthernLg Prem Div 89-90

FACT FILE
Founded: 1944 Nickname: The Boro'
Sponsors: Cawte & Elms
Colours: Yellow/blue/yellow
Change colours: All red
Midweek matchday: Tuesday
Reserves ' League: Wessex Combination
Programme:40 pages, £1.00
Editor: Roy newman (02392 799198)
Local Press: Portsmouth Evening News,
Southampton Evening Echo
**A club record 14 consecutive victories
were achieved in 00-01 season**
CLUB PERSONNEL
Chairman: JohnStimpson
President: H.Mizen
Manager: Mick Marsh Coach Hugh Doyle
Physio: Dave Topliss
2001-02
Captain.: Stuart Hensman
Top Scorer & P.o.Y.:: Neil Scammell 37

HAMBLE AEROSTRUCTURES
SPORTS & SOCIAL CLUB

Secretary: Matthew Newbold, Flat 6, 70-72 Portsmouth Road, Woolsten, Southampton,
              Hants. SO19 9AN   Tel: 023 803 24147 (H) 023 804 53371(W)

Ground: Folland Park, Kings Avenue, Hamble.,Southampton SO31 4NF
              Tel: 02380452173

Directions: M27 junction 8, then B3397 to Hamble. Half mile fromHamble (BR); turn right
              out of station, proceed for one mile then turn right before shops into Kings
              Avenue. Ground 1000 yards on right in works sports ground.

              Capacity: 1000   Seats: 150   Cover: 150   Floodlights: Yes
Clubhouse: 300 capacity social club. Cricket & bowls

HONOURS: Hampshire Lg Div 3 80-81 (Div 4 79-80), Hampshire Intermediate Cup 79-90,
              Southampton Senior Cup 84-85 86-87 91-92
              As Hamble AS&SC: Jewson Wessex League Cup 97-98
PREVIOUS   Name: Folland Sports (pre-1990), Aerostructures SSC 90-97
RECORD   Defeat: 1-10 v Andover (A), Wessex League 93-94

FACT FILE

Colours: Maroon and Sky Blue
Change colours: All navy blue
Midweek Matches: Tuesdays & Wednesdays
Reserves ' League: Wessex Comb
Under 18 & Under16: So'ton Youth Lgs

CLUB PERSONNEL

President: Alistair Tritten
Assistant Secretary: Matthew Newbold
Treasurer:Barry Morse
SeniorManager: Larry Clay

LYMINGTON & NEW MILTON

Secretary: John Osey, 9 Samphire Close, Lymington, Hants SO41 9LR Tel: 01590 676995
Ground: Fawcett Fields,Christchurch Rd., New Milton,Hants BH25 6QF (01425 6281910
Directions: M27 Jct 1 follow A337 to Lyndhurst one way system(A35) towards Christchurch. Left in Hinton Admiral at Cat & Fiddle.Follow Ringwood road ,then left at A337 roundabout to New Milton. Ground one mile on left past Chewton Glen Hotel.
Capacity: 3,000   Seats: 262   Cover: 262   Floodlights: Yes
Clubhouse: Open seven days a week 11.0 am to 11.0 pm. Hot food and functions availab le
HONOURS Wessex Lg 92-93 96-97 97-98, 98-99 , 99-00,00-01R-up 91-92 95-96, Wessex Lg Cup 88-89, R-up 94-95, 98-99 Wessex Comb. 92-93, Hants Snr Cup R-up 89-90, Texaco Cup 91-92, Bournemouth Snr Cup 92-93, R-up 96-97, Russell Cotes Cup 93-94 94-95, R-up91-92 92-93; Pickford Cup R-up 92-93. Jewson Champions Shield 98-99
BEST SEASON   FA Cup: 4th Qual. Rd. 99-00, 1-3 v Aldershot Town (H)
          FA Vase: 98-99 Quarter Final, 1-3 v Taunton Town (A)
PREVIOUS   Names: Lymington Town (until 1988 merger with Wellworthy Ath.),
              AFC Lymington 88-98 (until merger with New Milton Town)
          Ground: Ampress Ground (Wellworthy Ath.), until 1988 merger
RECORD   Attendance: 2,900 v Karen Mills Memorial Day 12.3.95
          Scorer: Darren Pitter 197   **Appearances:** Graham Kemp 504
          Win: 11-1 v Romsey Town (H), Wessex League 9/11/92
          Defeat: 0-8 v Basingstoke Town (A), Hampshire Senior Cup 10/4/90

FACT FILE

Founded as Lymington & New Milton: 1998
Nickname: Linnets
Sponsors:Parkcrest Construction
Colours: Maroon & Blue Stripes/blue/maroon
Change colours: White/black/black
Midweek Matches: Tuesday
Reserves ' League: Wessex Comb

Programme: 48 pages, £1.00
Editors: Jack Holliday & Keith Williams

CLUB PERSONNEL

Chairman: Charlie Hewlett
President: Jack Holliday & Ted Goodyer
Press Officer: Keith Williams (01202 476898)

Manager: Graham Kemp

MONEYFIELDS

Secretary: Paul Lipscombe,5 Braunston Close,Paulsgrove,Hants. PO6 4EN (07766 222718)
Ground: Moneyfields Sports Ground, Moneyfields Avenue, Copnor, Portsmouth,Hants.
Tel: 023 9266 5260 (Club), 023 9265 2424 (Office) **Club Shop:** Yes
Capacity: 1,500 Seats: 150 Cover: 150 Floodlights: Yes
Clubhouse: Daily 7-11 p.m. Saturday 11-11p.m. (food from 1.0 pm)
Directions: From Southampton & the west - travel east on M27 onto A27. Take exit marked
Southsea A2030. (From east take the same exit). Head south along A2030 exit
and turn right into Tangier Road (4th right). Follow until'Tangiers' PH & take next
right into Folkestone Road. Carry on into Martin Rd & club is in front of you.
Records: **Attendances:** Matthew Lafferty 156 (Jewson Wessex)
Goalscorer: Kevin Marsh 49 (Jewson Wessex)
Attendance: 152 v Fareham Town, Jewson Wessex League, 98-99
Best Seasons: F.A.Cup: 1st Qual. Rd. 01-02 **Previous Name:** Portsmouth Civil Service
F.A.Vase: 3rd Rd 01-02
Records: **Goalscorer:** Neil Damley 62 **Appearances** Matthew Lafferty 168
Attendance v Fareham T 232 01-02
Honours: Portsmouth Senior Cup: 90-91 R-up 91-92 Hampshire League Div 3 91-92, Div 2
92-93,Div 196-97,R-up 97-98 Portsmouth Premier champions 90-91,91-92 Billy Hill Cup 90-91
Hampshireb Intermediate Cup Winners 91-92, 92-93 Russell Cotes Cup Finalists 98-99 Hants
Youth Cuip (under 18) (4), Under 16 (98-99),Hants Youth League 00-01 R-up 98-99

FACT FILE
Founded:1987 Nickname: Moneys
Sponsors: Icee Ltd
Colours: Yellow/& navyblue/yellow
Change: Green & white/ green/green.
Midweek Fixtures: Tuesday
Reserves League: Wessex Combination
Prog 20pages 50p Eds: David Hayter(023
9264 3986)
CLUB PERSONNEL
Chairman: David Jupe
Tel: 023 9235 9571
Manager: Calvin Hore
Assistant Manager: Terry Arnold
Physio: Adie Hylands
2001-02
Captain: Matthew Lafferty
Ps.o.Y:Mark stewart & James Dunk
Top Scorer: Lee Mould

PORTLAND UNITED

Chairman: Phillip Laming, Acorn Bungalow, 1b, Straits, Portland, Dorset.
Tel: 01305 822756 (B)

Secretary: David Naerger, 5 Three Yards Close, Portland, Dorset DT5 1JN
Tel: 01305 821553 (H) 01305 768888 (B) 07811 518453 (M)

Ground: New Grove Corner, Grove Road, Portland, Dorset
Tel: 01305 861489

Directions A354 to Portland, follow one way system to the top of island, roundabout
(hotel on left, garage on right), over roundabout for 500m, turn left into Grove
Road, ground on left hand side.

Cover: Yes
Clubhouse: Yes

FACT FILE
Colours: All blue
Change colours: Red/black/red
Midweek matches: Tuesday
Programme: Yes

THATCHAM TOWN

Football Secretary: Peter Woodage, 5 Elm Grove, Thatcham, Berks. RG18 3DJ
Tel: 01635 861937

Ground: Waterside Park, Crookham Rd, Thatcham, Berks Tel: 01635 862016
Capacity: 3,000 Seats: 300 Cover: 300 Floodlights: Yes

Directions: M4 junc 13, take A34 to Newbury, then left onto A4 towards Reading
InThatcham turn right to the railway station. The ground is on the left
beyond the station - 2 minutes walk.From South A34 to Newbury,take
A339 to Basingstoke,left to Thatcham then left again down Crookham Rd.
Ground on right just before station

Clubhouse: Open every evening & lunchtimes **Club Shop:** Yes
HONOURS Wessex Lg 95-96,R-up 98-99, Cup 90-91 91-92 94-95 96-97, (R-up twice)
PREVIOUS Ground: Station Road 46-52; Lancaster Close 52-92
BEST SEASON **FA Cup:** 4th Qual Rd 96-97
RECORD **Attendnace:** 1,400 v Aldershot, FA Vase

FACT FILE
Founded: 1895
Sponsors: Panasonic Gsm Mobile Phones
Colours: Blue & white stripes/blue/blue
Change colours:Red,black,black
Midweek Matches: Tuesday
Programme: 28 pages, 50p
Editor: Les Wiunkworth

CLUB PERSONNEL
Chairman: Phil Holdway
General Secretary: John Haines
Press Officer: Chairman (01635 867803)
Manager:Neil Baker
Coach:Jason Braidwood

WHITCHURCH UNITED

Secretary: Joanna Cozzi, 39 Hartley Meadow, Whitchurch,Hants RG26
Tel: 01256 892579(H) 01344 401129 (B) 07780 663494 (M)

Ground: Longmeadow, Winchester Road, Whitchurch Tel: 01256 892493

Directions: From Whitchurch (BR) station; turn left after Railway Inn, follow road to end, turn right into main road, arriving in town turn left alongWinchester Road. Ground three quarters of a mile on left

Capacity: 2,000	Seats: 200	Cover: Yes	Floodlights: Yes

Clubhouse: Hot food on matchdays. Sports hall with squash courts and indoor bowling green

PREVIOUS Leagues: Hampshire (pre-1992)

BEST SEASON FA Vase: Extra-Preliminary Rd 93-94, 1-3 v Peppard (H)

FACT FILE

Founded: 1903
Colours: Red &white/black/black
Change colours: White/blue/blue.
Midweek Matches: Tuesday
Programme: 24 pages

CLUB PERSONNEL

Chairman: Tony Chivers
8 Bloswood Drive, Whichurch, Hants. RG28 7AZ
Tel: 01256 893696 (H) 07702 692200 (M)

WIMBORNE TOWN

Secretary: Paul Christopher, 31 Brookside Rd, Bransgore, Christchurch, Dorset. Bh23 8NA
Tel No: 01425 674084 (H) 07765 167848 (M)
Ground: The Cuthbury, Cowgrove Road, Wimborne, Dorset BH21 4EL Tel: 01202 884821
Capacity: 3,250 Seats: 275 Cover: 150 Floodlights: Yes
Directions: Wimborne to Blandford Road, behind Victoria Hospital
Clubhouse: Eves 7-11, Sat noon-11, Sun 12-6 Bar & Skittle alley **Club Shop:** Yes
HONOURS FA Vase 91-92; Wessex Lg 91-92 93-94 ,99-00(R-up 92-93 96-97), Lg Cup 93-94,99-00 (R-up 90-91 95-96); Dorset Lg Div 1 80-81 81-82 (R-up 38-39 72-73), Div 2 31-32 34-35 36-37(R-up 35-36), Lg Cup R-up (4) 72-74 80-82; Dorset Snr Cup 91-92 96-97, (R-up 80-82 85-86 98-99,99-00); Mark Frowde cup 92-93 94-95;01-02 Dorset Snr Amateur Cup 36-37 63-64;Dorset Jnr Cup 31-32 36-37 (R-up 13-14 34-35); Dorset Minor Cup 12-13; Dorset Jnr Amateur Cup (3) 34-36 38-39; Bankes Charity Cup 89-90 94-95 95-96, TexacoF/Light Cup 90-91
PREVIOUS Leagues: Dorset Lge, Dorset Comb, Western 81-86
BEST SEASON FA Vase: Winners 91-92 **FA Cup:** 1st Rd Proper 82-83
RECORDS Attendance: 3,250 v Bamberbridge FA Vase Semi-Final 28/3/92
Goalscorer: Jason Lovell **Win** (Wessex Lg): 9-0 v E.Cowes V 98-99, Brockenhurst 99-00
Appearances: James Sturgess **Defeat** (Wessex Lg): 2-6 v Thatcham Town 91-92
Fee paid: £5,500 for J P Lovell (Bashley, 1992)
Fee received: £6,000; for J P Lovell (Bashley, 1989) & for Tommy Killick(Dorchester, 1993)

FACT FILE

Founded: 1878 Nickname: Magpies
Sponsors: Nicolas O'Hara
Colours: Black & white stripes/black/black
Change colours: Yellow/green/yellow
Midweek Matches: Tuesday
Reserve League: Wessex Combination
Programme: 24 pages, 50p
Editor: Ken Fergus
2001-02 Captain: Tony White
Top Scorer: Mark Dancer
P.o.Y.: Paul Roast
CLUB PERSONNEL
Chairman: Nicholas O'Hara
President: Brian Maidment
Press Officer: Secretary
Manager:Paul Arnold
Asst. Mgr: John Macey
Coach: Darren Powell
Physio: Steve Churchill

Andover, champions of the Wessex League, with manager Ken Cunningham-Brown back right and top scorer Andy Forbes back left. Photo: Arthur Evans

HAMPSHIRE FOOTBALL LEAGUE
Established: 1896

President: N L White
Chairman: G Cox
Secretary: I J Craig
56 Ecton Lane, Anchorage Park, Hilsea, Portsmouth PO3 5TA
Tel: 023 9267 1155   Fax: 023 9265 1147 Email: secretary@hantsfl.freeserve.co.uk

League Development Officer: J Moody

At last season's AGM we welcomed David Munday who took on the position of League Registrations Secretary from Ray Taylor, who in turn became Assistant League Secretary. I took on the Fixtures Secretary position.

The League welcomed three new clubs this season, Portsmouth Royal Navy who were relegated from the Jewson Wessex League, Headley Athletic and King's Somborne, winners and runners-up respectively of the North Hants Senior League, while three weeks after the AGM came the news that West Wight Mayflower had withdrawn from the League, then Bishopstoke Social withdrew their reserve side from the Combinaiton Division a couple of weeks later, and congratulations to Broughton FC and Netley Central Sports FC who celebrated their centenaries this year.

Three clubs, Alton Town, Amesbury Town and Lymington Town represented the League in this season's FA Vase competition, but unfortunately all were eliminated by the Second Qualifying Round.

The first round of the Trophyman League Cup was played during August and September and a number of Premier Division clubs fell at the first hurdle. League newcomers Headley Athletic and King's Somborne beat Bishops Waltham Town and Esso (Fawley) respectively whilst Division Two Netley Central Sports defeated Alton Town.

Disappointingly a number of clubs were unable to fulfil fixtures during the early part of the season and the Committee took the decision to deduct points as well as fining the clubs in an effort to encourage clubs to make an extra effort to fulfil fixtures but meanwhile floodlights were appearing on the horizon throughout the Counties. AFC Aldermaston, Bishops Waltham Town, Brading Town, Esso (Fawley), Locksheath, Poole Town, Stockbridge, Vosper Thornycroft and Winchester City are all to be congratulated on their efforts.

Round Two of the Trophyman Cup saw King's Somborne gaining another Premier scalp by beating Ringwood Town, and notable efforts by Broughton and Laverstock and Ford, who took Premier Division sides Winchester City and Horndean to extra time before bowing out of the competition. Cup holders Hayling United needed extra time to beat Otterbourne, scoring in the last minute of the match.

The Hampshire Senior Cup in October saw eleven Hampshire League clubs progress into the second round. Pick of the results were Andover New Street's and Winchester City's wins over Jewson Wessex League clubs BAT and Fleet Town while the Second Round of the competition saw only three successful clubs enter the hat for the Third Round. East Cowes Victoria and Esso (Fawley) beat Jewson Wessex League sides Fareham Town and Whitchurch United respectively and Vosper Thornycroft. Unfortunately no club progressed any further.

At October's League Management Meeting the League appointed Russell Evans as next season's League Fixtures Secretary and Ricky Pyle as Results and Media Secretary, although this post was re-advertised the following month due to work commitments. November saw Hilsea become the third club to withdraw from the League due to a lack of players and helpers.

After last season the weather was being kind to me, but after mentioning this in my December report, guess what - frost! A number of matches over the festive season became the first to be postponed due to the weather this season.

Ian J Craig, Hon. League Secretary

FINAL LEAGUE TABLES 2001-02

PREMIER DIVISION

	P	W	D	L	F	A	Pts		P	W	D	L	F	A	Pts
Alton Town	40	31	4	5	95	35	97	Stockbridge	40	15	6	19	65	79	51
East Cowes Vics	40	30	5	5	125	52	*92	Pirelli General	40	13	7	20	71	100	46
Winchester City	40	28	6	6	132	35	90	Lymington Town	40	12	9	19	55	80	45
Vosper Thornycroft	40	25	7	8	86	35	82	Petersfield Town	40	11	6	23	56	78	39
Poole Town	40	24	8	8	86	49	80	Hythe & Dibden	40	10	8	22	49	77	38
Locksheath	40	23	3	14	90	61	72	Bishops Waltham Tn	40	10	7	23	40	79	37
Liss Athletic	40	21	5	14	81	84	68	Andover New Street	40	10	6	24	55	86	36
Brading Town	40	18	10	12	83	61	64	Esso (Fawley)	40	9	4	27	53	111	31
Horndean	40	17	7	16	78	66	*61	Amesbury Town	40	8	6	26	46	114	30
Ringwood Town	40	16	11	13	67	63	59	AFC Aldermaston	40	5	3	32	44	121	18
Portsmouth RN	40	15	10	15	69	60	55								

DIVISION ONE

	P	W	D	L	F	A	Pts		P	W	D	L	F	A	Pts
AFC Portchester	28	21	2	5	74	26	65	Verwood Town	28	10	7	11	36	38	37
Farnborough NE	28	18	4	6	102	49	58	Fareham Sacred Hearts	28	9	5	14	63	64	32
Hayling United	28	17	5	6	56	31	56	Fleetlands	28	8	5	15	54	60	29
Colden Common	28	17	3	8	80	32	54	Clanfield	28	8	5	15	50	63	29
Paulsgrove	28	17	5	6	73	37	*52	Tadley Town	28	7	3	18	35	83	24
CO-OP Sports	28	14	7	7	54	40	*46	Yateley Green	28	4	2	22	33	93	14
Fleet Spurs	28	13	6	9	61	46	45	Romsey Town	28	1	4	23	28	132	*1
Micheldever	28	11	7	10	56	61	40								

DIVISION TWO

	P	W	D	L	F	A	Pts		P	W	D	L	F	A	Pts
Headley Athletic	30	24	3	3	91	34	75	Broughton	30	12	4	14	56	61	40
Alresford Town	30	22	7	1	99	27	73	Otterbourne	30	11	6	13	49	53	39
Laverstock & Ford	30	20	4	6	87	25	64	Hedge End	30	12	3	15	50	69	39
Overton United	30	17	9	4	87	33	60	Awbridge	30	10	8	12	53	41	38
Netley Central	30	17	7	6	70	28	58	QK Southampton	30	8	4	18	42	57	28
Hamble Club	30	13	6	11	71	52	45	Hadleigh	30	9	3	18	50	61	*27
King's Somborne	30	14	2	14	70	58	44	Compton	30	1	1	28	26	181	4
Ordnance Survey	30	12	6	12	53	45	42	Bishopstoke Social	30	0	3	27	22	151	*0

PREMIER DIVISION RESULTS CHART 2001-02

		1	2	3	4	5	6	7	8	9	10	11	12	13	14	15	16	17	18	19	20	21
1	Aldermaston	X	1-4	5-1	1-1	0-2	0-5	4-7	1-2	3-0	1-1	4-6	1-2	1-2	2-1	1-3	0-2	1-4	1-4	1-6	0-3	1-5
2	Alton Town	4-1	X	3-1	2-0	4-0	2-1	1-2	5-1	3-0	5-0	6-2	3-2	2-0	4-0	1-3	2-0	1-0	2-1	1-0	1-0	3-3
3	Amesbury T	1-0	0-3	X	1-5	2-1	2-3	2-3	2-5	1-5	2-1	1-1	3-2	3-3	1-4	1-2	0-3	1-0	0-4	0-4	0-5	0-6
4	Andover NS	2-2	1-2	1-0	X	1-1	4-4	1-4	0-2	0-2	0-1	1-5	1-2	1-0	1-0	3-1	1-2	0-2	2-1	0-2	0-1	1-0
5	Bishops W	2-0	0-2	1-1	2-2	X	1-3	0-1	0-2	0-4	3-4	1-3	2-3	2-0	0-0	1-4	0-5	4-2	1-2	2-1	1-2	0-4
6	Brading Tn	5-0	1-3	2-0	7-0	3-0	X	1-1	4-1	0-2	5-1	3-2	2-0	2-1	3-1	0-3	1-1	1-1	2-2	1-2	3-2	1-1
7	E Cowes Vics	7-2	2-1	2-0	6-2	6-0	1-0	X	3-1	3-3	2-0	5-0	3-1	5-0	3-0	6-1	6-4	0-0	0-2	4-0	1-2	3-2
8	Esso (Fawley)	3-1	1-1	1-1	5-0	1-2	2-5	1-7	X	2-1	1-3	3-5	0-3	4-2	3-0	2-5	0-1	0-4	1-2	2-2	0-5	0-9
9	Horndean	3-1	0-2	2-3	2-0	1-0	3-0	1-3	6-0	X	0-2	0-3	3-2	3-3	0-0	3-1	5-5	1-0	2-2	3-1	0-2	2-3
10	Hythe & Dib	2-1	1-3	2-2	1-0	1-2	1-1	1-2	1-0	0-2	X	1-2	1-3	1-0	0-2	3-3	0-3	1-2	2-0	1-2	4-4	1-1
11	Liss Athletic	2-0	0-1	3-1	0-0	0-1	2-4	4-2	2-1	3-2	1-0	X	1-3	1-0	2-1	2-2	1-0	3-2	3-2	2-0	0-1	2-8
12	Locks Heath	7-0	1-3	4-0	4-2	2-1	0-2	2-5	6-2	2-0	2-1	6-1	X	2-0	1-1	4-0	1-3	1-0	1-1	2-1	1-1	2-1
13	Lymington T	0-2	0-2	5-1	1-7	0-0	3-2	2-4	5-2	0-2	1-0	3-3	3-2	X	1-0	6-1	2-1	0-0	2-2	2-1	0-4	0-3
14	Petersfield T	3-1	2-0	1-3	3-5	1-2	1-1	0-2	1-0	2-2	1-4	2-6	2-1	0-2	X	5-0	2-4	4-1	0-2	4-0	1-2	1-1
15	Pirelli Gen	0-1	1-1	6-2	3-4	1-3	0-0	2-4	2-0	0-4	3-2	2-0	0-1	1-1	0-4	X	0-4	2-6	4-1	2-4	2-1	1-5
16	Poole Town	2-1	1-2	0-0	5-2	1-0	1-1	2-0	4-0	3-0	2-0	2-3	0-3	2-1	4-2	2-1	X	3-1	1-1	3-3	1-1	1-0
17	Portsmouth	6-2	1-2	5-2	2-1	0-0	0-0	1-1	2-0	2-2	0-2	0-3	3-0	1-1	1-2	1-1	3-2	X	2-3	2-6	3-1	2-1
18	Ringwood T	3-0	2-1	2-0	2-1	1-0	1-2	2-4	3-0	1-1	1-1	1-2	2-0	4-6	6-0	1-0	1-1	1-2	X	3-1	0-5	0-3
19	Stockbridge	3-0	0-3	1-3	1-0	2-2	3-2	0-2	2-2	0-5	2-0	3-1	1-2	2-3	3-0	1-5	1-1	1-3	2-1	X	0-6	0-4
20	Vosper Th	1-0	1-2	4-1	2-1	2-0	4-0	2-2	1-0	3-0	1-0	2-0	2-1	0-0	5-1	4-1	1-1	2-1	1-1	0-1	X	0-1
21	Winchester C	4-0	2-2	4-1	2-1	5-0	5-0	2-1	2-0	5-3	7-1	6-0	5-2	2-0	4-1	5-1	0-1	3-0	5-0	0-0	3-0	X

AFC ALDERMASTON
Secretary: Christine Collier, 14 Brackenwood Drive, Tadley RG26 4YB (01256 363344)
Ground: Aldermaston Rec. Society, Automatic Weapons Establishment, Aldermaston, Reading, Berks. Tel: 0118 982 4544
Colours: All blue

AMESBURY TOWN
Secretary: Ken Lawes, 9 Bincombe Drive, Crewkerne, Som. TA18 7BE (01460 73189)
Ground: Amesbury Recreation Ground, Amesbury, Wiltshire. Tel: 01980 623489
Colours: All blue

ANDOVER NEW STREET
Secretary: Mr J Dunn at ground address (01264 337678)
Ground: Foxcotte Park, Charlton, Andover, SP11 0HS (01264 358358)
Colours: Green & black/black/green

BISHOPS WALTHAM TOWN
Secretary: Jim Bailey, 46 Claylands Road, Bishops Waltham, Southampton SO32 1BH (01489 894888)
Ground: Priory Park, Elizabeth Way, Bishops Waltham, Southampton, Hants. Tel: 01489 894269
Colours: Red & black/black & red/red & black

BRADING TOWN
Secretary: Scott Wright, 73 Station Ave, Sandown, Isle of Wight PO36 8HB (01983 407635)
Ground: Vicarage Lane, Brading, Isle of Wight (01983 405217)
Colours: Red & White/red/red

EAST COWES VICTORIA ATHLETIC
Secretary: Jim Thorn, 12 Brigstocke Terrace, Ryde, Isle of Wight PO33 2PD (01983 614075)
Ground: Beatrice Avenue Ground, Whippingham, East Cowes, I.O.W. Tel: 01938 297165 Directions: From the ferry: 1 mile from town centre on lower main road to Newport or Ryde near Whippingham Church adjacent to Osborne Middle School   Colours: Red/black/white

FAWLEY AFC
Secretary: Steve Amos, 3 Charmwood Crescent, Chandlers Ford, Southampton SO53 5QN (023 80 255721)
Ground: Waterside Sports & Social Club, Long Lane, Holbury, Southampton. Tel: 023 80 893750
Colours: All blue

HORNDEAN
Secretary: Mick Austin, 22 Abbas Green, Havant, Hants PO9 4EP (023 92645335)
Ground: Five Heads Park, Five Heads Road, Horndean. Tel: 023 92591363
Colours: Red/black/red

HYTHE & DIBDEN
Secretary: Mr A Moyst, 105 Hobart Drive, Hythe, Southampton, Hants SO45 6FD (023 8084 7335)
Ground: Ewart Rec Ground, Jones Lane, Hythe, Southampton (023 8084 5264)
Colours: Green & white/white/green

LISS ATHLETIC
Secretary: Neil Noble, 11 Southdown View, Waterlooville PO7 6BJ (023 9224 0795)
Ground: Newman Collard PF, Hill Brow Rd, Liss, Hants (01730 894022)
Colours: All Blue

LOCKS HEATH
Secretary: Peter Smith, 20 Wildrose Crescent, Locksheath, Hants SO31 6TG (01489 602256)
Ground: Locksheath Rec, Warsash Rd, Titchfield Common, Eastleigh (01489 600932)
Colours: Red & black/black/red & black

LYMINGTON TOWN
Secretary: Mike Woodfield, 6 Genoa Close, Pennington, Lymington SO41 8AU (01590 676705)
Ground: Sports Ground, Southampton Road, Lymington, Hants. Tel: 01590 671305
Colours: Red/white/black

PETERSFIELD TOWN
Secretary: M Nicholl, 49 Durford Rd, Petersfield, Hants GU31 4ER (01730 300518)
Ground: Love Lane, Petersfield, Hants (01730 233416)
Colours: Red & Black/Black/Black

PIRELLI GENERAL
Secretary: Mrs Vera Tuck, 47 Gurneys Mead, West Wellow, Romsey, Hants SO51 6BP (01794 322168)
Ground: Jubilee Spts Ground, Chestnut Ave., Eastleigh (023 8061 2725)
Colours: Blue & white/blue/blue & white

POOLE TOWN
Secretary: Bill Read, 15 Addison Close, Romsey, Hants SO51 7TL (01794 517991)
Ground: Tatnum Ground, Oakdale School, off Palmer Rd, School Lane, Poole, Dorset. Tel: 07771 604289
Colours: Red & white/red/white

PORTSMOUTH ROYAL NAVY
Secretary: John Thomas, 21 Elizabeth Court, Fareham, PO14 1DQ (01329 221881)
Ground: Victory Stadium, HMS Temeraire, Burnaby Road, Portsmouth PO1 2EJ Tel: 0239 229 1660
Colours: Navy/navy/lt blue

RINGWOOD TOWN
Secretary: Mrs Shirley Crewe, 278 Windham Road, Bournemouth, Dorset BH1 4QU (01202 398975)
Ground: Long Lane, Ringwood, Hants. Tel: 01425 473448
Colours: Red & black/black/red & black

STOCKBRIDGE
Secretary: Robin Smith, Curlews Farm, Quarley, Andover SP11 8PT (01980 629781)
Ground: The Recreation Ground, High Street, Stockbridge, Hants
Colours: All red

VOSPER THORNYCROFT
Secretary: A Fox, 22 Thornleigh Road, Woolston, Southampton SO19 9DH (023 8049 3346)
Ground: Vosper Thornycroft Spts Ground, Portsmouth Rd, Sholing, Southampton (023 8040 3829)
Colours: Yellow & blue/blue & yellow/yellow & blue

WINCHESTER CITY
Secretary: Ray Murphy, Petals, 21 Villett Close, Christchurch, Dorset BH23 2NR (023 8042 0859)
Ground: Hillier Way, Abbotts Barton, Winchester (01962 863553)
Colours: Red & black/black/black

DIVISION ONE CLUBS

AFC PORTCHESTER
Secretary: Colin Brans, 2 Eden Rise, Fareham, Hants PO16 0UL (01329 311560)
Ground: Portchester Community School, White Hart Lane, Portchester, Hants. Tel: 02392 364399
Colours: Tangerine/black/tangerine

ALRESFORD TOWN
Secretary: Trevor Ingram, 18 Corfe Close, Alresford, Hants SO24 9PH (01962 733012)
Ground: Arlesbury Park, The Avenue, Alresford, Hants (01962 735100)
Colours: Black & white/black/black

CLANFIELD
Secretary: Stuart Wallis, 42 Glamorgan Road, Catherington, Waterlooville, Hants (023 92 570231)
Ground: Peel Park, Charlton Lane, Clanfield, Waterlooville, Hants.
Colours: Blue & black/black/black

COLDEN COMMON
Secretary: Angela Banford, 19 Fleming Place, Colden Common, Winchester, Hants SO21 1SL (01962 712777)
Ground: Colden Common Recreation Ground, Main Road, Colden Common (01962 712365)
Colours: Red & white/black/red

CO-OP SPORTS & HILSEA
Secretary: Nigel Fisher, 228 Fawcett Road, Southsea, Portsmouth, Hants PO4 0DP (023 9234 2323)
Ground: Langstone Harbour Sports Ground, Eastern Rd., Portsmouth. Tel: 023 9282 4798
Colours: Yellow & navy/navy/navy

FAREHAM SACRED HEARTS
Secretary: Wallace Arnold, 48 Wallington Shore Road, Fareham, Hants PO16 8SA (01329 510438)
Ground: Thorney Island Bakers Barracks, Emsworth
Colours: Black & white/black/black

FARNBOROUGH NORTH END
Secretary: John Marchment, 4 Linstead Road, Cove, Farnborough, Hants GU14 9HH (01276 34254)
Ground: Farnborough Gate, Ringwood Rd., Farnborough, Hants.
Colours: Red/black/red

FLEETLANDS
Secretary: David Bell, 72 White Hart Lane, Portchester, Hants. PO16 9BQ.(023 9232 1781)
Ground: Lederle Lane, Gosport, Hants (01329 239723)
Colours: Red & black/black/black

FLEET SPURS
Secretary: Steve Houghton, 61 Earlsbourne, Church Crookham, Hants GU52 8XG (01252 815463)
Ground: Kennels Lane, Farnborough, Hants
Colours: Red & blue/blue/blue

HAYLING UNITED
Secretary: Mrs S Westfield, 14 Harold Road, Hayling Island, Hants PO11 9LT (023 9246 3305)
Ground: Hayling Sports Centre, Mengham Park, Hayling Island, Hants Tel: 023 9263 7758
Colours: Black & white/black/black

HEADLEY ATHLETIC
Secretary: Colin Panting, St Helens, 47 Hambridge Road, Newbury, Berks RG14 5ST (01635 32579)
Ground: Headley Rec Ground, Thornford Road, Headley, Thatcham, Berks (01635 268543)
Colours: Blue/white/blue

MICHELDEVER
Secretary: Mrs Mary Green, 19 Southbrook Cottages, Micheldever, Winchester, Hants SO21 3DJ (01962 774251)
Ground: Lord Rank Playing Fields, Duke St., Micheldever, Winchester.
Colours: Navy & white/navy/navy

PAULSGROVE
Secretary: Jim Garcia, 112 Falmouth Road, Paulsgrove, Portsmouth, Hants PO6 4JT
Ground: The Grove Club, Marsden Rd (off Allaway Avenue), Paulsgrove, Portsmouth (023 9232 4102)
Colours: All blue

TADLEY TOWN
Secretary: Steve Blackburn, 7 Bramdean Close, Tadley, Hants RG26 3RD (0118 981 6697)
Ground: The Green, Tadley, Hants
Cols: Yellow & blue/blue/blue

VERWOOD TOWN
Secretary: Mrs J A Fry, 19a Noon Hill Rd, Verwood, Dorset BH31 7DB (01202 822826)
Ground: Potterne Park, Pottern Way, Verwood, Dorset
Colours: Red & white & black/black/red

YATELEY GREEN
Secretary: Alan Baynes, 7 Borderside, Yateley, Camberley Surrey GU46 6LJ (01252 409703)
Ground: Sean Deveraux Park, Chandlers Lane Playing Fields, Yateley
Colours: Green/blue/green

DIVISION TWO CLUBS

BROUGHTON
Ground: The Sportsfield, Buckholt Road, Broughton, Stockbridge, Hants. Tel: 01794 301150

DC AFC
Ground: Victoria Park, Salisbury. Tel: 01722 415089

HAMBLE CLUB
Ground: College Playing Fields, Hamble-le-Rice, Hampshire

HEDGE END
Ground: Norman Rodaway Playing Fields, Heathhouse Lane, Hedge End, Southampton, Hants

KING'S SOMBORNE
Ground: The Recreation Ground, Romsey Road, King's Somborne, Stockbridge, Hants. Tel: 01794 388421

LAVERSTOCK & FORD
Ground: The Dell, Laverstock & Ford Social Club, 23 Church Road, Laverstock, Salisbury, Wilts. Tel: 01722 327401

LUDGERSHALL SPORTS
Ground: Astor Crescent, Ludgershall. Tel: 01264 398200

M & T AWBRIDGE
Ground: Mannyngham Way, Timsbury. Tel: 01794 368955

NETLEY CENTRAL SPORTS
Ground: Station Road Recreation Ground, Netley Abbey, Southampton Tel: 023 8045 2267

ORDNANCE SURVEY
Ground: Stoneham Park, Southampton. Tel: 023 8061 8812

OTTERBOURNE
Ground: Oakwood Park, off Oakwood Ave, Otterbourne, Hants Tel: 01962 714681

OVERTON UNITED
Ground: Overton Recreation Centre, Bridge Street, Overton, Hants Tel: 01256 770561

QK SOUTHAMPTON
Ground: Lordshill Recreation Centre, Southampton Tel: 023 8074 0417

ROMSEY TOWN
Ground: The Bypass Ground, South Front, Romsey, Hants Tel: 01794 512003

KEYLINE DORSET COMBINATION LEAGUE

Founded: 1957

President: Jack Cruickshank   **Chairman:** Alan Burt

Secretary: Geoff Theobald, 41 South Road, Corfe Mullen
Wimborne, Dorset BH21 3HZ   Tel: 01202 697994

FINAL LEAGUE TABLE 2001-02

		P	W	D	L	F	A	Pts
1	Hamworthy Recreation	34	25	5	4	79	27	80
2	Sherborne Town	34	23	6	5	66	34	75
3	Shaftesbury	34	21	8	5	74	37	71
4	Holt United	34	21	6	7	81	42	69
5	Hamworthy United*	34	21	6	7	85	42	66
6	Dorchester Town Res.	34	21	2	11	88	50	65
7	Gillingham Town	34	20	5	9	61	30	65
8	Westland Sports	34	19	4	11	82	55	61
9	Bournemouth Sports*	34	12	6	16	56	63	36
10	Weymouth Sports	34	8	9	17	46	77	33
11	Blandford United	34	9	6	19	30	71	33
12	Bridport Res.	34	9	5	20	35	68	32
13	Cobham Sports	34	7	10	17	38	71	31
14	Sturminster Newton U	34	7	7	20	48	70	28
15	Wareham Rangers*	34	7	9	18	44	73	27
16	Witchampton United	34	6	9	19	38	79	27
17	Allendale	34	6	8	20	46	73	26
18	Stourpaine	34	7	3	24	42	77	24

* points deducted

RESULTS CHART 2001-02

		1	2	3	4	5	6	7	8	9	10	11	12	13	14	15	16	17	18
1	Allendale	X	3-1	2-2	1-0	4-0	2-1	1-3	0-2	5-0	0-2	1-6	1-3	1-2	1-1	1-2	1-3	0-1	1-1
2	Blandford Utd	2-1	X	1-2	1-0	1-0	0-3	0-1	0-3	2-1	3-1	0-1	2-1	1-3	2-2	0-6	0-3	0-0	1-1
3	Bournemouth S	2-0	0-1	X	3-1	1-1	1-1	1-3	3-0	0-3	1-4	1-1	1-4	7-1	3-1	5-1	2-5	5-0	2-0
4	Bridport Res.	0-7	0-1	0-3	X	1-1	3-2	0-1	2-4	2-0	1-1	2-3	0-1	1-2	1-0	2-0	1-2	1-0	1-1
5	Cobham Sports	3-3	5-0	2-0	0-1	X	0-3	1-2	1-0	0-4	1-1	1-2	0-0	2-1	2-0	0-4	0-3	1-2	2-0
6	Dorchester T Rs	8-1	5-0	3-2	4-1	4-0	X	1-2	0-4	3-5	1-2	2-0	0-1	1-0	4-0	5-1	1-0	3-2	4-0
7	Gillingham Town	3-0	3-0	4-1	4-1	6-1	1-1	X	0-1	0-2	1-3	3-2	0-1	0-0	3-1	6-0	4-1	0-0	2-1
8	Hamworthy Rec	2-0	1-0	0-0	3-1	2-2	3-1	1-0	X	1-0	7-0	1-1	4-0	3-0	2-1	2-0	3-2	2-2	5-1
9	Hamworthy Utd	6-0	4-1	2-0	6-0	5-0	4-2	0-0	3-0	X	1-1	0-0	2-2	3-2	3-1	4-2	3-1	1-1	2-2
10	Holt United	2-2	2-2	1-0	6-0	5-1	5-1	3-1	2-0	2-1	X	1-2	2-1	2-1	2-0	0-0	3-1	5-0	1-0
11	Shaftesbury	3-0	2-0	6-1	2-1	3-0	2-1	1-0	0-0	3-2	4-2	X	0-5	2-0	1-1	3-0	2-0	1-3	3-0
12	Sherborne Town	3-1	2-0	2-1	2-0	1-1	1-3	0-0	1-2	1-0	3-2	2-0	X	1-0	2-1	3-1	2-2	2-1	4-0
13	Stourpaine	1-1	2-3	1-1	2-3	3-1	0-5	0-1	0-2	3-4	1-2	1-2	0-1	X	1-4	1-4	0-4	1-2	2-0
14	Sturminster N U	4-3	4-2	4-0	0-0	2-2	2-3	0-1	0-3	1-3	0-3	0-1	2-4	0-4	X	4-0	3-4	5-3	1-0
15	Wareham Rngrs	2-1	1-0	1-2	1-1	1-1	1-2	0-1	0-1	1-3	0-5	1-1	2-2	1-3	1-1	X	0-3	3-3	1-2
16	Westland Sports	1-1	5-0	5-2	2-1	2-1	1-3	3-1	1-2	2-5	3-2	2-4	0-1	3-0	3-1	1-1	X	2-0	7-3
17	Weymouth Spts	1-0	2-2	0-1	1-2	0-2	1-4	2-0	3-1	0-1	0-5	0-8	2-5	7-3	1-1	2-3	1-1	X	1-4
18	Witchampton U	0-0	1-1	2-0	1-4	1-2	2-3	0-4	0-9	1-2	2-1	2-2	1-2	2-1	2-0	2-2	1-4	2-2	X

COMBINATION LEAGUE CUP 2001-02

FIRST ROUND

Bournemouth Sports	v	Hamworthy Utd	1-0		Dorchester Town Res.	v	Sturminster N U	1-0

SECOND ROUND

Allendale	v	Hamworthy Rec	0-4		Blandford United	v	Dorchester Tn Rs. 1-0, 0*0
Bridport Res.	v	Westland	0-1		Gillingham	v	Stourpaine	5-0
Sherborne	v	Cobham Sports	4-3		Wareham	v	Holt United	4*1
Weymouth Sports	v	Shaftesbury	1-2		Witchampton United	v	Bournemouth Sports 2-3

QUARTER-FINALS

Dorchester Town Res	v	Westland Sports	1-2		Hamworthy Rec'n	v	Shaftesbury	1-0
Sherborne Town	v	Bournemouth Sports	2-0		Wareham	v	Gillingham	1-3

SEMI-FINALS

Hamworthy Recreation	v	Gillingham Town	2-3		Sherborne	v	Westland Sports	1-2

FINAL

Gillingham Town	v	Westland Sports	2*1		at Sherborne Town

DORSET COMBINATION CLUBS 2002-03

BLANDFORD UNITED

Chairman:M.Westwood
Secretary: Mrs Catherine Johnson, 37 Damory Street, Blandford Forum, Dorset DT117EU (01258 455899)
Ground: Recreation Ground, Park Road, Blandford Forum, Dorset. (HQ Tel: 01258456374)
Cover: No   Clubhouse: No   Programme: Yes
Colours: All Royal Blue
Change colours: Red/black/green

HAMWORTHY RECREATION

Chairman: M,Robson
Secretary: Ray Willis, 52 Heckford Road, Poole BH15 2LY (01202 773 290)
Ground: Hamworthy Rec. Club, Magna Rd, Canford Magna, Wimborne, Dorset BH21 3AE(01202 881922)
Cover: No   Clubhouse: Yes   Programme: No
Colours: All green.
Change colours: Blue & White stripes/blue/blue.

BOURNEMOUTH SPORTS CLUB

Chairman: I.Hansford

Secretary: Mrs June Johnson,19 Lawns Road, Wimborne,. Bh21 2JP
Tel No: 01202 887195
Ground: Chapel Gate, East Parley, Christchurch, Dorset BH23 6BD (01202 581933)
Cover: No   Clubhouse: Yes   Programme: Yes
Colours: Gold/black/gold   Change colours: All blue

HAMWORTHY UNITED

Chairman: D.Manuel
Secretary: Peter Gallop, 51A Symes Road, Hamworthy, Poole, Dorset BH15 4PR(01202 670792)
Ground: The County Ground, Blandford Close, Hamworthy, Poole, Dorset (01202674974)
Cover: Yes   Floodlights: Yes
Programme: Yes   Clubhouse: Yes
Colours: Maroon & Sky Blue stripes/maroon/maroon
Change colours:Yellow & black stripes/black/black

BRIDPORT Reserves

Chairman: David Fowler
Secretary: Keith Morgan, 95 Orchard Crescent, Bridport DT6 5HA
01308 456142 (H) 01308 424 269 (W)
Ground: The Beehive, St Mary's Field, Bridport, Dorset (01308 423834)
Colours: Red & black/black/red & black
Change colours:All blue.

HOLT UNITED

Ground: Gaunts Common, Holt, Wimborne, Dorset.
    Tel: 01258 840379

Previous League: Dorset County League

COBHAM SPORTS (formerly Flight Refuelling)
Chairman: A Miles
Secretary: Harry W Doyle, 27 Fairview Crescent, Broadstone, Poole BH18 9AL Tel: 01202 698393 (H) 07718 896211 (M)
Ground: Merley Park, Merley, Wimborne, Dorset (01202 885773)
Cover: No   Clubhouse: Yes   Programme: Yes
Colours:Sky blue/navy blue/navyblue.
Change colours: All red

DORCHESTER TOWN Reserves
Chairman: C E Clarke
Secretary: David Martin, 21 Diggory Crescent, Dorchester DT1 2SP
          Tel: 01305 262345 (H)   07971 172795 (M)
Ground: The Avenue Stadium, Dorchester. (01305 262451)
Cover: Yes   Floodlights: Yes   Clubhouse: Yes
Programme: Yes
Colours: Black & white stripes/black/black
Change: All red.

GILLINGHAM TOWN
Chairman: E Murphy
Secretary: David J Ayles, 37 Sylvan Way, Bay Road, Gillingham SP8 4EQ (01747822065)
Ground: Hardings Lane, Gillingham (01747 823673)
Cover: Yes
Programme: Yes   Clubhouse: Yes
Colours: Tangerine/black/tangerine
Change colours: Yellow & green/green/green

STOURPAINE
Chairman: C.Hardiman
Secretary: Rob Turner, 35 Hod View, Stourpaine, BLandford DT11 8TN
Tel : 01258 451691
Ground: Dick Draper Memorial Fields, Stourpaine, Blandford Forum, Dorset Tel: None
Previous league: Dorset County League
Colours: Navy blue & Yellow/navy blue/ yellow & navy blue.
Change Colours: Red & white stripes/red & white/red & white

STURMINSTER NEWTON UNITED
Chairman: A.Stockley
Secretary: Richard Frear 44 Green Close, Sturminster Newton DT10 1BL (01258473036)
Ground: Barnetts Field, Honeymead Lane, Sturminster Newton, Dorset. (01258471406)
Cover: Yes   Clubhouse: No   Programme: Yes
Colours:Red & Black stripes /red/red
Change colours:Blue & Black stripes/blue/blue.

SWANAGE TOWN & HERSTON
Chairman: Len Marsh
Secretary: Eric Webster, 24 James Day Mead, Ulwell Road, Swanage BH191NQ Tel: 01929 423522 (H & Fax)
Ground: Days Park, off De Moulham Road, Swanage, Dorset BH19 Tel: 01929 424633
Previous Leagues: Dorset Combination, Wessex
Colours: White,black and blue.Change colours: All yellow & sky blue
Midweek matchday: Tuesday

POOLE BOROUGH
Ground: Turlin Moor Recretaion Ground, Blandford Moor, Hamworthy, Poole, Dorset. Club Office: 01202 674973
Previous League: Dorset County Lge.

SHAFTESBURY
Chairman: A.P.Humphries
Secretary: Phil Watts, 4 Willow Cottages, Compton Abbas, Shaftesbury SP70NF (01747 811037)
Ground: Cockrams, Coppice Street, Shaftesbury (01747 853990)
Cover: Yes   Floodlights: Yes   Clubhouse: Yes
Colours: Red & white striped/Red/Red
Change colours: Yellow/black/black

SHERBORNE TOWN
Chairman: F Henderson
Secretary: Mike Mock, 67 Yew TRe Close, Yeovil. BA20 2PB Tel Nos: 01935 426219 (H) 01935 703934 (W)
Ground: Raleigh Grove, The Terrace Playing Fields, Sherborne (01935 816110)
Cover: Yes   Clubhouse: Yes   Programme: Yes
Colours: Yellow/black/yellow
Change colours: Black& white/white/black.

WAREHAM RANGERS
Chairman: G.Hawkes
Secretary: Mrs Carol White, 18 Folly Lane, Wareham, Dorset BH20 4HH (01929551765)
Ground: Purbeck Sports Centre,Worgret Rd, Wareham, Dorset
Cover: No   Clubhouse: No   Programme: Yes
Colours: Amber & black/black/black
Change colours:Navy & light blue/ navy/ light blue

WESTLAND SPORTS
Chairman:A.Fisher
Secretary: Dean Vincent, 8 Whitemead, Abbey Manor Park, Yeovil. BA21 3RX Tel NOs: 01935 479971 (H) 01935 705381 (W)
Ground: Westland Sports Ground, Westbourne Close, Yeovil (01935 703810)
Cover: No   Clubhouse: No   Programme: Yes
Colours: Red & Black/Black/Black
C hange colours: All White

WEYMOUTH SPORTS
Chairman: M.Richards
Secretary: Alan Burt, 32 Preston Road, Weymouth, DT3 6PZ Tel Nos: 01305 833256 (H) 01305 773536 (W)
Ground: Weymouth College, Cranford Ave., Weymouth, Dorset (01305 208859/208860)
Colours: Blue & yellow stripes/yellow/blue.
Change: Red/black/red
Prev. Lge: Dorset (champs 1993)

SOUTHERN FINAL LEAGUE TABLES 2001-02

SOUTHAMPTON SENIOR LEAGUE

PREMIER DIVISION

	P	W	D	L	F	A	Pts
Brendon	22	18	3	1	65	20	57
Nursling	22	14	5	3	78	33	47
Botley Village	22	12	5	5	51	29	41
Sporting BTC	22	11	2	9	42	33	35
Durley	22	10	3	9	46	43	33
Fair Oak	22	10	3	9	50	51	33
BTC Soton	22	9	2	11	32	27	29
Eastleigh Comrades	22	9	2	11	43	56	29
Old Tauntonians	22	7	1	14	32	45	22
North Baddesley	22	7	1	14	31	56	22
Lyndhurst	22	6	3	13	33	51	21
Solent Youth	22	3	2	17	22	81	11

PORTSMOUTH SATURDAY LEAGUE

PREMIER DIVISION

	P	W	D	L	F	A	Pts
Shearer Vat	14	11	0	3	72	32	*30
Kingston Arrows	14	9	2	3	68	44	29
Havelock Rovers	14	9	2	3	45	29	29
Fareham Sacred Heart	14	6	2	6	45	42	20
Alite Glazing	14	5	1	8	38	49	16
Royal TML	14	4	2	8	32	39	14
Portsmouth University	14	4	0	10	34	55	12
Wanderers	14	2	3	9	29	61	9

ISLE OF WIGHT SATURDAY LEAGUE

DIVISION ONE

	P	W	D	L	F	A	Pts
West Wight	22	15	4	3	53	17	49
Shanklin	22	15	2	5	79	26	47
East Cowes Vic	22	14	1	7	73	32	43
Binstead	22	13	3	6	56	35	42
W/B Sports	22	11	4	7	37	35	37
Redstar Spartans	22	11	3	8	60	43	36
Cowes Sports	22	10	2	10	51	36	32
Oakfield	22	9	4	9	46	37	31
Newport	22	9	3	10	46	39	*28
Brading Town	22	6	4	12	42	56	22
Brighstone	22	3	0	19	20	85	*7
Seaview	22	1	0	21	11	134	3

WEST SUSSEX LEAGUE

PREMIER DIVISION

	P	W	D	L	F	A	Pts
Midhurst E	22	21	0	1	96	15	63
Yapton	22	14	3	5	50	29	45
The Ship Aldwick	22	13	3	6	39	34	42
Alford	22	13	1	8	66	41	40
Henfield	22	12	2	8	60	41	38
Rustington	22	9	3	10	41	53	30
Rogate	22	9	2	11	50	48	29
Stedham United	22	7	4	11	30	40	25
Royal Sun Insurance	22	6	5	11	37	52	23
Ferring	22	6	1	15	47	72	19
Faygate United	22	4	4	14	22	51	16
Southwater	22	3	2	17	23	85	11

ANDOVER & DISTRICT LEAGUE

DIVISION ONE

	P	W	D	L	F	A	Pts
Picket Piece S & S	16	10	3	3	42	24	33
Vernham Dean	16	9	4	3	35	25	31
Inkpen Sports	16	8	4	4	50	33	28
ABC United	16	9	0	7	56	37	27
Borough Arms	16	8	3	5	41	36	27
Welly	16	8	2	6	50	51	26
St Ives (Andover)	16	5	2	9	44	48	17
Kings Somborne	16	3	0	13	23	62	9
Inkpen Exiles	16	2	2	12	17	42	8

KINGSTON & DISTRICT LEAGUE

PREMIER DIVISION

	P	W	D	L	F	A	Pts
Heathfield	16	10	2	4	40	26	32
Kingston ACAS	16	8	4	4	37	26	28
Kingston Albion	16	7	5	4	34	23	26
Westside	16	6	5	5	31	34	23
Chessington KC	16	6	4	6	36	34	22
Surbiton Griffins	16	6	3	7	36	31	21
Maori Park	16	6	3	7	31	36	21
HBG Double H	16	4	3	9	20	35	15
Hook Venturers	16	3	3	10	23	43	12

HERTS & DISTRICT LEAGUE

PREMIER DIVISION

	P	W	D	L	F	A	Pts
Hertford Heath	20	16	1	3	74	22	33
Little Munden	20	16	1	3	56	19	33
Westmill	20	14	2	4	60	27	30
Knebworth	20	11	3	6	34	25	25
Bengeo Trinity	20	8	6	6	37	36	22
Watton-At-Stone	20	7	3	10	32	41	17
Broxbourne Badgers	20	6	4	10	41	65	16
Greenbury United	20	6	3	11	44	65	15
Sawbridge Gate	20	5	2	13	34	73	12
Wodson Park	20	4	2	14	35	47	10
Allenburys Sports	20	2	3	15	32	59	7

EAST SUSSEX LEAGUE

PREMIER DIVISION

	P	W	D	L	F	A	Pts
Hollington United	18	13	2	3	51	28	41
Bexhill AAc	18	12	1	5	42	22	37
Wadhurst United	18	12	0	6	52	21	36
Little Common	18	11	3	4	55	28	36
Willingdon Athletic	18	8	2	8	33	35	26
Rock-A-Nore	18	8	3	7	33	39	27
Peche Hill Select	18	4	8	6	22	35	20
East Hoathly	18	4	3	11	37	47	15
Northiam '75	18	4	2	12	24	53	14
Sandhurst	18	2	0	16	16	57	6

694

SCREWFIX DIRECT
WESTERN LEAGUE

President: Rod Webber   **Chairman:** Cliff Ashton

Secretary: Ken Clarke, 32 Westmead Lane, Chippenham, Wiltshire SN15 3HZ
Tel: 01249 464467 **Fax:** 01249 652952 **Email:** westernleague@aol.com
www.firsteleven.co.uk/western

It was January and most clubs had played more than half their games before Bideford moved into the top three. This was due to the North Devon club's progress in both the FA Cup and FA Vase as well as the Les Phillips Cup. Going out to Basingstoke in the third qualifying round was the best any Western League club managed in last term's FA Cup.

Bideford settled down and always looked good for the league and cup double, which they achieved. Taunton Town made their intentions to accept promotion to the Southern League known to all – leaving the team the job of achieving a top two position. It was very much fought to the wire, with Odd Down making sure that Taunton's very last match was no walkover, with Taunton grabbing the required point needed, from the penalty spot, with almost the last kick of the season. Taunton could not defend their FA Vase achievement of the previous year, failing to take home advantage in the replay against Tiptree United in the fifth round proper.

Brislington narrowly failed to thwart Taunton's plans, missing second spot on goal difference. Team Bath finished strongly, but never recovered from a very poor start to their campaign. Devizes Town, Dawlish Town, Paulton Rovers and Bridgwater were good, above average sides, and kept everyone guessing by regularly exchanging positions. Backwell United, Melksham Town and Barnstaple proved to be solid, middle table, teams, and each produced good football at times. Keynsham Town, Elmore and Bishop Sutton were close to the relegation zone at various stages of the season, but never looked in any real danger. The woes of the Yeovil Town pitch continued, and the reserve side finished the campaign as visitors to all opponents, when the playing surface was declared unable to sustain matches at both Conference and Western League level. The club had already signalled their intention to resign at the end of the season.

Bridport, Welton Rovers, Bristol Manor Farm and Westbury United fought to avoid the drop, but the last two named failed to amass enough points to stay in the top flight.

Bath City Reserves stated their aims very early and sat in the top two of the First Division for the whole campaign. Frome Town moved steadily up the table, but were also playing a major part in the Les Phillips Cup, missing out in the final to on-song Bideford. When Frome Town moved to top spot it was left for Bath City Reserves and Exmouth Town to contest the second promotion spot, which the Twerton Park outfit almost gave away with a player registration mess-up. Exmouth Town were well worth their third position, and must start favourites in the new campaign. Torrington surprised many by finishing fourth and fifth placed Clyst Rovers suffered no ill effects from the, enforced, premature end to the 2000-01 season. Bitton, Shepton Mallet, Street and Corsham all looked possible of greater things, and certainly deserved to be above mid-table. Hallen faced catastrophe when the sacked manager took all but two or three players away with him, and to finish mid-table bore testament to a strong backroom setup. Larkhall Athletic, Weston St Johns, Ilfracombe Town and Willand Rovers seemed to promise more than their lowly positions suggest, but continued to enjoy their football. Cadbury Heath, Wellington and Minehead were troubled much of the season by lack of consistency, reflecting uncertainty at management level. Calne Town and Warminster Town looked likely relegation candidates from mid season, and it was only a lack of promotion candidates from lower down that saved Calne from the drop, for a second successive season. Warminster Town were the unlucky club to return to County football, but with the Western League committed to movement within the pyramid of football the decision was inevitable.

The Les Phillips Cup produced some excitement, but few surprises. However, Bitton only fell to Frome Town on penalties. The final, an impressive looking prospect with the top of each division the contestants, proved to be a fairly dull affair, with neither Bideford or Frome Town producing displaying their league flair, with a formbook result 2 – 1 in Bideford's favour. Hosted by Bath City the organisation and hospitality were a credit both to the Club and the League. The Western League continues to enjoy a fine reputation in all aspects of the non-league game and have been active in promoting planned changes to the structure, after receiving a clear mandate from member clubs via an extensive questionnaire.

FINAL LEAGUE TABLES 2001-02

PREMIER DIVISION

		P	W	D	L	F	A	Pts
1	Bideford	38	28	7	3	105	37	91
2	Taunton Town	38	26	5	7	104	43	83
3	Brislington	38	24	11	3	72	32	83
4	Team Bath	38	22	7	9	74	36	73
5	Devizes Town	38	22	4	12	72	51	70
6	Dawlish Town	38	21	6	11	86	56	69
7	Paulton Rovers	38	18	11	9	77	54	65
8	Bridgwater Town	38	17	9	12	53	45	60
9	Backwell United	38	16	9	13	56	41	57
10	Melksham Town	38	15	9	14	47	46	54
11	Odd Down	38	13	11	14	49	45	50
12	Barnstaple Town	38	12	8	18	57	66	44
13	Keynsham Town	38	11	9	18	47	71	42
14	Elmore	38	10	7	21	47	96	37
15	Bishop Sutton	38	9	8	21	53	89	35
16	Yeovil Town Res	38	10	4	24	57	86	34
17	Bridport	38	9	6	23	51	86	33
18	Welton Rovers	38	7	9	22	46	67	30
19	Bristol Manor Farm	38	7	8	23	30	80	29
20	Westbury United	38	7	4	27	35	91	25

DIVISION ONE

		P	W	D	L	F	A	Pts
1	Frome Town	38	29	5	4	104	22	92
2	Bath City Reserves*	38	24	12	2	79	22	81
3	Exmouth Town	38	23	11	4	84	39	80
4	Torrington	38	23	5	10	87	49	74
5	Clyst Rovers	38	18	11	9	73	53	65
6	Bitton	38	18	9	11	66	55	63
7	Shepton Mallet Town	38	18	8	12	59	47	62
8	Street	38	17	10	11	76	58	61
9	Corsham Town	38	14	13	11	55	48	55
10	Hallen	38	16	6	16	69	60	54
11	Chard Town	38	14	8	16	66	59	50
12	Larkhall Athletic	38	13	8	17	55	71	47
13	Weston St Johns	38	13	7	18	71	78	46
14	Ilfracombe Town	38	14	4	20	59	84	46
15	Willand Rovers	38	9	15	14	59	58	42
16	Cadbury Heath	38	10	7	21	55	84	37
17	Wellington	38	9	8	21	48	89	35
18	Minehead Town	38	9	5	24	52	90	32
19	Calne Town	38	6	7	25	40	86	25
20	Warminster Town	38	2	3	33	35	140	9

* points deducted

25 in 25

A review of the progress made by the **Western League** and its member clubs during the twenty-five year life span of the F.A. Non-League Club Directory (1978 - 2002) will be available in the next year. It will be one of a series of 25 and will contain features, statistics and photos in at least 160 pages dedicated purely to the Western League members.

Further details can be found on page 17 so make sure of your copy of this exciting limited edition.

PREMIER DIVISION RESULTS CHART 2001-02

		1	2	3	4	5	6	7	8	9	10	11	12	13	14	15	16	17	18	19	20
1	Backwell U	X	5-0	0-2	1-1	1-2	1-1	1-2	3-1	3-0	0-0	3-0	0-1	1-3	0-1	1-1	1-3	2-1	4-1	1-0	3-1
2	Barnstaple T	1-2	X	4-2	2-3	0-2	2-0	0-2	3-0	3-2	3-0	0-2	0-2	1-1	1-0	3-3	0-2	1-2	1-2	1-1	5-3
3	Bideford	2-2	2-0	X	5-1	4-1	3-1	3-3	3-0	2-0	1-1	5-0	2-1	1-0	1-1	4-2	2-1	0-1	2-1	7-0	6-0
4	Bishop Sutton	1-2	0-4	0-5	X	0-3	5-3	0-4	0-0	0-4	2-2	4-1	6-0	2-2	0-2	0-4	3-3	0-0	1-1	2-0	0-1
5	Bridgwater T	0-0	1-1	2-3	2-3	X	2-1	0-2	1-0	0-3	1-3	2-0	1-1	3-1	1-0	0-1	1-3	1-1	1-0	5-0	4-3
6	Bridport	1-1	2-3	0-3	0-1	0-1	X	0-2	3-0	1-2	0-5	1-0	3-4	0-1	3-3	0-4	0-5	0-6	2-2	2-0	2-0
7	Brislington	1-0	4-1	3-3	1-0	0-0	4-1	X	3-1	4-2	2-1	4-0	3-2	3-0	2-1	0-0	0-0	1-2	4-1	2-0	1-0
8	Bristol M F	0-4	0-0	1-2	1-4	2-0	1-0	1-1	X	0-3	1-3	1-1	0-2	0-2	1-0	0-2	0-5	1-1	2-1	3-1	1-1
9	Dawlish T	1-1	3-2	1-2	2-1	2-2	2-4	4-1	8-1	X	2-3	3-0	3-2	1-1	2-1	1-0	3-1	1-0	3-1	4-0	5-0
10	Devizes T	0-4	1-0	2-0	3-0	1-0	6-3	1-2	0-0	1-3	X	5-2	3-1	3-0	0-2	4-1	3-2	0-2	2-1	4-0	2-1
11	Elmore	1-2	2-1	3-3	3-0	1-0	3-4	0-0	3-1	0-6	0-4	X	3-1	3-1	3-3	0-1	1-2	0-6	1-1	2-1	3-4
12	Keynsham T	0-2	2-2	0-4	2-1	1-1	0-4	0-0	1-1	0-0	0-2	1-2	X	0-1	2-2	0-0	0-1	1-2	1-3	5-0	3-1
13	Melksham T	1-0	1-1	1-1	2-1	1-2	1-1	0-0	4-1	3-0	3-0	2-1	0-2	X	1-0	1-2	0-3	1-2	2-1	2-0	2-1
14	Odd Down	2-0	0-1	1-0	1-1	0-4	1-0	2-0	3-1	2-1	3-1	0-0	1-1	0-0	X	1-1	0-0	0-1	2-3	4-1	2-0
15	Paulton R	2-1	2-5	1-3	4-2	1-1	3-1	2-2	6-0	1-1	0-1	2-3	6-0	1-1	1-0	X	1-4	2-2	2-1	7-2	4-2
16	Taunton T	1-2	3-1	1-4	7-2	1-2	3-1	2-3	2-1	5-1	1-0	6-0	1-0	1-0	3-3	5-0	X	0-0	3-2	3-0	4-1
17	Team Bath	0-1	2-0	1-2	4-0	3-1	1-2	0-2	1-0	5-1	5-0	4-2	7-0	2-1	1-0	1-1	1-6	X	0-1	2-0	2-2
18	Welton R	0-0	2-3	0-1	3-1	1-2	1-1	0-0	1-2	0-1	0-1	1-1	1-4	1-0	0-3	1-2	3-4	0-1	X	2-2	2-2
19	Westbury U	2-0	3-1	1-4	0-3	0-0	1-2	1-3	2-1	2-2	1-3	1-0	1-2	4-0	2-0	0-3	1-3	0-1	1-3	X	4-0
20	Yeovil T	4-1	0-0	0-2	5-2	0-1	3-1	0-1	0-3	1-3	2-1	10-0	1-2	0-4	1-3	0-1	0-4	3-1	2-1	2-0	X

LES PHILLIPS CHALLENGE CUP 2001-02

PRELIMINARY ROUND

Bath City Reserves	v	Westbury United	5-1	Bishop Sutton	v	Wellington	1-2
Brislington	v	Team Bath	4-0	Chard Town	v	Paulton Rovers	1-7
Clyst Rovers	v	Bideford	1-9	Hallen	v	Taunton Town	2-6
Minehead Town	v	Melksham Town	2*4	Welton Rovers	v	Ilfracombe Town	3-1

FIRST ROUND

Backwell United	v	Bristol Manor Fm	4p3, 1*1	Barnstaple Town	v	Larkhall Athletic	2-1
Bitton	v	Welton Rovers	3-0	Brislington	v	Bridport	2-1
Calne Town	v	Street	1-2	Corsham Town	v	Shepton Mallet Town	2-0
Dawlish Town	v	Keynsham Town	4-3	Devizes Town	v	Cadbury Heath	2-1
Elmore	v	Warminster Town	5-0	Exmouth Town	v	Frome Town	2-3
Melksham Town	v	Wellington	7-0	Odd Down	v	Paulton Rovers	0-3
Taunton Town	v	Bath Res	3-1	Torrington	v	Yeovil Town Res	2-0
Weston St Johns	v	Bridgwater Town	1-0	Willand Rovers	v	Bideford	1*3

SECOND ROUND

Backwell United	v	Corsham Town	1*0	Barnstaple Town	v	Paulton Rovers	0-1
Brislington	v	Elmore	2-0	Devizes Town	v	Bideford	1-2
Melksham Town	v	Dawlish Town	3-2	Taunton Town	v	Street	4-2
Torrington	v	Bitton	1*2	Weston St Johns	v	Frome Town	1-5
Brislington expelled							

QUARTER FINALS

Bideford	v	Backwell	1*0	Bitton	v	Melksham Town	2-0
Frome Town	v	Elmore	3-1	Taunton Town	v	Paulton Rovers	2-1

SEMI FINALS

Bitton	v	Frome Town	2p3, 3*3	Taunton Town	v	Bideford	2-3

FINAL

Bideford	v	Frome Town	2-1	at Bath City

PREMIER DIVISION RESULTS CHART 2001-02

		1	2	3	4	5	6	7	8	9	10	11	12	13	14	15	16	17	18	19	20
1	Bath City Res	X	3-1	3-1	3-0	2-0	0-0	1-1	5-1	0-0	2-0	5-0	3-1	4-0	1-1	2-0	1-1	1-1	0-0	2-0	1-1
2	Bitton	0-2	X	3-0	3-0	2-1	0-0	3-1	0-0	0-1	1-1	2-1	3-1	3-1	1-2	1-1	1-0	2-0	3-2	3-3	2-1
3	Cadbury Heath	2-1	1-1	X	2-1	2-1	0-1	0-1	2-3	0-1	2-3	3-4	1-2	2-2	1-2	1-0	0-3	4-3	2-0	4-2	2-2
4	Calne Town	0-1	1-1	2-1	x	0-0	2-3	0-3	0-3	0-1	1-2	2-2	0-1	0-1	1-1	0-3	1-4	4-0	5-2	1-1	1-1
5	Chard Town	1-3	1-2	2-2	3-2	X	1-3	0-1	2-4	2-3	1-3	5-0	1-2	1-0	1-1	0-3	2-3	3-0	3-0	1-1	2-1
6	Clyst Rovers	3-2	5-1	3-3	3-0	1-1	X	0-0	0-1	0-1	4-3	3-1	2-2	4-1	1-2	2-1	5-2	3-0	0-1	2-1	0-2
7	Corsham Town	1-1	2-1	4-1	2-1	1-1	2-4	X	3-3	0-4	1-1	2-2	1-1	4-0	1-2	2-3	1-0	3-0	2-2	2-2	0-1
8	Exmouth Town	2-3	4-1	3-1	6-0	0-0	1-1	1-0	X	0-0	0-1	2-0	4-0	2-1	1-1	3-1	4-3	6-1	3-0	3-2	1-1
9	Frome Town	0-2	4-0	6-0	3-0	2-1	3-0	3-1	1-1	X	4-1	4-1	4-0	7-0	1-0	4-1	0-2	6-0	6-0	4-0	3-2
10	Hallen	0-4	1-2	0-2	7-0	0-2	4-0	0-1	1-4	1-0	X	4-2	0-1	6-2	0-1	1-2	1-4	6-0	3-2	1-2	1-1
11	Ilfracombe Town	0-3	3-2	3-1	2-1	1-4	2-0	0-2	1-0	0-1	2-2	X	3-1	1-0	1-2	1-0	0-1	3-1	4-6	1-3	1-4
12	Larkhall Athletic	1-2	2-5	1-1	1-2	3-1	0-2	0-0	2-4	3-1	1-0	3-1	X	1-1	1-2	1-1	0-1	0-1	2-1	3-3	3-4
13	Minehead Town	1-3	2-1	1-3	1-3	0-1	0-2	2-2	1-2	0-4	1-1	4-3	1-0	X	0-2	3-2	1-4	5-2	6-0	0-2	1-5
14	Shepton Mallet Tn	0-1	2-2	1-0	4-1	4-2	4-0	1-1	0-3	1-1	1-2	2-3	1-3	2-1	X	1-2	2-0	3-1	1-1	1-2	2-0
15	Street	1-1	1-3	5-3	1-0	1-3	3-3	2-0	0-0	1-1	3-3	2-1	4-1	3-1	0-2	X	1-1	8-0	1-1	2-1	3-2
16	Torrington	0-3	3-2	4-1	3-0	1-1	1-1	2-1	0-0	0-2	3-1	2-3	3-1	3-2	4-1	0-2	X	3-2	3-0	1-3	6-0
17	Warminster Town	0-4	0-1	1-3	2-4	2-6	0-3	1-2	1-4	1-7	1-3	1-2	2-3	1-5	1-4	2-2	1-5	X	0-1	0-10	1-1
18	Wellington	1-1	0-2	4-0	4-2	1-3	3-3	0-2	1-2	1-6	0-2	1-0	2-3	1-1	1-0	0-5	1-3	2-1	X	3-2	0-3
19	Weston St Johns	0-3	1-4	4-0	2-2	2-4	0-4	2-1	1-2	0-3	0-2	1-2	2-3	2-1	2-0	4-1	1-6	2-3	2-1	X	1-1
20	Willand Rovers	0-0	1-1	1-1	3-0	0-2	2-2	0-1	1-1	0-2	0-1	2-2	1-1	1-2	2-0	3-4	0-2	6-1	2-2	1-2	X

PAST RECORDS
WESTERN FOOTBALL LEAGUE CHAMPIONS

1981-82	Bideford	1992-93	Tiverton Town
1982-83	Bideford	1993-94	Tiverton Town
1983-84	Exmouth Town	1994-95	Tiverton Town
1984-85	Saltash United	1995-96	Taunton Town
1985-86	Exmouth Town	1996-97	Tiverton Town
1986-87	Saltash United	1997-98	Tiverton Town
1987-88	Liskeard Athletic	1998-99	Taunton Town
1988-89	Saltash United	1999-00	Taunton Town
1989-90	Taunton Town	2000-01	Taunton Town
1990-91	Weston-super-Mare	2001-02	Bideford
1991-92	Clevedon Town		

WESTERN FOOTBALL LEAGUE FIRST DIVISION CHAMPIONS

1981-82	Shepton Mallet	1992-93	Odd Down
1982-83	Bristol Manor Farm	1993-94	Barnstaple Town
1983-84	Bristol City Reserves	1994-95	Brislington
1984-85	Portway-Bristol	1995-96	Bridgwater Town
1985-86	Portway-Bristol	1996-97	Melksham Town
1986-87	Swanage Town & Herston	1997-98	Bishop Sutton
1987-88	Welton Rovers	1998-99	Minehead
1988-89	Larkhall Athletic	1999-00	Devizes Town
1989-90	Ottery St Mary	2000-01	Team Bath
1990-91	Minehead	2001-02	Frome Town
1991-92	Westbury United		

LES PHILLIPS CHALLENGE CUP WINNERS

1989-90	Plymouth Argyle Reserves	1996-97	Tiverton Town
1990-91	Elmore	1997-98	Tiverton Town
1991-92	Plymouth Argyle Reserves	1998-99	Yeovil Town Reserves
1992-93	Tiverton Town	1999-00	Chippenham Town
1993-94	Tiverton Town	2000-01	Chippenham Town
1994-95	Elmore	2001-02	Bideford
1995-96	Tiverton Town		

BACKWELL UNITED

Secretary: Jonathon Rpogers,114 Wellington Hill West,Westbury on Trym, Bristol BS9 4QY
Tel No: 0117 985 6138
Ground: Backwell Recreation Ground, West Town Rd, Backwell, Avon Tel: 1275 462612

Directions: Near centre of Backwell on main A370 Bristol to Weston-super-Mare road. Buses from Bristol or Weston, or 20 mins walk from Nailsea & Backwell(BR) station; turn right out of station, right at traffic lights (half mile),ground quarter mile on right just past car sales
Capacity: 1,000   Seats: 60 Cover: 150   Floodlights: Yes
Clubhouse: Open 6-11pm weekdays, 12.30-11pm Sat. Snacks available   Club Shop: No

HONOURS   Somerset Snr Lg 77-78 79-80 80-81 81-82 82-83 (Lg Cup 82-83 (R-up 79-80)
Div 1 72-73); Somerset Snr Cup 81-82; SW Co.'s Sutton Transformer Cup 81-82.
Western Lge Div 1 89-90 Champions, 94-95 promoted in 3rd place
PREVIOUS   Leagues: Clevedon & Dist; Bristol C. of E.; Bristol Surburban (pre 1970);
Somerset Senior 70-83
Grounds: Two in Backwell prior to 1939. Club reformed in 1946
RECORD   Attendance: 487 v Brislington, Gt Mills Lg. 2/5/94
Goalscorer: Steve Spalding   **Appearances:** Wayne Buxton
Win: 10-1 v Dowton, F.A.Cup 1st Qualifying Round. 1998-99
Defeat: 2-6 v Tiverton Town (H), Les Phillips Cup QF 1.2.94

FACT FILE
Founded: 1911
Nickname: Stags
Club Sponsors: C W Jones Carpets
Colours: Red & black,white,red &black
Change colours: Black & white
Midweek Matches: Tuesday
Programme: 42 pages, 50p
Editor: Dick Cole (01275 463627)

CLUB PERSONNEL
Chairman: John Southern
Vice-Chairman: Peter Higgins
President: John Southern
Press Officer:Mike Naylor (01275 858576)
Manager:Jamie Patch
Asst Manager: Shaun Penny
Physio: Steve Tregale

BARNSTAPLE TOWN

Secretary: David Cooke, 51 Walnut Way, Whiddon Valley, Barnstaple, Devon. EX32 7RF
Tel: 01271 326088
Ground: Mill Road, Barnstaple, North Devon Tel: 01271 343469
Directions: A361 towards Ilfracombe (from M5 Jct 26), in Barnstaple follow A36 1Ilfracombe signs, second left after crossing small bridge is Mill Road
Capacity: 5,000   Seats: 250   Cover: 1,000   Floodlights: Yes
Clubhouse: Full license with canteen on match days.
HONOURS   Western Lg 52-53 79-80 (R-up 80-81 81-82), Div 1 49-50 94-95, Merit Cup74-75
83-84 84-85, Comb. 92-93), Devon Professional Cup 62-63 64-65 67-68 69-70
71-73 (X2) 74-75 76-81 (X5), Devon Lg, Devon St Lukes Cup 87-88, Devon Snr
Cup 92-93, Devon Youth Cup 48-49 51-52
PREVIOUS   Leagues: Nth Devon, Devon & Exeter, S. Western   **Name:** Pilton Yeo Vale
Grounds: Town Wharf (> 1920); Highfield Rd, Newport (> 35), Pilton Pk, Rock Pk
RECORDS   Attendance: 6,200 v Bournemouth, FA Cup 1st Rd, 54**Appearances:** Ian Pope
Win: 12-1 v Tavistock (H), FA Cup 3rd Qual. Rd 1954 **Defeat:** 1-10 v Mangotsfield Utd (A), West
Lge Prem. Div. 90-91 **Fee out:** £4,000 to Hungerford T for Joe Scott **Fee in** £6,000 for Ian Doyle
from Bristol City **BEST SEASON** F.A Cup: 1st Rd replay 51-52 **FA Vase:** 4th Rd 94-95
Players progressing: Len Pickard (Bristol R. 51), John Neale (Exeter72), Barrie Vassallo
(Torquay 77), Ian Doyle (Bristol C. 78), Ryan Souter (Swindon 94), Jason Cadie (Reading 94),
Simon Heal (Cardiff City -02)

FACT FILE
Founded: 1906
Nickname: Barum
Sponsors:Blue Sky
Colours: Red/red/red
Change colours: All Blue
Midweek Matches: Tuesday
Reserve League: Devon & Exeter
Programme: 70p
Programme Editor: David Cooke
Local Press: N. Devon Journal Herald

CLUB PERSONNEL
President: Wilf Harris
Chairman: John Cann
Manager: John Hore
Physio: Paul Brown
2001-02
Captain & P.o.Y.: Danny Harris.
Top Scorer: Kevin Squire 21

BATH CITY RESERVES

Secretary: Quentin Edwards c/o the club.
Tel: 01225 359087 (H) 01225 423087 (B) & 07785 795532 (M)
Email Address: office@bathcityfc.freeserve.co.uk

Ground: Twerton Park, Twerton, Bath Avon BA2 1DB
Tel: 01225 423087/313247 Fax: 01225 481391

Directions: Twerton Park is situated on the A4/A36 Lower Bristol Road - on the Bristol side
of Bath City Centre (Approx 2.5 miles). The area is serviced by J18 on the M4.
From the centre of Bath the bus route is No.5 - Twerton High Street
Capacity: 8,840   Seated: 1,017   Covered Terracing: 4,800

Clubhouse: Several bars open all week and full service with menu on match-days catering
for up to 250 people
Club Shop: Contact Mr M. Brush c/o the club

FACT FILE
Founded: 1889
Nickname: Stripes & The City
Midweek matchday: Wednesday
Colours: Black & white stripes/black/b & w
Change: All yellow
Website: www.bathcityfc.com

CLUB PERSONNEL
Chairman: Stephen Hall
Commercial Director: G Todd
Press Officer: P Weaver

Manager: Dave Hobb s Tel: 01225 840619

2001-02
Capt & P.o.Y.: Lee Burns
Top scorer: Graham Maclean

BIDEFORD

Secretary: Kevin Tyrrell, 69 Laurel Ave., Bideford, devon EX39 3AZ Tel: 01237 4707747

Ground: The Sports Ground, Kingsley Road, Bideford Tel: 01237 474975

Directions: A361 for Bideford - ground on right as you enter the town
Capacity: 6,000   Seats: 120   Cover: 1,000   Floodlights: Yes
Clubhouse: 'Robins Nest' - on ground. Open lunchtimes and evenings, snacks and bar menu.
Mgr: Mrs Sue Tyrell

HONOURS Western Lg 63-64 70-7171-72 81-82 82-83, Div 1 51-52, Div 3 49-50, Lg Cup 71-72 84-85; Alan Young Cup 64-65 69-70; Merit Cup 68-69; Subsidiary Cup 71-72; Devon Snr Cup 79-80; Devon St Lukes Cup 81-82 83-84 85-86 95-96 (R-up 86-87 91-92 94-95)

PREVIOUS   Leagues: Devon & Exeter 47-49; Western 49-72; Southern 72-75
Name: Bideford Town   **Ground:** Hansen Ground (1 season)

BEST SEASON   FA Cup: 1st Rd 64-65(replay) 73-74 77-78 81-82. **FA Vase:**

RECORD   Gate: 6,000 v Gloucester C., FA Cup 4th Qual. Rd 60
Scorer: Tommy Robinson 259   **Appearances:** Derek May 527
Win: 16-0 v Soundwell 50-51   **Defeat:** 0-12 v Paulton 96-97

Players progressing: Shaun Taylor (Swindon Town) Tony Dennis (Cambridge)

FACT FILE
Founded: 1949
Nickname: Robins
Colours: All Red
Change colours: All Blue
Midweek Matchday: Tuesday
Prog: 32 pages, 50p Editor: Ian Knight

CLUB PERSONNEL
Chairman: Paul Mitchell
President: Jimmy McElwee
Hon.Vice Predident: Kevin Keegan
Company Secretary: B.Weston
Marketing & Promotions Exec. Sean Joyce
Assistant Secrtary: Ron Ackland
Manager: Sean Joyce Ass. Man: Mike Jones
Reserves Manager: Dave Matthews
Chief Scout Dudley Barry
Physio: Tony Beal

BISHOP SUTTON

Secretary: Roy Penney, 53 Ridgway Lane, Whitchurch, Bristol BS14 9PJ Tel: 01275 541392

Ground: Lakeview Football Field, Bishop Sutton Tel: 01275 333097

Directions: On A368 at rear of Butchers Arms pub - ground signposted on left entering village from the West
Capacity: 1,500   Seats: None   Cover: 200   Floodlights: yes
Clubhouse: Open matchdays. Rolls, pies and usual pub food available   Club Shop: No

HONOURS Somerset Snr Lg R-up 89-90 (Div 1 83-84 (R-up 81-82), Div 2 82-83), Bristol & Avon Lg 80-81 (Div 2 79-80), Somerset Jnr Cup 80-81, Weston Yth Lg77-78, Chew Valley KO Cup 83-84, Mid-Somerset Lg(Res) R-up 82-83 (Div 3 81-82)

PREVIOUS   Leagues: Weston & Dist. Yth; Bristol & Avon; Somerset Snr (pre 1991)
Ground: Adjacent cricket field

BEST SEASON   FA Cup: **FA Vase: 3rd Rd 1998**

CLUB RECORDS Attendance: 400 v Bristol City, friendly
Win: 15-0 v Glastonbury Res

Players progressing: David Lee (Chelsea), S Williams (Southampton), J French(Bristol R.)

FACT FILE
Founded: 1977
Nickname: Bishops
Sponsors: Symes Off License
Colours: All blue
Change colours: All yellow
Midweek Matches: Wednesday
Youth team's League: Somerset Mid Week
Programme: Yes
Editor: G Williams

CLUB PERSONNEL
Chairman: George Williams
Vice Chairman: Roy Penney
President: Bob Redding
Manager: Tony Cornelious
Coach: Peter Wills
Physio: Chris Bailes

BRIDGWATER TOWN (1984)

General Secretary: Mrs Glenda Fletcher,18 Dunkery Road, Bridgwater Tel:01278 425599
Football Secretary: Ray Heard, 4 Bush Road,Spaxton, Bridgwater
Tel Nos: 01278 671373 (H) 01278 446922 (W)
Ground: Fairfax Park, College Way, Bath Road, Bridgwater Tel: 01278 446899
(matchdays and weekday mornings only -it is not a postal address).
Website: www.bridgwatertownfc.com
Directions: M5 jct 23, follow signs to Glastonbury (A39), turn right for Bridgwater (A39).
Follow sign to Bridgwater College via College Way.Ground on rt after Rugby Club
One mile from Bridgwater (BR) station

Capacity: 2,500   **Seats:** 150   **Cover:** 400   **Floodlights:** Yes

Clubhouse: Robins social club on the Ground with refreshmants cabin on matchdays

HONOURS Somerset Senior Cup 93-94, Somerset Senior Lge 89-90 90-91 91-92 , Lg Cup winners (3) ,Western Lge Div 1 95-96, Merit cup 96-97 Somerset Senior Cup: 93-94 95-96

PREVIOUS   League: Somerset Snr (pre-1994)**Names:** None
BEST SEASONFA Cup: 2nd Q Rd   **FA Vase:** First Round Proper

RECORDS   Attendance: 1,112 v Taunton Town 26.2. 97

FACT FILE
Founded: 1984 after collapse of previous BTFC
Nickname: The Robins
Sponsor: TMB Patterns Ltd
Colours: Red,white & black/black/red
Change colours: All blue
Midweek matchday: Tuesday
Youth League.: Somerset U18 Floodlight
Prog. Editor: Mark Hollidge ,8 Conway Road, Cannington , Bridgwater TA5 2NP

CLUB PERSONNEL
Chairman: Steve French
Patron & President: Tom Pearce
Press Officer: Gordon Nelson (01823 271167)
Manager: Trevor Senior
Sports Injury Therapist: Dave Callow
L.C.S.P.(Assoc): F.A.Dip.

BRIDPORT

Secretary: Keith Morgan,95 Orchard Crescent, Bridport,Dorset DT6 5HA (01308 425113)
Email Address: ian@newsport.freeserve.co.uk and FAX: 01308 867422
Ground: The Beehive, St Mary's Field, Bridport, Dorset Tel: 01308 423834
Directions: Take West Bay road from town centre, turn right just before Palmers Brewery
Capacity: 2,000 Seats: 200 Cover: 400 Floodlights: Yes Club Shop: No
Clubhouse: Yes, open matchdays and for functions. Hot and cold snacks available

HONOURS Western Lg Cup 70-71 72-73 77-78 (R-up 76-77, Div 1 R-up 94-95, Merit Cup 69-70 71-72 73-74); Dorset Comb.(3) 85-88 (Lg Cup 86-87 87-88); Dorset Snr Cup(8) 63-64 69-71 75-76 78-81 87-88; Dorset Snr Amtr Cup(6) 48-50 54-55 56-57 70-72; W. Dorset Chal. Bowl 07-08; Perry Str. Lg 22-23; Mark Frowde Cup 76-77 88-89
PREVIOUS Leagues: Perry Street; Western 61-84; Dorset Combination 84-88
Grounds: Pymore (pre 1930s); Crown Field (pre 1953)
BEST SEASON FA Cup: FA Vase:5th Round 88-89
RECORD Attendance: 1,150 v Exeter City, 1981; 3,000 v Chelsea, at Crown, 1950
Scorer (in a season): Ellis Hoole 36
Fee received: £2,000 for Tommy Henderson
Fee paid: £1,000 for Steve Crabb

FACT FILE
Founded: 1885
Nickname: Bees
Sponsors:Newrlands Holidays
Colours: Red & black/black/red
Change colours: Blue & black/blue/blue
Midweek Matches: Tuesday
Reserves ' League: Dorset Combination
Programme: 40pages, #1.00
Editor: Ian Hallett (01308 868795)

CLUB PERSONNEL
President: Barry Williams
Chairman: David Fowler
Manager: Peter Conning

BRISLINGTON

Secretary: David Braithwaite, 3 Ashcott, Whitchurch, Bristol BS14 0AG
Tel: 01275 542040 (H) 0794 701 2253 (M) Email: brizzsec@aol.com
Ground: Ironmould Lane, Brislington, Bristol Tel: 0117 977 4030
Directions: 4 miles out of Bristol on main A4 to Bath - turn left up lane opposite Garden Centre just before dual carriageway (500 yards past Park & Ride on right)
Capacity: 2000 Seats: 144 Cover: 1500 Floodlights: Yes
Clubhouse: Yes - on ground, open matchdays **Club Shop:** No

HONOURS Somerset Senior Cup 92-93 R-up 93-94;
Somerset Senior League, Les Phillips Cup SF 93-94 99-00, Premier Cup 95-96
Somerset County League Champions 2001-02 (Reserves)
PREVIOUS League: Somerset Senior (pre-1991)
BEST SEASON FA Vase: 3rd Rd 89-90, 2-3 v Abingdon T. (A)

FACT FILE
Formed: 1956
Nickname: Bris
Sponsors: Balson 7 Co(Accountants)
Colours: Red & black/black/black & red
Change colours: White/red/red
Midweek matches: Tuesday
Reserves ' League: Somerset Senior
Programme: 50p
Editor: Laserset (0117 969 5487)
CLUB PERSONNEL
President: Paul Bishop
Chairman: M.Richardson
Vice-Chairman:B.Perrott
Manager: Nigel Webb
Asst Manager: Richard Cowley
Physio: Dave Sutor
2001-02
Leading goalscorer: Noel O'Sullivan 22
Captain: Dean Smart
P.o.Y.: Dean Radford

DAWLISH TOWN

Secretary: John Banks: 6 Luscombe Crescent, Paignton, South Devon, TQ3 3TW
Tel no: 01803 555919
Ground: Playing Fields, Sandy Lane, Exeter Road, Dawlish Tel: 01626 863110
Website: www.dawlishtownfc.co.uk
Directions: Approx 1 mile from centre of town, off main Exeter road (A379)
Capacity: 2,000 Seats: 200 Cover: 200 Floodlights: Yes
Clubhouse: Open nightly, all day Saturday and Sunday situated in car park opposite ground

HONOURS Western Lg Div 1 R-up 98-99, Lg Cup 80-81 83-84, Devon Premier Cup 69-70 72-73 80-81, Devon Snr Cup 57-58 67-68, Devon St Lukes Cup 82-83 (R-up 81-82), Carlsberg Cup 96
BEST SEASON FA Cup: FA Vase: Quarter Finals 86-87
PREVIOUS League: Devon & Exeter Ground: Barley Bank 1875-1900
RECORD Gate: 1,500 v Heavitree Utd, Devon Prem. Cup Q-Final
Defeat: 0-18 v Clevedon (A), Western Lge Prem. Div. 92-93

FACT FILE
Founded: 1889
Colours: Green /black/green
Change Colours:Blue/white/white
Midweek matchday: Wednesday
Programme: 34 pages, 50p
Programme Editor: Roy Bolt

CLUB PERSONNEL
President: Bob Webster
Manager: Tony Bowker

2001-0
Leading Goalscorer: Sean Friend Captain: Jason Heath
P.o.Y.: Andy Rollason

Barnstaple Town who drew 3-3 away to Clevedon United in the FA Cup Preliminary Round. Back Row (l-r): Paul Brown (physio), Martin Davey, Nick Murray, Danny Harris, David Penberthy, Kevin Squire, Simon Ovey, Paul Allen. Front Row: Richard Green, Craig Dann, Sean Watts, David Amooie, Danny Bell, Ross Middleton, Paul Williams, John Hore (Manager). Photo: Arthur Evans

Frome Town. Back Row (l-r): Simon White (Manager), Dick Pickersgill (Physio), Andy Turner, Mark Salter, Paul Thorpe, Stuart Parris, Nick Bunyard, Kieron White, Neil Smith, Tony Pounder, Ken Randell (Asst Manager), Giuseppe Sorbara. Front Row: Steve Jenkins, Bradley Peters, Lee Ashton (Captain), Aaron Blacker, Gary Lewis, Steve Grimshaw. Photo: Gordon Whittington

Torrington. Back Row (l-r): Paul Hutchings, Kevin Pickard, Lee Langhead, Karl Baggaley, Richard Fry, Jeff Parish, Trevor Haslet, Mike Heddon, Jeff Evans (Manager). Front Row: Paul Leach, Neil Bettiss, Jon Vooght, Dave Newsome, Karl Madge, Stuart Dymond. Photo: Gordon Whittington

DEVIZES TOWN

Secretary: Roy King, 20 Sand Leaze,Worton, Devizes , Wiltshire BN10 5SA
Tel Nos: 01380 720648   Email: royking100uk@hotmail.com

Ground: Nursteed Road, Devizes. Tel: 01380 722817

Directions: Off Nursteed Road (A342 signposted Andover); leaving town ground on right
opposite Eastleigh Rd
Capacity: 2,500   Seats: 130   Cover: 400   Floodlights: Yes

HONOURS Western League Div. 1 99-00; Wilts Snr Cup 07-08 49-50 56-57 57-58 58-59
60-61 61-62 62-63 65-66 67-68 70-71 71-72 73-74 78-79

PREVIOUS **Leagues:** Wilts Comb.; Wilts Premier
Name: Southbroom (until early 1900s)   **Ground:** London Rd (pre 1946)

FACT FILE

Founded: 1883

Colours: Red & white stripes/black/red
Change colours: All Blue
Midweek Matchday: Tuesday

CLUB PERSONNEL

Chairman: Chris Belcher

Manager: Brian Newlands

ELMORE

Secretary: Neville Crocker, Rivercroft,4 Little Silver, Tiverton, Devon EX16 4PH
Tel: 01884 2456634 (H) 07966 642094 (M)

Ground: Horsdon Park, Tiverton, Devon EX16 4DE Tel: 01884 252341

Directions: M5 Jct 27, A373 towards Tiverton, leave at 1st sign for Tiverton &Business Park,
ground 500yds on right
Capacity: 2,000   Seats: 200   Cover: Floodlights: Yes
Clubhouse: 11am-11pm Mon-Sat. Full canteen service - hot & cold meals & snacks
Club Shop: Yes

HONOURS East Devon Snr Cup 72-73 75-76, Western Lge R-up 94-95. Lge Cup 90-91,94-
95, Div 1 R-up 90-91, Prem Div Merit Cup R-up 91-92, Div 1 Merit Cup 86-87
89-90 90-91, Devon St Lukes Cup R-up 90-91, Devon Snr Cup 87-88, Devon
Intermediate Cup 60-61, Football Express Cup 60-61, Devon & Exeter Lg Div
2A 73-74 86-87(res)(Div1 A 76-77(res)), Devon Yth Cup 77-78.

PREVIOUS **Leagues:** Devon & Exeter 47-74; South Western 74-78   Grounds: None

RECORD **Attendance:** 1,713 v Tiverton Town Fri.April 14th 95
Appearances: P Webber   **Goalscorer:**
Win: 17-0   **Defeat:** 2-7

FACT FILE

Founded: 1947
Nickname: Eagles
Club Sponsors: Ken White Signs
Colours: All Green
Change colours: Red /black/black
Midweek matches: Tuesday
Reserve League: None
Programme: 12 pages, 30p
Editor: Richard Tapp(01884 252341)

CLUB PERSONNEL

Chairman: Alan J Cockram
Vice Chairman: P.J.Garnsworthy
Manager: Peter Buckingham
Asst Manager: R Moore
Physio: M Crocker

FROME TOWN

Secretary: Geoff Norris, 10 Clumber Drive, Frome, Somerset BA11 2LG (01373 464 803)

Ground: Badgers Hill, Berkeley Road, Frome Tel: 01373 453643

Directions: On the Westbury Road, 1 mile from town centre and Frome BR station
Capacity: 5,000   Seats: 250   Cover: 800   Floodlights: Yes   Club Shop: No
Clubhouse: Evenings & weekends. Cold food only

PREVIOUS **League:** Somerset Senior, Wilts League and Wilts Premier
BEST SEASON **FA Trophy:** 2nd Rd v Boston Utd (a) 0-4, 1984-85
FA Cup: 1st Rd Proper v L.Orient 1954-55
FA Vase: 2nd Rd v Paulton R (a) 1-2

RECORD **Attendance:** 8,000 v Leyton Orient, F.A.Cup 1st Rd. 58
Victory: 15-0 v Glastonbury, Somerset Senior League (h) 1906-07
Defeat: 1-11 v Dorchester, Western League (a) 1958-59

HONOURS Wiltshire Lge 1909-10,1910-11; Western Lg 78-79 (Div 2 19-20, Div 2 R-up 54-
55, Lg Cup 79-80 82-83, Merit Cup 82-83, Alan Young Cup 79-80, Subsidiary Cup 59-60),
Somerset Prem Cup 66-67 68-69 82-83, Wilts Prem Lg 62-63, Western Co's F'lit Cup 83-84,
Somerset Snr Cup 32-33 33-34 50-51, Somerset Snr Lg 06-07 08-09 10-11 also Div 1 (res) 90-91,
Div 3 (res) 85-86, Lg Cup (res) 91-92

FACT FILE
Founded: 1904
Nickname: Robins
Sponsors: Telewest Communications
Colours: Red & Black/black/red
Change colours: All yellow
Midweek matchday: Tuesday
Reserves ' League: Somerset Senior
Programme: 24 pages, 50p
Editor: Geoff Norris, Secretary

CLUB PERSONNEL
President: Mr C W M Norton
Chairman: Paul McGuinness
Vice Chairman: Steve Porter, Geoff Norris

Manager: Paul Thorpe
Player-coach: Tony Pounder
Physio: Bob Stokes

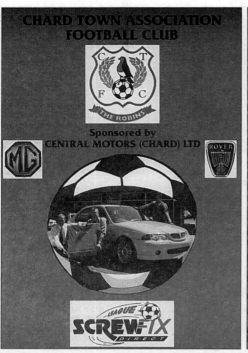

CHARD TOWN ASSOCIATION
FOOTBALL CLUB

Sponsored by
CENTRAL MOTORS (CHARD) LTD

SCREWFIX WESTERN LEAGUE 2001-2002

SOUTHBANK REVIEW

Sunday
10th March 2002
Corsham Town F.C.
versus
Minehead F.C.

Kick off 2.00pm

THE OFFICIAL PROGRAMME OF
CORSHAM TOWN FOOTBALL CLUB

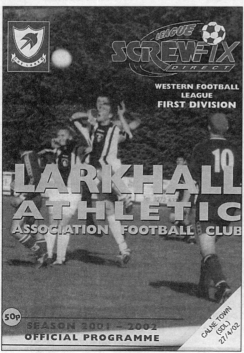

WESTERN FOOTBALL
LEAGUE
FIRST DIVISION

LARKHALL
ATHLETIC
ASSOCIATION FOOTBALL CLUB

50p

SEASON 2001 – 2002
OFFICIAL PROGRAMME

CALNE TOWN
(SDL)
27/4/02

DAWLISH TOWN

Programme

Sponsored By:

FULFORDS
STREETS AHEAD

Estate Agents
Devon's & Cornwall's favourite Estate Agent

KEYNSHAM TOWN

Secretary: Iain Anderson, 195 Mount Hill Road, Hanham, Bristol BS15 9SU Tel: 0117 961 6426

Ground: Crown Field, Bristol Road, Keynsham Tel: 0117 986 5876

Directions: A4 from Bristol to Bath, ground on left before entering village opposite Crown Inn. Bus service every 30 mins from Bristol passes ground. 10mins walk from Keynsham BR station
Capacity: 2,000   Seats: 120   Cover: 500   Floodlights: Yes
Clubhouse: Evenings & before & after games. Snacks   Club Shop: No

HONOURS   Somerset Lg Div 1 77-78; Somerset Snr Cup 51-52 57-58, 00-01; Div. 2 00-01
GFA Jnr Cup 25-26; Somerset & Avon (South) Premier Cup 79-80 (SF 93-94);

BEST SEASON   FA Cup: 4th Qual. Rd   **FA Vase:**

PREVIOUS   **Leagues:** Bristol District, Bristol Comb., Bristol Premier, Somerset Senior
Grounds: The Hams 1886-1910; Gaston 1910-25; Park Road 25-30; Charlton Rd 30-39

RECORD   **Attendance:** 3,000 v Chelsea, f'light opening 88-89.
Competitive:2,160 v Saltash, Amateur Cup, Oct 1952

FACT FILE
Founded: 1895
Nickname: K's
Sponsors: Hollywood Frames
Colours: All amber
Change: All blue
Midweek matchday: Wednesday
Reserves ' League: Somerset County
Programme: 32 pages, 50p
Editor: Mark Brown (0117 969 5487)

CLUB PERSONNEL
President: Lester Clements
Chairman: Martin Coles
Press Officer: Ray Parker

Manager: Nigel Lee
Physio: Guy Linley

2001-02
Leading goalscorer: Gary Silverthorne 17
Captain: Neil Harris

MELKSHAM TOWN

Secretary: David Phillips, 37 Duxford Close, Bowerhill,Melksham,Wlts. SN12 6XN
Tel No: 01225 706 904)
Ground: The Conigre, Melksham (01225 702843)
Capacity: 3,000   Seats: 150   Cover: 1,500   Floodlights: Yes

Directions: Just off main square in grounds of Melksham House

Clubhouse: Inside ground, open every evening & weekend lunchtimes

HONOURS   Wilts Lg 03-04 93-94 (R-up 24-25 29-30 59-60 67-68 68-69 71-72),
Western Lg Div 1 79-80, 96-97, Wilts Snr Cup 03-04 69-70 77-78 (R-up 57-58
67-68 68-69), Wilts Shield 80-81 81-82 84-85 ,85-86,97-98 ,99-00(R-up 86-87).

PREVIOUS   **Leagues:** Wiltshire 1894-1974 93-94; Western 74-93
Grounds: Challymead; Old Broughton Road Field

BEST SEASON **FA Cup:** 2nd Q Rd 57-58   **FA Vase:** 3rd Rd 81-82,98-99,01-02
FA Amateur Cup: 1st Rd 68-69

RECORD   **Attendance:** 2,821 v Trowbridge Town, FA Cup 57-58

FACT FILE
Founded: 1876
Sponsors: Cooper Avon Tyres
Colours:yellow/black/yellow Change :All white
Midweek Matchday: Tuesday
Prog Editor: Mike Miller ()1225 791873)

CLUB PERSONNEL
President: Mike Harris
Chairman: Mike Perrin
Vice Chairman: Paul Smith
Manager:Robert Lardner
Ass.Manager: Keith McCrum
Physio: Neil Young

ODD DOWN ATHLETIC

Secretary: Mike Mancini, 36 Caledonian Rd., East Twerton, Bath BA2 3RD
Tel: 01225 423293 Mobile: 07788 635560

Ground: Lew Hill Memorial Ground, Combe Hay Lane, Odd Down

Directions: On main Bath/Exeter road - leaving Bath turn left into Combe Hay Lane opposite
The Hustler Pub .opposite Park & Ride car park. 40 mins walk from Bath (BR)
Capacity: 1,000   Seats: 160   Cover: 250   Floodlights: Yes

Clubhouse: Yes, open noon-3 & 7-11pm. Hot & cold food available
Club Shop: No

HONOURS   Western Lg Div 1 92-93, Som. Snr Cup 91-92,Som, Premier Cup: R-up 2000-01

PREVIOUS   **Leagues:** Wilts Premier, Bath & District, Somerset Senior

BEST SEASON FA Cup: **FA Vase: Last 64 1983-84**

RECORD   **Appearances:** Steve Fuller 424
Scorer: Joe Matano 104
Win: 11-1 v Minehead (H), Western Lge Prem. Div. 19/3/94

FACT FILE
Founded: 1901
Sponsors: First Bus/Streamline
Colours: Black & white stripes/black/black
Change :All Yellow
Midweek Matches: Tuesday (7-30)
Reserves ' League: Somerset Senior
Programme: 12 pages with admission
Editor: Secretary

CLUB PERSONNEL
President:: T.B.A.
Chairman: Ian Robertson
Vice Chairman: Eric Clarke
Manager: Chris Mountford

PAULTON ROVERS

Secretary: Tracy Curtis,12 Linden Close,Waterford Park, Westfield,Radstock Somerset BA3 3EJ
Ground: Athletic Ground, Winterfield Road, Paulton Tel: 01761 412907

Directions: Leave A39 at Farrington Gurney (approx 15 miles south of Bristol),follow A362 marked Radstock for two miles, left at junction B3355 to Paulton,ground on right. Bus services from Bristol and Bath

Capacity: 5,000   Seats: 138   Cover: 200   Floodlights: Yes

Club Shop: Old programmes available - contact Chairman
Clubhouse: 3 bars, lounge, skittle alley, dance hall. Capacity 300. Cateringfacilities

HONOURS   Western Lg Div 2 R-up 1900-01; Somerset Snr Cup 00-01 02-03 03-04 07-08 08-09 09-10 34-35 67-68 68-69 71-72 72-73 74-75; Somerset Snr Lg 00-01 03-04 04-05 70-71 71-72 72-73 73-74; Somerset F/Lit Youth Lge 96-97

PREVIOUS   **Leagues:** Wilts Premier; Somerset Snr
              Grounds: Chapel Field; Cricket Ground; Recreation Ground 1946-48

BEST SEASON   **FA Cup:**   **FA Vase:**

RECORDS   **Attendance:** 2,000 v Crewe, FA Cup, 1906-07
            Appearances: Steve Tovey   **Goalscorer:** D Clark

FACT FILE
Founded: 1881
Nickname: Rovers
Sponsors: Barons Property Centre/Bass Breweries
Colours: White & maroon/maroon/maroon
Change colours: Yellow/navy/navy
Midweek matches: Tuesday
Reserves' League: Somerset Snr
Programme: 20 pages, 50p
Editor: D Bissex (01761 412463)
Local Press: Bath Evening Chronicle, Bristol Evening Post, Western Daily Press

CLUB PERSONNEL
President: Mr T Pow
Chairman: David Bissex
Vice Chairman: D Carter
Manager: Paul Hirons
Physio: Mike Brown

TEAM BATH

FACT FILE

Secretary: Matt Birch, Barn Cottage, Edgar Rise, Worle, Weston-s -Mare, Som. BS22 9JG
             Tel: 01934 418645 (H) 01225 826339 (B) 01225 826755 (F)
             e-mail: adsmab@bath.ac.uk

Ground: University of Bath, Sports Training Village, Claverton Down, Bath.
             Tel: 01225 826339

Directions: Follow signs to Claverton Down and Park & Ride (University).
             Take the Norwood Ave. entrance to the campus and as you drive towards the
             university you will approach two "hanger" like buildings on the right.
             This is the Sports Training Village. Follow signs to free car park.

Honours: Western Lge Div. 1 00-01

Formed: 2000
Colours: Yellow & Blue/blue/gold
Change colours: All blue
Midweek Matchday: Monday

CLUB PERSONNEL

Chairman: Ivor Powell
c/o Univ. of Bath, Sports Development, Claverton Down, Bath BA2 7AY
Tel: 01225 826656

Manager: Ged Roddy
Tel: 01225 826339
Coach: Paul Tisdale

WELTON ROVERS

Secretary: Geoff Baker, 6 Longfellow Road, Westfield Road, Westfield, Radstock BA3 3YZ
Email Address: weltonrovers@ yahoo.com

Ground: West Clewes, North Road, Midsomer Norton, Somerset Tel: 01761 412097

Directions: A367 Bath to Radstock õ right at lights at foot of hill onto A362,ground on right.

Capacity: 2,400   Seats: 300   Cover: 300   Floodlights: Yes   Club Shop: No

Clubhouse: 7.30-11pm daily, plus Sat matchdays 1.30-2.45pm, Sun 12-2pm

HONOURS Western Lg 11-12 64-65 65-66 66-67 73-74, Div 1 59-60 87-88,Amateur Cup 56-57 57-58 58-59 59-60, Alan Young Cup 65-66 66-67 67-68(jt); Somerset Snr Cup 06-07 11-12 12-13 13-14 19-20 24-25 25-26 60-61 61-62 62-63, Som. I'mediate Cup 77-78,   Som. Jnr Cup 06-07(jt) 24-25 30-31, WBC Clares City of Wells Cup 78-79

PREVIOUS   **Leagues:** None   **Names:** None   **Grounds:** None
BEST SEASON **FA Cup:**   **FA Vase:**   **FA Amateur Cup:**
RECORD   **Attendance:** 2,000 v Bromley, FA Amateur Cup 1963
              Goalscorer: Ian Henderson, 51

FACT FILE
Formed: 1887
Nickname: Rovers
Sponsors: Young Bros (Roofing)
Colours: Green & navy/navy &green/green
Change colours: Yellow/black/yellow
Midweek matchday: Wednesday
Reserve s' League: Somerset Senior
Programme: 12 pages, 25p
Editor: M Brown
Website: www.geocities.com/weltonrovers
2000-01
Captain: Mark Evans P.o.Y.: Steve Jenkins
Top Scorer: Gareth Wright 16
CLUB PERSONNEL
Chairman: Rae James
Manager: T.B.A.
Physio: John Carver

BITTON

Secretary: Mark Tilling, 71 Howes Close, Barrs Court, Bristol BS30 8SB
Tel Nos: 0117 9604550 (H) 0781 5086198 (M)

Ground: The Recreation Ground, Bath Road, Bitton, BS30 6HX Tel: 0117 932 3222
Capacity:1000 Cover: 200 Seats: 48 Floodlights: Yes Club Shop: No

Directions: M4 junc 18. Take A46 towards Bath, at first roundabout take A420 for Wick/
Bridgeyate. On approach to Bridgeyate turn left at mini-roundabout onto A4175 and
follow for 2.2 miles, then left for Bath on the A431. The ground is 100 yards on right.
Nearest station: Keynsham, Bristol

Clubhouse: Weekdays 7.30-11, Sat.& Sun all day.
HONOURS Glos. Jun Cup r-up 90; Avon Prem. Lg r-up 94, 95; Glos Sen amat Cup 95;
Glos Chall Trophy r-up 97; Glos County Lg r-up 97.
PREVIOUS Leagues: Avon Premier Comb.ination, Glos County

FACT FILE
Founded: 1922
Sponsors: John Dean Builders
Colours: Red & white stripes/black/black
Change colours: Yellow/green/yellow
Midweek Matcday : Monday 7.45
Programme: 36 pages Editor: Paul Cater
CLUB PERSONNEL
Chairman: John Langdon
V- Chairman: Paul Cater Pres: Roy Ewans
Treas: Steve Webb , Manager: Roger Sealey
2001-02
Captain: Richard Lee P.o.Y.Simon Crawford
Top Scorer: Mike Branch

BRISTOL MANOR FARM

Secretary: John Scriven, 44 Woodleaze,Sea Mills,Bristol BS9 2HY (0117 968 4916)
Email: christopher-davis2000@hotmail.com
Ground: `The Creek', Portway, Sea Mills, Bristol BS9 2HS Tel: 0117 968 3571

Directions: M5 jct 18 (Avonmouth Bridge), follow A4 for Bristol - U-turn on dual carriageway by
Bristol & West sports ground and return for half mile on A4- ground entrance is down narrow lane
on left (hidden entrance). Near to Sea Mills station (BR Temple Meads-Severn Beach line)

Capacity: 2,000 Seats: 84 Cover: 350 Floodlights: Yes Club Shop: No

Clubhouse: Open every evening & lunchtime Sat & Sun. Lounge bar, skittle alley, bar meals.

HONOURS Western Lge Prem 00-01 Sportsman Awards, Western Lg Div 1 82-83, Glos
Tphy 87-88, Glos Amtr Cup 89-90, Somerset Snr Lg Div 1 (Lg Cup, Div 2)
PREVIOUS Leagues: Bristol Suburban 64-69; Somerset Snr 69-77
Name: Manor Farm O.B. 1964-68 Grounds: None

FACT FILE
Formed: 1964
Nickname: The Farm
Club Sponsors: M.T.I. Ltd
Colours: Yellow
Change colours: Red& black/black/red& black
Midweek Matchday: Tuesday
Reserve s' League: Suburban League
Programme: 28 pages, 50p
Editor: Natalie & Michelle Lawrence

CLUB PERSONNEL
Chairman: Geoff Selleck
Manager: Geoff Bryant
Assistant Manager: Pete McCall

CADBURY HEATH

Secretary: Colin Trotman, 51 Deanery Road, Kingswood, Bristol BS15 9JB
Tel: 0117 983 7510 (H)

Ground: Springfield, Cadbury Heath Road, Warmley, Bristol. Tel: 0117 967 5731

Directions: Situated in East Bristol on the road between Warmley & Oldeland.
Tower Road (North & South) runs from Warmley to Oldland and passes Cadbury
Heath road. Look for Spar shop and King William P.H..
Turn into Cadbury Heath Road. 20 yds on right entrance to Social Club.

PREVIOUS League: Gloucestershire County Lge.
HONOURS Glos. County Lge 98-99, R-up 99-00

FACT FILE
Colours: All red
Change Cols.: yellow/black/black
Midweek Matchday: Wednesday
CLUB PERSONNEL
Chairman: Dave Smart
1 Farm Close, Emerson Green,
Bristol BS16 7RU
Tel: 0117 956 1223

Manager: Glen Smart

CALNE TOWN

Secretary: Laurie Drake, 22 Falcon Rd, Calne, Wilts SN11 8PL . Tel: 01249 819186
Ground: Bremhill View, Lickhill Rd., North End, Calne. 01249 816716.
Directions: Take A4 from Chippenham near Calne turn L. at 1st R'abt onto A3102 Calne B'pass
at next R'abt turn R., next L, then R and R. again. Email: calnetownfc@btinternet.com
Capacity: 2,500 **Seats:** 78 **Cover:** 250 **Floodlights:** Yes **Club Shop:** No
Clubhouse: Mon-Fri 7-11pm, Sat-Sun 12-11pm. Filled rolls, hot food, tea,coffee, sweets etc
HONOURS Western Lg Div 1 R-up 92-93; Wilts Snr Cup 12-13 34-35 84-85 (R-up1894-95
94-95 1911-12 49-50); Wilts Lg 33-34, (`Ghia' Cup 8) 1-81 85-86, Div 279-81,
Div 3 85-86, Div 4 81-82
PREVIOUS League: Wilts Co. (pre-1986) Ground: Anchor Road Rec. 1887-1967
Names: Calne Town (1886) & Harris Utd merged; Calne & Harris Utd (1921-67)
RECORD Attendance: 1,100 v Swindon, Friendly 25/7/1987
Scorer: Robbie Lardner Appearances: Gary Swallow, 259
Win: 11-1 v Heavitree (H) Defeat: 2-7 v Odd Down (A)

FACT FILE
Founded: 1887 Nickname: Lilywhites
Sponsors: The Bug & Spider
Colours: White/black/black
Change colours: Yellow/blue/blue
Midweek Matchday: Tuesday 7.45
Programme: 20 pages, 50p
Editor: Kath Brindle (01249 815198)

CLUB PERSONNEL
Chair: Steve Walker
President: Bill Burt
Manager: Paul Rankin

CHARD TOWN

Secretary: Michael Froom,30 Helliers Close, Chard , Somerset TA20 1LJ (01460 63670)
Ground: Town Ground, Zembard Lane, Chard TA20 1JL Tel: 01460 61402
         Capacity: 1,500   Seats: 60   Cover: 200   Floodlights: Yes

Directions: Follow sports centre signs off main A30 High Street along Helliers Road. Right into Upper Combe Street and left into Zembard Lane . BR 7miles Axminster or 8 miles Crewkerne
Clubhouse: Matchdays & most evenings. Snacks served

HONOURS   Som. Snr Lg 49-50 53-54 59-60 67-68 69-70 (Lg Cup 61-62 71-72 76-77); Western Lg Div 1 R-up 83-84 87-88 95-96, (Merit Cup 82-83, Comb. Cup(Res) 91-92 (R-up 92-93)); Som. Snr Cup 52-53 66-67; S W Co's Cup 88-89; Western Com Lge 96-97, Cup 96-97.

BEST SEASON   **FA Cup:** 2nd Qual Rd. 77-78 82-83   **FA Vase:**

PREVIOUS   **Leagues:** Somerset Snr 20-24 48-75; Perry Street 25-48 **Grounds:** None

FACT FILE
Founded: 1920 Nickname: Robins
Colours: Red with white trim/red/red
Change : Blue with yellow trim/blue/yellow
Midweek matches: Wednesday
Prog: 24 pages with entry Ed: Ian Hallett
2001-02
Captain: Stuart Larcombe
Ps.o.Y.: Paul Nicholls & Danny Wilson
Top Scorer: Danny Wilson 14
CLUB PERSONNEL
Chair: James Lovery V-Chair: R Glentworth
Gen Man: Malcolm Adcock
Manager: Steve Ritchie Ass.Man:Billy Morris
Physio: Michael J Gue

CLYST ROVERS

Secretary: Bob Chamberlain, Orchard Cottage, Clyst St George, Exeter EX3 0NZ(01392 873498)
Ground: Waterslade Park, Clyst Honiton, Devon Tel: 01392 366424
Directions: A30 following signs for Exeter Airport. Coming from Exeter take 1st right after airport turning (ground signposted) up narrow 200yds past Duke of York Pub
Capacity: 3,000   Seats: 130   Cover: 300   Floodlights: Yes
Club Shop: Yes, Programmes, souvenirs etc
Clubhouse: Open one and a half hours before kick off and after game. Excellent food available
HONOURS   Devon St Lukes Cup R-up 92-93, Western Lg Cup SF 92-93
PREVIOUS   **Leagues:** Exeter & District 26-44 51-66; Exeter & District Sunday 67-82;
                 South Western 81-92   **Grounds:** Fair Oak 1926-44
RECORD   **Gate:** 768 v Tiverton, Devon St Lukes final 11/5/93
               Win: 6-0 v Heavitree United, 1993
               Defeat: 0-12 v Torpoint Athletic, South Western League, October 1990

FACT FILE
Founded: 1926   Reformed: 1951
Nickname: Rovers
Sponsors: Vantage Pharmacy, Paignton
Colours: All yellow
Change colours: All green
Midweek Matches: Tuesday
Programme: 32 pages, 30p
Editor: Ray Dack (01392 215075)

CLUB PERSONNEL
President: Mr P W Brown
Chairman: Bob Chamberlain
Vice Chairman: Colin Dadson
Managers:Bill Potter & Martin Tooze
Physio: Bill Wreford

CORSHAM TOWN

Secretary: Richard Taylor, 7 Cresswells, Corsham, Wilts SN13 9NJ   Tel: 01249 714406
               Website: www.corshamtownfc.co.uk   Email: cup@corshamtownfc.co.uk

Ground: Southbank Ground, Lacock Road, Corsham, Wilts. SN13 9HS Tel: 01249 715609
Directions   From the A4 turn into Corsham at the Hare & Hounds PH roundabout, taking the
               Melksham Road, B3353, past the Methuen Arms PH then straight across the next
               mini-r'about into Lacock Road. The ground is situated 1/2 mile on right
               Capacity:1,500Seats: No   Cover: Yes   Floodlights: Yes .
Clubhouse: Yes   Club Shop: Yes

HONOURS   Wiltshire Lge. 97-98, Wiltshire FA Sen. Cup 75-76 96-97,
               Wiltshire Lge. KO Cup 95-96 96-97
PREVIOUS   **League:** Wiltshire Co. Lge

FACT FILE
Founded: 1893
Sponsors: Hong Kong House Vanitec
Colours: All red
Change colours: Yellow/blue/blue
Midweek matchday: Monday

CLUB PERSONNEL
Chairman: Colin Hudd
Manager: Mark Godley
Assistant Manager: Dave King
2001-02
Leading goalscorer:J.Freegard 19
Captain: Craig Tuck
P.o.Y.: Graham Ford

EXMOUTH TOWN

Secretary: David Richardson J.P.,44 Whitchurch Avenue, Exeter. EX2 1NT (01392 430985)
Ground: King George V Ground, Southern Road, Exmouth Tel: 01395 263348
Email Address: davidrich43@hotmail.com

Directions: On right side of main Exeter to Exmouth road (A376). Half mile from Exmouth (BR)

Capacity: 2,500   Seats: 100   Cover: 250   Floodlights: Yes   Club Shop: Yes
Clubhouse: Open every night and weekend lunchtimes. Snacks available

HONOURS   Western Lg (3) R-up (2) Lg Cup 88-89; Div 1 R-up 81-82; Sportmanship Tphy (2); Devon Premier Cup (2) Devon St Lukes Cup (3); Devon Snr Cup 50-51; East Devon Snr Cup (2 Harry Wood Mem. Cup 81-82; Exmouth Chal. Cup [7] Les Phillips Cup 00-01
PREVIOUS   **League:** Devon & Exeter 1933-73 **BEST SEASON**   **FA Vase:** SF 84-85
RECORD   **Gate:** 2,395 v Liverpool XI, friendly in 1987   **Scorer:** Mel Pym, 117
               Appearances: Keith Sprague, Geoff Weeks 410 (Western Lg)
               Victory: 11-0 v Pewsey Vale 7/10/00 (A) 10-0 v Glastonbury 27'3/99 (H)

FACT FILE
Formed: 1933
Nickname: `Town' or `Blues'
Colours: Blue & white/blue/blue
Change colours: All Red
Midweek matchday: Tuesday
Reserves' League: Devon & Exeter
Prog: 36 pages, 30p Editor: P.Hiscock

CLUB PERSONNEL
President: Brian Bradley
Chairman: Phillip Rugg
Manager:Russell Wilson
2000-01 Capt: Steve Taylor
Top Scorer: Richard Spiller 14

HALLEN

Secretary:	T.B.A.
	Email Address jrogers.gosw@go-region.gsi.gov.ok
Ground:	Hallen Playing Fields, Moorhouse Lane, Hallen, Nr Bristol Tel: 0117 950 2265
Directions:	M5 jct 17, A4018 to Henbury r'bout, right, right again at junction,next right to
	Station Road, left into Avonmouth Road at r'bout. One mile toHallen, ground first

left, then right into lane to ground

Capacity: 2,000   Seats: 200   Cover: 200   Clubhouse: **YHO-**

HONOURS	Glos County Lg 92-93, Glos Snr Trophy 92-93
PREVIOUS	**League:** Glos County (pre-1993), Hellenic 93-00
	Names: Lawrence Weston Athletic (80's), Lawrence Weston Hallen (pre-1991)
	Ground: Kings Weston (early 1980's)
RECORD	**Attendance:** 803 v Bristol Rovers 1997

FACT FILE
Founded: 1949
Colours: All Royal Blue
Change Colours: All Yellow
Midweek Matchday: Wednesday
Programme: No
CLUB PERSONNEL
Chairman: Barrie Phillips
Tel: 0117 950 1754
President: Ken Naish
Manager: Terry HareCoach: John Payne
Physio: Charlie Baldwin
2001-02
Captain: Paul Owen P.o.Y.: Top Scorer:

ILFRACOMBE TOWN

Secretary: Tony Alcock, 2 Worth Road, Ilfracombe, North Devon EX34 9JA Tel: 01271 862686.
Mobile: 07977 589199

Ground: Marlborough Park, Ilfracombe, Devon Tel: 01271 865939
Directions: A361 to Ilfracombe. Turn1st right in town after lights and follow Marlborough Rd to
the top, ground on left.**Capacity:** 2,000 **Seats:** 60 **Cover:** 450**Floodlights:** Yes Club Shop: No
Clubhouse: Every night 7-11pm and weekend lunchtimes. Hot & cold meals on matchdays

HONOURS	E Devon Prem Lg 25-26 28-29 29-30, N Devon Senior Lg, N Devon Prem Lg 66-
	67 70-71 81-82 82-83, Western Lg Div 2 R-up 52-53, Les Phillips Cup R-up 91
PREVIOUS Leagues:	North Devon 04-14 20-22 60-84; EDevon Premier 22-31;Exeter & District
	t 32-39 46-49; Western 49-59 **Grounds:** Shaftesbury Field; Brimlands; Killacleave (all pre-1924)
Names:	Ilfracombe FC 02-09; Ilfracombe Utd 09-14; Ilfracombe Comrades 14-20
RECORDS	**Attendance:** 3,000 v Bristol City, Ground opening, 2/10/24
	Goalscorer: Paul Jenkins 77 **Appearances:** Bobby Hancock 45

Players progressing: Jason Smith (Coventry City and Swansea City via Tiverton Town)

FACT FILE
Founded: 1902   Nickname: Bluebirds
Sponsors: K&J Electrical
Colours: Blue/black/blue
Change : White/navy/navy
Midweek matchday: Tuesday
Reserves ' League: North Devon
Programme: 8 pages, 40p Editor: Phil Hill

CLUB PERSONNEL
Chairman: Phil Hill
Vice-Chairman: Barry Jones
President: Mrs Jo Rose
Manager: Kevin Constantine
Physio: Ray Wooff

LARKHALL ATHLETIC

Secretary:	Garry Davy, 84 London Road West, Batheaston, Bath, BA1 7DA 01225 852729
	Email: garrydvy@aol.com
Ground:	"Plain Ham", Charlcombe Lane, Larkhall, Bath. 01225 334952
Directions	A4 from Bath, 1 mile from city centre turn left into St Saviours Rd. In Larkhall
	Square fork left, and right at junction, road bears into Charlcombe Lane.
	Ground on right as lane narrows

Capacity: 1,000   Seats: None   Cover: 50**Floodlights:** No

HONOURS	Somerset Senior Cup 75-76, Somerset Senior Lg,; Western Lg Div 1 88-89 93-94
	94-95(Div 1 Merit Cup (4) 83-86 87-88 (jt with Yeovil Res)
PREVIOUS	**League:** Somerset Senior

FACT FILE
Founded: 1914
Nickname: Larks
Colours: Royal & white/royal & white/royal
Change colours: Red & white/red & white/red
Midweek Matches: Tuesday
Programme: Yes
CLUB PERSONNEL
President: Tony Codd
Chairman: Jim McLay   Tel: 01373 834050
Manager: Chris Jeffrey
2001-02
Leading goalscorer: Duncan fear 7
Captain: Tommy Gilbert
P.o.Y.: Julian Bowen

MINEHEAD

Secretary:	Alex Knight,Swallowdale,Watery Lane,Doniford,Watchet,Somerset.TA3 0TW
	Tel No: 01984 639212
Ground:	The Recreation Ground, Irnham Road, Minehead, Somerset (01643 704989)

Directions: Entering town from east on A39 turn right into King Edward Road at Police station,
first left into Alexandra Rd and follow signs to car park;ground entrance within. Regular buses to
Minehead from Taunton, the nearestrailhead. (Steam train 'holiday route' Taunton to Minehead)

Capacity: 3,500   Seats: 350   Cover: 400   Floodlights: Yes

Clubhouse: Yes   **Club Shop:** No

HONOURS	Southern Lg R-up 76-77, Div 1 Sth 75-76, Merit Cup 75-76;
	Western Lg R-up 66-67 71-72, Div 1 90-91 98-99, Alan Young Cup 67-68 (jt with
	Glastonbury),Somerset Premier Cup 60-61 73-74 76-77
PREVIOUS	**Leagues:** Somerset Senior; Southern 72-83

FACT FILE
Founded: 1889
Colours: All Blue
Change colours: Yellow/black/black
Midweek Matches: Tuesday
Reserves League: TBA
Programme: Yes
Editor: Brian Walder

CLUB PERSONNEL
Chairman: Colin Gardner
Tel: 01984 633932
Manager: Andy Hodgson

Dave Osgood of visitors Bracknell crashes in a volley whilst Team Bath player Alex Ball turns from the draught! This effort flew wide of the target. Photo: Ken Gregory

Above left: Melksham player manager Robbie Lardner climbs above his opposite number Jon Bowering to get in a header. Fallen Bridgwater keeper and Melksham's Dave Clayton are in close attendance. Photo: Ken Gregory
Above right: Melksham keeper Darren Chitty wins this aerial duel with home striker Bridgwater's Chris Young. The Wiltshiremen went home with a 3-2 victory. Photo: Ken Gregory

Team Bath FC captain Ellis Wilmot charges for the gap between Bracknell defenders during their FA Vase tie at the Sports Village. Photo: Ken Gregory

SHEPTON MALLETT

Secretary: John Bell, 43 Victoria Grove, Shepton Mallet, Somerset BA4 5NJ
Tel Nos: 01749 344687 (H) 01749 830332 (W) 07866 762372 (M)

Ground: The Playing Fields, Old Wells Rd., West Shepton, Shepton Mallett, Som. BA4 5XN
Tel: 01749 344609
Capacity: 2500   Covered Seating: 120   Floodlights: Yes

Directions: Take the Glastonbury road from Shepton Mallett town centre then turn right at the junction with Old Wells Rd (approx. 1/2 mile, near the "King William" P.H.) - the ground is 300 yards on the left.

PREVIOUS   League: Somerset Senior

HONOURS   Somerset Senior League 2000-01

FACT FILE
Founded: 1986
Colours: Black & white/black/black
Change colours: Red & black/white/red
Midweek matchday: Tuesday

CLUB PERSONNEL
Chairman: Brian Blinman
Manager: Gary Banfield

STREET

Secretary: Mark Clarke, c/o 6 Clemence Road, Street, Somerset BA16 0SR
Tel Nos: 01458 442249 (H) 07979 5144181 (W) 07979 514181 (M)

Ground: The Tannery Ground, Middlebrooks, Street, Somerset
Tel: 01458 445987 Matchdays 01458 448227
Directions: Sign posted from both ends of A39 & B3151, Station Castle Cary
Capacity: 2,000   Seating: 120   Cover: 25   Floodlights: Yes   Club Shop: No

HONOURS: Western Lge R-up 52-53

RECORDS: **Attendance:** 4,300 v Yeovil Town FA Cup 17/11/47

PREVIOUS: **Grounds:** Victoria Field, Tunpike Ground

FACT FILE
Founded: 1880   Nickname The Cobblers
Sponsors C I C A
Colours: Green & white/white/white& green
Change colours: Red & black/black/black
Midweek home matchday: Tuesday
Programme: 44 pages 50p
Editor: M Clarke
CLUB PERSONNEL
Chairman: Andrew Walton
Manager: Gerry Pearson
Asst Mgr: Simon Culliford
Physios: Dick Pickersgill, Andrew Lee

TORRINGTON

Secretary: David Priscott, 6 Highfield Terrace, Bishops Talton, Barnstaple EX32 0AN
Tel: 01271 328316 (H) 07751-149900 (M) e-mail AFC. torrington@bushinternet.com
Ground: Vicarage Field, School Lane, Great Torrington Tel: 01805 622853   **Directions:** In town centre turn left by parish church, right at swimming pool, ground behind swimming pool. Good parking. Red Bus from Bideford & Barnstaple (nearest BR station).Bus stop 300yds from ground
Capacity: 4,000   Seats: 100   Cover: 1,000   Floodlights: Yes   Shop: No
Clubhouse: Weekdays 7-11pm, Sat 11-11 & Sun 12-3. Light snacks available on matchdays.
HONOURS   Western Lg R-up 90-91; Merit Cup 91-92 93-94 95-96; South Western Lg Cup 81;
Devon St Lukes Cup R-up 95-96 96-97; Devon & Exeter Lg & Cup 73-74;
Festival of Britain Cup 96-97; Les Phillips Cup R-up 91-92; Torridge Cup (13)
Somerset Youth Floodlight League 99-00
PREVIOUS   Leagues: N Devon; Devon & Exeter; S Western 77-84   Grounds: None
BEST SEASON   FA Vase: 5th Rd 84-85   FA Cup: 2nd Qual Rd. 81-82,94-95,96-97
RECORDS:Scorer: Trevor Watkins, 254 **Apps:**Mike Gilbert 527 **Fee Rcd:**£3,000 D.Walter(Yeovil)

FACT FILE
Formed: 1908
Nickname: Torrie or Supergreens
Sponsors: R & S Ware
Colours: Green & white Change : All white.
Midweek Matches: Wednesday
Programme: 48 pages, 50p Editor: Secretary
Local Press: North Devon Journal
CLUB PERSONNEL
Pres: Keith Curtis Chairman: Winston Martin
Manager: Jeff Evans Coach: Paul Hutchings
Physio: Albert Williams
2001-02 Captain: Richard Fey
P.o.Y.: John Vooght
Top Scorer:Lee Langmead 29

WELLINGTON

Secretary: Dave Grabham, 12 Drakes Park, Wellington, SomersetTA21 8TB
Tel: 01823 664946 (H), 01823 355687 (B) 07817 274585 (M) email:djgrabham@msn.com

Ground: Wellington Playing Field, North Street, Wellington, Somerset Tel: 01823 664810

Directions: At town centre traffic lights turn into North St., then first left by Fire Station into the public car park that adjoins the ground
Capacity: 3,000 **Seats:** None **Cover:** 200 **Floodlights:** Yes **Clubhouse:** Yes **Club Shop:** No

HONOURS   Western Lg Div 1 R-up 80-81, Merit Cup 91-92, Comb Lge 95-96;Comb Lge
KO Cup 95-96 98-99; Somerset Snr Lg Div 1 R-up; Rowbarton & Seward Cup, Bill Slee Trophy
PREVIOUS   Leagues: Taunton Saturday, Somerset Senior
RECORD   Attendance: **Goalscorer:** Ken Jones
BEST SEASON   FA Cup: 1st Qual Rd. 81-82, 84-85   **FA Vase:** 2nd rd Prop 98-99
99-00 Captain: Stuart Parris   P.o.Y.: Matthew Burfield   Top Scorer: Simon Towler
Players progressing: Nick Jennings and Ian Stonebridge (Plymouth)

FACT FILE
Founded: 1892
Sponsors: A J Shire & Wadham Fencing
Colours: All tangerine
Change cols: Blue & claret stripes/blue/blue
Midweek Matches: Tuesday
Reserve Lge: Devon & Exeter Sen Div
Programme: Yes   Editor: Jane Brown
CLUB PERSONNEL
Chairman: Ken Bird
Vice-Chair:Graham Aspin Pres: Alan Shire
Manr: Dave Sheehan Res Man: Ian Jackson
Physio: Ken Pearson
2001-02 Capt & Top Scorer: Matthew Brereton
P.O.Y.: Richard Jenkins

WESTBURY UNITED

Secretary: Michael Taylor, c/o W. U. F .C. Westury, Wiltshire BA13 3AF (01373 865406)

Ground: Meadow Lane, Westbury Tel: 01373 823409

Directions: In town centre, A350, follow signs for BR station, Meadow Lane on right (club signposted). Ten mins walk from railway station (on main London-South West and South Coast-Bristol lines)

Capacity: 3,500   Seats: 150   Cover: 150   Floodlights: Yes

Clubhouse: Evenings 7-11pm, Fri, Sat & Sun lunchtimes 12-3pm   Club Shop: No

HONOURS Western Lg Div 1 91-92, Wilts Senior Cup 31-32 32-33 47-48 51-52, Wilts Combination, Wilts Lg 34-35 37-38 38-39 49-50 50-51 55-56, Wilts Premier Shield R-up 92-93

PREVIOUS **Leagues:** Wilts Comb.; Wilts Co. (pre-1984)
Ground: Redland Lane (pre-1935)

FACT FILE
Formed: 1921
Nickname: White Horsemen
Colours: Green /white/green
Change colours: Sky & navy/navy/sky
Midweek Matches: Wednesday
Reserves' league: Wilts County Lg.
Programme: 16 pages, 50p
Editor: Mike Taylor (01373 865406)

CLUB PERSONNEL
Chairman: Phillip Alford
Vice Chairman: Bert Back
President: Ernie Barber
Managers: Derek Graham
Physio: Dave Prescott

WESTON ST. JOHNS

Secretary: Andy Jarrett,2 College Court, Uffculme,Cullompton, Devon EX15 3EQ Tel No: 01934 515260 (H)

Ground: Coleridge Road, Bournville Estate, Weston-s-Mare, Somerset Tel: 01934 612862

Directions: Leave M5 at J21and take main road into Weston-s-Mare. Turn left at the 4th r'about into Winterstoke Road, then take the 2nd right into Byron Road and then 1st left into Coleridge Road.

PREVIOUS **League:** Somerset Senior Lge.
Names: Worle & Weston St. Johns amalgamated 2000

HONOURS R-up Somerset Sen. Lge. 99-00 (Worle)

FACT FILE
Colours: blue & black/black/ black
Change Colours: All yellow
Midweek Matchday: Tuesday

CLUB PERSONNEL
Chairman: Bob Flaskett

Manager: Martin Dancey
Tel: 01934 517792

WILLAND ROVERS

Secretary: Andy Jarrett, 2 College Court, Uffcombe, Cullompton, Devon EX15 3EQ Tel: 01884 841210 (H) 01884 253238 (B) 07836 472708 (M) email: henry.jarrett1@btopenworld.com

Ground: Silver Street, Willand, Devon. Tel: 01884 33885 Capacity: 2000   Covered Seating: 75   Floodlights: Yes

Directions: Leave the M5 at Junction 27 (signed Tiverton & N. Devon). Follow signs to Willand and the ground is on the left hand side about 1/4 mile after passing Willand village sign.

PREVIOUS **League:** Devon County League >01

BEST SEASON **FA Vase:** 1st Round proper 00-01, 1-4 v Falmouth Town (A)

FACT FILE
Founded: 1946
Colours: White/black/black
Change colours: Red/white/red
Midweek matchday: Tuesday

CLUB PERSONNEL
Chairman: Mike Mitchell
Manager: Clive Jones

SOUTH WESTERN FINAL LEAGUE TABLES 2001-02

CORNWALL COMBINATION

	P	W	D	L	F	A	Pts
St Agnes	38	30	4	4	126	39	94
Penzance Reserves	38	27	2	9	92	49	83
St Just	38	25	5	8	72	35	80
Mullion	38	23	5	10	91	42	74
St Ives Town	38	22	5	11	69	44	71
Hayle	38	18	7	13	82	69	61
Goonhaven	38	18	5	15	77	65	59
Illogan RBL	38	17	7	14	69	59	58
Penryn Athletic Res	38	16	10	12	68	59	58
Helston Athletic	38	16	9	13	57	49	57
Truro City Reserves	38	17	6	15	75	85	57
Perranwell	38	16	7	15	81	66	55
Newquay Reserves	38	14	2	22	57	88	44
Mousehole	38	11	10	17	53	66	43
Falmouth Town Res	38	10	11	17	53	66	41
Marazion Blues	38	10	5	23	51	94	35
Porthleven Res	38	8	8	22	56	80	32
RNAS Culdrose	38	7	9	22	53	94	30
Ludgvan	38	6	7	25	44	106	25
Wendron CC Utd	38	4	6	28	39	110	18

DEVON & EXETER LEAGUE

	P	W	D	L	F	A	Pts
University of Exeter	30	21	3	6	131	40	66
Witheridge	30	20	4	6	85	40	64
Tap & Barrel	30	19	4	7	103	57	61
Exeter Civil Serv Res	30	15	7	8	50	34	52
Budleigh Salterton Res	30	14	7	9	51	55	49
Seaton Town	30	12	7	11	52	56	43
St Martins	30	12	6	12	55	62	42
Elmore Reserves	30	13	3	14	52	61	42
Cullompton Rngrs Res	30	12	4	12	64	67	40
Okehampton Argyle	30	10	10	10	50	66	40
Hatherleigh Town	30	11	3	16	60	70	36
Pinhoe	30	9	6	15	45	61	33
Exeter St Thomas	30	9	5	16	52	73	32
Sidmouth Town	30	8	7	15	48	71	31
Feniton*	30	9	2	19	50	90	27
Newton St Cyres	30	4	6	20	37	82	18

GLOS NORTHERN SENIOR LEAGUE

DIVISION ONE

	P	W	D	L	F	A	Pts
Wotton Rovers	30	19	8	3	76	32	65
Taverners	30	20	4	6	64	26	64
Broadwell Amateurs	30	16	7	7	51	27	55
Smiths Athletic	30	17	3	10	66	46	54
Bredon	30	15	7	8	66	36	52
Sharpness	30	15	5	10	58	41	50
Lydney Town	30	14	6	10	56	45	48
Shortwood Utd Res	30	12	10	8	50	48	46
Kings Stanley	30	12	9	9	62	53	45
Bourton Rovers	30	13	5	12	57	49	44
Cheltenham CS	30	10	9	11	59	62	39
Brockworth	30	10	7	13	40	52	37
Tuffley Rovers Res	30	7	6	17	50	73	27
Lydbrook Athletic	30	6	5	19	36	57	23
Longford	30	3	4	23	30	102	13
Cam Bulldogs	30	1	5	24	24	96	8

DORSET COUNTY LEAGUE

DIVISION ONE

	P	W	D	L	F	A	Pts
Poole Borough*	30	25	3	2	135	25	75
Dorchester United	30	22	3	5	106	33	69
Chickerell United	30	20	3	7	99	50	63
Weymouth United	30	19	4	7	88	46	61
Gillingham Town Res	30	18	4	8	90	47	58
Beaminster	30	16	8	6	79	45	56
Portland United Res	30	15	5	10	71	43	50
Sturminster Marshall	30	13	4	13	71	62	43
Shaftesbury Res	30	9	7	14	40	74	34
Hamworthy Utd Res	30	9	6	15	45	61	33
Cobham Sports Res*	30	9	4	17	50	74	28
Weymouth Consignia	30	6	9	15	49	90	27
Blandford Utd Res	30	7	5	18	37	74	26
Lytchett Red Triangle*	30	6	7	17	41	92	24
Dorchester Sports	30	7	2	21	45	122	23
Okeford United	30	1	2	27	30	138	5

DIVISION TWO

	P	W	D	L	F	A	Pts
Cranborne	26	19	2	5	83	30	59
Wareham Rngrs Res	26	15	5	6	63	37	50
Allendale Res	26	13	7	6	57	32	46
Marina Sports	26	14	3	9	65	44	45
Moreton*	26	13	7	6	59	31	43
Crossways	26	12	5	9	54	44	41
Kingston*	26	13	5	8	65	63	41
Chickerell Utd Res	26	11	4	11	52	59	37
Royal Oak Cougars	26	8	10	8	47	46	34
Stalbridge	26	9	5	12	39	50	32
Child Okeford	26	6	5	15	46	94	23
Dorchester YMCA	26	6	4	16	52	64	22
Sturminster Newton Rs	26	5	4	17	31	57	19
Piddletrenthide Utd	26	2	6	18	26	88	12

EAST CORNWALL PREMIER LEAGUE

	P	W	D	L	F	A	Pts
Liskeard Athletic Res	36	29	4	3	116	26	91
Saltash United Res	36	27	6	3	102	44	87
Foxhole Stars	36	23	3	10	92	53	72
Torpoint Athletic Res	36	20	9	7	96	45	69
St Cleer	36	20	7	9	96	59	67
St Blazey Res	36	17	7	12	90	78	58
St Dennis	36	17	7	12	67	57	58
Padstow United	36	17	4	15	75	83	55
Camelford	36	14	10	12	52	48	52
Nanpean Rovers	36	12	12	12	66	55	48
Roche	36	12	11	13	63	70	47
Bodmin Town Res	36	10	13	13	85	85	43
Bude	36	12	7	17	51	73	43
Wadebridge Town Res	36	11	7	18	51	72	40
Launceston Res	36	9	8	19	52	73	35
Millbrook Res	36	8	6	22	51	97	30
Probus	36	7	7	22	55	105	28
St Austell Res	36	4	7	25	46	104	19
Sticker	36	4	3	29	28	107	15

SOUTH WESTERN FINAL LEAGUE TABLES 2001-02

PLYMOUTH & DISTRICT COMBINATION

PREMIER DIVISION	P	W	D	L	F	A	Pts
Mount Gould BP	26	20	3	3	108	34	63
University	26	16	7	3	84	36	55
Wessex Rangers RM	26	14	6	6	65	53	48
Plympton United	26	14	4	8	80	49	46
Plymouth Parkway	26	14	4	8	78	55	46
Compton Inn	26	14	4	8	61	46	46
Civil Service S & L	26	12	4	10	56	40	40
Plymstock United	26	10	7	9	60	61	37
Princerock	26	10	7	9	66	68	37
Plymouth Command	26	8	3	15	73	79	27
Vospers Oak Villa	26	7	4	15	38	67	25
Tavistock AFC	26	8	2	16	45	75	23
Mainstone Sports	26	4	4	18	32	88	16
Plymouth CS	26	0	3	23	32	127	3

BATH & DISTRICT LEAGUE

PREMIER DIVISION	P	W	D	L	F	A	Pts
Westgate	18	18	0	0	93	13	54
Oval Sports	18	10	2	6	51	46	32
Raleigh Sports	18	9	3	6	49	39	30
Odd Down	18	8	4	6	62	47	28
Bath University	18	7	4	7	37	32	25
Larkhall	18	5	5	8	33	48	20
T & H Sports	18	5	4	9	40	51	19
Weston Wanderers	18	4	4	10	38	69	16
Saltford AFC	18	4	4	10	28	65	16
Claverton Academy	18	3	4	11	26	47	13

PERRY STREET & DISTRICT LEAGUE

PREMIER DIVISION	P	W	D	L	F	A	Pts
Merriott Rovers	20	18	2	0	72	17	56
Coombe St Nicholas	20	13	4	3	48	22	43
Lyme Regis	20	11	4	5	60	27	37
Crewkerne	20	8	5	7	33	41	29
South Petherton	20	9	2	9	41	55	28
Farway	20	6	5	9	45	53	23
Axminster Town	20	5	7	8	27	30	22
Forton Rangers	20	6	4	10	29	38	22
Shepton Beauchamp	20	6	2	12	32	43	20
Norton Athletic	20	3	5	12	25	55	14
Chard United	20	3	4	13	26	57	13

WESTON SUPER MARE LEAGUE

DIVISION ONE	P	W	D	L	F	A	Pts
Worle	24	21	1	2	114	33	64
East Worle EP	24	21	1	2	90	31	64
Blagdon	24	15	4	5	80	45	49
Westland United	24	11	4	9	64	65	37
Worle Lions	24	9	5	10	76	67	32
Nailsea United	24	9	5	10	48	42	32
Clevedon United	24	9	3	12	48	55	30
Kenn Valley	24	8	5	11	43	52	29
Bournville Rangers	24	7	8	9	49	61	29
Draycott	24	6	8	10	52	72	26
Portishead WMC	24	6	4	14	39	67	22
Hutton	24	3	6	15	37	75	15
Wrington Redhill	24	2	4	18	36	111	10

BRISTOL PREMIER COMBINATION

PREMIER DIVISION	P	W	D	L	F	A	Pts
Thornbury Town	25	19	1	5	71	24	58
Hanham Athletic	26	13	6	7	64	34	45
Hartcliffe	25	12	5	8	59	38	41
Bitton Reserves	26	11	8	7	46	31	41
Sea Mills Park	25	13	2	10	54	42	41
Hillfields OB	26	12	5	9	65	58	41
RMC Wick	26	12	5	9	48	42	41
Hallen Reserves	25	12	4	9	72	47	40
Longwell Green Sports	26	11	6	9	37	30	39
St Philips Mas	25	9	6	10	60	58	33
Bristol Union	26	9	5	12	52	53	32
Highridge United Res	26	9	5	12	44	53	32
Bristol 5 O B	26	5	5	16	42	67	20
Chipping Sodbury	25	0	1	24	15	152	1

BRISTOL & WESSEX LEAGUE

SENIOR DIVISION	P	W	D	L	F	A	Pts
Yate West End	22	16	4	2	91	28	62
City Darts Res	22	16	1	5	95	44	49
Blue Bowl Hanham	22	13	5	4	50	34	44
Crosscourt United	22	13	4	5	65	42	43
South Avon Sunday	22	12	1	9	70	44	37
Shadwell Rovers	22	8	4	10	32	57	28
Glasshouse Nailsea	22	8	3	11	52	71	27
Knowle PA	21	8	1	12	59	52	25
Hillfields 1883	21	7	2	12	32	59	23
Prince of Orange	22	4	5	13	40	60	17
Bristol Athletic S & S C	22	4	2	16	23	70	14
Royal Oak Nailsea	20	3	2	15	22	75	11

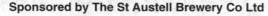

CARLSBERG SOUTH WESTERN FOOTBALL LEAGUE

Sponsored by The St Austell Brewery Co Ltd

President: Tristan H Scott   **Chairman:** Bob Bell

Secretary: Ray Rowe, 5 Alverton Gardens, Truro, Cornwall TR1 1JA
Tel/Fax: 01872 242190   **Email:** ray@rowe57.fsbusinessco.uk

Press Officer: Mike Sampson, 23 Eliot Street, Weston Mill, Plymouth, Devon PL5 1AX
Tel/Fax: 01752 514326   **Email:** mikewrite@mikewrite.eurobell.co.uk

The Carlsberg South Western League was dominated by St Blazey last season as Trevor Mewton's Green & Blacks made a clean sweep of all four domestic trophies.

This was the first time that a club had won all four trophies and also saw the Saints retain the championship, and it is hard to see where a serious challenge will come from to prevent them from completing a hat-trick.

Runners-up Porthleven have lost several of their squad with the most notable top scorer Lee Harvey (30 goals last season) and highly-rated midfielder Dave Larsen to Liskeard Athletic and Cornwall County central defender Wayne Hillson to Plymouth Parkway.

Liskeard have been busy in the close seaso adding Mike Preston, Huw Morgan and Andy Sargent, who has agreed to return from Taunton, to a strong looking squad at Lux Park. Manager Chris Burchell has also enlisted the services of Roger Fice as his assistant manager after the tragic death of John Hillson in the latter stages of last season.

There also appears to be little possibility of change at the other end of the table where St Austell are once again favourites to struggle despite the return of Glyn Rowett as manager. Penryn Athletic are making a determined effort to avoid the ignomy of applying for re-election in the second season by appointing Ronnie Barr as their manager.

Porthleven were again the League's most successful club in the FA Vase and the league has increased its participation in the competition to five clubs with Launceston and Liskeard joining St Blazey, Porthleven and Falmouth in this season's competition. Holsworthy's bid failed as their pitch was just too small for the Vase criteria, but this could be rectified in time for 2003. More South Western League clubs will also be participating in the FA Cup this season and hopefully earning more prize money and perhaps national headlines.

FINAL LEAGUE TABLE 2001-02

	P	W	D	L	F	A	GD	Pts		P	W	D	L	F	A	GD	Pts
St Blazey	36	33	3	0	120	25	95	102	Bodmin Town	36	13	9	14	66	81	-15	48
Porthleven	36	27	4	5	105	32	73	85	Torpoint Ath	36	13	6	17	67	74	-7	45
Liskeard Athletic	36	25	4	7	121	53	68	79	Wadebridge Town	36	13	6	17	58	70	-12	45
Holsworthy	36	24	5	7	94	47	47	77	Launceston	36	12	2	22	65	91	-26	38
Plymouth Pkway	36	21	6	9	88	50	38	69	Millbrook	36	8	7	21	44	93	-49	31
Penzance	36	16	8	12	79	62	17	56	Callington Town	36	8	5	23	57	112	-55	29
Falmouth Town	36	16	6	14	82	86	-4	54	Truro City	36	6	10	20	57	82	-25	28
Tavistock	36	15	7	14	61	53	8	52	Penryn Athletic	36	8	3	25	42	84	-42	27
Saltash United	36	15	5	16	62	76	-14	50	St Austell	36	2	3	31	20	125	-105	9
Newquay	36	14	7	15	76	68	8	49									

ROLE OF HONOUR 2001-02

South Western Football League
Champions   St Blazey
Runners Up   Porthleven

League Challenge Cup
Winners   St Blazey
Runners Up   Liskeard Athletic

Sporting Trophy
1st   Wadebridge Town

Ground Trophy
1st   Penryn Athletic

Jack Hawke Trophy for the Leading Goalscorer
Lee Harvey (Porthleven) 30
Dominic Richardson (St Blazey) 30

Top Referee
Dave Goldstone

Best Programme
Penzance

SOUTH WESTERN FOOTBALL LEAGUE

RESULTS CHART 2001-02

#	Team	1	2	3	4	5	6	7	8	9	10	11	12	13	14	15	16	17	18	19
1	Bodmin Town	X	1-0	4-6	1-1	3-0	2-2	2-2	3-6	3-1	5-1	2-1	2-1	3-0	0-2	0-3	2-2	4-1	4-3	2-1
2	Callington Town	1-3	X	1-3	1-2	2-3	4-7	4-1	1-6	0-3	4-2	1-4	1-7	3-3	1-1	0-2	1-2	5-3	1-0	2-2
3	Falmouth Town	2-2	3-1	X	4-3	3-1	1-4	1-4	1-1	2-1	2-2	1-4	1-4	4-1	6-2	1-3	3-0	0-1	3-3	3-1
4	Holsworthy	2-2	7-1	5-3	X	4-0	3-1	3-1	2-0	2-0	3-1	3-0	1-1	3-0	6-0	0-5	2-1	1-0	4-1	5-1
5	Launceston	1-2	1-4	2-2	2-2	X	1-4	4-0	2-4	1-0	4-0	3-1	1-2	0-4	0-3	1-2	0-4	4-1	5-1	1-1
6	Liskeard Athletic	2-2	9-0	4-1	1-0	5-0	X	5-0	4-2	4-2	0-2	4-3	1-2	3-4	6-1	1-5	2-2	3-0	1-1	2-0
7	Millbrook	0-0	3-1	3-1	2-5	0-2	1-5	X	0-5	1-1	2-1	0-3	1-0	2-1	4-0	0-6	0-2	1-3	3-3	1-1
8	Newquay	3-2	1-2	5-2	0-1	1-0	2-3	5-1	X	3-1	0-0	0-1	2-2	1-1	5-0	0-2	1-0	1-1	3-1	2-3
9	Penryn Athletic	5-2	0-0	1-2	1-4	1-3	0-3	1-0	1-3	X	3-1	0-2	0-1	2-2	2-1	0-8	2-4	1-0	1-2	1-2
10	Penzance	3-0	5-0	3-1	0-5	6-4	1-2	4-2	7-0	1-0	X	0-0	1-1	4-0	4-0	2-4	3-1	3-0	1-1	2-0
11	Plymouth Parkway	7-0	2-1	4-3	1-4	5-2	2-4	5-0	2-1	2-0	3-2	X	2-1	1-1	0-0	2-2	3-0	2-0	1-1	1-4
12	Porthleven	4-1	5-1	4-1	3-0	2-1	3-1	6-0	4-1	2-0	2-0	5-2	X	2-1	2-0	4-0	1-1	4-1	6-0	3-0
13	Saltash United	3-0	2-1	1-2	1-3	3-0	0-7	3-1	3-2	3-1	1-2	0-2	0-5	X	3-0	0-4	2-2	2-4	3-2	3-2
14	St Austell	0-4	2-3	1-3	0-2	1-5	0-6	0-4	0-0	2-4	2-4	1-9	0-4	0-2	X	0-4	0-2	3-1	0-3	0-1
15	St Blazey	4-1	4-0	3-1	4-0	3-1	1-0	0-0	6-2	6-0	1-3	3-1	3-1	2-1	5-0	X	1-0	6-2	5-2	2-1
16	Tavistock	1-0	3-3	1-2	2-0	1-3	2-3	2-0	4-1	4-2	1-1	0-2	1-5	2-0	6-0	0-1	X	4-0	1-1	4-0
17	Torpoint Athletic	5-1	0-1	1-2	4-2	6-2	1-3	3-3	2-2	2-1	2-1	1-1	1-5	2-3	7-1	1-2	1-0	X	2-1	1-0
18	Truro City	1-1	6-3	1-3	1-3	2-4	1-4	2-1	1-1	1-3	0-3	3-2	0-0	1-3	2-0	1-2	1-1	1-2	X	1-2
19	Wadebridge Town	4-0	4-1	3-3	1-1	1-3	1-5	3-0	2-1	5-0	1-1	0-3	0-1	1-2	3-0	1-1	0-1	4-3	2-1	X

CARLSBERG SOUTH WESTERN LEAGUE CHALLENGE CUP 2001-02

PRELIMINARY ROUND

Falmouth Town	v	Holsworthy	0-2	Millbrook	v	Porthleven	1-4
Newquay	v	Plymouth Parkway	2-8, 2*2				

FIRST ROUND

Callington Town	v	Bodmin Town	0-1	Launceston	v	Saltash United	1-2, 1*1
Liskeard Athletic	v	Torpoint Athletic	3-0	Porthleven	v	Holsworthy	4-1
Penzance	v	Wadebridge Town	3-0	St Austell	v	Tavistock	0-4
St Blazey	v	Plymouth Parkway	4*3	Truro City	v	Penryn Athletic	3*4

QUARTER FINALS

Bodmin Town	v	Penzance	2-3	Liskeard Athletic	v	Porthleven	4-3
Saltash United	v	Tavistock	2-0	St Blazey	v	Penryn Athletic	8-0

SEMI FINALS

Liskeard Athletic	v	Saltash United	4-2	Penzance	v	St Blazey	2-4

FINAL

Liskeard Athletic	v	St Blazey	1-3, 0*0	both at Tavistock

LEADING GOALSCORERS 2001-02

Lee Harvey	Porthleven	30	Ian Rowe	Holsworthy	24
Dominic Richardson	St Blazey	30	Jeff Babb	(18 Liskeard, 5 Tavistock)	23
Lee Doncaster	Liskeard Athletic	28	Glynn Hooper	St Blazey	22
Alan Clark	Holsworthy	25	Andy Sargent	Liskeard	22
Dave Burt	Penzance	25	Damian Stevens	Falmouth	20

BODMIN TOWN

Secretary: Sheila Chapman, c/o Bodmin AFC, Bodmin, Cornwall PL31 2AF
Tel: 01208 77974 (H) 07786 923638 (M)

Ground: Priory Park, Bodmin. Tel: 01208 269033 (office) or 021208 78165 (clubhouse)
Directions: Just off town centre in Priory Park complex, at rear of town car park

Capacity: 5,000 Cover: 400 Seats: 400 Floodlights: Yes

Clubhouse: Mon-Fri 6.30-11pm (matchdays 6-11), Sat 12-11pm,
Sun 12-10.30pm Bar snacks available most times
Club Shop: No

Honours: South Western Lg 90-91 93-94 (R-up 76-77, 92-93, 94-95, Lg Cup 93-94 ,97-98
(R-up 7-78 88-89 94-95,95-96), Cornwall Snr Cup Winners 98-99 R-up 93-94, Cornwall Charity
Cup 86-87 89-90,96-97.Cornish Guardian E.C.P.L.Supplimentary Cup 91-92 (R-Up. 93-94)-
GordonSweet Cup 90-91,92-93,98-99, 01-02.

FACT FILE
Founded: 1889 Nickname: Black & Ambers
Sponsors: Parc Signs
Colours: Amber/black/amber
Change colours: All white
Midweek Matchday: Wednesday
Reserves' League: East Cornwall Premier
Programme: 60 pages, 40p
Programme Editor: Secretary

CLUB PERSONNEL
Chairman: Colin.Hooper
Vice-Chairman: Dave Dunckley
President: A.Gynn
Manager: Paul Hicks
Physio: Stev Trotman

CALLINGTON TOWN

Secretary: Philip Brown, Mount Pleasant Cottage, Harrowbarrow, Callington PL17 8JL
Tel: 01822 833851 (H) 01752 307102 (B)

Ground: Ginsters Marshfield Park, Callington Comm. College, Launceston Rd., Callington,
Cornwall Tel: 01579 382647 **Directions** Turn into Callington
Community College from the A388, Callington to Launceston road. Go to the top
of the drive and bear left - the ground is 100m ahead.

Capacity: 1,500 **Seats:** No **Cover** Yes **Floodlights** : Soon **Clubhouse:** Yes

2001-02: Captain .: Matthew Hawke P.o.Y: Chris Tllbury Top scorer: Gary Williams 21

FACT FILE
Colours: Red & black/black/red & black
Change Cols.: All blue
Midweek Fixtures: Wednesday
Website: www.callington townfc.com

CLUB PERSONNEL
Chairman: Andrew Long
34 Coombe Road, Callington
Tel: 01579 383982 (H) 01752 220881 (B)

Manager: Ian Southcott
Tel: 01579 383561 (H) 07973 109609

FALMOUTH TOWN

Secretary: Colin Spargo,2 Grenville Crescent, Falmouth, CVornwall TR11 2NR
Tel: 0794 1591764 Website http://www.users.globalnet.co.uk/~cgdf
Ground: Bickland Park, Bickland Vale, Falmouth, Cornwall Tel: 01326 375156
Directions: Follow A39 to Tregonigie Industrial Estate - will pass ground on left.
1 1/2 miles from Penmere Halt (BR) on Falmouth-Truro branch line. Bus service from town centre
Capacity: 6,000 **Seats:** 350 **Cover:** 1,200 **Floodlights:** Yes **Club Shop:** c/o club
Clubhouse: Mon-Fri 7-11pm, Sat 11 am-11pm, Sun 12-10.30pm. Meals available
HONOURS: Cornish Senior Cup x 11 R-up x 8; Western Lg x 4, Lg Cup 74-75, Alan Young
Cup x 3; South Western Lg x 14 R-up x 5, Lg Cup x 13 R-up x 5; Pratten Cup 73-74,
Cornwall Charity Cup (2) R-up 00-01
BEST SEASON **FA Cup:** 1st Round 62-63 & 67-68 & 69-70
FA Vase: Quarter Final 86-87 **FA Trophy:** 2nd Round 77-78
PREVIOUS **Leagues:** Cornish Senior 50-51; South Western 51-74; Western 74-83
RECORDS **Gate:8,000**v Oxford United, FA Cup 1st Round 3/11/62

FACT FILE
Founded: 1949 Nickname: Town
Club Sponsors: Stralfors
Colours: Amber/black
Change colours: Red/white
Midweek Matchday: Tues/Wed
Reserves' League: Cornwall Comb
Programme: 44 pages, 50p
Editor/ Press Off.: Gary Spiller 0781 6339729
CLUB PERSONNEL
Chairman:Roger Fenner V.Chair:Trevor Jones
President: Sid Ridgeon Manager: Neil Phillips
Coach:
20001-02 Top Iscorer: Damien Stevens 21
Captain: Dave Sweet P.O.Y: Greg White

HOLSWORTHY

Secretary: Mel Goodenough, 114 B New Street, Torrington, Devon EX38 8BT
Tel Nos: 01805 625049(H) 01805 622315 (emergency W)
078117 32422 (M) Email: holsafc@btpenworld.com

Ground: Upcott Field Tel: 01409 254295
Capacity: 1.000 **Cover:** 100 **Seats:** No **Floodlights:** Yes **Clubhouse:** Yes

Directions: Leave town on A388 towards Bideford, 100 yds past mini-roundabout on left.

Honours: Devon Senior Cup 53-54 (Prem. Cup 71-72 78-79), Devon Junior Cup 38-39

2001-02 **Captain:** Danny Bryant **P.o.Y:** Matt Parnell **Top Goalscorer:** Ian Rowe 30

FACT FILE

Nickname: Magpies
Colours: Black & White/Black/black & red
Change colours:yellow/green/green & yellow
Programme: 36 pages, ¨2 with entry
Editor: Bob Thomson

CLUB PERSONNEL
Chairman: Mike Pett
Manager: Leigh Cooper
Assistant Manager: Joe Scott

LAUNCESTON

FACT FILE
Founded: 1891 Nickname: Clarets
Colours: Alll Claret
Change colours: Yellow/blue/blue
Midweek matchday: Tues/Wed
Reserves' League:East Cornwall Prem.
Programme: Yes

Secretary: Chris Martin, 3 Tavistock Road, Launceston, Cornwall PL15 9HA
Tel: 01566 776175 (H) Email: launcestonfc.co.uk

Ground: Pennygillam, Pennygillam Industrial Estate, Launceston PL15 7ED
Tel: 01566 773279 **Web site:** www.launcestonfc.co.uk

Directions: Follow signs to Pennygillam Ind. Est., just off main A30 -ground 400yds on left

Capacity: 1000 **Seats:** 150 **Cover:** 150 **Floodlights:** Yes
Clubhouse: Open after every game. Bar meals available. Club Shop: No

HONOURS South Western Lg Winners 94-95, R-up 84-85, S.W Lg.Cup Winners: 95-96
Cornish Snr Cup 1899-1900 00-01 82-83 (R-up 92-93, Charity Cup R-up 88-89)

CLUB PERSONNEL
Chairman: Keith Ellacott
President: Mr.S.Dawe
General Manager: Keith Ellacott
Manager: Gary Shirley
Physio: B.Medland

LISKEARD ATHLETIC

FACT FILE
Formed: 1889 Nickname: Blues
Sponsors: J P Leisure & Gilbert Outfitters
Colours: Blue & White/blue/blue or white
Change colours: Yellow & blue
Midweek matchday: Tuesday
Prog: 40 pages, 50p Editor: I.Pook

Football Secretary: Brian Oliver, Windrush, Tremeddan Lane, Liskeard, Cornwall PL14 3DS
Gen. Secretary: J.Melhuish,16 Maddever Crescent,Liskeard PL14 3PT
Ground: Lux Park, Liskeard, Cornwall (01579 42665) **Directions:** Take Tavistock Road (A390) from town centre, after 1/2 mile turn left on St Cleer Road (follow signs to Lux Park Sports Complex) & ground is 200 yards on left. Half mile from Liskeard BR station
Capacity: 2,000 **Seats:** 50 **Cover:** 300 **Floodlights:** Yes **Club Shop:** No
Clubhouse: (01579 342665) Normal licensing hours. Hot & cold food available
HONOURS: South Western Lg 76-77 78-79 (R-up 75-76 77-78; Lg Cup 76-77 78-79) Western Lg 87-88 (85-86 89-90, Merit Cup 80-81); Cornwall Snr Cup 04-05 83-84 84-85 85-86 88-89 89-90 93-94 (R-up., 5); Cornwall Charity Cup 21-22 79-80, Cornwall Jnr Cup 05-06 13-14 26-27; SWPratten Cup 78-79; E Cornwall Prem RAOB Cup 67-68, Plymouth & Dist. Lg 60-61(Div 1 59-60 (R-up 54-55 73-74), Div 2 76-77(Res)), Victory Cup 60-61, Charity Cup 59-60), E Cornl Prem. Lg (Res) (3) R-up:(3) Lg.Cup (4) Evely Cup (Res) 01-02
PREVIOUS Leagues: E. Cornwall Prem., Plymouth & Dist., South Western 66-79, Western 79-95
RECORDS **Goalscorer:** T Turner 59, 60-61 **Appearances:** Brian Bunney, 500+

CLUB PERSONNEL
Chairman:Ian Pook V. Chair: B.Harding
President: W.N.Rawlings
Man: Chris Burchell Asst Man: roger File
Physio: Hayley Collin
2001-02 Captain: Darren Gilbert,
Top Scorer: Lee Doncaster 31
P.O.Y.: Leigh Underhay & Darren Gilbert

MILLBROOK

FACT FILE
Founded: 1973 Nickname: The Brook
Sponsors: Plymouth Boat Cruises Ltd
Colours: Black & white/black/red
Change colours: All Royal blue
Midweek matchday: Tuesday
Reserve's League: Plymouth & District
Programme: 20 pages, 10p
Editor: J Weekes (01752 822637)

Secretary: Lee Collins, Goosaford Cottage, St John, Torpoint, Cornwall PL11 3AR
Tel No: 01752 822892 (H)
Ground: Mill Park, Millbrook, Cornwall (01752 822113)

Directions: From Torpoint Ferry - 3 miles to Antony on A374, fork left, after 1 mile turn left again and follow B3247 to Millbrook (3 miles), take road marked 'Town Centre Southdown', right at mini-r'bout after 1/4 mile, ground clearly visible. From Tamar Bridge - follow signs for Torpoint, 2 miles after Polbathic right turning marked Millbrook, 5 miles to Millbrook then proceed as above
Capacity: 2,000 **Seats:** 50 **Cover:** 200 **Floodlights:** Yes **Club Shop:** No
Clubhouse: Weekdays 7-11pm, Sat 11am-11pm, Sun noon-3 & 7.30-10.30. Hot food (chips, burgers etc) available during and after matchdays
HONOURS: South Western Lg R-up 81-82, Cornwall Snr Cup R-up 83-84 (Charity Cup 84-85, Jnr Cup 75-76), Plymouth & District Lg 80-81 (Div 1 R-up 76-77)
PREVIOUS **Leagues:** Plymouth Comb.(8yrs)/ Plymouth & Dist.(6yrs)
CLUB RECORDS **Scorer:** Unknown **Appearances:** John Horne 215

CLUB PERSONNEL
President: Mrs E Weekes
Chairman: Martin Bettridge
Vice Chairman: K Townsend
Press Officer: W Linney
Manager: Paul Stewart
Asst Manager: S Matthews

NEWQUAY

FACT FILE
Founded: 1890 Nickname: Peppermints
Sponsors:Hunters Sports
Colours: Red & white stripes/white/white
Change colours: Blue & white/white/white
Midweek Matchday: Tuesday
Reserve League: Cornwall Combination
Programme: 24 pages, 50p Editor: J Hawkey

Secretary: Bob Steggles, 12 Clemens Close, Newquay, Cornwall, TR7 2SG. Tel: 01637 872677
Ground: Mount Wise, Newquay 01637 872935
Directions: .5 mile from Newquay BR, follow 2way system for .5 mile grd sign on L.eft at Clevedon Road Website: www.newquayafc.com Email: bob@steggles.net
Capacity: 3,500 **Seats:** 250 **Cover:** 500 **Floodlights:** Yes **Club Shop:** No
Clubhouse: 7-11pm w/days, 12-11pm Sat, 12-10.30 Sun. Hot & cold snacks during matches
HONOURS: Cornish Senior Cup 34-35 52-53 54-55 56-57 91-92 (R-up (10) , S. Western Lg (7) 58-60 77-78 79-80 81-82 83-84 87-88 (R-up 3) Lg Cup 55-56 88-89 (R-up 4) Cornwall Charity Cup (13) & R-up (10) , W.Cornwall Lg 06-07,(R-up 2) ,Cornish Snr Lg Herald Cup 34-35 (R-up (7)
PREVIOUS **Leagues:** West Cornwall; Plymouth & District 21-27; Cornish Senior 31-51
BEST SEASON **FA Vase:** 3rd Round 90-91
Pl;ayers progressing: Chris Morris (Sheffield Wednesday), David Philip (Plymouth Argyle), Kevin Miller and John Hodge (Exeter City

CLUB PERSONNEL
Chairman:Roy Swift
V.-Chairman: M.Jago
President: A.Kendall
Manager: Conrad Robins
Physio: Ross McOnie
Coach: Kelvin Hunkin

St Blazey. Back Row (l-r): Dave Jones (asst manager), Steve Hancock, Dominic Richardson, Nigel Pugh, Daniel Nancarrow, Steve Taylor, Glynn Hooper, Matt Parsons, Neil Burton, Adam Trudgian, Martine Eade (physio), Terry Huddy (coach). Front Row: Trevor Mewton (manager), Dave Leonard, Chris Morris, Graham Waters, Ian Gosling, Adrian Street, Barry Pappin, Justin Harrington, Shaun O'Sullivan.

Porthleven. Back Row (l-r): Vidal James (secretary), Daniel Reed, Nigel Thwaites, Matt Witts, Luke Hodge, Dave Sweet, Richard Triggs, Matt Shiels, John Herbert, James Miller, Darren Holsey, Gary Penhaligon, Diane Ellis (physio), Sam Mellows. Front Row: Heather Mudge, Dave Gardner (coach), Liam Hennan, Jamie Morrison-Hill, Chris Stirke, Bryn Wheeler, Adrian Bleasdale, Alan Roberts, Nicky Medlin, Craig Swiggs.

Liskeard Athletic. Back Row (l-r): Chris Burchell (manager), Haly Colin (physio), Lee Harvey, Jamie Ahearn, Mike Arscott, Roger Fice (Asst manager), Mar Penprase, Huw Morgan, Paul Edwards, Paul Goodwin (coach). Front Row: Mike Preston, Darren Gilbert, Graeme McMillan, Adrian Walton, Ryan Honey, Andrew Sargent, John Dawe.

PENRYN ATHLETIC

Secretary: Mike Young, 1 Dunvegan Road, Penryn, Cornwall TR10 8HJ
Tel: 01326 374098 (H) 01326 212974 (B) 01326 374098 (F)

Ground: "Kernick", Kernick Road, Penryn, Cornwall   Tel: 01736 75182 (Clubhouse)
Capacity: 800   **Seats** 20   **Cover** 40   **Floodlights** No:

Directions: From Truro take the NEW Falmouth road at Treluswell and at the Treleiver roundabout follow signs for Kernick Industrial Estate.
Turn left at the new Asda store.

PREVIOUS   **League:** Cornwall Comb.
2000-20001   **Captain:** Steve Jewell **P.o.Y.:** Steve Coggin
Top Goalscorer: Paul Kneebone (central defender) 10

FACT FILE
Colours: Yelow/Blue/Yellow
Change colours: Light & dark blue stripes/
Navy Blue/Royal Blue
Midweek Matchday: Wednesday

CLUB PERSONNEL
Chairman: Peter Young
146 Little Oaks, Penryn
Tel: 01326 378035 (H)

Manager: Ronnie Barr
Tel: 01736 366742 (H) 07866 313816 (M)

PENZANCE

Secretary: John Mead, 8 Chyanclare, St Clare Street, Penzance TR18 2PG
Tel./Fax: 01736 369066 (H)

Ground: Penlee Park, Alexandra Place, Penzance Tel: 01736 361964
Capacity 3000 **Seats** 250 **Cover** 250 **Floodlights** No

Directions: Seafront road past harbour, after amusement arcade turn right at r'bout (Alexander Rd), ground second right.
Fifteen minutes walk from Penzance(BR); directions as above

HONOURS Cornish Snr Cup 1892-93 95-96 97-98 98-99 1903-04 07-08 47-48 60-61 72-73
80-81 (R-up 1896-97 99-1900 00-01 04-05 48-49 49-50 54-55 56-57 74-75),
South Western Lg 55-56 56-57 74-75 (Lg Cup R-up 60-61), Cornwall Charity Cup 47-48 48-49 (R-up 21-22 63-64), Cornwall Snr Lg Div 2 57-58 (Div 2 Cup 53-54 54-55), Cornwall Comb. R-up 65-66 (Lg Cup 69-70 (R-up 81-82)), Cornwall Jnr Cup(West) 03-04 04-05 05-06 07-08 09-10

Players progressing: Gerry Gazzard (West Ham), Tony Kellow (Exeter)

FACT FILE
Founded: 1888
Nickname: Magpies
Colours: Black & white/black/black
Change colours: All sky blue
Midweek matchday: Tuesday - no lights
Reserves' league: Cornwall Comb

CLUB PERSONNEL
President: Jim Dann
Chairman: Peter George
Manager:Gary Marks
Trainer: John Mead

PLYMOUTH PARKWAY

Secretary: Stuart Cadmore, 71 Trelawny Road, Menheniot, Liskeard, Plymouth PL14
3TS
Tel: 01579 340820 (H) 01752 304096 (B) 07776 14102 (M)

Ground: Brickfields, Cumberland Road, Devonport, Plymouth
Floodlights: Yes Clubhouse : Yes

Directions: Torpoint Ferry - Ferry Road and right to Park Avenue- Chapel Street- the le
then bear into Cumberland Road. Ground is on left in Madden Road

FACT FILE

Colours: Yellow/royal blue/white
Change colours: Navy/navy/white
CLUB PERSONNEL

Chairman: Mark Rowles
Tel: 01752 790436 (H) 01752 201918 (B)

Manager: Gez Baggott
Tel: 01752 302596 (H) 0966 542982 (M)

PORTHLEVEN

Team Secretary: Vidal James, 23 Parc-an -Bans,Camborne, TR14 7RW (01209 710618)
Ground: Gala Parc, Mill Lane, Porthleven (0208 574181) Clubhouse (01326 574754)
Directions: From Penzance on A394, B3304 into Porthleven, ground on left immediately before town. From Helston on B3304 ground on right as you exit town. Buses from Helston & Penzance
Capacity: 1,500   **Seats:** 50   **Cover:** 100   **Floodlights:** Yes   **Shop:** No
Clubhouse: Mon 7-11pm, Tue-Fri 12 pm-4.30 pm, Sat 12pm 12 am, Sun 12 pm -10.30 pm
Full food menu at week-ends   **PREVIOUS Grounds:** Treza Downs; Sunset Farm
Previous Leagues: West Penwith; Cornwall Snr; South Western 66-77; Cornwall Comb. 77-89
HONOURS S outh Western League R-up 72-73, 98-99 00-0 ,01-02 Lg Cup R-up Winners 00-01
98-99, Cornwall Comb.ination (6), (Lg Cup(6), Cornwall Charity Cup 70-71, 97-98 R-up: 01-02
Cornwall Senior Cup R-up 68-69, 97-98 ,99-00 ,00-01 George Evely Cup 64-65 65-66 83-84 86-
87, West Penwith Lg, Penzance Hosp. Cup, Penzance Charity Cup
Best Performance: F.A.Vase: Quarter Finalists 1997-98
Season 2001-02: Captain: Adrian Bleasdale **P.o.Y.:**Nicky Medlyn **Top Scorer** Lee Harvey 45

FACT FILE
Founded: 1896
Nickname: Fishermen
Colours: Yellow / black/blue
Change colours: All blue
Midweek Matchday: Wednesday
Reserves' League: Cornwall Combination
Programme: 50p

CLUB PERSONNEL
President: P F Johns
Chairman: Len.Williams
Vice Chairman: J.Cowles
Manager: Alan Carey

SALTASH UNITED

Secretary: Ian Mountford, 48 Castle View,Saltash, Cornwall PL12 4RD(01752 316963)
Ground: Kimberley Stadium, Callington Road, Saltash, Cornwall Tel: 01752 845746

Directions: First left after crossing Tamar Bridge, through town centre, at top of town fork right at min- roundabout, ground 400 yds ahead on left.
Capacity: 3,000   **Seats:** 250   **Cover:** 600   **Floodlights:** Yes
Clubhouse: Club attached to stand and caters for dancing and clubactivities.Sapphire Lounge caters for wedding receptions,quiz nights and private functions etc

PREVIOUS   **Leagues:** Cornwall Snr; Sth Western 51-59 62-76; E Cornwall Prem 59-62; Western 76-95
HONOURS   Cornwall Snr Lg 49-50 50-51, Western Lg 84-85 86-87 88-89 (R-up 83-84 87-88, Lg Cup 86-87 87-88 (R-up 88-89), Div 1 76-77, Merit Cup 79-80 87-88), Sth Western Lg 53-54 75-76 (R-up 3), Lg Cup 3, Cornwall Snr Cup 6

FACT FILE
Formed: 1945
Nickname: The Ashes
Colours: Red & white stripes/black/white
Change: All light blue with white trim
Midweek Matchday:Tuesday/ Wednesday
Programme: 52 pages,50p
Editor: Marian Gammage

CLUB PERSONNEL
President: P Skinnard
Chairman: Darren Bennetts
Manager:Allan Evans

St. AUSTELL

Secretary: Peter Beard, 24 Alexandra Rd, St Austell, Cornwall PL25 4QP
Tel: 01726 64138 (H) 07867 675460(M)
Ground: Poltair Park, Poltair Road, St. Austell   Tel: 01726 66099

Directions: 5 mins walk north of St Austell (BR)

          Capacity: 4,000   **Seats:** 200   **Cover:** 200   **Floodlights:** No
Clubhouse: Mon-Fri 7-10.30 & Sat 12-11pm Food is available

PREVIOUS   **Leagues:** Rocky Park (1890s)
RECORD   **Gate:** 15,000 v Penzance, Senior Cup 49
HONOURS   South Western Lg 68-69 (R-up 4), Lg Cup 64-65 71-73 87-88 (R-up 4), Cornish Senior Cup(11)

FACT FILE
Founded: 1890
Sponsors: Kwik Print
Colours: White/black/black
Change colours: Yellow/red/red
Midweek Matchday: Tuesday
Reserves' League: East Cornwall Prem.

CLUB PERSONNEL
Chairman:Andrew Millington
Asst Chairman: Alan Lucas
Manager: Glyn Rowett
Asst Manager: Keith Hosbani

St. BLAZEY

Secretary: Martin Richards, c/o St Blazey F.C.
Email Address: admin@stblazey-football.co.uk
Ground: St Blaise Park, Station Road, St Blazey Tel: 01726 814110
Directions: A390   Liskeard-St Austell road, turn into Station Road at lights inSt Blazey village; ground 100 yards on left. One and a half miles from Par (BR)

Capacity: 3,500   **Seats:** 200 **Cover:**600   **Floodlights:** Yes **Club Shop:** No
Clubhouse: Mon- Sat 11-11.00pm, Sun 12-11pm. Bar snacks
HONOURS   S Western Lg (9), R-up (10), Lg Cup 7, (R-up 5), Cornish Snr Cup (11) Cornis Charity Cup (5) Cornwall Snr Lg Cup (Herald Cup) 35-3648-49
RECORDS   Gate: 6,500 v St Austell, Cornwall Snr Cup 48-49
Goalscorer: B Tallamy   **Appearances:** W Isbell
2001-02:   **Capt:** Glynn Hooper **P.o.Y.:** Ian Gosling **Top scorer:** Damien Richardson

FACT FILE
Founded: 1896 Nickname: Saints
Sponsors: Eden Project
Colours: Green/Green /White
Change colours: Blue & white/blue/yellow
Midweek matchday: Wednesday
Reserve's League: East Cornwall Premier
Prog: 24 pages,50p Editor: Steve Paynter
Website: stblazey-football.co.uk

CLUB PERSONNEL
Chairman: Harry Cooke.V- Chair: MrA Putt
Manager: Trevor Mewton
Assistant Manager: Dave Jones
Treasurer Brian Brokenshire

TAVISTOCK AFC

Secretary: Philip Lowe, 14 Anderton Court, Whitchurch, Tavistock PL19 9EX
Tel: 01822 614447 (Club) 01822 613715 (W)
Ground: Langsford Park, Crowndale Rd, Tavistock (01822 614447)
Directions: A386 from Plymouth, 2nd left after Macdonalds into Crowndale Road and the ground is half mile on left opposite Tavistock College
Capacity: 2,000   **Seats:** 200   **Cover:** 200   **Floodlights:** Yes **Club Shop:** No
Clubhouse: Open all day Saturday and evenings 6.30-10.30 or 11pm. Hot & cold food
HONOURS   Devon Premier Cup 01-02 R-up 94-95, Devon Snr Cup 1889-90 1968-69 77-78 81-82, South Western Lg Cup 68-69 (R-up 76-77 83-84 99-00), Bedford Cup -numerous times; Devon Charity Cup 78-79, R-up 77-78, .Plymouth & District Comb Premier Cup 01-02
RECORDS   Gate: 5,000 v Calstock, Bedford Cup final 1952
Appearances: A Pethick 1,000+
Players progressing: Peter & Neil Langman (Plymouth A., 51 & 53); Robbie Pethick (Portsmouth); Mike Trebilcock (Plymouth A. 65); Harold Redmond & Danny Sullivan (Crystal Pal. 57 - £100)

FACT FILE
Founded: 1888
Nickname: `Tavy' or `Lambs'
Sponsors: RM Builders & Contractors
Colours: Red& blackblack/black
Change : All Blue
Midweek matchday: Wednesday
Reserves' Lge: Plymouth & Dist Comb. (Prem)
Programme: 32 pages £1.Editor:Ereic Pinch
Website: www.tavistock.afc.co.uk
CLUB PERSONNEL
Chairman: Robin Fenner
Vice Chairman:Steve Metters
Managers:Chris Abbott & Craig Smith
Asst Manager: Graeme Kirkup
Physio: Les Mewton

TORPOINT ATHLETIC

Secretary: Vic Grimwood, 43 Hemerdon Heights, Plympton PL7 3EY Tel: 01752 344263 (H)

Ground: The Mill, Mill Lane, Torpoint, Cornwall Tel: 01752 812889

Directions: Bear left from Torpoint ferry, ground down hill on left after half a mile

Capacity: 1,000   **Seats:** 100   **Cover:** 100   **Floodlights:** Soon

Clubhouse: Yes

PREVIOUS   **League:** Plymouth & District League.(Premier)

BEST SEASON   **FA Vase:** 4th Round 93-94, 0-3 v Diss Town (H), eventual winners

HONOURS   South Western Lg 64-65 66-67 (Lg Cup R-up 65-66), Cornish Snr Cup 8

FACT FILE

Colours:Gold & black stripes/gold& black/black
Change colours: Red & white hoops/white/red
Programme: Yes

CLUB PERSONNEL

Chairman: Colin Phillips
Tel: 01752 705845 (H)

Manager: Phil Cardew
Tel: 01752 812721 (H)

TRURO CITY

Secretary: Brian Fisher, 33 Southview Road, Biscosey, Par Pl24 2HJ(01726 812238)

Ground: Treyew Road, Truro, Cornwall (01872 278853)

     Capacity: 3,000 **Seats:** 20 **Cover** : 150 **Floodlights:** Yes **Clubhouse:** Yes

Directions: On A39 by-pass south of city.
10 mins walk from BR station; up hill and left at junction

HONOURS   South Western Lg 60-61 69-70 92-93 95-96 97-98, (R-up 54-55 62-63 66-67 67-68 70-71 96-97), Lg Cup 59-60 66-67(jt) 92-93 (R-up 54-55 58-59 67-68 93-94 95-96 97-98); Cornish Snr Cup x13; Cornish Charity Cup x7; Cornish Snr Lg 31-32 32-33; Cornwall Combination 94-95 98-99 League Cup: 1968,78,86,88,99

FACT FILE
Formed: 1889
Colours: All red
Change colours: All Blue
Midweek Matchday: Tuesday
Programme: Yes

Reserve s' League: Cornwall Combination

CLUB PERSONNEL
Chairman: Steve Cudmore
Manager: Robbie Black

WADEBRIDGE TOWN

Secretary: Brian Williams, 4 School Walk, Wadebridge, PL27 6DY

Ground: Bodieve Park, Bodieve Road, Wadebridge   (01208 812537)

     Capacity 1,500 **Seats:** 20   **Cover:** 80 **Floodlights**: No **Clubhouse:** Yes

Directions: At junction of A39 and B3314 to east of Wadebridge

HONOURS   South Western Lg R-up 68-69 78-79 79-80 (Lg Cup 5), (R-up 3),
CornishSenior Cup 79-80, Cornish Charity Cup 8

FACT FILE

Nickname: Bridgers
Colours:All red/white
Change colours: All blue/white
Reserve s' League: East Cornwall Premier

CLUB PERSONNEL

Chairman: Steve Cudmore
Manager:Robbie Black

Holsworthy. Back Row (l-r): Ian Rowe, Lee Fox, Danny Ryan, Chris Tomlinson, Adrian Lamerton, Spencer Dennis, Rob Francis, Symon Chadwick, Mark Thomas. Front Row: Ryan Swiggs, Dave Broad, Darren Butcher, Leigh Cooper (manager), Dean Chidley, Alan Clarke, Nicky Griffiths.

Penryn. Back Row (l-r): Ronnie Barr (manager), Paul Kneebone, Jamie Burr, Phil Willey, Damon Mulready, Duane Britton, Paul Wolstencroft, Martin Tuffery, Richard Pascoe (coach). Front Row: Tom Randall, Ian Humble, Andy Avery, Peter Grant, Jonny Perrow, Tim Hooper, Steve Jewell. Not in picture: Martin Day, Malcolm Moyle.

Tavistock. Back Row (l-r): James Cole, Steve Daymond, John Gosling, Steve Brownlow, Chris Gott, Simon Parnell. Middle Row: Lew Hewton (first aid), Chris Short, Mark Wall, Lee Beer, Andy Meeds, Darren Babb, Paul Smith, Graeme Kirkup (coach), Phil Lowe (secretary). Front Row: Lee Doncaster, Nathan Blamey, Craig Smith (jnt manager), Roger Lowe (president), Robin Fenner (chairman), Chris Abbott (jnt manager), Rob Hawkins

FIREWATCH
DEVON COUNTY LEAGUE

President: Carl Throgmorton

Chairman: Stephen Ware   **Vice Chairman:** Nigel Gooding

Hon. Secretary: Philip Hiscox, 19 Ivy Close, Wonford, Exeter EX2 5LX

Tel/Fax: 01392 493995   Email: pahiscox@hotmail.com

The 2001-02 season was the tenth year of existence for the League and provided much excitement and celebrations.

To celebrate the tenth year the League ran a Sportsman's Evening in October at the Langstone Cliff Hotel in Dawlish where Peter Shilton MBE OBE was the Chief Guest. We concluded the season with a Veterans Match at Newton Abbot between a team of players from our first year against a team of other veterans who have played in the League over the years.

The League Championship went to Dartmouth who were worthy champions as they racked up a record breaking 91 points and 125 goals in their 38 matches. For Dartmouth it is their first Devon League honour, but few would bet against it being their last. Newton Abbot came home in second place and were able to play the season back at Coach Road on their new level pitch and under their new floodlights. Newton Abbot will join Cullompton Rangers in representing the League in the FA Vase again next season.

There may well have been eight teams from the east of the county this year, but not one of them finished in the top six as south and west Devon teams dominated. Vospers Oak Villa finished in third place and equalled the highest ever finish by a Plymouth based club. Vospers were also unlucky to lose in the final of the Devon Premier Cup when an own goal was all that separated them from the eventual winners.

The Throgmorton Cup was won by Topsham Town for the third time in their history, and it took extra time to beat Buckland Athletic in the May Day final.

At the bottom end of the table Buckfastleigh Rangers were cast adrift and ended the season a whopping 27 points behind the nineteenth placed side Appledore. Buckfastleigh Rangers had won the first ever League Championship, but will ply their trade in the South Devon League after they were relegated.

Despite having no fewer than five applications to join the League only one side managed both a ground grading and a top two finish, and that was the University of Exeter. Having taken assurances that they will be available to play throughout the season we welcome them and their superb new home on Topsham Road into the Devon League.

Again many clubs improved their facilities, and as mentioned earlier Newton Abbot led the way on their County FA HQ shared ground, but also Budleigh Salterton erected new floodlights and managers' boxes, and Plymstock United completed three sides of hard standing around their Deans Cross home. Looking ahead a new stand at Newton Abbot and a new home for Buckland Athletic show commitment that others must follow as facilities are updated.

The League also faced the task of finding new sponsors this year as we planned ahead, so we have been fortunate to agree two separate deals, each lasting until 2005, with Firewatch South West Ltd for the League Sponsorship and with Carl Throgmorton for the Cup Sponsorship. We look forward to working with sponsors old and new as we move into the new season.

Looking ahead the new FA Standard Rules will keep us on our toes and with more than a passing interest in any restructure of the "pyramid" we are unlikely to be able, even if we wished, to rest on our laurels. But with a settled Senior Management in place and improved co-operation with the County FA on referee appointments we can all look forward with confidence to the next ten years.

Philip Hiscox, League Secretary

FINAL LEAGUE TABLE 2001-02

	P	W	D	L	F	A	W	D	L	F	A	Pts
Dartmouth	38	15	3	1	65	20	13	4	2	60	25	91
Newton Abbot	38	12	5	2	52	21	13	3	3	55	24	83
Vospers Oak Villa	38	10	3	6	39	21	14	1	4	43	17	76
Ivybridge Town	38	13	0	6	64	30	10	6	3	45	29	75
Newton Abbot Spurs	38	13	0	6	36	26	10	1	8	38	37	70
Buckland Athletic	38	10	4	5	50	29	9	5	5	41	30	66
Budleigh Salterton	38	10	2	7	38	38	10	0	9	32	49	62
Topsham Town	38	11	3	5	47	32	7	4	8	48	40	58
Ottery St Mary	38	11	3	5	46	21	5	4	10	31	31	55
Alphington	38	10	3	6	36	35	5	5	9	29	51	53
Heavitree United	38	8	3	8	41	38	8	1	10	30	38	52
Cullompton Rangers	38	9	1	9	35	33	5	6	8	29	34	49
Exeter Civil Service	38	8	4	7	34	32	5	5	9	26	40	48
Elburton Villa	38	7	4	8	33	40	7	2	10	31	42	48
Plymstock United	38	7	3	9	29	37	6	4	9	32	34	46
Dartington SC	38	6	7	6	34	36	5	2	12	29	40	42
Stoke Gabriel	38	6	2	11	33	45	4	2	13	30	59	34
Crediton United	38	6	2	11	36	42	3	3	13	16	32	32
Appledore	38	2	6	11	21	37	6	1	12	36	47	31
Buckfastleigh Rangers	38	1	1	17	13	87	1	0	18	19	83	4

725

RESULTS CHART 2001-02

		1	2	3	4	5	6	7	8	9	10	11	12	13	14	15	16	17	18	19	20
1	Alphington	X	3-1	2-1	3-0	2-3	3-3	2-0	1-3	2-2	1-1	3-2	5-3	5-3	1-3	2-1	2-1	0-3	2-1	0-4	0-3
2	Appledore	1-4	X	2-3	1-1	0-1	1-0	2-2	0-0	1-3	0-3	1-2	1-3	3-2	2-2	2-3	0-0	1-2	0-1	3-3	0-2
3	Buckfastleigh Rngrs	1-2	1-6	X	1-6	1-2	1-0	0-3	0-5	0-8	1-4	0-4	3-4	2-6	0-8	0-5	0-6	0-0	1-4	0-10	1-4
4	Buckland Athletic	2-0	2-1	10-1	X	6-0	2-2	1-1	3-0	1-1	0-1	6-1	1-0	2-1	0-5	2-3	3-2	4-4	3-0	2-3	0-3
5	Budleigh Salterton	1-1	3-1	4-1	2-2	X	1-0	3-0	2-0	1-6	2-1	2-3	3-1	1-3	1-5	0-5	2-4	1-2	2-1	5-1	2-1
6	Crediton United	2-2	0-4	9-2	0-2	5-2	X	1-5	4-2	0-4	3-1	2-3	3-2	0-1	0-1	0-1	1-2	0-3	5-2	0-0	1-3
7	Cullompton Rngrs	5-3	4-1	4-1	0-1	1-2	1-0	X	0-4	2-3	1-3	1-0	1-2	0-3	1-3	4-2	2-0	3-1	2-2	3-1	0-1
8	Dartington	0-0	1-1	3-1	2-2	2-4	0-1	0-0	X	5-2	3-1	4-2	1-0	3-3	4-4	0-2	1-6	2-1	1-1	2-4	0-1
9	Dartmouth	3-3	4-0	4-1	1-1	4-1	2-1	3-0	5-1	X	3-1	0-0	7-0	3-4	4-1	1-0	2-1	7-2	5-0	4-2	3-1
10	Elburton Villa	8-0	3-4	2-1	1-1	3-2	0-3	0-0	0-4	1-8	X	1-1	1-0	1-2	0-2	4-1	2-0	1-4	3-2	2-2	0-3
11	Exeter Civil Service	5-3	1-2	5-1	0-5	2-0	2-0	3-0	2-2	2-0	1-1	X	1-2	1-1	0-2	0-1	1-1	2-1	3-2	2-4	1-4
12	Heavitree United	1-1	3-1	4-0	3-6	3-2	0-2	1-2	2-1	2-4	3-0	2-3	X	2-2	1-2	4-0	2-1	2-2	3-5	2-1	1-3
13	Ivybridge Town	8-1	5-2	4-0	1-2	7-0	2-0	3-7	1-2	1-2	0-3	5-1	3-1	X	4-2	3-1	2-0	3-1	6-0	4-1	2-4
14	Newton Abbot	1-0	4-1	6-1	0-4	5-1	2-2	4-1	3-1	2-2	4-0	3-1	1-2	1-1	X	1-1	6-1	1-1	4-0	2-1	2-0
15	Newton Abbot Spurs	1-3	3-1	4-3	0-2	1-2	2-0	3-0	3-0	0-3	3-1	3-0	2-1	0-1	1-0	X	2-1	1-0	3-2	1-5	3-1
16	Ottery St Mary	1-2	3-0	6-1	2-1	1-2	4-0	2-0	4-0	2-3	4-1	0-0	0-1	3-3	1-3	4-1	X	2-1	3-2	4-0	0-0
17	Plymstock United	4-1	2-4	3-1	4-0	0-2	1-0	2-2	2-3	1-4	2-4	1-0	2-1	1-1	1-2	1-9	1-1	X	0-1	1-0	0-1
18	Stoke Gabriel	3-0	2-1	4-0	3-5	1-3	5-1	1-4	3-2	1-1	2-4	2-2	2-4	0-2	1-5	0-1	2-1	0-3	X	1-4	0-2
19	Topsham Town	3-1	3-2	3-0	4-0	2-3	1-0	2-1	3-2	1-1	6-0	2-1	2-2	0-3	2-2	0-1	0-3	3-1	9-3	X	1-6
20	Vospers Oak Villa	1-2	0-3	4-0	2-0	3-0	2-1	1-1	1-0	1-2	2-0	4-1	1-2	1-3	0-3	9-0	0-0	1-0	4-1	2-2	X

THROGMORTON CUP 2001-02

FIRST ROUND

Appledore	v	Topsham Town	1-5
Ottery St Mary	v	Newton Abbot	0-2
Cullompton Rngrs	v	Ivybridge Town	0-1
Plymstock United	v	Stoke Gabriel	1-3

SECOND ROUND

Alphington	v	Buckfastleigh Rngrs	4-0
Dartington SC	v	Newton Abbot Spurs	1-4
Heavitree United	v	Crediton Utd	2-4, 6-6
Topsham Town	v	Elburton Villa	3-2
Buckland Athletic	v	Newton Abbot	3-0
Dartmouth	v	Stoke Gabriel	4-0
Ivybridge Town	v	Exeter Civil Service	2-3
Vospers Oak Villa	v	Budleigh Salterton	4-1

THIRD ROUND

Alphington	v	Vospers Oak Villa	0-3
Crediton United	v	Newton Abbot Spurs	1-0*
Dartmouth	v	Buckland Athletic	1-2
Exeter Civil Service	v	Topsham Town	0-1

* Newton Abbot Spurs awarded tie after Crediton played ineligible player

SEMI FINALS

Buckland Athletic	v	Vospers Oak Villa	3-0
Newton Abbot Spurs	v	Topsham Town	0-1

FINAL

Buckland Athletic	v	Topsham Town	1-2

LEADING GOALSCORERS 2001-02

Mark Collins	Dartmouth	55
Gary Fisher	Buckland Athletic	42
Graham White	Exeter Civil Service	27
Lee Johnson	Vospers Oak Villa	23
Ricky Lennie	Crediton United	23
Tom Sercombe	Newton Abbot Spurs	23
Danny Hall	Topsham Town	22
Darren Pengelly	Alphington	22
Rob McGahey	Topsham Town	21

BASS SPORTING TROPHY 2001-02

Position	Club	Marks
1	Ottery St Mary	277
2	Exeter Civil Service	267
3	Vospers Oak Villa	253
4	Plymstock United	250
5=	Heavitree United	249
5=	Stoke Gabriel	249
7	Buckland Athletic	247
8	Newton Abbot Spurs	243

LEAGUE ALL TIME RECORDS

		P	W	D	L	F	A	Pts	P/G
1	Stoke Gabriel	356	187	68	101	829	525	629	1.76
2	Newton Abbot	356	183	74	99	838	511	623	1.75
3	Willand Rovers	318	183	61	74	755	429	610	1.91
4	Alphington	356	160	72	124	691	644	552	1.55
5	Vospers Oak Villa	356	165	56	135	772	641	551	1.54
6	Cullompton Rangers	356	155	64	137	654	585	529	1.48
7	Dartmouth	264	149	51	64	653	380	498	1.88
8	Budleigh Salterton	264	151	44	69	626	399	497	1.88

ALL TIME LEADING GOALSCORERS

Justin Osborne	175
Mark Seatherton	161
Darren Pengelly	119
Mark Collins	116
Leon Newnham	110
David Downing	109
Roger Bonaparte	108

SOMERSET COUNTY FOOTBALL LEAGUE

President: L J C Heal   **Chairman:** Miss S A Wright

Hon Secretary: C R J Rose, Sutley House, Pilton, Shepton Mallet BA4 4BL
Telephone: 01749 890767

FINAL LEAGUE TABLES 2001-02

PREMIER DIVISION

		P	W	D	L	F	A	Pts
1	Brislington Reserves	34	27	4	3	88	29	85
2	Portishead	34	21	7	6	55	30	70
3	Wells City	34	20	5	9	72	43	65
4	Mangotsfield Utd Res	34	18	5	11	72	49	59
5	Bridgwater Town Res	34	17	8	9	66	45	59
6	Castle Cary	34	14	9	11	55	47	51
7	Radstock Town	34	13	9	12	52	51	48
8	Burnham United	34	13	7	14	74	64	46
9	Nailsea United	34	13	7	14	58	52	46
10	Peasedown Athletic*	34	13	7	14	70	70	45
11	Clevedon United	34	12	6	16	51	68	42
12	Backwell United Res	34	12	4	18	63	70	40
13	Welton Rovers Res	34	10	7	17	48	74	37
14	Nailsea Town*	34	11	5	18	51	81	37
15	Fry Club*	34	10	10	14	51	60	36
16	Robinsons*	34	10	6	18	44	69	32
17	Shirehampton	34	8	6	20	41	59	30
18	Timsbury Athletic	34	5	6	23	33	83	21

FIRST DIVISION

		P	W	D	L	F	A	Pts
1	Westland United	34	25	3	6	86	44	78
2	Stockwood Green	34	23	5	6	73	30	74
3	Keynsham Town Res	34	21	8	5	102	34	71
4	University of Bath	34	18	7	9	89	46	61
5	Watchet Town	34	17	7	10	66	34	58
6	Cleeve West Town	34	15	8	11	56	54	53
7	Blackbrook	34	13	6	15	65	74	45
8	Long Sutton Somertonians	34	12	7	15	50	72	43
9	Glastonbury	34	11	9	14	46	45	42
10	Hengrove Athletic*	34	11	9	14	48	51	41
11	Congresbury	34	11	8	15	33	64	41
12	Paulton Rovers Res	34	12	4	18	65	82	40
13	Cheddar	34	11	7	16	43	62	40
14	Oldland Abbotonians*	34	10	10	14	56	56	39
15	Winscombe	34	10	8	16	54	70	38
16	Banwell	34	9	9	16	59	69	36
17	Clevedon United Res	34	8	9	17	44	89	33
18	Clandown	34	4	6	24	37	96	18

* denotes points adjustment

FINAL LEAGUE TABLES 2001-02

SECOND DIVISION

	P	W	D	L	F	A	Pts
Weston Super Mare Res	34	23	5	6	131	44	74
Crewkerne	34	19	7	8	71	42	64
Bishop Sutton Res	34	19	6	9	85	54	63
Odd Down Res	34	18	9	7	62	37	63
Frome Town Res	34	16	6	12	77	65	54
Dundry Athletic	34	16	6	12	87	80	54
Cutters Friday	34	16	3	15	66	77	51
Ilminster Town	34	15	5	14	63	53	50
Larkhall Athletic Res	34	13	9	12	58	64	48
Imperial	34	12	8	14	53	59	44
Nailsea United Res	34	12	7	15	67	62	43
Tunley Athletic	34	13	3	18	63	73	42
Churchill Club	34	12	5	17	70	86	41
Portishead Res	34	10	10	14	63	58	40
Saltford	34	10	6	18	53	75	36
Frome Collegians	34	10	6	18	46	72	36
Peasedown Ath Res	34	10	1	23	39	110	31
Wells City Res	34	8	6	20	55	98	30

THIRD DIVISION

	P	W	D	L	F	A	Pts
Backwell Utd A	34	24	4	6	89	45	76
St George Easton in G	34	23	6	5	98	42	75
Langford Rovers	34	21	7	6	110	55	70
Long Ashton	34	17	5	12	75	61	56
Shepton Mallet Tn Res	34	14	8	12	74	78	50
Hengrove Athletic Res	34	14	7	13	66	52	49
Bristol Spartak	34	15	1	18	85	100	46
Weston St Johns Res	34	14	3	17	87	101	45
Cheddar Reserves	34	11	11	12	64	58	44
Clutton	34	13	5	16	62	80	44
Fry Club Res	34	12	7	15	64	72	43
Timsbury Athletic Res	34	11	6	17	53	59	39
Robinsons Res	34	11	6	17	63	73	39
Yatton Athletic	34	11	6	17	53	75	39
Wrington-Redhill	34	12	2	20	69	77	38
Burnham Utd Res	34	11	5	18	60	83	38
Street Reserves*	34	9	11	14	64	76	37
Kewstoke	34	9	8	17	67	116	35

* points deducted

PAST WINNERS

	PREMIER DIVISION	DIVISION ONE	DIVISION TWO	DIVISION THREE
2000-01	Shepton Mallet Town	Castle Cary	Keynsham Town	Weston super Mare
1999-00	Shirehampton	Welton Rovers	Nailsea Town	University of Bath
1998-99	Clevedon United	Mangotsfield Utd	Paulton Rovers	Dundry Athletic 82
1997-98	Portishead	Timsbury Athletic	Mangotsfield Utd	Wrington Redhill
1996-97	Street	Radstock Town	Worle	Clevedon Utd Res
1995-96	Portishead	Nailsea United	Ilminster Town	Worle
1994-95	Portishead	Stockwood Green	Robinsons	Shepton Mallet Res
1993-94	Portishead	Longwell Green	Odd Down	Street
1992-93	Long Sutton	Clevedon Town	Saltford	Keynsham Cricketers
1991-92	Bridgwater T (1984)	Portishead	Bishop Sutton	Blackbrook
1990-91	Bridgwater T (1984)	Frome Town	St George E in G	Bishop Sutton Res
1989-90	Bridgwater T (1984)	Clevedon Town	Keynsham Town	Clutton
1988-89	Brislington	Stockwood Green	Ilminster Town	Fry's Club
1987-88	Robinson's DRG	Weston super Mare	Stockwood Green	Mendip Hospital
1986-87	Robinson's DRG	Bridgwater T (1984)	Shepton Mallet	Stockwood Green

LEAGUE CONSTITUTION 2002-03

Premier Division

Backwell United Res
Bridgwater Town Res
Brislington Reserves
Burnham United
Castle Cary
Clevedon United
Fry Club
Keynsham Town Res
Mangotsfield Utd Res
Nailsea Town
Nailsea United
Peasedown Athletic
Portishead
Radstock Town
Stockwood Green
Wells City
Welton Rovers Res
Westland United

Division One

Bishop Sutton Res
Blackbrook
Cheddar
Cleeve West Town
Congresbury
Crewkerne
Glastonbury
Hengrove Athletic
Long Sutton Somert'ns
Oldland Abbotonians
Paulton Rovers Res
Robinsons
Shirehampton
Timsbury Athletic
University of Bath
Watchet Town
Weston super Mare Res
Winscombe

GLOUCESTERSHIRE COUNTY LEAGUE

Chairman: A C Barrett

Hon. Secretary: D J Herbert, 8 Fernhurst Road, St George, Bristol BS5 7TQ
Tel: 0117 951 7696

FINAL LEAGUE TABLES 2001-02

		P	W	D	L	F	A	Pts
1	Roman Glass St George	32	22	3	7	83	40	69
2	Slimbridge Town	32	21	5	6	81	33	68
3	Highridge United	32	20	8	4	68	33	68
4	Ellwood	32	19	5	8	57	36	62
5	Patchway Town	32	15	11	6	55	27	56
6	Almondsbury	32	17	5	10	65	38	56
7	DRG Stapleton	32	13	10	9	51	41	49
8	Henbury Old Boys	32	11	12	9	50	46	45
9	Tytherington Rocks	32	10	8	14	35	49	38
10	Viney St Swithins	32	11	5	16	43	68	38
11	AXA	32	10	7	15	47	60	37
12	Whitminster	32	10	7	15	38	61	37
13	Hardwicke	32	9	5	18	44	56	32
14	Pucklechurch Sports	32	7	10	15	31	43	31
15	Old Georgians	32	8	5	19	31	62	29
16	Totterdown Port of Bristol	32	5	9	18	39	69	24
17	Broad Plain House OB	32	3	7	22	41	97	16

RESULTS CHART 2001-02

		1	2	3	4	5	6	7	8	9	10	11	12	13	14	15	16	17
1	AXA	X	2-2	1-1	0-4	5-0	2-1	3-0	0-2	1-0	2-2	1-4	2-3	1-4	3-1	1-3	1-0	3-3
2	Almondsbury	4-2	X	3-0	6-2	2-1	5-0	3-0	1-1	5-0	1-1	1-1	1-2	0-1	0-2	1-0	5-0	6-2
3	Broad Plain House OB	2-3	0-1	X	2-2	0-1	0-4	2-4	1-4	2-0	0-1	0-1	0-2	1-4	3-1	1-1	2-2	2-3
4	DRG Stapleton	1-0	0-1	6-1	X	2-1	4-3	0-0	1-1	1-1	0-0	0-0	3-0	1-4	2-1	0-0	5-0	3-0
5	Ellwood	0-1	2-1	2-2	1-1	X	3-2	1-2	4-0	1-0	2-1	2-0	3-1	1-0	1-0	1-2	3-1	4-3
6	Hardwicke	2-0	2-1	7-1	3-1	0-2	X	1-1	1-3	1-0	1-1	1-0	0-4	1-4	1-3	0-2	1-4	0-2
7	Henbury Old Boys	2-2	3-1	5-1	2-0	3-2	0-0	X	1-1	1-1	1-1	1-2	0-3	2-2	6-0	4-1	0-1	1-0
8	Highridge United	5-1	3-1	2-0	1-1	0-0	1-1	3-2	X	5-0	1-0	3-0	1-2	3-5	2-1	3-2	1-1	1-0
9	Old Georgians	1-3	3-0	2-3	0-2	0-3	3-1	2-1	1-2	X	1-5	1-0	0-2	0-7	0-2	1-0	2-3	0-0
10	Patchway Town	3-0	0-0	6-1	0-1	2-2	1-0	6-0	0-3	0-2	X	3-0	1-0	0-2	2-2	3-0	1-0	4-0
11	Pucklechurch Sports	0-1	3-0	2-2	3-1	0-0	0-2	0-0	1-4	0-2	0-1	X	3-3	0-1	1-1	1-0	2-3	1-1
12	Roman Glass St George	3-2	1-3	7-2	5-1	3-1	1-1	3-1	3-0	3-1	1-1	4-3	X	4-2	3-1	4-0	4-0	5-0
13	Slimbridge Town	2-1	2-0	2-1	0-0	1-3	2-1	0-0	1-2	1-3	0-0	3-1	4-1	X	6-1	4-0	6-0	4-0
14	Totterdown Port of Bristol	1-1	2-4	4-4	1-4	1-4	0-5	1-2	0-1	0-0	2-3	0-0	1-0	1-2	X	1-1	4-1	2-2
15	Tytherington Rocks	1-1	0-1	4-2	1-0	0-2	2-1	2-2	0-2	2-1	1-2	0-0	1-0	1-1	1-1	X	3-1	1-2
16	Viney St Swithins	1-0	0-2	7-1	2-0	0-2	2-0	1-1	1-1	4-2	1-4	1-0	1-3	2-4	2-1	1-2	X	0-5
17	Whitminster	2-1	0-3	3-1	1-2	0-2	1-0	0-2	0-5	1-1	0-0	0-2	0-3	1-0	2-0	4-1	0-0	X

SOUTH WESTERN FINAL LEAGUE TABLES 2001-02

BOURNEMOUTH LEAGUE

DIVISION ONE

	P	W	D	L	F	A	Pts
Westover Bournemouth	22	14	8	0	50	13	50
Pennington St Mks	22	15	2	5	56	25	47
Bournemouth Electric*	22	14	3	5	62	37	44
Dorset Knob	22	13	3	6	57	36	42
Bournemouth CS	22	13	3	6	43	29	42
Hamworthy Rec Res	22	11	4	7	50	27	37
Burton	22	9	6	7	45	42	33
Redlynch & W*	22	6	10	6	35	35	25
Southbourne	22	4	5	13	32	49	17
Sway*	22	2	5	15	22	68	14
St Marys	22	2	4	16	21	64	10
Highcliffe	22	1	3	18	30	78	6

BRISTOL & DISTRICT LEAGUE

SENIOR DIVISION

	P	W	D	L	F	A	Pts
Long Shore United	28	21	5	2	88	21	68
BAWA Aces	28	15	9	4	76	33	54
Totterdown United	28	15	5	8	65	46	50
Brimsham Green	28	13	8	7	51	45	47
Oldland Abb. Res.	28	13	3	12	65	58	42
South Bristol Cent.	28	11	7	10	66	59	40
Seymour United	28	11	5	12	51	46	38
Knowle United	28	11	5	12	50	59	38
Highridge Utd A	28	11	3	14	47	63	36
AXA Res	28	9	8	11	56	60	35
Fishponds Athletic	28	9	7	12	60	66	34
Pucklechurch Res	28	9	6	13	49	54	33
St Stephens	28	9	5	14	41	67	32
Lawrence Rovers	28	5	6	17	32	94	21
Hartcliffe Com C	28	5	4	19	38	64	19

DUCHY LEAGUE

PREMIER DIVISION

	P	W	D	L	F	A	Pts
Dobwalls	26	20	4	2	93	39	64
	26	16	5	5	65	34	53
Callington Tn Res	26	14	6	6	73	31	48
St Columb Minor	26	14	3	9	69	53	45
Southgate United	26	11	9	6	59	48	42
St Stephen	26	13	0	13	53	57	39
Polperro	26	10	8	8	59	42	38
Godolphin Atlantic	26	10	3	13	58	56	36
Pensilva*	26	10	3	13	58	56	36
Boscastle*	26	10	5	11	46	46	32
Mevagissey*	26	9	6	11	59	63	30
St Dominick	26	6	10	10	41	61	28
Biscovey	26	7	6	13	57	63	27
Lanreath*	26	4	8	16	38	80	18
St Teath	26	2	1	23	25	119	7

MID SOMERSET LEAGUE

PREMIER DIVISION

	P	W	D	L	F	A	Pts
Meadow Rangers	22	15	5	2	66	28	50
Mells & Vobster Utd	22	11	6	5	44	32	39
Chew Magna	22	11	5	6	63	39	38
Coleford Athletic	22	10	7	5	61	38	37
Inveresk	22	12	1	9	53	40	37
Chilcompton	22	10	3	9	56	51	33
Stoke Rovers	22	9	2	11	44	37	29
Evercreech Rovers*	22	9	2	11	50	56	28
Belrose	22	7	6	9	35	47	27
Pensford	22	6	6	10	39	54	24
Radstock Town Res*	22	4	3	15	28	82	13
Pilton United	22	3	4	15	28	82	13

NORTH DEVON LEAGUE

PREMIER DIVISION

	P	W	D	L	F	A	Pts
Shamwickshire R	30	28	1	1	155	38	85
Braunton	30	20	4	6	120	34	64
Morwenstow	30	18	5	7	98	47	59
Bradworthy United	30	18	4	8	77	36	58
Appledore Reserves	30	19	1	10	70	59	58
Ilfracombe Town Res	30	16	4	10	73	63	52
Northam Lions	30	11	10	9	69	68	43
Putford	30	12	4	14	53	56	40
High Bickington	30	11	4	15	60	72	37
Combe Martin	30	7	10	13	56	87	31
Holsworthy Res*	30	8	7	15	43	55	28
South Molton	30	5	10	15	44	102	25
Dolton Rangers*	30	8	3	19	58	104	24
Torrington Admirals	30	7	3	20	62	116	24
Kilkhampton	30	7	2	21	37	104	23
Boca Seniors*	30	7	4	19	54	92	22

TAUNTON & DISTRICT LEAGUE

DIVISION ONE

	P	W	D	L	F	A	Pts
Sydenham Rangers	18	15	2	1	74	17	47
Bishops Lydeard	18	12	2	4	64	16	38
Galmington	18	10	1	7	50	36	31
Wyvern	18	10	1	7	43	30	31
Staplegrove	18	8	4	6	42	37	28
Norton Fitzwarren	18	9	1	8	46	47	28
Nether Stowey*	18	7	0	11	35	42	18
Bridgwater Sports	18	5	3	10	28	40	18
Redgate	18	5	2	11	33	55	17
Highbridge Town	18	1	0	17	20	115	3

YEOVIL & DISTRICT LEAGUE

PREMIER DIVISION

	P	W	D	L	F	A	Pts
Ilchester	20	15	4	1	62	20	49
Barwick & Stoford	20	13	3	4	47	21	42
Henstridge United	20	12	2	6	59	28	38
Stoke sub Hamdon	20	9	5	6	42	32	32
Bradford Sports	20	9	4	7	45	42	31
Normalair RSL	20	8	5	7	41	38	29
Milborne Port	20	8	3	9	39	51	27
Keinton Mandeville	20	6	3	11	38	49	21
Glastonbury Sports	20	5	4	11	32	52	19
Baltonsborough	20	6	1	13	36	65	19
Camel	20	2	0	18	23	66	6
Ash Rovers withdrew							

* points adjustment

SKURRAYS WILTSHIRE FOOTBALL LEAGUE

Secretary: Peter Ackrill, 3 Dallas Avenue, Swindon SN3 3NP
Tel: 01793 520334

FINAL LEAGUE TABLES 2001-02

PREMIER DIVISION

	P	W	D	L	F	A	Pts
Shrewton United	30	25	3	2	121	22	78
Stratton Crosslink	30	19	7	4	76	33	64
Wroughton	30	19	5	6	68	30	62
Trowbridge Town	30	16	6	8	53	34	54
Devizes Town Res	30	14	9	7	62	47	51
Bradford Town	30	14	5	11	65	54	47
Melksham Town Res	30	13	6	11	53	46	45
Corsham Town Res	30	12	5	13	49	62	41

	P	W	D	L	F	A	Pts
Biddestone	30	11	7	12	44	47	40
Pewsey Vale Res	30	9	9	12	49	49	36
Westbury United Res	30	10	6	14	39	50	36
Purton Reserves	30	10	6	14	42	65	36
Aldbourne	30	5	11	14	34	71	26
Marlborough Town	30	7	1	22	40	87	22
Malmesbury Vic Res	30	6	2	22	26	81	20
Cricklade Town	30	4	4	22	44	87	16

SENIOR CUP 2001-02

FIRST ROUND
Trowbridge v Purton Reserves 4-0

SECOND ROUND
Cricklade	v	Corsham Reserves	0-4		Devizes Town Res	v	Aldbourne	6-2
Marlborough Town	v	Biddestone	1-4		Melksham Town Res	v	Pewsey Vale Res	1-0
Shrewton United	v	Wroughton	6-2		Trowbridge Town	v	Bradford Town	4p5, 1*1
Warminster Town Rs	v	Malmesbury Victoria	2-1		Westbury Utd Res	v	Stratton Crosslink	2-4

THIRD ROUND
Bradford Town	v	Devizes Town Res	0-3		Shrewton United	v	Corsham Town Res	6-1
Stratton Crosslink	v	Biddestone	2-3		Warminster Town Rs	v	Melksham Town Res	0-5

SEMI FINALS
Melksham Town Rs	v	Biddestone	0-3		Shrewton United	v	Devizes Tn Rs	5p4, 0*0

FINAL
Shrewton United v Biddestone 4p3, 1*1 at Corsham Town

CONSTITUTION OF LEAGUE 2002-03

PREMIER DIVISION

Aldbourne	Melksham Town Reserves
Biddestone	Pewsey Vale Reserves
Bradford Town	Purton Reserves
Chiseldon Castrol	Shrewton United
Corsham Town Reserves	Stratton Crosslink
Cricklade Town	Trowbridge Town
Devizes Town Reserves	Warminster Town Reserves
Malmesbury Victoria Reserves	Westbury United Reserves
Marlborough Town	Wroughton

Letchworth ground staff battle to get their ground fit for their team to win the last match of the season and the Spartan South Midlands Division title. Photo: Gordon Whittington

Maybe he's the leader! Photo: Graham Cotterill at Pagham

Crowd segregation at Oving FC. Photo: Graham Cotterill

MIDLAND FOOTBALL ALLIANCE

President: Bernard Davis   **Chairman:** Pat Fellows

Secretary: Peter Dagger, 32 Drysdale Close,
Wickhamford, Worcestershire WR11 7RZ
Tel: 01386 831763   Fax: 01386 833488
E-mail: PDagger@talk21.com

Following the problems caused by the weather in 2000-01 it was a relief that season 2001-02 was completed by the end of April.

For a second campaign we did not have a main sponsor which is a concern to members of the Management Committee and club officials. The current uncertainty regarding the revision of the non-League pyramid does not help in the search for a sponsor and it is to be hoped that the Football Association resolves the situation as soon as possible. However, we reamin grateful to Rameses Associates for sponsoring the League Cup competition and to Baker and Joiner for their continued sponsorship of the Hospitality award. Malcolm Lycett, a life member of the League, through his company Polymac Services, continues to sponsor the annual awards for the Team Manager and the highest goalscorer and Clubcall provide awards for the team of the month.

Last season the championship was won on goal difference and once again the championship was not determined until the last day of the season. Stourbridge needed a point at Stafford Town, but it was only a goal in the last few minutes of the match that saw them clinch the title from Bromsgrove Rovers. These two teams together with Wednesfield, Stratford Town and Rushall Olympic had challenged for the championship for most of the season and all had a chance of winning the League until near the end of April.

Unfortunately Stourbridge could not be considered for promotion to the Dr Martens League because they ground share with a local cricket club and this means that they are not able to carry out the necessary improvements to their ground. This means that Bromsgrove Rovers will return to the Dr Martens League after one season and the league will miss their large following of supporters which saw them attract over 1000 spectators to their home match with Stourbridge, more than doubling the record attendance for a match in this League.

The League Cup was keenly contested, the semi-finalists being Barwell, Oadby Town, Rushall Olympic and Stourbridge. The final saw Rushall Olympic beat Barwell 2-1 after extra time.

Once again we had high hopes of success in the FA Cup and particularly the FA Vase with the final being played locally at Villa Park. Rushall Olympic had a good run in the Vase and looked as if they might have a chance of making at least the semi-finals, but disappointingly lost at home to a team they normally would and should have beaten. In the County Cup competitions Studley BKL won the Worcestershire Senior Urn and Oadby Town were beaten finalists in the Westerby Cup.

Prior to the start of the season the match for the Joe McGorian Trophy, competed for by the previous season's League Champions and the League Cup winners, saw Stourbridge take the trophy after defeating Stourport Swifts.

After struggling for several years Stapenhill were forced to resign halfway through the season when lack of financial resources meant they were unable to retain the majority of their players. Financial problems also meant that Paget Rangers tendered their resignation at the end fo the season and tragically it will look as if this well known club will cease to exist, although it was only seven years ago that they were the first champions of the Midland Football Alliance and sold their old ground to build a new stadium. It must be of great concern to all people with an interest in non-League football that these two clubs, together with Blakenall, Bloxwich United and Bilston Town who all resigned from the Dr Martens League in the last twelve months, have been forced to close or look to compete at a much lower level of football. These resignations meant that there was no relegation from either the Dr Martens League or the Midland Football Alliance.

As usual our Referees and Assistant Referees received many prestigious appointments during the campaign. At the end of the season Andy Penn was promoted to the National List of Referees, Phil Gibbs and Michael Murphy entered the Panel list of Referees and Ian Evans, Peter Grove, Tom Sim and Mark Weaver were appointed to the National List of Assistant Referees. Oliver Langford was also promoted to the National Contributory list of Referees.

Finally, following the decision of the Football Association to take over the appointment of match officials for contributory leagues, Peter Brandwood, Referees Secretary, decided to retire at the end of the season. Peter has given over 50 years service to football as both a referee and an administrator and received an award from the Football Association for his long service. His experience and wisdom will be greatly missed by his colleagues on the Management Committee.

P G Dagger, General Secretary/Treasurer

FINAL LEAGUE TABLE 2001-02

	P	W	D	L	F	A	Pts		P	W	D	L	F	A	Pts
Stourbridge	42	27	7	8	82	39	88	Willenhall Town	42	16	9	17	65	62	57
Bromsgrove Rovers	42	26	9	7	94	41	87	Boldmere St Michaels	42	15	11	16	43	51	56
Wednesfield	42	24	9	9	73	39	81	Halesowen Harriers	42	16	8	18	56	69	56
Stratford Town	42	24	7	11	81	49	79	Paget Rangers	42	10	19	13	58	55	49
Rushall Olympic	42	22	11	9	81	50	77	Stafford Town	42	13	6	23	59	88	45
Oadby Town	42	21	12	9	78	62	75	Pelsall Villa	42	10	12	20	39	70	42
Quorn	42	20	10	12	76	55	70	Chasetown	42	9	13	20	43	74	40
Barwell	42	15	17	10	67	44	62	Shifnal Town	42	9	10	23	36	77	37
Studley BKL	42	16	12	14	76	57	60	Knypersley Victoria	42	10	5	27	51	82	35
Ludlow Town	42	15	14	13	58	53	59	Oldbury United	42	7	11	24	39	77	32
Bridgnorth Town	42	18	5	19	74	73	59	Cradley Town	42	5	11	26	36	98	26

RESULTS CHART 2001-02

	1	2	3	4	5	6	7	8	9	10	11	12	13	14	15	16	17	18	19	20	21	22	23
1	X	0-1	1-0	1-1	1-1	0-0	5-0	3-1	0-1	2-0	4-1	1-1	2-0	1-1	2-2	3-1	0-0	2-3	0-0	2-0	3-3	0-2	4-1
2	2-1	X	0-0	0-2	1-1	1-0	3-0	2-1	1-1	1-1	4-0	2-2	2-0	0-3	1-1	2-1	1-0	6-2	2-3	0-3	0-0	0-2	0-1
3	3-2	3-0	X	3-1	1-1	3-1	4-2	8-2	5-3	3-3	4-2	0-3	0-1	0-0	1-0	3-2	4-1	-	2-0	0-1	0-2	3-0	2-0
4	0-3	1-0	2-1	X	6-0	2-1	2-1	3-2	2-0	5-1	3-0	1-0	4-0	3-1	6-0	7-0	2-2	6-1	0-2	0-1	2-2	0-1	0-0
5	0-2	1-0	2-1	0-1	X	0-1	1-0	2-1	0-0	0-1	0-0	1-1	2-2	2-1	1-3	0-1	0-2	-	0-2	1-1	3-1	1-1	0-4
6	1-1	1-2	0-2	0-3	4-4	X	1-1	0-2	1-5	0-1	0-0	3-1	2-2	0-0	1-6	1-0	1-3	-	0-5	0-1	2-2	1-3	1-4
7	1-2	1-2	2-1	3-1	1-1	3-1	X	2-0	2-1	4-2	0-1	2-2	3-1	1-5	2-2	3-1	1-0	-	4-0	3-2	2-1	0-1	1-1
8	2-2	0-2	4-2	1-3	2-3	4-1	2-1	X	1-1	2-1	2-3	0-3	3-0	0-3	4-1	2-0	0-1	2-1	1-3	0-1	1-3	2-4	0-1
9	1-1	1-1	3-2	1-2	1-2	2-0	1-1	2-1	X	1-2	5-1	1-1	2-1	0-2	0-2	1-1	0-1	1-4	1-0	2-2	1-1	0-0	2-1
10	1-0	4-0	2-0	1-1	2-1	8-2	1-0	1-1	2-1	X	2-0	0-0	2-1	1-0	1-4	1-1	3-3	1-1	1-1	2-1	1-0	1-1	3-2
11	0-0	0-1	0-4	3-3	1-0	0-2	0-0	0-0	1-1	2-4	X	3-3	0-0	1-2	1-2	1-2	3-0	-	1-2	0-2	1-3	1-1	1-0
12	3-1	2-2	2-0	0-0	1-1	0-0	3-0	0-0	0-1	2-2	0-0	X	3-2	0-1	2-4	0-0	0-1	3-0	0-3	1-1	1-3	0-3	2-0
13	2-2	0-2	1-2	0-6	3-0	1-1	1-2	1-0	2-0	1-1	1-1	1-0	X	0-0	0-2	1-0	0-3	-	2-0	3-1	2-1	0-0	1-1
14	0-0	0-0	2-3	1-2	2-2	3-0	4-0	4-1	3-2	3-2	4-1	1-2	3-2	X	2-1	1-1	4-2	7-0	2-2	2-5	1-5	0-0	0-1
15	1-5	4-1	4-0	0-0	3-1	3-0	2-0	1-0	1-1	3-2	2-1	3-0	3-0	3-2	X	2-0	3-1	1-0	1-2	3-0	1-1	0-1	1-1
16	1-3	2-0	1-1	3-2	1-2	2-0	0-1	0-2	1-0	1-3	3-1	3-3	0-0	0-1	0-0	X	1-1	-	0-2	1-5	0-0	0-2	1-2
17	1-3	1-0	2-1	0-4	1-1	3-2	2-1	1-3	1-3	2-4	3-0	0-3	1-2	1-2	2-1	1-2	X	-	1-1	1-4	2-1	1-2	1-4
18	-	2-0	0-4	-	0-1	2-0	1-2	-	-	-	1-3	-	1-0	-	-	4-1	-	X	2-5	-	-	0-5	1-1
19	1-0	1-0	1-0	1-2	6-1	4-0	3-0	2-0	0-1	5-1	1-0	3-3	1-0	3-1	1-1	3-0	4-3	-	X	3-2	3-0	2-0	0-1
20	3-1	2-0	2-0	2-2	3-1	4-0	1-2	2-0	1-2	0-2	1-0	1-1	2-2	0-6	1-0	2-0	5-1	5-1	2-0	X	1-2	3-0	3-2
21	2-2	1-3	2-1	2-3	2-1	6-1	1-2	3-0	0-0	0-0	3-1	2-0	6-0	0-2	1-3	5-1	4-1	4-0	1-3	1-1	X	1-0	0-0
22	1-0	2-0	2-0	0-1	3-2	0-2	1-1	3-1	1-2	2-3	3-1	2-1	3-0	5-0	2-2	7-0	4-2	-	1-1	0-2	2-1	X	3-0
23	1-1	1-1	11-1	1-3	1-0	1-1	3-0	3-0	3-4	3-2	0-3	0-6	1-0	0-1	0-0	0-1	4-3	2-2	1-2	0-4	3-1	1-2	X

Stapenhill withdrew during the season. Their results are shown above but have been expunged from the league table

1	Barwell	9	Ludlow Town	17	Stafford Town
2	Boldmere St Michaels	10	Oadby Town	18	Stapenhill
3	Bridgnorth Town	11	Oldbury United	19	Stourbridge
4	Bromsgrove Rovers	12	Paget Rangers	20	Stratford Town
5	Chasetown	13	Pelsall Villa	21	Studley BKL
6	Cradley Town	14	Quorn	22	Wednesfield
7	Halesowen Harriers	15	Rushall Olympic	23	Willenhall Town
8	Knypersley Victoria	16	Shifnal Town		

CLUBCALL TEAM OF THE MONTH AWARDS 2001-02

August/September	Stapenhill	January	Wednesfield
October	Stourbridge	February	Wednesfield
November	Rushall Olympic	March	Bromsgrove Rovers
December	Wednesfield	April/May	Willenhall Town

LIST OF HONOURS

	1995-96	1996-97	1997-98	1998-99	1999-00	2000-01	2001-02
LEAGUE CHAMPIONSHIP							
Winners	Shepshed D	Blakenall	Bloxwich T	Rocester	Oadby Town	Stourport Swifts	Stourbridge
Runners up	Blakenall	Hinckley Ath	Rocester	Kings Norton	Stratford T	Rushall Olympic	Bromsgrove Rvrs
LEAGUE CUP							
Winners	Blakenall	Willenhall T	Knypersley V	Oldbury Utd	Willenhall T	Stourbridge	Rushall Olympic
Runners up	Oldbury Utd	Bloxwich T	Bloxwich T	West Mids Pol.	Knypersley V	Bridgnorth T	Barwell
INVITATION CUP							
Winners	Pelsall Villa	Oldbury Utd	Atherstone U	Atherstone U	Bridgnorth T	Willenhall T	
Runners up	Oldbury Utd	Bridgnorth T	Blakenall	Bandon	Darlaston T	Stratford T	
HOSPITALITY CUP							
Winners	Halesowen H	West Mids Pol.	Halesowen H	Halesowen H	Halesown H	Halesowen H	Halesowen H
KEVIN KEEGAN - PLAYER OF THE YEAR							
Player	Simon Hyden	Adrian Horne	John Powell	Ian Long	David Davis	John Powell	Marcus Johnson
Club	Rushall O	Pelsall Villa	Shifnal Town	Oldbury Utd	Oldbury Utd	Shifnal Town	Rushall Olympic
TOP GOALSCORER - THE GOLDEN BOOT							
Player	M Biddle	C Blakemore	S Bradbury	A Lucas	S Bradbury	L Booth	Craig Pountney
Club	Knypersley V	Willenhall T	Chasetown	Barwell	Chasetown	Stourport S	Studley BKL
BEST DISCIPLINARY AWARD							
Club	Barwell	Barwell	Stapenhill	Rocester	Boldmere St M	Stafford Town	Barwell
BEST PROGRAMME AWARD							
Club	Boldmere St M	Pelsall Villa	Rocester	Willenhall T	Shifnal Town	West Mids Pol.	Kypersley Vic
MANAGER OF THE YEAR							
Manager	M O'Kane	B Green	Knox/Folland	T Greer	T Hussy	R Brown	Joe Jackson
Club	Shepshed D	Blakenall	Bloxwich T	Rocester	Oadby T	Stourport S	Stourbridge
J McGORIAN CUP							
		Shepshed D	Willenhall T	Knypersley V	Oldbury Utd	Oadby Town	Stourbridge

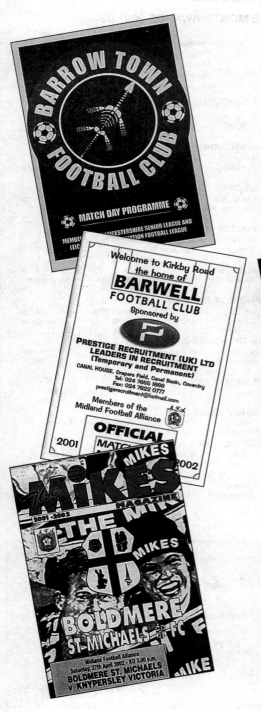

BARWELL

Secretary: Mrs Shirley Brown, 101 Eskdale Road, Hinckley, LE10 0NW (01455 446048)
Email address: steven.brown16@ntlworld.com

Ground: Kirkby Rd, Barwell, Leics (01455 843067)
Directions: M42 jct 10 (Tamworth Services), A5 towards Nuneaton. Remain on A5for approx 11 miles, go straight on at traffic lights at the Longshoot Motelthe 400 yards at r/about take 1st exit left sign A47 Earl Shilton, in 3 milesat traffic lights go straight ahead and in 1 mile at r/about take first leftexit sign Barwell in village centre 1/2 mile go straight over mini r/about, 20yards turn right into Kirkby Rd, ground 400 yards on right.
Capacity: 2,500   **Seats:** 256   **Cover:** 750   **Floodlights:** Yes
Clubhouse: Evenings & lunchtimes. Snacks available.   **Club Shop:** No

HONOURS: Barwell Ath.: Leics Snr Lg Tebbutt Brown Cup 91-92, Leics Sen Cup 96-97.

PREVIOUS   Names: Barwell Athletic F.C., Hinckley F.C. - amalgamated in 1992.
            Leagues: Midland Combination 92-94
            (Barwell Ath.: Leics Senior. Hinckley: Central Midlands 86-88)
Ground: Barwell Ath.: Kirkby Road pre 1992, Hinckley: groundshare at Hinckley Ath. pre-'92

RECORDS   Goalscorer: Andy Lucas
            Appearances: Kevin Johnson.

FACT FILE
Founded: 1992.
Nickname: The Kirkby Roaders
Sponsors: T.B.A.
Colours: Yellow,black& white/black/yellow
Change colours: All blue with white trim
Midweek matchday: Tuesday
Programme: 36 pages #1.00
Editor: I Backhouse
2001-02 Captain: Darren Grassby
Top Scorer: Jason Percival
Ps.o.Y.: Paul Grears & Jason Percival

CLUB PERSONNEL
Chairman: David Laing.
Vice Chairman: Colin Burton
President: Derek Withers
Press Officer: Merv Nash.
Manager: Mark O'Kane
Asst Manager: Mark Harbottle
Physio: Viv Coleman

BIDDULPH VICTORIA

Secretary: Steve Chawner, 18 John St., Biddulph, Stoke on Trent. ST6 6BB (01782 518998)
Email Address: secretary@knypersleyvics.co.uk
Ground: Tunstall Road, Knypersley, Stoke-on-Trent, (01782 522737 club).
Directions: M6 Jct 15 join A500, 4th exit, pick up A527, follow through Tunstall, Chell, to Biddulph. Ground is situated on A527 just before Biddulph. From M6 jct 18 follow signs to Holmes Chapel then Congleton, A527 to Biddulph,continue thru lights, ground on left.
Capacity: 1,200   **Seats:** 200   **Cover:** 200   **Floodlights:** Yes **Club Shop:** Yes
Clubhouse: Open from 1pm Saturdays, 7pm weekdays. Hot snacks at tea bar

HONOURS   West Mids Lg Div 1 92-93, Staffs Snr Lg 84-85 (Lg Cup 84-85 85-86), Staffs Co. Lg R-up 79-80, Staffs FA Vase 83-84 86-87, Sentinel Cup 86-87,   Leek & Moorlands Lg 72-73 (Div 2 71-72). Industrial Rewinds Cup 98,
            Joe McGorian Cup 88.
BEST SEASON   FA Cup 3rd Qual Rd 96-97 **FA Vase:**
PREVIOUS   Leagues: Leek & Moorlands 69-78; Staffs Co. (North) 78-83; Staffs Sen 83-90; W Midland (Reg) 90-94. **Grounds:** None **Names:** Knypersley Victoria
RECORDS   Attendance: 1,100 v Port Vale, friendly 1989
            Goalscorer: J Burndred 128   **Appearances:** Terry Stanway 601
            Fee paid: £1,000 M Biddle (Congleton 93) **Defeat:** 0-9 v Meir KA, Staffs Sen.
            Win: 10-0 v Clancey Dudley, West Midls (Reg.) Div. 1 90-91

FACT FILE
Founded: 1969.
Nickname: The Vics.
Sponsors: Chrysalis Fibres
Colours: Claret & sky/claret/claret & sky.
Change colours; Blue & Yellow/ Blue/Yellow
Midweek matchday: Tues/Thurs
Reserve League: Staffs Senior.
Programme: 40 pages 60p.
Editor/ Press Officer: J A Shenton
(01782 517962).
Website: www.knypersleyvics.co.uk

CLUB PERSONNEL
Chairman: Alan farr
President: G Quinn

Manager: Terry Stanway
Coach: Mick Biddle
Physio: T.B.A.

BOLDMERE St. MICHAEL

Secretary: Dave Holvey, 38 Aldridge Road, Streetly, Sutton Coldfield, B743TT
            Tel: 0121 353 6321 (H & FAX)   07787 106698 950102 (M)
Ground: Church Road, Boldmere, Sutton Coldfield
            Tel: 0121 373 4435 or 0121 384 7531
Directions: A38 & A5127 from City towards S. Coldfield, left at Yenton lights onto A452 (Chester Rd), Church Rd, 6th turning on the right.
            Nearest station: 400yds from Chester Road (BR).
Capacity: 2,500   **Seats:** 230   **Covered:** 400   **Floodlights:** Yes
Clubhouse: Bar & lounge, every evening and four lunchtimes.

HONOURS: Birmingham AFA 36-37; Birmingham AFA Snr Cup; Birmingham Jnr Cup, FA Amtr Cup SF 47-48; AFA Snr Cup 47-48; Central Amtr Lg 48-49; Midland Comb 85-86 88-89 89-90, Challenge Cup 77-78 89-90; Tony Allden Mem.Cup 78-79 88-89 91-92; Challenge Trophy 86-87; Sutton Charity Cup 96-97. Midland Comb. Reserve Div 2001-02
PREVIOUS   **Leagues:** West Mids 49-63; Midland Combination 63-94.

Players Progressing: John Barton (Everton, Derby County),Kevin Collins (Shrewsbury), Jack Lane (Birmingham City, Notts Co.), John Lewis(Walsall), Don Moss (Cardiff, C Palace), Harry Parkes (Aston Villa), Wally Soden (Coventry). Mike Griffiths (Torquay Un ited) , Robin Elmes, Jimmy Quiggin (Hereford United) and Paul Devlin (Birmingham City)

FACT FILE
Founded: 1883 Nickname: Mikes.
Sponsor: Swift Forwarding
Colours: White/black/black
Change Colours: Yellow/yellow/yellow
Midweek matches: Tuesday
Programme: 32 pages, £1.00
Editor: D.Holvey (0121 3536321)

CLUB PERSONNEL
Chairman: Keith Fielding
Match Secretary: as secretary
Manager: Alan Parsons
2001-02
Captain: Steve Behan
P.o.Y.: Darren Owen
Top Goalscorer: Chris Busby

BRIDGNORTH TOWN

Secretary: Mary Boot, 68 Wellmeadow,Bridgenorth,Shropshire WV15 6DE (01746 764204)
Ground: Crown Meadow, Innage Lane, Bridgnorth, Salop WV16 6PZ (01746 762747)
Directions: Follow signs for Shrewsbury (A458) over river bridge on by-pass,turn right for town centre at island, right at T junction, 1st left into Victoria Road, right at cross-road, follow road into Innage Lane, ground on left.
Capacity: 1,600   Shop: Yes   Seats: 250   Cover: 700   Floodlights: Yes
Clubhouse: Evenings & weekend lunches, Dancehall, darts, pool, hot food on matchdays
Record Fee Recieved: £10,000 for Delwyn Humphries from Kidderminster Harriers
Players Progressing: Roger Davies (Derby county) and Paul Jones (Wolves via Kidd'ter H)

HONOURS: Midland Comb 79-80 82-83 (R-up 76-77 80-81); Lg Cup 78-79, Tony Allden Mem Cup R-up, Kidderminster & Dist Lge,Shropshire Snr Cup 85-86; Shropshire County Cup 70-71 75-76 76-77 78-79 79-80;Welsh Amt Cup 70-71; Shropshire County Jun Cup 98-99.
BEST SEASON: FA Cup: 3rd Qual Rd 64-65FA Vase: 5th Rd 75-76, 94-95
PREVIOUS Leagues: Kidderminster & Dist until 68; Midland Comb 68-83; Southern Lge, Midland Div. 83-96   Names: St Leonards Old Boys pre 46
RECORDS Goalscorer: Roger Davies 157   Appearances: Kevin Harris 426
Attendance: 1,600 v South Shields FA Vase 5th Rd 1976

FACT FILE
Founded: 1946
Nickname: The Town
Sponsors:
Colours: All Blue
Change colours: All red
Midweek matchday: Tuesday
Programme: 24 pages,60p
Editor: Simon Bromley
Local Press : Shropshire Star, Bridgnorth Journal, Express & Star.. Local Radio:
Beacon, BBC Radio Shropshire
Youth League: West Mids Regional Regional
CLUB PERSONNEL
Chairman: Simon Bromley
Vice Chairman: Ian Thomas
President: Mike Williams
Manager:Les Bristow
Asst Manager: Paul Blakeley
Physio: Andy Perry

CAUSEWAY UNITED

Secretary: Frank Webb, 10 Moorfield Drive, Halesowen, West Midlands B63 3TG Tel: 0121 550 5219 (H) 0121 550 9916 (B)

Ground: Halesowen Town F.C., The Grove, Old hawne Lane, Halesowen Tel: 0121 550 2179

Directions: M5 jct 3, A456 (signed Kidderminster) to 1st island turn right (signed A459 Dudley), left at next island (signed A458 Stourbridge), at next island take 3rd left into Grammar School Lane, then Old Hawne Lane - ground 400 yds on left

Capacity: 5,000   Cover: 1,420   Seats: 420   Floodlights: Yes

Colours: All blue

Change Colours: All white

Chairman:Steven Hulston

CHASETOWN

Secretary: Chris Harris, 38 Naden House, Stafford Rd., Cannock, Staffs. WS12 4NU tel: 01543 572927 (H) 01889 583306 (B)
Ground: The Scholars, Church Street, Chasetown, Walsall WS7 8QL Tel: 01543 682222/684609
Directions: Follow Motorways M5, M6 or M42 and follow signs for A5. A5 to White Horse Road/Wharf Lane, left into Highfields Rd (B5011), left into Church Street at top of hill, ground at end just beyond church. Buses 394 or 395 W Mids Travel, 94 Chase Bus,from Walsall, 860 Midland Red from Cannock.
Capacity: 2,000   Seats: 112   Cover: 250   Floodlights: Yes   **Club Shop:** Yes
Clubhouse: Mon-Fri 7.30-11pm, Sat 11.30am-11pm, Sun 8-10.30pm. Basic snacks

HONOURS West Mids Lg R-up 90-91 92-93 (Lg Cup 89-90 90-91, Div 1 77-78 (R-up73-74 74-75 75-76 80-81 82-83), Div 1 Cup R-up 80-81 82-83, Div 2 R-up 87-88,Div 2 Cup R-up 86-87); Walsall Snr Cup 90-91 92-93; Staffs Snr Cup R-up 91-92.

PREVIOUS Name: Chase Terrace Old Scholars 54-72 Ground: Burntwood Rec Cte (pre'83)
Leagues: Cannock Yth 54-58; Lichfield & Dist. 58-61; Staffs Co. 61-72; West Mids 72-94.
RECORDS Attendance: 659 v Tamworth, FA Cup 2nd Qual Rd 1/10/88.
Appearances: A Cox 469 (+15)   **Win:** 14-1 v Hanford (H), Walsall Snr Cup 17/10/92.
Goalscorer: T Dixon 172   **Defeat:** 1-8 v Telford U Res., West Mids (Reg.) Lge Div. 1

FACT FILE
Founded: 1954.
Nickname: Scholars
Colours: All blue
Change Colours: All Red.
Sponsors: Aynsley Windows
Midweek matchday: Tuesday
Reserves League: West Midlands
Programme: 26 pages, 50p
Editor/Press Officer: Mike Fletcher

CLUB PERSONNEL
Chairman: Brian Baker
Vice Chairman: B Simpson
President: A Scorey.
Manager: Paul darby
Asst Manager: Brian Fox
Physio: E Highfield.

CRADLEY TOWN

Secretary: David Attwood, 4 Birch Coppice, Quarry Bank, Brierley Hill, W Midlands DY5 1AP
Tel: 01384 637430
Ground: Beeches View, Beeches View Ave, Cradley, Halesowen, B63 2HB. (01384 569658)
Directions: M5-jct3.A456 right at 2nd island into Hagley Rd. Third left to Rosemary Rd. Straigh
into Lansdowne Rd/Dunstall Rd then left at T jct into Huntingtree Rd/Lutley Mill Rd.Left at next T
jct into Stourbridge Rd and left into Beecher Rd East.First left into Abbey Rd and right into
Beeches View Avenue at end .Ground entrance is between houses 48 & 50,20yyds on left.
Capacity: 3,000 **Seats:** 200 **Cover:** 1,500 **Floodlights:** Yes
Clubhouse: Open matchdays only. Food available **Club Shop:** No
HONOURS West Mids Lg Div 1 90-91, Midland Comb. Div 2 72-73 R-up 75-76 77-78,
Presidents Cup 74-75 75-76, Invitation Cup 72-73); Metropolitan Lg 70-71,
Wednesbury Charity Cup 90-91, Dudley Guest Hosp. Cup 71-72 72-73 75-76 90-91
PREVIOUS Leagues: Metropolitan; Brierley Hill; Kidderminster; West Mids Amtr; Midland
Comb. 71-82; West Midlands 82-99 **Name:** Albion Haden United **Grounds:** None
RECORDS Gate: 1,000 v Aston Villa, friendly **Goalscorer:** Jim Nugent **Apps:** R J Haywood
Win: 9-1 v Wolverhampton U (H), West Midlands Lge 1990 **Defeat:** 0-9 v Paget Rangers (A)
Invitation Cup 97 **Transfer fee paid:** £1,000 for Darren Marsh (Oldswinford, 1992)
Received: £20,000 for John Williams (Swansea, 1991)
Players progressing: Alan Nicholls (Plymouth), John Williams, Jon Ford, Andy McFarlane (all
Swansea), Duane Darby (Torquay)

FACT FILE
Founded: 1948
Nickname: Lukes
Sponsors:Commercial Risk Insurance
Colours: White/black/black
Change colours: All Yellow
Midweek matchday: Tuesday
Programme: Yes

CLUB PERSONNEL
President: Alf Hill
Chairman:Alan Hankon
Vice Chairman: Trevor Thomas
Press Officer: Trevor Thomas (01384 569658)
Manager: Trevor Thomas
Assistant Manager:Morton Bartlett
Physio: Mark Holloway
2001-02
Captain: Matthew Aston
P.o.Y.: Matthew Aston
Top Goalscorer: Ian Aldridge 9

GROSVENOR PARK (formerly Sutton Town)

Secretary: Peter Yates, 8 Crome Road, Great Barr, Birmingham B43 7NL
Tel: 0121 360 1611 (H) email: py@otal.com

Ground The Red Lion Ground, Somerfield Rd, Bloxwich,Walsall WS3 2EJ (01922 405835)

Directions: From Jct 10 M6 follow signs to Walsall town centre. Left at first lights into Bloxwich
Lane. At first traffic island turn right and follow signs for A34. Ground is on A34 on right after
Four Crosses public house. Clubhouse at ground

Honours: Mid Comb Div 1 99-00, B'ham County Cup R-up 99-00, Endsleigh Cup 99-00 (first
non Premier club for 30 years), 00-01 R-up B'ham County Vase 00-01, MFC team of 99-00
Tony Allden Memorial Cup 2001-02. Midland Combination Champions 2001-02
Previous Leagues: Midland Comb.

FACT FILE
Founded: 1959
Colours: Tangerine/black/tangerine
Change colours: All white

Chairman: John O'Hara
Tel: 0121 360 1611
Match Secretary: Ray Fisher
Tel: 0121 360 9904

2001-02
Captain: Mel Henry
P.o.Y.: Rash Anifowose
Top Scorer: Rash Anifowose 29

HALESOWEN HARRIERS

Secretary: Mrs Christine Beasley, 43 Hawne Lane, Halesowen, West Midlands, B63 3RN.
Tel: 0121 550 3788 (H) 01384 896748 (B) 07788 697167 (M)

Ground: Hayes Park, Park Rd, Colley Gate, Halesowen Tel: 01384 896748

Directions: On A458 Birmingham to Stourbridge Rd (B'ham 10 miles, Stourbridge 4 miles).
M5 Jct 3 (towards Kidderminster), right at 1st island (towards Dudley),
turn left at island (towards Stourbridge), straight over next island then 3m to
ground on left side, 200yds past Park Lane next to McDonalds. 1 mile from Lye BR
Capacity: 4,000 Seats: 350 Cover: 500 Floodlights: Yes **Club Shop:** Yes
Clubhouse: Open every evening. Limited range of hot snacks, but full cold snack kitchen.
HONOURS West Mids League Div 1 85-86 (Div 2 84-85, Div 2 Cup 84-85),
Inter City Bowl 67-68 68-69, Festival League x5, R-up x9,
FA Sunday Cup SF 79-80, Midland Sunday Cup, Birmingham Sunday Cup.
PREVIOUS Leagues: Festival (Sunday)/ West Midlands (pre-1994)
Grounds: Birmingham Parks 61-70/ Halesowen Town FC 70-84 (both whilst in Sunday football).
RECORDS Attendance: Friendly matches 750 v Walsall and Wolves in 1985
Competitive: 450 v Lye, Lge 1988
Defeat: 2-8 v Frickley Athletic (A), F.A. Cup 2nd Qual Rd 26/9/92.
Win: 12-1 v Lichfield & v Malvern Town, 1986. **Fee paid:** £750 to Oldswinford for L Booth, 1991.

FACT FILE
Founded: 1961
Nickname: None
Sponsors:Ludlow Coaches,Bevan Contracts
Colours: All Blue.
Change colours: White/black/white
Midweek matchday: Tuesday or Wednesday.
Programme: 28-36 pages
Editor: Rob Shinfield 01922 42205
7
CLUB PERSONNEL
Chairman: Derek Beasley
Tel: 01384 896748(W) 07759 608 680 (M)

2001-02
Captain: Giles Parry
P.o.Y.: Dave Evans
Leading goalscorer: Phil Bridge 14

Barwell. Back Row (l-r): Viv Coleman (physio), Frank Williamson (coach), John Allcock, Scott Mackay, Adrian Greatex, Philip Mifsud, Scott Clamp, Jason Percival, Mark Harbottle (Asst Mngr), Mark O'Kane (Mngr). Front Row: David Hart, Darren Grassby (capt), Tim Warner, David Lucas, Keith Morris, Michael Skubala, Joe Harbottle

Boldmere St Michaels. Back Row (l-r): D Owen, C Dwyer, T Bayley, S Behan (Capt), C Busby, M Knight, A Parsons (Manager), A Bagley, L Colvin. Front Row: N Gough, N Watkins, A Richardson, M Burgess, L Inman, N Hylton, M Hawkins (Coach)

Pelsall. Back Row (l-r): Martin Seal (Asst Mngr), Neil Coles, Craig Davison (Player/Manager), Ryan Price, Ian Whitehouse, Gavin Edwards, Darren France, Keith Russell. Front Row: Matt Cartweight, Stuart King, Peter Howell, Craig Machin, Damian Taylor, Cameron Morgan, Chris Wilkins. Photo: Marshall's Sports Services

LUDLOW TOWN

Secretary: Mr J Nash, 58 Hucklemarsh Road, Ludlow, Shropshire (01584 874337)

Ground: The County Ground,Bromfield Road, Ludlow, Shropshire SY8 2BN

Directions: From Kidderminster and West Midlands, take A4117 and turn right at roundabout onto A49 to Shrewsbury. Then exit on B4361 after one and a half miles towards Ludlow. Ground is on right after passing under bridge after half a mile. From South , follow A49 to north end of Ludlow by-pass and turn right onto B4361.From north,Telford and Shrewsbury , at northern approach to Ludlow, exit left from A49 onto B4361.

Capacity: Seats: No   Cover: 150   Floodlights: Yes   Clubhouse: Yes

HONOURS: West Mids. Lg. Prem 00-01, Div. 2 78-79, Lg. Cup R-up 94-95. Div 1 Cup 90-91;
Shropshire Co. Cup: 73-7493-94, 94-95 96-97; Presteigne-Otway Cup 90-91.94-95:

PREVIOUS: League: Kidderminster League 1961-63, Shropshire Co. Lg.: 1963-1978
Ground: Riddings Park, Riddings Road, Ludlow, Shropshire

BEST SEASON **F.A.Vase:** 1st Q Rd. 98-99 (1st season)   **F.A.Cup:** Never Entered

FACT FILE
Formed: 1890
Colours: Red & white/black/black
Change colours: Blue & white/white/blue
Midweek Matchdays: Tuesday
Reserve League: West Midlands
Programme: Yes

2000-01
Leading goalscorer: Ashley Davies 58
Captain: Shaun Parker
P.O.Y.: Shaun Parker

CLUB PERSONNEL
Chairman: P.Gwilliam
Vice Chaiman: Robert Leech
Co Managers: Steve Frisby - Les Bristow
Asst Manager: Bob Jones
Physio: Miss J Stretton

OADBY TOWN

**Football
Secretary:** Kevin Zupp c/o Club. Tel Nos: 01455 557674 (H) 07790 728384 (M)
Ground: Events & Leisure Park, Wigston Rd,Oadby, Leics LE2 5QG Tel: 0116 271 5728

Directions: M69/M1 Jct 21. Follow A46 to Leicester take 4th turning off roundabout towards Narborough/ Enderby.Turn left on the outer ring road A563 ,towards Oadby.Turn right at lights after 2.5 miles towardsWigston.One mile to roundabout turn left first exit to Oadby follow Oadby road for another mile ground on right opposite Oval Park Leicester Tigers training ground.
Capacity: Cover: 224   Seating: 224   Floodlights: Yes
Clubhouse: Yes   Shop: Yes

HONOURS Leicestershire Senior Lge: (8) Midland Football Alliance 99-00
Div. 2 51-52; Lge Cup 77-78 93-94 94-95;
Leics Senior Cup 62-63 63-64 75-76 76-77 80-81
Charity CupsRolleston 58-59 59-60 68-69 74-75 88-89 93-94 96-97 97-98;
Coalville 60-61 63-64 65-66 69-70; Harborough 83-84 88-89; Oadby 70-71;
Battle of Britain 93-94 94-95 96-97
PREVIOUS **Leagues:** Leicestershire Senior League

FACT FILE
Founded:1939
Colours: All red
Change colours: All blue
Midweek matchday: Wednesday
Programme Editor: Rob Campion

CLUB PERSONNEL
Chairman: Brian Fletcher-Harrington
Vice Chairman: Martin Reid
Directors:S.g.Blyth,K.G.Farrant.,
M.V.BurtionI.Lockhead and L.Adam
President: Bob Mallet
Club Secretary: Ken Farrent
Manager: Lee Adam
Assistant Manager: Ian Lockhead
Physio: Derek Hewitt

OLDBURY UNITED

Secretary: Lee Tomkinson, 36 Bryan Road, Walsall,WS2 9DW
Tel. Nos: 01922-447834 (H)   0121 3034468 (W) 07790 295141 (M)
Ground: The Cricketts, York Road, Rowley Regis, Warley, West Midlands (0121 5595564)
Directions: M5 jct 2, follow Blackheath & Halesowen signs, first left at lights and fourth right
into York Road (turning before motorway flyover), ground 200yds on left.
One and a half miles from Sandwell & Dudley and Rowley Regis BR stations.
Bus 404 from West Bromwich, Oldbury and Blackheath.
Capacity: 3,000   Seats: 300   Cover: 1,000   Floodlights: Yes
Clubhouse: Mon-Fri 7.30-11pm, Sat-Sun 12-2.30 (12-11pm Sat matchdays).
Snacks available on matchdays.   **Club Shop:** No

HONOURS West Mids Lg 92-93, Staffs Snr Cup 87-88, Midland Comb. R-up 78-79(Presidents Cup 72-73(res), Div 3 R-up 82-83(res), Chal. Vase 82-83(res)),Walsall Snr Cup 82-83, B'ham Snr Amtr Cup, Oldbury Lg Div 2 61-62, Worcs Snr Urn 86-87, Sandwell Charity Cup 86-87, Interlink Invitation Cup 96-97. Industrial Rewinds League Cup: 98-99
PREVIOUS **Leagues:** Oldbury 58-62/ Warwick & W Mids All. 62-65/ Worcs (later Midland) Comb. 65-82/ Southern 82-86.**Names:** Queens Colts 58-62/ Whiteheath Utd 62-65
Grounds: Brittania Park 61-63/ Newbury Lane (Oldbury Stadium) 63-78.
RECORDS **Attendance:** 2,200 v Walsall Wood, Walsall Snr Cup Final 1982.
Win: 10-1 v Blakenall   **Defeat:** 1-9 v Moor Green.

FACT FILE
Founded: 1958
Nickname: Cricketts,The Blues.
Sponsors: Beswick Paper Group, Oldbury.
Colours: Navy with sky trim/blue/blue
Change colours: All amber
Midweek matchday: Tuesday
Programme: 28 pages, 60p
Editor: Football Secretary.

CLUB PERSONNEL
Chairman: Roy Keeling.
Vice Chairman: Ken Harris.
Press Officer: Ian Whitmore

Manager: John Morris
Asst Mgr: Kevin Sweeney
Physio: Paul Millard

PELSALL VILLA

Secretary: Dave Law, 29 Blithfield Road,Brownhills West, Walsall (Tel No: 01543 361693)
Ground: The Bush, Walsall Road, Pelsall, Walsall
Tel: 01922 682018 Club, 01922 692748 Ground
Directions: M6 jct 7 marked A34 B'ham. Take A34 towards Walsall to 1st island,turn right
(marked Ring Road), cross two islands. At large island at bottom of hill take last exit marked
Lichfield, up hill, cross next island to lights.Continue to next set of lights and turn left (B4154
Pelsall). Over railway bridge to Old Bush pub on right (next to Pelsall Cricket & Sports Club).
Capacity: 2,000   Seats: Yes   Cover: 624   Floodlights: Yes   **Club Shop:** Yes
Clubhouse: Mon-Fri 7-11pm, Sat noon-11pm, Sun noon-3 & 7-10.30pm. Hot &cold meals.

HONOURS West Mids Lg - Prem. Lge 94-95 (R-up 95-96) Div Cup 95-96, Div 1 Cup 88-89 (R-
up 89-90, Div 2 Cup R-up 83-84, Walsall Snr Cup R-up 89-90 92-93, Wednesbury Charity Cup 6,
(R-up 7), D Stanton Shield(2) 73-75 (R-up 75-76), Sporting Star Cup 76-77 (R-up 61-62), Prem
Div Tphy(res)89-90), Rugeley Charity Cup 78-79 (R-up 69-70), Bloxwich Charity Cup(2), Edge
Cup 83-84, Ike Cooper Tphy R-up 89-90. Midland Triangle Cup 95-96.
BEST SEASON   FA Cup: 3rd Qual. Rd 92-93, 2-4 V Gainsborough T. (A).
FA Vase: 5th Rd 92-93, 0-1 v Buckingham T. (A)
PREVIOUS   League: Staffs County (South) 61-81, West Midlands 82-96 Grounds: None
RECORDS   Attendance 2,060 v Aston Villa 29.7.98
Goalscorer: Dean Walters 244   **Appearances:** Neil Coles 679

FACT FILE

Reformed: 1961
Nickname: Villians
Sponsor: Spe-al
Colours: Red & black/blackblack
Change colours: Sky & navy/navy/sky
Midweek home matchday: Tuesday
Programme: 68 pages, 80p
Editor: Gareth Evans

CLUB PERSONNEL

Chairman: RonNew
Vice Chairman: J H Gough
President:M.Clark
Press Officer: D.Law

Manager: Steve Hinks
Asst Manager:Pall Baker
Physio:Martin Seal

QUORN

Secretary: Margaret Berry, 214 BarrowRd.Sileby,Leics.LE12 7LR   Tel: 01509 813259

Ground: Farley Way, Quorn, Leics (01509 620232)

Colours: Red/white/red

RUSHALL OLYMPIC

Secretary: Peter Athersmith, 46 Blakenall Lane, Leamore, Walsall, W Mids WS31HG
Tel: 01922 712632 (H) 0121 553 5525 (W) 07909 792422(M)
Ground: Dales Lane, off Daw End Lane, Rushall, Nr Walsall (01922 641021).
Directions: From Rushall centre (A461) take B4154 signed Aldridge. Approx., 1mile on right,
directly opposite Royal Oak P.H., in Daw End Lane. Grd on right. 2 miles Walsall (BR) station.
Capacity: 2,500   Seats: 200   Cover: 200   Floodlights: Yes   **Club Shop:** No
Clubhouse: Bar/lounge, every night 8-11pm, Sat matchdays, Sun noon-2.30pm
HONOURS   West Mids Lge Div 1 79-80; Walsall Amtr Lge Div 1 55-56, Div 2 52-53, Snr Cup
54-55 55-56, Jabez Cliff Cup 55-56 ; Staffs Co. Lge Div 1(4) (Div 2 56-57); Walsall Charity Cup
52-53; Walsall Chal.Cup (2).Walsall Mem. Charity Cup (x7) 55-62; W Preston Chal. Cup 56-57;
Cannock &   Dist. Charity Cup 56-57; Wednesbury Snr Cup (3) Sporting Star Cup (5) J W
Edge 62-63 66-67; Walsall Snr Cup 64-65;99-00 Lichfield Charity64-65 66-67; Staffs Yth Cup
81-82. Mid Alliance R-up 00-01 Lg.Cup Winners 2001-02
PREVIOUS   Leagues: Walsall Amateur 52-55/ Staffs County (South) 56-78/ West
Midlands (Reg) 78-94. **Grounds:** Rowley Place 51-75/ Aston University 76-79.
RECORDS   Attendance: 2,000 v Leeds Utd Old Boys Goalscorer: Graham Wiggin
Appearances: Alan Dawson (400+ apps) **Players progressing:** Lee Sinnott (Watford), Lee
Palin (Aston Villa),Stuart Watkiss (Walsall), Steve Taylor (Crystal Palace via Bromsgrove
£1,500 + £18,000 sell on-record club fee)

FACT FILE

Founded: 1951Nickname: Pics.
Sponsors: Staus Systems
Colours: Amber with black trim/black/black
Change colours: White & Black/white/white
Midweek matchday: Tuesday
Youth League: West Mids (Reg.)
Programme: 36 pages, 50p
Editor/ Press Officer: Darren Stockall
(01922 379153).

CLUB PERSONNEL

Chairman: John Allen
Vice Chairman: Gary Cooper
President: Brian Greenwood.
Manager: Kevin Hadley
Asst Manager:Dave Beasley
Physio: Gary McHale,Mick andrews
2001-02 Capt: Richard Brown
P.o.Y.: Richard Brown
Top Scorer: Gary Piggott 20

SHIFNAL TOWN

Secretary: Glyn Davies, 30 Drayton Road, Shifnal, Shropshire, TF11 8BT (01952460326 H)

Ground: Phoenix Park, Coppice Green Lane, Shifnal, Shropshire.

Directions: M54 jct 3, A41 towards Newport, 1st left for Shifnal (3 miles), in Shifnal take 1st right, and sharp right again up Coppice Green Lane, ground800yds on left past Idsall School.

Capacity: 3,000 **Seats:** 224 **Cover:** 300 **Floodlights:** Yes

Clubhouse: Not on ground but in Newport Rd, Shifnal. Open Mon-Fri 7.30-11pm, Sat 7.30-11pm , Sun 12-3 & 7.30-10-30

Club Shop: No

HONOURS	West Mids Lg 80-81 81-82 Div 1 78-79, Shropshire Snr Cup 80-81 90-91 92-93.
BEST SEASON	**FA Cup:** 1982-83 **FA Vase:** 1983-84
PREVIOUS	**Leagues:** Wellington (Dist.) 64-69; Shropshire County 69-77 85-93; West Midlands 77-85; Midland Combination 94-95. **Grounds:** Admirals Park 80-85
RECORDS	**Attendance:** 1,002 v Bridgnorth T., FA Vase 3rd Rd 83-84 (Admirals Park) **Goalscorer:** Steve Kelly 35 **Appearances:** John Powell 321 **Win:** 10-1 v Malvern, 82-83 **Defeat:** 1-6

FACT FILE

Founded: 1964
Nickname: None.
Sponsors:Clarkes (solicitors)
Colours:All Red & white
Change cols: Blue & white/white/blue & white
Midweek matchday: Tuesday
Reserves' League: West Midlands
Programme: 30 pages, 60p
Editor: J.Wilson (01952 274855).
01-02 Player of the Year: Neil Jones

CLUB PERSONNEL

Chairman: T.B.A.
Vice Chairman: Mr. R Owen
President: Mr.D.Adams
Press Off:K.Fullerton 01952 405274
Manager: Bernard Mackey
Assistant Manager: Dave Meachin
Physio: Charlott Lewis

STAFFORD TOWN

Secretary: Dave Rowley, 32 Lodge Rd, Brereton, Rugely, Staffs WS15 1HG Tel: 01889 800779 (H) 07971 454217 (Mobile) Email: info@staffordtownfc.co.uk

Ground: Stafford Rangers FC, Marston Road, Stafford

Directions: From M6 junction 14, Take 3rd left to Red Hill Roundabout and follow signs for Aston Fields Ind Est along Beaconside. Aston Fields is signposted 3rd right along Common Road, having travelled over railway bridge, Stafford Rangers FC ground is on the right

Capacity: 6,000 **Cover:** 3,000 **Seats:** 426 **Floodlights:** Yes **Club Shop:** No

Club address: Chamley Club, Beconside, Stafford Tel: 01785 665739 (Mr N Payne)

HONOURS	WMRL Div 1 93-94, Staffs Snr Lg R-up 91-92, Midland Comb. Div 2 78-79, Staffs Vase 84-85 92-93 (R-up 87-88,99-00, Bourne Sports Trophy 84-85, Walsall Sen Cup SF 91-92 W.Mids Champions 99-00 Lg.Cup R-up 99-00 Laegue Discipline Award 00-01
PREVIOUS	**Leagues:** Staffs Co. (North) 74-77 82-84; Midland Comb. 77-82; Staffs Sen. 84-93, W.M.R.L. 93-2000 **Grounds:** Silkmore Lane 74-77 Burton Manor Spts 77-88; Riverway 88-91 Park Stadium 91-94 ;
RECORD	**Win:** 14-0 v Leek CSOB (H), Staffs Senior League 8/10/88 **Goalscorer:** Mick Stark : 54 goals in the 1999-2000 season

FACT FILE

Founded: 1974
Nickname: Reds or Town
Colours: All red
Change colours:All Blue
Midweek matches: Mon/Wed
Programme: 36 pages, #1.00
Editor: Chris Curtis & Graham Whitehall
(01785 605561)
Website: www.staffordtownfc.co.uk

CLUB PERSONNEL

Chairman: Gordon Evans
01785 254073 (H) 01785 283863 (B)
President: Graham Hollinshead
Press Officer: Chris Curtis/Alan Bowers
Manager: Dave Downing
2000-01
Captain: Nick Anthony
P.o.Y.: Mark Tilston
Top Scorer: Russell Demmatteo 25

STOURBRIDGE

Secretary: Hugh Clark,10 Burnt Oak Drive, Stourbridge, W. Mids DY8 1HL Tel: 01384 392975

Ground: War Memorial Ath. Grd, High St., Amblecote, Stourbridge DY8 4HN (01384 394040)

Directions: Take A491, signposted Wolverhampton, from Stourbridge ring-road -ground 300yds on left immediately beyond traffic lights and opposite `RoyalOak' pub. Buses 311, 246 from Dudley, and 256 from Wolverhampton, pass ground. 1 mile from Stourbridge Town (BR)

Capacity: 2,000 **Cover:** 1,250 **Seats:** 250 **Floodlights:** Yes

Clubhouse: Open every evening from 8pm and Sunday lunchtimes

Club Shop: Programmes & souvenirs. Contact Nigel Gregg

PREVIOUS Name: Stourbridge Standard **Leagues:** West Midlands (prev. Birmingham) 1892-1939 54-71, Birmingham Comb. 45-53, Southern 71-00 **Ground:** None

HONOURS	Welsh Cup R-up 73-74; Southern Lg Midland Div 90-91 (Lg Cup 92-93), Div 1 North73-74, Merit Cup 73-74; West Mids (prev. B'ham) Lg 23-24 (R-up 4); B'ham Comb. R-up 51-52; B'ham Snr Cup 49-50 45-46 75-76 (R-up 3); Worcs Snr Cup 9, (R-up 12); Herefordshire Snr Cup 54-55; Camkin Cup R-up 69-70; Camkin Presidents Cup 70-71; Albion Shield 43-44; Keys Cup 37-38 62-63, Worcs Comb. R-up 27-28; Worcs Jnr Cup R-up 27-28; Tillotson Cup R-up 39-40, MFC Davis League Cup 00-01. Joe McGorian Cup 01-02 Midland Alliance: 01-02
BEST SEASON	**FA Cup:** 4th Qual Rd: 67-68, 84-85 85-86 98-99 **FA Trophy:** Qtr Final 70-71
CLUB RECORDS	**Career Goalscorer:** Ron Page 269 **Career Appearances:** Ron Page 427

FACT FILE

Formed: 1876 Nickname: The Glassboys
Sponsors: Plumbing World
Colours: Red & white stripes
Change colours: Yellow & blue
Midweek matchday: Tuesday
Programme: Pages: 28 Price: £1
Editors: Hugh Clark & Nigel Gregg

CLUB PERSONNEL

Chairman: Mark Serrell
Chief Executive: Nick Pratt
Press Officer: Richard Clark
Manager/Coach: Joe Jackson
Assistant Manager: Tom Stokes
Physio: Gavin Blackwell
2001-02
Leading goalscorer: Brian Gray 27
Captain: Jim Conway
P.o.Y. Lewis Baker

STRATFORD TOWN

Secretary: Roger Liggins, 17 Hammerton way, Wellesbourne, Warwicks. CV35 9NS
Tel Nos: 01789 840755 (H) 02476 539401 (W)
Ground: Masons Road, off Alcester Road, Stratford-upon-Avon, Warks (01789 297479).
Directions: Follow the signs for Alcester/Worcester A422 from the town centre.
Masons Road is the 1st right afterthe railway bridge.
400 yards from Stratford-on-Avon (BR)station.
Local buses for West Green Drive.
Capacity: 1,100   Seating/Cover: 200   Floodlights: Yes

Clubhouse: Open every night except Sunday   **Club Shop:** No.

HONOURS Midland Comb 56-57 86-87; Chal. Cup 86-87 88-89 (R-up 55-56); Chal. Vase 81-82; Jack Mould Tphy 81-82; Tony Allden Mem. Cup 86-87; B'ham Snr Cup62-63.

BEST SEASON   **FAVase:**   **FA Cup:**

PREVIOUS   **Leagues:** W Mids 57-70/ Mid Com. 70-73 75-94/ Hellenic 70-75.

RECORDS   **Attendance:** 1,078 v Aston Villa, Birmingham Snr Cup, Oct 1996

Players progressing: Martin Hicks (Charlton '77), Roy Proverbs (Coventry, '56)

FACT FILE
Founded: 1944
Nickname: The Town
Sponsors: Porters Precision Products
Colours: All Blue
Change Colours: All Tangerine
Midweek Matchday: Tuesday
Reserves' League: Midland Comb. Res. Div..
Programme: 20 pages, 50p
Editor:

CLUB PERSONNEL
Chairman: Stuart Dixon
Vice-Chairman: T.B.A.
President: P Chatburn
Commercial Mgr: J Carruthers.
Manager: S Dixon
Physio: N Dixon

STUDLEY

Secretary: Mark Sealey c/o club.

Ground: Beehive, BKL Sports Ground, Abbeyfields,Birmingham Rd., Studley, Warwicks
Tel: 01527 853817
Directions: M42 Jct.3 onto A435 to Redditch.Over island at Dog Pub on left continue
towards Studley. Ground on left signposted to Abbeyfields.
Capacity : 1,500   **Seats:** 200   **Cover :** Yes   **Floodlights:**Yes   **Clubhouse:** Yes,on ground.

HONOURS Midland Comb.: Prem Div R-up 2000-01,Div 1 91-92, Chall Cup R-up 91-92,
MFC Challenge Vase 87-88 R-up 88-89
Presidents Cup R-up 91-92,Div2 Cup 87-88; WFA Senior Urn 2000-01,01-02
Smedley Crooke Char. Cup 90-91 91-92; Jack Mould Trophy R-up 1987-88
Birmingham Vase R-up 96-97, Tony allden memorial Cup: 2001-02

PREVIOUS   **League:** Redditch & South Warwickshire Sunday Combination 71-87
Name: BKL Works

CLUB RECORDS **Appearances:** Lee Adams 523
Goalscorer: Brian Powell
Attendance: 600 v Tamworth 1998-99

FACT FILE
Founded: 1971
Nickname: Bees
Sponsors: BKL Fittings
Colours: All Skyblue & navy blue.
Change colours: All Yellow
Programme: 50p   Editor: Gordon Wilkie
Reserve's League:

CLUB PERSONNEL
Chairman: David Robinson
Vice-Chairman:Gordon Wilkie
General Manager: John Mitchell
Press Officer: Dave Chiswell

Manager:Mark Chambers
Asst Manager: Nicholas Cross
Coach: Trevor Whittington
Physio: ted Tghompson

WEDNESFIELD

Secretary: Ron Brown,8 Hazel Grove,Wednesfield, WV11 1LN Tel No: 07796 975634 (M)
Ground: Cottage Ground, Amos Lane, Wednesfield, Wolverhampton (01902 735506).
Directions: From Wolverhampton on the A4124 Wednesfield Rd. Stay on road right through
Wednesfield until island. Leave island at 1st exit (Wood End Rd), left after 200yds into Amos
Lane. Ground on right, approx. 400yds along. 3 miles Wolverhampton BR station. Bus 559 to
Wood End or 560 to Red Lion.
Capacity: 1,000   Seats: 148   Cover: 250   Floodlights: Yes

Clubhouse: Evenings 7-11pm. Food (burgers, chips etc) on 1st team matchdays.
Club Shop: No.

HONOURS   West Mids Lg Div 1 76-77 (R-up 77-78).
BEST SEASON   FA Vase: FA Cup:
PREVIOUS   **League:** Wolverhampton & District Amateur 61-76/West Midlands 77-97.
Ground: St Georges PF 61-76   **Name:** Wednesfield Social 61-89.
RECORDS   **Attendance:** 480 v Burton Albion, FA Cup 1981.

FACT FILE
Founded: 1961.
Nickname: Cottagers.
Sponsors: T.B.A.
Colours: Red/black/black& white
Change : Black & White Stripes/white/white
Midweek matchday: Tuesday
Programme:£1.00
Editor: Ron Brown

CLUB PERSONNEL
Chairman: Surinda Ghattaura
Managers: Brian and David Saville
Physio: Mark Rowberry
Press Officer: J Massey (01902 781819).

WILLENHALL TOWN

Secretary: Simon Haynes, 6 Ingledew Close, Briarsleigh, Walsall, West Mids (01902 411758)
Ground: Noose Lane, Willenhall, West Midlands (01902 605132-club, 636586-office).
Directions: M6 Jnc 10 follow 'new' Black Country route and then 'Keyway'. On leaving 'Keyway' follow signs to Wolverhampton(A454). At 'Neachells' P H house right into Neachells Lane, and first right again into Watery Lane. At island turn left onto Noose Lane, ground is 200yds on left.
Capacity: 5,000   Seats: 324   Cover: 500   Floodlights: Yes   Shop: Yes
Clubhouse: Open Mon-Fri 12-2 & 7-12pm,Sat & Sun All Day Hot food available.
HONOURS   FA Vase R-up 80-81; West Mids Lg 78-79, Div 1 75-76, Prem. Div Cup 79-80, Div 2 Cup 78-79(res); Southern Midland 83-84; Birmingham Snr Cup R-up 82-83; J W Hunt Cup 73-74., Mid Alliance Cup R-up 99-00, Rameses Invitation Cup 2000-01.
BEST SEASON   FA Vase: Finalists 80-81**FA Cup:** 1st Rd Proper v Crewe Alexander 1981
PREVIOUS   **Leagues:** Wolverhampton Amateur/ Staffs County/ West Mids 75-82 91-94/Southern 82-91.
RECORDS   Attendance: 3,454 v Crewe Alexandra, FA Cup 1st Rd 1981.
Goalscorer: Gary Matthews   Appearances: Gary Matthews.
Players progressing: Sean O'Driscoll (Fulham),Joe Jackson (Wolves), Stuart Watkiss (Wolves), Tony Moore (Sheff U), Andy Reece (Bristol R.), Wayne O'Sullivan (Swindon). Adie Smith (Kidderminster H) and Peter Smith (Brighton & H)

FACT FILE
Founded: 1953 Nickname: Reds
Colours: All Red
Sponsors: Aspray Transport Ltd.
Change colours: Yellow & Blue/Blue/Blue
Midweek matchday: Tuesday.
Reserves League: Midland Comb.
Programme: 44-46 pages, £1.00
Editor: Russ Brown (01902 681011)
CLUB PERSONNEL
President: Jack Williams
Chairman: JackWilliams -Chair: Ed Edmunds
Football Sec: Neil Arrowsmith (01902 450613)
Manager:Rob SmithAsst Man:Larry Chambers
Physio: Steve Ball Commercial Dept: Russ
Brown & Robert Fletcher
2001-02
Capt: Mark Creighton P.o.Y.: Aaron Skelding
Top Scorer: Lee Bullimore 17

Rushall Olympic.
Back Row (l-r): Damian Currier, Gary Piggott, Wayne Lloyd, Gary Price, Andy Wright, Jimmy Conroy, Jason Dyer, John Worsey.
Front row: Darren Evans, Steve Round, Stuart Darby, Richie Allen, Robbie Holcroft, Chris Homer. Photo: Marshall's Sports Services

Shifnal Town.
Back Row (l-r): Reg Priest, Wayne Brown, Iain Turnbull, Neil Jones, Russell Morris, John Powell, Shaun Ralph, Dean Walters, Warren Campbell.
Front Row: Steven Oldaker, Darren Barnwell, Stephen Manley, James Palmer, Dominic Heath, Peter Fell

Stafford Town. Back Row (l-r): Mick Collins (Manager), Dan Rochester, Russell Peake, Mark Tilstor, Paul Mottram, Robert Plant, Russell Pemberton, Gary Tinkler, Neil Walters. Front Row: Steve Lyons, Ian Brown, Russell Peake, Jimmy Bullimore, Mark Holland, Carl Wallace. Photo: Marshall's Sports Services

Studley FC. Back Row (l-r): Ken Somner (Kit Mngr), Trevor Whittington (Coach), Andy Biddle, Steve Hands, Simon Redhead, Duncan Turk, Martin Keight, Steve Duncan, Kevin Rowlands, Matt Pugh, Rob Powell, Gavin Barratt, John Mitchell (Asst Mngr), Mark Chambers (Mngr). Front Row: Paul Harmer, Andy Grubb, Craig Poutney, Craig Gillett (Capt), Mark Neath, Kenny Fergie, Dean Meyrick, Andy Devlin, Jamie Bailey, Ted Thompson (Physio)

ICIS MIDLAND COMBINATION

FEEDER TO THE MIDLAND FOOTBALL ALLIANCE

Chairman & Treasurer: David Prust
Hon. Secretary: Norman Harvey
115 Millfield Road, Handsworth Wood, Birmingham B20 1ED   Tel: 0120 357 4172

It has been a marvellous season in many respects. Grosvenor Park and Coventry Sphinx went hammer and tongs for the championship, Rugby Town and Leamington did likewise in the First Division, Burman Hi-Ton lead all of the way in Division Two but newcomers Stockingford never gave up and in the Third Division two more newcomers Littleton and Halfords headed the ladder with yet another newcomer, Handsworth Wesleyan Youth just off the pace. The Reserve Division saw Boldmere St Michaels out in front until Solihull Borough pipped them right at the post. That, in a nutshell, was the season but it doesn't begin to tell the stories behind the struggles.

We have had our triumphs but also a few real tragedies in our 75th anniversary year, in particular, the death of Sphinx manager Willie Knibbs in a car crash. The fact that more than 400 people turned up to the Memorial night for Juliette and the lads Lee, Adam and Ryan proved just how popular he was.

Nuneaton Griff began the Premier Division season chasing a third successive title under manager Mark Green, but struggled early on leaving the way open for Coventry Sphinx, Grosvenor Park and Romulus to forge ahead. Park had a six point lead by the start of the New Year and by early March it was down to four over Coventry Sphinx, who had two games in hand, but Grosvenor held their nerve to clinch the title on the last day of the season. Congratulations to everyone at Grosvenor Park on their promotion to the Midland Alliance, especially hard working secretary Peter Yates and manager Andy Biddle. Good luck for next season.

Rugby Town and Leamington continued their rivalry after promotion to the First Division with Town roaring away with 22 straight wins leaving the Brakes many points in arrears but with games in hand. Their meeting at Webb Ellis Road saw the visitors end that 100 per cent record by an amazing 5-0 scoreline in front of 560 fans, whilst the return game at the New Windmill on April Fools Day attracted a huge crowd of 1,204 who were rewarded with a cracking game that ended two all. Rugby went on to clinch the title three points ahead of Leamington with Knowle in third spot and Loughborough enjoyed their best season in the MFC to finish fourth.

In the Second Division, Burman Hi-Ton forced the pace winning eleven of their opening twelve games, but Barnt Green Spartak overtook them by Christmas having won a dozen consecutive matches, whilst newcomers Stockingford, aka The Cabbage, steadily climbed the ladder. Burman came back strongly to finish champions seven points ahead of the Cabbage with Enville Athletic in third place.

Littleton and Halfords soon opened up a gap in the Third Division but, with the former playing only three league games in a few weeks due to cup ties, Halfords grabbed pole position and stayed top until the closing day of the season. Littleton went on to set a new club record by remaining unbeaten in 25 matches, which they extended to 30 by completing the season as the only undefeated side in the MFC as they took the title. Halfords finished second twelve points behind with another newcomer, Handsworth Wesleyan Youth, third.

Boldmere St Michaels and Solihull Borough soon got into their stride in the Reserve Division and that was the way until virtually the last game of the season when 'Boro snatched the top prize from The Mikes with Hinckley United in third place.

The publication of the history of the Midland Football Combination by Bob Bannister was an unprecedented success, being superbly researched and written. For those who still haven't got a copy, it is available from Les James at 175 Barnett Lane, Kingswinford DY6 9QA at a cost of only £7.50 which includes postage and packing. Cheques or postal orders can be made payable to the MFC, please.

On the internal cup scene, the Endsleigh Insurance Challenge Cup final saw an all Coventry clash when Sphinx defeated Marconi at Hinckley United's ground by two clear goals watched by a crowd of 348 fans. As a fitting tribute to Willie Knibbs, the victorious Sphinx all sported tee shirts with the Gaffer's picture and the words 'the Willie Knibbs Cup' for the presentation ceremony. Briliant.

The President's Cup was played at Solihull Borough's Damson Park between the big boys, Leamington and Rugby Town who won by the only goal late in the second half in front of 563 spectators who witnessed a thrilling encounter. This was adequate revenge for the meeting in the Jack Mould Trophy which the Brakes won.

Chasetown hosted the Challenge Vase which saw Burman Hi-Ton defeat Stockingford, again by a single goal watched by 131 fans who got their money's worth in a closely fought game, whilst Coleshill Town Reserves snatched an extra time winner in their struggle with Halfords in the Challenge Urn final held at Alveston.

In the Challenge Bowl final at Noose Lane, Willenhall Town Reserves and Barwell Reserves shared four goals before the visitors won 4-2 on penalties and the last final of the season saw Hinckley United Reserves lose a hard fought match against Solihull Borough Reserves at Middlefield Lane, yet another single goal affair.

In outside cup competitions it was another great season with Coventry Marconi departing from the FA Vase in the Second Round Proper at highly fancied Rushall Olympic of the MFA, but only by the odd goal in three despite being the better side on the day. The Birmingham County FA Vase ended up in Combination hands as Grosvenor Park demolished Wolverhampton United by six goals to two after extra time thanks to a hat trick from Rashid Anifowose and a further brace from substitute Duncan Ferguson.

Littleton completed a tremendous season by capturing the Worcestershire Junior Cup and the Evesham Hospital Cup, while the Walsall Senior Cup is in the good hands of Bolehall Swifts. Feckenham gave MFA Studley BKL the fright of their lives in the final of the Worcestershire Senior Urn holding them to a one all draw only to lose the shoot out on penalties. Studley also collected the Tony Allden Memorial Trophy defeating Nuneaton Griff. Shirley Town went two goals down early in the Smedley Crooke final to give themselves too much to do and Bromyard Town hung on to win a five goal thriller. With Shepshed Dynamo winning the Leicestershire Junior Cup we do not think our clubs have ever held so many county cups in one season.

We set ourselves a target at the start of our 75th anniversary celebrations of raising money to fund the opening of a burns unit at the Diana, Princess of Wales Children's Hospital here in Birmingham and we are pleased to announce that the hospital has already received the sum of £10,000. The appeal does not end until the last day of thie year and we confidently expect to hand over another bumper cheque for this most worthy cause.

We are also pleased to announce that the league is to be sponsored by ICIS Clubwear Limited for the next three seasons and will be known as the ICIS Midland Combination. We welcome Sales Director Nick Maley and his ICIS team to the MFC and hope that the partnership will be a long and fruitful one to both parties. *Paul Vanes, MFC Press Officer*

FINAL LEAGUE TABLES 2001-02

PREMIER DIVISION

	P	W	D	L	F	A	Pts
Grosvenor Park	42	31	4	7	111	39	97
Coventry Sphinx	42	27	13	2	91	41	94
Nuneaton Griff	42	26	6	10	98	54	84
Romulus	42	22	7	13	88	59	73
Feckenham	42	20	11	11	78	64	71
Pershore Town	42	20	7	15	86	68	67
West Mids Police	42	18	7	17	69	75	61
Coventry Marconi	42	16	12	14	74	66	60
Massey Ferguson	42	17	9	16	82	81	60
Coleshill Town	42	18	5	19	76	68	59
Shirley Town	42	18	5	19	97	102	59
Handsworth C Star	42	16	9	17	76	75	57
Highgate United	42	13	12	17	70	74	51
Kings Heath	42	14	9	19	61	71	51
Meir K A	42	13	11	18	64	71	50
Handrahan Timbers	42	12	13	17	49	66	49
Cheslyn Hay	42	14	6	22	51	83	48
County Sports	42	11	13	18	64	108	46
Bolehall Swifts*	42	11	11	20	68	84	41
Alvechurch	42	10	10	22	58	79	40
Alveston	42	11	5	26	56	89	38
Southam United	92	8	7	27	52	102	31

DIVISION TWO (top five)

	P	W	D	L	F	A	Pts
Burman Hi-Ton	30	26	1	3	96	26	79
Stockingford AA	30	23	3	4	77	28	72
Enville Athletic	30	20	8	2	91	33	68
Barnt Green Spartak	30	19	4	7	64	42	61
Central Ajax	30	15	3	12	46	40	48

DIVISION ONE

	P	W	D	L	F	A	Pts
Rugby Town	36	30	3	3	100	25	93
Leamington	36	28	6	2	107	30	90
Knowle	36	23	8	5	91	41	77
Loughborough	36	18	8	10	77	45	62
Fairfield Villa	36	15	6	15	70	87	51
Thimblemill REC	36	15	5	16	72	69	50
Brownhills Town	36	15	5	16	70	70	50
Dudley Sports	36	14	7	15	66	55	49
Polesworth N Warwick	36	13	9	14	72	57	48
Wilmcote S & S	36	13	7	16	64	68	46
Handsaker	36	11	10	15	39	66	43
Old Hill Town	36	13	3	20	51	70	42
Mile Oak Rovers*	36	14	2	20	59	67	41
Blackheath Ivensys	36	11	6	19	43	77	39
Northfield Town	36	9	11	16	44	64	38
Burntwood Town	36	11	4	21	45	85	37
Cadbury Athletic	36	11	3	22	47	77	36
*Holly Lane	36	10	8	18	52	76	35
Kenilworth Town	36	10	5	21	56	96	35

DIVISION THREE (top five)

	P	W	D	L	F	A	Pts
Littleton	30	26	4	0	107	24	82
Halfords	30	21	7	2	72	23	70
Handsworth W Youth	30	17	5	8	85	62	56
Droitwich Sports	30	16	5	9	100	54	53
Coleshill Town Res	30	14	8	8	68	47	50

* points deducted

TOP GOALSCORERS 2001-02

PREMIER DIVISION

31	Brian Powell	Feckenham
29	Justin Rowe	Handsworth C Star
29	Rasheed Anifowose	Grosvenor Park
22	Carl Fairhurst	Feckenham
22	Lee Martin	Shirley Town
22	David Inniss	Massey Ferguson
21	Mark Cartwright	Kings Heath
20	David Aston	Nuneaton Griff

DIVISION ONE

29	Paul O'Callaghan	Loughborough
28	Gavin Mole	Dudley Sports

DIVISION ONE cont.

27	Mark Wells	Kenilworth Town
22	Joshua Blake	Leamington
20	Paul Nicholls	Leamington

DIVISION TWO

24	Paul Clark	Stockingford AA

DIVISION THREE

42	Des Cox	Littleton

RESERVE DIVISION

21	Justin Jenkins	Hinckley United

TOP ATTENDANCES

1,204
Leamington v Rugby Town
League   01.04.02

563
Leamington v Rugby Town
President's Cup Final 29.04.02

560
Rugby Town v Leamington
League 26.02.02

Left: Coventry Marconi.
Photo: Alan Watson

ALVECHURCH F.C.

Secretary: Stephen Denny,11 Shawhurst Croft,Hollywood,Birmingham.B47 5PB (01564 822302)
Ground: Lye Meadow, Redditch Rd, Alvechurch, Worcs (0121 445 2929)
Directions: M42 jct 2, follow signs to Redditch, taking dual carriageway. At island turn right
(signed Alvechurch) ground approx one mile on right. Ground is actually on Redditch Road, just
south of Alvechurch village
Capacity: 3,000   **Seats:**100   **Cover:**Yes   **Floodlights:**Yes
Clubhouse: Evenings and matchdays   **Club shop:** No
HONOURS   Mid Comb Chall Cup R-up 95-96, Smedley Crooke Cup R-up 94-95
CLUB RECORDS   **Goalscorer:** Dean Meyrick   **Appearances:** Dean Meyrick
PREVIOUS   **Leagues:** None
   Name: None (predecessors, Alvechurch FC, founded 1929, folded in 1992)

Founded: 1994
Nickname: The Church
Sponsors: Centreprint
Colours: Gold/black/black
Change colours: Black &White,white/black
Midweek matchday: Wednesday
Chairman: Michael Rowley
Director of Football: Lee Shaw
Patron: Roy Yardley
Manager:Mick Preece

ALVESTON

Secretary: Martin Beese, 16 The Smallholdings, Bubbenhall Road, Baginton, CV8 3BB
   Tel: 02476 305294H   077744 23641M

Ground: Home Guard Club, Main Street, Tiddington, Stratford-upon-Avon. Tel: 01789 297718
   Social Club Telephone : 01789 297718 Club Email martin.beese@fleet.gecapital.com

Floodlights: Yes

Directions: ground is on the Stratford - Wellesbourne Road (B 40860) Home Guard Club is
last building on right through Tiddington

Chairman: Martin Beese (02476 305294)

Colours: Maroon & Sky Blue/Sky Blue/ Maroon
& Sky Blue
Change Colours: Black & White Stripes/
White/White
2001-02
Leading Goalscorer: Tyrone Fagan 18
Captain: Rob Riley
Player of the Year: Mat Traynor

BOLEHALL SWIFTS

Secretary: Philip Hill, 64 Rene Road, Bolehall,Tamworth,Staffs. B77 3NN (07812 449054- M)
Ground: Rene Road, Bolehall, Tamworth (01827 62637)
Directions: A51 signs south to Bolebridge island, left under railway archesinto Amington Rd, 4th
left into Leedham Ave, fork right into Rene Rd, ground onright by school. From Tamworth BR sta-
tion walk up Victoria Road for threequarters of a mile and catch No.3 or No.6 mini-bus to Bolehall.
Alight atLeedham Avenue or Rene Road and follow as above
Capacity: 2,000   **Seats:** 500   **Cover:** 600   **Floodlights:** Yes   **Club Shop:** No
Clubhouse: Large Social Club. Open evenings 7-11 & lunchtimes. Snacks available
HONOURS: Midland Comb. Div 2 84-85, F/Lit Cup R-up 96-97, Chall. Vase 84-85, Presidents Cup
R-up 85-86; Fazeley Char Cup 84-85 (R-up 85-86); Ernie Brown Mem. Cup R-up 89-90 90-91 91-
92 92-93 94-95 98-99, Jack Mould Cup R-up 85-86 Tony Allden Nenorial Cup 98-99

Founded: 1953   Nickname: Swifts
Colours: Yellow/black/yellow
Change Colours: All Blue
Sponsors: Need -A-Skip-Hire Ltd.
Midweek matches: Tuesday
Programme: 24 pages, 70p
Editor: W Gould (01827 64530)
President: mr.L. Fitzpatrick
Chairman: James Latham
Vice-Chairman: K.Norchi
Manager: Ron Tranter Ass.Man: D.Finney
Coach: J.Capaldi
Physio: D.Crump

CHESLYN HAY

Secretary: J Rogers, 22 John Riley Dr., New Invention, Willenhall WV12 5AS   (01922 860064)
Ground: Scholars Ground, Chasetown F.C., Church St., Chasetown, Walsall. 01543 682222
Directions: M6 Junct 11, A460 to Cannock, A5 to Brownhills, to Whitehouse Rd and Wharf
Lane, at junction turn left into Highfield Rd., leading to Church St., ground on left.
Capacity: 2,000   Seats: 200   Cover: 300   Floodlights: Yes   Club Shop: Yes
Clubhouse: Evenings 7-11pm. Food (burgers, chips etc) on 1st team matchdays
HONOURS: Midland Comb. Prem Div. R-up 98-99, Div. 3 R-up 94-95;
   Wolves Cup 86-87 87-88, Staffs. Chall. Cup 96-97; Walsall Chall. Cup 96-97;
   W H Johns Mem. Cup 96-97; J W Hunt Cup R-up 96-97
CLUB RECORDS   **Appearances:** Gary Osborne 522
   Goalscorer: Ian Morgan 142 (in 113 games)

Founded: 1984
Sponsors: Pro Clean Ind. Services
Colours: Orange/white/black
Change colours: Blue & white stripes/blue/white
Programme: Yes
Editor/Press Off: As Sec. Fax: 01922 421460
Chairman: Ivor Osborne (01922 414755)
Manager: Carl Oulton Assistant: Paul Baker
Physio: M Bailey
2000-01 Leading goalscorer: Dave Marriott 15
Captain: Paul Miller
P.o.Y.: Everton Francis

COLESHILL TOWN

Secretary: George Phillips,49 Circus Avenue, Chelmsley Wood, Birmingham (0121 770 9513)
Ground: Pack Meadow, Packington Lane, Coleshill, Birmingham B46 3JQ (0167563259)
Directions: A446 to A4117 towards Coleshill, Packington Lane forks from A4117,south of village
and ground is 150 yds on right. M6 jct 4, 1 mile away
Capacity: 3,000Seats: 50Cover: 50 Floodlights: Yes
Clubhouse: Bar open 7 nights a week. Bar manager resident
HONOURS   Mercian Lg 75-76, Walsall Snr Cup 82-83 R-up 83-84, Midland Comb. R-up
   83-84, Div 2 69-70 R-up 74-75, Invitation Cup 70, Presidents Cup R-up x2 67-69
CLUB RECORDS: Attendance: 1,000
Players progressing: Gary Shaw (Aston Villa)

Founded: 1894
Nickname: Coalmen
Colours: Green & white/green/green
Change Colours: All blue
Midweek matches: Tues/Thurs
Programme: 30p,
Editor: Mavis Gordon

Chairman:
Manager: Christopher Davies

COVENTRY MARCONI F.C.

Chairman: D.Ryan   **Vice-Chairman:** S.Canliani   **Press Officer:** P Scanlon

Secretary: D.Wilson, 60 Craven Avenue, Binley Woods, Coventry. CV3 2JT (02476 544296)

Ground: Allard way, Copswood, Coventry   Tel: 02476 562831
    Capacity 1,500   **Seats:** 92   **Cover:** Yes, Seats and standing   **Floodlights:** Yes

Clubhouse: 12-11 Saturdays 6.00-11.00 weekdays

HONOURS: Midland Comb Div 1 96-97, Presidents Cup 96-97 , Endsleigh Comb.Cup 2001-02.
Only winners of Coventry Evening Telegraph Cup (3 years), R-up Endslegh Comb Cup 99-00

Formed: 1923
Sponsors: Home Heating
Colours: White with blue trim/bluewhite
Change colours: All red
Programme: 32 pages Price: 50p
Editor P.Scanlon

Manager: P.Mills
Assistant Manager:S.Shaw
Physio: S.Wilson

COVENTRY SPHINX

Secretary: David Rees. 15 Pleydell Close, Willenhall Wood, Coventry CV3 3EF2 (02476 305921)

Match Secretary: Kevin Monks: Tel Nos: 02476 659249 (H) 0403 508358 (M)

Ground: Sphinx Drive, off Siddeley Avenue, Stoke Aldermoor, Coventry Tel: 01203 451361
  Social Club Telephone Number: 02476 451361

Chairman: Vic Jones
Manager: Willie Knibbs

Colours:
Sky blue & white/black/white
Change Colours
White/white/Sky Blue

FECKENHAM

Secretary: M G Hawkes4 Mill Lane, Feckenhamk, Redditch, Worcs B96 6HY (01527 893341)

Ground: Redditch United F.C. See details in Dr. Martens Section **Floodlights:** Yes

Directions: M42 , Junction 4 take A38 towards Bromsgrov to Golf Course. Left at roundabout -
A448 towards Redditch. Aftyer five miles take third exit off roundabout, cross over dual carriageway, . First right into Birchfield Road, pastthe Foxlydiate Pubkic House.. First left into Red Lane
leading into Bromsgrove rRoad. Vallley Stadium is approx 3/4 mile on the left

Acting Chairman: R.Freeman
28 Milford Close,Walkwood,Redditch B97 5PZ
Tel Nos: 01527 67450 (H) 01527 401819 (W)

Colours: Green & White Hoops/Green/Green
Change Colours: All Yellow

FERNHILL COUNTY SPORTS

Secretary: Geoff Woodward, 2 Lansdowne Road, Worcester WR1 1ST
     Tel: 01905 23341 (H) 01905 612342 (B)
     email: sports@woodward2.worldonline.co.uk

Ground: King George V Playing Fields, King George Way, Pershore, Worcs.
     Tel: 01386 556902
Directions: Leave M5 at Junction 7 (Worcester South) - take first left A44 to Pershore.
     On entering town at second set of lights turn left. Ground 300 yards on left.
Clubhouse: Yes   Floodlights: No

Founded: 1968
Colours: Yellow/blue/blue
Change Colours: White/jade green/black
Midweek matches:

Chairman: Martin Pinches
Tel: 01905 457944 (H)
Match Secretary: Brian Evans
Tel: 01905 456122 (H)

HANDRAHAN TIMBERS

Secretary: Darren Mansell, 56 Windermere Drive, Kingswinford DY6 8AN (01384 830815)
Ground: Mile Flat Sports Ground, Mile Flat, Wallheath, Kingswinford, W. Mids (01381 484755)
     Cover: 200   Seats: 40   Floodlights: Yes
Clubhouse: Teas and refreshments   Club Shop: No
HONOURS   Midland Comb. Div 1 R-up 93-94, Birmingham Chall. Vase R-up 93-94,
     Wednesbury Charity Cup 91-92, J W Hunt Cup 92-93; Invitation Cup 94-95
PREVIOUS   **Leagues:** Staffs County Lg (South) 82-86   **Grounds:** None
CLUB RECORDS   **Goalscorer:** Paul Baker   **Appearances:** Jonathan Pole
         Win: 9-0   **Defeat:** 0-6

Founded: 1982 Nickname: Timbers
Sponsors: W J Handrahan & Son
Colours: Red & black stripes/black/black
Change colours: Blue & white stripes/navy/navy
Midweek matchday: Tuesday
Programme: All first eam games
Chairman: T.B.A.
President: W J Handrahan
Manager: Stev Newton
Asst Manager: Dominic Horton
Press Officer:Secretary
Fitness Coach: Eddie Wedderburn

HANDSWORTH CONTINENTAL STAR

Secretary: Gary Christie, 21 Spouthouse Lane, Great Barr B43 5PX
Tel: 0121 357 1044 (H) 07752 202802 (M)
email: soccer@continentalstar.fsnet.co.uk
Ground: Red Lion Ground,Somerfield Road, Walsall WS32EJ (019222 405835)
Clubhouse: Bar open 7 nights a week and is available for hire. Bar manager resident

HONOURS: Midland Comb Div One R-up 96-97; Birmingham Vase.

Jack Mould Cup R-up.Invitation Cup Winners. JW Hunt Cup winners

Founded: 1973
Colours: All white
Change Colours: All blue
Website:
www..continentalstar.fsnet.co.uk

Chairman:Keith John
Tel: 07956429046 (M)

HIGHGATE UNITED

Secretary: Simon Pretty,8 Monastry Drive,Solihull,B91 1DN (0121 706 0933)
Ground: The Coppice, Tythe Barn Lane, Shirley, Solihull B90 1PH (0121 7444194)
Directions: A34 from City through Shirley, fork right B4102 (Tanworth Lane), half mile then right
into Dickens Heath Rd, then first right & ground on the left. 100yds from Whitlocks End (BR)
Capacity: 5,000   Seats: 250   Covered: 750   Floodlights: Yes
Clubhouse: Members Club open Tue to Thur, Sat & Sun. Light refreshments available weekends
HONOURS Midland Comb (3) 72-75 (Div 2 66-67 68-69 71-72), Lg Cup (5) 72-74 75-77 84-85
(R-up 78-79 92-93); Presidents Cup 70-71 85-86); Tony Allden Mem. Cup 74-75;
Invit. Cup 68-69 71-72 85-86; West Mids All. 63-64; Birmingham Snr Cup 73-74
CLUB RECORDS Attendance: 4,000 v Enfield, FA Amateur Cup QF 1967
Players progressing: John Gayle (Wimbledon), Keith Leonard (A Villa), Geoff Scott (Leicester C.)

Founded: 1947   Nickname: The Gate
Colours:Red/Black/Red & Black
Change Colours: All white
Midweek matches: Tuesday
Programme: 28 pages, 50p
Editor: Terry Bishop (0676 22788)

Chairman: Terry Bishop
Treasurer: G Read
Press Officer: N C Sawyer
Manager: Jim Simms
Physio: Richard Flynn

KINGS HEATH

Secretary: Stuart Maddocks, 37 Rowheath Road, Cotteridge, Birmingham B30 2EP
Tel No: 0121 604 7543
Ground: Alvechurch F.C. See their section for details
Directions: As for Alvechurch F.C.
HONOURS Midland Comb. Div 1 R-up 92-93, Div 2 R-up 82-83, Presidents Cup R-up 79-80 81-82
92-93; Birmingham Chall. Vase R-up 86-87; Worcester Sen Urn 96-97,Chall. Cup R-up 96-97
PREVIOUS   Names: Horse Shoe FC/ Kings Heath Amateur
Ground: Shirley Town (pre-1994)
Player progressing: Geoff Scott (Stoke C.)

Founded: 1964
Nickname: The Kings
Colours: Old Gold/black/gold
Change Colours: All white
Midweek Matchday:
Programme: 12 pages
Editor: M Kite

Chairman: Ray Kite
Manager: Clive Seeley

LEAMINGTON

Secretary: Brian Knibb, 61 Villiers Street, Leamington Spa,Warwicks. CV32 5YA
Tel: 01926 429066

Ground: New Windmill Ground, Harbury Lane, Whitnash, Leamington Spa, Warwicks CV33 9JR
Tel: 07866 348712

Colours: Gold/ Black/ Gold.

MASSEY-FERGUSON

Secretary: Terry Borras, Masey Ferguson, c/o Massey Ferguson social Club, Broad Lane,
Coventry CV5 9LA.   Tel Nos: 02476 675745 (H) 07909 685137 (M)
Ground: Massey-Ferguson Sports Ground, Banner Lane, Tile Hill, Coventry   (01203 694400)
Directions: A45 to Meridan turn (B4104). Over two traffic islands, turn rightat 3rd island into
Pickford Grange Lane, continue to Pickford Green Lane, &Hockley Lane, left into Broad Lane,
right into Banner Lane, 3rd entrance right
Seats: 70   Cover: 200   Floodlights: Yes   Clubhouse: Not on ground

HONOURS   Midland Comb. Div 1 94-95, Div 2 93-94, Chall. Vase 93-94, Chall Cup 94-95,
Presidents Cup 94-95; Coventry Evening Telegraph Cup 95-96
PREVIOUS   League: Coventry Alliance (pre-1993)

Colours: Red & Black stripes,Black,Black
Change Colours: Yellow/ Blue / White
Programme: Yes

Chairman: Joe Swords

Manager: John Halford, Geoff Brassington
Coach: Carl Lascelles
Physio: Joe Doolan

MEIR K.A.

Secretary: Chris Robinson , 19 Tthe Square, Meir, Stoke -on- Trent, Staffs ST3 6DW
Tel No: 01782 332152
Ground: Kings Park, Hilderstone Road, Meir Heath, Stoke-on-Trent (01782 388465)
Directions: M6 jct 14, A34 to Stone, A520 to Rough Close then Meir Heath, turnright (B5066)
ground approx 1 mile on right. 3m Blythe Bridge (BR)
Capacity: 5,000 Seats: 200 Cover: 250 Floodlights: YesClub Shop: No
Clubhouse: open matchdays. Hot food
HONOURS: Staffs Snr Lg 88-89, 90-91; Staffs FA Vase 93-94; Walsall & Dist Sen Cup
89-90;Mid Comb Prem Lge R-up 96-97; Mid Comb Lge Chall Cup R-up 97-98
PREVIOUSLeagues: Staffs Alliance/ Staffs Snr 84-92
Ground: Normacot Rec   **Name:** 'The Station'&'Shoulder of Mutton.'

Founded: 1972   Nickname: Kings
Colours: Yellow/navy/navy
Change colours: All Red
Midweek matchday: Wednesday
Programme: 32 pages 50p
Editor: Kelly Reaney (01782 325624)
President: Peter Bott
Chairman: Des Reaney
Vice Chairman: Graham Lovatt
Manager: Des Reaney Coach: Bernie Bramwell
Press Officer: Mark Allen (01782 304472)
Commercial Mgr: Paul Robinson

NUNEATON GRIFF

Secretary: Bob Archer, 27 Park Lane, Robinsons End, Nuneaton, Warwicks. CV10 8LX
Tel: 024 76 74 1831 (H)   Email Address: a.archer3@ntlworld.com
Ground: The Pingles Stadium, Avenue Road, Nuneaton. Tel: 024 76 37 0688
Directions: Avenue Road (A4252) leads to Cedar Tree Pub traffic lights, where you turn left into
the stadium car park service road - unsuitable for coaches.
Capacity: 2,000   **Seats:** 238   **Cover:** 400   **Floodlights:** Yes
Clubhouse: Yes / Usual Licensing hours Tel: 024 7673 5344 (Social Club)   **Club Shop:** No No
HONOURS: Coventry Alliance 97-98, Coventry Telegraph Cup 98, Cov. Charity Cup 99, BCFA
Junior Cup Winners 98-99 R-up 99-00, Midland Comb Prem Div 99-00 00-01 (NB Only club to be
placed in Premier Division on application and win title in first season.) Cov Tel Challenge Cup
00-01, Endsleigh Challenge Cup 00-01, BCFC Challenge Vase R-up 00-01

Founded: 1972-73 Nickname: Griff
Colours: Blue & white/blue/red & blue
Change colours: All yellow
Midweek Matchday:Wednesday
Programme:16 pages £1.00

Chairman: John Gore Manager: Mark Green
2000-01 Captain: Lee Bateman P.o.Y.: Adam
Banks Top Scorers Dave Aston & Mark
Whitehead   33 each

PERSHORE TOWN 88

Secretary: T.B.A.
Ground: King George V Playing Fields, King Georges Way, Pershore, Worcs (01386556902).
Directions: M5 jct 7, A44 to Pershore (8 miles) cross 1st lights in Pershore,at 2nd lights turn left
& fold road round into King Georges Way, ground immediately on left.
Capacity: 4,000   Seats: 200 Cover: 200   Floodlights: Yes (138 lux)   Club Shop:No
Clubhouse: Open every evening, Sun lunch & all day Sat. Snack available during matches.
HONOURS Midland Comb Prem 93-94, Div 2 89-90; Worcs Jnr Cup 90-91, Robert Biggart Cup
(5), R-up (3); Worcs Snr Urn 95-96, R-up 92-93, Jack Mould Cup 90-91, Alfred Terry Cup 90-91
Martley Hosp. Cup(`A') 90-91. Pershore Hospital Charity Cup 2001-02
RECORDS   **Atttendance:** 1,356 v Yeading, FA Cup 4th Qual. Rd 23/10/93
PREVIOUS   League: Midland Comb 89-90 90-94 Midland Alliance 94-95,99-00

Founded: 1988   Nickname: The Town
Colours: Blue & White,blue,blue
Change colours:All Red
Midweek matchday:Tuesday
Programme: 20 pages,60p
Editor: Terry Conway (01386554390)
Reserves' Lge: Banks's W.Mid Lg Div 1 (S)
2001-02 Captain: Colin Fulloway
P.o.Y.:Joe Maidment T.Scorer: R.Congrave19
Chair: Anthony Cosnett V-Ch Terry Conway
Manager: Dave Connell
Match Sec: Miike Pugh (01386 554120)

ROMULUS

Secretary: Andy Fitchett, 7 Saveker Drive, Sutton Coldfield, Birm. B76 1FT Tel: 0121 3111115H
07768 852784M
Ground: Vale Stadium, Farnborough Road, Castle Vale, Birm. B35 7BE. Tel: 0121 7476969
Fax: 0121 7476868 Email: information@romulus-fc.co.uk Website: www.romulus-fc.co.uk

Directions: From Birmingham City Centre take No. 67 bus alight at terminus. Ground is 3 mins
walk. Train - exit at New Street station. Catch No. 67 bus from City centre. If travelling by car
contact the secretary for directions.

Capacity: 2,000   Seats: 500   Cover: 600   Floodlights: Yes

Founded: 1979
Colours: Red & white stripes/red/red
Change colours: White/white/black
Chairman: John Matthews
Tel: 01827 899583 (H) 0121 693 4747 (B)

2000-01
Leading goalscorer: S. Gossage 18
Captain: J. Preston
P.o.Y.: S. Gossage

RUGBY TOWN

Secretary: David Badger, New House, Halfway Lane, Dunchurch Nr Rugby, Warwicks.CV22 6RP
Tel: 01788 522538 (H) 01812 392842 (M)

Ground: The Rugby Lions R.F.C. Webb Ellis Rd., Rugby, Warwicks. CV22 7AU   Tel: 01788 334466

Capacity: 3,396   Seated: 240   Standing: Covered 600 Uncovered 2,556

Directions: Second turn right, half mile south west of town centre on A4071,Bilton Road.
From NW: M6 Jnc 1 A426 Rugby A4071
From NE: M1 Jnc 20 A426 Rugby A4071
From SE: M1 Jnc 17/M45/A4071 towards Rugby.
Nearest Railway Station: Rugby - recommend taxi 2 miles to ground   **Colours:** All Tangerine and Black

Alveston Photo: Gordon Whittington

Handsworth Continental Star Photo: Gordon Whittington

Loughborough Back Row (l-r): Steven Hewitt (Asst Mngr), Mick Barret (Mngr), Mark Edwards, Sean O'Callaghan, Bryn Foweather, Paul O'Callaghan, Paul Springthorne, Paul Gunn, Simon Tebbutt, Simon Bailey (Physio), Steve Mould. Front Row: Steven Davey, Darrell Brookes, Stuart Bell, Gareth Rogers, Andrew McIntosh. Photo: Gordon Whittington

Pershore Town Back Row (l-r): C Jew, G Smith, J Preece, C Downing, N Turner, P Jones, C Fulloway, T Concannon, J Maidment. Front Row: R Pincher, J Gregory, D Emerson, T Conway (Vice Chair), M Preece (Mngr), D Connell (Asst Mngr), P Court, S Brain, Mascot: Ashley Biggam

SOUTHAM UNITED

Secretary: Alan D Freeman,3 Old Road, Southam, Warwickshire Cv47 1GF (01926 817711)
Ground: Banbury Road Ground, Southam, Leamington Spa.Warwicks CV 47 0BJ
Tel: 01926 812091

Directions: A423 - 12 miles south of coventry on the Banbury side of Southam
Capacity: 2000   **Seats:** 200   **Cover:** 250   **Floodlights:** Yes
Clubhouse: Yes, with food available   **Club Shop:** No
HONOURS   Midland Comb. Prem. Div. R-up 97-98: Birmingham County Sat. Vase 97-98;
Coventry Chall. Cup; Coventry City Cup; Coventry & N. Warwicks. Lge Pre. Div.
RECORD   **Attendance:** 1,500 v Coventry City, friendly 86-87

Founded: 1905
Colours: Yellow & Royal Blue/blue/blue
Change colours:White & Black/black/black
Midweek Matchday: Tuesday
Programme: 24 pages 50p Editor: Charles Hill
Chairman: Charles Hill
Presss Officer: Czaire Hughes
Manager: Ian Clarke
Assistant Manager: Dave Sturman
Player/Coach: Rob Morey
Physio: Bill Rutledge

WEST MIDLANDS POLICE

Secretary: John Black, 57 Grosvenor Close, Sutton Coldfield, W.Mids. B75 6RP. 0121 308 7673

Ground: Police Sports Ground, `Tally Ho', Pershore Road, Edgbaston, Birmingham B57RN
Tel: 0121626 8228 Website: www.wmpfc.org.uk
Directions: 2 miles south west of city on A441 Pershore Road. Ground is on the left 50yds past Priory Road lights (Warks County Cricket Ground).
3 miles from Birmingham New Street (BR) - buses 45 & 47 from city.
Capacity: 2,500   **Seats:** 224   **Covered:** 224   **Floodlights:** Yes
Clubhouse: 3 bars including snooker room, ballroom, kitchen. Hot &cold food. Open all day.
BEST SEASON   FA Vase: Quarter Final 91-92   **FA Cup:** 2nd Q ual Rd 91-92

Founded: 1974
Colours: Red & black/ black/black
Change Colours: All Blue
Midweek matchday: Tues/Thurs.
Programme: 32 pages, £1.00
Editor: D.Coulson (01283 533791)
President: Chief Constable Paul Scott-Lee
Chairman: Ass. Chief Constable: Paul Blewitt
Manager: Jim Scott Coach: Mark Fogarty
2001-02
Captain & P.o.Y.: Darren Carmell
Top Scorer: Chris Burton 18

DIVISION ONE CLUBS

BLACKHEATH
Secretary: Paul Boswell, 34 Princes Rd., Tividale, W. Mids. B69 2LR
Tel: 0121 532 4032 (H) 07720 956309 (M)
Ground: Invensys Brook Crompton Sports Ground, Oakemore Rd.,
Rowley Regis Tel: 0121 698 3253   **Colours:** Red & white/red/red

BLOXWICH TOWN
Ground: Abbey Pk, Glastonbury Crnt, Bloxwich, Walsall. Tel: 01922 477640

BROWNHILLS TOWN
Secretary: Paul Dixon, 263 Chase Rd, Burntwood, WS7 0EA Tel: 01543 683730
Ground: Holland `Park, The Parade, Brownhills, Walsall (0956535545)
Colours: All Blue

BURMAN HI-TON
Ground: Triplex Sports Ground, Eckersall Road, Kings Norton, Birmingham.
Tel: 0121 458 4570

BURNTWOOD
Secretary: David Cox, 12 Galway Road, Burntwood, Staffs. WS7 8DT
Tel No: 07931 626887 (M)
Ground: Memorial Institute, Rugeley Road, Burntwood. Tel: 01543 675578
Colours: Red and Blue stripes/Blue/Red

CADBURY ATHLETIC
Secretary: Gerry Boyle,1 Greenway Gardens, Kings Norton, Birmingham
B38 9RY (0121 628 6533 (H) 07974 382986 (M)
Ground: Cadbury Recreation Ground, Bournville Lane, B'ham. B14 6DL Tel
No: 0121 458 2000 x 3316 or 0121 454 4264   **Colours:** All Purple.

DUDLEY SPORTS
Secretary: John Lewis, 6 Hern Rd., Brieley Hill, West Mids DY5 2PW
Tel: 01384 895782
Ground: Hillcrest Avenue, Brierley Hill, West Mids (01384 826420)
Colours: Green & white /white/ green

FAIRFIELD VILLA
Secretary/Press Officer: C W Harris, 28 ShelleyClose, Catshill,
Bromsgrove B61 0NH Tel: 01527 877203
Ground: Bromsgrove Rvrs F.C. See their details.   **Colours:** All Red & Black

HANDSAKER
Secretary: Claire Handsaker, 43 Bridle Lane, Streetly, Sutton Coldfield.
Tel: 0121 580 9308 (H) 07956 517258 (M)
Ground: Hollyfields Centre Club Ltd., Woodacre Road, Erdington
Birmingham B24 0JT Tel: 0121 373 1018
Colours: Navy & white stripes/navy & red trim/navy & red trim

HOLLY LANE '92
Secretary: R G Ashton, 19 Grange Rd, Erdington,B24 0DG Tel: 0121 350 2352
Ground: Holly Sports & Social Centre, Holly Lane, Erdington, Birmingham
B249LH. tel: 01213 730979   **Colours:** Yellow/black/yellow

KENILWORTH TOWN
Secretary: Mrs Sally McKenzie, K.T.F.C.,Marlborough House, Holly Walk,
Leamington Spa CV32 4JA 01926 855247 (H) 886632 (W)
Ground: K.T.F.C. Gypsy Lane (off Rouncil Lane), Kenilworth, Warwicks. Tel:
01926 50851   **Colours:** All blue

KNOWLE
Secretary: Roger Whittick, 149 Richmond Road, Solihull B92 7RZ
Tel No :0121 684 2753 (H) 07944 753551 (M)
Ground: Hampton Rd, Knowle, Solihull , W.Mid B93 0NX
Tel: 01564 779807   **Colours:** Red/black/black

LOUGHBOROUGH F.C.
Secretary: John Belton: 51 Farndale Drive, Loughborough, Leics.LE112RG
Tel No: 01509 231583 (H) 01509 231583 (W)
Ground: The Drome, Derby Road Playing Fields, Derby Road,
Loughborough Tel: 01509 610022   **Colours:** All white and blue.

NORTHFIELD TOWN
Secretary: Matthew Kirby, 53 Park Dale Drive, Birmingham B31 4RN
Tel: 0121 604 2202 (H) 07876 143121 (M)
Ground: Shenley Lane Comm. Assoc. & Sports Centre, 472 Shenley Lane,
Birmingham B29 4HZ Tel: 0121 478 3900   **Colours:** yellow/blue/yellow

OLD HILL TOWN
Secretary: Scott Wilshaw, 10 Rowley Hill View, Cradley Heath, West
Midlands. B64 7ER 01384 564466 (H) 07976 849022 (M)
Ground: Hingleys, Bluebell Rd, Cradley Heath, West Midlands. (01384 566827)
Colours: All maroon

POLESWORTH NORTH WARWICK
Secretary: Mrs Lynn Wright, 69 Chaytor Rd,.Polesworth, Tamworth Staffs.
B78 1JS (01827 892896 or 0797 389 8523)
Ground: North Warwick Sports Ground, Hermitage Hill, Tamworth Road,
Polesworth, Warks.   **Colours:** Green/ Black/ Black

STOCKINGFORD AA
Ground: The Pavilion, Ansley Road, Stockingford, Nuneaton, Warwicks. Tel:
02476 387743

THIMBLEMILL R.E.C.
Secretary: Gerry Houten, 86 Gower Road, Halesowen, W.Midlands, B62
9BT Tel Nos: 0121 422 3357 (H) 07966 374771 (M)
Ground: Thimblemill Recreation, Thimblemill Road, Smethwick, Warley. Tel:
0121 429 2459   **Colours:** Red & Blue/ Blue/ Blue.

WILMCOTE SPORTS & SOCIAL
Secretary: Jennifer Smith, 19 Nightingale Close, Spernal Lane, Great Alne,
Warwicks. B49 6PE 01789 488077 (H)
Ground: The Patch, Rear of Wilmcote S.S.Club, Astton Cantlow Road,
Wilmcote, Stratford on Avon (01789 297895)
Colours: Green & yellow / Green / Yellow

EXPRESS & STAR
WEST MIDLANDS (REGIONAL) LEAGUE

FEEDER TO: MIDLAND ALLIANCE

Hon Secretary: Neil Juggins
14 Badgers Lane, Blackwell, Bromsgrove

The 2001-02 season was the one in which Causeway United made the anticipated next stop and won the League championship, after finishing fifth and second in the previous two seasons. They emerged at the head of the table after a mammoth 46 game programme, the longest since 1953-54. However, the early pace setters were, perhaps surprisingly, Bridgnorth-based works side Star. Star took top spot at the end of August and went on to extend an unbeaten opening sequence to no less than twenty league games, before inexplicably being thrashed 6-0 by Brierley & Hagley Alliance at the end of November. The club never really recovered from this blow and eventually had to settle for seventh, although it still ended up being the club's highest ever placing in the competition.

Causeway assumed top spot shortly after Star's major setback and led the table for the remainder of the season, although they were strongly challenged initially by Wolverhampton Casuals, and latterly by Tividale. The championship was eventually ensured with a couple of games remaining when Heath Hayes were defeated by the only goal of the game on 1st May. Tividale's form deserted them at the end, winning just two of their last six games, but they had done enough to claim the Keys Cup for the first time through finishing as runners up. It was the club's highest end-of-season placing since reaching the Premier Division for the first time in 1973. Other clubs achieving their highest ever positions in the WMRL were Wolverhampton Casuals (third) and Ledbury Town (fourth), the latter appearing in the Premier Division for the first time since 1983.

Down at the bottom Dudley Town endured a miserable campaign, losing the first eight games (although by this stage they were still level on points with Bustleholme, who had lost seven games) and only picking up two points in the first sixteen. Ettingshall was then beaten 2-1 but it proved to be one of just three league victories all season as last place was guaranteed with four games still remaining. The total of 37 defeats was just one short of the WMRL's all time record. If there had been a prize for the leakiest defence it would have gone to Smethwick Rangers. Runners up a season earlier as Warley Rangers, major changes in personnel saw the goals against tally hit three figures in just the thirtieth game, with a final tally of 147. However, Walsall Wood's inability to turn games in hand into points left the Oak Park club to occupy the second relegation place.

Causeway were denied the league and cup double by Hereford-based Westfields, winners by the only goal of the final at Rushall.

In most seasons a c lub that lost just two games out of 30, and rattled in a massive 127 goals in the process, would consider itself highly unlucky not to win the championship. Unfortunately, this was the fate that befell Great Wyrley after they went to the head of the table on November 17th, courtesy of a 14-1 thrashing of hapless Walsall Wood Reserves, leading the way virtually until the season's end. It was Brereton Social that had made the early running, opening the season with eight straight wins and not tasting defeat until their fifteenth game, and, although overtaken by Great Wyrley, it was these two clubs that occupied the top two places for the majority of the season. However, Ounsdale, having conceded just 21 goals in 26 games the previous season, took defensive meanness a stage further by conceding just fifteen in 30 games this time round, and suffering their only defeat as early as their eighth game. As late as mid-March Ounsdale had as many as five games in hand and, as a result, briefly slipped into the bottom half of the table. However, a 1-0 victory at Great Wyrley on 6th April proved decisive and nine wins out of eleven for Ounsdale meant that Great Wyrley's own finishing sequence of eight wins and a draw in their last nine games was not quite enough. A 5-2 victory over Wyrley Rangers on May 11th secured the championship for Ounsdale, and victory in their last game meant that Great Wyrley's three point penalty for fielding an ineligible player had not proved decisive at all. At least Great Wyrley had the consolation of winning the Division One League Cup, overcoming Lucas Sports 2-0 in the final after the latter club had surprisingly beaten the champions in the semi final a few days earlier.

Walsall Wood Reserves endured a miserable campaign. The first fifteen games all ended in defeat and the dubious privilege of being the first side to fail to beat them fell to fellow strugglers Darlaston Reserves on 9th February. It was not until April 6th that a victory finally arrived at the 24th attempt, but remarkably bottom place was not ensured until yet another defeat was suffered in the penultimate game of the season, due to the form of fellow strugglers Darlaston Reserves and Wolverhampton Sports.

In Division One (South) things were much more clear cut. Kidderminster based works side Brintons were the early pacesetters but Sedgley White Lions overtook them at the beginning of December and were still unbeaten when the championship was secured with a 3-1 victory over Bustleholme Reserves on April 13th, with five games still remaining. With the title secured a single defeat was finally recorded in the 27th game. Bewdley Town eventually overcame their annual fixture backlog, largely attributable to their ground's proximity to the River Severn, to clinch the runners up spot.

Steve Carr

Bromyard Town. Back Row (l-r): Chalky White (Mngr), Andrew Cooke, Keith Aingel, Andrew Chalmers, Dave Kearney, Jamie Lambert, Neil Mogford, Paul Krivosic, Luke Willetts, Richard Silk, Scott Morris. Front Row: Ian Latimer (Asst Mngr), Darryl Gormley, Jon Jenkins, David Phillips, Chris Billings (Capt), Gordon Beauchamp, Adam Davies, Nathan Owen, Eric Birch (Physio)

Causeway United, West Midland League Premier Division Champions
Photo: Mark Wood

Darlaston. Back Row (l-r): Chris Horton, Chris Salt, Peter Rose, Dale Roberts, Neil Olden, Michael Lloyd, Richard Bullock, Stuart Ball, Steve Blameman, Richard Steeples, Dave Powers (Sec). Front Row: Martin Green, Chris Mario, Martin Townsend, Stuart Edwards, Paul Madders, Jimmy Tough, Mike Pope, Jason Paddock, David Ratcliffe. Photo: Marshall's Sports Services

Ettingshall. Back Row (l-r): Enoch Tipton, Chris Keating, Martin Bradburn, Tommy Johnson, Scott Bamford, James Revrant, Dean Hubbard, Riad Erradji, Winton Hardy, Albert Mills. Front Row: Gareth Mees, Philip Domeney, Teddy Pearson, Mike Elliott, Noel Smith, Dale Mills, Rob Perks.
Photo: Marshall's Sports Services

FINAL LEAGUE TABLES 2001-02

PREMIER DIVISION

	P	W	D	L	F	A	Pts
Causeway United	46	29	12	5	107	55	99
Tividale	46	27	10	9	94	57	*88
W'ton Casuals	46	26	8	12	89	69	86
Little Drayton Rngrs	46	24	13	9	98	54	85
Westfields	46	24	9	13	89	53	81
Ledbury Town	46	26	3	17	103	85	81
Star	46	24	8	14	91	65	80
Kington Town	46	20	14	12	76	42	74
Malvern Town	46	20	11	15	87	57	71
Heath Hayes	46	19	13	14	60	54	70
Tipton Town	46	19	12	15	76	50	69
Brierley & Hagley	46	18	15	13	74	60	69
Wellington	46	18	11	17	63	69	65
Lye Town	46	16	15	15	59	47	63
Ettingshall Holy Trin	46	16	13	17	66	73	61
Bustleholme	46	16	10	20	80	92	58
W'ton United	46	15	11	20	79	81	56
Shawbury United	46	13	14	19	69	83	53
Darlaston Town	46	13	12	21	69	99	51
Bromyard Town	46	11	10	25	73	97	43
Gornal Athletic	46	7	15	24	54	113	36
Smethwick Rangers	46	11	3	32	70	147	36
Walsall Wood	46	7	12	27	52	96	33
Dudley Town	46	3	6	37	42	122	15

DIVISION ONE NORTH

	P	W	D	L	F	A	Pts
Ounsdale	30	24	5	1	101	15	77
Great Wyrley	30	24	4	2	127	33	*73
Brereton Social	30	22	5	3	83	31	71
Newport Town	30	16	5	9	69	48	53
Sikh Hunters	30	15	5	10	79	63	50
Morda United	30	13	9	8	43	36	48
Marston Wolves	30	13	8	9	58	45	47
Wrockwardine Wood	30	13	6	11	80	49	45
Shenstone Pathfinders	30	11	8	11	54	60	41
Lucas Sports	30	10	8	12	58	63	38
Wyrley Rangers	30	9	6	15	56	70	33
Eccleshall Res	30	9	5	16	43	60	32
Heath Hayes Res	30	7	8	15	50	70	29
Darlaston Town Res	30	4	4	22	35	88	16
W'ton Sports Gnst	30	3	4	23	24	106	13
Walsall Wood Res	30	1	2	27	20	143	5

DIVISION ONE SOUTH

	P	W	D	L	F	A	Pts
Sedgley White Lions	26	22	3	1	77	18	69
Bewdley Town	26	15	3	8	56	31	48
Hinton	26	13	7	6	54	44	46
Leominster Town	26	13	4	9	49	38	43
Wyre Forest	26	10	10	6	44	34	40
Brintons Athletic	26	12	3	11	41	47	39
Bridgnorth Town Res	26	11	5	10	50	45	38
Ludlow Town Res	26	11	4	11	62	50	37
Chaddesley Corbett	26	10	1	15	56	61	31
Mahal	26	8	4	14	37	50	28
Malvern Town Res	26	8	4	14	38	54	28
Lye Town Res	26	6	8	12	35	54	26
Malvern Rangers	26	7	4	15	47	63	25
Bustleholme Res	26	5	2	19	32	89	17

*points deducted

RESULTS CHART 2001-02

	1	2	3	4	5	6	7	8	9	10	11	12	13	14	15	16	17	18	19	20	21	22	23	24
1	X	6-0	5-3	0-1	3-1	0-0	2-3	2-0	2-1	2-2	2-1	1-1	0-1	1-1	0-2	0-0	6-0	2-1	2-3	0-3	1-1	3-0	3-2	1-0
2	2-2	X	0-3	1-1	5-0	3-0	0-0	3-3	0-0	1-3	2-3	3-1	0-2	2-3	3-1	1-2	1-1	0-2	1-2	1-2	1-2	2-0	1-1	1-0
3	0-0	1-7	X	1-6	3-3	4-1	1-1	4-1	2-2	0-2	3-4	1-2	0-1	0-4	4-2	4-0	1-2	0-0	3-4	2-2	1-2	1-1	3-2	3-3
4	3-2	1-1	1-1	X	2-2	1-0	5-3	2-1	1-0	5-1	7-0	1-3	1-0	1-2	3-1	3-2	4-1	1-1	1-0	5-0	4-3	4-1	3-4	1-1
5	2-1	3-7	0-3	1-1	X	0-0	0-2	2-2	1-3	2-1	4-2	0-1	1-2	3-1	4-2	4-0	4-1	1-0	1-2	1-2	3-1	4-0	1-4	2-1
6	1-2	4-3	1-3	2-2	0-1	X	2-1	3-4	0-3	0-1	1-3	0-1	1-3	0-3	1-3	7-0	0-2	0-4	0-4	0-1	3-5	1-1	0-1	0-5
7	2-0	2-4	0-1	3-1	3-3	3-1	X	0-1	0-1	1-1	2-0	1-4	3-1	0-0	1-0	3-2	1-2	0-0	3-2	1-1	2-3	1-1	1-0	1-4
8	1-3	1-1	1-3	2-3	1-1	2-1	2-2	X	1-1	0-2	0-2	1-5	1-1	1-0	1-1	1-1	0-5	1-6	0-5	1-2	1-2	0-0	0-1	1-3
9	3-0	1-3	1-0	0-2	3-0	2-2	3-0	2-2	X	0-0	1-0	1-0	1-2	1-0	3-0	1-1	0-6	1-0	0-1	2-0	2-1	2-2	0-0	2-2
10	1-2	4-0	0-1	1-1	0-0	5-0	1-1	4-0	1-1	X	5-0	1-3	0-0	1-0	4-1	4-0	2-0	0-1	1-3	1-2	0-1	0-3	0-0	
11	2-0	2-1	2-1	1-2	3-1	7-0	3-0	5-0	2-3	1-2	X	1-0	2-1	3-2	5-2	2-1	2-1	1-1	1-4	2-2	4-0	6-1	2-1	
12	1-1	3-0	2-1	0-1	4-1	2-0	1-1	5-2	1-1	3-0	6-3	X	1-1	2-0	1-1	7-0	0-2	1-1	2-2	2-3	2-1	2-1	4-1	
13	1-0	2-1	1-1	0-2	4-0	3-0	0-0	2-0	3-0	0-1	1-4	2-2	X	1-1	2-5	0-4	4-1	3-1	2-2	0-1	1-1	2-3	2-0	0-0
14	0-1	4-0	6-0	2-2	3-4	4-0	2-1	4-0	3-0	0-3	1-5	4-2	0-0	X	1-2	3-1	1-2	2-2	0-1	2-1	1-1	2-0	1-1	1-2
15	1-0	1-1	0-2	1-1	0-0	5-2	0-0	3-3	3-1	0-2	4-0	2-2	1-1	3-3	X	3-0	1-5	0-3	0-3	1-2	3-4	0-1	4-2	2-2
16	3-4	5-2	2-4	0-2	5-0	2-1	5-1	3-4	1-4	1-9	2-3	2-1	2-0	2-6	2-3	X	2-4	3-2	1-2	4-1	4-1	0-1	1-2	1-5
17	2-2	2-0	1-0	0-3	2-2	3-1	4-1	3-2	3-0	0-0	3-0	1-1	3-0	4-3	3-0	3-0	X	1-0	1-1	1-2	1-1	2-0	5-0	1-5
18	0-1	4-3	2-1	1-2	3-3	2-1	0-4	4-0	0-1	2-1	2-0	2-1	0-1	1-1	6-0	3-1	X	1-0	0-0	2-0	7-0	4-0	1-1	
19	3-3	2-0	1-2	0-0	2-0	3-1	0-0	2-1	1-1	2-2	0-5	1-0	1-3	0-1	8-1	2-0	3-0	X	2-2	3-2	3-1	3-1	4-1	
20	1-1	6-2	1-0	4-2	5-0	2-1	1-3	5-1	0-2	0-0	4-0	2-2	1-0	1-3	3-2	2-3	0-4	2-2	0-1	X	0-4	2-3	3-0	
21	1-2	0-2	5-1	1-2	3-2	3-1	1-3	2-3	0-0	0-0	1-1	3-4	1-1	0-1	0-2	5-0	2-0	0-1	1-2	1-4	X	5-2	0-2	2-1
22	0-0	5-0	2-3	2-3	2-1	2-2	1-2	2-2	1-2	1-3	0-4	1-3	1-0	1-1	0-0	4-2	1-1	0-1	2-3	4-6	1-1	X	1-2	0-1
23	1-1	2-1	2-1	1-3	3-0	4-2	0-0	1-1	1-0	1-1	3-2	0-0	1-2	1-0	0-1	2-1	1-0	0-1	0-2	0-1	3-3	1-1	X	0-1
24	2-2	2-0	4-1	1-1																				X

1	Brierley & Hag	6	Dudley Town	
2	Bromyard Town	7	Ettingshall HT	
3	Bustleholme	8	Gornal Athletic	
4	Causeway Utd	9	Heath Hayes	
5	Darlaston Town	10	Kington Town	

- 1 Brierley & Hag
- 2 Bromyard Town
- 3 Bustleholme
- 4 Causeway Utd
- 5 Darlaston Town
- 6 Dudley Town
- 7 Ettingshall HT
- 8 Gornal Athletic
- 9 Heath Hayes
- 10 Kington Town
- 11 Ledbury Town
- 12 Little Drayton R
- 13 Lye Town
- 14 Malvern Town
- 15 Shawbury Utd
- 16 Smethwick Rgs
- 17 Star
- 18 Tipton Town
- 19 Tividale
- 20 W'ton Casuals
- 21 W'ton United
- 22 Walsall Wood
- 23 Wellington
- 24 Westfields

PREMIER DIVISION LEAGUE CUP 2001-02

FIRST ROUND

Darlaston Town	v	Brierley & Hagley All.	5-0		Kington Town	v	Tipton Town	3-4
Malvern Town	v	Walsall Wood	1-0		Ledbury Town	v	Causeway Utd	3p4, 3-3
Bromyard Town	v	W'ton Casuals	1-3		Little Drayton Rngrs	v	Tividale	4-0
Shawbury United	v	Bustleholme	5-1		Star	v	Heath Hayes	5-1

SECOND ROUND

Ettingshall H T	v	W'ton Casuals	0-1		Darlaston Town	v	Gornal Athletic	0-1
Star	v	Westfields	0-3		Dudley Town	v	Tipton Town	1-3
Lye Town	v	W'ton United	2-1		Wellington	v	Malvern Town	0-3
Causeway United	v	Smethwick Rangers	4-1		Shawbury United	v	Little Drayton Rngrs	2-3

THIRD ROUND

Gornal Athletic	v	Causeway United	1-3		Westfields	v	Malvern Town	3-1
Lye Town	v	W'ton Casuals	3-4		Tipton Town	v	Little Drayton Rngrs	3-2

SEMI FINALS
(1st leg)

Tipton Town	v	Westfields	1-0		W'ton Casuals	v	Causeway United	2-6

(2nd Leg)

Tipton Town	v	Westfields	0-3		W'ton Casuals	v	Causeway United	1-2

FINAL

Causeway United	v	Westfields	0-1		at Rushall Olympic FC

DIVISION ONE LEAGUE CUP 2001-02

FIRST ROUND

Chaddesley Corbett	v	Wyrley Rangers	3-1		Bridgnorth Town Rs	v	Leominster Town	2-4
Sikh Hunters	v	Hinton	5-3		Brintons Athletic	v	Ludlow Town Res	2-1
Malvern Rangers	v	Eccleshall Reserves	5-4		Lucas Sports	v	Wrockwardine Wood	3-2
W'ton Sports Gnst	v	Lye Town Reserves	1-5		Newport Town	v	Shenstone Path.	4-3
Sedgley White Lions	v	Walsall Wood Res	2-0		Mahal	v	Bustleholme Res	2-1
Darlaston Town Res	v	Marston Wolves	4-0		Malvern Town Res	v	Brereton Social	1-4
Morda United	v	Ounsdale	1-5		Great Wyrley	v	Bewdley Town	7-1

SECOND ROUND

Darlaston Town Res	v	Malvern Rangers	4-3		Chaddesley Corbett	v	Heath Hayes Res	0-2
Newport Town	v	Sedgley White Lions	1-0		Wyre Forest	v	Leominster Town	1-4
Mahal	v	Ounsdale	0-2		Brereton Social	v	Sikh Hunters	4-0
Brintons Athletic	v	Great Wyrley	1-3		Lye Town Reserves	v	Lucas Sports	0-2

THIRD ROUND

Heath Hayes Res	v	Great Wyrley	2-3		Leominster Town	v	Lucas Sports	0-3
Newport Town	v	Brereton Social	2-1		Ounsdale	v	Darlaston Town Res	2-1

SEMI FINALS

Ounsdale	v	Lucas Sports	0-1		Newport Town	v	Great Wyrley	1-2

FINAL

Great Wyrley	v	Lucas Sports	2-0		at Gornal Athletic FC

BRIERLEY HILL & HAGLEY ALLIANCE

Secretary: Tony Gore, 114 Dobbins Oak Road, Pedmore, Stourbridge, W.Mids DY9 0XY
Tel: 01562 720158 (H) 07932 493128 (M)

Ground: Halesowen Harriers FC, Park Road, Halesowen, West Mids.
Tel: 01384 896748

Directions: From M5 junction 3, follow A456 towards Kidderminster to first island. Turn right onto A459 towards Dudley. Turn left at next island onto A458 towards Stourbridge. Follow this road for 2 miles. Ground is on left-hand side.

Chairman: Lee Robson

Founded: 1955
Nickname: Lions
Colours: Blue & white shirts & shorts, white socks
Change colours: Green & white hoops, white shorts, black socks
Programme: 20 pages, 50p
Editor: Secretary

BROMYARD TOWN

Secretary: Tony Haverfield, 16 Highwell Avenue, Bromyard, Hereford HR7 4EL
Tel & Fax: 01885 483655 (H) 07885 849948 (M)
Ground: Delahay Meadow, Stourport Road, Bromyard HR7 4NT Tel: 01885 483974
Directions: 1/4 mile outside Bromyard on the Stourport/Kidderminster road (B4203). The ground is on the right through iron gates, adjacent to O'Malleys Irish restaurant.
Honours: Smedley Cooke Memorial Cup: 2001-02, West Mid REgional Lg.: Div1 South 1999-2000, Herefordshire Cup Winners 96-97 and 99-2000
Best seasons: F.A.Vase: 2nd Rd 2001-02

Founded: 1893

Colours: Blue & black/black/blue
Change colours: Yellow/red/yellow
Chairman: Tony Watkins
Tel: 01885 483509

BUSTLEHOME

Secretary: Peter John Lewis, 19 Bernard Street, West Bromwich B71 1DJ
Tel No: 0121 580 0573
Ground: Tipton Sports Academy, Wednesbury Oak Road, Tipton DY4 0BS

Directions: From M6 Junction 9, take A461, through Wednesbury Town centre to Ocker Hill Island. Follow signpost here taking a full right turn towards Bilston A4098 for half a mile, turning left at traffic lights A4037. Ground is 50 yards on left.

FACT FILE
Founded: 1975
Colours: Yellow/green/green
Change colours: All white

CLUB PERSONNEL
Chairman: Colin Hall

DUDLEY TOWN

Secretary: Margaret Turner, 3,Straits Road, Lower Gornal, Dudley, DY3 2UY Tel: 01384 214741
Ground: The Beeches, Packwood Road, Tividale W,Mids Tel : 01384 211743
Directions: M5 Jct 2 signs to Dudley (A4123). One mile past school and playing fields under walkway to lights. Left into Regent Road.,left into Elm Terrace then left again into BirchTerrace and 2nd left into Packwood Road. Ground is at end of cul-de-sac.
Capacity: 500 Cover: 1000 Seats: 100 Floodlights: Yes Club Shop: No
Clubhouse:Social club open on matchday . Food available from snackbar
HONOURS Southern Lg Midland Div 84-85, Birmingham Comb 33-34 (R-up 34-35 47-48), Midland (Worcs) Comb 31-32 (R-up 29-30 30-31), West Mids Lg Cp R-up 75-76 (Div2 Cp R-up 80-81), Birmingham Senior Cup 85-86 (R-up 64-65 83-84)Worcs SeniorCp 45-46(joint)(R-up 84-85), Camkin Cp 64-65, Worcs Junior Cp 83-84

FACT FILE
Formed: 1893 Nickname: The Robins
Colours: Red/black/black
Change: Yellow/black oryellow/grey or red
Midweek matchday: Tuesday 7.45pm
Progr: Pages :28 Price75p Editor: T.B.A.
Website: www.dtfc.net
Chairman: Nevil Jeynes V Chair: Alan Guest
President: N D Jeynes
Man: Ivor Chambers Asst Man:Andy Male/Brian.Hampson 2000-01 P.o.Y.: Chris Walwyn Top Scorer:Mark Woodall 8

ETTINGSHALL HOLY TRINITY

Secretary: Graham Mills, 27 Ashen Close, Sedgley, Dudley, West Mids DY3 3UZ(01902 66222)
Ground: Aldersley Stadium, Aldersley Road, Tettenhal, Wolverhampton (01902 556200)
Directions: From Wolverhampton take A41 Tettenhall Road, 1.5 miles turn right into Lower Street, then right into Aldersley Road, ground on right
HONOURS West Mids Lg Div 1 Cup R-up 85-86 (Div 2 R-up 84-85), Sporting Award 85-86,Staffs Co. Lg R-up 82-83 (Lg Shield 82-83 83-84), Ike Cooper Cup 82-84 83-84,Sporting Club Award 81-82, Wolverhampton & District Amateur Lg 80-81 (Div 1 65-66, Div 2 64-65), Div 1/2 Cup 64-65 65-66, A H Oakley Cup 80-81, J W Hunt Cup 82-83 83-84 (R-up 79-80), Wolverhampton Cup 83-84 (R-up 82-83)
PREVIOUS   **League:** Wednesbury Church & Chapel (early 1900s), Bilston Youth (1950s),Wolverhampton & District Amateur (1960s), Staffs County (South)

FACT FILE

Founded: 1920 Nickname: Trins
Club Sponsors: DKB Electric/ John O'Dell
Colours: Green & white/green/green& white
Change colours: Red/white/red
Midweek matchday: Wednesday
Prog. Editor: John Edwards (01785 713458)
Chairman:John Robinson Pres: David Gadd
Manager: Graham Mills Physio: David Gads

GORNAL ATHLETIC

Secretary: Richard Gwinnett,166 Wolverhampton Rd.,Sedgley, DudleyW.Mids(01902 825191 (H)
Ground: Garden Walk Stadium, Lower Gornal, Dudley, West Midlands (01384 358398)
Directions: From Dudley take A459 to Sedgley past the Burton Rd Hospital. 1ston left at the Green Dragon public house on the B4175 (Jews Lane). Follow theroad until you come to the Old Bull's Head, turn left into Rednall Road, 2ndleft to Garden Walk
Capacity: 3,000   Seats: 100   Cover: 500   Floodlights: Yes   Club Shop: No

HONOURS   West Mids Lg Div 1 R-up 83-84 (Div 1 Cup 92-93), Birmingham Vase 91-92
PREVIOUS   **League:** Midland Comb. 51-63
          Name: Lower Gornal Ath
RECORDS   **Transfer fees received:** £1,500 for Gary Bell and for George Andrews both toCardiff City, 1965

FACT FILE
Founded: 1945   Nickname: Peacocks
Sponsors: Jasper Steels
Colours: All blue
Change colours: Yeloe/green/green
Reserves' Lge: West Mids (Reg.) Lge Res. Div
Chairman: Ian Hall
Commercial Manager: Martin Wedgebury
Manager: John Gwinnell
Coach: Ian Clark/ Ross Hill
Reserves' Manager: Ian Davies

HEATH HAYES

Secretary: John Deans,280 Hednesford Road,Heath Hayes,Cannock, Staffs. WS12 5DS
Terl No: 01543 279849 (H)
Ground: Coppice Colliery Ground,Newlands Lane, Heath Hayes, Cannock,Staffs.(07976 269280)

Directions: From Cannoc, take Lichfield Rd. After 2.5 miles first right past Texaco garage on right
Seaon 2000-01: Captain: Stuart Turnbull
         Player of the Year: Lyndon Davies
         Top Scorer: Warren Inskip (27)

Colours: Blue & white stripes/blue/blue
Change Colours: Red & black/black/black

CLUB PERSONNEL

Chairman John Weldon
Manager: Paul Kent
Coach: Geraint Jones
Reserve Team Manager: Andrew Cox
Physio: John Thacker

KINGTON ATHLETIC

Secretary: Pauline Shaw, 9 Banley Drive, Headbrook, Kington, Herefordshire HR5 3FD
Tel No: 01544 231777

Ground: Park Road Ground, Mill Street, Kington, Hereford (01544 231007)

Directions: Follow signs for kington Town Centre, look for left turn betweenthe Town Clock and the Burton Hotel. Carry on this road for 500 metres, groundon left as road bends

FACT FILE

Colours: Yellow /black/black
Change colours: All Red

CLUB PERSONNEL
Chairman: William Mayglothing

LEDBURY TOWN

Secretary: Mike Clueit, 55 Lawnside Road, Ledbury, Herefordshire, HR8 2AE.
Tel: 01531 633 182

Ground: New Street, Ledbury, Hertfordshire Tel: 01531 631 463

Directions: Leave M50 at junction 2. Take A417 to Ledbury. At first island take first exit and at second island take fourth exit. ground is 100 yards on right.

FACT FILE
Formed: 1893

Colours: Black/white shirts, black shorts & socks.
Change colours: Red & blue shirts, red shorts, red socks.

CLUB PERSONNEL
Chairman: Chris Stephens

LITTLE DRAYTON RANGERS

Chairman: John Thorneycroft

Secretary: Brian Garratt, 4 Quarry Bank Road, Market Drayton, Shropshire TF9 1DR
Tel: 01630 654618 (H)

Ground: Greenfield Sports Club, Greenfield Lane, Market Drayton. Tel: 01630 655088

Directions: A41 to Tern Hill island, turn right for Newcastle-u-Lyme. Over 1st island and turn right at next, by Gingerbread P.H. towards town centre. After 200 yds turn right, before going over bridge, into Greenfields Lane. Ground is 150 yds down lane on right.

Colours: Royal & pale blue stripes/royal/royal
Change Colours:Red & Blue stripes/blue/red

LYE TOWN

Secretary: John Woodhouse, 46 Surfeit Hill, Cradley Heath, Warley, West Midlands. B64 7EB
Tel Nos: 01384 633976(H) 0121 627 6600(W) **Ground:** Sports Ground, Stourbridge Road, Lye
(01384 422672) **Directions:** On A458 Birmingham-Stourbridge road about 400yds
afterlights/crossroads at Lye. From M5 jct 3 take road marked Kidderminster as faras lights at bottom
of Hagley Hill, right at island, 3rd turn off at nextisland,turn off left at crossroads/lights, ground
about 400yds on left. Quarter mile from Lye (BR)
Capacity: 5,000 **Seats:** 200 **Cover:** 600 **Floodlights:** Yes **Clubhouse:** Yes (01384 822672)
HONOURS West Mids Lg R-up 76-77 78-79 79-80 80-81 (Prem. Div Cup 75-76), Midland
Comb.35-36 (R-up 32-33 34-35 37-38), W.Mid Lg Winners 97-98-99
PREVIOUS **Leagues:** Midland Combination 31-39
RECORD **Gate:** 6,000 v Brierley Alliance

FACT FILE
Founded: 1930 Nickname: Flyers
Colours: Blue & white stripes/blue/blue
Change Colours: Yellow/green/yellow
Programme: 24 pages, 40p
Editor: Roy Pearson
Chairman: Roy Pearson
President: Ian Cole
Manager: Geoff Moss
Coach: John Woodhouse
Physio: Harry Hill

MALVERN TOWN

Secretary: Margaret Caldicott, 20 Nixon Court, Callow End, Worcester WR2 4UU 01905 831327
Ground: Langland Stadium, Langland Avenue, Malvern, Worcs Tel: 01684 574068
Directions: From Worcester take A449 to Malvern.Turn left at roundabout signposted B4208 to
Welland. Left at traffic lights into Pickersleigh Road. Turn left at Longford Arms Pub, into
Maddesfield R oad. 2nd left into Langland Ave., ground 100yds on right. 1 mile from Malvern (BR)
Capacity: 4,000 **Seats:** 140 **Cover:** 310 **Floodlights:** Yes **Shop:** No
Clubhouse: 2 bars, large dance area, teabar matchdays **Best F.A.Vase Season:** 99-00 2nd Rd
HONOURS Worcester/ Midland Comb. 55-56 Mid Comb Cup R-up 75-76, WFA Senior Urn (7),
WFA Sat Junior Cup Winners (4) Banks's Brewery Premier League Cup R-up 87-88 WFA Nursing
Cup Winners 97-98, Robert Biggart Cup Winners 97-98, 98-99 ,Evesham Hosp Cup 99-00
PREVIOUS League: Midland Comb. 55-79 **RECORD Gate:** 1,221 v Worcester, FA Cup

FACT FILE
Founded:1947 Sponsors: Malvern Instruments
Colours: All Claret Change:White/black/maroon
Reserves League: Banks's Brewery Div 1 S
Midweek Matchday: Tuesday
Programme: 28 pages 50p Editor: Brian Scott
Chairman: Geoff Brewer President: R Box
Manager: Joe Rawle
Asst. Manager: Richard Anson
2001-02 Leading goalscorer: Lee Hooper
Captain: Sean Cotterill P.o.Y.:Dave Alden

SEDGLEY WHITE LION

Secretary: David Ferguson, 3 Earl Street, Coseley, West. Mids. WV14 8JT
Tel: 0121 520 8324 (H) 07881 856039 (M)

Ground: c/o Gornal Athletic - Garden Walk Stadium, Lower Gornal, Dudley, West Mids.
Tel: 01384 358398
Directions: From Dudley take A459 to Sedgley past the Burton Road Hospital.
1st on left at the Green Dragon public house on the B4175 (Jews Lane).
Follow the road until you come to the Old Bull's Head, turn left into Rednall Road,
2nd left to Garden Walk
Capacity: 3,000 **Seats:** 100 **Cover:** 500 **Floodlights:** Yes **Club Shop:** No

Founded: 1985
Colours: White/royal blue/red
Change: All royal blue.
Chairman: Kevin Lockley
Tel: 01902 674246 (H) 07802 931346 (M)
Match Secretary: Elaine Harris
Tel: 0121 530 3257 (H)

SHAWBURY UNITED

Secretary: Dave Thomas, 183 Cordwell Park,Wem, Shropshire SY3 9JB
Tel: 01743 245457 (H)

Ground: The Butler's Sports Centre, Bowen's Field, Wem. Tel: 01939 233287

Directions: Go into Wem town centre and at the Church junction turn right.
Take the first left after pedestrian crossing, then first left with Hawkestone pub on
corner. 2nd left into car park and ground.

Formed: 1992
Colours: Blue & yellow/blue/blue
Change Colours:White/yellow/yellow
Chairman: Ron Humphreys
Tel: 01939 251076

SMETHWICK RANGERS

Secretary: Joginder Singh, 134 Sandwell Road, Handsworth, Birmingham B21 8PS
Tel No: 0121 523 0259
Ground: Hadley Stadium, Wilson Road, Smethwick Tel No: 0121 434 4848
Directions: From Wolverhampton Centre, proceed along A459 to junc Parkfields Rd & Sedgley
Rd. Turn left at the main Parkfield traffic lights A4039, sign Ettingshall, travel 500yds, left into
Myatt Ave, 1st right into Lawn Rd. Ground on right

FACT FILE
Founded :1972
Colours: Red & black/black/black
Change Colours: Blue & white/blue/blue

CLUB PERSONNEL
Chairman: Mohan Singh Gill

TIPTON TOWN

Secretary: Ruth Archer, 34 Speakers Close,Oakham Park, Tividale.W.Midlands B69 1PB
Tel No: 01384 242912 (H)
Ground: Tipton Sports Acadamy, Wednesbury Oak Road, Tipton, West Midlands
Directions: M6 Jct 9 through Wednesbury taking A461 until right at island signto Tipton. At next island - Ocker Hill - turn full right owards Bilston & Wolverhampton. After 1/3 mile turn left at traffic lights and ground is on left.
Capacity: 1000 **Seats:** 200 **Cover:** New covered stand and dressing rooms **Floodlights:**Yes
Clubhouse: Open with excellent food available week-ends. 12noon - 7.00 p.m.**Club Shop:** no
Honours: West Mid Regional League DIv One Championship and League Cup, Wednesbury Senior Charity Cup (5)
Record Attendance: Approx 1100 v Wolverhampton Wanderers in a pre season friendly 1.8.88

FACT FILE
Founded: 1948
Sponsors: Tipton & Cseley Building Society
Colours: Black & white stripes/black/black
Change colours: White/blue/blue
Midweek Matchday: Wednesday
Reserves League:Kidderminster & District
Programme Editor: Ruth Shinfield
CLUB PERSONNEL
Chairman: Kevin Jennings
Manager:Neil Hickinbottom

TIVIDALE

Secretary: Leon Murray ,59 Peel Way, Tividale, Oldbury, W.Mids B69 3JZ(0121 532 6979)
Ground: The Beeches, Packwood Rd, Tividale, Warley, W. Midlands B69 1UL tel: 01384 211743
Directions: Dudley Port Station to Burnt tree, left towards Birmingham, ground1 mile on right. Or, M5 jct 2, follow Dudley signs A4123, after approx 2 miles turn left into Regent Rd & left again into Elm Terraces, 1st left into Birch Crescent. Packwood Rd is second left - ground at end of cul-de-sac
Capacity: 3,500 Seats: 200 Cover: 1,000 Floodlights: Yes Club Shop: No
Clubhouse: Mon-Fri 8-11pm, Sat 12-11pm, Sun 12-3 & 8-10.30. Cobs, rolls,sandwiches available
HONOURS West Midlands Lg Div 1 72-73 (Prem. Div Cup 76-77, Div 1 Cup 72-73),
Wednesbury Charity Cup 76-77
PREVIOUS Ground: City Road **Leagues:** Handsworth & District 56-60; inactive 60-62; West Mids Alliance 62-66 **RECORD Attendance:** 2,400 v Telford United, FA Cup

Founded: 1954 Nickname: Dales
Sponsors: Midland & North Security Consultants
Colours: All Yellow
Change colours: All Blue
Midweek matchday: Tuesday
Programme: 40 pages, 60p Editor: c/o Club
Newsline: 0891 66 42 52
Chairman: Donald Ashton
President: Lord Peter Archer
Press Officer: T Clark
Manager: Paul Madders
Asst Manager: Ron Blackwood
Physio: John Cotton

WALSALL WOOD

Secretary: David Cartwright, 299 Walsall Road, Stone Cross, West Bromwich B71 3LN
Tel: 0121 588 6021 (H) 01922 652633 (B) 07932 390381 (M)
Ground: Oak Park, Lichfield Rd, Walsall Tel: 01543 361084 **Directions:** Off A461 Walsall-Lichfield Rd, 4 miles from Walsall centre and100yds south of jctn with A4152(Aldridge-Brownhills.)
Capacity: 3,000 **Seats:** 400 **Cover:** 400 **Floodlights:**Yes Clubhouse:Eves,Matches +Sun lunch
HONOURS Midland Comb. 51-52 R-up (5), Lg Cup 54-55 60-61 (R-up 56-57 58-59), B'ham Junior Cup 76-77.(Walsall Sportsco: Mids Comb. Lg Cup 79-80) Walsall& District Sen.Cup (9) R-up (7) ,Wednesbury Charity Cup (oldest cup competition in England) 2001-02 Walsall & Dist F.A Challenge.Cup 1977-8, R-up (2) Midland floodlit Youth Lg.Champions 1998-99
Record Attendances: 3,600 v Smethwick Highfield Midland Comb union decider in 1952
3,014 V Walton & Hersha m in 1953 in The F.A. Amateur Cup (2-3)

FACT FILE
Founded: 1919
Colours: All Red
Change :Yellow +blue & white trim/blue/blue
Chairman: Scott Drew
MatchSec:DavidCollinsTel: 01922 428417 (H)
Previous Leagues: Mid. Comb. 51-92
Staffs Snr 92-93 **Names:** Walsall Wood Prims, Walsall Wood, Walsall Sportsco merged in 1982 to form Walsall Borough.
Name later reverted
Previous Grounds: Walsall Wood village

WELLINGTON

Secretary: Michael Perkins, haworth, Wellington, Hereford HR4 8AZ
Tel: 01432 830523 (H) 01432 345432 (B) 07974 447817 (M)

Ground: Wellington Playing Fields, Wellington. No telephone.

Directions: The ground is situated off the A49, 8 miles south of Leominster & 5 miles north of Hereford. At the end of the dual carriageway turn for Wellington. The ground is 1/4 mile from A49, on the left , behind Wellington School and opposite the Church.

2000-0001: Captain: Mark Fish P.o.Y.: Pete Wallace Top Scorer: Peter Wallace 21

Formed: 1968

Colours: tangerine & blue/blue/tangerine
Change colours: Blue & white/blue/blue

Chairman: Philip Smith
Tel: 01432 830096 (H)
Match Secretary: Colin Williams
Tel: 01432 830620 (H) 0374 101316 (M)

WESTFIELDS

Secretary:& Chief Executive: Andrew Morris, 17 Fayre Oaks Green, Kings Acre, Hereford HR4 0QT(01432 264711)
Ground: Thorn Lighting, Holme Lacy Rd, Rotherwas, Hereford Tel: 0860410548
Directions: Proceed 1.5 mile from Hereford on A49, left in Home Lacy Rd at Broadleys Inn.One mile to Thorn Lighting Rotherwas, ground on the right on Ind. Estate. 2 miles from Hereford (BR)
Capacity: 2,000 Seats: 100 Cover: 150 Floodlights: Yes Club Shop: Yes
Clubhouse: K's Pool Club, Berington StreetHereford (1/2 mile from ground)
HONOURS West Mids Lg Div 1 86-87, Div 2 R-up 83-84 (Div 2 Cup 79-80 83-84), H.County Snr Cup 85-86 88-89 91-92 95-96 01-2(Yth Cup 92-93 95-96), Kington Chall. Cup x5; Kington Invit. Cup x4; Presteigne Ottway Cup x4, Worcs Jnr Cup 79-80,Wye Guild Cup x2, Hereford Sunday Lg Prem 75-76 76-77 (Div 1 71-72, Div 2 76-77, Div 3 75-76, Prem Div Cup x3, Div 1 Cup x2, Div 3 Cup 72-73), Smart Brown Cup 67-68, Fair Play Cup 67-68. D.Hartland Mem Trophy 95-96,99-00 00-01 RBiggart Trophy 96,99-00

Founded: 1966 Nickname: The Fields
Sponsors: Left Bank Village
Colours: Maroon & sky/sky/sky
Change colours: Sky/white/sky & maroon
Midweek matchday: Tuesday
Programme: Yes Editor: Andy Morris
Chairman: Alan Dunsford V .Chair:John Morgan
President: Graham Preece
Joint Managers: Sean Edwards & Clive Harris
Coach:Owain Meale Physio: Neil Preece
2001-02 Capt: Matt Phillips P.o.Y.: Mark Hibbard
Top Scorer: Paul Burton 23

WOLVERHAMPTON CASUALS

Secretary: Michael Green, 63 St Phillips Avenue, Pennfields Wolverhampton WV67ED
Tel: 01902 333677
Ground: Brinsford StadiumBrinsford Lane, Coven Heath, Wolverhampton (01902 783214)
Directions: Onto M54 from M6 North, at Junc 2 turn right (A449 to Stafford).Ground half a mile,
turn right into Brinsford Lane. Billbrooke (BR) 2 miles
Seats: 50Cover: 50Capacity: 2,000Floodlights: No
Clubhouse: Bar & snacks, open Tues/Wed/Thurs/Sat/Sun & alternate Mondays
HONOURS WMRL Div 1 94-95, R-up (3) 85-88, Div 1 Cup 85-86
PREVIOUS Name: Staffs Casuals (pre 81)
Ground: Aldersley Stadium

FACT FILE
Founded: 1899
Colours: All Green & White
Change colours: Gold/black/gold
Programme: 28pages 30p
Editor: G Smith

CLUB PERSONNEL
Chairman: Barry Austin
President: Clive Hammond
Manager: Gary Walters

WOLVERHAMPTON UNITED

FACT FILE
Formed: 1976

Secretary: John Lee, 105 Milton Road, Fallings Park, Wolverhampton WV10 0NE
Tel: 01902 723 940 (H) 07774 299 628 (M)

Colours: Yellow & blue/ blue/blue
Change : Black & white/black&white/black

Ground: Wednesfield FC, Amos Lane, Wednesfield, Wolverhampton. Tel: 01902 735 506

CLUB PERSONNEL
Chairman: Clifford Dulstone
Match Secretary: Tom Ryan
Tel: 01543 422 012 (H)

Directions: From Wolverhampton, leave on B4124 Wednesfield Road. Stay on this road until you come to a traffic island. Straight over into Wood End Lane, then immediately left into Amos Lane. Ground is 400 yards on right.

Westfields FC, Express & Star West Midland League Premier Division Cup Winners and Herefordshire FA County Senior Challenge Cup winners. Back Row (l-r): Darren Hall, Sean Edwards (Joint Manager), Neil Preece (Physio), Rob Cooper-Tomkins, Dave Perkins, Richard Legdon, Alec Winstone, Jon Pugh, Wayne Hoskins, Mark Newman (Goalkeeping Coach), Darren Lynch (Player Coach), Clive Harris (Joint Manager), Andy Merris (Chief Executive). Front Row: Ben Vale, Paul Price, Matt Morris, Matt Phillips (Capt), Mark Hibbard, Rob Weaver, Paul Burton, Kevin Jinks, Matt Beale, Derek Craddock

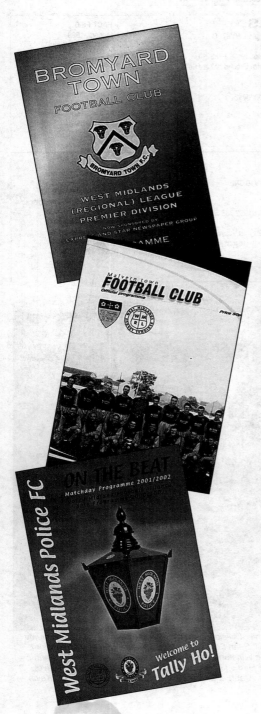

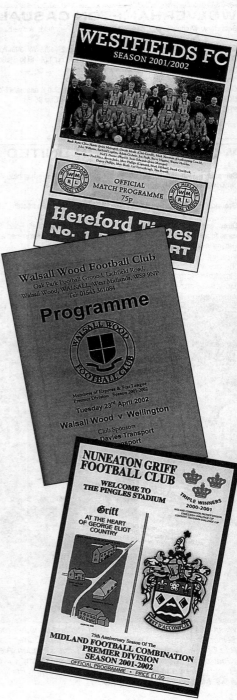

EVERARDS BREWERY
LEICESTERSHIRE SENIOR FOOTBALL LEAGUE
Founded 1903
President: John M Elsom F.C.A.   **Chairman:** David Jamieson
Hon Secretary: Robert J Holmes, 8 Huntsman Close, Markfield, Leics LE67 9XE
Tel/Fax: 01530 243093   Email: robertholmes@leicssenior1.freeserve.co.uk
www.leicestershireseniorfootballleague.com
Press Officer: Dave Lumley, 8 Pinewood Close, Countesthorpe, Leicester LE8 5TS
TelFax: 0116 277 8455   Email: davelumley@leicssenior.freeserve.co.uk

FINAL LEAGUE TABLES 2001-02

PREMIER DIVISION

	P	W	D	L	F	A	GD	Pts
Coalville Town	34	23	6	5	90	42	48	75
Friar Lane OB	34	21	9	4	88	39	49	72
Thurnby Rangers	34	20	6	8	77	39	38	66
St Andrews	34	19	3	12	73	50	23	60
Kirby Muxloe	34	17	9	8	63	44	19	60
Blaby Whetstone	34	16	6	12	37	48	-11	54
Leics YMCA	34	15	8	11	51	43	8	53
Holwell Sports	34	15	6	13	63	43	20	51
Ibstock Welfare	34	14	8	12	52	46	6	50
Highfield Rangers	34	13	10	11	51	49	2	49
Downes Sports	34	13	8	13	55	47	8	47
Thurmaston Town	34	12	9	13	59	65	-6	45
Ellistown	34	11	7	16	42	61	-19	40
Barrow Town	34	10	9	15	44	50	-6	39
Anstey Nomads	34	7	7	20	34	64	-30	28
Birstall United	34	6	9	19	28	69	-41	27
Aylestone Park	34	7	3	24	32	68	-36	24
Thringstone	34	3	5	26	22	94	-72	14

DIVISION ONE

	P	W	D	L	F	A	GD	Pts
Loughborough Dyn.	28	19	6	3	72	27	45	63
Ratby Sports	28	18	5	5	66	27	39	59
Lutterworth Town	28	16	8	4	57	34	23	56
Sileby Town	28	16	5	7	62	36	26	53
Huncote S & S	28	13	5	10	52	38	14	44
Bardon Hill	28	12	5	11	79	51	28	41
Anstey Town	28	9	12	7	38	28	10	39
Cottesmore Am	28	11	6	11	52	44	8	39
Leics Constabulary	28	11	4	13	53	45	8	37
Earl Shilton Alb	28	11	4	13	34	39	-5	37
Saffron Dynamo	28	8	9	11	39	49	-10	33
Asfordby Ams	28	8	3	17	29	66	-37	27
Narborough	28	6	8	14	32	60	-28	26
Stoney Stanton*	28	6	4	18	41	69	-28	19
North Kilworth	28	3	2	23	19	112	-93	11

* points deducted

LEADING GOALSCORERS

27	Ian Pitt	Coalville Town
23	Roger Brailsford	Blaby & Whetstone Ath
21	Richard Saunders	Coalville Town

LEADING GOALSCORERS

31	Carl Eagling	Bardon Hill
25	Darren Roberts	Ratby Sports

BEACON BITTER FINAL

Highfield Rangers	1	v	5	Thurnby Rangers
Lawrence				*McCathie (2), Nelson, Walker, Roland*

Coalville Town, Premier Division Champions. Back Row (l-r): Paul Bray, Rob Smith (Asst Mngr), Wayne Handford, Dave Tonge, Darren Hearne, Lee Harriman (Player/Manager), Dean Smith, Maurice Rowe, Tony Robinson, Andy Howarth *Capt), Greg Bault. Front Row: Ian Pitt, Chris Whitmore, Darren Warne, Dave Hollis, Dave Tansley, Richard Saunders, Ashley Brown. Photo: Gordon Whittington

ANSTEY NOMADS

Secretary: Martin Almen, 86 Rockhill Drive, Mountsorrel, Leicester LE12 7DT (0787 651 3494)
Ground: Llimah International Park, Cropston Road, Anstey, Leicester (0116 236 4868)
Directions: Take jct 21A off M1 to Newark on A46 .Turn to Anstey after 2 miles then take third exit at village roundabout and ground is half amile on right.
Capacity: 1,500 **Seats:**100 **Cover:** 100 **Floodlights:**Yes **Clubhouse:** Yes (available for bookings) **Club shop:** N o. **Best season in F.A.Vase:** 5th Round 1994-95
HONOURS   Leics Senior Lge: (4), Leics Comb. 93-94 ,Leics Seenior Cup 94-95, Leics Junior Cup 1994-95 Presidents Cup 95-96Battle of Britain Cup (8) Rolleston Charity Cup (4)

Founded: 1947
Nickname: Nomads
Sponsors: Ford Signs
Colours: Red/white/white
Change colours: Blue & white/blue/blue.
Midweek matchday: ?????
Programme: Yes / No
Club Personnel: eg - Chairman: Tony Ford
Manager: Jim Johnson
Ass.Man: Robert Coileman

BARROW TOWN

Secretary: Alan Dawkins, 72 Beaumont Road, Barrow-on-Soar, Loughborough, Leics LE12 8PJ (01509 413288) Email Address; alan@dawkins 9-freeserve.co.uk
Ground: Riverside Park, Meynell Road, Quorn, Leics (01509 620650)
Directions: Access via Quorn Lodge Drive & Barrow road.
Capacity: 2,000**Seats:** None **Cover:** 50 **Floodlights:**Yes **Clubhouse:** Yes **Shop:**No(BadgesYes)
HONOURS: Leics Sen Lg. 92-93 R-up 94-95.Loughboro.Charity Cup 68-69,96-97,98-99,00-**BEST SEASONFA Vase:** 2nd Rd Proper. 2000-01 ,01-02
2001-02: Captain: Darren Wagg **Ps.o.Y.**Russ pitman **Top Scorer:** Leroy Johnson 22

Re-formed 1947
Nickname: Riversiders
Colours: Red & black/black/red
Change colours: Navy Blue
Midweek matchday: Tuesday
Programme: Yes
Club Personnel: Chairman: Michael Bland
Managers: Brian Cleave & Louis Carr
Treasurer: Paul Carnell
Press Officer : Alan.Dawkins

BIRSTALL UNITED

Secretary: Bob Gerrard, 58 Halstead Rd, Mountsorrel, Leicester LE12 7HF (0116 237 6886)

Ground: Meadow Lane, Birstall (0116 267 1230)

Colours: White/navy/navy

BLABY & WHETSTONE ATHLETIC

Secretary: Mrs Sandra Morris, 10 Winchester Road, Blaby, Leics LE8 3HJ   Tel: 0116 277 3208

Ground: Blaby & Whetstone Boys Club, Warwick Road, Whetstone (0116 286 4852)

Colours: Navy & white/navy/navy

COALVILLE TOWN

Secretary: Robert Brooks, 17 Ashland Drive, Coalville, Leics LE67 3NH (01530 833269)
Ground: Owen Street Sports Ground, Owen Street, Coalville (01530 833365)
Directions: From M1 jct.22 take A511 towards Coalville.At third roundabout take third exit,then at fourth roundabout bear left to Coalvuille centre. Second lights, left into Belvoir Road and second right into Owen Street.Ground is onleft at top of road
Capacity: 1000 **Seats:**24 **Cover:**200 **Floodlights:**Yes **Clubhouse:** Yes: Match & Training Days
Previous Names: Ravenstoke Miners Ath 1926-58, Ravenstoke F.C.1958-95 Coalville F.C. 9-98
2001-02: Captain: Andy Howarth P.o.Y.: Dave Tonge Top Scorer: Ian Pitt 38

Founded: 1926 (as Ravenstone Miners Ath)
Nickname: The Ravens
Colours: Black&White/black/red
Change colours: All Yellow
Midweek matchday: Tuesday
Programme: Yes 36 Pages with admission
Ed & Press Officer: Tony Moore()1530459055
Club Personnel: Chairman:Steve Price
Vice-Chair:Glyn Rennocks Pres: Mick Jordan
Manager: LeeHarriman.

DOWNES SPORTS

Secretary: Tony Jacques, 17 Merton Close, Broughton, Astley Leicester LE9 6QP
Tel No: 01455 28402 (H) 01455 282028 (W)

Ground: Leicester Rd,Hinckley (01455 615062)
Directions: Off northern perimeter road round Leicester
Capacity: 2000   **Seats:**1 **Cover:**Yes **Floodlights:**Yes
Clubhouse: Yes **Club shop:** No
Honours: Leics. Sen. Lge. Div Two R-up 1986-87

Founded: 1968
Nickname: The Builders
Colours: Tangerine/black/tangerine
Change colours:t.b.a.
Midweek matchday: Tuesday
Programme:No
Club Personnel
Chairman: F. Down
Manager: S. Greenhill

ELLISTOWN

Secretary: John Measom, 29 Standard Hill, Coalville, Leicster LE67 3HN
Tel: 01530 810941

Ground: 1 Terrace Road, Ellistown

Colours: Yellow/blue shirts, yellow shorts, blue socks
Change colours: Red shirts, black shorts, red socks

FRIAR LANE OLD BOYS

Secretary: Kevin Brooks, 299 Milligan Rd, Leicester LE4 2RJ Tel: 0116 224 3854

Ground: Knighton Lane East, Leicester (0116 283 3629)

Colours: Black & white stripes/black/black

HIGHFIELD RANGERS

Secretary: Maurice Christian, 18 Blanklyn Avenue, Leicester LE5 5FA Tel: 0116 273 4002

Ground: 443 Gleneagles Ave., Rushey Mead, Leicester   Tel: 0116 266 0009

Colours: Yellow/blackyellow

HOLWELL SPORTS

Secretary: Mrs Anne Marriott, 24 Church Lane, Croxton Kerrial, Grantham, Lincs NG32 1PZ
Tel: 01476 870658

Ground: Welby Road, Asfordby Hill, Melton Mowbray, Leics Tel: 01664 812663

Colours: Green & gold/green/green

IBSTOCK WELFARE

Secretary: Ralph A Wilkinson, 6 Valley Rd, Ibstock, Leicester LE67 6NY (01530 450243)
Ground: The Welfare, Leicester Road, Ibstock (01530 260656)

Capacity: 1500   **Seats:** 50 **Cover:** 150   **Floodlights:** Yes
Clubhouse: Yes , open evenings and match days   **Club shop:** No
Website: www.footballnews.co.uk/clubs/22/2244/home.page
HONOURS: Leics Sen Cup Winners 93-94 R-Up 97-98; Leics Sen Lg Div 1 R-Up 90-91; Coalville
Ch Cup Winners (4) R-up (4); Loughborough Ch.Cup (4) R-up (2) Atherstone Nursing CXup (1)

Founded: 1962
Nickname: The Welly
Colours: Red/black/red
Change colours: All blue or all green
Midweek matchday: Tuesday
Programme: Yes
Email: lbstockwelfarefc@ntlworld.com
Club Personnel:
Manager: Simon Cook
Press Officer: Craig Wheatley (07967797648)

KIRBY MUXLOE S.C.

Secretary: Philip Moloney, 16 Church Lane, Ratby, Leics LE6 0JE (0116 239 2916)

Ground: Ratby Lane, Kirby Muxloe (0116 239 3201)

Colours: Blue/black/black

LEICESTER YMCA

Secretary: Colin Chappell, 132 South Knighton Rd, Leicester, LE2 3LQ   Tel: 0116 270 2721
Ground: YMCA Sports Ground, Belvoir Drive, Leicester Tel: 0116 244 0740
Directions: M1 Jct21 (M69) onto A563, Soarvalley Way, Aylestone Rd. Left at lights, to city.
Belvoir Drive 2nd Right after next lights.
Capacity: 1,500   **Seats**No **Cover:** 100   **Floodlights:**Yes   **Club shop:** No
Clubhouse: Yes . Sats & Suns 12.30p.m. onwards
HONOURS   Leics. Sen. Lge. Div. 1 99-00; **PREVIOUS Leagues:**Mid Comb. 97-9
BEST SEASON   FA Vase: N/A   **FA Cup:** N/A

Founded: 1910
Nickname: Beavers
Colours: Red & black/black/black
Change colours: Green/white/white
Midweek matchday: Wednesday
Programme: No
Club Personne
Chairman: Fred Smith
Manager: Tony Yeoman

LOUGHBOROUGH DYNAMO

Secretary: Max Hutchinson, 3 Wythburn Close, Loughborough, Leics LE11 3SZ
Tel: 01509 266092
Ground: Nanpanton Sport Ground, Loughborough Tel: 01509 612144
Capacity: 1,500   **Cover:**Yes   **Floodlights:**No
Clubhouse: Open match days only   **Club shop:** No
BEST SEASON   FA Vase: N/A   **FA Cup:** N/A
HONOURS: Leics. Sen. Lge: Div. 1 01-02, 64-65, Div 3 59-00; Cobin Trophy 62-63, 63-64, 64-65,
County Medals R-up 60-61; District Lg Div 1 69-70, Three Sons Trophy 80-81; Charity Cup 87-88

Founded: 1955
First Competitive Season: 57-58
Nickname: The Moes
Colours: Gold/black/black
Change colours:All Blue
Midweek matchday: Monday
Programme: Yes
Club Personnel
Chairman: Frank Fall
Managers: Frank Fall& Kev Laundon

RATBY SPORTS

Secretary: John Rowe, 57 Danehill, Ratby, Leicester LE6 0NG Tel: 0116 238 6806

Ground: Ratby Sports Club, Desford Lane, Ratby.   Tel: 0116 239 2474

Colours: All red

St ANDREWS SOCIAL CLUB

Secretary: Les Botting, 2 Neston Road, Saffron Lane, Leicester LE2 6RD Tel: 0116 224 3961   Colours: Black & white/black/black

Ground: Canal Street, off Aylestone Rd, Old Aylestone,Leicester Tel: 0116 283 9298

Directions: (next to Big City Tyres)

HONOURS: Leics Sen Lg. Premier Champions: 89-90,93-94,95-96

THURMASTON TOWN

Secretary: Kevin Sadler, 81 Woodgreen Road, Leicester LE4 9UD Tel: 0116 246 0093   Colours: Black & white stripes, black,black.

Ground: Elizabeth Park, Checklands Road, Thurmaston. Tel: 0116 260 2519

HONOURS: Dist. Lg Champs 97-99, Page & Moy Junior Cup Winners 97-98 Leics Div One
Champions & Beacon Bitter Cup Winners 98-99

THURNBY RANGERS

Secretary: Ian Henson, 13 Dudley Avenue, Thurnby Lodge, Leicester LE5 2EE
Tel: 0116 241 2741 07761 227 586 (M)

Ground: Dakyn Road, Thurnby Lodge, Leicester.
Tel: 0116 243 3698

Colours: All green
Change colours: All red

ISTHMIAN LEAGUE

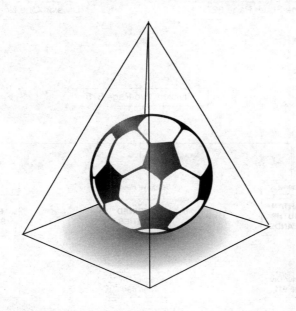

PYRAMID SECTION

Ryman
ISTHMIAN LEAGUE

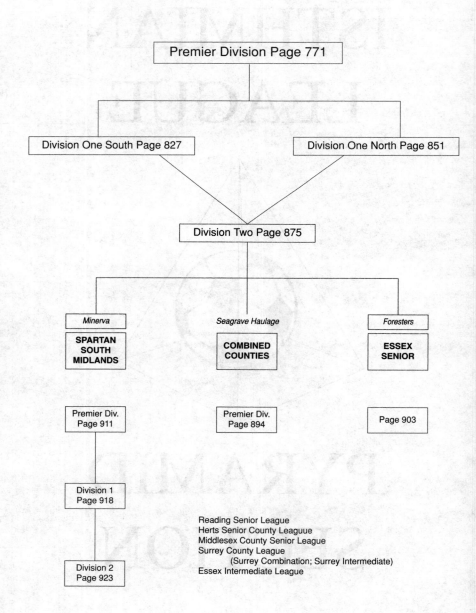

Premier Division Page 771

Division One South Page 827

Division One North Page 851

Division Two Page 875

Minerva

**SPARTAN
SOUTH
MIDLANDS**

Seagrave Haulage

**COMBINED
COUNTIES**

Foresters

**ESSEX
SENIOR**

Premier Div.
Page 911

Premier Div.
Page 894

Page 903

Division 1
Page 918

Reading Senior League
Herts Senior County Leaguue
Middlesex County Senior League
Surrey County League
        (Surrey Combination; Surrey Intermediate)
Essex Intermediate League

Division 2
Page 923

RYMAN LEAGUE

Chairman: A C F Turvey, MCIM, 18 Apple Way, Old Basing,
Basingstoke, Hants RG24 7HA
Secretary: N R Robinson FCRArb, 226 Rye Lane, Peckham, London SE15 4NL
Tel: 020 8409 1978 (H)   020 7639 5726 (B)   Fax: 020 8409 1979 (H)   020 7277 6061 (B)
Email: nickrob@clara.net   secretary@isthmian.co.uk

With the race lasting to the last Saturday of the season the Ryman League Championship went to Kent for the first time in over 40 years as Gravesend & Northfleet held their nerve and finally finished four points clear of runners-up Canvey Island.

In front of over 1,700 Gravesend won 1-0 at Bedford Town and were presented with the Championship Trophy by League Administration Secretary Clive Moyse immediately after the final whistle, while Canvey, who had led the Premier Division almost continuously from October to early April, ended their campaign with a 2-1 defeat at Braintree Town.

Despite a tense closing ten minutes Ford United held on for a 2-1 home win over Uxbridge to win the First Division Championship. With Bishop's Stortford winning at Whyteleafe, Ford needed all three points to take the title. They held on and were presented with the trophy by League Secretary Nick Robinson.

In DivisionTwo Lewes ended one of their most successful seasons ever with a 3-0 win at Wivenhoe Town. Having enjoyed success in the FA Cup and FA Vase, they finished their league campaign six points clear of Horsham.

Third Division Champions Croydon Athletic beat Egham Town 3-0 in their final game of the campaign to preserve their perfect record at Mayfields this season. The side took 63 points from a possible 63 at home, scoring 83 goals in the process.

Division One Northwood lifted the Isthmian League Cup for the first time by beating Premier Division Hampton & Richmond Borough at Clarence Park. Andy Cook broke the deadlock for Northwood in the 43rd minute only for Neil Gough to equalise two minutes later. Cook scored his and Northwood's second after 74 minutes, but within another three minutes Richard O'Connor equalised for the 'Beevers' to force extra time. The winning goal came in the 92nd minute from Northwood's top scorer Lawrence Yaku.

Lewes have been awarded the presitigious Football Association Charter Standard Certificate, the National Award for Excellence in Coaching. The club is the only senior side in Sussex to have achieved the accolade which is awarded to clubs that show exceptional commitment to the development of Youth and Women's football.

Sutton United played a friendly match against the Middlesex Wanderers representative side at Gander Green Lane in May, as a memorial game for Ralph Carr, the former England amateur goalkeeper who was a player, official and director for Sutton during an association with the club which lasted over 60 years until he passed away in March 2001. He also had connections with the Wanderers dating back to the 1930's as a player, committee member and Vice President.

Dorking had their best ever FA Vase run before being knocked out in unfortunate circumstances by way of a penalty shoot out in their Fifth Round replay against Burgess Hill in a tie that attracted a total of around 1,200 fans over the two matches.

After more than 70 years at Sandy Lane, Tooting & Mitcham United played their final game at the ground in April. They marked the occasion with a 3-2 victory over Wealdstone.

PREMIER DIVISION FINAL LEAGUE TABLE 2001-02

		P	HOME					AWAY					TOTAL						
			W	D	L	F	A	W	D	L	F	A	W	D	L	F	A	GD	Pts
1	Gravesend & Northfleet	42	14	4	3	43	18	17	2	2	47	15	31	6	5	90	33	57	99
2	Canvey Island	42	15	3	3	55	25	15	2	4	53	16	30	5	7	108	41	67	95
3	Aldershot Town	42	12	4	5	44	23	10	3	8	32	28	22	7	13	76	51	25	73
4	Braintree Town	42	15	2	4	37	20	8	2	11	29	41	23	4	15	66	61	5	73
5	Purfleet	42	11	8	2	39	20	8	7	6	28	24	19	15	8	67	44	23	72
6	Grays Athletic	42	12	5	4	33	21	8	5	8	32	34	20	10	12	65	55	10	70
7	Chesham United	42	11	7	3	40	27	8	3	10	29	26	19	10	13	69	53	16	67
8	Hendon	42	10	3	8	26	22	9	2	10	40	33	19	5	18	66	55	11	62
9	Billericay Town	42	8	6	7	32	34	8	7	6	27	26	16	13	13	59	60	-1	61
10	St Albans City	42	9	5	7	29	25	7	4	10	42	35	16	9	17	71	60	11	57
11	Hitchin Town	42	7	4	10	31	39	8	6	7	42	42	15	10	17	73	81	-8	55
12	Sutton United	42	8	9	4	33	26	5	6	10	29	37	13	15	14	62	63	-1	54
13	Heybridge Swifts	42	7	6	8	34	40	8	3	10	34	45	15	9	18	68	85	-17	54
14	Kingstonian	42	10	4	7	34	27	3	9	9	16	29	13	13	16	50	56	-6	52
15	Boreham Wood	42	6	4	11	24	36	9	2	10	26	26	15	6	21	50	62	-12	51
16	Maidenhead United	42	9	3	9	27	30	6	2	13	24	33	15	5	22	51	63	-12	50
17	Bedford Town	42	10	1	10	39	32	2	11	8	25	37	12	12	18	64	69	-5	48
18	Basingstoke Town	42	8	5	8	28	31	3	10	8	22	37	11	15	16	50	68	-18	48
19	Enfield	42	4	4	13	20	44	7	5	9	28	33	11	9	22	48	77	-29	42
20	Hampton & Richmond Borough	42	5	8	8	26	32	4	5	12	25	39	9	13	20	51	71	-20	40
21	Harrow Borough	42	2	5	14	26	54	6	5	10	24	35	8	10	24	50	89	-39	34
22	Croydon	42	5	3	13	24	40	2	2	17	12	53	7	5	30	36	93	-57	26

PREMIER DIVISION RESULTS CHART 2001-02

#	Team	1	2	3	4	5	6	7	8	9	10	11	12	13	14	15	16	17	18	19	20	21	22
1	Aldershot Town	X	2-2	4-0	1-1	0-2	4-0	1-3	1-0	2-0	3-1	1-2	0-1	4-1	2-1	2-1	3-3	1-2	3-0	4-1	4-1	1-1	1-0
2	Basingstoke Town	1-1	X	1-1	0-1	1-0	1-2	0-4	1-1	1-0	2-0	1-4	0-2	1-1	2-1	2-1	1-3	2-3	2-1	1-2	2-2	3-1	3-0
3	Bedford Town	1-2	3-0	X	3-4	2-0	2-0	1-3	2-0	3-2	2-2	0-1	4-0	4-1	3-4	0-5	5-2	0-1	2-1	1-2	1-0	0-1	0-1
4	Billericay Town	2-0	2-0	0-0	X	0-1	2-4	0-3	0-0	2-0	2-2	1-3	3-2	2-0	1-1	4-6	1-2	1-1	1-1	2-2	2-0	1-5	2-1
5	Boreham Wood	1-3	0-0	1-0	1-1	X	1-2	0-3	0-0	1-1	1-3	0-2	2-2	3-2	1-2	1-2	2-4	2-1	1-3	2-1	1-0	0-1	1-2
6	Braintree Town	2-0	3-2	2-1	1-0	2-0	X	2-1	2-0	2-1	2-3	0-2	2-3	3-2	0-0	2-0	2-0	0-1	1-0	2-1	2-2	2-1	3-0
7	Canvey Is;amd	1-3	5-1	3-3	3-0	2-1	3-2	X	2-1	3-0	3-1	0-2	1-2	1-1	3-0	3-1	6-1	5-3	2-0	2-0	3-0	3-2	1-1
8	Chesham United	2-1	1-1	1-1	2-0	1-0	4-1	1-5	X	2-1	0-0	2-2	3-5	2-1	5-0	0-2	3-0	1-2	2-0	1-0	3-0	3-2	2-0
9	Croydon	1-2	1-3	3-3	0-0	0-5	0-4	2-1	0-1	X	0-2	3-4	1-0	0-0	2-1	1-3	2-3	1-2	4-0	0-2	0-1	2-1	1-2
10	Enfield	1-1	3-0	1-0	0-2	0-1	1-2	0-3	0-3	3-1	X	1-5	1-2	0-2	1-2	0-6	4-2	0-5	2-2	0-2	0-1	0-0	2-2
11	Gravesend & Northfleet	2-1	0-0	4-1	1-0	0-1	3-0	0-1	1-4	6-1	3-0	X	2-0	2-1	2-2	3-0	1-1	2-0	2-0	3-2	0-0	3-2	3-1
12	Grays Athletic	3-1	0-0	2-1	0-0	3-2	3-0	0-1	2-1	1-0	0-0	2-0	X	1-1	2-1	2-0	1-3	2-1	2-0	0-1	1-3	3-2	3-3
13	Hampton & Richmond	1-1	1-1	1-1	1-2	1-2	0-2	1-5	0-2	6-0	2-1	0-2	0-0	X	0-1	0-0	1-1	6-3	0-0	2-1	1-1	0-5	1-6
14	Harrow Borough	2-3	3-3	2-4	0-2	2-3	1-2	1-1	2-1	2-0	2-4	0-3	1-1	1-1	X	0-2	1-3	1-1	1-3	0-3	1-2	2-6	1-6
15	Hendon	0-1	1-3	1-2	1-3	2-1	3-0	0-1	1-2	0-1	2-0	1-1	1-0	1-0	0-1	X	1-0	2-2	2-0	1-1	1-0	1-0	4-3
16	Heybridge Swifts	1-2	5-1	1-1	2-3	0-2	1-1	0-7	2-1	2-0	4-2	0-4	1-0	1-3	1-1	1-6	X	3-1	1-1	2-0	3-3	0-2	2-0
17	Hitchin Town	0-3	0-1	2-2	3-2	4-1	1-1	2-1	2-3	3-0	1-2	0-4	2-4	2-4	3-0	3-0	1-0	X	0-0	1-0	0-3	2-4	0-2
18	Kingstonian	2-1	1-1	3-0	4-1	1-1	0-2	2-1	1-0	3-0	0-2	0-1	2-3	3-0	1-0	1-2	1-2	2-2	X	1-0	1-5	4-2	1-1
19	Maidenhead United	1-2	2-2	2-1	0-2	2-0	2-0	0-1	0-4	0-1	0-1	0-3	2-1	2-1	4-2	3-1	1-0	1-1	0-1	X	1-3	2-1	2-2
20	Purfleet	2-1	0-0	1-1	1-1	0-1	3-2	0-0	2-2	5-1	1-0	0-3	3-0	3-0	0-3	2-0	3-1	3-1	1-1	5-2	X	2-2	1-1
21	St Albans City	0-3	2-0	0-0	0-0	1-0	3-1	2-4	3-1	5-0	1-1	0-3	2-1	1-3	1-0	1-1	1-2	1-2	2-2	1-0	0-1	X	2-0
22	Sutton United	2-0	2-1	2-2	2-2	2-2	3-1	1-4	0-1	2-0	1-1	1-1	2-2	2-0	1-1	2-1	4-1	2-4	0-0	2-1	0-0	1-1	X

LEAGUE CUP 2001-02

PRELIMINARY ROUND

Abingdon Town	3 v 1	Ashford Town (Mx)	50
Arlesey Town	4 v 0	Wingate & Finchley	134
Aveley	2 v 3	Corinthian-Casuals	66
Banstead Athletic	3 * 3	Barton Rovers	28
Berkhamsted Town	2 * 3	Leighton Town @LT	70
Camberley Town	1 v 0	Chertsey Town	57
Clapton	0 v 2	Epsom & Ewell	30
	(at Hertford Town)		
Croydon Athletic	4 v 3	Ware	36
Dorking	2 v 4	Hertford Town	32
Egham Town	2 v 0	Wivenhoe Town	32
Flackwell Heath	2 * 5	Marlow	136
Hml Hempstead T	5 v 1	East Thurrock Utd	58
Hornchurch	0 * 0	Wokingham Town	45
Hungerford Town	2 v 1	Cheshunt	25
Kingsbury Town	1 v 0	Barking & E Ham U	42
Leatherhead	2 v 3	Leyton Pennant	72
Lewes	4 v 0	Witham Town	106
Metropolitan Police	2 v 1	Gt Wakering Rovers	50
Romford	1 v 3	Molesey	60
AET Tilbury	3 * 2	Tring Town	66
Tooting & Mitch. U	3 v 2	Bracknell Town	154
Wealdstone	5 v 2	Edgware Town	167
Wembley	2 v 0	Horsham	60
Windsor & Eton	1 v 0	Chalfont St. Peter	90

PRELIMINARY ROUND REPLAYS

Barton Rovers	1 v 0	Banstead Athletic	33
Wokingham Town	0 v 4	Hornchurch	33

FIRST ROUND

Aldershot Town	5 v 1	Croydon	623
Aylesbury United	1 v 3	Metropolitan Police	201
Barking & E Ham U	3 v 8	Hampton & Rich B	96
Basingstoke Town	2 v 0	Kingstonian	187
Boreham Wood	1 v 2	Leyton Pennant	55
Braintree Town	2 * 2	Abingdon Town	153
Bromley	2 v 0	Billericay Town	178
Canvey Island	3 v 2	Lewes	192
Carshalton Athletic	0 v 2	Worthing	103
Chesham United	2 v 0	St. Albans City	164
Corinthian-Casuals	2 v 1	Whyteleafe	56
Enfield	4 v 1	Egham Town	34
Ford United	1 v 0	Epsom & Ewell	36
Gravesend & N'fleet	2 v 1	Arlesey Town	218
Grays Athletic	5 v 1	Bedford Town	119
Harlow Town	1 * 2	Northwood	105
Harrow Borough	3 v 0	Camberley Town	81
Hml Hempstead T	1 * 3	Croydon Athletic	63
Hertford Town	0 v 3	Hendon	98
Hitchin Town	8 v 2	Walton & Hersham	109
Hornchurch	5 v 2	Bognor Regis Town	60
Hungerford Town	0 v 3	Maidenhead United	48
Marlow	1 v 2	Barton Rovers	87
Molesey	4 v 1	Leighton Town	83
Oxford City	0 v 4	Bishop's Stortford	102
Purfleet	0 v 1	Yeading	73
Staines Town	2 v 0	Heybridge Swifts	52
Sutton United	5 * 3	Dulwich Hamlet	205
Thame United	1 * 0	Windsor & Eton	71
Uxbridge	1 * 1	Tooting & Mitch. U	109
Wealdstone	6 * 1	Tilbury	97
Wembley	4 v 6	Slough Town	99

FIRST ROUND REPLAYS

Abingdon Town	0 v 4	Braintree Town	95
Tooting & Mitch. U	3 v 1	Uxbridge	165

SECOND ROUND

Bishop's Stortford	2 v 4	Canvey Island	218
Braintree Town	4 v 1	Molesey	122
Bromley	0 v 1	Corinthian-Casuals	118
Chesham United	0 v 2	Enfield	111
Ford United	4 v 1	Barton Rovers	66
Gravesend & Nflt	4 * 1	Basingstoke Town	140
Hampton & Rich. B	5 v 3	Maidenhead United	118
Harrow Borough	1 v 4	Northwood	136
Hendon	0 v 2	Aldershot Town	584
	(at Aldershot Town FC)		
Hornchurch	0 * 2	Leyton Pennant	45
Metropolitan Police	1 * 2	Wealdstone	90
Slough Town	0 v 1	Hitchin Town	229
Staines Town	0 v 2	Grays Athletic	47
Thame United	1 v 3	Sutton United	46
Tooting & Mitch. U	2 v 0	Croydon Athletic	171
Yeading	3 * 2	Worthing	50

THIRD ROUND

Aldershot Town	3 v 0	Corinthian-Casuals	376
Braintree Town	3 v 5	Canvey Island	320
Enfield	4 v 0	Hitchin Town	89
Gravesend & Nthflt	1 v 2	Tooting & Mitch. U	190
Leyton Pennant	0 v 1	Northwood	46
Sutton United	1 v 7	Grays Athletic	203
Wealdstone	3 v 2	Ford United	82
Yeading	1 v 3	Hampton & Rich B	93

FOURTH ROUND

Grays Athletic	2 * 3	Aldershot Town	281
Hampton & Rich. B	1 v 0	Enfield	153
Northwood	3 v 1	Canvey Island	213
Wealdstone	0 v 1	Tooting & Mitch. U	151

SEMI-FINALS FIRST LEG

Aldershot Town	2 v 2	Hampton & Rich. B	752
Northwood	4 v 2	Tooting & Mitch. U	211

SEMI-FINALS SECOND LEG

Hampton & Rich. B	1 * 0	Aldershot Town	718

Hampton & Richmond Borough won 3-2 on aggregate

Tooting & Mitch. U	1 v 1	Northwood	245

Northwood won 5-3 on aggregate

FINAL

Hampton & Rich. B 2 * 3 Northwood
Gough 45, O'Connor 77   Cook 43, 74, Yaku 92
Attendance: 262
At St. Albans City F.C. on 1st May 2002

Hampton & Richmond Borough: Stuart MacKenzie, Richard O'Connor, Ronnie Girvan, Phil Dicker, Matt Flitter, Aidan O'Brien, Ronnie Gould, Tony Houghton, Sam Sloma, Craig Maskell, Neil Gough.
Subs: Steve Omonou (for Gould), Steve French (for Flitter), Eseyas Yhdego (for Gough).

Northwood: Andy Felton, Dave Nolan, Dave Sargent, Danny Butler, Alan Hamlet, Craig McIntosh, Andy Cook, Chris Gell, Wayne Carter, Lawrence Yaku, Ryan Ashe.
Subs: Mark Buchannon (not used), Gavin Hart (for Cook), Gary Williams (for Butler).

RYMAN LEAGUE REPRESENTATIVE MATCHES

F.A. XI	0	v	2	Ryman Football League

Duku 35, Parratt 84

at Bishop's Stortford FC
Att: 403

Ryman League: Lance Key (Kingstonian), Gary Wraight (St Albans City), Jason Chewins (Aldershot Town), Ryan Kirby (Aldershot Town), Francis Duku (Gravesend & Northfleet), Aaron Barnett (Gravesend & Northfleet), Lee Spiller (Chesham United), Dale Rainsford (Grays Athletic), Craig Wilkins (Gravesend & Northfleet), Adam Parker (Aldershot Town), Davis Haule (Hendon).
Substitutes: Vinnie John (Bishop's Stortford) for Haule, Scott Tarr (Basingstoke Town) not used, Dean Parratt (braintree Town) for Wraight, Dale Binns (Hendon) for Chewins, John Morgan (Grays Athletic) not used, Gary Waters (Braintree Town) not used.
Manager: John Kendall

Combined Services	0	v	1	Ryman Football League

John 50

at Aldershot Military Stadium
Att: 102

Ryman League: Lance Key (Kingstonian), Gary Wraight (St Albans City), Jason Chewins (Aldershot Town), Ryan Kirby (Aldershot Town), Grant Cooper (Enfield), Corey Campbell (St Albans City), Dale Rainsford (Grays Athletic), Lee Spiller (Chesham United), Nic McDonnell (Croydon), Vinnie John (Bishop's Stortford), Adam Parker (Aldershot Town)
Substitutes: David Sadler (Kingstonian) for John, Steve Blaney (Braintree Town) for Spiller, Leon Townley (Aldershot Town) not used, Dean Parratt (Braintree Town) not used, Scott Tarr (Basingstoke Town) for Key.
Manager: John Kendall

---

25 in 25

A review of the progress made by the **Isthmian League** and its member clubs during the twenty-five year life span of the F.A. Non-League Club Directory (1978 - 2002) will be available in the next year. It will be one of a series of 25 and will contain features, statistics and photos in at least 160 pages dedicated purely to the Isthmian members.

Further details can be found on page 17 so make sure of your copy of this exciting limited edition.

ALDERSHOT TOWN

CLUB OFFICIALS
Chairman: Karl Prentice
Vice Chairman: John McGinty
Company Secretary: tba
Press Officer: Nick Fryer Tel:01252 32011

FACT FILE
Formed: 1992   Nickname: The Shots
Sponsors: Hi-Speed Services Ltd
Colours: Red /Blue Trim
Change: White/Red Trim
Midweek matchday: Tuesday
Reserves League: Capital League
Club Newsline: 09066 55585
Official Website: www.theshots.net
Unofficial Website: www.shotsweb.co.uk

FOOTBALL MANAGEMENT TEAM
Manager: Terry Brown
Asst Man.: Stuart Cash
Physio: Alan McCreanney

2001-02
Captain: Jason Cousins
Top Scorer: Stafford Browne
P.O.Y: Jason Chewins

GROUND   Recreation Ground, High Street, Aldershot, Hants GU11 1TW
Tel: 0870 112 4112 Fax: 0870 112 5112

Pages: 44   Price: £2.00
Editors: Karl Prentice, Rachel Pearce
Tel No: 01256 471630
Tel: 01256 471630

Directions: Ground situated on eastern end of High Street next to large multi-storey B.T. building. From M3 (jct 4) take A325 to Aldershot. After five miles at r'bout take 1st exit marked town centre (A323) into Wellington Ave. At Burger King r'bout take 2nd exit into High Street - ground on left, large carpark adjacent. 5 mins walk from Aldershot (BR)
Capacity: 7,500   Cover: 6,850   Seats: 1,800   Floodlights: Yes

Local Press: Aldershot News, Farnham Herald
Local Radio: County Sound (96.4, 1476 khz), BBC Southern Counties (104.6 fm)

Clubhouse: Matchdays and special functions   Steward: Wally Clarke 01252 320211 x212
Club Shop: Range of souvenirs, programmes, replica kits.
Open matchdays or contact Janet Guess (01252-528007) for mail order

PREVIOUS   Leagues: None   **Names:** None   **Grounds:** None

CLUB RECORDS Attendance: 7,500 v Brighton & Hove Albion F.A.C. First Round 18.11.00
"Ground record: 19,138 Aldershot FC v Carlisle United, FA Cup 4th Rd replay 28/1/70
Win: 8-0 v Bishop's Stortford (a) League 5.9.98 **Defeat:** 0-6 v Worthing (a) Puma Cup 2.3.99
9-1 v Andover (n) Hants Senior Cup Final 99-00
Career Goalscorer: Mark Butler 155. (92-98)   **Career Appearances:** Jason Chewins 400 (93 – Present)
Transfer Fee Paid: £20,000 to Woking for Grant Payne (11.99)
Transfer Fee Received: £6,000 for Leon Gutzmore from Bedford Town (11.99)
BEST SEASON   FA Cup: Second Round 99-00 v Exeter City   **FA Trophy:** Fourth Rd Replay 99-00
FA Vase: Quarter Final 93-94

HONOURS Isthmian Premier Division R-up: 1999/00, Isthmian Division 1 1997/98, Isthmian Division 2 Promoted: 1993/94, Isthmian Division 3 1992/93, Isthmian League Cup: 1998/99, Isthmian Charity Shield: 1999/00; Hampshire Senior Cup 1998/99, 1999/00, 2001/02; Suburban West Division 1994/95; Allied Counties (West) 1993/94; Suburban Shield 1995/96; Hampshire Floodlit Cup 1997/98, 1998/99, 2001/02; Southern Youth League 1999/00, 2001/02, Southern Youth League Cup 1998/99

(L-R) Back Row: Jamie Taylor, Roscoe D'Sane, Adam Parker, Dominic Sterling, Lee Holsgrove, Dave Carroll, John Nutter, Richard Gell, Nick Roddis, Jason Chewins. **Middle:** Paul Priddy (GK Coach), Dean Hooper, Lee Charles, Mark Kleboe, Anthony Charles, Gareth Howells, Jason Cousins (Captain), Nikki Bull, Paul Moody, Martin Kuhl (Football Development Officer), Paul Buckle, Alan McCreeney. **Front:** Ally Shaw, Paul Andrews, Nick Sowden, Simon Pullen (Football Development Officer), Terry Brown (Manager), Stuart Cash (Assistant Manager), Brett Cooper, Julian Thompson, Michael Harper.

Date	Comp.	Opponents	Att.	Score	Goalscorers
18.08	Ryman P	ENFIELD	2057	3 - 1	Watson 26, Bentley 68, Kirby 75
21.08	Ryman P	Canvey Island	1120	3 - 1	Watson 7, Payne 28, Chewins 43
25.08	Ryman P	Heybridge Swifts	492	2 - 1	Watson 52, Nutter 90
27.08	Ryman P	GRAVESEND & NORTHFLEET	2252	1 - 2	Watson 79
01.09	Ryman P	BRAINTREE TOWN	1752	4 - 0	Holsgrove 5, Payne 37, Browne 68, Forrester 90
08.09	Ryman P	Hitchin Town	851	3 - 0	Brown 65 69, Forrester 82
11.09	Ryman P	PURFLEET	1751	4 - 1	Browne 16 86, Nutter 67, Forrester 90
15.09	Ryman P	Grays Athletic	738	1 - 3	Watson 78
18.09	Ryman P	MAIDENHEAD UNITED	1663	4 - 1	Coll 5, Brown 37 69, Gell 40
22.09	Ryman P	BILLERICAY TOWN	2308	1 - 1	Watson 44
25.09	Ryman P	Harrow Borough	670	3 - 2	Protheroe 61 66, Forrester 76
29.09	FA Cup Q2	Maidenhead United	917	1 - 1	Protheroe 84
02.10	FA Cup Q2 R	MAIDENHEAD UNITED	1742	1 - 0	Forrester 38
09.10	Ryman P	Sutton United	944	0 - 2	
13.10	FA Cup Q3	SUTTON UNITED	1961	3 - 0	Browne 41 49, Payne 45
20.10	Ryman P	KINGSTONIAN	2276	3 - 0	Payne 5, Browne 73, Parker 81
27.10	FA Cup Q4	HITCHIN TOWN	2238	2 - 1	Parker 32, Browne 64
30.10	Ryman P	HAMPTON & RICHMOND BOR.	1801	4 - 1	Bentley 21, Browne 68 78, Forrester 86
01.11	Hants SC 2	BRADING TOWN	570	5 - 1	Watson 31 74, Reid 44, Coll 55, Thompson 81
03.11	Ryman P	Chesham United	865	1 - 2	Parker 42
10.11	Ryman P	BOREHAM WOOD	1805	0 - 2	
17.11	FA Cup 1	BRISTOL ROVERS	5059	0 - 0	
24.11	Ryman P	Bedford Town	1070	2 - 1	Coll 27 86
27.11	FA Cup 1 R	Bristol Rovers	4848	0 - 1	
01.12	FA Trophy 2	Aylesbury United	876	2 - 0	Harford 22, Payne 58
04.12	Hants SC 3	FARNBOROUGH TOWN	n.k	4 - 3	
08.12	Ryman P	CROYDON	1674	2 - 0	Payne 7, Coll 56
11.12	Lge Cup 1	CROYDON	623	5 - 1	Payne ?? ?? Own-Goal Bentley
15.12	Ryman P	Enfield	439	1 - 1	Payne 32
18.12	Ryman P	Hendon	315	1 - 0	Bentley 38
26.12	Ryman P	BASINGSTOKE TOWN	2203	2 - 2	Parker 46, Chewins 60
29.12	Ryman P	CANVEY ISLAND	2630	1 - 3	Browne 35
05.01	Ryman P	CHESHAM UNITED	1541	1 - 0	Kirby 61
10.01	Hants SC QF	BROCKENHURST	548	4 - 0	Watson 10 22 39, Parker 44
13.01	FA Trophy 3	Forest Green Rovers	1138	1 - 1	Browne 46
15.01	FA Trophy 3 R	FOREST GREEN ROVERS	1487	2 - 3	Watson 54, Harford 81
19.01	Ryman P	HITCHIN TOWN	1505	1 - 2	Browne 67
02.02	Ryman P	Croydon	292	2 - 1	Browne 11, Harford 32
09.02	Ryman P	BEDFORD TOWN	1801	4 - 0	Gell 18, Browne 52 78[p], Chewins 88
14.02	Lge Cup 2	HENDON	584	2 - 0	Ward 39, Payne 77
16.02	Ryman P	Maidenhead United	753	2 - 1	Parker 23 90
19.02	Ryman P	Gravesend & Northfleet	1216	1 - 2	Coll 38
23.02	Ryman P	GRAYS ATHLETIC	1646	0 - 1	
27.02	Lge Cup 3	CORINTHIAN CASUALS	376	3 - 0	Holsgrove 47, Payne 49, Forrester 51
02.03	Ryman P	Billericay Town	1052	0 - 2	
05.03	Lge Cup QF	Grays Athletic	n.k	3 - 2	
09.03	Ryman P	HARROW BOROUGH	1458	2 - 1	Harford 15, Gell 58
12.03	Hants SC SF(1)	NEWPORT IOW	782	2 - 0	Payne 50, Browne 79
16.03	Ryman P	Hampton & Richmond Bor.	220	1 - 1	Forrester 72
19.03	Ryman Cup SF(1)	HAMPTON & RICHMOND BOR.	751	2 - 2	Browne 37, Gell 51
23.03	Ryman P	SUTTON UNITED	1618	1 - 0	Browne 44
26.03	Hants SC SF(2)	Newport IOW	441	2 - 0	Chewings 1, Parker 53
30.03	Ryman P	HEYBRIDGE SWIFTS	1507	3 - 3	Watson 40, Parker 69, Carroll 88
01.04	Ryman P	Basingstoke Town	1136	1 - 1	Allen 10
03.04	Lge Cup SF(2)	Hampton & Richmond Borough	718	0 - 1	
06.04	Ryman P	HENDON	1511	2 - 1	Browne 58, Parker 85
09.04	Ryman P	St Albans City	421	3 - 0	Watson 8, Browne 55 57
13.04	Ryman P	Kingstonian	1063	1 - 2	Payne 90
16.04	Ryman P	Purfleet	384	1 - 2	Townley 3
18.04	Ryman P	Braintree Town	300	0 - 2	
20.04	Ryman P	ST ALBANS CITY	1637	1 - 1	Bentley 22
27.04	Ryman P	Boreham Wood	439	3 - 1	Parker 33 80, Holsgrove 20
01.05	Hants SC F	Havant & Waterlooville	3523	3 - 1	Browne(3) Southampton

Match Facts 2001-02

PLAYING SQUAD

Goalkeepers: Gareth Howells (Sutton Utd), Nikki Bull (Hayes)
Defenders: Anthony Charles (Hayes), Dominic Sterling (Hayes), Jason Chewins (Wealdstone), Jason Cousins (Wycombe Wanderers), John Nutter (Wycombe Wanderers), Stuart Cash (Enfield)
Midfielders: Adam Parker (Hitchin T), David Carroll (Wycombe Wanderers), Dean Hooper (Peterborough), Nick Roddis (Margate), Paul Buckle (Exeter), Richard Gell (Chesham)
Forwards: Chris Allen (Dover Ath), Ivan Mballa (Raith Rovers), Jamie Taylor (Horsham), Lee Charles (Nuneaton), Nana Achamfuur (Egham T), Paul Moody (Oxford Utd), Roscoe D'sane (Woking)

AYLESBURY UNITED

CLUB OFFICIALS

Chairman: Bill Carroll
Vice Chairman: Les Baycroft
Secretary: Tony Graham
c/o the club.
Press Officer: Tony Graham
Email: info@aylesburyutd.co.uk

FOOTBALL MANAGEMENT TEAM

Manager: Steve Cordery
Assistant Manager: Floyd Street
Physios: Tyrone Matthews & Jon Hay

FACT FILE

Formed: 1897 Nickname: The Ducks
Sponsors: Shanks Waste Systems
Colours: Green & w hite/white/white
Change colours: Yellow & black, black,black
Midweek home matchday: Tuesday
Reserve Team's League: Suburban
Newsline: 0906 655 5811

2001-02
Captain: Stuart Maynard
P.o.Y.: Greg Williams
Top Scorer: Dwight Marshall 22

GROUND The Stadium, Buckingham Road, Aylesbury HP20 2AQ Tel: 01296 436350/436891
Fax: 01296 395667
Directions: On A413 to Buckingham, just off ring road opposite Horse & Jockey PH. Arriving from Buckingham ground is on left - from all other directions follow Buckingham signs and ground on right. Half hour walk from Aylesbury rail and bus stations
Capacity 4,000   Cover: 1000   Seats: 500   Floodlights: Yes
Clubhouse: Pub hours. Bar snacks available
          Function room available for hire(01296 428000).
Club Shop: Sells programmes, magazines, leisurewear, badges etc.
          Contact DebbieGamage c/o The Club

Programme
Pages: 36 Price: £1.50
Editor: 21st Century Ducks.

Local Press: Bucks Herald, Bucks Advertiser
Local Radio: Three Counties Radio,
Chiltern Radio, Mix 96

PREVIOUS   **Leagues:** Bucks Contiguous 1897-1903, South Eastern 03-07, Spartan 07-51, Delphian 51-63, Athenian 63-76, Southern 76-88, GMV Conference 88-89
          Grounds: Printing Works Ground 1897-1935, Sports Stadium, Wendover Rd (ground name changed to The Stadium, Turnfurlong Lane) 35-85, shared grounds 85-86   **Name:** Night School, Printing Works (merged in 1897)

CLUB RECORDS   **Attendance:** 6,000 v England 1988 (at old ground: 7,500 v Watford, FA Cup 1st Rd1951)
          Career goalscorer: Cliff Hercules   **Career appearances:** Cliff Hercules
          Transfer fee paid: £15,000 for Glenville Donegal (Northampton, 1990)
          Transfer fee received: Undisclosed forJermaine Darlington (Q.P.R. 1999)

BEST SEASON   **FA Trophy:** Quarter-Final replay 80-81   **FA Cup:** 3rd Rd 95. League clubs defeated: Southend Utd 89-90

HONOURS   Southern Lg 87-88 (Mids Div R-up 84-85, Sth Div R-up 79-80); Athenian Lg Div 2 R-up 67-68; Delphian Lg 53-54 (R-up 52-53, Lg Cup 59-60); Spartan Lg 08-09 (R-up 52-53), West Div 28-29 (R-up 45-46), Div 1 38-39 (R-up 34-35); Berks & Bucks Snr Cup 13-14 85-86 96-97; Isthmian League Cup 94-95, Isthmian Charity Shield 95-96 Isthmian League R-up 98-99

Players progressing: Ray Mabbutt (Bristol Rovers), Phil Barber (Crystal Palace 1986), Jermaine Darlington (Q.P.R. 99),Lee Cook (watford 00)

Back row,left to right: Sam Sloma,Kesie Ibe, Daniel Gordon, Lewis Pritchard, Stuart Corbould, Rory Hunter, John Marsh, Danny Gray and Dwight Marshall. **Middle row:** Peter Remnant (Reserve Team Manager), John Hay (Physio), Roni Joe, Steve McGrath,Gareth Risbridger, Phil Dicker, Chris Bangura, Tony Houghton, John Winter, Danny Grimsdell, Fiston Manuella, Ron Schmidt (Kit man) and Peter Wright (Director of Football) **Front row:** Greg Williams, Gary McCann, Scott Honeyball, Steve Cordery (Manager), Craig Maskell (Assistant Manager),Adam Cam[pion,Adam Wheeler and Mark Burgess.

ISTHMIAN LEAGUE PREMIER DIVISION

Date	Comp.	Opponents	Att.	Score	Goalscorers
18.08	Ryman 1	Staines Town	247	1 - 2	Clark 64
21.08	Ryman 1	THAME UNITED	437	2 - 0	Joe 29, Clark 75
25.08	Ryman 1	BARKING & EAST HAM UNITED	446	3 - 2	Honeyball 62, Silvestri 64, Clifford 80
27.08	Ryman 1	Tooting & Mitcham United	290	4 - 2	Bennetts 62, Williams 82, McCormack 89, Silvestri 90
01.09	FA Cup P	BRENTWOOD	301	10 - 1	Bangura, Silvestri 2, Clark 5 Williams, Marshall
04.09	Ryman 1	Windsor & Eton	177	3 - 1	Honeyball 5, Marshall 16, Bangura 41
08.09	Ryman 1	BOGNOR REGIS TOWN	465	2 - 2	Marshall 12 30
11.09	Ryman 1	NORTHWOOD	330	3 - 2	S Clark 41, Marshall 75, Bangura 86
15.09	FA Cup Q1	SUDBURY	408	4 - 3	Maynard 24, S Clark 27, Stanbridge 29, Bangura 74
22.09	Ryman 1	Whyteleafe	195	2 - 1	Marshall 61 90
25.09	Ryman 1	YEADING	362	4 - 1	Maynard 42, Marshall 45, Bangura 51, Honeyball 70
29.09	FA Cup Q2	ARLESEY TOWN	414	2 - 0	Bangura 50, Clark 77
02.10	Ryman 1	Bishop's Stortford	316	2 - 2	Bangura 53, Clark 72
05.10	Ryman 1	Bromley	232	2 - 0	Joe 20, McCormack 62
09.10	Ryman 1	WEALDSTONE	470	2 - 2	Honeyball 63, Clifford 86
13.10	FA Cup Q3	ATHERSTONE UNITED	543	3 - 1	Bangura 64, D Clarke 81, Marshall 85
16.10	Ryman 1	Slough Town	413	4 - 3	Clarke 25, Marshall 82 85, Bangura 90
20.10	Ryman 1	FORD UNITED	477	3 - 4	Clifford 8, Gerraghty 13[og], Bangura 64
27.10	FA Cup Q4	Yeading	340	5 - 0	Marshall 17 18 48, Maynard 37, Clarke 64
03.11	FA Trophy 1	Slough Town	441	2 - 0	Maynard 61, Stanbridge 73
10.11	Ryman 1	WORTHING	566	1 - 1	Joe 86
17.11	FA Cup 1	Port Vale	4956	0 - 3	
20.11	Ryman 1	CARSHALTON ATHLETIC	335	2 - 1	Joe 41, Paris 86
24.11	Ryman 1	WALTON & HERSHAM	558	4 - 2	Marshall 17[p] 77[p], Clark 73, Bangura 75
27.11	Berks & BS 1	WYCOMBE WANDERERS	400	2 - 3	Honeyball 16, Clarke 19
01.12	FA Trophy 2	ALDERSHOT TOWN	876	0 - 2	
04.12	Lge Cup 1	METROPOLITAN POLICE	n.k	1 - 3	
08.12	Ryman 1	Dulwich Hamlet	312	3 - 3	Marshall 74 87, Clarke 78
11.12	Ryman 1	Oxford City	187	2 - 0	S Clarke 57, Joe 70
15.12	Ryman 1	STAINES TOWN	687	2 - 1	Marshall 26, D Clarke 32
22.12	Ryman 1	Uxbridge	300	1 - 3	Clark 6
29.12	Ryman 1	Thame United	549	1 - 0	S Clark 32
05.01	Ryman 1	WINDSOR & ETON	564	3 - 2	Joe 9, S Clark 26 78
16.01	Ryman 1	Harlow Town	220	3 - 1	Joe 12, Maynard 30, Bangura 90
19.01	Ryman 1	WHYTELEAFE	502	8 - 0	Bangura 3 (9 48 52), S Clark 22 37, Silvestri 61, Williams 73, Maynard
02.02	Ryman 1	DULWICH HAMLET	567	3 - 3	Silvestri 3, Stanbridge 12, Maynard 66
09.02	Ryman 1	Walton & Hersham	260	1 - 1	Maynard 1
12.02	Ryman 1	Bognor Regis Town	337	1 - 1	Joe 42
16.02	Ryman 1	BROMLEY	802	3 - 1	Bangura 59, Clark 61, Paris 63
23.02	Ryman 1	Yeading	212	2 - 1	Bangura 7, Silvestri 8
02.03	Ryman 1	BISHOP'S STORTFORD	863	3 - 3	Bangura 17, Paris 31, Williams 70
05.03	Ryman 1	Northwood	261	2 - 3	Joe 28, Marshall 81
09.03	Ryman 1	Wealdstone	367	0 - 1	
16.03	Ryman 1	SLOUGH TOWN	707	4 - 0	D Clarke 6, Bangura 43, Marshall 47, Williams 78
23.03	Ryman 1	Carshalton Athletic	343	1 - 2	Marshall 43
30.03	Ryman 1	Barking & East Ham United	189	1 - 2	Scotchmer 5[og]
01.04	Ryman 1	UXBRIDGE	602	0 - 0	
06.04	Ryman 1	HARLOW TOWN	605	1 - 0	D Clarke 10
13.04	Ryman 1	Ford United	294	3 - 0	Risbridger 6, Paris 34, Bangura 69
20.04	Ryman 1	OXFORD CITY	1412	1 - 4	S Clark 88
23.04	Ryman 1	TOOTING & MITCHAM UNITED	445	3 - 2	Bangura 2 36, S Clark 16
27.04	Ryman 1	Worthing	502	0 - 2	

PLAYING SQUAD

Goalkeepers: Adam Wheeler (Baldock T), Gary McCann (Hendon), David Lovell (Barnet)

Defenders: Danny Gordon (Youth), Greg Williams (Thame Utd), Phil Dicker (Hampton & Richmond Bor.), Enzo Silvestri (Barton Rov.), Peter Risely (St Albans), Richard Horner (Wealdstone), Scott Honeyball (Gravesend & N'fleet)

Midfielders: Dwain Clarke (Yeading), Gareth Risbridger (Salisbury C), Keiran Knight (Northwood), Ollie Stanbridge (Brackley T), Frank McCormack (Sutton Utd), Jason Shaw (Wealdstone), Martin Carter (Hampton & Richmond), Rennie Joe (Thame Utd)

Forwards: Chris Bangura (Tottenham Hotspur), Daniel Gray (Youth), Lee Tunnell (Oxbridge), Steve Clark (Canvey Is.), Craig Maskell (Hampton & Richmond Bor.), Dwight Marshall (Slough T), Mitchell Murphy (Edgeware T)

BASINGSTOKE TOWN

TOWN FC

v
Purfleet
Ryman Premier Division
Saturday 9th February 2002
Kick-off 3.00pm

Basingstoke Town Official Sponsor: Centerprise International
Programme Sponsors: Ericsson Mobile Communications Ltd   Aston Press Printing Ltd
OFFICIAL PROGRAMME OF BASINGSTOKE TOWN F.C.

Pages: 24   Price: £1.50
Editor: T.B.A.

Local Press: Basingstoke Gazette (461131)
Local Radio: Radio 210 (01189 413131),
Kestrel Radio (01256 694000)

CLUB OFFICIALS

Chairman: David Knight
President: Rafi Razzack
Secretary: Richard Trodd
5 Lehar Close, Brighton Hill,
Basingstoke RG22 4HT
Tel: 01256 413076
Press Officer: Ian Trodd
Commercial Manager: AlanHumphries

FOOTBALL MANAGEMENT TEAM

Manager: Ernie Howe
Asst Manager: Pete Peters
Coach: Steve Richardson
Physio: Mark Randall

FACT FILE

Formed: 1896
Nickname: Stoke
Sponsors: Centerprise International
Colours: Blue & gold stripes/blue/blue
Change colours: All Red
Midweek home matchday: Tuesday
Reserves' League: Suburban (Prem Div)
and Capital league
2001-02
Captain : Paul Wilkinson
Top Scorer:Jason eaton
P.O.Y.:Jason Bristol

GROUND Camrose Road, Western Way, Basingstoke RG22 6EZ   Tel: 01256 325063
or01256 327575   Email Address: info@btfc.co.uk   Club Website http // www.btfc.co.uk
Directions: Exit 6 off M3 and follow A30 west, ground off Winchester Road.
Two miles from bus and rail stations
Capacity: 6,000   Cover:2,000   Seats: 651   Floodlights: Yes

Clubhouse: Open every day (incl. lunchtime)   Steward: Cheryl Fox (01256 464353)
Club Shop: Open daily 10-5pm, selling programmes, books, scarves, shirts, badges etc.

PREVIOUS   **Leagues:** Hants 1900-40 45-71; Southern 71-87   **Ground:** Castle Field 1896-1947
CLUB RECORDS Attendance: 5,085 v Wycombe Wanderers, FA Cup 1st Rd replay 97-98
Win: 10-0 v Chichester City (H), FA Cup 1st Qualifying Round, September 1976
Defeat: 0-8 v Aylesbury United, Southern League, April 1979.
Goalscorer: Paul Coombs 159 (Oct 91 99)   **Appearances:** Billy Coombs
TransferFees - Paid: £4,750 for Steve Ingham (Gosport Borough)   **Received:** £6,750 for Steve Ingham (Bashley)

BEST SEASON   **FA Trophy:** 3rd Rd 98-99, 0-2 v Yeovil T. (H)
FA Cup: 2nd Rd replay 97-98, 3-4 pens aet 0 -0 v Northampton (H) after 1-1; 2nd Rd 89-90, 2-3 v Torquay U. (H)
League clubs defeated: Wycombe Wanderers 97-98

HONOURS   Southern Lge Southern Div 85-86; Isthmian League Div 1 R-up 88-89 96-97; Hants League 67-68 69-70 70-71 (R-up 65-66
66-   67 68-69, North Div 11-12 19-20); HantsSenior Cup 70-71 89-90 95-96 96-97

Players progressing: Tony Godfrey (Southampton 58), John Neale (Exeter 72),Mike Doherty (Reading 82), Micky Cheetham (Ipswich 88),
Matt Carmichael(Lincoln), Tony Franklin (Exeter), Steve Welsh (Peterborough 90)

Back row left to right: Rob Cook, Mike Davis, Scott Tarr,Jason Eaton, Paul Wilkinson, Craig McAllister and Jason Bristow.
Front row: Chris Honor, Matt Hayfield, Toby Summer and Mark Lisk.   **Photo:** Alan Coomes

ISTHMIAN LEAGUE PREMIER DIVISION

Date	Comp.	Opponents	Att.	Score	Goalscorers
18.08	Ryman P	Hitchin Town	271	1 - 0	Gorman 38
21.08	Ryman P	KINGSTONIAN	529	2 - 1	Newbery 50, Cook 72
25.08	Ryman P	CROYDON	331	1 - 0	Newbery 34
27.08	Ryman P	Chesham United	348	1 - 1	Gorman 18
01.09	Ryman P	Enfield	102	0 - 3	
04.09	Ryman P	GRAYS ATHLETIC	352	0 - 2	
08.09	Ryman P	BILLERICAY TOWN	364	0 - 1	
11.09	Ryman P	St Albans City	224	0 - 2	
15.09	Ryman P	Hendon	226	3 - 1	Gorman 12, Davis 61, Sills 73
18.09	Ryman P	SUTTON UNITED	278	3 - 0	Davis 8, Sills 32, Gorman 90
22.09	Ryman P	BEDFORD TOWN	507	1 - 1	Gorman 15
25.09	Ryman P	Hampton & Richmond Borough	268	1 - 2	Eaton 56
29.09	FA Cup Q2	CORINTHIAN CASUALS	369	6 - 0	Beaton 34 57, Fraser 70 82, T Sills 85, Cook 89
09.10	Ryman P	Braintree Town	331	2 - 3	Eaton 35 87
13.10	FA Cup Q3	BIDEFORD	523	3 - 1	Sills 58, Eaton 68, Davies 71
20.10	Ryman P	Canvey Island	521	1 - 5	Davis 6
27.10	FA Cup Q4	DAGENHAM & REDBRIDGE	1089	2 - 2	Davis 30, Sills 38
30.10	Ryman P	BOREHAM WOOD	257	1 - 0	Cook 41
03.11	Hants SC 2	Andover	208	0 - 1	
06.11	FA Cup Q4 R	Dagenham & Redbridge	1752	0 - 3	
10.11	Ryman P	Harrow Borough	131	3 - 3	Newbery 72, Sills 80, Honor 83
13.11	Ryman P	GRAVESEND & NORTHFLEET	340	1 - 4	Sills 8
17.11	Ryman P	HEYBRIDGE SWIFTS	329	1 - 3	Sumner 33
24.11	Ryman P	Purfleet	232	0 - 0	
27.11	Lge Cup 1	KINGSTONIAN	n.k	2 - 0	Sills 9, Newbery 76
01.12	FA Trophy 2	Braintree Town	342	1 - 1	Newbery 57
04.12	FA Trophy 2 R	BRAINTREE TOWN	236	0 - 2	
08.12	Ryman P	MAIDENHEAD UNITED	327	1 - 2	Elad 30
11.12	Lge Cup 2	Gravesend & Northfleet	n.k	1 - 4	
15.12	Ryman P	HITCHIN TOWN	265	2 - 3	Hayfield 15, Eaton 54
26.12	Ryman P	Aldershot Town	2203	2 - 2	Houghton 12 79
29.12	Ryman P	Kingstonian	487	1 - 1	Eaton 70
05.01	Ryman P	Grays Athletic	277	0 - 0	
12.01	Ryman P	ENFIELD	417	2 - 0	Howes 14, Gorman 90
19.01	Ryman P	Billericay Town	565	0 - 2	
22.01	Ryman P	CHESHAM UNITED	233	1 - 1	Elad 71
02.02	Ryman P	Maidenhead United	218	2 - 2	Elad 42, Girdler 59
09.02	Ryman P	PURFLEET	322	2 - 2	Honor 18, Bristow 86
16.02	Ryman P	Sutton United	557	1 - 2	Eaton 6
23.02	Ryman P	HENDON	315	2 - 1	Sills 63, Eaton 83
02.03	Ryman P	Bedford Town	591	0 - 3	
09.03	Ryman P	HAMPTON & RICHMOND BOR.	293	1 - 1	McAllister 47
12.03	Ryman P	ST ALBANS CITY	235	3 - 1	McAllister 3, Eaton 29, Gorman 90
17.03	Ryman P	Boreham Wood	215	0 - 0	
23.03	Ryman P	BRAINTREE TOWN	295	1 - 2	Bristow 45
30.03	Ryman P	Croydon	90	3 - 1	Davis 16, Eaton 35, Hayfield 61
01.04	Ryman P	ALDERSHOT TOWN	1136	1 - 1	Eaton 16
06.04	Ryman P	Gravesend & Northfleet	802	0 - 0	
13.04	Ryman P	CANVEY ISLAND	546	0 - 4	
20.04	Ryman P	Heybridge Swifts	208	1 - 5	Gorman 32
27.04	Ryman P	HARROW BOROUGH	346	2 - 1	McAllister 11, McKenna 52[og]

PLAYING SQUAD

Goalkeepers:	Clive Lyttle (Redding - Junior), Scott Tarr (Yeading)
Defenders:	Jason Bristow (Redding), Nathan Wallace (Basingstoke), Simon Herbert (Youth Team), Tom Foster (Youth Team)
Midfielders:	Glenn Howes (Eastleigh), Matt Hayfield (Woking), Paul Wilkinson (Dorchester T), Stuart Girdler (Woking), Tinio Christie (Bisley Sports), Toby Sumner (Aldershot)
Forwards:	Craig McAllister (Eastleigh), Raymond Spence (Youth Team), Richard Newbery (Carshalton Ath.), Sean Gorman (Goldalming & Guildford)

BEDFORD TOWN

CLUB OFFICIALS	FACT FILE
Chairman: **David Howell**	The Eagles Founded 1908 Reformed: 1989
Directors: **Dave Redman,Tony Luff,Gerry Edmonds.**	Sponsors: Paul Riches Skips,Bergordien Coaches and Charles Wells.
Secretary: **Dave Swallow** c/o club	Colours: Blue with white trim Change Colours: All Orange
Company Secretary: **Barry Stephenson**	Midweek Matchday: Tuesday Reserves' League: Capital
	2001-02
FOOTBALL MANAGEMENT TEAM	Captain: Gary Williams
Manager: Roger Ashby	Top Scorer: Kevin Slinn32
Asst. Manager: Andy Lomas	P.o.Y.: Lee Harvey
Physio: John Clare	

GROUND: The New Eyrie, Meadow Lane, Cardington, Bedford MK44. 3SB
Fax: 01234 831990 Tel: 01234 838448. Club Website: www.eagles.co.uk
Directions: BR station Bedford Midland 3miles from ground. Bus station 5 mins walk from BR station. Service 171 & 172 stop outside ground (Canvins stop). Trains from London Thameslink run every 30 mins to Bedford. By road:**A1** going north take L. turn Bedford A603 at Sandy r'abt. Over small bridge keep on this road for 5 miles, ground on right. **M1** going North A603. Next r'abt straight over to Cambridge A1 & Bedford A603. Take 3rd turn to Bedford. At r'abt take 4th exit to Sandy A603. Ground is half a mile on left.
Capacity: 3,000   Seats: 300   Cover: 1000   Floodlights: Yes
Clubhouse: Matchdays bar snacks
Club Shop: Good range of merchandise   Mick Spavins (01234 402822)

Pages: 40 Price: £1.50Editor: Dave Swallow
Supporters Website: www.bedfordeagles.net

Local Press:Beds Times, Beds on Sunday
Local Radio: Chiltern Radio,Three Counties

PREVIOUS **Leagues:** South Midlands 91-94 (predecessors: Utd Co's 08-39; Southern 46-82)
Grounds: Allen Park, Queens Park, Bedford (park pitch) 1991-93
(predecessors: London Rd; Gasworks; Queens Pk; The Eyrie, Raleigh Street)
CLUB RECORDS Attendance: 3,000 v Peterborough Utd, ground opening 6/8/93. (predecessors: 18,407 v Everton, FA Cup 4th Round 12/2/66)
At Allen Park: 1,227 v Bedford Utd, South Midlands Lge Div. One, 26/12/91
Career scorer: Jason Reed   **Career appearances:** Jason Reed
Win: 9-0 v Ickleford, and Caddington   **Defeat:** 0-5 v Hendon
BEST SEASON   **FA Cup:** 1st Rd proper 01-02 **FA Vase:** 5th Round 1998-99, 1-2 v Tiverton Town (H) **F.A.Trophy:** 4th Rd v Yeovil Town 99-00

HONOURS: Isthmian League: Div 1 R-up. 00-01 Div. 2 98-99; South Midlands Lg 94-95 (Div 1 92-93, F'lit Cup 94-95); Hinchingbrook Cup 94-95 94-95; Beds Sen Cup 94-95.   (Predecessors: Southern Lg 58-59 (Div 1 69-70), Utd Co's Lg 30-31 32-33 33-34 (R-up 7 Times) Vandanal Cup 97-8 Beds Prem , Beds Premier Cup 97-98 **FA Cup** 4th Rd 63-64 65-66. **FA Trophy** Semi-Final 74-75.
Players progressing: Bill Garner (Southend 69), Nicky Platnaeur (Bristol Rovers 77). Ray Bailey/Derek Bellotti/Billy Brown/Bert Carberry/PeterHall/Dave Quirke/Bobby Fold (Gillingham 56-67), Phil Driver (Wimbledon 78), Joe Dubois (Grimsby T 53), Ted Duggan (Luton T 56), Harry Duke (Noprwich C 46),John Fahy (Oxford U 64), Ken Flint (Spurs 47), Joe Hooley (Accrington 61), Joe Kirkup (Reading 55), Graham Moxon (Exeter C 75), Bela Olah (Northampton 58),Gary Sergeant (Peterborough U 77), Neil Townsend (Southend U 73)

Back Row, Left To Right: Glen Botterill (Reserve Physio), John Clare (1st Team Physio), Lee Harvey, Paul Wilson, Derek Brown, Gary Williams (Reserve Manager), James Heeps, Andy Lomas (Assistant Manager), Steve Jackman, Eddie Lawley, Paul Turner, Kevin Slinn, Steve Gee (Reserve Team Assistant), Kenny Mist (Chief Scout)
Front Row: Grant Haley, Carl Adams, Josh Sozzo, Paul Covington, Roger Ashby (Manager), Ian Edge, Rob Miller, Mark Paul, Steve Berry

Date	Comp.	Opponents	Att.	Score	Goalscorers
18.08	Ryman P	Boreham Wood	456	0 - 1	
21.08	Ryman P	ST ALBANS CITY	647	0 - 1	
25.08	Ryman P	BILLERICAY TOWN	539	3 - 4	Dyer 5, Harrison 27 36
27.08	Ryman P	Braintree Town	454	1 - 2	Lawley 3
01.09	Ryman P	Grays Athletic	274	1 - 2	Adams 51
04.09	Ryman P	MAIDENHEAD UNITED	472	1 - 2	Harrison 59[p]
08.09	Ryman P	HARROW BOROUGH	449	3 - 4	Slinn 42, Lawley 50, Paul 53
11.09	Ryman P	Hendon	285	2 - 1	O'Donnell 72[og], Perna 90
15.09	Ryman P	CROYDON	554	3 - 2	Slinn 6, Paul 43 90
18.09	Ryman P	Heybridge Swifts	135	1 - 1	Elding 75
22.09	Ryman P	Basingstoke Town	507	1 - 1	Paul 56
25.09	Ryman P	CANVEY ISLAND	641	1 - 3	Wilson 87
26.09	Beds SC 1	STOTFOLD	n.k	1 - 3	Hancock 58
29.09	FA Cup Q2	LEYTON	436	3 - 0	Tucker 19, Slinn 73[p], Miller 78
02.10	Ryman P	Kingstonian	469	0 - 3	
09.10	Ryman P	CHESHAM UNITED	481	2 - 0	Nuttell 11, Paul 49
13.10	FA Cup Q3	HEDNESFORD TOWN	736	2 - 0	Paul 42, Slinn 65
20.10	Ryman P	Hampton & Richmond Borough	384	1 - 1	Dyer 30
27.10	FA Cup Q4	Harlow Town	940	2 - 1	Paul 13, Slinn 48
03.11	FA Trophy 1	WORTHING	653	4 - 0	Paul 44, Edge 60, Dyer 70, Slinn 90
10.11	Ryman P	Gravesend & Northfleet	656	1 - 4	Paul 39
13.11	Ryman P	ENFIELD	435	2 - 2	Edge 29, Paul 74
17.11	FA Cup 1	PETERBOROUGH UNITED	2626	0 - 0	
20.11	Beds PC 1	STOTFOLD	n.k	5 - 1	
24.11	Ryman P	ALDERSHOT TOWN	1070	1 - 2	Turner 74
27.11	FA Cup 1 R	Peterborough United	5751	1 - 2	Slinn 54
01.12	FA Trophy 2	Eastbourne Borough	518	0 - 0	
04.12	FA Trophy 2 R	EASTBOURNE BOROUGH	404	1 - 2	Slinn 70
08.12	Ryman P	Sutton United	591	2 - 2	Jackman 3, Slinn 38
11.12	Lge Cup 1	Grays Athletic	n.k	1 - 5	
15.12	Ryman P	BOREHAM WOOD	524	2 - 0	Paul 3, Slinn 75
26.12	Ryman P	Hitchin Town	879	2 - 2	McNamara 34, Slinn 72[p]
29.12	Ryman P	St Albans City	760	0 - 0	
05.01	Ryman P	Maidenhead United	294	1 - 2	Slinn 15
19.01	Ryman P	Harrow Borough	394	4 - 2	Miller 45, Dyer 50, Slinn 62, O'Flynn 90
29.01	Beds PC QF	ARLESEY TOWN	n.k	0 - 4	
02.02	Ryman P	SUTTON UNITED	488	0 - 1	
09.02	Ryman P	Aldershot Town	1801	0 - 4	
12.02	Ryman P	GRAYS ATHLETIC	389	4 - 0	Slinn 5, Paul 12 35 89
16.02	Ryman P	HEYBRIDGE SWIFTS	525	5 - 2	Slinn 23 65 75, Paul 57, Brown 62
23.02	Ryman P	Croydon	173	3 - 3	Slinn 8, Edge 17, Paul 76
26.02	Ryman P	PURFLEET	417	1 - 0	Slinn 32
02.03	Ryman P	BASINGSTOKE TOWN	591	3 - 0	Slinn 31 38 83
09.03	Ryman P	Canvey Island	805	3 - 3	Flynn 50 51 70
12.03	Ryman P	BRAINTREE TOWN	534	2 - 0	Williams 2, Slinn 58
16.03	Ryman P	KINGSTONIAN	719	2 - 1	Slinn 9, Paul 20
23.03	Ryman P	Chesham United	416	1 - 1	Slinn 31[p]
26.03	Ryman P	HENDON	556	0 - 5	
30.03	Ryman P	Billericay Town	650	0 - 1	
01.04	Ryman P	HITCHIN TOWN	766	0 - 1	
06.04	Ryman P	Enfield	201	0 - 1	
13.04	Ryman P	HAMPTON & RICHMOND BOR.	481	4 - 1	Slinn 9 63, Brown 20, Paul 45
20.04	Ryman P	Purfleet	301	1 - 1	Paul 9
27.04	Ryman P	GRAVESEND & NORTHFLEET	1743	0 - 1	

PLAYING SQUAD

Goalkeepers: Jimmy Heeps (Leighton T), Steve Wilson (Kings Lynn)

Defenders: Eddie Lawley (Buckingham T), Gary Williams (Hitcham T), Ian Edge (Emley), Lee Harvey (Stevenage Bor.), Liam Folds (Aston Villa), Mark Tucker (Worcester), Paul Covington (Buckingham T), Robbie Miller (Stevenage Bor.), Steve Jackman (Raunds T), Stuart Smeathers (Raunds)

Midfielders: Carl Williams (Hitchin), Josh Sozzo (Hemel Hempstead), Lee Broughton (Arseley T), Paul Turner (St Albans), Steve Berry (Stevanage Borough)

Forwards: Kevin Slinn (Raunds T), Ross Harrison (Bedworth), Mark Paul (Kettering Town)

BILLERICAY TOWN

BILLERICAY TOWN *football club*

CLUB OFFICIALS
Chairman: Rod Moore
V. Chair: John Stacey **Pres:** Jim Hall
Secretary: Len Dewson14 Graham Close
Biillericay,Essex CM12 0QW(01277622375)
Email: len.dewson@billericay-
essex.freeserve.co.uk
Press Officer: Rob Moore

FOOTBALL MANAGEMENT TEAM
Manager: Gary Calder
Asst. Man.: Chris Snowsill
Coach: Joe Dunwell
Physio: Dave Lawson

FACT FILE
Formed: 1880 **Nickname:** The Town
Sponsors: Faurecia Ltd
Colours: Royal Blue/White/ Royal Blue
Change colours: T.B.A.
Midweek Matches: Tuesday

2001-02
Captain: Lee Williams
P.o.Y.: Martin Carthy
Top Scorer: Martin Carthy 16

GROUND: New Lodge, Blunts Wall Rd, Billericay CM12 9SA. 01277 652188
Directions: From Shenfield (A129) right at 1st lights then 2nd right. FromBasildon (A129)
over 1st lights in town, then left at next lights and 2nd right. Half mile from Billericay (GER)
(London Liverpool St. - Southend line). 5 mins walk from buses 222, 251, 357, 255, 551
Capacity: 3,500 **Seats:** 424 **Cover:** 2000 **Floodlights:** Yes
Clubhouse: Open every evening 8-11pm (except Monday)(1pm-11pm Sat) and weekend-
lunch times noon-2.30pm. Discos, live entertainment
Club Shop: Open matchdays for souvenirs, metal badges, old progs, programme swaps
Nigel Harris (01268 558114) Club Website: www.billericaytownfc.co.uk

Pages: 32 .Price: £1.50
Editor: Mark Kettley (01277 636149)
Local Press: Evening Echo, Billericay
Gazette, Billericay Recorder
Local Radio: BBC Radio Essex,
Essex Radio, Essex FM

PREVIOUS	**Leagues:** Romford & Dist. 1890-1914; Mid Essex 18-47; South Essex Comb. 47-66; Essex Olympian 66-71; Essex Snr 71-77; Athenian 77-79 **Grounds:** Laindon Road (pre-1971).	
CLUB RECORDS	**Attendance:** 3,841 v West Ham Utd, Floodlight opener 77. Comp match: 3,193 v Farnborough Tn, FA Vase SF 1st leg 76	
	Win: 11-0 v Stansted (A), Essex Senior League 5/5/76	
	Defeat: 3-10 v Chelmsford City (A), Essex Senior Cup 4/1/93	
	Goalscorer: (career) F Clayden 273, (season) Leon Gutmore 51 (97-98) **Appearances:** J Pullen 418	
	Fees - Paid: Undisclosed **Received:** £22,500+ increments for Steve Jones (West Ham, Nov. 1992)	
BEST SEASON	**FA Cup:** 1st Rd Proper 97-98 **FA Vase:** Winners - 75-76, 76-77 & 78-79	
	FA Trophy: 5th Rd 00-01 **FA Amateur Cup:** 3rd Qual Rd 73-74	
HONOURS:	Essex Lge Lg 72-73 74-75 75-76, R-up 71-2 73-4, Lg Cup 71-72, Challenge Cup 72-73, 76-77 (R.up 74-75); Isthmian Lge Div 2 79-80, Div 1 R-up 80-81, 97-98; Athenian Lg 77-79 (Lg Cup 77-78); East Anglian Cup R-up 79-80 84-5; Essex Snr Cup 75-76 (R-up 85-6 93-4,4,5,5-6); Essex Snr Tphy 77-78 79-80; Essex Thameside Tphy 86-87 91-92 (R-up 90-1); Essex F'lit Tphy 77-78; Phillips F'lit Tphy 76-77; Rothmans Merit Award 1978	

Players progressing: D Westwood (QPR) 75, A Hull, D Carter (Peterborough,Orient), D Cass (Orient) 88,
D Ludden (Orient) 92, S Jones (West Ham Utd) 92

Left to right - Back row: Russell Penn, Chris Moore, Juho Rantala, Neil Fay, Paul Fewings, Jerome John, Jamie Wallace, Richard Graham and Martin Carthy. **Front row:** Dave McDonald, Danny Kerrigan, Nick Savidge, Gary Henty, Scott Forrester, Lee Williams, Joe Baker, Mark Graham and Mark Brennan. **Photo** courtesy of the Basildon Evening Echo.

Match Facts 2001-02

Date	Comp.	Opponents	Att.	Score	Goalscorers
18.08	Ryman P	GRAYS ATHLETIC	707	3 - 2	Opara 5, Simba 16, Moore 40
21.08	Ryman P	Hendon	258	3 - 1	Opara 30, Woolsey 44, Morgan 48
25.08	Ryman P	Bedford Town	539	4 - 3	Carthy 45, Opara 51 54, Wallace 85
27.08	Ryman P	SUTTON UNITED	627	2 - 1	Opara 40, Carthy 76
01.09	Ryman P	HAMPTON & RICHMOND BOR.	557	2 - 0	Tomlinson 62, Baker 80
04.09	Ryman P	Braintree Town	478	0 - 1	
08.09	Ryman P	Basingstoke Town	364	1 - 0	Carthy 48
11.09	Ryman P	BOREHAM WOOD	511	0 - 1	
15.09	Ryman P	CHESHAM UNITED	634	0 - 0	
18.09	Ryman P	Kingstonian	412	1 - 4	Woosley 90
22.09	Ryman P	Aldershot Town	2308	1 - 1	Dixon 38
25.09	Ryman P	GRAVESEND & NORTHFLEET	565	1 - 3	Dixon 15
29.09	FA Cup Q2	St Albans City	441	1 - 0	Carthy 72
02.10	Ryman P	Heybridge Swifts	235	3 - 2	Williams 26 53, Baker 90[p]
09.10	Ryman P	ENFIELD	451	3 - 2	Simba 41 48, L Williams 44
13.10	FA Cup Q3	GRANTHAM TOWN	642	2 - 1	Simba 5 20
20.10	Ryman P	Harrow Borough	202	2 - 0	Carthy 9, Baker 55
27.10	FA Cup Q4	TIVERTON TOWN	926	1 - 2	Leonard 57[og]
03.11	FA Trophy 1	Rothwell Town	206	1 - 1	Morgan 2
06.11	FA Trophy 1 R	ROTHWELL TOWN	273	5 - 3	Simba 46, Carthy 95 105 118, Moore 110
10.11	Ryman P	Purfleet	268	1 - 1	Woolsey 70
13.11	Essex SC 3	Romford	n.k	2 - 1	
17.11	Ryman P	HITCHIN TOWN	591	1 - 1	Opara 10
24.11	Ryman P	Croydon	130	0 - 0	
27.11	Lge Cup 1	Bromley	n.k	0 - 2	
04.12	FA Trophy 2	Dulwich Hamlet	165	1 - 2	Carthy 7
08.12	Ryman P	ST ALBANS CITY	519	1 - 5	Baker 67[p]
11.12	Ryman P	MAIDENHEAD UNITED	281	2 - 2	Carthy 58, Baker 77[p]
15.12	Ryman P	Grays Athletic	312	0 - 0	
26.12	Ryman P	CANVEY ISLAND	1408	0 - 3	
29.12	Ryman P	HENDON	505	4 - 6	L Williams 9, Opara 22, Carthy 54, Hook 62[og]
05.01	Ryman P	BRAINTREE TOWN	665	2 - 4	Darlington 7, Baker 59
12.01	Ryman P	Sutton United	570	2 - 2	Woolsey 11, Opinel 59
15.01	Essex SC 4	WITHAM TOWN	n.k	4 - 2	
19.01	Ryman P	BASINGSTOKE TOWN	565	2 - 0	L Williams 14, Baker 75
02.02	Ryman P	Boreham Wood	206	1 - 1	Williams 8
09.02	Ryman P	CROYDON	508	2 - 0	Wallace 12, Baker 80
16.02	Ryman P	KINGSTONIAN	614	1 - 1	Henty 19
19.02	Essex SC QF	DAGENHAM & REDBRIDGE	n.k	0 - 2	
23.02	Ryman P	Chesham United	203	0 - 2	
02.03	Ryman P	ALDERSHOT TOWN	1052	2 - 0	Baker 22 90
05.03	Ryman P	St Albans City	229	0 - 0	
09.03	Ryman P	Gravesend & Northfleet	862	0 - 1	
16.03	Ryman P	HEYBRIDGE SWIFTS	685	1 - 2	Baker 34[p]
23.03	Ryman P	Enfield	185	2 - 0	Moore 54 73
28.03	Ryman P	Hampton & Richmond Borough	n.k	2 - 1	Baker 37[p], Moore 45
30.03	Ryman P	BEDFORD TOWN	650	0 - 0	
01.04	Ryman P	Canvey Island	1027	0 - 3	
06.04	Ryman P	Maidenhead United	191	2 - 0	Gilley 24, Carthy 59
13.04	Ryman P	HARROW BOROUGH	484	1 - 1	L Williams 88
20.04	Ryman P	Hitchin Town	359	2 - 3	Carthy 7, Opinel 9
27.04	Ryman P	PURFLEET	681	2 - 0	Simba 6, Dickinson 90

PLAYING SQUAD

Goalkeepers: Jermone John (Grays Athletic)

Defenders: Chris Moore (Canvey Island), David McDonald (Boreham Wood), Gary Hoy (Enfield), Juho Rantala (HIFK- Finland), Nicky Savage (Ford Sports), Sasha Opinel (Aldershot T)

Midfielders: Gary Henty (Barking), Jimmy Porter (Bowers Utd), Mark Brennan (Dagenham and Redbridge), Mark Graham (Alsershot), Martin Carthy (Purfleet), Pasi Pihamaa (HIFK _Finland), Richard Graham (Chesham Utd), Scott Williams (Hertford T)

Forwards: Jamie Wallace (Ford Utd), Jimmy Sugrue (St Albans), Joe Baker (Sutton Utd), Lee Williams (Enfield), Paul Fewings (Chesham Utd), Scott Forrester (Aldershot)

BISHOPS STORTFORD

CLUB OFFICIALS

Chairman: John Goodwin
President: B W A Bayford
Secretary: Ian Kettridge,25 Cox Ley,Hatfield Heath,Bishop,s Stortford, Herts. CM22 7ER Tel No: 07904169017 (M)
Press Officer: Daniel Smart
Tel No: 07736 459052 (M)

FOOTBALL MANAGEMENT TEAM

Team Manager: Martin Hayes
Assistant Manager: Tim Moylette
Physio: Peter Fox & Brian Curtis

FACT FILE

Formed: 1874 Nickname: Blues or Bishops
Colours: Blue & white stripes/blue/blue
Change colours: Yellow/yellow/yellow
Midweek matchday: Tuesday
Local Press: B.Stortford Citizen,
Herts & Essex Observer, Herald
Local Radio: BBC Essex, Essex FM,
Breeze AM, Mercury FM
2001-2002
Captain: Al James Hannigan
P.o.Y.: Vinnie John
Top Scorer: Vinnie John 33

Pages: 72 Price: £1.50
Editor: Dan Smart
Tel No: 07736 459052

GROUND Woodside Park, Dunmow Road, Bishop 's Stortford (01279 306456)
Directions: M11 jct 8, A1250 towards town centre, left at first roundabout. Woodside is first on right opposite Golf Club. Entrance is between industrial units on right. By rail: British Rail: W. Anglia Line (London, Liverpool Str.-Cambridge)
Capacity: 4,000   Cover: 700   Seats: 298   Floodlights: Yes
Clubhouse: Open lunchtimes,evenings and matchdays
Function room(seating 250) available for hire .
Club Shop: Full stock inc. scarves, badges and other souvenirs.
Massive stock of programmes and books etc. Contact Mark Pulfervia club.

PREVIOUS   **Leagues:** East Herts 1896-97, 02-06, 19-21; Stansted & Dist. Lg 06-19; HertsCounty 21-25 27-29; Herts & Essex Border 25-27; Spartan 29-51; Delphian 51-63;Athenian 63-73
CLUB RECORDS   **Attendance:** 6,000 v Peterborough Utd, FA Cup 2nd Rd 1972 & v Middlesbrough FACup 3rd Rd replay, 1983
Win: 11-0: Nettleswell & Butntmill, Herts Jun Cup 2nd Rd 1911   **Defeat:** 0-13 v Cheshunt (H), Herts Sen. Cup 1st Rd 9/1/26
Fee Paid: For Vinnie John to Grays Athletic (1999)   **Fee Received:** £10,000 for Carl Hoddle (Leyton O., 89)
Scorer: (Since 29) Jimmy Badcock 123   **Appearances:** Phil Hopkins 543
BEST SEASON   **FA Amateur Cup:** Winners 73-74   **FA Trophy:** Winners 80-81
FA Cup: 3rd Rd rep. 82-83 (above) - League clubs beaten: Reading 82-83
HONOURS   Isthmian Lg Div 1 80-1 94-5 (Lg Cup 88-9, Full Mem. Cup 90-1); Prem. Inter Lg Cup 89-90; Athenian Lg 69-70 (R-up 66-7, Div 1 65-6, Div 2 R-up 64-5); Delphian Lg 54-5; London Snr Cup 73-4; Herts Snr Cup 58-9 59-0 63-4 70-1 72-3 73-4 75-686-7; E Anglian Cup 81-2; Herts Charity Cup 62-3 65-6 73-4 81-2 82-3 84-5 87-896-7; Herts Charity Shield 54-5; Herts I'mediate Cup (res) 94-95; Eastern F'lit Cup 84-5; Essex F'lit Cup 67-8; Essex & Herts Border Comb 81-2 88-9 R-up (2) 92-4; Fred Budden Tphy R-up 78-9 90-1 92-3
Players progressing: P Phelan (Southend 61), M Hollow (Orient 62), P Phillips(Luton 69), T Baker (Colchester 86), T Sorrell (Maidstone, Colchester, Barnet 88), C Hoddle (Leyton O., Barnet 89), T English (Colchester 89), L Fortune-West (Gillingham 95), L Braithwaite (Exeter City 96)

Back row, left to right: Les Whitton (Coach), Onaldo, Colin Taylor, Ray Taylor, Alex Riches, Richard Hayward, Vinnie John, Tim Langer, Lee Mitchell, Andy Keepence, Owen Beale and Tom Moylette (Coach) **Front row:** Martin Hayes (Player/Manager), Charlie Goodwin, Glen Southam, Mark McGibboin, Jimmy Sygrue, Freddie Hyatt, Troy Braham, Carl Allison, Danny Wolf, Rob French and Trevor Paul

ISTHMIAN LEAGUE PREMIER DIVISION

Date	Comp.	Opponents	Att.	Score	Goalscorers
31.07	Herts CC 1	St Albans City	111	3 - 4	
18.08	Ryman 1	BOGNOR REGIS TOWN	295	1 - 3	John 56
21.08	Ryman 1	Bromley	230	1 - 1	John 45
25.08	Ryman 1	Oxford City	163	0 - 1	
27.08	Ryman 1	WINDSOR & ETON	291	2 - 0	D Gentle 87, John 90
01.09	FA Cup P	Northwood	196	3 - 3	John 14 88[p], Riches 90
04.09	FA Cup P R	NORTHWOOD	294	0 - 1	
08.09	Ryman 1	Barking & East Ham United	148	4 - 0	John 12[p] 78 90, Gridelet 60
11.09	Ryman 1	Carshalton Athletic	182	0 - 2	
22.09	Ryman 1	STAINES TOWN	338	2 - 0	John 29 79
26.09	Ryman 1	Ford United	94	1 - 2	Graham 51 Barking & East Ham United
29.09	Ryman 1	TOOTING & MITCHAM UNITED	282	5 - 0	Braham 4 11 26, Hayes 71, John 83
02.10	Ryman 1	AYLESBURY UNITED	316	2 - 2	Hayes 2, John 75
06.10	Ryman 1	UXBRIDGE	294	2 - 4	Fannon 2, Paul 71
09.10	Ryman 1	Thame United	138	2 - 0	Paul 50, John 84
13.10	Ryman 1	Worthing	282	4 - 2	Kimble 75, Paul 20 89, Braham 27
20.10	Ryman 1	SLOUGH TOWN	340	3 - 2	John 42 43, Purcell 67
23.10	Ryman 1	WEALDSTONE	359	7 - 1	John 8 40 70, Purcell 18, Beale 52, Southam 80, Paul 84
27.10	Ryman 1	Walton & Hersham	189	1 - 0	Riches 61
01.11	East Ang. 2	Stotfold	n.k	1 - 2	Paul 44
04.11	FA Trophy 1	Wealdstone	327	1 - 1	Shaw 85[p]
06.11	FA Trophy 1 R	WEALDSTONE	286	3 - 2	Braham 43, Southam 64, Paul 74
10.11	Ryman 1	WHYTELEAFE	240	3 - 0	Braham 31, Paul 45, Double 81
13.11	Ryman 1	Northwood	232	2 - 2	Paul 2, Southon 20
17.11	Ryman 1	Yeading	137	2 - 3	Fannon 14 64
20.11	Herts SC 2	Tring Town	n.k	2 - 2	Paul 9, Hayes 45 7 6
24.11	Ryman 1	DULWICH HAMLET	322	2 - 2	John 16[p], Braham 44
27.11	Lge Cup 1	Oxford City	n.k	4 - 0	
01.12	FA Trophy 2	GRAYS ATHLETIC	503	1 - 1	John 82
04.12	FA Trophy 2 R	Grays Athletic	226	2 - 3	Hall 4, Southon 7
11.12	Lge Cup 2	CANVEY ISLAND	n.k	2 - 4	
15.12	Ryman 1	Bognor Regis Town	265	0 - 0	
26.12	Ryman 1	HARLOW TOWN	717	4 - 1	Paul 30, Hyatt 42, John 63, Allison 86
29.12	Ryman 1	BROMLEY	266	3 - 0	John 20, Paul 32, Braham 48
05.01	Ryman 1	Wealdstone	291	2 - 2	Allison 44, Paul 72
08.01	Herts SC QF	LONDON COLNEY	n.k	2 - 3	
12.01	Ryman 1	BARKING & EAST HAM UNITED	310	3 - 1	Hunt 26[og], John 63[p] 82
19.01	Ryman 1	Staines Town	119	0 - 0	
29.01	Ryman 1	CARSHALTON ATHLETIC	132	2 - 1	Paul 80, John 90
02.02	Ryman 1	WORTHING	267	1 - 1	Langer 25
05.02	Ryman 1	Windsor & Eton	109	7 - 1	**John 3** (24[p] 26[p] 48), Barham 45, Hyatt 62, Bowen 74, Paul 90
09.02	Ryman 1	Dulwich Hamlet	282	2 - 1	Paul 5 47
16.02	Ryman 1	Tooting & Mitcham United	267	3 - 2	Hannigan 24, Paul 38, John 52
23.02	Ryman 1	FORD UNITED	359	4 - 1	Paul 39 56, Thompson 61, John 80[p]
02.03	Ryman 1	Aylesbury United	863	3 - 3	Paul 35, Hyatt 38, John 88
09.03	Ryman 1	THAME UNITED	347	3 - 0	Paul 42 43, Hyatt 90
16.03	Ryman 1	Uxbridge	160	3 - 1	Thompson 2, Paul 40, Hyatt 90
23.03	Ryman 1	NORTHWOOD	515	1 - 2	Bowen 80
30.03	Ryman 1	OXFORD CITY	456	2 - 0	Fannon 70, Riches 79
01.04	Ryman 1	Harlow Town	628	2 - 1	John 74[p] 90
06.04	Ryman 1	WALTON & HERSHAM	553	2 - 0	Hannigan 60, Langer 87
13.04	Ryman 1	Slough Town	390	1 - 0	Paul 20
20.04	Ryman 1	YEADING	516	6 - 4	Paul 12 32 44, Southam 47, Langer 58, John 61
27.04	Ryman 1	Whyteleafe	309	4 - 2	John 16 90, Hyatt 42, Langer 80

PLAYING SQUAD

Goalkeepers: Micky Desborough (Grays Ath.)
Defenders: Al-James Hannigan (Dulwich Hamlet), Alex Riches (Saffron Walden T), Andy Keepence (Ware), Danny Wolf (Avely), Ray Taylor (Grays Ath.), Andrew Denney (Youth), Danny Foot (Baldock T), Mark McGibbon (Tooting & Mitcham Utd)
Midfielders: Carl Allison (Saffron Waldon), Freddie Hyatt (Chelmsford C), Joel-Marie Sainte (USM Senlis-France), Owen Beale (Youth), Tim Langer (Aveley), Carl Fannon (Grays Athletic), Glen Southam (Enfield), Lee Double (East Thurrock Utd), Rob French (Dulwich Hamlet), Troy Braham (Romford)
Forwards: Martin Hayes (Romford), Roy Essandoh (Cambridge C), Vinnie John (Grays Ath.), Paul Armstrong (Stevenage Bor.), Trevor Paul (Romford)

BOREHAM WOOD

CLUB OFFICIALS

Chairman: **Danny Hunter**
President: **W F O'Neill**
Secretary:**Peter Smith**,26 Briarwood
Road,Stoneleigh,Epsom, Surrey KT19
2LYTel: 020 8393 2902(H) 07711745987(W)
Press Officer: **John D Gill** (020 8723 6407)

FACT FILE

Formed: 1948 Nickname: The Wood

Sponsors: One 2 One

Colours: White/black/black

Change : Alll yellow

Midweek matchday: Tuesday

FOOTBALL MANAGEMENT TEAM
Manager: Micky Engwell
Asst Manager: Roger Goodhind
Physio: Dave Dickens

Pages: 44 Price: £1.50
Editor: John Gill
(020 8723 6407)
Local Radio: Chiltern Radio
Local Press: Boreham Wood Times, Watford
Observer, Herts Advertiser

GROUND: Meadow Park, Broughinge Rd, Boreham Wood,Herts WD6 5AL (020 8953 5097)
Directions: A1 towards London from M25, 1st turn for Boreham Wood, head for town centre, into Brook Rd at r'bout before town centre, Broughinge Rd is 1st right. 1 mile from Elstree & Boreham Wood station (Thameslink),or bus 292 or107 to McDonalds (5 minutes walk)
Capacity: 4,502 Cover: 1,568 Seats: 600 Floodlights: Yes
Clubhouse: (020 8953 5097). Open during normal licensing hours. Snacks available.
Function room (250) available for hire
Club Shop: Sells good selection of souvenirs & programmes.
Contact: Dell Ward (020 8363 7345)

PREVIOUS **Leagues:** Mid Herts 48-52, Parthenon 52-57, Spartan 56-66, Athenian 66-74
Ground: Eldon Avenue 1948-63 **Names:** Boreham Wood Rovers and Royal Retournez, amalgamated in 1948
CLUB RECORDS Attendance: 3,892 v Arsenal , 9 July 99 (friendly) **Goalscorer:** Micky Jackson, 208
Appearances: Dave Hatchett, 714
BEST SEASON **FA Amateur Cup:** 3rd Rd. replay 70-71 **FA Trophy:** 3rd Rd 1995-96. Replay at Chorley 3-4, 3rd Rd replay 97-98
FA Cup: 2nd Round v Luton Town 1996-97. v Cheltenham Town 97-98
HONOURS: Isthmian Lg.Prem Div R-Up 97-98 Div I 94-95, 00-01 Isthmian Lg Div 2 76-77 (Yth Cup R-up 80-81), Isthmian Lge. Cup 96-97;
R-Up 94-95,95-96 ,98-99 Athenian Lg 73-74 (Div 2 68-69, Div 1 R-up 69-70), Spartan Lg R-up 65-66, Herts Senior Cup 71-72 ,98-99 (R-up 66-67
74-75 79-80 87-88,96-97,97-98), Herts Junior Cup 51-52, Parthenon Lg 55-56 (R-up(2) 53-55 56-57, Herts Charity Shield 64-65, Herts
Interm Cup 69-70, Herts Charity Cup (5) 80-81 83-84 85-86 88-90 (R-up 71-72 84-85 86-87 90-91 91-92 92-93), London Senior Cup R-
up89-90, London Intermediate Cup 70-71, Neale Trophy 69-70, Essex & Herts BorderComb 72-73 (Lg Cup 72-73), Western Div R-up 82-83 89-90),
Mithras Cup 76-77, Middx Border Lg 81-82 (Lg Cup 79-80), Wallspan Floodlit 86-87, London Challenge Cup 97-98
Players progressing: Colin Franks (Watford & Sheff Utd), Charles Ntamark (Walsall), Dean Samuels (Barnet 96),Justin gentle (Colchester
U),Kenny Veyse (Plymouth Argyle), Matthew Brady (Wycombe Wanderers)

Back row left to right: Jeran Meah, Chima Eberendu, Chris Harvey, David Kirby, Gary Wotton, Noel Imber, Gary Dixon,
Paul Lamb, Brian Jones, Daniel Hewitt, Paul Davies and Corey Browne.
Front row: Steve Gracie (Physio), Steve Sinclair, Dean Parratt, Lee Harvey (Assistant Manager), Micky Engwell (Manager),
Dominic Grime, Dave McDonald, Sam McCarthy and Dave Dickens (Kit Manager)

Match Facts 2001-02

Date	Comp.	Opponents	Att.	Score	Goalscorers
18.08	Ryman P	BEDFORD TOWN	456	1 - 0	Selby 48
21.08	Ryman P	Sutton United	483	2 - 2	Meah 26, Dixon 45
25.08	Ryman P	Hendon	261	1 - 2	McDonald 20
27.08	Ryman P	GRAYS ATHLETIC	203	2 - 2	Lawford 62[p], Meah 82
01.09	Ryman P	Harrow Borough	220	3 - 2	Lawford 61 85[p], Capone 67
04.09	Ryman P	ST ALBANS CITY	312	0 - 1	
08.09	Ryman P	MAIDENHEAD UNITED	201	2 - 1	Meah 27, Lawford 64
11.09	Ryman P	Billericay Town	511	1 - 0	Meah 32
15.09	Ryman P	PURFLEET	189	1 - 0	Howard 45[og]
18.09	Ryman P	Canvey Island	411	1 - 2	Drew 69
22.09	Ryman P	Chesham United	343	0 - 1	
25.09	Ryman P	HEYBRIDGE SWIFTS	149	2 - 4	Meah 11, Wotton 53
29.09	FA Cup Q2	HARLOW TOWN	168	2 - 2	Wotton 12, Eberendu 86
03.10	FA Cup Q2 R	Harlow Town	216	0 - 0	Lost 2-4 after pens.
09.10	Herts SC 1	St Margaretsbury	n.k	4 - 2	
20.10	Ryman P	Croydon	96	5 - 0	Mead 15, Kodra 36, Drew 47 51, Dixon 90
27.10	Ryman P	HAMPTON & RICHMOND BOR.	202	3 - 2	Capone 2, Drew 31 71
30.10	Ryman P	Basingstoke Town	257	0 - 1	
03.11	FA Trophy 1	Purfleet	195	2 - 4	Sinclair 12, Lawford 59
06.11	Ryman P	HITCHIN TOWN	184	2 - 1	Jones 33, Eberendu 62
10.11	Ryman P	Aldershot Town	1805	2 - 0	Sinclair 35, Jones 90
20.11	Herts SC 2	SOMERSETT AMBURY V & E	n.k	2 - 0	
24.11	Ryman P	KINGSTONIAN	287	1 - 3	Harvey 47
27.11	Lge Cup 1	LEYTON PENNANT	n.k	1 - 2	Parratt 63
08.12	Ryman P	Braintree Town	373	0 - 2	
15.12	Ryman P	Bedford Town	524	0 - 2	
22.12	Ryman P	GRAVESEND & NORTHFLEET	272	0 - 2	
26.12	Ryman P	ENFIELD	207	1 - 3	Jones 5
29.12	Ryman P	SUTTON UNITED	216	1 - 2	Dixon 39
01.01	Ryman P	Grays Athletic	301	2 - 3	Grime 50, Markman 65
08.01	Herts SC QF	St Albans City	n.k	1 - 1	Won 4-3 after pens.
12.01	Ryman P	HARROW BOROUGH	197	1 - 2	Markman 53
19.01	Ryman P	Maidenhead United	232	0 - 2	
02.02	Ryman P	BILLERICAY TOWN	206	1 - 1	Brown 61
09.02	Ryman P	Kingstonian	503	1 - 1	Browne 6
16.02	Ryman P	CANVEY ISLAND	372	0 - 3	
19.02	Herts SC SF	HITCHIN TOWN	n.k	6 - 1	
23.02	Ryman P	Purfleet	152	1 - 0	Dixon 50
02.03	Ryman P	CHESHAM UNITED	242	2 - 1	Meah 48, Lamb 52
09.03	Ryman P	Heybridge Swifts	215	2 - 0	Grime 45, Harvey 49
17.03	Ryman P	BASINGSTOKE TOWN	215	0 - 0	
19.03	Ryman P	BRAINTREE TOWN	134	1 - 2	Meah 79
23.03	Ryman P	Hitchin Town	335	1 - 4	Dixon 90
26.03	Ryman P	St Albans City	318	0 - 1	
29.03	Ryman P	HENDON	391	1 - 2	Meah 89
01.04	Ryman P	Enfield	132	1 - 0	Jones 90
06.04	Ryman P	Hampton & Richmond Borough	185	2 - 1	Meah 19, Marvey 80
13.04	Ryman P	CROYDON	142	1 - 1	Sinclair 81
20.04	Ryman P	Gravesend & Northfleet	1844	1 - 0	Browne 81
27.04	Ryman P	ALDERSHOT TOWN	439	1 - 3	Dixon 28
30.04	Herts SC F	LONDON COLNEY	n.k	3 - 2	@ St Albans City

PLAYING SQUAD

Goalkeepers: Noel Imber (St Albans C)

Defenders: Colin Wall (Tiptree Utd), Domonic Grime (Stevenage Borough), Gary Wotton (Chesham Utd), Daniel Mehmet (Youth T), Gary Howard (Purfleet), Kofi Nyamah (Hayes), Lee Harvey (St Albans), Micky Engwell (Purfleet)

Midfielders: Andre Delisser (Hayes), Corey Browne (Harlow T), Jeran Miah (Hitchin T), Marvin Walker (Enfield), Brian Jones (Wealdstone), Dean Parratt (Youth), Mark Cartilidge (Billeracay)

Forwards: Gary Dixon (Hitchin T), Scott Holding (St Albans), Luke Baulkham (Purfleet)

BRAINTREE TOWN

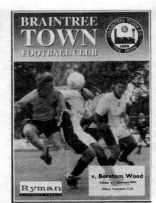

Programme
Pages: 40 Price: £1.50
Editor: Len Llewellyn (01277 363103 T/Fax)
Local Radio: BBC Essex (103.5 fm),
Essex Radio (102.6 fm)

CLUB OFFICIALS	FACT FILE
Chairman: **George Rosling**	Founded: 1898
Vice Chairman: **Ivan Kibble**	Nickname: The Iron
President: **Ron Webb**	Sponsors: T.B.A.
Secretary: **T A Woodley**, 19a Bailey Bridge	Colours:Yellow with navy side panel
Rd., Braintree, Essex CM7 5TT	Change colours: White
(01376 326234)	Reserves' Lg: Essex/Herts Border Comb
Press Officer: **Ron Webb** (01376 325338)	Email Address:
	10665.3036@ compuserve.com
FOOTBALL MANAGEMENT TEAM	**2001-02**
Manager:Ben Embery	Captain: Nicky Smith
Ass Manr Steve Jackson Coach:Ken Varney	P.o.Y.: Dean Parratt
Physio: Tony Brightwell	Top Goalscorer: Nicky Simpson

GROUND   Cressing Road Stadium, Clockhouse Way, Braintree, Essex (01376 345617)
Directions: From Braintree by-pass, turn into Braintree at the McDonalds r'bout, follow signs for East Braintree Ind. Est. - floodlights on left 3/4 mile into town just past. Orange Tree Pub. Entrance next left in Clockhouse Way, then left again. 1 mile from Braintree & Bocking (BR). Bus 353 from Witham or town centre Town centre 20 mins walk

Capacity: 4,000   Cover 1,500   Seats 250   Floodlights:Yes
Clubhouse: Open evenings 7-30-11, Sun 12-3, Sat matchday 12.00- 11.00 Full bar facilities
Club shop: ContactTom Marshallc/o club (75 year History of Braintree £15.99)

PREVIOUS   **Leagues:** North Essex 1898-1925; Essex & Suffolk Border 25-28 55-64; Spartan 28-35; Eastern Co's 35-37 38-39 52-55 70-91; Essex Co. 37-38; London 45-52; GtrLondon 64-66; Metropolitan 66-70; Southern 91-96
    Names: Manor Works 1898-1921; Crittall Ath. 21-68; Braintree & Crittall Ath. 68-81; Braintree FC 81-82
    Grounds: The Fair Field 1898-1903; Spaldings Meadow, Panfield Lane 03-23

CLUB RECORDS Attendance: 4,000 v Spurs, charity challenge match, May 1952
    Career Goalscorer: Chris Guy 211, 63-90.   **Seasonal Record Scorer:** Gary Bennett 57, 97-98
    Career Appearances: Paul Young 524, 66-77   **Fee Paid:** £2,000 for Shane Bailey (Sudbury Town)
    Fee Received: £10,000 Matt Metcalf (Brentford 93) & John Cheesewright(Colchester 93)
    Win: 15-3 v Hopes (Birmingham Friendly 39), 12-0 v Thetford Tn (Eastern Lge 35-36)
    Defeat: 0-14 v Chelmsford City A (Nth Essex Lge 23)

BEST SEASON   FA Cup: 4th Qual. Rd 69-70 85-86 94-95 97-98
HONOURS: Isthmian Lge Div 2 R-up 97-98, Div 3 R-up 96-97; Guardian Insurance Cup R-up 96-97; Eastern Counties Lg 36-37 83-84 84-85 (R-up 86-87 87-88 88-89 90-91), Lg Cup 87-88 (R-up 35-36 74-75); Essex County Lg R-up 37-38; London Lg (East) R-up 45-46, Lg Cup 47-48(jt) 48-49 51-52 (R-up 49-50); Metropolitan Lg Cup 69-70; Essex Elizabethan Tphy R-up 68-69; E. Anglian Cup 46-47 68-69 95-96; Essex Sen.Tphy 86-87 (R-up 90-91); Essex & Suffolk Border Lg 59-60 84-85 (Lg Cup 59-60); Nth Essex Lg 05-06 10-11 11-12; Essex Sen Cup 95-96 R-up 96-97; Essex Jnr Cup R-up 04-05 05-06 22-23; RAFA Cup 56-57; Gtr Lon. Ben. Cup 65-66; Worthington Evans Cup (3) R-up (4); Eastern F'lit Cup 85-86 96-97 (R-up 94-95 97-98); Anglian F'lit Lg 69-70; Jan Havanaar Inter. Tour. 94-95 (R-up 92-93)
Players progressing : J Dick (West Ham 53), S Wright (Wrexham 83), J Cheesewright (Birmingham C. 91), G Bennett, M Metcalf (Brentford 93),R Reinelt (Gillingham 93), M de Souza (Birmingham C.), G Culling (ColchesterU 94) , S.Forbes (Southend U), S.Brown (Tottenham H) and D.Theobald (Brentford)

Back row: Andrew Potter, Paul Catley, Gavin Cowan, Tommy Noble, Adam Gillespie and Mark Jones.
Front row: Matt Hayter, Brett Girling, Neil Cousins, Dean Parratt and Nicky Hayden.

ISTHMIAN LEAGUE PREMIER DIVISION

Date	Comp.	Opponents	Att.	Score	Goalscorers
18.08	Ryman P	SUTTON UNITED	393	3 - 0	Gutmore 27 68, Simpson 49
21.08	Ryman P	Grays Athletic	214	0 - 3	
25.08	Ryman P	Hampton & Richmond Borough	255	2 - 0	Culverhouse 4, Smith 75
27.08	Ryman P	BEDFORD TOWN	454	2 - 1	Reinelt 29, Noble 90
01.09	Ryman P	Aldershot Town	1752	0 - 4	
04.09	Ryman P	BILLERICAY TOWN	478	1 - 0	Waters 32
08.09	Ryman P	HENDON	357	2 - 0	Reinelt 15 19
11.09	Ryman P	Harrow Borough	138	2 - 1	Reinelt 65[p], Simpson 75
15.09	Ryman P	KINGSTONIAN	518	1 - 0	Simpson 81
18.09	Ryman P	Chesham United	206	1 - 4	Simpson 27
22.09	Ryman P	Croydon	105	4 - 0	Reinelt 30, Cowan 63, Simpson 87 90
25.09	Ryman P	PURFLEET	315	2 - 2	Reinelt 73, Cowan 84
29.09	FA Cup Q2	CHELMSFORD CITY	1093	0 - 1	
02.10	Ryman P	Enfield	87	2 - 1	Gutzmore 73, Simpson 90
09.10	Ryman P	BASINGSTOKE TOWN	331	3 - 2	Reinelt 9, Noble 29, Smith 85
13.10	Ryman P	HAMPTON & RICHMOND BOR.	353	3 - 2	Reinelt 63, Simpson 68 83
20.10	Ryman P	Gravesend & Northfleet	779	0 - 3	
04.11	FA Trophy 1	Dartford	272	3 - 0	Reinelt 48[p] 67[p], Jones 76
10.11	Ryman P	Canvey Island	1284	2 - 3	Noble 32, Quinton 67
17.11	Ryman P	MAIDENHEAD UNITED	363	2 - 1	Reinelt 46, Cowan 84
20.11	Essex SC 3	Stansted	n.k	5 - 1	Simpson 15, Reinelt 55 80 88, Gutzmore 90
24.11	Ryman P	St Albans City	502	1 - 3	Noble 44
27.11	Lge Cup 1	ABINGDON TOWN	n.k	2 - 2	Jones 85, Reinelt 90
01.12	FA Trophy 2	BASINGSTOKE TOWN	342	1 - 1	Noble 69
04.12	FA Trophy 2 R	Basingstoke Town	236	2 - 0	Noble 58, Reinelt 72
08.12	Ryman P	BOREHAM WOOD	373	2 - 0	Gutzmore 61, Davidson 83
11.12	Lge Cup 1 R	Abingdon Town	n.k	4 - 0	
15.12	Ryman P	Sutton United	515	1 - 3	Simpson 88
18.12	Ryman P	HITCHIN TOWN	268	0 - 1	
29.12	Ryman P	GRAYS ATHLETIC	389	2 - 3	Reinelt 31, Simpson 69
05.01	Ryman P	Billericay Town	665	4 - 2	Reinelt 37[p], Noble 64, Simpson 68 71
08.01	Lge Cup 2	MOLESEY	n.k	4 - 1	
12.01	FA Trophy 3	Dulwich Hamlet	379	4 - 3	Noble 27, Simpson 41 90, Parratt 85
16.01	East Ang.	TIPTREE UNITED	n.k	2 - 0	
22.01	Essex SC 4	PURFLEET	n.k	0 - 3	
29.01	Lge Cup 3	CANVEY ISLAND	n.k	3 - 5	Simpson ?? Blackery ??
30.01	Eastern FL	HAVERHILL ROVERS	n.k	0 - 0	
02.02	FA Trophy 4	North Ferriby United	381	4 - 4	Simpson 10 57 69, Blaney 78
12.02	FA Trophy 4 R	NORTH FERRIBY UNITED	580	2 - 2	Cowan 30, Simpson 57 5 4
13.02	Eastern FL	HALSTEAD TOWN	n.k	3 - 3	4 2
16.02	Ryman P	CHESHAM UNITED	302	2 - 0	Simpson 31, Reinelt 83
19.02	Ryman P	HEYBRIDGE SWIFTS	460	2 - 0	Davidson 31, Noble 86
23.02	FA Trophy 5	Margate	802	1 - 1	Noble 82
02.03	Ryman P	CROYDON	277	2 - 1	Simpson 28, Noble 38
05.03	FA Trophy 5 R	MARGATE	846	1 - 2	Culverhouse 88
09.03	Ryman P	Purfleet	301	2 - 3	Simpson 7, Smith 71
12.03	Ryman P	Bedford Town	534	0 - 2	
16.03	Ryman P	ENFIELD	283	2 - 3	Reinelt 18, Simpson 25
19.03	Ryman P	Boreham Wood	134	2 - 1	Reinelt 42, Good 90
19.03	Eastern FL	Halstead Town	n.k	1 - 1	
23.03	Ryman P	Basingstoke Town	295	2 - 1	Quinton 27, Jones 78
26.03	Ryman P	Kingstonian	383	2 - 0	Jones 13, Quinton 51
01.04	Ryman P	Heybridge Swifts	333	1 - 1	Simpson 75
06.04	Ryman P	Hitchin Town	364	1 - 1	Noble 29
09.04	Ryman P	HARROW BOROUGH	265	0 - 0	
13.04	Ryman P	GRAVESEND & NORTHFLEET	663	0 - 2	
16.04	Ryman P	Hendon	189	0 - 3	
18.04	Ryman P	ALDERSHOT TOWN	300	2 - 0	Jones 42, Cowan 48
20.04	Ryman P	Maidenhead United	181	0 - 2	
23.04	Ryman P	ST ALBANS CITY	263	2 - 1	Noble 16, Reinelt 35
27.04	Ryman P	CANVEY ISLAND	1104	2 - 1	Jones 62 88

PLAYING SQUAD

Goalkeepers: Paul Catley (Chelmsford)
Defenders: Brett Girling (Chelmsford), Gavin Cowan (Youth), Wayne Houghton (Tiptree Utd),
Gary Waters (Heybridge Swifts), Mark Jones (Romford)
Midfielders: Adam Gillespie (Heybridge Swifts), David Kreyling (Heybridge S.), Dean Parrat (Billericay T)
Forwards: Bradley Quinton (Bishop Stortford), Neil Cussons (Maldon T), Tom Noble (Maldon T),
Steve Good (Romford)

CANVEY ISLAND

CLUB OFFICIALS
Chairman: **Ray Cross,** 95 Lakeside Path,
Canvey Island, Essex SS8 5PD.
Tel: 01268 684357 (H)
Secretary: **Mrs Frances Roche,** 56
Harvest Road, Canvey Island SS8 9RP.
Tel: 01268 698586 (H/Fax)
Press Officer: **Tony Roche**
Tel: 01268 698586

FOOTBALL MANAGEMENT TEAM
Manager: Jeff King. 01268 511555 (B)
07850654321 (Mobile)
Asst Manager: Glenn Pennyfather
Physio: Harry Johnson

FACT FILE
Formed: 1926
Nickname: Gulls
Sponsors: Kings Park Homes
Colours: Yellow/blue/white
Change colours: Red & Blue/White/white
Midweek matchday: Tuesday
Reserves' League:
Essex & Herts Border Comb
Club Website: www.canveyfc.com
2001-02
Captain Steve Tilson
Supporters P.o.Y.: Lee Boylan
Top Goalscorer: Lee Boylan 43

GROUND: Park Lane, Canvey Island, Essex SS8 7PXTel: 01268 682991
Directions: A130 from A13 or A127 at Sadlers Farm r/about, 1 mile through town centre, 1st
right past old bus garage. Bus 3 or 151 fromBenfleet (BR) to stop after Admiral Jellicoe (PH)
Capacity: 4,308   Seats: 500   Cover: 827   Floodlights: Yes
Clubhouse: Open Tues, Thurs & Sats. Full licence. Food avaiable
Club Shop: Open matchdays. Selling programmes, badges, shirts etc.
Contact Keith Johnson (07773 959125)

Pages: 52 Price: £1.50
Editor: Keith Johnson (07773 959125)
Local Press: Evening Echo
Local Radio: Essex FM, BBC Essex

PREVIOUS   **Leagues:** Southend & Dist.; Thurrock & Thameside Comb.; Parthenon; Metropolitan;Gtr London 64-71; Essex Senior
Grounds: None   **Names:** None

CLUB RECORDS Attendance: 3,250 v Brighton & Hove Albion F.A. Cup 95-96
Win: 9-1 v Somersett Ambury   **Defeat:** 7-0 v Halstead
Career Appearances: Steve Price (407)   **Career Goalscorer:** Andy Jones
Fee received: £3,000 for Ian Durrant from Grays Athletic
Fee paid: £ 5,000 for Chris Duffy to Northwich Victoria

BEST SEASON   FA Cup: 3Rd Round, 1-4 v Burnley (A) 01-02   League clubs defeated: Port Vale 2-1(A) after 1-1 (H)
FA Vase: Semi-final v Tiverton 27/3/93   **FA Trophy:** Winners 2000-01 v Forset Green Rovers 1-0
HONOURS: Ryman Lge Prem R-up 00-01,01-02 ,Div 1 98-99 - Div 2 95-96, 97-98,R-up 98-99 Div 3 R-up 94-95; Carlton Trophy 95-96;
Essex Sen Lg 86-87 92-93 (Lg Cup 79-80 92-93),Trophy R-up 93-94; Harry Fisher Mem.Tphy 93-94; Essex Thameside Trophy 93-94; Parthenon
Lge Cup 58-59; Metropolian Lge 67-68 68-69, Cup 67-68 68-69; Thameside 95-96 97-98, Essex Sen Cup 98-99,99-00,01-02

Players progressing: Peter Taylor (Spurs), Gary Heale (Luton T)

Back row left to right: Mark Stimson, Ben Chenery, Peter Smith, Glen Johnson, Ashl;ey Harrison, Chris Duffy, Mick Bodley and Neil Gregory .
Middle Row: Harry Johnson (Physio), Adam Tanner, Steve Tilson, Jeff King (Manager), Paul Cobb, Micky Bennett and Glenn Pennyfather (coach)
Front Row: Steve Parmenter, Ian Thompson, Lee Boylan, John Kennedy, Wayne Vaughan and Adam Miller.

Date	Comp.	Opponents	Att.	Score	Goalscorers
18.08	Ryman P	Chesham United	336	5 - 1	Tilson 42[p] 55[p], Vaughan 48, Parmenter 50, Gregory 58
21.08	Ryman P	ALDERSHOT TOWN	1120	1 - 3	Boylan 41
25.08	Ryman P	HITCHIN TOWN	406	5 - 3	Gregory 33, Boylan 37 64, Vaughan 60, Miller 90
27.08	Ryman P	Purfleet	693	0 - 0	
01.09	Ryman P	Croydon	211	1 - 2	Tilson 64[p]
04.09	Ryman P	ENFIELD	435	3 - 1	Cobb 40, Tilson 52, Miller 72
08.09	Ryman P	KINGSTONIAN	632	2 - 0	Miller 5 56
11.09	Ryman P	Heybridge Swifts	289	7 - 0	Tilson 17 35, Parmenter 38 68, Stimson 49 90, Vaughan 87[p]
15.09	Ryman P	St Albans City	499	4 - 2	Tilson 11 69, Kennedy 35, Cobb 60
18.09	Ryman P	BOREHAM WOOD	411	2 - 1	Parmenter 42, Miller 47
22.09	Ryman P	HENDON	522	3 - 1	Duffy 48, Cobb 74, Vaughan 78
25.09	Ryman P	Bedford Town	641	3 - 1	Cobb 23, Gregory 70, Boylan 79
29.09	FA Cup Q2	SOMERSETT AMBURY V & E	453	9 - 1	Bennett 20, Gregory 44 47, Boylan 61 66 90, Cobb 72 80, Vaughan 85
09.10	Ryman P	Harrow Borough	203	1 - 1	Duffy 9
13.10	FA Cup Q3	Halesowen Town	823	2 - 0	Cobb 42, Miller 80
16.10	Ryman P	MAIDENHEAD UNITED	415	2 - 0	Gregory 11 50[p]
20.10	Ryman P	BASINGSTOKE TOWN	521	5 - 1	Stimson 50, Miller 60, Vaughan 63, Vaughan 77, Boylan 85
27.10	FA Cup Q4	STAFFORD RANGERS	561	5 - 1	Tilson 17[p] 68 72, Miller 35, Vaughan 36
30.10	Essex SC 3	Leyton Pennant	76	4 - 0	Smith 10, Boylan 44 58, Miller 84
06.11	Ryman P	Grays Athletic	704	1 - 0	Parmenter 40
10.11	Ryman P	BRAINTREE TOWN	1284	3 - 2	Parmenter 35, Cobb 43 46
13.11	Ryman P	Sutton United	574	4 - 1	Boylan 72, Vaughan 79 81, Knight 87
17.11	FA Cup 1	Wigan Athletic	3671	1 - 0	Gregory 88
24.11	Ryman P	Hampton & Richmond Borough	449	5 - 1	Duffy 14, Vaughan 64 70, Stimson 75, Kennedy 80
27.11	Lge Cup 1	LEWES	n.k	3 - 2	Miller 19, Boylan 31, Stimson 44
01.12	FA Trophy 2	ST ALBANS CITY	480	5 - 1	Kennedy 3, Parmenter 11, Vaughan 42 45, Gregory 56
09.12	FA Cup 2	NORTHAMPTON TOWN	3232	1 - 0	Gregory 48
11.12	Lge Cup 2	Bishop's Stortford	n.k	4 - 2	
15.12	Ryman P	CHESHAM UNITED	486	2 - 1	Ward 70, Duffy 90
22.12	Ryman P	PURFLEET	641	3 - 0	Smith 34, Boylan 56 78
26.12	Ryman P	Billericay Town	1408	3 - 0	Cobb 33, Boylan 70[p], Chenery 76
29.12	Ryman P	Aldershot Town	2630	3 - 1	Boylan 53 57, Kennedy 84
05.01	FA Cup 3	Burnley	11496	1 - 4	Boylan 67
08.01	Ryman P	GRAVESEND & NORTHFLEET	2111	0 - 2	
12.01	FA Trophy 3	PURFLEET	483	2 - 2	Cobb 30, Chandler 42[og]
14.01	FA Trophy 3 R	Purfleet	471	1 - 0	Miller 115
19.01	Ryman P	Kingstonian	754	1 - 2	Boylan 70
22.01	Essex SC 4	SOUTHEND MANOR	214	6 - 1	Thompson 52, Vaughan 70, Gregory 74, Knight 80 82 83
29.01	Lge Cup 3	Braintree Town	n.k	5 - 3	F
02.02	FA Trophy 4	Grantham Town	1222	4 - 1	Boylan 60 84, Duffy 70, Gregory 72
05.02	Lge Cup QF	Northwood	213	1 - 3	Vaughan 60
09.02	Ryman P	HAMPTON & RICHMOND BOR.	560	1 - 1	Stimson 45
12.02	Ryman P	Enfield	121	3 - 0	Boylan 39, Knight 59, Duffy 63
16.02	Ryman P	Boreham Wood	372	3 - 0	Boylan 29 90, Nicholls 88
19.02	Ryman P	CROYDON	426	3 - 0	Gregory 64, Boylan 67, Parmenter 85
23.02	Ryman P	ST ALBANS CITY	425	3 - 2	Boylan 32[p], Gregory 35, Parmenter 56
26.02	Ryman P	HEYBRIDGE SWIFTS	289	6 - 1	Boylan 4 15 47 86, Tilson 13, Parmenter 76
02.03	Ryman P	Hendon	314	1 - 0	Bodley 23
05.03	FA Trophy 5	Yeovil Town	3616	1 - 2	Cobb 89
09.03	Ryman P	BEDFORD TOWN	805	3 - 3	Cobb 45, Miller 77, Boylan 89
13.03	Essex SC QF	Harlow Town	88	1 - 0	Boylan 88
16.03	Ryman P	Maidenhead United	306	1 - 0	Boylan 45
20.03	Essex SC SF	Chelmsford City	307	3 - 2	Cobb 4, Gregory 18 70
23.03	Ryman P	HARROW BOROUGH	482	3 - 0	Knight 25, Chenery 49, Boylan 69
26.03	Ryman P	Gravesend & Northfleet	4098	1 - 0	Gregory 33
30.03	Ryman P	Hitchin Town	550	1 - 2	Vaughan 90
01.04	Ryman P	BILLERICAY TOWN	1027	3 - 0	Gregory 5, Blackwell 29[og], Chenery 50
06.04	Ryman P	GRAYS ATHLETIC	728	1 - 2	Boylan 5
13.04	Ryman P	Basingstoke Town	546	4 - 0	Gregory 20, Boylan 40, Duffy 45, Knight 74
15.04	Essex SC F	DAGENHAM & REDBRIDGE	n.k	6 - 1	Gregory 9 70 90, Boylan 43 51 61 @ Southend United
20.04	Ryman P	SUTTON UNITED	808	1 - 1	Tilson 45[p]
27.04	Ryman P	Braintree Town	1104	1 - 2	Boylan 67

PLAYING SQUAD

Goalkeepers: Ashley Harrison (Dover Ath.), Dean Greygoose (Stevenage Bor.), Danny Potter (Chelmsford), Glen Johnson (Youth)
Defenders: Ben Chenery (Kettering T.), David Gregory (Colchester Utd.), Lee Protheroe (Aldershot), Mickey Bennett (Brighton), Steve Ward (Grays A.), Craig Davidson (Braintree), Garry Britnell (Enfield), Mick Bodley (Dagenham & Red.), Ollie Adedeji (Aldershot T)
Midfielders: Adam Tanner (Colchester Utd), Ian Thompson (Norwich C), Jeff Minton (Grays Ath), Kevin Dobinson (Chelmsford C), Scott Forbes (Southend), Chris Duffy (Northwich Vic.), Jason Dozell (Colchester Utd), John Kennedy (Ipswich T), Matt Jones (Dagenham & Redbridge)
Forwards: Andy Jones (Billerachy), Lee Boylan (Heybridge Swifts), Paul Cobb (Dagenham & Redbridge), Steve Parmenter (Dorchester), Bert Brayley (Swindon T), Neil Gregory (Colchester Utd), Spencer Knight (Harrow Bor.)

Match Facts 2001-02

CHESHAM UNITED

CLUB OFFICIALS

President: Bill Wells
Chairman: Tony O'Driscoll
Secretary: T.B.A.
c/o Chesham United FC.
Tel: 01494 775490 (H) 0181327 4016(B)
Commercial Manager: T.B.A.
Press Officer: Phil Morgan

FOOTBALL MANAGEMENT TEAM
Manager: Colin Lippiatt
Physio: Kevin Campbell

FACT FILE
Formed: 1886 Nickname: The Generals
Sponsors: T.B.A.
Colours: Claret & blue quarters/claret/claret
Change colours: White & blue/blue/white
Midweek home matchday: Tuesday
Reserve Team's League: Suburban North
Match information: 09068 335505

2001-02
Captain & P.o.Y.:Derek Brown
Top Scorer: Wayne Andrews 26

Ryman football league

THE **MEADOW**
matchday magazine 2001/02

Ryman Premier Division
v
Maidenhead United
Wednesday 26th December 2001 Kick-off 3.00pm

Pages: 52   Price: £1.50
Editors: Alan Calder
(01442 230420 [H])

Local Radio: Three Counties
Local Press: Bucks Examiner, Bucks
Advertiser, Bucks Free Press

GROUND: The Meadow, Amy Lane, Amersham Road, Chesham, Bucks. HP5 1NE
Tel: 01494 783964 (ground clubhouse) Fax: 01494 794244 Club Website: www.cheshamunit-edfc.co.uk Email Address: jimchamberschesham@talk21.com

Directions: M25 junction 18, A404 to Amersham, A416 to Chesham - go down to r-about at foot of Amersham Hill, then sharp left. 10 mins walk from Chesham station (Metropolitan Line)
Capacity: 5,000   Cover: 2,500   Seats: 284   Floodlights: Yes

Clubhouse: Open every evening & matchdays. Bar snacks. Available for hire(business training meetings, weddings etc)
Club Shop: Open matchdays   Metal Badges: Yes

PREVIOUS   **Leagues:** Spartan 17-47; Corinthian 47-63; Athenian 63-73

CLUB RECORDS **Attendance:** 5,000 v Cambridge Utd, FA 3rd Rd 5/12/79
Goalscorer: John Willis   **Appearances:** Martin Baguley (600+)
Record Fees - Paid & Received: Undisclosed (club policy)

BEST SEASON **FA Cup:** 3rd Rd 79-80. 1st Rd 66-67 68-69 76-77 82-83
FA Amtr Cup: R-up 67-68   **FA Trophy:** 3rd Rd 92-93 (1-3 v Sutton United [H])

HONOURS: FA Amtr Cup R-up 67-68, Isthmian Lg 92-93 (Div 1 90-91 96-97), Div 2 Nth 86-87, Associate Members Cup R-up 90-91, Charity Shield 94-95; Athenian Lg Div 1 Cup 63-64 68-69; Corinthian Lg R-up (2) 60-62 (Lg Cup 60-61); Spartan Lg(4) 21-23 24-25 32-33 (R-up 26-27 29-30 33-34); Berks & Bucks Snr Cup 21-22 25-26 28-29 33-34 47-48 50-51 64-65 66-67 75-76 92-93. 00-01 (R-up 94-95, 01-02)

Players progressing: Bill Shipwright & Jimmy Strain (Watford 53 & 55), StewartScullion (Charlton 65), John Pyatt (L'pool 67), Brian Carter (Brentford 68),Kerry Dixon (Spurs 78), Tony Currie (Torquay 84), Dwayne Plummer (Bristol Rovers)

Chesham United, August 2002.
Back row from left: Clive Howse (assistant manager), Kevin Mealor, Marc Leach, Julian Capone, Steve Dogbe, Julian Mehdi Mehamha, Scott Ward, Delroy Preddie, Dwain Clarke, Grant Cooper, Jermaine Hunter, Leon White and Colin Lippiatt (manager). **Front row:** Dave Fotheringham, Steve Miles, Kieran Corcoran, Steve Sinclair, James Bent, Andre Scarlett, Conrad Thorpe and Tom Neil.

Picture: BUCKINGHAMSHIRE EXAMINER

ISTHMIAN LEAGUE PREMIER DIVISION

Date	Comp.	Opponents	Att.	Score	Goalscorers
18.08	Ryman P	CANVEY ISLAND	336	1 - 5	Fewings 31
21.08	Ryman P	Gravesend & Northfleet	391	4 - 1	Fewings 4, Andrews 18 81, Barnes 44
25.08	Ryman P	Sutton United	532	1 - 0	Andrews 48
27.08	Ryman P	BASINGSTOKE TOWN	348	1 - 1	Statham 55[p]
01.09	Ryman P	St Albans City	393	1 - 3	Andrews 9[p]
08.09	Ryman P	HEYBRIDGE SWIFTS	218	3 - 0	Andrews 25 38, Graham 87
11.09	Ryman P	Kingstonian	402	0 - 1	
15.09	Ryman P	Billericay Town	634	0 - 0	
18.09	Ryman P	BRAINTREE TOWN	206	4 - 1	Andrews 43 68 88, Goddard 60
22.09	Ryman P	BOREHAM WOOD	343	1 - 0	Graham 12
25.09	Ryman P	Grays Athletic	242	1 - 2	Goddard 88
29.09	FA Cup Q2	EAST THURROCK UNITED	238	2 - 0	Andrews 2 79
02.10	Ryman P	HARROW BOROUGH	242	5 - 0	Cooksey 21, Andrews 31[p], Hall 45, Boyle-Renner 84 90
09.10	Ryman P	Bedford Town	481	0 - 2	
13.10	FA Cup Q3	CAMBRIDGE CITY	436	0 - 1	
20.10	Ryman P	Hitchin Town	291	3 - 2	Andrews 23, Bowes 57, Boyle-Renner 82
27.10	Ryman P	PURFLEET	270	0 - 0	
03.11	Ryman P	ALDERSHOT TOWN	865	2 - 1	Cooksey 4, Bowes 90
10.11	Ryman P	Croydon	78	1 - 0	Graham 90
24.11	Ryman P	Hendon	244	2 - 1	Darlington 2, Pickett 78[og]
27.11	Lge Cup 1	ST ALBANS CITY	164	2 - 0	Graham Armstrong ??
01.12	FA Trophy 2	WEYMOUTH	416	4 - 0	Cooksey 17, Graham 38, Walton 49, Fewings 63
08.12	Ryman P	HAMPTON & RICHMOND BOR.	306	2 - 1	Andrews 10, Spiller 32[p]
15.12	Ryman P	Canvey Island	486	1 - 2	Andrews 46
22.12	Ryman P	ENFIELD	276	0 - 0	
29.12	Ryman P	GRAVESEND & NORTHFLEET	424	2 - 2	Doyle-Renner 15, Solomon 50[p]
05.01	Ryman P	Aldershot Town	1541	0 - 1	
08.01	Ryman P	MAIDENHEAD UNITED	179	1 - 0	Boyle-Renner 9
12.01	FA Trophy 3	HEREFORD UNITED	831	2 - 2	Andrews 35, Fewings 76
15.01	FA Trophy 3 R	Hereford United	1075	0 - 4	
19.01	Ryman P	Heybridge Swifts	236	1 - 2	Hall 90
22.01	Ryman P	Basingstoke Town	233	1 - 1	Graham 26
24.01	Lge Cup 2	ENFIELD	n.k	0 - 2	
05.02	B & B S QF	CHALFONT ST PETER	n.k	5 - 0	Fewings 30 47 70[p], Spiller 60[p], Andrews 83
09.02	Ryman P	HENDON	323	0 - 2	
16.02	Ryman P	Braintree Town	302	0 - 2	
23.02	Ryman P	BILLERICAY TOWN	203	2 - 0	Cooksey 1, Spiller 83[p]
02.03	Ryman P	Boreham Wood	242	1 - 2	Graham 43
05.03	Ryman P	Hampton & Richmond Borough	163	2 - 0	Campbell 27, Fewings 90
09.03	Ryman P	GRAYS ATHLETIC	229	3 - 5	Campbell 12 45 74[p]
16.03	Ryman P	Harrow Borough	206	1 - 2	Andrews 49
19.03	Ryman P	ST ALBANS CITY	205	3 - 2	Andrews 3, Fewings 32, Graham 76
23.03	Ryman P	BEDFORD TOWN	416	1 - 1	Fewings 15
26.03	B & B S SF	BURNHAM	155	3 - 1	Fewings 25 85, Spiller 52[p]
30.03	Ryman P	SUTTON UNITED	266	2 - 0	Andrews 14 50
01.04	Ryman P	Maidenhead United	246	4 - 0	Graham 38 45, Fewings 41, Andrews 69
06.04	Ryman P	Purfleet	203	2 - 2	Brown 36, Graham 40[p]
13.04	Ryman P	HITCHIN TOWN	230	5 - 5	Andrews 27 58, Cook 28, Graham 45[p], Kersey 89
16.04	Ryman P	KINGSTONIAN	221	0 - 0	
20.04	Ryman P	Enfield	121	3 - 0	Cooksey 62, Fewings 88 90
27.04	Ryman P	CROYDON	239	2 - 1	Andrews 10, Fewings 37
06.05	Berks & B S F	MAIDENHEAD UNITED	n.k	0 - 0	2 4 Wycombe Wanderers

PLAYING SQUAD

Goalkeepers: Delroy Preedie (Walton and Hesham), Scott Ward (Luton T)
Defenders: Grant Cooper (Enfield), Keiran Corcoran (Aylesbury Utd), Tom Neill (Watford), Leon White (Sutton Utd), Marc Leach (Wycombe Wanderers)
Midfielders: Andre Scarlett (Hitchin Utd), Steve Dogbe (Luton T), Dave Fotheringham (Youth Team), Steve Sinclair (Borenham Wood)
Forwards: Jamie Bent (Chippenham T.), Julian Capone (Boreham Wood), Mark Nwokeji (Leatherhead), Jermaine Hunter (Harrow Borough), Kevin Mealor (Youth Team), Steve Miles (Marlow)

ENFIELD

Official Matchday Programme — Season 2001-2002

Enfield Football Club

Sponsored by
EVERBRITE
WINDOWS & DOORS

Ryman

Boreham Wood FC
1 April 2002: Ryman League : Premier Division
Kick off 3.00 pm

Official Website: www.enfieldfc.com £1.50

CLUB OFFICIALS

Chairman: A Lazarou
President: R.Prosser
Secretary & Match Sec: Derek Bird,17
Fishers Close, Waltham Cross,Herts.
Tel No: 01992 301741
07765 837246 (M)
07992 066605 (Fax)

FOOTBALL MANAGEMENT TEAM

Manager: Terry Back

FACT FILE
Formed: 1893
Nickname: The E's
Sponsors:
Newsline: 0930 555845
Colours: White/blue/white
Change colours: Blue/white/blue
Midweek matchday: Tuesday
Reserves' League: Middlesex Co.
2001-002: Captain Nicky Gyoury
P.O.Y.: Lee Allen
Top Scorer: George Georgiou 19

Pages: 48 Price: £1.50
Editor: Steven Edwards, Derek Bird and Edward Penn
Local Press: Enfield Gazette,
Enfield Advertiser, Enfield Independent

GROUND: Boreham Wood FC. Meadow Park, Broughinge Rd, Boreham Wood, Herts WD6 5AL. Tel: 0208 9535097 Email: efcltd@lineone.net Website: www.enfieldfc.com
Directions: A1 towards London from M25, 1st turn for Boreham Wood, head for town centre, into Brook Rd at r'bout before town centre, Broughinge Rd is 1st right. 1 mile from Elstree & Boreham Wood station (Thameslink), or bus 292 or 107 to McDonalds (5 minutes walk)
Capacity: 4,502 Cover: 1,568 Seats: 500 Floodlights: Yes
Club Shop: Alan Farmer (0208366 6066)

PREVIOUS **Leagues:** Tottenham & Dist 1894-95; Nth Middx 96-1903; London 03-13 20-21; Middx 08-12, 19-20; Athenian 12-14 21-39 45-63; Herts & Middx Comb 39-42; Isthmian 63-81; GMV Conference 81-90
Name: Enfield Spartans 1893-1900 **Grounds:** Baileys Field 1893-96; Tuckers Field 96-1900; Cherry Orchard Lane1900-36

CLUB RECORDS **Attendance:** 10,000 (10/10/62) v Spurs, floodlight opener Southbury Road 1936-1999
Win: 18-0 v Stevenage FA Cup 2nd Qual 22/10/27 (H) **Defeat:** 0-12 v Woolwich Polytechnic, London Lge Div 2 27/4/04
Fee Paid: for Gary Abbott (Barnet) **Fee Received:** for Paul Furlong (Coventry City)
Scorer: Tommy Lawrence, 191 1959-1964. **Appearances:** Steve King 617 (77-89)

BEST SEASON FA Amateur Cup: Winners 66-7 69-70 R-up 63-4 71-2 FA Trophy: Winners 81-2 87-8
FA Cup: 4th Rd replay 80-81, 0-3 v Barnsley (at Spurs), Att 35,244, after 1-1.
League clubs beaten: Wimbledon, Northampton 77-78, Hereford, Port Vale 80-81, Wimbledon 81-82, Exeter 84-85, Orient 88-89, Aldershot 91-92, Cardiff City 94-95, Torquay Utd 94-95, Chesterfield 99-00

HONOURS: Alliance Premier Lge 82-83 85-86 (R-up 81-82), Lg Cup R-up 81-82; IsthmianLg(8) 67-70 75-78 79-80 94-95 (R-up 64-65 71-72 74-75 80-81 90-92 95-96), LgCup(2) 78-80 (R-up 91-92 94-95); Athenian Lg(2) 61-63 (R-up 34-35); London LgDiv 1 11-12 (R-up 04-05 06-07); Middx Snr Cup 13-14 46-47 61-62 65-66 68-71 77-81 88-89 90-91 97-98, (R-up 10-11 20-21 47-48 51-52 57-60 62-63 66-67 72-73 75-76 84-85); London Snr Cup 34-35 60-61 66-67 71-73 75-76 (R-up 63-64 67-68 70-71); Middx Lg (West) 09-10 (R-up 10-11); European Amtr Cup Winners Cup 69-70

Players progressing: Terry McQuade (Millwall 61), Roger Day (Watford 61), Jeff Harris (Orient 64), Peter Feely (Chelsea 70), Carl Richards & Jon Bailey (B'mouth 80 & 95), Paul Furlong (Coventry 91), Andy Pape (Barnet 91), GregHeald (Peterborough 94), Lee Marshall (Norwich City 97)

Back row, left to right: Tom Loizow (ex manager), John Sitton (ex Asst Manager), George Gregoriou, Simon Peddie, N icky Gyoury, Ricky Millard , Kenny Addai, Michael Kalli, James Ayres, Dave Reddington, Steve Magona, Malik Sesay, Dwayne Minors, Kevin Ellis (P(hysio) and Frank Fuschillo **Front row:** Patrick Yembe, George Georgiou,Gary Hoy ,Glen Wilkie, Marvin Rufus, Clive Walker, Lee Allen, Vas Soteriou and Dean Fenton.

Match Facts 2001-02

Date	Comp.	Opponents	Att.	Score	Goalscorers
18.08	Ryman P	Aldershot Town	2057	1 - 3	Koulamanou 49
21.08	Ryman P	CROYDON	89	3 - 1	Allen 26, Georgiou 34, Nartey 51
25.08	Ryman P	PURFLEET	103	0 - 1	
27.08	Ryman P	Kingstonian	560	2 - 0	Allen 36, Georgiou 89
01.09	Ryman P	BASINGSTOKE TOWN	102	3 - 0	Georgiou 45, Soteriou 45, Nartey 90[p]
04.09	Ryman P	Canvey Island	435	1 - 3	Nartey 62
08.09	Ryman P	Gravesend & Northfleet	473	0 - 3	
11.09	Ryman P	HITCHIN TOWN	89	0 - 5	
15.09	Ryman P	Sutton United	509	1 - 1	Georgiou 51
18.09	Ryman P	HAMPTON & RICHMOND BOR.	83	0 - 2	
22.09	Ryman P	MAIDENHEAD UNITED	114	0 - 2	
25.09	Ryman P	St Albans City	252	1 - 1	Gant 27
29.09	FA Cup Q2	Newmarket Town	219	3 - 1	Petersen 28, Nartey 59, Cooper 88
02.10	Ryman P	BRAINTREE TOWN	87	1 - 2	Gant 24
09.10	Ryman P	Billericay Town	451	2 - 3	Allen 86, Peterson 90
13.10	FA Cup Q3	YEADING	81	3 - 4	Ayres 28, Georgiou 31 85
20.10	Ryman P	GRAYS ATHLETIC	111	1 - 2	Ayres 45
03.11	FA Trophy 1	HASTINGS TOWN	126	2 - 1	Georgiou 8, Petersen 45
10.11	Ryman P	HENDON	137	0 - 6	
13.11	Ryman P	Bedford Town	435	2 - 2	Walker 31, Georgiou 82
15.11	Middx SC 1	VIKING GREENFORD	n.k	6 - 3	
24.11	Ryman P	Harrow Borough	188	4 - 2	Georgiou 22, Walker 30, Gregoriou 65, Minors 72
01.12	FA Trophy 2	HISTON	121	2 - 2	Walker 4, Rufus 33
08.12	Ryman P	HEYBRIDGE SWIFTS	99	4 - 2	Ayres 5, Gregorio 55[p], Georgiou 70, Sesay 87
15.12	Ryman P	ALDERSHOT TOWN	439	1 - 1	Gregoriou 16
18.12	FA Trophy 2 R	Histon	114	1 - 3	Ayres 23
22.12	Ryman P	Chesham United	276	0 - 0	
26.12	Ryman P	Boreham Wood	207	3 - 1	Georgiou 60 90[p], Gyoury 73
29.12	Ryman P	Croydon	83	2 - 0	Chin 49[og], Walker 62
08.01	Middx SC 2	Uxbridge	n.k	0 - 4	
10.01	Lge Cup 1	EGHAM TOWN	n.k	4 - 1	
12.01	Ryman P	Basingstoke Town	417	0 - 2	
19.01	Ryman P	GRAVESEND & NORTHFLEET	306	1 - 5	Lee 50[og]
24.01	Lge Cup 2	Chesham United	n.k	2 - 0	
26.01	Ryman P	Hitchin Town	343	2 - 1	Walker 24, Georgiou 90
29.01	Ryman P	KINGSTONIAN	129	2 - 2	Georgiou 41, Wilkie 90
02.02	Ryman P	Heybridge Swifts	221	2 - 4	Georgiou 27, Cooper 45
05.02	Lge Cup 3	HITCHIN TOWN	n.k	4 - 0	
09.02	Ryman P	HARROW BOROUGH	143	1 - 2	Gregoriou 76
12.02	Ryman P	CANVEY ISLAND	121	0 - 3	
16.02	Ryman P	Hampton & Richmond Borough	264	1 - 2	Soteriou 63
19.02	Lge Cup QF	Hampton & Richmond Borough	n.k	0 - 1	
23.02	Ryman P	SUTTON UNITED	159	2 - 2	Allen 15, Georgiou 45
02.03	Ryman P	Maidenhead United	168	1 - 0	Rufus 90
09.03	Ryman P	ST ALBANS CITY	221	0 - 0	
16.03	Ryman P	Braintree Town	283	3 - 2	Georgiou 34 58, Walker 54
23.03	Ryman P	BILLERICAY TOWN	185	0 - 2	
29.03	Ryman P	Purfleet	236	0 - 1	
01.04	Ryman P	BOREHAM WOOD	132	0 - 1	
06.04	Ryman P	BEDFORD TOWN	201	1 - 0	Walker 15
13.04	Ryman P	Grays Athletic	237	0 - 0	
20.04	Ryman P	CHESHAM UNITED	121	0 - 3	
27.04	Ryman P	Hendon	335	0 - 2	

PLAYING SQUAD

Goalkeepers: Kenny Addai (Beaconsfield Sycob), Mark Whittamore (Hemel Hempstead), Michael Kalli (Wingate and Finchley), Ricky Millard (Barnet)

Defenders: Dave Reddington (Cheshunt), Mark Boyce (Chesham Utd), Simon Peddie (Youth), James Ayres (Kettering Town), Paul Kyriacou (Bishop Stortford)

Midfielders: Adam Gant (Witham T), Chris Perifimou (Cheshunt), David Preece (Torquay Utd), Glen Wilkie (Cheshunt), Mike Rodosthenous (Cheshunt), Stuart Maynard (Aylesbury Utd), Dean Coppard (Hayes), Marvin Rufus (Romford), Oliver Petersen (Harrow Bor.)

Forwards: Chris Boothe (Aylesbury), George Gregorid (Cheshunt), Kelechi Opara (Billencay T), Leon Hall (Cheahunt), Mike Koulamanou (Wembly), Dwayne Lewis (Harrow Borough), Jody Loomes (Cheahunt), Kevin Warren (Barking & E. Ham Utd), Malik Sesay (SISK Trelleborgs-Sweden), Warren Waugh (Crawley T)

FORD UNITED

Official Program £1.50p

CLUB OFFICIALS

Chairman: Jimmy Chapman
President : Nick Scheeler
Secretary: Alan Wetherall,23 Warley Avenue, Dagenham, Essex RM8 1JS
Tel : 02085172419 H) 07712365424 (M)
Chief Execs: John Rowe & George Adams

FOOTBALL MANAGEMENT TEAM
Manager: Dennis Elliott
Coach: Stevie Brice
Assistant Coach: Johnny Burrows
Physio.: Paul Baskin

FACT FILE
Founded: 1934
Nickname: Motormen
Sponsor: Sky Sports
Colours: Blue/white/red
Change: red/red/blue.
Midweek home matchday: Tuesday
Res Lg. Essex & Herts Border Comb

2001-02
Captain: Jay Devereux
Top Scorer: Chris Rose 25

Ford United
vs
Basingstoke Town
Saturday 31st August 2002
kick-off 3:00pm

Ryman
Premier Division
2002 - 2003

sponsored by
SKY SPORTS

Programme
Pages: 72   Price: £1
Editor: Michael Ewen
Tel: 01708 724178 (H)

GROUND Oakside Stadium,Station Road, Barkingside, Ilford, Essex
Directions: From London Take A12 ,Eastern Avenue and turn left into Horns Road., Barkingside (Greengate). Right into Craven Gardens, right again into Carlton Drive and left into Station Road..Go over bridge and ground is on right next to Barkingside (Central Line). From Ilford BR station take 169 bus to Craven Gardens.
Capacity: 3,000   **Seats:** 316   **Cover:** 1000   **Floodlights:** Yes   **Club Shop:** Yes
Clubhouse: Large bar which is open every day 12.00 midday until 11.00 p.m.

HONOURS: London Snr Cup 55-56 56-57 94-95 97-98; 00-01 Essex Snr Lge 91-92 96-97,R-up 94-95, Essex Sen. Trophy 90-91 91-92,00-01 Essex Senior Cup 39-40 49-50 50-51 51-52 85-86, R-up Spartan Lg 49-50 50-51 55-56 56-57 57-58; London Lg 36-37 38-39; Essex Elizabethan 59-60 60-61 70-71; Gtr London Lg 70-71; Sportsmanship Award 77-78 79-80 80-81; Essex Thameside Trophy 98-=99Essex & Herts Border Comb.(res) 94-95 (Lg Cup 94-95); Isthmian League Div 3 98-99, Promoted from Div 2 99-00, Promoted to Isthmian Premier 01-02

RECORDS: **Attendance:** 58,000 Briggs Sports v Bishop Auckland, at St James Park, Newcastle, FA Amateur Cup
Appearances: Roger Bond   **Goalscorer:** Jeff Wood 196
Win: Unknown   **Defeat:** Unknown

PREVIOUS: **Leagues:** Spartan, Spartan, Aetolian, Metropolitan, Essex Senior
Names: Brigg Sports (1934) & Ford Sports (1934) amalgamated in 1958   **Grounds:** Ford Sports & Social Club, Rush Green Road, Romford.
BEST SEASON: **FA Vase:** 98-99, 5th Round, 1-2 v Bedlington Terriers (H)
FA Amateur Cup: Semi-Final 53-54
Players progressing: Les Allen (Spurs), Mick Flanagan (QPR, Charlton, Crystal Palace), Jim Stannard (Fulham, Southend, Millwall), Nicky Hammond (Arsenal,Swindon), Laurie Abrahams (Charlton), Doug Barton (Reading, Newport)

Date	Comp.	Opponents	Att.	Score	Goalscorers
18.08	Ryman 1	Thame United	158	2 - 1	Read 58, Hoddy 65
21.08	Ryman 1	TOOTING & MITCHAM UNITED	132	1 - 1	Aransibia 90 F
25.08	Ryman 1	WORTHING	122	2 - 1	Bajeda 33 75
27.08	Ryman 1	Staines Town	151	4 - 2	Rose 15, Read 31, Cole 47, Bajeda 61
01.09	FA Cup P	ROYSTON TOWN	112	3 - 2	Rose 9 76, Willis 11 @ Dagenham & Redbridge
08.09	Ryman 1	WINDSOR & ETON	82	4 - 2	Read 2, Rose 13, Woodards 51, Bejada 56
12.09	Ryman 1	WHYTELEAFE	80	2 - 2	Bejada 45, Salmon 89
15.09	FA Cup Q1	Brackley Town	80	1 - 1	Aransibia 89
18.09	FA Cup Q1 R	BRACKLEY TOWN	89	4 - 2	Woodward 31, Rose 90 109, Bejada 101 @ Dagenham &
22.09	Ryman 1	Bromley	199	2 - 1	Rose 45, Aransibia 84
26.09	Ryman 1	BISHOP'S STORTFORD	94	2 - 1	Aransibia 69, Rose 90 @ Barking & E. Ham U.
30.09	FA Cup Q2	YEADING	97	1 - 2	Rose 44
13.10	Ryman 1	SLOUGH TOWN	97	0 - 2	
16.10	Ryman 1	Bognor Regis Town	313	1 - 1	Read 4
20.10	Ryman 1	Aylesbury United	477	4 - 3	Benstock 42 44, Bajeda 52, Read 78[p]
23.10	Ryman 1	Northwood	154	2 - 1	Bajeda 42, Rose 66
30.10	Essex TST 1	Brentwood	n.k	5 - 1	Aransibia 10 40, Benstock 27, Read 77, Rose 85
03.11	FA Trophy 1	Croydon	71	1 - 3	Read 24
10.11	Ryman 1	Uxbridge	79	2 - 1	Rose 34 53
13.11	Essex SC 3	Tiptree United	37	7 - 1	
17.11	Ryman 1	DULWICH HAMLET	73	2 - 2	Willis 24, Heighway 65
20.11	Lge Cup 1	EPSOM & EWELL	n.k	1 - 0	
24.11	Ryman 1	WEALDSTONE	152	2 - 1	Aransibia 55, Reed 71
01.12	Ryman 1	Oxford City	117	2 - 0	Read 22, Aransibia 75
08.12	Ryman 1	Harlow Town	137	1 - 4	Aransibia 83
15.12	Ryman 1	THAME UNITED	47	4 - 2	Aransibia 17, Bajeda 56, Read 78, Livett 86
29.12	Ryman 1	Tooting & Mitcham United	204	4 - 0	Devereaux 9, Poole 53, Bajada 59, Livett 81
05.01	Ryman 1	NORTHWOOD	95	2 - 0	Aransibia 37, Poole 66
08.01	Ryman 1	YEADING	86	3 - 2	Rose 1 76, Bajada 45[p]
12.01	Ryman 1	Windsor & Eton	153	5 - 1	Devereux 17 35, Rose 26 83, Heighway 75
15.01	Essex SC 4	Dagenham & Redbridge	543	1 - 5	Woodward 31
17.01	Lge Cup 2	BARTON ROVERS	n.k	4 - 1	
19.01	Ryman 1	BROMLEY	152	1 - 1	Benstock 67
21.01	London SC 4	Ilford	n.k	1 - 1	Aransibia 87 Lost 5-6 after pens.
22.01	Lge Cup 3	Wealdstone	82	2 - 3	
02.02	Ryman 1	HARLOW TOWN	167	0 - 2	
09.02	Ryman 1	Wealdstone	266	1 - 1	Rose 84
16.02	Ryman 1	OXFORD CITY	114	5 - 0	Woodards 33, Rose 71 82, Benstock 86, Sale 90
19.02	Ryman 1	Barking & East Ham United	171	4 - 1	Salmon 29, Poole 69, Bajeda 80, Adolphe 81
23.02	Ryman 1	Bishop's Stortford	359	1 - 4	Rose 17
02.03	Ryman 1	WALTON & HERSHAM	112	6 - 1	Marsh 39, Bejada 50 76, Salmon 61, Benstock 67 86
05.03	Ryman 1	CARSHALTON ATHLETIC	130	1 - 1	Adolphe 12
09.03	Ryman 1	Yeading	67	1 - 0	Aransibia 45
12.03	Ryman 1	Whyteleafe	121	0 - 1	
16.03	Ryman 1	BOGNOR REGIS TOWN	168	1 - 3	Read 73
23.03	Ryman 1	Slough Town	303	2 - 1	Rose 33, Marsh 45
26.03	Ryman 1	Walton & Hersham	101	2 - 0	Marsh 71, Aransibia 90
30.03	Ryman 1	Worthing	285	2 - 1	Marsh 13, Aransibia 63
01.04	Ryman 1	BARKING & EAST HAM UNITED	224	2 - 1	Reed 25, Rose 30
06.04	Ryman 1	Carshalton Athletic	209	1 - 2	Read 63[p]
13.04	Ryman 1	AYLESBURY UNITED	294	0 - 3	
16.04	Ryman 1	STAINES TOWN	120	2 - 1	Aransibia 20, Rose 39
20.04	Ryman 1	Dulwich Hamlet	267	5 - 0	Rose 10 24 74 88, Aransibia 17
27.04	Ryman 1	UXBRIDGE	149	2 - 1	Rose 23, Aransibia 25

Match Facts 2001-02

PLAYING SQUAD

Goalkeepers: Chris Harvey (Youth Team), Jimmy Chapman (Barking)

Defenders: Andy Polston (Boreham Wood), Ashley Marsh (Barking & E. Ham Utd), Ben Willis (Youth Team), Ben Wood (Aveley), Garry Kimble (Harlow T), Jay Devereux (Enfield), Paul Salmon (Leyton Pennant), Warren Hackett (Grays Ath)

Midfielders: Billy Read (Leyton Pennant), Bradley Woodlands (Youth Team), Glen Poole (Yeovil T.), Greg Heighway (Grays Ath), John Sullivan (Grays Ath), Kevin Hoddy (Barking), Paul Adolphe (Harrow B), Ross White (Grays Ath), Simon Livett (USA)

Forwards: Andy Aransibia (Barking), Chas Murray (Youth Team), Chris Rose (Grays Ath), Dean Allen (Barking & E. Ham Utd), Lela Bejada (Grays Ath)

GRAYS ATHLETIC

CLUB OFFICIALS

Chairman: Alan Barnard

Secretary & Press Officer: Phil O'Reilly
102 Luxborough Lane,Chigwell,Essex IL7
5AA Tel: 07980 643832

FOOTBALL MANAGEMENT TEAM
Manager: Craig Edwards
Asst Man.: Lyndon Lynch Coach: John
Frostick Physio: Marrtin Stevens

FACT FILE

Formed: 1890
Nickname: The Blues
Sponsors: F.S.McKenzie
Colours: Yellow
Change colours: Yellow & Blue
Midweek matchday: Tuesday

2000-2001 Captain:Andy Sussex
P.o.Y.:Mel Capleton
Top Scorer: Nathan Thomas

GROUND Recreation Ground, Bridge Road, Grays RM17 6BZ (01375 391649)
Directions: Seven minutes walk from Grays station - turn right round one way system, right into Clarence Road, and at end into Bridge Road. Bus No. 370. By road - A13 towards Southend from London, take Grays exit and follow signs to town centre, keep left on one-way system, continue up hill for about 1/2 mile, turn right into Bridge Road, ground 1/2 mile on right
Capacity: 4,500 Cover: 1,200 Seats: 300 Floodlights: Yes
Clubhouse: Bar, pool, darts, bar snacks available. Indoor sports hall(.Steward: Chris Riley)
Club Shop: Sells `The First Hundred Years', sweaters, T-shirts, replica shirts, scarves, ties, etc.
Contact Bill Grove 01375 391649

Pages: 48 Price: £1
Editor: Jeremy Mason (01375 400188)
Local Press: Thurrock Gazette
Local Radio: BBC Essex, Radio Essex

Club Website: grays.ath.btinternet.co.uk

PREVIOUS **Leagues:** Athenian 12-14, 58-83; London 14-24, 26-39; Kent 24-26; Corinthian 45-58

CLUB RECORDS **Attendance:** 9,500 v Chelmsford City, FA Cup 4th Qual. Round 1959
Win: 12-0 v Tooting (H) London Lge 24/2/23 **Defeat:** 0-12 v Enfield (A) Athenian Lge 20/4/63
Goalscorer: Harry Brand 269 (1944-52) **Appearances:** Phil Sammons. 673. 1982-97
Fee Paid: For Ian Durant (Canvey Island 85)
Fee Received: Undisclosed for Tony Witter (C. Palace), Dwight Marshall(Plymouth 1991) and Matthew Lawrence(Wycombe W)

BEST SEASON **FA Cup:** 1st Rd 51-52 88-89 ,00-01,01-02 **FA Trophy:** 3rd Rd 92-93, 01-02 **FA Amateur Cup:** 3rd Rd 63-64

HONOURS Isthmian Div 1 R-up 87-88 ,99-00(Div 2 Sth 84-85, Lg Cup 91-92); Athenian Lg R-up 82-83, Res. Sect. R-up 58-59 (Cup R-up 59-60); Corinthian Lg 45-46 (R-up 51-52 54-55 56-57), Lg Cup(2) 45-47, Mem. Shield(4) ; Essex Snr Cup 8(R-up 9; Essex SenTr 98-99; East Ang Cup 44-45 (R-up 43-44 54-55); Essex Thameside Tphy x 8 (R-up 7); Essex Elizabeth Tphy 76-77 (R-up 65-66); Claridge Tphy 87-88 88-89; Mithras Cup 79-80; Essex Int Cup(3) 56-57 58-60 (Jun Cup 19-20 (R-up 58-59); Essex & Herts ,Border Comb. East 87-88 (Ancillary Cup 78-79, Comb Cup 82-83); Fred Budden Tphy 86-87; Hornchurch Charity Cup 78-79 86-87; Neale Tphy 50-51; Ford Rate Tphy 83-84 85-86 87-88 (R-up 84-85 86-87); Stan Veness Mem. Tphy (8) 87-96

Players progressing: J Jordan (Spurs 47), R Kemp (Reading 49), B Silkman & TBanfield (Orient), G O'Reilly (Spurs), W Entwhistle (Bury 83), M Welch(Wimbledon 84), T Witter (C Palace 90), D Marshall (Plymouth 91), M Lawrence(Wycombe W. 96-97)

Back row left to right: John Frostick (Coach), Johnny Buffony, John O'Sullivan, Andy Sussex, Steve Robinson, Mel Capleton, Jeff Woolsey, Alan Keeper, David Rainford, Craig Edwards (Manaager)
Front row: Sam Cooper, Tony Lock, Craig Edwards, Allan McLeod, Alex Fiddes and Mervin Abraham. **Photo:** Alan Coomes

ISTHMIAN LEAGUE PREMIER DIVISION

Date	Comp.	Opponents	Att.	Score	Goalscorers
18.08	Ryman P	Billericay Town	707	2 - 3	Abraham 38, Halle 48
21.08	Ryman P	BRAINTREE TOWN	214	3 - 0	Douglas 56 74 84
25.08	Ryman P	ST ALBANS CITY	259	3 - 2	Sussex 15, Thomas 66 82
27.08	Ryman P	Boreham Wood	203	2 - 2	Douglas 34, O'Sullivan 58
01.09	Ryman P	BEDFORD TOWN	274	2 - 1	Thomas 50, Douglas 78
04.09	Ryman P	Basingstoke Town	352	2 - 0	Douglas 6 67
08.09	Ryman P	Hampton & Richmond Borough	245	0 - 0	
11.09	Ryman P	SUTTON UNITED	206	3 - 3	Abraham 27, Fiddes 32, Cooper 43
15.09	Ryman P	ALDERSHOT TOWN	738	3 - 1	Edwards 60, Rainsford 73, Sussex 90
18.09	Ryman P	Hitchin Town	195	4 - 2	Edwards 37, Rainford 43, Douglas 55, Allen 81
22.09	Ryman P	Kingstonian	571	3 - 2	Abraham 40, Douglas 45, Cooper 62
25.09	Ryman P	CHESHAM UNITED	242	2 - 1	Douglas 52 57
29.09	FA Cup Q2	WINGATE & FINCHLEY	186	4 - 1	M Thomas 7 20 44, Robinson 37
01.10	Ryman P	Purfleet	389	0 - 2	
09.10	Ryman P	GRAVESEND & NORTHFLEET	453	2 - 0	Abraham 18, Thomas 75
13.10	FA Cup Q3	Purfleet	389	1 - 1	O'Sullivan 55
16.10	FA Cup Q3 R	PURFLEET	487	3 - 2	Thomas 17 68, Fiddes 66
20.10	Ryman P	Enfield	111	2 - 1	Thomas 71 77
27.10	FA Cup Q4	MARGATE	832	2 - 0	Boardman 10[og], Fiddes 27
03.11	FA Trophy 1	Havant & Waterlooville	411	3 - 2	Abraham 48 90, Rainsford 78
06.11	Ryman P	CANVEY ISLAND	704	0 - 1	
10.11	Ryman P	Maidenhead United	184	1 - 2	Andrews 29
17.11	FA Cup 1	HINCKLEY UNITED	1133	1 - 2	Lock 53
20.11	Essex SC 3	TILBURY	n.k	0 - 1	
24.11	Ryman P	Heybridge Swifts	239	1 - 1	Lock 31
01.12	FA Trophy 2	Bishop's Stortford	503	1 - 1	Lock 90
04.12	FA Trophy 2 R	BISHOP'S STORTFORD	226	3 - 2	Fiddes 25, Southgate 48 58
08.12	Ryman P	HENDON	239	2 - 0	Lock 2, Clarke 16[og]
11.12	Lge Cup 1	BEDFORD TOWN	n.k	5 - 1	
15.12	Ryman P	BILLERICAY TOWN	312	0 - 0	
18.12	Lge Cup 2	Staines Town	n.k	2 - 0	
22.12	Ryman P	HARROW BOROUGH	220	2 - 1	Abraham 75, Fiddes 90
26.12	Ryman P	Croydon	107	0 - 1	
29.12	Ryman P	Braintree Town	389	3 - 2	Fletcher 8 70, Thomas 24
01.01	Ryman P	BOREHAM WOOD	301	3 - 2	Sussex 15[p], Rainford 20, Fletcher 26
05.01	Ryman P	BASINGSTOKE TOWN	277	0 - 0	
12.01	FA Trophy 3	WELLING UNITED	378	2 - 4	Cooper 51, Robinson 80
15.01	Lge Cup 3	Sutton United	203	7 - 1	Thomas 15 50 73, Cooper 47 75, Morgan 55, Fletcher 71
19.01	Ryman P	HAMPTON & RICHMOND BOR.	231	1 - 1	Fiddes 83
09.02	Ryman P	HEYBRIDGE SWIFTS	254	1 - 3	Cooper 60
12.02	Ryman P	Bedford Town	389	0 - 4	
16.02	Ryman P	HITCHIN TOWN	229	2 - 1	Harold 25, Cooper 60
23.02	Ryman P	Aldershot Town	1646	1 - 0	Halle 90
02.03	Ryman P	KINGSTONIAN	322	2 - 0	Hunter 3, Thomas 71
05.03	Lge Cup QF	ALDERSHOT TOWN	n.k	2 - 3	
09.03	Ryman P	Chesham United	229	5 - 3	Thomas 41 46, Fiddes 65, Lock 60, Abraham 75
16.03	Ryman P	PURFLEET	401	1 - 3	Thomas 11
23.03	Ryman P	Gravesend & Northfleet	920	0 - 2	
30.03	Ryman P	St Albans City	327	1 - 2	Thomas 30
01.04	Ryman P	CROYDON	118	1 - 0	McCloud 74
06.04	Ryman P	Canvey Island	728	2 - 1	Lock 39, McLeod 45
09.04	Ryman P	Hendon	197	0 - 1	
13.04	Ryman P	ENFIELD	237	0 - 0	
20.04	Ryman P	Harrow Borough	344	1 - 1	Abraham 77
23.04	Ryman P	Sutton United	440	2 - 2	Abrahams 89, Fiddes 90
27.04	Ryman P	MAIDENHEAD UNITED	227	0 - 1	
30.04	Essex TST F	Tilbury	n.k	3 - 1	Rainford 16, Lock 54 79

PLAYING SQUAD

Goalkeepers: James Lunan (Southend), Melvin Capelton (Southend Utd)

Defenders: Alan Keeper (Braintree T), Andy Sussex (Barking), Jeff Woolsey (Billerachy), Owen Coll (Aldershot), Peter Smith (Canvey Is.), Alan Mcloud (Arsenal), Ben Lewis (Chelmsford C), Michael Haswell (Southend), Paul Hatch (Barking), Steve Robinson (Edgware T)

Midfielders: Adam Miller (Canvey Is.), Craig Edwards (Southend), Jason Broom (Dagenham & Redbridge), Mark Stimson (Canvey Is.), Sam Cooper (Canvey Is.), Alex Fiddes (Heybridge Swifts), Dave Collis (Charlton Ath), Jonathon Buffong (Barking), Nathan Thomas (Barking)

Forwards: Andy Douglas (Sheffield Wed.), Gary Abbott (Welling Utd), Mervn Abraham (Dulwich Hamlet), Robbie Reinelt (Braintree T), John Morgan (Stevanage Bor.), Stafford Browne (Aldershot), Tony Lock (Dagenham & Redbridge)

HAMPTON & RICHMOND BOROUGH

CLUB OFFICIALS
Chair:Mervyn Cox **Pres:** AlanSimpsonOBE
Vice Chairman: Michael Holland
Press Officer: Les Rance
Secretary: Adrian Mann,
30 Burniston Court, Manor Rd, Wallington,
Surrey SM6 0AD (0208 773 0858)

FOOTBALL MANAGEMENT TEAM
Manager: Ian McDonald
Coach: Matt Beard
Physio: Gareth Workman

FACT FILE
Formed: 1921
Nickname: Beavers/Borough
Sponsors: M.M Cox.Properties Ltd.
Colours: Red & blue/white/blue
Change Colours: White/blue/white
Midweek Matchday: Tuesday

Website: http://www.hamptonfc.co.uk

2001-02
Captain: Fiston Manuella
Top scorer: Craig Maskell
P.o.Y.: Craig Maskell

**Hampton &
Richmond
Borough
F.C.**

Ryman
Football
League
Premier
Division

2001/2002

**B e v e r e e
R e v i e w**

Ryman

Main Sponsor -
M.M. Cox Properties

AQUATINT

GROUND: Beveree Stadium, Beaver Close, off Station Rd, Hampton TW12 2BX
Tel: Office 020 8979 2456(matchdays only) Club: 020 8941 4936 Boardroom: 020 8941 2838
Directions: A3 out of London, fork left (signed Staines/Esher/Sandown Pk) onto A243, A309
Staines exit to Hampton Ct at `Scilly Isles' r'bout, left at r'bout after Hampton Court Bridge
onto A308, after 1 mile right into Church St (A311), left after White Hart after 200yds into High
St, Station Rd on right just before junction with A308
Capacity: 3,000   Seats: 300   Cover: 800   Floodlights: Yes
Clubhouse: (020 8979 2456). Lounge bar and hall, open on matchdays and training nights.
     Hall available for hire.
Club Shop: Sells various souvenirs & prog. Contact: David Rees

Pages: 28 Price: £1.50p
Editor: Nick Taylor
Local Press: Middx Chronicle, Surrey Comet,
Richmond & Twickenham Times, The Informer

PREVIOUS **Leagues:** Kingston & District 21-33; South West Middx 33-59; Surrey Snr 59-64; Spartan 64-71; Athenian 71-73
Grounds: Hatherop Rec (until 1959)
CLUB RECORDS **Win:** 11-1 v Eastbourne Utd, Isthmian Lge Div 2 (S), 90-91   **Defeat:** 0-13 v Hounslow Town, Middlesex Senior Cup 62-63
Goalscorer: Peter Allen (176) 1964-73   **Appearances:** Tim Hollands (700) 1977-95
Fees - Paid: £3,000 for Matt Flitter (Chesham United) June 2000
Fees - Received: £40,000 for Leroy Griffiths from Q.P.R.May 2001
BEST SEASON **FA Cup:** 1st Rd Proper 00-01 (1-2 v Barnet)   **FA Amateur Cup:** 1st Rd Prop 73-74 (2-4 v Leytonstone)
FA Trophy: 4th Rd 01-02 .1-4 v Hereford United (A)
FA Vase: 3rd Rd 91-92 (0-1 v Newport IOW), 95-96 (0-1 v Colllier Row)
HONOURS: London Snr Cup(2) 86-88; Spartan Lg(4) 64-67 69-70, (R-up 67-68), Lg Cup(4) 64-68 (R-up 2); Surrey Snr Lg 63-64 (Lg Cup
R-up 60-61); Middx Charity Cup 69-70 95-96 97-98,98-99 (R-up 68-69 71-72 89-90 94-95); Middx Snr Cup R-up 71-72 76-77
95-96; Athenian Lg Div 2 R-up 72-73; Southern Comb. Cup 68-69 71-72 76-77 81-82 83-84 85-86 96-97 (R-up 77-78 79-80
97-98); Isthmian Lge promotion from Div 1 97-98, Div 2 95-96, Div 3 91-92. Isthmian Lg.Cup Finalists 01-02
Players progressing: Andy Rogers (Southampton), Dwight Marshall (Plymouth), Paul Rogers (Sheffield Utd via Sutton Utd), Derek Bryan
Brentford 97), Darren Powell (Brentford 98), Julian Charles (Brentford 99.), Leroy Griffiths (Q.P.R. 01)

Back row. left to right: Aiden O'Brien, Matt Flitter, Phil Dicker, Fiston Manuella, Gavin Rose, Stuart Mackenzie, Terry Buss, Ronnie Gould, Steve
French and Raphael Nade. **Front row:** Kasey Ibe, Craig Maskell,Marvyn Watson, Ronnie Girvan, Richard O'Connor, Sam Sloma and Esayas
Yhdego with 'Bertie the Beaver" resting at the front!

Match Facts 2001-02

Date	Comp.	Opponents	Att.	Score	Goalscorers
18.08	Ryman P	St Albans City	315	3 - 1	Green 2, Maskell 50, O'Connor 62
21.08	Ryman P	HITCHIN TOWN	217	6 - 3	Green 5 50, Manuella 15, Holloway 40, O'Connor 65, Maskell 71
25.08	Ryman P	BRAINTREE TOWN	255	0 - 2	
27.08	Ryman P	Croydon	141	0 - 0	
01.09	Ryman P	Billericay Town	557	0 - 2	
04.09	Ryman P	HENDON	263	0 - 0	
08.09	Ryman P	GRAYS ATHLETIC	245	0 - 0	
11.09	Ryman P	Maidenhead United	184	1 - 2	O'Connor 21
15.09	Ryman P	GRAVESEND & NORTHFLEET	330	0 - 2	
18.09	Ryman P	Enfield	83	2 - 0	Burnham 8, Carter 14
22.09	Ryman P	Heybridge Swifts	164	3 - 1	Maskell 24 32 68
25.09	Ryman P	BASINGSTOKE TOWN	268	1 - 1	Maskell 58
29.09	FA Cup Q2	HITCHIN TOWN	298	1 - 1	Maskell 65[p]
02.10	FA Cup Q2 R	Hitchin Town	243	1 - 2	Deegan 53
09.10	Ryman P	PURFLEET	183	1 - 1	Green 15
13.10	Ryman P	Braintree Town	353	2 - 3	Maskell 33, Williams 48
20.10	Ryman P	BEDFORD TOWN	384	1 - 1	Maskell 40
27.10	Ryman P	Boreham Wood	202	2 - 3	Maskell 21 44
30.10	Ryman P	Aldershot Town	1801	1 - 5	Omonna 36
03.11	FA Trophy 1	Whyteleafe	152	5 - 0	Williams 33 90, O'Connor 31 90, Deluca 75
10.11	Ryman P	SUTTON UNITED	391	2 - 1	De Luca 67 78
17.11	Ryman P	Kingstonian	714	0 - 3	
24.11	Ryman P	CANVEY ISLAND	449	1 - 5	Nade 29
27.11	Lge Cup 1	Barking & East Ham United	n.k	8 - 3	
01.12	FA Trophy 2	HARLOW TOWN	245	2 - 2	Lee 47, Nade 55
05.12	FA Trophy 2 R	Harlow Town	113	2 - 1	Nade 16, Lee 55
08.12	Ryman P	Chesham United	306	1 - 2	Ibe 82
12.12	Middx SC 2	Southall Town	42	4 - 0	
15.12	Ryman P	ST ALBANS CITY	308	0 - 5	
18.12	Lge Cup 2	MAIDENHEAD UNITED	n.k	5 - 3	
26.12	Ryman P	Harrow Borough	184	1 - 1	Doogan 47
29.12	Ryman P	Hitchin Town	276	4 - 2	Maskell 71, Vicker 80, Nade 81 90
05.01	Ryman P	Hendon	202	0 - 1	
12.01	FA Trophy 3	NEWPORT COUNTY	505	2 - 0	Flitter 48, Ibe 88
15.01	Lge Cup 3	Yeading	n.k	3 - 1	
19.01	Ryman P	Grays Athletic	231	1 - 1	O'Connor 52
22.01	Middx SC QF	Uxbridge	n.k	0 - 1	
05.02	Ryman P	CROYDON	140	6 - 0	O'Connor 21, Flitter 53, Marsh 69, Deagan 80, Maskell 85, Nade 87
09.02	Ryman P	Canvey Island	560	1 - 1	Marsh 45
12.02	FA Trophy 4	Hereford United	1167	1 - 4	Nade 43
16.02	Ryman P	ENFIELD	264	2 - 1	Marsh 50, Maskell 53
19.02	Lge Cup QF	ENFIELD	n.k	1 - 4	
02.03	Ryman P	HEYBRIDGE SWIFTS	248	1 - 1	Maskell 47
05.03	Ryman P	CHESHAM UNITED	163	0 - 2	
09.03	Ryman P	Basingstoke Town	293	1 - 1	Rose 15
12.03	Ryman P	MAIDENHEAD UNITED	194	2 - 1	Marsh 36, Maskell 45
16.03	Ryman P	ALDERSHOT TOWN	220	1 - 1	Maskell 90
19.03	Lge Cup SF(1)	Aldershot Town	751	2 - 2	Maskell 35 45
23.03	Ryman P	Purfleet	247	0 - 3	
28.03	Ryman P	BILLERICAY TOWN	n.k	1 - 2	Maskell 90[p]
01.04	Ryman P	HARROW BOROUGH	230	0 - 1	
03.04	Lge Cup SF(2)	ALDERSHOT TOWN	718	1 - 0	Maskell 92
06.04	Ryman P	BOREHAM WOOD	185	1 - 2	Ibe 50
09.04	Ryman P	Gravesend & Northfleet	1076	1 - 2	Nade 80
13.04	Ryman P	Bedford Town	481	1 - 4	Rose 87
20.04	Ryman P	KINGSTONIAN	732	0 - 0	
27.04	Ryman P	Sutton United	514	0 - 2	
01.05	Lge Cup F	Northwood	262	2 - 3	Gough 45, O'Connor 77 @ St Albans City

PLAYING SQUAD

Goalkeepers: Andrew Iga (Whyteleafe), Chris Bouchez (Tooting & Mitcham Utd), Stuart Mackenkie (Farnborough)
Defenders: Aidan O'Brein (Harrow Bor.), Ben Proudfoot (Tooting & Mitcham), Gary McCracken (Linfield), Ben Ferris (Tooting & Mitcham), Dean Berry (Ashford T), Ronnie Girvan (Chelsea-Junior)
Midfielders: Ashley Sestanovich (Royal Antwerp -Belgium), Billy Mead (Kingstonian), Dudley Gardner (Egham T), Steve Moss (Newport I.W.), Chris Rose (Farnborough), Richard O'Connor (Leatherhead)
Forwards: Adam Pittwood (Tooting & Mitcham), David Cross (Notts County), Enrico Grimm (Youth Team), Lee Riddell (Farnborough), David Cory (Walton & Hersham), Dean Thomas (Bromley), Esyas Yhdego (Farnborough T)

HARROW BOROUGH

Harrow Borough Football Club

Season 2001/02

CLUB OFFICIALS

Chairman: Jim Ripley **President:** Jim Rogers
Secretary: Peter Rogers,
21 Ludlow Close, South Harrow, Middx HA2
8SR (0208 248 8003H)(0208 423157W)
Commercial Manager:
Paul Carter c/o the club
Press Officer: Paul Carter (07971 848385)

FOOTBALL MANAGEMENT TEAM
Manager: Edwin Stein
Asst Manager: David Howell
Physio: Suzanne Bowen

FACT FILE

Formed: 1933
Nickname: The Boro
Sponsors: Sodexho Land Technology
Colours: Red, white trim/white/red, white hoops
Change cols: White/navy blue trim/navy/navy
Midweek matchday: Tuesday
Captains: Christian Hyslop & Richard Clarke
P.o.Y.:Richard Clarke
Top Scorer: Fabio Valenti 12

2001-02

Grays Athletic
Ryman League Premier Division
Saturday 20th April 2002

Sodexho Official Programme £1.50 Ryman

Premier Division

GROUND: Earlsmead, Carlyon Avenue, South Harrow, Middx HA2 8SS Tel: 0208 422 5989 or 5221. Website: www.harrowboro.com Email: paul@harrowboro.com
Directions: Underground to Northolt (Central Line) then 140 bus to Northolt Park BR, 282 bus, to Eastcote Arms or to South Harrow (Piccadilly Line) then 114 or H10 to Kings Rd.Junction. By road leave A40 at Macdonalds roundabout towards Northolt station (A312 north), left at lights, right at next island (Eastcote Arms pub), ground 5th turning on right.
Capacity: 3,070 **Cover:** 1,000 **Seats:** 350 **Floodlights:** Yes
Clubhouse: Open daily, normal pub hours. Four bars, games room, equipped for all social events. Hot and coldfood available, buffets by prior request
Club Shop: Sells progs, scarves, badges, T-shirts, etc. Contact Tony Trowbridge c/o club

Pages: 32 Price: £1.50p
Editor: Paul Carter (07971 848385)

Local Press: Harrow Observer

PREVIOUS	**Leagues:** Harrow & Dist 33-4; Spartan 34-40, 45-58; W Middx Comb 40-1; Middx Sen41-45; Delphian 58-63; Athenian 63-75;	
	Names: Roxonian 1933-8; Harrow Town 38-66	**Ground:** Northolt Road 33-4
CLUB RECORDS	**Attendance:** 3,000 v Wealdstone, F.A. Cup 1st Qualifying Round 1946 Fee Received: £16,000 for Lee Endersby (Enfield 97)	
	Scorer: Dave Pearce, 153 **Appearances:** Steve Emmanuel 522 (1st team only), Les Currell 582, Colin Payne 557	
	Fee Paid: Unspecified to Dagenham for George Duck & Steve Jones, Summer 81	
	Win: 13-0 v Handley Page (A), Middlesex Snr Lg 18/10/41. **Defeat:** 0-8 5 times: Wood Green T. (A) Middx Lge 40, Met Police (A) Spartan Lg 52, Briggs Spts (A) Spartan Lg 53, Hertford T. (A) Spartan Lge 53, Hendon (A) Middx Snr Cup 65	
BEST SEASON	**FA Trophy:** Semi final 82-83 **FA Cup:** 2nd Rd 83-84 (1-3 at home to Newport Co)	
HONOURS:	Isthmian Lg 83-84 (Div 1 R-up 78-79); Athenian Lg Div 2 R-up 63-64; Spartan Lg R-up 57-58 (Div 2 West 38-39 (R-up 37-38); Middx Senior Cup 82-83 92-93; Harrow & Dist. Lg Div 1 R-up 33-34; Middx Charity Cup 79-80 92-93 (R-up 78-79); Middx Intermediate Cup 55-56,R-up 75-76, Middx Premier Cup 81-82,R-up 82-83, Harrow Sen Cup 95 97, London Interm'te C 78-79	

Players progressing: D.Russell (Arsenal), M.Lucas (L.Orient), R.Shaw (Torquay U), T.Eden (Raith R), T. Carpenter (Watford), M Bottoms (QPR 60), C Hutchings (Chelsea 80), R Holland (Crewe 85), J Kerr (Portsmouth 87), D Howell, A Pape & E Stein, (Barnet), D .Byrne (Gillingham), R.Rosario (Norwich), D Kemp (Crystal Palace), M Doherty (Reading), D Bassett (Wimbledon), G Borthwick (Bournemouth), B.Shaw, (Torquay U),T.Evans (Scunthorpe U), L.Charles (Q.P.R.), P.Barrowcliff (Brentford) M.Richardson (Camb Utd & Torquay U). **International:** K Karamoko(Mali)

L-R - Back row: Edwin Stein (Team Manager), Michael Currie, Michael Jatto, Kevin Green, Ross Fitzsimon, Pat Gavin, Daniel Dyer, Danny Gladman, Keita Karamoko, Dean Marney, Richard Goddard, Julian Renner-Thomas, Mekel Hackett, Godfrey Torto, Suzanne Bowen (Physio) and David Howell (Assistant Manager). **Front row:** Robert Charles, Davis Haule, Adam Everitt, Fabio Valenti, Richard Clarke, Perry Norman, Phil Gridelet, John Lawford, Chris Jones, Wayne Walters and Michael Barima. **Photo:** Paul Carter

Date	Comp.	Opponents	Att.	Score	Goalscorers
18.08	Ryman P	MAIDENHEAD UNITED	267	0 - 3	
21.08	Ryman P	Heybridge Swifts	168	1 - 1	Knight 18
25.08	Ryman P	Gravesend & Northfleet	395	2 - 2	Valenti 66, Xavier 82
27.08	Ryman P	HENDON	290	0 - 2	
01.09	Ryman P	BOREHAM WOOD	220	2 - 3	Hurlock 52, Knight 75
04.09	Ryman P	Sutton United	440	1 - 1	Hurlock 29[p]
08.09	Ryman P	Bedford Town	449	4 - 3	Adolphe 36, Valenti 46, Clarke 48, Hurlock 60
11.09	Ryman P	BRAINTREE TOWN	138	1 - 2	Valenti 38
15.09	Ryman P	HITCHIN TOWN	168	1 - 1	Adolphe 18
19.09	Ryman P	Croydon	88	1 - 2	Hingley 4
22.09	Ryman P	Purfleet	387	3 - 0	Hyslop 18, Adolphe 42, Gavin 90
25.09	Ryman P	ALDERSHOT TOWN	670	2 - 3	Valenti 40, Woodruffe 50
29.09	FA Cup Q2	King's Lynn	916	0 - 1	
02.10	Ryman P	Chesham United	242	0 - 5	
09.10	Ryman P	CANVEY ISLAND	203	1 - 1	Knight 34
20.10	Ryman P	BILLERICAY TOWN	202	0 - 2	
27.10	Ryman P	St Albans City	334	0 - 1	
03.11	FA Trophy 1	DORCHESTER TOWN	180	2 - 3	Everitt 8, Woodruffe 59
10.11	Ryman P	BASINGSTOKE TOWN	131	3 - 3	Marivat 39, Gavin 45, Bloor 90[p]
24.11	Ryman P	ENFIELD	188	2 - 4	Lawford 36, Barima 77
27.11	Lge Cup 1	CAMBERLEY TOWN	n.k	3 - 0	
04.12	Middx SC 2	Hayes	n.k	1 - 3	
08.12	Ryman P	Kingstonian	558	0 - 1	
11.12	Lge Cup 2	NORTHWOOD	n.k	1 - 4	
15.12	Ryman P	Maidenhead United	209	2 - 4	Lawford 84 90
22.12	Ryman P	Grays Athletic	220	1 - 2	Lawford 30
26.12	Ryman P	HAMPTON & RICHMOND BOR.	184	1 - 1	Oktay 80
29.12	Ryman P	HEYBRIDGE SWIFTS	179	1 - 3	Adolphe 78
05.01	Ryman P	SUTTON UNITED	262	1 - 6	Valenti 10
12.01	Ryman P	Boreham Wood	197	2 - 1	Xavier 67, Barima 77
19.01	Ryman P	BEDFORD TOWN	394	2 - 4	Adolphe 45, Hurlock 70
29.01	Middx CC 2	SOUTHALL TOWN	n.k	6 - 1	F
02.02	Ryman P	KINGSTONIAN	260	1 - 3	Dyer 23
09.02	Ryman P	Enfield	143	2 - 1	Valenti 9, Protain 83
16.02	Ryman P	CROYDON	186	2 - 0	Marney 16, Lawford 81
23.02	Ryman P	Hitchin Town	248	0 - 3	
02.03	Ryman P	PURFLEET	151	1 - 2	Fitzsimon 75
09.03	Ryman P	Aldershot Town	1458	1 - 2	Lawford 65
16.03	Ryman P	CHESHAM UNITED	206	2 - 1	Cook 45[og], Lawford 65
19.03	Ryman P	Hendon	207	1 - 0	Walters 56
23.03	Ryman P	Canvey Island	482	0 - 3	
26.03	Middx CC QF	Uxbridge	n.k	0 - 1	
30.03	Ryman P	GRAVESEND & NORTHFLEET	381	0 - 3	
01.04	Ryman P	Hampton & Richmond Borough	230	1 - 0	Currie 51
06.04	Ryman P	ST ALBANS CITY	225	2 - 6	Lawford 69, Gavin 90
09.04	Ryman P	Braintree Town	265	0 - 0	
13.04	Ryman P	Billericay Town	484	1 - 1	Haule 34
20.04	Ryman P	GRAYS ATHLETIC	344	1 - 1	McKenna 35
27.04	Ryman P	Basingstoke Town	346	1 - 2	Haule 54

PLAYING SQUAD

Goalkeepers: Danny Gladman (Northwood), Keita Karamoko (Wembley)
Defenders: Adam Everitt (Luton T), Christian Hyslop (Boldock T), Dean Marney (Greenwich B),
Emond Protain (Wembley), Perry Norman (Cherstsey T), Richard Clark (Stanway Rovers),
Richard Goddard (Chesham U), Sean James Halesowen T.), Wayne Walters (Wembley)
Midfielders: Fabio Valenti (Edgware T), Kevin McKenna (Hillington B), Nicolaj Lund (Grombak Utd-Singapore),
Phil Gridelet (Bishop Stortford), Phil Johnson (Runcorn), Ross Fitzsimon (Norwich C)
Forwards: Daniel Dyer (Wembley), Godfrey Torto (Aresley T), John Lawford (Boreham Wood), Mekel Hackett
(Ford Utd), Michael Barima (Hampton & Richmond), Michael Currie (Northwood), Pat Gavin (Farnborough)

HAYES

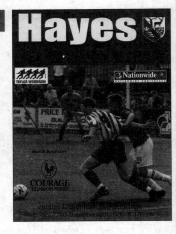

CLUB OFFICIALS
President Les Lovering
Chairman Derek Goodall
Vice Chairman Trevor Griffith
Financial Director Charles Mackintosh
Directors D Goodall, C Porter, E Stevens, T Griffith, C Mackintosh, A Bond, J Bond, N Griffith, T Gorman.
Football Secretary John Bond Jnr.
Press Officer Trevor Griffith
c/o the club Tel: 0208 573 2075

FOOTBALL MANAGEMENT TEAM
Manager: Willy Wordsworth
Player/Asst Manager: Paul Holsgrove
Physio: Carl Ballard

FACT FILE
Founded: 1909
Nickname: The Missioners
Club Sponsors: Taylor Woodrow
Club colours: Red & white shirts, black shorts, black socks
Change colours: Blue shirts, blue shorts, blue socks
Reserve team's league: Suburban Premier
Midweek home matchday: Tuesday

GROUND	Townfield House, Church Road, Hayes, Middx. UB3 2LE Tel: 0208 573 2075
Simple Directions:	M25, M4, A312 (Hayes By-Pass), A4020 (Uxbridge Road) and Church Rd. is on the left.
Capacity: 6,500	**Seated:** 450 **Terracing - Covered:** 2,000 **Uncovered:** 4,050
CLUBHOUSE:	Open Sat 12 - 11pm. Sun 12 - 3pm, 7 - 11pm. Midweek 6.30 - 11pm. Hot and cold snacks are available.
CLUB SHOP:	Wide range of programmes & souvenirs. Contact Lee Hermitage, c/o the club.

Pages: 32   Price: £1.50
Editor: Ken Green
Other club publications: None
Local Press: Hayes Gazette
Local Radio: Capital Radio

PREVIOUS	**Leagues:** Local leagues 1909-14; Gt. Western Suburban 19-22; London 22-24; Spartan 24-30; Athenian 30-71; Isthmian 71-96; Conference 96-02. **Names:** Bokwell Mission **Ground:** Botwell Common
CLUB RECORDS	**Attendance:** 15,370 v Bromley, FA Amateur Cup, 10.2.51
	Win: Unknown **Defeat:** Unknown
	Career Goalscorer: Unknown **Career Appearances:** Reg Leather 701
	Transfer Fee Paid: £6,000 for Gary Keen (Hendon) 1990 & for Joe Francis (Enfield) 1996
	Transfer Fee Received: £30,000 for Les Ferdinand (Q.P.R.) 1987
BEST SEASON	**FA Cup:** 2nd Round (replay) 72-73: 0-1 v Reading (H) after 0-0; 99-00: 2-3 aet v Hull City (A) after 2-2; also 2nd Round 90-91 & 91-92 League clubs defeated: Bristol Rov.72-73, Cardiff C.90-91, Fulham 91-92
	FA Trophy: Quarter Final 78-79, 1-2 v Runcorn (A); 97-98, 0-1 v Cheltenham Town (A)
	FA Amateur Cup: Runners Up 1930-31 **League:** 3rd Conference 98-99
HONOURS	Isthmian League 95-96; Athenian League 56-57 Spartan League 27-28; Great Western Suburban League 1920-24 (x4) Middlesex Senior Cup 19-20, 20-21, 25-26, 30-31, 35-36, 39-40, 49-50, 81-82, 95-96, 99-00; London Senior Cup 31-32, 80-81; Middlesex Charity Cup - 15 Times; London Charity Cup 60-61

Players Progressing: Cyril Bacon (Orient 46), Phil Nolan (Watford 47), Dave Groombridge (Orient 51), Jimmy Bloomfield (Brentford 52), Derek Neate & Les Champlevoer(Brighton 56 & 57), Gordon Phillips (Brentford 63), Robin Friday (Reading 74), Les Smith (A Villa), Cyrille Regis (WBA 1977), Les Ferdinand (QPR 87),Derek Payne (Barnet 88), Paul Hyde (Wycombe 91), Dean Hooper (Swindon95), Jason Roberts (Wolverhampton W. 97)

L-R - Back: Paul Hamer, Peter Collins, Josiah Hunt, Danny Julienne, Mark Molesey, Chris Andrews, Bertrand Bossu, Sean O'Connor, Andrew Cooper, Peter Holsgrove, Ian Addele, Glen Harris. **Middle**: Caroline Bosley (Matchday asst.), John Case, Paul Johnson, Darren Crane, John Murphy, Jamie Jarvis, James Shipperley, Rob Bixby, Yiadom Yeboah, Leeyon Phelan, Elis Kodra, John Ellis, David Warner, Sarah Phillips (reserve team physio). **Front**: Mick Harvey (chief scout), Gary Austin, Dean Clark, Matt Gray, Justin Cochrane, Willy Wordsworth (manager), Derek Goodall (chairman), Paul Holsgrove (player/asst. manager), Ryan Williams, Richard Jolly, Kevin Warner, Ian Hodges, Mick Geraghty (reserve team manager). **Photo:** Ray Peploe, HFC Photography

Date	Comp.	Opponents	Att.	Score	Goalscorers
18/08	Conf	Leigh RMI	546	1 - 1	Watts 90
21/08	Conf	STEVENAGE BOROUGH	685	0 - 2	
25/08	Conf	CHESTER CITY	507	1 - 3	Clark 39
27/08	Conf	Yeovil Town	2782	1 - 2	Molesley 90
01/09	Conf	MORECAMBE	503	3 - 1	Clark 26 53, Hodge 78
03/09	Conf	Dover Athletic	817	2 - 3	Sodje 5, Sterling 45
08/09	Conf	Scarborough	896	2 - 1	
11/09	Conf	FOREST GREEN ROVERS	548	1 - 1	Dyer 36
15/09	Conf	DONCASTER ROVERS	821	1 - 5	Hodge 64
18/09	Conf	Barnet	947	1 - 3	Clark 47
22/09	Conf	Boston United	1709	1 - 4	Spencer 31
29/09	Conf	HEREFORD UNITED	634	4 - 1	
02/10	Conf	Margate	1205	0 - 1	
06/10	Conf	NUNEATON BOROUGH	417	1 - 2	
09/10	Conf	WOKING	818	4 - 1	Clark 23, Hodge 42 82, Sterling 45
13/10	Conf	Northwich Victoria	698	0 - 1	
20/10	Conf	Farnborough Town	884	2 - 1	
27/10	FA Cup Q4	YEOVIL TOWN	1182	3 - 1	Hodges 2 39 89
03/11	Conf	TELFORD UNITED	629	1 - 4	
10/11	Conf	Stalybridge Celtic	660	0 - 1	
16/11	FA Cup 1	WYCOMBE WANDERERS	3475	3 - 4	K Warner 36, Clark 41[p], D Warner 85
24/11	Conf	SOUTHPORT	528	1 - 0	
01/12	Conf	LEIGH RMI	507	2 - 1	
04/12	Middx SC 2	HARROW BOROUGH	n/k	3 - 1	
08/12	Conf	Nuneaton Borough	962	2 - 0	Sterling 45, Dyer 57
15/12	Conf	Stevenage Borough	1572	1 - 1	Holsgrove 90
26/12	Conf	DAGENHAM & REDBRIDGE	820	2 - 4	Everitt 45, Hodges 71
29/12	Conf	Chester City	1250	1 - 3	Clark 90
05/01	Conf	DOVER ATHLETIC	655	2 - 1	Holsgrove 13, Clark 57
12/01	FA Trophy 3	Margate	625	1 - 3	Warner 44
19/01	Conf	Morecambe	1149	1 - 2	Clark 48
26/01	Conf	YEOVIL TOWN	708	0 - 4	
12/02	Conf	Dagenham & Redbridge	1585	1 - 1	Molesley 49
16/02	Conf	NORTHWICH VICTORIA	543	1 - 2	Charles 90
19/02	Middx SC QF	HENDON	n/k	1 - 5	Everett 76
02/03	Conf	BARNET	804	0 - 2	
09/03	Conf	Forest Green Rovers	635	1 - 2	Hale 78
12/03	Conf	MARGATE	350	2 - 4	Molesley 45, K Warner 56
16/03	Conf	SCARBOROUGH	631	1 - 2	Charles 54
22/03	Conf	Doncaster Rovers	1651	2 - 5	Charles 36, Molesley 80
26/03	Conf	Woking	2202	1 - 0	Clark 62[p]
30/03	Conf	FARNBOROUGH TOWN	617	0 - 3	
01/04	Conf	Telford United	762	2 - 1	Warner 38, Holsgrove 90
06/04	Conf	STALYBRIDGE CELTIC	510	0 - 0	
13/04	Conf	Southport	683	3 - 2	Clark 17, Hodges 65 90
20/04	Conf	Hereford United	1494	1 - 0	Case 84
28/04	Conf	BOSTON UNITED	3249	0 - 2	

Match Facts 2001-02

PLAYING SQUAD

Goalkeepers: Bertrand Bossu (Barnet), Sean O,Connor (Berkhamsted T), Steve Sladen (Youth Team)
Defenders: Brendan Gallen (Youth Team), Elis Kodra (Boreham Wood), Jamie Spencer (Youth Team), Jon Ashton (Exeter C), Jon Case (Youth Team), Mark Boyce (Watford)
Midfielders: Alex Dick (QPR), Ben Hodson (Forest Green Rovers), Daniel Tilbury (Youth Team), Dean Clark (Uxbridge), Jamie Jarvis (Maidenhead U), Mark Molesey (Youth Team), Paul Holsgrove (Slough T), Peter Holsgrove (Wycombe Wanderers), Scott Taylor (Carterton T)
Forwards: Cherif Diallo (Exeter C), David Warner (Watford), Ian Hodge (St Ives), Kevin Warner (Brook House), Leeyon Phelan (Wycombe Wanderers)

HENDON

CLUB OFFICIALS
Chairman: **Ivor Arbiter**

Secretary: **Graham Etchell,** c/o Hendon FC.
Tel: 020 8201 9494(Club)

Marketingl Manager:**Sue Damary**
PressOfficer: **David Ballheimer**

FOOTBALL MANAGEMENT TEAM
Man: Dave Anderson Ass.Man: John Turner
Player/Coach: Warren Kelly
Physio: Fernanda Chappinelli

FACT FILE
Formed: 1908 Nickname: Dons or Greens
Sponsors: UK Packaging
Colours: Green& white stripes/green/white
Change Colours: Azure/azure/white
Midweek matchday: Tuesday
Reserve League: Suburban (Premier)
Club Line: 09066 555 836
Club Website: www.hendonfc.net
2001-02
Captain: Jon Barrie-Bates
P.o.Y: Simon Clarke
Top Scorer: Ricci Crace & Martin Randall

GROUND: Claremont Road, Cricklewood, London NW2 1AE.
Tel: 020 8201 9494 Fax: 020 8905 5966
Directions: From Brent Cross station (Northern Line) to the east take first left after flyover on North Circular - Claremont Rd is then left at 3rd mini-r'bout. Buses 102, 210, 226 and C11 pass ground
Capacity: 3,029   Cover: 601   Seats: 329   Floodlights: Yes
Clubhouse: (contact Sue Damary 020 8455 9185). Two banqueting suites,conference centre, room hire, restaurant & bars open licensing hours 7 days aweek. Hot & cold food, pool, darts, bingo, members club, satelite TV,entertainments
Club Shop: Contact Derek Furmedge, 020 8459 2042 (H) Sells football souvenirs

Pages: 40 Price: £1.50p
Editor: Secretary
Local Press: Hendon Times,
Willesden & Brent Chronicle
Hampstead & Highgate Express
Local Radio: Capital, GLR, LBC

PREVIOUS **Leagues:** Finchley & Dist. 08-11, Middx 10-11, London 11-14, Athenian 14-63.
Names: Christ Church Hampstead to 08, Hampstead Town to 26, Hampstead to 33,Golders Green to 46
Grounds: Kensal Rise 08-12; Avenue Ground, Cricklewood Lane 12-26
CLUB RECORDS Attendance: 9,000 v Northampton, FA Cup 1st Rd 1952
Goalscorer: Freddie Evans 176 (1929-35)   **Appearances:** Bill Fisher 787 (1940-
Defeat: 2-11 v Walthamstow Ave. (A), Athenian Lge 9/11/35   **Win:** 13-1 v Wingate (H), Middx Senior Cup 2/2/57
Fee Paid: Paul Whitmarsh (undisclosed)   **Fee Received:** £30,000 for Iain Dowie (Luton)
BEST SEASON F.A. Cup: First Rd 20 times, Second Rd 5 times   **F.A.Trophy:** 5th Rd 98-99
HONOURS: European Am Champions 72-3; Isthmian Lg 64-5 72-3 (R-up 63-4 65-6 73-4) Lg Cup 76-7 (R-up 86-7), Full Members Cup 94-5 97-8 98-99, Premier Inter-Lge Cup R-up 86-7; Middx Lge 12-3 13-4; Athenian Lg 52-3 55-6 60-1 (R-up 28-9 32-3 47-8 48-9 51-2); London Lg Div 1 R-up 12-13 (Amtr Div 3-4); Finchley & Dist. Lg 10-1; London Snr Cup 63-4 68-9 (R-up 35-6 50-1 54-5 58-9 71-2); Middx Snr Cup (13) (R-up 83-4), Middx Interm 64-5 66-7 72-3, Middx Charity Cup(14); London IntermCup (4) (R-up (2); Suburban Lg 92-3 (R-up 84-5 97-8)
Players progressing: Peter Shearing (WHU 60), Iain Dowie (Luton 88), PeterAnderson (Luton), Jeff Harris (Orient), Phil Gridelet (Barnsley 90), GerrySoloman (Leyton O 91), Junior Hunter & Micah Hyde (both Cambridge 94-95),Simon Clark (Peterboro' 94-95),Junior Lewis(Gillingham 99-00)

Back row left to right: Andrew Landesberg (Director), Paul Towler, Steve Butler, Simon Clarke, Steve Forbes, Mark Cooper, Gary McCann, David Hook, Ross Pickett, Martin Randall, Leon Woodruffe, Michael Woolner, Mark Burgess, Roz Burns (physio) and Fernander Chappinelli (Physio).
Front row: Eugene Ofori, Paul Yates, Ricci Crace, James Burgess, Warren Kelly (Coach) Dave Anderson (Manager),jon Turner (Assistant Manager),jon Barrie-Bates, Byron Bubb, Dale Binns and Iain Duncan.

ISTHMIAN LEAGUE PREMIER DIVISION

Date	Comp.	Opponents	Att.	Score	Goalscorers
18.08	Ryman P	Purfleet	309	0 - 2	
21.08	Ryman P	BILLERICAY TOWN	258	1 - 3	Clarke 25
25.08	Ryman P	BOREHAM WOOD	261	2 - 1	Harvey 33[og], Binns 46
27.08	Ryman P	Harrow Borough	290	2 - 0	Haule 4, Binns 51
01.09	Ryman P	SUTTON UNITED	292	4 - 3	Haule 5, Bates 48, Binns 54 62
04.09	Ryman P	Hampton & Richmond Borough	263	0 - 0	
08.09	Ryman P	Braintree Town	357	0 - 2	
11.09	Ryman P	BEDFORD TOWN	285	1 - 2	Towler 40
15.09	Ryman P	BASINGSTOKE TOWN	226	1 - 3	Haule 38[p]
18.09	Ryman P	Gravesend & Northfleet	394	0 - 3	
22.09	Ryman P	Canvey Island	522	1 - 3	Street 90
25.09	Ryman P	KINGSTONIAN	232	2 - 0	Ruggles 67, Binns 90
29.09	FA Cup Q2	Southend Manor	203	2 - 1	Towler 39, Robson 90
09.10	Ryman P	HEYBRIDGE SWIFTS	157	1 - 0	Ruggles 9
13.10	FA Cup Q3	HITCHIN TOWN	325	0 - 0	
16.10	FA Cup Q3 R	Hitchin Town	338	1 - 3	Ruggles 68
20.10	Ryman P	Maidenhead United	236	1 - 3	Ruggles 11
30.10	Ryman P	Hitchin Town	264	0 - 3	
03.11	FA Trophy 1	SUTTON UNITED	287	2 - 1	Haule 44, Pickett 90
06.11	Middx SC 1	Kingsbury Town	n.k	5 - 0	Ofori 12, Bubb 34, Haule 50, Binns 64, Fewings 80
10.11	Ryman P	Enfield	137	6 - 0	Ofoiru 7 55, Fewings 39, Bubb 75, Preddie 82[og], Nartey 86
17.11	Ryman P	CROYDON	216	0 - 1	
24.11	Ryman P	CHESHAM UNITED	244	1 - 2	Forbes 20
27.11	Lge Cup 1	Hertford Town	n.k	3 - 0	Nartey 23 90, Bubb 62
01.12	FA Trophy 2	Maidenhead United	209	2 - 1	Pickett 1, Yates 62
08.12	Ryman P	Grays Athletic	239	0 - 2	
11.12	Middx SC 2	STAINES TOWN	84	5 - 0	Binns 14, Pickett 15 49, Bubb 78, Ruggles 89
15.12	Ryman P	PURFLEET	152	1 - 0	Woodruffe 40
18.12	Ryman P	ALDERSHOT TOWN	315	0 - 1	
29.12	Ryman P	Billericay Town	505	6 - 4	Cooper 4, Forbes 48, Woolner 50, Binns 82 88, Otari 90
05.01	Ryman P	HAMPTON & RICHMOND BOR.	202	1 - 0	Woodruffe 9
12.01	FA Trophy 3	Cambridge City	404	1 - 1	Ofori 78
02.02	FA Trophy 3 R	CAMBRIDGE CITY	281	2 - 0	Randall 37 78 St Albans City
05.02	FA Trophy 4	Gravesend & Northfleet	542	1 - 2	Forbes 86
09.02	Ryman P	Chesham United	323	2 - 0	Forbes 28, Randall 34
12.02	Ryman P	St Albans City	545	1 - 1	Fiori 71
14.02	Lge Cup 2	Aldershot Town	584	0 - 2	
16.02	Ryman P	GRAVESEND & NORTHFLEET	364	1 - 1	Bates 60[p]
19.02	Middx SC QF	Hayes	n.k	5 - 1	Hodges 12[og], Ofori 51, Randall 60, Crace 83, Forbes 88
23.02	Ryman P	Basingstoke Town	315	1 - 2	Crace 90
02.03	Ryman P	CANVEY ISLAND	314	0 - 1	
05.03	Middx SC SF	ENFIELD TOWN	234	1 - 0	Butler 75
09.03	Ryman P	Kingstonian	420	2 - 1	Bubb 4, Crace 29
12.03	Ryman P	Sutton United	438	1 - 2	Butler 87
16.03	Ryman P	HITCHIN TOWN	302	2 - 2	Bubb 5, Butler 43
19.03	Ryman P	HARROW BOROUGH	207	0 - 1	
23.03	Ryman P	Heybridge Swifts	193	6 - 1	Randall 16 54, Ofori 28, Woolner 40, Bubb 45, Crace 87
26.03	Ryman P	Bedford Town	556	5 - 0	Randall 32[p], Ofori 38 70, Brown 74[og], Wilson 88[og]
29.03	Ryman P	Boreham Wood	391	2 - 1	Randall 54, Ofori 59
01.04	Middx SC F	NORTHWOOD	853	4 - 2	Randall 56 103, Crace 105, Binns 120 @ Hayes
04.04	Ryman P	ST ALBANS CITY	307	1 - 0	Binns 63
06.04	Ryman P	Aldershot Town	1511	1 - 2	Binns 73
09.04	Ryman P	GRAYS ATHLETIC	197	1 - 0	Crace 55
13.04	Ryman P	MAIDENHEAD UNITED	221	1 - 1	Crace 81
16.04	Ryman P	BRAINTREE TOWN	189	3 - 0	Crace 7 13, Randall 76
20.04	Ryman P	Croydon	116	3 - 1	Crace 2 29 40
27.04	Ryman P	ENFIELD	335	2 - 0	Crace 2, Randall 63

PLAYING SQUAD

Goalkeepers: Dan Burton (Poole Borough), David Hook (Harrow B)

Defenders: Iain Duncan (Aylesbury U), Mark Cooper (Windsor and Eton), Pat Sappleton (Youth Team), Paul Towler (Metropolitan Police), Warren Kelly (St Albans C)

Midfielders: Byron Bubb (Millwall), Dale Binns (Youth Team), Jon-Barrie Bates (Harrow Bor.), Keiran Gallagher (Slough), Leon Woodruffe (Harrow Bor.), Michael Woolner (Ruislip), Paul Yates (Brook House), Steve Forbes (Dagenham & Redbridge)

Forwards: Eugene Ofori (Liberty Profesionals), Martin Randall (Woking), Nathan Edwards (Youth Team), Ricci Crace (Ware), Rob Haworth (Sutton Utd), Ross Pickett (Hendon)

HEYBRIDGE SWIFTS

CLUB OFFICIALS

Chairman: Mike Springett
President: T.B.A.
Vice Chairman: Michael Gibson
Secretary: Dennis Fenn
c/o cl;ub
Match Secretary: Terry Stowers
74 Wood Road, Heybridge, Maldon,
Essex CM9 4AW   Tel: 01621 857226
Press Offr: Tony Foster (M) 07931 330756
(H) 01376 519712
Treasurer: John Williams

FACT FILE
Formed: 1880   Nickname: Swifts
Sponsors: Towermaster.
Midweek matchday: Tuesday
Colours: Black & white stripes/black/black
Change colours: All Red or Amber/ white
Reserves' Lge: Essex & Herts Border Comb

2001-002
Captain John Pollard

FOOTBALL MANAGEMENT TEAM
Manager: David Greene
Coach: Dean Curtis   Physio: Glenn Churchet

Pages: 556 Price: £1.50
Editors: Tony Foster
Local Press: Maldon & Burnham Standard
: BBC Essex, Essex FM,Essex
Chronicle,Green Un
Dream FM
Club Website: www.robert-e-lee.couk\swifts

GROUND: Scraley Road, Heybridge, Maldon, Essex CM98JATel: 01621 852978
Directions: Leave Maldon on the main road to Colchester, pass through Heybridge then turn right at the sign to Tolleshunt Major (Scraley Road). The ground on the right. Six miles from nearest station (Witham). By bus via Chelmsfordand Maldon
Capacity: 3,000 Cover: 1,200   Seats: 550   Floodlights: Yes
Clubhouse: Two bars open every night. Games room, boardroom, kitchen (on matchdays)
Club Shop: Open matchdays, selling club sweaters, shirts, scarves, baseball hats, enamel
badges, old programmes etc.   Contact Tony Foster, c/o club.

PREVIOUS   **Leagues:** Essex & Suffolk Border, North Essex, South Essex, Essex Senior 1971-84
CLUB RECORDS **Attendance:** 2,477 v Woking FA Trophy 97 and pre season v West Ham United , 3,000 +, 99-00.
Goalscorer: Julian Lamb 115 (post war), Dave Matthews 112 (Isthmian)
Appearances: Hec Askew 500+, Johnpollard 414
Fee Paid: None   **Fee Received:** £35,000, Simon Royce (Southend Utd)

BEST SEASON **FA Trophy:** Qtr finals v Woking 22/3/97 (lost 0-1)
FA Cup: First round 0-2 v Gillingham 11/11/94, 0-3 v Bournemouth 15.11.97 **League clubs defeated:** None

HONOURS: Isthmian Lg Div 1 R-up 95-96, Div 2 North 89-90; Essex Senior Lg 81-82 82-83 83-84, Lg Cup 82-83, Trophy 81-82; JT Clarke Cup 82-83; Thorn EMI National Floodlit Competition R-up 82-83; Eastern Floodlit Cup 93-94; East Anglian Cup 93-94 94-95; Essex & Suffolk Border Lge 31-32; Essex Jun Cup 31-32; North Essex Lge 46-47 Ryman League Cup 00-01

Players progressing: Simon Royce (Southend United & Charlton Athletic), Peter Cawley & Ben Lewis (Colchester Utd), Alan Hull (Leyton Orient), Jonathan Hunt (Birmingham City), Dominic Naylor (Leyton Orient), Haken Hayrettin (Doncaster Rovers), Derek Payne & Tom Meredith (Peterborough Utd), Ben Barnett, Eddie Stein & Tim Alexander (Barnet), Ashley Vickers (Peterborough United), James Pullen (18 year old ,goalkeeper to Ipswich Town) 99-00.

Back row left to right: Dave Greene (Manager), Andy Tomlinson, Kevin Budge, Mark Cranfield, Kingsley Black, John Pollard, Josh Leeke, Ross Taylor, Dean Curtis (Coach) and Ricky Clarke (Coach). **Front row:** Ron Walker, Sean Caton, Lewis Baillie, Jamie Window, Dave Streetley, Dominic Gentle, and Danny Roberts

ISTHMIAN LEAGUE PREMIER DIVISION

Date	Comp.	Opponents	Att.	Score	Goalscorers
11.08	Ryman Shld	FARNBOROUGH TOWN	301	0 - 4	
18.08	Ryman P	Croydon	103	3 - 2	Lee 37 59, Taylor 87
21.08	Ryman P	HARROW BOROUGH	168	1 - 1	Bloor 38[og]
25.08	Ryman P	ALDERSHOT TOWN	492	1 - 2	Lee 12
27.08	Ryman P	Hitchin Town	264	0 - 1	
01.09	Ryman P	PURFLEET	187	3 - 3	Lee 21, Abraham 44, Roberts 45
04.09	Ryman P	Gravesend & Northfleet	420	1 - 1	Wall 72
08.09	Ryman P	Chesham United	218	0 - 3	
11.09	Ryman P	CANVEY ISLAND	289	0 - 7	
15.09	Ryman P	Maidenhead United	193	0 - 1	
18.09	Ryman P	BEDFORD TOWN	135	1 - 1	Parker 51
22.09	Ryman P	HAMPTON & RICHMOND BOR.	164	1 - 3	Gould 60
25.09	Ryman P	Boreham Wood	149	4 - 2	Gould 4 87, Taylor 45, Parker 76
29.09	FA Cup Q2	Clacton Town	302	2 - 3	Streetley 74, Parker 82
02.10	Ryman P	BILLERICAY TOWN	235	2 - 3	Hazell 18, Streetley 70
09.10	Ryman P	Hendon	157	0 - 1	
20.10	Ryman P	ST ALBANS CITY	191	0 - 2	
27.10	Ryman P	Sutton United	494	1 - 4	Parker 50
03.11	FA Trophy 1	ERITH & BELVEDERE	196	2 - 3	Parker 74 90
10.11	Ryman P	KINGSTONIAN	215	1 - 1	Gentle 61[p]
17.11	Ryman P	Basingstoke Town	329	3 - 1	Gentle 6 47, Budge 70
20.11	Essex SC 3	Great Wakering Rovers	n.k	3 - 1	D Gentle 32, Parker 54, Caton 88
24.11	Ryman P	GRAYS ATHLETIC	239	1 - 1	Budge 65
27.11	Lge Cup 1	Staines Town	n.k	0 - 2	
01.12	Ryman P	HITCHIN TOWN	216	3 - 1	Budge 39, Parker 81, Roberts 89
08.12	Ryman P	Enfield	99	2 - 4	Gentle 14, Budge 22
15.12	Ryman P	CROYDON	153	2 - 0	Roberts 76, Budge 90
29.12	Ryman P	Harrow Borough	179	3 - 1	Parker 41[p], Caton 65, Abrahams 79
05.01	Ryman P	GRAVESEND & NORTHFLEET	266	1 - 2	Abrahams 74
19.01	Ryman P	CHESHAM UNITED	236	2 - 1	Abrahams 14 33
29.01	Essex SC 4	BARKING & EAST HAM UNITED	n.k	8 - 1	Abrahams 13 14 25 40, Haydon 36, Leeke 44, Budge 63 70
02.02	Ryman P	ENFIELD	221	4 - 2	Abrahams 7 57 62, A N Other
09.02	Ryman P	Grays Athletic	254	3 - 1	Payne 16, Budge 35 59
11.02	Essex SC QF	Purfleet	n.k	0 - 3	
16.02	Ryman P	Bedford Town	525	2 - 5	Budge 30, Abrahams 42
19.02	Ryman P	Braintree Town	460	0 - 2	
23.02	Ryman P	MAIDENHEAD UNITED	219	2 - 0	Budge 62, Barber 64
26.02	Ryman P	Canvey Island	289	1 - 6	Budge 51
02.03	Ryman P	Hampton & Richmond Borough	248	1 - 1	Abrahams 42
04.03	Ryman P	Purfleet	189	1 - 3	Gentle 45
09.03	Ryman P	BOREHAM WOOD	215	0 - 2	
16.03	Ryman P	Billericay Town	685	2 - 1	Pollard 85, Gentle 90[p]
23.03	Ryman P	HENDON	193	1 - 6	Budge 90
30.03	Ryman P	Aldershot Town	1507	3 - 3	Budge 20 53, Kirby 43[og]
01.04	Ryman P	BRAINTREE TOWN	333	1 - 1	Abrahams 77
06.04	Ryman P	SUTTON UNITED	204	2 - 0	Budge 31, Windows 33
13.04	Ryman P	St Albans City	334	2 - 1	Abrahams 17, Window 63
20.04	Ryman P	BASINGSTOKE TOWN	208	5 - 1	Window 24, Budge 43 53 57, Taylor 70
27.04	Ryman P	Kingstonian	389	2 - 1	Budge 64 76
28.04	St Clares Cup	MALDON TOWN	150	3 - 2	Bailey 13[p], Clark 60[p], Cressy 80

PLAYING SQUAD

Goalkeepers: Kingsley Banks (Witham T)

Defenders: Danny Barber (Clacton T), Josh Leeke (Braintree T), Nicky Haydon (Chelmsford C), Richard Halle (Grays Ath), Dave Culnerhouse (Braintree), Leon Hunter (Grays Ath), Ollie Blacknell (Billerachy)

Midfielders: Andy Tomlinson (Billerachy), David Rainford (Grays Ath), Glen Moss (Youth Team), Dave Streeley (Halstead T), Gino Defoe (Witham T), Jason Shepphard (Maldon T), John Pollard (St Albans), Rob Walker (Chelmsford C), Ross Taylor (Chelmsford C), Lewis Baillie (Wivenhoe T), Ronnie Bridge (Youth Team), Tommy Santer (Youth Team)

Forwards: Chris Payne (Chelmsford C), Jamie Windows (Southend), Paul Abrahams (Wivenhoe T), Dominic Gentle (Slough T), Kevin Budge (Braintree T), Tresor Kandol (Cambridge Utd)

HITCHIN TOWN

The
Yellow & Green 'Un
The Matchday Magazine of
Hitchin Town Football Club 2001-02

CLUB OFFICIALS
Chairman: **Terry Barratt**
Secretary: **Roy Izzard**
2 Bedford Road, Ickleford, Hitchin, Herts
Tel: 01462 433171

Media Officer: **Neil Jensen**
Tel: 01462 454678   0207 5457921
Email: neiljensen@hitchintownfc.co.uk

FOOTBALL MANAGEMENT TEAM

Manager: Robbie O'Keefe
Assistant Manager: Ian Donnelly
Physio: Peter Prince

FACT FILE
Formed: 1865   Reformed 1928
Nickname: The Canaries
Sponsors: Alma Engineering
Colours: Yellow/green/green
Change colours: white/black/white
Midweek matchday: Tuesday
Clubcall Line: 09066 555 817
Website: www.hitchintownfc.co.uk
2001-02
Captain: David bass
P.O.Y.: Carl Drew
Top Scorer:Shaun Marshall 23

Pages: 24 (A4)   Price: £1.50
Editor: Neil Jensen

Local Press: Hitchin Comet, Herts on Sunday
Local Radio: Chiltern, BBC Three Counties

GROUND: Top Field, Fishponds Road, Hitchin SG5 1NU (01462434483) + 01482 459028 on match days only **Directions:** On A505 near town centre opposite large green. 1 mile from Hitchin(BR). From A1(M) Jct 8,A602 towards Bedford into Hitchin.Over two roundabouts through lights on one way system. Turn right at next roundabout for Fishponds Road.
Capacity: Cover: 1,250   Seats: 500   Floodlights: Yes
Clubhouse: (01462 434483). Members bar, Function Hall (available for hire). Open every-day. Steward: Eamonn Watson/ Nigel Collins
Club Shop: Yes, Contact - Chris Newbold on chris@bewvikd013.freeserve.co.uk

PREVIOUS	**Leagues:** Spartan 28-39; Hert & Middx 39-45; Athenian 39,45-63	
CLUB RECORDS	**Attendance:** 7,878 v Wycombe Wanderers, FA Amateur Cup 3rd Rd 18/2/56	
	Win: Spartan Lge 29-30 13-0 v Cowley, 13-0 v RAF	
	Defeat (Isthmian Lge): 0-10 v Kingstonian (A) 65-66, v Slough T. (A) 79-80	
	Career Appearances: Paul Giggle 769 (68-86) **Career Goals:** Paul Giggle, 214	
	Fee paid: £2,000 Ray Seeking Potton United, July 1989 **Fee received:** £30,000 Zema Abbey to Cambridge Utd Jan 00	
BEST SEASON	**FA Trophy:** 5th Rd 98-99 **FA Amateur Cup:** Semi Final 60-61, 62-63	
	FA Cup: 2nd Rd on four occasions -	
	v Swindon 1-3 (A) 76-77, v Boston Utd, 0-1 (A) 73-74, v Wycombe Wand. 0-5 (H) 94-95, v Gillingham 0-3 (A) 95-9	
HONOURS:	Isthmian Lge R-up 68-69Div 1 92-93 R-up 98-99, Spartan Lge 34-35; AFA Sen Cup 30-31; Herts Snr Cup (19-record); London Sen Cup 69-70 (R-up 72-73); E Anglian Cup 72-73; Herts Charity Cup(17), Herts I'mediate Cup (8); Woolwich Trophy 82-83; Televised Sport International Cup 88-89 90-91; Southern Comb. Senior Floodlit Cup 90-91	

Back row left to right: Matt Nolan, Craig Rydehead, Cliff Akurang, Jon Bone, Darren Sarll, Nick Grime and Louie Evans.
Middle row : Bunny Dear(physio), Nick Sopowski(Physio Team), Syd Springett(Kit Manager), Scott Cretton, Shaun Marshall, Nick Webb, Ian Morris, James Robinson, Carl Williams, Stuart Beavor, Ian Donnelly (Asst. Man.), Gavin Covington (Coaching Staff) & Richard Springett (Kit Manager).
Front row: Peter Prince (Physio Team), Jon Barnett, Robbie O'Keefe (Manager), Tim Allpress, Adam Parker, Ian Scott, Andy Malvin (Director), Rob Simpson and Mark Burke.

Date	Comp.	Opponents	Att.	Score	Goalscorers
11.08	Herts CC QF	HEMEL HEMPSTEAD TOWN	n.k	3 - 1	Marshall 43 44, Beevor 90
18.08	Ryman P	BASINGSTOKE TOWN	271	0 - 1	
21.08	Ryman P	Hampton & Richmond Borough	217	3 - 6	Allpress 34, Marshall 47, Deagan[og] 70
25.08	Ryman P	Canvey Island	406	3 - 5	Kean 69, Akurang 71, Marshall 73
27.08	Ryman P	HEYBRIDGE SWIFTS	264	1 - 0	Beevor 32[p]
01.09	Ryman P	Kingstonian	488	2 - 2	Marshall 36, Akurang 55
04.09	Ryman P	CROYDON	232	2 - 2	Allpress 73, Parker 90
08.09	Ryman P	ALDERSHOT TOWN	851	0 - 3	
11.09	Ryman P	Enfield	89	5 - 0	Marshall 55 70 78[p], Nolan 79, Barnett 84
15.09	Ryman P	Harrow Borough	168	1 - 1	Nolan 20
18.09	Ryman P	GRAYS ATHLETIC	195	2 - 4	McMenamin 11, Bone 90
22.09	Ryman P	SUTTON UNITED	352	0 - 2	
29.09	FA Cup Q2	Hampton & Richmond Borough	298	1 - 1	Marshall 75
02.10	FA Cup Q2 R	HAMPTON & RICHMOND BOR.	243	2 - 1	Bone 86, Akurang 107
06.10	Ryman P	Maidenhead United	194	1 - 1	Kean 13
09.10	Herts SC 1	Cheshunt	n.k	1 - 0	
13.10	FA Cup Q3	Hendon	325	0 - 0	
16.10	FA Cup Q3 R	HENDON	338	3 - 1	Scott 89, Nolan 105, Marshall 110
20.10	Ryman P	CHESHAM UNITED	291	2 - 3	McMenamin 14, Akurang 56
27.10	FA Cup Q4	Aldershot Town	2238	1 - 2	Sarll 72
30.10	Ryman P	HENDON	264	3 - 0	Nolan 33, Marshall 60[p], Akurang 63
03.11	FA Trophy 1	KINGSTONIAN	383	1 - 2	Marshall 69
06.11	Ryman P	Boreham Wood	184	1 - 2	Marshall 60
10.11	Ryman P	ST ALBANS CITY	398	2 - 4	Drew 53, Scott 56
13.11	Herts SC 2	SAWBRIDGEWORTH TOWN	90	2 - 0	Drew 50, Nolan 73
17.11	Ryman P	Billericay Town	591	1 - 1	Allpress 68
24.11	Ryman P	Gravesend & Northfleet	706	0 - 2	
27.11	Lge Cup 1	WALTON & HERSHAM	n.k	8 - 2	
01.12	Ryman P	Heybridge Swifts	216	1 - 3	Drew 14
08.12	Ryman P	PURFLEET	297	0 - 3	
15.12	Ryman P	Basingstoke Town	265	3 - 2	Nolan 36 59, Marshall 42
18.12	Ryman P	Braintree Town	268	1 - 0	Beaver 67
22.12	Lge Cup 2	Slough Town	n.k	1 - 0	
26.12	Ryman P	BEDFORD TOWN	879	2 - 2	Beevor 11, Marshall 18
29.12	Ryman P	HAMPTON & RICHMOND BOR.	276	2 - 4	Marshall 31[p], Drew 39
05.01	Ryman P	Croydon	97	2 - 1	Drew 30, Marshall 88[p]
08.01	Herts SC QF	STEVENAGE BOROUGH	n.k	3 - 1	
12.01	Ryman P	MAIDENHEAD UNITED	305	1 - 0	Drew 76
19.01	Ryman P	Aldershot Town	1505	2 - 1	Scott 50, Nolan 81
26.01	Ryman P	ENFIELD	343	1 - 2	Robertson 83
29.01	Herts CC SF	Cheshunt	n.k	3 - 2	
02.02	Ryman P	Purfleet	207	1 - 3	Scott 48
05.02	Lge Cup 3	Enfield	n.k	0 - 4	
09.02	Ryman P	GRAVESEND & NORTHFLEET	439	0 - 4	
12.02	Ryman P	KINGSTONIAN	276	0 - 0	
16.02	Ryman P	Grays Athletic	229	1 - 2	Nolan 6
19.02	Herts SC SF	Boreham Wood	n.k	1 - 6	
23.02	Ryman P	HARROW BOROUGH	248	3 - 0	Nolan 44, Dyer 45[og], Marshall 73
02.03	Ryman P	Sutton United	531	4 - 2	Nolan 14 28, Brennan 34, Drew 85
16.03	Ryman P	Hendon	302	2 - 2	Marshall 38, Bone 60
23.03	Ryman P	BOREHAM WOOD	335	4 - 1	Drew 3 68, Marshall 57, Francis 77
30.03	Ryman P	CANVEY ISLAND	550	2 - 1	Drew 55 65
01.04	Ryman P	Bedford Town	766	1 - 0	Drew 43
06.04	Ryman P	BRAINTREE TOWN	364	1 - 1	Francis 85
13.04	Ryman P	Chesham United	230	5 - 5	Drew 5, Nolan 29, Brennan 37, Scarlett 67, Simpson 87
20.04	Ryman P	BILLERICAY TOWN	359	3 - 2	Simpson 37[p], Beevor 41, Nolan 54
27.04	Ryman P	St Albans City	604	2 - 1	Williams 22, Brennan 66
01.05	Herts CC F	BERKHAMSTED TOWN	n.k	4 - 7	

PLAYING SQUAD

Goalkeepers: James Robinson (Inter Cardiff)
Defenders: Dean McElroy (Youth), Mark Burke (Luton T), Scott Gretton (Stevenage Bor.), John Bone (Bedford T), Nick Grime (Boreham Wood), Tim Allpress (St Albans C)
Midfielders: Chris Menamin (Boreham Wood), Darren Sarll (Youth), Daen Brennan (Luton T), Neil Butler (Woking), Craig Rydeheard (Youth), David Bass (Kingstonian), Ian Scott (St Albans), Stuart Beevor (St Albans), Tony Fontanelle (Arseley T)
Forwards: Anthony Francis (Youth), Jonathon Barnett (Stevenage Borough), Matthew Nolan (Youth), Shaun Marshall (Boreham Wood), Carl Drew (Boreham Wood), Robbie Simpson (St Albans C)

Match Facts 2001-02

KINGSTONIAN

CLUB OFFICIALS
Chairman:
Chief Executive: Victor Searle
Directors : G Rajesh Khosla,Anup Hhosla,
and Rishi Khosla
Club Secretary:
Graham Richards, 1 Bridge Court, Bridge
Street, Leatherhead, Surrey KT22 8BWTel No:
01372 377076
Commercial Man.: Anup Khosla
Press Officer: Gary Ekins (07764 745904)

FACT FILE
Founded: 1885
Nickname: The Ks
Sponsors: Bass Brewers
Club Colours: Red & white hooped shirts,
black shorts, black socks
Change Colours: Yellow shirts, royal blue
shorts,white socks
Midweek matchday: Tuesday
Reserves' League: Suburban

www.kingstonian.net
Official Matchday Programme - £1.50

RYMAN LEAGUE PREMIER DIVISION 2001-2002

FOOTBALL MANAGEMENT TEAM
Manager: Steve Sedgley
Coach: Kim Harris

20001-02
Leading Scorer: Greg Ball
Captain: Peter Barnsby

GROUND: Kingsmeadow Stadium, Kingston Road, Kingston-upon-Thames, Surrey. KT13PB
Tel: 0208 547 3335/6 Fax: 0208 974 5713
DIRECTIONS: From town centre - Cambridge Rd on to Kingston Rd (A2043) to Malden Rd.
From A3, turn off at New Malden, turn left on to A2043 - grd 1 mile on left. Half mile from
Norbiton (BR)
CAPACITY: 6,255 **COVERED TERRACING:** 3700 **SEATED:**1125
SOCIAL FACILITIES: Banqueting centre, open 7 days. 3 bars capacity 400.
Contact Anup Khosla (0208 647 3335)
CLUB SHOP: Sells programmes, shirts, badges etc.
Contact Brian Gifford: 0208 747 3336

Pages: 32 Price: £1.50
Editor: Robert Wooldridge Tel: 020 8669 3824

Local Press: Surrey Comet 020 8546 2261
Local Radio: County Sound;
Southern Counties

RECORDS **Win:** 15-1 v Delft, friendly 5/9/51; Competitive 10-0 v Hitchin (H) Isthmian Lge 19/3/66)
Attendance: 4,582 v Chelsea (Friendly) 22.7.95 **Defeat:** 0-11 v Ilford (A) Isthmian Lge 13/2/37
Fee Paid: £18,000 for David Leworthy to Rushden & Diamonds '97 **Goalscorer:** Johnny Whing 295
Fee Received: £150,000 for Gavin Holligan from West Ham Utd. '99 **Appearances:** Micky Preston 555

PREVIOUS **Leagues:** Kingston & Dist.; West Surrey; Southern Suburban; Athenian 1919-29; Isthmian League 29-98; Conference 98-01
Names: Kingston & Surbiton YMCA 1885-87, Saxons 87-90, Kingston Wanderers 1893-1904, Old Kingstonians 08-19
Grounds: Several to 1921; Richmond Rd 21-89

HONOURS FA Trophy 98-99 99-00; Isthmian League 33-34, 36-37, 97-98, R-up 47-48 62-63, Div 1 R-up 84-85, League Cup 95-96;
Athenian Lge 23-24 25-26, R-up 26-27; London Senior Cup 62-63 64-65 86-87, R-up x 5; Surrey Senior Cup x 9, R-up 90-91.

BEST SEASON FA Amateur Cup: Winners 32-33 R-up 59-60 **FA Trophy:** Winners 98-99 99-00
FA Cup: 4th Round replay 00-01, 0-1 v Bristol City (H), after 1-1 **League:** 5th Conference 99-00
League clubs defeated: Brighton & H.A. 94-95, Brentford & Southend Utd. 00-01

PAST PLAYERS: C Nastri (C Palace), H Lindsay (Southampton 65), G Still (Brighton 79), D Byrne (Gillingham 1985), J Power (Brentford 87),
Jamie Ndah (Torquay), Gavin Holligan (West Ham '99)

Back row left to right: Dave Clarke, Max Hustwick, Danny Bolt, Peter Barnsby (captain), Lance Key, Dave Sadler, Bashiru Alimi and Greg Ball
Front row : Jon Leacock, Liam Collins, Billy Mead, Mark Jones, Liam Garman and Ronnie Green

ISTHMIAN LEAGUE PREMIER DIVISION

Date	Comp.	Opponents	Att.	Score	Goalscorers
18.08	Ryman P	GRAVESEND & NORTHFLEET	723	0 - 1	
21.08	Ryman P	Basingstoke Town	529	1 - 2	Bolt 39
25.08	Ryman P	Maidenhead United	335	1 - 0	Green 75
27.08	Ryman P	ENFIELD	560	0 - 2	
01.09	Ryman P	HITCHIN TOWN	488	2 - 2	Cretton 64[og], Barnsby 89
03.09	Ryman P	Purfleet	486	1 - 1	Brown 90
08.09	Ryman P	Canvey Island	632	0 - 2	
11.09	Ryman P	CHESHAM UNITED	402	1 - 0	Sadler 24
15.09	Ryman P	Braintree Town	518	0 - 1	
18.09	Ryman P	BILLERICAY TOWN	412	4 - 1	Beard 23, Ball 53 76 89
22.09	Ryman P	GRAYS ATHLETIC	571	2 - 3	Stewart 3, Sadler 29
25.09	Ryman P	Hendon	232	0 - 2	
29.09	FA Cup Q2	Brockenhurst	452	1 - 2	Bolt 50
02.10	Ryman P	BEDFORD TOWN	469	3 - 0	Stewart 31, Bolt 54, Abini 66
06.10	Ryman P	St Albans City	307	2 - 2	Bolt 45[p], Ball 50
20.10	Ryman P	Aldershot Town	2276	0 - 3	
27.10	Ryman P	CROYDON	504	3 - 0	Sadler 23 76, Ball 56
03.11	FA Trophy 1	Hitchin Town	383	2 - 1	Ball 47, Green 90
10.11	Ryman P	Heybridge Swifts	215	1 - 1	Ball 50
17.11	Ryman P	HAMPTON & RICHMOND BOR.	714	3 - 0	Green 41 79, Ball 69
24.11	Ryman P	Boreham Wood	287	3 - 1	Ball 31, Green 33 75
27.11	Lge Cup 1	Basingstoke Town	n.k	0 - 2	
01.12	FA Trophy 2	CIRENCESTER TOWN	404	6 - 2	Green 8 59, Mead 48, Ball 51 55, Sadler 90
08.12	Ryman P	HARROW BOROUGH	558	1 - 0	Green 50
15.12	Ryman P	Gravesend & Northfleet	691	0 - 2	
29.12	Ryman P	BASINGSTOKE TOWN	487	1 - 1	Sadler 55
05.01	Ryman P	PURFLEET	459	1 - 5	Green 34
12.01	FA Trophy 3	Woking	2474	1 - 2	Sadler 52
19.01	Ryman P	CANVEY ISLAND	754	2 - 1	Sills 5, White 88
22.01	Surrey SC 4	WALTON & HERSHAM	n.k	1 - 2	
29.01	Ryman P	Enfield	129	2 - 2	Green 10, Sills 18
02.02	Ryman P	Harrow Borough	260	3 - 1	Ball 34, Marney 50[og], Sills 57
09.02	Ryman P	BOREHAM WOOD	503	1 - 1	Ball 44[p]
12.02	Ryman P	Hitchin Town	276	0 - 0	
16.02	Ryman P	Billericay Town	614	1 - 1	Sadler 65
02.03	Ryman P	Grays Athletic	322	0 - 2	
09.03	Ryman P	HENDON	420	1 - 2	Collins 62
16.03	Ryman P	Bedford Town	719	1 - 2	Sadler 64
23.03	Ryman P	ST ALBANS CITY	418	4 - 2	Sadler 40 61, Thurgood 47, Mead 59
26.03	Ryman P	BRAINTREE TOWN	383	0 - 2	
30.03	Ryman P	MAIDENHEAD UNITED	404	1 - 0	Sills 90[p]
01.04	Ryman P	Sutton United	949	0 - 0	
06.04	Ryman P	Croydon	225	0 - 4	
09.04	Ryman P	SUTTON UNITED	762	1 - 1	Sills 43
13.04	Ryman P	ALDERSHOT TOWN	1063	2 - 1	Ball 43, Elverson 64
16.04	Ryman P	Chesham United	221	0 - 0	
20.04	Ryman P	Hampton & Richmond Borough	732	0 - 0	
27.04	Ryman P	HEYBRIDGE SWIFTS	389	1 - 2	Ball 10

PLAYING SQUAD

Goalkeepers: Lance Key (Northwich Victoria)
Defenders: Liam Garmer (Walton and Hersham), Luke Dowling (Lewes), Matt Elverson (Basingstoke T), Peter Barnsby (Hampton and Richmond Borough), Mark Jones (Wimbledon), Max Hustwick (Walton and Hersham), Sean Thurgood (Youth)
Midfielders: Bashiru Alimi (Millwall), David Clarke (Dover Athletic), Liam Collins (Walton and Hersham), David Sadler (Hinckley Utd), James Pinnock (Gillingham), Tim Sills (Basingstoke T), Phil Wingfield (Sutton Utd), Greg Ball (Walton and Hersham), Ronnie Green (Youth)

MAIDENHEAD UNITED

THE MAGPIE
2002-2003
£1.50

IN TOWN TODAY
BEDFORD TOWN

CLUB OFFICIALS

Chairman: **Roger Coombs**
Vice Chairman: **Jon Swan**
President: **Jim Parsons**
Secretary: **Ken Chandler**
c/o Maidenhead United
Press Off .: **Jon Swan** (01344 372027

FOOTBALL MANAGEMENT TEAM
Manager: Alan Devonshire
Asst. Man. & Coaches: Carl Taylor,Phil
Parkes,Dave Harrison & Phil Heggie
Physios:Jon Urry & Bryan Clements

FACT FILE

Formed: 1870
Nickname: Magpies
Sponsors: Trademark Windows & The
Honeypot
Colours: Black & white stripes/black/black
Change colours: Red/white/white
Midweek matchday: Tuesday
Reserve League: Suburban
Local Press: Maidenhead Advertiser,
Reading Evening Post, Slough Observer

Pages: 36   Price: £1
Editor: J Swan Tel: 01344 723750

Local Radio: 2-Ten FM, Star FM,
Thames Valley FM

GROUND   York Road, Maidenhead, Berks SL6 1SQ Tel: 01628 624739/636314

Directions: From Maidenhead BR station proceed eastwards down Bell St - 500 yds
Ground is 5 miles from M4 in town centre.
Capacity: 4,500   Cover: 2,000   Seats: 400   Floodlights: Yes
Clubhouse: Open evenings & matchdays. Some hot food
Club Shop: Wide range of programmes and club souvenirs.
Contact Mark Smith (01753 854674)

PREVIOUS   **Leagues:** Southern 1894-1902; West Berks 02-04; Grt West Sub 04-22; Spartan 22-39; Grt West Comb 39-45;
Corinthian 45-63; Athenian 63-73, Isthmian 1973-
Names: Maidenhead FC, Maidenhead Norfolkians. **Grounds:** None

CLUB RECORDS   **Attendance:** 7,920 v Southall, FA Amat Cup Q/F 7/3/36   **Season's goalscorer:** Jack Palethorpe 66, 1929-30
Career appearances: Bert Randall 532, 1950-64   **Career goalscorer:** George Copas 270, 1924-35
Win: 14-1 v Buckingham Town (H), FA Amat. Cup 6/9/52   **Defeat:** 0-14 v Chesham United (A), Spartan Lge 31/3/23
Transfer fee paid: Undisclosed   **Transfer fee received:** £5,000 from Norwich for Alan Cordice, 79

BEST SEASON   FA Cup: Qtr Finals 1873-74 74-75 75-76   F A Trophy: 3rd Qual Rd   FA Amateur Cup: Semi Final 35-36
HONOURS   Isthmian Lg Div 2 Sth R-up 90-91,Promotion to Premier Division 99-00 Full Members Cup 96-97; Spartan Lg x3 R-upx2;
Corinthian Lg 57-58 60-61 61-62 R-up 58-59 59-60, Mem. Shield 56-57 61-62,R-up x4, Neale Cup 48-49 57-58 60-61; Gt Western Suburban Lg
19-20 R-up 20-21; Berks & Bucks Snr Cup x18, Berks & Bucks Benev. Cup x6 R-up x2; Mithras Cup R-up x4; Southern Comb. Cup R-up 81-82;
Sub Lge West 97-98; Allied Counties Champ 97-98
Players progressing: A Cordice (Norwich 79), P Priddy (Brentford 72), D Kemp (Plymouth), L Sanchez (Reading),E Kelsey, J Palethorpe (Reading
30), B Laryea(Torquay), R Davies (Torquay), Mark Harris (C.Palace & Swansea C 1985),Ben Abbey (Oxford U via Crawley 99)

Back row,left to right: Paul Lagerman (Physio), Carl Levene, Nick Hart, Phil Heggie (Coach), Richard Barnard, Steve Croxford, Rickey Ibe, Lee Channell, Rob Saunders, Brian Connor, Adrian Allen, Orlando Jeffrey, Alan Devonshire (Manager) and Roger Coombs (Chairman). **Front row:** Richard Goddard (Reserve Team Manager), Adam Durrant, Andy Morley, Paul Kelly, Obinna Ulasi, Andy Rose, Chris Ferdinand, John Urry (Physio) with Dave Harrison (Coach) at the front.   **Photo:** Maidenhead Advertiser

ISTHMIAN LEAGUE PREMIER DIVISION

Date	Comp.	Opponents	Att.	Score	Goalscorers
18.08	Ryman P	Harrow Borough	267	3 - 0	Croxford 4, Scott 45, Channell 75[p]
21.08	Ryman P	PURFLEET	184	1 - 3	Lawrence 52[og]
25.08	Ryman P	KINGSTONIAN	335	0 - 1	
27.08	Ryman P	St Albans City	281	0 - 1	
01.09	Ryman P	GRAVESEND & NORTHFLEET	217	0 - 3	
04.09	Ryman P	Bedford Town	472	2 - 1	Morley 39, Rake 53
08.09	Ryman P	Boreham Wood	201	1 - 2	Croxford 49
11.09	Ryman P	HAMPTON & RICHMOND BOR.	184	2 - 1	Allen 42 61
15.09	Ryman P	HEYBRIDGE SWIFTS	193	1 - 0	Rake 65
18.09	Ryman P	Aldershot Town	1663	1 - 4	Channell 49
22.09	Ryman P	Enfield	114	2 - 0	Wilkie 40[og], Rake 83
29.09	FA Cup Q2	ALDERSHOT TOWN	917	1 - 1	Ibe 86
02.10	FA Cup Q2 R	Aldershot Town	1742	0 - 1	
06.10	Ryman P	HITCHIN TOWN	194	1 - 1	Jarvis 44
09.10	Ryman P	CROYDON	174	0 - 1	
16.10	Ryman P	Canvey Island	415	0 - 2	
20.10	Ryman P	HENDON	236	3 - 1	Ulasi 51, Kelly 73, Allen 89
03.11	FA Trophy 1	Northwood	214	1 - 0	Allen 12
10.11	Ryman P	GRAYS ATHLETIC	184	2 - 1	Allen 21 28
17.11	Ryman P	Braintree Town	363	1 - 2	Scott 90
24.11	Ryman P	SUTTON UNITED	253	2 - 2	Cook 41, Channell 47
27.11	Lge Cup 1	Hungerford Town	n.k	3 - 0	
01.12	FA Trophy 2	HENDON	209	1 - 2	Ibe 63
08.12	Ryman P	Basingstoke Town	327	2 - 1	Channell 10 61
11.12	Ryman P	Billericay Town	281	2 - 2	Jeffrey 62, Channell 82
15.12	Ryman P	HARROW BOROUGH	209	4 - 2	Channell 18 32, Allen 73 90
18.12	Lge Cup 2	Hampton & Richmond Borough	n.k	3 - 5	
29.12	Ryman P	Purfleet	172	2 - 5	Channell 75, Allen 84
05.01	Ryman P	BEDFORD TOWN	294	2 - 1	Saunders 50, Cook 69[p]
08.01	Ryman P	Chesham United	179	0 - 1	
12.01	Ryman P	Hitchin Town	305	0 - 1	
19.01	Ryman P	BOREHAM WOOD	232	2 - 0	Channell 17 59
02.02	Ryman P	BASINGSTOKE TOWN	218	2 - 2	Channell 16, Jarvis 58
05.02	Berks & BS QF	FLACKWELL HEATH	n.k	3 - 0	Ibe 30 80, Allen 49
09.02	Ryman P	Sutton United	495	1 - 2	Saunders 40
16.02	Ryman P	ALDERSHOT TOWN	753	1 - 2	Channell 12
23.02	Ryman P	Heybridge Swifts	219	0 - 2	
26.02	Ryman P	ST ALBANS CITY	138	2 - 1	Allen 29, Ibe 83
02.03	Ryman P	ENFIELD	168	0 - 1	
05.03	Ryman P	Gravesend & Northfleet	626	2 - 3	Ibe 28, Ulasi 90
12.03	Ryman P	Hampton & Richmond Borough	194	1 - 2	Scott 76
16.03	Ryman P	CANVEY ISLAND	306	0 - 1	
19.03	Berks & BS SF	SLOUGH TOWN	n.k	3 - 0	Channell, Ibe, Jarvis
23.03	Ryman P	Croydon	78	2 - 0	Channell 61, Scott 46
30.03	Ryman P	Kingstonian	404	0 - 1	
01.04	Ryman P	CHESHAM UNITED	246	0 - 4	
06.04	Ryman P	BILLERICAY TOWN	191	0 - 2	
13.04	Ryman P	Hendon	221	1 - 1	Channell 27
20.04	Ryman P	BRAINTREE TOWN	181	2 - 0	Morley 29 35
27.04	Ryman P	Grays Athletic	227	1 - 0	Saunders 60[p]
06.05	Berks & BS F	Chesham United	n.k	0 - 0	Won 4-2 after pens @ Wycombe Wanderers

PLAYING SQUAD

Goalkeepers: Richard Barnard (Millwall)

Defenders: Andy Morley (Basingstoke), Andy Rose (Harrow Bor.), Brian Connor (Marlow)
Chris Elsegood (Crystal Palace), Obinna Vlasi (Hayes), Rob Paris (Aylesbury Utd),
Craig Webster (Youth Team), Orlando Jeffrey (Burnham), Steve Croxford (Hampton & Richmond Bor.)

Midfielders: Andy Cook (Northwood), Jamie Pritchard (Marlow), Michael Gorman (Yeading), Ryan Ashe (Northwood),
Tom Hickey (Feltham), Barry Rake (Slough), Matthew Glynn (Windsor & Eton),
Paul Kelly (Boreham Wood), Steve Brown (Feltham)

Forwards: Adrian Allen (Leyton Pennant), Lawrence Yaku (Northwood), Mark Nicholls (Chesham Utd),
Ayodeji Ahochin (Enfield), Lee Channell (Feltham), Micky Creighton (Uxbridge)

PURFLEET

CLUB OFFICIALS
Chairman: **Grant Beglan**
V/Chairman/Chief Executive: **Tommy Smith**
Secretary: Norman Posner, 1 Chase House
Gardens, Hornchurch, Essex, RM11 2PJ,
Tel: 01708 458301
Match Secretary/Press Officer:
Norman Posner
Comm Mger: **Tony Joy** (01375 392906)

FACT FILE
Founded: 1985
Nickname: Fleet
Colours:Yellow &green/green/yellow & green
Change colours: All white
Midweek home matchday: Tuesday
Reserve's League: None
Sponsors: Daybreak Windows, Lakeside
Shopping Centre and T&P Lead Roofing Ltd.

FOOTBALL MANAGEMENT TEAM
Manager: Colin McBride
Asst Manager: Jimmy McFarlane
Coach: Ronnie Hanley
Physio: Michelle Sheehan

2001-02
Leading Goal Scorers:
Cliff Akurang & Paul Linger
Captain: Jimmy McFarlane
P.o.Y.: Jimmy McFarlane

PURFLEET v ENFIELD
RYMAN LEAGUE PREMIER DIVISION
Friday 29th March 2002 Kick off 7.30pm
TONIGHT'S MATCH SPONSOR: L & D FOOD PRODUCTS

GROUND: Thurrock Hotel, Ship Lane, Grays, Essex. 01708 868901 Fax: 01708 866703
Webside: www.purfleetfootballclub.com
Directions: M25 or A13 to Dartford tunnel r'bout. Ground is fifty yards on right down Ship
Lane. Nearest station is Purfleet, two miles from ground
Capacity: 4,500   Cover: 1,000   Seats: 300   Floodlights: Yes
Clubhouse: Steward: Tommy South
Club Shop: Selling programmes & magazines. Contact Tommy South (01708 868901)

Pages: 60 Price: £1.50
Editor: Norman Posner (01708 458301 H)
Local Press: Romford, Thurrock Recorder,
Thurrock Gazette
Local Radio: Essex Radio, BBC Radio
Essex

PREVIOUS   **League:** Essex Senior 85-89.   **Grounds:** None

CLUB RECORDS **Attendance:** 2,572 v West Ham United, friendly 1998.
Goalscorer: George Georgiou 106.   **Appearances:** Jimmy McFarlane 452
Win: 10-0 v Stansted (H) 86-87, v East Ham Utd (A) 87-88 (both Essex Senior League)
Defeat: 0-6 v St Leonards Stamco(A), FA Trophy 96-97. 0-6 v Sutton United(H) Isthmian Lge 97-98

BEST SEASON **FA Cup:** Fourth Qualifying Round Replay 95-96 (lost 1-3 away to Rushden & D)
FA Trophy: Second Round Prop 95-96 (lost 1-2 away to Macclesfield Tn)
HONOURS: Isthmian Lg Div 2 91-92 Div 1 R-up 93-94, Div 2 Nth R-up 88-89, Associate Members Tphy 91-92; Essex Snr Lg 87-88 (Lg
Cup (2) 86-88; Essex Snr. Cup R-up 97-98, 99-00, Stanford Charity Cup 87-88 (R-up 85-86); Essex Thames-Side Trophy 94-
95; Essex Bus Houses Sen L/Cup 93-94; F Budden Trophy 94-95; Essex & HertsBorder Comb R-up 94-95; Full Members Cup
R-up 99-00, 00-01.

Players progressing to Football League: Paul Cobb & Lee Williams (Leyton O.)

L-R - Back Row: P. Smith (Coach) B. Leggit (Coach) R. Gould, M. Lawrence, C. Simpson, D. Chandler, M. Goodfellow,
A. O'Reilly, N. Fillery, S. Pashley, J. Southon, K. Gray (Coach) C. McBride (Manager)
Middle Row: C. Akurang, J. Purdie, P. Linger, J. McFarlane (Asst manager), S. Brown, D. Jones
Front Row: T. Bowes, W. Vaughan, D. Smith, L. Allen.   **Photo:** T. Hoskins.

Date	Comp.	Opponents	Att.	Score	Goalscorers
18.08	Ryman P	HENDON	309	2 - 0	Buglione 8, Ling 37
21.08	Ryman P	Maidenhead United	184	3 - 1	Buglione 2, Linger 75, Kelly 75[og]
25.08	Ryman P	Enfield	103	1 - 0	Buglione 47[p]
27.08	Ryman P	CANVEY ISLAND	693	0 - 0	
01.09	Ryman P	Heybridge Swifts	187	3 - 3	Marshall 5, Buglione 14, Limber 41
03.09	Ryman P	KINGSTONIAN	486	1 - 1	Linger 24
08.09	Ryman P	CROYDON	290	5 - 1	Keeling 48 69, Marshall 50 67, Adams 78
11.09	Ryman P	Aldershot Town	1751	1 - 4	Martin 89
15.09	Ryman P	Boreham Wood	189	0 - 1	
17.09	Ryman P	ST ALBANS CITY	301	2 - 2	McFarlane 22 90
22.09	Ryman P	HARROW BOROUGH	387	0 - 3	
25.09	Ryman P	Braintree Town	315	2 - 2	Martin 14 58
29.09	FA Cup Q2	WEALDSTONE	190	3 - 2	Linger 41, Southon 45, Martin 81
01.10	Ryman P	GRAYS ATHLETIC	389	2 - 0	Adams 17, Martin 71
09.10	Ryman P	Hampton & Richmond Borough	183	1 - 1	Pashley 64
13.10	FA Cup Q3	GRAYS ATHLETIC	389	1 - 1	Marshall 8
16.10	FA Cup Q3 R	Grays Athletic	487	2 - 3	Pashley 51, Marshall 84
20.10	Ryman P	SUTTON UNITED	272	1 - 1	Etherington 68
27.10	Ryman P	Chesham United	270	0 - 0	
31.10	Essex SC 3	SOUTHEND UNITED	n.k	3 - 0	Simpson 1, Buglione 11, Martin 87
03.11	FA Trophy 1	BOREHAM WOOD	195	4 - 2	Linger 17 51, Marshall 18 81
10.11	Ryman P	BILLERICAY TOWN	268	1 - 1	Marshall 7
24.11	Ryman P	BASINGSTOKE TOWN	232	0 - 0	
26.11	Lge Cup 1	YEADING	n.k	0 - 1	
01.12	FA Trophy 2	KETTERING TOWN	261	2 - 1	Buglione 46, Brown 78
08.12	Ryman P	Hitchin Town	297	3 - 0	Southon 47, Jones 50, Marshall 84
15.12	Ryman P	Hendon	152	0 - 1	
22.12	Ryman P	Canvey Island	641	0 - 3	
29.12	Ryman P	MAIDENHEAD UNITED	172	5 - 2	Chandler 15, Akurang 24 40, Keeling 48, Simpson 90
05.01	Ryman P	Kingstonian	459	5 - 1	Akurang 8 21, Brown 33, McFarlane 51, Simpson 85
12.01	FA Trophy 3	Canvey Island	483	2 - 2	Martin 47, Linger 80
14.01	FA Trophy 3 R	CANVEY ISLAND	471	0 - 1	
19.01	Ryman P	Croydon	86	1 - 0	Akurang 78[p]
22.01	Essex SC 4	Braintree Town	n.k	3 - 0	
02.02	Ryman P	HITCHIN TOWN	207	3 - 1	Linger 26 81, Brown 75
09.02	Ryman P	Basingstoke Town	322	2 - 2	Akurang 3 54
11.02	Essex SC QF	HEYBRIDGE SWIFTS	n.k	3 - 0	
16.02	Ryman P	St Albans City	403	1 - 0	Linger 13
23.02	Ryman P	BOREHAM WOOD	152	0 - 1	
26.02	Ryman P	Bedford Town	417	0 - 1	
02.03	Ryman P	Harrow Borough	151	2 - 1	McFarlane 88, Bowes 90
04.03	Ryman P	HEYBRIDGE SWIFTS	189	3 - 1	Akurang 9[p], Brown 54, Lawrence 83
09.03	Ryman P	BRAINTREE TOWN	301	3 - 2	Akurang 6 48, McFarlane 90
11.03	Ryman P	GRAVESEND & NORTHFLEET	713	2 - 0	Linger 41, McFarlane 68
16.03	Ryman P	Grays Athletic	401	3 - 1	McFarlane 59, Simpson 75 90[p]
23.03	Ryman P	HAMPTON & RICHMOND BOR.	247	3 - 0	Bowes 4, Simpson 13 60
29.03	Ryman P	ENFIELD	236	1 - 0	Simpson 66
01.04	Ryman P	Gravesend & Northfleet	1085	0 - 0	
06.04	Ryman P	CHESHAM UNITED	203	2 - 2	Bowe 1, McFarlane 90
13.04	Ryman P	Sutton United	480	0 - 0	
16.04	Ryman P	ALDERSHOT TOWN	384	2 - 1	Lawrence 47, Simpson 71
20.04	Ryman P	BEDFORD TOWN	301	1 - 1	Cartlidge 49
27.04	Ryman P	Billericay Town	681	0 - 2	

PLAYING SQUAD

Goalkeepers: Alex O'Reilly (Bristol Rovers), Steve Mead (Concord Rangers)
Defenders: Dean Chandler (Woking), Jamie Southon (Chelmsford), Jim McFarlane (Concord Rangers), Steve Pashley (Aveley)
Midfielders: Greg Berry (Millwall), Jon Keeling (Tilbury), Lee Allen (Enfield), Mark Cartlidge (East Thurrock), Mark Goodfellow (Youth Team), Martin Ling (Leyton Orient), Paul Linger (Billericay T), Terry Bowes (Chesham)
Forwards: Cliff Akurang (Hitchin T), George Georgiou (Enfield), Martin Buglione (Ashford T), Martyn Lawrence (Concord Rangers), Steve Brown (Kingstonian), Wayne Vaughan (Canvey Island)

St ALBANS CITY

CLUB OFFICIALS
Chairman: John Gibson
President: Cllr Malcolm MacMillan
Vice Chairman: SteveCarroll
Secretary: Steve Eames c/o Club
Safety Officer: Rex Winn 0966 175124 (M)
Commercial Manager: Michele Sinclair

FOOTBALL MANAGEMENT TEAM
Manager: Gary Roberts & Steve Cook
Physio: Adie Blundell

FACT FILE
Formed: 1908
Nickname: The Saints
Colours: Yellow & blue
Change colours: Sky Blue
Midweek home matchday: Tuesday
Newsline: 09066 555822
Club Website:http://www.sacfc.co.uk
E-Mail: info@sacfc,co,uk

Programme: Pages: 32 Price: £1.50
Editor: T.B.A.
Local Press: St Albans & District Observer, Herts Advertiser
Local Radio: BBC Three Counties, Chiltern Radio, Oasis

GROUND: Clarence Park, York Rd, St Albans, Herts AL1 4PL Tel: 01727 864296
Directions: Left out of St Albans station - Clarence Pk 200yds ahead acrossHatfield Rd. M25, jct 21 to Noke Hotel island, straight on thru Chiswell Green towards St Albans, straight over 2 mini-r'bouts and one larger island, thru 2sets of lights and right at island at far end of city centre (St Peters St.) into Hatfield Rd, over mini-r'bout, left at 2nd lights into Clarence Rd, ground on left
Capacity: 6,000 Cover: 1,900 Seats: 904 Floodlights: Yes
Clubhouse: Open matchdays and available for functions. Manager:James Brewer
Tea bar within ground serves hot food
Club Shop: Club merchandise & League & non-League progs,magazines,videos etc
Managers:Barry Hillard c/o club

PREVIOUS **Leagues:** Herts County 08-10; Spartan 08-20; Athenian 20-23
CLUB RECORDS **Attendance:** 9,757 v Ferryhill Ath., FA Amtr Cup QF 27/2/26
Appearances: Phil Wood 900 (62-85) **Goalscorer:** W H (Billy) Minter 356 (top scorer for 12 consecutive seasons 1920-32)
Win: 14-0 v Aylesbury United (H) Spartan Lge 19/10/12 **Defeat:** 0-11 v Wimbledon (H), Isthmian Lge 9/11/46.
Fee Paid: £6,000 for Paul Turner (Yeovil Town Aug 97) **Fee Received:** £92,750 for Dean Austin (Southend 90/Spurs 92)

BEST SEASON **FA Amateur Cup:** Semi final 22-23 24-25 25-26 69-70. **FA Trophy:** Semi-Final 1998-99 1-2 & 2-3 v Forest Green Rovers
FA Cup: 2nd Rd replay 68-69 (1-3 at Walsall after 1-1 draw), 80-81 (1-4 atTorquay after 1-1 draw), 96-97 (9-2 at Bristol City)

HONOURS: Isthmian Lg 23-24 26-27 27-28 (R-up 54-55 92-93), Div 1 85-86, Div 2 R-up 83-84, Lg Cup R-up 89-90, Res. Sect. R-up 48-
49 60-61 61-62; Athenian Lg 20-21 21-22 (R-up 22-23); Spartan Lg 11-12 (R-up 12-13, East Div 09-10); Herts Co. Lg 09-10 (West Div 08-09, Aubrey Cup(res) 61-62); London Snr Cup 70-71 (R-up 69-70); AFA Snr Cup 33-34 (R-up 30-31 32-33 34-35); E Anglian Cup 92-93; Herts SnrCup(13) (R-up 10), Herts Snr Tphy 86-87, Herts Charity Cup(25) (R-up(18);Mithras Cup 64-65 71-72 (R-up 76-77); Wycombe F'lit Cup(2) 68-70; St AlbansHosp Cup 45-46; Hitchin Centenary Cup 70-71 (R-up 71-72); Victory Cup 25-26 27-28, Liege Cup 26-27; Billy Minter Invit. Cup (3) 90-93

Players progressing: A Grimsdell (Spurs 11), G Edmonds (Watford 14), R Burke(Man Utd 46), J Meadows (Watford 51), M Rose (Charlton 63), J Kinnear (Spurs 65), J Mitchell (Fulham 72), A Cockram (Brentford 88), D Austin (Southend 90),T Kelly (Stoke 90), M Danzey (Cambridge 92), D Williams (Brentford 93).

Back row left to right: Steve Cook (co-manager), Tom Upsher, Simon Martin, Ryan Moran, Derek Brown, Corey Campbell, Rob Smith, Richard Evans and Gary Roberts (co-manager). **Front row:** Richard Wilmot, Gary Wraight, Jon Rattle, Mike Bignall and Jimmy Sugrue.

Date	Comp.	Opponents	Att.	Score	Goalscorers
18.08	Ryman P	HAMPTON & RICHMOND BOR.	315	1 - 3	Smith 47
21.08	Ryman P	Bedford Town	647	1 - 0	Ansell 59[p]
25.08	Ryman P	Grays Athletic	259	2 - 3	Smith 61, Wraight 80
27.08	Ryman P	MAIDENHEAD UNITED	281	1 - 0	Smith 17
01.09	Ryman P	CHESHAM UNITED	393	3 - 1	Martin 5, Rattle 42, Nabil 64
04.09	Ryman P	Boreham Wood	312	1 - 0	Nabil 15
08.09	Ryman P	Sutton United	553	1 - 1	Nabil 7
11.09	Ryman P	BASINGSTOKE TOWN	224	2 - 0	Martin 2, Wilkinson 41[og]
15.09	Ryman P	CANVEY ISLAND	499	2 - 4	Wraight 2, Fenton 90
17.09	Ryman P	Purfleet	301	2 - 2	Metcalfe 59, Martin 66
22.09	Ryman P	Gravesend & Northfleet	604	2 - 3	Smith 54, Brown 90
25.09	Ryman P	ENFIELD	252	1 - 1	Blaney 89
29.09	FA Cup Q2	BILLERICAY TOWN	441	0 - 1	
03.10	Ryman P	Croydon	119	1 - 2	Moran 54
06.10	Ryman P	KINGSTONIAN	307	2 - 2	Martin 38, Browne 62
20.10	Ryman P	Heybridge Swifts	191	2 - 0	Smith 44, Martin 56
27.10	Ryman P	HARROW BOROUGH	334	1 - 0	Martin 84[p]
03.11	FA Trophy 1	Wisbech Town	376	1 - 1	Ansell 57
06.11	FA Trophy 1 R	WISBECH TOWN	200	3 - 0	Deare 2[og], Martin 45, Evans 85
10.11	Ryman P	Hitchin Town	398	4 - 2	Sugrue 34, Martin 62, Nabil 75, Ansell 90
13.11	Herts CC QF	Hertford Town	n.k	2 - 4	Ansell 7[p], Duncliffe 70
20.11	Herts SC 2	Hertford Town	n.k	2 - 0	
24.11	Ryman P	BRAINTREE TOWN	502	3 - 1	Bignall 47, Wraight 79, Kean 90
27.11	Lge Cup 1	Chesham United	164	0 - 2	
01.12	FA Trophy 2	Canvey Island	480	1 - 5	Martin 72
08.12	Ryman P	Billericay Town	519	5 - 1	Campbell 31, Martin 40 71[p], Bignall 63, Smith 85
15.12	Ryman P	Hampton & Richmond Borough	308	5 - 0	Martin 4 37, Stowell 36[og] 44[og], Brown 60
29.12	Ryman P	BEDFORD TOWN	760	0 - 0	
08.01	Herts SC QF	BOREHAM WOOD	n.k	1 - 1	Bignall ?? 3 4
12.02	Ryman P	HENDON	545	1 - 1	Martin 50
16.02	Ryman P	PURFLEET	403	0 - 1	
23.02	Ryman P	Canvey Island	425	2 - 3	Martin 15[p], Armstrong 83
26.02	Ryman P	Maidenhead United	138	1 - 2	Wraight 57
02.03	Ryman P	GRAVESEND & NORTHFLEET	451	0 - 3	
05.03	Ryman P	BILLERICAY TOWN	229	0 - 0	
09.03	Ryman P	Enfield	221	0 - 0	
12.03	Ryman P	Basingstoke Town	235	1 - 3	Moran 81
16.03	Ryman P	CROYDON	372	5 - 0	Kean 45, Ansell 54[p] 86, Martin 65, Bignall 77
19.03	Ryman P	Chesham United	205	2 - 3	Martin 23, Kean 65
23.03	Ryman P	Kingstonian	418	2 - 4	Martin 80 85
26.03	Ryman P	BOREHAM WOOD	318	1 - 0	Nabil 2
30.03	Ryman P	GRAYS ATHLETIC	327	2 - 1	Martin 7 76
04.04	Ryman P	Hendon	307	0 - 1	
06.04	Ryman P	Harrow Borough	225	6 - 2	Smith 28 72, Cook 37, Martin 44 66 67
09.04	Ryman P	ALDERSHOT TOWN	421	0 - 3	
13.04	Ryman P	HEYBRIDGE SWIFTS	334	1 - 2	Moran 45
16.04	Ryman P	SUTTON UNITED	213	2 - 0	Martin 42, Evans 51
20.04	Ryman P	Aldershot Town	1637	1 - 1	Bignall 58
23.04	Ryman P	Braintree Town	263	1 - 2	Smith 73
27.04	Ryman P	HITCHIN TOWN	604	1 - 2	Martin 59

PLAYING SQUAD

Goalkeepers: Duncan Roberts (Harrow Bor.), Richard Wilmot (Hendon)

Defenders: Beckett Hollenbach (Northampton T.), Corey Campbell (Gravesend & N'fleet), Lee Townley (Aldershot T.), Ryan Moran (Luton T.), Derek Brown (Bedford T.), Rob Gould (Tamworth)

Midfielders: Craig Maikall-Smith (Youth), John Challinor (Kalamazoo Kingdom-USA), Richard Evans (Chertsey T.), Rob Smith (Baldock T.), Steve Castle (Stevenage Bor.), Hamid Barr (QPR), Robbie Kean (Hitchin T.), Scott Oakes (Leyton Orient)

Forwards: Gary Crawshaw (Farnborough), Gary Sippetts (London Colney), Miguel de Souza (Farnborough), Simon Martin (Hucknall T)

SUTTON UNITED

CLUB OFFICIALS
Chairman: Bruce Elliott
President: Andrew W Letts
Secretary: Dave Farebrother,
38 Plevna Rd Hampton.TW12 2BP
Tel: 0771 2682415 (M)
Press Officer: Tony Dolbear
Tel: Mobile 07966 507023

FOOTBALL MANAGEMENT TEAM
Manager: John Rains
Assistant Manager: Tony Rains
Coach: Micky Cook **Physio:** Ben
McDonald**Res Team Manager:** Phil Dunne

FACT FILE
Formed: 1898   Nickname: The U's
Sponsors: Securicor
Colours:
Amber & chocolate/chocolate/amber & chocolate
Change colours: Green & white/black/black
Midweek matchday: Tuesday
Reserve League: Suburban League
Local Press: Sutton Advertiser, Sutton
Guardian, Sutton Independent, Sutton Comet
Local Radio: Thames Radio, County Sound
2001-02
Leading Scorer: Rob Haworth 18
Player of the Year: Paul Honey
Captain: Mike Mison

Pages: 48   Price: £1.50
Editor: Mackrory - Lyall Reynolds
Email: LReynolds@TARP.co.uk

Other club publications:
'Touchliner' (Supporters' Club)

GROUND: Borough Sports Ground, Gander Green Lane, Sutton, Surrey SM1 2EY Tel: 0208 6444440 Fax: 0208 6445120   Website: www.btinternet.com/~suttonunited
Directions: Gander Green Lane runs between A232 (Cheam Road - turn by Sutton Cricket Club) and A217 (Oldfields Road - turn at 'Goose & Granite' PH lights). Ground opposite 'The Plough' 50 yards from West Sutton BR station. Bus 413 passes ground
Capacity: 7,032   **Seated:** 765   **Terracing - Covered:** 1,250 **Uncovered:** 5,000
Clubhouse: Open every day, food. Available for hire with five function rooms
Club Shop: Open matchdays selling a full range of souvenirs, etc, contact Tony Cove via club

PREVIOUS   **Leagues:** Sutton Junior, Southern Sub 10-21, Athenian 21-63, Isthmian 63-86, 91-99, GMVC 86-91, 99-00
Names: Sutton Association, Sutton Guild Rovers   **Grounds:** Western Road, Manor Lane, London Road, The Find.
CLUB RECORDS Attendance: 14,000 v Leeds United,FA Cup 4th Rd 24/1/70
Victory: 11-1 v Clapton 66, & leatherhead 82-83   **Defeat:** 13-0 v Barking 25-26
Scorer: Paul McKinnon (279)   **Appearances:** Larry Pritchard 781 (65-84)
Fee Paid: to Malmo FF for Paul McKinnon 83   **Fee Received:** £100,000 for Efan Ekoku (Bournemouth 90)
BEST SEASON   **FA Amateur Cup:** Runners-up 62-63 68-69; SF 28-29 36-37 67-68 **FA Trophy:** Runners-up 80-81; SF 92-93,99-00 **FA Cup:**
4th Rd-69-70, 0-6 v Leeds Utd (H); 88-89, 0-8 v Norwich C.(A), 3rd Rd 87-88 v Middlesbrough 1-1, 0-1, 93-94 v Notts Co(A)2-3
HONOURS   Bob Lord Trophy 90-91; **Isthmian League** 66-67 84-86 98-99 R-up 67-68 70-71 81-82, Lge Cup (3) 82-84 85-86 97-98 R-up
79-80; Loctite Cup 91-92; Carlton Cup 95-96; **Athenian Lge** 27-28 45-46 57-58 R-up 46-47, Lg Cup 45-46 55-56 61-62 62-63, Res Sec 61-62 R-
up 32-33; Anglo Italian Semi-Pro Cup 79 R-up 80 82; London Snr Cup 57-58 82-83; London Charity Cup 69-70 R-up 67-68 68-69 72-73; Surrey
Snr Cup x14 R-up x9; Surrey Interm. Cup x4 R-up x6; Surrey Jnr Cup R-up 09-10; Surrey Snr Char. Sh. x3 R-up x6; Surrey Interm Char. Cup 31-
32 R-up 34-35 38-39; Dylon Char. Sh. 84 R-up 80 82 83 85; Groningen Yth tournament 83 85 R-up 79 81 89 91; John Ullman Invit. Cup 88-89
Past Players progressing: Numerous including the following since 1980 - S Galloway (C Palace 84), P McKinnon (Blackburn 86), R Fearon
(Ipswich 87), PHarding (Notts Co), E Ekoku (Bournemouth 91), M Golley (Maidstone), A Barnes (C Palace 91), P Rogers (Sheff U 92), S Massey
(C Palace 92), A & R Scott (Sheff U 93), O Morah (Cambridge 94), M Watson (West Ham 95), E Hutchinson (Brentford 2000)

L-R - Back Row: Micky Cook (coach), Paul Honey, Ryan Palmer, Matt Hanlon, Mark Watson, Tom Dunn, John Rains (manager), Jamie Ribolla,
Scott Corbett, Danny Hodges, Matt Gray, Darren Beale, Tony Rains (asst. manager).
Front: Ben Shannon, Nick Bailey, Mike Hollands, Danny Bolt, Matt Fowler, Lewis Gonsalves, Dave Timothy.   **Photo:** Garry Letts

ISTHMIAN LEAGUE PREMIER DIVISION

Date	Comp.	Opponents	Att.	Score	Goalscorers
18.08	Ryman P	Braintree Town	393	0 - 3	
21.08	Ryman P	BOREHAM WOOD	483	2 - 2	Mison 54, Fowler 72
25.08	Ryman P	CHESHAM UNITED	532	0 - 1	
27.08	Ryman P	Billericay Town	627	1 - 2	Haworth 85
01.09	Ryman P	Hendon	292	3 - 4	Mison 18, Boothe 26[p] 90[p]
04.09	Ryman P	HARROW BOROUGH	440	1 - 1	Mison 13
08.09	Ryman P	ST ALBANS CITY	553	1 - 1	Boothe 57[p]
11.09	Ryman P	Grays Athletic	206	3 - 3	Haworth 34, Palmer 59, Murray 73
15.09	Ryman P	ENFIELD	509	1 - 1	Murray 20
18.09	Ryman P	Basingstoke Town	278	0 - 3	
22.09	Ryman P	Hitchin Town	352	2 - 0	Arkwright 20 76
25.09	Ryman P	CROYDON	458	2 - 0	Haworth 16, Akuamoah 73
29.09	FA Cup Q2	EASTLEIGH	402	5 - 1	Akuamoah 17 28 61, Keevill 35, Haworth 90
02.10	Ryman P	Gravesend & Northfleet	582	1 - 3	Boothe 14
09.10	Ryman P	ALDERSHOT TOWN	944	2 - 0	J Palmer 65, Haworth 74
13.10	FA Cup Q3	Aldershot Town	1961	0 - 3	
20.10	Ryman P	Purfleet	272	1 - 1	Akuamoah 27
27.10	Ryman P	HEYBRIDGE SWIFTS	494	4 - 1	Arkwright 42, Boothe 53[p], Wall 72[og], Murray 88
03.11	FA Trophy 1	Hendon	287	1 - 2	Honey 90
10.11	Ryman P	Hampton & Richmond Borough	391	1 - 2	Timothy 68
13.11	Ryman P	CANVEY ISLAND	574	1 - 4	Dicks 29[og]
24.11	Ryman P	Maidenhead United	253	2 - 2	Haworth 8, R Palmer 74
27.11	Lge Cup 1	DULWICH HAMLET	205	5 - 3	Haworth 43 120, Palmer 48, Gonsalves 62, Akuamoah 96
08.12	Ryman P	BEDFORD TOWN	591	2 - 2	Boothe 10, Akuamoah 73
11.12	Lge Cup 2	Thame United	46	3 - 1	
15.12	Ryman P	BRAINTREE TOWN	515	3 - 1	Akuamoah 1, R Palmer 47, Howarth 49
29.12	Ryman P	Boreham Wood	216	2 - 1	Akuamoah 23, Harvey 57[og]
05.01	Ryman P	Harrow Borough	262	6 - 1	Akuamoah 9 49 83, Haworth 47[p], Wingfield 55, Brown 77
12.01	Ryman P	BILLERICAY TOWN	570	2 - 2	Wingfield 16, Haworth 41[p]
15.01	Lge Cup 3	GRAYS ATHLETIC	203	1 - 7	Haworth 38
29.01	Surrey SC 4	WESTFIELD	161	2 - 0	Haworth 38, Akuamoah 78
02.02	Ryman P	Bedford Town	488	1 - 0	Corbett 52
09.02	Ryman P	MAIDENHEAD UNITED	495	2 - 1	Timothy 83, Mison 84
16.02	Ryman P	BASINGSTOKE TOWN	557	2 - 1	Wingfield 46, Corbett 64
23.02	Ryman P	Enfield	159	2 - 2	Howorth 18, Corbett 81
02.03	Ryman P	HITCHIN TOWN	531	2 - 4	Haworth 40, Akuamoah 62[p]
05.03	Surrey SC QF	TOOTING & MITCHAM UTD.	246	0 - 3	
09.03	Ryman P	Croydon	175	2 - 1	Akuamoah 30, Fowler 64
12.03	Ryman P	HENDON	438	2 - 1	Wingfield 15, Gray 36[p]
16.03	Ryman P	GRAVESEND & NORTHFLEET	689	0 - 1	
23.03	Ryman P	Aldershot Town	1618	0 - 1	
30.03	Ryman P	Chesham United	266	0 - 2	
01.04	Ryman P	KINGSTONIAN	949	0 - 0	
06.04	Ryman P	Heybridge Swifts	204	0 - 2	
09.04	Ryman P	Kingstonian	762	1 - 1	Akuamoah 86
13.04	Ryman P	PURFLEET	480	0 - 0	
16.04	Ryman P	St Albans City	213	0 - 2	
20.04	Ryman P	Canvey Island	808	1 - 1	Haworth 62
23.04	Ryman P	GRAYS ATHLETIC	440	2 - 2	Gray 70, Mison 84
27.04	Ryman P	HAMPTON & RICHMOND BOR.	514	2 - 0	Gray 8, Haworth 58

Match Facts 2001-02

PLAYING SQUAD

Goalkeepers: Tommy Dunn (Youth Team)

Defenders: Craig Howard (Youth Team), Danny Arkwright (Whyteleafe), Danny Hodges (Tooting and Mitcham), Lewis Gonsalves (Youth Team), Nick Drew (Fulham-Junior), Ryan Palmer (Brighton)

Midfielders: Aaron Smith (Youth Team), Danny Bolt (Canvey Island), David Timothy (Slough T), Graham Tydeman (Youth Team), Michael Mison (St Albans), Paul Honey (Youth Team), Scott Corbett (Farnborough)

Forwards: Jon Palmer (Kings Lynn), Mark Watson (Aldershot T), Matt Fowler (Carshalton), Matt Gray (Youth Team), Nick Bailey (Youth Team)

CROYDON

Date	Comp.	Opponents	Att.	Score	Goalscorers
18.08	Ryman P	HEYBRIDGE SWIFTS	103	2 - 3	Garland 44, Dundas 45
21.08	Ryman P	Enfield	89	1 - 3	Coleman 78
25.08	Ryman P	Basingstoke Town	331	0 - 1	
27.08	Ryman P	HAMPTON & RICHMOND BOR.	141	0 - 0	
01.09	Ryman P	CANVEY ISLAND	211	2 - 1	McDonnell 66, Thompson 74
04.09	Ryman P	Hitchin Town	232	2 - 2	McDonnell 45 50
08.09	Ryman P	Purfleet	290	1 - 5	McDonnell 73
12.09	Ryman P	GRAVESEND & NORTHFLEET	153	3 - 4	Dundas 66, McDonnell 74, Chin 84
15.09	Ryman P	Bedford Town	554	2 - 3	Coleman 53, Allen 76
19.09	Ryman P	HARROW BOROUGH	88	2 - 1	Coleman 31, Bower 47
22.09	Ryman P	BRAINTREE TOWN	105	0 - 4	
25.09	Ryman P	Sutton United	458	0 - 2	
29.09	FA Cup Q2	Carshalton Athletic	256	2 - 1	McDonnell 16 64[p]
03.10	Ryman P	ST ALBANS CITY	119	2 - 1	McDonnell 15 19
09.10	Ryman P	Maidenhead United	174	1 - 0	Dickinson 70
13.10	FA Cup Q3	HAVANT & WATERLOOVILLE	168	0 - 1	
20.10	Ryman P	BOREHAM WOOD	96	0 - 5	
27.10	Ryman P	Kingstonian	504	0 - 3	
03.11	FA Trophy 1	FORD UNITED	71	3 - 1	McDonnell 31 52, Coleman 88
10.11	Ryman P	CHESHAM UNITED	78	0 - 1	
17.11	Ryman P	Hendon	216	1 - 0	McConnell 54
24.11	Ryman P	BILLERICAY TOWN	130	0 - 0	
01.12	FA Trophy 2	Tiverton Town	740	0 - 6	
08.12	Ryman P	Aldershot Town	1674	0 - 2	
11.12	Lge Cup 1	Aldershot Town	623	1 - 5	
15.12	Ryman P	Heybridge Swifts	153	0 - 2	
26.12	Ryman P	GRAYS ATHLETIC	107	1 - 0	Barclay 65
29.12	Ryman P	ENFIELD	83	0 - 2	
05.01	Ryman P	HITCHIN TOWN	97	1 - 2	Chatelier 25
12.01	London SC 4	ERITH & BELVEDERE	58	4 - 2	Hill 20 65, Chatelier 63, Barclay 78
19.01	Ryman P	PURFLEET	86	0 - 1	
29.01	Surrey SC 4	Molesey	n.k	2 - 0	
02.02	Ryman P	ALDERSHOT TOWN	292	1 - 2	Barclay 53
05.02	Ryman P	Hampton & Richmond Borough	140	0 - 6	
09.02	Ryman P	Billericay Town	508	0 - 2	
13.02	London SC QF	ILFORD	n.k	3 - 0	
16.02	Ryman P	Harrow Borough	186	0 - 2	
19.02	Ryman P	Canvey Island	426	0 - 3	
23.02	Ryman P	BEDFORD TOWN	173	3 - 3	Barclay 44, Mitchell 53, McDonnell 57
27.02	Surrey SC QF	WALTON & HERSHAM	n.k	4 - 2	
02.03	Ryman P	Braintree Town	277	1 - 2	Favata 24
09.03	Ryman P	SUTTON UNITED	175	1 - 2	McDonnell 35
13.03	London SC SF	HANWELL TOWN	n.k	2 - 0	Patton 12[og], Barclay 43
16.03	Ryman P	St Albans City	372	0 - 5	
19.03	Ryman P	Gravesend & Northfleet	673	1 - 6	Greene 80
23.03	Ryman P	MAIDENHEAD UNITED	78	0 - 2	
25.03	Surrey SC SF	CRYSTAL PALACE	210	1 - 3	Hill 12
30.03	Ryman P	BASINGSTOKE TOWN	90	1 - 3	Harper 87
01.04	Ryman P	Grays Athletic	118	0 - 1	
06.04	Ryman P	KINGSTONIAN	225	4 - 0	Favata 13, McDonnell 37, Greene 53 85
13.04	Ryman P	Boreham Wood	142	1 - 1	Dundas 2
20.04	Ryman P	HENDON	116	1 - 3	Mitchell 88
27.04	Ryman P	Chesham United	239	1 - 2	Chatelier 26
01.05	London SC F	DULWICH HAMLET	n.k	2 - 1	McDonnell 30 90[p] @ Leyton Orient

DIVISION ONE FINAL LEAGUE TABLE 2001-02

		Home					Away					Total						
	P	W	D	L	F	A	W	D	L	F	A	W	D	L	F	A	GD	Pts
Ford United	42	12	5	4	44	30	15	2	4	48	26	27	7	8	92	56	36	88
Bishop's Stortford	42	15	3	3	60	25	11	6	4	44	26	26	9	7	104	51	53	87
Aylesbury United	42	13	6	2	57	33	10	4	7	39	31	23	10	9	96	64	32	79
Bognor Regis Town	42	10	8	3	36	20	10	5	6	38	35	20	13	9	74	55	19	73
Northwood	42	11	5	5	53	34	8	6	7	39	30	19	11	12	92	64	28	68
Carshalton Athletic	42	11	5	5	38	28	6	11	4	26	25	17	16	9	64	53	11	67
Harlow Town	42	9	4	8	36	30	10	5	6	41	35	19	9	14	77	65	12	66
Slough Town	42	10	4	7	41	24	7	7	7	27	27	17	11	14	68	51	17	62
Uxbridge	42	11	1	9	44	35	7	5	9	24	30	18	6	18	68	65	3	60
Oxford City	42	10	6	5	32	23	7	3	11	27	43	17	9	16	59	66	-7	60
Thame United	42	10	4	7	44	27	5	10	6	31	34	15	14	13	75	61	14	59
Tooting & Mitcham U	42	7	7	7	40	36	9	4	8	30	34	16	11	15	70	70	0	59
Walton & Hersham	42	6	6	9	27	25	10	4	7	48	45	16	10	16	75	70	5	58
Yeading	42	9	6	6	40	31	7	4	10	44	59	16	10	16	84	90	-6	58
Worthing	42	7	2	12	43	41	8	6	7	26	24	15	8	19	69	65	4	53
Staines Town	42	5	9	7	22	26	7	2	12	23	34	12	11	19	45	60	-15	47
Dulwich Hamlet	42	6	5	10	33	42	5	8	8	31	34	11	13	18	64	76	-12	46
Wealdstone	42	6	9	6	32	31	5	3	13	28	51	11	12	19	60	82	-22	45
Bromley	42	7	5	9	20	27	3	6	12	24	47	10	11	21	44	74	-30	41
Whyteleafe	42	6	6	9	30	39	4	5	12	16	47	10	11	21	46	86	-40	41
Barking & East Ham	42	6	3	12	31	50	2	4	15	30	73	8	7	27	61	123	-62	31
Windsor & Eton	42	5	3	13	34	46	2	2	17	19	47	7	5	30	53	93	-40	26

DIVISION ONE RESULTS CHART 2001-02

		1	2	3	4	5	6	7	8	9	10	11	12	13	14	15	16	17	18	19	20	21	22
1	Aylesbury	X	3-2	3-3	2-2	3-1	2-1	3-3	3-4	1-0	3-2	1-4	4-0	2-1	2-0	3-2	0-0	4-2	2-2	8-0	3-2	1-1	4-1
2	Barking	2-1	X	0-4	1-2	2-2	1-2	1-0	1-4	0-6	0-5	1-1	0-1	2-0	2-3	2-1	2-3	3-3	2-1	3-0	2-4	1-3	3-4
3	Bishop's	2-2	3-1	X	1-3	3-0	2-1	2-2	4-1	4-1	1-2	2-0	3-2	2-0	3-0	5-0	2-4	2-0	7-1	3-0	2-0	1-1	6-4
4	Bognor R	1-1	8-3	0-0	X	2-0	1-1	1-0	1-1	0-0	3-1	3-1	0-0	0-2	2-1	3-1	0-1	3-3	0-1	2-0	2-1	1-1	3-1
5	Bromley	0-2	3-2	1-1	1-1	X	0-1	1-0	1-2	1-3	2-0	1-0	0-3	0-1	1-1	1-3	1-0	2-1	1-2	0-0	1-0	0-2	2-2
6	Carshalton	2-1	1-1	2-0	0-2	3-0	X	0-0	2-1	1-2	1-1	3-2	2-1	1-0	2-2	2-3	4-1	3-2	3-0	2-0	2-2	0-2	2-5
7	Dulwich	3-3	7-1	1-2	2-1	5-3	0-3	X	0-5	1-1	1-4	1-2	0-0	0-1	2-2	0-2	1-1	0-3	0-3	3-1	1-2	2-0	
8	Ford Utd	0-3	2-1	2-1	1-3	1-1	1-1	2-2	X	0-2	2-0	5-0	0-2	2-1	4-2	1-1	2-1	6-1	2-1	2-2	4-2	2-1	3-2
9	Harlow T	1-3	4-0	1-2	4-0	0-1	2-2	1-2	4-1	X	3-2	1-2	1-4	2-2	2-0	2-1	2-2	0-1	2-0	1-0	2-1	2-1	
10	Northwood	3-2	2-2	2-2	5-1	2-2	1-1	1-3	1-2	2-1	X	4-1	1-1	4-3	3-1	3-4	2-0	3-5	3-1	5-0	0-1	2-0	4-1
11	Oxford C	0-2	0-1	1-0	2-2	0-1	1-1	0-0	0-2	1-2	2-2	X	3-0	3-1	1-1	1-0	1-1	2-3	4-2	3-2	2-0	1-0	2-1
12	Slough T	3-4	2-1	0-1	0-1	3-0	1-1	3-2	1-2	4-0	2-1	1-2	X	2-0	1-1	3-1	3-0	0-3	6-0	0-0	3-0	0-1	3-3
13	Staines T	2-1	2-1	0-0	1-1	0-0	0-0	0-0	2-4	1-3	1-3	0-0	0-1	X	0-0	1-3	1-2	3-1	1-1	0-0	3-0	4-3	0-2
14	Thame U	0-1	10-2	0-2	1-1	4-1	0-0	4-2	1-2	1-4	2-1	3-0	3-0	0-4	X	0-0	1-0	3-4	4-2	3-0	1-0	0-1	3-4
15	Tooting	2-4	5-0	2-3	2-3	2-0	1-1	1-1	0-4	2-4	1-1	3-0	1-1	4-1	2-2	X	0-1	1-0	3-2	2-3	2-1	0-0	4-4
16	Uxbridge	3-1	3-1	1-3	2-0	1-0	2-0	0-3	1-2	2-3	0-2	3-1	3-1	2-3	1-3	1-1	X	3-4	1-0	2-0	5-3	2-3	6-1
17	Walton	1-1	4-0	0-1	1-0	2-4	2-2	1-1	0-2	1-1	0-0	1-2	1-1	0-1	2-1	1-2	2-1	X	1-2	1-2	4-0	2-0	0-1
18	Wealdstone	1-0	2-2	2-2	2-3	4-1	1-2	1-3	1-1	1-1	2-2	3-0	2-1	1-0	1-3	0-1	2-1	3-3	X	1-1	1-1	1-1	0-2
19	Whyteleafe	1-2	2-4	2-4	1-5	1-1	0-0	2-1	1-0	1-1	1-3	4-2	0-2	1-1	2-2	3-0	0-1	2-5	1-2	X	1-0	2-1	2-2
20	Windsor	1-3	4-0	1-7	3-4	2-1	1-2	3-0	1-5	4-2	0-3	1-4	3-3	1-2	0-0	0-1	1-2	3-3	4-0	X	0-1	1-2	
21	Worthing	2-0	2-2	2-4	0-2	2-3	2-3	6-2	1-2	6-1	0-1	2-2	0-3	4-2	0-2	1-2	3-2	1-2	0-2	0-3	2-0	X	7-1
22	Yeading	1-2	5-2	3-2	3-1	3-3	4-1	1-4	0-1	1-1	3-3	0-1	0-0	1-0	1-1	3-2	1-1	0-1	2-1	4-0	3-1	1-1	X

DIVISION TWO FINAL LEAGUE TABLE 2001-02

	P	Home					Away					Total						
		W	D	L	F	A	W	D	L	F	A	W	D	L	F	A	GD	Pts
Lewes	42	17	3	1	65	15	12	6	3	43	16	29	9	4	108	31	77	96
Horsham	42	17	3	1	59	14	10	6	5	45	30	27	9	6	104	44	60	90
Berkhamsted Town	42	12	5	4	47	26	11	5	5	35	25	23	10	9	82	51	31	79
Arlesey Town	42	12	5	4	52	28	11	1	9	37	27	23	6	13	89	55	34	75
Banstead Athletic	42	12	3	6	44	25	10	5	6	39	29	22	8	12	83	54	29	74
Leyton Pennant	42	15	2	4	47	27	7	6	8	37	33	22	8	12	84	60	24	74
Great Wakering	42	12	4	5	43	17	9	4	8	21	20	21	8	13	64	37	27	71
East Thurrock Utd	42	11	5	5	37	25	10	3	8	30	34	21	8	13	67	59	8	71
Marlow	42	10	5	6	33	26	8	8	5	40	37	18	13	11	73	63	10	67
Hemel Hempstead T	42	10	6	5	46	28	8	4	9	36	38	18	10	14	82	66	16	64
Leatherhead	42	11	3	7	42	24	6	3	12	30	38	17	6	19	72	62	10	57
Ashford Town (Mx)	42	8	7	6	33	29	7	4	10	25	42	15	11	16	58	71	-13	56
Metropolitan Police	42	10	4	7	49	35	6	3	12	35	49	16	7	19	84	84	0	55
Barton Rovers	42	9	2	10	28	24	6	7	8	26	36	15	9	18	54	60	-6	54
Hungerford Town	42	7	7	7	27	32	7	2	12	29	43	14	9	19	56	75	-19	51
Tilbury	42	7	4	10	24	28	8	2	11	31	46	15	6	21	55	74	-19	51
Chertsey Town	42	7	6	8	45	52	3	8	10	34	60	10	14	18	79	112	-33	44
Wembley	42	7	4	10	31	35	2	6	13	20	47	9	10	23	51	82	-31	37
Molesey	42	6	6	9	21	32	4	0	17	19	61	10	6	26	40	93	-53	36
Cheshunt	42	2	8	11	28	39	5	5	11	23	45	7	13	22	51	84	-33	34
Wivenhoe Town	42	6	2	13	33	52	2	7	12	22	59	8	9	25	55	111	-56	33
Romford	42	2	4	15	27	59	2	3	16	15	46	4	7	31	42	105	-63	19

DIVISION THREE FINAL LEAGUE TABLE 2001-02

	P	Home					Away					Total						
		W	D	L	F	A	W	D	L	F	A	W	D	L	F	A	GD	Pts
Croydon Athletic	42	21	0	0	83	14	9	5	7	55	27	30	5	7	138	41	97	95
Hornchurch	42	13	7	1	54	20	12	4	5	42	26	25	11	6	96	46	50	86
Aveley	42	14	4	3	74	28	12	2	7	35	27	26	6	10	109	55	54	84
Bracknell Town	42	17	2	2	59	17	8	6	7	37	37	25	8	9	96	54	42	83
Epsom & Ewell	42	9	9	3	41	24	11	6	4	40	27	20	15	7	81	51	30	75
Egham Town	42	12	6	3	37	23	9	5	7	35	36	21	11	10	72	59	13	74
Wingate & Finchley	42	10	5	6	39	26	10	4	7	41	34	20	9	13	80	60	20	69
Dorking	42	12	5	4	42	27	6	9	6	35	39	18	14	10	77	66	11	68
Tring Town	42	12	4	5	42	25	7	7	7	22	37	19	11	12	64	62	2	68
Corinthian Casuals	42	12	5	4	40	16	6	8	7	29	28	18	13	11	69	44	25	67
Hertford Town	42	12	5	4	45	25	8	2	11	43	49	20	7	15	88	74	14	55
Witham Town	42	11	2	8	38	29	4	8	9	28	43	15	10	17	66	72	-6	55
Ware	42	8	6	7	43	36	6	4	11	31	40	14	10	18	74	76	-2	52
Chalfont St Peter	42	9	2	10	35	39	6	2	13	34	53	15	4	23	69	92	-23	49
Wokingham Town	42	9	3	9	46	47	5	3	13	33	60	14	6	22	79	107	-28	48
Abingdon Town	42	7	5	9	27	27	6	2	13	34	48	13	7	22	61	75	-14	46
Leighton Town	42	6	6	9	35	47	2	6	13	21	48	8	12	22	56	95	-39	36
Kingsbury Town	42	4	6	11	28	42	4	5	12	30	49	8	11	23	58	91	-33	35
Edgware Town	42	4	5	12	38	50	5	2	14	27	51	9	7	26	65	101	-36	34
Flackwell Heath*	42	4	3	14	32	62	5	5	11	21	37	9	8	25	53	99	-46	32
Clapton	42	6	2	13	23	46	3	2	16	22	72	9	4	29	45	118	-73	31
Camberley Town	42	6	7	8	26	36	1	2	18	11	59	7	9	26	37	95	-58	30

* points deducted

ISTHMIAN LEAGUE DIVISION ONE SOUTH

ASHFORD TOWN (Middlesex)

CLUB OFFICIALS
Chairman: Robert Parker
Vice Chairman: Mark Vaughan
President: T.B.A.
Secretary: Alan B J Constable
3 Craigwell Close, Chertsey Lane,
Staines, Middx. TW18 3NP
Tel: 01784 440613 (H) 07956 930719 (M)
01784 451614 (Fax) Email: alanc52@aol.com
Press Secretary: Kerry Vertannes

FOOTBALL MANAGEMENT TEAM
Manager: Nathan Wharf

FACT FILE

Formed: 1964
Nickname: Ash Trees
Colours: Tangerine & white/white/black
Change colours:Blue/Black/Blue
Midweek matchday: Tuesday

2001-02
Captain: Tony Nolan
Top Scorer:Tony Nolan 16
P.o.Y .Vince O'Sullivan

ASHFORD TOWN
(Middlesex)
Football Club

PROGRAMME
Pages: 24   Price: £1
Editor: Alan B J Constable (Secretary)

GROUND   Short Lane, Stanwell, Staines, Middx Tel: 01784 245908
Club Website: www.ashfordtownmxfootballclub.co.uk
Directions: M25 jct 13, A30 towards London, 3rd left at footbridge after Ashford Hospital
crossroads - ground signposted after 1/4 a mile on right down Short Lane.
2 miles from Ashford (BR) & Hatton Cross (tube) stations.
Bus route - Westlink 116
Capacity: 2550   **Seats:** 150   **Cover:** 300   **Floodlights:** Yes
Clubhouse: Open 7 days a week. Refreshments always available - hot food on matchdays
Club Shop: No

PREVIOUS   **Ground:** Clockhouse Lane Rec
Leagues: Hounslow & Dist. 64-68; Surrey Intermediate 68-82;
Surrey Premier 82-90 Combined Counties League 90-00

CLUB RECORDS   **Appearances:** Alan Constable 650
Attendance: 750 v Brentford, friendly 29/7/8
Goalscorer: Andy Smith

BEST SEASON   **FA Vase:**
FA Cup:

HONOURS: Combined Co's Lg Champions 94-95, 95-96, 96-97, 97-8, 99-00; Chall Cup R-up 92-93 94-95, Lg Vase Cup R-up 91-92
94-95; Surrey I'mediate Lg, Surrey Prem. Cup 89-90; Middx Prem. Cup R-up 89-90; Southern Comb Cup 95-96,
R-up 01-02 World Wide Carpets Prem Ch Cup 98-99

Back row ,left to right: Leeyon Phelan, Leon Canning, Jamie Keith, Tony Nolan, Mick Mahoney-Johnson and Simon Kent.
Front row: Mark Donnelly, Andy Frost, Ross Davidson, Andy Sherwood, Vince O'Sullivan, Richard Butler and Des Vertannes

BANSTEAD ATHLETIC

CLUB OFFICIALS

Chairman: Terry Molloy
President: Gordon Taylor
Press Officer: Colin Darby
Secretary: Gordon Harrison
69 Chipstead Lane, Lower KIngswood,
Surrey KT20 6RD (01737 833817)

FOOTBALL MANAGEMENT TEAM

Manager: Bob Langford
Coaches: Ray Best & Michael Stratford
Physio: John Steerwood

FACT FILE

Founded: 1944
Nickname: A's
Sponsors: PDM Marketing
Colours: Amber/black/amber
Change colours: All red
Midweek Matchday: Tuesday
Club Website: www.bansteadathletic.co.uk

2001-2002
Captain: Kristien Sorensen
P.o.Y.: David Moore
Top scorer: Gary Whelan 20

PROGRAMME

Pages: 38 Price: £1.00
Editor: Colin Darby (0208 643 5437)

GROUND	Merland Rise, Tadworth, Surrey KT20 5JG (01737 350982)
Directions:	Follow signs to Tattenham Corner (Epsom racecourse), then to Banstead Sports Centre. Ground adjacent to swimming pool. Half a mile from Tattenham Corner (BR) Bus 420 from Sutton stops outside ground. Also buses 406 & 727 from Epsom
Capacity:	3,500 Seats: 250 Cover: 800 Floodlights: Yes
Clubhouse	All week 11am-11pm. 2 bars, real ale, bar snacks
Club Shop	Yes

PREVIOUS
CLUB RECORDS

Leagues: Surrey Int., Surrey Snr 49-65, Spartan 65-75, London Spartan 75-79, Athenian 79-84

Attendance: 1,400 v Leytonstone, FA Amateur 1953

Win: 11-0   **Defeat:** 0-11

Career goalscorer: Harry Clark   **Career appearances:** Dennis Wall

Transfer fee received: None   **Transfer fee paid:** None

BEST SEASON   **FA Cup:** 3rd Qual.Rd. 86-87. 00-01 FA Vase: Semi - finals 96-97

HONOURS: Surrey Snr Lg(6) 50-54 56-57 64-65, R-up(5) 49-50 54-56 57-59, Lg Cup 57-58, Charity Cup 52-53 58-59; London Spartan Lg R-up 77-78 (Lg Cup(2) 65-67);Surrey Prem. Cup R-up 91-92, 95-96; Surrey Snr Shield 55-56; Gilbert Rice F'lit Cup 81-82 86-87 (R-up(4) 82-86); Athenian Lg Cup(2) 80-82 (R-up 82-83 (SF 79-80); Surrey Int. Lg(2) 47-49, Cup 46-47 54-55; E. Surrey Charity Cup (4) 59-6066-67 76-78, R-up 79-80, I'mediate Sect. 75-76 (R-up 76-77), Jnr Sect. 81-82;Southern Comb. Cup R-up 69-70; Suburban Lg R-up 86-87; Carlton T.V. Trophy R-Up 95-96

Players Progressing: W Chesney & B Robinson (Crystal Palace)

Back row, left to right: Mick Stratford (Coach), Gary Whelan, Barry Langford, Glyn Shimell, Kristian Sorensen (Captain), Mark Russell, Steve Shaw and Danny Wise **Middle Row:** John Sherwood (Physio), Terry Molloy (Chairman),Graham Knight, Aaron Day, Wayne Finnie, Kevin Cooper, Marl Leahy (Vice Captain), Martin Beard, Jeroime Richards, Ray Best (Assistant Manager) and Gordon Harrison (Secrtary) **Front row:** Gordon Taylor (President), James Greenaway, David Moore, Bob Langford (Manager), Grant Hutchinson and Bobby George.

BOGNOR REGIS TOWN

CLUB OFFICIALS

Chairman: Tom Martin
President: S Rowlands
Secretary: Peter Helsby, c/o The Club.
02392 291388
Press Officer: Jack Pearce
Comm. Manager: Maurice Warner

FOOTBALL MANAGEMENT TEAM
Manager: Jack Pearce
Coach: Paul Holden M.B.E.
Physios: S Sidaway & Heidi Simpson

FACT FILE

Founded: 1883
Nickname: The Rocks
Sponsors: Butlins South Coast World
Colours: White (green trim)/green/white
Change colours: Blue/white/red
Midweek home matchday: Tuesday
Reserves ' League: None

2001-02
Leading Goalscorer: Matt Russell

GROUND
Nyewood Lane, Bognor Regis PO21 2TY
Tel: 01243 822325

Directions: West along sea front from pier, past Aldwick shopping centre then turn right into Nyewood Lane

Capacity: 6,000   Cover: 3,800   Seats: 243   Floodlights: Yes

Clubhouse: Open every night, matchdays and Sunday lunchtimes. Hot food available

Club Shop: Selling programmes and normal club items

Pages: 36   Price: £1
Editor: Maurice Warner Tel: 01243 822325

Local Radio: Radio Sussex, Ocean Sound, Radio Solent, Southern Sound, Spirit FM
Local Press: Bognor Regis Journal & Guardian, Bognor Observer, Brighton Argus, Portsmouth News

PREVIOUS
Leagues: W Sussex Lge 1896-1926; Brighton, Hove & District Lge 26-27; Sussex County Lge 27-72; Southern Lge 72-81

CLUB RECORDS
Attendance: 3,642 v Swansea FA Cup 1st Rd replay, '84
Goalscorer: Kevin Clements (206)
Appearances: Mick Pullen, 967 (20 seasons)
Transfer Fee Paid: £2,200 Guy Rutherford 95-96
Fee Received: £10,500
for John Crumplin & Geoff Cooper (Brighton & Hove Alb, 87)
& for Simon Rodger (C Palace 89)

BEST SEASON
FA Amateur Cup: 1st Round 71-72
F A Trophy: 3rd Round 95-96
F A Cup: 2nd Rd on four occasions -League clubs beaten: Swansea 84-85, Exeter 88-89 84-85 2-6 v Reading (A), 85-86 1-6 v Gillingham (A), 88-89 0-1 v Cambridge (H), 95-96 0-4 v Peterborough (A)

HONOURS:
Isthmian Lg Div 1 R-up 81-82, (Lg Cup 86-87); Southern Lg R-up 80-81 (Lg Cup R-up 80-81), Merit Cup 80-81; Sussex Lg 48-49 71-72 (R-up 38-39 51-52), Div 2 70-71, Invitation Cup 40-41 49-50 62-63 71-72; Brighton Lg R-up 26-27; W Sussex Lg (5) 20-25 (R-up 1896-97, 25-26), Jnr Lg 10-11 13-14; Southern Co's Comb 78-79; Sussex Snr Cup(9) 54-56 79-84 86-87 94-95 R-up 51-52 58-59 84-85 00-01); Sussex Prof. Cup 73-74, Sussex RUR Cup 71-72; Sussex I'mediate Cup 52-53, Littlehampton Hosp. Cup 29-30 33-34; Bognor Charity Cup(8) 28-29 30-31 32-33 37-38 47-48 58-59 71-73; Gosport War Mem. Cup (2) 81-83 (R-up 86-87); Snr Midweek F'lit Cup R-up 74-75

Players progressing: E Randall (Chelsea 50), J Standing (Brighton 61), A Woon (Brentford 72), J Crumplin & G Cooper (Brighton 87), Simon Rodger (C Palace 89)

Matt Russell, last season's leading goalscorer, is congratulated by Richard Hudson.

ISTHMIAN LEAGUE DIVISION ONE SOUTH

BRACKNELL TOWN

CLUB OFFICIALS

Chairman: Chris Nixon
President: Jack Quinton
Vice-Chairman & Match Secretary:
Malcolm Hutt, 3 Livingstone Gardens,
Woodley, Reading RG5 3LT
01189 694946 (H) 07977 822148 (M)
Secretary: David Mihell, 51 Upshire Gdns.,
The Warren,Bracknell, Berks RG12 9YZ
Tel: 01344 488369 (H) 07712 489415 (M)
Press Off.: Robert Scully 01344 640721

FOOTBALL MANAGEMENT TEAM
Manager: Alan Taylor
Coach: Paul Harford
Physio: Richard Lansiquot

FACT FILE
Founded: 1896
Nickname: Robins
Colours: Red & white quarters/red/red
Change colours: Blue & white
stripes/blue/blue
Sponsors: GAME (www.game.uk.com)
Midweek Matchday: Tuesday
Reserve's League: Suburban (west)

01-02
Top Goalscorer:
Gavin Smith & Simon Teague (19 goals)
Player of the Year: Giles Marchant

GROUND   Larges Lane, Bracknell RG12 9AN.
Tel: 01344 412305 (club), 01344 300933 (office- T & Fax)
Directions: Off A329 just before Met Office r'bout by Bracknell College, ground 200 yards.
From Bracknell (BR)/bus station - right out of station, follow pathover bridge, left down steps
and follow cycle path ahead, after 300yds follow curve over footbridge, right and follow lane
to end, left and ground on leftafter bend
Capacity: 2,500   Seats: 190   Cover: 400   Floodlights: Yes
Clubhouse: Members' bar open 11am-11pm Mon-Sat, 12-3 & 7-10.30pm Sun.
Club Shop: Yes, selling metal badges, programmes, scarves, club sweaters, club ties

PROGRAMME
Pages: 48   Price: £1.00
Editor: Robert Scully 01344 640721
Local Press: Bracknell News

PREVIOUS   **Leagues:** Great Western Comb.; Surrey Snr 63-70; London Spartan 70-75
Grounds: None   **Names:** None

CLUB RECORDS   **Attendance:** 2,500 v Newquay, FA Amateur Cup 1971
Career Goalscorer: Richard Whitty   **Career Appearances:** James Woodcock

BEST SEASON   **FA Cup:** 1st Round Proper, 00-01 (0-4 v Lincoln City)

HONOURS: Isthmian Lg Div 3 93-94; Berks & Bucks Snr Cup R-up; Spartan Lg 74-75, (Lg Cup 81-82 82-83);
Surrey Snr Lg 68-69 (Lg Cup 68-69 69-70)

Players progressing: Willie Graham (Brentford)

Back row (from left to right): Chris Nixon (chairman), Paul Harford (player/coach), Ben Edwards, Neil Baker, Jon Underwood, Martin Hutt, Kevin Butcher, Paul Gower, Stuart Hammonds, Gavin Smith, Alan Taylor (manager), Malcolm Hutt (vice-chairman/match secretary), Jack Quinton (president).
Front row: Richard Lansiquot (physio), Gary Sargeant, Adam Crittenden, Simon Teague, Stuart Harte, James Glynn, Gavin Taylor, Giles Marchant, Jeff Dennis (fitness coach)

830

BROMLEY

CLUB OFFICIALS

Chairman: Jerry Dolke
Secretary: John Self
22 Faringdon Avenue, Bromley,
Kent BR2 8BS

FOOTBALL MANAGEMENT TEAM

Manager:Stuart McIntyre
Ass.Manager/Coach:Mark Harris

FACT FILE

Formed: 1892
Nickname: The Lilywhites
Colours: White/black/black
Change colours: All red
Midweek home matchday: Tuesday
Reserve's League: None
Youth League: Kent Youth League
Newsline: 0930 555 838
2001-02
Captain: Mark Harris
P.o.Y.: Dean Frost
Top Scorer: Carl Bartley (8)

GROUND Hayes Lane, Bromley, Kent BR2 9EF Tel: 0208 460 5291 or 0208 313 3992

Directions: One mile from Bromley South (BR). Buses 314, 146 and 119 pass ground.
Junction 4 off M25, then A21 towards London
Capacity: 5,000   Cover: 2,500   Seats: 1,300 Floodlights: Yes
Clubhouse: Open matchdays. Food available
Club Shop: Yes. contact Jim Brown

Pages: 32 Price: £1.20
Editor: Steven McCartney (07979 418 360)

Local Press: Bromley Times
Local Radio: Radio Kent,
Bromley Local Radio

PREVIOUS   **Leagues:** South London - 1894; Southern 94-96; London 96-98 99-1901; West Kent 01-04; Southern Suburban 04-07;
Kent 1898-99, 11-14; Spartan 07-08; Isthmian 08-11; Athenian 19-52
Grounds:White Hart Field Cricket Ground, Widmore Rd & Plaistow Cricket Field (pre-1904),Hayes Lane 1904-37 .New Ground

RECORDS   **Attendance:** 12,000 v Nigeria, 1950
Goalscorer: George Brown 570 (1938-61)   **Appearances:** George Brown
Win: 131 v Redhill, Athenian League 1945-46   **Defeat:** v Barking ,Athenian League 1933-34
Fee Paid: Unknown   **Fee Received:** £50,000 for Jon Goodman (from Millwall 90)

BEST SEASON   **FA Amateur Cup:** Winners 10-11, 37-38, 48-49
FA Trophy: Second Round 91-92   **FA Cup:** 2nd Rd replay v Scarborough 37-38, Lincoln 38-39, Watford 45-46

HONOURS: Isthmian League(4) 08-10 53-54 60-61 (R-up 52-53 55-56 87-88), Div 1 R-up 79-80 5-86 90-91, Prince Phillip 5-a-side Cup
1979; Athenian League 22-23 48-49 50-51 (R-up 35-36); London League Div 2 1896-97; Spartan League 07-08; London
Snr Cup 09-10 45-46 50-51; Kent Senior Cup 49-50 76-77 91-92 96-97; Kent AmateurCup (12) 07-08 31-32 35-36 36-37 38-39
46-47 48-49 50-51 52-53 53-54 54-55 59-60; LondonChallenge Cup 1995-96.

Players progressing: Roy Merryfield (Chelsea), Stan Charlton (Arsenal 52), RonHeckman (Orient 55), John Gregory (West Ham 51), Bill Lloyd
(Millwall 56), Brian Kinsey (Charlton 56), Harold Hobbs (Charlton & England), Matt Carmichael (Lincoln 90), Leslie Locke (QPR 56), Jon Goodman
(Millwall 90), Dean Wordsworth (Crystal Palace 97), Landry Zahana-ONI (Luton Town 98)

Back row left to right: Chris Cooke (Physio), Dean Frost, Vladimir Lazic, John Wilfort, Mark Harris, Danny Harwood, Carl Bartley, Billy Manuel,
Grant Watts and Stuart McIntyre (Manager).
Front row: Kwabena Amaning, Michael Harney, Kris Hollidge, John Myatt, Andy Silk,Kirk Watts, DeanThomas   **Photo:** Alan Coomes

CARSHALTON ATHLETIC

CLUB OFFICIALS

Chairman: Steve Friend
President: John Carpentiere
Vice Chairman: T.B.A.
Secretary: Janey Gould,394 Winchcombe Road, Carshalton, Surrey SM5 1SB
Chief Executive: Barry Gartell
General Manager: Andy Abrehart
Press Officer: Roger Fear
Commercial Manager: Roger Fear

FOOTBALL MANAGEMENT TEAM
Man: Graham Roberts Ass Man:Clive Gartell Coach: Graham Baker
Physios: Tanya Clarke & Mark Davis

FACT FILE
Formed: 1905 Nickname: Robins
Sponsors: CDL Exhibition Contractors
Colours: White, maroon trim/maroon/white
Change colours: Maroon/white
Midweek matchday: Tuesday
Reserve League: Suburban
Newsline: 0930 555 877
2001-02
Captains Mark Costello & Gary Elliot
Top Scorer: Wade Falana P.o.Y.: Gary Elliot

Carshalton Athletic v Whyteleafe 20th April Ryman League Division One

Season 2001/02 Price £1.20 Ryman

THE ROBINS REVIEW

GROUND War Memorial Sports Ground, Colston Av, Carshalton SM5 2PW
Tel: 0181 642 8658

Directions: Turn right out of Carshalton BR Station, and Colston Avenue is first left. Entrance 150 yards on right. London Transport bus 151 from Morden to Wrythe Green Lane
Capacity: 8,000   Cover: 4,500   Seats: 240   Floodlights: Yes
Clubhouse: Open every evening and lunchtime. Licenced bar, pool, darts,machines, discos on Saturday. Separate function hall (bookings taken). Food:sandwiches, rolls, burgers, hot dogs, teas, coffees and soft drinks. (0181 642 8658)
Club Shop: Sells hats, scarves, T-shirts, badges, programmes etc

Pages: 20 Price: £1.50p
Editor: Andy Hill (020 8644 7928)

Local Press: Sutton Comet, Sutton Herald
Local Radio: BBc Southern Counties

PREVIOUS   Leagues: Southern Sub (pre-1911); Surrey Snr 22-23; London 23-46; Corinthian46-56; Athenian 56-73
Grounds: Wrythe Recreation Ground 1907-14; Culvers Park 19-20

CLUB RECORDS Attendance: 7,800 v Wimbledon, London Senior Cup
Career goalscorer: Jimmy Bolton(242)   **Career appearances:** Jon Warden (504)
Transfer fee paid: £5,000 for Junior Haynes 1998 **Transfer fee received:** £15,000 for Curtis Warmington (Enfield)
Win: 13-0 v Worthing, Loctite Cup Third Round 28/2/91
F.A.Trophy : 3rd Rd 95-96 lodst away at Hyde United (2-3)
FA Cup: 2nd Rd 82-83, lost 1-4 at Torquay. - League clubs defeated: None

HONOURS: Isthmian League Div 2 R-up 76-77, Corinthian League 52-53 53-54, Surrey Senior League R-up 22-23, Surrey Senior Cup(3) Runners-up (5) Surrey Senior Shield 75-76 Runners-up (2)), London Challenge Cup 91-92 Isthmian Lg Cup R-up 90-91

Players progressing: Roy Lunnes (Crystal Pal. 60), Les Burns (Charlton 67), Ron Walker (Watford), Nobby Warren (Exeter),Terry Stacey (Plymouth A.), Frank GeorgelLeyton Orient) ,Tommy Williams (Colchester U), Alan Eagles (Leyton Orient), Derek Razzell (Q.PR),Muray Jones Crystal Pal.) Gus Caesar (Arsenal), Darren Annon (Brentford) 94, Ian Cox (Crystal Pal.) 94, Carl Asaba (Brentford)

L-R - Back Row: Steve Lang (coach), Graham Baker (coach), Steve Darlington, Mark Costello, Berandeh Ouefio,Tutu Henriques, Mark Pye, Stuart Searle, Peter Wood, Gary Elliott, John Hamsher, Romuald Bouadji, John(JJ)Johnson (Kit Manager)
Front Row: Matt York, Byron Glasgow, Nigel Webb, Michael Johnson, Barry Gartell (Chief Executive), Graham Roberts (Manager), Steve Friend (Chairman), Keith Dublin (Captain), Tommy Williams, Baroan Tagro, Scott Todd

ISTHMIAN LEAGUE DIVISION ONE SOUTH

CHERTSEY TOWN

CLUB OFFICIALS

Chairman: Steve Powes
President: Cllr Chris Norman
Vice Chairman: Nick Keel
Press Officer/Secretary: Ben O'Conner
2 Monaveen Gardens,Weat MOlesey,Surrey
KT8 1SB Tel No: 0208 224 1387

FOOTBALL MANAGEMENT TEAM
Manager: Steve Johnson
Asst Manager: Tom Maloney
Coach: Ian Barrado
Physio: Peter Chessman

FACT FILE
Formed: 1890 Nickname: Curfews
Sponsors: Holly Tree
Colours: Blue & white stripes/white/blue
Change colours: Yellow & Black
Midweek Matchday: Tuesday
Club Website: www.curfews.com

2001-02
Captain: Colin Gould
Top Scorer: John Pomroy 26
P.o.Y.:Colin Gould

Welcome to Alwyns Lane

Official Matchday Programme

Saturday 13th April 2002
Ryman League
Division Two

CHERTSEY TOWN
Versus
HUNGERFORD TOWN
Kick Off 3.00pm

Ryman

Pages: 36 Price: £1
Editor: Chris Gay (01276 20745)
Local Press: Surrey Herald
Local Radio: BBC Southern Counties,
County Sound

Address: Alwyns Lane, Chertsey, Surrey KT16 9DW
Tel:01932 561774 Email: ctfc.freeserve.co.uk
Directions: Alwyns Lane is off Windsor Street at north end of shopping centre.
10 mins walk from Chertsey (BR). London Country bus
Capacity: 3,000   Seats: 250   Cover: 1000   Floodlights: Yes

Clubhouse: Open weekday evenings and weekend lunchtimes
Club Shop: Open matchdays, selling club & football souvenirs. Contact Daniel Dullaway

PREVIOUS	**Leagues:** West Surrey (pre-1899); Surrey Jnr 1899-1920; Surrey Intermediate 20-46; Surrey Snr 46-63; Metropolitan 63-66; Gtr London 66-67; Spartan 67-75; London Spartan 75-76; Athenian 76-84; Isthmian 84-85; Combined Counties 85-86. **Grounds:** The Grange (pre-World War 1), The Hollows (pre-1929)
CLUB RECORDS	**Attendance:** 2,150 v Aldershot, Isthmian Lge Div. 2 4/12/93 **Goalscorer:** Alan Brown 54, 1962-63 **Win:** 10-1 v Clapton (H), Isthmian Lge Div. 3, 91-92 **Defeat:** 1-12 v Bromley (H), FA Cup Preliminary Rd, 82-83 **Transfer fee received:** £67,500. Paid: Nil
BEST SEASON	**FA Vase:** Quarter Final 87-88 91-92 **FA Cup:** 3rd Qual. Rd 92-93, 1-3 v Kingstonian (H) **FA Trophy:** 2nd Qual Rd 95-96 **FA Amateur Cup:** 3rd Qual Rd 61-62
HONOURS	Isthmian Lge Cup 94-95 (Assoc. Members Trophy 94-95), Div 2 R-up 94-95, Div 3 R-up 91-92; Surrey Snr Lge 59-60 61-62 62-63 (Lge Cup 59-60 61-62); Combined Co's Lge R-up 85-86 (Concours Tphy 85-86); Surrey Snr Cup R-up 85-86; Spartan Lge & Lge Cup R-up 74-75

Players progressing: Rachid Harkouk (Crystal Palace), Peter Cawley (Wimbledon 87), Lee Charles (Q.P.R. 95)

L-R - Back row: Steve Johnson, Tom Moloney; John Pomroy, Warren Burton, Lee Taylor, Mark Lewis, Paul Seuke, Kevin Bere, Colin Gould, James Verseci.
Front row: Abby Nsubuga, Neil Breslin, James Crowe, Terry Davies, Billy Jones, Michael Griffin, Paul Mercer

833

CORINTHIAN CASUALS

CORINTHIAN CASUALS F.C.
2002/03

RYMAN LEAGUE • DIVISION ONE SOUTH

Ryman

CLUB OFFICIALS

Chairman: Geoff Hewitson

President: Jimmy Hill

Press Officer & MatchSecretary
Rob Cavallini (0208 4042763)

Secretary: Brian Wakefield
5 Martingales Close, Richmond, Surrey
Tel: 020 8940 9208

FOOTBALL MANAGEMENT TEAM
Manager: Mickey Stephens

FACT FILE
Founded: 1939
Sponsors: London Catering Services
Colours: Chocalte & Pink/sky/sky
Change colours: White/navy/white
Midweek Matchday: Tuesday
Reserves' League: Suburban

2001-02
Captain: Simon Shergold
Top Goalscorer: Iain Waghorn 26

GROUND King George's Field, Hook Rise South, Tolworth, Surrey KT6 7NA
Tel: 020 8397 3368   Email Address: rob@corinthians.freeserve.co.uk
Directions: A3 to Tolworth r'bout (The Charrington Bowl). Hook Rise is slip road
immediately after the Toby Jug pub. Turn left under railway bridge after
a 1/4mile - grd on right. Half mile from Tolworth (BR); turn left, contin-
ue to Toby Jug, then as above.
Capacity: 2,700   Seats: 161   Cover: 700   Floodlights: Yes
Clubhouse: Open evenings, matchdays, Sunday lunchtimes.
Hot & coldsnacks on matchdays
Club Shop: Yes

PROGRAMME
Pages: 24-48   Price: £1
Editor: Rob Cavallini

Club Website:
www.corinthians.freeserve.co.uk

PREVIOUS **Leagues:** Isthmian 39-84, Spartan 84-96; Combined Counties 96-97

HONOURS FA Amateur Cup R-up 55-56 (SF 56-57), London Spartan Lg R-up 92-93 (Lg Cup R-up 91-92);
Combined Counties Lg R-up 96-97

CLUB RECORDS
Career Records: Goals Cliff West 219   **Appearances** Bruce Martin 504

BEST SEASON **FA Cup:** 1st Rd 65-66 1st Rd replay 85-86   **FA Vase:** 5th Rd 83-84
FA Amateur Cup: Runners-up 55-56

Players progressing: Peter Phillips (Luton Town),Andy Gray, Tony Finnegan, Alan Pardew (Crystal Palace),Leroy Griffiths (Q.P.R.)

Corinthian Casuals 2002/03
L-R - Back Row: Iain Waghorn, Leon Raishbrook, Simon Sobihy, Nathan Jupp, Elliott Lyward, Jamie Goodwin, John Russell-Smith, Clive Offer, Paul Midwinter (Physio) **Front**: Simon Shergold, Jamie White, Mark Webb, John Hotchkiss, Tony Blunt, Dave Roberts, Andy Gibbons.

CROYDON

CLUB OFFICIALS

Chairman: Ken Jarvie
Secretary: Mrs Jacqueline Jarvie
2 Spa Close, London SE25 6DS
Tel: 020 86537250(H),
Press Officer: Russell Chandler
Dartnell Rd, Croydon, Surrey. CR0 6JA
: 0208 406 4573 (H) 0208 654 8555 (B)
Match Secretary: Gordon Tennant

FOOTBALL MANAGEMENT TEAM
Manager: Micky Read
Asst. Manager: Dave Garland
Physio: Ian Fairs

FACT FILE
Formed: 1953
Nickname: The Trams
Sponsors:
Colours: Sky & navy /
navy & sky/navy & sky
Change colours: Whte
Midweek home matchday: Wednesday
Reserve Team's League: Suburban Capital

OUND Croydon Sports Arena, Albert Road, South Norwood, London. SE25 4QL
Tel: 0208 654 3462/8555
ections: Train to East Croydon or Norwood Junction, then bus 12 to either Belmont or
adee Road. Walk down either - ground at bottom. 5 mins walk from Woodside (BR)
acity: 8,000   Cover: 1,000   Seats: 450   Floodlights: Yes
bhouse: Open every evening and lunchtime, holds 250, snacks available
Dancing, discos, bingo. Lounge bar available for private hire
b Shop: Yes Badges £2.50, Croydon Women's F.C. Champions badges £3.00
VIOUS **Leagues:** Surrey Senior 53-63; Spartan 63-64; Athenian 64-74
Name: Croydon Amateurs 1953-74

Pages: 28 Price: £1.00
Editor: Russell Chandler (0181 406 4573 H)

Local Press: Whyteleafe Advertiser,
Croydon Midweek Post, Times, Guardian

B RECORDS **Attendance:** 1,450 v Wycombe, FA Cup 4th Qualifying Rd 1975
Career appearances: Alec Jackson (1977-88) 452 + 111goals and Tony Luckett(1962-73) 411 appearances + 411 goals
Transfer fee paid: Steve Brown   **Transfer fee received:** Peter Evans (to Sutton Utd)

T SEASON **FA Cup:** 2nd Round replay 79-80, 2-3 v Millwall after 1-1
FA Trophy: 2nd Round 81-82, 82-83   **FA Amateur Cup:** 3rd round 71-72

OURS Isthmian Lg Div. 1 99-2000, Div 2 R-up 75-76 95-96, Lg Cup: R-up 74-75 FM Cup 99-2000; Surrey Snr Cup 81-82 (R-up 76-77
), Surrey Prem Cup 86-87, Spartan Lg 63-64, Athenian Lg R-up 71-72 (Div 2 65-66 (R-up 70-71)), Surrey Snr Lg R-up 56-57 60-61 62-63 (Lg
60-61, Charity Cup 53-54 62-63, Res Section 57-58), London Senior Cup R-up 77-78, Suburban Lg South 86-87(Lg Cup(2), Southern Yth Lg
(Lg Cup 85-86 87-88), Berger Yth Cup 78-79, Southern Youth Lg Cup 96-97. Womens F.A.Cup 95-6,99-00 R-up 97-98 Premier Lg 99-00

rs progressing: Alan Barnett (Plymouth 1955), Peter Bonetti (Chelsea), Leroy Ambrose (Charlton 1979), Steve Milton (Fulham - via
eleafe), Murray Jones (Crystal Pal. - via Carshalton)

- Back row: John Finch (coach), James Cecil, Roy Newman, Michael Riley, Matt Martin, Graham Chappel, Craig Dundas,
y Edwards (capt.), Dave Garland (asst. manager), Micky Read (manager).
t: Sean Jarvie, Darren Hall, David Smith, Jamie White, Andrew Frith, Nicky Greene, Jeff Goulding, Jeff Okai. **Photo:** David West

CROYDON ATHLETIC

CLUB OFFICIALS

Chairman: Keith Tuckey
V Chairman/ Press Officer:
Clive Thompson
Chief Executive: Dean Fisher
153 Chipstead Valley Road,
Coulsdon, Surrey CR5 3BQ
Tel: 020 8407 3296 (H & Fax)
020 7556 6092

FOOTBALL MANAGEMENT TEAM
Manager: Haydon Bird
Asst Man.: Peter Thomas
1st Team Coach: Simon Liddle
Chief Scout: Leon Maxwell
Physio: Mick Reed

FACT FILE

Founded: 1990

Sponsors: T.C.S. Media

Colours: Maroon & white/maroon/maroon

Change colours: Yellow/royal/royal/royal

Midweek matches: Tuesday

Reserve League: Suburban (S)

PROGRAMME
Pages: 52   Price: £1
Editor: Secretary
Club Website:
www.croydonathletic.co.uk

GROUND	Mayfields, off Mayfield Road, Thornton Heath, Surrey, CR7 6DN. Tel: 0208 6648343: Email: dfisher@croydonathletic.co.uk
Directions:	Follow A23 from London & continue on A23 into Thornton Road. After roundabout take !st on right into Silverleigh Road, left fork into Trafford Road which continues into Mayfield Road. To end and turn left and follow narrow road to ground. 1 mile from Norbury (BR). Buses 109, 60

Capacity: 3,000   Seats: 163   Cover: 660   Floodlights: Yes
Clubhouse: Open every evening & weekends   **Club Shop:** Yes

PREVIOUS   **Leagues:** None

RECORDS   **Attendance:** 550
Goalscorer: John Fowler
Appearances: Graham Edginton/ Paul Gall/Leon Maxwell

BEST SEASON   **FA Vase:** 4th Rd 00-01
FA Cup: 2nd Qual. Rd 94-95

HONOURS: London Spartan Lg 94-95, R-up 88-89 93-94, (Reserve Div 88-89, R-up 88-89); London Snr Cup R-up 91-92; Southern Youth Lg 92-93; Bearman Harber MemTrophy 87-88; Wirral Prog 86-87 96-97; Umbro Fair Play 97-98; Isthmian League Div 3 2001-02

Players progressing to Football League: Jamie Ndah (Torquay Utd)

Back row, left to right: Simon Liddle, Jamie Gibson, Danny Cecil, John Fowler, Tony Quinton and Gavin Harrison.
Middle row: Mick Reed (Physio), Tyrone Myton, Billy Jackson, Rob Frank;land, Leon Raishbrook, Leon Johnson and Peter Thomas (Assistant Manager) **Front row:** Jon Waite, Justin Brauer-Jones, Dean Davenport, Hayden Bird (Manager), Danny Stassinos, Adrian Moses and James Evans.

DULWICH HAMLET

CLUB OFFICIALS

Chairman: Martin Eede
President: Tommy Jover
Vice Chairman: Brian Shears
Secretary:: John Leahy, 58 Newquay
House,Black Prince Road, Kennington,
London S.E.11 6HL Tel No: 0207 582 9296
Press Officer: John Lawrence
Tel: 020 8761 2091

FOOTBALL MANAGEMENT TEAM

Manager: Martin Eede
Physio: Danny Keenan

FACT FILE

Formed: 1893 Nickname: The Hamlet
Sponsors: T.B.A.
Colours: Navy blue & pink
stripes/navy/navy
Change colours: Red & light blue
squares/red/red
Midweek matchday: Tuesday
Reserve League: Suburban

2000-01 Captain: Ian Savage
P.o.Y.: Dave Richards
Top Scorer: Matt Fowler 17

GROUND: Champion Hill Stadium, Edgar Kail Way, East Dulwich, London SE22 8BD
Tel: 020 7274 8707

Directions: East Dulwich station, 200yds. Denmark Hill station, 10 mins walk. Herne Hill station then bus 37 stops near grd. Buses 40 & 176 from Elephant & Castle, 185 from Victoria
Capacity: 3,000 **Cover:** 1,000 **Seats:** 500 **Floodlights:** Yes
Clubhouse: Open 7 days a week, bar. Function rooms and meeting room available for hire
Health Club,Gymnasium,Squash courts (020 7274 8707)
Club Shop: Sells programmes, pennants, badges, scarves, baseball caps, replica shirts (by
order only). New shop opening in 2001-02.

Pages: 48   Price: £1.20
Editor: John Lawrence
Local Press: South London Press,
Southwark News

PREVIOUS   **Leagues:** Camberwell 1894-97; S/thern Sub 1897-1900 01-07; Dulwich 00-01; Spartan 07-08
Grounds: Woodwarde Rd 1893-95; College Farm 95-96; Sunray Avenue 96-1902; Freeman's Ground, Champion Hill 02-12;
Champion Hill (old ground) 1912-92; Sandy Lane (groundshare with Tooting & Mitcham F.C.) 91-92

CLUB RECORDS Attendance: 20,744, Kingstonian v Stockton, FA Am Cup Final 1933 (at refurbished ground): 1,835 v Southport FAC 98-99
Career Goalscorer: Edgar Kail 427 (1919-33)   **Career Appearances:** Reg Merritt 571 (50-66)
Fee Paid: T Eames (Wimbledon), G Allen (Carshalton Ath 80)   **Fee Received:** E Nwajiobi (Luton 83)
Win: 13-0 v Walton-on-Thames, 37-38   **Defeat:** 1-10 v Hendon, 63-64

BEST SEASON FA Amateur Cup: Winners 19-20 31-2 33-4 36-7   **FA Trophy:** Quarter Final 79-80
FA Cup: 1st Rd replay 30-31 33-34. 1st Rd on 14 occasions

HONOURS: Isthmian League 19-20 25-26 32-33 48-49, (R-up(7) Div 1 77-78; London Senior Cup 24-25 38-39 49-50 83-84 (R-up 05-06 07-08
20-21 27-28); Surrey Senior Cup 14 (R-up -6); London Chal. Cup 98-9 R-up 91-92; 99-00 London Charity Cup(12); Surrey Senior Shield 72-73;
Surrey Centen. Shld 77-78; Sth of the Thames Cup (4) 56-60; Southern Comb Cup 73-74

Players progressing: W Bellamy (Spurs), A Solly (Arsenal), L Fishlock/A Gray/APardew (C Palace), J Moseley & E Toser (Millwall), R Dicks
(Middlesborough), GJago/J Ryan (Charlton Ath 51/63), G Pearce (Plymouth), R Crisp (Watford 61), ENwajiobi (Luton 83), C Richards & J Glass
(Bournemouth), P Coleman (Millwall86), A Perry (Portsmouth 86), N Kelly (Stoke City), C Emberson (Rotherham), CAsaba (Brentford)S.Watts
(Leyton O), M.King (Barnet),J Darlington (Q.P.R.), D.McEwen (Spurs)

EGHAM TOWN

CLUB OFFICIALS
Chairman: Peter Atkins
Vice Chairmen:
Peter Barnes & Brian Askew
President: Peter Barnes
Press Officer: Secretary
Club Administrator:
Alison Thompson, 138A Thorpe Lea Rd,
Egham, Surrey. TW20 8BL
Tel: 01784 463562

FOOTBALL MANAGEMENT TEAM
Manager:Byron Walton
Coaches: Alf Coulton Physio: Ken Weaver

FACT FILE
Founded: 1877
Nickname: Sarnies/Town
Colours: Yellow & Green/green/yellow
Change colours: All blue
Midweek Matches: Tuesday
Reserves' League: Suburban

Local Press: Herald & News
Local Radio: County Sound

Egham Town
Football Club

SPONSORED BY
COURAGE

RYMAN DIVISION 1
SOUTH

Ryman
Football League

PROGRAMME SPONSOR

Arena Mechanical Handling Group Ltd
OFFICIAL PROGRAMME **SEASON 2002-2003**

GROUND: Runnymeade Stadium, Tempest Road, Egham, Surrey TW20 8HX
Tel: 01784 435226   Club email: eghamtownfc.co.uk

Directions: M25 jct 13, follow signs to Egham, under M25 at r'bout, left to end, left at mini
r'bout, over railway crossing, left to end (Pooley Green Rd), right, Tempest Rd.
2nd right.   Bus 41 43 441 from Staines to Pooley Green Rd.
30 mins from Egham or Staines (BR)

Capacity: 5,635 Seats: 335 Cover: 1,120 Floodlights: Yes Club Shop: No
Clubhouse: (01784 435226) 7-11pm daily & weekend lunchtimes. Function hall

PROGRAMME
Pages: 40   Price: £1
Editor: A lisonThompson
Tel: 01784 463562 (H)

PREVIOUS **Leagues:** Hounslow & District 1896-1914; Surrey Intermediate 19-22; Surrey Senior 22-28 65-67; Spartan 29-33 67-74;
Parthenon 64-65; Athenian 74-77
Names: Runnymede Rovers 1877-1905; Egham FC 05-63
Grounds: Anglers Rest 1877-1914; Manorcroft Rd 19-26; Vicarage Rd 26-27 28-39;Green Lane 27-28
RECORD **Attendance:** 1,400 v Wycombe Wanderers, FA Cup 2ndQual Rd 72
Scorer: Mark Butler 50 (91-92) Career record scorer as well   **Appearances:** Dave Jones 850+
Win: 10-1 v Camberley, 81-82   **Defeat:** 0-10 v Fisher Ath. (A), Parthenon League 64-65
Transfer Fee Paid: £3,000 for Mark Butler, 1990
Transfer Fee Received: £4,000 for Mark Butler (Wycombe Wanderers, 1988)
BEST SEASON **FA Cup:** 4th Qual Rd 90-91, 0-2 v Telford Utd (A)
HONOURS Isthmian Lg Assoc Members Tphy R-up 91-92; Spartan Lg 71-72 (Lg Cup R-up 67-68); Athenian Lg R-up 75-76 (Div 2 74-75);
Surrey Snr Cup R-up 91-92, Surrey Snr Lg 22-23, Lg Charity Cup 22-23 (R-up 26-27 34-35); Surrey Intermediate Lg 20-21,
Charity Cup 19-20 20-21 (R-up 26-27); North West Surrey Charity Cup 20-21;
Egham Twinning Tournament 67-68 71-72 74-75 75-76 76-77 80-81; S.Comb. F'lit Cup 77-78 (R-up 83-84).
Promotion to Div 1.

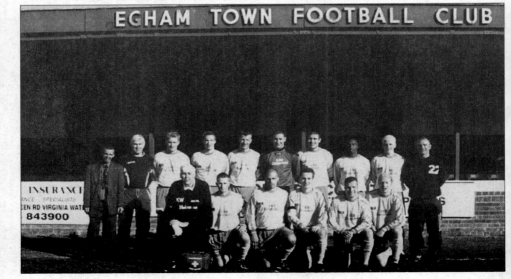

EPSOM & EWELL

EPSOM & EWELL Football Club

Rymar
DIVISION ONE SOUT

A & M Transport UK Ltd
Same-Day Express Couriers

OFFICIAL PROGRAMME
£1

CLUB OFFICIALS
President: Stella Lamont
Chairman: Peter Lumm
Vice Chairman: Derick Hayles
Secretary: D Wilson, 33 Delaporte Close,
Epsom, Surrey KT17 4AF
Tel: 01372 729817
email: d.wilson@nbad.co.uk

FACT FILE
Founded: 1917
Nickname: E's
Colours: Royal & white
Change: All yellow
Midweek Matches: Tuesday
Reserves' League: Suburban

FOOTBALL MANAGEMENT TEAM
Manager: Adrian Hill
Coaches: Barry Barnes
Physio: Kevin Taylor

2001-02
Captain: Graham Morris
Top Scorer: Simon Huckle 18
P.o.Y.: Simon Huckle

GROUND:GROUND: Groundshare with Banstead Athletic FC.
Merland Rise, Tadworth, Surrey KT20 5JG Tel: 01737 350982
Directions: Follow signs to Tattenham Corner (Epsom racecourse), then to Banstead
Sports Centre. Ground adjacent to swimming pool.
Half a mile fromTattenham Corner (BR)
Bus 420 from Sutton stops outside ground.
Also buses 406 & 727 from Epsom
Capacity: 3,500   Seats: 250   Cover: 800   Floodlights: Yes
Clubhouse: Normal licensinghourd, food available   **Club Shop:** No

PROGRAMME
Pages: 28/32   Price: £1.00
Editor: Stella Lamont (01737 356245)

Club Website www.eefc.net

PREVIOUS

Leagues: Surrey Snr 24-27 73-75; London 27-49; Corinthian 49-63; Athenian 63-73 75-77
Grounds: Horton Lane, Epsom 1925-26 and West Atreet, Ewell 1926-93
Names: Epsom Town (previously Epsom FC) merged with Ewell & Stoneleigh in 1960

CLUB RECORDS

Attendance: 5,000 v Kingstonian, F.A. Cup 2nd Qual. Rd, 15/10/49
Record Goalscorer: Tommy Tuite

BEST SEASON

FA Cup: 1st Round 33-34   **FA Trophy:** 2nd Roundd 81-82
FA Vase: Runners-up 74-75

HONOURS

FA Vase R-up 74-75; London Lg 27-28, R-up (5); Corinthian Lg Memorial Shield 59-60 (R-up 51-52 56-57);
Athenian Lg Div 2 R-up 75-76 (Lg Cup R-up 76-77, Div2 Cup R-up 67-68); Isthmian Lg Div 2 77-78 (Div 1 R-up 83-84),
Div 2 S . Promotion 01-02 Vandanel Ass Members Trophy R-up 97-98; Surrey Snr Lg 25-26 26-27 74-75 (R-up 73-74),
Lg Cup 73-74 74-75, Charity Cup 26-27 (R-up 73-74), Surrey Snr Cup 80-81 (R-up 3); Surrey Snr Shield 32-33 54-55;
Surrey Interm'te Cup 29-30,Charity Cup 57-58; S Comb. Cup 79-80 (R-up 82-83 92-93)
Players progressing: Matt Elliott (Leicester), Chris Powell(Derby), Paul Harding (Notts County, Birmingham), Murray Jones (Grimsby),
Alan Pardew (Charlton), Mick Leonard (Chesterfield)

HORSHAM

CLUB OFFICIALS
Chairman: Frank King
Vice Chairman: Tim Hewlett
President: Geoff Holtom
Press Officer: Jeff Barrett (01403 267730)
Secretary: Jef Barrett, 3Bunting Close, Horsham, West Sussex RH13 5PA.
Tel: 01403 267730
Email : jeff.barrett@btinternet.com

FOOTBALL MANAGEMENT TEAM
Manager: John Maggs
Asst Mgr/Coach:Ali Rennie
Physio: Geoff Brittain

FACT FILE
Founded: 1885
Nickname: Hornets
Club Sponsors: Sunley Homes
Colours: Amber & Green
Change colours: Maroon & Sky Blue
Midweek Matches: Tuesday

2001-02
Captain: Stuart Hardy
P.o.Y.: Jamie Taylor
Top scorer: Jamie Taylor

CROYDON
Ryman Division One South
Saturday 24th August 2002

OFFICIAL MATCHDAY PROGRAMME   £1.20

PROGRAMME
Pages: 40   Price: £1.20
Editor:Adam Hammond (01403 217316)

Local Press: West Sussex County Times: Market Square, Horsham (01403 253371

GROUND:	Queen St, Horsham RH12 5AD
	Tel: 01403 252310 E mail address : c/o Sec
Directions:	From the station turn left into North Street. Pass the Arts Centre to the traffic lights and turn left. At the next set of lights (200 yards) turn left again into East Street. East Street becomes Queen Street after the Iron Bridge and the ground lies opposite Queens Head public house
Capacity:	3,500 Seats: 300 Cover: 2,000 Floodlights: Yes
Clubhouse:	Matchdays only. Hot and cold snacks. Dancehall
Club Shop:	Yes

PREVIOUS	**Leagues:** W Sussex Sen; Sussex County 26-51; Metropolitan 51-57; Corinthian 57-63; Athenian 63-73
	Grounds: Horsham Park, Hurst Park, Springfield Park
CLUB RECORDS	**Attendance:** 8,000 v Swindon, FA Cup 1st Rd, November 1966
	Victory: 16-1 v Southwick Sususssex Co Lg 1945-46
	Defeat: 1-11 v Worthing Sussex Sen Cup 1913-14
BEST SEASON	**FA Cup:** 1st Rd 47-48 (lost 1-9 at Notts County), 66-67 (lost 0-3 v Swindon)
	F.A. Trophy: 1st Rd Proper Replay 76-77 **F.A.Vase:** 4th Rd Replay 85-86
HONOURS	Sussex Snr Cup 33-34 38-39 49-50 53-54 71-72 73-74 75-76; Sussex RUR Cup (13); Sussex Floodlight Cup 77-78;01-02 Sussex County Lg (7), R-up (4), Lg Cup 45-46 46-47; Metropolitan Lg 51-52; Ryman League Div 2 R-up 2001-02 Athenian Lg Div 1 72-73, Div 2 69-70 72-73; West Sussex Sen Lge (4); ICIS Div 3 95-96
Players progressing:	Jamie Ndah (Barnet), Darren Freeman (Fulham)

LEATHERHEAD

RYMAN FOOTBALL LEAGUE DIVISION 1 SOUTH

THE tanners

Vs

SEASON 2002 - 2003

Bromley

Tuesday 24th September 2002 : 7.45pm
RYMAN LEAGUE DIVISION ONE SOUTH

CLUB OFFICIALS

Chairman: Tim Edwards
President: Gerald Darby
General Manager: Keith Wenham (at club)
Secretary: Gerald Darby
Ranmore, 31 Harriots Lane, Ashtead,
Surrey, KT21 2QG
Press Office/Comm. Director: Tim Edwards

FACT FILE

Founded: 1946
Nickname: Tanners
Sponsors: The Beer Seller
Colours: Green and White/green/green
Change colours: Blue & white
Midweek Matchday: Tuesday

FOOTBALL MANAGEMENT TEAM

Manager: Chick Botley
Asst. Manager: Clive Howse
Youth Team Manager: Alex Inglethorpe
Physio: Steve Young

Ryman football league

KIT SPONSOR
MILNER CARPETS

Pages: 24   Price: £1
Edito: Robert Wooldridge (0208 669 3824)

Local Press: Leatherhead Advertiser,
Surrey Advertiser
Local Radio: County Sound

GROUND	Fetcham Grove, Guildford Rd, Leatherhead, Surrey KT22 9AS
	Tel: 01372 360151, Fax: 01372 362705
Directions:	M25 jct 9 to Leatherhead; follow signs to Leisure Centre, ground adjacent.
	Half mile from Leatherhead (BR)
	London Country Buses 479 and 408 - ground opposite bus garage
Capacity:	3,400 Seats: 200 Cover: 445 Floodlights: Yes
Clubhouse:	Bar open 12-11pm matchdays. Full catering. Tel: 01372 360151
Club Shop:	Yes. Tel: 01372 362705

PREVIOUS	**Leagues:** Surrey Snr 46-50; Metropolitan 50-51; Delphian 51-58; Corinthian 58-63; Athenian 63-72
CLUB RECORDS	**Attendance:** 5,500 v Wimbledon, 1976
	Win: 13-1 v Leyland Motors 46-47 Surrey Sen Lge **Defeat:** 1-11 v Sutton United
	Career goalscorer: Steve Lunn 96-97 (46) **Career appearances:** P Caswell
	Fee paid: £1,500 to Croydon (B Salkeld)
	Fee received: £1,500 from Croydon (B Salkeld)
BEST SEASON	**FA Amateur Cup:** Semi finalists 70-71 73-74
	FA Trophy: Runners-up 77-78
	F A Cup: 4th Round 74-75, 2-3 v Leicester C.(A). Also 2nd Rd 75-76 76-77 78-79,1st Rd 77-78 80-81
	League clubs defeated: Colchester, Brighton 74-75, Cambridge Utd 75-76,Northampton 76-77

HONOURS   FA Trophy R-up 77-78; Isthmian Lg Cup 77-78; Corinthian Lg 62-63; Athenian Lg Div 1 63-64; Surrey Snr Cup 68-69 (R-up 64-65 66-67 74-75 78-79); Surrey Snr Lg 46-47 47-48 48-49 49-50(Lg Cup 49-50), Snr Shield 68-69, Charity Cup 46-47 49-50); E. Surrey Charity Cup 68-69 (R-up 67-68); London Snr Cup R-up 74-75 77-78; Surrey Inter Cup 89-90; Southern Comb. Cup 89-90

Players progressing: Chris Kelly (Millwall), B Friend (Fulham), L Harwood (Port Vale), John Humphrey (Millwall)

Back row,left to right: Wesley Cain, Danny Lavender, Tommy Smith, Danny Oliver, Justin Gray, Michael Webb, Adam Gray, Darrell Teasdale, and Alex Inglethorpe (Player-Manager) **Front row:** Ali Chabaan, Paul McKay, Jamie Beer, Peter Maynard, Phil Ruggles, Jonathon Lloyd and Jeremy Jones

LEWES

SEASON 2002/2003
Official Programme & Matchday Magazine
Season 2002/2003 Ryman League Division 1 South

LEWES FOOTBALL CLUB

LEWES

Ryman
FOOTBALL LEAGUE

Ryman League Team of the Year

£1.00

CLUB OFFICIALS
President: T. Carr
Chairman: T. Parris
Secretary: Laurie Pilbeam
Lewes F.C.,Westgate Street,Lewes.
East Sussex BN7 1YR
Tel: 01273 474518

FACT FILE
Founded: 1885
Nickname: Rooks
Colours: Red & Black /black/black
Change colours: All white
Midweek matches: Tuesday
Reserves' League: Sussex Co. Res. Sect

FOOTBALL MANAGEMENT TEAM
Manager: Jimmy Quinn

GROUND: The Dripping Pan, Mountfield Road, Lewes BN7 1XN
Tel: 01273 472100

Directions: Two minute walk from Lewes (BR) - turn left out of station and left into Mountfield Road. Ground 100 yards on right

Capacity: 2,600   Cover: 400   Seats: 400   Floodlights: Yes
Club Shop: Yes
Clubhouse: (01273 472100). Bar, tea bar

PROGRAMME
Pages: 32 pages   Price: £1
Editor: Laurie Pilbeam
Local Press: Evening Argus, Sussex Express
Local Radio:
Southern F.M.,B.B.C. Southern Counties

PREVIOUS: **Leagues:** Mid Sussex 1886-1920; Sussex Co 20-65; Athenian 65-77

RECORDS: **Attendance:** 2,500 v Newhaven, Sussex County Lg 26/12/47
Goalscorer: Mark Stafford 192   **Appearances:** Terry Parris 662
Transfer Fee Paid: None   **Transfer Fee Received:** £2,500 for Grant Horscroft (Brighton)

BEST SEASON: **FA Cup:** 1st Rd Proper 2001-02 v Stoke City 0-2
FA Trophy: 1st Rd 82-83   **FA Amateur Cup:** 2nd Rd 67-68
FA Vase: Quarter Final 2001-02

HONOURS Isthmian Lg Div 2 Champions 01-02, R-up 79-80 91-92; Div 3 R-up 00-01. Ath'n Lg Div 1 69-70 (Div 2 67-68); Sussex Co. Lg 64-65 (R-up 24-25 33-34 58-59 63-64, Lg Cup 39-40); Mid Sussex Lg 10-11 13-14; Sussex Snr Cup 64-65 70-71 84-85 00-01(R-up 79-80 82-83 87-88); Sussex Royal Ulster Rifles Charity Cup(3) 61-63 64-65; Gilbert Rice F'lit Cup 82-83 88-89; Neale Tphy 68-69; Sussex F'lit Cup 76-77 (SF 83-84); Southern Counties Comb Div 1 80-81

Players progressing: (to Brighton unless stated) Don Bates(1950), Peter Knight (1964), Terry Stanley (1969), Colin Woffuden (1970), G Elphick & Steve Ford (Stoke 1981), Glen Geard, Grant Horscroft (1987), J Hammond (Fulham), S Funnell, L Allen (Wimbledon), M Rice (Watford)

METROPOLITAN POLICE

CLUB OFFICIALS
Chairman: Des Flanders QPM
Vice Chairman: Ian Carter
President: Sir John Stevens QPM
Secretary: Tony Brooking
15 Westmoreland Ave,
Hornchurch, Essex. RM112EJ.
Tel: (01708 450715)

FOOTBALL MANAGEMENT TEAM
Manager: John Cottam
Physio: Dick Pierce

FACT FILE
Founded: 1919
Nickname: Blues
Club Sponsors: Hatch Associates
Colours: All blue
Change colours: Black & White stripes
Midweek Matches: Tuesday
Reserves' League: Suburban
2001-02
Leading Goalscorer: Jason Prins 37
Captain: Adam Wickens
P.o.Y.: Jon Daly

GROUND: Metropolitan Police Sports Ground, Imber Court, East Molesey
Tel: 0208 398 7358)

Directions: From London: A3 then A309 to Scilly Isles r'bout, right into Hampton Court Way, left at 1st r'bout into Ember Court Rd - ground faces in 300yds. From M25 jct 10: A3 towards London for 1 mile, A307 through Cobham, left immd. after Sandown Park into Station Rd - ground 1 mile on left.
Half mile from either Thames Ditton or Esher BR stations

Capacity: 3,000 Seats: 297 Cover: 1,800   Floodlights: Yes   **Club Shop:** No
Clubhouse: (0181 398 1267). Four bars, dancehall, cafeteria open 9am-11pm. Hot & cold food

Pages: 10   Price: 50p
Editor/ Press Officer:
Cliff Travis (01932 782215)
Local Press: Surrey Comet, Surrey Herald
Local Radio: County Sounds

REVIOUS: **Leagues:** Spartan 28-60; Metropolitan 60-71; Southern 71-78
Grounds: None   **Name:** None

CLUB RECORDS: **Attendance:** 4,500 v Kingstonian, FA Cup 1934
Goal Scorer: Mario Russo
Appearances: Pat Robert
Win: 10-1 v Tilbury 1995
Defeat: 1-11 v Wimbledon, 1956

BEST SEASON **FA Cup:** 1st Rd - 32-33, 0-9 v Northampton T. (A); 84-85, 0-3 v Dartford (H); 94-95, 0-3 v Crawley T. (H)

HONOURS: Isthmian Lg Div 2 R-up 77-78 87-88; Spartan Lg 28-29 29-30 36-37 38-39 45-46 53-54 54-55, (R-up 47-48), Lg Cup 59-60 (R-up 57-58); Middx Snr Cup 27-28;Surrey Snr Cup 32-33, Charity Shield 38-39; Metropolitan Lg Cup 68-69 (Amtr Cup 68-69 69-70); London Snr Cup R-up 34-35 40-41; Herts & Middx Comb. 39-40;Diadora Lg Carlsberg Trophy 94-95

Back row, left to right: Ian Batten, Jason Prins, Eric Tomlinson, Andy Whyte, Jon Daly, Graeme Thompson and Dave Newman.
Front row: Peter Thackeray, Lee Cormack, Steve Boswell, Adam Wickens (Captain), Andy kemp and Carl Naylor

MOLESEY

CLUB OFFICIALS
Chairman: Norman Clark
President: Fred Maynard
Pres Officer: Peter Bowers
Secretary : Fiona Bowers
(c/o the club)

FOOTBALL MANAGEMENT TEAM
Manager: Pete Johnson
Asst Man/Coach: Gary Ross
Reserve Team Manager: Andy Graves
Youth Team Manager: John Lampard

FACT FILE
Formed: 1952 (as senior club)
JUBILEE SEASON

Nickname: The Moles
Colours: White/black/black
Change colours: Yellow/royal
Midweek home matchday: Tuesday
Reserve Team's League: Suburban
Youth Team: Southern Yth Lge

PROGRAMME
Pages:12 Price: £1
Editor: Pete Bowers c/o the club

Local Press: Surrey Comet,
Surrey Herald, Molesey News
Local Radio: Thames 107.8 FM
Hospital Radio, County Sound,
Three Counties, Star FM.

GROUND **Address:** 412 Walton Road, West Molesey, Surrey KT8 0JG
Tel: 0181 941 7989 (Boardroom)   0181 979 4823 (Clubhouse)

Directions A3 from London to Hook, thenA309 to Marquis of Granby pub, right to Hampton
Court station, turn left forWest Molesey, ground one mile on left
Capacity 4,000   Cover: 600   Seats: 400   Floodlights: Yes
Clubhouse Open every evening and weekend lunchtimes
2 bars, discos, live artists, darts, bingo, pool. Steward: John Chambers
Club Shop: Contact John Chambers

PREVIOUS **Leagues:** Surrey Intermediate 53-56; Surrey Snr 56-59; Spartan 59-72; Athenian72-77
Name: Molesey St Pauls 1950-53.   **Grounds:** None

CLUB RECORDS **Attendance:** 1,255 v Sutton United, Surrey Senior Cup Semi-Final 1966
CareerGoalscorer: Michael Rose, 139
Career Appearances: Frank Hanley, 453
Transfer fee paid: £500 for Chris Vidal (Leatherhead 88)
Transfer fee received: £5,000 for Chris Vidal (Hythe Town 89)

BEST SEASON **FA Vase:** 6th Rd 81-82.   **FA Trophy:** 1st Rd replay 90-91
FA Cup: First Round Proper 94-95, 0-4 v Bath City (H)

HONOURS Isthmian Lg Div 1 R-up 92-93, Div 2 South R-up 89-90, Lg Cup R-up 92-93,   Surrey Senior Lg 57-58, Lg Charity Cup 56-57,
Spartan Lg R-up 59-60. Lg Cup 61-62 R-up 63-64, Surrey Senior Shield R-up 74-75, Southern Combination Cup 90-91 94-95

Players progressing: John Finch (Fulham), Cyrille Regis (WBA, Coventry &England)

STAINES TOWN

CLUB OFFICIALS

Chairman: Alan Boon
Vice Chairman: Ken Williams
Secretary: Steve Parsons
3 Birch Green, Staines, Middx TW18 4HA
Tel: 01784 450420
General Manager: Chris Wainwright
Commercial Manager: Ken Williams
Press Officer: Stuart Moore (01784 421118)

FOOTBALL MANAGEMENT TEAM

Manager: Ken Ballard Asst Man: Danny Pipe
Physios: Chris Wiltcher,Mike Critchall,Mike
Savage ,Den Collins and Alan Gregory

FACT FILE

Formed: 1892
Nickname: The Swans
Sponsors: The Exchange Nightclub
Colours: Old gold (blue trim)/royal/royal
Change colours: All white
Midweek matchday: Tuesday
Reserve league: Sutton & District Vets Lg.

2000-01

Captain & P.o.Y : Jon Underwood
Top Scorer: Nick Hooper (18)

Staines Town
Football Club

Ryman League
Division One
Season 2001/02

Ryman
Football league

Official match day programme
Price £1.50

Pages: 44   Price: £1.50
Editor: Sec. & Stuart Moore (01784 421118)
Local Press: Staines & Ashford News,
Middx Chronicle, Informer,Staines Gaurdian
Local Radio: County Sound, GLR, Capital,
Star FM, Radio Wey.

GROUND Wheatsheaf Park, Wheatsheaf Lane,Staines,Middlesex TW18 2PD(01784 455988)
Directions: M25 Jct13 to A30 Staines by-pass to Crooked Billet roundabout.Take town centre exit(A308) and left into South St., at iron bridge. Pass bus staion and bear left into Laleham Rd. Wheatsheafe Lane is 1km on right Buses 481, 570,and 573 pass Wheatsheaf Lane.
Capacity: 2,500 **Cover:** 850 **Seats:** 250 **Floodlights:**Yes **Food:** Rolls and snacks available
Club HQ & Clubhouse: Staines Town FC, Wheatsheaf Lane, Staines (01784 455988).
Club Shop: Souvenirs available from Ray Moore c/o STFC.
Completely new ground on old site due to open in August 2002

PREVIOUS   **Leagues:** W London All (pre-1900), W London, W Middx (pre-1905), Gt WesternSuburban 05-13 20-24, Gt Western Comb, Munitions Lg (World War 1), London Works(World War 1), Hounslow & Dist 19-20, Spartan 24-35 58-71, Middx Sen 43-52; Parthenon 52-53, Hellenic 53-58, Athenian 71-73
Names: Staines Albany and St Peters Institute (merged) in 1895, Staines 05-18,Staines Lagonda 18-25, Staines Vale (2nd World War)
Grounds: Edgell Rd (St Peters Inst) ; The Lammas, Shortwood Common, Mill Mead(Hammonds/Wicks/Pursers Farm); Shepperton Road (to 51); Wheatsheaf Lane (From 51-except) ,Alwyns Lane Chertsey (1996-8) and Stompond Lane ,Walton & Hersham (2001-002)
CLUB RECORDS Attendance: 2,750 v Banco di Roma (Barassi Cup) 1975 (70,000 saw 1st leg in Rome)
    Goalscorer: Alan Gregory 122   **Appearances:** Dickie Watmore 840
    Win: 14-0 v Croydon (A), Isthmian League Div. 1 19/3/94 **Defeat:** 1-18 v Wycombe Wanderers (A), G West Sub Lge 27.12.09
    Fee Paid: For R Teale (Slough 81)   **Fee Received:** For Scott Taylor (Millwall 95-96)
BEST SEASON FA Amateur Cup: 3rd Rd 23-24   **FA Trophy:** 2nd Rd 2nd Replay 76-77l (Last 32)
    FA Cup: 1st Rd 84-85, 0-2 v Burton Alb (A) & 1879-80 & 80-81 (as St Peters Institute)
HONOURS Isthmian Lg Div 1 74-75 88-89 (Div 2 74-75); Athenian Lg Div 2 71-72 (Div 1 R-up 72-73); Spartan Lg 59-60 (R-up 70-71), Lg Cup 68-69 (R-up 60-61 70-71); Hellenic Lg R-up 55-56 (Lg Cup R-up 53-54 55-56); Gt Western Suburban Lg Div 1R-up 11-12 22-24 (Div 2 (Middx) 20-21); W London All Div 1 1899-1900; W LondonLg Div 1 00-01; W Middx Lg 04-05 (R-up 03-04); London Snr Cup R-up 76-77 80-81; Middx Snr Cup(7), (R-up 09-10 32-33 79-80), Snr Charity Cup 94-95; Barassi Cup76; Southern Comb. Chall. Cup 64-65 66-67 68-69 94-95 96-97,(R-up 67-68 94-95,99-00);W Middx Cup 23-24; Staines Cottage Hosp Cup 24-25; Merthyr Middx Charity Shield 90-91,(R-up 94-95); El Canuelo Trophy 92-93 94-95 94-95; Carlsberg Cup 94-95; Melksham Middx Charity Shield 96-97 Jim Lawford Memorial Cup 99-00, Midd'x Bowl 2001-2 (shared)

Back row left to right: Danny Pipe (Assistant Manager), Paul McCarthy, Danny Hayward,Andrew Sullivan, Mark Parker, Matthew Lovett, Richard Taylor, Damien Smith, Paul Johnson, Paul Greaves,Ken Ballard (Manager) and Chris Witcher (Physio).
Front row: Kohei Iio, Steve Battams, Joe O'Shea, Nick Hooper and Neil Selby.   **Photo:** Mick Gaughan.

TOOTING&MITCHAM UTD

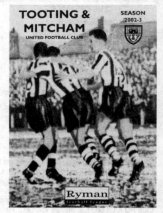

TOOTING &
MITCHAM
UNITED FOOTBALL CLUB

SEASON
2002-3

CLUB OFFICIALS

Chairman: John Buffoni
President: Cliff Bilham
Vice Chairman: Alan Simpson

Secretary: Les Roberts, 91 Fernlea Road,
Mitcham, Surrey CR4 2HG (01816 465275)

Commercial Manager: John Pollard
Press Officer: Steve Taylor c/o club

FOOTBALL MANAGEMENT TEAM
Manager: Ian Hazell
Coach: Peter Shaw
Physio: Danny Keenan

FACT FILE

Formed: 1932
Nickname: Terrors
Sponsors: Claremont Coaches
Colours: Black & white stripes/black/white
Change colours: All red
Midweek matchday: Tuesday
Reserve League: Suburban

Local Press: Mitcham News, South London
Press, South London Guardian
Local Radio: Capital

Programme: Pages: 24 Price: 80p
Editor: Steve Taylor

GROUND
Address: Imperial Fields, Bishopsford Road, Morden, Surrey SM4 6BF
Tel Nos: 020 8648 3248 (ground) 020 8685 9229 (board room)
Directions: Phone club please.

Capacity: 8,000 Cover: 1,990 Seats: 1,990 Floodlights: Yes
Clubhouse: Open every evening and weekend lunchtimes. Wide variety of food available
Club Shop: Sells souvenirs & confectionary

PREVIOUS: **Leagues:** London 32-37, Athenian 37-56 **Ground:** None **Name:** None

CLUB RECORDS: **Attendance:** 17,500 v QPR, FA Cup 2nd Rd 56-57
Goalscorer: Alan Ives 92 (1972-78) **Appearances:** Danny Godwin 470
Win: 11-0 v Welton Rovers, FA Amateur Cup 62-63
Defeat: 1-8 v Kingstonian, Surrey Snr Cup 66-67 v Redbridge Forest (H), LoctiteCup 3rd Rd 19/2/91
Fee Paid: £9,000 for Dave Flint (Enfield) **Fee Received:** £10,000 for Herbie Smith (Luton)

BEST SEASON: **FA Trophy:** 2nd Qualifying Rd Replay 71-72 81-82
FA Amateur Cup: 1st Rd replay 22-23 **FA Vase:**
FA Cup: 4th Rd 75-76, 1-3 v Bradford C. (A) 3rd Rd 58-59; 2nd Rd 56-57 76-77;1st Rd 5 other occasions
League clubs defeated: Bournemouth & Boscombe Ath, Northampton 58-59, Swindon 75-76

HONOURS: Isthmian League 57-58 59-60 (Full Members Cup 92-93); Athenian League 49-50 54-55; London Challenge Cup R-up 59-60;
Surrey Senior Cup 37-38 43-44 44-45 52-53 59-60 75-76 76-77 77-78; Surrey Senior Shield 51-52 60-61 61-62 65-66
London Senior Cup 42-43 48-49 58-59 59-60 (R-up 43-44 44-45); South Thames Cup 69-70;

Players progressing: Trevor Owen (Orient 58), Dave Bumpstead (Millwall 58), Paddy Hasty (Aldersot 58), Walter Pearson(Aldershot), Richie Ward &
Alex Stepney (Millwall 62 & 63), Vic Akers(Watford 75), Paul Priddy (Wimbledon 78), Carlton Fairweather & Brian Gayle(Wimbledon 84)

The start of a new era.
Tooting & Mitcham United (stripes) pictured before the opening of the new stadium with the opposing Chelsea XI.

WALTON & HERSHAM

CLUB OFFICIALS

Chairman: A.Smith
President: TBA
Secretary: Michael Groom,15 Windsor Walk, Weybridge, Surrey KT13 9AP
Tel No: 01932 842982
Press Officer: Mervyn Rees
Tel: 01932 245756

FOOTBALL MANAGEMENT TEAM

Manager: Matt Alexander

Physio: Stuart Smith

FACT FILE
Formed: 18960 Nickname: Swans
Sponsors: Beales
Colours: Red /white/red
Change colours: Yellow/Blue/yellow
Midweek home matchday: Tuesday
Reserve Team's League: Suburban
Club Website: waltonandhershamfc.org.uk
2001-02 Captain: Chris Whelan
P.o.Y.:Nicky Andrews
Top Scorer: Scott Edgar

Official Match Day Programme
Walton Hersham F.C.
The Ryman Football League
£1.50
SHIRT SPONSORS F.A. CUP 1st Qualifying Round WALTON & HERSHAM
BEALES Saturday 14th September 2002 v
of Walton Kick off 3.00 p.m. COVE
Ryman
The Ryman Football League

Pages: 36 Price: £1.20
Editor: Mark Massingham Tel: 01932 885814

Local Press: Surrey Herald, Surrey Comet
Local Radio: County Sound,
BBC Southern Counties

GROUND: Sports Ground, Stompond Lane, Walton-on-Thames Tel: 01932 245263 (club)
Directions: From North: Over Walton Bridge & along New Zealand Ave., down 1-way street and up A244 Hersham Rd - grd 2nd right. From Esher: Down Lammas Lane then Esher Rd, straight over 1st r'bout, 4th exit at next r'bout (WestGrove) 2nd left at end of Hersham Rd and Stompond Lane 1/2 mile on left.Ten min walk Walton-on-Thames (BR). Bus 218 passes grd
Capacity: 6,500 Cover: 2,500 Seats: 500 Floodlights: Yes
Clubhouse: (01932 245263). Open every night. TV, darts, pool, refreshments on matchdays
Club Shop: Open matchdays. Contact Richard Old, c/o the club

PREVIOUS **Leagues:** Surrey Senior; Corinthian 45-50; Athenian 50-71
CLUB RECORDS Attendance: 6,500 v Brighton, FA Cup First Round 73-74
Scorer: Reg Sentance 220 in 11 seasons **Appearances:** Terry Keen 449 in 11 seasons
Win: 10-0 v Clevedon, FA Amateur Cup 1960 **Defeat:** 11-3 v Kingstonian Surrey Sen Shield 58
Transfer fee paid: £6,000 **Transfer fee received:** £150,000 for Nathan Ellington 99

BEST SEASON **FA Trophy:** 4th Round 99-00 **FA Amateur Cup:** Winners 72-73, (SF 51-52, 52-53)
FA Cup: 2nd Rd 72-73 (v Margate), 73-74 (v Hereford). League clubs defeated: Exeter 72-73, Brighton 73-74

HONOURS: Isthmian Lg R-up 72-73, Barassi Cup 73-74; Athenian Lg 68-69 (R-up 50-51 69-70 70-71, Lg Cup 69-70); Corinthian Lg 46-49 (R-up 49-50), Premier Midweek F'litLg 67-69 70-71 (R-up 71-72); Surrey Snr Cup 47-48 50-51 60-61 61-62 70-71 72-73(R-up 46-47 51-52 59-60 69-70 71-72 73-74); London Snr Cup R-up 73-74); SouthernComb. Cup 82-83 88-89 91-92; 99-00 Surrey Comb.Cup 49-50 91-92; John Livey Memorial Trophy 91-92

Players progressing: Andy McCulloch (QPR 1970), Mick Heath (Brentford 1971),Paul Priddy (Brentford 1972), Richard Teale (Q.P.R. 1973), SteveParsons (Wimbledon 1977), Stuart Massey (Crystal Palace), Ross Davidson(Sheffield Utd), Nathan Ellington (Bristol Rovers), Tommy Williams (West Ham United) and Basir Savage (Reading)

L-R - Back Row: Stuart Smith (physio), Luke Garrard, Lee O'Donnell, Chris Whelan, Nicky Andrews, Scott Edgar, Alan Dowson, Tristan Frontin, Jamie Laister. **Front:** Adam Thompson, Marcus Rose, Adam Fennell, Paul Harkness, Ben Loney, Francis Dolan, Wes Goggin. **Photo** courtesy of the Surrey Herald

WHYTELEAFE

CLUB OFFICIALS	FOOTBALL MANAGEMENT TEAM	FACT FILE

CLUB OFFICIALS
Chairman: Tony Lidbury
Secretary: Robin Clements, 7 Orchard End,
Caterham, Surrey CR3 5UR
TelNo: 01883 3400-77 (H) 07767 233698 (M)
Press Sec:: Brian Davis,Tel: 020 8651 2999
Commercial Manager: T Douce
Tel: 01883 343450
Match Secretary: Edward Lucas:
Braeside,Johns Road,Tatsfield,Westerham,
Kent TN16 2AP.Tel No: 01959 577361 (H)

FOOTBALL MANAGEMENT TEAM
Manager: Lee Richardson
Assistant Man.: Bernie Donnelly
Coach: Stuart Massey
Physio: John Knapton

Programme
Pages: 36 Price: £1.00
Editor: Chris Layton (01883 381169)
Local Press: Croydon Advertiser
Local Radio: Mercury

FACT FILE
Formed: 1946
Nickname: Leafe
Sponsors: Custom cables
Colours: Yellow/green/green
Change colours: Yellow & black/black/black
Midweek matchday: Tuesday
Reserve Team's League: Suburban

GROUND 15 Church Road, Whyteleafe, Surrey CR3 0AR Tel: 020 8660 5491 (Ground) 020 8645 0422 (Boardroom)
Directions: Five minutes walk from Whyteleafe (BR) - turn right from station, and left into Church Road
Capacity: 5,000 Cover: 600 Seats:400 Floodlights: Yes
Clubhouse: Open every lunchtime & evening. Hot & cold food, pool, darts, gaming machines **Clubshop:** Yes

PREVIOUS **Leagues:** Caterham & Edenbridge, Croydon, Thornton Heath & Dist., SurreyIntermediate (East) 54-58, Surrey Senior 58-75, Spartan 75-81, Athenian 81-84
Names: None **Grounds:** None
CLUB RECORDS Attendance: 2,210 v Chester City F.A.Cup 1st Rd 99-00.
Transfer fee paid: £1,000 for Gary Bowyer (Carshalton)**Transfer fee received:** £25,000 for Steve Milton

BEST SEASON FA Vase: 5th Rd 80-81 85-86
FA Trophy: 4th Rd 98-99 v Kingstonian **FA Cup:** First Round proper, 99-00 v Chester City (H)

HONOURS Isthmian Lge Div 2 South R-up 88-89; Surrey Senior Lge 68-69 (Lge Cup R-up 68-69, Lge Charity Cup 71-72, Res Sect 62-63 (Chall. Cup 62-63 (R-up 59-60); Surrey Sen. Cup 68-69 (R-up 87-88); Surrey Prem. Cup R-up 84-85; E. Surrey Charity Cup 79-80 (R-up 76-77 77-78); Thornton Heath & Dist Lge 51-52(Lge Cup 51-52) Div 4 R-up 51-52; Edenbridge Charity Cup 51-52; Caterham & Purley Hospital Cup 51-52; Surrey County Interm Lge East Sect 1 55-56; Surrey Jun. Cup R-up 51-52; Caterham & Edenbridge Lge Div 3 51-52; Borough of Croydon Charity Cup 56-57; Southern Yth Lge 89-90 (R-up 88-89), Lge Cup 88-89 89-90; Southern Counties M'week F'lit Cup 95-96
Players progressing: Steve Milton (Fulham), Ian Cox and Alan Pardew (Crystal Palace)

WINDSOR & ETON

CLUB OFFICIALS
Chairman: Peter Simpson
President: T.B.A.
Secretary: Steve Rowland,
c/o Football Club
Tel No: 07887 770630 (M)
Press Officer: Secretary
FOOTBALL MANAGEMENT TEAM
Manager: Dennis Greene
Asst Manager:Colin Ferguson

FACT FILE
Founded: 1892
Nickname: Royalists
Sponsors: T.B.A.
Colours: All red with green trim
Change colours: Blue
Midweek matches: Tuesday
Reserves' League: Suburban (South)

PROGRAMME
28 pages Price: £!.00
Editor: Malcolm Williams
Local Press: Windsor & Eton Express,
Windsor & East Berks Observer,
Evening Post
Local Radio: BBC Radio Berkshire,Star FM

GROUND Stag Meadow, St Leonards Road, Windsor, Berkshire SL4 3DR (01753 860656)
Directions: A332 from M4 junct 6. Third left at r'bout , left into St Leonards Rd at lights on T-junction, ground 500 yards on right on B3022 opposite Stag &Hounds PH. 1 mile from town centre - BR to Windsor Central station (from) Slough or Windsor Riverside (change at Staines from Waterloo)
Capacity: 4,500 Cover: 650 Seats: 400 Floodlights: Yes
Clubhouse: Yes **Club Shop:** Yes

PREVIOUS **Leagues:** Southern 1895-96; West Berks; Great Western Suburban 1907-22; Athenian 22-29 63-81; Spartan 29-32; Great Western Comb; Corinthian 45-50; Metropolitan 50-60; Delphian 60-63 **Ground:** Ballon Meadow 1892-1912
CLUB RECORDS Attendance: 8,500 (Charity match) **Appearances:** Kevin Mitchell
Fee Paid: £9,000 for Keith White (Slough Town)
Fee Received: £45,000 for Michael Banton & Michael Barnes (Barnet)
BEST SEASON FA Amateur Cup: 4th Rd 21-22 **FA Vase:** Semi-Final 80-81 (QF 79-80) **FA Trophy:** 3rd Rd 88-89
FA Cup: 2nd Rd replay 83-84. 1st Rd 7 times 25-26 80-81 82-86 91-92. League clubs defeated: None
HONOURS Isthmian Lg Div 1 83-84 Div 2 R-up 82-83 2000-01,
Athenian Lg 79-80 80-81 Lg Cup 79-80 R-up 78-79 80-81, Div 2 Cup 63-64 R-up 68-69, Spartan Lg R-up 36-37 37-38 Div 1 30-31, Metropolitan Lg R-up 53-54 Lg Amtr Cup 51-52 52-53, Lg Cup 52-53 R-up 53-54 54-55, Gt Western Suburban Lg R-up 21-22, Berks & Bucks Snr Cup (11) 10-11 36-38 40-45 61-62 87-89 R-up 07-08 24-25 26-27 38-39 46-47 62-63, Berks & Bucks Benev. Cup 35-36 37-38 46-47 62-63 R-up 38-39 47-48 49-50
Players progressing: Reg Dare (Southampton 1949), Steve Adams (Charlton 1979), Dave Barnett (Colchester 1988), Vic Woodley (Chelsea & England), Billy Coward (QPR, Walsall), Ken Groves (Preston), Dave Regis (Notts County), Damian Spencer (1998)

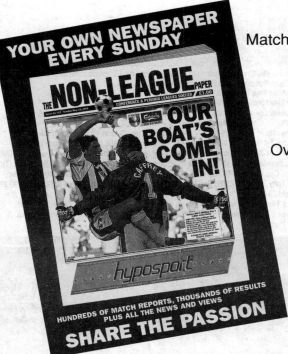

849

WORTHING

CLUB OFFICIALS

Chairman: **Beau Reynolds**
President: **Morty Hollis**
Vice Chairman: **Ray Smith**

Secretary/Press Off.: **Paul Damper**
19 Fletcher Road, Worthing,
West Sussex BN14 8EX
Tel: 01903 210290

FOOTBALL MANAGEMENT TEAM
Manager: Barry Lloyd
Assistant Manager:Keith Rowley
Physio: Alan Robertson

FACT FILE
Formed: 1886
Nickname: The Rebels
Sponsors:Worth F.M.
Colours: Red, with white trim/red/red
Change : White withbluetrim/ white/white
Midweek matches: Tuesday

2001-02
Captain: Mark Burt
P.o.Y: James Wastell
Top Scorer: Gavin Geddes 27

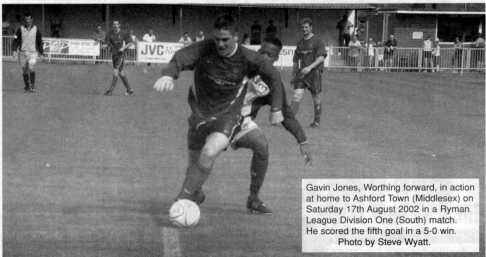

THANK YOU FOR YOUR
MAGNIFICENT
SUPPORT

GROUND Woodside Road, Worthing, West Sussex BN14 7HQ (01903 239575)

Directions: Follow A24 to town, at end of Broadwater Rd having gone over railway bridge,
1st right into Teville Rd, right into South Farm RD, 2nd left into Pavilion Rd,
Woodside Rd is first right. Half a mile fromWorthing (BR)
Capacity: 4,500   Seats: 450   Cover: 1,500   Floodlights: Yes
Clubhouse: Open 2 hrs before kick-off & closes 11pm. Hot & cold food available
Club Shop: Yes

Pages: 40 Price: £1 Editor: Ian Fowler
Local Press: Evening Argus, Worthing Herald
Worthing Guardian
Local Radio: Southern FM,
Southern Counties Radio

PREVIOUS **Leagues:** West Sussex Sen 1896-04, 05-14, 19-20; Brighton, Hove & Dist 19-20; Sussex County 20-40, 45-48;
Corinthian 48-63; Athenian 63-77 **Names:** Worthing Association pre 1899 **Grounds:** Homefield Park, Beach House Park
CLUB RECORDS **Attendance:** Claimed to be 4,500 v Depot Battalion Royal Engineers, FA Amtr Cup 07-08
Transfer fee paid: Undisclosed fee forMarc Rice (Havant & Waterlooville1998)
Transfer fee received: £7,500 for Tim Read (Woking, 1990)
Win: 25-0 v Littlehampton (H) West Sussex Lge 1911-12 **Defeat:** 0-14 v Southwick (A), Sussex County Lge 1946-47
Career Goalscorer: Mick Edmonds 276   **Career Appearances:** David Bloom 397
BEST SEASON **FA Vase:** 5th Rd 78-79   **FA Trophy:** 4th rd Replay 85-86   **FA Amateur Cup:** Quarter-Final replay 07-08
FA Cup: 2nd Rd 82-83, 0-4 v Oxford Utd; 1st Rd 36-37, 94-95 (1-3 v AFC Bournem'th), 99-00 (0-3 v Rotherham United)
HONOURS Isth.Lg R-up (2) 83-85 (Div 1 82-83, Div 2 81-82 92-93);Isth Full members Cup r-up98-99, Athenian Lg Div 1 R-up 63-64, Div 2
R-up 71-72, Lg Cup R-up 72-73, Mem. Shield R-up 63-64; SussexSnr Cup (21); Sussex RUR Char. Cup (13); Sussex Co. Lg(8)W Sussex Lg (7);
Brighton Char. Cup(10) Worthing Char. Cup (11); AFA Invit. Cup 63-64 68-69 73-74 75-76 (Snr Cup R-up 36-37 46-47 48-49); Corinth. Lg Mem.
Shield R-up 49-50 (NealeTphy 58-59); Roy Hayden Mem. Tphy 75(jt), 77 78,99. Don Morecraft Tphy 72 73 76 8182; Sussex F'lit Cup(3) 88-90 97-
98; Sussex I'mediate Cup 34-35 64-65; BrightonChal. Shield 29-30 31-32
Players progressing: Ken Suttle (Chelsea 48), Alan Arnell & Fred Perry (Liverpool 54), Craig Whitington (Scarborough, via Crawley Town) 93,
Darren Freeman (Gillingham), Paul Musselwhite (Scunthorpe), Trevor Wood (Port Vale), Richard Tiltman (Brighton), David Cameron (Lincoln C),
Charlie Webb (Brighton 1908),Vince Taylor (Arsenal), Eric Parsons (West Ham U & Chelsea), E.C.D. Wright (Hull City)

Gavin Jones, Worthing forward, in action
at home to Ashford Town (Middlesex) on
Saturday 17th August 2002 in a Ryman
League Division One (South) match.
He scored the fifth goal in a 5-0 win.
Photo by Steve Wyatt.

ARLESEY TOWN

ARLESEY TOWN
FOOTBALL CLUB
Est 1891
OFFICIAL MATCH PROGRAMME
sponsored by the
WAYBURY PARTNERSHIP

HUNGERFORD TOWN
Saturday 27th April 2002
Ryman League Division II
Kick Off 3:00pm   £1.00

Ryman
football league

CLUB OFFICIALS

Chairman: Bryan Ellis (01462 682612)
Vice-Chairman: Scott Geekie (01462 732396)
President: Maurice Crouch
Secretary: John Albon
13 St Johns Rd, Arlesey, Beds SG15 6ST.
Tel: 01462 731318 (H & B),
Mob 07711 566044
Email: j.albon1@ntlworld.com

FACT FILE

Founded: 1891
Nickname: Blues
Colours: Sky & navy/navy/navy
Change Colours: All white.
Midweek matchday: Tuesday
Reserves' Lge: S. Midlands Lge Res Div 1

2001-02
Captain & P.o.Y.: Dave Hatchett
Top Scorers:
Tony Fontenelle & Dean Harding

FOOTBALL MANAGEMENT TEAM

Manager: Nicky Ironton
Asst Man:Alan Dawson
Physio: Eric Turner

GROUND: Hitchin Rd, Arlesey, Beds SG15 6RS
Tel: 01462 734504

Directions: A1 take A507 to Shefford, at 3rd roundabout turn left, 1st left follow road
through village, ground 1.5 miles on left

Capacity: 2,920   Seats: 150   Cover: 600   Floodlights: Yes

PROGRAMME

Price: £1.00
Editor: Pete Brennan (01462 834455)

Club Website: www.arleseyfc.co.uk

Club Shop: Yes
Clubhouse: Open daily 7- 11.30, Sat 12-11.30, Sun 12-2.30 7-11.30
Members bar & function suite

PREVIOUS: **Leagues:** Biggleswade & Dist.; Beds. Co. (S. Mids) 22-26 ,27-28; Parthenon;
London 58-60; Utd Co's 33-36 82-92. Spartan South Midlands 92-99

RECORDS: **Attendance:** 2,000 v Luton Res, Beds Snr Cup 1906
Appearances: Gary Marshall

BEST SEASON: **FA Vase:** Winners 94-95   **FA Cup:** 3rd Qual.Round

HONOURS: FA Vase Winners 1994-5; Isthmian League (Ryman) Div 3 Champions 00-01,
Beds Sen Cup 65-66 78-79 96-97, Prem Cup 83-84, 01-02, Interm Cup 57-58; S Mids Lge Prem Div 51-52 52-53 94-95
95-96.99.99-00, Div 2 29-30 31-32 35-36, Chall Trophy 79-80, Prem Shield 64-65, O'Brien Prem Cup 93-94, F'litCup 90-91;
Utd Co Lge Prem Div 84-85, KO Cup 87-88; Hinchingbrooke Cup 77-78 79-80 81-82 96-97;
Biggleswade KO Cup 77-78 80-81

Players Progressing: Roland Legate (Luton), Pat Kruse (Brentford, Leicester) & Dave Kitson(Camb U)

Back row,left to right: Nathan Beckett, Steve Magona, Justin Griffith, Damian Matthews, Matt Cope and Marvin Samuel.
Middle row: Helen Bardell (Physio), Eric Turner, James Ougham, Micky Simpson, Andy Theodosiou, Martin Patching,Trevor
Wilkinson, Jamie Lever, Roy Parkin, Barry Dellar and Margaret Brabrook (Physio).**Front row:** Dean Harding,Craig Reynolds
Lee Tekell, Dave Hatchett, Nicky Ironton,Matt Corbould, Dwayne Clarke,Phil Dean,Phil Leggatt with mascot George Ironton

AVELEY

CLUB OFFICIALS
Chairman: David Patient
President: Ken Clay
Press Officer: Terry King
Secretary: Craig Johnston
10 San Juan Drive, Chafford Hundred,
Grays, Essex RM16 6LQ.
Tel: 01375 650220 (H) 07946 438540 (M)

FOOTBALL MANAGEMENT TEAM
Manager: Steve Mosely
Asst. Manager & Coach: Keith Day
Coach: Lee Malcolm
Physio Phil Hunter

FACT FILE
Founded: 1927
Sponsors: Freightmaster
Colours: All Royal blue
Change: All Red
Midweek matches: Tuesday
Reserves' Lge: Essex Business House

2001-02
Captain: Ricky Hazel
P.o.Y.: Darren Smith
Top Scorer: Kenny Leslie 23

GROUND: `Mill Field', Mill Road, Aveley, Essex RM15 4TR
Tel: 01708 865940

Directions: London - Southend A1306, turn into Sandy Lane at Aveley.
Rainham or Purfleet BR stations then bus No. 723 to the ground. Bus from Rainham No 324
Capacity: 4,000   Cover: 400   Seats: 400   Floodlights: Yes
Clubhouse: Normal pub hours. Bar snacks and hot food available
Club Shop: No

Pages: 48   Price: £1
Editor: Terry King
Local Press: Thurrock Gazette
Romford Recorder
Local Radio: Radio Essex, Essex Radio

PREVIOUS	**Leagues:** Thurrock Com 46-49; London 49-57; Delphian 57-63; Athenian 63-73	
RECORDS	**Attendance:** 3,741 v Slough T., FA Amateur Cup 27.2.71	
	Goalscorer: Jotty Wilks, 214 **Appearances:** Ken Riley, 422	
	Win: 11-1 v Histon, 24/8/63	
	Defeat: 0-8 v Orient, Essex Thameside Trophy, 11/4/85	
BEST SEASON	**FA Cup:** 1st Rd 70-71, 0-1 v Yeovil League clubs defeated: None	
	FA Amateur Cup QF 70-71 **FA Trophy** 3rd Qual Rd replay 74-75 **F.A.Vase** 3rd Rd 89-90	
HONOURS:	Isthmian Lg Div 2 (North) R-up 89-90, Lg (AC Delco) Cup 89-90; London Lg 51-5254-55 (R-up 55-56, Lg Cup 53-54); Delphian Lg R-up 57-58 (Lg Cup 61-62);Athenian Lg 70-71 (Div 2 R-up 68-69); Essex Junior Cup 47-48 48-49; Essex Thameside Trophy 79-80 R-up 97-98; Hornchurch Charity Cup 81-82 (R-up 83-84); East Anglian Cup 88-89, R-up 97-98	

Players progressing: David Case & Alan Hull (Orient), Alan Parkinson (Orient 1967), Yilmaz Orhan (W Ham 1972), Keith Day (Colchester 1984), Paul Williams (Charlton, Sheff Wed & C.Palace) Paul Wilson (Barnet), David Morrison (Peterborough U), Tony Sorrell (Maidstone Utd), Steve Crane (Gillingham), David Matthews (Walsall, Southend United)

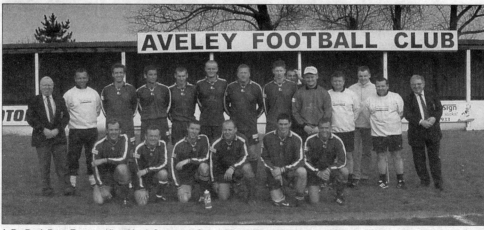

L-R - Back Row: Terrance King (Match Secretary), Steven Mosely (Manager), Robert Bird, Neil Cannon, Wesley Faulkner, Lucas Bauckham, William Goldstone, Matthew Harrold, Darren Smith, Christopher King (Coach), Rikky Hazle, Lea Melcolm (Fitness Trainer), Philip Additer (Ground Supervisor).
Front Row: James Stevens, Gareth Lynch, Daniel Stanley, Bartolomew Mas, Daniel Curran, Marcus Robson.

BARKING & EAST HAM UNITED

CLUB OFFICIALS

Chairman: John Edgeworth
Vice-Chairman: Paul Lovell
President: Terry Lovell
Secretary: Roger Chilvers
50 Harrow Rd, Barking, Essex IG11 7RA Tel: 020 8591 5313
Press Officer: Derek Pedder
Tel: 020 85292 483

FOOTBALL MANAGEMENT TEAM

Manager: Richard Thomas
Asst Manager: Mark Lord
Reserves' Manager: Dorian West
Goalkeeping Coach: Marc Baker
Physio: Shuc Davis

FACT FILE

Founded: 1880 Nickname: The Blues
Main Sponsors: Capital Coin and Peter Webster Property management and Surveying
.Other Sponsors: Global Games, New Spice & Docklands Coachworks
Colours: Blue & white Change Cols: White
Midweek matchday: Tuesday
Reserves' Lge: Essex & Herts Border Div 1
Ladies Lg: F.A. Prem Div 1 (South)
Youth League: Eastern Junior Alliance
Club Website: www.barkingfc.co.uk
2001-02
Capt,P.o.Y.& Top Scorer: Michael Black

BLUES NEWS & VIEWS

OFFICIAL MATCHDAY PROGRAMME OF BARKING & EAST HAM UNITED
INCORPORATING 'BLUE THRU & THIN'

Saturday 20th October 2001 Ryman League Division One
versus
Oxford City

Ryman
football league
£1

Peter Webster
020 7467 3949
Email: info@Peterwebster.co.uk
94/96 Wigmore Street, London W1U 3RF

PROGRAMME

Pages: 16   Price: £1.00
Editor: Mark Harris
Local Press: B arking & Dagenham Post
B & D Recorder.
Local Radio: Active FM

GROUND Mayesbrook Park, Lodge Avenue, Dagenham RM8 2JR Tel: 020 8595 6900/6511
Email Address: john@capitalcair.co.uk

Directions: Off A13 on A1153 (Lodge Ave), and ground 1 mile on left.
Bus 162 from Barking station or Nos 5 or 87 to Robin Hood. Nearest tube Becontree.

Capacity: 2,500   Cover: 600   Seats: 200   Floodlights: Yes
Clubhouse: 2 large bars, open daily 11am-11pm (Sundays Noon-11pm).
Hot & cold food and drinks.
Club Shop: Yes. Manager: Brad Robinson

PREVIOUS **Grounds:** Eastbury Field, Kennedy Estate,Movers Lane,Barking Recreation Ground Merry Fiddlers,Vicarage Field (until 1973)
Names: Barking Rovers,Barking Woodville, Barking Institute,Barking Town and Barking
Leagues: London 1896-98 09-23, South Essex 1898-21, Leyton & Dist 1899-1900,Athenian 12-13 + 23-52 S.E.Combination 39-40

CLUB RECORDS **Attendance:** (At Mayesbrook) 1,972 v Aldershot FA Cup 2nd Rd 78
Win: 14-0 v Sheppey Utd Mithras Cup 69-70   **Defeat:** 0-8 v Marlow.
Fee received: £6,000 for Alan Hull (Orient)   **Fee paid:** None over £1,000
Goal scorer: Neville Fox 241 (65-73)   **Appearances:** Bob Makin 566

BEST SEASON **FA Vase:** 96-97 5th Rd   **FA Amateur Cup:** Runners-up 26-27   **F.A.Trophy:** 2nd Rd 79-80
FA Cup: 2nd Rd rep. 81-82 1-3v Gillingham (A) after 1-1. Also 2nd Rd 78-79 79-80 83-84, and 1st Rd 26-27 28-29 78-80.
League clubs defeated: Oxford Utd 79-80.

HONOURS FA Amateur Cup R-up 26-27; Isthmian Lg 78-79 (Lg Cup R-up 76-77); Athenian Lg 34-35 (R-up 24-25); London Lg 20-21 (Div 1 (A) 09-10); South Essex Lg Div 1 (2),R-up (3), Div 2 (4); London Senior Cup (4), R-up (3); Essex Senior Cup (7), R-up (8); Dylon Shield 79-80; Eastern Floodlit R-up (3); Essex Elizabethian 66-67, R-up (2); Essex Thameside (4), R-up (4); London Charity Cup 61-62 R-up 21-22; London Intermediate Cup (3) ,R-up(1); East Anglian Cup 37-38 53-54;Mithras Cup (3), R-up (2); Premier Midweek (2). Vandanel Trophy R-up 99-00

Players progressing:39 players to date including: - 1956; Peter Carey (Orient 57), Lawrie Abrahams (Charlton 77), Kevin Hitchcock (Nottm Forest83 & Chelsea), Dennis Bailey (Fulham 86), Alan Hull (Orient 87) Joe Sibley1939, Hedley Sheppard 1932, Paul Wilson (Barnet) John Still (Ex-Manager Barnet), Mark Lazarus (Leyton O),J.Tresarden 1922 (West Ham U & England) and H.j.Holse,1908 (Manchester U & England)

Back row, left to right: Steve Davies (Physio), Danny Vincent, Mark Lord (Assisitant Manager), Richard Halle, Dean Cleaver, Dean Allen, Richard Thomas (Player Manager), Robin Ruston, Stewart Moody, Terry Schotchmer, and Jay Murray.
Front row: Jamie Dormer, Steve Shaw, Michael Black, Paul Carr, Sam Taylor and David Hunt.

BARTON ROVERS

CLUB OFFICIALS
Chairman: Trevor Capon
President: Pat Howarth
Vice Chairman: Richard Carey
Football Secretary: Owen Clark,
c/o Barton Rovers F.C.
Tel: 01582 882398
Press Officer: Nick Rhodes
Tel: 01582 881865

FOOTBALL MANAGEMENT TEAM
Manager: Ian Allinson
Assistant Manager: Geoff Livingstone
Physio: Mark Boulding

FACT FILE
Formed: 1898
Nickname: Rovers
Sponsors: Hillson Builders
Colours: All royal blue with white trim
Change colours: All yellow
Midweek Matchday: Tuesday
Reserves' League: None
Local Press: Luton News, Herald,
Beds on Sunday
Local Radio: Radio Chiltern, Radio Beds
Three Counties Radio

Season 2002-2003

Match Day Magazine

£1.20

RYMAN FOOTBALL LEAGUE
DIVISION ONE NORTH

GROUND   Sharpenhoe Road, Barton-le-Clay, Bedford MK45 4SD
Tel: 01582 707772

Directions: M1 Jct 12, from London exit turn right, take 2nd right through Harlington and Sharpenhoe. Entrance to ground 44 yds on right down concrete drive entering village. 41/2 miles from Harlington (BR), 6 miles from Luton (BR), good bus or taxis service from Luton
Capacity: 4,000   Seats: 160   Cover: 1,120   Floodlights: Yes

Clubhouse: Noon-3pm weekends (no football), noon-11pm (matchdays), 7-11pm weekdays.
Real ale, hot & cold snacks, pool, darts, gaming machines
Club Shop: Yes (contact 01582 751013)

PROGRAMME
Pages: 64 Price: £1.20
Editor: Sec & Nick Rhodes (01582 881865)

PREVIOUS   **Leagues:** Luton & Dist. 47-54; Sth Midlands 54-79
Grounds: Church Pitch 1898-1912; Barton Cutting 1912; Sharpenhoe Rd 12-33; Faldo Rd 33-38; Barton Rec. 46-75

CLUB RECORDS   **Attendance:** 1,900 v Nuneaton, FA Cup 4th Qual. Rd 1976
Win: 17-1 v Flitwick Athletic (H), S Midlands Lge Div 1 55-56
Defeat: 1-11 v Leighton United (H), S Midlands Lge Prem Div 62-63
Scorer: Richard Camp 152, 1989-98   **Appearances:** Tony McNally 514 (1988-2000)
Fees - Paid: £1,000 for B Baldry (Hitchin Town, 1980)   **Received:** £1,000 for B Baldry (Bishop's Stortford, 1981)

BEST SEASON   **FA Cup:** 1st Round 1980-81, 0-2 v Torquay United (A)
FA Vase: Runners-up 77-78 (SF 76-77 81-82, QF 75-76 78-79)
FA Trophy: 2nd Rd 98-99, 99-00

HONOURS: Sth Mids Lg(8) 70-73 74-79 (R-up 67-68), Div 1 64-65 (R-up 55-56), Div 2 54-55, Lg Shield 57-58 60-61 68-69, Chal. Tphy 71-72 74-75 77-78 78-79; Beds Snr Cup 7), R-up (5); Beds Premier Cup 95-96, R-up 81-82 83-84 88-89, 99-00 01-02 Beds Intermediate Cup 53-54; Luton & Dist. Lg Div 3 47-48; North Beds Charity Cup 72-73 74-75 76-77 77-78 79-80 80-81 (R-up 70-71); Isthmian Lge Div 2 R-Up 94-95, Assoc. Members Trophy R-up 92-93; South Midlands Floodlight Cup 98-99. Hinchingbroke Cup   2001-02 R-up: 98-99,99-00

Players progressing: Kevin Blackwell (Huddersfield T.)

L-R - Back Row: Kevin Thoburn (u18 Manager), Paul Donnelly, Mark Boulding (Physio), Steve Turner, Keiran Carey, Dave Cook, Leon Cashman, Brad Gillham, Brett Donnelly, Chris Payne, Danny Kennoy, Robert Messina, Matt Endersby, Owen Clark (secretary)
Front: Dave Brown, Jermaine Daley, Keith Coughlin, Ian Allinson (Manager), Stuart Lochhead (Cpatain), Geoff Livingstone (Asst. Manager), Drew Roberts, Paul Ayling, Richard Fisher
Mascots Karen Sterry & Anthony Rhodes with the Hitchinbrooke Cup (left) and the Southern Counties Brian Hitchings Challenge Cup

BERKHAMSTED TOWN

CLUB OFFICIALS

Chairman: Danny Jennings

Secretary: David Stanley
17 Old Vicarage Gardens, Markyate,
St Albans, Herts. AL3 8PW.
Tel: 01582 840707

Press Officer: Bob Sear
Tel: 01442 864547 (H & B)

FOOTBALL MANAGEMENT TEAM
Manager: Steve Bateman
Coach: Mark Pearson
Physio: Bryan Hardy

FACT FILE
Formed: 1895
Nickname: Lilywhites
Sponsors: T.B.A.
Colours: White/black/black
Change Colours: Yellow/blue/blue
Midweek Matchday: Tuesday
Reserves' Lge: Suburban League Prem Div

Website: www.berkhamstedfc.co.uk

2001-02
Captain: Paul Lowe
Top scorer: Ben Smith 27
P.o.Y.: Graham Hall

GROUND Broadwater, Lower Kings Road, Berkhamsted, Herts HP4 2AA
Tel: 01442 862815

Directions: Adjacent to Berkhamsted station (Euston-Birmingham line). A41 toBerkhamsted town centre traffic lights, left into Lower Kings Road

Capacity: 2,500 Seats: 170 Cover: 350 Floodlights: Yes

Clubhouse: Open 7 days a week. Pool & darts - Big screen

Club Shop: Contact Doug Pearcey

PROGRAMME
Pages: 64 Price: £1
Editor:David Stanley
Local Press: Berkhamsted Herald, Berkhamsted Gazette
Local Radio: Chiltern Radio, Mix '96', Three Counties Radio

PREVIOUS **Leagues:** Herts Co. 1895-1922; Herts Co: 1921,Spartan 22-51, 66-75; Delphian 51-63; Athenian 63-66, 83-84; London Spartan 75-83
Grounds: Sunnyside Enclosure 1895-1919, Sports Ground 1919-83
Name: Bekhamsted Comrades 1919-22

CLUB RECORDS **Attendance:** 1,732 v Bedlington Terriers F.A.Vase Semi Final 2nd Leg 2001
Career appearances: Ray Jeffrey (612)
Victory: 14-0 **Defeat:** 2-12

BEST SEASON **FA Cup:** 3rd Qual Rd v Barnet 87-88, v Slough 91-92, v Chesham U. 92-93, v Burton Albion 2001-02
FA Vase: Finalists 2000-01
FA Trophy: 1st Rd v Kidderminster Harriers 97-98

HONOURS Herts Senior Cup 52-53; London Spartan Lge 79-80 (Div 2 26-27);Herts Charity Cup: 2001-02
Herts Charity Shield 50-51(jt) 73-74 79-80 84-85 90-91; Herts Senior County Lge Aubrey Cup 52-53; St Marys Cup(13); Apsley Senior Charity Cup (9); Southern Comb 84-85/F/lit Cup 84-85)

Players progressing: Frank Broome(Aston Villa & England), Maurice Cook (Fulham), Keith Ryan(Wycombe), Maurice Telling (Millwall)

Berkhamsted Town Football Club: Herts Charity Cup Winners 2001-2002. Photo:Malcolm Armstrong

EAST THURROCK UNITED

CLUB OFFICIALS

Chairman: Gary Snell
Secretary: Peter Lambert
30 Thames Cres., Corringham,
Essex, SS17 9DU
Tel: 01375 643418
Press Officer: Malcolm Harris

FOOTBALL MANAGEMENT TEAM
Manager: Andy McDonald
Assistant Manager.: Kevin Rolls
Physio: Richard Mainwaring

FACT FILE

Founded: 1969
Nickname: Rocks
Colours: Amber/black/black
Change: All Blue
Midweek Matchday: Tuesday
Reserves' Lge: Essex/Herts Border Comb.

2001-02
Leading Goalscorer: Rikki Finning 16
Player of the Year: Nick Dickson
Captain: T.B.A.

GROUND: Rookery Hill, Corringham, Essex
Tel: 01375 644166-club

Directions: A13 London-Southend, take 1014 at Stanford-le-Hope for two and a half miles - ground on left. Two miles from Stanford-le-Hope and Basildon BR stations

Capacity: 3,000   **Seats:** 160   **Cover:** 500   **Floodlights:** Yes
Clubhouse: Open all day seven days a week. Hot and cold snacks
Club Shop: No

PROGRAMME
36 pages £1.00
Editor: Tony Smith (01375 892855)
Local Press:
Thurrock Gazette/ Thurrock Recorder
Local Radio: BBC Essex

PREVIOUS   **Leagues:** Sth Essex Comb.; Gtr London; Metropolitan 72-75; London Spartan 75-79; Essex Snr 79-92
Grounds: Billet, Stanford-le-Hope 70-73 74-76; Grays Athletic 73-74; Tilbury FC 77-82; New Thames Club 82-84
Name: Corringham Social (pre-1969 Sunday side)

CLUB RECORDS   **Attendance:** 947 v Trevor Brooking XI, May 1987. Competitive: 845 v Bashley, FA Vase 1989
Goalscorer: Graham Stewart 102   **Appearances:** Glen Case 600+
Win: 7-0 v Coggeshall (H) 1984
Defeat: 0-9 v Eton Manor (A) 1982, both Essex Snr League
Transfer Fee Paid: £22,000 for Greg Berry (Leyton Orient)

BEST SEASON   **FA Cup:** 3rd Qual 93-94   **FA Vase:** 5th Rd 84-85

HONOURS: Metropolitan Lg Div 2 72-73, Essex Snr Lg R-up 88-89 (Lg Cup 88-89 91-92, Harry Fisher Mem. Tphy 83-84 90-91,
Sportsmanship Award 81-82 86-87 89-89), Essex SnrTphy R-up 91-92 95-96, Fred Budden Tphy R-up 89-90,
Essex & Herts Border Comb.89-90,01-02 (Lg Cup 89-90) , Isthmian League Div. Three 99-00

Players progressing to Football League: Greg Berry (Leyton Orient & Wimbledon)

Back row,left to right: Chris Marshall, Steve Carter, Tim Bird, Neil Cullis, Mick Dickson, Danny Dafter and Jamie Bowler.
Front row: Wayne Tomkins, Marc Wingrove, James Dwyer, Keith Wilson, Lee Carter, Eliot Caton and Paul Hume.**Photo:** Alan Coomes

GREAT WAKERING ROVERS

CLUB OFFICIALS
Chairman: Roy Kettridge
Vice-Chairman: Barry Beadle
President: Eddie Ellis
Secretary: Roger Sampson
37 Lee Lotts, Gt. Wakering,
Southend SS3 0HA
Tel: 01702 217812
Press Officer: Nobby Johnson
Tel: 01702 297840

FOOTBALL MANAGEMENT TEAM
Manager: Alan Hull
Physio: Clive Taylor

FACT FILE
Founded: 1919
Nickname: Rovers
Sponsors: I.M.S.
Colours: Green & white /green/green
Change Coours: All Red
Midweek Matchday: Tuesday
Reserves' Lge: Essex & Herts Border Comb

2000-01
Captain: Danny Scopes
P.o.Y.: John Heffer
Leading Goalscorers: Mark Hampshire (17)

GROUND: Borroughs Park, Little Wakering Hall Lane, Gt. Wakering, Southend SS3 OHQ
Tel: 01702 217812

Directions: 4a bus from Shoeburyness (BR), 4a or 4b from Southend - alight at British Legion in Gt Wakering alongside which runs Little Wakering Hall Lane. A127 past Southend signed Gt Wakering. In Gt Wakering, .5 mile past large
Total garage along High Street is Little Wakering Hall Lane, ground 250 yds along on left

Capacity: 2,500   **Cover:** 300   **Seats:** 150   **Floodlights:** Yes
Clubhouse: Open every eve., Sat 11-11, Sun 12-3 & 7.30-10.30.
Hot meals, snacks etc matchdays only   **Club Shop:** No

PREVIOUS   **Leagues:** Southend & Dist. 19-81, Southend All. 81-89, Essex I'mediate 89-92
Ground: Gt Wakering Rec

RECORDS   **Attendance:** 659 v Potters Bar FA Vase 5th Rd 7-2-98
Win (in Senior Football): 9-0 v Eton Manor 27/12/93
Defeat (in Senior Football): 1-7 v Bowers Utd, Essex Snr Lge 1-4-98

BEST SEASON   **FA Cup:** 2nd Qual 98-99
FA Vase: 5th Round 97-98, 01-02

HONOURS   Isthmian League div. 3 R-iup 99-00; Essex I'mediate Cup 91-92, Essex I'mediate Lg Div 2 91-92, Div 3 90-91, Lg Cup 91-92, Southend Charity Shld 90-91 91-92, Essex Snr Lg. 94-95, Lg Res. Sect. 94-95
(Wirral Programme Essex Sen. Lg. Award 92-93 94-95)

Players progressing: Les Stubbs (Southend, Chelsea) 1947, Jackie Bridge(Southend Utd) 1948, Kevin Maddocks (Maidstone Utd)

PROGRAMME
Pages: 24-32   Price: £1.00
Editor: Nobby Johnson (01702 468243)
Website: great wakeringroversfc.co.uk

Chairman Roy Kettridge makes the presentation to Neville Hickton on his 300th appearance for the club.

HARLOW TOWN

CLUB OFFICIALS

Chairman: **Jeff Bothwell**

President: **Ron Bruce**

Press Officer: **T.B.A.**

Secretary: **Graeme Auger**
58 Braziers Quay, South Street,Bishop's
Stortford, Herts (01279 465998)

FOOTBALL MANAGEMENT TEAM

Manager: John Kendall
Coach: Jeff Wood
Physio: T.B.A.

FACT FILE

Founded: 1879

Nickname: Hawks

Sponsors: BritSec Int. Ltd

Colours: Red & white/white/white

Change: White / Black/ Black

Midweek Matchday: Wednesday

Reserves' Lg: Essex & Herts Border Comb.

Website:www.harlowtown.co.uk

2001-02

Captain: David Gray

P.o.Y.: Tony McNally

Top Scorer: Martin Young 24

36 pages £1.00

Editor: Phil Tuson (01279 416743)

Local Press: Harlow Citizen, Harlow Star, Harlow Herald & Post

Local Radio: Essex Radio, BBC Essex, Ten 17

GROUND Harlow Sports Centre, Hammarskjold Rd, Harlow CM20 2JF Tel: 01279 445319
Email: jeff.bothwell@ britsec.co.uk

Directions: Near town centre, 10 mins walk from Harlow Town (BR) station

Capacity: 10,000   Cover: 500   Seats: 400   Floodlights: Yes

Club Shop: Yes

Clubhouse: Open daily 11-11 (10.30 Sundays). Hot & cold food available

PREVIOUS   **Leagues:** East Herts (pre-1932); Spartan 32-39 46-54; London 54-61; Delphian 61-63; Athenian 63-73; Isthmian 73-92; Inactive 92-93
Grounds: Marigolds 1919-22; Green Man Field 22-60

CLUB RECORDS   **A ttendance:** 9,723 v Leicester, FA Cup 3rd Rd replay 8/1/80
Goalscorer: Jeff Wood (45 in 88-89)   **Appearances:** Norman Gladwin 646 (1949-70)
Win: 12-0 v Hertford Ath. (H), E. Herts Lge 5/10/29   **Defeat:** 0-11 v Ware (A), Spartan Lge Div. One (East) 6/3/48

BEST SEASON   **FA Amateur Cup:** 2nd Rd 72-73   **FA Trophy:** 2nd Rd(2) 80-82   **FA Vase:** 3rd Rd 88-89
FA Cup: 4th Rd 79-80 (lost 3-4 at Watford). Also 1st Rd 80-81 81-82   League clubs defeated: Southend, Leicester 79-80

HONOURS   Isthmian Lg Div 1 78-79 (R-up 82-83, Div 2 Nth 88-89, Yth Cup 77-78), Ath'n LgDiv 1 71-72, E Angl. Cup 89-90, 01-02Knight F'lit Cup R-up 87-88, Essex Snr Cup 78-79, Essex F'lit Competition R-up 71-72, London Lg Chal. Cup 59-60, Spartan LgCup 52-53, Epping Hosp. Cup (3) 46-49, Essex & Herts Border Comb Cup 75-76, Fred Budden Trophy 88-89 89-90, Chelmsford Yth Lg 86-87 (Lg Cup 86-87 87-88)

Players progressing: Jeff Wood (Charlton 75), Neil Prosser (B'mouth 80)

Back row left to right: Nigel Tester (coach), Neil Moore, Marvin Samuel, Tony McNally, James Hasell, Glenn Southgate, Danny Cowley, Steve Blaney, Dave Cook, and John Kendall (Manager) **Front Row:** Micky Stevens (Physio), Marc Salmon, Justin Gentle, Chris Wilson, Liam Tremayne (Mascot), Martin Young, Soner Zumrutel, Nick Cowley and Ian Green (Coach)

HEMEL HEMPSTEAD TOWN

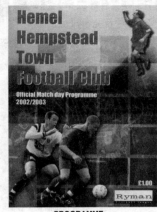

CLUB OFFICIALS

Chairman: David Boggins

President:

Vice President: Dave Lloyd

Secretary & Press Officer: T.B.A.

FOOTBALL MANAGEMENT TEAM
Manager: Gary Phillips
Asst Manager: Roy Butler
Physio: Zoey

FACT FILE

Founded: 1885

Nickname: Hemel

Sponsors: Barling

Colours: All red with white trim

Change colours: Green/white trim

Midweek Matches: Tuesday

Local Press: Hemel Gazette, Herald

Local Radio: Beds Radio, Chiltern,

Three Counties Radio

PROGRAMME
Pages: 48   Price: 80p
Editor/Press Off.: Paul Bullen

GROUND: Vauxhall Ground, Adeyfield Rd, Hemel Hempstead HP2 4HW
Tel: 01442 259777

Directions: Euston to Hemel Hempstead Station.
H2 or H3 bus to Windmill Rd., Longlands

Capacity: 3,000   Seats: 175   Cover: Yes   Floodlights: Yes

Clubhouse: Open 7-11pm weekdays, 12-11pm weekends & Bank Hols.
Tea bar open matchdays.   Tel: 01442 259777.

Club Shop: None

PREVIOUS **Leagues:** Spartan 22-52; Delphian 52-63; Athenian 63-77
Names: Apsley 1885-1947; Hemel Hempstead Town (merged with Hemel Hempstead Utd in1947)
Grounds: Crabtree Lane (til '71)

CLUB RECORDS **Attendance:** 2,000 v Watford 1985 (at Crabtree Lane: 3,500 v Tooting, FA AmtrCup 1st Rd 1962)
Goalscorer: Dai Price   **Appearances:** John Wallace, 1012

BEST SEASON **FA Cup:** Never past Qualifying Rounds
FA Vase: 4th Rd 98-99 v Taunton Town

HONOURS Ryman Lge Div 3 98-99; Herts Snr Cup 05-06 07-08 08-09 25-26 61-62 65-66 91-92,
Herts Charity Cup/Shield 25-26 34-35 51-52 63-64 76-77 83-84 (R-up 90-91), Spartan Lg 33-34,
Herts Intermediate Cup 54-55 65-66 83-84, West Herts St Mary Cup 70-71 75-76 82-83 85-86 90-91 91-92 93-94,
Athenian Lg Div 1 R-up 64-65 (Res Cup 65-66), Delphian Lg (res) 54-55 (Res Cup 54-55 61-62)

L-R - Back Row: Chris Walton (coach), Lee Graves, Rene Street, Darren Grieves, Robbie Simpson, Danny Turner, Mat Rawdon, Fergus Moore, Paul Lamb, Darren Bonfield, James Hannington, Daniel West, Gary Fitzgerald, Steve Baker, Marvyn Watson, John Simon White. **Front Row:** Joe Narty, Marcelle Bruce, Nick Jackson, Bobby Highton, Danny Adams, Vinnie Ryan (coach), Tony Kelly (manager), Bryan Hammett, Vinnie Somers, Chris Watters, Richard McDonagh

HERTFORD TOWN

CLUB OFFICIALS

President: John Hedley

Chairman: David Thomas
01992 500123 (H) 07777 556 6771 (M)

Secretary & Press Officer: Stephen Hedley
29 Upper field Road,Wewyn Garden City,
Herts AL7 3LP
Tel: 01707 333712

FACT FILE

Founded: 1908
Nickname: The Blues
Sponsors: Simply Health
Colours: Blue & yellow stripes/blue/blue
Change colours: White & Blue
Midweek Matches: Tuesday
Reserves' Lge: Essex & Herts Border Comb

FOOTBALL MANAGEMENT TEAM
Manager: Andy Prutton
Physio: Ian Priest

2001-02
Captain: David Crate
P.o.Y. & Top Scorer: Kevin Cooper

GROUND:

Hertingfordbury Park, West Street, Hertford
Tel: 01992 583716

Directions: Rail to Hertford Nth (from Moorgate) or Hertford East (LiverpoolStr.);
both 15 mins walk. Green Line bus to town centre then 10 mins walk.
By road; off bypass heading east, turn off at Ford garage

Capacity: 6,500   Seats: 200   Cover: 1,500   Floodlights: Yes

PROGRAMME
Pages: 28   Price: 50p
Editor: Matt Darrington (01992 447927)
Local Newspapers: Hertfordshire Mercury

Club Shop: Souvenirs   **Clubhouse:** Yes

PREVIOUS **Leagues:** Herts Co.; Spartan 21-47 48-59; Delphian 59-63; Athenian 63-72; Eastern Co's 72-73
Names: None   **Grounds:** None

BEST SEASON **FA Cup:** 4th Qual. Rd. 73-74 (lost 1-2 at Hillingdon Borough)

CLUB RECORDS **Gate:** 5,000 v Kingstonian, F.A. Amateur Cup 2nd Rd 55-56
Appearances: Robbie Burns

HONOURS Herts Char. Cup 72-73, 89-90, Herts Snr Cup 66-67, Hertford Char.Shd 19-20 20-21 35-36 49-50 55-56 59-60,
Eastern Co's Lg Cup 72-73, East Anglian Cup 62-63 69-70, Southern Co's Comb. F-lit Cup 94-95,
Mithras Cup SF 85-86, Ryman Div 3 R-up 97-98

Players progressing to Football League: G Mazzon (Aldershot), J.Hooker (Brentford)

Back row,left to right: Jamie Nicholson, Lee Munt, Matt Barnaby, Chris Fitkin, Glenn Draper and Neil Jordan. **Front row:** Kevin
Cooper, Jon Moore, Leo Turner, Adam Warner and Paul Jordan.   Photo: Arthur Evans.

HORNCHURCH

CLUB OFFICIALS
Chairman: Tony Wallace

Vice Chairman: Brian Davie

Secretary: Brian Eagling
20 Tindall Close, Harold Wood
Esssex RM3 0PB
Tel: 01708 373027

FOOTBALL MANAGEMENT TEAM
Manager: Mick Marsden
Physio: D Edkins

FACT FILE
Founded: 1923
Nickname: Urchins
Sponsors: Premier Snacks
Colours: Red & white/red/red
Change Colours: Yellow/blue
Midweek Matches: Tuesday
Reserve Lge: Essex & Herts Border Comb

2001-02
Leading goalscorer: Chris Wolff 31
Captain: Jon Bates
P.o.Y.: Kevin Jopson

HORNCHURCH
FOOTBALL CLUB
The Stadium, Bridge Avenue, Upminster, Essex RM14 2LX

BRYCO **BRYCO**

Founded 1923
http://www.urchins.org

Ryman
football league

GROUND: The Stadium, Bridge Avenue, Upminster, Essex RM14 2LX
Tel: 01708 220080 Email: enquiries@urchins.org
Website: www.urchins.org

Directions: Fenchurch Street to Upminster (BR) then 10 mins walk.
Or tube to Upminster Bridge (LT), right outside station, 2nd right into Bridge Ave. ground 150yds on right.
By road Bridge Avenue is off A124 between Hornchurch and Upminster.
Buses 248, 348, 370, 373 from Romford or Upminster BR stations

Capacity: 3,000 Seats: 300 Cover: 350 Floodlights: Yes Club Shop: Yes,

Clubhouse: Mon-Fri 7.30-11, Sat 12-11, Sun 12-3. Cafeteria open matchdays

Club Shop: Yes, selling programmes, handbooks, scarves, hats, souvenirs etc.
Contact : Ron Quantock (01708 455529)

PROGRAMME
16-20 pages with admission
Editor: Brian Davie 01708 445107

Local Press: Romford Recorder
Local Radio: Essex Radio, Active FM

PREVIOUS: **Leagues:** Romford 25-38; Spartan 38-52; Delphian 52-59; Athenian 59-75
Names: Hornchurch & Upminster (Upminster FC pre-1950s) merged with Upminster Wanderers in 1961
Ground: Upminster Rec

RECORDS: **Attendance:** 3,000 v Chelmsford, FA Cup 66-67

BEST SEASON: **FA Cup:** 4th Qual Rd 66-67   **F.A. Vase:** 5th Rd 74-75

HONOURS: Athenian Lg 66-67, Romford Lg(2), Essex Snr Trophy R-up 86-87, Essex Jnr Cup, Essex Thameside Tphy 84-85, Isthmian Yth Cup, Carlsberg Trophy R-up 93-94, Ryman Lg Div3 R-up.2001-02

Players progressing to Football League: D Armstrong (Millwall), R Lee(Charlton, Newcastle U & England), Nicky Bissett (Brighton), Jesse Roast (Maidstone United), Nicky Hammond (Swindon Town)

Back row l-r: Mick Marsden (manager), Kevin Marsden, Ian Bower, Nick McDonald, Chris Wolff, Paul Wood, Oliver Woodman, Barrie Fox, Kevin Jopson, Nathan Elder, Lee Pyne, Nick Lowery
Front row: Derek Edkins (physio), Grant Apicella, Glen Dyson, Jon Bates, Craig Cripps, Joe Tungate, Steve Taylor

LEYTON PENNANT

LEYTON PENNANT F.C.

SEASON 2002-3

CLUB OFFICIALS

Chairman: Dave Salmon

Vice-Chairman: Dave Crabb

President: George Cross

Secretary / Press Officer: Andy Perkins
4 Chestnut Drive,Wanstead, London E11 2TA
Tel: 02085304551

FOOTBALL MANAGEMENT TEAM

Team Manager Colin Richards

Asst.Man : Marc Mennell Physio: Lee Elliot

FACT FILE

Formed: 1868

Nickname: Lilywhites

Sponsors: Kay Sports

Colours: White/navy/navy

Change colours: All Navy Blue

Midweek home matchday: Tuesday

Reserves' Lge: Essex & Herts Border Comb

2001-02

Captain: Simon Tickner

P.o.Y.: Simon Tickner

Top Scorer: Jermaine Hughes 18

£1

Ryman

Pages: 32   Price: £1
Editor: Tony Hampford

Local Press: Waltham Forest Guardian,
Hackney Gazette
Local Radio: LBC
Website: www.leyton-pennant.net

GROUND: Wadham Lodge Sports Ground,Kitchener Road, Walthamstowe,London E17
Tel: 020 8527 2444 **Email:** andyperkins@btinternet.com
Directions: Take the North Circular Road to The Crooked Billet,then turn right into Chingford
Road and into Brookscroft Road , ground is in Kitchener Road first on left .Walthamstowe
Central (Victoria Line tube) is one mile away then buses W21 or 256
Capacity: 2,000   Cover: 600   Seats: 200   Floodlights: Yes
Clubhouse: Open 11-11 Mon-Sat 12-3 & 7-10-30 Sun. Tel: 0208 527 2444
No hot food but snacks available on match days from tea bar.
Club Shop: Sells progs, pennants, scarves, badges etc. Contact Ian Ansell c/o club

PREVIOUS   **Leagues:** Leyton * Dist Alliance, South Essex,Southern 05-11,London 20-26 Athenian 27-82 Spartan (Walthamstowe Pennant)
Name: Leyton FC, Leyton Wingate (75-92), Walthamstow Pennant (64-92)
Grounds: Brisbane Rd (Home of Leyton Orient), Hare & Hounds Leabridge Rd
CLUB RECORDS   **Attendance:** 676 v Aldershot, Isthmian Lge 10/2/96
100,000, Leyton v Walth'stow Ave., FA Am Cup final, Wembley, April 26th 1952)
Win: 10-2 v Horsham 1982   **Career goalscorer:** Steve Lane 118
Defeat: 1-11 v Barnet 1946   **Career appearances:** Steve Hamberger 387
Transfer Fee Paid: £200 for Dwight Marshall (Hampton) **Received:** £6,000 for T Williams (Redbridge Forest)
BEST SEASON   **FA Amateur Cup:** Winners 26-27 27-28, R-up x6   **FA Vase:** Sixth Rd 83-84
FA Trophy: 3rd Rd 86-87   **FA Cup:** 3rd Rd 09-10   League clubs defeated: None
HONOURS   Isthmian Lg Div 1 R-up 86-87 (Div 2 North 84-85); Essex Snr Tphy R-up 84-85; National Floodlight Cup 84-85;
London Sen. Cup 03-04 (R-up 33-34 37-38 45-46); London Charity Cup 34-35 36-37 R-up (4) London 23-24 24-25 25-26 (R-up 26-27),
Lg Cup 56-57; Athenian Lg 28-29 65-66 66-67 76-77 81-82 ,R-up (3), Div 2 Cup R-up 69-70; London Chall. Cup R-up 09-10 27-28 95-96;
East Anglian Cup R-up 45-46 72-73; Essex Thameside Trophy 64-65 66-67 81-2 (R-up 63-64); Leyton & Dist. All 1892-93 94-95;
Eastern F'lit Comp 97-98, 99-00

Players progressing: C Buchan (Sunderland 10), Casey (Chelsea 52), K Facey (Orient 52), M Costello (Aldershot 56), D Clark (Orient 61),
D Marshall (Luton)

MARLOW

CLUB OFFICIALS
Chairman: Terry Staines

Secretary: Paul Burdell,
69 Wycombe Rd., Marlow.
Tel: 01628 890540

Press Off./Comm. Man.: Terry Staines

FOOTBALL MANAGEMENT TEAM
Manager: Derek Sweetman
Coach: Ian Parsons
Physio: Mark Skoyles

FACT FILE
Formed: 1870
Nickname: The Blues
Sponsors: North West Estates
Colours: Royal, white trim/royal/royal
Change colours: White & black
Midweek matchday: Tuesday
Reserves' League: Suburban Premier
2001-02
Captain: james Pritchard
P.o.Y.: John Beale
Top scorer:James Pritchard 24

PROGRAMME
Pages: 40   Price: £1
Editor: Terry Staines
Local Press: Bucks Free Press,
Maidenhead Advertiser, Evening Post
Local Radio: Eleven 70, Radio 210,
Thames Valley Radio

GROUND: Alfred Davis Memorial Ground, Oak Tree Road, Marlow SL7 3ED
Tel: 01628 483970   Information Line (normal call rates): 01932 710215

Directions: A404 to Marlow (from M4 or M40), then A4155 towards town centre.
Turn right into Maple Rise (by ESSO garage), ground in road opposite
(Oak Tree Rd).
1/2 mile from Marlow (BR). 1/4 mile from Chapel Street bus stops

Capacity: 3,000   Cover: 600   Seats: 250   Floodlights: Yes

Clubhouse: Open matchdays & most evenings. Snack bar open matchdays

PREVIOUS: **Leagues:** Reading & Dist.; Spartan 1908-10 28-65; Great Western Suburban;Athenian 65-84
Name: Great Marlow   **Grounds:** Crown Ground 1870-1919); Star Meadow 19-24

CLUB RECORDS: **Attendance:** 3,000 v Oxford United, FA Cup 1st Rd 1994.
(Ground - 8,000 SloughT. v Wycombe W., Berks & Bucks Snr Cup Final, 1972)
Goalscorer: Kevin Stone 31
Appearances: Mick McKeown 500+
Fees - Paid: £5,000 for Richard Evans (Sutton Utd. 94)
Received: £8,000 for David Lay from Slought Town 94

BEST SEASON: **FA Cup:** Semi-Finals 1882;   3rd Rd 94-95 (0-2 v Swindon), 92-93 (1-5 v Tottenham);
1st Rd - 19 times -1871-85 86-88 92-93 1991-92 94-95
FA Trophy: 1st Rd 1987-88, 91-92
FA Vase: 5th Rd replay 74-75, 5th Rd 00-01

HONOURS: Isthmian Lg Div 1 87-88, Div 2 South R-up 86-87, Lg Cup 92-93, Associate Members Trophy: 2000-01;
SpartanLg Div 1 37-38 (Div 2 West 29-30); Berks & Bucks Sen Cup (11)

Players progressing: Leo Markham (Watford 1972), NaseemBashir (Reading)

NORTHWOOD

CLUB OFFICIALS

Secretary: Steve Williams, 35 Evelyn Drive
Hatch End, Pinner, Middx HA5 4RL
Tel: 020 8428 1533(H) 020 8421 5923 (F)
Chairman: Andy Johnson
Vice Chairman: Martin Ellis
President: Lothar Hahn
Press Off: M Russell (01923 827690)

FOOTBALL MANAGEMENT TEAM
Manager: Tony Choules
Coaches:Gary Farrell & John Toogood
Physio: George Price

FACT FILE
Founded: 1899
Nickname: Woods
Sponsors: IFS Freight Forwarding
Colours: All red
Change colours: All yellow
Midweek Matches: Tuesday
Reserve League: Suburban

2001-02
Captain: Chris Gell
P.o.Y: Dave Sargent
Top Scorer: Lawrence Yaku 39

Pages: 60   Price:£1.00
Editor: A Evans (020 8566 2880)
Local Press: Ruislip & Northwood Gazette,
Watford Observer

GROUNDNorthwood Park, Chestnut Avenue, Northwood (01923 827148)
Email Address: evansa@ealing, gov,uk   **Club Website:** www.northwoodfc.com
Directions: A404 (Pinner-Rickmansworth) - Chestnut Ave. on left by large grey iron rail way bridge. Third of a mile from Northwood Hills station (Metropolitan Line) - turn right out of station to r'bout, left into Pinner Road, left into Chestnut Avenue after 300yds. Buses 282 and H11 to Northwood Hills   **Club Shop:** No
Capacity: 2,580   Seats: 200   Cover: 500   Floodlights: Yes
Clubhouse: Weekends & most eves from 6pm. Bar. Hot and cold food. Pool, juke-box

HONOURS: Isthmian Lg Associate Members Cup 92-93,99-00; London Spartan Lg 91-92 (R-up 89-90), Lg Cup 89-90 91-92;Hellenic Lg Div 1 78-79 (Prem Div Cup R-up 81-82); Middx Lg 77-78 (R-up 72-73 76-77), Div 1 R-up 71-72, Challenge Cup 74-75 76-77 77-78; Middx Snr Charity Cup R-up 93-94; Middx Snr Cup SF 91-92 92-93 98-99; R-up 99-00 Jnr Cup 46-47 47-48 48-49; Harrow & Wembley Lg (9); Middlesex Premier Cup 94-95 Finallists 99-00, 01-02.Isthmian Div 2 R-up 99-00, Isthmian League Cup Winners 2001-02

PREVIOUS: **Leagues:** Harrow & Wembley 32-69; Middlesex 69-78; Hellenic 79-84; London Spartan 84-92
                         Names: Northwood Town   **Grounds:** None

CLUB RECORDS: **Attendance:** 1,642 v Chelsea Friendly July 1997
                         Goal Scorerin Season: Lawrence Yaku 61 (99-00) **Career Appearances:** Chris Gell
                         Win: 15-0 v Dateline (H) Middlesex Inter Cup 1973   **Defeat:** 0-8 v Bedfont (Middlesex Lg.1975)

BEST SEASON: **FA Cup:** 4th Qual Rd 00-01   **F.A.Trophy:** 3rd Rd 00-01   **FA Vase:** Quarter Final 96-97

Players progressing: Gavin Maguire, Derek Payne (Barnet), Warren Patmore (Cambridge United)

L-R - Back row: Christian Matcalfe, Dave Sargent, Gary Williams, Mark Buchanan, PaulRiordan, Andy Felton, Danny Butler, Andy Cook and Paul Watkins. **Front row:** Kieran Knight, Wayne Carter, Dave Nolan, Gavin Hart, Ryan Ashe, Chris Gell and Lawrence Yaku.
Photo: Paul Evans.

OXFORD CITY

CLUB OFFICIALS

Chairman: **M Woodley**
President: T.B.A.
Vice Chairman: **B.Cox**
Press Officer/Secretary: **John Shepperd**
20 Howe Close, Wheatley, Oxford OX33 1SS
Tel: 01865 872181 (& Fax)

FOOTBALL MANAGEMENT TEAM

Manager: Paul Lee
Asst Manager:
Physio: C. Perkins

FACT FILE

Formed: 1882
Nickname: City
Sponsors: S.M.C.
Colours: Blue & white hoops/white/white
Change colours: yellow,black,black
Midweek Matchday: Tuesday
Reserves Lge: Suburban
Website: oxfordcityfc.co.uk

2000-01
Captain: Julian Dark
Top Scorer: John Mitchell 18
P.o.Y.: Stuart Nelson

GROUND Court Place Farm, Marsh Lane, Marston, Oxford. OX3 0NQ.
Tel: 01865 744493.**Directions:** From London M40/A40, ring-road to North, take 1st slip road,
follow signs to John Radcliffe hospital and Court Place Farm Stadium, ground on left after
leaving flyover. From the north same ring-road.
Capacity: 3,000 Seats: 300 Cover: 400 Floodlights: Yes
Clubhouse: Open matchdays, most refreshments available
Club Shop: Yes, open matchdays, selling souvenirs. Contact Paul Cotterell

Pages: 60 Price: £1
Editor: Colin Taylor
Local Press: Oxford Mail
Local Radio: Radio Oxford FM, Fox FM

PREVIOUS **Leagues:** Isthmian 07-88; South Midlands 90-93
Grounds: The White House 1882-1988; Cuttleslowe Pk 90-91; Pressed Steel,Romanway 91-93

CLUB RECORDS **Attendance:** 9,500 v Leytonstone, FA Amateur Cup 50
Win: 9-0 v Harlow Town, Isthmian League 9/10/76
Defeat: 0-8 v Wycombe Wanderers, Isthmian League - date unknown
Scorer: John Woodley **Appearances:** John Woodley
Fee Paid: £3,000 for S Adams (Woking) **Fee Received:** £17,500 for Howard Forinton (Yeovil T. 1.97)

BEST SEASON **FA Amateur Cup:** Winners 05-06 Runners-up 02-03 12-13 **FA Vase:** Runners-up 94-95
FA Cup: Second Round 69-70, 1-5 v Swansea City (H) **FA Trophy:** 1st Rd Prop 96 v Merthyr Tydfil

HONOURS FA Amateur Cup 05-06 (R-up 02-03 12-13); F.A.Vase R-up 94-95; Isthmian Lg R-up 34-35 45-46, Div 1 95-96 R-up 77-78
South MidlandsLg 92-93; Oxon Senior Cup - 28 times
Players progressing: A Blakeman (Brentford 46), C Holton (Arsenal 50), K Savin (Derby 50), R Adams (Blackpool 48), A Jeffries (Brentford 49),
P James (Luton 49), D Gordon/E Wilcox (WBA 47/48), V Mobley (Sheffield Wed 63), J Varney (Hull 50), P Lee (Hereford 73),
H Poole (Port Vale 55), G Parker (Luton 81), M Keown (Arsenal 84), D Meeson (Wolves 52)

Back row. left to right: Oliver Davies (Assistant Physio), Mickey Lewis (Player Coach),John Mitchell, Mark Druce, Steve Atkins, Paul
Woodhouse, Chris Brain, Phil Wilson, Andy Smith, Matt Hayward, Nick McCrea, Lewis Craker, Chris Perkins (Physio) and Paul Lee
(Manager) **Front row:** Danny Morgan, Kelvin McIntosh, Jemaine Ferreira, Jorden Holder, Julian Dark, Shaun Wimble, Danny Wise
and Matty Whitehead. **Ballboys:** Tom Whitehead and Tom Freeman.

SLOUGH TOWN

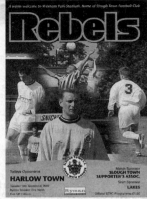

CLUB OFFICIALS
Chairman: Martin Deaner
Secretary / Press Off.: Roy Merryweather
Tel: 01753 554833 (Ground)
01735 534033(W)
01189 722871(H)
01753 533949 (Fax)

FOOTBALL MANAGEMENT TEAM
Manager: Steve Browne
Coach: Steve Stott
Physio: Kevin McGoldrick

FACT FILE
Formed: 1890
Nickname: The Rebels
Sponsor:Lakes Video-HiFi of Slough
Colours: Amber/navy blue/amber
Change colours: All white
Midweek home matchday: Tuesdays
Website: www.sloughtownfc.net

2001-02
Captain: Steve Daly
P.o.Y.: Velli Hakki
Top Scorer: Neville Roach

GROUND: Wexham Park Stadium, Wexham Road, Slough, Berkshire. SL2 5QR.
Tel: 01753 554833 Fax: 01753 533949

Directions: From North : M25 J16 East London M40 J1 - South A412 through Iver Heath to George Green. 2nd set lights turn right by George PH, George Green.Church Lane 1 mile to end, then small roundabout, turn left, ground 1/4 mile onright
Capacity: 5,000   Cover: 1,890   Seats: 450   Floodlights: Yes
Clubhouse: Lounge bar open weekdays 7pm-11pm, weekends, lunchtimes, evenings.
Banqueting hall for all types of functions
Club Shop: Contact: Graham Gowland 01252 873620

Pages: 36 Price: £1.50
Editor: John Tebbit
Local Press: Slough Observer Slough Express
Local Radio: Thames Valley FM, Star FM Radio Berkshire

PREVIOUS   **Leagues:** Southern Alliance 1892-93; Berks & Bucks 1901-05; Gt Western Suburban1906-19; Spartan 1920-39; Herts & Middx 1940-45; Corinthian 1946-63; Athenian1963-73; Isthmian 1973-90, 94-95; Alliance Prem. (GMVC) 90-94
Grounds: Dolphin Playing Fields & Stadium, Chalvey Rd Sports Grd, YorkRd Maidenhead 1920, Centre Sports Ground 36-42

CLUB RECORDS **Attendance:** 8,000 - Schoolboys u15 Final Slough v Liverpool - 1976
Win: 17-0 v Railway Clearing House - 1921-22   **Defeat:** 1-11 v Chesham Town 1909/10
Transfer fee paid: £18,000 for Colin Fielder from Farnborough - 1991   **Career appearances:** Terry Reardon 458 - 64/81
Received: £22,000 from Wycombe Wanderers for Steve Thompson   **Career goalscorer:** E.J.C. Tory Norris 84 - 25/26

BEST SEASON   **FA Cup:** 2nd Round Proper, 79-80 (Yeovil T), 82-83 (Bishop's Stortford), 85-86 (Leyton O.), 86-87 (Swansea C.).
League clubs defeated: Millwall, 1-0 (H) Jan. 1983
FA Trophy: Semi-Final 1976-77, 2-6(agg) v Dagenham; 97-98, 1-2(agg) v Southport

HONOURS: FA Amateur Cup R-up 72-73; Great Western Suburban League R-up 19-20: Spartan League R-up 20-21 21-22 31-32 32-33 38-39; Herts & Middx League R-up 43-44; Corinthian League 50-51 (R-up 45-46 46-47 57-58); Athenian League 67-68 71-72 72-73 (R-up 68-69),LgCup 71-2 72-3 Div 1 64-65, Memorial Shield 64-65 71-72 72-73); Isthmian League 80-81 89-90 R-up 94-95, (Div 2 R-up 73-74),Lg Cup 75-76 80-81 R-up 94-95 Lge Shield 89-90 ; Berks & Bucks Sen Cup (10) 02-03 19-20 23-24 26-27 35-36 54-55 70-72 76-77 80-81

THAME UNITED

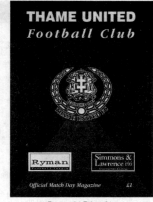

THAME UNITED
Football Club

CLUB OFFICIALS

Chairman: **Jim Tite**

Vice Chairman: **Mike Dyer**

Secretary: **Sally Hunt**
c/o Thame United.

FOOTBALL MANAGEMENT TEAM

Manager: Andy Sinott
Assistant Manager: Mark West

FACT FILE

Founded: 1883
Sponsors:T.B.A.
Nickname: United
Colours: Red & blacks/black/red & black.
Change colours: Green & white
Midweek Matchday: Tuesday
Reserves' League: Suburban
2001-2002
Top Scorer: Wayne Cort
P.o.Y.:Andy Williams
Captain: Martin Brown

Official Match Day Magazine £1

Pages: 24 Price: £1
Editor: Sally Turner (c/o Club)
Local Press: Oxford Mail, Thame Gazette,
Bucks Free Press
Local Radio: Radio Oxford, Fox FM, Mix 96

GROUND: Windmill Road, Thame, Oxon OX9 2DR (01844 213017)
Club Website: www.thameunitedfc.co.uk

Directions: Into Nelson Street from Market Square. 3 miles from Haddenham &Thame Parkway (BR). Nearest bus stop at Town Hall (half mile away)

Capacity: 3,600   Seats: 284   Cover: 850   Floodlights: Yes

Clubhouse: Open every evening and weekend lunch times   **Club Shop:** No - Banqueting facilities for 200 (weddings, dinners, dances etc)

PREVIOUS **Leagues:** Oxon Senior; Hellenic 1959-87; South Midlands 1987-91
Name: Thame FC   **Ground:** None

CLUB RECORDS **Attendance:** 1,035 v Aldershot, Isthmian Div 2 4/4/94
Win:11-3 v Barton Rovers 16/09/01   **Defeat:** 2-11 v Hungerford, FA Cup Prelim. Rd 1984
Career Goalscorer: Not known   **Career Appearances:** Steve Mayhew
Transfer Fee received: **Fee paid:**

BEST SEASON **FA Cup:** Third Qualifying Round 91-92, 0-4 v Salisbury
FA Vase: Semi Final 1998/99

HONOURS Isthmian Lg Div 2 94-95, Div 2 R-up 98-99 Div 3 R-up 92-93; Hellenic Lg 61-62 69-70, Premier Div Cup (4);
Sth Mids Lg 90-91; Oxon Snr Cup 1894-95 05-06 08-09 09-10 75-76 80-81 92-93;00-01,01-02.
Oxon Interm Cup 76-77 78-79 91-92,99-00; Oxon Charity Cup
Players progressing to the Football League: None

TILBURY

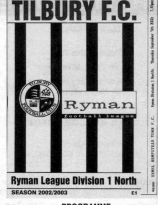

TILBURY F.C.

Ryman League Division 1 North
SEASON 2002/2003   £1

CLUB OFFICIALS
Chairman: Robin Nash
Vice Chairman: Daniel Nash
President: T.B.A.
Secretary / Press Officer: Lloyd Brown
52 Lionel Oxley House, New Road,
Grays, Essex RM176PP
Tel: 01375 409938 (H)
0776 232 6519 (M)

FOOTBALL MANAGEMENT TEAM
Manager: Bill McMeekin
Physio: Steve Bell

FACT FILE
Founded: 1900
Nickname: Dockers
Colours: Black& white stripes,black,black
Change: Red & white stripes,white,red
Midweek Matches: Tuesday
Reserves' Lge: Essex & Herts Border Comb.

2001-02
Captain: Craig Dennis
P.O.Y.: Kevin Mully
Top Scorer: Jean-Marie Okita

PROGRAMME
36 Pages   Price: £1.00
Editor: Lloyd Brown

Local Press: Thurrock Gazette, Thurrock Recorder
Local Radio: Essex Radio, BBC Essex

GROUND:	Chadfields, St Chad's Rd, Tilbury, Essex RM18 8NL
	Tel: 01375 843093
Directions:	BR from Fenchurch Street to Tilbury Town then one mile walk.
By road:	M25 (jct 30 or 31) - A13 Southend bound, Tilbury Docks turn off after 4 miles, Chadwell St Mary turn off (left) after another 1.5 miles, right after 400 metres, rt at r'bout (signed Tilbury), right into St Chad's Rd after .5 mile, 1st rt into Chadfields for ground.
Capacity:	4,000 Seats: 350 Floodlights: Yes **Club Shop:** No
Clubhouse:	Open evening, all day Fri. & Sat. and Sun. lunchtimes. Hot &cold food

PREVIOUS   **Leagues:** Grays & Dist.& Sth Essex (simultaneously); Kent 27-31; London 31-39 46-50 57-62;
Sth Essex Comb. (war-time); Corinthian 50-57; Delphian 62-63; Athenian 63-73
Grounds: Green & Silley Weir Ground 1900-11; Orient Field 19-38   **Names:** None

RECORDS   **Attendance:** 5,500 v Gorleston, FA Cup 4th Q Rd 19/11/49
Goalscorer: Ross Livermore 282 (in 305 games, 1958-66)   **Appearances:** Nicky Smith 424 (1975-85)
Fee received: £2,000, Tony Macklin to Grays A. 1990 & for Steve Conner to Dartford, 1985
Win: 17-0 v No.9 Coy Royal Artillery (H), South Essex Lg 4/10/02.
In Senior Football; 13-2 v Chalfont National (A), London Lg 28/4/92
Defeat: 1-10 - v Maidstone U. (A), Corinthian Lge 4.9.62 & v Met. Police (A), Isthmian Lg. 6.5.95

BEST SEASON   **FA Cup:** 3rd Rd 77-78, 0-4 v Stoke City (A)
FA Amateur Cup: Quarter Final v Wimbledon 46-7
FA Vase: Round 4 v Cowes Sports (a) 99-00

HONOURS: Isthmian Lg Div 1 75-76, (Div 1 Cup 74-75), Div 3 Prom.: 91-92, 99-00); Athenian Lg 68-69 (Div 2 62-63);
London Lg 58-59 59-60 60-61 61-62, Lg Cup 58-59 60-61 61-62, R-up (3); DelphianLg 67-68 (Div 2 62-63);
Essex Snr Cup 60-61 63-64 72-73 74-75 (R-up 46-47 47-48 69-70 71-72 78-79);
Players progressing to Football League: L Le May, T Scannell, T Oakley, JEvans

L-R - Back Row: Lloyd Brown (Sec.), Kevin Stubbs. John Ray, Mark Hardingham, Jean-Marie Okita, Scott Larkin, Kevin Mully.
Centre: Bill McMeekin (manager), Kitman, Lee Mpensah, Danny Whybrow.
Front: Ricky Downs, Paul Talbot, Jason White, Steve Jones.

UXBRIDGE

CLUB OFFICIALS
Chairman: Alan Holloway
President: Alan Odell
Secretary: Mick Burrell,39 Newton Road,New Denham,Uxbridge,Middx. UB9 4BE Tel No: 07889 442562 (M)
Match Sec: Mick Burrell Tel: 01895 443094
Match Sec Res: PeterGranville 01595 233208
Commercial Manager: Derek Marshall
Press Officer: Richard Russell
Youth Team Sec: David Gill 0208 581 6517

FACT FILE
Formed: 1871
Nickname: The Reds
Sponsor:
Colours: Red/white/red
Change: Yellow & Black
Midweek matchday: Tuesday
Reserves' League: Suburban (North Div)
2001-02
Captain: Gavin Bamford
Ps.o.Y.: Stuart Bamford & Kevin Cleary
Top Scorer: Lee Tunnell 21

FOOTBALL MANAGEMENT TEAM
Manager: George Talbot Ass. Manager: Sean Dawson
Coach: Mark Gill   Physios:Ian Doubleday & Paul Donnell
Res Manager: Phil Granville   Youth Manager: Robert Frape

GROUND Honeycroft, Horton Road, West Drayton, Middx UB7 8HX Tel: 01895 443557
Directions: From West Drayton (BR) turn right then 1st right (Horton Road).Ground 1 mile on left. From Uxbridge (LT) take 222 or U3 bus to West Draytonstation, then follow as above. By road, ground 1 mile north of M4 jct 4 takingroad to Uxbridge and leaving by first junction and turning left into Horton Rd- ground 500yds on right
Capacity: 3,770   Cover: 760   Seats: 339   Floodlights: Yes
Clubhouse: Open every evening and weekend/bank holiday lunchtimes. (01895 443557)
Hot & cold snacks available on matchdays
Large clubhouse with bar and function room availablefor hire.

Pages: 44 Price: £1.00
Editor: Richard Russell

Local Press: Uxbridge Gazette & Leader, Uxbridge Recorder
Local Radio: Capital, G L R, Star FM

PREVIOUS **Leagues:** Southern 1894-99; Gt Western Suburban 1906-19, 20-23; Athenian 1919-20, 24-37, 63-82; Spartan 37-38; London 38-46; Gt Western Comb. 39-45;Corinthian 46-63
Name: Uxbridge Town 23-45   **Grounds:** RAF Stadium 23-48, Cleveland Rd 48-78
CLUB RECORDS **Attendance:** 1,000 v Arsenal, opening of floodlights 1981
Career Scorer: Phil Duff, 153   **Career Appearances:** Roger Nicholls, 1054
BEST SEASON **FA Trophy:** 2nd Rd.1998-99, 99-00, 00-01   **FA Vase:** 4th Rd 83-84
FA Cup: 2nd Rd 1873-74. Also 1st Rd 1883-84 84-85 85-86   **FA Amateur Cup:** Runners-up 1897-98
HONOURS FA Amateur Cup R-up 1897-98; London Chall. Cup 93-94 96-97 98-99, R-up 97-98; IsthLge Div 2 S. R-up 84-85; Athenian Lge Cup R-up 81-82, Res. Sect. 69-70, Res. Cup R-up 68-69; Corinthian Lge 59-60 (R-up 48-49), Lge Mem. Shield 50-51 52-53; Middx Sen.Cup 1893-94 95-96 1950-51, 2000-01 R-up 97-98; Middx Sen. Charity Cup 07-08 12-13 35-36 81-82 (R-up 69-70 82-83 85-86); Middx PremCup 95-96 (R-up 2000-01; Allied Counties Yth Lge [East] 92-93 (Lge Cup R-up 86-87), Lge Shield 88-89 92-93, R-up 97-98; AC Delco Cup R-up 85-86; Suburban Lge North Div 95-96 97-98, R-up 96-97; Middx Sen Yth Cup 96-97
Players progressing: William Hill (QPR 51), Lee Stapleton (Fulham 52), Gary Churchouse (Charlton A.), Tony Witter (QPR), Guy Butters (Spurs), Michael Meaker (QPR)

Back row, left to right: George Talbot(Manager), Kevin Cleary, Gavin Bamford, John Swift, Daryl Pelton, Stuart Bamford, Steve Higgins, Mark Gill and Sean Dawson. **Front row:** Steve Walters, Jamie Cleary, Danny Yeoman, Stuart Goodall, Paul Mills, Saidu Hamid, Barry Bamford and Lee Tunnell.

WEALDSTONE

football club   ryman lge div I

wealdstone

royal blue review 2001/02

Saturday 30th March 2002 K.O. 3.00pm
Ryman League Division One
WEALDSTONE v
HARLOW TOWN
Programme £1.50

CLUB OFFICIALS
Chairman: **Paul Rumens**
Vice Chairman: **Nick Dugard**
Secretary: **Roger Slater,** c/o 31 Jersey
Avenue,Stanmore,Middlesex HA7 2JG
Tel: 0208 552 3595
Commercial Director: **Howard Krais**
Press Officer: **Roger Slater**
Company Secretary: **Graham Clark**

FOOTBALL MANAGEMENT TEAM

Manager: Gordon Bartlett
Asst Mgr: Leo Morris Coach: T.B.A.
Physio: Joe O'Reilly

FACT FILE
Formed: 1899
Nickname: The Stones
Sponsors:Fleetline
Colours: Blue & white quarters
Change colours: Navy & Yellow Quarters
Midweek matches: Tuesday
Reserves' League: Suburban
Club Website: http://come.to/wealdstonefc

2001-02
Captain: Fergus Moore
P.o.Y: Andy Carter
Top Scorer: Brian Hammatt 21

Pages: 36-40 Price: £1.50
Editor: Roy Couch (0208 907 4421)

Local Press:
Harrow Observer, Harrow Times
Local Radio: None give reports
Stones Soccerline: 09003 800 160

GROUND: (Sharing with Edgware FC) White Lion Ground, High Street,Edgware,Middlesex
(Ground Tel No: 020 8952 6799)   Email Address: roge@ dircon.co.uk
Directions: Left out of Edgware station(Northern Line), left again at crossroads and ground
is on right , 300 yards down Edgware High Street opposite Warwick Wright behind Premier
Lodge Hotel
Clubhouse: Open nightly and Friday, Saturday and Sunday lunch time. Hot and cold food on
matchdays.

PREVIOUS   **Leagues:** Willesden & Dist. 1899-1906 08-13; London 1911-22; Middx 13-22; Spartan 22-28; Athenian 28-64; Isthmian 64-71;
Southern 71-79 81-82,88-95; GMVConference 79-81 82-88
Grounds: College Farm 03-10; Belmont Rd 10-22; Lower Mead Stad 22-91; Vicarage Rd (Watford FC) 91-93; The Warren (Yeading F.C.) 93-95

CLUB RECORDS Attendance: 13,504 v Leytonstone FA Amateur Cup Fourth Round replay 5/3/49
Goalscorer: George Duck, 251   **Appearances:** Charlie Townsend, 514
Win: 22-0 v The 12th London Regiment (The Rangers)(H), FA Amateur Cup 13/10/23
Defeat: 0-14 v Edgware Town (A), London Senior Cup 9/12/44
Fees Paid: £15,000 for David Gipp (Barnet, 90)   **Received:** £25,000 for Stuart Pearce (Coventry City 83); for Sean Norman (Chesham, 1989)

BEST SEASON   FA Amateur Cup: Winners 1965-66   **FA Trophy:** Winners 1984-85
FA Cup: Third Round 77-78, 0-4 v Q.P.R. (A). 1st Rd on 13 occasions. League clubs defeated: Hereford Utd and Reading, 77-78

HONOURS: FA Trophy 84-85; FA Amateur Cup 65-66; GMV Conference 84-85; Isthmian Lge - Div3 96-97; Southern Lg Southern Div 81-
82, Div 1 South 73-74, Lg Cup 81-82; Athenian Lg 51-52 (R-up 52-53 58-59 60-61); Spartan Lg R-up 22-23; London LgDiv 2 12-13 (R-up 11-12);
London Snr Cup 61-62 (jt) (R-up 39-40 51-52 60-61); Middx Snr Cup (11); Middx Senior Charity Cup (11); Capital League 84-85 86-87

Players progressing: Stuart Pearce (Coventry City 83), Vinnie Jones(Wimbledon 86), Danny Bailey (Exeter 89), Phil White (Orient 53), Tom
McGhee & John Ashworth (Portsmouth 54 & 62), Charlie Sells (Exeter City 62), Eddie Dilsworth (LincolnCity 67), Colin Franks (Watford 69)

Back row left to right: Gordon Bartlett (Manager), Martin Carter, Andy Carter, Joel Marie-Saint, Tom Bryson, Marvin Morgan, Richard
Horner, Kevin Ramsay, Fergus Moore, Mick Swaysland, Danny Tilbury, Leo Morris (Asst. Manager), and Joe O'Reilly.
Front row: Robin Tucker, Andre Scarlett, Jason Shaw, (Captain), Tyronne Hercules,Carl Hunt and Olatunji Bangbola.

Photo: Graham Smith

WEMBLEY

CLUB OFFICIALS

Chairman: Brian Gumm
President: Eric Stringer
Secretary: Mrs Jean Gumm
14 Woodfield Avenue, North Wembley,
Middx. HA0 3NR   (0208 908 3353)
Press Officer: Richard Markiewicz
(0208 902 0541 before 9pm)
Commercial Manager: Nick Bennett

FOOTBALL MANAGEMENT TEAM
Manager:Scott Cousins
Asst. Manager: Roger Linton

FACT FILE

Formed: 1946
Nickname: The Lions
Sponsors: G & B Builders
Colours: Red & white/red/red
Change colours: All gold
Midweek matchday: Tuesday
Reserves' League: Suburban

WEMBLEY FOOTBALL CLUB

VERSUS
BERKHAMSTED TOWN

Saturday, 17th August, 2002
RYMAN LEAGUE - DIVISION ONE NORTH
Kick-off 3.00p.m.

Ryman
football league

OFFICIAL PROGRAMME ONE POUND

Pages: 28 Price: £1
Editor: Richard Markiewicz
(0208 902 0541 - before 9pm)
Local Press: Wembley & Harrow Observer
Local Radio: Capital, G.L.R

GROUND:Address:	Vale Farm, Watford Road, Sudbury, Wembley HA0 4UR Tel: 0181 908 8169
Directions:	Sudbury Town station (Underground) 400 yds, or 10 mins walk from North Wembley (BR) station. Buses 18, 92, 245 & 182
Capacity:	2,000 Cover: 350 Seats: 350 Floodlights: Yes
Clubhouse:	Open every night & weekend lunchtimes. Hot food on matchdays (0181 904 8169)
Club Shop:	No

PREVIOUS   **Leagues:** Middx 46-49; Spartan 49-51; Delphian 51-56; Corinthian 56-63; Athenian 63-75

CLUB RECORDS   **Attendance:** 2,654 v Wealdstone, FA Amateur Cup 52-53
Career goalscorer: Bill Handrahan 105 (1946-52)
Career appearances: Spud Murphy 505 (78-88)
Win: 11-1 v Hermes, London Senior Cup 1963
Defeat: 0-16 v Chelsea, London Challenge Cup 59-60
Fee received: £10,000 for Gary Roberts (Brentford, 1981)   **Transfer Fee paid:** Nil.

BEST SEASON   FA Trophy: 1st Round proper 91-92   **FA Amateur Cup:** 2nd Round 66-67, 68-69
FA Cup: 1st Round Proper 1980-81, 0-3 v Enfield (A)

HONOURS   Middx Sen Cup 83-84 86-87 (R-up 55-56 68-69 78-79 87-88 91-92 92-93 98-99); Middx Lge 47-48 (Lge Cup 46-47), Middx Charity Cup 67-68 (jnt) 80-81(jnt) 82-83 86-87 94-95,(R-up 83-84 87-88 96-97); Middx Invitation Cup 56-57; Athenian Lge R-up 74-75 (Div 1 R-up 67-68); Corinthian Lge Mem Shield R- up 58-59; Delphian Lge R-up 55-56; Spartan Lge Div 1 West 50-51 (Dunkel Trophy 50-51 jnt); London Sen Cup R-up 55-56; Hitachi Cup SF 83-84; Suburban Lge North 85-86, Lge Cup 84-85 (R-up 83-84)

Players progressing Keith Cassells (Watford 1977), MikeO'Donague (Southampton 1979), A McGonigle (Olympiakos), Gary Roberts (Brentford1980), Richard Cadette (Orient 1984)

L-R - Back Row: Knut auf dem Berge (manager), Dave Drury, Gareth Paxton, Michael Haastrup, Mariusz Tryc, Deji Davies, Kevin Beckles, Erald Kunigi, Luke Dockwray, Renee Fontaine, Nelson Heldt (coach). **Front:** Leigh Halfteck (physio), Alberto Scarampi (trainer), Myron Ramsey, Richard Allicock, Gary McLaughlin, Ian Bates (captain), Avi Schwarz, Steve O'Carroll, Kevin Mason-Thompson.

WINGATE & FINCHLEY

Wingate & Finchley fc

Ryman

Official Programme... One Pound

F.A. Challenge Cup - 1st Qualifying Round
Wingate & Finchley v Ware
Saturday September 14th • Kick-Off 3:00pm

PROGRAMME
32 pages   Price: £1.50
Editor: Peter Rebak (0208 8371 6001)

CLUB OFFICIALS
Chairman: Peter Rebak
Chief Executive: John E Barnett
Presidents: Peter Rebak& Harvey Ackerman
Press Off.: Harvey Ackerman
Tel: 07860 444763(M) 020 83490160(H)
Secretary: Maurice Hanover,c/o Club.
Tel : Club - as below.
020 8501 0607(H)   07976 265588(M)

FACT FILE
Founded: 1991
Nickname: Blues
Colours: SkyBlue & white stripes/white/white
Change Colours: All yellow
Midweek matches: Tuesday
Reserve's Lge: Sub Lge U18

FOOTBALL MANAGEMENT TEAM
Manager: Tommy Cunningham
Coach: Adam Lee Physio: Jim Connolly

GROUND: The Abrahams Stadium, Summers Lane, Finchley, London N12 0PD
Tel: 0208 446 2217 Fax: 020 8343 8194
Directions: North Circular (A406) to junction with High Road Finchley (A1000).
Go north and Summers Lane is 200 yds on right - parking for 80 cars.
Tube to East Finchley (Northern Line) and then 263 bus to Summers Lane towards North Finchley
Capacity: 8,500 **Seats:** 500   **Cover:** 500   **Floodlights:** Yes   **Club Shop:** No
Clubhouse: Open during matches. Also tea-bar selling most refreshments

PREVIOUS: **Names:** Wingate (founded 46), Finchley (founded late 1800s) merged in 91
Leagues: (as Wingate & Finchley) South Mids 89-95
Finchley: London 02-12 14-15 23-25 30-39; Athenian 12-14 29-30 45-73; Isthmian73-91
Wingate: Middx 46-52; London 52-62; Delphian 62-63; Athenian 63-75; Barnet Yth,Hendon & Dist. Sunday 75-84; Herts 84-89
CLUB RECORDS: Attendance: 9,555 - Finchley v Bishop Auckland, F.A. Amat Cup QF 49-50
Career Goalscorer: Marc Morris 578   **Career Appearances:** Marc Morris 587(1975-93)
Win: 9-0, Wingate v Sarratt, Herts Co. Lge Div. 1, 20/4/85
Defeat: 0-9 v Edgware,Ryman League Division Two. 15.1.2000
BEST SEASON   **FA Vase:** 74-75 Quarter Final (Wingate)
FA Amateur Cup: Semi-Final (Finchley)
HONOURS: Isthmian League Div. 3 R-up 98-99, Promoted (7th) 2001-02, London Senior Cup winners 94-95
Previous Honours   Finchley: London Snr Cup, London Charity Cup, FA Amtr Cup SF, Athenian Lg 53-54(R-up 63-64 65-66),
London Lg 36-37 (R-up 35-36, Div 2 06-07(jt with Enfield),Lg Cup 34-35, Park Royal Cup 37-38)
Wingate: Middx Lg(2)(R-up(1), Lg Cup), London Lg R-up(2)(Lg Cup(1)), Middx SnrCup SF, Athenian Lg Div 2 69-70,
Herts Co. Lg Div 1 84-85 (Aubrey Cup 85-86),Herts I'mediate Cup 84-85, Herts Snr Tphy 86-87,
Sth Mids Lg Div 1 R-up 89-90(Lg Cup SF 89-90), Barnet Yth Lg 75-76, Pete Morrison Cup 82-83 83-84 (R-up 79-80 84-85),
Hendon & Dist. Int. Div 79-80. Win & Fin: London Sen Cup 79-80

Back row, left to right: Adam Lee, Marcus Davis, A Newman, Andy Walker, Daniel Boateng, Steve Forwell and Robert Donn
Front row: Daniel Nielson, Daniel Fitzpatrick, John Butterfield, Dean Williams, Paul Wood, Daniel Berg, Clive Wilson and Guy Morris.
Photo: Arthur Evans

WIVENHOE TOWN

Official Matchday Programme   Season 02/03

WIVENHOE TOWN
FOOTBALL CLUB

Sponsored by
Jones & Whymark

CLUB OFFICIALS

Chairman: Maz Brook

Secretary / Press Officer: Mike Boyle,
15 Daniell Drive, Colchester, Essex
Tel: 01206 573223

FACT FILE
Formed: 1925
Nickname: The Dragons
Colours: Royal blue/white
Change colours: Red/black
Reserves' League: Essex & Suffolk Border
Midweek matchday: Tuesday

Ryman
Football League

Saturday 31st August 2002
The Dragons V Yeading
FA Cup Preliminary Round

FOOTBALL MANAGEMENT TEAM
Manager: Steve Pitt

Official Website: www.wivenhoetown.com

GROUND: Broad Lane Ground, Elmstead Road, Wivenhoe CO7 7HA
Tel: 01206 825380

48 Pages   Price: £1.00
Editor: J. Gooding

Directions: Coming out of Colchester towards Clacton take first turning (right) towards Wivenhoe, then 1st left and the ground is clearly visible on the right at the cross-roads.   1 mile from Wivenhoe (BR)

Capacity: 3,000   Cover: 1,300   Seats: 250   Floodlights: Yes

Clubhouse: Open normal pub hours. Tel: 01206 825380

Club Shop: A full range of souvenirs etc

Local Press: East Anglian Daily Times,
Colchester Evening Gazette
Local Radio: BBC Radio Essex, S.G.R.

PREVIOUS: **Leagues:** Brighlingsea & District 1927-50; Colchester & East Essex 50-71; Essex & Suffolk Border 71-79; Essex Senior 79-86
Name: Wivenhoe Rangers
Grounds: Spion Kop; Broomfield (twice); Claude Watcham's Meadow; Vine Farm; King George V Playing Fields; Essex University

CLUB RECORD   **Attendance:** 1,912 v Runcorn, FA Trophy 1st Rd, Feb 1990
Transfer fee received: £5,875 for Bobby Mayes (Redbridge Forest)
Win: 18-0 v Nayland. **Defeat:** 0-8 v Carshalton A. (H), Isthmian Lg 28/8/93
Career goalscorer: Paul Harrison, 258 in 350 games   **Career appearances:** Keith Bain, 536

BEST SEASON   **FA Cup:** 4th Qual Rd 89-90 2-3 v Halesowen Tn (A), 94-95 1-2 v Enfield (H)
FA Trophy: 2nd Rd replay 89-90   **FA Vase:** 5th Rd 82-83;

HONOURS   Isthmian Lg Div 1 89-90 (Div 2 Nth 87-88); Essex Snr Lg R-up 79-80 81-82 85-86(Harry Fisher Tphy 83-84 85-86); Essex & Suffolk Border Lg 78-79, Div 1 72-73,Div 2 71-72, Lg Cup R-up(2); Colchester & East Essex Lg 52-53 55-56 (R-up 70-71), Div 1 59-60 69-70, Div 2 R-up 68-69, Lg KO Cup 51-52 52-53 54-55 55-56 (R-up 59-60), Challenge Cup 52-53); Brighlingsea & Dist Lg Div 1 35-36 36-37 47-48(R-up 37-38), Lg KO Cup 36-37 37-38 47-48, Challenge Cup 36-37; Essex Snr Tphy87-88 Essex Jnr Cup R-up 55-56 78-79; Amos Charity Cup(7) (R-up 72-73); StokesCup(3); Wivenhoe Charity Cup (4), (R-up [4]); Cristal Monopole Cup (5), (R-up 2); Sidney James Mem. Tphy 69-70 (R-up 72-73), Tolleshunt D'Arcy Mem. Cup(3)(R-up 2); Walton & District Charity Cup 73-74 78-79; Coggeshal Brotherhood Cup80-81; Brantham Charity Cup R-up 82-83; Worthington Evans Cup 81-82 (R-up 80-8185-86); Harwich Snr Cup R-up 84-85; Woodbridge Chal. Cup 91-92; Mat FowlerShield 92-93 94-95

Players progressing: Robert Reinelt (Gillingham) 1993

YEADING

Yeading FC
at The Warren

CLUB OFFICIALS
Chairman: Philip Spurden
Secretary: Joanne Powell,
42 Roberts Ride, Hazlemere, Bucks. HP15 7AF
Tel: 01494 712442
Email: yeading@yeadingfc.co.uk
Commercial Manager: Bill Perryman
Tel: 020 8756 1200
Press Officer: Tim Fuell (0709 1214576)

FOOTBALL MANAGEMENT TEAM
Managers: Johnson Hippolyte
Asst. Manager: Dereck Brown
Coaches: Erskine Smart & Jason Tucker

FACT FILE
Formed: 1965
Nickname: The Ding
Colours: Red & black stripes/black/black
Change colours: All white
Midweek matchday: Tuesday
Reserves League: Capital

Website: www.yeadingfc.co.uk
Local Newspapers: Hayes Gazette,
Hillingdon Times

GROUND The Warren, Beaconsfield Rd.Hayes, Middx.
Tel: 020 8848 7362   Fax: 020 8756 1200   email: yeading@yeadingfc.co.uk
Directions: 2 miles from Hayes (BR) - take Uxbridge Road and turn right towards Southall,
right into Springfield Rd and then left into Beaconsfield Rd. Bus 207 stops 1/2 mile from ground
Capacity: 3,500   Cover: 1,000   Seats: 250   Floodlights: Yes
Clubhouse: Open normal pub hours.' The Warren' Conference & Banquetting suite available
for hire.
Club Shop: No   Metal Badges: Yes

Programme - Pages: 32   Price: £1
Editor: Tim Fuell

PREVIOUS **Leagues:** Uxbridge & Dist. 65-67; W. Middx. Comb. 67-68; S W Middx 68-74; Middx 74-84; Spartan 84-87
CLUB RECORDS **Attendance:** 3,000; v Hythe Town, FA Vase SF 1990; v Tottenham Hotspur, friendly
Career Goalscorer: Dave Burt 327   **Career Appearances:** Norman Frape 457
Fee Paid: £3,000 for Matt Edwards to Hucknall Town   **Fee Received:** £45,000 for Andrew Impey (QPR)
BEST SEASON **FA Cup:** First Round Proper 93-94 & 94-95
FA Vase: Winners 89-90
FA Trophy: 2nd Round 97-98, 98-99, 00-01
HONOURS FA Vase 89-90; Isthmian League Div 2 Sth 89-90 (Div 1 R-up 91-92);Spartan League 86-87 (R-up 85-86, Senior Div R-up 84-85, League Cup 85-86 86-87); Middlesex Snr League (6) 71-73 74-76 81-82 83-84 (R-up 73-74 74-75 78-79, LeagueCup (6) 72-73 75-76 79-83); South West Middlesex League (2) 69-71; Middlesex Snr Cup 89-90 91-92, Middlesex Prem. Cup 80-81, Middlesex I'mediate Cup (5) 70-7274-76 77-78, Middlesex Jnr Cup (4) 68-69 70-72 74-75; Uxbridge League 66-67; Middlesex Border League Cup 86-87 (AJA Cup 86-87); Suburban League Nth 87-88; Allied Counties Yth League 89-90 (Lge Cup 89-90)
Players progressing: Andrew Impey (Leicester City ,West Ham United , QPR and England U 21) and Lee Charles (Q.P.R.via Chertsey Town)

Matt Edwards, Dwane Lee, David Tilbury, Jason Tricker, Otis Hutchings, Matt Hodson, Nevin Saroya, Stephen Griffiths,
Johnson Hippolyte (manager). Front: Naz Bashir, Jesse Hall, Mattt Miller, Daniel Hawksworth, Lee White, Bobby Behzadi,
Errol Telemaque, Jo Gritt.

ABINGDON TOWN

GROUND
Address: Culham Road, Abingdon OX14 3HP (01235 521684)
Directions: On A415 road to Dorchester-on-Thames half a mile south of town centre. Nearest rail station is Culham. Main line: Didcot Parkway or Oxford. Bus service from Didcot & London
Capacity: 3,000   Cover: 1,771   Seats: 271   Floodlights: Yes
Clubhouse: (01235 521684). 7.30-11pm. 6pm matchdays. 12.30-2.30, 4-11 Sat. Hot food on matchdays. Pool, darts, jukebox, canteen
Club Shop: Selling programmes, magazines, scarves. Metal Badges: £2
HONOURS
Berks & Bucks Sen Cup 58-59 (R-up 88-89 92-93); Isthmian League Div 2 (Sth) 90-91 (Assoc. Mem. Tphy R-up 90-91); London Spartan Lg 88-89 Hellenic Lge(4) 56-57 58-60 86-87, R-up(3) 70-72 87-88,Lg Cup 57-58 70-71 81-82 (R-up 83-84 86-87), Div 1 75-76, Div 1 Cup 75-76,Res. Div(3) 69-71 86-87, Res. Div Cup 70-71 85-86, Res. Div Suppl. Cup 74-75;Oxford & Dist. Lg (3) 1898-1901; Reading & Dist. Lg 47-48; Berks & Bucks Jnr Cup 06-07; Abingdon Centenary Cup 58-59; Joan Lee Mem. Cup 69-70 70-71 86-87
PREVIOUS
Leagues: Oxford & Dist.; West Berks; Reading Temperance; North Berks; Reading & Dist. 1927-50; Spartan 50-53; Hellenic 53-88; London Spartan 88-89
Name: Abingdon FC (merged with St Michaels in 1899).
CLUB RECORDS
Attendance: 1,400 v Oxford City, FA Cup September 1960
Career appearances: John Harvey-Lynch
BEST SEASON
FA Vase: Fifth Round, replay, 1989-90.
FA Cup: 4th Qualifying Round
60-61 0-2 v Hitchin,   89-90 1-3 v Slough(H),   92-93 1-2 v Merthyr T.(A) after 0-0
Players progressing: Maurice Owen (Swindon Town), George Buck (Stockport County& Reading), Sammy Chung (Reading, Norwich City, Watford & WolverhamptonWanderers), Jermaine McSporran (Wycombe Wanderers via Oxford City), Howard Forinton (Birmingham City,Plymouth Argyle via Oxford City and Yeovil Town)

FACT FILE
Formed: 1870
Nickname: The Abbotts
Sponsors: Wootton Trucks
Colours: Yellow & green/yellow
Change colours: Black & white

Programme: Pages: 40 Price:£1.00
Editor: Kevin Rowland(01235 522115)

Midweek Matchday: Tuesday
Reserves ' League: Suburban (North)

Local Press: Oxford Mail, Oxford Times,
Abingdon Herald, South Oxon Guardian

CLUB PERSONNEL
Chairman: Phil Evans
President: Dr Tim Reynolds
Secretary: Ted Quail,
107 Park Lane, Thatcham,
Newbury, Berks RG18 3BZ
Tel: 01635868967
Press Off : Roger Nicholl
Tel: 07768 427268 (M)

Manager: Alan Thorne
Asst Manager: Peter Lamont
Physio: Anton Titcombe
Coach: T.B.A.

CAMBERLEY TOWN

GROUND
Address: Krooner Park, Krooner Road, off Frimley Rd, Camberley, Surrey, GU15 2QP.
Tel: 01276 65392

Directions: M3 Jct 4, follow signs to Frimley, then B3411 towards Camberley, ground on left opposite `The Standard' pub

Capacity: 3,000 Seats: 195 Cover: 280   Floodlights: Yes   Club Shop: Yes
Clubhouse: Open matchdays & 2 evenings. Food available from burger bar matchdays

HONOURS:
Isthmian Lg Div 2 R-up 78-79; Surrey Snr Lg 30-31 31-32 32-33 (R-up 46-47 61-62), Lg Charity Cup 37-38 51-52 (R-up 31-32 36-37 54-55 72-73); Surrey Snr Cup 78-79 (R-up 35-36); W. Surrey Lg 13-14 (R-up 12-13); Ascot & Dist Lg 03-04; Surrey Jnr Charity Cup R-up 08-09; Surrey Jnr Cup 1897-98 1909-10 (R-up 07-08); Aldershot Snr Lg 12-13 (Lg Charity Cup R-up 21-22); Southern Comb. Cup 80-81 (R-up 78-79 85-86 87-88); Aldershot Sen Cup 96-97 97-98

PREVIOUS   **Leagues:** Ascot & District; West Surrey; Aldershot Snr;
Surrey Snr 22-73 Spartan 73-75; Athenian 75-77 82-84; Isthmian 77-82
Names: Camberley & Yorktown 1896-1946; Camberley FC 46-67
Grounds: London Rd Rec 1898-1905 12-18/ Southwell Park Rd 05-09/ Martins Meadow 09-12

CLUB RECORDS: **Attendance:** 3,500 v Crystal Pal. friendly 14.10.74
Competitive: 2,066 v Aldershot Town, Isthmian Lge Div. 3, 10.11.92
Appearances: Brian Ives
Win: 15-0 v Royal Engineers, friendly, 20/9/19
Defeat: 0-11 v Abingdon Town (A), Isthmian Lge Div. 2 (South) 25/8/90

BEST SEASON: **FA Vase:** Quarter Final 85-86, 98-99 v Woodbridge
FA Cup:1st Rd Prop 98-99 v Brentford 4th Qual. 32-33 33-34 97-98

FACT FILE
Founded: 1896
Nickname: Krooners, Reds or Town
Colours:Red & White Stripes/ Red/Red
Change colours: L & D Blue strips
Midweek Matches: Tuesday
Reserve's League: Suburban

Programme: 24 pages, £1
Local Press: Camberley News
Bracknell News

CLUB PERSONNEL
Chairman: Ian Waldren
Press Office & Prog.Ed,: Andy Vaughan
Secretary: David Clifford
63 Inglewood Ave, Camberley,
Surrey. GU15 1RS
Tel & Fax: 01276 516613
Website: www.cambrleytownfc .co.uk

Managers: Martin Paterson
Physio: T.B.A.

2001-02
Top Scorer: Jamie Shannon 14
Captain: Anthony Bruty
P.o.Y.: Ricky McNamara

CHALFONT ST. PETER

GROUND

Address: Mill Meadow, Amersham Road, Chalfont St Peter SL9 7BQ
Tel: 01753 885797

Directions: A413 from Uxbridge (London) to Chalfont. Turn left 100 yds after 2nd major roundabout (between Ambulance station and Community Centre.
Two miles from Gerrards Cross (BR)
Regular buses from Slough & Uxbridge

Capacity: 4,500   Cover: 120   Seats: 220   Floodlights: Yes   Club Shop: Yes

Clubhouse: Open every evening, Saturday afternoons and Sunday lunchtimes

PREVIOUS   **Leagues:** Great Western Combination 1948-58; Parthenon 58-59; London 60-62; Spartan 62-75; London Spartan 75-76; Athenian 76-84

BEST SEASON   **FA Trophy:** 3rd Qual Rd 89-90 91-92
FA Vase: 4th Rd 87-88
FA Cup: 3rd Qual Rd85-86 (wins over Banbury, King's Lynn and Barking)

HONOURS   Isthmian Lg Div 2 87-88; Athenian Lg R-up 83-84 (Lg Cup 76-77 82-83); London Spartan Lg Div 2 75-76; Berks & Bucks Intermediate Cup 52-53; Berks & Bucks Benevolent Cup 64-65

CLUB RECORDS   **Attendance:** 2,550 v Watford, benefit match 85
Career Goalscorer: Unknown **Career Appearances:** Colin Davies
Transfer Fee Paid: £750 to Chertsey (Steve Church, March 1989)

Players progressing to Football League: Paul Barrowcliff (Brentford), Dean Hooper (Swindon)

FACT FILE
Founded: 1926
Nickname: Saints
Colours: Red, green trim/green/green & red
Change colours: Yellow/black/black
Midweek matchday: Tuesday
Reserves' League:

Programme: Pages: 30 Price: 50p
Editor: Mal Keenan
Local Press: Bucks Advertiser,
Bucks Examiner, Bucks Free Press,
Wycombe Midweek
Local Radio: Chiltern Radio

CLUB PERSONNEL
Chairman:Nigel Payne
Press Officer: Chairman (01494 875195)
Secretary: Alan Thompson,
4 Dane Close, Amersham, Bucks. HP7 9LZ
Tel: 01494 724260

Manager: Martin Dean

CHESHUNT

GROUND Address: The Stadium, Theobalds Lane, Cheshunt, Herts . Tel: 01992 626752
Secretary's Email addess: cheshunt@brassett.net

Directions: M25 to junction 25, A10 north towards Hertford, next roundaboutthird exit to next roundabout, turn left proceed under railway bridge, turnleft, ground approx 400 yards on right. 400yds from Theobalds Grove BR station,Buses 310, 242, & 311 to Theobalds Grove station

Seats: 285   Cover: 700   Capacity: 2,500   Floodlights: Yes
Clubhouse: Yes   Club Shop: No

HONOURS:
Athenian Lg 75-76 (R-up 73-74), Div 1 67-68, Div 2 R-up 65-66, Lg Cup74-75 75-76; Spartan Lg 62-63, Lg Cup 63-64 92-93, (R-up 89-90); London Lg 49-50 (R-up 56-57), Div 1 47-48 48-49 (R-up 46-47), Div 1 Cup 46-47, Lg Cup R-up58-59, Park Royal Cup 46-47; Isthmian Lg Div 2 R-up 81-82 (Div 3 R-up 94-95);Herts Snr Cup 23-24 (R-up 48-49 49-50 68-69 69-70 71-72 73-74); Herts CharityCup 00-01 05-06 (R-up 70-71 74-75 80-81); Herts Charity Shield 46-47 65-66 (52-53 53-54 54-55 63-64 64-65); Herts Snr Centenary Tphy 91-92; East Anglian Cup74-75 (R-up 75-76); Mithras Floodlit Cup 69-70 (R-up 75-76); London Charity Cup73-74; Roy Bailey Tphy 90-91 94-95 97-98 98-99 99-00

PREVIOUS: **Leagues:** Athenian 19-20 21-31 64-77; London 20-21 24-25 46-51 55-59; Delphian51-55; Aetolian 59-62; Spartan 62-64; Isthmian 77-87
Name: None   **Ground:** None

RECORDS: Attendance: 7,000 v Bromley, London Senior Cup 1947

BEST SEASON: **FA Vase:** Quarter Final 81-82
FA Cup: 4th Qual. Rd(4)

Players progressing: Ian Dowie, Ruben Abgula, SteveSedgeley, Lee Hodges, Paul Marquis, Steve Terry, Neil Prosser, Mario Walsh

FACT FILE
Founded: 1946
Nickname: Ambers
Sponsors: Brasilia
Colours: Gold & black/Black/Black
Change colours: All blue
Midweek matchday: Tuesday
Reserves' Lge: Essex & Herts Border Comb
Programme: Pages: 28 Price: £1
Editor: Jim Tuite (07956 324 525)
Website: Jftuite@aol.com

CLUB PERSONNEL
Secretary:
Robert Brassett, 32 Firbank Close,
Windmill Chase, Enfield, Middl'x EN2 7ER
Nos :0208 364 4058(H) 0788 060 3108 (M)
Chairman:Vince Satori
Vice Chairman: Paul Cully
President: Paul Philips
Press Officer: Alfie Norman
Manager: Andrew Leese
Asst Manager: John Meakes & Kevin Mudd
Physio: T.B.A.
2000-01
Captain:Glenn Wilkie
P.O.Y.: Omar Dervish
Top Scorer: Tom Moody

Camberley Town FC. Photo: Eric Marsh

Chalfont St Peter, home victors over Thetford Town by 2-0 in the FA Vase First Qualifying Round. Back Row (l-r): Darren Keeley, Christian Ayres, Gary Attrell, Kevin Eldred, Kevin Davies, Mark Lee, Gavin Akers, Matt Holian. Front Row : Fraser Fennel-Ball, Adam Cooper, Simon Rodgers, Anthony Baker, Luke Blackmore, Andy Goddard, Lewis Foster. Photo: Arthur Evans

Hungerford Town. Back Row (l-r): Gary Ackling (Manager), Martin Fox, Elliott Jackson, Simon Cadle, Tim North, Ben Hopkins, Gary Swann, Jason Brizel, Richard Fox (Physio). Front Row: Bobby Tong, Matt Jack, Lee Howell, Dean Mildenhall, Jon Quinton, Darren Howell, Andy Phillpot, Mark Rivers

CLAPTON

GROUND

Address: The Old Spotted Dog, Upton Lane, Forest Gate, London E7 9NP
Tel: 0208 4720822

Directions: BR to Forest Gate.Tube to Plaistow (District Line).
Official entrance in Upton Lane.
Docklands Light Railway to Prince Regent then 325 bus to ground

Capacity: 2,000 Seats: 100 Cover: 180 Floodlights: Yes

Club Shop: No

Clubhouse: Match days. Light snacks available. To hire please contact club

HONOURS: FA Amateur Cup: 06-07 08-09 14-15 23-24 24-25 (R-up 04-05);
Isthmian Lg 10-11 22-23 (R-up 05-06 07-08 09-10 24-25), Div 2 82-83; Essex Thames-side Tphy(2); A.F.A.Invitation Cup (2); London Snr Cup (2); London Charity Cup; Essex Snr Cup (4); Middlesex Snr Cup; Essex Sen Trophy; First English team to play on the continent, beating a Belgian Select XI over Easter 1890.

PREVIOUS **Leagues:** Southern 1894-96 (founder members); London 1896-97
Grounds: None

CLUB RECORDS **Attendance:** 12,000 v Tottenham Hotspur, FA Cup 1898-99
Defeat: 0-14 v Nottingham Forest (H), FA Cup 1st Rd 1890-91

BEST SEASON **FA Cup:** 3rd Rd Proper 25-26 (lost 2-3 to Swindon at Upton Park)
League clubs defeated Norwich City 25-26.
FA Amateur Cup: 06-07 08-09 14-15 23-24 24-25 (R-up 04-05);

Players progressing to Football Lge: Numerous over past 116 years. Currently:, Gary Charles (West Ham)

FACT FILE
Founded: 1878
Nickname: Tons
Sponsors: T.B.A.
Colours: Red & white stripes/black/black
Change colours: All blue
Midweek Matchday: Tuesday

Programme: up to 30 pages £1.00
Editor: Linda C Ambrose

CLUB PERSONNEL
Chairman: Neville Watson
Chief Executive: Vince McBean

Secretary: Linda Ambrose,
8 Sylvan Hill, Crystal Palace, SQ19 2QF
Tel: 0208 6538000
Press Officer: Alexander Cole

Manager: Vince McBean

DORKING

FACT FILE
Formed: 1880
Nickname: The Chicks
Colours: Green & white hoops/green/green
Change colours: All navy blue
Midweek matches: Tuesday
Reserve League: Suburban

GROIUND

Address: Meadowbank, Mill Lane, Dorking, Surrey RH4 1DX
Tel: 01306 884112

Directions: Mill Lane is off Dorking High St. next to Woolworths and Marks &Spencers, & opposite the White Horse pub. Fork right in Mill Lane past the Malthouse pub. 1/2 mile from both Dorking and Deepdene (BR) stations

Capacity: 3,600 Cover: 800 Seats: 200 Floodlights: Yes

Club Shop: Yes

Clubhouse: All week &Sun. 4-11 p.m. Sats 12-11pm Hot & cold food on matchdays

HONOURS Isthmian Lge Div 2 Sth 88-89, (Full Members Cup R-up 92-93); Surrey Sen Cup R-up 1885-86 1989-90; Surrey Senior Shield (2), R-up (3); Surrey Sen Lge (4), R-up (2), Lge Cup (3); Lge Charity Cup (4), R-up (5); Gilbert Rice F'lit Cup 87-88 (R-up 89-90); Surrey I'mediate Cup 56-57 (R-up 54-55); Southern Comb.Challenge Cup 92-93

PREVIOUS **Ground:** Prixham Lane (until 1953)
Leagues: Surrey Senior 22-56 77-78; Corinthian 56-63; Athenian 63-74 78-80; Southern 74-77
Names: Dorking Town 77-82; Guildford & Dorking United (when club merged with Guildford in1974)/

CLUB RECORDS **Attendance:** 4,500 v Folkestone Town, FA Cup 1st Qual. Rd 1955 and v Plymouth Argyle 1st Rd F.A.Cup 92-93
Goalscorer: Andy Bushnell **Appearances:** Steve Lunn
Win: 7-0 v Barking, Isthmian Lge Div. One, 31/10/92

BEST SEASON **FA Cup:** 1st Round Proper 92-93, 2-3 v Plymouth A. (H)
FA Vase: 5th Round 2001-2002 **FA Trophy:** 2nd Rd 91-92

Players progressing to Football League:
Steve Scrivens & John Finch (Fulham), Andy Ansah (Brentford 1989)

Programme
48 pages £1 Editor: Bryan Bletso
Local Press: Dorking Advertiser,
Surrey Mirror, Surrey Advertiser
Local Radio: County Sound, BBC Southern
Counties, Radio Mercury

CLUB PERSONNEL

Chairman: Jack Collins
President: Ingram Whittingham
Vice-Chairman: Ray Collins
Co. Sec.: Martin Collins
Secretary: Ray Collins
11 Richmond Way, Fetcham,
Surrey KT22 9NP
Tel: 01372 453867
Press Officer: Bryan Bletso

Managers: Steve Lunn & Nick Torpey
Physio: Bennie Fishlock

Above: Tring Town
Back Row (l-r): Howard Cowley (Manager), Keith Hardy (Assistant Manager), Lee Johnson, Scott Walters, Anthony Beamish, Simon Bartley, Ben Chesters, David Butler, Brian Johnson, Gary Kinsley (Assistant Manager)
Front Row: Tony Oliver, Chris Gibson, Neal Bartlett, Wayne Barber, Sean Sangster, Alex Kinsley, Joe Gibson.
Photo: Arthur Evans

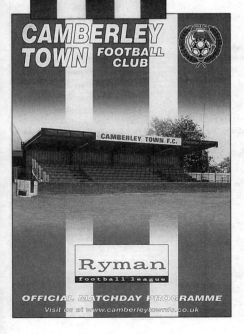

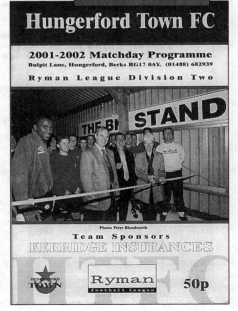

EDGWARE TOWN

GROUND
Address: White Lion Ground, High Street, Edgware HA8 5AQ. Tel: 0181 9526799

Directions: Left out of Edgware tube station (Northern Line), left again at crossroads and ground is 300yds on right in Edgware High St. . Buses 32, 288 142

Capacity: 5,000   **Seats:** 220   **Cover:** 1,500   **Floodlights:** Yes
Club Shop: No
Clubhouse: Open nightly and Fri, Sat, Sun lunchtimes.
Hot & cold food matchdays, cold food lunchtimes

HONOURS: Isthmian Lg Div 3 91-92; London Spartan Lg 87-88 89-90 (Lg Cup 87-88); Corinthian Lg R-up 53-54, Memorial Shield 52-53 61-62; Athenian Lge R-up 81-82; Middx Snr Lg 40-41 41-42 42-43 43-44 44-45, Cup 47- 48 (R-up 73-74 94-95); London Snr Cup R-up 47-48; Middx Border Lg Cup 79-80; Suburban Lg Div R-up 89-90

PREVIOUS   **Leagues:** Corinthian 46-63; Athenian 64-84; London Spartan 84-90
            Names: Edgware F.C.   **Grounds:** None

CLUB RECORDS   **Attendance:** 8,500 v Wealdstone, FA Cup 1948
                 Career Appearances: John Mangan
                 Career Goalscorer: Steve Newing

BEST SEASON   **FA Vase:** 5th Round, 1991-92

Players progressing: Brian Stein (Luton), Dave Beasant (Wimbledon), Scott McGleish (Charlton 94)

FACT FILE
Founded: 1939
Nickname: Wares
Colours: Green & white quarters/green/green
Change colours: All yellow
Midweek Matchday: Tuesday
Reserve League: Suburban
Sponsor: Philiam Construction

Programme:
Pages: 16   Price: 50p
Editor: Paul Gregory (0181 959 2535)
Website: www.edgwaretownfc.com

CLUB PERSONNEL
Chairman: Paul Karaiskos
President: Mr V Deritis
Patron: Russell Grant

Secretary: Peter Evans,
5 Windmill Ct., Windmill Lane, Bushey,
Herts WD23 1NG
Tel: 0208 420 4750
Fax: 0208 950 8924

Manager: John Harding
Asst Manager: Noel Blackwell
Physio: Sarah Gow

FLACKWELL HEATH

GROUND:
Address: Wilks Park, Heath End Rd, Flackwell Heath, High Wycombe. HP10 9EA
Tel: 01628 523892

Directions: M40 jct 3 Wycombe East, follow signs for F/Heath left up Treadway Hill & right at top of hill at roundabout. Wilks park 800yds on right, grd at rear of Magpie (PH). Bus 301 either from bus station or High Street near bottom of Crendon Street which comes from BR station. Ask for Oakland Way

Capacity: 2,000   **Seats:** 150   **Cover:** Yes   **Floodlights:** Yes

Club Shop: No
Clubhouse: Open every night 6.30-11pm & before & after matches. Hot food in tea bar

HONOURS: Gt Western Combination 57-58 62-63; Hellenic Lg Div 1 R-up 76-77; Berks & Bucks Snr Cup SF 85-86

PREVIOUS: **Leagues:** Wycombe & District; Gt Western Comb.; Hellenic 76-82; Athenian 82-84

RECORDS: **Attendance:** 4,500 v Oxford U., charity game 1986
(competitive: 700 v Aldershot Town, 27/10/92)
Goalscorer: Tony Wood   **Appearamces:** Lee Elliott
Win: 6-0 v Clapton & v Petersfield (both away)
Defeat: 0-7 v Aveley (H)

BEST SEASON: **FA Cup:** 2nd Qual. Rd replay 90-91, 0-3 v Grays A (A) after 2-2

FACT FILE
Founded: 1907
Colours: Red/red/white & black
Change colours: Yellow/black/black
Midweek Matches: Tuesday
Reserves' League: Suburban
Programme: 18 pages £1

CLUB PERSONNEL
Chairman: T Glynn
Vice Chairman: G.Turner
President: Ken Crook

Secretary: Mrs Christine Hobbs
23 Southfield Rd., Flackwell Heath,
Bucks. HP10 9BT
Tel: 01628 521051

HUNGERFORD TOWN

GROUND

Address: Town Ground, Bulpit Lane, Hungerford RG17 0AY
Tel: 01488 682939 (club) 01488 684597 (boardroom) 01488 684597 (Fax)

Directions: M4 jct 14 to A4, right and left at Bear Hotel, through town centre on A338, left into Priory Rd, second left into Bulpit Lane, over crossroads, ground on left. 3/4 mile from Hungerford BR station

Capacity: 3,000 Seats: 300 Cover:320 Floodlights: Yes Club Shop: Yes

Clubhouse: Open every evening and lunchtimes including Sunday. 2 bars,dancehall, boardroom/committee room, darts, pool, fruit machines. Hot & coldsnacks. Steward: Dianne Tanner (01488 682939)

HONOURS: Berks & Bucks Snr Cup 81-82 (R-up 75-76 76-77); Hellenic Lg Div 1 70-71, PremDiv Cup 77-78, Div 1 Cup 70-71, Benevolent Cup 60-61; Hungerford Cup 96-97, Isthmian Lge Representatives in Anglo-Italian Tournament 81.

PREVIOUS **Leagues:** Newbury & D.; Swindon & D.; Hellenic 58-78
Names: None **Grounds:** None

CLUB RECORDS Attendance: 1,684 v Sudbury Town, FA Vase SF 1st leg 88-89
(20,000 v Modena inItaly 1981) Anglo-Italian Tournament
Scorer: Ian Farr (268) **Appearances:** Dean Bailey (approx 400)
Transfer Fee Paid: £4,000 for Joe Scott (Yeovil Town)
Received: £3,800 for Joe Scott (Barnstaple Town)

BEST SEASON **FA Cup:** 1st Rd 79-80, 1-3 v Slough T. (A)
FA Vase: Semi-Final 77-78 79-80 88-89

Players progressing to Football League: Steve Hetzke (Reading, Blackpool,Sunderland), Bruce Walker (Swindon, Blackpool), Des McMahon (Reading), BrianMundee (Bournemouth, North'ton)

FACT FILE
Founded: 1886
Nickname: Crusaders
Club Sponsors: Kerridge Insurance
Colours: White/navy blue/blue
Change colours: All yellow
Midweek Matchday: Tuesday
Reserves' League: Suburban (North)
Programme: 24 pages, 50p
Editor:Martyn Leach (01488 683682)
Local Press: Newbury Weekly News,
Newbury Evening Post
Local Radio: Radio Berkshire , Radio 210
Kick F.M.

CLUB PERSONNEL
Chairman: Alan Holland
Vice Chairman: Ron Tarry
President: Sir Seton Wills
General Secretary: Eric Richardson
Match Secretary: Norman Matthews
Press Officer: Ron Tarry (01488 682539)
Manager: Gary Ackling
Asst.Man: Tim North
Reserve Team Managers:
Nicky Harrison & Mike Butler
Youth Team Manager: Mark Rivers
Physio: Richard Fox

KINGSBURY TOWN

GROUND:

Address: Silver Jubilee Park, Townsend Lane, Kingsbury, London NW9 7NE
Tel: 0208 2051645 Website:www.madasafish.com/~kingsbury-town

Directions: Underground to Kingsbury, cross road and take bus 183 to TownsendLane (2 miles) - ground in far left-hand corner of Silver Jubilee Park

Capacity: 2,500 Seats: 165 Cover: 400 Floodlights: Yes

Club Shop: Sells club ties, pennants, metal badges
Contact Allan Davies (01895 443761)

Clubhouse Mon-Fri 7-11, Sat 12-11, Sun 12-2.30 & 7-10.30. Food on matchdays

HONOURS: Isthmian Lg Div 2 Nth R-up 85-86; Spartan Lg Cup R-up 59-60 64-65; Parthenon Lg 51-52 (Prem Charity Cup 52-53 53-54; Snr Charity Cup 53-54); Middx Snr Cup R-up 88-89; Middx Charity Cup 85-86 (R-up 88-89); Middx Lg Charity Cup (3) 44-47; Willesden & Dist. Lg R-up 30-31 (Div 2 34-35)

PREVIOUS: **Leagues:** Hellenic 27-30 (as Davis Sports); Willesden & District 30-43; MiddxSnr 44-47; Parthenon 47-59; Spartan 59-76 78-81; Athenian 76-78 81-84
Grounds: None **Name:** Davis Sports

RECORDS: **Attendance:** 1 ,300 v Wealdstone, FA Amateur Cup 1971
Appearances: Mick Coffey (goalkeeper)
Win: 8-0 v Eastbourne United, 91-92. **Defeat:** ?????
Record Fees - Paid: £500 **Received:** £600

BEST SEASON: **FA Vase:** 4th Rd 74-75
FA Cup: 3rd Qual. Rd. 87-88, 0-1 v Leytonstone-Ilford (H)

Players progressing to Football League: Billy Dare (Brentford & West Ham), JohnMeadows, Dave Underwood, Dwight Marshall (Plymouth (via Grays Ath.), Ashley Bayes (Leyton Orient)

FACT FILE
Founded: 1927
Nickname: Kings
Sponsors:
VPA Entertainment Technology
Colours: Royal blue & White/white/royal
Change colours: Yellow/navy/yellow
Midweek Matches: Tuesday
Reserves' League: Suburban

Programme
16-20 pages 50p
Editor: Dave Thomas
Local Press: Harrow Observer, Willesden
Chronicle, Allsport Weekly,
Edgware & Finchley Times

CLUB PERSONNEL
Chairman: Mark Harrt
Press Officer: Dave Thoomas
Secretary: David Thomas,
9 Hillview Gardens, Kingsbury, NW9 0DE

Manager: Toni Kelly
Physio: Ann Bryan

LEIGHTON TOWN

FACT FILE
Founded: 1885
Nickname: Reds
Colours: Red & white
Change colours: Orange & black
Midweek Matchday: Tuesday
Reserves' League: Suburban

Programme: £1.00
Editor: James Ullyett
Local Press:
Leighton Buzzard Observer, The Citizen
Local Radio: Three Counties Radio,
Radio Chiltern, Mix 96
Website: www.leightontownfc.co.uk

GROUND:

Address: Bell Close, Lake Street, Leighton Buzzard, Beds
Tel: 01525 373311

Directions: From bypass (A505) take A4146 (Billington Rd) towards Leighton Buzzard,
straight overfirst roundabout then straight over mini-r'bout & 1st left into car park -
ground behind Camden Motors just before town centre.
Half mile from Leighton Buzzard (BR) station.
Buses from Luton, Aylesbury and Milton Keynes

Capacity: 2,800   Seats: 155   Cover: 300   Floodlights: Yes

Club Shop: No

Clubhouse: Normal licensing hours.
Snack bar on matchdays - full range of hot snacks & drinks

HONOURS Isthmian Lge Div 3 R-up 95-96; Sth Midlands Lg 66-67 91-92, Lg Cup 90-91,
O'Brien Tphy 90-91, Reserve Div 1 87-88 91-92 94-95, Res Div 2 76-77, Res Challenge Cup
93-94 94-95; Beds Snr Cup 26-27 67-68 68-69 69-70 92-93; Bucks Charity Cup 94-95;98-99
Spartan Lg Div 2 23-24 27-28; Leighton & District Lg, Beds Intermediate Cup (res) 90-91; Beds
Yth Cup 91-92 92-93,94-95 94-95; Chiltern Youth Lg 94-95, Lg Cup 93-94; East Anglian Yth.
Cup 94-95; Assoc Mem. Cup 96-97.98-99, S.E. Co.Youth F'lit Lge (Corinthian Div.) 99-00, 01-02

BEST SEASON **FA Cup:** Third Qual. Round 70-71, 1-2 v St Albans City (A)
FA Vase: 2nd Round 1980-81, 94-95, 95-96, 00-01

PREVIOUS **Leagues:** Leighton & Dist; South Midlands 22-24 26-29 46-54 55-56 76-92;
Spartan 22-53 67-74; United Counties 74-76
Name: Leighton United 1922-63   **Ground:** Wayside

CLUB RECORDS **Attendance:** 1,522 v Aldershot T., Isthmian Lg Div 3, 30/1/93
As Leighton Utd. **Win:13-0** v Met. Railway 1925/6 (H) Spartan League
Defeat: 0-12 v Headington Utd (A) 18.10.47 Spartan League
As Leighton Town **Win:10-1** v Skefko(H) 31.12.66
Defeat: 0-8 v Electrolux(A) 16.10.65 & **0-8** v Harpenden 1965/66 4.11.65

CLUB PERSONNEL
Secretary: James Ullyett,
22 Windsor Avenue, Leighton Buzzard,
Beds. LU7 IAP
Tel: 01525 851986
Chairman: Iain S McGregor
President: M.Hide
Press Officer: James Ullyett

Manager: Paul Burgess
Physio: Geoge Lathwell & Roy Parker

2001-02 Captain:Paul Matthews
P.o.Y.: Paul Matthews
Top scorer: Bill Perry 18

LEYTON

FACT FILE
Founded: 1868
Nickname: Lilywhite
Colours: White/ blue/ white
Change colours: Blue/ white/ blue
Midweek Matches: Tuesday
Reserves' Lge: Essex & Herts Prem. Div.
Programme Editor: Tony Hampford

Secretary/Press Officer/Match Sec.:
Tony Hampford, 282 Lea Bridge Road, Leyton, London E10 7LD
Tel: 0208 539 5405 (B) 07904 012402 (M)

Ground: Wingate Leyton Stadium, 282 Lea Bridge Road, Leyton, London E10 7LD
Tel: 0208 539 5405   Email: enquiries@leytonfc.co.uk

Directions: Lea Bridge Rd. is A104, ground next to Hare & Hounds PH.
Leyton (Central Line) thence bus 58 or 158 to Lea Bridge Road.
Clapton (BR) Walk 100 yds to Lea Bridge Rd. roundabout, buses 48, 55, 56 to
ground. Bus 48 runs direct to ground from London Bridge (BR) station

Capacity: 2,500   Seats: Yes   Cover: Yes   Floodlights: Yes

Clubhouse: open

PREVIOUS **Leagues:** Essex Senior >02; Essex Intermediate; London Spartan

CLUB PERSONNEL
Chairman: Costa Sophocleous
Hon. Life President: Doug Digby
President: Peter Lewis

Manager: TBA
Assistant Manager: John Bass
Club Physio: Simon Purton

TRING TOWN

FACT FILE

Founded: 1904
Nickname: T's
Colours: Red & white /red/red
Change: Yellow & blue stripes/blue/yellow
Midweek Matchday: Tuesday
Reserves' Lge: Suburban Lge
Programme: 24 pages £1
Editor/Press Officer:
Alan Lee (01702 216063)

GROUND:

Address: Pendley Sports Centre, Cow Lane, Tring, Herts HP23 5NS
Tel: 01442 824018

Directions: One mile from Tring centre on A41
- direct connection to M25 (jct20) via new A41 bypass.
One and a half miles from Tring (BR).
Numerous busesfrom station and Watford-Aylesbury routes serve ground

Capacity: 2,500   Seats: 150   Cover: 250   Floodlights: Yes

Club Shop: No

Clubhouse: All licensing hours. Dancehall, pool, darts, kitchen.

HONOURS: Spartan Lg 67-68, R-up 68-69. Herts Charity Shield winners 4,
R-up 2. Athenian Lg Div 2 R-up 76-77, Herts Snr Cup R-up 77-78

PREVIOUS: **Leagues:** Gt Western Combination; Spartan 53-75; Athenian 75-77
Names: None   Ground: Tring Cricket Ground (40 yrs)

RECORD: **Attendance:** 2,500 v West Ham, friendly
Competitive: 2,000 - Aylesbury U. v Slough T., FA Cup 1st Rd replay, 86
Goalscorer & Appearances: Gary Harthill
Win: 8-1 v Willesdon Isthmian Lge 77
Defeat: 1-11 v Epsom & Ewell Isthmian Lge 96

BEST SEASON: FA Cup: 3rd Qual. Rd replay 84-85, 0-5 v Fisher(A) after 1-1
FA Vase: 5th Rd 76-77, 0-2 v Farnborough Town (H)

Players progressing: Peter Gibbs (Watford)

Local Radio: Chiltern, Mix 96
BBC Three Counties Radio

CLUB PERSONNEL

Chairman: Harry Bowden

Secretary: Laurie McParland,
125 Bennetts End Rd,
Hemel Hempstead, Herts HP3 8DX
Tel: 01442 263902 (H) 07836 265105 (M)

Manager: Howard Cowley
Physio: Keith Hardy

WARE

FACT FILE
Founded: 1892
Nickname: Blues
Sponsors: Charvill Bros Ltd
Colours: Blue & white stripes/blue/blue
Change colours: Amber/black
Midweek Matchday: Tuesday
Reserves' Lge:
Essex & Herts Border Comb

GROUND:
Address: Wodson Park, Wadesmill Road, Ware Herts SG12 0HZ
Tel: 01920 463247
Directions: A10 off at junction A602 & B1001 (Ware North), turn right at roundabout
300yds, and follow Ware sign, past Rank factory, turn left at main round
about onto A1170 (Wadesmill Rd). After 3/4 mile stadium on right

Capacity: 3,300   Seats: 312   Cover: 500   Floodlights: Yes
Club Shop: Yes
Clubhouse: Licensed bar open matchdays. Light snacks at refreshment bar

HONOURS: Herts Snr Cup 1898-99 03-04 06-07 21-22 53-54, Herts Char. Shield 26-
27 56-57 58-59 62-63 85-86, Herts Char. Cup R-up 64-65 65-66 78-79 89-90, Spartan Lg
52-53 (Div 1 Sect.B 51-52, Div 2 Sect.A 26-27), Athenian Lg Div 2 Cup 65-66 72-73,East
Anglian Cup 73-74, Herts Co. Lg 08-09 21-22, East Herts Lg 04-05 06-07 (LgCup 06-07),
Perry Cup 26-27 28-29 37-38 51-52 52-53 53-54 55-56, Dunkels Cup 52-53, Rolleston
Cup 39-40 51-52

PREVIOUS: **Leagues:** East Herts; North Middx 07-08; Herts County 08-25;
Spartan 25-55;Delphian 55-63; Athenian 63-75
Grounds: Highfields; Canons Park;
London Rd, Presdales Lower Park 1921-26
RECORDS   **Attendance:** 3,800 v Hendon Amt Cup 56-57
Career Goalscorer: M Hibbert 229.
Goalscorer (season): George Dearman 98(1926-27)
Career Appearances: Gary Riddle 654
Win: 10-1 v Wood Green Town   **Defeat:** 0-11 v Barnet

BEST SEASON: FA Cup: First Round Proper 68-69, 1-6 v Luton Town.

Players progressing: Derek Saunders (Chelsea), Ken Humphrey (QPR)

Programme: 24 pages, 50p
Editor : K.Mynott (01992 551605
Local Press: Herts Mercury, Herts Star,
Herald & Post

CLUB PERSONNEL
Chairman: W ally Luck
Press Officer: Secretary

Secretary: Ian Bush,
42 Burnett Square, Hertford SG14 2HD
Tel: 01992 587334

Manager: Grah am Norcott
Coach: Dermot Drummy
Physio: Frank Roberts

WITHAM TOWN

FACT FILE
Founded: 1947
Nickname: Town
Colours: Red & black stripes/black/black
Change colours: Blue & white
Midweek Matchday: Tuesday
Reserves' Lge: Essex & Herts Border Comb

Programme: 24 pages, 60p
Editor: Nigel Dudley
Local Press: Witham & Braintree Times,
Essex Chronicle, East Anglian DailyTimes,
Evening Gazette
Local Radio: BBC Essex, Essex Radio,
Chelmer Radio

CLUB PERSONNEL
Chairman: Dave Knott
Vice Chairman: Dave Puttock
President: B Olley
Press Officer: G Vale (01376 513861)

Secretary: Jim Claydon,
58 Silver Street, Silver End, Witham,
Essex CM8 3QG
Tel: 01376 584086 (H)
01376 583241 x 426 (B)

Manager: Tony Kinsella
Asst Mgr: Derek Robinson
Physio: Derek Robinson

Ground: Spa Road, Witham, Essex CM8 1UN
Tel: 01376 511198 (lounge) 500146 (reception) 520996 (boardroom)

Directions: From Witham BR (network S.E.) station; through pub car park and follow road to Faulkbourne, at main r'bout turn left and ground is on the right. By road: Off A12 at Witham sign, left at 1st lights (Spinks Lane), right at end of road, follow road under railway bridge - ground 100yds on left

Capacity: 2,500   Seats: 150   Cover: 300   Floodlights: Yes

Clubhouse: Open every night and weekend lunctimes.Hot bar snacks.
Club Shop: No

HONOURS: Essex Snr Lg 70-71 85-86 (R-up 84-85 86-87), Tphy 85-86 (R-up 88-89); Essex Thameside Trophy R-up 95-96; Loctite Tphy SF 90-91

PREVIOUS: **Leagues:** Mid Essex; Essex & Suffolk Border; Essex Senior 71-87
Ground: Spa Road   **Names:** None

CLUB RECORDS **Attendance:** 800 v Billericay Town, Essex Senior League, May 1976
Win: 7-0 v Banstead 27/9/94   **Defeat:** 0-9 v Collier Row 21/10/95
Goalscorer: Colin Mitchell   **Appearances:** Keith Dent (16 years)
Fee received: for Steve Tilson (Southend)

BEST SEASON: **FA Vase:** 5th Round, 85-86
FA Cup: 2nd Qual. Rd   87-88 (v Gravesend),
88-89 (v B. Stortford), 89-90 (v Dartford)

Players progressing to Football League: Steve Tilson (Southend)

WOKINGHAM TOWN

FACT FILE
Formed: 1875
Nickname: The Town
Sponsors: Swan Hill Homes
Colours: Amber & black/black/black
Change colours: All w hite
Midweek matchday: Tuesday

Programme: Pages: 32 Price: £1
Editor: Alan Glenny
Local Press: Wokingham Times,
Wokingham News, Reading Evening Post
Local Radio: 210 FM

CLUB PERSONNEL
Chairman: Phillip Butt MA
President: John Aulsberry

Secretary: John Aulsberry,
8 Paice Green, Wokingham RG40 1YN
Tel: 01189 790441

Manager: John Osborne
Assistant Manager: Dane Carstairs
Physio: Dave Carstairs

2001-02
Captain: Jason Walkington
P.o.Y.: Jason Walkington
Top scorer: Gavin Ward 23

GROUND
Address: c/o Flackwell Heathr F.C.
Directions: M40 jct 3 Wycombe East, follow signs for F/Heath left up Treadway Hill & right at top of hill at roundabout. Wilks park 800yds on right, grd at rear of Magpie (PH). Bus 301 either from bus station or High Street near bottom of Crendon Street which comes from BR station. Ask for Oakland Way

Capacity: 2,000   Seats: 150   Cover: Yes   Floodlights: Yes

Club Shop: No
Clubhouse: Open every night 6.30-11pm & before & after matches. Hot food in tea bar

HONOURS Isthmian Lg R-up 89-90 (Div 1 81-82, Full Members Cup R-up 94-95), Berks & Bucks Snr Cup 68-69 82-83 84-85 95-96, Berks & Bucks I'mediate Cup 52-53

PREVIOUS **Leagues:** Reading & Dist.; Great Western Comb 07-54; Metropolitan 54-57; Delphian 57-59; Corinthian 59-63; Athenian 63-73.
Grounds: Oxford Road 1875-1883; Wellington Road 83-96; Langborough Rd 96-1906, Finchampstead Road 06-99

BEST **FA Trophy:** Semi finals 87-88   **FA Amateur Cup:** 4th Rd 57-58
SEASONS **F.A Cup:** 1st Rd replay 82-83, 0-3 v Cardiff (A) after 1-1

CLUB **Career Appearances:** Dave Cox, 533
RECORDS **Fee received:** £25,000 for Mark Harris (C Palace 88)
Fee paid: £5,000 for Fred Hyatt (Burnham, 1990)

Players progressing: Ian Kirkwood (Reading 53), John Harley (Hartlepool 76), Kirk Corbin (Cambridge 78), Phil Alexander (Norwich 81), DougHatcher (Aldershot 83), Steven Butler & George Torrance (Brentford 84), MarkHarris (C Palace 88), Gary Smart (Oxford 88), Darren Barnard (Chelsea 90), PaulHolsgrove (Luton Town 91), Darron Wilkinson (Brighton) 92

Always look on the bright side of life!

Over the twenty-five years in which we have had the pleasure of compiling non-league annuals in all shapes and sizes, our happy band of photographers, who so loyally trudge out in all weathers, have recorded the highs and lows of the game we love so much.

Included amongst their treasured work are some lighter moments which they have caught for posterity. Here are a few wonderful examples of their work and who knows there could be the making of a Christmas book here!

A favourite photographers' ploy, having taken a team group, is to ask the players to turn around for easy identification from the shirt numbers. Eastwood Town put a different meaning to 'exposure'

Photo: Gordon Whittington

We are proud of our "Team" photos in the Directory - Harrow Borough and Steve & Sarah Stroud.

Photo: Paul Carter.

A new meaning to "moving the goalposts"

If you can't line up the defensive wall correctly then maybe you should make other arrangements!
Kettering's Adam Sollitt at Wembley.
Photo: Neil Thaler

Do they have a blonde lion at Arlesey Town?
Photo: Steve Ayre.

You get a better type of supporter in the Eastern Counties.

A nice touch from the Burton Albion fans!

When Burton Albion visited Yeovil Town in the first leg of the FA Umbro Trophy semi-final the Yeovil supporters, who virtually sang throughout the match, many times referred to the Burton Albion fans as "Northern 'whatevers'" - displaying a rather poor knowledge of geography which some Burton fan(s) very cleverly and amusingly pointed out to them in the second leg! **Photo**: Peter Barnes.

Haven't we seen them somewhere before?

AFC Wimbledon   **Back Row**: Lee Harwood (Assistant Manager), John Harris (Sports Therapist), Dennis Lowndes (Kit Man), Danny Oakins, Danny Roberts, Andy Bell, Glyn Shimell, Sim Johnston, Daniel Couch, Joe Sheerin (Captain), Terry Eames (Manager). **Front Row**: Andy Sullivan, Keith Ward, Lee Sidwell, Glenn Mulcaire, Julian King (Coach), David Fry, Lee Passmore, Kevin Cooper.

Right: Enfield Town

Left:
Maidstone's Ross Edwards outjumps Ramsgate's Mark Jackson . **Photo**: Alan Coomes

Three famous names are once again making their mark in non-League football as Maidstone United celebrate success in the Kent League, and Enfield Town flex their muscles with encouraging support and success in the Essex Senior League. Now we can also look forward to AFC Wimbledon proving themselves to be the real "Dons" as huge crowds follow them through the Combined Counties fixtures this season.
Good luck to them all!

The "Cornish Hop"

The 'Cornish Hop' was a great success and very well run by the South Western League. The keenness, dedication and love shown towards football at lower pyramid levels really gives non-league football tremendous foundations on which all the glamour is built. These four photos were sent to us by Mark Wood and show action in four of the games watched by the touring hundreds of "Hoppers". Hopefully this will be among many such occasions!

SEAGRAVE HAULAGE COMBINED COUNTIES LEAGUE

President: Ron Monkley   **Chairman:** John Bennett
General Secretary: Clive Tidey, 22 Silo Road, Farncombe, Godalming, Surrey GU7 3PA
Tel: 01483 428453 Fax: 01483 426117

The 2001-02 season duly commenced in August with 22 clubs in the Premier Division and just one change from last year's constitution, with Withdean 2000 FC being admitted to the League following approval from the Football Association and their successful negotiation of a ground sharing agreement with Horsham FC. The introduction of Withdean meant that the League now had coverage in five different counties.

Champions Cove FC were again expected to be strong and started well enough. There had been rumours circulating throughout the summer, though, that the successful manager from last season, Steve Beeks, was likely to be moving on and so it proved with Beeks and many of the playing staff moving over to Fleet Town in September. This caused an enormous problem for the club, not helped by pitch problems which led the League to close it down for several weeks while renovations took place.

The early season runners were Feltham, Raynes Park Vale and Chessington & Hook, but all fell away as the campaign progressed and it was not too long before pre-season favourites Ash United and AFC Wallingford came to the fore. By the beginning of November these two had taken over at the top two places, and, although Chipstead, Bedfont, Withdean and Hartley Wintney all put up some resistance, it soon became clear that the championship was already destined for either Ash or Wallingford.

For a long time neither club gave an inch, but as the season drew to a conclusion both teams dropped some unexpected points. Ash were the more susceptible though, and in the final weeks the advantage turned to Wallingford and they went into their final home game of the season needing to beat Merstham to clinch the championship, before their last match in which they would be travelling to Ash. An emphatic 10-1 win over a Merstham side that held out for the first 35 minutes of the game ensured that only pride would be at stake on the Tuesday evening at Ash.

It was congratulations, therefore, to manager Dave Crowdy and the club now look forward to embarking upon further ground improvements to enable them to move up the ladder in the future. Their team was strong all round but their success owed much to the goal scoring talents of Andy Shildrick, well known in the Combined Counties for his efforts with Peppard a few seasons back. Andy finished as the League's top scorer with 37 goals.

Ash, who also topped the 100 point mark, accepted the runners-up spot with great dignity and with their planned and ongoing ground improvements should ensure that they will continue to be a force to be reckoned with.

Chipstead finished third, closely followed by Bedfont, and the consistency of both clubs over several seasons cannot be faulted. Withdean were more than happy with their fifth spot in their first season, whilst a much improved Hartley Wintney side under new manager Mick Wollen did well to clinch sixth place.

At the other end of the table, it was Cranleigh who were unable to improved upon last season's bottom placing and they will now face relegation to the Surrey Senior League if, as expected, they are replaced by Frimley Green, likely to be back in the League after an absence of several seasons.

No club was able to satisfy the requirements of the Ryman League so there will be no promotion or relegation from that competition for the 2002-03 season.

As well as Frimley Green coming in from the Surrey Senior League, however, North Greenford United from the Middlesex County League are likely to be elected. Both clubs have carried out extensive ground improvements in a very short time and are to be congratulated in reaching the required standards. The Combined Counties League is grateful to the Middlesex County League for allowing North Greenford, with their much improved facilities, to progress.

It seemed for some time that Wokingham Town would enter the League voluntarily for the 2002-03 season, but at the death they decided to stay in the Ryman League. As this goes to press there is the possibility of AFC Wimbledon gaining admittance, following their failure to achieve direct entry to the Ryman League. This would leave the League in a strong position with a constitution of 24.

Fortunately the season was kind weather-wise and the first annual fixture list was reckoned to be a success, with all postponed matches for whatever reason being re-arranged with a minimum of delay.

In the Premier Challenge Cup competition, as has become the norm in recent seasons, most of the clubs in the higher reaches of the table made early exits and it was Cobham FC, under the managership of Ken Reid, who belied their indifferent league form, to beat favourites Bedfont in a very close Final played at Woking's magnificent ground, by three goals to two.

In outside competitions, only three clubs made it as far as the First Qualifying Round of the FA Cup, namely Ash United, Bedfont and Chessington & Hook, and they all went out at this stage. A special mention goes to Bedfont though, who did well to draw at Brockenhurst, later conquerors of Kingstonian, only to lose narrowly in the home replay.

The FA Vase saw Cove and Westfield exempted to the Second Round stage, but neither were able to make progress with both clubs losing at home to Bemerton Heath and AFC Wallingford respectively. Ash, however, went on to the Third Round with an impressive 4-0 home win over Falmouth Town to join Wallingford.

Wallingford, somewhat unexpectedly, then went out at that stage, losing by a solitary goal at home to Abingdon Town, but Ash marched on with a 3-1 home win over United Counties League club, Stotfold. They were rewarded with another home tie, this time against tough Northern League opponents Tow Law Town, who were good enough to win 3-0 and end Ash's and the Combined Counties League's direct interest in the competition. A large crowd, superbly handled by the Ash officials, was their reward for an exciting run.

In County competitions there was more success for AFC Wallingford, who won the Berks & Bucks Senior Trophy by beating neighbours Didcot Town, from the Hellenic League, by three goals to two, in an exciting match.

In the meantime, Ash United won the Aldershot Senior Cup whilst pride of place in the Surrey Senior Cup went to Westfield who progressed in a very strong county competition to the Fourth Round before going down 0-2 at Sutton United. Bedfont Reserves also did very well to reach the semi-finals of the Middlesex Premier Cup before losing to Hendon Reserves and in other competitions, Chessington & Hook won the Southern Combination Challenge Cup, beating Ashford Town 5-3, whilst Sandhurst Town reached the Semi-finals of the Southern Counties Floodlit Cup, losing out to Fleet Town in a two-legged affair.

Alan Constable, League Fixture Secretary

HONOURS 2001-02

Premier Division Champions	AFC Wallingford	Programme of the Season Winners	Merstham
Premier Division Runners up	Ash United	Programme of the Season R/U	Hartley Wintney
Premier Challenge Cup Winners	Cobham	Ladbrokes Sportsmanship Award	Westfield
Premier Challenge Cup R/U	Bedfont	President's Monthly Award:	
Division One Champions	Ash United	Sept:	Chessington & Hk
Division One Runners up	AFC Wallingford	Oct:	Ash United
Div One Challenge Cup Winners	Sandhurst Town	Nov:	AFC Wallingford
Div One Challenge Cup R/U	Westfield	Dec:	Hartley Wintney
Div One Challenge Shield Winners	Bedfont	Jan:	Ash United
Div One Challenge Shield R/U	Westfield	Feb:	Farnham Town
Prem Div Fair Play Champions	Westfield	Mar:	AFC Wallingford
Prem Div Fair Play Runners up	Ash United	Apr:	Withdean 2000
Div One Fair Play Champions	Merstham		
Div One Fair Play Runners up	Cove		

FINAL LEAGUE TABLES 2001-02

PREMIER DIVISION

	P	W	D	L	F	A	Pts	GD
AFC Wallingford	42	33	5	4	134	39	104	95
Ash United	42	31	7	4	137	44	100	93
Chipstead	42	24	8	10	90	55	80	35
Bedfont	42	23	8	11	80	58	77	22
Withdean 2000	42	21	13	8	84	52	76	32
Hartley Wintney	42	21	9	12	109	77	72	32
Raynes Park Vale	42	18	13	11	79	56	*69	23
Southall	42	20	7	15	97	77	68	20
Walton Casuals	42	20	7	15	88	63	67	25
Feltham	42	18	10	14	77	64	64	13
Chessington & Hk	42	16	9	17	81	73	57	8
Westfield	42	15	12	15	69	61	57	8
Sandhurst Town	42	16	6	20	73	74	54	-1
Farnham Town	42	15	6	21	54	75	51	-21
Cove	42	15	6	21	72	86	*49	-14
Chessington Utd	42	13	8	21	60	79	47	-19
Godalming & G	42	12	9	21	57	88	45	-31
Cobham	42	12	7	23	62	76	43	-14
Viking Greenford	42	11	7	24	55	106	*42	-51
Merstham	42	9	8	25	59	106	35	-47
Reading Town	42	8	5	29	47	115	29	-68
Cranleigh	42	4	3	35	26	166	15	-140

DIVISION ONE

	P	W	D	L	F	A	Pts	GD
Ash United	26	17	5	4	96	39	56	57
AFC Wallingford	26	16	6	4	65	42	54	23
Hartley Wintney	26	15	6	5	75	38	51	37
Bedfont	26	15	6	5	71	30	*50	41
Raynes Park Vale	26	13	6	7	53	51	45	2
Westfield	26	13	4	9	71	36	43	35
Sandhurst Town	26	14	2	10	63	49	*41	14
Cobham	26	10	4	12	48	56	34	-8
Merstham	26	10	2	14	46	59	32	-13
Feltham	26	8	4	14	48	50	*31	-2
Chessington Utd	26	8	5	13	55	77	*31	-22
Chessington & Hk	26	6	8	12	41	59	26	-18
Farnham Town	26	3	3	20	26	89	12	-63
Cove	26	3	1	22	27	110	10	-83

* points adjustment

LEADING GOALSCORERS 2001-02

PREMIER DIVISION

37	A Shildrick	AFC Wallingford
31	E Barrs-James	Walton Casuals
30	S Mitchell	Ash United
29	S Joyce	Ash United
28	M Nolan	Chipstead
25	P Mulvaney	Sandhurst Town

DIVISION ONE

43	T Finlayson	Ash United
36	S Shepherd	Ash United
26	L Aberdein	AFC Wallingford
17	T Peters	Hartley Wintney
16	S Holman	Hartley Wintney
15	R Burns	Chessington & Hook

PREMIER DIVISION RESULTS CHART 2001-02

	1	2	3	4	5	6	7	8	9	10	11	12	13	14	15	16	17	18	19	20	21	22
1 AFC Wall.	X	2-2	3-0	4-1	3-1	2-1	3-1	5-0	6-0	3-0	2-4	10-2	4-2	10-1	2-1	4-1	7-1	7-1	7-0	1-0	3-2	0-1
2 Ash Utd	0-0	X	3-1	0-3	4-0	1-0	3-0	2-2	8-0	4-0	5-0	8-1	2-1	9-0	5-4	5-4	3-0	4-0	2-2	4-2	0-0	0-0
3 Bedfont	0-1	0-2	X	2-1	0-2	2-2	1-0	3-4	8-0	2-0	1-2	1-2	2-0	3-1	2-2	5-1	2-0	4-2	1-0	2-1	5-2	1-1
4 Chess & H	2-2	3-2	2-3	X	3-0	1-1	0-1	4-1	5-0	0-3	2-0	3-0	2-3	2-3	1-0	4-1	1-0	2-3	2-1	1-4	2-1	1-2
5 Chess Utd	0-1	2-0	1-1	3-0	X	0-1	0-0	2-6	5-1	1-1	0-3	5-0	2-4	3-2	1-1	1-1	1-1	0-6	4-0	1-4	1-2	0-3
6 Chipstead	1-2	2-4	5-0	2-2	2-1	X	5-4	4-1	9-0	4-0	1-0	2-3	2-1	2-2	2-0	0-3	4-1	2-2	1-0	2-1	1-0	2-2
7 Cobham	1-1	2-6	0-1	2-3	3-1	0-2	X	0-2	8-0	1-1	0-1	0-0	1-2	4-1	0-3	2-1	5-3	0-2	1-0	2-1	5-0	0-4
8 Cove	2-3	1-6	2-3	0-2	4-1	0-4	1-0	X	8-0	1-0	1-1	2-1	1-2	1-2	3-3	2-0	1-0	1-3	1-1	1-5	0-1	0-1
9 Cranleigh	0-3	0-7	1-2	0-3	0-1	1-2	2-1	2-1	X	0-3	1-1	2-2	1-4	0-3	1-5	1-5	1-2	1-4	0-0	1-4	1-4	2-4
10 Farnham	1-1	4-3	2-4	2-0	3-1	1-1	2-0	1-4	4-0	X	4-1	2-4	1-4	3-0	0-2	0-2	2-1	2-3	1-3	1-6	0-2	2-0
11 Feltham	1-0	0-2	1-2	2-2	5-1	3-1	0-1	3-2	11-0	0-1	X	3-0	0-0	5-1	2-2	4-1	3-2	3-2	1-1	0-2	3-3	1-3
12 God & G	0-1	1-4	2-3	0-0	1-3	0-2	1-2	1-1	2-0	2-0	2-1	X	2-4	3-0	1-2	4-1	1-0	1-2	1-0	2-3	2-1	0-1
13 Hartley W	2-1	1-2	0-2	2-2	3-1	4-1	2-2	4-0	9-0	0-3	1-1	5-3	X	4-3	1-1	5-2	1-4	3-4	2-3	2-1	2-2	6-1
14 Merstham	1-3	2-0	2-3	1-1	0-2	0-2	1-1	0-2	2-3	2-0	5-1	1-1	2-3	X	2-2	3-1	1-1	3-1	2-7	0-2	0-2	1-1
15 RP Vale	1-3	0-2	2-2	2-1	1-0	0-2	5-2	4-0	1-0	3-0	0-1	2-2	2-1	1-3	X	7-0	0-1	2-1	4-1	0-1	2-1	3-3
16 Reading	0-4	1-2	0-0	0-5	2-3	0-1	1-0	0-2	4-0	1-2	2-0	1-0	2-2	0-2	2-3	X	0-3	2-3	1-2	1-7	0-6	0-5
17 Sandhurst	2-3	1-3	0-3	4-2	1-0	1-1	4-1	3-0	1-3	0-0	0-2	1-0	2-4	3-2	0-0	3-0	X	4-0	6-0	11-2	3-1	2-3
18 Southall	1-4	3-5	2-0	3-0	1-1	6-1	2-3	2-4	5-0	F	3-0	2-2	2-2	1-0	1-1	4-0	1-4	X	5-0	1-1	1-3	1-1
19 Viking Gr	0-4	0-8	2-1	5-3	1-2	2-5	2-1	0-0	2-1	2-1	2-2	2-2	3-7	2-1	0-1	1-2	0-1	1-5	X	2-4	1-4	0-1
20 Walton Cs	1-4	1-1	2-3	3-2	2-1	0-1	2-3	3-5	2-0	2-0	1-2	0-1	1-1	4-1	2-2	1-1	2-2	0-3	3-0	X	1-3	2-3
21 Westfield	0-2	0-1	0-0	3-3	2-2	0-3	0-2	1-0	1-0	4-0	1-1	2-2	2-0	2-0	2-1	0-0	5-2	1-2	3-2	0-1	X	0-0
22 Withdean	1-3	0-1																				X

PREMIER CHALLENGE CUP 2001-02

SEMI-FINALS

Bedfont	v	Godalming & Guildford	3-0		Chessington United	v	Cobham	1-4

FINAL

Bedfont	v	Cobham	2-3

DIVISION ONE CHALLENGE CUP 2001-02

SEMI-FINALS

AFC Wallingford	v	Westfield	0-2		Sandhurst Town	v	Ash United	4*2

FINAL

Sandhurst Town	v	Westfield	4-0	at Ashford Town (Middx) FC

DIVISION ONE CHALLENGE SHIELD 2001-02

SEMI-FINALS

Ash United	v	Westfield	1-3		Hartley Wintney	v	Bedfont	1-2

FINAL

Bedfont	v	Westfield	1-1	aet. Bedfont won 4-3 on penalties

AFC WALLINGFORD

Secretary: Richard may, 27 Chiltern Crescent, Wallingford, Oxon OX100PG
Tel Nos: 01491 837391 (H) 01491 823612 (W) 07748 828574(M)
Ground: Wallingford Sports Park, Hithercroft Road,Wallingford,Oxon.(Tel:01491 835044
Directions : Nearest Railway station: Cholsey & Moulsford. Bus - Thames Transit.
Capacity: 1,500 Cover: 100 Seats: 40 Floodlights: Yes
Clubhouse: Open evenings 7.30-11.00, Sat & Sun Tea & snacks available 01491 835044
HONOURS: Chiltonian Prem Lge 97-98; Bon Accord Trophy 95-96 Combined Counties
League Premier Division Champions 01-02,Runners Up 2000-01, Berks & Bucks Senior Trophy :
Winners 01-02 Finalists 2000-01, North Bucks Nairne Paul Cup Winners 2000-01
RECORDS: **Attendance:** 280 v Reading Town **Goalscorer:** Carl Henry 62, 97-98
In Career: Steve Wood 130 92-98 **Appearances:** Anthony Hill 243
PREVIOUS: **Leagues:** Chiltonian Lge 95-98
2000-01 **Captain:** Gary Stevens **P.o.Y.:** James McKinney **Top Scorer:**Andy Shildrick48

FACT FILE
Founded: 1995
Colours: Red & black hoops/black/red & black
Change colours: Blue & white
Midweek matchday: Tuesday
Programme: 20 pages; price 50p
Editor: Andy Ham (01491 837608)

CLUB PERSONNEL
President: Ken Lester
Chairman: Lindsay Townsend
Tel: 01491 839103 (H)
Match Secretary: G Lee
21 Orchard Close, Brightwell, Wallingford,
Oxon. Tel: 01491 836921 (H)
Manager: Dave Crowdy

AFC WIMBLEDON

Secretary: Trevor Williams, 110B Cavendish Road, Colliers Wood, London SW19 2EZ
Tel: 0208 401 1702 or 0208 540 0771 (H) 0208 540 7396 (B)
email: clubsec@afcwimbledon.co.uk

Ground: Kingsmeadow Stadium, Jack Goodchild Way, 422a Kingston Rd.,
Kingston-upon-Thames, Surey KT1 3PB
Tel: 0208 547 3335/6 0208 974 5713 (Fax)
Website: www.afcwimbledon.co.uk
Directions: From town centre - Cambridge Rd on to Kingston Rd (A2043) to Malden Rd.
From A3, turn off at New Malden, turn left on to A2043 - grd 1 mile on left.
Half mile from Norbiton (BR)
Capacity: 9,000 **Covered - Terracing:** 3,500 **Seating:** 690

FACT FILE
Founded: 2002
Nickname: The Dons
Colours: All blue

CLUB PERSONNEL
President: Alan Batsford
Chairman: Kris Stewart
0208 540 7396 (B) 07970 702798 (M)
Press Secretary: Ivor Heller
0208 946 4664 (H) 0208 542 9535 (B)
07973 322409 (M)

ASH UNITED

Secretary: James Avenell, 82 Ewins Close,Ash,Aldershot, Hants. GU12 6SB
Tel/FAX No: 01252 321528
Email: alex@smith-gander.freeserve.co.uk.
Ground: Youngs Drive, off Shawfield Rd, Ash, Nr Aldershot Tel: 01252 745757
Directions: A323 towards Ash, left into Shawfield Rd, left into Youngs Drive
1 mile from both Ash and Ash Vale BR stations. Bus - Stagecoach 20A, 550
Capacity: 1,500 **Seats:** None **Cover:** Yes **Floodlights:** Yes
HONOURS: Prem Chall Cup 97-98; Comb Co Lge 81-2, 86-7, 98-99; Aldershot Sen Cup
98-99,01-02
CLUB RECORDS **Attendance;** 650 v Tiverton Town FA Vase
Goalscorer: Shaun Mitchell 44 **Appearances:** Tommy Burton 540
BEST SEASON **FA Cup:** 2nd Qual Rd v Walton & Hersham 98-99
FA Vase: 4th Rd v Tiverton Town 98-99 & v Tow Law 2001-02
PREVIOUS **Ground:** Ash Common Rec. 70-71**Leagues:** Surrey Snr, Aldershot Snr.

FACT FILE
Founded: 1911
Colours: Green with red trim/green/green
Change colours: All blue
Midweek Matchday: Tuesday
Programme: 36 pages, #1.00
Editor: T.B.A.
Captain : Mattie Everard
Top Scorer: Shaun Mitchell (44)

CLUB PERSONNEL
President; Paul Murray Chairman: Robert J
Atkins Vice Chairman: Geoff Hills
Gen Manager: Alex Smith-Gander
Manager: Mick Wollen Asst.Man Jamie Horton

BEDFONT

Secretar Les King, 14 Harlequin Close, Isleworth, Middlesex. TW7 7LA
Tel No: 0208 894 5525 (H) 0208 392 3021 (W)
Ground: The Orchard, Hatton Rd, Bedfont, Middx. Tel: 0208 8907264
Directions: Turn down Faggs Rd opposite Hatton Cross (Picadilly Line) station on Great
South Western Rd (A30), then sharp right into Hatton Rd. Ground opposite
Duke of Wellington pub. Bus - Westlink 203
Capacity:2,000 **Seats:** 100 **Cover:** 50**Floodlights:** Yes **Clubhouse:** Yes

HONOURS: Comb. Co's Chal. Vase 92-93 (Res. Div R-up 88-89, Res. Cup R-up 89-90,
Grant McClennan Yth Cup 91-92), Middx Lg 73-74 76-77 (Div 1 (Res) & Div 1 Cup 71-72 78-79
79-80, Surrey Prem. Lg 84-85 86-87, Middx I'mediate Cup 69-70 76-77, Inter. Contois Tour. 1992,
Liege Euromann Tour. 89, Harold Clayton Cup 90-91, Hounslow & Dist. Div 1 (Res) 86-87

PREVIOUS Names: Bedfont Inst.(1900), Bedfont Rangers(1950) & Fairholme Utd(1953) merged
1968. Club later merged with Interharvester(1973) & Bedfont Eagles(1988). **Ground:** Bedfont Rec.

FACT FILE
Founded: 1968
Colours: Yellow & blue stripes/blue/blue
Change colours: All red or White/navy/navy
Midweek matches: Tuesday
Programme: 20 pages, 50p. Editors: Les King
(020 8891 1985)

CLUB PERSONNEL
President: Roger Cooper
Chairman: Mick Carroll
Manager: John Morris
Coach: Ron Griffin
Asst. Man.: Mark Wilson

CHESSINGTON & HOOK UNITED

Secretary: Alan Warwick, 38 Hartfield Road, Chessington, Surrey. KT9 2PW
Tel:020 8397 1843(H)

Ground: Chalky Lane, Chessington, Surrey. Tel: 01372 729892

Directions: Turn off A243 into Chalky Lane opposite Chessington World of Adventure
Theme Park Railway - Chessington South. Bus - London Transport 71.

Capacity: Seats: Cover: Floodlights: Yes

HONOURS: Combined Counties Lge Prem Cup R-up 97-98, Surrey County Lge Prem Div
R-up 96-97, Div 1 70-71, Combination Cup 2001-02

PREVIOUS **Leagues:** Middx Lge 68-69, Surrey County 69-72, Home Counties 72-78
Comb Co 78-81, Surrey Prem, Surrey Comb, Surrey Prem.

FACT FILE
Founded: 1968
Colours: All blue
Change colours: Yellow/black/yellow
Midweek Matchday:
Programme: Yes

CLUB PERSONNEL
Chairman: Graham Ellis
63 Stormont Way, Chessington,
Surrey. KT9 2QW
Tel: 020 8391 4829(H)
Manager: Paul Ellis 020 8397 8499 (H)

CHESSINGTON UNITED

FACT FILE

Secretary: John Carleton, 22 Dawson Road, Kingston upon Thames, Syurrey KT1 3AT
Tel No: 0208546 8266 & 0208241 8461 FAx: 0208241 8461 Mombilr: 07785 986943
Email: carleton-john@ hotmail.com

Colours: Gren & white hoops/white/green
CLUB PERSONNEL

Ground: Fetcham Park Utd., Riverlane, Leatherhead, Surrey. Tel: 01372 363995
Nearest Railway Station: Leatherhead
Buses: London Country 465 & 479

President:R.Jaramillo

Chairman: Richard Jaramillo
19 Purbeck Close, Merstham, Redhill
Surrey RH1 1PG
Tel: 01737 644588

2001-02 Captain: Mark Arnett P.o.Y.:Gary Lyon Top Scorer: Kevin Wareham 8

Match Secretary: as Secretary

CHIPSTEAD

Secretary: Geoff Corner, 20 Sunnymede Avenue, Carshalton Beeches, Surrey SM54JF
Tel: 0181 642 0827 (H)

Ground: High Road, Chipstead, Surrey. Tel: 01737 553250

Directions: Brighton Road northbound, left into Church Lane, left into HogcrossLane, right
High Road. 1 1/2/ miles from Chipstead (BR). Bus -London County 405, 407
Capacity: 2,000 Seats: 30 Cover: 100 Floodlights: Yes

HONOURS Surrey Premier Lg R-up 82-83 83-84 85-86 (Lg Cup 82-83 84-85 85-86),
Combined Co's Lge 89-90 (R-up 90-91 92-93, Lg Cup 86-87 90-91 92-93, Elite Class Cup R-up 89-
90, Reserve Section Cup 92-93)

BEST SEASON **FA Cup:** 1998-99 **FA Vase:** 1998-99

CLUB RECORDS Attendance: 903
Goalscorer: Appearances:

PREVIOUS **Leagues:** Surrey Intermediate 62-82; Surrey Premier 82-86

FACT FILE
Founded: 1906 Nickname: Chips
Colours: Green & white/black/black
Change colours: Purple/yellow/yellow
Midweek matchday: Tuesday
Programme: 36pages
2001-02
Captain: Chris Roberts P.o.Y.:Paul Stanford
Top Scorer: Mick Nolan 30
CLUB PERSONNEL
President: Dave Argent
Chairman:D.Faircloth, 156 St Andrews Road,
Coulsdon,Surrey CR5 3HF(0208 668 8348)
Manager: R.ussellHarmsworth
Coach: Ricky Kidd

COBHAM

Secretary: Craig Swift, 28 Brushfield Way, Knaphill, Woking, Surrey GU21 2TG
Tel Nos: 01407 891 2429 (W) 07815 108504 (M)

Ground: Leg O'Mutton Field, Anvil Lane, Downside Bridge Rd, Cobham, Surrey
Tel: 01932 865959

Directions: A3 turnoff A245, A307 (Portsmouth) towards Leatherhead, right intoBetween Streets,
rt to Downside Rd then rt opposite car park. Cobham & StokeD'Abernon (BR) 2 miles. Bus -
Green Line 715, London Country 501, 513

Capacity: 2,000 Seats: None Cover: Yes Floodlights: Yes Club Shop: No
Clubhouse: Yes

HONOURS Combined Co's Lge Cup, Res Lge (3)

BEST SEASON **FA Cup:** **FA Vase:** 1998-99 3rd Rd.

CLUB RECORDS **Attendance:** 2,000 v Showbiz XI, charity game 1975

PREVIOUS **League:** Surrey Senior **Grounds:** Cobham Rec

FACT FILE
Founded: 1892
Nickname: Hammers
Sponsor: Peter Haworth Consultancy
Colours: Red & Black /black/black
Change colours:Black & White stripes
Midweek matchday: Tuesday
Programme: Yes

CLUB PERSONNEL
Chairman: Chris Woolston
President: E D Strange
Manager: John Mephan
Player-Coach: Alan Carey
Physio: C Bird

COVE

Secretary: Graham Brown, 6 Longfield Close,Haley Estate, Farnborough. GU14 8HQ
Tel: 01252 650920 - Club Email: covefc1897@aol.com
Ground: Oak farm Fields,7 Squirrels Lane, Farnborough, Hants GU14 8PB. Tel.: 01252 543615
Directions: Farnborough (BR) 2 miles; right into Union Street, right at lights into Prospect Rd, left into
West Heath Rd, right into Romayne Close and follow signs to Cove FC. Or, M3 jct 4, follow A325 signed
Aldershot & Farnham, right into Prospect Rd. (signed Cove FC & Farnborough Town FC), then as above
Capacity: 3,500   Seats: 75   Cover: 475   Floodlights: Yes   Club Shop: No
Clubhouse: Mon-Fri 7-11, Sat 12-11, Sunday 12-3 & 7-11. Hot food on matchdays
HONOURS: Surrey I'mediate Lg; Surrey Prem. Lg x5, R-up x3, Lg Cup x3, Res.Section x4 ,R-up
x4, Res. Cup x2; Combined Co's Lg Cup 81-82; Hants Lg Div 3, Div 4, Div 2 R-up;
Aldershot - Snr Cup x5, R-up, Snr Shield x4, Snr Lg, Div 2x3, Div 2 Cup, Div 4 Cup
PREVIOUS Leagues: Aldershot Jnr; Aldershot I'mediate 45-48; Surrey I'mediate 48-71; Surrey
Snr 71-73; Hants 74-81; Combined Counties 81-90 &95-01; Isthmian 90-95;
CLUB RECORDS Attendance: 1,798 v Aldershot, Isthmian Lg Div 3, 1/5/93
BEST SEASON   FA Cup: 2nd Rd 2000-01 **FA Vase:** 5th Rd 00-01 2-3 v Chippenham Tn. (H)

FACT FILE
Founded: 1897
Sponsors: Sunnyside Removals
Colours: Yellow & black stripes/yellow/yellow
Change colours: Red & white stripes/red/red
Midweek Matches: Tuesday
Reserves' League: Comb. Cos. 1st Div
Programme: 30 pages, 50p
Editor: Graham Brown (01252 650920)

CLUB PERSONNEL
Chairman: P.Wentworth
President: Ron Brown

FARNHAM TOWN

Secretary: Mrs Barbara Fripp, 70 Lower Farnham Rd., Aldershot. GU12 4EA (01252 657184)

Ground: Memorial Ground, West Street, Farnham, Surrey (01252 715305)

Directions: From A31, direction Winchester, take 2nd turning into town at Coxbridge roundabout.
Follow West Street until you come to new mini roundabout - the Memorial Ground is on the right.

Capacity: 2,000   Seats: 30 Cover: 150   Floodlights: Yes
Clubhouse: Open every evening and match daysClub Shop: Yes

HONOURS	Combined Counties Lg 90-91 91-92, Challenge Cup Prem Div 95-96, Challenge Tphy 91-92 (R-up 89-90).
CLUB RECORDS	**Attendance:** 500 v Kingstonian, Surrey Snr Cup 1960.
PREVIOUS	**Leagues:** Surrey Intermediate; Surrey Snr 47-71; Spartan 71-75; London Spartan 75-80: Combined Counties 80-92.
BEST SEASON	**FA Cup:** Never past Qualifying Rounds

FACT FILE
Founded: 1921   Nickname: The Town
Sponsors:T.B.A.
Colours: All claret & blue.
Change: All Yellow
Midweek Matchday: Tuesday
Reserve League: Comb Counties Res Div
Programme: 32 pages 50p
Editor: T,B,A,
CLUB PERSONNEL
Chairman: DerekWythe
President: Paul Cooper
Press Officer: Charlie White
Manager: Andy Nunn
Asst Manager: Dave Ward
Coach: Simon Musslewhite

FELTHAM

Secretary: John Cronk,Flat 8 Wyvern Court, 24 Gordon Rd, Ashford, Middsx TW15 3EZ
Tel: 01784 243122 (H) 0208 839 2104 (B) Website: http://www.felthamfc.freeserve.co.uk/
Ground: Feltham Arena(All weather surface), Shakespeare Ave., Feltham, Middx.Tel: 0208 890
6164 (club), 0208 890 6905 (ground)**Directions:** BR to Feltham & 5 mins walk thro' Glebelands
Park. Buses 90, 285,117, 237, H24 or H25 to Feltham station, or 116 to top of Shakespeare Ave.
By car: M3, M4, A312 Staines road towards Bedfont, 2nd left is Shakespeare Ave
Capacity: 10,000   Seats: 650   Cover: 1,500   Floodlights: Yes
Clubhouse: Open 7 days a week. 2 bars, dancehall available for hire Club Shop: No

HONOURS	Surrey Snr Lg R-up 65-66 (Lg Cup 65-66), Charity Cup 63-64 65-66),Southern Comb. Cup(2)(R-up(2)), Middx Summer Cup, Isthmian Div 2 80-81, Comb.Cos. Lge Co. 96-97
PREVIOUS	**Leagues:** Feltham: West Middx Sunday; Staines & Dist.; Hounslow & Dist.; Surrey Snr 63-68; Spartan 68-73; Athenian 74-77; Isthmian 78-95
CLUB RECORDS	**Attendance:** 1,9 38 v Hampton,Middlesex Senior Cup 1968 **Goalscorer:** Paul Clarke 130**Appearances:** Paul Clarke 326
BEST SEASON	**FA Cup:** 3rd Qual.Rd.77-78, 1-4 v Tilbury; 82-83, 0-1 v Chesham U

FACT FILE
Founded: 1946 Sponsors: Feltham first
Colours: Royal blue & white halves/blue/blue
Change colours: Red /White or Blue/White
Midweek Matches: Wednesday
Programme: 20 pages, 50p
Editor:Chris Thompso
Email: cjthompson-uk@yahoo.co.uk
CLUB PERSONNEL
Chairman: Brian Barry
Press Officer: Secretary
Managers: Sammy Boyd & Dave Patience
Players progressing:Rachid Harkouk,Tony
Witter(CrystalP) Andy Pape (QPR), Pat Gavin
(Gillingham) Bobby Wilson (Brentford)

FRIMLEY GREEN

Secretary: Mark O'Grady, 8 Rokers Place, Yateley, Hants. GU46 6FF
Tel: 01252 879883 (H) 01923 234300 (B) 07812 026390 (M)
email: mogradyuk@yahoo.co.uk

Ground: Frimley Green Recretarion Ground, Frimley Green Road, Frimley Green,
Camberley, Surrey GU16   Tel: 01252 835089

Travel: Nearest railway station: Frimley or Farnborough (North)
Bus: Stagecoach, Hants & Surrey 49, 50 & 530

FACT FILE
Founded: 1919

Colours: Blue & white halves/white/white

CLUB PERSONNEL
President: Paul Grace
Chairman: Craig Fennell
Tel: 01252 317325 (H) 07831 248260 (M)

GODALMING & GUILDFORD

Secretary: Eddie Russell, 31 Harts Gardens, Guildford, Surrey GU2 9QB. 01483 535287 (H & B)

Ground: Weycourt, Meadrow, Godalming, Surrey (01483 417520)
Directions: A3100 from Guildford - past Out & About Hotel on left, then 'Save' petrol station on right, then 1st right 50 yards on. From Godalming on A3100, grd on left by Leathern Bottle pub. Three quarters of a mile from Farncombe BR station

Capacity: 3,000   Seats: 200   Cover: 200   Floodlights: Yes   Club Shop: No
Clubhouse: Open Tues, Thurs eves, matchdays. Hot & cold snacks available
HONOURS   Combined Co's Lg 83-84, Lge Chall. Trophy 82-83, Res Lge 95-96 96-97, Res Chall Cup 92-93 97-98, Chall Shield 96-97: Southern Comb Chall Cup 97-98
PREVIOUS   **Leagues:** Guildford & Dist 50-71; Surrey Intermediate 71-78; Surrey Co. Senior 78-79
RECORDS   **Attendance:** 600+ ex-Guildford City XI v ex-Football Lg XI. Tony Burge benefit 91
Goalscorer: Sean Gorman 127   **Appearances:** Paul Monger 356
BEST SEASON FA Cup: 1st Q.Rd.   **FA Vase:** 2nd Rd.
Players progressing: John Humphreys (MIllwall)

FACT FILE
Founded: 1950
Nickname: The Gees
Colours: Green & yellow/black/black
Change colours: Blue & white/white/blue.
Midweek matchday: Tuesday
Programme: Yes

CLUB PERSONNEL
Chairman: Jane Phillips
Life President: W F Kyte
Press Officer: Secretary
Manager: Roger Steer
Asst Managers: Andy Dear
Physio: Jan Eaton

HARTLEY WINTNEY

Secretary: Steve Shimwell, 13 Clayton Close, Hartley Wintney, Hook, Hants. RG27 8HD
Tel No: 01252 844421 (H) 01252 844402 (W) 07703 193689 (M)
Ground: Memorial Playing Fields, Green Lane, Hartley Wintney, Hants
Tel: 01252 843586
Directions: A30 west through Camberley, left at parade of shops at beginning of village then sharp right - ground on right. Two miles from Winchfield (BR)
Buses: Stagecoach 200, Bee Line 111, 112
Capacity:4,000   Seats: None   Cover: Yes   Floodlights: Yes
HONOURS: Aldershot Senior League winners: 73-74,74-75,75-76. Alderhot Senior Cup Winners 76-77,80-81 CoCo.League Winners 82-83,R-up 80-81
BEST SEASON   **FA Cup:** Do not compete   **FA Vase:** Do not compete
PREVIOUS   **Leagues:** Basingstoke/ Aldershot

ACT FILE
Founded: 1897
Nickname: The Row
Colours: Orange & black/black/black & orange
Change colours: All white or Red/black/black
Midweek matchday: Tuesday
Programme: Yes

CLUB PERSONNEL
Chairman: James Cooke
President: W A Mitchell
Treasurer: D.Willoughby
Press Officer: Luke Mullen (07860 729608 (M)

MERSTHAM

Secretary: Richard Baxter, 2 Wood Street, Merstham, Surrey. RH1 3PF
Tel: 01737 645748 (H) 01293 450809 (B) Email: the.baxters@virgin.net
Ground: Merstham Rec., Weldon Way, Merstham, Redhill, Surrey RH1 3QB (01737 644046)
Directions: Leave Merstham village (A23) by School Hill, take 5th right (WeldonWay), clubhouse and car park 100m on right. 10 mins walk from Merstham (BR);down School Hill, under railway bridge, then 5th turning on right into WeldonWay. Bu98-99s - London Country 430, 432 & 435
Capacity: 2,000   Seats: 100   Cover: 100   Floodlights: Yes   Club Shop: No
Clubhouse: Across adjacent footpath. Open daily (am & pm). Snacks available
HONOURS Combined Co's Lg R-up 87-88 89-90 (Elite Class Cup 89-90 (R-up 90-91), Res. Sect. 90-91), Spartan Lg 78-79 (Lg Cup 79-80), Surrey Snr Lg 71-72, Surrey Snr Char. Cup 79-80, E. Surrey Char. Cup 80-8 98-99, Surrey I'mediate Lg 52-3.Fair Play & Prog Awards 01-02
CLUB RECORDS Attendance: 532
BEST SEASON   **FA Cup:** 3rd Q Rd   **FA Vase:** 4th Rd.
PREVIOUS   **Leagues:** Redhill & Dist.; Surrey Co.S.E. I'mediate; Surrey Snr 64-78; London Spartan 78-85   **Grounds:**None

FACT FILE
Founded: 1892
Club Sponsors: Brewers
Colours: Amber & black stripes/black/amber
Change colours:White,navy, red.
Midweek matches: Tuesday/Thursday
Programme: Yes Editor:Mrs S Fish

CLUB PERSONNEL
Chairman:Ted Hickman President: Bill Lawton
Press Officer: Roger Peerless
Manager: Mick Sullivan
Asst Manager: Peter Gibson
2001-002 Captain: Shane Traynor
P.o.Y.:Ben Jupp
Top Goalscorer Rhod Davies

NORTH GREENFORD UNITED

Secretary: Mrs B Bivens, 1 The Green, sarratt, Hertfordshire WD3 6AY
Tel: 01923 270057 (H & Fax)

Ground: Berkeley Fields, Berkeley Avenue, Greenford, Middlesex UB6
Tel: 0208 422 8923

Travel: Nearest railway station: Greenford (Central Line) & Sudbury Hill (Piccadilly)
Bus: Metro Link 92

FACT FILE
Founded: 1944

Colours: Blue & white/blue/blue

CLUB PERSONNEL
President: John Bignell
Chairman: Mick Hardwick
Tel: 0208 423 0702 (H)

Press Secretary: Secretary

Merstham. Photo: Gordon Whittington

AFC Wallingford, Champions of the Combined Counties League. Photo: Eric Marsh

Sandhurst Town: The first team did not win any competitions this season despite reaching three cup semi-finals, but the club submitted, as something a little different, a photograph of the club officers, most of whom have given numerous years of service to the club. The club treasurer, John 'Lofty' Parker, has been associated with the club as a player and officer for over thirty years. Back Row: Brian Levey (Vice President), Mick Morgan (Vice Chairman), Phil Long (General Manager), Phil Sigley (Chairman). Middle Row: John 'Lofty' Parker (Treasurer), Ian Bealey (Committee Member), Ray Clark (Groundsman), Tony Ford (Secretary. Front: Roger Inions (Asst Secretary).

RAYNES PARK VALE

Secretary: Dave Brenen, 22 The Crescent, Belmont, Surrey SM2 6BJ
Tel No: 0208 296 8626 (H&W)) Fax: 0208286 4858
e-mail: davidbrenen@blueyonder.co.uk

Ground: Prince George's Playing Field, Raynes Park. SW20 9NB Tel: 07714 339747
Directions: Bus - London Transport 163 & 152
Nearest railway station - Raynes Park.
Buses: Nos: 152 & 163

HONOURS: None

FACT FILE
Formed 1995
Nickname: The Vale
Colours:Red& blue/red/blue
Change colours: Green & white
hoops/green/white
Website: http://m25football.tripod.com

CLUB PERSONNEL

President: Robert Hallett
Chairman: Nigel Thorn
43 Granville Avenue, Hounslow, Middlesex
Tel No: 0208 572 2331
Press Secretary: Secretary

READING TOWN

Secretary: Richard Grey, 6 Milestone View Court, Lowfield Road, Caversham Park,
Reading RG4 6ND Tel: 0118 948 4920 Email:richardigrey@aol.com
Ground: Reading Town Spts Ground, Scours Lane, Tilehurst, Reading, Berks (0118 945 3555)
Directions: Out of Reading on Oxford road (A329), past Battle Hosp. Scours Lane 1st right after
roundabout ,Nearest station - Tilehurst or Reading (General). Bus -Reading Bus 17(Tilehurst)
Capacity: 2,000   Seats: No   Cover: Yes   Floodlights: Yes   Clubhouse: Yes
PREVIOUS Leagues: Chiltonian 89-95, Reading 66-89 **Ground:**Adwest Spts Grd,Kings Meadow
Names: Lower Burghfield, XL United, Vincents Utd, Reading Garage, ITS Reading Town
CLUB RECORDS Attendance: 253 v Banstead Ath FA Vase 96-97
Defeat: 0-10 v Feltham(A) 96-97
Win: 7-0 v Cranleigh/Viking Spts/AFC Wallingford all Home 97-98

BEST SEASON FA Cup: 1st Qual. Rd. 00-01   FA Vase: 4th Rd 96-97
HONOURS Comb. Counties Lge R-up 97-98; Chiltonian Lge Champions 94-95,
Berks &Bucks Sen. Trophy 95-96, R-up 96-97

FACT FILE
Founded: 1968
Colours: Red & black stripes/black/black
Change colours: Navy/navy/red
Midweek Matchday: Tuesday
Programme: 20 pages 50p
Editor: Richard Grey
CLUB PERSONNEL
Chairman: Roland Ford, 103 Little Heath
Road, Tilehurst, Berkshire RG31 5TG
Tel: 0118 941 2270
Fixture Sec.: As Secretary
Manager:Colin Millard
2001-02 Leading goalscorer: Karl Leighton 9
Captain: James Hancock

SANDHURST TOWN

Secretary: Tony Ford, Pennings Cottage, Aldershot Road, Guildford, Surrey GU3 3AA
Tel Nos: 01483 567284 (H) 07778 628547(M)
Ground: Bottom Meadow, Memorial Ground, Yorktown Rd, Sandhurst (07831 366140)
Directions: M3 Jn4- A331 -A321 or M4 Jn10 -A329 -A321. Park in main council offices car park
off A321. Walk down tarmac path to ground. Nearest station: Sandhurst. Buses: 174,193 & 194
Capacity: 2,000   Seats: Eight Cover: Yes Floodlights: Yes Clubhouse: after matches only
PREVIOUS Leagues: Reading & Dist.; East Berks; Aldershot Snr 79-84; Chiltonian84-90
CLUB RECORDS Attendance: 353 v Aldershot Town (Friendly)
Win: 9-1 v Cranleigh (08.01.2000)   **Defeat:** 0-8 v Cobham 26.10.1991)
Goalscorer: Glenn Price   **Appearances:** John Parker
BEST SEASON FA Vase: 2nd Rd 01-02   FA Cup: 1st Rd Qualifying
HONOURS Combined Co's Lge Chal. Vase R-up 92-93 (Reserve Chal. Cup R-up 91-92),
Chiltonian Lg R-up 86-87, Aldershot Snr Lg R-up 83-84; Berks & Bucks Sen.Trophy R-up 92-93
Aldershot Senior Cup: 00-01 , Co.Co. Res Cup 00-01, 01-02

FACT FILE
Founded: 1910
Nickname: Fizzers
Colours: Red/black/black
Change colours: Yellow,blue,yellow
Midweek matchday: Tuesday
Programme: Yes   Editor:Tony Ford
CLUB PERSONNEL
Chairman:Phil Sigley (01276 32742)
President: Malcolm Watts
Match Sec.: as Secretary
Manager:Peter Browning
Coach:Dave Hawtin
2001-02 Capt: Aaron Roberts P.o.Y.: Darren
Wilson Top Scorer: Peter Mulvaney 29

SOUTHALL

Secretary: Phillip Temple, 196A Cromwell Road, London SW5 0SN Tel No: 0208 566 4748 (W)
07879 403572 (M)   Email: ptemp@btconnect.com
Ground: Ground share with Chalfont St. Peter FC, The Playing Fields, Amersham Road, Chalfont
St Peter SL9 7BQ Tel: 01753 885797 **Directions:** A413 from Uxbridge (London) to Chalfont. Turn
left 100 yds after2nd major roundabout (between Ambulance station and Community Centre. 2
miles from Gerrards Cross (BR), regular buses from Slough & Uxbridge
Capacity: 4,500   Cover: 120   Seats: 220   Floodlights: Yes
PREVIOUS: Leagues: Southern 1896-1905; Gt Western Suburban; Herts & Middx;
Athenian 19-73, Ryman 73-00
BEST SEASON: FA Cup: 3rd Round 35-36, 1-4 v Watford (H)
FA Vase: Runners-up 85-86   **FA Amateur Cup:** Runners-up 24-25
HONOURS: FA Amtr Cup R-up 24-25, FA Vase R-up 85-86, Isthmian Lg Div 2 R-up 74-75,
Gt Western Suburban Lg 12-13, Athenian Lg 26-27 R-up 54-55,
Middx Snr Cup x12, Middx Charity Cup x9

FACT FILE
Founded: 1871   Nickname: Fowlers
Colours: Red & white stripes/redrred
Change: Yellow & black
Midweek Matchday: Wednesday
Res' Lge: Middx County
Prog: 6 pages, 50p   Ed: Steve Hawkins
2000-01 P.o.Y.: Andre Robinson
Top Scorer: Andre Robinson 12
CLUB PERSONNEL
Chairman: B.S.Gill
Manager: Keith Chamberlin
Physio: Keith Chamberlin
Club Website: www.southallfootballclub.co.uk
Club Email: geoff@southallfootballclub..co.uk

VIKING GREENFORD

Secretary: trevor Hern, 54 Jeymer Drive, Greenford, Miiddlesex UB6 8NS Tel No: 07958 521392 (M)

Ground: Avenue Park, Western Avenue, Greenford, Middx (020 8578 2706)

Directions: On London-bound carriageway of A40, 300 yds before Greenford flyover and slip road to A4127. 12 mins walk from Greenford (Central Line) station - turn right out of station to A40, turn right - grd 1/4 mile on rght

Capacity: 450   **Seats:** 50   **Cover:** 100   **Floodlights:** Yes   **Club Shop:** No
Clubhouse: Open every evening except Sunday. Hot & cold snacks on matchdays

HONOURS   Hellenic Lg Div 1 85-86 (Div 1 Cup R-up 90-91).Co.Counties Lg.(R-Up.94-95)
CLUB RECORDS   **Att:** 180 v Wealdstone,Middx.SenCup,Sept.96 **Goalscorer:** Frank Healy, 43
                PREVIOUS   **Leagues:** Middlesex 70-80; Hellenic 80-91
BEST SEASON   **FA Cup:** 1st Q Rd 96 F,A.Vase: 2nd Rd v Diss Town 1991
Players progressing: Gordon Bartlett (Portsmouth), AlanDevonshire (West Ham), Peter Shaw (Charlton A.)

FACT FILE
Founded: 1945   Nickname: Vikings
Sponsors: Measham Self-Drive/ Greeene King
Colours: Tangerine/black/tangerine
Change colours: Sky blue & maroon/sky/sky
Midweek matchday: Tuesday
Programme: 12 pages, 50p
Editor: John Bennett

CLUB PERSONNEL
Chairman: Greg Dusgate B.Sc.(Hons)
President: Roy Bartlett
Andy Myhill (0207 271 8876)T.B.A.
Manager: Wayne Haley
Asst Man.:Steve Parsons
Physio: Ernie Stockwell

WALTON CASUALS

Secretary: Stuart Roberts, 47 Foxholes, Weybridge, Surrey. KT13 0BN. Tel: 01932845923
Email: sroberts@cattronuk.com

Ground: Franklyn Road Sports Ground, Waterside Drive, Walton-on-Thames, Surrey KT12 2JG
Tel No: 01932 787749   Website: http://www.waltoncasualsfc.co.uk
Directions: Next to Elmbridge Leisure Centre, left off Terrace Rd at first roundabout out of Walton centre. Hersham (BR), then bus 564 to Elmbridge Leisure Centre.
Capacity: 1,500   **Seats:** None   **Cover:** 80**Floodlights:** Yes
Clubhouse: Matchdays only. Hot food available from Tea Bar   **Club Shop:** No

HONOURS Suburban Lge (South) 82-83, (R-up 83-84); Surrey Prem Lge R-up 94-95, S.P.L. Chall Cup 93-94, (R-up 94-95); Surrey Premier Cup R-up 86-87,CoCo Lg Cup 99-00 R-up 00-01
BEST SEASON   **FA Vase:** 1Rd Proper 00-01   **FA Cup:** PrelimRd 2000-01,01-02
PREVIOUS   **Leagues:** Surrey Premier, Surrey Senior, Surrey Intermediate, Suburban.
CLUB RECORDS Attendance: 178 v Pagham FA Vase 96/97

FACT FILE
Founded: 1948
Nickname: The Stags
Sponsors: Browns Building Centre
Colours: Tangerine/black/tangerine
Change colours: All Blue
Midweek Matchday: Tuesday
Programme: 28 pages70p
Editor/Press Officer: Stuart Roberts

CLUB PERSONNEL
Chairman:Graham James (01932 227921)
General Manager: David Symonds
President: Grahan James
Manager: Ray Noad

WESTFIELD

Secretary: Michael Lawrence, 19 Ash Road, Barnsbury Estate, Woking, Surrey. GU22 0BJ
               Tel/Fax: 01483 722184 (H)

GROUND   Woking Park, Kingfield, Woking, Surrey Tel: 01483 771106

Directions: (Adjacent to Woking FC.)
               M25 J10 or 11, signposted from outskirts of Town.Ground 1 mile.
               Woking B.R.Station & buses from Woking
               Capacity: 1,000   **Seats:** None   **Cover:** Yes   **Floodlights:** Yes
Clubhouse   Yes - open matchdays when snacks are available.
Club Shop   No

PREVIOUS   **League:** Surrey County Senior League

FACT FILE
Founded: 1953
Colours: All yellow
Change colours:Yellow/Black/Yellow
Midweek Matchday:Tuesday
Programme: No
CLUB PERSONNEL
President: Richard Hill
Chairman: Steven Perkins
160 Coleford Bridge Road, Mytchett,
Camberley, Surrey
Tel: 01252 547900 (B)
Manager: John Cassidy
Asst. Managers:
Alan Morton & Brian Hennessy

WITHDEAN 2000

Secretary: Brian Davies, 119 Church Road, Hove BN3 2AF
               Tel: 01272 272776 (H) 01273 764874 (B)
               Email: briand@bdinsurance.demon.co.uk
Ground: Worthing F.C.,Withdean Stadium, Tongdean Lane, Brighton BN3 2AF
               Tel: 01273 542100
Capacity: 10,000   **Seats:** 6,000   **Cover:** 1,000   **Floodlights:** No

Directions: Off main London - Brighton road
Clubhouse: Pub on ground   **Club Shop:** No

HONOURS   Sussex Co. Lg Div 3 92-93 (Div 3 Cup 91-92)
PREVIOUS   **Leagues:** Brighton Hove & District
               Ground: Council pitch

FACT FILE

Founded: 1984
Colours: All white
Programme Editor: Gary Arnold
Local Newspaper: Brighton Evening Argus

CLUB PERSONNEL
Chairman: Desmond Ralfe
President: Stan Hunt
Manager: Dave Cole

FORESTERS
ESSEX SENIOR LEAGUE

President: Arthur Dimond   **Chairman & Publicity:** Robert Errington

Secretary: David Walls, 2 Hillsfield Cottage, Layer, Breton, Essex CO2 0PS

Tel & Fax: 01206 330146   Email: EssexSenior@wallsd.freeserve.co.uk

The season welcomed the county's latest senior squad, Enfield Town, to the fold and they gave the ultimate champions, Leyton, a true run for their money. The sheer consistency and 100 per cent home record at The Hare & Hounds was the telling factor in the Lillywhites' championship and this, with their success in the first ever Gordon Brasted Memorial Trophy over host club Burnham Ramblers, takes them on the promotion rung to the Ryman League with everyone's best wishes.

In the meantime, Enfield Town were setting the league alight with their loyal and brilliant fans, sometimes adding over 200 to normal club gates. Their first match in the league saw over 500 in attendance. In addition to the runners-up spot they won the League Cup final on penalties against Leyton in a thoroughly entertaining game at Basildon United.

A fabulous run around the Home Counties with every game away from home saw the Blues lift the Cherry Red Trophy against Pitstone & Ivinghoe. The season ended with a memorable Middlesex Charity Cup win over Wealdstone, and their match programme was the best in the league. Not bad for a first ever season.

We are still blessed with the excellent sponsorship of the Foresters Friendly Society for both League and Cup and now welcome back Romford FC from the Ryman League and Waltham Abbey FC from the Essex & Herts Border League. One club suffered a major crisis at the beginning of the season but, with the usual encouragement from fellow clubs, Woodford Town found a new committee and a new team, put the nightmare of a league record 0-15 defeat behind them and rallied well for the rest of the season. They now return to the FA Vase.

Brentwood won the Sportsmanship Award for the second successive season and Clive Thomas of Basildon United was the Secretary of the Year.

The season was overshadowed by the continuing saga of re-organisation of the National Game. Certainly, we now enter a new phase of our life in the Isthmian Pyramid wherein we sit, along with the Spartan South Midlands and Combined Counties, on a level with the new Division Two of the Ryman League. We are hoping that there will not be any further change to this situation . . . but time will tell.

Robert Errington, Chairman

Right: Leyton FC with the Gordon Brasted Memorial Trophy. Photo: Margaret Errington

FINAL LEAGUE TABLE 2001-02

| | | P | Home | | | | | Away | | | | | Pts |
			W	D	L	F	A	W	D	L	F	A	
1	Leyton	30	12	3	0	34	10	12	0	3	41	13	75
2	Enfield Town	30	13	0	2	52	12	9	3	3	31	16	69
3	Burnham Ramblers	30	8	0	7	33	25	9	2	4	24	17	53
4	Concord Rangers	30	9	1	5	37	22	7	1	7	28	29	50
5	Southend Manor	30	7	4	4	30	23	7	3	5	27	19	49
6	Bowers United*	30	7	3	5	41	27	6	6	3	29	24	46
7	Sawbridgeworth Town	30	7	5	3	30	19	6	2	7	29	35	46
8	Stansted	30	7	2	6	31	27	5	4	6	24	27	42
9	Ilford	30	5	4	6	25	26	6	1	8	26	23	38
10	Basildon United	30	5	1	9	28	30	5	6	4	30	34	37
11	Saffron Walden Town	30	5	4	6	16	26	5	2	8	24	36	36
12	Hullbridge Sports	30	5	3	7	21	34	4	3	8	23	42	33
13	Barkingside	30	5	5	5	27	26	3	3	9	17	24	32
14	Brentwood	30	5	2	8	29	21	3	4	8	16	32	30
15	Eton Manor	30	1	4	10	19	38	3	3	9	21	34	19
16	Woodford Town	30	1	3	11	12	41	4	1	10	17	60	19

* points deducted

RESULTS CHART 2001-02

		1	2	3	4	5	6	7	8	9	10	11	12	13	14	15	16
1	Barkingside	X	3-3	2-2	0-0	0-3	5-1	1-4	2-2	1-0	4-2	0-3	3-1	1-2	1-1	1-2	3-0
2	Basildon United	1-4	X	0-2	6-1	1-3	3-1	2-3	1-2	1-1	3-1	0-2	1-2	0-2	0-6	0-0	7-0
3	Bowers United	3-1	1-1	X	0-4	1-0	1-2	1-0	1-3	9-1	3-3	1-5	1-3	2-1	1-1	4-0	12-2
4	Brentwood	1-0	2-3	2-3	X	2-3	3-1	1-1	3-0	1-2	0-2	0-1	2-3	0-0	1-2	2-0	9-0
5	Burnham Ramblers	0-3	5-2	2-1	3-0	X	1-2	0-1	1-0	5-2	1-0	1-3	2-3	8-3	3-0	0-2	1-3
6	Concord Rangers	2-0	0-1	3-3	2-1	2-0	X	4-1	6-2	3-1	0-2	1-5	4-0	1-2	1-2	2-1	6-1
7	Enfield Town	2-0	4-0	2-1	6-0	4-0	0-1	X	2-1	5-0	2-1	3-1	6-2	6-0	4-1	0-3	6-1
8	Eton Manor	2-2	2-2	1-2	3-3	0-1	2-3	1-4	X	1-1	0-3	0-3	1-5	3-0	1-5	1-2	1-2
9	Hullbridge Sports	1-1	1-1	2-4	0-2	1-3	2-1	0-3	2-2	X	2-1	0-5	4-1	0-5	0-3	3-1	3-1
10	Ilford	2-0	3-5	1-1	1-0	2-4	2-2	0-1	2-2	4-2	X	0-1	4-1	0-3	2-1	1-1	1-2
11	Leyton	2-1	4-1	2-1	2-1	3-0	4-0	1-0	1-0	3-2	2-0	X	0-0	4-2	0-0	1-1	5-1
12	Saffron Walden Town	1-0	0-3	2-2	1-1	0-2	2-0	0-0	2-0	1-3	0-3	0-5	X	2-1	0-2	3-2	2-2
13	Sawbridgeworth Town	2-3	1-1	1-2	5-0	1-0	1-0	3-6	4-1	3-3	1-0	3-0	1-1	X	2-0	2-2	1-0
14	Southend Manor	3-1	3-3	3-3	1-0	0-0	1-4	2-2	3-0	1-2	2-3	0-3	2-0	5-1	X	2-1	2-0
15	Stansted	1-0	5-3	1-1	0-1	1-2	1-7	0-2	4-1	1-2	3-1	4-1	4-2	2-2	3-0	X	1-2
16	Woodford Town	1-1	0-1	0-1	2-2	0-3	1-3	0-3	0-5	1-1	0-4	0-3	1-0	1-5	0-3	5-6	X

ANCIENT ORDER OF FORESTERS LEAGUE CUP 2000-01

GROUP A	W	D	L	Pts	GROUP C	W	D	L	Pts
Enfield Town	3	2	1	11	Southend Manor	5	0	1	15
Sawbridgeworth Town	3	2	1	11	Hullbridge Sports	2	2	2	8
Eton Manor	1	3	2	6	Burnham Ramblers	1	2	3	5
Saffron Walden Town	0	3	3	3	Concord Rangers	1	2	3	5

GROUP B	W	D	L	Pts	GROUP D	W	D	L	Pts
Stansted	4	0	2	12	Leyton	4	2	0	14
Barkingside	4	0	2	12	Bowers United	3	1	2	7
Ilford	4	0	2	*9	Basildon United	2	1	3	7
Woodford Town	0	0	6	0	Brentwood	0	4	2	4

QUARTER-FINALS

Enfield Town	v	Bowers United	2-1	Leyton	v	Hullbridge Sports	4-2
Stansted	v	Barkingside	4p3, 2*2	Southend Manor	v	Sawbridgeworth Tn	1-2

SEMI-FINALS (Two Legs)

Stansted v Enfield Town 1-0, 0-2 Sawbridgeworth Tn v Leyton 2-2, W/O

Sawbridgeworth Town were ruled out due to rule infringement

FINAL

Enfield Town v Leyton 4p2, 1-1 at Gardiners Close, Basildon. Att: 658

GORDON BRASTED MEMORIAL TROPHY 2001-02

SEMI-FINALS (Two Legs)

Burnham Ramblers v Sawbridgeworth 2-1, 1-0 Barkingside v Leyton 0-4, 0-2

FINAL

Burnham Ramblers v Leyton 0-3

twentyfive in twentyfive twentyfive in twentyfive twentyfive in twentyfive twentyfive in twentyfive

25 *in* 25

A review of the progress made by the **Essex Senior League** and its member clubs during the twenty-five year life span of the F.A. Non-League Club Directory (1978 - 2002) will be available in the next year. It will be one of a series of 25 and will contain features, statistics and photos in at least 160 pages dedicated purely to the Essex Senior League members.

Further details can be found on page 17 so make sure of your copy of this exciting limited edition.

twentyfive in twentyfive twentyfive in twentyfive twentyfive in twentyfive twentyfive in twentyfive

BARKINGSIDE

Secretary: John Taylor, 2 Courage Close.Hornchurch, Essex RM11 2BJ (01708 456373)
Ground: Oakside, Station Road, Barkingside, Ilford, Essex Tel: 020 8550 3611
Directions: From London A12 Eastern Ave to Green Gate, left into Hurns Rd to Barkingside, right into Craven Gardens, right Carlton Drive to Station Rd, under bridge and grd on right. Next to Barkingside station (Central Line). From Ilford station (BR) take 169 Bus to Craven Gardens
Capacity: 2,500 Seats: 140 Cover: 240 Floodlights: Yes Club Shop: No
Clubhouse: Saturdays 1pm-12. midweeek matchnights 6.30-11pm. Rolls, hotdogs,hamburgers
HONOURS Spartan Lge. Prem. Div. 96-97, R-up 90-91 (Harry Sunderland Shld 83-84 (R-up 84-85); London Sen. Cup 96-97; S. Essex Lge R-up 46-47, L'don Lg R-up 49-50 (Lg Cup 55-56 (R-up 52-53 62-63)), Gtr L'don Lg 64-65,S.S.Mids Premier 98-99.Harry Fisher Mem Trophy 00-1
PREVIOUS: Leagues: Ilford & Dist. 1898-1925 44-47; Ilford Minor 25-44; Sth Essex 47-48; Walthamstow 48-50; London 50-64; Gtr London 64-71; Metropolitan-London 71-75; Spartan 76-South Midlands 1996-99 **Grounds:** Fulwell Cross PF 1898-1921; Clayhall Rec 21-29; Hainault PF 29-33; Barkingside Rec 33-57 **RECORDS: Gate:** 957 v Arsenal Res., London Lg 1957

FACT FILE
Founded: 1898

Colours: All Sky Blue
Change colours: All Red
Midweek matchday: Tuesday
Programme: Yes

CLUB PERSONNEL
Chairman: Tony Myers
Manager: Tony Myers

BASILDON UNITED

Secretary: Clive Thomas, 52 Conway Gardens, Grays, Essex RM17 6HG
Tel: 01375 390231 (H) Email: clivekarenzoe@aol.com
Ground: Gardiners Close, Gardiners Lane, Basildon, Essex SS14 3AW Tel: 01268 520268

Directions: A176 off Southend arterial (A127), left at r'bout into Cranes FarmRoad, proceed to end of duel carriageway, left at lights, Gardiners Close is 1st left (Football Club signed). Two and a half miles from Basildon BR station
Capacity: 2,000 Seats: 400 Cover: 1,000 Floodlights: Yes
Clubhouse: Open lunchtimes, evenings, weekends. Hot food sold Club Shop: No

HONOURS Isthmian Lge Div 2 83-83; Essex Senior Lge (5) 76-80 93-94, Lg Cup 77-78 93-94 97-98, Res. Cup 92-93; Essex Senior Trophy 78-79; Res. Lge &Shield 94-95
PREVIOUS Leagues: Grays & Thurrock; Gtr London 68-70; Essex Snr 70-80; Athenian 80-81; Isthmian 81-91 **Name:** Armada Sports **Ground:** Grosvenor Park 63-69
CLUB RECORDS Attendance: 4,000 v West Ham, ground opening 11/8/70

FACT FILE
Founded: 1963
Sponsors: T.B.A.
Colours: Amber & black stripes/black
Change: Royal Blue/black/black
Midweek Matches: Wednesday
Programme: 16 pages, 50p Editor: T.B.A.
2001-02 Top Scorer: John Doyle

CLUB PERSONNEL
President: J Oakes
Chairman: T.B.A.
Press Officer: Frank Ford (01268 552994)
Manager:Steve Wheeler

BOWERS UNITED

Secretary: Lee Stevens,59 Cross Green, Lee Chapel South, Basildon, Essex SS16 5Q
Tel No: 01268 548 493 (H)
Ground: Len Salmon Stadium, Crown Avenue, off Kenneth Rd,Pitsea, Basildon (01268 452068)
Directions: Turn into Rectory Rd from Old London Rd (B1464) at Pitsea Broadway into Kenneth Rd, right at top Crown Ave. 1.25 miles Pitsea (BR). Bus 5& 42 toRectory Rd, Bowers Gifford
Capacity: 2,000 Seats: 200 Stand: Yes Floodlights: Yes
Clubhouse: Open every night Club Shop: No
PREVIOUSLeagues: Thurrock & Thameside Comb.; Olympian**Ground:** Gun Meadow, Pitsea
HONOURS Thurrock & Thameside Comb. 58-59; Essex Snr Lg 80-81,98-99 R-up 83-84 Div 1 Cup 90-91,Lg Cup Winners 81-82,98-99 R-up (3) Harry FisherMem Trophy 91-92 R-up (4) E.S.L. Charity Cup 99-00
BEST SEASON FA Cup: 1st Rd Q 98-99 **FA Vase:** 4th Rd 98-99
CLUB RECORDS Attendance: 1,800 v Billericay F.A.Vase
Players progressing: Steve Tilson (Southend Utd)

FACT FILE
Founded: 1946
Colours: Red & white stripes/black/black
Change colours:All Yellow
Midweek Matches:Wednesday7.30
Res League; Essex & Herts Border Comb
Programme: 30pages 50p
Editor:Lee Stevens
CLUB PERSONNEL
Chairman:Barry Hubbard
Vice Chairman: Denis Osborne
Manager: Tony Cross
2001-02
Captain & Top Scorer: Lee Goodwin 15
P.o.Y.: Paul Hatch

BRENTWOOD

Secretary: Colin Harris, 56 Viking Way, Pilgrims Hatch, Brentwood, Essex CM15 9HY
Tel: 01277 219564 (H) Email Address: khobbs1057@aol.com
Ground: Brentwood Centre, Doddinghurst Rd, Brentwood, Essex. 01277 215151 Ext.713
Directions: From east end High St (Wilsons Corner) turn north into Ongar Rd. 3rd mini-round-about ,Right into Doddinghurst Rd, Centre half mile on right after A12 Bridge, ground far right.
Capacity: !,000 Cover: 100 Seats: Floodlights: Yes
Clubhouse: Open Tues & Thur evening & matchdays Club Shop: No
PREVIOUS Names: Manor Ath. 55-70, Brentwood Ath. 70-72
Grounds: King George, Hartswood, `Larkins', Ongar (pre-92), East Thurrock 92/93
Leagues: Romford & Dist., Sth Essex Comb., London & Essex Border,Olympian
HONOURS Olympian Lg Cup 67-68, Essex Inter. Cup 76-77, Essex Lg Cup 75-76 78-79 90-91; Harry Fisher Mem. Trophy 95-96 ,Essex Senior League 2000-01, League Sportsmanship Award 00-01,01-02
BEST SEASON FA Vase: 3rd Rd Prop 95-96

FACT FILE
Founded: 1955 Sponsor: CLC Construction
Nickname: Blues
Colours: All sky blue
Change colours: All Yellow
Midweek Matches: Tuesday
Programme: 50p
Club Website:www.brentwoodfc.co.uk

CLUB PERSONNEL

Chairman: Kevin O'Neale
Manager: Paul Delea (H) 01708 550630
2001-02 Top scorer: Paul Battram

BURNHAM RAMBLERS

Secretary: Mrs Christine Revell c/o Club
Ground: Leslie Fields Stadium, Springfield Rd, Burnham-on-Crouch CM0 8TE (01621 784383)
Club Website: www.burnhamramblersfc.co.uk
Directions: On B1010 from South Woodham Ferrers, trt,1/2 mile before town.
10 mins -Burnham on Crouch railway station
Capacity: 2,000   Seats:156   Stand: Yes   Floodlights: Yes   Club Shop: No
Clubhouse: Mon-Fri 7-11pm, Sat 12noon -11pm, Sun 12-3 & 7-9.30pm. Hot meals & snacks available

HONOURS Olympian Lg 65-66; Essex I'mediate Cup R-up 81-82; Essex Snr Lg Cup R-up 86-87 89-90 97-98, (Reserve Cup 89-90 (R-up 92-93), Reserve Shield R-up 90-91; Harry Fisher Mem. Trophy 96-97, R-up 97-98 99-00; Sportsmanship Award 96-97
PREVIOUS   Leagues: N Essex, Mid-Essex, Olympian, S.E. Essex
Grounds: Wick Rd ,Millfields and Saltcourts
BEST SEASON   **FA Vase:** 5th Rd 88-89
CLUB RECORDS   **Gate:** 1,500 v Arsenal at opening of new stand

FACT FILE
Founded: 1900   Nickname: Ramblers
Colours: Blue/black/black
Change colours: Yellow/black/yellow
Midweek matches: Tuesday
Reserves' Lge: Essex & Herts Comb.
Prog: 32 pages, £1.00 Editor: Chris Dobson
CLUB PERSONNEL
Chairman: Ron Hatcher
Vice Chairman: Chris Browne
President: R J Cole, Esq
Press Officer: Nigel Radcliffe, 016217774
Manager: John Hegley Physio:T.B.A.
2001-02: Top Scorer: Danny Greaves
Captain :Steven Dobson P.o.Y:Paul Harrison

CONCORD RANGERS

Secretary: Eddie Crace, 71 Tilburg Road, Canvey Island, Essex, SS8 9ER. Tel: 01268 681868H
07889 904109M   01268 2950288W
Ground: Thames Road, Canvey Island, Essex. SS8 0HP 01268 691780 / 515750
Website: www.concordrangersfc.co.uk   **Email:** ecrace@newholland.com
Directions: Follow A130 onto Canvey Island and turn right into Thorney Bay Road, then right again into Thames Road.
Capacity: 1,500   Cover: Yes   Seats: No   Floodlights: Yes

HONOURS Southend & Dist. Lge - Lge & Cup 84-85; Southend Alliance - Lge & Cup 87-88;
Essex Intermediate Lg Div 2 90-91; Essex Sen Lge 97-98, Cup 96-97;
Wirral Programme Award 93-94, Harry Fisher Trophy 99-00 ESL Charity Cup 00-01
PREVIOUS   **Leagues:** Southend & Dist. All., Essex I'mediate (pre-1991)   **Ground:** Waterside
CLUB RECORDS   **Gate:** 1,500 v Lee Chapel North, FA Sunday Cup 89-90
Win: 12-1 v Woodford, Essex Snr Lge 00-01

FACT FILE
Founded: 1967
Colours:Yellow & Blue/blue/yellow
Change colours: white/black/black
Midweek Matches: Tuesday
Clubhouse: Evenings & weekends
Programme: 20 pages, 50p
Editor: As Secretary

CLUB PERSONNEL
President: Albert Lant
Chairman: Antony Smith
Manager: Brian Horne
2001-02 Top Scorer: Lee Brent
Captain: Roger Gell

ENFIELD TOWN

Secretary: Roger Reed, 16 College Gardens, Enfield, Middx. EN2 0QX Tel: 020 8350 4064 (H) 020 8424 8524 x5 (B) 07736 776510 (M)
Press Officer: P J Coath, 33 Bertram Rd.,Enfield Middx EN11LR Tel: 020 8292 7783
Fixture Sec.:   Keith Wortley, Greenways, Appleby Street, Cheshunt, Herts EN7 6QZ Tel: 01992 6201690 07732 319897
Ground: Brimsdown Sports & Social Club, Goldsdown Road, Enfield, Middlesex
Tel: 020 8804 5491
Website: www.enfieldtownfootballclub.co.uk
Directions: BR from Liverpool Street to Brimsdown (half mile away) or Southbury Road.
By road off Green Street, itself off Hertford Road (A1010). Buses 191 or 307
HONOURS: Cherry Red Books Trophy 01-02, Essex Senior League Cup 01-02, Middlesex Senior Charity Cup 01-02, Essex Senior League Runners Up 01-02.
CLUB RECORDS: Gate: 516 v Leyton 12.09.01
Appearances: Daniel Clarke, Andy Hall (52 - 2001-02)
Goalscorer: Daniel Clarke 46 (2001-02)
Win: 7-1 v Eton Manor, Essex Senior League Cup 04.09.01

FACT FILE
Founded: June 2001
Nickname: ETs or Towners
Sponsors: Direct Boot & Embroidery
Colours: White/bluewhite
Change: All yellow
Midweek Matches: Variable
Programme: 32 pages £1.50
Editor: Peter Coath
CLUB PERSONNEL
Chairman: David Bryant
Manager:Jim Chandler
Physio: Colin Mardel
01-02 Top Scorer: Daniel Clarke
PoY: Andy Hall
Captain: Bradley Brotherton

ETON MANOR

Secretary: R.Curtis, 5 Foxwood Chase, Meridian Park, Waltham Abbey En9 3YW (01992 713497)
Ground: Waltham Lodge Sports Ground,Kitchener Rd.,Walthamstowe London E17 4JP(020 8527 2444)
Directions: Sharing with Leyton Pennant (Ryman League).
Capacity: 1,000   Seats: 60   Cover: 60Floodlights: Yes   Clubhouse: Yes
HONOURS Essex Snr Cup R-up 37-38, London Lg 33-34 37-38 52-53 53-54 (R-up 48-49 57-58, Lg Cup 55-56 (R-up 46-47 54-55)), Greater London Lg 64-65, Essex Intermediate Cup 64-65, London Intermediate Cup R-up 33-34 66-67, Essex Snr Lg Sportsmanship Award 75-76   (Div 1 Cup 90-91, Res. Div 76-77, Res. Div Cup 91-92).
PREVIOUS Leagues: London 33-59; Aetolian 59-64; Greater London 64-69; Metropolitan 69-75.
Grounds: Wildness, Hackney; GUS Sports Ground, Clapton; Walthamstow Ave. FC; Norwegian Ground, Barking; Roding Lane, Buckhurst Hill, ThurrockHotel   **Name:** Wilderness Leyton.
CLUB RECORDS Gate: 600 v Leyton Orient, opening of floodlights at Roding Lane.
Goalscorer: Dave Sams

FACT FILE
Founded: 1901
Nickname: The Manor
Colours: Sky/navy/navy
Change: Yellow/dark blue/light blue
Midweek Matches: Tuesday
Programme: 12 pages with entry Editor:
Secretary

CLUB PERSONNEL
Chairman: Reg Curtis
Manager:Alex Lee
Physio: Alf Jones
01-02 Top Scorer: Ben Ruocco

HULLBRIDGE SPORTS

Secretary: Beryl Petre, 58 Grasmere Ave., Hullbridge, Essex SS5 6LF
Tel: 01702 230630 (H) 01702 552211 (B)
Ground: Lower Road, Hullbridge, Hockley, Essex SS5 6BJ Tel: 01702 230420
Directions: Turn into Rawreth Lane from A130 (left if arriving fromChelmsford), down to
mini-r'bout, left, across next mini-r'bout, up hill, ground signed on right just past garage
Capacity: 1,500 **Seats:** No **Cover:** Yes **Floodlights:** Yes **Club Shop:** No
Clubhouse: Lounge bar, function hall with bar & changing rooms - set in 16 acres

HONOURS Essex Intermediate Snr Div Cup 87-88, Southend & District Lg Div 1 65-66 (Div 2
51-52, Div 3 56-57), French Cup 51-52, Essex Snr Lg Sportsmanship Award 91-92 92-93 93-94

PREVIOUS   **Leagues:** Southend & Dist., Alliance, Essex I'mediate
Grounds: Pooles Lane Rec

RECORD ATTENDANCE: 800 v Blackburn Rovers F.A.Youth Cup 99-00

FACT FILE
Founded: 1945
Sponsor: Thermo Shield
Colours: Royal Blue & white/blue/blue
Change colours: All yellow
Midweek matches: Tues/Thursday
Programme Editor: T.B.A.
Website: www.sportsworldwide.co.uk

CLUB PERSONNEL
Chairman: Terry Scourfield
Manager: Jayson Stephens
2001-02
Capt: Keith Scourfield
Top Scorer: Luke Slatford

ILFORD

Secretary: Bill Robertson,2 humphrey close,Clayhall,Ilford, Essex JG5 0RW
Tel Nos: 02085506680 (H) 07930 104076 (W)
Ground: Cricklefield Stadium, High Road, Ilford, Essex. IG1 1UB Tel: 0181 514 0019
Directions: 5 min walk from Seven Kings Station. Opposite 'TheCauliflower' publ, Or 86 Bus
Capacity: 5,000 **Seats** - 216 **Cover** - Yes **Floodlights** - Yes
Clubhouse: Open November 2002 with snack bar open on match days
HONOURS: FA Amateur Cup: 28-29 29-30, R-up 35-36 57-58 1973-74 Isthmian Lge Champ.
06-07 20-21 21-22 R-up 11-12 26-27 31-32 37-38 38-39 Essex Senior Cup x13 (record nos. of
wins), R-up x5; London Sen. Cup: x7 R-up x 5; London Charity Cup: x 6 R-up x 7: Essex I'mediate
Cup R-up x1; London I'mediate Cup R-up x1; Eastern F'lit Comp. Group Winners 96-97
PREVIOUS   **League:** Spartan 87-95
BEST SEASON   **FA Cup:** 73-74 2nd Rd, 0-2 v Southend Utd. (H)
FA Vase: 99-00 2nd Rd 1-2 v Watton United (a)
CLUB RECORDS Attendance: 17,000 Ilford Boys v Swansea Boys (Schools Trophy Final)

FACT FILE
Founded: 1881   Re-Formed: 1987
Sponsor: Kelvin Hughes
Colours: Blue & white hoops/blue & white
Change colours: Red & white qtrs/red/red
Midweek matches: Monday
Programme Editor: L Llewellyn
CLUB PERSONNEL
Chairman: George Hogarth
Vice Chairman: Melvin Attwell
President: Lord John Taylor of Warwick
FManager: Joe Simmonds (0208 9895560)
2001-02
Top Scorer: C.J.Emmanuel

ROMFORD

Secretary: Derek Robinson Tel: 01708 507803   Email: derek@romfordfc.freeserve.co.uk
Ground: `Sungate', Collier Row Road, Collier Row, Romford, Essex. Tel: 01708 722766
Club Call: 09066 555 841 Website: www.romfordfc.co.uk
Directions: Take the A12 from London as far as the Moby Dick junction.
Turn left and then right at the 1st r'about into Collier Row Rd. The ground entrance is
signposted 200 yards on the right. Nearest station is Romford (BR). From directly outside the sta-
tion the London bus 247 passes the ground.
Capacity: 2,500 **Cover:** 300   **Seats:** 175   **Floodlights:** Yes
Previous   **Leagues:** Essex Senior 92-96, Isthmian 96-02
Grounds: Hornchurch 92-95, Ford Utd 95-96
Club Records - Attendance: 820 v Leatherhead (IL2) 15/4/97; **Career Goalscorer:** Micky Ross
57; **Season goalscorer:** Vinny John 45 (97-98); **Career Appearances:** Danny Benstock 197
Best Season: FA Vase: 5th Rd 96-97 v Bedlington Terriers 2-1
HONOURS Essex Senior Lge 95-96, Lge Cup 95-96;
Isthmian Div 2 96-97; East Anglian Cup 97-98

FACT FILE
Reformed: 1992 Nickname: The Boro
Colours: Blue & old gold/blue/blue
Change colours: Red & black/black/black
Midweek home matchday: Tuesday (7.45)
Reserves' Lge: Essex & Herts Border Prem
Programme: Pages: 40 Price: £1.20
Editor: Derek RobinsonTel: 01708 507803
Local Press: Romford Recorder
Local Radio:Active FM
CLUB OFFICIALS
Chairman: Dave Howie
Vice-Chairman: Steve Gardener
Press Officer: Steve Gardener
Manager: Paul Withey
Physio: Colin Maherson

SAFFRON WALDEN TOWN

Secretary: Peter Rule, 48 Church Street, Saffron Walden, Essex, CB10 1VQ (Tel 01799 522417)
Ground: The Meadows,Catons Lane, Saffron Walden, Essex CB10 2DU (01799 522789)
Directions: In Saffron Walden High St turn into Castle St, left at T-junction, 1st left by Victory pub
Capacity: 5,000 **Seats:** 500 **Cover:** 2,000 **Floodlights:** Yes **Club Shop:** Yes **Clubhouse:** Yes -
PREVIOUS   **Leagues:** Haverhill & Dist.; Stansted & Dist.; Cambridgeshire; Nth Essex; Herts Co.;
Spartan 33-49 50-54; Parthenon 49-50; Essex Snr 71-74; Eastern Co's 74-84
HONOURS   Essex Snr Lg 73-74, 99-00Lg.Cup 99-00 Eastern Co's Lg 82-83,Spartan Lg Div 1
36-37,Essex Snr Tphy 82-83 83-84 84-85, Eastern Floodlit Comp. x3 (R-up 88-89),Nth Thames
Group B 82-83), Essex Jnr Cup 1896-97 (R-up x3), Cambs Lg R-up 22-23, Essex & Herts Border
26-27 joint)), Stansted & Dist. x 7, Haverhill & Dist. x 6 ,Harry Fisher Mem98-99 Uttlesford Ch Cup
x9,S.Mids Floodlit Cup 99-00 Sportsmanship Cup: 98-99.99-00,00-01
CLUB RECORDS Scorer: Alec 'Alf' Ramsey 192 **Appearances:** Les Page, 538
Attendance: 6,000 v Rainham Ath., Essex Jun. Cup Final 1926 (played at Crittals, Braintree)
BEST SEASON   **FA Cup:** 2nd Qual. Rd replay 84-85, 1-2 v King's Lynn (A)

FACT FILE
Founded: 1872
Nickname: Bloods
Club Sponsors: Coxvs.com PC Furniture
Colours: Red & black/black/black
Change cols: Blue & yellow/yellow/yellow
Midweek Matchday: Tuesday
Reserves' League: Essex & Herts Comb
Programme: 48 pages, 50p
Editor: R Smith (01799 500061)
CLUB PERSONNEL
Chairman: Steve Cox V-Chair: John Butchart
Press Officer: Secretary
Manager: Marc Das

Brentwood. Back Row (l-r): Dave Brewington, David White, Jason Fairweather, Dave Pether, Graham Wood, Paul Brewington, James Read, Ian McGowan (Asst Mngr). Front Row: Frank Everett, Dave Doel, Gran Delea, Dave Stittle, Craig Mead, Calum Foley, Paul Battram.
Photo:
Gordon Whittington

Enfield Town, winners of the Cerry Red Trophy, beating Pitstone & Ivinghoe in the final at Ware in front of a crowd of 620, scoreline 3-1.
Photo:
Gordon Whittington

Ilford
Photo:
Gordon Whittington

Southend Manor
Photo:
Gordon Whittington

SAWBRIDGEWORTH TOWN

Secretary: Leslie Atkins, c/o 49 Cambridger Road, Sawbridgeworth.CM21 9JP (01279 725665)
Ground: Crofters End, West Road, Sawbridgeworth, Herts. CM21 0DE (01279 722039)

Directions: Three quarters of a mile from the station; up Station Road then into West Road.

Capacity: 1,500   Seats: None   Cover: 250   Floodlights: Yes   Club Shop: No
Clubhouse: Yes/No - when is it open ??? is food available ???

HONOURS   Essex Olympian Lg 71-72; Essex Snr Lg R-up 92-93 94-95; Harry FisherMem.
Cup 87-88; Lg Cup 94-95 R-up 92-93 93-94, Res. Div 91-92 92-93 (R-up 93-94), Res. Shield R-up
92-93); Herts Snr Tphy 90-91 93-94 (R-up 92-93);Herts Charity Shield 92-93 94-95 95-96;
Uttlesford Charity Cup 92-93; Herts Intermediate Cup R-up 93-93(res); S. Midlands F'lit Cup R.up
94-95; Res. Sect S.M Lge & Lg.Cup R-Up 94-95
PREVIOUS   Leagues: Essex Olympian, Spartan 36-53
CLUB RECORDS Attendance: 610 v Bishop's Stortford.
PREVIOUS GROUNDS: Hyde Hall, Pishiobury, Hand & Crown.

FACT FILE
Founded: 1890
Nickname: Robins
Colours: Red & black stripes/black/black
Change colours: All blue
Midweek Matchday;
Prog Editor:Gary Bennett (01279 830306)
Wirral programme Award 99-00

CLUB PERSONNEL
Chairman: Barrie Hodges
President: Ron Alder
Manager:Don Watters
Physio: T.B.A.
2001-02op Scorer: Peter Lawrence

SOUTHEND MANOR

Secretary: Mrs Michele Frost, 16 Sharnbrook, North Shoebury, Essex SS3 8YE (01702 216299)
Ground: Southchurch Park Arena, Lifstan Way, Southend-on-Sea. Tel: 01702 615577
Directions: A127 then A1159 for 1 mile turn right at second roundabout by Invisible Man PH,
then due south for 1 mile, ground on right near sea front
Capacity: 2,000   Seats: 500   Cover: Yes   Floodlights: Yes
Clubhouse: Open every evening   Club Shop: No
HONOURS Essex Sen Trophy 92-93; Essex Interm'te Cup 78-79; Essex Sen League 90-91, R-
Up: 99-00 Essex Sen League Cup 87-88, R-Up:99-00,00-01 Challenge Cup 89-90;Harry Fisher
Mem Trophy 90-91 92-93 (R-up 91-92) Essex Sen Cup 2001-02 , ESL Charity Cup 2001-02
PREVIOUS Leagues: Southend Borough Combination, Southend Alliance
Grounds: Victory Spts/ Oakwood Rec
RECORDS   Attendance: 1,521 v Southend Utd, 22/7/91, floodlight opener
BEST SEASON   FA Vase: 1996-97

FACT FILE
Founded: 1955   Nickname: The Manor
Sponsors: Info-Line
Colours: Yellow/black/black
Change colours: All white
Midweek Matchday: Tuesday
Reserves Lge: Essex & Herts Border Comb
Programme: 10 pages, 50p
Editor/Press Off: Chris Hunt 01702 615897
Website: www.southendmanor.co.uk
CLUB PERSONNEL
Chairman: Robert Westley
Vice-Chairman: Geoff Gorham
Man: Mark Jenkins Coach: Andy Dixon
2001-02 Capt: Simon Nicks P.o.Y.: Simon Nicks
Top Scorer: John Boyle 25

STANSTED

Secretary: Terry Shoebridge ,2 Dawson Close,Saffron Walden ,Essex Home
Telephone Number: 01799 -527937 (H)
Ground: Hargrave Park, Cambridge Road, Stansted, Essex. (01279 812897)
Directions: B1383 north of Bishops Stortford on west side of Cambridge Rd.
Stansted (BR) - 1/2 mile
Capacity: 2,000   Seats: 200   Cover: Yes   Floodlights: Yes
Clubhouse: Matchdays till 11pm. Sandwiches available.   Club Shop: No

HONOURS   FA Vase Winners 83-84; Essex Snr Lg R-up 82-83; Essex Snr Lg Cup 83-84, (R-up
72-73 94-95); Harry Fisher Mem Cup 82-83 84-85 (R-up 92-93 93-94); E. AnglianCup 83-84;
Eastern F/lit Cup 83-84 R-up 01-02; Uttlesford Char. Cup 93-84 86-87 88-89 94-95 97-98 01-02
PREVIOUS   Leagues: Spartan; London; Herts Co. **Grounds:** Greens Meadow; ChapelHill
RECORDS   Attendance: 828 v Whickham (FA Vase 83-84)
BEST SEASON   FA Cup: 97-98   **FA Vase:** Winners 83-84

FACT FILE
Founded: 1902 Nickname: The Blues
Sponsor: Leyton Orient Community Sports
Programme
Colours: Blue /Blue/White
Change: Yellow & Black/Black/Black
Midweek matches: Tuesday
Reserves League:Essex & Herts Border Comb.
Under 18's : Eastern Junior Alliance

CLUB PERSONNEL
Chairman: Terry Shoebridge
President: Percy Heal
Manager: Tony Mercer

WALTHAM ABBEY

Ground: Capershotts, Sewardstone Road, Waltham Abbey, Essex. Tel: 01992 711287

Previous League: Essex & Herts Border Comb.

WOODFORD TOWN

Secretary: Larry McDonald,20 Heynes Road, Dagenham, essex RM8 2SX
Tel Nos: 0208590 2863 (H) 0207987 4811 (W) 07974 189 893 (M)
Ground: Clapton FC ground share
Old Spotted Dog Ground, Upton Lane, Forest Gate, London E7
Tel: 0181 472 0822
Directions: BR to Forest Gate,Tube to Plaistow (District Line).
Official entrance in Upton Lane.
Docklands Light Railway to Prince Regent then 325 bus to ground
Buses: Any bus fron Forest Gate station
Capacity: 2,000 Seats: 100 Cover: 180 Floodlights: Yes
Previous Leagues: South Essex 37-39,London 47-51,Delphian 51-61,Metropolitan 61-63
70-71 Junior Football 63-70, Southern 71-72,82-87 Essex Senior,76-79 and Athenian 79-82
Essex Senior 87-93 ,Spartan 93-97, No League 97-98 essex Senior League 1998-

FACT FILE

Founded: 1937
Colours: Red & white stripes/black/black
Change colours:Sky blue & white/white/sky blue
Programme Editor: T.B.A.

CLUB PERSONNEL

Chairman: Nexille Watson
Fixture Sec. as Secretary
Manager: Kirk Whitelock

Enfield Town skipper Bradley Brotherton (arm aloft beyond six yard line) celebrates as his header puts his side in front against Pitstone & Ivinghoe. Enfield Town went on to win this Cherry Red Trophy Final 3-1 at Ware.
Photo: Gordon Whittington

Essex Senior League action between Ilford and Brentwood.
Photo: Gordon Whittington

The dramatic late penalty from Ross Webster which clinched the Essex Intermediate League Division Three for Stambridge United, winning 2-1 at Great Baddow.
Photo: Gordon Whittington

footballs

SPARTAN
SOUTH MIDLANDS
FOOTBALL LEAGUE

President: B F Smith **Chairman:** Pat Burns

Hon. Gen. Secretary: M Mitchell, 26 Leighton Court, Dunstable, Beds. LU6 1EW

Tel: 01582 667291

This year's Premier Division champions were last year's runners-up, London Colney. In winning the title, Colney set four new records - the ten point difference between themselves and second place was one more than the previous largest, they had only two defeats (both by the odd goal), scored 119 goals and had a goal difference of 87. They were unbeaten for their first 27 league games. Colney went top after three games, and apart from a few days in December, maintained their position, winning 28 of their 38 games.

Runners-up Letchworth, who last season were promoted as Division One Champions, after a poor start established themselves into second place following an undefeated run of nineteen matches, a position they held for most of the season. They scored 105 goals and five of their six defeats were by only one goal. Third placed were Hanwell Town, whose twelve match undefeated run late in the season moved them up to second place, but they eventually finished one point behind Letchworth. Hanwell scored 114 goals and lost seven games. Milton Keynes City, who themselves were unbeaten in their first eight games finished fourth, six points behind Hanwell. St Margaretsbury, who won 20 of their last 28 games, finished fifth. For each of the top five clubs, this was the highest position they had ever finished in the league. The second promoted team, Dunstable Town, initially took the division by storm, winning their first five games with a goal difference of 25-2, but eventually finished seventh. Last season's champions, Beaconsfield, finished tenth. New Bradwell St Peter finished bottom with only three wins, with Brache Sparta thirteen points above them. The leading goalscorers were Gary Sippetts of London Colney with 45 and Keith Rowlands of Hanwell with 37.

Division One champions were Greenacres, who finished one point above Harefield United. For both teams, it was the first time either had finished in the top half. At one stage Greenacres were seventeen points clear, but in the end it depended on their last game. Tring Athletic were early leaders, but once Greenacres took over an unbeaten run of twelve matches established a good points lead, and they were top for the rest of the season. They lost only four games, and with 101 goals they were the only team in the division to reach three figures. Their goal difference of 61 was the best in the division. Harefield's success was based on an excellent second half season in which they lost only one of nineteen games, enabling them to finished eight points clear of third placed Colney Heath. Biggleswade United and Tring, both of whom have finished in the top five in each of the last four seasons, finished in fourth and fifth positions, with Langford sixth and Pitstone & Ivinghoe (promoted last season) in seventh place. Welwyn Garden City, relegated from the Premier last season, had a good start with only one defeat in seven games, but with only 33 goals scored finished sixteenth. Amersham Town, with only four wins, finished bottom, one point behind Winslow United. Top goalscorers were Alan Arthur (Greenacres) with 42 and Paul Sloley (Stony Stratford) with 35.

Division Two winners were Mursley United, undefeated for their first twenty games, who finished one point above Haywood United. Haywood moved into second place for the first time with their last victory of the season. Leading goalscorers were Darren Edwards (Crawley Green) with 42 and Chris Hill (Haywood United) with 37.

In the Premier Division Cup, St Margaretsbury beat Potters Bar 2-0. The Division One final was between the top teams, runners-up Harefield beating champions Greenacres 2-0, and in Division Two Crawley Green defeated Old Dunstablians 2-0.

In the FA Cup, the best effort was by St Margaretsbury, who beat teams from the Eastern Counties and Ryman Leagues before losing in the Third Qualifying Round. In the FA Vase a record 22 SSML teams played in the Second Qualifying Round, with five reaching the Second Round Proper. The most successful side was Milton Keynes City, who were knocked out by eventual winners Whitley Bay in the Fourth Round. Division One side Colney Heath had the distinction of the biggest victory in this year's competition, beating March Town 11-0 in the Second Qualifying Round.

In County Cups, an excellent performance by Division One Biggleswade United saw them beat UCL Premier Stotfold 4-1 to win the Beds Senior Cup, whilst another Division One side Tring Athletic, beat Premier Letchworth 4-1 in the Herts Charity Shield. Other finalists were London Colney, who lost 2-3 to Ryman Premier side Borehamwood, in the Herts Senior Cup, the winner coming in the last five minutes, Milton Keynes City who lost narrowly 2-3 to Wallingford in the Berks & Bucks Senior Trophy, and Pitstone & Ivinghoe, defeated 1-3 by Enfield Town in the Cherry Red Books Trophy.

S G Eaton

FINAL LEAGUE TABLES 2001-02

PREMIER DIVISION

	P	W	D	L	F	A	Pts
London Colney	38	28	8	2	119	32	92
Letchworth	38	25	7	6	105	45	82
Hanwell Town	38	25	6	7	114	64	81
Milton Keynes City	38	22	9	7	76	39	75
St Margaretsbury	38	20	8	10	74	55	68
Brook House	38	19	7	12	89	63	64
Dunstable Town	38	18	8	12	74	54	62
Royston Town	38	15	13	10	82	58	58
Biggleswade Town	38	16	9	13	74	64	57
Beaconsfield SYCOB	38	15	10	13	84	52	55
Somersett A V & E	38	16	5	17	75	61	53
Haringey Borough	38	13	9	16	53	74	48
Potters Bar Town	38	14	5	19	71	77	47
Hoddesdon Town	38	12	8	18	50	56	44
Holmer Green	38	12	6	20	59	98	42
Hillingdon Borough	38	11	6	21	63	76	39
Ruislip Manor	38	9	6	23	47	82	33
Bedford United	38	8	7	23	38	114	31
Brache Sparta	38	7	4	27	45	109	25
New Bradwell St P	38	3	3	32	25	144	12

DIVISION ONE

	P	W	D	L	F	A	Pts
Greenacres (Hemel)	38	24	10	4	101	40	82
Harefield United	38	25	6	7	85	36	81
Colney Heath	38	21	10	7	86	47	73
Biggleswade United	38	21	8	9	89	45	71
Tring Athletic	38	19	12	7	63	38	69
Langford	38	19	6	13	65	46	63
Pitstone & Ivinghoe	38	16	9	13	70	65	57
Leverstock Green	38	15	10	13	86	58	55
Stony Stratford	38	15	8	15	78	70	53
The 61 FC	38	14	10	14	59	65	52
Risborough Rangers	38	14	9	15	70	62	51
Kings Langley	38	14	8	16	58	69	50
Cockfosters	38	13	9	16	67	71	48
Ampthill Town	38	12	10	16	58	91	46
Harpenden Town	38	12	9	17	72	83	45
Welwyn Garden City	38	9	11	18	33	54	38
Brimsdown Rovers	38	9	10	19	55	79	37
Letchworth Bridger	38	8	9	21	55	103	33
Winslow United	38	7	3	28	30	86	24
Amersham Town	38	4	11	23	46	448	23

PREMIER DIVISION RESULTS CHART 2001-02

		1	2	3	4	5	6	7	8	9	10	11	12	13	14	15	16	17	18	19	20
1	Beaconsfield SYCOB	X	10-1	4-1	5-0	1-1	1-1	6-2	4-1	2-3	2-0	4-0	1-2	0-1	1-3	3-0	0-0	2-2	2-0	1-0	4-1
2	Bedford United	0-6	X	2-2	2-0	1-2	1-1	0-5	0-3	1-2	0-4	3-0	0-6	1-1	1-3	3-1	0-3	0-2	1-0	3-2	1-3
3	Biggleswade Town	1-0	4-1	X	2-0	0-1	3-0	1-2	2-0	4-4	1-4	5-0	3-3	1-1	1-2	3-0	3-3	0-0	2-3	1-0	
4	Brache Sparta	3-2	4-1	1-4	X	1-2	0-3	1-2	1-2	2-1	1-5	2-2	1-3	2-5	1-4	2-0	2-4	1-4	0-1	2-0	1-4
5	Brook House	1-0	10-2	4-1	2-0	X	2-1	1-7	2-2	4-0	3-0	5-2	1-5	2-3	2-4	8-1	5-1	2-2	1-1	4-1	0-3
6	Dunstable Town	3-0	1-1	1-0	4-1	3-1	X	1-3	0-3	1-0	4-0	4-2	4-4	1-2	0-0	2-3	2-1	1-0	2-0	0-0	
7	Hanwell Town	3-2	5-0	5-3	7-3	1-5	5-1	X	6-1	3-2	3-2	6-2	4-3	2-2	1-2	6-1	0-2	2-2	0-2	2-1	6-1
8	Haringey Borough	2-1	1-0	0-1	3-2	3-3	1-3	1-1	X	1-0	2-2	0-3	0-1	0-2	0-3	5-0	4-1	2-0	1-0	2-1	1-2
9	Hillingdon Borough	2-2	0-0	1-3	0-2	2-1	0-0	2-3	4-0	X	1-2	1-2	2-3	3-7	1-4	1-2	0-1	1-1	3-0	0-3	1-4
10	Hoddesdon Town	0-0	0-3	0-0	3-1	1-0	0-2	0-1	0-0	1-3	X	3-4	1-2	0-4	1-1	4-1	3-0	2-3	1-1	0-1	1-0
11	Holmer Green	1-3	1-2	2-4	4-1	2-2	1-2	1-1	3-2	0-3	2-1	X	1-1	1-3	1-0	4-1	1-3	1-1	2-1	3-0	1-2
12	Letchworth	4-2	5-0	4-0	1-0	1-2	2-0	1-3	3-3	1-3	0-1	5-0	X	0-0	4-3	5-0	0-2	4-0	3-0	1-1	4-2
13	London Colney	4-2	3-0	4-0	8-0	4-1	6-2	2-2	6-0	3-0	2-1	6-0	0-1	X	3-3	3-0	5-0	1-2	6-0	3-0	4-1
14	Milton Keynes City	2-1	2-0	2-1	0-4	1-0	1-0	1-1	6-0	2-0	1-1	4-1	0-1	0-0	X	5-0	2-1	1-3	1-0	0-0	2-4
15	New Bradwell St Peter	1-3	1-1	1-6	2-2	0-4	0-12	0-2	1-2	0-6	2-1	1-2	0-3	0-2	0-4	X	4-2	0-10	1-5	1-3	0-1
16	Potters Bar Town	3-3	1-2	1-0	7-0	2-1	2-1	0-2	2-2	2-3	0-2	2-2	3-8	0-1	0-2	4-0	X	1-2	1-2	1-3	1-0
17	Royston Town	0-0	2-2	4-1	4-0	0-1	5-1	2-1	2-2	5-0	0-0	1-4	1-2	1-3	3-3	X	3-1	2-2	3-1		
18	Ruislip Manor	0-1	7-2	1-2	0-0	1-1	1-3	3-5	1-1	1-4	4-1	0-2	0-7	2-4	0-1	5-0	1-6	3-2	X	1-1	
19	Somersett Ambury	4-3	7-0	0-3	0-1	0-2	1-2	4-0	3-0	1-0	6-1	0-1	0-2	3-2	7-1	2-6	1-1	5-0	X	4-1	
20	St Margaretsbury	0-0	4-0	3-3	5-0	3-0	1-1	3-2	1-0	2-1	0-0	3-2	2-2	2-2	0-2	2-0	2-0	2-1	4-0	2-2	X

PREMIER DIVISION CUP

SEMI-FINALS

Potters Bar Town	5 * 1	Hoddesdon Town	
St Margaretsbury	6 * 3	London Colney	

FINAL

Potters Bar Town	0 v 2	St Margaretsbury	

DIVISION ONE CUP

SEMI-FINALS

Harefield	2 v 0	Biggleswade Utd	
Langford	0 v 2	Greenacres (Hemel)	

FINAL

Harefield United	4 v 1	Greenacres (Hemel)	

BEACONSFIELD SYCOB

Secretary: Ken Barrett, 31 Stockey End, Abingdon, Oxon OX14 2NF. Tel: 01235202058 (H), 01235 537080 (B) Email: kj17ox@aol.com
GROUND: Holloway Park, Slough Road, Beaconsfield, Bucks (01494 676868).
Directions: M40 (Jct 2), 1st exit to A355. Club 100yds on right. 1.5 miles from Beaconsfield BR Bus 441Slough/ High Wyc'be**PREVIOUS NAMES:** SloughYCOB & Beaconsfield U merged 1994
Capacity: 3,000   **Cover:** 400   **Seats::** 250   **Floodlights:** Yes   C lub Shop: Clu
Clubhouse: Open eves & matchdays. Bar, Committee Room, Hall, Kitchen, Changing Room I
HONOURS: As Slough : Chilt.Lg R-up: 93-4,Lg Cup 92-3 Slough T Cup R-up 91-2
Champios Spartan South Midlands 2000-01
Leagues: Beaconsfield Utd: Wycombe & District; Maidenhead. Slough YCOB: Windsor, Slough & District; East Berks; Chiltonian (pre 1994) **Previous Grounds:** As Slough: Haymill Community Centre,Burnham Lane,slough (pre 1944)
Record Gate: 300 Beaconsfield Utd v Chesham Utd, Berks & Bucks Sen Cup 1985
BEST SEASONS: FA Cup: 3rd Q Rd 98-998 **FA Vase:** Beaconsfield: 1st Rd 83-84 85-86 87-88

FACT FILE
Founded: 1994   Nickname: The Rams
Colours:Red & white quarters/black/red & white
Change colours: Navy Blue
Midweek Matches: Monday or Tuesday
Reserves' League: Suburban
Programme: Yes, £1
Editor: Andy Jackson, 7 Boundary Lane, Chipperfield Rd., Bovingdon, Herts.HP3 0JT
Tel No: 01442 834203
CLUB PERSONNEL
President: D Piercy
Chairman: Fred Deanus
Manager: Colin Barnes

BEDFORD UNITED & VALERIO

Secretary: Jim McMullen,7 Buttermere Close, Kempston, Bedford MK42 8JU(01234 300765)
GROUND: McMullen Park, Meadow Lane, Cardington, Bedford MK45 3SB (01234 831024)

Directions: M1 jct 13, A421 to Bedford by-pass. Third exit, A603 ground 500 yards on left
Capacity: 5,000   Seats: 25   Cover: 100   Floodlights: Yes
Clubhouse: Open matchdays. Hot & cold snacks and drinks available

HONOURS: Bedford & Dist Lg Premier Division & Division One, County Junior Cup, Biggleswade KO Cup, Butchers Cup(2), Britania Cup, Bedford Charity Cup
PREVIOUS: **Leagues:** Bedford & Dist. Lge (57-70 & 80-89); United Cos. Lge 70-80
            Name: Printers Diemer-Reynolds (pre'72)
Grounds: Allen Park (57-80); Fairhill, Clapham Road (80-93); Hillgrounds, Kempston 93-96)

RECORD: Attendance: (at Fairhill) 1500 v Bedford Town, South Midlands Lge Div. 1 26/12/92
       Scorer: Neil Tysoe 220   **Appearances:** Simon Fordham 418

Founded: 1957   Nickname: United
Club Sponsors: JDP Finance
Colours: Blue & White/blue/blue
Change colours: Red & black/red/red
Midweek matches: Wednesday
Reserves' League: S. Mids Lge Res. sect
Programme: 24 pages, £1
Editor: Graham Williams (O1234 312 982)

Chairman: John Cleverley
Vice Chairman/Press Off Jim McMullen
President: D Rostron
Manager: Cliff Canavan -Smith
Asst. Man.: M Ackroyd
Coach/Physio: Dave Petrie

BIGGLESWADE TOWN

Secretary: Graham Arkwright, 47Honeysuckle Close Biggleswade, Beds SG188ST
       Tel: 01767 318370
GROUND: `Fairfield', Fairfield Road, Biggleswade, Beds (01767 312374).
Directions: A1 North r'bout, left immediately after bridge into car park.
       10 mins walk from Biggleswade (BR).
Capacity: 2,400   Seats: 50   Cover: 100   Floodlights: Yes   Club Shop: No.
Clubhouse: Open all matchdays. , teas, coffees, snacks.
HONOURS:S Mids Lge: Res Div 2 87-88, Res Chall Trophy 88-89, S.M. Floodlit Cup 95-96; Beds Snr Cup 02-03 07-08 46-47 51-52 61-62 62-63 66-67 73-74; Beds Premr Cup 22-23 27-28; N. Beds Charity Cup x13; Utd Co's Lg Cup 73-74; Hinchingbrooke Cup 03-04 12-13 92-93 Hunts Prem Cup 92-93 93-94(joint)00-01 94-95 97-98; Jess Piggott Trophy 87-88 89-90 91-92 92-93
PREVIOUS: Leagues: Biggleswade & Dist. 02-20; Bedford & Dist. 09-12; Utd Co's (prev. Northants Lg) 20-39 51-55 63-80; Spartan 46-51; Eastern Co's 55-63 **Name:** Biggleswade F.C.
RECORD: **Attendance:** 2,000

FACT FILE
Founded: 1874   Nickname: Waders
Club Sponsors: Mantles Ford & LetchworthCouriers
Colours: green/green/green
Change: All red
Midweek Matchday: Tuesday
Programme: 32 pages, admission
Editor: Brian Doggett (01767 318307 (H).
CLUB PERSONNEL
Chairman:M.Dorrington V. Chair:M Jarvis
President: R Dorrington
Manager: David Northfield Physio: A.Wellings
2001-02 Captain: Mark Winwood P.o.Y.:
MarkRainbow Top Scorer: Mark Phillips 24

BROOK HOUSE

Secretary: Barry Crump, 19 Bradenham Road, Hayes, Middlesex UB4 8LP.
       Tel: 0208 841 3959 (H), 0966 468029 (B)

Ground: Farm Park, Kingshill Avenue, Hayes, Middlesex (0208 842 1448)
Directions: From North Circular road: A40 Western Ave. to Target r'about, left towards Hayes (A312), over White Hart r'about towards Yeading/Hayes, right at traffic lights in to Kingshill Ave, ground 1 mile on right. Nearest BR stationis Hayes & Harlington, then bus 90 or 195 to Brook House pub. Nearest tube is Northolt (central line), then bus to ground
Capacity: 2,000   Cover: 100   Seats: 120   Floodlights: Yes   Club Shop: No
Clubhouse: Open weekdays 7-11pm, Sat noon-11pm, Sun noon-11.00pm

HONOURS: SSM Prem South 97-98, Prem Div R-Up 99-00, Lge Cup 99-00 R-up 91-92.
BEST SEASON: FA Vase: 3rd Round Proper 97-98   **FA Cup:** 1st Qual Rd 93-94
Players progressing: Neil Shipperley (Crystal Palace), MarkHyde (Orient), Mark Perry (QPR)
David Warner (To Watford for £10,000) and Anthony Charles (To Crewe Alexandrafor £6,000)

FACT FILE
Founded: 1974
Colours: Blue & white stripes/blue/blue
Change colours: All yellow
Midweek matchday: Tuesday
Reserve League: Suburban League
Programme: 28 pages, £3 with entry
Editor: Andrew Gavin (020 8581 8715)
CLUB PERSONNEL
President: Victor Kirby
Chairman: Mick Ralph
Vice-Chairman: JohnHandell
Press Officer: Lawrie Watts
Manager: Bob Strutton Ass Man: Joe Mitchell
Coach: Reg Leather

BROXBOURNE BOROUGHV & E

Secretary:	Peter Harris, 30 Lordship Road, Cheshunt, Herts. EN7 5DP
	Tel : 01992 429297 (H) 0208 345 1274(W) **Email address:** savefc@fcmail.com
Ground:	V & E Club, Goffs lane, Cheshunt, Herts. Tel: 01992 624281

Capacity: 500   Seats: 20   Cover: Yes   Floodlights: Yes   Club Shop: No

Directions: M25 junct. 25, A10 towards Cheshunt. Take the first left at the first roundabout onto the B198 (Cuffley & Goffs Oak). At the end of the road turn right off roundabout into Goffs lane. Clubhouse on immediate right. Open 11 a.m. 11 p.m. every day.

Previous League: Herts County

2000-01 Captain: Paul Kendall P.o.Y.: Steve Wales Top Goalscorer: John Dixon 18

Club Website www.savefc.thesportcity.com

FACT FILE
Founded: 1959
Colours: White & blue/blue/blue
Change Colours: Orange/white/orange
Midweek Matchday: Tuesday
Reserves League; Essex ,Herts Border
Programme Editor: Peter Harris
01992 429297 (H) 0208 1274 (B)

CLUB PERSONNEL
Chairman:Dave Bidwell
Tel: 01992 428187 (H)
Vice Chairman:Mario Persico
President: Doug Bacon
Manager:David Craig
Assistant manager: Mark Standen

DUNSTABLE TOWN

Chairman:	Ian Tompkins
Secretary:	Colin Howes, 3 Rotherwood Close, Dunstable, Beds LU6 1UA
	Tel: 01582 478395
Ground:	Creasey Park, Brewers Hill Rd, Dunstable
Directions:	Travel north on A5, Through centre Dunstable, left at 1st r/about into Brewers Hill Rd, str over mini r/about, grd on right

FACT FILE

Colours:
Blue & white stripes/blue/blue & white

Change Colours:
Red & black hoops/black/red & black

Programme Editor:
Paul Reeves: 0961 951103

GREENACRES (Hemel Hempstead)

Secretary:	Hayley Smith, 437 Barnacres, Hemel Hempstead, Herts. HP3 8JS
	Tel No: 01442 214739 (H) 01442 264300 (W)
Ground:	Hemel Hempstead FC, Vauxhall Rd., Adeyfield, Hemel Hempstead.
	Tel: 01442 259777
Directions:	M1 J8; over two roundabouts, then first right off dual carriageway. First left and then right at roundabout

Capacity: 3,000   **Seats:** 100   **Cover:** Yes   **Floodlight:** Yes   **Club Shop:** No

Clubhouse: as for Hemel Hempstead F.C.

Colours:
Green & white hoops/white/green & white
Change Colours: All red & white
Midweek Matchday: Wednesday
Programme: £1.00
Editor: William Cain

Chairman: David Boggins
01442 264300 (H)
Match Sec. David Lloyd
01442 259721 (H)

Manager: Paul Burgess

HANWELL TOWN

Secretary: John Wake, 38 Warwick Ave., S Harrow, Middx. HA2 8RD. Tel/Fax: 0208 4221048(H)
GROUND: Reynolds Field, Perivale Lane, Perivale, Greenford, Middx (0208 998 1701)
Directions: A40(M) west from London, leave opp Hoover building (B456 for Ealing), turn left into Argyle Rd, left into Perivale Lane. Grd on left. 500 yards from Perivale tube station (Central line)
Capacity: 2,000   Seats: 90   Cover: 200   Floodlights: Yes   Club Shop: No
Clubhouse: Saturday matchdays 2-11pm, Tuesdays 6-11pm, Non-matchdays 7.30-11pm

HONOURS:	Spartan Sen Lg R-up 98-99 83-84 (Lg Cup R-up 93-94, London Snr Cup 91-92 92-93 (R-up 93-94), Middx Charity Cup R-up 92-93, 99-00
PREVIOUS: RECORDS:	**Leagues:** Dauntless Lge, Harrow, Wembley & District and Middlesex County **Attendance:** 600 v Spurs, Floodlight opening October 1989 **Scorer:** Keith Rowlands **Appearances:** Phil Player, 20 seasons, 617 games
BEST SEASON:	**FA Cup:** 3rd Rd Qual 97-98
2001-002:	**P.o.Y.:**Aaron Patton **Captain:** Chris Beck **Top Scorer:** Keith Rowlands 45

FACT FILE
Founded: 1948   Nickname: The Town
Colours: Black & white stripes/black/black & white
Change colours: White with red trim
Midweek matchday: Tuesday
Reserves' League: S.S.M.Res Lg
Programme: 16 pages, with entry
Editor: Bob Fisher as below

CLUB PERSONNEL
Chairman/Press Officer: Bob Fisher
Tel: 0208 952 4142 (H) 0207 510 4954 (B)
President: Dave Iddiols
Patron: Stephen Pound MP
Manager: Ray Duffy

Biggleswade Town. Back Row (l-r): G Rogers (Asst Mngr), Warren Grieves, Barry Gulliford, David Allen, Ray Massey, Scott Waters, Colin Reid, Mark Gregory, Mark Rainbow. Front Row: Mel Franklin, Neil Mapletoft, Mark Phillips (now Letchworth), Peter Gatti, Adie Mapletoft, Mark Winwood. Photo: Gordon Whittington

Hanwell Town. Back Row (l-r): R Duffy (Mngr), J Clements (Physio), M Sroka, P White, L Holmes, C Beck, T Davis, G Brown, R Mundy, D Vincent (Asst Mngr), R Nairn (Coach). Front Row: S McLelland, D Webb, A Patton, K Nowlands, D Mills, J Spencer, K Dobson, M Elder.

Hoddesdon Town. Back Row (l-r): Darren White, Matt Anstey, Darren Gibbs, Ritchie Simmonds (Capt), Joe O'Driscoll, Neil Conner, Graham Howes, Wesley Pullen, Danny Atkins. Also standing: Bill O'Driscoll (Manager), John Briggs (General Manager). Front Row: Danny Swaile, Paul Mann, Paul Evitt, Pablo Ardiles, Ryan Redford, Neil Johnson, Albert Morris. Photo: Gordon Whittington

Leyton FC with the Gordon Brasted Memorial Trophy Photo: Margaret Errington

HAREFIELD UNITED

Secretary: Terry Devereux, 72 Williamson Way, Rickmansworth, Herts WD3 2GL.
Tel: 01923 711451 (H/B)

GROUND: Preston Park, Breakespeare Rd North, Harefield, Middx UB9 6DG (01895 823474)
Directions: M25 jct 16 to M40 East, left at 1st roundabout, then 2nd left into Harvill Rd. Follow road up the Church Hill into village, right at mini roundabout, ground on right. Denham (BR)
Capacity: 2,000 Seats: 100 Cover: Yes Floodlights: Yes Club Shop: No
Clubhouse: (01895 823474) Lunchtimes and evenings. Cold snacks (hot on matchdays)
HONOURS: Middx Premier Cup 85-86, Athenian Lg R-up 83-84, Parthenon Lg 64-65
(Div 1 Cup 65-66), Middx Lg 66-67 68-71 (Lg Cup 66-67 68-69)
Spartan South Mids Div. 1 R-up 01-02
BEST SEASON: **FA Cup:** 2nd Qual. Rd replay 80-81, 86-87 **F.A.Vase:** 6th Rd 1989-90
RECORD: **Gate:** 430 v Bashley, FA Vase
PREVIOUS **Leagues:** Uxbridge & Dist.; Gt Western Comb. 46-64; Parthenon 64-68;
Middx 68-75; Athenian 75-84, Isthmian 85-96

Founded: 1868
Nickname: Hares
Colours: Red & white stripes/black/red
Change colours: Yellow /green/yellow
Midweek Matches: Tuesday
Reserves' League: Suburban
Programme: 12-40 pages, 30p
Editor: Terry Deveraux (Sec.)

Chairman: Keith Ronald. Tel: 01895 824287
President: Dave West
Manager: Stuart Levy

HARINGEY BOROUGH

Secretary: John Bacon, 7 Everett Close, West Cheshunt, Herts., EN7 6XD Tel: 01707 873187
GROUND: Coles Park, White Hart Lane, Tottenham N17 (020 88891415) Clubhouse: Yes
Directions: M25 to J.25 turn south on A10 approx 6 miles, over jnct with N. Circular Rd (A406)
Turn R. at T.lght 1 mile into White Hart Lne grd approx 500yds on L. Bus W3 from Finsbury Park.
Mainline & Under-grd stn to Northumberland Park mainline station passes grd can be boarded at
Alexandra Palace or White Hart Ln. Mainline stations or Wood Green Underground station.
Capacity: 2,500 Seats: 280 Cover: Yes Floodlights: Yes
Best Seasons: F.A.Vase: 6th Rd 77-78 **F.A. Cup:** 3rd Qualifying Round 86-87
HONOURS: FA Am Cup R-up 19-20; London Sen Cup 12-13, 90-91; Athenian Lge 13-14; Div 2
Cup winners 67-68, 68-69; Spartan Lg Cup r-up 90-91 Spartan S. Mids Prem Div cup r-up 97-98
PREVIOUS: **Leagues:** London 07-14; Isthmian 19-52 84-88; Spartan 52-54; Delphian 54-63;
Athenian 63-84 **Names:** Edmonton; Tufnell Park; Tufnell Park Edmonton; Edmonton &
Haringey (merged with Wood Green Town in early seventies)

FACT FILE
Colours: Yellow/green/yellow
Change colours: Green/black/green
Midweek Matchday: Tuesday
Reserves League - London Intermediate
Programme Editor: As Secretary
CLUB PERSONNEL
Chairman: Peter Lawlor Tel: 020 8889 2726
Match Secretary : As Secretary
2001-02
Captain: Jason Hanson

HILLINGDON BOROUGH

Secretary: Garry Grant, 19 Leveret Close,Leavesden, Watford, herts WD2 7AX
Tel Nos: 01923 463602 (H) 0958 409678 (W)
GROUND: Middlesex Stadium, Breakspear Road, Ruislip, Middx HA4 7SB (01895 639544)
Website: www.hillingdonboroughfc.uk.co **E-mail:** alanhbfc@hotmail.com
Directions: From A40 take B467 (signed Ickenham), left at 2nd r'bout into Breakspear Rd South,
right after 1 mile by Breakspear pub - ground half mile on left. Nearest station is Ruislip. Bus U1
passes ground
Capacity: 1,500 Seats: 150 Cover: 150 Floodlights: Yes Club Shop: No
Clubhouse: Mon-Fri 7.30-11pm, Sat & Sun lunchtime & 7.30-11.00pm

RECORDS: **Win:** 12-0 v Hanwell T. (H), S.S.M. Prem 97/98
Defeat: 1-11 v St. Albans City (A), FA Cup 2nd Qual. Rd. 24.9.94
Transfer Fee Received: ˜1,000 for Craig Johnson (Wealdstone)
Top goalscoer 2000-01: Andy McCulloch - 18 **Captain:** Kevin Ford **P.o.Y:** Mark Donnelly

FACT FILE
Founded: 1990 Nickname: Boro
Sponsors: Airport Motor Radiator Co
Colours: White/blue/blue
Change colours: All red
Midweek Matches: Tuesday
Reserves' League: Suburban
Programme: 20 pages Editor/Press Off:
Alan Taylor (0181 581 0981)
CLUB PERSONNEL
Chairman: Dhally Dhaliwall
Commercial Mgr: Garry grant
Manager: Steve Hawkins
Asst Man.: Ian Lancaster
Physio: Dave Pook

HODDESDON TOWN

Secretary: Brenda Timpson, 82 Tolmers Rd,Cuffley, Herts EN6 4JY (01707 874028)
GROUND: `Lowfield', Park View, Hoddesdon, Herts (01992 463133)
Directions: A10, A1170 into Hoddesdon, over 1st r'about, right at 2nd r'aboutand follow signs to
Broxbourne, keeping to the left. Turn right at 1st mini r-about into Cock Lane and 1st right is Park
View. Ground 200yds on the left,entrance opposite Park Rd. BR station is Broxbourne
Capacity: 3,000 Seats: 100 Cover: 250 Floodlights: Yes Club Shop: Scarves,badges,hats &pens
Clubhouse: Bar and well-stocked Tea Bar with hot food. Open at every home game
HONOURS: FA Vase 74-75 (1st winners); S.S.M. Lg Prem Div Plate 97-98 (R-up 96-97,
SthMids Lge Lg Cup 85-86 86-87 91-92 (Prem Div Tphy R-up 92-93); Spartan Lg 70-71(R-up(3)
71-74), Div 1 35-36, Div 2 `B' 27-28, Lg Cup(2) 70-72; S.Mids Floodlit Cup 01-02
PREVIOUS: **Lges:** East Herts 1896-1908, 11-21; Herts Co. 08-25; N Middx Dist 10-22;
Spartan 25-75; London Spartan 75-77; Athenian 77-84; South Midlands 84-97
RECORDS: **Attendance:** 3,500 v West Ham, (Floodlight opening friendly), 1975
BEST SEASON: FA Vase: Winners 74-75

FACT FILE
Founded: 1879 Nickname: Lilywhites
Colours: White/black/black
Change Colours: yellow/blue
Midweek matchday: Tuesday
Reserves' Lge: Essex/Herts Border Com
Programme: 100 + pages £1.00
Editor: Mrs Jane Sinden Tel: 01767 631297
CLUB PERSONNEL
Pres: Peter Haynes Chairman: Roger Merton
Gen Man: Jim Briggs
Man : Bill O'Driscoll Ass.Man: Darren White
Coaches : Paul Wade and Kevin Butler
2001-02 Captain: Ritchie Simmonds
Top Scorer & P.o.Y.: Paul Evitt

HOLMER GREEN

Secretary: Stuart Moffat, 40 Broughton Avenue, Aylesbury HP20 1NH
GROUND: Watchet Lane, Holmer Green, High Wycombe (01494 711485)
Directions: From Amersham on A404 High Wycombe Road, after approx 2 miles turn right into Sheepcote Dell Road. Continue until end of road by Bat & Ball PH.Turn right then immediate left, continue approx 1/2 mile until 2 mini roundabouts, turn left in front of the Mandarin Duck into Watchet Lane. The ground is 150 yards on the right
Capacity: 1,000   Seats: 25   Cover:Yes   Floodlights:Yes   Club Shop:No
Clubhouse: Saturdays 12pm -11 pm midweek 7pm 11pm   Badges: Yes (£3)
HONOURS: Berks & Bucks Sen Tr.Finalists 98-99, BB Jun Cup Winners 52-53, 63-64 B&B Inter'iate Cup Winners 76-77; S.Mid Sen Div Winners (2), S.Mid Sen Cup Winners 96-97 Additional Honours: Cheshm Charity Cup Winners (6),Wycombe Sen Cup Winners: (5),Wycombe Lg Winners (4) and Lg Cup Winners 80-8181 Chiltonian League Winners: (3) Lg Cup Winners 94-95, Spartan South Midlands Sen Div Cup Winners: 97-98
PREVIOUS Leagues: 1908--34 Chesham. 34-84 Wyc Comb. 84-95 Chiltonian 95-98 S Mids

FACT FILE
Founded: 1908
Colours: Green & White/ Green/Green
Change colours: All blue
Midweek Matchday: Tuesday (7.45)
Prog: Yes - Inc.Admission
Club Website:
www.hgfc1908@freeserve.co.uk
2000-01
Captain & Top Scorer: Shaun Martin 18
P.o.Y.: Jason Quyincey
CLUB PERSONNEL
President: John Anderson
Chairman: Bill Scholes 01494 713867 (H)
Match Secretary: T.B.A. Manager JezHodges

LETCHWORTH

Secretary: Trevor Sostacenko,52 Jackmans Place,Letchworth , Herts SG6 1RH
Ground: Baldock Road, Letchworth, Herts SG6 2GN (01462 637979)
Directions: Jct 9 (A6141) off A1M straight over large r-about, right at next r-about, ground on right. From Luton (A505) thru Hitchin, ground 3 miles afterHitchin. 2 miles from Letchworth (BR)
Capacity: 3,200   Cover: 400 Seats: 300 Floodlights: Yes   Clubhouse: Yes
HONOURS: Herts Lg 11-12, Spartan Lg 29-30 35-36 51-52, Delphian Lg 57-58, Athenian Lg 74-75 (Mem. Shield 65-66 66-67), Herts Snr Cup 12-13 35-36 51-52, Herts Charity Shield 22-23 47-48 87-88 91-92, East Anglian Cup 76-77, Woolwich Cup 81-82, Hitchin Cup 81-82
Senior DivisionTrophy Winners: 99-00
PREVIOUS: **Leagues:** Herts Co. 06-07; Biggleswade 07-08; Nth Herts 08-22   , S Mids 22-23 24-29; Spartan 29-56; Athenian 63-77; Isthmian 77-90
    Names: Garden City; Letchworth Ath.; Letchworth Town
    Grounds: Letchworth Corner; Garth Rd; Cashio Lane
Players progressing to Football League: Imre Varadi, Keith Larner

FACT FILE
Founded: 1906
Nickname: Bluebirds
Colours: All Blue
Change Colours: Red & black/black/black
Midweek matchday: Tuesday
Programme:24 pages,50p
Editor: Nigel Crow
Email: info@letchworthfc.co.uk

CLUB PERSONNEL
Chairman: Graham Hopkins
Match Sec.: T.B.A.
Manager: Kerry Dixon & John Alder

LONDON COLNEY

Secretary: Dave Brock, 50 Seymour Rd., St Albans, Herts. AL3 5HW. Tel: 01727 761644 (H)

Ground: Cotslandswick, London Colney (01727 822132)
Directions: From London Colney r'bout (junction of A414/A1081) take A414 towards Watford, after layby (300yds) turn left (hidden turning marked `SportsGround') and follow around to gates.
Capacity: 1,000 Cover: 100   Seats: 30   Floodlights: Yes   Club Shop:
Clubhouse: Open after games. Hot food available

HONOURS   Sth Mids Lg Sen Div 94-95 R-up 93-94 (Chall. Tphy 93-94, Div 1 R-up 92-93, Res.Div 1 92-93), Herts Co. Lg 56-57 59-60 86-87 88-89 (R-up 57-58 58-59). Aubrey Cup 21-22 22-23 56-57 58-59 81-82, Res. Div 1 87-88 88-89 89-90 91-92, Res. Cup 62-63 89-90 91-92 (R-up 70-71)

PREVIOUS   **Leagues:** Mid Herts 1907-54; Herts Co. 07-92
    Ground: Whitehorse Lane 07-75
Record Attendance: 300 v St Albans City. Herts Senior Cup 98-99

FACT FILE
Founded: 1907   Nickname: Blueboys
Sponsors: City Glass
Colours: All Royal blue
Change Colours: Yellow/ & black/black/yellow
Midweek Matchday: Tuesday
Programme: £1 with entry
Editor: Bill Gash (01727 767556)
CLUB PERSONNEL
Chairman: Bill Gash
Vice Chairman: P Light
President: K.Parsons
Manager: Mick Wright
Physio: J Burt

MILTON KEYNES CITY

Secretary: Peter Baldwin,1 Wantage Close, Hackleton,Nirthants NN7 2AG (01604 870457 (H) 01908 245408 (W) FAX 01908 245088 (Fax at Work)
Ground: Wolverton Park,Old Wolverton Rd.,Wolverton,Milton Keynes MK12 5QH(01908 318317)
Directions: From A5 trunk road exit at Milton Keynes North onto Great Monks Way (V5). Continue over two oundabouts onto Old Wolverton Road. Ground is 1 milwe on right, between two railway arches and next to Wolverton BR station.p
Capacity: 3000   Cover: Yes   Seats: 150 Floodlights: Yes   Club Shop: No
Clubhouse: On ground and open normal opening hours.Closed Mondays
HONOURS: North Bucks Lge - Div 1 90-91, Prem. Div Cup 92-93, I'mediate Tphy 91-92; Daimler-Benz Austrian International Tournament R-up 1990
    S.S.M.Lg Trophy Winners 99-00 **Previous Name:** Mercedes - Benz F.C.
PREVIOUS: **Leagues:** Milton Keynes Sunday/ North Bucks & District (pre'93)
RECORD   **Scorer:** Stuart Collard 132   **Appearances:** Stuart Collard 206
    Win: 24-2 v Milton Keynes Saints, Berks & Bucks Jun Cup 1st Rd 16/10/93
    Defeat: 1-8 v Greenleys, Milton Keynes Sun Lge Cup 1st Rd 22/11/87

FACT FILE
Founded: 1967   Nickname: Blues or City
Sponsors: Wright Tile Centre
Colours: All Royal Blue
Change Colours: Old Gold/Black/Old Gold
Midweek matches: Tuesday
Reserves' league: S.S.M. Reserve Div
Programme: 25 pages,£1.00
Editor: Stuart Collard, 01908 505042 (H),
01908 600394 (B)
CLUB PERSONNEL
Chairman: Bob Flight. President: T.B.A.
Manager & Assistant T.B.A. Physio: Andy
Nicholls Captain: Mark McCarthy Top Scorer:
Darren Lynch (16). P.o.Y.: T.B.A.

London Colney and (right) those who did not make the main picture having 'hibernated' in the dressing room!
Photos: Arthur Evans

Stony Stratford. Back Row (l-r): Darren Long, Graham Boddy, Craig Jackman, Ben Carpenter, James Canwell, Hugo McGlue. Middle Row: Dean Valentine, Paul Sloley, Adam Knox, Joe Major, Reid Watson, Paul Calnan, Chris Johnson (Mngr). Front Row: Alex Carroll, Stuart Pullman, Brendan Quill, Ian King, Matty Herbert.

Leverstock Green. Back Row (l-r): B Chapman (Physio), B Jackson (Manager), M Burfoot, G Parkins, S Garnham, D Cartwright, N Starbrook, S Mazurek, A Phillips, P Copson (Coach). Front Row: C Nduka, L Daly, M Wardle, T Sears, J Juster, D Fisher, J Copson, R Males (Asst Manager)

POTTERS BAR TOWN

Secretary: Jeff.Barnes,38 Pinewood Drive, Potters Bar, Herts EN6 2BD Tel/FAX: 01707 660445
Email Address: jibarnes@supanet.com **GROUND:** Parkfield, The Walk, Potters Bar, Herts EN6
1QN, 01707 654833
Directions: M25 jct 24, enter Potters Bar along Southgate Rd (A111), at 1st lights right into the
High St (A1000), half mile left into The Walk, grd 200yds on right (opp. Potters Bar Cricket Club)
Capacity: 2,000   **Seats:** 150   **Cover:** 100   **Floodlights:** Yes   **Club Shop:** No   Contact Jeff
Barnesfor details of pennants,badges, car stickers and hangers etc.
Clubhouse: Sat 12.30-11pm, Sun noon-5pm, Tues & Thurs 7.30-11pm, midweek matchnights
HONOURS: South Midlands Lge. - Prem. Div. 96-97, Plate 96-97; Herts. Sen. Co. Lge. -Prem.
Div. 90-91, Div. 1 73-74, 81-82, Div. 2 68-69; North London Comb. - Prem.Div. 67-68, Div. 1 67-68,
Div. 2 R-up 65-66;SSMLg R-up 98-99   Prem Div North R-up 97-98 ,SML Floodlight Cup 99-00
PREVIOUS: **Leagues:** Barnet & Dist. 60-65/ N London Comb. 65-68/ Herts Snr Co. 68-91
RECORD: **Attendance:** 4000 v Eastenders XI, 20.4.97. 387 v Barnet, f/light open93
Competitive: 268 v Wealdstone ,F.A.Cup 1998
BEST SEASON: FA Vase: 6th Rd 97-98

FACT FILE
Founded: 1960
Nickname: The Grace or The Scholars
Colours: Red & royal stripes/royal/royal
Blue & Yellow stripes/ryellow/yellow
Midweek matchday: Tuesday or Wednesday
Prog Ed: Jonathon Gooding (01483 420731)
Programme: 40pages, £1 and Website-
fotballnews.co.uk/clubs/20/2055/home.page
CLUB PERSONNEL
Chairman: Peter Waller V Chair: Alan Bolt
President: B Wright General Mger: L Eason
Manager:JohnMeakes.Coach:Steve Hurd
Physio: Brian Simpson **00-01** Top Scorer Lee
Talbot Capt: Ryan Harris P.o.Y.: Neil Jord

ROYSTON TOWN

Secretary/Press Officer: Elaine Phillips, 14 Roan walk, Royston, Herts SG8 9HT
Tel No: 01763 241041 (H)
GROUND: Garden Walk, Royston, Herts SG8 7HP (01763 241204).
Directions: FromBaldock, A505 to Royston bypass, right at 2nd island onto A10 towards
London, 2nd left is Garden Walk; ground 100 yds on left.
Capacity: 4,000   Seats: 300   Cover: 300   Floodlights: Yes   Club Shop: Yes
Clubhouse: Mon-Thurs 7-11, Fri 11-3 & 7-11, Sat 11-3 & 4-11, Sun 12-3.
HONOURS   Herts Co. Lg 76-77 (Div 1 69-70 76-77); Sth Mids Lg R-up 79-80   (Div 1 78-
79,Chall. Cup R-up 78-79;
PREVIOUS   **Leagues:** Buntingford & Dist. 18-28; Cambs 28-50; Herts Co. 50-59 62-77;
SthMids 59-62 77-84; Isthmian 84-94
RECORDS   **Attendance:** 876 v Aldershot, 13/2/93
Scorer: Trevor Glasscock 289 (1968-82)   **Appearances:** Fred Bradley 713
BEST SEASON   FA Cup: 2nd Qual. Rnd 59-60, 0-9 v Barnet (A), 89-90, 0-3 V Bromley (A)

FACT FILE
Founded: 1875   Nickname: Crows
Res League: Essex & Herts Border Comb
Sponsors: ABA Consultants
Colours: White/black/black
Change colours: Red/white/white
Midweek Matches: Tuesday
Programme: 16 pages, 30p
Editor: Secretary
CLUB PERSONNEL
Chairman: Graham Phillips
Vice-Chairman: Bernard Brown
President: Alan Barlow
Manager: Gavin Head
Asst Mgr: S Salomone   Physio: C Mardell

RUISLIP MANOR

Secretary: John Price, 1 Filey Way, Ruislip,Middlesex (01895 631933)
Ground: Grosvenor Vale, off West End Rd, Ruislip, Middx 01895 637487-office,676168-boardroom
Directions: A40 to Ruislip, turn off on A4180, right at r'bout into West EndRd, right into Grosvenor
Vale after a 1 1/2 miles - ground at end. From RuislipManor station (Metropolitan Line) turn left out
of station, then 1st right intoShenley Ave, 3rd left into Cranley Dr - ground 150 yds on left
Capacity: 3,000   Seats: 250   Cover: 600   Floodlights: Yes   Club Shop: Yes
Clubhouse: Mon-Fri 12-3.30 & 5.30-11pm, Sat & Sun 12-3 & 7.30-10.30
HONOURS   London Lg R-up 51-52 (Div 1 R-up 47-48), Isthmian Lg Div 2 R-up 92-93
(Associate Members Tphy 90-91), Athenian Lg Div 2 72-73, Middx Snr Cup
SF (6), Middx Charity Cup R-up 90-91 95-96
PREVIOUS   **Leagues:** Uxbridge 38-39; Middx Snr 39-46; London 46-58; Spartan 58-65;
Athenian65-84; Isthmian 84-96
RECORDS   **Attendance:** 2,000 v Tooting & Mitcham United, F.A. Amateur Cup 1962
Appearances: Chris Balls, 350 **Goalscorer:** Kevin Quinn, 76
BEST SEASON   FA Cup: 4th Q Rd 90-91, 2-5 v Halesowen T (A) **F.A.Am.Cup:** 1st Rd 73-74

FACT FILE
Founded: 1938   Nickname: The Manor
Sponsors: Light Years
Colours: Black & White/black/black
Change colours: Blue & yellow/blue/blue.
Midweek Matches: Monday
Reserve League: Suburban Lge (North)
Programme: 24 Price: 50p
Editor/ Press Off.: Chris Thomas
01895 636930
CLUB PERSONNEL
Chairman: Tom O'Shea
Vice Chairman: Keith Cham berlain
Manager:Paul Pitfield
Physio: Gary Strudwick

St MARGARETSBURY

Secretary: Ashley Ward, 1 Village Close, Hoddesdon, Herts. EN11 0GJ (01992 410386)
GROUND: Station Road, Stanstead St Margarets, Nr Ware, Herts (01920 870473)

Directions: Harlow/Chelmsford exit from A10 to A414, take B181 at Amwell roundabout after
300yds towards Stanstead Abotts, ground quarter mile on right. 300yds from St Margaretsbury BR
station (Liverpool Str.-Hertford East line)
Capacity: 1,000   Seats: 60   Cover: 60   Floodlights: Yes   Club Shop: No

Clubhouse: Bar open every evening 7.30-11, plus Sat 12-2, Sun 12-3. Bar snacks available
HONOURS: Herts Snr Cent Tphy 92-93; Herts Co. Lg Div 2 48-49, Div 3 78-79; Aubrey
Cup 48-49 71-72; Res. Div 1 82-83 86-87; Res. Cup 84-85 86-87 87-88); Waltham &Dist Lg 46-47;
Spartan Lge 95-96; Roy Bailey Mem Trophy 95-96, Herts Charity Shield 97-98.
PREVIOUS: Lges: East Herts; Hertford & Dist.; Waltham & District 47-48; Herts Co. 48-92
RECORD: Attendance: 327 v Wisbech Town, FA Vase 3rd Round 14/12/85
BEST SEASON   FA Vase: 3 Rd 1985

FACT FILE
Founded: 1894   Nickname: The Bury
Sponsors: Lawfords Building Supplies
Colours: Red & black/white/white
White/Black/Black
Midweek matchday: Tuesday
Reserve League: Essex & Herts Border Comb.
Programme: £3.00 with entry
Editor/Match Sec.: Jon Gooding
Tel:07931 191026
CLUB PERSONNEL
Chairman: Dave Stock
President: R L Groucott
Manager:Martin Gutteridge
Physio: John Elliott

AMERSHAM TOWN

Secretary: Michael Gahagan, 7 Ely Close, Lincoln Pk,Amersham,Bucks.HP7 9HS (01494 24798)
GROUND: Spratley's Meadow, School Lane, Old Amersham, Bucks. (01494 727428)
Directions: From London A413 to Amersham Old town, in front of market hall, right into Church St., first left into School Lane, ground on left past Mill Lane. 1 mile from Amersham Station - BR & underground Metropolitan Line
Capacity: 1,500   Seats: 50   Cover: 100   Floodlights: Yes   Club Shop: No
Clubhouse: Open matchdays. Bar facilities. Teas, coffees and light snacks
HONOURS: Hellenic Lg 63-64 (R-up 64-65 65-66, Div 1 62-63, Cup 53-54), Ldn Spartan Lg R-up 79-80, St Marys Cup 89-90 96-97 (R-up 90-91,96-97), B & Bucks Jnr Cup 22-23 (Snr Cup SF 79-80 80-81), Wycombe Chal. Cup 23-24
2001-02 Captain: Neil Poulter   ScorerTony Haick(7)

FACT FILE
Founded: 1890   Nickname: Magpies
Colours: Black & white stripes/black/black
Change colours: All Yellow
Midweek matches: Tuesday
Reserve's League: S.S Mids.
Prog. Editor: Michael Gahagan
CLUB PERSONNEL
Chairman: David Holdcroft
President: Graham Taylor
Manager: Frank Figuero Coach:Colin Perkins

AMPTHILL TOWN

Secretary: Eric Turner, 34 Dunstable Street, Ampthill, Beds MK45 2JT.
Tel:01525 403128 (H & B)

Ground: Ampthill Park, Woburn Road, Ampthill, Beds. Tel: 01525 404440

Directions: From Ampthill Town Centre follow signs to Woburn then take the first right into Ampthill Park

Chairman: Peter Foxall
Tel: 01525 755041
Manager: Nicholas Burton
Programme Editor: As Secretary
Colours: Yellow & navy blue/navy/navy
Change Colours: Green/black/black
2000-01
Leading goalscorer: Danny Giggs 14
Captain: Carl Page
P.o.Y.: James Slack

BIGGLESWADE UNITED

Secretary: Tracey James, 17 Havelock Road, Biggleswade, Beds SG18 0DB.
Tel: 01767 316270 (H), 020 7270 6045(B), 0771 466 1827(M)
GROUND: Second Meadow, Fairfield Road, Biggleswade, Beds. (01767 600408)
Directions: From A1 Sainsbury's roundabout, cross over iron bridge and take 2nd left into Sun Street.(before Peugot Garage) Take first left into Fairfield Road ground at bottom of road in lane
Capacity: 2,000   Seats: 30   Cover: 130   Floodlights: Yes   Club Shop: No
Clubhouse: Open all matchdays, rolls available. Also refreshment hut with hot snacks
HONOURS: Hunts F.A. Prem Cup : 98-99,S.Mids Lg Div 1 96-97 Cup Winners 96-97Beds & District Prtem Div.94-95, 95-96, Div 1. 91-92,Div2 90-91,Div3 88-89 Beds F.A. Inter Cup (2)
Record Crowd: 250 v Biggleswade Town 28.12.98 **Previous Name:**Biggleswade F.C.
Best Season in F.A.Vase: 1st Rd Proper 95-96

Founded: 1959 (original club 1935)
Colours: Red & navy/navy/red
Change : Yellow & Black/black/yellow
Midweek Matchday: Tuesday /Thursday
Prog-With admission Editor: Secretary
Chairman: David McCormick (01767 316018)
Match Sec.: Mick Brown, (01767 221512)
Manager: 'Snowy' Wright
Physio: Phil Lunceford

BRACHE SPARTA

Secretary: Roy Standring, 37 Taunton Avenue, Luton, Beds. LU2 0LN. Tel: 01582 736574
GROUND: Foxdell Sports Ground, Dallow Rd, Luton LU1 1UP (01582 720751).
Directions: From M1 jct11, take A505 towards Luton. Right at Chaul End roundabout. Across A505 keep B&Q on left, into Dallow Rd. Ground 50 yds on right by Foxdell junior school.
Capacity: 400   Cover: 100   Seats: 25   Floodlights: Yes   Club Shop: No
Clubhouse: Open daily 12-3 & 7.30-11. Light snacks & refreshments etc available
HONOURS: South Mids Lg R-up 92-93, 96-97 (Div 1 R-up 83-84 87-88), Lg Cup R-up 75-76 80-81 92-93 97-98, Premier Div Cup Winners 97-98 R-up 91-92, Res Div 2 R-up 75-76, Res Cup R-up 87-88; Luton & Dist. Lg 67-68 69-70 70-71 71-72; William Pease Trophy 66-67 67-68 70-71 71-72; Beds Interm Cup 71-72 (R-up 68-69 70-71), BedsJnr Cup 82-83; Leighton Challenge Cup R-up 69-70 South Mids Lg Prem Div 1 North Champions 97-98, Beds Premier Cup R-up. 97-98

FACT FILE
Founded: 1960   Nickname: The Foxes
Colours: White/navy/white
Change Colours: All royal
Midweek matches: Tuesday
Prog: 32 pages, £2.50 (incl. admission)
Career Record Goalscorer: Keith Denness
CLUB PERSONNEL
Chairman: Roy Standring
President: Doug Smith
Manager: Steve Brinkman
Physio: Chris Garner

BRIMSDOWN ROVERS

Secretary: Mrs Lorraine Winter,,141 Kinwood Crescent,Enfield, Midd'x EN1 4US (Tel & Fax: 020 8366 1075 , Fax: 0208 8045491 and Mobile: 07747 681044) Email: lw@bssc.freeserve.co.uk
GROUND: Brimsdown Sports & Social Club, Goldsdown Road, Enfield, Middlesex EN3 7RR
Tel: 0208 804 5491 **Directions:** BR from Liverpool Street to Brimsdown (half mile away) or Southbury Road. By road off Green Street, itself off Hertford Road (A1010). Buses 191 or307
Capacity: 1,000   Seats: 25Cover: 50Floodlights: Yes   Club Shop
Clubhouse: Large lounge & clubroom, games room & stage. 3 bars (300 capacity)
HONOURS: Spartan Lg 92-93. Spartan Lg Cup 95-96
RECORD: **Gate:** 412 v Chesham Utd, FA Cup 3rd Qual. Rd 12/10/91
BEST SEASON: **FA Vase:** 3rd Rd 93-94   **FA Cup:** 3rd Qual. replay 91-92
PREVIOUS: **Leagues:** Northern Suburban   **Names:** Durham Rovers; Brimsdown FC

FACT FILE
Founded: 1947
Colours: Black & white stripes/black/black
Change colours: Yellow/Blue/Yellow
Midweek Matchday: Tuesday
Programme: With admission
Editor: Peter Wade
Chairman: Gary Simpson
Match Secretary: Peter Wade.
5 Goldsdown Close, Enfield Middlesex EN3 7RR Tel: 0208 804 7053
Manager:Dave Farenden

COCKFOSTERS

Secretary: Graham Bint, 15 Chigwell Park, Chigwell, Essex IG7 5BE (0208 500 7369)
GROUND: Cockfosters Sports Ground, Chalk Lane, Cockfosters, Barnet (0208 449 5833)
Directions: M25 Jct 24 (Potters Bar), take A111 signed Cockfosters - ground 2 miles on right.
Adjacent to Cockfosters underground station (Picadilly Line). Bus 298 to Cockfosters station
Capacity: 1,000   Seats: None   Cover: 50   Floodlights: Yes   Club Shop: No
Clubhouse: 7-11pm Tues & Thurs, 4-11pm Sat, 12-3pm Sun. Hot & cold food onmatchdays
HONOURS: London Interm Cup 70-71 89-90, Herts Snr Co. Lg 78-79 80-81 83-84 R-up
82-83 84-85, Aubrey Cup 78-79 84-85 R-up 70-71 77-78, Herts Interm Cup 78-79 R-up x3
Previous Leagues: Wood Green & Dist. 21-46/ Northern Suburban 46-66/ Herts Snr Co.66-91
BEST SEASON: FA Vase: 2nd Round 91-92
RECORDS: Gate: 408 v Saffron Walden, Herts Senior County Lg 68-69

Founded: 1921   Nickname: Fosters
Colours: All Red Change colours: All White
Midweek matches: Tuesday
Sponsors: T.S.I.Design
Programme: 12 pages with entry
Editor: A Simmons (0208 440 7998)
Chairman/Press Off.: Frank Brownlie
(0208 500 5930)
President: Les Langdale Manager: Dean Cole
2001-02 Captain: Dave Finch . P.o.Y.: Duncan
Field . Top Scorer: Jon Moniatis 24

COLNEY HEATH

Secretary: Ann Hutchins,15 Cobmead, Hatfield,

Ground: The Pavillion Recreaton Ground, High St., Colney Heath, St. Albans, Herts.
Tel: 01727 826188

Directions: Turn off the A414 (was A405) into Colney Heath village and the ground is
behind the school on the left.

HARPENDEN TOWN

Secretary: Neil Ludlow, 93 RussellSt.,Luton,Beds LU1 5EB 01582 486802(H) 01582 424233(W)
GROUND: Rothamsted Park, Amenbury Lane, Harpenden (01582 715724)
Directions: A1081 to Harpenden. Turn left/right at George public housel into Leyton Rd.Turn left
into Amenbury Rd, then left again (50yds) into `Pay and Display' carpark - entrance is signposted
thru car park to opposite corner
Capacity: 1,500   Seats: 25   Cover: 100   Floodlights: Yes   Club Shop: No
Clubhouse: Open matchdays
HONOURS: Sth Mids Lg 61-62 64-65, Ch'ship Shield 67-68, Lg Cup 70-71, Div 1 89-90, Prem Div
Tphy 89-90; Mid-Herts Lg 09-10 20-21, Div 1 99-00; Herts Co. Lg 11-12 49-50 51-52 53-54
PREVIOUS: **Leagues:** Mid-Herts; Herts County   **Best Seasons:** F.A.Cup: 1st Rd Q
Name: Harpenden FC 1891-1908   F.A.Vase: 2nd Rd

FACT FILE
Founded: 1891
Nickname: The Town
Colours: Yellow/blue/blue
Change:Red & Black Hoops/Black/Black
Midweek matches: Tuesday
Programme: 50pEditor: Chairman
CLUB PERSONNEL
Chairman: Stephen Whiting (01582 761606)
Manager: GrahamGolds & Gordon Guile
2000-01 Captain Nathan Dawes
Top Scorer: Chris Gregory 20

HAYWOOD UNITED
Secretary: Lynne Nappin, 6 Evesham Green, Aylesbury, Bucks. HP19 9RX
Tel: 01296 486924

Ground: Stocklake Sports & Social Club, Haywards Way, Aylesbury, Bucks. Tel: 01296 423324

Directions: Follow signs to Bicester from Aylesbury ring road.
At fifth road island, with Aylesbury Duck P.H. on right, turn right into Jackson Road
and then second left into Haywood Way.   Club is at bottom of the road.

Previous Leagues: Chiltonian

KINGS LANGLEY

Secretary: Andy Mackness, 79 Weymouth Street, Apsley, Hemel Hempstead, Herts HP3 9SJ
Tel: 01442 398186 (H) 020 7587 4153 (B) 07976 692801 (M)

Ground: Gaywood Park, Hempstead Road, Kings Langley. Tel: 01923 264489

Directions: From M25 leave at Junction 20. Take A4251 to Kings Langley.
The ground is approx. 1 mile on the right.

Colours: Black & white stripes/black/black
Change colours: All white
Programme: Yes
Editor: Adrian Marston Tel: 01923 893320 (H)

Chairman: Derry Edgar
Tel: 01923 268301 (H)

Manager: Colin Jones
Tel: 01442 394986 (H)

LANGFORD

Secretary: Frank Woodward, 4 West View, Langford, Biggleswade. Beds. SG18 9RT
Tel: 01462 701015 (H)   Club Email: langfordfc@talk21.com
GROUND: Forde Park, Langford Road, Henlow SG16 6AF   Tel: 01462 816106
Directions: Halfway between Langford and Henlow on A6001 Hitchin to Biggleswade road. Bus 177 on main Hitchin-Biggleswade route stops right outside ground
Capacity: 4,000   **Seats:** 50   **Cover:** 250   **Floodlights:** Yes   **Club Shop:** Yes
Clubhouse: Weekday evenings, matchdays 11am-11pm, Sun 12-3pm. Hot food on matchdays
HONOURS: S Mids Lg 88-89 (Lg Cup 73-74 75-76, Prem. Div Tphy 88-89,94-95.O'Brien Div 1 Tphy 84-85), N Beds Charity Cup 27-28 30-31 69-70 75-76 86-87 92-93 94-95 98-99 01-02Bedford & Dist. Lg 30-31 31-32 32-33, Bedfs l'mediate Cup 68-69, Hinchingbrooke Cup 72-73
RECORD: **Gate:** 450 v Q.P.R., 75th Anniversary and clubhouse opening, 22/8/85

Founded: 1908   Nickname: Reds
Sponsors:Armitage Asphalt
Colours: All red with white trim
Change Colours: Blue & white
Midweek matches: Tuesday
Programme: With admission.
Editors: Bob Davies (01438 238066)
Chairman: Mick Quinlan President: Ted Rutt
Com. Man: Diane Woodward Man: Roy Ryall
2001-02 Leading goalscorer:Eddie Fannon 13
Captain: Barry laurence
P.o.Y.: Lee Rogers

LETCHWORTH BRIDGER

Secretary: Mark Phillips, 72B Ickneild Way, Letchworth, Herts. SG6 4AT
Tel Nos: 01462 636862 (H) 07977 978426 (M)

Ground: Letchworth Corner Sports Club, Muddy Lane, Letchworth, Herts. SG6 3TB.
Tel: 01462 486459

Directions: A1(M) junc 9 towards Letchworth, over large roundabout, turn left at next roundabout A505 Hitchin, through lights, turn left at pelican crossing into Muddy Lane

Colours: Sky blue & yellow stripes/sky blue/
sky blue & yellow
Change Colours: All claret & blue.

Programme Editor: John Furness
Tel: 01462 627279 (H)

Chairman: Lawrence Bridger

Manager: Dean Cole

LEVERSTOCK GREEN

Secretary: Brian Barter, 11 Curlew Close, Berkhamsted, Herts HP4 2HZ (01442 862322)
GROUND: Pancake Lane, Leverstock Green, Hemel Hempstead. Tel: 01442 246280.
Directions: From M1 leave at A4147 to 2nd r-about. 1st exit to LeverstockGreen, Pancake Lane is on left 300 yrds past the `Leather Bottle' pub
Capacity: **Seats:** 25   **Cover:** 100   **Floodlights:** Yes **Club Shop:** Yes   **Clubhouse:** Yes, one hour before kick-off but no food

HONOURS: South Midlands Lge - Sen. Div 96-97, Sen Div Cup R-up 93-94, Herts CentenaryTphy R-up 91-92, Herts Charity Shield R-up 91-92, Frank Major Tphy 1991
PREVIOUS: **Leagues:** West Herts (pre-1950); Herts County 50-91
Players progressing to Football League: Dean Austin (Tottenham Hotspur)

Founded: 1895 Nickname: The Green
Sponsor: Sunshine Cabs
Colours: Yellow/Blue/Blue
Change Colours: Green & black/white/black
Midweek Matchday: Tuesday
Prog: 24 pages, 50p Ed: Chairman
Chairman: Bill Dawes, 01442 395748 (H)
Match Sec: Brian Pollard 01442 256720 (H)
Press Officer: Brian Pollard
Manager:Brian Jackson Coach: Brian Howard
2000-01Captain & P.o.Y.: Matt Griffin
Top Goalscorer: Tony Sears 14

NEW BRADWELL St PETER

Secretary: Les Smith, 25 Bishopstone,Bradville, Milton Keynes. MK13 7DQ (01908 315736)
Ground: Recreation Ground, Bradwell Rd, New Bradwell, Milton Keynes MK13 7AT
Tel.: 01908 313835
Directions: From M1 Jnt 14 go towards Newport Pagnell, left at 1st r-about into H3 (A422 Monks Way). Over 5 r-abouts, right at 6th island into V6 (GraftonSt.), At 1st roundabout go right the way round (back on yourself) then take 1st left at mini-r'about turn left into Bradwell Rd. Go straight over next mini r'about. Ground immediately on left.
Capacity: **Seats:** 30   **Cover:** 100   **Floodlights:** Yes
Clubhouse: Members only (member can sign in 2 guests). Evenings & w/e mid day. No food.
HONOURS: Sth Mids Lg Div 1 76-77 83-84 Sen Div Champs 97-98, (Res Div 2 R-up 76-7), Berks& Bucks Senior Trophy 1999-2000

FACT FILE
Founded: 1902   Nickname: Peters
Colours: All Maroon
Change: Amber/black/black.
Midweek matches: Tuesday
Programme: 32 pages, £3 with entry
Editor: Paul Smith 01908 550211 (H)
CLUB PERSONNEL
Chairman John Haynes President: J P Booden
Vice-Chairman: R.Creasey
Press Officer: P Smith
Managers:J. Gunn & E.Byrne

PITSTONE & IVINGHOE

Secretary: Jay Adlem, 22 Maud Janes Close, Ivinghoe, Leighton Buzzard. LU7 9ED.
Tel: 01296 668663 (H)

Ground: Pitstone Recreation Ground, Vicarage Road, Pitstone, Bucks Tel: 01296 661271

Directions: Tring Rd (B489) from Dunstable, turn right for Ivinghoe, and continue through to Pitstone r-about; ground left then right. From Aylesbury -left at `Rising Sun' in Aston Clinton, keep on that road to Pitstone r'bout; ground right then right.
Bus 61 from Luton or Aylesbury. Nearest BR stations are Tring or Cheddington.

Colours: Red & black/black/black
Change Colours:
Sky & navy stripes/navy/sky & navy hoops
Programme: Yes
Editor: Rob Adlem Tel: 01296 668663 (H)

Chairman: David Hawkins
Tel: 01296 661456
Manager: Sean Downey
Tel: 01525 634019

RISBOROUGH RANGERS

Secretary: Derrick J Wallace, 42 Ash Road, Princes Risborough, Bucks, HP27 0BQ
Tel: 01844 345179 (H), 01844 345435 (B)
GROUND: `Windsor', Horsenden Lane, Princes Risborough. (01844 274176)
Directions: Rear of Princes Risborough BR Station (Chiltern Line). A4010 fromAylesbury thru Princes Risborough, fork right onto A4009, left by thatched cottage, over railway bridge, immediate right ground 150 yds on right
Capacity: 2,000   Seats: 25   Cover: 100   Floodlights: No   Club Shop: No
Clubhouse: Yes. Snacks available matchdays
HONOURS: Berks & Bucks Jnr Cup 85-86, Wycombe & Dist Lg D 2 85-86 D 3 84-85
PREVIOUS: League: Wycombe & Dist. 71 -
RECORD: Gate: 1,200 v Showbiz XI   Scorer: Craig Smith

Founded: 1971
Club Sponsors: Systems 3R
Colours: Red & white/black/red
Change Colours: Blue & white/blue/white
Midweek matches: Tuesday
Programme: 20+ pages, £1 with entry
Editor: Richard Woodward
Chairman: Trevor Taylor
Tel: 01844 342202 (H)
Manager: Jon Franklyn

SHILLINGTON

Secretary: Aubrey Cole, 32 Greenfields, Shillington, Hitchin, Herts. SG5 3NX
Tel: 01462 711322

Ground: Playing Field, Greenfields, Shillington
Tel: 01462 711757

Directions: From Luton on A6 after bypassing Barton, turn right at large roundabout. Through Gobian to Shillington.
From Bedford or Hitchin, A600 to RAF Henlow. At Bird in Hand roundabout take exit to Upper Stondon.

STONY STRATFORD TOWN

Secretary: Maurice J Barber, 26 Boundary Cres., Stony Stratford, Milton Keynes MK11 1DF
Tel: 01908 567930 (H)
GROUND: Sports Ground, Ostlers Lane, Stony Stratford (01908 562267).
Directions: From Dunstable use old A5, Watling Street. Approaching Bletchley continue on A5 loop road (Hinkley) to end of dual c'way to A422/A508 r'bout. First exit, thru lights, 2nd right into Ostlers Lane.
Capacity: 600   Seats: 30   Cover: 120   Floodlights: Yes   Club Shop: No
Clubhouse: Open evenings & weekends
HONOURS: Sth Mids Lg R-up 70-71 71-72 (Div 1 93-94, Div 1 Cup 93-94)
PREVIOUS: Leagues: North Bucks & Dist.; Northampton Combination
RECORD: Attendance: 476 v Aston Villa U21, floodlight opening 12.11.96

Reformed: 1898
Sponsor:Amity Mortgages Ltd.
Colours:Sky blue/navy/navy
Change Colours:All yellow
Midweek matches: Tuesday
Reserves' League: SSM Res. Div. One
Programme: 28 pages, £3.00 (Incl. entrance)
Editor: Paul Grimsley   Chairman: Mike Judd
Mtch Sec.:Mrs. E. Sartain Man:Chris Johnson
2001-02 Leading goalscorer: Paul Sloley 55
Captain: Brendan Quill
P.o.Y.: 'Joe' Major

THE 61 FC

Secretary: Richard Everitt, 44 Somersby Close, Luton LU1 3XB. Tel: 01582 485095 (H)

Ground: Kingsway, Beverley Road, Luton, Beds. 01582 495417

Directions: M1 jct 11, A505 to Luton centre, right at 1st island, 1st left, Beverley Rd is 3rd left, entrance in Beverley Rd, exactly 1 mile junction 11.All Luton to Dunstable buses pass ground - alight at Beech Hill Bowling Club. 1mile from both Leagrave & Luton BR stations

Colours: Sky blue/royal blue/royal
Change Colours: Red & white/black/red
Programme: Yes
Editor: Richard Everitt Tel: 01582 485095

Chairman: Mark Davie
Tel: 01582 416011
Manager: Richard Everitt
Tel: 01582 485095 (H)

TRING ATHLETIC

Secretary: Ralph Griffiths, 42 Bedgrove, Aylesbury, Bucks HP21 7BD.Tel: 01296 426425 (H), email: ralph.griffiths@ntworld.com
Ground: Miswell Lane, Tring, Herts. HP23 4DR(01442 828331) Website: www.tafc.co.uk
Directions: Through Tring on main rd to Aylesbury, rt after Anchor PH into Miswell Lane, grd 500yds on rt opp Beaconsfield Rd. Tring station is several miles outside town, grd by bus ortaxi
Capacity: Seats: 25+   Cover: 100+   Floodlights: No   Club Shop: No
Clubhouse: Bar, open matchdays, training nights & Sunday lunchtimes
HONOURS: West Herts Div 1 (3), Lg R-up 72-73 ,Lg Cup 65-66. SSMIds: Senior Div 99-00,Lg Cup 89-90,Herts Charity Shield 99-00,01-02 Cherry Red Trophy (2) Herts Centenary Trophy (2)
PREVIOUS: League: West Herts 58-88
RECORD Scorer: Ian Butler   Appearances: Mark Boniface

Founded: 1958   Nickname: Athletic
Sponsors: R.O.Allum & Sons(Contractors)
Colours: Red & black/black/black
Change colours: yellow/green/yellow
Midweek matches: Wednesnay
Programme: 36 pages, £1.50 Editor: Sec
President: T.B.A.
Chairman: Barry Johnson
Manager: Mick Eldridge
Asst Manager: Ray Brimson
Coach &Physio: Richard Vincent

The Colney Heath squad line up after their tremendous 11-0 win against March Town United in their first ever Vase match.
Photo: Francis Short

Harefield United. Back Row (l-r): Mark Gibson, Steve Baker, Alex Brown, Dave Robinson, Shaka Mugal, James Keen, Dwayne Williams, Darryl Craft, Jeff Fanner, Eddie Richards. Front Row: Ben Herring, Leigh Curtin, Dean Harper, Josa Pena (Capt), Stuart Leavey (Mngr), Jesse Smith (Coach), John Whitfield, Andy McCullough, Robert Ursell, Ricky Pither.
Photo: Arthur Evans

Mursley United, Spartan South Midlands Division Two Champions line up before their win against Old Dunstablians which clinched the title.
Photo: Gordon Whittington

Tring Athletic. Back Row (l-r): Richard Vincent (Coach), Stuart Stedman, David Whicker, John Perry, Keith Eldridge, Tom Vincent, David Forskett, Steve Johnson, Mick Eldridge (Jnt Mngr), Ray Brimson (Jnt Mngr). Front Row: Ralph Griffiths (Sec), Julian James, Andy Humphreys, Trevor Gibb, Matt Strange, Mark Boniface (Capt), Paul Lewis, Rob Duncan, David Booles.
Photo: Arthur Evans

WELWYN GARDEN CITY

Secretary: James Bruce, 6 Autumn Grove, Welwyn G.C., Herts AL7 4DB. Tel: 01707331048 (H)
GROUND: Herns Lane, Welwyn Garden City (01707 328470)
Directions: From A1 follow signs for industrial area. Take one-way systemopposite Avdel Ltd (signed Hertford B195), take 2nd exit off one-way system.Ground 400 yards on left. One and a half miles from Welwyn GC (BR)
Capacity: 1,500   Seats: 40   Cover: 120   Floodlights: Yes   Club Shop: Yes
Clubhouse: Open every night and weekend lunchtimes. Members Bar, Hall.Steward:Gary Bevan
HONOURS: Herts Snr Centenary Tphy 84-85 (R-up 88-89), Herts Charity Shield 27-28 86-87
87-88 94-95 (R-up 48-49), Sth Mids Lg 73-74 (R-up 85-86, Div 1 69-70 81-82, LgCup R-up 74-75 81-82 88-89, Reserve Cup 85-86)
PREVIOUS: **Leagues:** Spartan; Metropolitan; Gtr London.   **Ground:** Springfields

Founded: 1921   Nickname: Citzens
Colours: Maroon & blue/blue/maroon
Change Colours: All white
Midweek Matches: Tuesday
Programme: 24 pages, 50p
Editor: Dave Fallon 01438 235701
Local Press: Welwyn & Hatfield Times,
Welwyn & Hatfield Herald & Post
Chairman: Terry Hazel
Manager: David Steedman
Assistant Manager: Ray Greenhall
Physio: Danny Milliken

WINSLOW UNITED

Secretary: David F Ward, 28 Park Road, Winslow, Buckingham MK18 3DL.
Tel: 01296713202 (H), 01865 781210 (B)

Ground: Recreation Ground, Elmfields Gate, Winslow, Bucks. Tel: 01296 713057

Directions: A413 from Aylesbury to Winslow, in High Street turn right into Elmfields Gate, ground on left opp. car park.A421 from Milton Keynes to Buck'ham then thro 'Gt Horwood

Colours: Yellow/blue/yellow
Change colours: Green & white/green/green
Programme: Yes
Editor: David Ward Tel: 01296 713202

Chairman: Jeff Robins
Tel: 01280 814974 (H)

Manager: Peter Miller
Tel: 01908 367832 (H)

DIVISION TWO CLUBS

ABBEY NATIONAL (Loughton.)
Secretary: Clare O'Connor, 18 Cranwell Close,Shenley Brook End, Milton Keynes MK5 7BU (01908 520370)
Ground: Loughton Sports & Social Club, Lincesdale Grove, Loughton, Milton Keynes. Tel: 01908 690668
Directions: From M1 Jct 14 follow H6, Childs Way for 5 miles until V4 Watling Way (Knowlhill r-about), right to Loughton r-about, right along H5 Portway 1st right Linceslade Grove

AMERSHAM TOWN
Secretary: Michael Gahagan, 7 Ely Close, Lincoln Pk,Amersham,Bucks.HP7 9HS (01494 24798)
Ground: Spratley's Meadow, School Lane, Old Amersham, Bucks. (01494 727428)
Directions: From London A413 to Amersham Old town, in front of market hall, right into Church St., first left into School Lane, ground on left past Mill Lane. 1 mile from Amersham Station - BR & underground Metropolitan Line

BUCKINGHAM ATHLETIC
Secretary: Neil Holman, 3 Chandos Close, Buckingham, Bucks. MK18 1AW (o1280 815539)
Ground: Stratford Fields, Stratford Rd, Buckingham Tel: 01280 816945
Directions: From Milton Keynes take the A422 Stony Stratford-Buckingham road -ground on left just before town centre. From Oxford, Aylesbury or Bletchley, take the ring road to the A422 Stony Stratford roundabout, turn left, theground is situated at the bottom of the hill on the left

CADDINGTON
Secretary: Dave Mark, 7 Heathfield Close, Caddington, Luton, Beds. LU1 4HD Tel: 01582 421404 (H) 01797 147968 (B)
Ground: Caddington Recreation Club, Manor Road, Caddington (01582 450151)
Directions: On entering village turn into Manor Road (adjacent to shops andvillage green), proceed 500 metres: Clubhouse and ground on left side next to Catholic Church

CRANFIELD UNITED
Secretary: Ed Frost, 9 Pollys Yard, Newport Pagnell MK16 8YU (01908 210877)
Ground: Crawley Road, Cranfield (01234 751444)
Directions: Take north Crawley/Newport Pagnell road from Cranfield village and ground is on left before leaving speed limit signs.

CRAWLEY GREEN
Secretary: Alan Burgess, 23 Higham Drive, Luton LU2 9SP (01582 483172)
Ground: Crawley Green Recreation Ground, Crawley Green Road, Luton, Beds. 01582 451058
Directions: From M1 jct 10 , to roundabout at end of motorway slip road into Airport Way. At fourth roundabout turn right into Crawley Green Road. Ground is 1/2 mile on left past Ashcroft High School.

FLAMSTEAD
Secretary: Mark McGreevy, 3 White Hill, Flamstead, Herts. AL3 8DN (01582 841 481)
Ground: Flamstead Sports Assoc., Friendless Lane, Flamstead, St Albans, Herts(0582 841307)
Directions: From Dunstable Town Centre travel south on A5 Trunk Roadtowards the M1. Follow for approximately 3 miles then turn right oppositeHertfordshire Moat House Hotel. Ground and parking approximately half a mile onthe corner of the first right turn

KENT ATHLETIC
Secretary: Irene Oodian, 9 Gafield Court, Handcross Road,Luton, Beds. LU2 8JZ (01582 483090)
Ground: Kent Social Club, Tenby Drive, Leagrave, Luton (01582 582723)
Directions: M1 jct 11 take A505 towards Luton. Take the first turning on theleft (Stoneygate Road), straight over at the roundabout and turn right attraffic lights into Beechwood Road. Take the first road on the left and then the first right into Tenby Drive. Ground and car park 100 yards on left

MURSLEY UNITED
Secretary: Geoff Curtis, 26 Berwick Drive, Bletchley, Milton Keynes MK3 7NB (01908 377196)
Ground: Station Road, Mursley, Milton Keynes
Directions: A421 Bletchley to Buckingham Road, first right in village

OLD BRADWELL UNITED
Secretary: Paul Mills, 36 Craddocks Close, Bradwell, Milton Keynes MK13 9DX (01908 227520)
Ground: Abbey Road, Bradwell, Milton Keynes (01908 312355)
Directions: M1 junction 14 go towards Newport Pagnell. Turn left at firstroundabout into H3 Honks Way. Go six r'abouts then left onto V6 Grafton Street.Take 1st right at mini-r'about into Rawlins Road and then 2nd left intoLoughton Road. Take 1st right into Primrose Road and at the 'T' junction turnright into Abbey Road

OLD DUNSTABLIANS
Secretary: Craig Renfrew, 75B Princes Street. Dunstable. LU6 3AS. Tel: 01582471794 (H), 01234 265444 (B)
Ground: Lancot Park. Dunstable Road, Totternhoe (01582 663735)
Directions: From Dunstable Town Centre take the B489 Tring Road. At the 4throundabout turn right, signposted Totternhoe. The pitch is located withinDunstable Town Cricket Club which is on the right just before entering thevillage of Totternhoe

PADBURY UNITED
Secretary: James Clarke, 41 Moorhen Way, Buckingham, Bucks. MK18 1GN (01280 824513
Ground: Springfields,Playing Fields, Padbury
Directions: From Buckingham follow ring road with signs,to Aylesbury (A413), then towards Buckingham and Padbury is two miles south of the town A413 and three miles north west of Winslow on A413. Turn off opposite bus shelter on Springfields Estate and follow road forward.

SCOT
Secretary: William Land, 18 Coleridge Close, Bletchley, Milton Keynes MK3 5AF (01908 372228)
Ground: Selbourne Avenue, Bletchley, Milton Keynes (01908 368881)
Directions: Main roads to Bletchley then A421 Buckingham road, at Glen Garageright into Newton Rd, 2nd left into Selbourne Ave., through railway bridge to bottom of road

TOTTERNHOE
Secretary: Jim Basterfield, 41 Park Avenue, Totternhoe, Dunstable, Beds LU6 1QF. Tel: 01582 667941 (H)
Ground: Totternhoe Recreation Ground, Dunstable (01582 606738)
Directions: Turn off the main Dunstable to Tring Road B489. Ground on right as you enter Totternhoe. Five miles from Leighton Buzzard (BR), 7 miles fromLuton. Bus 61 Luton-Aylesbury

WINSLOW UNITED
Secretary: David F Ward, 28 Park Road, Winslow, Buckingham MK18 3DL. Tel: 01296713202 (H), 01865 781210 (B)
Ground: Recreation Ground, Elmfields Gate, Winslow, Bucks. Tel: 01296 713057
Directions: A413 from Aylesbury to Winslow, in High Street turn right into Elmfields Gate, ground on left opp. car park.A421 from Milton Keynes to Buck'ham then thro 'Gt Horwood

HERTS SENIOR COUNTY LEAGUE

President: Eric Dear   **Chairman:** Cecil T Husdon

General Secretary: Kevin Folds, 6 Lanthony Court,
High Street, Arlesey, Beds SG15 6TU
Tel: 01462 734102   Email: KFoldsHSCL@aol.com

Website: www.football.mitoo.co.uk/News.cfm?LeagueCode=HSCL

FINAL LEAGUE TABLES 2001-02

PREMIER DIVISION

	P	W	D	L	F	A	Pts
Oxhey Jets	26	18	3	5	72	28	57
Sun Postal Sports	26	17	5	4	56	29	56
Bovingdon	26	15	3	8	64	31	48
Bedmond S & S	26	15	2	9	52	39	47
London Lions	26	12	5	9	44	41	41
Sandridge Rovers	26	11	6	9	60	50	39
Wormley Rovers	26	11	4	11	47	41	37
Cuffley	26	10	3	13	38	68	33
Chipperfield Corinth.	26	8	8	10	49	47	32
St Peters	26	8	6	12	38	49	30
Elliott Star	26	9	2	15	48	58	29
Met Police Bushey	26	8	2	16	39	57	26
Croxley Guild	26	7	3	16	34	72	24
Hatfield Town	26	6	2	18	40	71	20

DIVISION ONE

	P	W	D	L	F	A	Pts
Hadley	24	20	1	3	63	22	61
Bushey Rangers	24	18	3	3	71	28	57
Old Parmiterians*	24	16	3	5	56	29	53
Lemsford	24	11	5	8	64	40	38
Cheshunt Club*	24	11	3	10	66	60	38
North Mymms	24	10	5	9	43	51	35
Kimpton Rovers	24	10	2	12	58	57	32
Evergreen	24	7	10	7	36	29	31
Mill End S&S Athletic	24	7	7	10	55	64	28
Standon & Puck	24	6	4	14	34	56	22
Benington*	24	6	5	13	33	63	22
Welwyn	24	3	6	15	25	55	15
Sarratt*	24	2	4	18	25	75	9

* points adjustment

PREMIER DIVISION RESULTS CHART 2001-02

		1	2	3	4	5	6	7	8	9	10	11	12	13	14
1	Bedmond S & S	X	0-2	2-0	6-2	3-1	1-0	3-1	3-3	2-2	3-1	2-1	4-3	2-1	3-2
2	Bovingdon	2-1	X	4-1	3-0	1-2	0-1	2-1	1-2	4-0	3-2	1-1	1-2	0-1	3-2
3	Chipperfield Corinth.	0-1	2-2	X	5-0	2-3	3-1	3-1	1-1	1-3	1-5	4-5	1-3	0-1	0-0
4	Croxley Guild	0-4	0-4	1-4	X	2-2	1-2	2-3	1-6	2-1	0-4	0-4	2-0	1-4	1-3
5	Cuffley	1-0	5-2	1-2	0-0	X	2-1	4-1	0-1	0-2	0-3	2-0	1-7	1-1	0-6
6	Elliott Star	2-1	0-5	1-1	1-3	11-0	X	4-6	1-0	0-3	2-5	2-5	2-4	0-1	2-1
7	Hatfield Town	1-3	0-2	1-5	2-3	1-2	1-4	X	2-1	2-3	1-3	0-5	2-1	1-2	0-2
8	London Lions	1-0	0-4	2-2	0-3	1-2	1-0	4-0	X	1-0	1-2	3-2	3-1	3-3	0-1
9	Met Police Bushey	1-0	1-4	0-2	3-5	2-0	1-4	5-3	1-4	X	2-4	3-2	0-0	0-4	2-3
10	Oxhey Jets	0-2	3-1	1-1	2-0	5-1	5-0	4-2	1-2	3-1	X	4-0	1-2	2-0	4-0
11	Sandridge Rovers	4-2	3-2	2-2	4-1	4-1	2-5	0-0	2-2	2-1	2-2	X	1-3	2-0	1-3
12	St Peters	3-2	0-7	2-2	0-1	0-4	1-1	2-4	1-2	1-0	0-2	1-1	X	1-1	0-2
13	Sun Postal Sports	4-0	1-1	2-1	3-1	6-3	3-1	1-3	3-0	2-1	1-1	3-1	2-0	X	4-2
14	Wormley Rovers	1-2	0-3	2-3	2-2	4-0	2-0	1-1	4-0	2-1	0-3	1-4	0-0	1-2	X

DIVISION ONE RESULTS CHART 2001-02

		1	2	3	4	5	6	7	8	9	10	11	12	13
1	Benington	X	1-6	3-3	0-6	0-1	0-5	2-3	0-3	0-2	4-2	1-2	0-0	2-1
2	Bushey Rangers	6-1	X	1-1	3-1	3-2	5-4	4-1	6-0	0-3	6-2	1-2	2-0	5-1
3	Evergreen	1-1	0-1	X	2-3	4-1	1-1	2-2	0-0	0-1	1-1	3-0	3-0	0-0
4	Hadley	1-1	1-3	1-0	X	2-1	2-1	6-0	0-1	2-1	2-1	1-0	3-2	2-0
5	Kimpton Rovers	2-1	1-3	4-0	2-4	X	1-1	5-3	3-1	1-3	0-2	3-2	0-5	3-4
6	Lemsford	1-0	1-4	0-1	1-2	3-2	X	4-1	2-2	0-1	7-0	5-2	7-1	1-0
7	Mill End S & S Ath	1-3	0-1	1-1	1-5	4-4	2-2	X	3-1	2-5	5-0	1-1	3-0	6-0
8	North Mymms	6-2	1-1	2-0	1-4	0-5	0-2	1-1	X	3-3	5-1	4-2	2-1	2-1
9	Old Parmiterians	4-0	2-3	4-1	0-4	3-2	2-1	5-2	5-0	X	2-0	1-0	1-3	3-0
10	Sarratt	2-3	1-3	0-7	0-1	1-3	3-5	3-0	1-2	0-0	X	0-5	2-5	1-1
11	Standon & Puck.	1-3	0-0	1-3	0-2	5-3	2-2	1-4	0-4	2-1	2-0	X	1-1	1-1
12	The Cheshunt Club	3-3	2-0	1-1	0-6	3-6	6-4	5-6	6-2	2-3	5-1	6-1	X	2-1
13	Welwyn	1-2	0-4	0-1	1-2	0-3	0-4	3-3	2-0	1-1	1-1	3-2	3-4	X

AUBREY CUP 2001-02

FIRST ROUND

Bedmond S & S	v	Mill End S & S Ath	2-1		Benington	v	Chipperfield Cor.	3-4
Bovingdon	v	Sandridge Rovers	0-2		Croxley Guild	v	Old Parmiterians	2-0
Elliott Star	v	Lemsford	3-2		Kimpton Rovers	v	The Cheshunt Club	3-2
London Lions	v	Hadley	1*4		Oxhey Jets	v	St Peters	3*2
Standon & Puck.	v	North Mymms	0-1		Sun Postal Sports	v	Codicote	SPS WO
Welwyn	v	Cuffley	0-2		Wormley Rovers	v	Evergreen	2-0

SECOND ROUND

Bedmond S & S	v	Oxhey Jets	1-3		Chipperfield Corinth.	v	Hatfield Town	2p3, 3*3
Croxley Guild	v	Bushey Rangers	2-6		Cuffley	v	Wormley Rovers	1*4
Elliott Star	v	Sandridge Rovers	2-3		Hadley	v	Sarratt	7-0
Kimpton Rovers	v	Sun Postal Sports	0-8		Met Police Bushey	v	North Mymms	5-2

QUARTER-FINALS

Bushey Rangers	v	Met Police Bushey	3-7		Hadley	v	Oxhey Jets	0-3
Sandridge Rovers	v	Hatfield Town	7-0		Sun Postal Sports	v	Wormley Rovers	3-1

SEMI-FINALS

Oxhey Jets	v	Sandridge Rovers	2-1		Sun Postal Sports	v	Met Police Bushey	2-0

FINAL

Oxhey Jets	v	Sun Postal Sports	2-1	at Harefield United

CHAIRMAN'S CUP 2001-02

SEMI-FINALS

Bedmond S & S	v	Chipperfield Corinth.	2-1		Wormley Rovers	v	Standon & Puck.	3-0

FINAL

Bedmond S & S	v	Wormley Rovers	2-1	at Bedmond Sports & Social

RESERVE CUP 2001-02

FINAL

Oxhey Jets Res	v	London Lions Res	5-0	at Lemsford

PREMIER DIVISION CONSTITUTION FOR 2002-03

Bedmond Sports & Social
Toms Lane Recreation Ground, Toms Lane, Bedmont, Herts. Tel: 01923 267991

Bovingdon
Green Lane, Bovingdon, Hemel Hempstead, Herts. Tel: 01442 832628

Bushey Rangers
Moatfield, Bournehall Lane, Bushey, Herts. Tel: 020 8386 1875

Chipperfield Corinthians
Queens Street, Chipperfield, Herts. Tel: 01923 269554

Croxley Guild
Croxley Guild of Sport, The Green, Croxley Green, Herts. Tel: 01923 770534

Cuffley
King George's Playing Fields, Northaw Road East, Cuffley, Herts. Tel: 07815 174434

Elliott Star
Pursley Football Ground, London Road, Shenley, Herts. Tel: 020 8953 5087

Hadley
Hadley Sports Ground, Brickfield Lane, Arkley, Barnet, Herts. Tel: 020 8449 1144

London Lions
Barnet Copthall Sports Stadium, Great North Way, London NW4. Tel: 020 8457 9900

Metropolitan Police Bushey
Met Police SC, Aldenham Rd, Bushey, Watford. Tel: 01923 243947

Old Parmiterians
Parmiters School, High Elms Lane, Garston, Watford, Herts. Tel: 01923 682805

Oxhey Jets
Altham Centre, Little Oxhey Lane, South Oxhey, Herts. Tel: 020 8421 4965

Sandridge Rovers
Spencer Recreation Ground, Sandridge, St Albans, Herts. Tel: 01727 855159/835506

St Peters
William Bird Playing Fields, Toulmin Drive, St Albans, Herts. Tel: 01727 852401

Sun Postal Sports
Bellmount Wood Avenue, Watford, Herts. Tel: 01923 227453

Wormley Rovers
Wormley Sports Club, Church Lane, Wormley, Herts. Tel: 01992 460650

Oxhey Jets after retaining their Herts County League title. They also won the Herts County Intermediate Cup and the Aubrey (League) Cup. Photo: Gordon Whittington

Walthamstow Avenue (London Intermediate League). Back Row (l-r): Paul Wayling (Manager), Benji Campbell, Paul Fowler, Andy Antoniou, Paul Jackson, Mark Nisbet, Peter Bowden, Danny Garcia, Volkan Aksoy. Front Row: Dennis Mahadha, Simon Ryan, Umesh Gandvi, Mark Cornell, Gary Nisbet (Captain). Photo: Gordon Whittington

Little Oakley (Essex & Suffolk Border League). Photo: Gordon Whittington

MIDDLESEX COUNTY FOOTBALL LEAGUE
Founded 1984

President: Peter Rogers   **Chairman:** Reg Johnson

Secretary: Stephen C. Hosmer, 27 St Georges Road, Hanworth, Middx. TW13 6RD
Tel: (H) 020 8894 1244 (Fax) 020 8894 0499 (M) 07831 393559
Email: stephen@hosmer.freeserve.co.uk

FINAL LEAGUE TABLES 2001-02

PREMIER DIVISION

	P	W	D	L	F	A	Pts
Spelthorne Sports	24	15	6	3	63	23	51
Willesden Con.	24	14	4	6	50	32	46
Broadfields Utd	24	13	7	4	47	33	46
Hanworth Villa	24	11	6	7	47	31	39
Wraysbury	24	9	9	6	46	39	36
Technicolour CAV	24	9	5	10	37	41	32
Northolt Saints	24	6	9	9	46	59	27
CB Hounslow Utd	24	7	6	11	26	39	27
North Greenford*	24	7	8	9	30	30	26
Neasden	24	4	13	7	33	35	25
Brentford New Inn	24	4	11	9	25	34	23
Harefield Utd Res*	24	5	8	11	39	60	20
Deportivo Galicia	24	4	4	16	25	58	16

Edgware Town Reserves resigned

DIVISION ONE

	P	W	D	L	F	A	Pts
Stonewall	24	18	4	2	77	39	58
Western Command	24	14	4	6	67	31	46
Hounslow Wndrs	24	12	5	7	42	33	41
Southall Town Res	24	12	3	9	42	33	39
Hanworth Villa Res	24	11	3	10	49	45	36
Nth Greenford Res	24	9	7	8	43	45	34
AC Richmond*	24	9	8	7	31	21	32
Ealing Assyrians	24	10	2	12	44	36	32
Spelthorne Sp Res*	24	9	6	9	44	38	30
London Tigers	24	8	5	11	48	63	29
Neasden Res*	24	6	7	11	40	55	19
Southall Res	24	4	2	18	28	81	14
Broadfields Utd Res*	24	4	4	16	36	71	13

* points adjustment

NORTH BERKS LEAGUE

FINAL LEAGUE TABLES 2001-02

DIVISION ONE

	P	W	D	L	F	A	Pts
Kintbury Rangers	22	17	2	3	66	28	53
Saxton Rovers	22	15	2	5	56	36	47
Lambourn Sports	22	12	1	9	69	40	37
Long Wittenham	22	11	3	8	43	34	36
Blewbury	22	10	3	9	51	59	33
East Hendred	22	9	5	8	58	56	32
Childrey United	22	10	2	10	42	50	32
Marcham	22	7	4	11	37	53	25
Drayton	22	6	5	11	30	42	23
Sutton Courtenay	22	6	3	13	33	53	21
Faringdon Town	22	5	5	12	36	42	20
Harwell International	22	5	3	14	27	55	18

DIVISION TWO

	P	W	D	L	F	A	Pts
Benson	22	18	3	1	104	23	57
Warborough/Shillingford	22	16	2	4	86	42	50
Coleshill United	22	13	9	0	60	17	48
Shrivenham Res	22	14	3	5	57	35	45
Hanney United	22	10	5	7	38	42	35
Steventon	22	8	5	9	47	42	29
Stanford-in-Vale	22	7	3	12	37	49	24
Saxton Rovers Res	22	6	4	12	44	65	22
Harwell Village	22	6	4	12	54	79	22
Botley United	22	5	3	14	36	80	18
Faringdon Res	22	5	2	15	32	61	17
Harwell International Rs	22	1	3	18	22	82	6

CONSTITUTION 2002-03

DIVISION ONE: Benson, Blewbury, Childrey United, Drayton, East Hendred, Kintbury Rangers, Lambourn Sports, Long Wittenham Athletic, Marcham, Saxton Rovers, Sutton Courtenay, Warborough & Shillingford.

DIVISION TWO: Ardington & Lockinge, Botley United, Coleshill United, Faringdon Town, Grove Rangers, Hanney United, Harwell International, Harwell Village, Saxton Rovers Reserves, Shrivenham Reserves, Stanford-in-Vale, Steventon.

A QUOTE INSURANCE
READING FOOTBALL LEAGUE

President: Leon Summers   **Chairman:** John Dell
Secretary: David Jeanes, 6 Hawkesbury Drive, Fords Farm, Calcot, Reading RG31 5ZP
Tel: 01734 413926 (H)
http://www.rdgleague.mcmail.com

FINAL LEAGUE TABLES 2001-02

SENIOR DIVISION

	P	W	D	L	F	A	Pts
Mortimer	26	20	1	5	58	31	61
Forest Old Boys	26	17	4	5	72	37	55
Cookham Dean	26	14	4	8	61	38	46
Highmoor/IBIS	26	13	6	7	71	50	45
Vansitstart Wdrs	26	13	4	9	67	55	43
Royal Mail	26	13	3	10	49	33	42
Westwood United	26	13	3	10	52	38	42
Unity *	26	10	8	8	50	40	37
Checkendon Spts	26	10	5	11	52	55	35
Marlow United	26	10	3	13	43	51	33
West Reading	26	10	1	15	40	51	31
Ascot United	26	4	9	13	37	55	21
Sonning Common	26	3	4	19	28	100	13
Newtown Henley	26	2	5	19	33	79	11

PREMIER DIVISION

	P	W	D	L	F	A	Pts
Midgham	22	14	4	4	63	44	46
Woodley Town	22	12	6	4	49	37	42
Reading YMCA	22	10	8	4	63	48	38
Roundhead United	22	10	3	9	57	58	33
Goring United	22	8	6	8	52	47	30
Forest Old Boys Res.	22	8	6	8	49	57	30
Berks County Sports	22	8	4	10	54	46	28
Westwood Utd Res.	22	7	6	9	56	54	27
Emmbrook Sports	22	7	5	10	41	43	26
Finchampstead 'A'	22	6	5	11	46	44	23
Woodcote & Stoke R.	22	6	4	12	45	74	22
Reading Old Blues	22	5	5	12	34	57	20

DIVISION ONE KENNET

	P	W	D	L	F	A	Pts
Shinfield	18	13	2	3	49	28	41
Hurst	18	12	1	5	40	20	37
Highmoor/IBIS Res.	18	11	3	4	71	28	36
Spencers Wood	18	10	6	2	50	24	36
Frilsham/Yattendon	18	7	7	4	49	26	28
Rides United	18	7	2	9	55	51	23
Rabson Rovers	18	5	6	7	37	41	21
Wargrave	18	4	5	9	38	45	17
Calcot CA	18	3	4	11	29	57	13
Woodcote/SR Res.	18	0	0	18	12	110	0

DIVISION ONE THAMES

	P	W	D	L	F	A	Pts
Emmbrook Spts Res.	18	11	3	4	34	31	36
REME Arborfield	18	11	2	5	53	35	35
Cookham Dean Res.	18	10	5	3	35	23	35
AFC Maidenhead	18	10	2	6	43	31	32
Woodley Town Res.	18	7	3	8	36	38	24
Reading University	18	7	2	9	30	25	23
Westwood Utd 'A'	18	6	5	7	30	34	23
Victory Gladstone	18	6	2	10	35	49	20
Checkendon Sp. Res.	18	6	1	11	31	41	19
Mortimer Res.	18	3	1	14	19	39	10

SENIOR DIVISION RESULTS CHART 2001-02

		1	2	3	4	5	6	7	8	9	10	11	12	13	14
1	Ascot United	X	1-1	0-2	0-5	1-0	2-4	1-2	2-2	2-2	9-0	3-0	1-2	2-3	0-0
2	Checkendon Sports	7-1	X	3-3	4-4	3-5	L-W	2-1	6-2	1-4	W-L	1-6	4-1	1-0	2-4
3	Cookham Dean	1-1	1-0	X	1-2	1-1	4-1	1-3	2-0	0-4	15-1	1-3	2-1	3-0	4-0
4	Forest Old Boys	4-0	2-3	2-0	X	2-2	3-1	4-2	3-2	4-1	4-0	1-1	4-1	5-3	1-3
5	Highmoor/IBIS	3-2	2-1	5-1	2-2	X	3-1	1-3	4-1	1-0	10-2	2-2	0-2	4-2	2-2
6	Marlow United	1-1	0-0	2-3	1-4	5-4	X	0-1	6-1	1-0	1-1	1-0	1-4	4-0	0-4
7	Mortimer	3-0	1-2	1-0	1-0	2-0	2-1	X	2-1	2-1	3-0	0-3	2-0	2-1	2-1
8	Newtown Henley	3-2	0-0	0-1	0-4	1-4	2-5	2-3	X	0-4	2-2	1-4	2-2	4-3	2-4
9	Royal Mail	0-0	4-0	0-1	0-2	0-1	1-0	5-2	1-0	X	4-1	1-1	1-3	1-0	2-1
10	Sonning Common	1-1	0-3	0-4	1-3	1-3	3-1	1-7	4-2	1-3	X	1-4	1-5	1-0	0-3
11	Unity	3-3	2-5	1-3	0-3	1-1	4-2	0-2	2-2	1-3	2-2	X	W-L	1-1	W-L
12	Vansittart Wdrs	2-1	5-3	4-4	5-1	2-7	3-0	2-2	7-1	5-3	4-3	0-5	X	1-3	1-2
13	West Reading	0-1	2-0	3-2	1-2	7-2	0-2	0-3	1-0	2-1	3-1	1-0	0-3	X	3-2
14	Westwood United	4-0	4-0	0-1	2-1	1-3	2-4	1-0	2-1	4-0	0-4	2-2	3-1	X

R.S.R. TYRES SURREY COUNTY SENIOR LEAGUE

Chairman: Tony Osborn
General Secretary: Les Pharo, 17 Nigel Fisher Way, Chessington, Surrey KT9 2SN
Tel: 020 8391 0297

Congratulations to Frimley Green for gaining promotion to the Combined Counties League, and a welcome to Staines Lammas and Horley Town who have joined us on promotion, and also to Cranleigh on relegation from the Combined Counties Football League. The League's best wishes go to Virginia Water who, this season, have decided that it is in the club's best long term interest to join the Surrey Intermediate Western League. We hope that it is not long before they can rejoin us.

PREMIER DIVISION FINAL LEAGUE TABLE 2001-02

	P	W	D	L	F	A	GD	Pts
Seelec Delta	28	17	3	8	61	45	16	54
Frimley Green	28	16	5	7	70	44	26	53
Hersham RBL	28	13	6	9	49	41	8	44
Bookham	28	12	7	9	38	41	-3	43
Colliers Wood Utd	28	12	5	11	40	34	6	41
Worcester Park	28	12	4	12	40	43	-3	40
Ditton	28	12	6	10	60	38	22	39
Farleigh Rovers	28	11	6	11	52	52	0	39

	P	W	D	L	F	A	GD	Pts
Netherne Village	28	12	3	13	54	55	-1	39
Crescent Rovers	28	11	8	9	48	38	10	38
AFC Guildford	28	10	8	10	48	50	-2	38
Virginia Water	28	9	5	14	38	49	-11	32
Chobham & O	28	9	4	15	42	48	-6	31
Sheerwater	28	8	7	13	41	55	-14	31
Shottermill & Has.	28	4	7	17	24	72	-48	19

LEAGUE CUP 2001-02

FINAL
Hersham Royal British Legion v Worcester Park 0-1
at Walton Casuals FC

CHARITY CUP 2001-02

FINAL
Netherne Village v Ditton 1-2
at Netherne FC

PREMIER DIVISION RESULTS CHART 2001-02

		1	2	3	4	5	6	7	8	9	10	11	12	13	14	15
1	AFC Guildford	X	1-1	2-3	2-0	4-3	2-2	4-2	0-2	2-2	1-4	0-0	4-0	2-0	2-3	3-1
2	Bookham	1-1	X	1-0	2-1	2-0	1-1	1-0	0-0	1-4	4-1	0-2	3-0	4-2	0-0	2-0
3	Chobham & Ottershaw	5-0	1-2	X	0-1	0-0	0-1	1-1	4-2	1-0	1-3	2-0	2-4	0-0	2-1	1-2
4	Colliers Wood United	2-0	4-1	3-2	X	1-0	1-0	1-1	0-1	0-0	1-0	1-2	1-1	1-1	0-1	0-2
5	Crescent Rovers	2-0	2-2	1-1	3-1	X	1-0	2-2	3-1	2-0	2-3	3-2	0-1	3-1	1-1	3-0
6	Ditton	5-0	0-1	2-3	3-1	1-0	X	6-1	3-2	2-2	1-3	5-1	2-1	7-0	1-1	4-0
7	Farleigh Rovers	1-3	6-3	3-1	3-2	2-2	2-1	X	2-4	1-2	0-3	0-2	3-0	3-0	4-0	4-2
8	Frimley Green	3-1	7-1	5-3	0-3	1-1	3-3	1-1	X	1-0	5-3	3-0	3-3	5-0	3-2	4-1
9	Hersham Royal Brit Legion	1-1	2-0	1-0	1-4	2-1	2-1	0-1	0-3	X	2-4	3-4	1-0	1-1	2-0	4-2
10	Netherne Village	2-0	1-2	4-1	0-1	1-3	1-1	2-2	2-3	2-5	X	2-4	1-3	3-1	1-0	2-0
11	Seelec Delta	1-4	1-0	1-3	3-1	2-0	2-1	2-0	4-2	1-1	4-1	X	2-0	5-0	4-2	3-2
12	Sheerwater	1-1	2-0	4-1	1-3	1-3	0-5	1-2	1-0	3-4	3-2	3-3	X	2-3	2-3	1-1
13	Shottermill & Haslemere	1-5	0-0	1-4	1-0	0-0	0-2	3-2	0-3	0-2	4-1	2-4	2-2	X	0-4	0-2
14	Virginia Water	2-2	0-2	1-0	2-5	3-5	4-0	2-1	1-2	1-4	0-1	3-2	0-1	0-0	X	1-0
15	Worcester Park	0-1	2-1	2-0	1-1	3-2	3-0	1-2	2-1	2-1	1-1	1-0	0-0	5-1	2-0	X

LEADING GOALSCORERS

		Pld	Gls
Stephen Poole	Frimley Green	30	31
Mark Mohamed	Colliers Wood Utd	32	29
Errol Harris	Ditton	31	24
Michael Page	Hersham RBL	29	24
Lee Smith	Seelec Delta	33	23
Brendan Bernal-Soria	AFC Guildford	25	22
Danny Oakins	Netherne Village	26	18
Mark Dalrymple	Netherne Village	31	17
Eddie Edwards	Chobham & Ottershaw	22	16
Andy McGregor	Ditton	35	16

		Pld	Gls
Terry Morgan	Crescent Rovers	30	16
Paul Cross	Sheerwater	28	15
Kevin Dalrymple	Netherne Village	31	15
Jojo Kunii	Colliers Wood Utd	27	15
Thomas Mulcahy	Crescent Rovers	27	15
Graeme Purdy	Frimley Green	25	15
James Saunders	Colliers Wood Utd	18	15
David Harding	Ditton	30	14
David Hart	AFC Guildford	36	14
Leroy Hyett	Seelec Delta	29	14

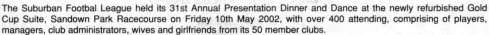

SUBURBAN FOOTBALL LEAGUE

Chairman: David Stanley
Chief Executive: Michael Bidmead
55 Grange Road, Chessington, Surrey KT9 1EZ
Tel/Fax: 0208 397 4834   Website: www.suburbanleague.org.uk

The Suburban Football League held its 31st Annual Presentation Dinner and Dance at the newly refurbished Gold Cup Suite, Sandown Park Racecourse on Friday 10th May 2002, with over 400 attending, comprising of players, managers, club administrators, wives and girlfriends from its 50 member clubs.

During the excellent meal, diners were introduced to the distinguished guests, which included John Young, Registrations Manager of the Football Association, Peter Adams, President, and Ray Lewis from the Surrey County Football Association, Peter Clayton and Ray Ward, respective Secretaries of Middlesex and Surrey County Football Associations, and representatives from both the Amateur Football Alliance and the Berks & Bucks County Football Associations.

The toast to the Suburban Football League was proposed by Ray Lewis, the well known former Football League Referee, and now Chairman of Council of The Surrey C.F.A., outlining that the ,with the assistance of other County Associations, had been successful in their lobbying for Match Officials on the League remaining in the national system.

The Chairman of the Suburban Football League, David Stanley, responded by thanking Ray for his kind words, and added that appreciation must go to the League Officials for all their hard work during the past season, and reminding all that the Suburban League is proud to provide high class football for reserve sides in the top echelon of non-League football.

Excellent entertainment for the second year running was provided by comedian Adger Brown, a former player himself, who provided 45 minutes of continuous laughter. Having certainly done his homework on the clubs in attendance, he is sure to receive an invitation to entertain again.

Next on the programme were the presentations to the various winners of league competitions. The Cups, Shields and medals were presented by Ray Lewis, assisted by the League Chairman. The Premier Division Champions were Hayes, with Basingstoke Town runners-up. The Divisional Champions were Crawley Town (South) and Brook House (North) with Carshalton Athletic and Wingate & Finchley the respective runners-up. Northwood won the League Cup defeating Carshalton Athletic 3-0 in an entertaining and competitive final, while Basingstoke Town triumphed in the Invitation Shield, 3-1 winners over Northwood. Sutton United secured the Champions Cup, defeating Berkhamsted Town over two legs, and Wilfred Smith of Fisher Athletic was presented with the golden boot award in recognition of his 37 goals scored during the season.

Dancing into the late hours concluded this highlight event of the season and left everyone eagerly looking forward to next year's Presentation Dinner and Dance. The evening was organised by the Master of Ceremonies and Chief Executive of the League, Michael Bidmead, who has been a leading administrator of the Suburban Football League since its inception in 1971, when the League was founded with just sixteen clubs.

FINAL LEAGUE TABLES 2001-02

PREMIER DIVISION

	P	W	D	L	F	A	Pts	GD
Hayes	30	24	0	6	102	44	72	58
Basingstoke Town	30	19	8	3	65	30	65	35
Sutton United	30	17	5	8	54	32	56	22
Maidenhead Utd	30	16	8	6	57	36	56	21
Dulwich Hamlet	30	15	5	10	56	42	50	14
Berkhamsted Town	30	15	2	13	65	62	47	3
Corinthian Casuals	30	12	7	11	46	43	43	3
Kingstonian	30	10	10	10	51	41	40	10
Met Police	30	11	5	14	61	67	38	-6
Northwood	30	11	3	16	39	47	36	-8
Walton & Hersham	30	10	6	14	64	93	36	-29
Hendon	30	11	2	17	49	57	35	-8
Thame United	30	8	7	15	43	61	31	-18
Marlow	30	7	7	16	39	63	28	-24
Whyteleafe	30	6	6	18	44	67	24	-23
Oxford City	30	4	7	19	45	95	19	-50

SOUTH DIVISION
(top seven)

	P	W	D	L	F	A	Pts	GD
Crawley Town	32	26	4	2	97	28	82	69
Carshalton Athletic	32	23	3	6	95	26	72	69
Tooting & Mitcham U	32	22	5	5	103	39	71	64
Ashford Town	32	22	2	8	93	41	68	52
Croydon Athletic	32	20	4	8	81	35	64	46
Fisher Athletic	32	17	3	12	82	74	54	8
Tonbridge Angels	32	16	3	13	62	61	51	1

NORTH DIVISION
(top seven)

	P	W	D	L	F	A	Pts	GD
Brook House	32	22	3	7	95	58	69	37
Wingate & Finchley	32	20	6	6	85	41	66	44
Thatcham Town	32	21	3	8	73	46	66	27
Hillingdon Borough	32	18	5	9	71	52	59	19
Uxbridge	32	18	2	12	59	44	56	15
Beaconsfield SYCOB	32	17	4	11	79	59	55	20
Chesham United	32	13	6	13	68	49	45	19

ESSEX & HERTS
BORDER COMBINATION

Hon Secretary: Fred Hawthorn, PO Box 115,
Upminster, Essex RM14 3AQ   Tel: 01708 225451

FINAL LEAGUE TABLES 2001-02

PREMIER DIVISION

		Home			Away			Totals						
	P	W	D	L	W	D	L	W	D	L	F	A	GD	Pts
East Thurrock United	26	8	4	1	11	1	1	19	5	2	73	25	48	62
Hornchurch	26	9	3	1	6	5	2	15	8	3	59	27	32	53
Braintree Town	26	7	3	3	8	2	3	15	5	6	73	35	38	50
Leyton	26	6	2	5	8	2	3	14	4	8	51	45	6	46
Cheshunt*	26	8	0	5	7	3	3	15	3	8	50	41	9	42
Canvey Island	26	5	4	4	5	3	5	10	7	9	57	53	4	37
Great Wakering Rovers	26	6	1	6	5	2	6	11	3	12	53	49	4	36
Heybridge Swifts	26	6	4	3	3	3	7	9	7	10	47	39	8	34
Potters Bar Town	26	7	0	6	2	4	7	9	4	13	44	66	-22	31
Ware	26	7	1	5	2	1	10	9	2	15	43	60	-17	27
Ilford	26	6	4	3	1	2	10	7	6	13	44	57	-13	27
Brentwood	26	5	3	5	2	2	9	7	5	14	35	51	-16	26
Witham Town	26	5	2	6	0	3	10	5	5	16	39	67	-28	22
Burnham Ramblers	26	2	3	8	1	1	11	3	4	19	23	76	-53	13

DIVISION ONE

	P	W	D	L	W	D	L	W	D	L	F	A	GD	Pts
Tilbury	24	6	6	0	8	1	3	14	7	3	61	34	27	49
Waltham Abbey	24	10	1	1	4	4	4	14	5	5	49	30	19	47
Somersett Ambury VE	24	7	3	2	6	2	4	13	5	6	55	36	19	44
Barking/East Ham Utd	24	9	2	1	2	6	4	11	8	5	48	29	19	41
Hullbridge Sports	24	3	5	4	5	5	2	8	10	6	53	46	7	34
Hoddesdon Town	24	6	1	5	4	2	6	10	3	11	43	53	-10	33
Hertford Town	24	3	2	7	6	1	5	9	3	12	39	46	-7	30
Southend Manor	24	2	2	8	5	4	3	7	6	11	46	41	5	27
Romford*	24	4	4	4	5	1	6	9	5	10	61	58	3	26
Concord Rangers	24	5	3	4	1	4	7	6	7	11	37	53	-16	25
Basildon United	24	3	3	6	3	4	5	6	7	11	30	50	-20	25
Bowers United*	24	3	2	7	3	3	6	6	5	13	24	4	-24	22
Sawbridgeworth Town	24	2	4	6	3	1	8	5	5	14	38	60	-22	20

* points deducted

Next season, our 32nd, will see Harlow Town, Purfleet, Maldon Town, St Albans City and Stansted all join to make two 16 strong Divisions.

COMBINATION CUP 2001-02

THIRD ROUND

Heybridge Swifts	v	Ilford	7p8, 3*3
Hullbridge Sports	v	Cheshunt	0-1
Burnham Ramblers	v	Ware	0-4
Potters Bar Town	v	Concord Rangers	0-1

SEMI-FINALS

Ilford	v	Cheshunt	4*2
Ware	v	Concord Rangers	3*1

FINAL

Ilford	v	Ware	2-0

FRED BUDDEN TROPHY 2001-02

THIRD ROUND

Braintree Town	v	Hornchurch	4-1
Ware	v	Leyton	0-2
Basildon United	v	Cheshunt	0-2
East Thurrock Utd	v	Somersett Ambury	0-1*

SEMI-FINALS

Braintree Town	v	Leyton	4-2
Cheshunt	v	East Thurrock Utd	4-0

FINAL

Braintree Town	v	Cheshunt	0-2

* *Somersett Ambury removed from competition - ineligible player*

CAPITAL FOOTBALL LEAGUE

Chairman & Treasurer: David Free **Secretary:** Adrian Cook
41 Amis Avenue, New Haw, Addlestone, Surrey KT15 3ET
Tel 01932 888474 Fax: 01932 345604

FINAL LEAGUE TABLE 2001-02

		Home					Away						
	P	W	D	L	F	A	W	D	L	F	A	GD	Pts
Grays Athletic	14	6	0	1	22	10	5	2	0	22	6	28	35
Farnborough Town	14	6	1	0	20	2	4	3	0	14	4	28	34
Stevenage Borough	14	4	2	1	19	8	5	0	2	26	9	28	29
Purfleet	14	4	1	2	12	10	3	2	2	17	9	10	24
Bedford Town	14	3	3	1	14	8	3	1	3	16	16	6	22
Hitchin Town	14	4	1	2	18	11	3	0	4	10	22	-5	22
Harrow Borough	14	2	2	3	12	14	4	1	2	11	10	-1	21
Yeading	14	3	2	2	11	15	3	0	4	15	15	-4	20
Havant & Waterlooville	14	3	0	4	10	14	3	1	3	13	17	-8	19
St Albans City	14	3	0	4	14	19	2	1	4	16	18	-7	16
Billericay Town	14	3	1	3	14	15	1	2	4	5	10	-6	15
Slough Town	14	3	3	1	13	10	0	0	7	6	16	-7	12
Croydon	14	3	0	4	13	16	0	1	6	6	18	-15	10
Bishop's Stortford	14	2	0	5	9	25	1	1	5	7	13	-22	10
Boreham Wood	14	2	0	5	11	21	1	1	5	14	29	-25	10

DOXHILL PRESIDENT'S CUP 2001-02

FIRST ROUND

Purfleet	v	Croydon	5-2	Farnborough Town	v	Havant & W'looville	2-0
Hitchin Town	v	Boreham Wood	4-1	Bishop's Stortford	v	Bedford Town	2-1
Slough Town	v	Yeading	0-5	Billericay Town	v	Grays Athletic	0-2
Harrow Borough	v	St Albans City	4-2	Bye: Stevenage Borough			

SECOND ROUND

Grays Athletic	v	Bishop's Stortford	4-1	Harrow Borough	v	Farnborough Town	4-2
Purfleet	v	Yeading	4p1, 3*3	Hitchin Town	v	Stevenage Boro	5p4, 2*2

SEMI-FINALS

Hitchin Town	v	Grays Athletic	3-4	Harrow Borough	v	Purfleet	1-0

FINAL

Harrow Borough	v	Grays Athletic	1-0

CONSTITUTION FOR SEASON 2002-03

SOUTH WEST DIVISION

Aldershot Town
Croydon
Farnborough Town
Harrow Borough
Havant & Waterlooville
Slough Town
Woking
Yeading

NORTH EAST DIVISION

Bedford Town
Billericay Town
Bishop's Stortford
Dagenham & Redbridge
Gravesend & Northfleet
Grays Athletic
Hitchin Town
Purfleet
Stevenage Borough

THE SYGNUS
CENTRAL CONFERENCE LEAGUE

Secretary: Jason Mills
25 Hewlett Road, Cheltenham, Gloucestershire GL52 6AD
Tel/Fax: 01242 700496

FINAL LEAGUE TABLE 2001-02

		Home					Away					
	P	W	D	L	F	A	W	D	L	F	A	Pts
Burton Albion	12	3	2	1	11	9	4	0	2	13	12	23
Telford United	11	3	1	2	10	8	3	2	0	11	7	21
Hereford United	12	3	1	2	13	12	2	1	3	6	10	17
Tamworth	10	3	0	2	18	7	1	0	4	7	15	12
Hednesford Town	10	1	2	2	6	8	2	1	2	11	9	12
Worcester City	10	0	1	3	6	12	2	2	2	6	10	9
Boston United	7	2	0	2	10	5	0	1	2	7	11	7

DOXHILL CHALLENGE CUP 2001-02

FIRST ROUND

Nuneaton Borough	v	Hereford United	HU t/a	Burton Albion	v	Worcester City	2-0
Hednesford Town	v	Tamworth	4-2	Telford United	v	Boston United	1-4

SEMI-FINAL

Hereford United	v	Hednesford Town	1-3	Burton Albion	v	Boston United	0-3

(Match awarded to Burton Albion after Boston United failed to fulfill their season's fixtures)

FINAL

Hednesford Town   v   Burton Albion   1-3

PROPOSED CONSTITUTION FOR SEASON 2002-03

BURTON ALBION
GRANTHAM TOWN (new club)
HEDNESFORD TOWN
HEREFORD UNITED
NUNEATON BOROUGH (new club)
STAFFORD RANGERS (new club)

* Boston United, Tamworth, Telford United and Worcester City have resigned from the League for the ensuing season. The officers of the League wish them well in the future and thank them for their participation. Also best wishes to Boston United who are about to compete in their first season in the Football League following their promotion from the Nationwide Conference League.

COUNTY
FOOTBALL
ASSOCIATIONS

Tel: 01582 565111 (B)   Fax: 01582 565222   Email: info@bedfordshirefa.com
Century House, Skimpot Road, Dunstable LU5 4JU
Secretary: Peter D Brown
Executives (Responsibility)   Century House for
                                   Coaching Exams/Courses, Referees, Womens Football

President: R Berridge

Number of Affiliated Clubs   Senior: 480
Number of Affiliated Leagues: Senior: 9   Junior: 4
County Representative Teams: Senior, U18, U16, Intermediate, Womens
Inter County Competitions: East Anglia Counties Intermediate, U18, U16 & Womens, FA County Youth Cup

BEDFORDSHIRE SENIOR CUP 2001-02
(15 ENTRIES)

LAST SEASON'S FINAL: Wootton Blue Cross v Dunstable Town   1*0

FIRST ROUND

Bedford Town	v	Stotfold	1-3	Barton Rovers	v	Leighton Town	3-0
Wootton Blue Cross	v	Brache Sparta	3-0	Arlesey Town	v	Dunstable Town	1-2
Kempston Rovers	v	Ampthill Town	0-7	Biggleswade United	v	Potton United	3-2
Bedford United	v	Langford	4p1, 1*1				

SECOND ROUND

Dunstable Town	v	Biggleswade United	0-3	Stotfold	v	Wtn Blue Cross	4p3, 2*2
Ampthill Town	v	Biggleswade Town	1-3	Barton Rovers	v	Bedford United	4p1 2*2

SEMI-FINALS

Biggleswade Town	v	Biggleswade United	1-3	Barton Rovers	v	Stotfold	2-3

FINAL

BIGGLESWADE U	v	STOTFOLD	4-1	at Hitchin Road, Arlesey Town FC

BEDFORDSHIRE PREMIER CUP 2001-02
(16 ENTRIES)

Holders: Luton Town

FIRST ROUND

Ampthill Town	v	Bedford United	3-2	Brache Sparta	v	Langford	2-0
Arlesey Town	v	Biggleswade United	2*1	Bedford Town	v	Stotfold	5-1
Wootton Blue Cross	v	Kempston Rovers	2-0	Leighton Town	v	Luton Town	2*4
Biggleswade Town	v	Barton Rovers	1-2	Dunstable Town	v	Potton United	4-2

SECOND ROUND

Bedford Town	v	Arlesey Town	0-4	Ampthill Town	v	Dunstable Town	2-3
Brache Sparta	v	Barton Rovers	0-2	Wootton Blue Cross	v	Luton Town	2-1

SEMI-FINALS

Arlesey Town	v	Dunstable Town	4-1	Barton Rovers	v	Wootton Blue Cross	3-0

FINAL

BARTON ROVERS	v	ARLESEY TOWN	1-4	at Roker Park, The Green, Stotfold FC

Biggleswade United, Bedfordshire Senior Cup winners for the first time, beating Stotfold 4-1 in the final. Photo: Gordon Whittington

Langford, winners of the North Beds Charity Cup Final. Back Row (l-r): Roy Ryall (Manager), Rob Groves, Luke Gregson, Paul Martin (white top), Simon Catmur, Eddie Fannon, Barry White, Darren Mattusa, Joe West. Front Row: Lee Rogers, Robbie Beckwith, Lewis Ryall (mascot), Barry Laurence (Capt), Kevin Thomas, Wayne Goldsmith, Mark Goddard, Lee Buck. Photo: Pete Felstead

BERKS & BUCKS F.A. LIMITED

Tel: 01367 242099   Fax: 01367 242158

15a London Street, Faringdon, Oxon SN7 7HD

Chief Executive: Brian Moore   **Press Officer:** Brian Moore

Responsibilities   J Kelman (Coaching Exams/Courses)

P R Hill (Referees)

A Glenny (Womens Football)

Number of Affiliated Leagues: Senior: 17   Junior: 10   **President:** W J Gosling

County Representative Teams: U18, Women   **Chairman:** J Atkins

Inter County Competitions: South/South West Counties Championship Youth

BERKS & BUCKS SENIOR CUP 2001-02

(14 entries)   (FOUNDED 1878-79)

LAST SEASON'S FINAL: Chesham United v Maidenhead United 1-0

MOST WINS: Wycombe 24   Maidenhead United 17   Marlow 13

FIRST ROUND

AylesburyUnited	v	Wycombe Wanderers	2-3	Abingdon Town	v	Hungerford Town	2-0
Bracknell Town	v	Slough Town	1-1, 0-1	Chalfont St Peter	v	Wokingham Town	4-3
Flackwell Heath	v	Windsor & Eton	2-0	Burnham	v	Marlow	2-1

QUARTER FINALS

Wycombe Wanderers	v	Burnham	3*3, 0-3	Slough Town	v	Abingdon Town	4-1
Chesham United	v	Chalfont St Peter	5-0	Maidenhead United	v	Flackwell Heath	3-0

SEMI-FINALS

Chesham United	v	Burnham	3-1	Maidenhead United	v	Slough Town	3-2

FINAL

CHESHAM UNITED v MAIDENHEAD U 2p4, 0*0   at Adams Park, Wycombe Wanderers FC. Att: 812

BERKS & BUCKS SENIOR TROPHY 2001-02

(13 ENTRIES)

LAST SEASON'S FINAL: Didcot Town v Wallingford 2-1

FIRST ROUND

Sandhurst Town	v	Wantage Town	5-4	Milton Keynes C	v	New Bradwell St Peter	2-1
Holmer Green	v	Beaconsfield SYCOB	0-1	Thatcham Town	v	Newbury	2-1
Buckingham Town	v	Abingdon United	3-4			

QUARTER-FINALS

Beaconsfield SYCOB	v	Wallingford	0-4	Reading Town	v	Milton Keynes City	0-4
Abingdon United	v	Didcot Town	0-1	Sandhurst Town	v	Thatcham Town	1*2

SEMI-FINALS

Wallingford	v	Didcot Town	1-0	Milton Keynes City	v	Thatcham Town	3-1

FINAL

MILTON KEYNES C v WALLINGFORD 2-3   at Buckingham Road, Aylesbury United FC

Darren Lynch of Newport Pagnell makes progress toward goal against Martin Baker Sports in the Berks & Bucks Intermediate Cup Semi-final. Photo: Steve Ayre

Andy Bailey (player in full view to right of keeper) celebrates his goal that gave Milton Keynes the lead at 2-1 for a short while in the Berks & Bucks Senior Trophy final. Photo: Steve Ayre

BIRMINGHAM COUNTY F.A.

Tel: 0121 357 4278 Fax: 0121 358 1661 Email: secretary@bcfa.co.uk or info@birminghamfa.com

Ray Hall Lane, Great Barr, Birmingham B43 6JF

Company Secretary: M Pennick F.F.A.

Secretary: D Selton   **PR Officer:** A Lacey

Executives (Responsibility)   T Stack (Coaching Exams/Courses) D Sheltonl (Referees)
                                    Natalie Justice (Football Development Officer)
                                    Rachael Dunlop (Womens Football)

Number of Affiliated Clubs   Senior: 1,663   U.18:   484   **President:** K H Goodfellow
Number of Affiliated Leagues: Senior: 55   Junior: 14
County Representative Teams: U18, U17, Womens Open, U18, U16
Inter County Competitions: FA County Youth, Midland County Youth (Men & Women)
County Publications: "The Centre Circle" bi-monthly newsletter

---

BIRMINGHAM SENIOR CUP 2001-02
(41 entries)   (FOUNDED 1875-76)

LAST SEASON'S FINAL: Moor Green v Tamworth 3-1

MOST WINS: Aston Villa 19   Birmingham City 9
Kidderminster Harriers 7   Wolverhampton Wanderers 7

FIRST ROUND

Gornal Athletic	v	Solihull Borough	0-4	Atherstone United	v	Studley BKL	3*3, 3-2
Tividale	v	Wednesfield	0-6	Sutton Coldfield Tn	v	Willenhall Town	0-1
Stratford Town	v	Banbury United	0*1	Coleshill Town	v	Paget Rangers	2-3
Rushall Olympic	v	Redditch United	2*1	Burton Albion	v	Cradley Town	1-0
Bedworth United	v	Racing Club Warwick	2*1	King's Heath	v	Dudley Town	1-2
Highgate United	v	Darlaston Town	0-1	Halesowen Harriers	v	Brierley & Hagley Alnce	1*0
Lye Town	v	West Midlands Police	2-1				

SECOND ROUND

Rushall Olympic	v	Paget Rangers	7-0	Moor Green	v	Darlaston Town	4-0
Willenhall Town	v	Wednesfield	1-3	Nuneaton Borough	v	Stourbridge	2*1
Tamworth	v	Boldmere St Michaels	2-3	Lye Town	v	Handrahan Timbers	2-1
Dudley Town	v	Halesowen Harriers	1-2	Banbury United	v	Oldbury United	2-1
Bolehall Swifts	v	Bedworth United	0-3	Atherstone United	v	Rugby United	3-0
Halesowen Harriers	v	Hednesford Town	2-0	Burton Albion	v	Solihull Borough	2-1

THIRD ROUND

Rushall Olympic	v	Wednesfield	0-2	Atherstone United	v	Boldmere St Michaels	4-2
Lye Town	v	Wolverhampton Wndrs	0-2	West Bromwich Alb	v	Halesowen Harriers	4-0
Halesowen Town	v	Birmingham City	0-3	Moor Green	v	Walsall	3-2
Nuneaton Borough	v	Banbury United	3-1	Bedworth United	v	Burton Albion	0-3

FOURTH ROUND

Moor Green	v	Burton Albion	3-1	Birmingham City	v	Wednesfield @W	0-1
West Bromwich Alb	v	Atherstone United	5-2	Nuneaton Borough	v	Wolverhampton W	3p2, 2*2

SEMI-FINALS

Moor Green	v	Nuneaton Borough	0-4	West Bromwich Alb	v	Wednesfield @W	1-0

FINAL

W BROMWICH ALB	v	NUNEATON BORO	0-2	at The Hawthorns, West Bromwich Albion FC

CAMBRIDGESHIRE F.A. LTD

Tel: 01223 576770   Fax: 01223 576780   Email: info@cambridgeshirefa.com
City Ground, Milton Road, Cambridge CB4 1FA
Secretary: Roger Pawley
Executives (Responsibility)   Richard Nichols (Asst Gen Sec, County Referees Sec)
                                  Jim Hill (Football Development Officer)
                                  Phil Mitcham (Competitions Secretary)
                                  Kirsty Prior (Girls/Womens Development Officer)

Number of Affiliated Clubs	Senior:	350	U.18:	50
Number of Affiliated Leagues:	Senior:	1	Junior:	6
County Representative Teams:	U18, U16, Womens			
Inter County Competitions:	East Anglian Counties			

President: W W Ashton
Chairman: J W Coad

CAMBRIDGESHIRE INVITATION CUP 2001-02
(12 entries)   (FOUNDED 1950-51)

LAST SEASON'S FINAL: Histon v Wisbech Town 2-0

MOST WINS: Wisbech Town 9   Cambridge City 9   Chatteris Town 7

PRELIMINARY ROUND

Cambridge City	v	Newmarket Town	7-1		Histon	v	Leverington Sports	10-1
March Town United	v	Over Sports	1-3		Mildenhall Town	v	Ely City	0-2

FIRST ROUND

Cambridge City	v	Cottenham United	3-0		Histon	v	Sawston United	6-0
Ely City	v	Over Sports	6-0		Soham Town Rngrs	v	Wisbech Town	2-1

SEMI-FINALS

Histon	v	Soham Town Rangers	3-0		Ely City	v	Cambridge City	2-0

FINAL

ELY CITY	v	HISTON	1-0	at the Abbey Stadium, Cambridge United FC

GROUNDTASTIC

The Football Grounds Magazine

Groundtastic is the acclaimed magazine featuring news, articles and special features on football grounds at all levels from the Premiership to non-league. Each glossy 80-page edition carries regular development updates, including 6 pages of non-league news, together with articles and photos chronicling the rich history of non-league grounds. The magazine usually retails at £3.50 but to receive a free sample issue send 2 first class stamps to: 21 Tiptree Grove, WICKFORD, SS12 9AL. To obtain details of back issues and our other publications, please visit our website at www.groundtastic.ukgateway.net

CHESHIRE F.A.

Tel: 01606 871166   Fax: 01606 871292   Football Development: 01606 871155
The Cottage, Moss Farm Recreation Centre, Winnington, Northwich CW8 4BG

Secretary & Press Officer:	Maureen J Dunford
Executives (Responsibility)	John Ackerley (Coaching Exams/Courses & Development Officer)
	Bob Cooper (Referees), Jacci Cooper (Women's Football)

Number of Affiliated Clubs Senior: 816   U.18: 325   **President:** Alan Burbidge
Number of Affiliated Leagues: Senior: 27   Junior: 13
County Representative Teams: Senior, U18s, Womens, U16 Girls teams
Inter County Competitions: FA County Youth, Northern Counties Youth Cup, Ladies Cup and Senior Cup

CHESHIRE SENIOR CUP 2001-02
(17 entries)   (FOUNDED 1879-80)

LAST SEASON'S FINAL: Stalybridge Celtic v Stockport County 5-1

MOST WINS: Macclesfield Town 20   Northwich Victoria 16   Crewe Alexandra 13   Runcorn 12

PRELIMINARY ROUND
Cheadle Town	v	Winsford United	2*5

FIRST ROUND
Crewe Alexandra	v	Winsford United	1-0		Hyde United	v	Warrington Town	0-1
Chester City	v	Congleton Town	2-0		Nantwich Town	v	Stockport County	1-3
Woodley Sports	v	Witton Albion	3-2		Altrincham	v	Northwich Victoria	3-2
Tranmere Rovers	v	Stalybridge Cltc @SC	1-2		Macclesfield Town	v	Vauxhall Motors	2-1

SECOND ROUND
Macclesfield Town	v	Warrington Town	5-1		Woodley Sports	v	Altrincham	1-8
Stockport County	v	Crewe Alexandra	1-6		Chester City	v	Stalybridge Celtic	1*2

SEMI-FINALS
Altrincham	v	Macclesfield Town	2-0		Stalybridge Celtic	v	Crewe Alexandra	2-7

FINAL
ALTRINCHAM	v	CREWE ALEXANDRA	0-3	at The Drill Field, Northwich Victoria FC. Att: 625

CORNWALL F.A.

Tel: 01726 74080   Fax: 01726 76174   E-mail: cornwallcfa@aol.com
1 High Cross Street, St Austell, Cornwall PL25 4AB
Secretary: Barry Cudmore
Executives (Responsibility)   David Bray (Youth Secretary)
Ian Anear (Referees)
Phil Cardew (Football Development Officer)

Number of Affiliated Clubs	Senior: 311	U.18: 84	**President:** B F Conyon
Number of Affiliated Leagues:	Senior: 20	Youth: 2	**Chairman:** D G Champion
County Representative Teams:	Senior, Youth U18		
Inter County Competitions:	South West Counties Senior, Youth & Womens, FA County Youth Cup		

CORNWALL SENIOR CUP 2001-02
(40 entries)   (FOUNDED 1892-93)

LAST SEASON'S FINAL: Porthleven v St Blazey   2-2, 4-0

MOST WINS: Truro City 12   St Blazey 12
St Austell 11   Penzance 10   Torpoint Athletic 10

FIRST ROUND

Illogan R B L	v	Helston Athletic	0-7		Marazion Blues	v	Mousehole	2-2, 1-2
Mullion	v	RNAS Culdrose	5-1		Nanpean Rovers	v	Sticker	5-0
Perranwell	v	St Ives Town	2-2, 1-2		Roche	v	Ludgvan	1-0
St Agnes	v	Camelford	1-1, 0-2		Wendron United	v	Padstow Utd	0-0, 2p3, 2*2

SECOND ROUND

Bodmin Town	v	Padstow United	3-2		Bude Town	v	Torpoint Athletic	0-1
Camelford	v	Mullion	1-2		Falmouth Town	v	Hayle	4V2
Heston Athletic	v	Callington Town	0-2		Launceston	v	Probus	7-1
Liskeard Athletic	v	St Austell	4-1		Nanpean Rovers	v	Truro City	2-3
Penryn Athletic	v	St Cleer	5-1		Penzance	v	Roche	1-1, 6-0
Porthleven	v	Newquay	5-1		St Blazey	v	St Ives Town	4-1
St Dennis	v	Millbrook	3V2		St Just	v	Mousehole	1-0
Saltash United	v	Foxhole Stars	0-3		Wadebridge Town	v	Goonhavern Athletic	2-1

THIRD ROUND

Callington Town	v	Foxhole Stars	2-2, 3p4, 2*2		Hayle	v	Truro City	1-1, 1-4
Millbrook	v	Bodmin Town	2-2, 3-6		Mullion	v	Liskeard Athletic	1-4
Penryn Athletic	v	Launceston	2-1		Porthleven	v	Wadebridge Town	3-3, 6-0
St Just	v	St Blazey	1-7		Torpoint Athletic	v	Penzance	5-2

QUARTER-FINALS

Bodmin Town	v	Liskeard Athletic	2-3		Penryn	v	Truro City	2-1
Porthleven	v	Callington Town	2-1		St Blazey	v	Torpoint Athletic	4-1

SEMI-FINALS

Liskeard Athletic	v	Penryn Athletic	2-1		Porthleven	v	St Blazey	0-2

FINAL

LISKEARD ATHL	v	ST BLAZEY	0-2	at Kimberley Stadium, Saltash United FC

CUMBERLAND F.A.

Tel: 01900 872310   Fax: 01900 872310
17 Oxford Street, Workington, Cumbria CA14 2AL

Secretary & Press Officer: Geoff Turrell
Development Officer: R Patterson
Executives (Responsibility) Keith Hunton (Coaching Exams/Courses)
Harry Upton & Thomas Jackson (Referees)

Number of Affiliated Clubs Senior: 187   U.18: 186   **President:** Brian Taylor
Number of Affiliated Leagues: Senior: 7   Junior: 4   **Chairman:** R J Turner
County Representative Teams: Senior, Youth, Womens
Inter County Competitions: FA County Youth, Northern Counties

CUMBERLAND SENIOR CUP 2001-02
(35 entries)   (FOUNDED 1960-61)

LAST SEASON'S FINAL: Northbank (NA) v Penrith 2-0

MOST WINS: Penrith 11   Gretna 9   Haig Colliery 3

FIRST ROUND
Aspatria	v	St Bees	5-1	Carlisle United	v	Carleton Rovers	7-0
Gretna	v	Northbank Carlisle	1-2				

SECOND ROUND
Whitehaven Miners	v	Wetheriggs United	2-3	Cockermouth	v	Penrith	0-6
Parton United	v	Frizington White Star	7-6	Harraby C C	v	Netherhall	1*3
Longtown	v	Cleator Moor Celtic Rs	3-2	Silloth	v	Greystoke	3-2
British Steel	v	Northbank Cody's	4-2	Windscale	v	Carlisle City	2-3
Whitehaven	v	Workington	2*1	Abbeytown	v	Mirehouse	1-4
Kirkoswald	v	Cleator Moor Celtic	2-8	Wigton Harriers	v	Windscale Res	1-3
Frizington W Star Rs	v	Whitehaven Res	2-3	Braithewaite	v	Carlisle United	0-20
Aspatria	v	Keswick	2-7	Penrith Rangers	v	Northbank Carlisle	0-7

THIRD ROUND
British Steel	v	Cleator Moor Celtic	3-2	Penrith	v	Northbank Carlisle	2-0
Mirehouse	v	Wetheriggs United	0-5	Keswick	v	Silloth	5*3
Carlisle United	v	Windscale Res	3-0	Longtown	v	Netherhall	0-3
Parton United	v	Whitehaven	1-4	Carlisle City	v	Whitehaven Res	3-1

QUARTER-FINALS
Keswick	v	Carlisle City	0-4	Carlisle United	v	Netherhall	1-0
Penrith	v	Wetheriggs United	1-0	Brit Steel Workington	v	Whitehaven	3-1

SEMI-FINALS
Carlisle City	v	British Steel Workington	4-0	Carlisle United	v	Penrith	4V2, replay 2-0

FINAL
CARLISLE CITY	v	CARLISLE UNITED	0-2	at Raydale Park, Dominion Road, Gretna FC	

Carlisle United's Michael Dickinson bursts between Carlisle City's Alan Hodgson (left) and Mike Algeo in the Cumberland Senior Cup Final. Photo: Alan Watson

DERBYSHIRE F.A.

Tel: 01332 361422   Fax: 01332 360130
Nos 8-9 Stadium Business Court, Millennium Way, Pride Park, Derby DE24 8HZ
Secretary & Press Officer: K Compton
Executives (Responsibility)   County Secretary (Referees)
                                   Craig Lee & Debbie Wood
                                   (Football Development & Womens Football)
No. Affiliated Clubs & Leagues 800
County Representative Teams: U16, U18
Inter County Competitions: Midlands Youth Football Championships

Chairman: R F Johnson

DERBYSHIRE SENIOR CUP 2001-02
(24 entries)   (FOUNDED 1883-84)

LAST SEASON'S FINAL: Glossop North End v Glapwell 5*5, 4p2 on aggregate
MOST WINS: Derby County 15   Ilkeston Town 13
Buxton 8   Chesterfield 8   Heanor Town 8

FIRST ROUND
Sth Normanton Ath	v	Shirebrook Town	1-3	Heanor Town	v	GAD Khalsa Sports	4-0
Long Eaton United	v	Stanton Ilkeston	3-1	Ripley Town	v	Graham Street Prims	7-4

SECOND ROUND
Holbrook	v	Long Eaton United	0-1	Ripley Town	v	Shardlow St James	5-0
Sandiacre Town	v	Heanor Town	5*4	Shirebrook Town	v	Blackwell M W	4-1

THIRD ROUND
Alfreton Town	v	Mickleover Sports	8-0	Buxton	v	Glossop North End	2-3
Gresley Rovers	v	Shirebrook Town	4-2	Matlock Town	v	Borrowash Victoria	3-2
Ripley Town	v	Glapwell	4-2	Sandiacre Town	v	Long Eaton United	1-4
Stapenhill	v	Belper Town	0-1	Staveley MW	v	Ilkeston Town	1-5

FOURTH ROUND
Long Eaton United	v	Ilkeston Town	0-4	Belper Town	v	Ripley Town	6-0
Matlock Town	v	Alfreton Town	0-4	Glossop North End	v	Gresley Rovers	1-4

SEMI-FINALS
Ilkeston Town	v	Gresley Rovers	4p5, 1*1	Alfreton Town	v	Belper Town	2-0

FINAL (Two Legs)
Gresley Rovers	v	Alfreton Town	2-2	Att: 330
Alfreton Town	v	Gresley Rovers	3-2	= 5-4 on aggregate. Att: 505

Leigh Grant (9) fires past Ripley's Shaun Machin to pull Graham St Prims back to 4-5. Photo: Bill Wheatcroft

DEVON F.A.

Tel: 01626 332077   Fax: 01626 336814
County Headquarters, Coach Road, Newton Abbot, Devon TQ12 1EJ

Secretary & Press Officer: Chris J Davidson
Executives (Responsibility)   R Soper (Coaching Exams)   C Cox (Referees)
                                   M Lawrence (Womens Football)   C Davey (Coaching Courses)
Number of Affiliated Clubs   Senior: 161   U.18:   252
Number of Affiliated Leagues: Senior: 50   Junior: 10   **Chairman:** Brian Williams
County Representative Teams: Senior, U18, Womens
Inter County Competitions: South West Counties Championship
County Publications: "Kick Off" - bi-monthly Newsletter

Per Temps DEVON PREMIER CUP 2001-02
(69 entries)
LAST SEASON'S FINAL Newton Abbot v Dartmouth   6p5, 3*3

FIRST ROUND

Watts Blake Bearne	v	Hatherleigh Town	5-2	Feniton	v	Seaton Town	1-2
Liverton United	v	Combe Martin	3-1	Chudleigh Athletic	v	Galmpton United	0-6
Breakwaters BKS	v	Civil Service S&L CS	W-O	Hele Rovers	v	Okehampton Atgyle	1*2
Victoria Rangers	v	Compton Inn	1-2	Mnt Gold Blk Prince	v	Plympton United	5-2
High Bickington	v	Braunton	0-5	South Molton	v	Elmore	0-10
Teignmouth	v	Shamwickshire Rvrs	2*3	Chelston	v	Northam Lions	2-0
Pinhoe	v	Mainstone Sports	2-0	Upton Athletic	v	Dolton Rangers	6-2
Torrington Admirals	v	Sidmouth Town	4-0	Wessex Rngrs RM	v	Putford	2*0
Plymouth Command	v	Bishopsteignton Utd	2-1	Plymouth Civil Serv.	v	Totnes Town	0-3
Kingskerswell	v	Tap & Barrel 6p7, 1*1		St Martins	v	Exeter St Thomas	2-5
Prince Rock	v	Newton St Cyres	4-1				

SECOND ROUND

Elmore	v	Galmpton	0-2	Torrington Admirals	v	Buckfastleigh Rgrs TA	W-O
Crediton	v	Shamwickshire Rovers	1-2	Witheridge	v	Compton Inn	6-3
Civil Service S & L	v	Stoke Gabriel	3-2	Chelston	v	Plymouth Parkway	1*4
Dartington Sports	v	Plymstock United	3-0	Kingsteignton Ath	v	Bradworthy United	4-1
Upton Athletic	v	Tap & Barrel	4*2	Seaton Town	v	Totnes Town	0-1
Exeter St Thomas	v	Liverton United	4-2	Plymouth Command	v	Prince Rock	5-3
Mnt Gould Blk Prince	v	Pinhoe	0-1	Okehampton	v	Braunton	1-2
Exeter Civil Service	v	Watts Blake Bearne	11-0	Wessex Rangers RM	v	Combined 89	3-5

THIRD ROUND

Dartmouth	v	Witheridge	2-1	Dartington Sports	v	Elburton Villa	2-1
Vospers Oak Villa	v	Plymouth Command	4-0	Tavistock	v	Newton Abbot	2-1
Torrington Admirals	v	Totnes Town	4-1	Pinhoe	v	Plymouth Parkway	1-3
Newton Abbot Spurs	v	Ottery St Mary	0-3	Appledore	v	Heavitree United	4*3
Upton Athletic	v	Cullompton	3-2	Ivybridge Town	v	Buckland Athletic	0-2
Alphington	v	Galmpton United	3-1	Topsham Town	v	Budleigh Salterton	4-0
Holsworthy	v	Combined 1989	4-1	Kingsteignton Ath	v	Exeter St Thomas	5-2
Shamwickshire Rvrs	v	Exeter Civil Service	2-3	Civil Service S&L	v	Braunton	3-2

FOURTH ROUND

Alphington	v	Torrington Admirals	7-2	Vospers Oak Villa	v	Kingsteignton Athletic	2-1
Plymouth Parkway	v	Upton Athletic	2*3	Topsham Town	v	Dartington Sports	2*4
Ottery St Mary	v	Holsworthy	0-2	Dartmouth	v	Buckland Athletic	4-1
Tavistock	v	Exeter Civil Service	4-0	Appledore	v	Civil Service S & L	1-2

QUARTER-FINALS

Dartington SC	v	Vospers Oak Villa	0-1	Upton Athletic	v	Dartmouth	2-1
Tavistock	v	Alphington	5p3, 2*2	Civil Service S&L	v	Holsworthy	0-2

SEMI-FINALS

Tavistock	v	Holsworthy	4p2, 0*0	Upton Athletic	v	Vospers Oak Villa	2-3

FINAL

TAVISTOCK	v	VOSPERS OAK VILLA 1-0	at Home Park, Plymouth Argyle FC

DEVON ST LUKES BOWL 2001-02

(13 entries)

HOLDERS (2000) Tiverton Town

FIRST ROUND

Barnstaple Town	v	Torquay United	1-4	Bideford	v	Plymouth Argyle	3*4
Elmore	v	Exeter City	0-5	Exmouth Town	v	Torrington	1-0
Tiverton Town	v	Dawlish Town	8-1				

SECOND ROUND

Clyst Rovers	v	Plymouth Argyle	2-1	Ilfracombe Town	v	Torquay United	0-3
Tiverton Town	v	Exmouth Town	7-1	Willand Rovers	v	Exeter City	0-2

SEMI-FINALS

Tiverton Town	v	Exeter City	1*2	Torquay United	v	Clyst Rovers	4-1

FINAL

EXETER CITY	v	TORQUAY UNITED	3-1	at St James Park, Exeter City FC

DORSET F.A.

Tel: 01202 682375   Fax: 01202 666577

County Ground, Blandford Close, Hamworthy, Poole BH15 4BF

Secretary: Peter Hough
Deputy Secretary: Colin Chainey
Press Officer: Ian Hallett
Executives (Responsibility) S N Whittle (Referees)
Sue Hough (Football Development)

County Representative Teams: Senior, U21, U18, Womens, Womens U18   **President:** Spencer Miles
Inter County Competitions: South West Championship for all the above   **Chairman:** Doug Smurthwaite

DORSET SENIOR CUP 2001-02

(37 entries)   (FOUNDED 1887-88)

LAST SEASON'S FINAL: Dorchester Town v Weymouth   2-1 after extra time

MOST WINS: Weymouth 27   Poole Town 10   Portland United 10   Bridport 9

FIRST ROUND

Blandford United	v	Lytchett Red Triangle	1-2	Dorchester Sports	v	Trinidad New Star	0-2
Gillingham Town	v	Stourpaine	5-0	Okeford United	v	Hamworthy Recreation	0-5
Shaftsbury	v	Witchampton United	2-1	Sherborne Town	v	Cosham Sports	3-0
St Mary's R C	v	Dorset Knob	1V6	Sturminster Newton U	v	Bournemouth Sports	0-2
Verwood Town	v	Wey. Consignia	VT W-O	Wareham Rangers	v	Weymouth United	2-1

SECOND ROUND

(St Mary's RC re-instated)

Allendale	v	Trinidad New Star	1*1, 5-2	Bournemouth Sports	v	St Pauls Jersey	2-1
Chickerell United	v	Beaminster	4-1	Dorchester United	v	Gillingham Town	1-4
St Mary's RC	v	Weymouth Sports	1-2	Hamworthy United	v	Hamworthy Recreation	1-0
Poole Borough	v	Sherborne Town	2-1	Poole Town	v	Portland United	1-2
Shaftsbury	v	Lytchett Red Triangle	4-1	Sturminster Marshall	v	Holt United	1-4
Verwood Town	v	Wareham Rangers	3-1				

THIRD ROUND

Portland United	v	Gillingham Town	2-0	Shaftsbury	v	Bridport	2-3
Weymouth	v	Weymouth Sports	0-5	Wimborne Town	v	Poole Borough	3-0
Bournemouth Sports	v	Verwood Town	1-2	Chickerell United	v	Allendale	1-3
Holt United	v	Swanage T & Herston	4-2	Hamworthy United	v	Dorchester Town	1-4

FOURTH ROUND

Holt United	v	Bridport	4-3	Dorchester Town	v	Portland United	2-1
Weymouth	v	Allendale	8-2	Wimborne Town	v	Verwood Town	8-2

SEMI-FINALS

Weymouth	v	Wimborne Town	4-1	at Dorchester Town FC
Dorchester Town	v	Holt United	3-0	at Wimborne Town FC

FINAL

DORCHESTER T	v	WEYMOUTH	1*1	at Weymouth Avenue, Dorchester Town FC. Att: 623

Weymouth won 3-1 after penalties

DURHAM F.A.

Tel: 0191 384 8653   Fax: 0191 384 3234
"Codeslaw', Ferens Park, Durham DH1 1JZ
Secretary: John Topping
Executives (Responsibility)   A Philliskirk (Coaching Exams/Courses)
                                   J C Topping (Referees)

Number of Affiliated Clubs	Senior:	1100	Junior:	900	**President:** F D Pattison
Number of Affiliated Leagues:	Senior:	50	Junior:	26	**Chairman:** F D Pattison

County Representative Teams: U18
Inter County Competitions: Association of Northern Counties, FA County Youth

Albany DURHAM CHALLENGE CUP 2001-02

(44 entries)   (FOUNDED 1883-84)

LAST SEASON'S FINAL: Bishop Auckland v Brandon United 2-0

MOST WINS: Sunderland 21   Spennymoor United 15   Bishop Auckland 15

PRELIMINARY ROUND

Easington Colliery	v	Billingham Synthonia	4-0		Washington I Hoover	v	Jarrow	7-2
Murton	v	Seaham Red Star	2*1		Boldon C A	v	Willington	0-5
Harton & Westoe	v	Cleadon S C	2-0		Ryhope CW	v	Evenwood Town	0-1
Consett	v	Norton & S Ancients	1-0		Annfield Plain	v	Jarrow R & Boldon C A	0-8
New Birtley	v	Stanley United	4-3		Peterlee Newtown	v	Wolviston	5-0
Spennymoor United	v	Birtley Town	3-0		Wickham	v	Esh Winning	1-2

FIRST ROUND

New Birtley	v	Harton & Westoe	4-3		Peterlee Newtown	v	Darlington	2-1
Bishop Auckland	v	Esh Winning	2-1		Billingham Town	v	Washington Nissan	5-1
Sunderland K Roker	v	Easington Colliery	1-5		Gateshead	v	West Auckland Town	4-2
Evenwood Town	v	Spennymoor United	2-1		Crook Town	v	Consett	3-1
Brandon United	v	Washington I Hoover	4-0		Chester Le Street Tn	v	Eppleton CW	7-1
South Shields	v	Shildon	3-1		Tow Law Town	v	Hartlepool United	0-1
Horden CW	v	Durham City	3-2		Willington	v	Shotton Comrades	4-1
Murton	v	Jarrow Roofing BCA	1-6		Dunston Federation	v	Hebburn Town	2-0

SECOND ROUND

Peterlee Newtown	v	South Shields	1-2		Dunston Federation	v	Bishop Auckland	1-2
Jarrow Roofing BCA	v	Horden C W	2-1		Gateshead	v	Brandon United	3*2
Hartlepool United	v	Crook Town	0-2		Willington	v	Easington Colliery	4p2, 2*2
Billingham Town	v	New Birtley	8-0		Chester Le Street Tn	v	Evenwood Town	4-1

THIRD ROUND

Chester Le Street Tn	v	South Shields	1-3		Gateshead	v	Crook Town	7-2
Jarrow R & Boldon CA	v	Bishop Auckland	2-4		Billingham Town	v	Willington	4-0

SEMI-FINALS

South Shields	v	Bishop Auckland	0-7		Billingham Town	v	Gateshead	1-0

FINAL

BISHOP AUCKLAND v   BILLINGHAM TOWN 1-0   at New Ferens Park, Durham County FA. Att: 302

Billingham's Stuart Jackson (centre) clears from Bishop Auckland's Tony Nelson in the Durham Senior Cup Final. Photo: Alan Watson

Bishop's substitute Andrew Shaw (partly hidden) scores the only goal of the Durham Senior Cup Final against Billingham Town. Photo: Alan Watson

EAST RIDING F.A. LTD

Tel: 01482 221158 Fax: 01482 221159 E.Mail: info@eastridingfa.com
50 Boulevard, Hull HU3 2TB

Secretary & Press Officer:	Dennis R Johnson
Football Development Officer:	Jonathan Day
Executives (Responsibility)	T Mason (Coaching Exams/Courses)
	A Youngs (Referees) M Edge (Womens Football)

Number of Affiliated Clubs Senior: 408   U.18: 214   **President:** Denis Grout
Number of Affiliated Leagues: Senior: 5   Junior: 3   **Chairman:** M Rawding
County Representative Teams: Senior, U18, Womens
Inter County Competitions: Association of Northern Counties, FA County Youth, East Midlands U18

EAST RIDING SENIOR CUP 2001-02

(20 entries) (FOUNDED 1902)
LAST SEASON'S FINAL: North Ferriby United v Hull City 1-0
MOST WINS: Hull City 25   Bridlington Town 12   North Ferriby United 9

FIRST ROUND

Discount Carpets FC	v	Automatrix	DC W-O	North Ferriby U Rs	v	Bridlington SC	3-0
Reckitts	v	Hall Road Rangers Res	4-0	Driffield	v	Hutton Cranswick Utd	2-0
Hider Foods	v	Beverley Town	1-2	East Hull Amateurs	v	Nightjar	2 Byes

SECOND ROUND

Westella & Willerby	v	Hall Road Rangers	1-2	Hedon United	v	Easington United	1-5
North Ferriby Utd Rs	v	East Hull Amateurs	4-0	Driffield	v	Sculcoates Amateurs	0-5
Discount Carpets	v	Nightjar	3-1	Chisholms	v	Reckitts	1-6
Beverley Town	v	Bridlington Town	1-3	North Ferriby United	v	Hull City	5-3

QUARTER-FINALS

Reckitts	v	Hall Road Rangers	1-2	Sculcoates Amateurs	v	Easington Town 2p4, 2*1	
Discount Carpets Hull	v	Bridlington Town	1-4	North Ferriby United	v	North Ferriby U Res	5-1

SEMI-FINALS

Bridlington Town	v	Easington United	2-1	North Ferriby United	v	Hall Road Rangers	3-0

FINAL

BRIDLINGTON T   v   NORTH FERRIBY U   0-2   at Boothferry Park, Hull City FC. Att: 471

EAST RIDING COUNTRY CUP 2001-02

(17 entries)
LAST SEASON'S FINAL: Ward v Nags Head Bridlington 4-0

FIRST ROUND

Long Riston   v   Filey Town   2-5

SECOND ROUND

Ward	v	Mills Lane Beverley	2-0	Hunmanby United	v	Nags Head Bridlington	8-3
Holme Rovers	v	Hornsea Town	3-2	Thorngumbald	v	Brandesburton	5-3
Pucklington Town	v	Withernsea	4-2	Dunnington	v	North Cave	1-3
Walkington Wanderers	v	Shiptonthorpe Utd	1-2	Filey Town	v	Riccall	9-1

QUARTER-FINALS

North Cave	v	Hunmanby United	1-2	Thorngumbald	v	Ward	1-2
Shiptonthorpe United	v	Pucklington Town	1-8	Filey Town	v	Holme Rovers	4-3

SEMI-FINALS

Filey Town	v	Ward FC	1-0	Hunmanby United	v	Pocklington Town	1-3

FINAL

FILEY TOWN   v   POCKLINGTON TN   1-2   at Queensgate, Bridlington Town FC

ESSEX F.A.

Tel: 01245 357727   Fax: 01245 344430   Email: info@EssexFA.com
31 Mildmay Road, Chelmsford CM2 0DN

Chief Executive: Philip Sammons
Number of Affiliated Clubs Senior: 1367   U.18: 463   Chairman: R Brooks
Number of Affiliated Leagues: Senior: 40   Junior: 15   Vice -Chairman: E Fairchild
County Representative Teams: Senior, Intermediate, U18, U16, Womens
Inter County Competitions: East Anglian, Southern Counties

ESSEX SENIOR CUP 2001-02
(42 entries)   (FOUNDED 1883-84)

LAST SEASON'S FINAL: Dagenham & Redbridge v Canvey Island 5p4, 2*2

MOST WINS: Ilford 13   Walthamstow Avenue 12   Grays Athletic 8   Leyton 8

FIRST ROUND
Brentwood	v	Waltham Abbey	1-0	Saffron Walden Town	v	Barkingside	2-1
Southend Manor	v	Burnham Rmbrs @BR	4-3				

SECOND ROUND
Concord Rangers	v	Saffron Walden Town	2-1	Ilford	v	Bowers United	2-3
Aveley	v	Southend Manor	1-2	Hornchurch	v	Brentwood	1-0
Hullbridge Sports	v	Basildon United	5-0	Clapton	v	Stansted	0-1
Leyton	v	Brightlingsea United	2-0				

THIRD ROUND
East Thurrock Utd	v	Stanway Rovers	4-1	Romford	v	Billericay Town	1-2
Dagenham & Red.	v	Harwich & Parkeston	7-2	Grays Athletic	v	Tilbury	0-1
Leyton Pennant	v	Canvey Island	0-4	Tiptree United	v	Ford United	1-7
Great Wakering Rvrs	v	Heybridge Sports	1-3	Witham Town	v	Halstead Town	2-1
Purfleet	v	Southend United	3-0	Bowers United	v	Harlow Town	0-5
Chelmsford City	v	Hornchurch	6-0	Hullbridge	v	Barking & East Ham U	2*3
Concord Rangers	v	Wivenhoe Town	3-1	Southend Manor	v	Maldon Town	3-0
Clacton Town	v	Leyton	0-2	Stansted	v	Braintree Town	1-5

FOURTH ROUND
Heybridge Swifts	v	Barking & E Ham U	8-1	Billericay Town	v	Witham Town	4-2
Dagenham & Red.	v	Ford United	5-1	Canvey Island	v	Southend Manor	6-1
Harlow Town	v	East Thurrock United	2-1	Tilbury	v	Leyton	2-4
Braintree Town	v	Purfleet	0-3	Concord Rangers	v	Chelmsford City	0-2

FIFTH ROUND
Purfleet	v	Heybridge Swifts	3-0	Billericay Town	v	Dagenham & R'bridge	0-2
Harlow Town	v	Canvey Island	0-1	Chelmsford City	v	Leyton	3-0

SEMI-FINALS
Purfleet	v	Dagenham & R.	D&R T-A	Chelmsford City	v	Canvey Island	2-3

FINAL
CANVEY ISLAND	v	DAGENHAM & R	6-1	at Roots Hall, Southend United FC	

ESSEX THAMES-SIDE TROPHY 2001-02
(21 entries) (FOUNDED 1945-46)

LAST SEASON'S FINAL: Grays Athletic v Great Wakering Rovers 3p0, 3*3

MOST WINS: Ilford 13   Walthamstow Avenue 12   Grays Athletic 8   Leyton 8

FIRST ROUND

Burnham Ramblers	v	Hullbridge Sports	5*1	East Thurrock United	v	Romford	1p2 1*1
Concord Rangers	v	Hornchurch	0-1	Basildon United	v	Ilford	0-3
Bowers United	v	Clapton	R-R				

(R-R = Both Clubs removed from Competition)

SECOND ROUND

Aveley	v	Grays Athletic	1-4	Brentwood	v	Ford United	1-5
Hornchurch	v	Burnham Ramblers	1-3	Leyton Pennant	v	Bowers Utd/Clapton	bye
Barking & E Ham U	v	Canvey Island	0-2	Great Wakering Rvrs	v	Romford	4*3
Barkingside	v	Maldon Town	1-2	Tilbury	v	Ilford	5p4 1*1

THIRD ROUND

Great Wakering Rvrs	v	Burnham Ramblers	2-1	Ford United	v	Grays Athletic	GA W-O
Leyton Pennant	v	Canvey Island	3-0	Maldon Town	v	Tilbury	0-1

SEMI-FINALS

Tilbury	v	Leyton Pennant	2-1	Grays Athletic	v	Great Wakering Rvrs	2*1

FINAL

TILBURY	v	GRAYS ATHLETIC	1-3	at Chadfields, St Chads Road, Tilbury FC

GLOUCESTERSHIRE F.A. LIMITED

Tel: 01454 615888   Fax: 01454 618088

Oaklands Park, Almondsbury, Bristol BS32 4AG

Company Sec. & Press Officer: Paul Britton
Executives (Responsibility)   Paul Britton (Coaching Exams/Courses, Womens Football)
   J W Hawkins (Referees)
Number of Affiliated Clubs   Senior: 868   U.18:   189   **President:** S Dyer
Number of Affiliated Leagues: Senior: 21   Junior: 10   **Chairman:** R F Burden
County Representative Teams: Senior, U18, Womens, Womens U18
Inter County Competitions: South & South West Counties Championship, FA County Youth Cup

GLOUCESTERSHIRE SENIOR CUP 2001-02
(8 entries)   (FOUNDED 1936-37)
LAST SEASON'S FINAL: Cinderford Town v Bristol City   1-0
MOST WINS: Cheltenham Town 32   Gloucester City 18   Forest Green Rovers 3

FIRST ROUND

Cirencester Town	v	Cinderford Town	5-1	Bristol Rovers	v	Gloucester City	3-0
Forest Green Rovers	v	Mangotsfield United	2-5	Bristol City	v	Cheltenham Town	3-1

SEMI-FINALS

Bristol Rovers	v	Bristol City	0-4	Cirencester Town	v	Mangotsfield United	1-0

FINAL pre-season TBA
Bristol City   v   Cirencester Town

GLOUCESTERSHIRE SENIOR TROPHY 2001-02
(35 entries)   (FOUNDED 1978-79)
LAST SEASON'S FINAL: Yate Town v Tytherington Rocks   4-2
MOST WINS: Mangotsfield United 6   Moreton Town 3   Shortwood United 2

PRELIMINARY ROUND

Patchway Town	v	DRG Stapleton	3-2	Old Georgians	v	Shirehampton	0-1
Mangotsfield Utd Rs	v	Ellwood	5-3				

FIRST ROUND

Winterbourne United	v	Highridge United	2-0	Viney St Swithins	v	Bishops Cleeve	0-3
Bitton	v	Axa	5-3	Broad Plain	v	Almondsbury FC	4-3
Cirencester United	v	Patchway Town	3-2	Henbury OB	v	Hardwicke	3-1
Harrow Hill	v	Cirencester Academy	0-4	Whitminster	v	Almondsbury T @AT	1-2
Cheltenmham Srcns	v	Hallen	0-3	Tuffley Rovers	v	Tytherington Rocks	1-0
Fairford Town	v	Gloucester United	1-3	Cadbury Heath	v	Totterdown POB	2-3
Slimbridge	v	Roman Glass St G	4-2	Pucklechurch Sprts	v	Shirehampton	1-0
Bristol Manor Farm	v	Yate Town	2-1	Mangotsfield U Res	v	Shortwood	2-1

SECOND ROUND

Bitton	v	Gloucester United	1-4	Henbury Old Boys	v	Cirencester United	1-2
Almondsbury Town	v	Cirencester Academy	2-7	Mangotsfield U Res	v	Bishops Cleeve	1-3
Winterbourne United	v	Broad Plain House	4-1	Bristol Manor Farm	v	Slimbridge	0-2
Hallen	v	Totterdown POB	2-1	Tuffley Rovers	v	Pucklechurch Sports	3-0

THIRD ROUND

Tuffley Rovers	v	Cirencester Academy	0-2	Bishops Cleeve	v	Hallen	0-2
Slimbridge	v	Winterbourne United	0-1	Cirencester United	v	Gloucester United	1-9

SEMI-FINALS

Gloucester United	v	Winterbourne United	2-1	Cirencester Academy	v	Hallen	2-0

FINAL

Cirencester Academy	v	Gloucester United	1-0	at County FA, Oaklands Park, Almondsbury. Att: 130

HAMPSHIRE F.A.

Tel: 02380 791110   Fax: 02380 788340   Email: secretary@hantsfa.co.uk   www.hampshire-fa.org
William Pickford House, 8 Ashwood Gardens, off Winchester Road, Southampton SO16 7PW

Chief Executive: L C Jones
Managers: N A Cassar (Football Operations)
S Nicholas (Football Development)
Number of Affiliated Clubs: Senior: 2000   U.18: 450
County Representative Teams: Womens, U21, Girls U16, Boys U18, Girls U18
Inter County Competitions: South West Counties, FA County Youth Cup

President: M E Turner
Chairman: E J Ward

HAMPSHIRE SENIOR CUP 2001-02
(44 entries)   (FOUNDED 1887-88)

LAST SEASON'S FINAL: Andover v Havant & Waterlooville 2-0

MOST WINS: Southampton 13   Newport 7   Cowes 6

FIRST ROUND

East Cowes Vic Ath	v	Hythe & Dibden	6-2	Totton	v	Blackfield & Langley	5-0
Horndean	v	Stockbridge	4-1	Cowes Sports	v	Bishops Waltham Tn	3-0
Pirelli General	v	R S Basingstoke	3-1	Bournemouth	v	Petersfield United	3-0
Ringwood Town	v	Moneyfields	0-5	Liss Athletic	v	Christchurch	0-3
Fleet Town	v	Winchester City	1-2	B A T Sports	v	Andover New Street	0-1
Portsmouth R N	v	Lymington Town	2-0	Hartley Wintney	v	Gosport Borough	1-3

SECOND ROUND

Pirelli General	v	Eastleigh	1-3	Christchurch	v	Winchester City	2-1
Farnborough Town	v	Portsmouth RN	7-1	Horndean	v	Vosper Thornycroft	0-1
Esso Fawley	v	Whitchurch United	3-1	Fareham Town	v	East Cowes Vics	2-3
Sylvans Sports	v	Hamble ASSC	2-0	Locksheath	v	Brockenhurst	0-5
Bashley	v	Lymington & N Milton	5-1	Cove	v	Totton	3-0
Newport IOW	v	Andover New St	9-0	Andover	v	Basingstoke Town	1-0
Havant & W'rlooville	v	Moneyfields	9-0	Cowes Sports	v	Bournemouth	3-1
Gosport Borough	v	Alton Town	2-0	Aldershot Town	v	Brading Town	5-1

THIRD ROUND

Andover	v	Sylvans Sports	5-0	Havant & W'looville	v	Christchurch	5-1
Brockenhurst	v	Totton	2-0	Bashley	v	East Cowes Victoria	2*1
Newport IOW	v	Esso Fawley	5-0	Aldershot Town	v	Farnborough Town	4-3
Cowes Sports	v	Gosport Boro	4p5, 3*3	Eastleigh	v	Vosper T'croft	5p4, 2*2

FOURTH ROUND

Aldershot Town	v	Brockenhurst	4-0	Andover	v	Newport IOW	1-2
Eastleigh	v	Gosport Borough	1-2	Havant & W'looville	v	Bashley	5-1

SEMI-FINALS Two Legs

Aldershot Town	v	Newport IOW	2-0, 2-0	=4-0
Havant-Waterlooville	v	Gosport Borough 2-1, 1-1		=3-2

FINAL

ALDERSHOT TOWN v   HAVANT & W'VILLE   3-1   at St Mary's Stadium, Southampton FC. Att: 3523

HEREFORDSHIRE F.A.

Tel: 01432 342179 Fax: 01432 279265 Email: herefordfa@ukonline.co.uk
County Ground Offices, Widemarsh Common, Hereford HR4 9NA

Secretary & Press Officer:	Jim Lambert
Assistant Secretary;	Val Lambert
Executives (Responsibility)	Alex Sykes (Football Development Officer)
	A Jenkins (Referees) G Stevens (County Coach)
	R J Perks (Womens Football)

Number of Affiliated Clubs	Senior: 125	U.18: 114	**President:** Sir Colin Shepherd
Number of Affiliated Leagues:	Senior: 1	Junior: 1	**Chairman:** E G Powell
County Representative Teams:	Under 18, Under 16		
Inter County Competitions:	Midland Counties U18, East Midland U16		

HEREFORDSHIRE CHALLENGE CUP 2001-02
(16 entries) (FOUNDED 1973-74)

LAST SEASON'S FINAL: Kington Town v Ross Town 2-0

FIRST ROUND

Leominster Town	v	Fownhope	3-0		Pegasus Juniors	v	Bromyard Town	1-2
Westfields	v	Ross Town	2-1		Hereford Civil Service	v	Kington Town	1-3
Wellington	v	Woofferton	3-0		Ewyas Harold	v	Hinton	1-4
Sutton United	v	Ledbury Town	2-3		Weson U Penyard	v	Ross United Services	1-5

SECOND ROUND

Leominster Town	v	Wellington	1-1 1-5		Hinton	v	Bromyard Town	1-3
Ross United Services	v	Kington Town	0-1		Westfields	v	Ledbury Town	3-1

SEMI-FINALS

Wellington	v	Westfields	2-4		Bromyard Town	v	Kington Town	0-2

FINAL

KINGTON TOWN	v	WESTFIELDS	1-3	at Edgar Street, Hereford United FC

HERTFORDSHIRE F.A.

Tel: 01462 677622   Fax: 01462 677624   E.Mail: competitions@hertsfa.demon.co.uk
County Ground, Baldock Road, Letchworth, Herts S96 2EN
Secretary: E W J King   **Press Officer:** County HQ
Company Secretary: Mrs D Button
Executives (Responsibility)   D Gorringe (Executive Officer)
  A Ackrell (Football Development Officer)
  R G Dowden (Referees)   M Spacey (Womens Football)

Number of Affiliated Clubs   Senior: 860   U.18:   190   **President:** R G Kibble
Number of Affiliated Leagues: Senior: 24   Junior: 11   **Chairman:** W H Dance
County Representative Teams: Senior, U18, U16
Inter County Competitions: East Anglian, EMYFC

ICIS CLUBWEAR HERTFORDSHIRE SENIOR CUP 2001-02
(21 entries)   (FOUNDED 1886-87)

LAST SEASON'S FINAL: Baldock Town v Ware 3-0

MOST WINS: Hitchin Town 21   Barnet 16   Watford 14

FIRST ROUND
Hertford Town	v	Potters Bar Town	4-2	Barnet	v	Watford	0-2
Cheshunt	v	Hitchin Town	0-1	Letchworth	v	Somersett Ambury	2-3
St Margaretsbury	v	Boreham Wood	2-4				

SECOND ROUND
Watford	v	Berkhamsted Tn @BT	0-1	Tring Town	v	Bishops Stortford	6p7, 2*2
Hitchin Town	v	Sawbridgeworth Tn	2-0	Boreham Wood	v	Somersett Amb'y V&E	2-0
London Colney	v	Ware	4-1	Hertford Town	v	St Albans City	0-2
Hoddesdon Town	v	Stevenage Borough	0-2	Royston Town	v	Hemel Hempstead T	2-1

THIRD ROUND
Bishops Stortford	v	London Colney	2-3	St Albans City	v	Boreham Wood	3p4, 1*1
Berkhamsted Town	v	Royston Town	4-2	Hitchin Town	v	Stevenage Borough	3-1

SEMI-FINALS
Boreham Wood	v	Hitchin Town	6-1	London Colney	v	Berkhamsted Town	2-0

FINAL
BOREHAM WOOD	v	LONDON COLNEY	3-2	at Clarence Park, St Albans City FC

GREEN KING HERTFORDSHIRE SENIOR TROPHY 2001-02
(22 entries)
LAST SEASON'S FINAL: Tring Athletic v Wormley Rovers 2-0

FIRST ROUND
London Lions	v	St Peters	7p8, 3*3	Welwyn Garden City v	Letchworth Bridger	0-4
Chipperfield Corinths	v	Kings Langley	0-4	Cuffley v	Colney Heath	2-3
Met Police Bushey	v	Bedmond S&S	2-1	Sandridge Rovers v	Croxley Guild	6-0

SECOND ROUND
Tring Athletic	v	L'worth Bridger	5p4, 2*2	Oxhey Jets v	Hatfield Town	4-0
Greenacres	v	Harpenden Tn	5p4, 6*6	Met Police Bushey v	Sun Postal Sports	1-4
St Peters	v	Elliott Star	2-5	Colney Heath v	Sandridge Rvrs	6p5, 3*3
Wormley Rovers	v	Leverstock Green	3*6	Kings Langley v	Bovingdon	2-4

THIRD ROUND
Tring Athletic	v	Elliott Star	1-3	Sun Postal Sports v	Bovingdon	1-0
Greenacres Hemel H	v	Colney Heath	4-2	Oxhey Jets v	Leverstock Green	2*1

SEMI-FINALS
Oxhey Jets	v	Sun Postal Sports	1-0	Elliott Star v	Greenacres Hemel H 2-1

FINAL
ELLIOTT STAR	v	OXHEY JETS	3-4	at The Herts FA County Ground, Letchworth.

Little Munden Sports FC, winners of the Hertfordshire Junior Cup (for the first time) after beating Hertford Heath 3-0.
Photo: Gordon Whittington

HUNTINGDONSHIRE F.A.

Tel: 01480414422   Fax: 01480 412691   Email: info@hunts-fa.org
Cromwell Chambers, 8 St Johns Street, Huntingdon, Cambs. PE29 3DD

Secretary & Press Officer: Maurice Armstrong
Executives (Responsibility)   M A Hair (Referees)
                                   S Batchelor (Football Development Officer)

Number of Affiliated Clubs   Senior: 130   U.18:   30   **President:** D A Roberts
Number of Affiliated Leagues: Senior: 1   Junior: 1   **Chairman:** E K Heads
County Representative Teams: Senior, Under 18, Under 16, Colts
Inter County Competitions: U18 & U16, Midlands Youth Football Championships

HUNTINGDONSHIRE SENIOR CUP 2001-02
(17 entries)   (FOUNDED 1888-89)

LAST SEASON'S FINAL: Somersham Town v St Neots Town 1-0
MOST WINS: St Neots 34   Eynesbury Rovers 14   Huntingdon Town 12

FIRST ROUND
Hemingford United   v   Huntingdon Utd 2000   1-5

SECOND ROUND

Ortonians	v	Hotpoint	0-1	St Ives Town	v	St Neots Town	0-8
Stilton United	v	ICA-Juventus	2-0	Huntingdon United	v	Ramsey Town	1-2
Great Paxton	v	Yaxley	0-5	Eynesbury Rovers	v	Godmanchester Rvrs	2-0
Somersham Town	v	Warboys Town	3-4	Alconbury	v	Bluntisham	2-1

THIRD ROUND

Stilton United	v	Ramsey Town	7-4	Hotpoint	v	Eynesbury Rovers	1-3
Yaxley	v	Warboys Town	4-0	Alconbury	v	St Neots Town	1-3

SEMI-FINALS

Eynesbury Rovers	v	Yaxley	1*1, 4-1	St Neots Town	v	Stilton United	7-0

FINAL
ST NEOTS TOWN   v   EYNESBURY RVRS   0-3   at Forge Way, High Street, Warboys Town FC

HUNTINGDONSHIRE PREMIER CUP 2001-02
HOLDERS: Biggleswade Town

SEMI-FINALS

St Ives Town	v	Ely City	0-4	St Neots Town	v	Stotfold	2-1

FINAL
ELY CITY   v   ST NEOTS TOWN   1*5   at Rowley Park, Cambridge Road, St Neots Town FC

Opposite page:

Top: Paul Carey's last minute spot-kick completes his hat-trick and Eynesbury Rovers 3-0 win over St Neots in the Huntingdonshire Senior Cup final.

Centre: Eynesbury Rovers celebrate their Huntingdonshire Senior Cup win.

Bottom: Brampton, Cambs League Senior 1B Champions and Huntingdonshire Junior Cup Runners-up.

Photos: Gordon Whittington

KENT F.A. Limited

Tel: 01634 843824 Fax: 01634 815369 E.Mail: enquiries@kent-fa.org
69 Maidstone Road, Chatham, Kent ME4 6DT

Chief Executive:	K T Masters
Press Officer:	Tony Hudd
Executives (Responsibility)	Alan Walker (Coaching) John Newson (Referees)
	Nici Rice (County Development)
	Liz Symons (Girls & Womens Football)

Number of Affiliated Clubs Adult: 1071   U.18: 217   **President:** N Chatfield
Number of Affiliated Leagues: Senior: 2   Junior: 41   **Chairman:** B W Bright
County Representative Teams: U18, U16, Womens, Girls

KENT FACIT SENIOR CUP 2001-02
(14 entries) (FOUNDED 1888-89)

LAST SEASON'S FINAL: Gravesend & Northfleet v Dover Athletic 4-0
MOST WINS: Maidstone United 15   Dartford 9   Northfleet United 9

FIRST ROUND

Folkestone Invicta	v	Tonbridge	2-1	Margate	v	Bromley	3-1
Chatham Town	v	Fisher Athletic London	1-4	Welling United	v	Erith & Belvedere 4p3, 1*1
Sittingbourne	v	Ashford Town	2-3	Dartford	v	Whitstable Town	2-1

QUARTER-FINALS

Ashford Town	v	Dover Athletic	5-1	Folkestone Invicta	v	Margate	1-2
Fisher Athletic London	v	Welling United	3-2	Dartford	v	Gravesend & Nthfleet	0-3

SEMI-FINALS

Fisher Athletic	v	Gravesend & Nthfleet	2-3	Margate	v	Ashford Town	5-0

FINAL

MARGATE   v   GRAVESEND & N   0-5   at Hartsdown Park, Margate FC. Att: 1668

KENT PLAAYA SENIOR TROPHY 2001-02
(21 entries) (FOUNDED 1874-75)

LAST SEASON'S FINAL: Whitstable Town v VCD Athletic 10p9, 1*1
MOST WINS: Ramsgate 3   Alma Swanley 2   Corinthian 2   Faversham Town 2   Fisher Athletic 2

FIRST ROUND

Crockenhill	v	Lydd Town	0-1	Faversham Town	v	Milton United	
Beckenham Town	v	West Wickham	1-0	Erith Town	v	Bearsted	3*3 rep
Maidstone United	v	Thames Poly	3-0				

SECOND ROUND

VCD Athletic	v	Hythe Town	3-0	Slade Green	v	Cray Wanderers	0-6
Lordswood	v	Thamesmead Town	0-3	Lydd Town	v	Greenwich Borough	1-0
Maidstone United	v	Erith Town	0-1	Deal Town	v	Ramsgate	4-1
Tonbridge Wells	v	Ramsgate	5-2	Milton United	v	Beckenham Town	1-0

THIRD ROUND

Erith Town	v	Cray Wanderers	0-1	Deal Town	v	VCD Athletic	2-0
Milton Athletic	v	Lydd Town	4-1	Thamesmead Town	v	Tunbridge Wells	3-0

SEMI-FINALS

Cray Wanderers	v	Deal Town (2/3)	116 3-1	Thamesmead Town	v	Milton Athletic	1-0

FINAL

CRAY WANDERERS v   THAMESMEAD TN   0-2   at Surrey Docks Stadium, Fisher Athletic. Att: 257

Tel: 01772 624000   Fax: 01772 624700
The County Ground, Thurston Road, Leyland PR25 2LF

Secretary & Press Officer	J Kenyon, ACIS
Assistant Secretary:	Ms C Banks
Executives (Responsibility)	D Egan (Development Officer) Tel: 01772 490440
	E J Parker (Referees)

Number of Affiliated Clubs   Senior: 1600   U.18:   300   **President:** D J Lewin
County Representative Teams: Senior, U18, Womens
Inter County Competitions: FA County Youth, Northern Counties Senior, U18 & Womens

MARSDEN LANCASHIRE TROPHY 2001-02

(28 entries)   (FOUNDED 1885-86)

LAST SEASON'S FINAL: Southport v Lancaster City 1-0

FIRST ROUND

Blackpool Mechanics	v	Burscough fog 0A0, 0-3		Squires Gate	v	Marine	2-1
Castleton Gabriels	v	Accrington Stanley	0-7	Darwen	v	Great Harwood Town	2-0
Barrow	v	Skelmersdale United	3-2	Chorley	v	Leigh RMI	2-4
Colne	v	Ramsbottom United	2-5	Bacup Borough	v	Fleetwood Freeport	2-0
Nelson	v	Atherton Laburnum R3p5 2*2		Clitheroe	v	Radcloiffe Borough	2-0
Holker Old Boys	v	Atherton Collieries	1-3	Flixton	v	Rossendale United	0-4

SECOND ROUND

Southport	v	Lancaster City	2-1	Accrington Stanley	v	Atherton Collieries	4-1
Leigh RMI	v	Rossendale United	4*3	Atherton L R	v	Ramsbottom United	4-5
Burscough	v	Squires Gate	3-1	Darwen	v	Morecambe	4-2
Bamber Bridge	v	Barrow	0-1	Clitheroe	v	Bacup Borough	3-0

QUARTER-FINALS

Southport	v	Barrow	0-2	Burscough	v	Darwen	4-1
Accrington Stanley	v	Leigh RMI	2-1	Ramsbottom United	v	Clitheroe	0-2

SEMI-FINALS

Barrow	v	Clitheroe	3-0	Burscough	v	Accrington Stanley	0-1

FINAL

ACCRINGTON S'LEY v   BARROW   2-0   at Christie Park, Morecambe FC. Att: 1330

LEICESTERSHIRE & RUTLAND F.A.

Tel: 0116 286 7828   Fax: 0116 286 4858   Email: leicscfa@aol.com
Holmes Park, Dog & Gun Lane, Whetstone LE8 6FA

Secretary & Press Officer:	Paul Morrison		
Executives (Responsibility)	J Ward (Referees)		
	Mrs G F Wait (Womens Football)		
Number of Affiliated Clubs	Senior: 500	U.18: 180	**President:** G E Cooper
Number of Affiliated Leagues:	Senior: 12	Junior: 7	**Chairman:** D J Jamieson
County Representative Teams:	Under 18, Under 16, Under 16 Girls		
Inter County Competitions:	Midlands Youth Combination U18 & U16 and U16 Girls		

LEICESTERSHIRE 'JELSON HOMES' SENIOR CUP 2001-02
(38 entries)   (FOUNDED 1887-88)
LAST SEASON'S FINAL: St Andrews v Friar Lane 2-0
MOST WINS: Leicester City 27   Enderby Town 6   Shepshed Dynamo 6

FIRST ROUND

Loughboro Dynamo	v	Sileby Town	2-0	Kirby Muxloe	v	Aylestone Park O B	0-1
Loughborough	v	Anstey Town	2*1				

SECOND ROUND

Friar Lane O B	v	Saffron Dynamo	7-1	Melton Mowvray	v	Coalville Town	2-6
Barrow Town	v	North Kilworth	4*3	Aylestone Park OB	v	Thringstone MW	1-0
Blaby & Whetstone A	v	Narborough & L	2-1	Ratby Sports	v	Loughborough	0-4
Downes Sports	v	Birstall United	4-3	Holwell Sports	v	Leics Constabulary	2-1
Bardon Hill Sports	v	Thurmaston Town	2-1	Leicester YMCA	v	Ellistown	1-0
Stoney Stanton	v	Anstey Nomads	2-1	St Andrews	v	Huncote Sports	10-2
Thurnby Rangers	v	Asfordby Amateurs	4-0	Loughboro Dynamo	v	Lutterworth Town	1-3
Earl Shilton Albion	v	Cottesmore Amateurs	2-1	Ibstock Welfare	v	Highfield Rangers	1*0

THIRD ROUND

Loughborough	v	Blaby & Whetstone A	0-1	Leicester YMCA	v	Ibstock Welfare	1-2
Barrow Town	v	Downes Sports	1*4	Bardon Hill Sports	v	Aylestone Park OB	4-3
Coalville Town	v	Lutterworth Town	5-1	St Andrews	v	Stoney Stanton	8-0
Earl Shilton Albion	v	Thurnby Rangers	1-5	Holwell Sports	v	Friar Lane Old Boys	0-1

FOURTH ROUND

Friar Lane OB	v	Coalville Town	0-1	Blaby & Whetstone	v	Downes Sports @DS	1-3
Thurnby Rangers	v	Bardon Hill Sports	3-0	St Andrews	v	Ibstock Welfare	0-1

SEMI-FINALS

Ibstock Welfare	v	Thurnby Rangers	0-4	Downes Sports	v	Coalville Town	1-2

FINAL

COALVILLE TOWN	v	THURNBY RANGERS 3-4	at Leics & Rutland County FA Ground, Whetstone

LEICESTERSHIRE WESTERBY CHALLENGE CUP 2001-02
(14 entries)
LAST SEASON'S FINAL: Hinckley United v Barwell 2-1

FIRST ROUND

Coalville Town	v	Thringstone M W	5-1	Downes Sports	v	Quorn	2-1
Highfield Rangers	v	Leicester City	0-2	Holwell Sports	v	Shepshed Dynamo	0-3

SECOND ROUND

Oadby Town	v	Barwell	3p2 2*2	St Andrews	v	Leicester City	4-3
Thringstone M W	v	Downes Sports	0-3	Hinckley United	v	Shepshed Dynamo	4-1

SEMI-FINALS

Downes Sports	v	Hinckley United	1-4	Oadby Town	v	St Andrews	3-1

FINAL

HINCKLEY UNITED	v	OADBY TOWN 3-1	at Filbert Street, Leicester City FC. Att: 885

LINCOLNSHIRE F.A.

Tel: 01522 524917 Fax: 01522 528859
PO Box 26, 12 Dean Road, Lincoln LN2 4DP

Secretary:	J Griffin
Press Officer:	K Weaver
Executives (Responsibility)	Board of Directors

| **Number of Affiliated Clubs** | Senior: | 896 | U.18: | 243 | **President:** N A Saywell |
| **Number of Affiliated Leagues:** | Senior: | 19 | Junior: | 13 | **Chairman:** R D Teanby |

County Representative Teams: U18, U16
Inter County Competitions: East Midlands Youth Combination, FA County Youth

LINCOLNSHIRE SENIOR CUP 2001-02
(8 entries)   (FOUNDED 1935-36)

LAST SEASON'S FINAL: Stamford AFC v Boston United 2-1

MOST WINS: Grimsby Town 14   Lincoln City 12   Boston United 5   Lincoln Moorlands 2

FIRST ROUND

| Stamford | v | Grimsby Town | 3-2 | | Gainsborough Trinity v | Grantham Town | 2p4, 0-0 |
| Boston United | v | Scunthorpe Utd | 7p8, 3-3 | | Lincoln City | v | Lincoln United | 5p4, 1-1 |

SEMI-FINALS

| Lincoln City | v | Grantham Town | 1-2 | | Stamford | v | Scunthorpe United | 2-3 |

FINAL TBA

| Grantham Town | v | Scunthorpe United |

LINCOLNSHIRE SENIOR 'A' CUP 2001-02
(12 entries)   (FOUNDED 1949-50)

LAST SEASON'S FINAL: Lincoln Moorlands v Louth United 5p3, 0-0

MOST WINS: Boston Town 6   Holbeach United 4   Skegness Town 4

PRELIMINARY ROUND

| Blackstone | v | Winterton Rangers 4p3 1*1 | | Holbeach United | v | Bourne Town | 3-0 |
| Brigg Town | v | Spalding United 2p3 3*3 | | Louth United | v | Bottesford Town | 1-6 |

FIRST ROUND

| Boston Town | v | Spalding United | 0-3 | | Holbeach United | v | Deeping Rangers | 2-1 |
| Nettleham | v | Bottesford Town | 1-0 | | Lincoln Moorlands | v | Blackstone | 1-0 |

SEMI-FINALS

| Nettleham | v | Lincoln Moorlands | 0-4 | | Holbeach United | v | Spalding United | 3-1 |

FINAL

| HOLBEACH UNITED v | LINCOLN M'LANDS | 0-1 | | at Sincil Bank Lincoln City FC |

LINCOLNSHIRE SENIOR 'B' CUP 2001-02
(12 entries) (FOUNDED 1949-50)

LAST SEASON'S FINAL: Deeping Rangers v Harrowby United 4-1

MOST WINS: Brigg Town 5   Appleby Frodingham Athletic 4   Lincoln Moorlands 3

FIRST ROUND

Barton Tn Old Boys	v	Horncastle Town	4-0	Limestone Rangers	v	Grimsby Immingham A	0-3
Wyberton	v	Barrowby	0-3	Hykeham Town	v	Skegness Town	0-3

SECOND ROUND

Barton Town	v	Wyberton	3-1	Appleby Frodingham	v	Skegness Town	2-4
Alstom Sports	v	Harrowby United	0-3	Grimsby Im'ham Am	v	Sleaford Town	1-2

SEMI-FINALS

Sleaford Town	v	Skegness Town	3-2	Barton Town OB	v	Harrowby United	3p4, 0*0

FINAL

HARROWBY UTD	v	SLEAFORD TOWN	2-3	at York Street, Boston United FC

LIVERPOOL F.A.

Tel: 0151 523 4488 Fax: 0151 523 4477 Email: info@liverpoolfa.com
Liverpool Soccer Centre, Walton Hall Park, Walton Hall Avenue, Liverpool L4 9XP

Secretary: F L Hunter   **Press Officer:** E McGrath
Executives (Responsibility)   M McGlyn (Coaching Exams/Courses)
                                  D Cleveland (Referees)
                                  Mrs Marley (Womens Football)
Number of Affiliated Clubs   Senior: 900   U.18:   600   **President:** N Dainty
Number of Affiliated Leagues: Senior: 18   Junior: 25
Inter County Competitions: All FA Competitions

Nat West LIVERPOOL SENIOR CUP 2001-02
(11 entries)   (FOUNDED 1977-78)

LAST SEASON'S FINAL: Burscough v Southport 1-0

MOST WINS: Marine 5   Liverpool 3   South Liverpool 3

FIRST ROUND

Runcorn F C Halton	v	Marine	3-0	Prescot Cables	v	St Helens Town	0-1
Warrington Town	v	Skelmersdale United	2-1				

SECOND ROUND

Runcorn FC Halton	v	Everton	1-2	St Helens Town	v	Southport	1-2
Burscough	v	Liverpool	1-7	Tranmere Rovers	v	Warrington Tn @WT	3-0

SEMI-FINALS

Tranmere Rovers	v	Liverpool	1*3	Southport	v	Everton	1-3

FINAL

Liverpool	v	Everton

LONDON F.A.

Tel: 020 8690 9626   Fax: 020 8690 9471   Email: enquiries@londonfa.fsnet.co.uk
6 Aldworth Grove, Lewisham, London SE13 6HY

Secretary: D G Fowkes

Executives (Responsibility): J Drabwell (Coaching Exams)   R Jenkins (Referees)
C Arundale (Womens Football)   Miss N Donnelly (Coaching Courses)

Number of Affiliated Clubs   Adult: 2134   U18:   476   **President:** F J Lock MBE

Number of Affiliated Leagues: Adult: 93   U18:   35   **Chairman:** N R J Moss

County Representative Teams: Senior, Womens, U16

Inter County Competitions: Southern Counties Cup (men), Southern Counties Cup (women), FA County Youth Cup

LONDON SENIOR CUP 2001-02
(38 entries)   (FOUNDED 1882)

LAST SEASON'S FINAL: Ford United v Croydon Athletic   3-2

PRELIMINARY ROUND

Cray Wanderers	v	Crown & Manor	5-0	Ilford	v	Woodford Town	6-1

FIRST ROUND

Ilford	v	Civil Service	3-1	Beckenham Town	v	Barkingside	4-1
Brimsdown Rovers	v	Haringey Borough	2-4	Cray Wanderers	v	Thamesmead Town	2-1

SECOND ROUND

Hoddesdon Town	v	Clapton	1-0	Kingsbury Town	v	Thames Poly	3-1
Cray Wanderers	v	Hornchurch	2-1	Erith Town	v	Hanwell Town	2-3
Leyton	v	VCD Athletic	4-2	Cockfosters	v	Haringey Borough	4-0
Waltham Abbey	v	Beckenham Town	1-3	Bedfont	v	Ilford	0-1

THIRD ROUND

Leyton Pennant	v	Beckenham Town BT	W-O	Ilford	v	Romford	3-0
Erith & Belvedere	v	Cockfosters	7-1	Metropolitan Police	v	Wingate & Finchley	3-0
Corinthian Casuals	v	Leyton	1-3	Cray Wanderers	v	Barking & East Ham U	4-1
Bromley	v	Hoddesdon Town	0-1	Hanwell Town	v	Kingsbury Town	5-4

FOURTH ROUND

Dulwich Hamlet	v	Beckenham Town	2-1	Welling United	v	Metropolitan Police	3-1
Fisher Athletic	v	Leyton	4-0	Hanwell Town	v	Croydon Athletic	1-0
Hoddesdon Town	v	Uxbridge	1-2	Tooting & Mitcham U	v	Cray Wanderers	0-1
Croydon	v	Erith & Belvedere	4-2	Ilford	v	Ford United	6p5, 1*1

FIFTH ROUND

Uxbridge	v	Welling United	5-2	Dulwich Hamlet	v	Fisher Athletic	1-0
Cray Wanderers	v	Hanwell Town	2-1	Croydon	v	Ilford	3-0

SEMI-FINALS

Dulwich Hamlet	v	Uxbridge	3-1	Croydon	v	Hanwell Town	2-0

FINAL

CROYDON	v	DULWICH HAMLET	2-1	at Brisbane Road, Leyton Orient FC	

INTERMEDIATE CUP FINAL	London City Athletic v Metrogas	4-1
JUNIOR CUP FINAL	Leone Stars S'wark v TC Sports	3*4
SUNDAY INTERMEDIATE CUP FINAL	Faithfold v Libra Arms	2-5
WOMEN'S CUP FINAL	Arsenal v Fulham	0-4
SUNDAY JUNIOR CUP FINAL	Black Horse v Ford Scorpio	4-0
VETERANS CUP FINAL	Reginald Vets v Canning Town	4-0
SUNDAY CHALLENGE CUP FINAL	Livingstone v Green Island Utd	1-3

MANCHESTER F.A.

Tel: 0161 881 0299 Fax: 0161 881 6833 E-mail: mancfa@cs.com

Brantingham Road, Chorlton, Manchester M21 0TT

Secretary & Press Officer: Jon Dutton
Executives (Responsibility)   Jason Wright (Education)
                                   Phil Morris (Referees)
                                   Fiona Miley (Development Officer)

Number of Affiliated Clubs	Senior:	542	U.18:	154	**President:** Frank Hannah
Number of Affiliated Leagues:	Senior:	29	Junior:	13	

County Representative Teams: U18, Womens
Inter County Competitions: FA County Youth, Association of Northern Counties Youth Competition

MANCHESTER PREMIER CUP 2001-02
sponsored by SPARTA SPORTSWEAR
(12 entries)   (FOUNDED1979-80)

LAST SEASON'S FINAL: Ashton United v Droylsden 4-0

MOST WINS: Curzon Ashton 5   Ashton United 4   Hyde United 3
Droylsden 3   Mossley 2

FIRST ROUND

Curzon Ashton	v	Oldham Town	1-0	Abbey Hey	v	Droylsden	2-1
Maine Road	v	Trafford	1-0	Salford City	v	Chadderton	4-2

SECOND ROUND

Mossley	v	Curzon Ashton	4-3	Abbey Hey	v	Flixton	0A0 f/f 30m 1-0
Ashton United	v	Trafford	2-0	Salford City	v	Stand Athletic	5-2

SEMI-FINALS

Abbey Hey	v	Ashton United	1-2	Mossley	v	Salford City	1-2

FINAL

ASHTON UNITED v SALFORD CITY 3-1   at Boundary Park, Oldham Athletic FC. Att: 319

GROUNDTASTIC

The Football Grounds Magazine

Groundtastic is the acclaimed magazine featuring news, articles and special features on football grounds at all levels from the Premiership to non-league. Each glossy 80-page edition carries regular development updates, including 6 pages of non-league news, together with articles and photos chronicling the rich history of non-league grounds. The magazine usually retails at £3.50 but to receive a free sample issue send 2 first class stamps to: 21 Tiptree Grove, WICKFORD, SS12 9AL. To obtain details of back issues and our other publications, please visit our website at www.groundtastic.ukgateway.net

MIDDLESEX COUNTY F.A.

Tel: 0208 424 8524   Fax: 0181 863 0627   E.Mail: peter.clayton@middlesexfa.com

39 Roxborough Road, Harrow, Middlesex HA1 1NS

Secretary: Peter Clayton   Executive Officer: Mark Frost

Executives (Responsibility)   P Clayton (Coaching Exams/Courses,
                                                    Womens Football, Referees)

Number of Affiliated Clubs   Snr: 32; Inter: 12; U18 232; Jnr 583; Wmn 19; Other 337   **President:** John Wake

Number of Affiliated Leagues: Adult: 30   Youth: 8   **Chairman:** Derek Mennell

County Representative Teams: Senior, Intermediate, U18, U16, Womens, U16, Womens U16

Inter County Competitions: FA County Yth, Home Counties Yth, Southern Counties (Intermediate, Women)

MIDDLESEX SENIOR CUP 2001-02

(26 entries)   (FOUNDED 1888-89)

LAST SEASON'S FINAL: Uxbridge v Harrow Borough 3-0

MOST WINS: Enfield 14   Southall 12   Wealdstone 11   Hendon 11   Hayes 10

FIRST ROUND

Brook House	v	Yeading	1-4		Hillingdon Borough	v	Bedfont	3-2
Edgware Town	v	Ruislip Manor	1-3		Enfield	v	Viking Greenford	E W-O
Feltham	v	Southall	4-2		Kingsbury Town	v	Hendon	0-5
Harefield United	v	Enfield Town	0-2		Wealdstone	v	Hanwell Town	2-1
Ashford Town	v	Northwood	0-5		Wembley	v	Southall Town	1-2

SECOND ROUND

Southall Town	v	Hampton & Rich Boro	0-4		Staines Town	v	Hendon @ H	0-5
Feltham	v	Hillingdon Borough	5-1		Ruislip Manor	v	Enfield Town	1-3
Northwood	v	Yeading	5-2		Hayes	v	Harrow Borough	2-1
Potters Bar Town	v	Wealdstone	0-3		Uxbridge	v	Enfield	4-0

THIRD ROUND

Hayes	v	Hendon	1-5		Northwood	v	Feltham	3-2
Uxbridge	v	Hampton & Richmond B	1*0		Enfield Town	v	Wealdstone	3-1

SEMI-FINALS

Hendon	v	Enfield Town @ET	1-0		Northwood	v	Uxbridge	6-2

FINAL

HENDON	v	NORTHWOOD	4*2	at Church Road, Hayes FC

NORFOLK F.A.
Tel: 01603 717177   Fax: 01603 717187
Plantation Park, Blofield, Norwich NR13 4PL

Chief Executive: Roger J Howlett
Executives (Responsibility) Through County Office
                           (Coaching Exams/Courses, Referees, Womens Football)

Number of Affiliated Clubs	Senior:	487	U.18:	167	**President:** R W Kiddell
Number of Affiliated Leagues:	Senior:	16	Junior:	9	**Chairman:** B Woodhouse

County Representative Teams: U18, Womens
Inter County Competitions: FA County Youth, East Anglian Counties

NORFOLK SENIOR CUP 2001-02
(30 entries)   (FOUNDED 1881-82)

LAST SEASON'S FINAL: Gorleston v Great Yarmouth 4-0

MOST WINS: King's Lynn 19   Great Yarmouth Town 14   Gorleston 13

FIRST ROUND
Hempnall	v	Thorpe Village	4-1		Watton United	v	Loddon United	5-0
Sprowston Wndrs	v	Ang.Windows Norwich	3-6		Acle United	v	Mattishall	2-1

SECOND ROUND
Norwich United	v	Downham Town	5-0		Sprowston Athletic	v	Wells Town	4-2
Thetford Town	v	Norwich Union	0-1		Halvergate United	v	Wymondham Town	5-1
Stalham Town	v	Ang Windows Norwich	2-3		Blofield United	v	St Andrews	5-0
Acle United	v	Attenborough Town	3-2		Hempnall	v	Watton United	2*2, 1-3
Cromer United	v	Mulbarton United	5-1		North Walsham Town	v	Kings Lynn Res	2*3

THIRD ROUND
Wroxham	v	Norwich United	2-1		Great Yarmouth Tn	v	Halvergate United	2-1
Watton United	v	Dereham Town	0-4		Norwich A Windows	v	Sprowston Athletic	4-6
Norwich Union	v	Comer United	204		Acle United	v	King's Lynn Res	0-2
Fakenham Town	v	Blofield United	1-0		Swaffham Town	v	Diss Town	1-0

FOURTH ROUND
Dereham Town	v	Wroxham	0-3		Fakenham Town	v	Cromer United	5-1
Great Yarmouth Town	v	Sprowston Athletic	2-1		Swaffham Town	v	Acle United	2*1

(Acle United are re-instated after King's Lynn Res were found to have fielded an ineligible player in the 3rd Rd)

SEMI-FINALS
Fakenham Town	v	Great Yarmouth Tn	0-1		Swaffham Town	v	Wroxham	210 0-2

FINAL
GT YARMOUTH TN	v	WROXHAM	1-2		at Carrow Road, Norwich City FC. Att: 870

NORTHAMPTONSHIRE F.A.

Tel: 01604 670741 Fax: 01604 670742

2 Duncan Close, Moulton Park, Northampton

Chief Executive: D Payne

Executives (Responsibility) N Levett (Football Development Officer)
Jim Wilkinson (Referees)
Mrs J Jeffrey (Womens Football)

Number of Affiliated Clubs	Senior:	466	U.18:	162
Number of Affiliated Leagues:	Senior:	12	Junior:	7

President: D Vernum

Chairman: D Joyce

County Representative Teams: U18 & Women's U16

Inter County Competitions: Midland Youth Combination

NORTHAMPTONSHIRE 'HILLIER' SENIOR CUP 2001-02
(17 entries) (FOUNDED 1883-84)

LAST SEASON'S FINAL: Kettering Town v Rushden & Diamonds 3-1

MOST WINS: Kettering Town 31   Northampton Town 11   Peterborough United 11

FIRST ROUND

Bugbrooke St M	v	Raunds Town	0-7	Daventry Town	v	Brackley Town	2-4
Desborough Town	v	Long Buckby	2-0	Northampton Spncr	v	Stewart & Loyds Corby	3-1

SECOND ROUND

Cogenhoe United	v	Brackley Town	2-3	Corby Town	v	Rothwell Town	2*4
Desborough Town	v	Raunds Town	2-3	Ford Spts Daventry	v	Northampton Spencer	2-3
Wellingborough Tn	v	Kettering Town @KT	1-10				

QUARTER-FINALS

Northampton Spencer	v	Northampton Town	0-2	Rothwell Town	v	Raunds Town	4-1
Brackley Town	v	Rushden & Dia	BT T-A	Kettering Town	v	Peterborough United	0-2

SEMI-FINALS

Northampton Town	v	Peterborough United	1-4	Rothwell Town	v	Brackley Town	2-0

FINAL

ROTHWELL TOWN v PETERBOROUGH U 2-1   at Home Close, Rothwell Town FC. Att: 151

Opposite page:

Top: Grant Stewart's header gives Sileby Rangers an early lead against Rothwell Corinthians in the Northants Junior Cup final. They finally won 2-1 in extra time at Rushden & Diamonds.

Bottom: Sileby Rangers celebrate their Northants Junior Cup win.

Photos: Gordon Whittington

NORTH RIDING F.A.

Tel: 01642 318603   Fax: 01642 318604   Email: enquiries@northridingfa.com
Southlands Centre, Ormesby Road, Middlesbrough TS3 0HB

Chief Executive: Mark Jarvis
Executives (Responsibility)   Andy Clay (Football Development Officer/Womens Football)
                               Contact County Office for Exams/Courses, Referees
Number of Affiliated Clubs   Senior: 500   U.18:   120
Number of Affiliated Leagues: Senior: 20   Junior: 10   **President:** K Boyer
County Representative Teams: Senior, U18, Ladies
Inter County Competitions: Northern Counties Competitions, FA Youth Competition

NORTH RIDING SENIOR CUP 2000-01

(14 entries)   (FOUNDED 1881-82)

LAST SEASON'S FINAL: Middlesbrough v York City   2-0

MOST WINS: Middlesbrough 47   Scarborough 17   South Bank 8   Stockton 8   York City 8

FIRST PRELIMINARY ROUND
Nunthorpe Athletic   v   Carlin How   0-1

SECOND PRELIMINARY ROUND
Guisborough Town	v	Fishburn Park	1-2	Thornaby	v	Bedale Athletic	0-3
Pickering Town	v	New Marske S C	2-1	Northallerton Town	v	Whitby Town	1-3
Marske United	v	Carlin How	4-1				

FIRST ROUND PROPER
Pickering Town	v	Bedale Athletic	1-2	Middlesbrough	v	York City	5-0
Whitby Town	v	Scarborough	4p1, 3*3	Fishburn Park	v	Marske United	0-1

SEMI-FINALS
Whitby Town   v   Bedale Athletic   7-1   Marske United   v   Middlesbrough   1-3

FINAL
Whitby Town   v   Middlesbrough   2p4, 3*3   at Turnbull Ground, Upgang Lane, Whitby Town FC

NORTHUMBERLAND F.A.

Tel: 0191 297 0101
Whitley Park, Whitley Road, Benton, Newcastle upon Tyne NE12 9SF
Chief Executive: Rowland E Maughan   **Press Officer:** Bill Gardner
Executives (Responsibility)   Barry Jones (Football Development Officer)
                                    Bill Darby (Referees)
                                    G Watson (Mini Soccer & Womens Football)
Number of Affiliated Clubs   Senior: 450   U.18:   480   **President:** E A Wright
Number of Affiliated Leagues: Senior: 18   Junior: 4
County Representative Teams: Senior, U18
Inter County Competitions: Northern Counties Senior & Youth Cups, FA County Youth Cup
County Publications: "The Far Corner" - Bi-monthly Newsletter

NORTHUMBERLAND SENIOR CUP 2001-02
Sponsored by "Absolut"
(14 entries)   (FOUNDED 1883-84)

LAST SEASON'S FINAL: Newcastle United Reserves v Bedlington Terriers
MOST WINS: Blyth Spartans 21   Newcastle United 21   North Shields 12

FIRST ROUND

Newcastle Blue Star	v	Prudhoe Town	3-4	North Shields	v West Allotment Celtic	1*2
Morpeth Town	v	Ashington	3-1	Blyth Spartans	v Whitley Bay	5-1
Shankhouse	v	Ponteland United	3-1	Alnwick Town	v Walker Central	0-1

SECOND ROUND

Shankhouse	v	Walker Central	2-0	Prudhoe Town	v Morpeth Town	3-1
Bedlington Terriers	v	Newcastle United Res	2-0	West Allotment Celtic v	Blyth Spartans	2-0

SEMI-FINALS

West Allotment Celtic v	Prudhoe Town	4*3	Bedlington Terriers	v Shankhouse	2-1

FINAL

Bedlington Terriers v West Allotment Celtic 2-1   at Croft Park, Blyth Spartans FC

NORTHUMBERLAND BENEVOLENT BOWL 2001-02
Sponsored by "Brother"
(12 entries)   (FOUNDED 1975-76)

LAST SEASON'S FINAL: North Shields v Amble Vikings 2-1
MOST WINS: Morpeth Town 2   Stobswood Welfare 2

FIRST ROUND

Seaton Delaval Ams	v	N Procter & Gamble	1-4	Cullercoats	v Cowgate Sports	3-2
Spittal Rovers	v	Heaton Stannington	2-3	N Benfield Saints	v Amble United	4-1

SECOND ROUND

N'castle Benfield Sts	v	Walker Fosse	8-1	Wark	v Cullercoats	5-0
Percy Main Amateurs v	Heaton Stan'ton	3p5, 3*3	Newcastle P & G	v Newbiggin CW	3-1

SEMI-FINALS

Heaton Stannington	v	Wark	1-0	N'castle Benfield Sts	v Procter & Gamble	4-1

FINAL

Heaton Stannington v Newcastle Benfield Sts 0-3   at Whitley Park, Benfield

Ian Archbold in the West Allotment goal prepares to save from Bedlington's Jonathon Milner. The Terriers won the Northumberland Senior Cup final tie 2-1 in extra time. Photo: Graham Brown

Dean Gibb of Bedlington Terriers fires wide during an early attack against West Allotment Celtic in the Northumberland Senior Cup final. Photo: Graham Brown

NOTTINGHAMSHIRE F.A. LIMITED

Tel: 0115 941 8954   Fax: 0115 941 5254   Email: NOTTSFA@aol.com

7 Clarendon Street, Nottingham NG1 5HS

Secretary: Mike Kilbee

Executives (Responsibility)	Tom Goodwin (Referees Administration Officer)
	Helen Bennett (Discipline Secretary)

Number of Affiliated Clubs   Senior: 630   U.18:   193   **President:** John Waterall

Number of Affiliated Leagues: Senior: 9   Junior: 4   **Chairman:** David Woolrich

County Representative Teams: U18

Inter County Competitions: FA County Youth Cup, East Midlands Youth Combination

NOTTINGHAMSHIRE SENIOR CUP 2001-02

(34 entries)   (FOUNDED 1883-84)

LAST SEASON'S FINAL: Hucknall Town v Gedling Town   1-0

MOST WINS: Nottingham Forest 17   Sutton Town 17   Notts County 11

FIRST ROUND

Linby C W	v	Hucknall Rolls	2-4	Woodhouse Athletic	v	Kimberley M W	1-3
Clifton	v	Selston	4*2	Pelican	v	Ollerton Town	2-3
Keyworth United	v	North Notts	1-2	Retford Town	v	Kimberley Town	3-0
Collingham	v	Retford United	2-0	Clipstone Welfare	v	Rainworth M W	2-0
Boots Athletic	v	Greenwood Meadows	2-1	Dunkirk	v	Blidworth Welfare	1-4
Radford	v	Southwell City	1-5	Cotgrave C W Utd	v	Attenborough	0-2

SECOND ROUND

Retford Town	v	Hucknall Rolls	0-1	Southwell City	v	Attenborough	3-1
Clipstone Welfare	v	Blidworth M W	2-1	Boots Athletic	v	North Notts	2-1
Kimberley M W	v	Collingham	4-3	Ollerton Town	v	Clifton	3-1

THIRD ROUND

Wollaton	v	Gedling Town	2-3	Welbeck M W	v	Notts Police	2-0
Clipstone Welfare	v	Eastwood Town	0-2	Hucknall Town	v	Teversal	4V1
Newark Flowserve	v	Southwell City	1-3	Ollerton Town	v	Hucknall Rolls	0-1
Kimberley M W	v	Boots Athletic	1-2	Sneinton	v	Arnold Town	4-1

Hucknall Town played an ineligible player, Teversal reinstated

FOURTH ROUND

Hucknall Rolls	v	Gedling Town	1-4	Southwell City	v	Eastwood Town	3p0, 1*1
Boots Athletic	v	Welbeck M W	4-1	Sneinton	v	Teversal	4-2

SEMI-FINALS

Sneinton	v	Gedling Town	5p6 1*1	Southwell City	v	Boots Athletic	1-0

FINAL

SOUTHWELL CITY	v	GEDLING TOWN	0-1	at Meadow Lane, Notts County FC

Tel: 01993 778586 Fax: 01993 772191 Email: Ian.Mason@oxfordshirefa.com
PO Box 62, Witney, Oxon OX28 1HA

Secretary:	Ian Mason
Executives (Responsibility)	Ted Mitchell (Football Development)
	Trevor Spindler (Coaching Exams/Courses)
	Paul Faulkner (Referees) Liz Verrall (Womens Football)

Number of Affiliated Clubs 320
Number of Affiliated Leagues: 12
County Representative Teams: Under 18, Under 16
Inter County Competitions: Under 18, Under 16

President: J Webb
Chairman: T Williams

OXFORDSHIRE SENIOR CUP 2001-02
(34 entries) (FOUNDED 1884-85)

LAST SEASON'S FINAL: Thame United v Banbury United 3-1

MOST WINS: Oxford City 31   Witney Town 9   Oxford United 8

FIRST ROUND

Kidlington	v	Middle Barton	1-2	Goring United	v	Charlton United	2-3
Adderbury Park	v	Witney Academy	5-1	Garsington	v	Stoke Row	5-2
Eynsham	v	Ardley United	1-7	Clanfield 1985	v	Broughton & N N'ton	2-0
Chinnor	v	Yarnton	11-2	Bicester Town	v	Ruscote Sports	3-1
Marston Saints	v	Carterton Town	0-3	Newtown Henley	v	Checkendon Sports	0-2
Headington Amateurs	v	Chipping Norton Town	0-2	Easington Sports	v	Hook Norton	1-2
Worcester & Ble'ton	v	Peppard	0-3	Sonning Common	v	Highfield Old Boys	0-8

SECOND ROUND

Chinnor	v	Ardley United	0-4	Henley Town	v	Middle Barton	1-2
Peppard	v	Bicester Town	2-4	Garsington	v	Highfield Old Boys	0-1
Charlton United	v	Carterton Yown	0-5	Quarry Nomads	v	Adderbury Park	3-2
Clanfield	v	Hook Norton	0-3	Checkendon Sports	v	Chipping Norton Town	0-2

THIRD ROUND

Carterton Town	v	Ardley United	3-1	Hook Norton	v	Chipping Norton Town	3-2
Quarry Nomads	v	Bicester Town	1-0	Middle Barton	v	Highfield Old Boys	7-0

QUARTER-FINALS

Banbury United	v	Oxford City	0-1	Quarry Nomads	v	Carterton Town	1-8
Thame United	v	Hook Norton	8-2	North Leigh	v	Middle Barton	5-0

SEMI-FINALS

Carterton Town	v	Thame United	0-2	at Oxford City. Att: 165
North Leigh	v	Oxford City	2-0	at Carterton Town FC. Att: 220

FINAL

NORTH LEIGH	v	THAME UNITED	3-4	at Grenoble Road, Oxford United FC

SHEFFIELD & HALLAMSHIRE F.A.

Tel: 0114 241 4999   Fax: 0114 241 4990
Clegg House, 69 Cornish Place, Cornish Street, Shalesmoor, Sheffield S6 3AF
Secretary & Press Officer: J P Hope-Gill
Executives (Responsibility)   John Warnock (Coaching Exams/Courses)
                                    Peter Jackson (Referees)   Julie Callaghan (Womens Football)
                                    Brian Peck (Development Officer)

Number of Affiliated Clubs	Senior:	888	U.18:	243	**President:** C L Milner
Number of Affiliated Leagues:	Senior:	17	Junior:	7	**Chairman:** M Matthews

County Representative Teams: Under 18, Under 16 Girls
Inter County Competitions: Midlands Youth Combination, FA County Youth Cup

SHEFFIELD & HALLAMSHIRE SENIOR CUP 2001-02
(51 entries)   (FOUNDED 1876-77)

LAST SEASON'S FINAL: Doncaster Rovers v Emley 2-1

SECOND QUALIFYING ROUND (No First Round)

The Wetherby	v	Dinnington Town @DT	2-3	Grapes Roy Hancock	v	The Forum	3-1
Parramore Sports	v	Avesta Polarit Sports	3-0	Wickersley	v	NCB Maltby MW	3-1
Ecclesfield Red Rose	v	Swinton Athletic	3-2	Sheffield Centralians	v	Harworth C Inst	3-1
Hemsworth M W	v	Yorkshire Main	9-0	Athersley Recreation	v	Hollinsend Amateurs	3-1
HSBC Shef. Bankers	v	Phoenix	2-1	Davy	v	South Kirkby Colliery	3-2
Georgia Pacific	v	Frecheville C A	3-1	Mexborough Tn Ath	v	Oughtibridge WM	1-3
Wombwell Main WMC	v	Hare&Hounds	1*1, 1-2	Mexborough Main St	v	Treeton Welfare	M W-O
Penistone Church	v	High Green Villa	1-0	Bentley Colliery	v	Caribbean Sports	3-2
Groves Social	v	Renishaw Juniors	0-2	Elm Tree	v	Kiveton Park	3-2
Sheffield Lane Top	v	Thorpe Hesley	2-3				

FIRST ROUND

Athersley Recreation	v	Stocksbridge Pk Steel	1-3	Penistone Church	v	Mexborough Mn St	0-2
Worksop Town	v	Parkgate	0-1	Dinnington Town	v	Doncaster Rvrs @DR	0-6
Swinton Athletic	v	Maltby Main	2-1	Emley	v	Davy	2-1
Sheffield	v	Frickley Athletic	1-3	Bentley Colliery	v	Parramore Sports	1-4
Worsbrough Bridge	v	Hare&Hnds	2*2, 2p4, 1*1	Hemsworth M W	v	HSBC Sheffield	1-2
Hallam	v	Rossington Main	7-0	Oughtibridge	v	Grapes Roy Hancock	1-2
Denaby United	v	Brodsworth Welfare	2-1	Wickersley	v	Renishaw Juniors	1*1, 0-2
Thorpe Hesley	v	Sheffield Centralians	1-2	Elm Tree	v	Gorgia Pacific	2-1

SECOND ROUND PROPER

Renishaw Juniors	v	Sheffield Centralians	4-0	Doncaster Rovers	v	Hallam	2-0
Emley	v	Parramore Sports	1-0	Denaby United	v	Swinton Athletic	5*2
Stocksbridge P S	v	Grapes Roy Hancock	7-1	Elm Tree	v	Hare & Hounds	2-0
HSBC Sheffield	v	Parkgate	1-3	Mexborough Mn St	v	Frickley Athletic @F	2-3

THIRD ROUND

Stocksbridge Pk Stls	v	Frickley Athletic	0-1	Emley	v	Elm Tree	2-0
Parkgate	v	Doncaster Rovers	0-3	Denaby United	v	Renishaw Juniors	1-2

SEMI-FINALS

Emley	v	Renishaw Juniors	4-1	Frickley Athletic	v	Doncaster Rovers	1-3

FINAL

DONCASTER RVRS v   EMLEY   3-0   at Hillsborough, Sheffield Wednesday FC. Att: 971

SHROPSHIRE F.A.

Tel: 01743 362769   Fax: 01743 240474
Gay Meadow, Abbey Foregate, Shrewsbury, Shropshire SY2 6AB
Secretary: David Rowe   **Press Officer:** Neil Sambrook
Football Development Officer: Mick Murphy
                                   Eric Adams (Referees)
Number of Affiliated Clubs   Senior: 330   U.18:   95
Number of Affiliated Leagues: Senior: 9   Junior: 5
County Representative Teams: U18, Womens, U16
Inter County Competitions: FA County Youth, Midland County Youth, Gilbert Trophy

President: A W Brett
Chairman: S T Farmer

SHROPSHIRE COUNTY CUP 2001-02

(23 entries)

LAST SEASON'S FINAL: Little Drayton v Star   4p3, 0*0

FIRST ROUND

Clee Hill United	v	Ludlow Town	2-1	Hanwood United	v	Wem Town	4-1
Belvidere	v	Meole Brace	3-4	Little Drayton Rngrs	v	Oakengates Town	9-0
Bridgnorth Town Res	v	Whitchurch Alport	WA W-O	Weston Rhyn	v	Wrockwardine Wood	1-4
Morda United	v	Brosley Juniors	1-0				

SECOND ROUND

Little Drayton Rngrs	v	Craven Arms	5-0	Belle Vue OB	v	Star	1-3
Morda United	v	Meole Brace	2-0	Hanwood United	v	Shawbury United	1-2
Broseley Town	v	W'dine Wood	WW W-O	Tibberton United	v	Newport Town	1-4
Clee Hill United	v	Whitchurch Alport	1-2	Wellington Amateurs	v	Haughmond	1-2

THIRD ROUND

Little Drayton Rngrs	v	Haughmond	3-1	Newport Town	v	Shawbury United	1-0
Star	v	W'dine Wood	8p9, 2*2	Whitchurch Alport	v	Morda United	3-0

SEMI-FINALS

Newport Town	v	Wrockwardine Wood	2-0	Whitchurch Alport	v	Little Drayton Rngrs	0-5

FINAL

Little Drayton Rngrs	v	Newport Town	5-1	at Gay Meadow, Shrewsbury Town FC

Tel: 01761 410280   Fax: 01761 410477   Email: info@somersetfa.com

30 North Road, Midsomer Norton, Bath, Somerset BA3 2QD

Secretary: Mrs H Marchment

Executives (Responsibility)   I Tincknell (Coaching Courses/Exams)

J H Day (Referees), K Hodges (Football Development)

Number of Affiliated Clubs   Senior: 78   U.18:   407   **President:** F P Hillier

Number of Affiliated Leagues: Senior: 1   Junior: 22   **Chairman:** A J Hobbs

County Representative Teams: Senior, U18, Womens

Inter County Competitions: FA County Youth, South West Counties Championship (Senior, Youth & Womens)

SOMERSET PREMIER CUP 2001-02

(24 entries)   (FOUNDED 1948-49)

LAST SEASON'S FINAL: Clevedon Town   v   Bath Odd Down   1-0

MOST WINS: Bath City   17   Yeovil Town   15   Bristol City   6

FIRST ROUND

Backwell United	v	Paulton Rovers	1-3		Keynsham Town	v	Chard Town	2-1
Bristol City	v	Bristol Manor Farm	3-0		Bitton	v	Wellington	1-4
Yeovil Town	v	Minehead Town	3-0		Brislington	v	Frome Town	3-1
Taunton Town	v	Bishop Sutton	3-2		Odd Down Bath	v	Mangotsfield United	0-1

SECOND ROUND

Welton Rovers	v	Clevedon Town	1-4		Yeovil Town	v	Street	0-1
Bristol City	v	Bath City	0-1		Team Bath	v	Shepton Mallet	3-0
Bridgwater Town	v	Weston super Mare	0-2		Taunton Town	v	Paulton Rovers	2-1
Wellington	v	Keynsham Town	1-4		Brislington	v	Mangotsfield United	1-2

THIRD ROUND

Clevedon Town	v	Keynsham Town	3-0		Weston super Mare	v	Team Bath	2*3
Taunton Town	v	Street	1-2		Bath City	v	Mangotsfield United	3-2

SEMI-FINALS

Street	v	Team Bath	0-1		Clevedon Town	v	Bath City	1-0

FINAL

TEAM BATH	v	CLEVEDON TOWN	1-2	at Athletic Ground, Winterfield Rd, Paulton Rovers FC

SOMERSET SENIOR CUP 2001-02
(53 entries)   (FOUNDED 1895-96)

LAST SEASON'S FINAL: Nailsea United v Cleeve West Town   2-1 aet

MOST WINS: Paulton Rovers 12   Radstock Town 12   Welton Rovers 9

FIRST ROUND

Weston s Mare Res	v	Banwell	1-2	Westland Sports	v	Clandown	3-0
Shepton Mallet Res	v	Long Sutton	3p4, 2*2	Peasedown Athletic	v	Welton Rvrs Rs	3p4, 2*2
Nailsea Town	v	Wells City	0-4	Cleeve Town Res	v	Weston St Johns	0-2
Hengrove Athletic	v	Larkhall Athletic	3-5	Glastonbury	v	Fry Club	1*0
Imperial	v	Kewstoke	5-2	Westland United	v	Clevedon United	1-3
Robinsons	v	Teyfont Athletic	4-2	Bridgwater Town	v	Nailsea United	6-2
Bristol Spartak	v	First Tower United	1-6	Cheddar	v	Cutters Friday (Bristol)	1-2
Clutton	v	Stockwood Green	1-2	Odd Down Bath Res	v	Brislington Res	0-1
Castle Cary	v	Burnham United	4-2	Watchet Town	v	Saltford	WT W-0
Crewkerne	v	Blackbrook	6-0	Wrington-Redhill	v	St George Easton in G	1-0
Radstock Town	v	Winscombe	4*3				

SECOND ROUND

Bishop Sutton	v	Keynsham Town Res	0-3	Congresbury	v	Castle Cary	1-2
Weston St Johns	v	Stockwood Green	4*3	Wells City	v	Bridgwater Town Res	1-0
Brislington Res	v	Radstock Town	0-1	Frome Collegians	v	Larkhall Athletic	1-3
Welton Rovers Res	v	Robinsons	2-4	Banwell	v	Ilminster Town	2-4
Watchet Town	v	Wrington Redhill	3-1	Crewkerne	v	Clevedon United	3-2
Glastonbury	v	First Tower United	1-2	Portishead	v	Long Sutton (Som'ns)	2-1
Timsbury Athletic	v	Imperial	2-3	Dundry Athletic	v	Westland Sports	1-4
Street	v	Paulton Rovers Res	3-4	Backwell United	v	Cutters Friday (Bristol)	4-0

THIRD ROUND

Paulton Rovers Res	v	Crewkerne	0-3	Brislington	v	Robinsons	4-1
Backwell United Res	v	Westland Sports	3*1	Watchet Town	v	Portishead	3-1
Weston St Johns	v	Wells City	1-3	First Tower United	v	Imperial	0-0, 5-0
Castle Cary	v	Larkhall Athletic	6-0	Ilminster Town	v	Keynsham Town Res	3-1

FOURTH ROUND

Backwell United Res	v	Castle Cary	4-1	Watchet Town	v	Brislington Res	2-1
Crewkerne	v	First Tower Utd	7p6, 4*4	Wells City	v	Ilminster Town	5-2

SEMI-FINALS

Backwell United Res	v	Wells City	0-1	Watchet Town	v	Crewkerne	4*1

FINAL

WATCHET TOWN	v	WELLS CITY	3*1	at Athletic Ground, Winterfield Rd, Paulton Rovers FC

STAFFORDSHIRE F.A.

Tel: 01785 256994   Fax: 01785 224334
County Showground, Weston Road, Stafford ST18 0BD

Secretary:	Brian Adshead
Executives (Responsibility)	Andy Weston (Football Development Officer)
	Nick Broad (Referees)
	Adam Evans (Competitions)

Number of Affiliated Clubs   Senior: 567   U18:   553
Number of Affiliated Leagues: Senior: 15   U18:   14
County Representative Teams: U 18 Boys, U 16 Boys, Ladies, U 16 Girls

President: P Savage
Chairman: P Hodgkinson

STAFFORDSHIRE SENIOR CHALLENGE CUP 2001-02
(17 entries)   (FOUNDED 1891-92)

LAST SEASON'S FINAL: Port Vale v Rocester 6-1

MOST WINS: Stoke City 18   Aston Villa 16   West Bromwich Albion 13

FIRST ROUND
Rushall Olympic	v	Stoke City	1-0

SECOND ROUND
Chasetown	v	Hednesford Town	2-2, 1-6		Pelsall Villa	v	Tamworth	2*2, 0-8
Kidsgrove Athletic	v	Stafford Rngrs @SR	0-15		Leek Town	v	Rushall Olympic	0-3
Newcastle Town	v	Port Vale	1-0		Shifnal Town	v	Rocester	0-2
Knypersley Victoria	v	Stafford Town	0-3		Bloxwich United	v	Bilston Town	4-1

THIRD ROUND
Stafford Rangers	v	Rocester	4-1		Tamworth	v	Bloxwich United	T W-O
Stafford Town	v	Newcastle Town	1-5		Hednesford Town	v	Rushall Olympic	1-1 0-1

SEMI-FINALS
Newcastle Town	v	Stafford Rangers	1-0		Tamworth	v	Rushall Olympic	4-2

FINAL First Leg
TAMWORTH v NEWCASTLE TOWN 3-1   at The Lamb Ground, Kettlebrook, Tamworth.

FINAL Second Leg
NEWCASTLE TOWN v TAMWORTH 0-0 = 1-3   at Lyme Valley, Parkway Stadium, Newcastle U Lyme.

SUFFOLK F.A.

Tel: 01473 407290   Fax: 01473 407291   Email: suffolkfa.office@dial.pipex.com
Felaw Maltings, 44 Felaw Street, Ipswich, Suffolk IP2 8SJ
Secretary: Martin Head
Executives (Responsibility)   Will Cook (Development Officer)
                                         Barry Felgate (Referees)
Number of Affiliated Clubs   Senior: 450   U.18:   200   **President:** Gordon Blake
Number of Affiliated Leagues: Senior: 13   Junior: 7   **Chairman:** George Whight
County Representative Teams: U18, U16, Womens
Inter County Competitions: All in East Anglian Counties Championships

SUFFOLK PREMIER CUP 2001-02
(9 entries) (FOUNDED 1958-59)
LAST SEASON'S FINAL: Lowestoft Town v Sudbury 4-3
MOST WINS: Sudbury Town 13   Bury Town 10   Lowestoft Town 6

PRELIMINARY ROUND
Mildenhall Town	v	Sudbury	0-5			

SECOND ROUND
Ipswich Wanderers	v	Felixstowe & Walton U	2-3	Woodbridge Town	v	Bury Town 4p5, 3*3
Stowmarket Town	v	Newmarket Town	5*4	Lowestoft Town	v	Sudbury 4-5

SEMI-FINALS
Sudbury	v	Stowmarket Tn	6p5, 0*0	Bury Town	v	Felixstowe & Walton U 0-3

FINAL
Felixstowe & Walton U v	Sudbury	1-3	at Millfield, Hadleigh United FC. Att: 425

SUFFOLK SENIOR CUP 2001-02
(33 entries) (FOUNDED 1885-86)
LAST SEASON'S FINAL: Kirkley v Ipswich Athletic 3-1
MOST WINS: Ipswich Town 16   Lowestoft Town 10   Stowmarket Town 8

PRELIMINARY ROUND
Sudbury Res	v	Whitton United	4*3

FIRST ROUND
Stanton	v	Walsham le Willows	0-2	Long Melford	v	Stowmarket Town Rs 5*3
Capel Plough	v	East Bergholt United	2-1	Brandon Town	v	Brantham Athletic 2-4
Cornard United	v	Melton St Audreys	1-3	Felixstowe & W U Rs v	Bungay Town 4-1
Sudbury Res	v	Sudbury Athletic	5-0	Lowestoft Town Res	v	Ransomes Sports 3*2
Haverhill Rovers	v	Woodbridge Athletic	3-0	Beccles Town	v	Haughley United 2-3
Ashlea	v	Leiston St Margarets	2-1	Hadleigh United	v	Needham Market 0-1
Achilles	v	Grundisburgh	1-2	Kirkley	v	Ipswich Athletic 4-1
Bramford United	v	Old Newton United	2-4	Stonham Aspal	v	Leiston 1-5

SECOND ROUND
Haverhill Rovers	v	Capel Plough	6-1	Sudbury Res	v	Felixstowe & W Utd R 4-0
Old Newton United	v	Ashlea	0-1	Leiston	v	Needham Market 3-1
Lowestoft Town Res	v	Walsham Le Willows	1-7	Melton St Audreys	v	Brantham Athletic 5-1
Kirkley	v	Long Melford	1*0	Grundisburgh	v	Haughley United 6-0

QUARTER-FINALS
Ashlea	v	Leiston	3*4	Haverhill Rovers	v	Melton St Audreys 4-2
Sudbury Res	v	Walsham Le Willows	3-1	Grundisburgh	v	Kirkley 1-3

SEMI-FINALS
Sudbury Res	v	Kirkley	0-5	Haverhill Rovers	v	Leiston 3-2

FINAL
HAVERHILL RVRS	v	KIRKLEY	3-4	at Portman Road, Ipswich Town FC. Att: 822

SURREY F.A.

Tel: 01372 373543   Fax: 01372 361310
Website: www.surreyfa.co.uk   Email: info@surreyfa.com
321 Kingston Road, Leatherhead, Surrey KT22 7TU
Secretary: Ray Ward
Executives (Responsibility)   Larry May (Football Development Officer)
                                 Phil Whatling (Referees)   Peter Adams (Womens Football)
                                 Michelle Jeffcoate (Women's Football Development Officer)
Number of Affiliated Clubs   Senior: 33   **President:** A P Adams
Number of Affiliated Leagues: Senior: 2   Junior: 20   **Chairman:** R S Lewis
County Representative Teams: Under 18, Womens
Inter County Competitions: Home Counties Womens Competition, FA County Youth Cup

SURREY SENIOR CUP 2001-02
(33 entries)   (FOUNDED 1882-83)

LAST SEASON'S FINAL: Crystal Palace   v   Tooting & Mitcham Utd   3-1

FIRST ROUND

Merstham	v	Camberley Town	4p1, 1*1	Corinthian Casuals	v	Dorking	1*3
Walton Casuals	v	Chessington Utd	5p4, 2*2	Farnham Town	v	Redhill	1-3
Banstead Athletic	v	Raynes Park Vale	6-0				

SECOND ROUND

Westfield	v	Cobham	3-2	Epsom & Ewell	v	Redhill	3-0
Godalming & G'ford	v	Molesey	1-4	Metropolitan Police	v	Ash United	1-3
Dorking	v	Banstead Athletic	1-2	Egham Town	v	Chessington & Hook U	4*2
Walton Casuals	v	Chipstead	2-0	Cranleigh	v	Merstham	0-9

THIRD ROUND

Walton Casuals	v	Molesey	1-3	Banstead Athletic	v	Merstham	4-0
Westfield	v	Egham Town	1-0	Ash United	v	Epsom & Ewell	2*4

FOURTH ROUND

Banstead Athletic	v	Woking @W	1-3	Kingstonian	v	Walton & Hersham	1-2
Dulwich Hamlet	v	Tooting & Mitcham U	4*5	Whyteleafe	v	Epsom & Ewell	1-3
Molesey	v	Croydon	0-2	Sutton United	v	Westfield	2-0
Leatherhead	v	Crystal Palace Res	1-3	Chertsey Town	v	Carshalton Athletic	2-0

QUARTER-FINALS

Sutton United	v	Tooting & Mitcham United	0-3	Epsom & Ewell	v	Crystal Palace Res	1-3
Woking	v	Chertsey Town	9-1	Croydon	v	Walton & Hersham	4-2

SEMI-FINALS

Woking	v	Tooting & Mitcham U	3-1	Crystal Palace	v	Croydon @ Croydon	3-1

FINAL

CRYSTAL PALACE	v	WOKING	3-0	at Imber Court, Metropolitan Police FC

SUSSEX F.A.

Tel: 01903 753547 Fax: 01903 761608
Website: sussex-fa.org E-mail: sussexfa@dial.pipex.co.uk
Culver Road, Lancing, West Sussex BN15 9AX

Chief Executive	Ken Benham
Executives (Responsibility)	L Thompson (Coaching Admin)
	M Bodenham (Head of Refereeing)
	H Millington (Football Development Officer)

Number of Affiliated Clubs Senior: 951   Youth: 246
Number of Affiliated Leagues: Senior: 18   Junior: 10
County Representative Teams: Senior, Inter, U18, U16, Womens, U18
Inter County Competitions: FA County Youth, Home Counties Youth U16's, U18's
South West Counties Senior, Womens U18's, Southern Counties Intermediate

President: John Davey
Chairman: Ron Pavey

Yellow Jersey SUSSEX SENIOR CUP 2001-02
(46 entries)   (FOUNDED 1882-83)

LAST SEASON'S FINAL: Lewes v Bognor Regis Town 2-1 aet

MOST WINS: Worthing 20   Eastbourne Town 12   Southwick 10

FIRST ROUND
Hailsham Town	v	East Grinstead Town	2-0	Shoreham	v	Oakwood	3-0
Rye & Iden United	v	Crawley Down	4-3	East Preston	v	Ringmer	1-3
Storrington	v	Lancing	0-2	Bosham	v	Oving	6-1
Seaford	v	Westfield	2-5	Arundel	v	Littlehampton Town	2-0
Worthing United	v	Wealden	2-1	Whitehawk	v	Mile Oak	2-0
Broadbridge Heath	v	Shinewater Assoc'n	4*3	Saltdean United	v	Hassocks	3*5
Southwick	v	Peacehaven & Tels.	2-3	Eastbourne United	v	Eastbourne Town	2-1

SECOND ROUND
Burgess Hill Town	v	Shoreham	4-1	St Leonards	v	Eastbourne Boro	2-2, 0-2
Chichester City Utd	v	Eastboune United	1-3	Broadbridge Heath	v	Selsey	0-1
Worthing United	v	Hailsham Town	0-1	Horsham	v	Bosham	10-1
Bognor Regis Town	v	Brighton & Hove Albion	0-3	Hassocks	v	Peacehaven & Tels.	1-0
Arundel	v	Horsham YMCA	5-4	Hastings Town	v	Lancing	8-0
Ringmer	v	Crawley Town	0-1	Rye & Iden United	v	Pagham	2-1
Westfield	v	Worthing	0-3	Lewes	v	Sidlesham	1-0
Wick	v	Whitehawk	1*1, 3-0	Three Bridges	v	Sidley United	0-1

THIRD ROUND
Burgess Hill Town	v	Eastbourne Borough	0-1	Eastbourne United	v	Selsey	0*0, 2*1
Hailsham Town	v	Horsham	0-2	Brighton & Hove Alb.	v	Hassocks @H	8-1
Arundel	v	Hastings Town	1-6	Crawley Town	v	Rye & Iden United	4-0
Worthing	v	Lewes	1-3	Wick	v	Sidley United	1-0

QUARTER-FINALS
Eastbourne Borough	v	Eastbourne U	2A0f/f 1-0	Horsham	v	Brighton & Hove Albion	0-2
Hastings Town	v	Crawley Town	2-0	Lewes	v	Wick	3-1

SEMI-FINALS
Eastbourne Borough	v	Brighton&Hove Albion	2-0	Hastings Town	v	Lewes	1*2

FINAL
Eastbourne Borough	v	Lewes	2-1	at Langney Sports Club, Eastbourne. Att: 1558

Sussex Senior Cup Final

Opposite page:
Top: Lewes line up before the match.
Centre: Match officials and captains before kickoff at Priory Lane.
Bottom:Captains and mascots lead Eastbourne Borough and Lewes on to the pitch.

This page:
Top: Lewes' Lee Newman (right) about to be challenged by Eastbourne Borough's Darren Baker.
Centre: Eastbourne Borough celebrate with the Sussex Senior Cup after beating Lewes 2-1 at Priory Lane.
Bottom: Darren Pearce, the Eastbourne Borough captain, with the Sussex Senior Cup.

Photos: Roger Turner

WESTMORLAND F.A.

Tel: 01539 730946   Fax: 01539 730946   E-mail: westfa@dial.pipex.com
Unit 1, Angel Court, 21 Highgate, Kendal, Cumbria LA9 4DA

Executive Officer: P G Ducksbury
Executives (Responsibility) County Office (Football Development, County Coaching Centre, Coaching Courses, Girls/Womens Football, Referees)

Number of Affiliated Clubs Senior: 61   U.18:   24   **President:** J B Fleming
Number of Affiliated Leagues: Senior: 3   Junior: 1   **Chairman:** G Aplin
County Representative Teams: Senior, U18, U16, U14, U12
Inter County Competitions: FA County Youth, Association of Northern Counties Senior & Youth Competitions

WESTMORLAND CAR SALES SENIOR CUP 2001-02

(FOUNDED 1896-97)

(23 entries)

HOLDERS: Appleby

MOST WINS: Corinthians 14   Netherfield 12   Burneside 7   Windermere 7

FIRST ROUND

Shap	v	Lunesdale United	2-5	Sedbergh Wanderers	v	Esthwaite Vale U	SW W-O
Wetheriggs United	v	Kendal County	0-1	Dent	v	Endmoor KGR	2-3
Kendal Town	v	Victoria Sports Club	4-2	Keswick	v	Appleby	@ A 4-0
Corinthians	v	Ambleside United	4-1				

SECOND ROUND

Coniston	v	Arnside	3-2	Milnthorpe Corinths	v	Carvetii United	8-1
Kendal Celtic	v	Greystoke	0-5	Kendal County	v	Keswick	4-0
Kirkby Lonsdale	v	Burneside	4-2	Lunesdale United	v	Sedbergh Wanderers	1-3
Staveley United	v	Endmoor KGR	2-0	Windermere S C	v	Kendal Town	0-2

THIRD ROUND

Coniston	v	Sedbergh Wanderers	1-2	Corinthians	v	Kirkby Lonsdale	2-0
Kendal County	v	Staveley United	1-2	Greystoke	v	Kendal Town @KT	0-3

SEMI-FINALS

Milnthorpe Corinths	v	Sedburgh Wanderers	3-2	Kendal Town	v	Staveley United	1-0

FINAL

Kendal Town	v	Milnthorpe Corinths	1-3	at Parkside Road, Kendal Town FC

WEST RIDING F.A.

Tel: 01132 821222   Fax: 01132 821525   Email: secretary@NRCFA.com
Fleet Lane, Woodlesford, Leeds LS26 8NX
Secretary & Press Officer: G R Carter
Executives (Responsibility)   Danny Philpott (Football Development Officer)
                                  Julie Chipchase (Womens/Girls Football)

Number of Affiliated Clubs	Senior:	950	U.18:	300
Number of Affiliated Leagues:	Senior:	40	Junior:	12

President: A C Taylor
Chairman: G Pawson

County Representative Teams: Senior, Junior U18, Womens
Inter County Competitions: Association of Northern Counties Senior, Junior U18 & Womens, FA County Youth

WEST RIDING COUNTY CUP 2001-02

(18 entries)   (FOUNDED 1924-25)

LAST SEASON'S FINAL: Farsley Celtic v Ossett Town 3-2 aet

MOST WINS: Goole Town 11   Farsley Celtic 9   Guiseley 5

FIRST ROUND

Goole	v	Armthorpe Welfare	2-0	Eccleshill United	v	Glasshoughton Welfare	0-2

SECOND ROUND

Garforth Town	v	Ossett Town	1-0	Ossett Albion	v	Bradford Park Avenue	3-6
Tadcaster Albion	v	Goole	1*2	Yorkshire Amateurs	v	Guiseley	2-4
Liversedge	v	Selby Town	2-1	Farsley Celtic	v	Glasshoughton Welfare	3-1
Hatfield Main	v	Thackley	0-3	Harrogate Town	v	Harrogate Railway	3-0

THIRD ROUND

Farsley Celtic	v	Thackley	3*1	Liversedge	v	Goole	3-2
Harrogate Town	v	Guiseley	2-	Garforth Town	v	Bradford Park Avenue	1-2

SEMI-FINALS

Farsley Celtic	v	Bradford Park Avenue 1-0	Harrogate Town	v	Liversedge	2-0

FINAL

FARSLEY CELTIC v HARROGATE TOWN 0-4   at West Riding County FA Ground, Leeds. Att: 470

WILTSHIRE F.A.

Tel: 01793 486047 or 525245   Fax: 01793 692699   Email: mikebenson@hotmail.com
18 Covingham Square, Covingham, Swindon, Wilts SN3 5AA

Secretary: Michael Benson
Executives (Responsibility): Ian Whitehouse (Referees)
B V Stephens (Development Officer)
Number of Affiliated Clubs: 502
Number of Affiliated Leagues: 17   **President:** T K Dowty
County Representative Teams: Senior, U21, U18, Womens Senior & U18   **Chairman:** R Gardiner
Inter County Competitions: All levels

WILTSHIRE PREMIER SHIELD 2001-02
(15 entries)   (FOUNDED 1926-27)

LAST SEASON'S FINAL: Salisbury City v Bemerton Heath Harlequins 1-0
MOST WINS: Swindon Town 26   Salisbury City 11   Trowbridge Town 9

FIRST ROUND

Amesbury Town	v	Chippenham Town	0-3	Corsham Town	v	Highworth Town	2-1
Devizes Town	v	Swindon Town	1-4	Downton	v	Westbury United	0-1
Melksham Town	v	Calne Town	4-0	Wootton Bassett T	v	Bemerton Hth Hquins	1-0
Swindon Supermarine	v	Salisbury City	2-1	Warminster Town	bye		

SECOND ROUND

Warminster Town	v	Westbury United	0-2	Wootton Bassett T	v	Swindon Supermarine	2-0
Chippenham Town	v	Melksham Town	5-0	Swindon Town	v	Corsham		2-0

SEMI-FINALS

Swindon Town	v	Wootton Bassett Tn	2-0	Westbury United	v	Chippenham Town	0-1

FINAL

CHIPPENHAM T	v	SWINDON TOWN	4-0	at Hardenhuish Park, Chippenham Tn FC. Att: 1205

WILTSHIRE SENIOR CUP 2001-02
(12 entries)   (FOUNDED 1886-87)

LAST SEASON'S FINAL: Wootton Bassett Town v Shrewton United 2-0
MOST WINS: Devizes Town 14   Swindon Town 10   Chippenham Town 8

FIRST ROUND

Stratton Crosslink	v	Aldbourne	4-1	Wroughton	v	Trowbridge Town	4p3 2*2
Bradford Town	v	Malmesbury Victoria	3*4	Marlborough Town	v	Pewsey Vale	1-8

SECOND ROUND

Biddestone	v	Stratton Crosslink	0-7	Purton	v	Pewsey Vale	0-2
Malmesbury Victoria	v	Cricklade Town	5-0	Wroughton	v	Shrewton United	3-2

SEMI-FINALS

Pewsey Vale	v	Wroughton (9/3)	5-2	Stratton Crosslink	v	Malmesbury Victoria	1-2

FINAL

Malmesbury Victoria	v	Pewsey Vale	1-0	at The Conigre, Melksham Town FC. Att: 165

WORCESTERSHIRE F.A.

Tel: 01905 827137 Fax:01905 798963 Email: secretary@worcs-fa.freeserve.co.uk
Craftsman House, De Salis Drive, Hampton Lovett Ind. Estate, Droitwich, Worcs WR9 0QE

Company Secretary:	Mervyn Leggett	**Treasurer:** Mick Thomson
Executives (Responsibility)	John Lovegrove (Disciplinary Secretary)	
	Andy Norman (Football Development Officer)	
	Julie Leroux (Girls' & Womens' FDO)	
	Bill Allsopp (Referees Co-ordinator)	

Number of Affiliated Clubs Senior: 17 Junior: 243 Youth: 101   **President:** Percy Rushton
Womens & Girls: 18 Small-Sided: 49   **Chairman:** Ken Clifford
Number of Affiliated Leagues: Senior: 7 Junior: 4
County Representative Teams: U18 Youth, U16 Girls'
Inter County Competitions: FA County Youth Cup, Midland Youth Football Championships

---

WORCESTERSHIRE SENIOR CUP 2001-02
(8 entries)   (FOUNDED 1893-94)

LAST SEASON'S FINAL: Moor Green v Evesham United 4-2 aet

FIRST ROUND

Redditch United	v	Solihull Boro	3-3, 0-3	Kidderminster Harr's	v	Stourport Swifts	5-1
Evesham United	v	Halesowen Town	1-1, 0-1	Worcester City	v	Moor Green	2-3

SEMI-FINALS

Kidderminster Harriers	v	Solihull Borough	2*1	Halesowen Town	v	Moor Green	1-1, 0-3

FINAL (TWO LEGS)

Moor Green	v	Kidderminster Harriers	0-2
Kidderminster Harr's	v	Moor Green	0-1	= 2-1 on aggregate

WORCESTERSHIRE SENIOR URN 2001-02
(10 entries)

LAST SEASON'S FINAL: Studley BKL v Malvern Town 2-0

FIRST ROUND

Pegasus Juniors	v	Lye Town	1-0	Pershore Town	v	Bromsgrove Rvrs Rs	0-3

SECOND ROUND

County Sports	v	Studley BKL	0-2	Bromsgrove Rvrs Rs	v	Feckenham	2-4
Malvern Town	v	Alvechurch	3*1	Worcester City Res	v	Pegasus Juniors	4-2

SEMI-FINALS

Studley B K L	v	Malvern Town	3p1, 1*1	Feckenham	v	Worcester City Res	2-0

FINAL

FECKENHAM	v	STUDLEY BKL	2p4, 1*1	at Aggborough, Kidderminster Harriers FC

EAST ANGLIAN CUP 2001-02
(44 entries)

HOLDERS: Clacton Town

FIRST ROUND

Cornard United	v	Thetford Town	4p2, 3*3	Spalding United	v	March Town United	8-1
Holbeach United	v	Chatteris Town	3-0	Royston Town	v	Letchworth	0-1
Hertford Town	v	Hoddesdon Town	4-0	Ware	v	Saffron Walden Town	2-1
Romford	v	Stansted	4-3	Biggleswade Town	v	Biggleswade United	2*1
Kempston Rovers	v	Eynesbury Rovers	1-3	Braintree Town	v	Tiptree Town	2-0
Concord Rangers	v	East Thurrock United	0-1	Harwich & Parkeston	v	Clacton Town	3-2

SECOND ROUND

Wroxham	v	Lowestoft Town	1-2	Cornard United	v	Sudbury	0-5
Spalding United	v	Holbeach United	2*1	Bourne Town	v	Downham Town	5p4, 2*2
Letchworth	v	Hertford Town	HT W-O	Stotfold	v	Bishop's Stortford	2-1
Ware	v	Romford	3-2	Harlow Town	v	Aveley	5-0
BiggleswadeTown	v	Eynesbury Rovers	3-1	Ely City	v	Soham Town Rangers	5-1
Hullbridge Sports	v	Maldon Town	1-2	Braintree Town	v	Halstead Town	4p3, 3*3
Burnham Ramblers	v	Southend Manor	0-2	East Thurrock	v	Basildon United	0-1
Felixstowe & Walton U	v	Ipswich Wanderers	2*1	Harwich&Parkeston	v	Gt Wakering Rovers	

THIRD ROUND Area/Group FINALS

Lowestoft Town	v	Sudbury	4*2	Bourne Town	v	Spalding United	1-2
Stotfold	v	Hertford Town	0-2	Harlow Town	v	Ware	3-1
Ely City	v	Biggleswade Town	5-0	Maldon Town	v	Braintree Town	4-2
Southend Manor	v	Basildon United	3-0	F'xstowe & Walton U	v	Gt Wakering Rovers	2-1

QUARTER-FINALS Proper

Spalding United	v	Hertford Town	1*2	Southend Manor	v	Ely City	3-1
Lowestoft Town	v	Maldon Town	3*4	F'xstowe & Walton U	v	Harlow Town	0-3

SEMI-FINALS

Southend Manor	v	Harlow Town	0-5	Hertford Town	v	Maldon Town	1-3

FINAL

MALDON TOWN	v	HARLOW TOWN	1-2	at Park Drive, Maldon Town FC

CAPITAL FEEDER LEAGUE'S TROPHY 2001-02
Sponsored by Cherry Red Books
(41 entries)

HOLDERS: Tring Athletic

FIRST ROUND

Frimley Green	v	Hartley Wintney	2-5	Feltham	v	Cranleigh	3-1
Oxhey Jets	v	Totternhoe	4-0	Winslow United	v	Wormley Rovers	0-3
Cuffley	v	Tring Athletic	1-8	Netherne Village	v	Sun Postal Sports	2-0
Bedmond Sports	v	Frenford Senior	1-2	Stambridge United	v	Eton Manor	0-1
Pitstone & Ivinghoe	v	Ditton	6p5, 1*1				

SECOND ROUND

Basildon United	v	Tring Athletic	5p4, 3*3	Spelthorne Sports	v	Elliott Star	3*4
White Notley	v	Wormley Rovers	4-1	Frenford Seniors	v	Amersham Town	2-0
Farleigh Rovers	v	Bovingdon	1-5	Virginia Water	v	Sandridge Rovers	1-3
Hartley Wintney	v	Croxley Guild	0-1	Epping	v	Met Police Bushey	2-0
Kent Athletic	v	Feltham	0-1	Caddington	v	Sheerwater	1-4
Netherne Village	v	Enfield Town	1-2	Chipperfield Corinths	v	North Greenford Utd	0-2
London Lions	v	Pitstone & Ivinghoe	2-5	Hatfield Town	v	Eton Manor	0-3
St Peters	v	Stony Stratford Town	2-4	Oxhey Jets	v	Barnston	OJ W-O

THIRD ROUND

Eton Manor	v	Elliott Star	8-2	White Notley	v	Enfield Town	3-4
Frenford Senior	v	Sandridge Rovers	1*2	Sheerwater	v	Oxhey Jets	1-2
Croxley Guild	v	Stony Stratford Town	0*1	Epping	v	Bovingdon	5-2
Pitstone & Ivinghoe	v	Basildon United	1-0	North Greenford Utd	v	Feltham	5-0

FOURTH ROUND

Epping	v	Eton Manor	2-0	Pitstone & Ivinghoe	v	Nth Greenford U	4p3, 3*3
Stony Stratford Town	v	Enfield Town	1*3	Sandridge Rovers	v	Oxhey Jets	2-1

SEMI-FINALS

Epping	v	Enfield Town	1-2	Pitstone & Ivinghoe	v	Sandridge Rovers	5p4, 0*0

FINAL

Enfield Town	v	Pitstone & Ivinghoe	3-1	at Wodson Park, Ware FC. Att: 620

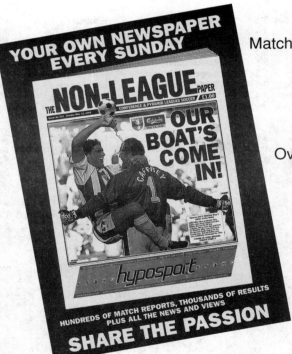

SOUTH WEST COUNTIES CHAMPIONSHIP

President: R F Reeve

Chairman: P S Hough

Hon. Secretary: L P Clements, 24 Holcombe, Whitchurch, Bristol BS14 0AT
Tel: 01275 543171

Overall 2001-02 was a very successful season, despite three games falling foul of the weather. All the matches were played in the true spirit of the game and the match officials were excellent.

For season 2002-03 in the Senior section Dorset have re-entered and Jersey are a new entry into the competition while Hampshire have withdrawn. In the Women's section Cornwall are a new entry, as are Sussex into the U18 section while Dorset have withdrawn. The Youth section sees Guernsey as a new entry with Sussex withdrawn.

SENIOR GROUP A

		1	2	3	4		P	W	D	L	F	A	Pts
1	Army	X	3-1	1-1	6-2		3	2	1	0	10	4	7
2	Cornwall	1-3	X	1-1	4-1		3	1	1	1	6	5	4
3	Gloucester	1-1	1-1	X	0-0		3	0	3	0	2	2	3
4	Somerset	2-6	1-4	0-0	X		3	0	1	2	3	10	1

Winners: Army   Runners up: Cornwall

SENIOR GROUP B

		1	2	3	4	5	P	W	D	L	F	A	Pts
1	Devon	X	5-4	2-2	5-3	0-1	4	1	2	1	12	10	7
2	Guernsey	4-5	X	2-1	1-2	1-1	4	1	1	2	8	9	4
3	Hampshire	2-2	1-2	X	3-1	3-3	4	1	2	4	9	8	5
4	Royal Navy	3-5	2-1	1-3	X	1-4	4	1	0	3	7	13	3
5	Sussex	1-0	1-1	3-3	4-1	X	4	2	2	0	9	5	8

Winners: Sussex   Runners up: Devon

UNDER 21

		1	2	3	4		P	W	D	L	F	A	Pts
1	Army	X	2-3	0-4	0-0		3	0	1	2	2	7	1
2	Dorset	3-2	X	2-3	1-3		3	1	0	2	6	7	3
3	Hampshire	4-0	3-2	X	0-6		3	2	0	1	7	8	6
4	Wiltshire	0-0	3-1	6-0	X		3	2	1	0	9	1	7

Winners: Wiltshire   Runners up: Hampshire

YOUTH GROUP A

		1	2	3	4	5	6	P	W	D	L	F	A	Pts
1	Army	X	X	0-1	2-1	3-4	0-5	4	1	0	3	5	11	3
2	Cornwall	X	X	1-2	6-0	2-2	0-4	4	1	1	2	9	8	4
3	Gloucester	1-0	2-1	X	3-0	2-3	0-4	5	3	0	2	8	8	9
4	Gwent	1-2	0-6	0-3	X	1-2	3-0	5	1	0	4	5	13	3
5	Somerset	4-3	2-2	3-2	2-1	X	0-1	5	3	1	1	11	9	10
6	Wiltshire	5-0	4-0	4-0	0-3	1-0	X	5	4	0	1	14	3	12

Winners: Wiltshire   Runners up: Somerset

YOUTH GROUP B

		1	2	3	4	5	6	P	W	D	L	F	A	Pts
1	Berks/Buck	X	2-0	7-1	0-1	3-2	0-3	5	3	0	2	12	7	9
2	Devon	0-2	X	1-2	2-5	2-1	1-0	5	2	0	3	6	10	6
3	Dorset	1-7	2-1	X	1-2	0-1	1-1	5	1	1	3	5	12	4
4	Hampshire	1-0	5-2	2-1	X	4-3	2-0	5	5	0	0	14	6	15
5	Oxford	2-3	1-2	1-0	3-4	X	1-4	5	1	0	4	8	13	3
6	Sussex	3-0	1-0	1-1	0-2	4-1	X	5	2	1	2	8	5	7

Winners: Hampshire   Runners up: Berks/Bucks

WOMENS GROUP A

	P	W	D	L	F	A	Pts
Gloucester	3	2	1	0	16	4	7
Sussex	3	2	1	0	8	3	7
Army	3	1	0	2	6	3	3
Dorset	3	0	0	3	1	21	0

WOMENS GROUP B

	P	W	D	L	F	A	Pts
Hampshire	2	2	0	0	8	2	6
Devon	3	2	0	1	8	4	6
Somerset	3	1	0	2	2	7	3
Wiltshire	2	0	0	2	2	7	0

WOMENS UNDER 18

	P	W	D	L	F	A	Pts
Devon	4	3	1	0	21	2	10
Gloucester	4	3	0	1	23	3	9
Hampshire	3	1	1	1	12	8	4
Wiltshire	4	1	0	3	5	22	3
Dorset	3	0	0	3	0	25	0

MICK PARRY MEMORIAL TROPHY

FIRST ROUND

Dorset	v	Devon	4p1, 4-4

SECOND ROUND

Army	v	Wiltshire	3-2
Berks/Bucks	v	Guernsey	3-2
Dorset	v	Oxford	2*1
Hampshire	v	Somerset	2-0

SEMI FINAL

Berks/Bucks	v	Dorset	2-1
Hampshire	v	Army	
(not played, tie awarded to Hampshire)			

FINAL

Berks/Bucks	v	Hampshire	2-1

SEASON 2001-02 FINALS RESULTS

SENIOR

Sussex	v	Army	1-0

U21

Hampshire	v	Wiltshire	4-2

YOUTH

Hampshire	v	Wiltshire	4-2

WOMEN

Hampshire	v	Gloucestershire	3-1

U18

Gloucestershire	v	Devon	3-0

Sussex FA after their victory over the Army FA in the South West Counties Championships, score 1-0
Photo: Eric Marsh

Above: Gary Green (Three Bridges) receives the trophy from the competition Chairman Peter Hough.
Below left: Dez Gullie (Burgess Hill) with his winners medal from the South West Championship
Below right: Goalscorer Chris Green (Bognor Regis Town) for the Sussex FA in the final at Aldershot Military Stadium
Photos: Eric Marsh

WIRRAL PROGRAMME CLUB

The non-profit making Club formed in March 1967

Secretary: I.R.W. Runham

3 Tansley Close, Newton, West Kirby, Wirral CH48 9XH   Tel: 0151 625 9554

27th NON-LEAGUE FOOTBALL PROGRAMME OF THE YEAR SURVEY 2001-2002

This season's survey saw 1039 clubs represented, one up on last season, with reserve and youth programmes there were 1099 places, four down on last season.

Again there were many superb programmes with many clubs showing an improvement on last season. It is again pleasing to see clubs issue for the first time or returning after a gap of many seasons. <u>All</u> clubs that issue a programme are to be congratulated, a single sheet is better than nothing. There would be no programmes without the hard work of the editors, plus any helpers they can find, put in to get them out. I'm sure that most supporters and many committee members have no idea of the time and effort needed to produce a programme, so our special thanks go to all these people. Our thanks are also due to all those who sent in programmes for the survey and to those who helped spread the word, the clubs themselves, their supporters, our members, other collectors, the Football Association, the County Associations, the League Secretaries, the Non League Directory, the Non League Paper, the Non League Magazine, the Football Traveller, Welsh Football, Programme Monthly, and those who lent programmes for the survey. Sincere apologies to anyone inadvertently omitted.

Some clubs only issue for a Saturday game, some for just cup games, some change the style, content, price, editor, etc, during the season; some have special connections with printers, etc., often we are not aware of these circumstances. Obviously we can only survey the programmes we receive. Some are from early in the season, others from just before the closing date, most from in between. The results always create a lot of interest with varying comments being expressed; some of these we hear, often second or third hand, but most miss our ears, if you have any comments on the survey please let us know. I am sure the day will never come when there is complete agreement over the results, however the more discussion there is over the survey the better, it will keep programmes to the forefront and hopefully encourage clubs at least to maintain or even improve the standards, better still it may encourage more clubs to issue next season.

The club with the overall winning programme will receive a framed certificate, the winners of each league will also receive a certificate. Please note the programmes have been surveyed, not as many assume voted upon. Marks were awarded to each programme as follows (the maximum marks in each section are given):

Cover 15 (design 10, match details 5),   **Page size** 10,   **Team layout and position within the programme** 10, **Results** 10, **League tables** 10,   **Price** 15,   **Pictures** 15,   **Printing and paper quality** 20, **Frequency of issue** 20, **Value for money** 20 (this takes into account the ratio of adverts to content, the club's league etc),

Contents 245 (other than those listed) taking into account the relevance to the club, its league, environs etc, the size of the print used, the spacing between the lines, the size of the margins, and if all the contents are original or reproduced (from League Bulletins, newspapers, magazines etc).

To gain full marks in the Frequency of issue section we needed to receive programmes from six different current season matches for each team entered (allowances were made if six home games were not played by the closing date and we were informed of this). The minimum entry was one programme.

As many programmes varied from issue to issue all programmes were surveyed, the marks in each section totalled and divided by the number of issues to get the final mark for each section, the marks from each section were then totalled to get the final score.

A new standard of marks is set each season so this season's total should not be compared with those of earlier seasons, as the comparison will almost certainly be inaccurate; a programme identical to last season's will almost certainly have gained a different points total.

We have already received many entries for the Specials section of the survey (for one-offs, big cup ties, friendlies, testimonials, charity matches, first/last matches at a ground, etc), the closing date for receiving these is 31st May 2002. To receive the results, expected by early July, we should appreciate it if you could pleae send a stamped sae. Thank you.

The results of this season's survey are as follows:

Best Non-League Programme Nationally 2001-2002	**1st**	Redhill	**218 points**
	2nd	Hoddesdon Town	206 points
	=3rd	Northwood	205 points

NATIONAL TOP 30: 1 Redhill 218; **2** Hoddesdon Town 206; **3** Northwood 205; **4** Eastbourne Borough 203; **5** Kings Langley 196; **6** Bryntirion A 192; **7** Bath City 190; **8** Lancing 189; **9** Poole Town 184; **10=** Hayes, Coalville Town 183; **12** Morecambe 182; **13** Yateley Green 181; **14** Arlesey Town 179; **15** Clacton Town 177; **16=** Woking, Weymouht, Horsham 176; **19** Atherton LR 173; **20=** Bedford Town, Caersws 172; **22=** Doncaster Rovers, Easington U, Barry Town 171; **25** Sutton United 170; **26** Yeovil Town 169; **27** Prestwich Heys 168; **28=** Dagenham & Redbridge, Felixstowe & Walton United 165; **30=** Bedworth United, Aldershot Town, Worthing 163

INDIVIDUAL LEAGUE RESULTS The first number after the club's name is the number of programmes received - 6 shows six or more different programmes were surveyed or every programme if less than six matches were played and all programmes received, the second number is the total points gained. The leagues are in no particular order.

LEAGUE + No of entries			FIRST		SECOND		THIRD	
Nationwide Conference		22	Hayes	6-183	Morecambe	1-182	Woking	1-176
Dr Martens	Overall	64	Eastbourne Borough	6-203	Bath City	6-190	Weymouth	6-176
	Prem Div	22	Bath City	6-190	Weymouth	6-176	Hinckley United	1-160
	West Div	21	Bedworth United	6-163	Swindon Supermarine	6-160	Mangotsfield United	6-151
	East Div	21	Eastbourne Borough	6-203	Corby Town	6-157	Bashley	6-156
Ryman	Overall	73	Northwood	6-205	Arlesey Town	6-179	Horsham	6-176
	Prem Div	22	Bedford Town	6-172	Sutton United	6-170	Aldershot Town	6-163
	Div 1	20	Northwood	6-205	Worthing	6-163	Bishop's Stortford	6-160
	Div 2	21	Arlesey Town	6-179	Horsham	6-176	Romford	1-142
	Div 3	10	Croydon Athletic	3-138	Epsom & Ewell	6-127	Bracknell Town	1-126
Unibond	Overall	45	Altrincham	6-161	Ossett Town	1-154	Bradford Park Avenue	6-145
	Prem Div	23	Altrincham	6-161	Bradford Park Avenue	6-145	Barrow	6-144
	Div 1	22	Ossett Town	1-154	Ashton United	1-136	Witton Albion	6-135
Minerva	Overall	45	Hoddesdon Town	6-206	Kings Langley	6-190	Somersett Ambury V&E	6-162
Spartan	Prem Div	18	Hoddesdon Town	6-206	Somersett Ambury V&E	6-162	Potters Bar Town	6-159
South Mids	Div 1	20	Kings Langley	6-196	Tring Athletic	6-143	Cockfosters	1-135
	Div 2	7	Old Dunstablians	5-92	Shillington	1-76	Cranfield United	1-70
							Mursley United	1-70
Combined Counties		12	Ash United	6-154	Sandhurst Town	6-136		
					Walton Casuals	6-136		
Kent		12	Cray Wanderers	6-146	Herne Bay	1-141	Deal Town	6-122
Essex Senior		10	Enfield Town	6-154	Burnham Ramblers	1-96	Basildon United	1-89
Wessex		16	Brockenhurst	6-143	Blackfield & Langley	1-124	Fleet Town	6-122
Sussex County	Overall	25	Redhill	6-218	Lancing	6-189	Ifield	6-146
	Div 1	12	Redhill	6-218	Ringmer	1-118	Saltdean United	2-112
	Div 2	8	Lancing	6-189	Oving	6-145	Crawley Down	6-124
	Div 3	5	Ifield	6-146	Upper Beeding	6-103	T.S.C.	1-100
Screwfix Direct Western	Overall	22	Minehead Town	6-133	Taunton Town	1-130	Calne Town	6-117
	Prem Div	9	Taunton Town	1-130	Bridport	1-114	Barnstaple Town	6-101
							Brislington	6-101
	Div 1	13	Minehead Town	6-133	Calne Town	6-117	Frome Town	1-112
Jewson Eastern	Overall	28	Clacton Town	6-177	Felixstowe & Walton Utd	6-165	AFC Sudbury	6-137
	Prem Div	19	Clacton Town	6-177	Felixstowe & Walton Utd	6-165	AFC Sudbury	6-137
	Div 1	9	Leiston	6-129	Wisbech Town Reserves	6-125	Needham Market	6-123
United Co		15	Eynesbury Rovers	6-153	St Neots Town	6-137	Daventry Town	6-122
Cherry Red Records Hellenic	Overall	56	Peppard	6-139	Wootton Bassett Town	5-136	Milton United	6-135
	Prem Div	22	Wootton Bassett Town	5-136	Abingdon United	4-131	Brackley Town	6-122
	West Div	18	Shrivenham	4-118	Winterbourne United	4-108	Purton	6-105
	East Div	16	Peppard	6-139	Milton United	6-135	Finchampstead	6-131
Mid Alliance		18	Stourbridge	6-161	Boldmere St Michael	5-154	Willenhall Town	6-139
North West Counties	Overall	28	Atherton LR	6-173	St Helens Town	6-157	Curzon Ashton	6-154
	Div 1	15	Atherton LR	6-173	St Helens Town	6-157	Curzon Ashton	6-154
	Div 2	13	Bootle	5-136	Daisy Hill	6-119	Padiham	6-112
Albany Northern	Overall	31	Newcastle Blue Star	6-142	Ashington	1-133	Whickham	6-130
	Div 1	18	Newcastle Blue Star	6.142	Ashington	1-133	Durham City	6-128
	Div 2	13	Whickham	6-130	Penrith	1-118	Prudhoe Town	6-111
Northern Counties East	Overall	33	Arnold Town	6-161	Glapwell	1-140	Lincoln Moorlands	6-139
							Pontefract Collieries	6-139
	Prem Div	20	Arnold Town	6-161	Glapwell	1-140	Garforth Town	1-131
	Div 1	13	Lincoln Moorlands	6-139			Bridlington Town	6-135
			Pontefract Collieries	6-139				
Essex Intermediate		11	Great Baddow Reserves	6-104	Bishops Stortford SW	6-102	Great Baddow	1-90
							Manford Way Reserves	1-90
Kent County		9	Crockenhill	6-112	Sheerness East	1-101	Sevenoaks Town	1-97
Hampshire	Overall	12	Poole Town	6-184	Yateley Green	6-181	Colden Common	6-158
	Prem Div	3	Poole Town	6-184	East Cowes Victoria A	6-123	Andover New Street	1-62
	Div 1	4	Yateley Green	6-181	Colden Common	6-158	Micheldever	1-68
	Div 2	5	Alresford Town	6-97	Laverstock & Ford	1-94		
					QK Southampton	1-94		
Dorset Comb		9	Witchampton United	1-88	Blandford United	1-83	Sherborne Town	3-82
Devon		7	Buckland Athletic	6-156	Cullompton Rangers	6-107	Crediton United	6-105
Sth Western		15	Falmouth Town	1-150	Saltash United	1-125	Penzance	1-120
Anglian Comb		6	Blofield United	6-127	Kirkley	4-102	Acle United	1-87
							Wells Town	1-87
Suffolk & Ipswich		6	Woodbridge Athletic	1-97	East Bergholt United	1-96	Claydon	6-86
Essex & Suffolk		6	Long Melford	6-144	Alresford Colne R	4-130	Alresford Colne R Res	2-126

Glos County		5	Highridge United	5-156	Tytherington Rocks	6-147	DRG Stapleton	1-92
Herts Snr Co		15	Oxhey Jets	4-105	Wormley Rangers	5-102	St Peters	2-101
Cornwall Comb		3	St Just	1-59	Hayle	1-52	Helston Athletic	1-50
Cambridgeshire		4	Lakenheath	6-141	Sawston United	1-111	Great Paxton	1-104
Central Mids	Overall	19	Blackwell MW	6-147	Teversal	1-122	Long Eaton United	1-118
	Sup Div	11	Teversal	1-122	Long Eaton United	1-118	South Normanton Athletic	1-114
	Prem Div	8	Blackwell MW	6-147	Retford United	1-114	Barton Town Old Boys	1-102
Express	Overall	13	Star	6-150	Marston Wolves	6-100	Bromyard Town	6-99
& Star							Malvern Town	1-99
	Prem Div	10	Star	6-150	Bromyard Town	6-99		
					Malvern Town	1-99		
	Div 1N	3	Marston Wolves	6-100	Shenstone Pathfinder	1-73	Lucas Sports	1-70
Midland	Overall	42	Loughborough	6-143	West Midlands Police	6-140	Alvechurch	6-136
Combination	Prem Div	22	West Midlands Police	6-140	Alvechurch	6-136	Bolehall Swifts	6-127
	Div 1	11	Loughborough	6-143	Brownhills Town	6-117		
					Rugby Town	6-117		
	Div 2	4	Stockingford AA	3-104	Earlswood Town	1-75	Wilnecote Sports	2-68
	Div 3	5	Wellesbourne	6-112	Droitwich Sports	4-108	Brownhills Town Res	3-96
Leics Senior		10	Coalville Town	6-183	Loughborough Dynamo	6-136	Ibstock Welfare	1-115
Notts Alliance		3	Rainworth MW	6-132	Cotgrave Coll W Utd	1-122		
					Cotgrave Coll W Utd Res	1-122		
Manchester		4	Prestwich Heys	6-168	Dukinfield Town	1-123	Prestwich Heys Reserves	6-122
West Cheshire		5	New Brighton	6-130	New Brighton Reserves	6-108	Manweb	1-76
Northern	Overall	11	Walker Fosse	6-132	Newcastle Benfield Snts	6-96	Carlisle City	1-91
Alliance	Prem Div	5	Newcastle Benfield Snts	6-96	Carlisle City	1-91	West Allotment Celtic	1-86
	Divs 1, 2	6	Walker Fosse	6-132	New Birtley	1-89	Newcastle E End Railway	1-86
West Yorks		3	Nostell MW	1-144	Knaresborough Town	6-122	Beeston	1-54
Other Leagues		40	Easington United	6-171	Colden Common Res	6-157	Hemsworth MW	6-154
Youth Clubs, Schools		8	Askern Spa Town	4-140	Warmley Rangers	6-109	Baginton Guild	6-88
Club Youth XI's		9	Wootton Bassett Town	6-135	Stowmarket Town	6-121	Prestwich Heys U18	5-117
FA YC		20	Sandhurst Town	1-104	Ipswich Wanderers	1-91		
					Potters Bar Town	1-91		
Reserves		27	Colden Common	6-157	Ifield	6-145	Alresford Colne Ran	2-126
Wales	Overall	80	Bryntirion Athletic	3-192	Caersws	6-172	Barry Town	1-171
League of Wales		17	Caersws	6-172	Barry Town	1-171	Flexys Cefn Druids	6-158
Welsh	Overall	22	Tillery	6-157	Newport YMCA	6-129	Ely Rangers	5-106
	Div 1	6	Ely Rangers	5-106	Cardiff Corinthians	6-101	Gwynfi United	5-89
	Div 2	5	Garden Village	1-90	Porth Tywyn Suburbs	1-71	Bettws	1-67
	Div 3	11	Tillery	6-157	Newport YMCA	6-129	Newcastle Emlyn	1-96
Cymru Allnce		10	Gresford Athletic	6-160	Denbigh Town	6-129	Porthmadog	1-124
Welsh Allnce		5	Rhyl Reserves	6-124	Llandudno Junction	1-122	Llanfairpwl	1-98
Welsh Nat Wrexham		4	Chirk AAA	6-145	Mold Alexandra	6-115	Chirk Town	1-92
Sth Wales Amat		5	Bryntirion Athletic	3-192	Cwmaman Institute	6-161	Llangeinor	1-145
Gwent County		12	Tillery Athletic	6-131	Abertillery Bluebirds	1-126	Panteg	1-96
Other Welsh Leagues		5	Cogan Coronation	1-101	Pretatyn Nova	6-96	Penrhyncoch	1-79
Scotland	Overall	42	Tayport	6-129	Edinburgh City	1-125	Forres Thistle	3-121
Highland		5	Buckie Thistle	1-108	Huntly	1-105	Forres Mechanics	1-104
East Scotland		5	Edinburgh City	1-125	Lothian Thistle	1-88	Gala Fairydean	1-82
Central	Overall	13	Pollok	6-107	Renfrew	6-108	Larkhall Thistle	1-94
Region	Prem Div	8	Pollok	6-107	Renfrew	6-108	Larkhall Thistle	1-94
	Divs 1, 2	5	Shettleston	1-87	Ashfield	1-77	Stonehouse Violet	1-68
Ayrshire Region		4	Kilwinning Rangers	6-109	Troon	1-69	Irvine Meadow	1-64
East Region		3	Dunbar United	6-119	Bathgate Thistle	1-71	Livingstone United	1-57
Fife Region		3	Thornton Hibs	1-104	Kelty Hearts	1-81	Steelend Victoria	1-58
Tayside Region		3	Tayport	6-129	Scone Thistle	6-87	Montrose Roselea	1-85
North Region		6	Forres Thistle	3-121	Formantine United	1-64	Lewis United	1-62
Ladies	Overall	62	Stockport Celtic	6-137	Huddersfield Town	6-132	Wolverhampton Wndrs	6-128
FA Premier	Overall	17	Wolverhampton W	6-128	Leeds United	1-114	Barking	1-107
	Nat Div	5	Leeds United	1-114	Brighton & Hove Albion	1-105		
					Sunderland	1-105		
	North Div	8	Wolverhampton W	6-128	Liverpool	3-86		
					Sheffield Wednesday	3-86		
	South Div	4	Barking	1-107	Ipswich Town	1-92	Wimbledon	1-91
Sth East Comb		3	Chelmsford City	6-120	Norwich City Racers	1-110	Chesham United	1-75
Other Ladies Leagues		13	Stockport Celtic	6-137	Huddersfield Town	6-132	Colchester U13	4-113
FA Womens Cup		38	Garswood Saints	1-133			Stockport Celtic	1-131
			West Ham United	1-133				
Sunday	Overall	55	Turnergraphic	6-148	Palace Court	6-119	Holly Lane Delta	1-116
Sunday Leagues		6	Turnergraphic	6-148	Palace Court	6-119	Palace Court Reserves	6-113
FA Sunday Cup		49	Holly Lane Delta	1-116	Theale	1-93	Standens Barn	1-88

The programme of Redhill FC of the Sussex County Football League won the Wirral Programme Survey by a clear twelve point margin and it was an accolade that was thoroughly deserved.

Boasting 68 A4 pages the programme is filled front to back with information, the only advertisements appearing on the inner covers. The articles cover not only what is happening at Redhill and the Sussex County League, but also a round up of non-League happenings across the country and in the particular issue illustrated here, match reports from the FA Vase and Trophy. Statistics are in plentiful supply as well with details of each match of the season, and even each season since the club's inception in 1894.

Included with this issue was a supplement with the match details of all the clubs in the Division and sponsors' adverts, meaning that anyone who attended this match against Wick and bought a programme came away with well over 100 pages for the unbelievable price of 50 pence.

The time, effort and enthusiasm that Editor Michael Stewart has put into the programme is very much in evidence and he should be justifiably thrilled with the award.

Left: Redhill's award-winning programme with the supplement below left. Below right: Poole Town's programme, ninth place nationally and the winning programme in the Hampshire League

ISLE OF MAN

FINAL LEAGUE TABLES 2001-02

DIVISION ONE

	P	W	D	L	F	A	Pts
Peel	24	17	3	4	56	27	54
Marown	24	17	2	5	63	30	53
St Mary's*	24	15	3	6	81	51	45
Rushen	24	13	5	6	58	34	44
Laxey	24	12	4	8	56	34	40
Ayre United	24	9	6	9	65	59	33
Douglas Royal	24	8	7	9	50	57	31
Castletown	24	8	6	10	49	58	30
Pulrose	24	7	6	11	60	66	27
St George's	24	7	4	13	56	65	25
Douglas HSOB	24	4	7	13	30	63	19
Ramsey	24	5	3	16	29	51	18
Gymns	24	6	0	18	23	81	18

DIVISION TWO

	P	W	D	L	F	A	Pts
Colby	24	21	2	1	122	21	65
Corinthians	24	18	5	1	103	32	59
Foxdale	24	16	2	6	91	43	50
Union Mills	24	15	3	6	73	36	48
RYCOB	24	16	3	6	64	43	48
St John's	24	14	2	8	66	42	44
Braddan	24	10	3	11	54	48	33
Ronaldsway	24	7	1	16	54	110	22
Onchan	24	5	5	14	41	71	20
Michael	24	4	6	14	41	63	18
Malew	24	4	5	15	41	78	17
Barclays	24	4	3	17	28	94	15
Jurby	24	2	2	20	21	118	8

* points deducted

Peel rewrote the Manx Football history books when they took the League Division One Title for the 29th time and for the third year in a row. For much of the season it looked as if Marown from Crosby would win their first crown but nerves overtook them at the end and the young Western team came past in the last month to take the honours, with Marown having to settle for a best ever finish under the guidance of Island International Chris Taggart. Peel were managed by Shaun Dickinson and David Cain and also winger Rick Holden who used to star for Oldham Athletic and Manchester City.

Peel, along with Corby, have the best Junior set up on the Island under the guidance of the ever young Roly Haughton and Sidecar passenger Dicke Gale. The relegation issue was always tight between Ramsey, Gymns and Old Boy's with Ramsey going down despite having the best stadium and a good defensive record.

After the awful start Gymns went on an unbeaten late run which just failed to save them so it was the Northerners and the Tomode side who will spend next season in the Second Division. The promotion issues were clear cut and Colby and Corinthians dominated the Second Division.

Top teams Marown and Rushen United were both beaten by Ramsey with young Craig Lunt hammering in goals galore. Colby eventually took the title alone, also winning the Cowell Cup for the Under 18's, Corinthians were promoted and also took Combination Two while Rushen United from Port St Mary were worthy Combination One winners.

Pulrose United dominated the Alan Hawley Under 17 Trophy while the Ladies National Team scored their first ever win defeating Guernsey in the Nat West Island Games, with Eleanor Gawne the Women's Player of the Year. Eleanor plays of course for Rushen United. Ramsey took Division Two in the 14/16 League.

The top League scorers in any division were Colby with 127 goals. The Island now looks forward to the Island Games in Guernsey in 2003.

Youngster Anthony Jubb has joined Chesterfield and a number of youngsters have had good trials at Hartlepool United. The North Eastern side now have an authorised scout on the Island, Eddie Christian from Ramsey.

Peel are looking to become the first Isle of Man team to have floodlights in time for season 2003-04. They are looking for friendly fixtures with good Non-League opposition from England, Scotland, Wales and Northern and Southern Ireland. Their best opponents so far were League of Wales European side TNS. Anyone interested can contact the writer of this article, David Phillips on 01624 814704, phone and fax on the same number.

The Isle of Man National Team had a very disappointing Island Games as well as all fixtures in the Isle of Man Steam Packet Summer Festival which was dominated by Wrexham.

St Mary's Peter Langridge was again top scorer as well as winning the Golden Boot. Craig Lunt from Corinthians was the Silver Boot winner. There was a new record penalty shoot out of 14-13 when Foxdale edged out Ramsey. St George's dominated Junior Football and look certain to have a top team in the none too distant future, some youngsters have already reached first team level at the tender age of fourteen years. Their top midfielder Johnny Myers is now at Stockport County.

A Manx Referees team took charge of an early FA Trophy fixture, and a number of youngsters and ex-players have taken up the whistle. In the Cups the honours were shared with St Mary's winning the FA Cup, Rushen United the Railway Cup and Peel the Hospital Cup. Peel won the Charity Shield and Foxdale won the Woods Cup.

Second Division Corinthians added the Woods Cup to their promotion while Rushen United won the day in the Junior Cup, a sign of their strength in depth.

The Isle of Man Football Association now has a Coaching Advisor in Manxman Andrew Wadsworth from Union Mills. He was formerly working in Sheffield.

Dave Phillips

LEAGUE OF WALES

President: D W Shanklin

Secretary: D G Collins **Chief Executive:** D G Collins
Plymouth Chambers, 3 Westgate Street, Cardiff CF10 1DP
Tel: 029 2037 2325 Fax: 029 2034 3961

THE STRUCTURE OF WELSH FOOTBALL

LEVEL ONE League of Wales
LEVEL TWO Welsh Football League Division One, Cymru Alliance
LEVEL THREE Welsh Football League Division Two, Central Wales League, Welsh National League (Wrexham Area) Division One, Welsh Alliance League

FINAL LEAGUE TABLES 2001-02

LEVEL ONE

LEAGUE OF WALES

	P	W	D	L	F	A	Pts		P	W	D	L	F	A	Pts
Barry Town	34	23	8	3	82	29	77	Carmarthen Town	34	13	9	12	51	37	45
TNS Llansantffraid	34	21	7	6	85	33	70	Caernarfon Town	34	12	8	14	64	64	44
Bangor City	34	21	6	7	83	38	69	Port Talbot Athletic	34	12	7	15	44	55	43
Caersws	34	18	4	12	65	44	58	Newtown	34	9	11	14	35	44	38
Afan Lido	34	18	4	12	42	38	58	Flexsys Cefn Druids	34	8	8	18	49	79	32
Rhyl	34	17	5	12	53	45	56	Llanelli	34	8	7	19	41	64	31
Cwmbran Town	34	17	4	13	66	53	55	Oswestry Town	34	8	6	20	39	84	30
Connah's Quay Nomads	34	14	9	11	56	46	51	Haverfordwest County	34	6	10	18	47	76	28
Aberystwyth Town	34	14	9	11	53	48	51	Rhayader Town	34	3	6	25	28	89	15

LEAGUE OF WALES RESULTS CHART

		1	2	3	4	5	6	7	8	9	10	11	12	13	14	15	16	17	18
1	Aberystwyth Town	X	2-0	2-1	2-2	0-0	1-3	1-1	2-0	3-0	1-1	0-0	3-1	2-2	3-0	4-1	1-0	1-1	1-3
2	Afan Lido	0-1	X	1-0	1-1	3-0	2-1	1-0	0-2	2-0	0-0	3-0	2-1	1-0	3-2	2-1	4-1	2-1	0-2
3	Bangor City	2-1	1-0	X	2-2	3-1	3-1	3-0	2-1	1-3	6-0	3-0	2-0	2-1	2-1	3-1	1-0	3-0	3-0
4	Barry Town	4-1	3-2	1-1	X	2-0	0-3	0-0	0-1	2-1	8-0	5-0	2-0	3-0	7-1	3-0	5-0	1-0	3-1
5	Caernarfon Town	4-1	2-1	1-3	1-5	X	3-3	1-2	2-1	0-2	4-2	6-0	4-5	0-0	4-1	1-2	2-0	3-2	0-1
6	Caersws	2-1	6-0	2-1	1-4	2-1	X	1-1	1-2	2-0	0-0	3-0	2-1	1-0	2-3	2-1	3-0	2-0	1-2
7	Carmarthen Town	2-1	3-0	0-0	1-2	5-1	3-0	X	2-2	1-2	0-2	1-2	0-0	3-1	3-2	0-1	5-0	1-0	3-1
8	Connah's Quay	1-2	2-0	4-2	2-2	1-2	1-2	0-0	X	4-2	2-1	2-2	0-6	2-2	5-1	0-0	4-0	2-1	0-0
9	Cwmbran Town	2-0	0-1	3-5	1-2	3-2	3-2	1-1	2-1	X	5-1	2-2	6-1	0-1	8-2	0-0	4-2	0-3	0-4
10	Flex. Cefn Druids	1-2	1-2	2-7	0-2	1-3	2-1	0-4	1-2	2-4	X	2-2	1-0	1-2	0-2	4-2	2-0	2-2	2-2
11	Haverfordwest Co	2-3	0-1	2-4	0-1	2-2	2-4	0-3	0-3	2-0	2-2	X	2-1	2-0	4-1	0-0	3-3	1-2	3-3
12	Llanelli	3-2	0-1	2-6	1-1	1-0	2-0	1-0	1-1	0-3	1-1	3-4	X	1-1	2-2	1-2	1-1	0-3	1-3
13	Newtown	1-1	1-3	2-0	0-1	3-3	1-0	1-0	1-0	1-1	2-2	2-1	1-0	X	1-1	1-3	1-0	2-2	0-1
14	Oswestry Town	2-5	0-3	0-1	0-2	1-1	1-3	1-1	1-0	0-2	0-5	3-2	0-1	0-0	X	3-0	2-0	2-2	1-5
15	Port Talbot Town	1-1	1-1	1-0	2-3	1-4	1-0	1-0	0-2	1-2	6-2	1-1	3-2	3-1	2-3	X	1-2	2-3	1-0
16	Rhayader Town	0-2	0-0	0-7	0-9	0-1	2-6	2-4	1-1	0-3	3-4	3-2	3-0	0-3	1-2	1-1	X	1-3	0-1
17	Rhyl	3-0	1-0	0-3	3-1	3-1	1-3	3-1	0-4	1-0	1-2	2-1	2-0	1-0	2-0	3-1	1-1	X	1-1
18	Total Net Solutions	2-1	2-0	1-1	1-1	2-2	1-0	3-0	5-1	0-1	2-1	2-1	1-0	3-2	1-0	4-0	4-0	1-2	X

LEVEL TWO

WELSH FOOTBALL LEAGUE DIVISION ONE

	P	W	D	L	F	A	Pts
Ton Pentre	36	26	6	4	81	22	84
Pontardowe	36	27	2	7	94	36	83
UWIC Inter Cardiff	36	23	7	6	81	45	76
Garw	36	16	10	8	74	49	64
Neath	36	19	7	10	64	47	64
Maesteg Park	36	18	6	12	61	53	60
Goytre United	36	14	13	9	61	48	55
Ely Rangers	38	15	9	12	69	52	54
Llanwern	36	13	8	15	76	62	47
Gwynfl United*	36	14	6	16	86	69	45
Caerleon	36	12	6	18	48	55	42
Penrhlwceiber	36	12	6	18	69	100	42
Cardiff Corinthians	36	12	5	19	54	66	41
Milford United	36	10	9	17	43	64	39
Cardiff Civil Service	36	10	7	19	54	62	37
Fields Park Pontllanfraith	36	10	7	19	50	76	37
AFC Rhondda	36	9	4	23	30	80	31
Ammanford	36	8	5	23	40	85	29
Bridgend Town	36	7	7	22	50	93	28

HGF CYMRU ALLIANCE

	P	W	D	L	F	A	Pts
Welshpool Town	34	25	5	4	101	29	80
Llangefni/Glantraeth	34	24	3	7	78	36	75
Cemaes Bay	34	23	4	7	81	45	73
Porthmadog	34	20	8	6	88	45	68
Buckley Town	34	21	4	9	72	38	67
Ruthin Town	34	17	7	10	78	51	58
Halkyn United	34	17	7	10	58	43	58
Airbus UK	34	16	6	12	55	55	54
Holyhead Hotspur	34	15	4	15	72	78	49
Llandudno	34	12	3	19	55	80	39
Gresford Athletic	34	10	7	17	47	59	37
Llanfairpwll	34	10	6	18	59	81	36
Flint Town United	34	8	7	19	40	58	31
Lex XI*	34	13	4	17	67	87	31
Guilsfield	34	8	6	20	48	82	30
Holywell Town	34	8	5	21	60	85	29
Brymbo Broughton	34	8	5	23	40	80	23
Denbigh Town*	34	5	5	24	29	83	17

*points deducted

LEVEL THREE

WELSH FOOTBALL LEAGUE DIVISION TWO

	P	W	D	L	F	A	Pts
Garden Village	30	21	2	7	69	38	65
Bettws	30	21	1	8	85	41	64
Briton Ferry	30	16	6	8	62	30	60
Porth Tywyn	30	18	4	8	58	48	54
Aberaman	30	15	5	10	71	52	50
Taffs Well	30	13	7	10	74	54	48
Blaenrhondda	30	13	6	11	88	54	45
AFC Llwydcoed	30	12	6	12	85	65	42
Tredegar Town*	30	17	2	11	66	80	41
Porthcawl	30	12	5	13	83	60	41
Portos Grange Quins	30	11	5	14	52	61	38
Morriston Town	30	8	7	15	52	67	31
Merthyr Saints	30	8	7	15	63	82	31
Treharris Athletic	30	7	5	18	9	72	26
Treowen	30	7	3	20	31	83	24
Chepstow Town	30	1	3	24	41	112	8

WELSH NATIONAL LEAGUE WREXHAM AREA PREMIER DIVISION

	P	W	D	L	F	A	Pts
Mold Alexandra	28	24	3	1	85	22	75
Penycae	28	22	5	1	84	22	71
Castell AC	28	20	1	7	90	47	61
Cefn United	28	16	4	8	45	28	52
Llangollen Town	28	13	8	7	69	54	47
Ruthin Town	28	14	4	10	55	46	48
Corwen	28	13	4	11	40	60	43
Chirk AAA	28	12	5	11	51	48	41
Borras Park Albion	28	9	3	16	57	83	30
Rhos Aelwyd	28	7	5	16	37	49	26
Brickfield Rangers	28	6	6	16	40	64	24
Penley	28	5	8	15	37	57	23
Llay Welfare	28	6	5	17	38	59	23
Bala Town	28	4	7	17	33	61	19
Brymbo Broughton	28	3	4	21	31	92	13

TYN LON VOLVO WELSH ALLIANCE

	P	W	D	L	F	A	Pts
Amlwch Town	24	20	3	1	94	28	63
Conwy United	24	18	2	4	57	28	56
Rhyl	24	13	5	6	43	31	44
Felinheli	24	13	4	7	44	34	43
Llandudno Junction	24	13	3	8	52	30	42
Bangor City	24	12	3	9	63	41	39
Bethesda Athletic	24	11	4	9	60	40	37

	P	W	D	L	F	A	Pts
Locomotive Llanberis	24	10	4	10	48	57	34
Prestatyn Town	24	8	5	11	40	49	28
Rhydymwyn	24	9	2	13	50	60	29
Penmaenmawr Phoenix	24	3	4	17	39	79	13
Glan Conwy	24	2	4	18	38	79	10
Caersws	24	1	3	20	32	96	6

FEEDERS TO LEVEL THREE

WELSH FOOTBALL LEAGUE DIVISION THREE

	P	W	D	L	F	A	Pts
Newport YMCA	34	27	3	4	90	33	84
Dinas Powys	34	26	5	3	96	25	83
Pontypridd	34	20	9	5	77	32	69
Caldicot	34	21	4	9	77	24	67
Newcastle Emlyn	34	18	4	12	64	59	58
Seven Sisters	34	15	10	9	86	62	55
Pontyclun	34	16	6	12	70	52	52
Tillery FC	34	15	7	12	70	52	52
Risca United	34	14	7	13	50	52	49
Pentwyn Dynamo	34	13	6	15	79	71	45
Troedyrhiw	34	10	12	12	58	53	42
Caerau Ely	34	11	8	15	58	64	41
Skewen Athletic	34	10	8	16	47	66	38
Pontlottyn	34	8	12	14	49	62	36
Albion Rovers	34	9	5	20	51	63	32
RTB Ebbw Vale	34	8	8	18	52	75	32
Caerau	34	6	3	25	50	106	21
Abercynon	34	0	1	33	21	175	1

WELSH NATIONAL LEAGUE WREXHAM AREA DIVISION ONE

	P	W	D	L	F	A	Pts
Mynydd Isa	22	15	5	1	70	29	53
Ruthin Town Reserves	22	14	3	5	54	34	45
Llanuwchllyn	22	12	2	8	57	46	38
Acrefair	22	11	3	8	52	46	36
Airbus UK Reserves	22	10	4	8	63	48	34
Summerhill	22	9	2	11	49	69	29
Gresford Reserves	22	9	1	12	44	50	28
Bradley	22	8	3	11	50	57	27
Glyn Ceiriog	22	7	4	11	57	57	25
Hightown*	22	8	2	12	53	75	23
Penycae Reserves	22	6	3	13	34	44	21
Corwen Reserves	22	4	4	14	26	53	16

SOUTH WALES SENIOR LEAGUE DIVISION ONE

	P	W	D	L	F	A	Pts
Bridgend Street	28	25	0	3	92	35	75
Grange Albion	28	19	5	4	89	29	62
Pant Yr Awel	28	16	5	7	86	56	53
Sully Sports	28	14	4	10	79	71	46
Cwmbach Royal Stars	28	12	6	10	63	59	42
Cogan Coronation	28	12	4	12	59	48	40
Butetown	28	10	8	10	46	48	38
Penydarren BC	28	11	5	12	57	61	38
Penrhiwceiber Cons*	28	11	8	11	69	57	36
Hopkinstown	28	9	9	10	60	58	36
Ynyshir Albion*	28	11	5	12	72	65	35
AFC Whitchurch	28	6	8	14	69	89	26
Llsvane	28	6	5	17	46	84	23
Llanrumney United*	28	6	1	21	53	86	16
Penrhiwfer*	28	6	1	21	46	108	16

GEORGE FORD GWENT COUNTY LEAGUE DIVISION ONE

	P	W	D	L	F	A	Pts
Croesycelliog	30	23	3	4	88	34	72
Cwmbran Celtic	30	19	6	5	80	38	63
Clydach Wasps	30	19	5	6	77	48	62
Aborbargoed Buds	30	18	2	10	75	45	56
Lucas Cwmbran	30	15	5	10	76	69	50
Blaina West Side	30	14	5	11	70	58	47
Spencer Youth & Boys	30	15	1	14	67	60	46
Trinant	30	12	7	11	59	57	43
Pill AFC	30	13	2	15	61	72	41
Panteg	30	9	8	13	55	65	35
Tillery Athletic	30	9	7	14	60	80	34
Abercarn United	30	9	6	15	85	73	33
Fairfield United	30	10	3	17	46	76	33
Mardy	30	8	8	14	54	55	32
Cromwell Youth	30	5	8	17	43	73	23
Abergavenny Thursdays	30	4	1	25	43	104	13

* points deducted

NORTH GWENT LEAGUE

DIVISION ONE

	P	W	D	L	F	A	Pts
Fochrlw Sports	24	19	2	3	94	43	59
Abarbargoed Town	24	17	2	5	54	35	53
Central Cars	24	15	4	5	108	54	49
Tillory United	24	13	5	8	91	65	44
Rhymney	24	13	4	7	87	52	40
Pantside	24	13	1	10	65	75	40
Maesycwmmor	24	12	2	10	80	70	38
RTS Sports	24	9	4	11	50	64	31
Pentwynmewr Wkms	24	7	3	14	50	75	24
Llanhilleth Athletic	24	6	2	16	50	86	20
Trinanl Athletic	24	6	1	17	43	79	19
Coln Forest United	24	5	2	17	39	84	17
Cwmtolltach Colts	24	3	4	17	51	108	13

PIC UP SPARES SWANSEA SENIOR LEAGUE

DIVISION ONE

	P	W	D	L	F	A	Pts
West End	22	16	3	3	74	20	51
Bonymaen Colts	22	15	3	4	52	29	48
St Josephs	22	15	2	5	58	33	47
Ragged School	22	15	0	7	58	37	45
D & L Scaffolding	22	11	2	9	46	47	35
Farmers Arms	22	10	4	8	50	37	34
South Gower	22	9	3	10	49	48	30
P T Starts	22	7	4	11	33	45	25
Cwm Press	22	7	4	11	28	47	23
Penplas	22	7	4	11	29	55	21
Malsters Sports	22	2	2	18	28	64	8
North End	22	2	1	19	20	62	7

L'HIRONDELLE CARDIGANSHIRE LEAGUE

DIVISION ONE

	P	W	D	L	F	A	Pts
Aberaeron	22	16	3	3	61	20	51
Crannog	22	13	7	2	51	17	46
St Dogmaels	22	12	4	6	66	37	40
Cardigan*	22	13	3	6	51	35	39
Lampeter	22	12	4	7	48	43	37
Felinfach	22	10	3	8	54	43	36
Dewi Stars	22	10	2	10	42	38	32
Ffostrasol	22	10	1	11	41	42	31
Llanybyddr*	22	10	3	9	54	42	30
Llanboldy	22	4	2	16	26	58	14
SDUC	22	3	3	16	21	61	12
New Quay*	22	1	1	20	23	105	1

ABERDARE VALLEY LEAGUE

PREMIER DIVISION

	P	W	D	L	F	A	Pts
Mount Ash Town	22	15	2	5	72	34	47
Aberaman All Stars	22	14	4	4	77	34	46
Aberaman Bt Lgn	22	14	4	4	80	44	46
FC Cwmaman	22	13	3	6	52	37	42
Penywaun FC	22	13	2	7	62	49	41
Tynte Rovers A	22	12	3	7	62	49	39
Glancynon	22	9	3	10	60	48	30
Cwmbach RS	22	9	3	10	47	47	30
Abernant Rovers 97	22	6	5	11	50	55	22
AFC Miskin	22	7	0	15	40	79	21
Bee Hive	22	2	3	17	36	97	9
Mackworth Arms	22	1	3	18	34	96	6

JAMES WILLIAMS PEMBROKESHIRE LEAGUE

DIVISION ONE

	P	W	D	L	F	A	Pts
Hakin United	26	24	1	1	134	22	73
Pennar Robins	26	17	4	5	80	35	55
Tenby	26	17	3	6	67	46	54
Goodwick United	26	16	3	7	78	39	51
Narbarth	26	15	1	9	76	41	49
Monkton Swifts	26	13	2	11	54	50	41
St Ishmaels	26	11	8	7	58	43	41
Milford United	26	11	3	12	58	52	36
Carew	26	9	6	11	54	44	33
Camrose	26	10	3	13	51	73	33
Merlins Bridge	26	8	3	15	33	55	27
Fish Sports	26	4	3	19	39	91	15
St Clears	26	2	2	22	23	91	6
Haverfordwest County*	26	2	2	22	28	156	2

SPAR MID WALES LEAGUE

	P	W	D	L	F	A	Pts
Penrhyncoch	28	21	5	2	117	27	68
Carno	28	21	2	5	100	33	65
Llanrhaeadr	28	20	3	5	71	20	63
Aberystwyth Reserves	28	20	2	6	86	35	62
Newtown Reserves	28	14	4	10	64	49	47
Caersws Reserves	28	12	4	12	50	48	41
Llanfyllin	28	12	4	12	70	65	40
Llanidloes	28	11	4	13	48	50	37
Kerry	28	10	6	12	51	47	36
Prestelgne	28	10	5	13	88	80	35
UWA	28	10	3	15	64	76	34
Waterloo	28	8	2	18	37	88	28
Rhayader Reserves	28	4	5	18	39	109	18
Melfod	28	4	3	21	44	87	15
Llandrindad	28	3	4	21	33	104	13

THREEWAYS VALE OF CONWY LEAGUE

	P	W	D	L	F	A	Pts
Llanfairfechan Town	14	11	2	1	50	18	35
Machno United	14	11	2	1	49	17	35
Cricketers	14	7	1	6	37	33	22
Mochdre Sports	14	7	1	6	35	37	22
Conwy United Reserves	14	5	0	9	27	45	15
Llanrwst United Reserves	14	4	2	8	24	41	14
Blaenau Amateurs Reserves*	14	3	3	8	27	45	9
Llandudno Junction Reserves	14	2	1	11	35	51	7

SOUTH WALES AMATEUR LEAGUE

DIVISION ONE

	P	W	D	L	F	A	Pts
Bryntirion Athletic	30	24	5	1	67	19	77
Cambrian S B	30	19	4	7	82	37	61
British Steel	30	18	10	4	73	35	58
Llanbradach	30	14	9	7	88	41	51
Cardiff Dracs	30	14	7	9	75	73	49
Barry Athletic	30	14	8	10	54	46	48
Cwmaman Inst	30	12	10	8	71	45	48
Llantwil Fardre	30	13	8	9	53	40	44
Llangeinor	30	11	5	14	48	52	38
Llantwit Manor	30	10	7	13	46	52	37
Rhydyfalln Zenith	30	9	6	15	53	73	33
Taffs Well	30	9	12	9	51	53	30
Cardiff Corries	30	8	6	16	38	67	30
Kenfig Hill	30	8	4	20	46	76	22
Carnotown	30	4	7	19	35	89	19
Trefalin	30	2	4	24	23	103	1

ABERYSTWYTH TOWN

Secretary: Rhun Owens, 31 Maesgogerddan, Aberystwyth.
Tel: 01970 623520 (H) 0777 323 0894 (M)
Ground: Park Avenue, Aberystwyth, Ceredigion. Tel: 01970 612122
Club Email: atfc@btopenworld.com
Directions: From south: A487, 1st right at Trefachan Bridge to r'bout, 1st right with Park Ave. being 3rd right. From north: A487 and follow one-way system to railway station, at r'bout 1st left with Park Avenue being 3rd right. 5 mins walk from Aberystwyth (BR) - follow as above

Capacity: 4,500   Seats: 650   Cover: 1,200   Floodlights: Yes
Clubhouse: Open daily noon-3 & 7-12pm. Snacks available   **Club Shop:** Yes

HONOURS Welsh Cup 1899-1900; Welsh I'mediate Cup 85-86 87-88; Mid Wales Lg (11) (Lg Cup(7); Welsh Amtr Cup (3); Welsh Lg Div 2 Sth 51-52; Cambrian Coast Lg (8) Central Wales Chal. Cup(6)

PREVIOUS **League:** Welsh 1896-97; Nth Wales Comb. 99-1900; Montgomeryshire & Dist. 04-20; Central Wales 21-25 81-87; Mid-Wales 26-32 51-81; Cambrian Coast 32-51; Welsh Lg South 51-63; Abacus 87-92

RECORD **Attendance:** 4,500 v Hereford, Welsh Cup 1971
Goalscorer: David Williams 476, 66-83
Appearances: David P Whitney 572, 62-81

FACT FILE
Founded: 1884
Nickname: Seasiders
Sponsors: Continental Cambria Tyres
Colours: Black & green/white/black
Change colours: Yellow/navy/white
Midweek Matchday: Tuesdays
Reserves League: Mid-Wales
Programme: 64 pages, £1.00
Editor: D.Roberts Young (01970 617705)
Website:www.atfcnews.co.uk

CLUB PERSONNEL

Chairman: Donald Kane
President: D Jones
Press Officer: Rhun Owens
Manager: Gary Finley
2001-02
Captain: Ged Hennigan P.o.Y.: Gary Finlay
Top Scorers: Gavin Allen 17

AFAN LIDO

Secretary: P.Robinson.56 Abbeyville Avenue,Sandfields Estate, Port Talbot SA12 6PY
Tel Nos: 01639 885638 (H) 07812 142 833(M)

Ground: Runtech Stadium, Princess Margaret Way, Aberavon Beach, Port Talbot.
Tel: 01639 892960 (Club) 01639 881432 (Office)

Honours: League of Wales R-up 94-95, League of Wales Cup 92-93 93-94

FACT FILE

Colours: All red
Change colours: All yellow
Midweek Rixtures: Tuesday

CLUB PERSONNEL

Chairman: David Dale
Tel: 01639 891579

Manager: Mark Robinson
Tel:01639 822026

Head of Youth Academy:
P.Robinson

BANGOR CITY

Secretary: Alun Griffiths, 12 Lon-Y-Bryn, Menai Bridge, Anglesey, Gwynedd LL575NM
Tel: 01248 712820
Ground: The Stadium, Farrar Road, Bangor, Gwynedd (01248 355852)
Directions: Old A5 into Bangor, 1st left before railway station, ground on leftby garage
Capacity 2,000   Seats: 700   Cover: 1,200   Floodlights: Yes
Clubhouse: Not on ground   **Club Shop:** Yes
HONOURS FA Tphy R-up 83-84; Northern Prem. Lg 81-82 (R-up 86-87, Lg Cup 68-69, Presidents Cup 88-89, Chal. Shield 87-88), Cheshire Co. Lg R-up 53-54 58-59,Lancs Comb. R-up 30-31, League of Wales 94-95 (Lg Cup R-up 94-95), WelshNational Lg 27-28 (R-up 26-27), Nth Wales Coast Lg 1895-96, Welsh Cup 1888-89 95-96 1961-62 (R-up 27-28 60-61 63-64 72-73 77-78 84-85), Nth Wales Chal. Cup 26-27 35-36 36-37 37-38 46-47 51-52 57-58 64-65 67-68, Welsh Amtr Cup 1894-9596-96 97-98 98-99 1900-01 02-03 04-05 05-06 11-12, Welsh Jnr Cup 1995-96 97-981919-20, Welsh All. Alves Cup 49-50 59-60 (Cookson Cup 61-62 68-69 84-85 86-87)
RECORD **Attendance:** 10,000 v Wrexham, Welsh Cup final 78-79
PREVIOUS **Leagues:** N Wales Coast 1893-98 1911-12; The Comb 1898-1910; N Wales Comb 30-33; WMids 32-38; Lancs Comb 38-39 46-50; Ches Co 50-68; NPL 68-79 81-82 84-92; AlliancePrem 79-81 82-84, Welsh Cup 97-98,North Wales Challenge Cup 1998-99

FACT FILE
Founded: 1876 Nickname: Citizens
Sponsors: Pentraeth Group
Colours: All blue
Change colours: All red
Midweek Matchdays: Tuesday
Reserve League: Welsh Alliance
Programme: 32 pages, £1.00
Editor: Sam Vilaski

CLUB PERSONNEL
President: Gwyn Pierce Owen
Marketing Manager: Hayle Meek
Chairman: Ken Jones
Vice Chairman: David Gareth Jones
Press Officer: Alun Griffiths
Manager: Peter Davenport
Assistant Manager: Marc Lloyd Williams
Coach:Stephen Owen Physio: Arwel Jones
Head of Youth Acadeny: M.Jones

BARRY TOWN

Secretary: Craig Griffiths, 15 Thistle Close, Barry, South Glam. 01446 733576
Ground: Jenner Park, Barry CF62 9BG Tel: 01446 735858 Fax: 01446 701884
Website: www.barrytown.cjb.net
Directions: M4 jct 33 via Wenvoe (A4050) to Barry. Left at 1st 2 r'bouts to Jenner Park.
Nearest rail station is Cadoxton
Capacity: 3,000   Seats: 3,000   Cover: Yes   Floodlights: Yes
Clubhouse: Open normal licensing hours, 11.00-11.00 daily
HONOURS Welsh Cup (3); Welsh Trophy 94-95; Southern Lg R-up 20-21;
Western Lg R-up 11-12, Welsh Lg (7), Lg Cup (4); South Wales Senior Cup (13);
SA Brain Cup (3); League of Wales 95-96 96-97 97-98 98-99 01-02, R-up 99-00;
UEFA Cup 2 Qual Rds 96-97, Prel Rd 97-98 Champs . 2nd . Prelim Rd 01-02

PREVIOUS   **Leagues:** Western 08-13; Southern 13-82 89-93; Welsh 82-89 94-95

BEST SEASON   **FA Cup:** 2nd Rd 29-30   **FA Trophy** 3rd Qualifying Rd replay 90-91

RECORD   **Attendance:** 7,400 v Queens Park Rangers, FA Cup 1st Rd 1961
Goalscorer: Clive Ayres   **Appearances:** Basil Bright
Players progressing Chris Simmonds (Millwall) 47, Derek Tapscott/Dai Ward(Arsenal) 53/54, Laurie
Sheffield/Gordon Fazer/Phil Green (Newport) 62/66/84,Chris Pike (Fulham) 85, Ian Love (Swansea)
86, Tony Bird/Dave O'Gorman (SwanseaCity) 97, Mark Ovendale (Bournemouth) 98 Eifion Williams
(Torquay United) 99

FACT FILE

Founded: 1923
Nickname: Dragons
Sponsors: Tango
Colours: Yellow & blue/yellow/blue
Change: Maroon & white trim
Midweek Matchdays: Tuesday
Programme: Yes

CLUB PERSONNEL

Chairman: Craig Griffiths
Player Manager: Kenny Brown
Head of Youth Academy: A.York

CAERNARFON TOWN

Secretary: I Sixsmith,Caernarfon Air Parc,Dinas Dinille, Caernarfon Gwynedd LL54 5TP
Tel Nos: 07970 220 066 (H) 08707 541 500 (W)
Ground: The Oval, Marcus Street, Caernarfon, Gwynedd Tel: 01286 675002
Directions: A55 coast road to A487 bypass to Caernarfon. At inner relief road r'bout follow
Beddlegert sign, then 2nd right - ground opposite.
Nearest BR station is 9 miles distant at Bangor. Local buses to Hendre estate
Capacity: 3,678   Seats: 178   Cover: 1,500   Floodlights: Yes
Clubhouse: 2 snooker tables, darts, pool, fruit machines & live entertainment **Club Shop:** Yes
HONOURS N West Co's Lg R-up 84-85 (Div 2 R-up 82-83); Lancs Comb 81-82 (Lg Cup 80-
81); Welsh Lg (North)(4) 46-47 65-66 77-79, R-up (4) 56-58 72-73 79-80; Alves
Cup(4) 38-39 74-75 77-79; Cookson 56-57 77-78; N Wales Combination 32-33;
Welsh National Lg 26-27 29-30 (R-up 28-29); N Wales Coast Lg 11-12
PREVIOUS **Leagues:** North Wales Coast 06-21; Welsh National 26-30; North Wales Comb.
32-33; Welsh Lg (North) 37-76 77-80; Lancs Comb. 80-82; North West Counties
82-85; Northern Premier
BEST SEASON   **FA Trophy:** 1st Round replay 87-88
FA Cup : 3rd Rd replay 86-87, 0-1 v Barnsley (A). Also 2nd Rd 29-30
RECORD   **Attendance:** 6,002 v Bournemouth, FA Cup 2nd Rd 1929
Goalscorer: W Jones 255 (1906-26)   **Appearances:** Walter Jones 306

FACT FILE
Founded: 1876
Nickname: Canaries
Sponsors: T.J. Fixit
Colours: Yellow & green/green/yellow
Change colours: Sky & claret/claret/claret
Midweek Matchday: Wednesday
Reserve Team: Yes
Programme: 48pgs 70p
Editor: Marc Roberts

CLUB PERSONNEL
President: Jack F Thomas
Chairman: G.Lloyd Owen
Vice-Chairmen: Eilian Angel
Press Officer: Geraint Lloyd Owen
Tel: 01286 830307
Manager: Adrian Jones
Coach: Alan McDonald
Head of Youth Academy: R.Holroyd
Physio: Ian Humphreys

CAERSWS

Secretary: T M B Jones, 3 Hafren Terrace, Caersws, Powys SY17 5ES
Tel: 01686 688103 (H/Fax)

Ground: The Recreation Ground, Caersws, Powys. Tel: 01686 688753
Directions: Entering Caersws, which lies between Newtown & Llanidloes on the A470, the
ground entrance is on the left by bridge
Capacity: 3,250   Seats: 250   Cover: 300   Floodlights: Yes **Club Shop:** No
Clubhouse: Not on ground, but in village centre. Normal licensing hours. Food available
HONOURS Welsh Amtr Cup 60-61, I'mediate Cup 88-89 (R-up 91-92); Mid-Wales Lg (9) 59-
61 62-63 77-78 82-83 85-86 88-90 96-97 (Lg Cup 79-80 82-83 87-88 89-90);
Cent. Wales Chall.Cup 77-78 82-83 87-88 89-90 (Yth Cup 69-70 72-73 Lg01-02);
Montgomeryshire Chall. Cup (18) 52-53 59-60 62-63 69-72 74-75 76-78 83-89
90-91 94-95 94-95 96-97 97-98 98-99; Montgomeryshire Lg 77-78 U.E.F.A. Inter
Toto Cup 01-02, 02-03.

PREVIOUS   **Leagues:** Mid-Wales (pre-1989)/Cymru Alliance 90-92

RECORD   **Attendance:** 2,795 v Swansea City, Welsh Cup 1990
Goalscorer: Gareth Davies

Players progressing: P Woosnam (Leyton O.), M Evans (Wolverhampton W.), KLloyd (Hereford U)
Graham Evans (Aston Villa)

FACT FILE
Founded: 1877
Nickname: Bluebirds
Sponsor: Dave Smith
Colours: Blue & white/white/blue
Change colours: Orange/black/black
Midweek Matchday: Tuesday
Reserve League: Mid-Wales
Programme: 44 pages, £1.00
Editor: Ian Baker

CLUB PERSONNEL
Chairman: Garth Williams
Vice Chairman: John Baker
President:: Dileryn Lewis
Patron: Phil Woosnam
Press Officer: Ivor Williams
Manager: Mickey Evans
Asst Manager: Barry Harding
Physio: Wynne Jones

CARMARTHEN TOWN

Secretary: G.O.Jones,Glaslyn,3 Nant Y Felin,Caerfyrddin SA 31 3DT
Tel Nos: 01267 234829 (H) 01267 221838 (W) 01267 222851 (Fax)

Ground: Richmond Park, Priory Street, Carmarthen Dyfed
Tel: 01267 232101 Fax: 01267 222851

Directions: Proceed into Carmarthen on A48, pick up A40 to Llandilo at the 1st rounabout and follow town centre signs for 800 meters.Ground on left in Priory Street

Capacity: 2,500 Seats: 500 Cover: 500 Floodlights: Yes

Clubhouse: Yes **Club Shop:** Yes

HONOURS Welsh Lge Div 2 59-60, Div 1 95-96, Cup Winners 95-96

RECORD **Attendance:** 3,000

PREVIOUS **Leagues:** Welsh League

FACT FILE
Founded: 1948
Nickname: The Town
Sponsors: R.S.V. Windows
Colours: Old gold/black/black
Change colours:White with blue trim
Midweek Matchday: Tuesday
Reserve League: C C Sports Welsh Lge
Programme: £1.00
Editor: Alun Charles

CLUB PERSONNEL
Chairman: Jeff Thomas
President: Anthony Jenkins
Manager : Tommi Morgan
Head of Youth Academy:C.Staples
Physio: Nigel Davies

CONNAH'S QUAY NOMADS

Secretary/Press Officer
Robert Hunter, 40 Brookdale Ave., Connah's Quay, Deeside, Clywd CH5 4LU
Tel: 01244 831212 (H)
Ground: Deeside Stadium Connah's Quay

Directions: On main coast road (A548) from Chester to Rhyl west end of Connah's Quay
Deeside College.
Capacity: 3,500 Seats: 500 Cover: 500 Floodlights: Yes
Clubhouse: Yes, in college. **Club Shop:** No

HONOURS Welsh Amtr Cup 52-53 54-55, Nth Wales FA Amtr Cup 52-53 54-55,
North Wales Coast Challenge Cup, Welsh Intermediate Cup 80-81,
Welsh Alliance CooksonCup 87-88, Welsh Youth Cup 47-48

PREVIOUS **Leagues:** Clywd; Welsh Alliance; Cymru Alliance 90-92

RECORD **Attendance:** 1,500 v Rhyl, Welsh Cup SF 29/3/93

FACT FILE
Founded: 1946
Nickname:Westenders
Sponsors: Copyrite
Colours: White/black/black&white
Change colours: Maroon/white/maroon
Midweek Matchday: Tuesday
Reserve League: Clwyd Premier
Programme: 26 pages, £1.00
Editor: D.Rapson

CLUB PERSONNEL
Chairman: Mr R Morris
President: Mr R Jones
Manager: Neville Powell
Asst Manager: S.Gelder
Physio: M Latter
2001-02
Captain: Stephen Hopkins
P.o.Y.: Paul Mazzarella
Top Scorer: Stuart Rain 22

CYMBRAN TOWN

Secretary: R L Langley, 77 Hampton Crescent East, Cyncoed, Cardiff CF23 6RG, Tel:
029 20764381 (H/Fax) 0771 892 3142 (M)
Ground: Cwmbran Stadium, Henllys Way, Cwmbran, Gwent
Tel: 01633 866192 Fax 01633 863324
Directions: M4 jct 26, follow signs for Cwmbran. At 1st r/about (approx 1.5miles) take 1st
exit & proceed along Cwmbran Drive umtil passing Stadium onright. At r/about
take 1st exit, then immediately at next r/about take 3rdexit.
Ground entrance 150 yardson right.
One and a half miles from Cwmbran(BR)
Capacity: 8,201 **Seats:** 2,201 **Cover:** 1,857 **Floodlights:** Yes **Club Shop:** Yes
Clubhouse: And clubhouse at 5/7 Commercial Street, Old Cwmbran (01633 483282
HONOURS Lg of W. 92-93; Welsh Lg Div 2 67-67, Welsh Lg Cup 90-91, Welsh Cup
Finalists 96-97,99-00 UEFA Champions Cup 93-4 ,UEFA CUP WInners `CUP 97-8 ,UEFA Cup
99-00,01-01, UEFA Inter Toto Cup 00-01
PREVIOUS **Leagues:** Monmouthshire Snr 51-59/ Welsh 60-92
RECORD **Attendance:** 8,148 v Manchester Utd Aug 1994
Goalscorer : Graham Reynolds **Appearances:** Mostyn Lewis

Players progressing: Simon King (Newport 1984), Mark Waite (Bristol Rovers1984), Nathan
Wigg (Cardiff 1993), Chris Watkins (Swansea 1993), Daniel Gabbidon(W.B.A.,Cardiff)C)

FACT FILE
Founded: 1951 Nickname: The Town
Sponsors:Colley Hyunda1
Colours: Dark blue.
Change colours: Black & white/black/black
Midweek Matches: Wednesday
Programme: 40 pages, £1.00
Programme Editor/Press Off: Terry Daley
CLUB PERSONNEL
President &Chairman: John Colley
Vice Chairman: Clive Edwrads
General Secretary: Roy Langley
Press Officer: Kevin Morris
Manager: Tony Willcox
Coach: Roger Gibbins Physio: Tommy Cosh
Youth Academy: Delwyn Cheedy
Fitness Coach: Richard Hughes
2001-02
Captain: Sean Wharton P.o.Y.: Richard
CarterTop Scorer: Craig Hughes 24

FLEXSYS CEFN DRUIDS

Secretary: Mr I.Williams,Hillview,Overton Road, St Martins, Oswestry. SY11 3DG
Tel Nos: 01691 777937 07779 433618 (M)

Ground: Plas Kynaston lane, Plas Kynaston, Cefn Mawr, Wrexham
Tel Nos: 01978 824279(Club) 01978 824332 (Office)

Website: www.cefndruids@ wrexham.gov.uk

FACT FILE

Colours: Black & white/black/black
Change colours: All Yellow

Midweek Fixtures: Tuesday

CLUB PERSONNEL

Chairman: Mr M Pritchard
Tel: 01978 812100 (H)

Manager: Steve O'Shaugnessy
Tel: 01978 855357 (H)
07787 805 075(M)

Head of Youth Academy: J.Hunter

HAVERFORDWEST COUNTY

FACT FILE

Secretary: Barry Vaughan   Tel: 01437 731779 (H) 01437 764331 (B)
Woodbine Cottage,Clarbeston Road, Haverfordwest, Pembs. SA63 4QS

Ground: Bridge Meadow Stadium, Haverfordwest, Pembs.
Tel: 01437 769048 Fax: 01437 769048

Directions: Off the Safeway roundabout near town centre

Capacity: 4,000   Covered Seats: 500   Floodlights: Yes   **Club Shop:** Yes

HONOURS West Wales Sen Cup 81-82 88-89 91-92 92-93 97-98 98-99, R-up 37-38 49-50
56-57 60-61 80-81; Welsh Lge 56-57, R-up 67-70 70-71, Prem Div 80-81,
National Div 89-90, Div 1 96-97, R-up 94-95 95-96; SA Brains Cup 88-89 R-up 84-85

Nickname: Bluebirds
Sponsor: Preseli Taxis
Colours: All Blue
Change cols: Orange & black/black/orange & black
Midweek Matchday: Tuesday
Programme: 28 Pages £1.00
Editor: JohnThomas

CLUB PERSONNEL

Chairman: W,Griffiths
Press Officer: Robert Nesbitt
Manager: Derwyn Brace
Head of Youth Academy: John Daniels

LLANELLI

Secretary: Mr R Davies, 29 Pemberton Park, Llanelli, Carmartenshire SA14 8NN
Tel: 01554 756176 (H) 01554 772973 (B) 01554 772973 (Fax)

Ground: Stebonheath Park, Llanelli, Carmarthenshire SA15 1HF
Tel: 01554 756216. Clubhouse Tel No: 01554 756216

Capacity: 3,700   Cover and seats: 700 Floodlights: Yes   Club Shop : No

PREVIOUS
Leagues Welsh League and Southern League

RECORD
Attendance: 15,000 1st Rd F.A.Cup 1950-51

2000-01
Captain & P.o.Y. Mark Dickeson
Top Scorer: Mark Dickeson 30

FACT FILE
Year Formed: 1896
Nickname : Reds
Sponsors : Panda Motors
Colours: All red
Change colours: All white
Midweek Fixtures: Wednesday
Programme: 42 pages Price: £1.00
Editor: Hugh Roberts (01554 750547)

CLUB PERSONNEL
Chairman: Mr R Jones
Tel: 01792 405301 (H)
Press Officer: Hugh Roberts
Manager: Peter Nicholas
Tel:01446 760138
Coach: Paul Compton
Physio: Bill Morris

NEWTOWN

Team Secretary: Howard Ellis, 30Court Close, Abermull, Montgomery, Powys (01686 630372 (H) 01686 626121 (W))

Ground: Latham Park, Newtown, Powys Tel: 01686 622666/623120, Fax: 623813
Directions: A43 to Newtown, right at 1st lights into Back Lane & town centre -400yds left into Park St., 500yds right (at Library) into Park Lane - ground at end
Capacity: 5,000   Seats:1,100   Cover: 850   Floodlights: Yes
Clubhouse: Open every evening & matchday afternoons. Hot/cold snacks, pool,darts
Club Shop: Yes

HONOURS League of Wales R-up 95-96 97-98; Welsh Cup 1878-79 94-95 (R-up 85-65 87-88 96-97), Welsh Amtr Cup 1954-55, Central Wales Lg 75-76 78-79 81-82 86-87 87-88 (R-up 51-52 52-53 55-56 56-57 74-75 82-83, Lg Cup 54-55 56-57 74-75 75-76 81-82 83-84), Arthur Barritt Cup 86-87, Central Wales Cup 74-75 80-81 92-93, Emrys Morgan Cup 80-81

PREVIOUS **Leagues:** The Combination/ Central Wales/ Northern Premier
RECORD **Attendance:** 5,002 v Swansea City, Welsh Cup 1954
BEST SEASON **FA Trophy:** 3rd Qual. 89-90
FA Cup: 2nd Rd 1884-85. Also 1st Rd 1885-86

FACT FILE
Founded: 1875Nickname: Robins
Sponsors: ControlTechniques & Elliott Presco
Colours: Red/white/red
Change : Yellow/blue/blue
Midweek Matchdays: Tuesday
Reserves League:Spar Mid Wales
Programme: 36 pages, £1
Editors: Keith Harding/ Nigel Bevan & Barry Gardiner
CLUB PERSONNEL
President: Richard Edwards
Chairman:Phil Trenbath
Exec Co-Ordinator: Mrs Lyn Barnett
Match Sec/Press Officer: John Annereau
Man : Brian Coyne Asst Man : Richard Pike
Physio:T.B.A.
Res.Team Manager: Jack Watkins
2001-02
Captain: Colin Reynolds P.o.Y,ChrisAdamson
Top Scorer: Steve McCormick 19

OSWESTRY TOWN

Secretary: James Bond c/o club

Ground: Park Hall Stadium, Burma Road, Park Hall, Oswestry, Shropshire
Tel: 01691 679499 (Social Club)
Directions: From A5 Oswestry bypass,take A495 "Whitchurch" away from Oswestry; second left into Burma Rd., go past rugby pitches on the left and the stadium is round bend on right.
Capacity : 6,100 **Seats:** 250 **Covered Standing** 3000 **Floodlights :**Yes **Clubhouse:** Yes

HONOURS: Founder Members of Welsh F.A., Welsh Cup Winners (3) Cymru Alliance Champions 1995,2000
Previous **Leagues:** Cymru Alliance, Welsh National, Northern Premier, Cheshire Birmingham
Ground: Victoria Road
Best Season Welsh Cup Winners (3)
Welsh Intermediate Cup: Quarter Finalists
North East Welsh Cup Winners
Record **Attendance:** 1,600 v Shrewsbury Yown 1993

Players Progressing: Many, includinhg Herbie Roberts (Arsenal)

FACT FILE
Founded 1860 Nickname 'Town'
Club Sponsors: Arthu's of Oswestry
Colours: All Blue
Change colours: All Maroon
Midweek Fixtures: Tuesday
Programme 32 Pages £1.00
Editors: David Owen & Mike Clarke

CLUB PERSONNEL
Chairman: Bill Jerman
Tel: 01691 661297 (H)
Press Officer: Secretary
Manager:Dave Norman
Assistant Manager: Mo Doytle
Physio: Syd Hardwick

2001-02
Captain & Top Scorer: Mo Doyle
P.o.Y. Mark Hobson

PORT TALBOT TOWN

Secretary: Mr P. Fisher, 87 Village Gardens, Baglan Moors, Port Talbot SA12 7LP
Tel: 01639 793689 (H) 07974 446720 (M) 01639 778886 (W)
Fax: 01639 778 884. Email: p.fisher@ntlworld.com

Ground: Victoria Road, Port Talbot, SA12 6AD
Tel: 01639 882465
Fax: 01639 886991

FACT FILE
Colours: Blue & white/blue/blue
Change colours: White/black/black

Midweek Fixtures: Tuesday

Website: www.porttalbotfc.co.uk

CLUB PERSONNEL

Chairman: Andrew Edwards
Tel: 01639 888515 (H)

Manager: M.Jones
Tel: 07885 118 115(H)

Head of Youth Academy: B.Wells
c/o Club

RHYL

Secretary: Dennis McNamee, 3 Maes Rhosyn, Rhuddlan. Tel: 01745 591287 (H)
Ground: Belle Vue, Grange Road, Rhyl, Clwyd Tel: 01745 338327
Directions: Leave A55 at the St Asaph/Rhyl turn off and take A525 to Rhuddlan.At roundabout take 2nd turn for Rhyl, then left at next roundabout and over next two roundabouts .After 1mile urn right into Pendyffryn Rd, then left at junction and ground is 300yds on left.

Capacity: 3,800   Cover: 1,200   Seats: 500   Floodlights: Yes
Club Shop: Yes   Clubhouse: No

HONOURS   Welsh Cup 51-52 52-53 (R-up 29-30 36-37 92-93), Welsh Amateur Cup 72-73, Northern Premier Lg Presidents Cup 84-85, North West Counties Lg R-up 82-83,North Wales Coast Challenge Cup, Cheshire County Lg 47-48 50-51 71-72 (R-up 48-49 49-50 51-52 55-56, Div 2 R-up 81-82, Lg Cup 48-49 51-52 70-71, Div 2 Shield 81-82), Cyrmu Alliance 93-94 (R-up 92-93, Lg Cup 92-93)

PREVIOUS LEAGUES: **North Wales Coast League,** Cheshire County; North West Counties; Northern Premier; Cymru Alliance 92-94
BEST SEASON   FA Cup : 4th Rd Proper 56-57 (lost 0-3 at Bristol City)
RECORD   **Attendance:** 10,000 v Cardiff City, Welsh Cup 1953
Goalscorer: Don Spendlove   **Appearances:** Not known
Players progressing:
Ian Edwards, Grenville Millington, Brian Lloyd, Andy Holden, Barry Horne, Andy Jones

FACT FILE
Founded: 1870 (as Rhyl Skull & Crossbones)
Nickname: Lilywhites
Sponsors: Webber Office Solutions of Rhyl
Colours: White/black/black
Change: Blue & maroon/ blue/blue
Midweek matches: Tuesday
Programme: 40 pages £1
Editor: Dave Jones (01745 334144)

CLUB PERSONNEL
Managing Director; P.Parry
Chairman: David Simmons
Vice Chairmen; N.C.Jones & J.Evans
President: R B G Webster
Company Secretary : David Milner
Press Officer: David .Williams

Manager: J.Hulse
Tel No: 0151 653 9874
Head of Youth Academy: J.Smith

TOTAL NETWORK SOLUTIONS

Secretary: Gwynfor Hughes, Birch Lea, Porthywaen, Oswestry, Shrops SY10 8LY
Tel: 01691 828645 (H)   Fax: 01691 828645

Ground: Recreation Park, Treflan, Llansantffraid Tel: 01691 828112 & Fax 01691 828862
Directions: A483 between Oswestry and Welshpool, right for Llansantffraid (A495) at Llyclys When from North Follow sign to village.Turn opposite Mill silos towards Llynclys Community Centre. Ground is behind housing estate.From south A483 turn left at B4393 to village and Mill
Capacity: 1,500   Seats: 500Cover standing: 1,500   Floodlights: Yes Shop: no
Clubhouse: Open every evening except Sunday, plus weekend afternoons.
HONOURS   League of Wales Champions 99-00 R-up 01-02, Welsh Cup 95-96; R-up: 00-01 Welsh Intermediate Cup 92-93; League of Wales Cup 94-95;Cymru Alliance Lge 92-93, R-up 91-92; Central Wales Sen Cup 98-99,R-up 92-93 97-98;Central Wales Lg R-up 90-91 94-95 95-96, Lge Cup 95-96; Montgomeryshire Amtr Cup (7), Village Cup (17); UEFA Champions League 00-01, European Cup Winners Cup Preliminary Rd 96-97 U.E.F.A. Cup: 2001-02,02-03

PREVIOUS   **League:** Mid-Wales; Cymru Alliance (pre-1993)

RECORD   **Attendance:** 2,100 v KS Ruch Chorzow Euro Cup Winners 96(at Wrexham F.C.)
Goalscorer: Adrian Jones   **Appearances:** Andy Mulliner

FACT FILE
Founded: 1959
Nickname: The Saints
Sponsors: Total Network Solutions
Colours: Green and white
Change: All Blue
Midweek Matchdays: Tuesday
Programme: 40 pages, £1
Editor:Tony Williams
CLUB PERSONNEL
Chairman: Edgar Jones
President: Mike Hughes
Manager:Ken McKenna
Assistant Manager: John Carroll
Physio: Gordon Evans
2001-02
Captain: Tim Alexander
Top Scorer: John Toner
P.O.Y.: Tommy Holmes

WELSHPOOL

Secretary: Mr C McNamee, Paradise Cottage, Hope, Leighton, Welshpool, Powys SY21 8JD
Tel: 01938 552 270 (H)   01938 553311 (B) 07989 429290 (M)
Fax::   01938 555885   email: clivemcnamee@lineone.net

Chairman: Mr B Jones, Park View, Forden, Nr. Welshpool, Powys.
Tel: 01938 580529 (H)   01938 552260 (B)

Ground: Maes y Dre Recreation Ground, Welshpool, Powys
Tel: 01938 553027
Capacity: Cover: 100   Seating:
Honours: Cymru Alliance 01-02

FACT FILE
Founded: 1878
Nickname: Seasiders
Colours: White/black/white
Change colours: Purple/white/purple
Midweek Matchday: Wednesday

Manager
Russ Cadwallader
Tel: 01686 668608

Wales against England in the Four Nations Tournament
Photos: Milton Haworth

SCOTTISH NON-LEAGUE FOOTBALL

Compiled by Bill Mitchell with thanks to Stewart Davidson

JUNIORS

OVD SCOTTISH JUNIOR CUP 2001-02

FIFTH ROUND

Camelon	v	Petershill	3-3	Cumbernauld	v	Shettleston	1-1
Cumnock	v	Bathgate Thistle	0-1	Irvine Meadow	v	Glenafton Athletic	0-2
Kilwinning Rangers	v	Hill of Beath Hawthorn	3-1	Oakley United	v	Auchinleck Talbot	2-2
Renfrew	v	Tayport	1-1	Vale of Leven	v	Linlithgow Rose	0-1

Replays

Auchinleck Talbot	v	Oakley United	5*3	Tayport	v	Renfrew	1-0

SIXTH ROUND

Auchinleck Talbot	v	Glenafton Athletic	2-1	Bathgate Thistle 2	v	Tayport	2-2
Camelon	v	Kilwinning Rangers	3-4	Shettleston	v	Linlithgow Rose	1-2

Replay:

Tayport	v	Bathgate Thistle	1-0

SEMI-FINALS

Tayport	v	Linlithgow Rose	1-2	At West Lothian Courier Stadium, Livingston. Att: 4,401
(McGlashan)		(Corcoran, Flynn)		

Auchinleck Talbot	v	Kilwinning Rangers	4-1	At Rugby Park, Kilmarnock. Att: 6,454
(Wallace (2), Traynor, McAulay)		(McLaren)		

FINAL

Auchinleck Talbot	v	Linlithgow Rose	0-1	Sunday, 19th May 2002. At Firhill Park, Glasgow.
		(Creaney 64)		Attendance: 6,966. Half-time: 0-0

AUCHINLECK TALBOT: McIntosh; Duncan, Davidson, Traynor, McAneyy, Hyslop, McAuley, Duffy, Aallace, Biggart, McCann. Substitutes: Friels for Duffy 68 minutes, Watson for McCann 83 minutes.
LINLITHGOW ROSE: Lamont; Gallacher, Finlayson, Landels, Beaton, Smith, Whyte, McLaughlin, Flynn, Creaney, Corcoran. Substitutes: Dickov for Creaney 78 mins, McGrotty for Flynn 85 mins, Mahon for McLaughlin 88 mins.
Referee: J Downie.

UNLIKE the 2002 final it could fairly be said that the better team had won this match, although only a single goal by James Creaney, the tiny striker, separated the sides, when referee Downie blew up for full-time.

For the most part Linlithgow were the best team on the afternoon and took the Junior Cup back to the Lothians town for the first time in 37 years.

The goal itself might have been disputed as some thought that Creaney had possibly fouled McLaughlin, who

came far off his goal line and then failed to intercept the ball, which was then poked into an empty net, but the Ayrshire supporters were nonetheless generous in their applause for both teams after a thoroughly entertaining match, which showed that they had no complaints about the eventual result.

Auchinleck Talbot before the OVD Scottish Cup Final May 2002. The Ayrshire side lost (0-1) to Linlithgow Rose from the East Region.
Photo: John B Vass

Above left: Kilwinning Rangers keeper Derek Barnes gathers the ball in the semi-final against Auchinleck Talbot
Above right: Wallace (Auchinleck Talbot), scorer of two goals, challenges Currie (Kilwinning Rangers).
Photos: John B Vass

WEST, CENTRAL & EAST LEAGUES

STAGECOACH AYRSHIRE REGION

DIVISION ONE

	P	W	D	L	F	A	Pts
Glenafton Athletic	18	15	1	2	49	13	46
Cumnock Juniors	18	11	3	4	40	21	36
Kilwinning Rangers	18	11	2	5	37	27	35
Auchinleck Talbot	18	7	3	8	23	26	24
Irvine Meadow	18	6	3	9	33	33	21
Kilbirnie Ladeside	18	5	4	9	22	28	19
Lugar Boswell This	18	0	0	18	10	66	0

DIVISION TWO

	P	W	D	L	F	A	Pts
Largs Thistle	21	15	3	3	58	17	48
Hurlford United	21	14	3	4	39	19	45
Beith	21	13	4	4	40	24	43

Other league positions: Troon (41 points), Irvine Victoria (21), Muirkirk (15), Kello Rovers (15), Craigmark Burntonians (11).

DIVISION THREE

	P	W	D	L	F	A	Pts
Dalry Thistle	21	15	2	4	49	25	47
Maybole	21	13	5	3	56	26	44
Ardrossan Winton Rs	21	10	4	7	43	41	34

Other league positions: Saltcoats Victoria (33 points), Whitletts Victoria (32), Ardeer Thistle (22), Annbank United (16), Darvel (10).

AYRSHIRE LEAGUE PLAY-OFFS

Beith 4   Dalry Thistle 1   (2-1, 2-0)
(3rd Division 2 v 1st Division 3)

Lugar Boswell Thistle 1   Troon 2   (1-2, 0-0)
(bottom Division 1 v 4th Division 2)

KERR & SMITH
SECTIONAL LEAGUE CUP

QUARTER-FINALS
Craigmark Burntonians 1   Auchinleck Talbot 2
Cumnock 5   Hurlford 1
Kilbirnie Ladeside 2   Irvine Meadow 2
(Irvine Meadow won 4-3 on penalties)
Kilwinning Rangers 1 Largs Thistle 1
(Kilwinning Rangers won 4-2 on penalties)

SEMI-FINALS
Auchinleck Talbot 1   Cumnock Juniors 3
Irvine Meadow 1   Kilwinning Rangers 0

FINAL
Friday, 5th October 2001. At Somerset Park, Ayr.

CUMNOCK JUNIORS   3 - 2   IRVINE MEADOW
Kerr (2), McGinty Campbell   Ferguson (pen)
Attendance: 1,000

IRVINE TIMES AYRSHIRE DISTRICT CUP

THIRD ROUND
Auchinleck Talbot 3   Beith 0
Cumnock 4   Lugar Boswell Thistle 1
Kilbirnie Ladeside 1   Irvine Victoria 2
Kilwinning Rangers 9   Muirkirk 0

SEMI-FINALS
Cumnock 1   Auchinleck Talbot 0
Irvine Victoria 2   Kilwinning Rangers 4

FINAL
Thursday, 30th May 2002. At Irvine Meadow FC

CUMNOCK   1 - 1   KILWINNING RANGERS
Kerr   Adams

(after extra-time
Kilwinning Rangers won 7-6 on penalties)

'ARDROSSAN & SALTCOATS HERALD'
AYRSHIRE CUP

THIRD ROUND
Irvine Victoria 2   Muirkirk 2
(after extra-time - Muirkirk won 5-4 on penalties)
Kello Rovers 0   Kilwinning Rangers 9
(played at Kilwinning)
Kilbirnie Ladeside 1   Irvine Meadow 0
Lugar Boswell Thistle 1   Hurlford United 0

SEMI-FINALS
Kilbirnie Ladeside 1   Kilwinning Rangers 2
Lugar Boswell Thistle 2   Muirkirk 0

FINAL
Thursday, 13th June 2002. At Hurlford FC

KILWINNING RNGRS 2-0 LUGAR BOSWELL THISTLE
Adams, Geoghegan

Cumnock, winners of the Kerr & Smith League Cup. The team celebrated winning the League Cup at Somerset Park, Ayr. They beat Irvine Meadow 3-2.

Photo: John B Vass

Lindsay (Auchinleck Talbot) watches McGinty (Cumnock) look at the name on the ball!
Photo: John B Vass

Troon v Arthurlie. Wyte & Mackay West of Scotland Cup Quarter Final. Troon won but lost in the semi-final to Benburb who went on to win the cup.
Photo: John B Vass

EAST AYRSHIRE CUP

SEMI-FINALS
Auchinleck Talbot 5   Hurlford United 1
Darvel 3   Kello Rovers 1

FINAL
Wednesday, 5th June 2002. At Glenafton Athletic FC

AUCHINLECK TALBOT   5 - 0   DARVEL
Friels (2), Hyslop (2), Watson

NORTH AYRSHIRE CUP

SEMI-FINALS
Irvine Victoria 0   Beith 4
Largs Thistle 0   Kilbirnie Ladeside 3

FINAL
Sunday, 2nd June 2002. At Largs Thistle FC
KILBIRNIE LADESIDE   2 - 1   BEITH
Lyon, Hughes pen   Anderson

SOUTH AYRSHIRE CUP

SEMI-FINALS
Annbank United 1   Troon 2
Whitletts Victoria 1   Maybole 1
(after extra-time - Maybole won 5-4 on penalties)

FINAL
Wedmesday, 29th May 2002. At Whitletts Victoria FC
MAYBOLE   2 - 1   TROON
Creamer (2)   Baxter

AYRSHIRE SUPER CUP

SEMI-FINALS
Kilbirnie Ladeside 1   Auchinleck Talbot 1
(after extra-time -
Kilbirnie Ladeside won 4-3 on penalties)
Troon 1   Maybole 0

FINAL
Wednesday, 12th June 2002. At Troon
TROON   0 - 1   KILBIRNIE LADESIDE
Grant

WEST OF SCOTLAND CUP
(for Ayrshire and Central Region clubs)

QUARTER-FINALS
Bellshill Athletic 0   Benburb 1
Neilston 1   Johnstone Borough 3
Troon 1   Arthurlie 1
(after extra-time - Troon won 6-5 on penalties)
Vale of Leven 3   Kilwinning Rangers 0

SEMI-FINALS
Benburb 3   Troon 1
(at Kilwinning Rangers FC)
Johnstone Borough 2   Vale of Leven 1
(at Pollok FC)

FINAL
Saturday, 11th May 2002. At Pollok FC
BENBURB   3 - 2   JOHNSTONE BOROUGH
Sharkey, Tinney   Donnelly
Fontana   McLay
Attendance: 1,500

CENTRAL LEAGUE

PREMIER DIVISION

	P	W	D	L	F	A	Pts
Johnstone Borough	22	12	6	4	36	27	42
Larkhall Thistle	22	12	3	7	39	30	39
Pollok	22	12	2	8	41	33	38
Neilston Juniors	22	12	2	8	41	36	38
Benburb	22	10	5	7	34	20	35
Maryhill	22	9	5	8	39	31	32
Arthurlie	22	9	4	9	33	29	31
Cambuslang Rangers	22	9	4	9	26	28	31
Cumbernauld United	22	6	7	9	24	38	25
Renfrew	22	6	4	12	26	34	22
Petershill	22	6	4	12	29	41	22
Lanark United	22	3	6	13	20	41	15

DIVISION ONE

	P	W	D	L	F	A	Pts
Shettleston	26	16	5	5	59	27	53
Shotts Bon Accord	26	14	8	4	50	30	50
Bellshill Athletic	26	14	7	5	52	32	49

The above were promoted.

Other positions: Rutherglen Glencairn (47 points), East Kilbride Thistle (43), Greenock (40), Blantyre Victoria (37), Kilsyth Rangers (37), Kirkintilloch Rob Roy (35), Vale of Leven (26), Lesmehagow (26), Dunipace (25), St Anthony's (18), Carluke Rovers (15).

DIVISON TWO

	P	W	D	L	F	A	Pts
Glasgow Perthshire	22	13	6	3	50	32	45
Vale of Clyde	22	14	0	8	45	29	42
St Rochs	22	12	4	6	34	28	40

The above were promoted.

Other positions: Port Glasgow (45 points), Thorniewood United (35), Baillieston (34), Yoker Athletic (31), Forth Wanderers (28), Royal Albert (26), Stonehouse Violet (24), Ashfield (20), Coltness United (40, Wishaw (0 - withdrew without completing the league).

EVENING TIMES CUP WINNERS CUP

SEMI-FINALS
Johnstone Borough 0   Shettleston 0
(after extra-time - Johnstone Boro won 3-1 on penalties)
Glasgow Perthshire 0   Bellshill Athletic 0
(after extra-time - Bellshill Athletic won 5-4 on penalties)

FINAL
Saturday, 8th June 2002 at Kirkintilloch Rob Roy FC

JOHNSTONE BOROUGH   3-1   BELLSHILL ATHLETIC
Donnelly, McLay,   *Brownlie*
Brolly
Attendance: 500

Ellis of Troon on the prowl in the Whyte & Mackay West of Scotland Cup semi-final, Troon v Benburb. Photo: John B Vass

BEATONS LEAGUE CUP

QUARTER-FINALS
Bellshill Athletic 0   Arthurlie 0
(after extra-time - Bellshill Athletic won 4-2 on penalties)
Larkhall Thistle 0   Cambuslang Rangers 0
(after extra-time - Larkhall Thistle won 5-4 on penalties)
Lanark United 2   Vale of Leven 1
Maryhill 1   Pollok 2

SEMI-FINALS
Larkhall Thistle 2   Lanark United 2
(after extra-time - Larkhall Thistle won 4-3 on penalties)
Pollok 2   Bellshill Athletic 2
(Bellshill Athletic won 4-3 on penalties)

FINAL
Tuesday, 2nd October 2000. At Firhill Park, Glasgow

BELLSHILL ATHLETIC   3 - 0   LARKHALL THISTLE

CENTRAL LEAGUE CUP

QUARTER-FINALS

Kirkintilloch Rob Roy 0   Greenock 1
Shettleston 2   Benburb 0
Shotts Bon Accord 4   East Kilbride Thistle 2
Vale of Clyde 1   Johnstone Borough 3

SEMI-FINALS
Greenock 2   Shettleston 3
Shotts Bon Accord 1   Johnstone Borough 3

FINAL
Saturday, 1st June 2002. At Petershill FC

SHETTLESTON   4 - 1   JOHNSTONE BOROUGH
Kelly (2)   *Anderson*
Thomson, Jack
Attendance: 1,000.

CLYDESDALE CHALLENGE CUP

SEMI-FINALS
Forth Wanderers 2   Lesmehagow 3
Lanark United 3   Carluke Rovers 1

FINAL
Monday, 6th August 2001 at Lesmehagow FC

LESMEHAGOW   2 - 3   LANARK UNITED
Melvin pen, Carr   *Young, Bratney, Irvine*

(NB: Lanark United won this competition for the
fifth successive season)

EAST REGION

DIVISION ONE

	P	W	D	L	F	A	Pts
Linlithgow Rose	22	18	1	3	60	20	55
Whitburn Juniors	22	12	4	6	46	28	40
Bathgate Thistle	22	11	5	6	40	32	38
Bonnyrigg Rose	22	10	2	10	35	31	32
Edinburgh United	22	9	5	8	32	32	32
Arniston Rangers	22	9	4	9	37	45	31
Bo'ness United	22	9	3	10	35	38	30
Camelon Juniors	22	8	3	11	38	43	27
Armadale Thistle	22	6	5	11	31	43	23
Newtongrange Star	22	6	5	11	28	46	23
Musselburgh Athletic	22	6	3	13	35	50	21
Haddington Athletic	22	5	4	13	33	48	19

DIVISION TWO

	P	W	D	L	F	A	Pts
Fauldhouse United	24	16	8	0	89	20	56
Bonnybridge	24	14	5	5	52	33	47

The above two clubs were promoted.
Other positions: Sauchie (45 points), Pumpherston (43), Dalkeith Thistle (40), Dunbar United (38), Broxburn Athletic (30), Blackburn United (28), Harthill Royal (23), Tranent (23), West Calder United (22), Livingston United (21), Stoneyburn (19)

LEADING GOALSCORERS

35	I McMurray (Fauldgouse United)
30	D Flynn (Linlithgow Rose)
31	D McGlynn (Whitburn)
28	M McGinlay (Broxburn Athletic)
23	D Beaton (Linlithgow Rose),
	G Herd (Sauchie),
	R McDonald (Pumpherston),
	C McFadden (Camelon).

CARLSBERG LEAGUE CUP

THIRD ROUND
Bonnybridge 1   Camelon 1
(Camelon won 5-4 on penalties after extra-time)
Dalkeith Thistle 0   Haddington Athletic 2
Dunbar United 5   Armadale Thistle 2
Linlithgow Rose 3   Newtongrange Star 2

SEMI-FINALS
Camelon 6   Dunbar United 4
(at Linlithgow)
Haddington United 1   Linlithgow Rose 2
(at Newtongrange)

FINAL
Wednesday 19th September 2001 at Bathgate Thistle

CAMELON   1 - 4   LINLITHGOW ROSE
McKeever   *Flynn (2), Whyte, McMahon*

Top:
OVD Scottish Junior Cup Second Round Whitletts Victoria v St Rochs
Photo: John B Vass

Bottom left:
OVD Scottish Junior Cup Third Round replay Auchinleck Talbot v Ashfield
Photo: John B Vass

Bottom right:
OVD Scottish Junior Cup Second Round replay Troon v Blantyre Victoria
Photo: John B Vass

CALDERS EAST OF SCOTLAND CUP

THIRD ROUND
Bathgate Thistle 2   Livingstone United 2
(after extra-time - Bathgate Thistle won 3-1 on penalties)
Camelon 2   Dunbar United 2
(after extra-time - Camelon won 3-1 on penalties)
Musselburgh Athletic 4   Bonnyrigg Rose 1
Sauchie 0   Whitburn 3

SEMI-FINALS
Musselburgh Athletic 1   Bathgate Thistle 0
Whitburn 1   Camelon 1
(after extra-time - Whitburn won 4-1 on penalties)

FINAL
Saturday, 8th June 2002 at Arniston Rangers FC

MUSSELBURGH ATHLETIC   1 - 2   WHITBURN
Hall   *Clouston, Gilmour*

DOUG M'AL CUP
(formerly Brown Cup)

QUARTER-FINALS
Blackburn United 1   Tranent 1
(after extra-time - Blackburn Utd won 4-2 on penalties)
Broxburn Athletic 1   Whitburn 1
(after extra-time - Broxburn won 4-3 on penalties)
Linlithgow Rose 2   Bonnybridge 1
Musselburgh 0   Fauldhouse United 1

SEMI-FINALS
Fauldhouse United 0   Linlithgow Rose 3
Whitburn 2   Blackburn United 1

FINAL
Wednesday, 12th June 2002 at Armadale

LINLITHGOW ROSE   3 - 2   WHITBURN
Flynn 2,1 pen, Whyte   *McGlynn, Ramage*

STREAMLINE TAXIS CUP
(Formerly St Michael's Cup)

QUARTER-FINALS
Bo'ness United 1   Camelon 1
(after extra-time - Bo'ness united won 5-4 on penalties)
Edinburgh United 1   Musselburgh Athletic 1
(after extra-time - Edinburgh Utd won 6-5 on penalties)
Fauldhouse United 4   Whitburn 1
Linlithgow Rose 5   Tranent 0

SEMI-FINALS
Bo'ness United 2   Fauldhouse United 2
(after extra-time - Fauldhouse Utd won 6-5 on penalties)
Linlithgow Rose 5   Edinburgh United 0

FINAL
Wednesday, 5th June 2002 at Whitburn FC

LINLITHGOW ROSE   2 - 1   FAULDHOUSE UNITED
Whyte, Corcoran   *Jaffa*

OVD Scottish Junior Cup First Round
Auchinleck Talbot v Edinburgh United. Talbot were the
beaten finalists
Photo: John B Vass

HEINEKEN FIFE & LOTHIANS CUP

FOURTH ROUND
Newtongrange Star 0   Armadale Thistle 1
Pumpherston 0   Linlithgow Rose 4
St Andrews United 0   Hill of Beath Hawthorn 2
Thornton Hibs 1   Whitburn 0

SEMI-FINALS
Hill of Beath Hawthorn 4   Thornton Hibs 2
Linlithgow Rose 3   Armadale Thistle 2

FINAL
Saturday, 1st June 2002 at Camelon FC

LINLITHGOW ROSE 6-5 HILL OF BEATH HAWTHORN
Flynn (3,1 pen),   Dair (3), Noble, Whitelaw
Beaton, Creaney,
Dickov

NB: After leading 2-0 the Hill of Beath went behind 3-5
before the final flourish and huge scoreline

FIFE REGION

FIFE LEAGUE

	P	W	D	L	F	A	Pts
Hill of Beath Hawthorn	28	22	3	3	98	27	69
Glenrothes	28	17	5	6	68	28	56
Oakley United	28	16	8	4	60	25	56
Thornton Hibs	28	17	5	6	62	34	56
Lochore Welfare	28	17	1	10	86	45	52
Kelty Hearts	28	15	7	6	46	28	52
St Andrews United	28	15	4	9	60	48	47
Crossgates Primrose	28	13	8	7	50	35	47
Dundonald Bluebell	28	14	3	11	58	49	45
Newburgh	28	10	7	11	42	40	37
Rosyth Recreation	28	10	2	16	44	53	32
Tulliallan Thistle	28	4	3	21	31	81	15
Lochgelly Albert	28	4	2	22	38	97	14
Steelend Victoria	28	3	4	21	27	76	13
Kirkcaldy YM	28	1	2	25	23	127	5

PEDDIE SMITH MALOCCO CUP

QUARTER-FINALS
Glenrothes 2   Lochore Welfare 1
Hill of Beath Hawthorn 4   Lochgelly Albert 0
Newburgh 2   Crossgates Primrose 1
(after extra-time)
Oakley United 2   Dundonald Bluebell 0

SEMI-FINALS
Newburgh 2   Hill of Beath Hawthorn 2
(after extra-time - Hill of Beath won 4-2 on penalties)
Glenrothes 2   Oakley United 0

FINAL
Sunday, 2nd September 2001 at Lochore Welfare FC

GLENROTHES   3 - 3   HILL OF BEATH HAWTHORN
(after extra-time - Hill of Beath won 5-3 on penalties)
Own goal, Andrew pen,   Smith, Thompson, Wardlaw
McPhee
Attendance: 400

STELLA ARTOIS CUP

SECOND ROUND
Dundonald Bluebell 0   Oakley United 1
Lochgelly Albert 1   Glenrothes 3
Lochore Welfare 2   Crossgates Primrose 1
Thornton Hibs 2   Hill of Beath Hawthorn 4

SEMI-FINALS
Hill of Beath Hawthorn 2   Lochore Welfare 0
Oakley United 1   Glenrothes 5

FINAL
Saturday, 29th May 2002 at Dundonald Bluebell FC
GLENROTHES   2 - 1   HILL OF BEATH HAWTHORN
Caithness,   Gray
McKinlay pen

INTERBREW CUP

QUARTER-FINALS
Dundonald Bluebell 0   Glenrothes 1
Hill of Beath Hawthorn 0   Oakley United 2
Lochore Welfare 3   Kelty Heart 1
Thornton Hibs 3   Steelend Victoria 1

SEMI-FINALS
Glenrothes 2   Thornton Hibs 1
Oakley United 2   Lochore Welfare 1

FINAL
Tuesday, 4th June 2001 at Hill of Beath Hawthorn

OAKLEY UNITED   2 - 0   GLENROTHES
Lister, Newbiggins

NORTH REGION

EAST SECTION

PRINTAGRAPH PREMIER DIVISION

	P	W	D	L	F	A	Pts
Formartine United	26	19	6	1	70	31	63
Culter	26	18	5	3	71	36	59
FC Stoneywood	26	13	8	5	62	42	47
Sunnybank	26	14	4	8	73	34	46
Banks o'Dee	26	13	3	10	56	34	42
East End	26	11		11	51	55	37
Hermes	26	10	5	11	55	59	35
Stonehaven	26	9	7	10	48	44	34
Longside	26	10	3	13	37	49	33
Cruden Bay	26	9	3	14	36	61	30
Wilsons XI	26	9	2	15	34	59	29
Glentanar	26	7	7	12	62	59	28
Deveronside	26	6	2	18	34	69	20
Buchanhaven Hearts	26	2	5	19	19	74	11

CAMSTRUCTION DIVISION ONE EAST

	P	W	D	L	F	A	Pts
Lads Club	27	15	8	4	63	26	53
Lewis United	27	10	10	7	53	36	40
Banchory St Ternan	27	10	10	7	57	46	40
Dyce Juniors	27	10	8	9	42	45	38
Ellon United	27	11	4	12	52	41	37
Fraserburgh Ubited	27	9	9	9	46	55	36

Other positions: Turriff United (34 points), Hall Russell United (33), Parkvale (28), Maud (24).

GRILL LEAGUE CUP
QUARTER-FINALS
Culter 3   Banks o'Dee 4
Glentanar 7   Buckie Rovers 1
Nairn St Ninian 0   Stonehaven 2
Sunnybank 3   Strathspey Thistle 1

SEMI-FINALS
Banks o'Dee 4   Glentanar 4
(after extra-time - Glentanar won 9-8 on penalties)
Sunnybank 3   Stonehaven 1

FINAL
Sunday, 28th October 2001 at Keith Park, Aberdeen
SUNNYBANK   1 - 0   GLENTANAR
(after extra-time)
Clark

ROLLSTUD REGIONAL CUP
QUARTER-FINALS
Banks o'Dee 0   New Elgin 1
Culter 4   Buchanhaven Hearts 0
Stonehaven 4   Glentanar 1
Wilsons XI 0   Sunnybank 4

SEMI-FINALS
New Elgin 1   Culter 3
(at Lossiemouth)
Sunnybank 2   Stonehaven 1

FINAL
Thursday 2nd May 2002 at Pittodrie, Aberdeen
CULTER   0 - 3   SUNNYBANK

*OVD Scottish Junior Cup Fourth Round replay
Auchinleck Talbot v Banks O'Dee, a much postponed
tie. Talbot lost in the final, while "Dee" were the North's
last survivors. Photo: John B Vass*

ACORN HEATING CUP
QUARTER-FINALS:
Banks o'Dee 1   Stoneywood 1
(after extra-time - Banks o'Dee won 4-3 on penalties)
Cruden Bay 0   Culter 1
Hermes 5   Buchanhaven Hearts 3
Wilsons XI 1   Formartine United 2

SEMI-FINALS
Banks O'Dee 0   Culter 6
Formartine United 4   Hermes 3

FINAL
Friday, 31st May 2002. At Sunnybank
FORMARTINE UNITED   1 - 0   CULTER

MORRISON TROPHY
QUARTER-FINALS
Hall Russell United 1   Fraserburgh United 2
Maud 2   Dyce Juniors 4
Parkvale 0   Lewis United 1
Turriff United 4   Banchory St Ternan 0

SEMI-FINALS
Dyce Juniors 2   Turriff United 2
(after extra-time - Dyce Juniors won 5-3 on penalties)
Lewis United 1   Fraserburgh United 0

FINAL
Friday, 10th May 2002 at Woodside Sports Complex
DYCE JUNIORS   2 - 1   LEWIS UNITED

CONCEPT GROUP
INTER-REGIONAL TROPHY
(for Tayside and North clubs)
FOURTH ROUND
Bankfoot Athletic 0   North End 5
Blairgowrie 0   Carnoustie Panmure 4
Sunnybank 3   Hermes 0
Tayport 5   Forfar West End 0

SEMI-FINALS
North End 1   Sunnybank 2
Tayport 1   Carnoustie Panmure 0

FINAL
Saturday, 25th May 2002 at Keith Park, Aberdeen
TAYPORT   5 - 1   SUNNYBANK
Craik (3), Stewart   Moreland
McGlashan
(North End won 3-0 on penalties)

WEST SECTION

SCOTSCOUP DIVISION ONE WEST

	P	W	D	L	F	A	Pts
Strathspey Thistle	28	21	5	2	102	29	68
Nairn St Ninian	28	18	7	3	71	38	61
Forres Thistle	28	18	6	4	92	27	60
Islavale	28	18	3	7	83	39	57
New Elgin	28	16	4	8	76	48	52
Dufftown	28	15	6	7	57	49	51

Other positions: Whitehills (47 points),
Bishopmill United (39), Buckie Rovers (36), Kinloss (32),
Burghead Thistle (31),   Lossiemouth United (27),
RAF Lossiemouth (16), Fochabers (13),
Portgordon United (7).

GORDON WILLIAMSON CUP

SECOND ROUND
Bishopmill United 1   Forres Thistle 3
Islavale 5   Burghead Thistle 1
New Elgin 0   Strathspey Thistle 2
Whitehills 1   Buckie Rovers 1

SEMI-FINALS
Buckie Rovers 1   Islavale 3
Forres Thistle 3   Strathspey Thistle 3
(after extra-time - Strathspey won 4-3 on penalties)

FINAL
STRATHSPEY THISTLE   3 - 2   ISLAVALE
Ross, Hendry, Rodgers   *Anderson og,*
                                      Massie

TOP SCORERS (SCOTSCOUP LEAGUE)
38   B Minty (Forres Thistle)
37   T Dagtas (Strathspey Thistle)
25   M Wood (Islavale)
24   D Woolam (Nairn St Ninian)
23   B Whitlock (Burghead Thistle)

TAYSIDE REGION

PREMIER DIVISION	P	W	D	L	F	A	Pts
Tayport	22	17	4	1	69	21	55
Carnoustie Panmure	22	18	1	3	60	24	55
Dundee North End	22	11	4	7			37
Dundee Violet	22	8	9	5	40	28	33
Forfar West End	22	9	6	7	41	36	33
Elmwood	22	7	5	10	34	47	26
Lochee United	22	6	6	10	32	41	24
Broughty Athletic	22	8	0	14	34	46	24
Downfield	22	5	8	9	31	48	23
Kirrie Thistle	22	5	8	9	26	43	23
Bankfoot Athletic	22	6	4	12	29	47	22
Arbroath SC	22	3	3	16	37	67	12

DIVISION ONE	P	W	D	L	F	A	Pts
Montrose Roselea	22	17	4	1	55	22	55
East Craigie	22	13	4	5	48	32	43

The above two clubs are promoted.
Other positions: Jeanfield Swifts (40 points), Arbroath
Victoria (38), Scone Thistle (35), Forfar Albion (33),
Blairgowrie (31), Kinnoull (28), Coupar Angus (20),
Lochee Harp (18), Brechin Victoria (18), Luncarty (12).

LEAGUE PLAY-OFF:
Arbroath Sports Club 2   Jeanfield Swifts 1
Arbroath Victoria 2   Bankfoot Athletic 1
Bankfoot Athletic relegated
Arbroath Sports Club stay in Premier Division.

DJ LAING CUP

QUARTER-FINALS
Arbroath Sports Club 0   Montrose Roselea 1
North End 5   Jeanfield Swifts 0
Tayport 5   Broughty Athletic 1
Dundee Violet 5   Luncarty 0

SEMI-FINALS
North End 3   Dundee Violet 1
Tayport 1   Montrose Roselea 0

FINAL
TAYPORT   2 - 0   NORTH END
Stewart, Kenneth

HERSCHEL TROPHY
Wednesday, 15th August 2001 at Dundee Violet FC
TAYPORT   3 - 0   BANKFOOT ATHLETIC
Grant, Harris,
Kenneth

REDWOOD LEISURE
FIFE & -TAYSIDE CUP

THIRD ROUND
Dundonald Bluebell 0   Hill of Beath Hawthorn 2
Kirrie Thistle 2   Glenrothes 3
Lochore Welfare 1   Carnoustie Panmure 1
(after extra-time - Lochore won 4-2 on penalties)
Thornton Hibs 3   Tayport 2

SEMI-FINALS
Lochore Welfare 1   Hill of Beath Hawthorn 3
Thornton Hibs 0   Glenrothes 1
(after extra-time)

FINAL
Saturday, 8th June 2002 at Dundonald Bluebell FC
HILL OF BEATH HAWTHORN   2 - 1   GLENROTHES
Smart pen, Noble   *Barr*

NORTH END CHALLENGE CUP

THIRD ROUND
Broughty Athletic 1   Carnoustie Panmure 2
Downfield 2   Arbroath Sports Club 1
Jeanfield Swifts 2   Montrose Roselea 4
Tayport 2   Dundee Violet 1

SEMI-FINALS
Carnoustie Panmure 2   Montrose Roselea 1
Tayport 2   Downfield 1

FINAL
Tuesday, 11th June 2002 at Dundee North End FC
TAYPORT   2 - 2   CARNOUSTIE PANMURE
(after extra-time - Carnoustie won 3-1 on penalties)
Kenneth, Evans   *Webster, Miller*

FINDLAY & COMPANY TROPHY

THIRD ROUND
Arbroath Sports Club 1   Dundee Violet 2
Forfar West End 0   Carnoustie Panmure 1
North End 3   Kinnoull 3
(after extra-time - North End won 3-2 on penalties)
Tayport 4   Arbroath Victoria 0
(at Arbroath)

SEMI-FINALS
Carnoustie Panmure 5   Dundee Violet 1
Tayport 2   North End 0

FINAL
Saturday, 1st June 2002 at Lochee United FC
TAYPORT   2 - 1   CARNOUSTIE PANMURE
Craik, Stewart   *Bonella*

ROSEBANK CAR CENTRE CUP

SECOND ROUND
Arbroath Victoria 4   Coupar Angus 0
Blairgowrie 1   Kinnoull 4
East Craigie 2   Lochee Harp 0
Forfar Albion 2   Montrose Roselea 0

SEMI-FINALS
Forfar Albion 2   Arbroath Victoria 2
(after extra-time - Forfar Albion won 4-3 on penalties)
Kinnoull 2   East Craigie 1

FINAL
Thursday, 30th May 2002 at Downfield FC
KINNOULL   5 - 5   FORFAR ALBION
(after extra-time - Kinnoull won 4-2 on penalties)
Kelly (3),   Duncan, Anderson,
Boylan,   Lawson, Nesbitt,
Dunlop   West

DOWNFIELD SC CUP

SECOND ROUND
Arbroath Victoria 1   East Craigie 2
Brechin Victoria 1 Montrose   Roselea 2
(after extra-time)
Jeanfield Swifts 3   Kinnoull 2
Lochee Harp 3   Blairgowrie 2

SEMI-FINALS
East Craigie 1   Montrose Roselea 4
Jeanfield Swifts 1   Lochee Harp 0

FINAL
Monday, 10th June 2002 at Downfield
JEANFIELD SWIFTS 4 - 3 MONTROSE ROSELEA
(after extra-time)
Hamilton, D Mitchell,   Simpson, own goal,
S Mitchell, Christie   Ferrie

SUMMARY
THE outstanding Junior club in Scotland was without doubt Linlithgow Rose, who not only won the OVD Scottish Junior Cup in a most entertaining final against Auchinleck Talbot, but also topped their own East Region League and took four other knock-out cups, one of them - the Heineken Cup for Fife and Lothians teams - in a final of eleven goals with Rose scoring the all important extra one against Hill of Beath Hawthorn, Fife's top club.

Further North in Tayside both Tayport and Carnoustie Panmure had good seasons and the best team in the North Region was Formartine United, who were League champions and winners of one of the cup competitions, although the likes of Culter, Stoneywood and Sunnybank could look back with satisfaction on their performances.

In the West Glenafton had a fine league season to finish comfortably clear to take the Ayrshire honours ahead of Cumnock, Kilwinning Rangers and Auchinleck Talbot, the cup exploits of the latter two probably harming their league chances, while the Central League had two good sides in champions Johnstone Borough and Larkhall Thistle, although to many people they play in the strongest Junior competition in Scotland.

All in all it was a fine campaign and possibly emphasised the point that, if Scotland is to prosper in international terms against other nations in the semi-professional sphere, players from junior clubs should be considered for selection.

Highland League Cup Final

Forres Mechanics. Back Row (l-r): Charles Brown, William McLean (Trainer), Stephen MacLean, Martin Murphy (Capt), Mark McRitchie, Johnston Bellshaw, Gary Ross, Steven McIntosh, Neil Whyte, Gordon Connelly (Mngr). Front Row: Stuart Cameron, Craig Reid, Ewwn Grigor, Andrew MacLeod, Roy Main, Gavin Hayden, Scott Moore, David McIvor

Deveronvale. Back Row (l-r): Lenny Binnie (Trainer), Steve Dolan, Darren McAllister, David Henderson, Fraser Speirs, Derek Craigie, Barry Thompson, Mark Smith, Mike McKenzie, Mark Chisholm, Ian McIvor. Front Row: Paul Urquhart, Barrie Stephen, Franny More, Nigel Montgomery (Capt), Gregg Carrol (Mngr), Paul Stewart, Robbie Brown, Jamie Watt, Mathew Kinghorn

SENIORS

HIGHLAND LEAGUE TABLE

	P	W	D	L	F	A	Pts
Fraserburgh	28	20	4	4	71	36	64
Deveronvale	28	19	4	5	68	27	61
Buckie Thistle	28	15	8	5	51	28	53
Clachnacuddin	28	13	10	5	60	39	49
Keith	28	14	5	9	57	37	47
Cove Rangers	28	12	7	9	72	60	43
Inverurie Locos	28	12	4	12	48	43	40
Brora Rangers	28	12	4	12	47	55	40
Huntly	28	11	6	11	46	36	39
Forres Mechanics	28	9	10	9	49	47	47
Lossiemouth	28	9	6	13	24	40	33
Nairn County	28	6	8	14	44	61	26
Fort William	28	7	2	19	30	61	23
Wick Academy	28	5	4	19	21	59	19
Rothes	28	2	6	20	24	83	12

Fraserburgh won the championship for the first time since the 1937-38 season. In a thrilling final match they needed a point at Allan Park, Cove, to clinch the title and a crowd of 2,000 was there to see them do it by the odd goal in three against the defending champions thanks to two opportunist first half goals from the youthful striker McLaren.

Two goals up at half-time and against ten men, Cove defender Murphy having been sent off for an alleged head-but on Stephen, they had to avoid some anxious moments before the crowning ending.

QUALIFYING CUP NORTH

FIRST ROUND:
Cove Rangers 3   Brora Rangers 1
Fort William 2   Clachnacuddin 2
Fraserburgh 1   Forres Mechanics 2
Huntly 1   Buckie Thistle 3
Keith 1   Nairn County 2
Lossiemouth 0   Wick Academy 1
Rothes 1   Golspie Sutherland 1
Replays: Clachnacuddin 4   Fort William 0
Golspie Sutherland 2   Rothes 1

SECOND ROUND
Deveronvale 3   Clachnacuddin 1
Buckie Thistle 8   Golspie Sutherland 0
Forres Mechanics 2   Cove Rangers 2
Nairn County 2   Wick Academy 2
Replays: Cove Rangers 2   Forres Mechanics 3
Wick Academy 5   Nairn County 0

SEMI-FINALS
Buckie Thistle 0   Forres Mechanics 0
Wick Academy 1   Deveronvale 2
Replay
Forres Mechanics 0   Buckie Thistle 2

FINAL
Saturday, 27th October 2001. At Kynoch Park, Keith
BUCKIE THISTLE   1 - 5   DEVERONVALE
Thomson   Murray 2, Watt 2, Brown
H.T. 0-5   Attendance: 1,800.

BUCKIE THISTLE: Rae; Grant, Lamberton, Anderson, McPherson, Davidson, Holmes, Stephen, Thomson, Bruce, Reid. Substitutes: Craik for Davidson, 46 minutes, Rattray for Bruce 74 minutes, Green for Holmes 76 minutes. Substitutes not used: Milne, Rowley. Sent off: Anderson 11 minutes. Yellow card: Grant.
DEVERONVALE: Thompson; Dolan, Kinghorn, Chisholm, Henderson, Montgomery, More, Pressley, Murray, Watt, Urquhart. Substitutes: Brown for Chisholm 16 minutes, Smith for More 67 minutes. Substitutes not used: Stephen, Craigie, Speirs. Yellow card: Henderson.
Referee: C MacKay.

This match, which provided the Banff club with its first Qualifying success for 50 years, was over as a contest at half-time, by which point they had taken a five-goal lead and had to face the second half with only ten Buckie players to oppose them, Anderson having been dismissed after only eleven minutes for a foul when he was the last man.

Murray scored from the resulting free kick and was again on the scoresheet eight minutes later, with substitute Brown adding to the tally after 25 minutes.

Two fine efforts by Watt in the closing stages of the first half effectively settled the issue and Buckie could only say in reply that Thomson's magnificent drive to bring his team some consolation was the best goal of the game.

The losers could also claim that they might have been awarded a penalty in the very first minutes of the match when Davidson seemed to be pulled down in the area, but the referee waved play on and Holmes brought the best out of Thompson after fifteen minutes, when a goal-bound shot was tipped over the crossbar, but then came the Anderson disaster - and the rest is history.

ABERDEENSHIRE CUP

FIRST ROUND
Fraserburgh 0   Deveronvale 8
Huntly 2   Aberdeen 'A' 0
Inverurie Locos 0   Cove Rangers 1
Keith 1   Buckie Thistle 1
Replay: Buckie Thistle 1   Keith 4

SEMI-FINALS
Deveronvale 2   Keith 1
Huntly 0   Cove Rangers 2

FINAL
22nd September 2001. At Pittodrie Stadium. Aberdeen
COVE RANGERS   1 - 1   DEVERONVALE
(Score at 90 minutes - 0-0;
Cove Rangers won 5-4 on penalties)
Beattie 98   Chisholm 106

COVE RANGERS: M Coull; Pilichos, Mullen, Adams, Megginson, Baxter (captain), Coutts, Taylor, K Coull, Beattie, Brown. Substitutes not used: Marwick, Jappie, McHattie, Emslie, Charles. Booked: Beattie 44 for foul, Pilichos 44 for foul.
DEVERONVALE: Thompson; Dolan, Kinghorn, Henderson, Chisholm, Montgomery, Smith, Brown, McKenzie, Watt, Moore. Substitutes: McAllister 61 for Smith, Presslie 67 67 for Brown. Not used: Urquhart, Craigie, Stewart. Booked: Brown 40 for foul, Henderson 78 for foul.
Referee: A Freeland.

McEWAN'S LAGER
NORTH OF SCOTLAND CUP

FIRST ROUND
Golspie Sutherland 0 Inverness Caledonian Thistle 'A' 2
Lossiemouth 3 Forres Mechanics 3
(after extra time -Lossiemouth won 4-3 on penalties)
Ross County 'A' 5 Elgin City 'A' 1
Wick Academy 0 Rothes 1

QUARTER-FINALS
Brora Rangers 0 Nairn County 1
Clachnacuddin 2 Lossiemouth 1
Inverness Caledonians Thistle 'A' 1 Ross County 'A' 0
(after extra-time)*
Rothes 1 Fort William 2

SEMI-FINALS
Clachnacuddin 2 Nairn County 2
(after extra-time: Clachnacuddin won 8-7 on penalties)
Fort William 1 Inverness Caledonian Thistle 'A' 1
(after extra-time. Inverness won 9-8 on penalties)

FINAL
22 September 2001. At Caledonian Stadium, Inverness
CLACHNACUDDIN 2 - 0 INV CAL THISTLE 'A'
McPherson 15, Polworth 89

CLACHNACUDDIN: Rae; Skinner, S MacLeod, Allan, Matheson, MacCuish, Mitchell, B MacLeod, MacPherson, Polworth, Brennan. Substitutes: Bruce MacCraw for MacPherson 60 minutes, Douglas for Matheson 89 minutes. Not used: Sanderson, Barry MacCraw, Williamson.
INVERNESS CALEDONIAN THISTLE 'A': Ridgers; Chisholm, Smith, Gilfillan, G Munro, McRae, Stewart, McMillan, D MacDonald, Calder, Low. Substitute: MacKinnon for McMillan 55 minutes. Not used: J Munro, MacInnes, Rich, Sutherland.
Referee: E Robertson.

ABERDEENSHIRE SHIELD

FIRST ROUND
Deveronvale 0 Inverurie Loco Works 1
Fraserburgh 1 Cove Rongers 0
Huntly 3 Buckie Thistle 3
(after extra-time - Huntly won 4-3 on penalties)

SEMI-FINALS
Keith 4 Inverurie Loco Works 1
Fraserburgh 2 Buckie Thistle 1

FINAL
28th November 2001. At Harlaw Park, Inverurie
FRASERBURGH 2 - 3 KEITH
*Stephen pen, Main   Patterson, Still,
                                        McKenzie*
H.T. 0-3. Attendance: 527.
FRASERBURGH: Gordon; Milne, Geddes, Bisset, Finnie, Fleming, Norris, Mackie, Main, Wemyss, Stephen. Sebstitutes: Hunter for Finnie 56 minutes, McLaren for Mackie 85 minutes.
KEITH: Thain; Cheyne, Simmers, Craig, McKenzie, Morrison, Still, Robertson, Cadger, Smith, Patterson.
Subs: Henderson for Patterson 79 mins, Nicol for Cadger 87 mins.
Referee: C Mackay.

INVERNESS CUP

SECOND ROUND
Brora Rangers 1 Ross County 'A' 3
Elgin City 'A' 3 Fort William 1 *(after extra-time)*
Inverness Caledonian Thistle 'A' 8 Forres Mechanics 1
Nairn County 1 Clachnacuddin 3

SEMI-FINALS
Inverness Caledonian Thistle 'A' 7 Elgin City 'A' 1
Ross County 'A' 5 Clachnacuddin 0

FINAL
12 December 2001. At Caledonian Stadium, Inverness
INV CAL THISTLE 'A' 3 ROSS COUNTY 'A' 2
Bavidge, Munro, MacDonald   Mackay, Hislop
Attendance: 508

INVERNESS CALEDONIAN THISTLE 'A': Calder; Duncan, Golabeck, Jardine, Tokely, Munro, MacRae, MacDonald, Bavidge, Bagan, McBain, Substitutes: Stewart for MacRae 62 minutes, Robson for McBain 62 minutes.
ROSS COUNTY 'A': Gonet; Campbell, Hastings, Maxwell, Webb, Cowie, Anselin, Tarrant, Gethins, Hislop, MacKay. Substitutes: Bookras for Gethins 53 minutes, McCormick for Tarrant 63 minutes. Sent off: McCormick 90 minutes.
Referee: E Robertson.

SOCCER WORLD INTER LEAGUE CUP

FIRST ROUND
Buckie Thistle 1 Annan Athletic 1
(after extra-time - Buckie Thistle won 4-3 on penalties)
Cove Rangers walked over Tarff Rovers (scratched)
Girvan walked over Whitehill Welfare (scratched)
St Cuthbert Wanderers 1 Huntly 2

SEMI-FINAL
Huntly 1 Buckie Thistle 0
Cove Rangers walked over Girvan (scratched)

FINAL
Wednesday, 1st June 2002. At Harlaw Park, Inverurie
COVE RANGERS 1 - 0 HUNTLY
Copland

COVE RANGERS: Charles; Summers, MacCraw, McHattie, Murphy, Adam, Brown, Craig, K Coull, Beattie (captain), Coutts. Substitutes: Emslie for Coutts nine minutes, Pilichos for Craig 60 minutes, Copland for Summers 87 minutes.
HUNTLY: Bremner; Campbell, Hendry, Allan, Small, Guild, Nicol, Stewart, Munro, Wilson, Farmer. Substitute: Cairns for Wilson nine minutes. Yellow card: Wilson.
Referee: E Robertson. Attendance: 350 (approx).

Substitute Copland landed a last minute goal to bring success to Cove Rangers, their second of the season, and on the whole it was just about deserved in a well contested match.

Cove Rangers' young star Coutts was the victim of an early bad challenge from Huntly's Wilson, who was also assisted off the field after being yellow-carded, a lenient penalty for the offence.

HIGHLAND LEAGUE CUP

FIRST ROUND
Buckie Thistle 1 Forres Mechanics 1
(Forres Mechanics won 5-4 on penalties)
Clachnacuddin 4 Deveronvale 4
(3-3 at 90 minutes, Deveronvale won 5-3 on penalties)
Cove Rangers 5 Nairn County 2
Fort William 0 Inverurie Loco Works 3
Huntly 2 Wick Academy 0 *(after extra-time)*
Keith 3 Rothes 0
Lossiemouth 4 Fraserburgh 2

QUARTER-FINALS
Cove Rangers 2 Inverurie Loco Works 1
Deveronvale 3 Keith 0
Forres Mechanics 2 Brora Rangers 1
Lossiemouth 2 Huntly 1 *(after extra-time)*

SEMI-FINALS
Forres Mechanics 3 Cove Rangers 0
Deveronvale 5 Lossiemouth 0

FINAL
Saturday, 11th May, 2002. At Kynoch, Park, Keith
DEVERONVALE 1 - 1 FORRES MECHANICS
Watt pen   *Ross*
Half-time: 0-0. 90 minutes and after extra-time: 1-1
Forres Mechanics won 4-3 on penalties

FORRES MECHANICS: McRitchie; Hayden, Main, Reid, McLean, MacIntosh, Whyte, Murphy (captain), Ross, Connelly, MacLeod. Substitutes: Brown for MacLeod 70 minutes, Grigor for Main 71 minutes, Moore for Connelly 113 minutes. Johnston and McIver did not play. Booked: Reid, MacLean, McIntosh.
Penalties (all successful): Reid, Hayden, Murphy, Ross.

DEVERONVALE: Thompson; Dolan, Kinghorn, Chisholm, Henderson, Montgomery (captain), More, Pressley, Craigie, Murray, Urquhart. Substitutes: Watt for Craigie 51 minutes, McAllister for More 65 minutes, Nicol for Chisholm 75 minutes. Stewart and Speirs did not play. Booked: McAllister.
Penalties: McAllister, Urquhart, Nicol (missed), Murray, Pressley (missed). **Referee:** S Duff. **Attendance:** 1,100.
Man of the Match: Main (Forres Mechanics)

THE SEASON for the Highland League clubs ended in appropriate fashion with a thrilling League Cup Final at Kynoch Park, Keith, on a beautiful afternoon in a delightful setting and two hours of end to end action could only be best settled by a penalty shoot-out, which the Can-Cans (the cup holders) duly won thanks to having cooler heads available.

Although the retiring Forres veteran Roy Main was made man of the match by the club's goalkeeper, Mark McRitchie, must have run him close, as he not only saved two of the vital penalties, but had a similar success after fifteen minutes of the first half, when he correctly guessed the intended direction of a rather harshly awarded decision.

Vale did in fact have the better of the first half, but the Morayshire club came into their own after the break and took the lead through an excellent lob by their striker Gary Ross.

They looked as if they would hold onto the advantage until another penalty award in injury time gave Watt the chance to equal accounts, but early in extra time he

was injured and could not continue, which left Vale playing the rest of the match a man short. This left them with an inability to take advantage of much territorial pressure.

The referee, 26-year-old Steven Duff, had a sound game and looks to have a good future. He had also handled the match at Allan Park, Cove, earlier in the week when Fraserburgh won the Championship for the first time since 1938, and on that occasion too he had been impressive especially when matters looked likely to go out of control.

HIGHLAND LEAGUE YOUTH CUP

FINAL
Sunday, 12th May 2002. At Kynoch Park, Keith
FRASERBURGH 1 - 0 HUNTLY
McLaren
Half-time: 0-0

QUALIFYING CUP SOUTH

PRELIMINARY ROUND
Burntisland Shipyard 2 Edinburgh University 0
St Cuthbert Wanderers 2 Spartans 3
Selkirk 1 Girvan 2
Vale of Leithen 7 Wigtown & Badenoch 1
Whitehill Welfare 2 Hawick Royal Albert 0

FIRST ROUND
Annan Athletic 2 Civil Service Strollers 0
Coldstream 3 Dalbeattie Star 2
Gala Fairydean 2 Vale of Leithen 1
Glasgow University 0 Preston Athletic 1
Spartans 3 Edinburgh City 1
Tarff Rovers 6 Newton Stewart 0
Threave Rovers 3 Girvan 0
Whitehill Welfare 6 Burntisland Shipyard 1

SECOND ROUND
Annan Athletic 2 Spartans 3
Coldstream 2 Tarff Rovers 4
Preston Athletic 1 Gala Fairydean 1
Threave Rovers 1 Whitehill Welfare 0
Replay: Gala Fairydean 1 Preston Athletic 0

SEMI-FINALS
Gala Fairydean 2 Tarff Rovers 3
Spartans 0 Threave Rovers 0
Replay: Threave Rovers 0 Spartans 2

FINAL
3rd November 2001. At Palmerston Park, Dumfries
SPARTANS 2 - 1 TARFF ROVERS
Hughes, Manson   *Beattie*

EAST OF SCOTLAND LEAGUE

PREMIER DIVISION	P	W	D	L	F	A	Pts
Spartans	22	18	3	1	61	16	57
Whitehill Welfare	22	16	4	2	49	16	52
Annan Athletic	22	11	3	8	53	40	36
Threave Rovers	22	10	3	9	40	36	33
Vale of Leithen	22	9	6	7	32	33	33
Edinburgh City	22	8	4	10	35	36	28
Lothian Thistle	22	8	3	11	38	43	27
Craigroyston	22	7	5	10	42	52	25
Coldstream	22	6	7	9	42	52	25
Gala Fairydean	22	6	5	11	24	48	23
Pencaitland & Ormiston	22	4	5	13	28	52	17
Edinburgh University	22	4	2	16	22	55	14

DIVISION ONE	P	W	D	L	F	A	Pts
Preston Athletic	22	17	2	5	63	27	53
Peebles Rovers	22	15	5	2	58	23	50
Easthouses Lily	22	12	3	7	45	38	39
Kelso United	22	11	3	8	50	42	36
Dalbeattie Star	22	10	6	6	42	39	36
Eyemouth United	22	11	2	9	40	39	35
Civil Service Strl	22	11	0	11	49	34	33
Edinburgh Athletic	22	8	5	9	39	44	29
Tollcross United	22	6	3	13	35	48	21
Selkirk	22	4	6	12	35	47	18
Heriot Watt University	22	6	0	16	26	54	18
Hawick Royal Albert	22	2	3	17	21	68	9

IMAGE PRINTERS
EAST OF SCOTLAND CUP

FIRST ROUND
Civil Service Strollers 7 Pencaitland-Ormiston 1
Coldstream 2 Eyemouth United 0
Edinburgh University 0 Craigroyston 2
Preston Athletic 0 Tollcross United 0
Vale of Leithen 3 Edinburgh Athletic 2
Replay: Tollcross United 3 Preston Athletic 2

SECOND ROUND
Coldstream 2 Whitehill Welfare 3
Craigroyston 2 Spartans 8
Easthouses Lily 3 Civil Service Strollers 3
Gala Fairydean 4 Edinburgh City 1
Hawick Royal Albert 2 Lothian Thistle 4
Heriot Watt University 3 Selkirk 2
Kelso United 2 Tollcross United 0
Peebles Rovers 1 Vale of Leithen 2
Replay: Civil Service Strollers 3 Easthouses Lily 1

THIRD ROUND
Kelso United 2 Heriot Watt University 0
Lothian Thistle 1 Civil Service Strollers 2
Spartans 3 Gala Fairydean 2
Vale of Leithen 1 Whitehill Welfare 2

SEMI-FINALS
Spartans 3 Kelso United 1
Whitehill Welfare 5 Civil Service Strollers 2

FINAL
Saturday, 27th April 2002. At Lothian Thistle
SPARTANS 2 - 1 WHITEHILL WELFARE
(after extra-time - 1-1 after 90 minutes)
Hobbins (2)   *Gowrie og*

KING CUP

FIRST ROUND
Easthouses Lily 3 Kelso United 3
(Kelso United won 4-2 on penalties)
Edinburgh Athletic 0 Peebles Rovers 2
Edinburgh University 2 Coldstream 1
Lothian Thistle 0 Tollcross United 4
Selkirk 0 Pencaitland-Ormiston 3

SECOND ROUND
Craigroyston 4 Tollcross United 0
Edinburgh University 3 Edinburgh City 2
Eyemouth United 1 Preston Athletic 0
Gala Fairydean 1 Vale of Leithen 0
Hawick Royal Albert 3 Peebles Rovers 6
Kelso United 1 Pencaitand-Ormiston 1
(Kelso United won 7-6 on penalties)
Spartans 3 Civil Service Strollers 1
Whitehill Welfare 2 Heriot Watt University 0

THIRD ROUND
Edinburgh University 0 Gala Fairydean 2
Kelso United 2 Spartans 4
Peebles Rovers 1 Craigroyston 2
Whitehill Welfare 2 Eyemouth United 1

SEMI-FINALS
Craigroyston 0 Gala Fairydean 2
Spartans 1 Whitehill Welfare 0

FINAL
Friday, 3rd May 2002. At Preston Athletic
SPARTANS 4 - 2 GALA FAIRYDEAN
Hobbins, Own goal,   *Martin (2, 1 pen)*
Hughes, Tulloch

ALEX JACK CUP

FIRST ROUND
Heriot Watt University 1 Pencaitland-Ormiston 2
Tollcross United 2 Easthouses 4

SECOND ROUND
Easthouses Lily 4 Craigroyston 0
Edinburgh Athletic 4 Eyemouth United 2
Lothian Thistle 0 Kelso United 1
Pencaitland-Ormiston 1 Peebles Rovers 2

SEMI-FINALS
Easthouses Lily 4 Peebles Rovers 3
Kelso United 1 Edinburgh Athletic 1
Replay: Edinburgh Athletic 2 Kelso United 3

FINAL
Sunday, 4th November 2001. At Vale of Leithen.
EASTHOUSES LILY 1 - 2 KELSO UNITED
Sinnett   *Jackson, Tait*

EAST LEAGUE CUP

FIRST ROUND
Coldstream 2   Eyemouth United 1
Dalbeattie Star 1   Annan Athletic 4
Gala Fairydean 4   Heriot Watt University 3
Kelso United 0   Lothian Thistle 3
Preston Athletic 1   Spartans 2
Selkirk 2   Easthouses Lily 1
Tollcross United 1   Pencaitland-Ormiston 2
Vale of Leithen 0   Whitehill Welfare 2

SECOND ROUND
Easthouses 2   Civil Service Strollers 3
Edinburgh Athletic 0   Whitehill Welfare 1
Edinburgh City 4   Threave Rovers 2
Gala Fairydean 1   Coldstream 2
Hawick Royal Albert 0   Craigroyston 2
Peebles Rovers 0   Edinburgh University 2
Pencaitland-Ormiston 3   Annan Athletic 1
Spartans 5   Lothian Thistle 1

THIRD ROUND
Coldstream 0   Civil Service Strollers 1
Edinburgh City 2   Pencaitland-Ormiston 0
Spartans 3   Craigroyston 0
Whitehill Welfare 3   Edinburgh University 1

SEMI-FINALS
Civil Service Strollers 3   Spartans 5 *(after extra-time)*
Edinburgh City 2   Whitehill Welfare 2
(after extra-time - Edinburgh City won 6-5 on penaltieS)

FINAL
Tuesday, 7th May 2002. At Whitehill Welfare
EDINBURGH CITY   1 - 0   SPARTANS
Rennie

LEADING SCORERS
28	P Hobbins (Spartans)	24	C Manson (Spartans)
24	S O'Donnell (W'hill W)	22	J Bird (Spartans)
22	J Martin (Gala F'dean)	21	T Currie (C.S. Strllers)
21	B Davies (C.S. Strllers)	21	S Shennan (C'stream)
20	A Sinnett (East. Lily)	17	G Harley (Peebles R)

SOUTH OF SCOTLAND LEAGUE

	P	W	D	L	F	A	Pts
Tarff Rovers	28	22	0	6	119	32	66
Girvan	28	21	3	4	93	42	66
St Cuthbert Wanderers	28	18	4	6	100	45	58
Creetown	28	17	4	7	86	55	55
Stranraer Athletic	28	17	3	8	81	50	54
Dumfries FC	28	13	5	10	61	71	44
Annan Athletic A	28	13	4	11	74	65	43
Dalbeattie Star A	28	10	6	12	60	63	36
Gretna A	28	11	3	14	63	86	36
Threave Rovers A	28	11	1	16	52	67	34
Nithsdale Wanderers	28	7	6	15	45	58	27
Crichton Royal	28	8	3	17	52	96	27
Wigtown & Badenoch	28	7	3	18	42	94	24
Abbeyvale	28	5	4	19	35	76	19
Newton Stewart	28	4	3	21	50	113	15

POTTS CUP

FIRST ROUND
Gretna 'A' 3   Creetown 4 (after extra-time)
Newton Stewart 3   Abbeyvale 1
Stranraer Athletic 4   Annan Athletic 2 (after etxra-time)
Tarff Rovers 2   Dumfries FC 6

SECOND ROUND
Creetown walked over Newton Stewart
Crichton Royal 2   St Cuthbert Wanderers 6
Tarff Rovers 5   Dumfries FC 2 (played at Dumfries)
Wigtown & Badenoch 2   Stranraer Athletic 3

SEMI-FINALS
St Cuthbert Ewanderers 3   Stranraer Athletic 0
Tarff Rovers 6   Creetown 0

FINAL
ST CUTHBERT WANDERERS   1-3   TARFF ROVERS
McGill   *Beattie(2), Lamont*

HAIG GORDON CUP

FIRST ROUND
Dumfries FC 0 Annan Athletic 1
St Cuthbert Wanderers 6 Abbeyvale 1
Tarff Rovers walked over Newton Stewart (disqualified)
Threave Rovers 3 Stranraer Athletic 4
Wigtown & Badenoch 0 Creetown 1

SECOND ROUND
Creetown 1   Tarff Rovers 3
Crichton Royal 3   Dalbeattie Star 0
Gretna 'A' 0   Stranraer Athletic 2
St Cuthbert Wanderers 1   Annan Athletic 0

SEMI-FINALS
Crichton Royal walked over Stranraer Athletic
Tarff Rovers 3   St Cuthbert Wanderers 0

FINAL
CRICHTON ROYAL   1 - 4   TARFFF ROVERS
Glendinning   *Hanlon, Montgomery,*
                       Lamont, R Paterson

CREE LODGE CUP

FIRST ROUND
Abbeyvale 1 Crichton Royal 2
Annan Athletic 0 Tarff Rovers 3
Creetown 3 Gretna 'A' 2
Newton Stewart 2 St Cuthbert Wanderers 6
Stranraer Athletic 2 Dalbeattie Star 1
Wigtown & Badenoch 1 Threave Rovers 6

SECOND ROUND
Crichton Royal 1   Tarff Rovers 3
Dumfries FC 0   Girvan 3
St Cuthbert Wanderers 4   Creetown 0
Threave Rovers 2   Stranraer Athletic 2
(after extra-time - Threave Rovers won 9-8 on penelties)

SEMI-FINALS
Girvan 3   Tarff Rovers 0
St Cuthbert Wanderers 1   Threave Rovers 1
(after extra-time - St Cuthbert won 6-5 on penalties)

FINAL
GIRVAN   1 - 0   ST CUTHBERT WANDERERS
Wilson

TWEEDIE CUP

FIRST ROUND
Abbeyvale 2 Girvan 4
Creetown 1 St Cuthbert Wanderers 3
Crichton 2 Annan Athletic 1
Dumfries FC 0 Gretna 'A' 4
Newton Stewart 1 Tarff Rovers 8
Wigtown & Badenoch 4 Threave Rovers 2

SECOND ROUND
Dalbeattie Star 1 Stranraer Athletic 0
(Dalbeattie Star disqualified after match)
Girvan 0 Gretna 'A' 4
Tarff Rovers 2 Crichton Royal 3 (at Crichton Royal)
Wigtown & Badenoch 0 St Cuthbert Wanderers 2

SEMI-FINALS
Crichton Royal 0 Gretna 'A' 2
Stranraer Athletic 2 St Cuthbert Wanderers 2
(after extra-time - St Cuthbert won 5-4 on penalties)

FINAL
6th April 2002. At St Cuthbert Wanderers, Kirkcudbright

ST CUTHBERT WANDERERS 2 - 1 GRETNA 'A'
Crosbie (2)   *Milligan*

SOUTHERN COUNTIES CHALLENGE CUP

FIRST ROUND
Abbeyvale 1 Gretna 'A' 5
Crichton Royal 0 Annan Athletic 4
Dumfries FC 1 Tarff Rovers 1
(after extra-time - Tarff Rovers won 4-3 on penalties)
Stranraer 'A' walked over Newton Stewart
Stranraer Athletic 3 Dalbeattie Star 3
(after extra-time -Stranraer won 9-8 on penalties)
Threave Rovers 2 St Cuthbert Wanderers 0
Wigtown & Badenoch 0 Queen of the South 'A' 6

SECOND ROUND
Creetwon 2 Tarff Rovers 2
(after extra-time - Tarff Rovers won 4-2 on penalties)
Dalbeattie Star 1 Gretna 'A' 2
Queen of the South 'A' 4 Threave Rovers 1
Stranraer 'A' 1 Annan Athletic 2

SEMI-FINALS
Queen of the South 'A' 0 Annan Athletic 2
Tarff Rovers 5 Gretna 'A' 1

FINAL
Monday, 29th April 2002. At Tarff Rovers, Kirkcowan

TARFF ROVERS 3 - 0 ANNAN ATHLETIC
Lamont (2), Irving

DETROIT TROPHY

TOP SIX FINAL POSITIONS:
Tarff Rovers (86 points), Girvan (78 points)
St Cuthbert Wanderers (69 points)
Stranraer Athletic (64 points) Creetown (57 points)

NORTH CALEDONIAN LEAGUE

	P	W	D	L	F	A	Pts
Invergordon	18	14	3	1	58	13	45
Alness United	18	12	3	3	53	21	39
Golspie Sutherland	18	12	2	4	45	24	38
Thurso	18	10	4	4	33	22	34
Halkirk United	18	7	4	7	39	28	25
Tain St Duthus	18	7	1	10	39	26	22
Bunilidh Thistle	18	5	4	9	26	47	19
Balintore	18	4	3	11	33	52	15
Bonar Bridge	18	4	1	13	35	50	13
Dornoch	18	2	1	15	21	89	7

'POST SERVICES' CHIC ALLAN CUP

1ST ROUND
Dornoch 0 Alness United 5
Halkirk 2 Invergordon 1

SECOND ROUND
Balintore 1 Golspie Sutherland 5
Bonar Bridge 1 Thurso 3
Bunilidh Thistle 0 Alness United 9
Tain St Duthus 0 Halkirk 4

SEMI-FINALS
Alness United 2 Halkirk 1
Thurso 1 Golspie Sutherland 2

FINAL
Saturday, 3rd November 2001. At Brora Ronagers
GOLSPIE SUTHERLAND 3 - 1 ALNESS

PCT CUP

FIRST ROUND
Bunilidh Thistle 5 Dornoch 0
Halkirk 3 Thurso 5

SECOND ROUND
Balintore 0 Alness United 5
Bunilidh Thistle 1 Golspie Sutherland 5
Invergordon 2 Bonar Bridge 1
Thurso 3 Tain St Duthus 0

SEMI-FINALS
Alness United 4 Invergordon 1
Golspie Sutherland 0 Thurso 1

FINAL
Saturday, 6th April 2002. At Golspie
THURSO 2 - 1 ALNESS UNITED

MORRIS NEWTON CUP

FIRST ROUND
Bonar Bridge 4 Bunilidh Thistle 1
Tain St Duthus 1 Balintore 3

SECOND ROUND
Bonar Bridge 5 Dornoch 0
Golspie Sutherland 2 Alness United 1 *(after extra-time)*
Halkirk United 1 Thurso 6 *(after extra-time)*
Invergordon 1 Balintore 0

SEMI-FINALS
Golspie Sutherland 4 Bonar Bridge 0
Thurso 0 Invergordon 0 *(aet, 6p7)*

FINAL
Saturday, 27th April 2002. At Ross County FC, Dingwall
GOLSPIE SUTHERLAND 4 - 1 INVERGORDON

FOOTBALL TIMES CUP

FIRST ROUND
Bunilidh Thistle 2 Tain St Duthus 1
Thurso 1 Golspie Sutherland 1 (after extra-time -
Golspie Sutheralnd won 5-4 on penalties)

SECOND ROUND:
Balintore 1 Alness United 2
Dornoch 1 Bunilidh Thistle 5
Halkirk United 1 Golspie Sutherland 2 *(after extra-time)*
Invergordon 0 Bonar Bridge 1 *(after extra-time)*

SEMI-FINALS
Alness United 3 Bonar Bridge 4 *(after extra-time)*
Golpsie Sutherland 1 Bunilidh 5

FINAL
Saturday, 11th May 2002. At Brora Rangers
BONAR BRIDGE 1 - 2 BUNILIDH THISTLE

NON-LEAGUE CLUBS IN THE SCOTTISH CUP

FIRST ROUND
Stirling Albion 2 Buckie Thistle 1
Tarff Rovers 1 Montrose 4
Wick Academy 2 Threave Rovers 3

SECOND ROUND
Deveronvale 0 Spartans 0 (Replay: 2-1)
East Stirlingshire 1 Forres Mechanics 1 *(Replay: 1-3)*
Forfar Athletic 2 Threave Rovers 0
Gala Fairydean 1 Stirlng Albion 0

THIRD ROUND
Deveronvale 0 Ayr United 6
Dundee United 3 Forres Mechanics 0
Gala Fairydean 0 Forfar Athletic 5

SENIOR NON-LEAGUE SUMMARY

THERE are in effect four senior non-League competitions in Scotland with 64 teams, some of them reserve sides, which is a small number considering the size of competitions elsewhere and the toughest tournaments are the Highland League and East of Scotland League, from whose numbers Scotland's selectors foolishly restricted their range of choice for the Home Nations Semi-Professional matches at the end of the season in England with three losses from three outings being the inevitable outcome.

The outstanding sides over the season were Spartans, who won all but one of the five competitions in the East, which involved them, including the South Qualifying Cup, but they narrowly lost a Scottish Cup Second Round tie after a replay against Highland League Deveronvale, who themselves not only won the North Qualifying Cup, but also were runners-up in the league narrowly to Fraserburgh (their first success since 1938), in the Aberdeenshire Cup and the Highland League Cup, both finals being lost on penalties to Cove Rangers and Forres Mechanics respectively.

With Clachnaccuddin and Keith also winning good cup competitions the North was no one-club show, nor was this the case in the South of Scotland League where Tarff Rovers from Kirkcowan eventually won the title, but Girvan and St Cuthbert Wanderers from Kirkcudbright did well enough to banish any complacency. In fact the South did well to go through a season without too many hassles after the dreadful foot and mouth horrors of the previous campaign.

Any competition in Britain, which takes place near the Arctic Circle and survives, can also congratulate itself, so the North Caledonian League, won well by Invergordon, can take a bow as should Wick Academy, who late in 2001 staged the furthest North national cuptie ever held in Britain, when they entertained Threave Rovers from way down in Castle Douglas - and lost narrowly in a thriller!

In general it is a struggle for the clubs to survive, but no-one should underestimate them, as Stirling Albion will testify from their Second Round Scottish Cup defeat against Gala Fairydean in the Borders.

Anyone, who attends matches in the various competitons, should be heartened by the marvellous enthusiasm of the fans and on that very basis they will survive and entertain.

SCOTTISH AMATEUR CUP

FINAL
Sunday, 19th May 2002. At Hampden Park, Glasgow
DUMBARTON 2 - 4 HARESTANES (Kirkintilloch)
Rennie,   *Davies (2), Whitson, Tennent*
McDonald pen   Half-time: 2-2

DUMBARTON: Grindley; K Brown, Graham, Paterson, McBride, Kemp, McCuaig, McDonald (captain), KR Brown, Marshall. Susbtitutes: Docherty, McGinley (both played), Burns, Connolly, McGilvray.

HARESTANES; McNab, Gillon, Gallagher, Harrison, Tennent, Whitson, Keaveney, Cameron, Meghan, McGoldrick, Davies. Substitutes: Hart, Stevenson (both played), Currie, Findlay, Hunter.

A THOROUGHLY entertaining match was eventually settled thanks in no small way to Man of the Match Mark Davies, who scored twice and was always a thorn in the flesh of 'Accies', who were the better side in the first half and deserved to reach the interval ahead, but were foiled by an equalising goal from the Harestanes hero.

AMATEUR FOOTBALL ALLIANCE

President: F J Banner

Company Secretary: Mike Brown, 55 Islington Park Street, London N1 1QB
Tel: 020 7359 3493   Fax: 020 7359 5027
Website: www.amateur-fa.org   Email: A.F.A.@dial.Pipex.com

A.F.A. CUP COMPETITIONS

In addition to the Challenge Cups there are two other AFA Cup competitions:
The Invitation Cup - presented by Wellesley Jack - for some time held in abeyance, until recently.
The Greenland Memorial Cup - presented by Pegasus FC - is competed for in an annual memorial game between AFA League Champions, selected by the Cup Committee.

W E GREENLAND MEMORIAL CUP
(Inaugurated 1971)

Ignatians	v	Wokingians	4-0

SENIOR CHALLENGE CUP
(Inaugurated 1908)

Roe'n O Meadonians	v	O Actonians	4p2, 1*1

INTERMEDIATE CHALLENGE CUP
(Inaugurated 1908 as the Junior Cup -
re-named 1977-78)
(all 2nd XI's unless otherwise stated)

Acton O. Aloysians	v	O. Owens	1*0

JUNIOR CHALLENGE CUP
(Inaugurated 1923 as the Minor Cup -
re-named 1977-78)
(all 3rd XI's unless otherwise stated)

Wal'stow O.Challon'rs Res	v	O. Aloysians	1-0

MINOR CHALLENGE CUP
(Inaugurated 1955 as Novets Cup -
aka Novets Senior 1973-77)
(all 4th XI's unless otherwise stated)

Carsh'n O. Tenisonians	v	Nat Westmin'r Bank	3-0

SENIOR NOVETS CHALLENGE CUP
(Inaugurated 1973 as the Junior Novets Cup -
re-named 1977)
(all 5th XI's unless otherwise stated)

E Barnet Civil Service	v	O. Finchleians	3-1

INTERMEDIATE NOVETS CHALLENGE CUP
(Inaugurated 1985)
(all 6th XI's unless otherwise stated)

Mill Hill Norsemen	v	O. Actonians Assn	2-1

JUNIOR NOVETS CHALLENGE CUP
(Inaugurated 1980)

Hampton Outcasts 1st	v	O. Actonians 8th	3-2

VETERANS' CHALLENGE CUP
(Inaugurated 1978 - All Veterans' Teams)

Wal'stow Winchmore Hill	v	O. Parmiter'ns A'	2-1

OPEN VETERANS' CHALLENGE CUP
(Inaugurated 1986 - All Veterans' Teams)

W. Hill Frenford Snr	v	Old Parmiterians	4-2

COUNTY DIVISIONAL CUP COMPETITIONS
FINALISTS - SEASON 2001 - 02

SENIOR:

Essex			
Hale End Ath	v	O. Parmiterians	5-3
Middlesex			
O. Actonians Assn	v	Polytechnic	1-3
Surrey			
Carshalton	v	HSBC	0-2

INTERMEDIATE:

Essex			
Hale End Athletic Rs	v	O. Buckwellians	5-0
Kent			
J P Morgan	v	Dresdner K W	2-3
Middlesex			
O. Hamptonians Rs	v	BB Eagles Res	1-2
Surrey			
Nottsborough Res	v	Carshalton Res	3-2

AMATEUR FOOTBALL ALLIANCE

A.F.A. REPRESENTATIVE GAMES - 2001-02

Civ Serv Nat'l XI (Trial)	(Chiswick)	Won 4-2
Oxford University	(Iffley Rd)	Won 4-0
Army F.A.	(Dulwich)	Drawn 1-1
Royal Navy F.A.	(Portsm'h)	Won 2-1
London University	(Motspur Pk)	Won 2-1

RAF F.A., Cambridge University & London FA cancelled

PLAYERS GAINING REPRESENTATIVE TIES
SEASON 2001 - 02

Neil Backers (Carshalton)
Neil Gillard (UCL Academicals)
Harry Hoffen (Old Harrovians)
Dennis Watson (Old Ignatians)
Martin Woodrow (UCL Academicals)

UNDER 16 HOME COUNTIES YOUTH COMPETITION
(Entered for the first time)

02.12.01	v	Sussex County F A	Lost 0-2
27.02.02	v	London F A	Lost 1-2
10.03.02	v	Middlesex County FA	Lost 0-2
24.03.02	v	Surrey County F A	Lost 4-5
24.04.02	v	Kent County F A	Lost 0-3

U-16 YOUTH CHALLENGE CUP
(Inaugurated 1997)

1997
Roeh'n O. Salesians	v	O. Actonians Ass'n	2-1

1998
Roeh'n O. Salesians	v	Norsemen	3-1

1999
W. Hill Norsemen	v	O. Parmiterians	4-0

2000
W'side Pk Norsemen	v	O. Parmiterians "A"	8-0

2001
Barnet Norsemen	v	O. Parmiterians	8-2

2002
Alex'a Pk Aloysians	v	Carshalton	3*2

OTHER YOUTH CUP FINALS

Saturday
U-18
Battersea Park Rngrs	v	Young Parmiterians	4-1

U-16
Thornton United	v	Young Parmiterians	2-1

Sunday
U-18
Latymerians	v	Alexandra Park	2-0

U-16
Aloysians	v	Carshalton	3*2

U-15
Sheen Tigers	v	Providence	2-1

U-14
Parmiterians "A"	v	Providence	3-1

U-13
St John's Walworth	v	London Lions	1-7

U-12
Bethwin Boys	v	Providence	1-5

U-11
Bec United	v	Bethwin Boys	5-0

U-13
Palace North	v	Palace South	4-0

U-12
Palace South	v	Palace North	1-3

U-11
Parmiterians	v	Palace Raiders	2*3

ARTHUR DUNN CUP

Old Chigwellians	v	Old Reptonians	2-1

ARTHURIAN LEAGUE

PREMIER DIVISION	P	W	D	L	F	A	Pts
Old Reptonians	16	11	3	2	43	23	25
Old Brentwoods	16	9	5	2	39	21	23
Old Carthusians	16	8	3	5	39	30	19
Old Etonians	16	6	2	8	42	35	14
Lancing Old Boys	17	7	0	9	37	38	14
Old Harrovians	16	6	2	8	33	39	14
Old Salopians	16	6	1	9	35	40	13
Old Chigwellians	16	5	3	8	24	41	13
Old Cholmeleians	16	3	3	10	24	49	7

DIVISION 1	P	W	D	L	F	A	Pts
Old Westminsters	14	13	1	0	50	9	27
Old Foresters	14	11	0	3	59	18	22
Old Bradfieldians	14	8	1	5	46	21	17
Old Wykehamists	14	6	2	6	26	38	14
Old Witleians	14	6	0	8	26	40	12
Old Malvernians	14	4	1	9	21	41	9
Old Aldenhamians	14	4	1	9	23	45	9
Old Wellingburians	14	1	0	13	18	57	0

DIVISION 2	P	W	D	L	F	A	Pts
Old Salopians Res	12	7	2	3	40	26	16
Old Etonians Res	12	7	2	3	33	21	16
Old Carthusians Res	12	6	2	4	22	23	14
Old Chigwellians Res	12	6	1	5	22	24	13
Old Etonians 3rd	12	4	2	6	23	24	10
Old Brentwoods Res	12	4	2	6	26	38	10
Lancing Old Boys Res	12	1	3	8	16	26	5

DIVISION 3	P	W	D	L	F	A	Pts
Old Cholmeleians Res	12	9	1	2	35	9	17
Old Carthusians 3rd	12	6	3	3	26	17	15
Old Foresters 3rd	12	4	4	4	19	24	12
Old Bradfieldians Res	12	4	3	5	25	22	11
Old Aldenhamians Res	12	3	4	5	30	49	10
Old Foresters Res	12	4	1	7	34	29	9
Old Harrovians Res	12	3	2	7	18	37	8

DIVISION 4	P	W	D	L	F	A	Pts
Old Haileyburians	14	12	0	2	49	13	24
Old Cholmeleians 3rd	14	12	0	2	39	13	22
Old Malvernians Res	14	9	1	4	51	23	19
Old Brentwoods 3rd	14	8	1	5	42	27	17
Old Reptonians Res	14	7	1	6	37	38	15
Old Eastbournians	14	2	0	12	19	53	4
Old Foresters 4th	14	2	1	11	16	41	3
Old Cholmeleians 4th	14	2	0	12	16	61	0

DIVISION 5

6 Teams. Won by: Old Westminsters Res

JUNIOR LEAGUE CUP

O. Haileyburians 1st v O. Etonians 3rd   5-1

J DIXSON 6-A-SIDE CUP

Won by O. Chigwellians

DERRIK MOORE VETERANS' CUP

O. Cholmeleians v O. Brentwoods   3-0

LONDON FINANCIAL F A

DIVISION ONE	P	W	D	L	F	A	Pts
Dresdner Kleinwortt W	16	12	3	1	60	23	39
Coutts & Co.	16	11	2	3	38	21	35
Mount Pleasant P O	16	8	4	4	47	27	28
J P Morgan	16	6	4	6	36	28	22
Granby	16	5	6	5	32	31	21
Bank of America	16	5	5	6	35	41	20
Royal Sun Alliance	16	3	4	9	30	48	13
Chelsea Exiles	16	3	3	10	25	65	11
Citibank	16	1	5	10	25	44	8

DIVISION TWO	P	W	D	L	F	A	Pts
Churchill Insurance	21	16	2	3	94	46	50
Zurich Eagle Star	21	16	1	4	107	38	49
Marsh	21	11	4	6	62	50	37
Royal Sun Alliance Rs	21	7	7	7	63	49	28
Granby Res	21	4	7	10	39	66	19
C Hoare & Co	21	5	4	12	50	88	19
Coutts & CO. Res	21	4	5	12	37	71	17
Foreign & C'wealth Off.	21	3	6	12	34	78	15

DIVISION THREE	P	W	D	L	F	A	Pts
Citibank Res	16	10	4	2	49	24	34
Marsh Res	16	10	3	3	63	26	33
Salomon Smith Barney	16	10	2	4	47	30	32
Royal Bank of Scotland	16	9	3	4	59	37	30
Royal Sun Alliance 3rd	16	8	1	7	50	32	25
Credit Suisse First Bstn	16	6	1	9	42	57	19
Temple Bar	16	3	5	8	33	45	14
Zurich Eagle Star Res	16	4	2	10	28	61	14
Customs & Excise	16	1	1	14	19	78	4

DIVISION FOUR	P	W	D	L	F	A	Pts
Marsh 3rd	16	11	2	3	58	39	35
Granby 4th	16	10	2	4	45	35	32
Temple Bar Res	16	9	1	6	56	36	28
Standard Chrtd Bank	16	7	3	6	40	28	24
GEFC	16	7	2	7	45	47	23
Granby 3rd	16	6	3	7	30	37	21
Bank of Ireland	16	5	4	7	42	39	19
Royal Bank of Scot Rs	16	5	1	10	30	52	16
South Bank Cuaco 5th	16	2	2	12	32	65	8

CHALLENGE CUP

Bank of England v Coutts & Co.   3-1

REPRESENTATIVE MATCHES

v Southern Amateur League	Lost 1-4
v Old Boys' League	Lost 1-5
v Royal Marines	Drawn 0-0

LONDON LEGAL LEAGUE

DIVISION 1	P	W	D	L	F	A	Pts
Denton Wilde Sapte "A"	18	12	3	3	52	18	39
Eversheds	18	11	1	6	40	25	34
Slaughter & May	18	10	2	6	47	34	32
Gray's Inn	18	9	3	6	36	19	29
KPMG ICE	18	9	1	8	31	33	28
Linklaters & Alliance	18	9	0	9	35	40	27
Lovells	18	7	5	6	31	39	26
Fleet FRK	18	5	3	10	25	30	17
Clifford Chance	18	4	3	11	30	46	15
Nabarro. Nathanson	18	3	1	14	19	62	10

DIVISION II	P	W	D	L	F	A	Pts
Watson Farley & Wllms	18	15	2	1	53	17	47
CMS Cameron McKenna	18	12	1	5	49	27	37
Allen & Overy	18	8	3	7	48	34	27
Baker & McKenzie	18	8	3	7	28	40	27
Norton Rose	18	8	1	9	49	45	25
Herbert Smith	18	7	4	7	26	43	25
Simmons & Simmons	18	8	0	10	41	33	24
Nicholson Graham & J	18	7	2	9	34	38	21
Barlow Lyde & Gilbert	18	6	2	10	30	43	20
Taylor Joynson Garrett	18	1	2	15	16	54	3

DIVISION III	P	W	D	L	F	A	Pts
Freshfields	18	14	2	2	60	20	44
Richards Butler	18	13	1	4	78	33	40
Titmuss Sainer Dechert	18	11	1	6	49	31	34
Macfarlanes	18	8	2	8	51	50	24
Financial Services A	18	5	7	6	43	49	22
S J Berwin & Co	18	6	3	9	31	23	21
Hammonds Sds Edge	18	7	1	10	16	29	21
Denton Wilde Sapte (B)	18	6	0	12	21	63	18
Pegasus (Inner Temple)	18	4	4	10	36	55	16
Stephenson Harwood	18	5	1	12	30	62	16

CHALLENGE CUPS:

LEAGUE
Denton Wilde Sapte 'A'   v   KPMG ICE   4-2

WEAVERS ARMS
Herbert Smith   v   Allen & Overy   6-4

LONDON OLD BOYS' CUPS

Senior:
Old Wilsonians   v   Latymer Old Boys   1-0

Intermediate:
Albanian Res   v   Old Bradfieldians   2-0

Junior:
Old Challoners Res   v   Old Suttonians 3rd 1-0

Minor:
Holland Park OB Res v   Old Edmontonians 3rd 2-1

Novets:
Old Edmontonians 4th v   Old Uffingtonians 3rd 3-2

Drummond:
Old Actonians An. 6th v Albanian 6th   3-0

Nemean:
Old Actonians 8th   v   Old Edmontonians 6th 1-0

Jack Perry Veterans':
Phoenix Old Boys   v   Old Meadonians   1-0

OLD BOYS' INVITATION CUPS

Senior:
Old Wilsonians   v   Old Salesians   3*2

Junior:
Old Finchleians Res v   Old Owens Res   3*2

Minor:
Old Minchend'ns   v   Old Tenisonians 3rd 3-1

4th XIs:
Old Finchleians 4th v   Old Stationers 4th 4-2

5th XIs:
Old Finchleians 5th v   O W'minster Ctzns 5th 4*2

6th XIs:
Old Minchend'n 6th   v   Old Finchleians 6th 5*2

7th XIs:
Glyn Old Boys 7th   v   Old Parkonians 7th 4-0

Veterans':
Old Esthameians   v   Old W'minster Cit's 3p0,0*0

MIDLAND AMATEUR ALLIANCE

PREMIER DIVISION

	P	W	D	L	F	A	Pts
Caribbean Cavaliers	24	19	3	2	87	38	60
Nottingham Trent Univ.	24	15	4	5	84	40	49
Nottinghamshire	24	15	4	5	64	28	49
Old Elizabethans	24	12	3	9	66	56	39
Ashland Rovers	24	11	4	9	64	54	37
Squareform Stealers	24	10	5	9	69	65	35
Bassingfield	24	11	1	12	58	59	34
Magdala Amateurs Res	24	10	3	11	48	50	33
Lady Bay	24	9	3	12	54	67	30
Woodborough United	24	9	3	12	45	62	30
ASC Dayncourt Res	24	9	2	13	45	75	29
Racing Athletic	24	5	3	16	38	68	18
Wollaton 3rd	24	2	0	22	34	94	6

DIVISION 1

	P	W	D	L	F	A	Pts
Bracken Park	26	20	6	0	75	22	66
Pakistan Centre	26	18	4	4	92	28	58
Nottinghamshire Res	26	17	3	6	78	45	54
Beeston Old Boys Assn	26	15	4	7	68	45	49
Wollaton 4th	26	15	4	7	61	43	49
Sherwood Forest	26	12	2	12	57	66	38
F L L Aerospace	26	11	3	12	65	61	36
Old Elizabethans Res	26	9	5	12	55	75	32
County NALGO	26	8	7	11	70	67	31
Southwell Arms	26	8	6	12	52	69	30
Bassingfield Res	26	8	2	16	42	64	26
Old Bemrosians	26	6	4	16	30	60	22
Derbyshire Amat Res	26	5	0	21	35	83	15
Brunts Old Boys	26	3	4	19	37	89	13

DIVISION 2

	P	W	D	L	F	A	Pts
ASC Dayncourt 3rd	28	20	2	6	80	36	62
Edwinstowe FC	28	17	5	6	91	42	56
Magdala Arms 3rd	28	18	1	9	92	66	55
Nottinghamshire 3rd	28	16	3	9	65	45	51
Caribbean Cavaliers Rs	28	15	4	9	87	64	49
Old Elizabethans 3rd	28	15	4	9	65	49	49
West Bridgford United	28	14	2	12	70	54	44
Beeston O. B Assn Res	28	12	6	10	55	47	42
F L L Aerospace Res	28	11	5	12	73	67	38
Tibshelf Old Boys	28	11	4	13	64	67	37
Derbyshire Amat 3rd	28	11	2	15	65	91	35
Wollaton 5th	28	10	2	16	76	71	32
Dynamo	28	8	3	17	74	99	27
EMTEC	28	5	2	21	47	146	17
Old Bemrosians Res	28	3	3	22	33	93	12

LEAGUE CUPS:

SENIOR
Nott'm Trent Univ v Lady Bay 3-1
INTERMEDIATE
Southwell Amateurs v Pakistan Centre 0-2
MINOR
ASC Dayncourt 3rd v Wollaton 5th 2-1

OLD BOYS' LEAGUE

PREMIER DIVISION	P	W	D	L	F	A	Pts
Old Meadonians	20	13	3	4	52	22	42
Old Danes	20	12	5	3	50	28	41
Old Aloysians	20	10	6	4	53	30	36
Old Ignatians	20	10	5	5	44	35	35
Old Hamptonians	20	10	4	6	44	38	34
Old Wilsonians	20	7	6	7	43	32	27
Old Salvatorians	20	7	5	8	26	37	26
Old Vaughanians	20	6	4	10	44	41	22
Cardinal Manning O B	20	5	4	11	39	67	19
Phoenix Old Boys	20	4	2	14	33	66	14
Shene Old Gramm'ns	20	3	2	15	35	67	11

SENIOR DIVISION 1	P	W	D	L	F	A	Pts
Latymer Old Boys	18	16	1	1	77	14	49
Old Tiffinians	18	12	2	4	55	22	38
Old Isleworthians	18	11	2	5	53	28	35
Old Manorians	18	9	3	6	36	33	30
Old Dorkinians	18	6	7	5	30	32	25
Glyn Old Boys	18	8	1	9	27	48	25
Old Suttonians	18	4	4	10	24	46	16
Old Tenisonians	18	4	3	11	18	48	15
Enfield Old Gramm'ns	18	3	3	12	20	47	12
Old Minchendenians	18	3	2	13	32	54	11

SENIOR DIVISION 2	P	W	D	L	F	A	Pts
Old Wokingians	20	18	2	0	54	17	56
Queen Mary Cllge O B	20	13	3	4	46	26	42
Old Buckwellians	20	11	4	5	62	38	37
Wood Green Old Boys	20	11	2	7	64	47	35
Old Reigatians	20	10	2	8	46	29	32
John Fisher Old Boys	20	8	2	10	32	31	26
Old Sedcopians	20	6	3	11	44	64	21
Latymer Old Boys Res	20	6	3	11	34	56	21
Old Kingsburians	20	5	3	12	40	59	15
Phoenix Old Boys Res	20	4	2	14	31	56	14
Old Vaughanians Res	20	4	2	14	38	68	14

SENIOR DIVISION 3	P	W	D	L	F	A	Pts
Old Aloysians Res	22	14	2	6	62	33	44
Old Tenisonians Res	22	13	5	4	44	23	44
Old Egbertians	22	12	4	6	42	24	40
Old Salvatorians Res	22	10	7	5	56	47	37
Clapham Old Xav'ns	22	10	4	8	51	39	34
Old Wilsonians Res	22	10	3	9	52	34	33
Old Hamptonians Res	22	10	2	10	33	36	32
Mickleham Old Box'ns	22	7	7	8	43	50	28
Old Meadonians Res	22	7	5	10	53	67	26
Old Manorians Res	22	6	3	13	33	54	21
Old St Marys	22	5	3	14	30	67	18
Fitzwilliam Old Boys	22	4	3	15	37	62	15

OTHER DIVISIONS:

Intermediate Division South
12 teams — Won by Chertsey Old Salesians

Intermediate Division North
12 teams — Won by Old Challoners

Northern:
Division 1
11 teams — Won by Old Edmontonians Res

Division 2
10 teams — Won by Old Minchendenians 3rd

Division 3
9 teams — Won by Old Edmontonians 4th

Division 4
9 teams — Won by Old Edmontonians 5th

Division 5
8 teams — Won by Holland Park O B 5th

Division 6
9 teams — Won by Old Egbertians 6th

Southern:
Division 1
10 teams — Won by Old Tenisonians 4th

Division 2
11 teams — Won by Old Guildfordians

Division 3
9 teams — Won by Sinjuns Res

Division 4
10 teams — Won by Clapham Old Xav'ns 4th

Division 5
9 teams — Won by Glyn Old Boys 6th

Division 6
11 teams — Won by Old Strandians

Division 7
9 teams — Won by Mickleh'm O. Boxhill's R

Division 8
8 teams — Won by Old Tiffinians 5th

Western:
Division 1
10 teams — Won by Old Challoners Res

Division 2
10 teams — Won by Old Salvatorians 4th

Division 3
11 teams — Won by Old Uxonians Res

Division 4
11 teams — Won by Old Uffingtonians Res

Division 5
10 teams — Won by Old Uffingtonians 3rd

SOUTHERN AMATEUR LEAGUE

FIRST DIVISION	P	W	D	L	F	A	Pts
Old Owens	22	16	1	5	50	18	49
BB Eagles	22	12	6	4	53	33	42
Civil Service	22	13	1	8	46	34	40
Broomfield	22	11	3	8	49	34	36
Old Esthameians	22	10	5	7	45	34	35
Polytechnic	22	11	2	9	40	42	35
Old Actonians Assn	22	9	6	7	36	26	33
Alleyn Old Boys	22	8	5	9	36	42	29
Norsemen	22	8	1	13	39	47	25
E Barnet O. Gramm'ns	22	6	4	12	28	56	22
Carshalton	22	5	2	15	29	59	17
Crouch End Vampires	22	4	2	16	30	56	14

SECOND DIVISION	P	W	D	L	F	A	Pts
Old Salesians	22	16	5	1	69	21	53
HSBC	22	16	3	3	62	30	51
West Wickham	22	15	5	2	46	15	50
Old Bromleians	22	12	4	6	48	26	40
Old Parkonians	22	10	5	7	42	39	35
Old Lyonians	22	8	5	9	42	53	29
Old Finchleians	22	6	7	9	37	53	25
Lensbury	22	6	5	11	34	36	23
Winchmore Hill	22	7	2	13	24	37	23
Lloyds TSB Bank	22	5	3	14	36	52	18
Old Stationers	22	4	1	17	24	15	13
National West Bank	22	3	3	16	27	78	10

THIRD DIVISION	P	W	D	L	F	A	Pts
Nottsborough	22	18	3	1	92	16	57
South Bank CuacO.	22	14	6	2	44	21	48
Bank of England	22	15	1	6	56	22	46
Alexandra Park	22	13	3	6	50	33	42
Kew Association	22	11	4	7	55	54	37
Old Parmiterians	22	10	3	9	60	48	33
Southgate Olympic	22	7	2	13	31	62	23
Merton	22	6	4	12	36	51	22
Ibis	22	5	6	11	30	48	21
Old Latymerians	22	6	2	14	37	52	20
O Westminster Citizens	22	5	3	14	32	72	18
Brentham	22	3	1	18	43	87	10

2ND TEAMS:
First Division
12 teams — Won by E Barnet O Gramm's Res

Second Division
12 teams — Won by Polytechnic Res

Third Division
12 teams — Won by Nottsborough Res

3RD TEAMS:
First Division
12 teams — Won by Old Finchleians 3rd

Second Division
12 teams — Won by Old Latymerians 3rd

Third Division
12 teams — Won by Carshalton 3rd

4TH TEAMS:
First Division
12 teams — Won by Old Finchleians 4th
Second Division
11 teams — Won by West Wickham 4th
Third Division
11 teams — Won by Nottsborough 4th

5TH TEAMS:
First Division
11 teams — Won by Old Finchleians 5th
Second Division
10 teams — Won by HSBC 5th
Third Division
9 teams — Won by Old Esthameians 5th

6TH TEAMS:
First Division
12 teams — Won by Old Parmiterians 6th
Second Division
10 teams — Won by Kew Association 6th

MINOR SECTION:
First Division
10 teams — Won by Old Finchleians 7th
Second Division
10 teams — Won by Kew Association 7th
Third Division
11 teams — Won by Old Parmiterians 9th

CHALLENGE CUPS:

Junior:
Crouch End V. v Nottsborough 4p2, 3*3
Minor:
HSBC 4th v West Wickham 4th 1-4
Senior Novets:
HSBC 5th v Norsemen 5th 1-3
Intermed. Novets:
Carshalton 6th v Norsemen 6th 3-0
Junior Novets:
Polytechnic 7th v Carshalton 7th 3-1

HAMILTON TROPHY

for Hospitality & Sportsmanship: Old Stationers Club

REPRESENTATIVE MATCHES

16.09.01	v	West Wickham	Lost 0 - 3
30.09.01	v	Old Finchleians	Draw 6 - 0
14.10.01	v	Old Actonians Association	Draw 0 - 3
07.11.01	v	London Legal League	Won 4 - 1
21.11.01	v	Old Boys' League	Won 4 - 0
04.12.01	v	Oxford University	Drawn 1 - 1
22.01.02	v	Cambridge University	Lost 0 - 2
05.03.02	v	Arthurian League	Won 1 - 0
03.04.02	v	Southern Olympian League	Lost 1 - 2

SOUTHERN OLYMPIAN LEAGUE

Senior Section:
DIVISION ONE

	P	W	D	L	F	A	Pts.
Hale End Athletic	18	12	4	2	44	17	40
UCL Academicals	18	10	2	6	47	27	32
Parkfield	18	8	6	4	29	23	30
Albanian	18	8	5	5	25	24	29
Honorary Artillery Co	18	7	5	6	36	30	26
Mill Hill Village	18	7	3	8	40	41	24
Southgate County	18	6	4	8	31	42	22
Ulysses	18	5	5	8	30	40	20
Old Grammarians	18	5	4	9	33	43	19
Old Woodhouseians	18	1	4	13	27	55	7

DIVISION TWO

	P	W	D	L	F	A	Pts.
Old Bealonians	18	14	1	3	66	29	43
St. Mary's College	18	11	2	5	36	21	35
King's Old Boys	18	10	3	5	44	27	33
University of Hertford	18	9	2	7	46	33	29
Economicals	18	9	2	7	38	32	29
Pegasus	18	7	5	6	38	26	26
Wandsworth Borough	18	6	2	10	28	52	21
Brent	18	6	2	10	25	53	20
Centymca	18	3	4	11	28	50	13
City of London	18	1	4	13	30	56	7

DIVISION THREE

	P	W	D	L	F	A	Pts.
B.B.C.	20	18	1	1	96	28	55
The Rugby Clubs	20	13	2	5	88	42	41
London Welsh	20	11	5	4	65	40	38
Witan	20	9	6	5	43	43	33
Hampstead Heathens	20	9	5	6	52	43	32
London Airways	20	8	1	11	42	71	25
Bluepoint	20	6	4	10	38	46	22
Ealing Association	20	6	2	12	39	81	20
The Comets	20	4	4	12	35	51	16
Fulham Compton O.B	20	4	4	12	32	57	16
Inland Revenue	20	3	4	13	24	52	13

Intermediate Section:

Division One:
10 teams — Won by Old Woodhouseians Res

Division Two:
10 teams — Won by H A C Res

Division Three:
8 teams — Won by Mill Hill Village 3rd

Junior Section North:

Division One
9 teams — Won by Mill Hill Village 4th

Division Two
9 teams — Won by Old Bealonians 5th

Division Three
7 teams — Won by UCL Academicals 6th

Junior Section South & West:

Division One:
9 teams — Won by Witan Res

Division Two:
9 teams — Won by Witan 3rd

LEAGUE CUP FINALS:

Senior Bowl:	Won by Southgate County
Senior Shield:	Won by UCL Academicals
Intermediate Cup:	Won by Albanian Res
Intermediate Shield:	Won by UCL Academicals Res
Junior Cup:	Won by Mill Hill Village 3rd
Junior Shield:	Won by Albanian 3rd
Mander Cup:	Won by Mill Hill Village 4th
Mander Shield:	Won by Old Woodhouseians 4th
Burntwood Trophy:	Won by Mill Hill Village 5th
Burntwood Shield:	Won by Old Bealonians 5th
Veterans' Cup:	Won by Albanian Veterans
Veterans' Shield:	Won by UCL Academicals Vet's

LEAGUE REPRESENTATIVE XI

28.11.01	v London Legal League	Draw 1 - 1
20.01.02	v London University	Lost 0 - 3
29.01.02	v Cambridge University	Won 2 - 0
27.03.02	v Old Boy's League	Lost 0 - 1
03.04.02	v Southern Amateur League	Won 2 - 1

LONDON UNIVERSITY REPRESENTATIVE XI

13.12.01	v Southern Olympian League	Won 3-0
11.02.02	v Cambridge University	Draw 0-0
13.02.02	v Old Boys' League	Draw 1-1
24.02.02	v Army Crusaders H	Won 6-0
27.02.02	v Amateur Football Alliance	Lost 1-2
20.03.02	v Arthurian League	Lost 2-3
24.04.02	v London Legal League	Won 5-1
	v Oxford University - Cancelled by OU	

UNIVERSITY OF LONDON UNION
MEN'S COMPETITIONS
(Limited to one game against each member)

PREMIER DIVISION	P	W	D	L	F	A	Pts
London Sch of Econ	11	9	1	1	35	8	28
University College	11	9	1	1	34	14	28
Royal Holloway College	11	7	0	4	16	15	21
R Free, UC & Mx H MS	11	6	1	4	35	20	19
Imp College Sch Med	11	5	1	5	17	20	16
Imperial College	11	5	1	5	19	18	15
Goldsmiths' College	11	4	2	5	15	11	13
Q Mary Westfield Cllge	11	3	4	4	16	27	13
King's College	11	2	6	3	28	26	11
Guy's, King's & St. T MS	11	3	1	7	10	30	9
St George's Hosp M S	11	1	3	7	14	23	5
St Barts & R L Hosp MC	11	0	3	8	11	38	3

DIVISION 1	P	W	D	L	F	A	Pts
Ryl Holloway Cllge Rs	11	10	0	1	61	15	30
University College Res	11	8	1	2	35	11	25
King's College 3rd	10	6	2	2	43	22	20
Imperial College Res	11	6	0	5	32	18	18
Lon'n Sch of Econ 3rd	10	5	3	2	21	19	18
Lon'n Sch of Econ Res	11	6	1	4	29	16	17
Q Mary West'd Cllge Rs	11	5	2	4	23	26	17
University College 3rd	11	3	3	5	21	22	12
Imp Cllge Sch Med Rs	11	3	2	6	21	36	11
Goldsmiths' College Rs	10	2	2	6	13	27	7
King's College 4th	10	1	0	9	10	55	3
King' College Res	9	0	0	9	6	48	0

DIVISION 2	P	W	D	L	F	A	Pts
Ryl Holloway Cllge 4th	10	9	0	1	29	10	27
Imperial College 3rd	10	5	4	1	19	9	19
Ryl Holloway Cllge 3rd	10	6	1	3	32	25	19
Guy's, King's, St. T Rs	10	5	2	3	34	19	17
R Free, UC & Mx Hsp R	10	5	2	3	22	17	17
Lon'n Sch of Econ 4th	10	4	2	4	26	30	14
University College 4th	9	3	3	3	15	15	12
Imperial College 4th	10	3	1	6	19	28	10
Imp Cllge Sch Med 3rd	10	2	2	6	16	29	7
Q Mary West'd Cllge 3rd	8	1	1	6	20	32	4
Wye College	9	1	0	8	7	25	2

DIVISION 3	P	W	D	L	F	A	Pts
Sch Oriental & African S	11	10	1	0	54	11	31
R School of Mines	11	9	1	1	28	8	28
Guy's, Kng's, St T MS 3	11	9	0	2	37	21	27
Birkbeck Cllge Students	11	7	1	3	44	24	22
St B'ts & R. Lon H MC R	11	6	1	4	32	23	19
Guy's, ing's, St.T MS 4	11	5	1	5	23	30	16
St George's Hsp M S R	10	4	2	4	21	15	13
R Free, UC & Mx H MS 3	10	4	0	6	23	19	12
Imp College Sch Med 4	11	3	1	7	19	35	10
St Bts & R Lon H MC 3	11	1	2	8	9	45	4
R Free, UC & Mx H S 4	11	1	2	8	6	33	3
Goldsmiths' College 4th	11	0	0	11	10	42	0

DIVISION 4

13 teams   Won by London Sch Economics 5th

DIVISION 5

11 teams   Won by R College of Science (ICSTM)

CHALLENGE CUP

L S E	v	Royal Holloway	1:2*-1:1*

RESERVES' CUP

L S E Res	v	Imperial	1:2*-1:1*

RESERVES' PLATE

L S E 4th	v	RF Mx UC 3rd	1:2*-1:1*

VASE

U C 6th	v	Imperial 6th	0-2

UNIVERSITY OF LONDON UNION
WOMEN'S COMPETITIONS

Premier Division	P	W	D	L	F	A	Pts
Guy's, King's & St T MS	10	9	1	0	81	8	28
Q Mary Westfield Coll	10	8	1	1	69	11	25
University College	9	4	0	5	35	35	12
London School of Econ	10	4	0	6	29	40	12
Imperial College	9	2	0	7	10	58	6
School Oriental & African	8	0	0	8	5	77	0

Division 1	P	W	D	L	F	A	Pts
Royal Holloway College	10	8	1	1	64	15	25
King's College	10	6	3	1	41	9	21
R Free, UC & Mx H MS	10	3	1	6	8	19	10
Royal Veterinary Cllge	9	2	3	4	10	17	9
Goldsmiths' College	9	3	0	6	2	65	9
St George's Hospital MS	10	2	2	6	19	19	8

Division 2	P	W	D	L	F	A	Pts
Guy's, King's, St.T Res	8	7	0	1	30	7	21
R Free, UC & Mx H Rs	8	5	0	3	18	15	15
University College Res	8	5	0	3	17	17	15
Wye College	8	3	0	5	10	26	9
Royal Holloway Cllge Rs	8	0	0	8	8	18	0

CHALLENGE CUP

Guy's, King's, St. Thomas'	1:2*
Queen Mary Westfield	1:1*

SERVICES FOOTBALL

INTER-SERVICE (MEN)

Royal Navy	6	v	1	RAF
RAF	3	v	3	Army
Army	0	v	0	Royal Navy

Winners: Royal Navy

INTER-SERVICE (WOMEN)

Royal Navy	4	v	2	RAF
Army	3	v	3	Royal Navy
RAF	0	v	5	Army

Winners: Army

INTER-SERVICE (YOUTH)

| Royal Navy | 0 | v | 1 | Army |

Winners: Army

COMBINED SERVICES FOOTBALL ASSOCIATION

CSFA	1	v	0	Hayes
CSFA	0	v	2	Ryman League
CSFA	0	v	3	England Nat Game

KENTISH CUP

Netherlands	2	v	0	Belgium
CSFA	1	v	1	Netherlands
Belgium	1	v	2	CSFA

Winners: Netherlands

NAAFI JUBILEE CUP

1 Kings	2	v	2	42 CDO RM
42 CDO RM	3	v	2	RAF Leeming
RAF Leeming	0	v	4	1 Kings

Winners: 1 Kings

The huddle didn't work - Kings Regiment (Catterick) prior to the Army Cup Final at Aldershot. They lost 2-1 to 28 Eng Regiment. Photo: Eric Marsh

Above: Team Talk Photographers enjoyed a get together at the Lakeside, Frimley. (l-r): Roger Turner, Graham Cotterill, Kevin Rolfe, Gordon Whittington, Gary Letts and Peter Lirettoc.
Photo: Jan Turner

Right: Lee Hoenig was one of the greatest supporters in the early days of the Directory. Eric Marsh catches up with him at Bookham v Frimley Green. Both stars must be as keen as ever! Photo:
Eric Marsh

Below: Northern photographer Alan Watson has brought his wife and pet dog to join him when on holiday at Lowestoft Town! Photo:
Alan Watson

CHANNEL ISLANDS REVIEW

THE GUERNSEY VIEWPOINT

25 years ago, Rangers were at the top of Guernsey football. Manager Harold Allen, who later sat in the island's parliament, led a team containing his son Craig, who went on to play professionally in the United States, to the Priaulx League Championship in 1978. Meanwhile, Sylvans' perennial struggle against the wooden spoon seemed as tough as ever. The Westerners were too often the whipping boys of the local game and seldom troubled the top teams.

In a quarter of a century, however, things have changed a great deal. Last season, Rangers once again finished bottom of the Priaulx League - they won only two of their eighteen matches - while Sylvans finished two points ahead of Vale Rec to clinch a record-equalling ninth successive championship.

Sylvans maintained their domination of local football in spite of another managerial change at the start of the season. At one stage, Richard Packman, a former Wimbledon youth team player, looked set to lead Sylvans to every possible trophy but their form against Jersey opposition in Channel Islands knock out cups let them down. Indeed, against Jersey champions St Peters, Sylvans turned in yet another woeful end of season performance and lost a replay 3-0, thus becoming the first team to lose four successive Upton Park Cups (CI club championships).

At home, Vale Rec, League winners nine times in the last 25 years but without a championship since 1993, pushed Sylvans hard but were undone by two bad defeats either side of Christmas. In mid-December, in the 'Northern' derby, Vale were beaten 1-0 by North and, three weeks later, their title bid collapsed when they lost 7-2 at Sylvans.

Northerners finished third and St Martin's, who started the season as joint favourites to lift the title, endured a nightmare campaign - they went through three managers - and finished fourth, nineteen points behind the champions.

On the representative front, Guernsey lost a classic Muratti match 2-1. Jersey's winner was scored just five minutes from time and stretched Guernsey's run without an away Muratti win to eleven years. Guernsey did, however, win the Junior Muratti 1-0 - against the odds and with a very young side. Guernsey also won the Under 21 Muratti - 3-1 after extra time in a replay - and shared the Under 15 Muratti after a draw in Jersey.

Looking ahead to this season, Rangers are growing increasingly desperate to turn back the clock and have made a number of potentially significant summer signings. It is inconceivable that they will repeat their championship-winning feat of 25 years ago but their new-look squad should be enough to lift them off the foot of the table.

Sylvan's golden period could, however, be about to end. This season promises to be one of the most intriguing yet - Sylvan's band of ageing stars is bidding to break the record of successive title wins but they are likely to be challenged to a greater extent than ever before by a number of rejuvenated clubs.

Off the field, meanwhile, a series of recommendations aimed at reforming Guernsey football have just been announced for discussion by the clubs, who effectively control the game. The most concerning problem of the last 25 years - that of plummeting attendances - is unlikely to be reversed, however. Big club games now attract perhaps 200 people, whereas a quarter of a century ago crowds of several hundred or even a couple of thousand were not at all uncommon.

Matt Fallaize

GUERNSEY FINAL LEAGUE TABLES 2001-02

PRIAULX LEAGUE
(1st Team)

DIVISION 1	P	W	D	L	F	A	Pts
Sylvans	18	14	2	2	77	13	44
Vale Rec.	18	13	3	2	61	13	42
North	18	11	4	3	38	14	37
St Martin's	18	6	7	5	24	23	25
Bels	18	3	3	12	13	56	12
Rovers	18	2	3	13	10	60	9
Rangers	18	2	2	14	14	58	8

JACKSON LEAGUE
(Reserves)

	P	W	D	L	F	A	Pts
St Martin's	21	18	0	3	69	16	54
Sylvans	21	16	3	2	76	25	51
Port City	21	12	3	6	72	33	39
North	21	11	3	7	75	49	36
Vale Rec.	21	10	3	8	67	46	33
Rovers	21	5	1	15	27	56	16
Bels	21	3	1	17	23	85	10
Rangers	21	2	1	18	15	114	7

RAILWAY LEAGUE
(3rd Team)

	P	W	D	L	F	A	Pts
North	18	17	0	1	68	21	51
Vale Rec.	18	14	0	4	75	25	42
Sylvans	18	12	1	5	66	30	37
St Martin's	18	12	0	6	82	29	36
Port City	18	10	0	8	58	38	30
Bavaria Nom.	18	9	0	9	53	47	27
Bels	18	6	1	11	42	51	19
Rovers	18	5	0	13	24	62	15
Police	18	4	0	14	25	99	
Rangers	18	0	0	18	18	109	0

YOUTH ONE

	P	W	D	L	F	A	Pts
St Martin's	18	15	1	2	82	13	46
Northerners	18	13	1	4	93	28	40
Belgraves	18	13	1	4	69	23	40
Sylvans	18	7	1	10	42	54	22
Rangers	18	6	0	12	30	81	18
Rovers	18	3	3	12	19	44	12
Vale Rec	18	2	1	15	14	106	7

YOUTH TWO

	P	W	D	L	F	A	Pts
North	12	10	1	1	50	11	31
Bels	12	10	1	1	39	5	31
Sylvans	12	7	1	4	32	24	22
St Martin's	12	6	0	6	34	24	18
Rangers	12	4	2	6	28	32	14
Rovers	12	1	1	10	5	39	4
Vale Rec.	12	1	0	11	6	59	3

JERSEY BRITISH EUROPEAN FOOTBALL COMBINATION

FINAL LEAGUE TABLES 2001-02

DIVISION ONE

	P	W	D	L	F	A	Pts
St Paul's	18	14	1	3	47	21	43
St Peter	18	13	2	3	54	20	41
Scottish	18	10	2	6	39	24	32
First Tower	18	9	4	5	40	23	31
Rozel Rovers	18	8	3	7	43	33	27
Wanderers	18	8	3	7	25	26	27
Magpies	18	7	3	8	16	24	24
St Martin	18	4	3	11	19	44	15
Portuguese	18	4	1	13	21	48	13
St John	18	1	2	15	14	53	5

DIVISION TWO

	P	W	D	L	F	A	Pts
Trinity	18	16	2	0	84	13	50
Sporting Acs	18	11	4	3	55	21	37
Oaklands/SS	18	10	4	4	60	28	34
St Clement	18	10	2	6	40	36	32
Grouville	18	8	5	5	31	19	29
St Ouen	18	8	1	9	36	30	25
St Brelade	18	5	3	10	25	51	18
St Lawrence	18	4	5	9	33	40	17
Beeches OB	18	3	4	11	22	46	13
Sporting Club	18	0	0	18	14	116	0

THE JERSEY SEASON

ST PAUL'S won the Jersey European Combination Division I title for the first time since 1988. On the night of the penultimate league matches of the season, they recorded a comfortable 4-1 victory at Le Couvent against Rozel Rovers while title challengers St Peter failed to maintain their challenge after drawing 3-3 against First Tower at La Hague Manor. The points lifted St Paul's into an unassailable five-point lead over St Peter and the clash between the clubs a few days later was purely academic.

However, St Paul's players and officials had to endure a tense fourteen minutes before they knew they were champions. After defeating Rozel 4-1, in a game which was reduced to 40 minutes each way because of a possibilty of bad light, St Paul's players huddled around a radio to listen to the final minutes of challengers St Peter's game against First Tower at La Hague Manor.

With St Paul's three points won, St Peter now had to win their game to retain an interest in the title race and they were 3-2 behind when the St Paul's game finished. St Peter were awarded a late penalty, their third of the game, and Tower goalkeeper Sean McDonald saved it. The St Paul's contingent leapt for joy - but their happiness was short-lived because in their excitement and shouting they hadn't heard that St Peter had equalised from the rebound.

Worried looks quickly replaced grinning faces until, after several more nail-biting minutes, the final whistle went and St Paul's were champions for the first time since 1988. Back came the happy faces, handshakes of congratulations and the sound of popping champagne bottles.

So St Peter's championship hopes were dashed in a match packed with drama and controversy. It was a heart-breaking end to the title campaign for Peter Vincenti's side as they were condemned to runners-up spot for the third consecutive year.

But Tower were seething with referee Chris Gouyette who awarded THREE penalties against them after they had built a seemingly unassailable 3-0 lead. The Saints players, too, were unhappy with the referee over one of Tower's goals. The official waved aside their offside appeals, 'keeper John McCulloch thought the whistle had gone and threw the ball outside of the penalty area for a free kick ó only for Tower striker Colin Roworth to race in and hit the ball into the unguarded net.

Vincenti said: "St Paul's didn't win the league we gave it away. I'm extremely disappointed for the players and the club, everyone has put a lot of hard work in. At the end of the day it wasn't about last night but over the season. We didn't get enough points earlier in the season to be in strong enough contention. We have dominated so many games this season but it's an inherent problem we've got, we press the self-destruct button. The first goal we conceded we didn't clear our lines while the second was a total farce and it effectively ended our title hopes. I'm not being critical of the ref. He didn't signal an infringement so you can't expect him to go back and give offside just because a team goes on to score a goal."

St Paul's also won a hard-fought Junior Upton against Guernsey's St Martin's with Paul Aitken's goal settling the issue with just three minutes of extra-time remaining. Racing up St Paul's left, Aitken danced his way past a couple of sliding tackles before then cutting inside. He made further ground and from 25 yards his low shot beat goalkeeper Nathan Pattimore inside his right-hand post.

St Paul's joint-manager Bill Begbie said: 'I thought we just about deserved in the end. We got stronger as the game went on, especially in extra time. St Martin's tired before us and that surprised me because we had a lot of younger players than them. Both teams worked extremely hard and Andy Chevalier was my man-of-the-match because he didn't stopping running.'

St Martin joint coach Nigel Gavey said: 'We're all very disappointed, it was a big game. We prepared well but on the day three or four of our players didn't perform. Full credit to St Paul's, they are a very young side and they played some good football. For the goal Nathan thought the ball was going wide. When he realised it wasn't it was too late for him to do anything about it. Nobody is blaming him because he kept us in the game with his penalty save. If it hadn't been for him we wouldn't have got to extra-time.

St Paul's Portsmouth Trophy success was their fourth in nine appearances.

The club has now won two Upton's this season after the first-team's 2-1 success against Sylvans in Guernsey.

LATE saves from goalkeeper Steve Carlyon helped Jersey to regain the Muratti Vase at Springfield in May. With Jersey leading 1-0 in the 84th Muratti final by captain Ricky Muddyman's 28th minute penalty kick, Carlyon produced two excellent saves in the closing three minutes to prevent Guernsey forcing extra time.

Carlyon, who was making a Channel Islands record 21st appearance for a goalkeeper, came good at the death after a nervous opening period when Jersey were fortunate Guernsey didn't capitalise on three excellent opportunities in the opening ten minutes.

Jersey weathered Guernsey's early storm and for the latter part of the first half they gained the upperhand - Muddyman striking the apex of the crossbar and upright with a thunderous shot from 35 yards. Just before the half-hour Jersey, who were playing well and full of inventiveness and running, got what turned out to be the match-winning goal. Yazalde Santos, later named man-of-the-match, picked up a loose ball in midfield. He produced a fantastic weaving run and after beating three defenders he was upended by Stuart Polson's lunging foul tackle. Muddyman stepped up crash the ball wide to Ian Drillot's left for his second Muratti penalty goal in three years at Springfield. It was an excellent game and both goalkeepers pulled off fine saves.

The match was the best seen at the level in the Islands for over a decade and Jersey's victory puts them 43-39 ahead in the series.

BRITISH UNIVERSITIES SPORTS ASSOCIATION

The British Universities Sports Association (BUSA) provides competitive sport to students in higher education through the organisation of championships, representative fixtures and British teams for international events. Football is the largest of the 44 sports that BUSA organise with 429 men's teams and 127 women's teams entered for the forthcoming season at 1st XI level and below.

The final of the men's championship was played at Stevenage Borough's, Broadhall Way ground in early May and featured Loughborough University and the University of Bath. These two institutions are at the forefront of raising the profile of University football in England as they have recently implemented scholarship programmes to attract players released from the professional game. The players are offered excellent facilities, quality coaching and a fresh start in education in return for competing for the institution. Both Universities are competing in the non-league pyramid with the Conference their ultimate goal. In a closely contested final Loughborough prevailed with a 2-0 scoreline. In the Shield final Southampton Institute defeated Glasgow University 3-2.

The women's final is usually hosted prior to the men's championship game. Unfortunately this year one of the finalists had international fixture commitments, so the game was played in late March at the University of Nottingham. Crewe + Alsager played the slight favourites Loughborough and in an extremely competitive match Crewe were able to secure a 3-2 victory.

At the annual British University Games held at the University of Exeter in April 2002 the English Men and Women's teams won their respective competitions. A late Phil Denney (Ashton Utd) goal in the final game against Scotland proved to be the decisive factor in securing overall victory in what is always a competitive tournament.

In the women's competition England's squad was made up of players all who represent teams in the National League. Their strength in depth counted as they ran out worthy winners of the tournament. Wales showed great improvement by finishing runners-up.

The Men's England Universities Team played three representative matches during the season, the results being:

1-1	v. RAF played at Lilleshall -	*(Eade)*
4-1 (won)	v. Sheffield Wednesday -	*(Elford, Ewin (2), Wareham)*
0-1 (lost)	v. Sheffield United	

The England Women's University team have played representative games with the Arsenal Academy and England under - 19's, who used this fixture as a warm-up game to the U19 World Cup, hosted in Canada last month.

The World University Games is a multi-sport event held once every two years and is second only in size and standard to the Olympic Games. There will be in excess of 6000 world class athletes in attendance at the forthcoming Games, which are to be held in Daegu, Korea from the 21 - 31 August 2003.

The World University Games comprises of 8 core sports one of which is Football. This competition is sanctioned by FIFA and for the 2003 Games will consist of 16 teams from around the world in both men and women's competitions. The tournament will take place in Korea's newly built World Cup stadium. Large crowds are expected to support this event as in previous years with the football final in Beijing 2001 watched by 36,000 people.

Graeme Dell (Head Coach - Team GBR - Men's Football) and his coaching team are committed to improving on the last result in the 2001 Beijing Games of reaching the quarter-finals, losing to the eventual winners Japan on penalties 7 - 6. The squad captained by Luke Anderson (Welling) also included Steve Perkins (Dag + Red), Simon Travis (Stevenage) and Nick Roddis (Aldershot) competing in his third World University Games. The two-year development programme has already identified eligible players from the traditional University representative level through appearances for their home nation, as well as over 40 players playing in the non-league at Unibond Premier, Ryman Premier, Dr.Martens Premier and Conference level. National Coach Dell commented: "Korea in 2003 will be a fantastic chance for a new group of players to represent GB and some will go on to play professionally on completion of their studies"

During the 2001-02 season a young British Universities squad, including Neil Glasser (Burton Albion), John Turner (Nuneaton) and Joe Taylor (Burscough) drew 1-1 with a FA National Game XI played at Hednesford Utd. A GB Development Squad also travelled to Libya at the request of the Libyan Students Union and played two matches against the Libyan U21 team and the French National student team. The results of both matches were 1-1 draws. The experience of travelling, training and playing in such an environment is invaluable in the selection process for the World University Games. The players that represented their country were a credit to their institutions and the hospitality extended to the GB party was exemplary.

The GB student's women's squad is in its infancy and will hopefully compete for the first time at the World University Games in Korea next year. It will be a great opportunity for the players to attend such an event of this scale and there is no question that they will be competitive in the tournament.

Blundell 16   Eade 86

STUDENTS DEDICATION EARNS DESERVED DRAW

On a bitterly cold night in Staffordshire, the annual FA XI v British Universities fixture was played out in front of a small but vocal crowd of 301. Some of those hardy supporters were guests of the Stafforshire County FA, whilst others had made the short trip from Telford to support the five-strong 'Lillywhites' contingent in the FA XI.

With Nuneaton Borough, Chester City, Forest Green Rovers and Hereford United all required to play F.A. Umbro Trophy 3rd Round Replays on the previous night, John Owens, manager of the FA XI was forced to replace 10 of his orginal 16-man squad, drafting in two players from host club Hednesford Town, one from Unibond Northern Premier League side Droylesden, and three from current Unibond league leaders Burton Albion.

Graeme Dell, manager of the British Universities side was also forced to re-shuffle his pack, replacing Kevin Langan and Simon Travis from Forest Green Rovers, as well as losing Yeovil's Anthony Tonkin and Morecambe's Robbie Talbot.

As the FA XI slowly began to exert some pressure, Mark Barnard had a shot blocked on the edge of the box, whilst at the other end, James Bent, who recently signed for Chippenham Town after impressing on trial from Conference side Yeovil Town, ballooned only a half-chance high and wide for the students.

On 16 minutes the deadlock was finally broken after a patient build up from the FA XI. Gareth Hanmer from Telford United made good progress down the left flank, and whipped in a cross that found Blundell ten yards from goal. Still with work to do and under pressure from the Universities defence, Blundell planted his header past a flat-footed Kalli to give the FA XI the lead.

Three minutes later, and the FA XI could have had the chance to double their lead. Steve Palmer fed his fellow Telford teammate Peter Smith who went down under a heavy challenge in the box. Whilst Smith was expecting the referee to point to the spot, he instead waved play on, and this coincided with the best spell of pressure from the Universities side.

Up until this point, the three centre backs in John Owens' back-line were soaking up any pressure, with Captain Neil Moore looking composed and assured in the middle. Dropping deep for the students and intelligently linking up the play was Simon Tucker, a Loughborough University student who also plays for Leek Town, currently third in Unibond Northern League Division One.

It was Tucker who had a rasping drive blocked after 27 minutes, and seven minutes later nearly got on the end of a James Bent flick-on, with Telford United stalwart Paul Edwards needing to be quick off his line to smother the danger.

That was to be the nearest either side got to adding to the scoreline in the first-half, with The FA XI failing to capitalise on a goalmouth scramble after forty minutes when another cross from Hanmer was dropped by Kalli. Hanmer then hit a free-kick high and wide on the stroke of half-time.

At half-time, John Owens made all five of his substitutions, which saw 17 year old Hednesford Town Goalkeeper Adam Jenkins enter the fray, as well as the Burton Albion forward partnership of Dale Anderson and Alan Bailey.

After 59 minutes, the unlucky Alan Bailey had to be replaced after a heavy challenge left him limping badly. Five minutes later, and the FA XI should have extended their lead. James Wall of Burton Albion who had come back on to replace Bailey swung in a high cross from the right which once more was missed by Kalli, but could only be headed wide of the left-hand post by the on-rushing Steve Garvey.

That was to be the final goal-bound effort from the FA XI, as the tide which had slowly begun to turn in favour of the students during the second-half, started to creep further and further towards the FA XI goal.

On 76 minutes, British Universities Manager Graeme Dell brought on Rob Eade of Exeter University to replace James Bent who had fought gamely up front.

Three minutes later, another substitute Steve Wareham forced FA XI 'keeper Jenkins into a smart save with his feet, after beating Northwich defender Denny Ingram to a cross. Two corners in the next five minutes continued to build the pressure on the FA XI rearguard, until with just four minutes left on the clock, Eade produced a huge leap at the far post to guide a header low to the left of Jenkins' despairing dive, and bring the students level.

Man-of-the-Match Awards went to Neil Moore (Captain of the FA XI) and Ellis Wilmot of the University of Bath.

FA SQUAD: Dale Anderson (Burton Albion FC), Alan Bailey (Burton Albion FC), James Wall (Burton Albion FC), Iain Brunskill (Droylesden FC), Adam Jenkins (Hednesford Town FC), Adam Shakespeare (Hednesford Town FC), Mark Barnard (Northwich Victoria FC), Mark Blundell (Northwich Victoria FC), Steve Garvey (Northwich Victoria FC), Denny Ingram (Northwich Victoria FC), Richard Norris (Northwich Victoria FC), Paul Edwards (Telford United FC), Gareth Hanmer (Telford United FC), Neil Moore (Telford United FC), Steve Palmer (Telford United FC), Peter Smith (Telford United FC)

MIDDLESEX WANDERERS

Last year was a most rewarding and successful one for Middlesex Wanderers. The Annual Dinner and Reunion at the Cafe Royal, a match with Sutton United in memory of that great stalwart of both clubs Ralph Carr and a tour to Indonesia and Vietnam contributed to a most enjoyable programme.

Ralph Carr Memorial Match

A wonderful evening was had by all who attended Sutton United on Wednesday 8th May 2002, when 'The Wanderers' met Sutton in a memorial match in memory of the late Ralph Carr. We were indeed pleased to welcome Ralph's widow Maisie and daughter Pauline to the match. The following players represented 'The Wanderers': Glen Knight (Welling United), Lance Key (Kingstonian), Scott Tarr (Basingstoke), Chris Sharpling (Woking), Francis Duku (Gravesend & Northfleet), Adam Parker (Aldershot), Gary Abbot (Welling United), Mark Brennan (Dagenham & Redbridge), Steve Ward (Capt.) (Canvey Island), John Kennedy (Canvey Island), Jake Leberl (Dover Athletic), Che Stadhart (Gravesend & Northfleet), Mark Smith (Dagenham & Redbridge), Steve Perkins (Woking). The team was managed by Nigel Ransom, assisted by Terry Moore, David Lawson acted as physio.

After something of a shaky start, going behind twice, The Wanderers eventually began to play some excellent football and were worthy winners by five goals to two. The match was refereed by FIFA Referee Steven Bennett of Orpington.

Tour to Indonesia and Vietnam

The club completed its 107 tour this year to Indonesia and Vietnam.

The touring party: Glen Knight (Welling United), Steve Dickinson (Southport), Francis Duku (Gravesend & Northfleet), John Kennedy (Canvey Island), Chris Sharpling (Woking), Timmy Ryan (Doncaster Rovers), Mark Brennan (Dagenham & Redbridge), Steven Canning (Queens Park Rangers), Gary Abbott (Welling United), Mark Smith (Capt.) (Dagenham & Redbridge), Steve Nicholson (Emley), Jake Leberl (Dover Athletic), Steve Perkins (Woking), Steve Ward (Canvey Island), Jay Saunders (Margate), Adam Parker (Aldershot), Neill Collins (Queens Park Rangers), Che Stadhart (Gravesend & Northfleet). Team Manager: Nigel Ransom, Assistant Manager: Terry Moore, Physio: David Lawson, Tour President: Brian Wakefield, Tour Secretary: Keith Masters, Executive Committee: T Barr, Vice Presidents: Billy Miller and A C Nash. The club was greatly assisted by Strata Sports of Stanstead, Herts. Representing them on the tour was Miss N Bondi.

The party met at the Heathrow Business Centre on Friday 24th May 2002 and then proceeded to Terminal Two at Heathrow Airport. After checking in and entering the Departure Lounge the players got to know each other over a meal in 'Cafe Uno'.

We boarded a Lufthansa plane and began something of a marathon journey! First to Frankfurt, then, following a two hour stop over to Jakarta and via further stop overs at Singapore and Bangkok, where, incidentally, other travellers and staff in the various airports were quite taken with the players' ever improving renditions of the Wanderers Anthem - 'Mary had a Little Lamb'.

We actually arrived at the Hotel Century Atlet in Jakarta some 21 hours after leaving Heathrow at 9.00pm local time and were pleased with the comfort of the rooms and other accommodation provided. All wer very pleasantly surprised when waking up on Sunday morning when the first glance from the bedroom windows was of the Olympic Stadium in which our match with Indonesia was to take place the following day. After breakfast we went to the Stadium to train and from the inside it looked much bigger having accommodation for 110,000 spectators. Training was in some 95 degrees.

The following day we were pleased to see a reasonable crowd in the stadium for the match. They were most friendly and welcoming. The match was also televised live.

Above: Mark Smith and Mark Brennan with the Wanderers mascot, The Lamb

The Indonesians had been described both by Dato Peter Velappan and club President Sir Bobby Robson as 'the Brazilians of Asia'.

Below: The two Steves - Dickinson and Nicholson

The Wanderers had something of a dream start. After only four minutes a dazzling run by Steve Perkins set up Gary Abbott. Although Abbott crashed his shot against the post, Che Stadhart was on hand to score from the rebound. The lead was short lived. Three minutes later Glen Knight in the Wanderers goal was adjudged to have fouled the Indonesian's brilliant striker Sudiman and a penalty was awarded. Sudiman himself took the penalty and scored. For the next half hour Wanderers were under pressure from a very good side who were still 'smarting' from being beaten by China for a place in the World Cup finals. Riyadi put the home side in the lead on 37 minutes with a strong header.

Manager Nigel Ransom made changes at half time and this appeared to work. Wanderers came much more into the game. Stadhart went close and Abbott was unlucky with a strong header which flew just the wrong side of the post.

With ten minues left on the clock the intense heat and a bit of jet-lag started to take its toll. Whilst the club were still competing well Indonesia went further ahead when a deflected shot gave Glen Knight no chance. Two minutes later Indonesia scored a fourth. A truly brilliant goal. Man of the Match Suprioni made a

searching run down the right hand side of the pitch before pulling the ball back to Riyadi who volleyed home from twenty yards. Final score Indonesia 4 Middlesex Wanderers 1.

Wanderers: Glen Knight (Steve Dickingson), Steve Nicholson, Mark Brennan (Neill Collins), Mark Smith, Timmy Ryan, John Kennedy (Francis Duku), Steven Canning (Steve Ward), Steve Perkins (Jake Leberl), Gary Abbott, Che Stadhart (Chris Sharpling), Jay Saunders (Adam Parker).

We left Indonesia with happy memories to travel to Ho Chi Minh City (Saigon). The flight was again via Bangkok and, once again, whilst waiting for the connecting flight other travellers and duty free retail staff were enthralled by the rendition of the Wanderers Anthem, the party being prevailed upon to sing it on seveal occasions.

The time in Saigon was a wonderful experience. A most magical place with lovely people who, considering the country's turbulent past in very recent history, were most welcoming and friendly.

We were pleased, the day before the match, to have the opportunity of training in the Thong Nhat Stadium and the following evening when we arrived for the match were again wonderfully received. The game was also televised live.

The first half was something of a disaster. After dominating the match for most of the half, three errors in a mad ten minutes cost the Wanderers the match.

To their credit Wanderers picked themselves up and shortly afterwards Gary Abbott reduced the arrears from the penatly spot after Che Stadhart had been fouled.

The second half was all Wanderers pressure and Abbott, Stadhart and Ryan were close. The best move of the match was by Francis Duku who beat four opponents before setting up Gary Abbott for a chance. Shortly before the end of the game Nguyen Liem Thanh scored the fourth for Vietnam. Final score Vietnam 4 Middlesex Wanderers 1.

Middlesex Wanderers: Steve Dickinson, Steve Ward (Francis Duku), Mark Brennan (Adam Parker), Mark Smith, John Kennedy (Jay Saunders), Che Stadhart (Chris Sharpling), Timmy Ryan, Neill Collins, Gary Abbott, Jake Leberl (Steve Nicholson), Steve Perkins, Steven Canning.

In conclusion it was an excellent tour, thoroughly enjoyed by all. The one lesson to be learned was that we played the first game too soon before becoming acclimatised to the weather and conditions.

Strata Sports are speaking provisionally of a possible tour in 2003 to Cambodia and Laos, however this is something which will need very careful consideration and not a little philanthropy as the 2002 tour cost the club in the region of £22,000 and has greatly reduced our financial resources.

The club has lost some highly respected and much loved members during the past year. We extend our sincere condolences to the families of:

Ken Aston (Former Referee and Vice President), Alf Gover (Vice President), Roy Ullyett OBE (Vice President), David Boon (Member), Sir Walter Winterbottom (Former England Manager and Vice President), Dr David Kelleher (Vice President), Kenneth Wolstenholme DFC (Vice President), Rivaltz Marot (Vice President - Maurtius). To live in our hearts is not to die!

So another year has passed by. A good year, in many respects for the club. A year when the World Cup in the Far East showed us just how much 'smaller' the world is becoming in football related matters. it is only a few short years ago that the club toured, successfully, to Korea. This year saw the Koreans reach the latter stages of the World's greatest competition. Times change and we must ensure we change with them.

Keith T Masters, Secretary

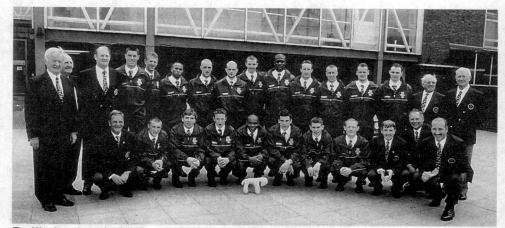

The Wanderers squad at Heathrow Airport prior to departure for the Tour to Indonesia and Vietnam. Back Row (l-r): Tony Fay (Chairman), Brian Wakefield (Vice Chairman and Tour President), Keith Masters (Secretary), Glen Knight, Steve Ward, Che Stadhart, Jay Saunders, Adam Parker, John Kennedy, Francis Duke, Gary Abbott, Chris Sharpling, Steve Dickinson, Timmy Ryan, Billy Miller (Vice President), Albert Nash (Vice President). Front Row: Tommy Barr (Executive Member), Steven Canning, Mark Brennan, Jake Leberl, Mark Smith (Captain), Steve Perkins, Neill Collins, Steve Nicholson, David Lawson (Physio), Terry Moore (Assistant Manager), Nigel Ransom (Manager).

ENGLISH SCHOOLS' FOOTBALL ASSOCIATION

Publicity: Mike Simmonds, 19 The Spinney, Bulcote, Burton Joyce, Nottingham NG14 5GX
Tel: 0115 931 3299   Fax: 0115 931 2758

THE INTERNATIONAL SEASON

THE E.S.F.A. UNDER 18 SQUAD

After Malaysia and Singapore in season 2000-01, the England Schools' F.A. Under 18 Squad selected from those students still in full time education had a week's tour to the United States to start their international season. Three matches were played against Pembroke College (1-1), a High School Select XI (9-0) and Coastal University (2-2). The week was a resounding success and valuable coaching sessions helped the squad prepare for the Centenary Shield programme.

England's opening match was on a wet and blustery night in Belfast when the visitors coped with the conditions admirably, running out 4-1 winners thanks to goals from Chris Bass, Alex Cunliffe, Drew Roberts and Alex Harrison. There was also a very strong wind when England travelled to Newport to meet Wales. Harrison's early goal seemed likely to win the game but the last kick of the game, a speculative shot from 30 yards was caught by the wind and drifted into the net for the equaliser.

This left England requiring victory over Scotland at the Don Valley Stadium, Sheffield if they were to win the Centenary Shield. In a match full of fluctuations inlcuding two penalties and some brilliant saves, England finally triumphed 4-3 thanks to goals from Harrison, Roberts, Kirk Wheeler and Anthony Stazicker.

England's programme ended with three friendly matches. For the first time an international match was staged as part of the Pakefield Festival in early April. A crowd of 2722 packed Lowestoft Town's ground to see England meet the Republic of Ireland. Goal scoring opportunities were limited but seven minutes from time, Alex Harrison picked up a through ball, looked up and fired home a 25 yard shot to leave the Irish keeper stranded.

The season finished with a short tour of Finland in early May when two games were played against the Finnish Under 18 national side with the first bringing England's only defeat of the season (3-0). England gained revenge with a 3-1 win two days later with two goals from Drew Roberts and one from Robert O'Brien.

INTERNATIONAL CAPS
Awarded to the ESFA Under 18 Schoolboys Season 2001-02

	A	B	C	D	E	F		A	B	C	D	E	F
Adrian Adams (Wiltshire)	1	1	1	1	1	1s	Robert O'Brien (W Yorkshire)	1	1			1	1g
Daniel Allen (Wiltshire)	1	1	1	1s	1		Gary Ray (West Midlands)	1s			1	1s	1
Simon Arthur (Hampshire)				1			Drew Roberts (Bedfordshire)	1g	1	1s	1	1s	1sg
Chris Bass (Gloucestershire)	1g	1	1	1	1s	1	Anthony Stazicker (Notts)		1s	1g	1	1	1
Alex Cunliffe (Gt Manchester)	1+g	1+	1+	1+		1+	Lee Summerscales (Norfolk)	1	1	1	1	1	1
Alex Harrison (Suffolk)	1sg	1g	1g	1sg	1+	1s	Kirk Wheeler (Humberside)	1	1	1g	1	1	
John Hastings (Surrey)	1		1s	1	1	1	Daniel Whitmarsh (Beds)	1s	1s	1s	1	1	1
Joe Manning (Leicestershire)	1	1	1				Craig Sudderby (Humberside)					1	1
Daniel Mudd (Humberside)	1	1	1		1	1	Graeme Black (Merseyside)					1s	

KEY:	A	N Ireland (Glentoran)	D	Eire (Pakefield)	1+	Captain
	B	Wales (Newport)	E	Helsinki (Finland)	g	Goalscorer
	C	Scotland (Sheffield)	F	Helsinki (Finland)	s	Substitute

The ESFA U18 Squad Back Row (l-r): Arthur Tabor (Doctor), Mark Wallington (GK Coach), John Hastings, Daniel Mudd, Simon Arthur, Alex Cunliffe, Vic Bragg (Asst Coach), Alan Gallafant (Physio). Middle Row: Anthony Stazicker, Robert O'Brien, Joe Manning, Lee Summerscales, Gary Ray, Kirk Wheeler, Adrian Adams, Daniel Whitmarsh. Front Row: Daniel Allen, Chris Bass, Malcolm Hird (Manager), Dave Woollaston (Chairman), John Reid (Chief Executive), Alex Harrison, Drew Roberts

THE INTER-ASSOCIATION COMPETITIONS

ENGLISH SCHOOLS' F.A. WIZARDS TROPHY

FINAL

1st Leg

Cardiff   2   v   1   North Tyneside

2nd Leg

North Tyneside   2   v   0   Cardiff

North Tyneside won 3-2 on aggregate

For the third time in four years, another new name will be engraved on the Inter-Association Trophy as North Tyneside came from a one goal first leg deficit to defeat Cardiff on aggregate. Cardiff compete in the competition which was sponsored for the first time by game card manufacturers, Wizards of the Coast, as a guest team and were one of the early winners back in 1915 but North Tyneside were appearing in their first ever final.

In the first leg at Ninian Park, the home side had the better of the early exchanges and edged ahead after 22 minutes with a goal from Abdi Ahmed but North Tyneside equalised with a Jan Martin goal six minutes before the break. The two sides were evenly matched in the second period but Ahmed's second goal of the game gave Cardiff a narrow lead to take into the second leg.

In that game, North Tyneside made the most of home advantage and scored a goal in each half to take the trophy.

E.S.F.A./F.A. PREMIER LEAGUE UNDER 19 COUNTY CHAMPIONSHIP

FINAL

Merseyside   1   v   4   Somerset

at Goodison Park, Everton

There was another first time national title winner when Somerset were crowned Under 19 County Champions with a surprise but well deserved victory over Merseyside. Not overawed by the venue or the reputation of their opponents, Somerset started brightly with Craig Thomas almost opening the scoring in the first minute. Merseyside then got on top but the Somerset back four of captain Mark Hughes, Matt Villis, Piers Govier and Alex Stephens protected goalkeeper Luke Buckingham so well that he was called upon to make only one save.

The deadlock was broken in the 30th minute when a Somerset free-kick was only partially cleared to Graham Burne who played it wide to Hughes and his cross was turned in by Dan Bulley.

An injury early in the second half to Craig Thomas unsettled Somerset and their loss of concentration was punished by a Merseyside equaliser scrambled home by Danny Byrne. Within five minutes, Somerset were ahead again when a Shane Gage free-kick was turned in by Wayne Barry and within four minutes, another Gage free-kick was magnificently headed in by Bulley to make it 3-1.

Somerset ensured that the Trophy would be theirs with the goal of the game when substitute Richard Heath received a short pass from Andy Turner, tricked his way round four defenders and the goalkeeper before slotting the ball in. Manager Graham Clarke was a proud man afterwards, being most pleased with the discipline the squad had shown throughout their impressive run.

Somerset: Luke Buckingham, Matt Villis, Piers Govier, Craig Thomas, Wayne Barry, Leighton Ballantine, Kewvin Ballantine, Ben Kirk, Mark Hughes, Alex Stephens, Graham Burne, Shane Gage, Dan Bulley, Andy Turner, Richard Heath, Simon Keates, Clive Parsons, Matt Grimes.

Merseyside: Graeme Black, Kevin Price, Tony Dunne, Ben Carson, James Hengler, Paul Roberts, Paul Tilley, Gary Greenall, Michael Dawn, David Walsh, Danny Byrne, Michael Sawtell, Matthew Parry, Lee Mulvaney, Philip Martin, Kevin McCormack

Left: Somerset Schools U19 Squad, winners of the ESFA Under 19 County Championship, pictured at their semi-final match against Suffolk.

E.S.F.A. PREMIER LEAGUE UNDER 16 COUNTY CHAMPIONSHIP

FINAL

Nottinghamshire   2   v   0   Kent

at Meadow Lane, Nottingham (Notts County FC)

Nottinghamshire became the third side to win a national title for the first time with a comfortable 2-0 victory over Kent in the final, completing a run of five matches in which only one goal was conceded. The highlight of their progress to the final was an outstanding game of schoolboy football against Merseyside. The latter led from the seventh minute but Notts equalised four minutes from time and an extra goal from Chris Robertson brought them a 2-1 victory.

The final against Kent was spoiled as a spectacle when Kent goalkeeper Daniel Knowles was sent off in the second minute for handling the ball outside the penalty area in stopping a goal bound shot from Will Hoskins. Although Michael Fox's free-kick was blocked, Kent's task of playing with ten men for 78 minutes gave Notts a tremendous boost and it came as no surprise when they took the lead after eighteen minutes. Hoskins' 25-yard shot was brilliantly saved by Kent substitute goalkeeper Scott Chalmer-Stevens but the rebound fell to Ian Brown who made no mistake from close range.

Hoskins hit the post with a fierce drive and Robertson's effort was cleared off the line by Corbishley as Notts continued to dominate but as they failed to score again, frustration mounted. Jukes and Rook both went close for Kent but Notts scored the second they deserved seven minutes from time. A corner from Brown was met by Chris Robertson whose header was pushed out to captain Andy Jones who poked in the clinching goal.

Nottinghamshire Route to the Final				**Kent Route to the Final**			
v Leicestershire	(A)	Midland Counties Group	3-0				
v Lincolnshire	(A)	Midland Counties Group	1-3	v Sussex	(H)	S.E. Counties Group	3-0
v Humberside	(A)	Midland Counties Group	2-3	v Buck'shire	(A)	S.E. Counties Group	1-0
v Derbyshire	(H)	Midland Counties Group	3-0	v Surrey	(A)	S.E. Counties Group	4-0
v Staffordshire	(A)	Midland Counties Semi-final	5-0	v Middlesex	(H)	S.E. Counties Semi-final	2-1
v Merseyside	(H)	National Quarter-final	2*1	v Hampshire	(A)	National Quarter-final	2-1
v Cleveland	(A)	National Semi-final	2-0	v Bedfordshire	(A)	National Semi-final	2-0

Above left: Nottinghamshire Schools' Under 16's, winners of the ESFA/FA Premier League County Championship. Back Row (l-r): Tom Bailey, Francis Chapman, Michael Fox, Peter Ryalls, Chris Wraithmell, Will Hoskins, Ally Barcherini, Andrew Jones, Chris Robertson, Chris O'Grady. Front Row: Luke Parfitt, Alex Baptiste, Daniel Tonks, Martin Smith, Daniel Ward, Ian Brown, Robert Limb, Sam Shepherd. Above right: Peter Ryalls (Notts) is thwarted by the Kent keeper.

E.S.F.A. UNDER 16 GIRLS' COUNTY CHAMPIONSHIP

FINAL

Merseyside   3   v   1   Kent

at Goodison Park, Everton FC

Merseyside gained compensation for their defeat in the Under 19 County Final when their Under 16 girls' side had a comfortable victory over Kent at Goodison Park. Kent had the better of the early exchanges, taking the lead after only five minutes but Merseyside were quick to equalise when Jody Taylor converted the penalty awarded when Amy Kane was brought down. Kane herself was on target tewlve minutes alter with a superb twenty yard left foot shot to give the home side a 2-1 interval lead.

Merseyside dominated the second half and were unlucky not to go further ahead with Taylor who scored twelve goals in seven games on the way to the final, twice going close. Their pressure paid off late in the game when Leanne Jones lobbed the keeper from close range to ensure their hold on the Trophy.

THE INDIVIDUAL SCHOOLS' COMPETITIONS

E.S.F.A. UNDER 19 SCHOOLS AND COLLEGES CHAMPIONSHIP

FINAL

West Nottinghamshire College   0   v   6   Cirencester College
at Meadow Lane, Nottingham (Notts County FC)

Gloucestershire's Cirencester College continued a remarkable sequence by winning the Under 19 Schools and Colleges Cup for the fourth time in five seasons when they romped to a 6-0 win over West Notts College, competing in the competition for the first time. Cirencester had a hat-trick of successes between 1998 and 2000 and after a year's break, resumed possession of what they seem to consider their right!

West Notts started well, having the best of the early chances but Cirencester went ahead with a wind assisted goal from their England Schools' international, Chris Bass after fourteen minutes. West Notts responded well to this setback and but for two fine saves by Kevin Scriven could well have been on level terms at the interval.

Cirencester increased their lead after only 30 seconds of the second period when Ben Fitch coolly latched on to a flick from Ashley Read and this opened the floodgates. As the Gloucestershire side piled on the pressure, West Notts lost their defensive shape and James Blastland made it 3-0 after Read had crossed from the left. This seemed to knock the confidence of the keeper Adam Jones and he was beaten three more times as Cirencester ensured that they scored the goals which matched their dominance. Jones was unable to hold a shot from Adam Mayo and Fitch knocked in the rebound. Mayo himself added a fifth and Fitch completed his hat-trick with ten minutes remaining.

ESFA Schools and Colleges Trophy Final Winners Cirencester College Football Academy.
Back Row (l-r): Ivor Gumm (Senior Coach), Ashley Read, Matthew Dale, Gavin Lewis, Kevin Scriven, James Blastland, Adam Mayo, Matthew McEntegart, Daniel Sollis, Steve Lowndes (Academy Director). Front Row: Dean Gilewicz, James Constable, Ben Fitch, Chris Bass, Gary Probert, Lee Stevens, Tony Clark (captain), John Cant

E.S.F.A. UNDER 19 INDIVIDUAL SCHOOLS' CHAMPIONSHIP

SEMI-FINALS

Bluecoat School (Merseyside)   1   v   0   Thomas Telford CTC (Shropshire)
Hartridge High School (Gwent)   3   v   1   East Barnet High School (Middlesex)

FINAL

Bluecoat School   2   v   3   Hartridge High School
at Anfield, Liverpool FC

E.S.F.A. UNDER 16 SCHOOLSNET CUP

FINAL

Arrow Vale School (Worcestershire)   2   v   1   Kingshurst CTC (West Midlands)
at Redditch United FC

E.S.F.A. UNDER 16 GIRLS' INDIVIDUAL SCHOOLS' CUP

FINAL

Frome Community College (Somerset)   2   v   1   Countesthorpe College (Leicestershire)
at Ashton Gate, Bristol (Bristol City FC)

Not for the first time in recent seasons, the final of the E.S.F.A. Under 16 Girls' competition outshone many of the other thirteen Cup Finals staged by the Association, both for skill and excitement. It was certainly a case of the favourites coming second as in the national rounds alone, Countesthorpe College had scored 49 goals and conceded just one. Moreover, Frome had suffered, like many other teams, in having to omit several Year 9 players who had been an integral part of their success in the Somerset competition so that in the national rounds, they had to rely on just twelve players.

Those twelve girls were heroines throughout but especially in the final when they had to withstand almost constant second half pressure from the Leicestershire school. Frome had been under pressure from the start but thanks to the hard work of Stacey Anstis and Tina Wakefield and excellent stops by Josie McCulloch, they kept Countesthorpe at bay and then surprised them by taking the lead. An alert Katie Gomes turned smartly to set up Ali Hudd who netted with a dipping shot which looped over Charlotte Ward in Countesthorpe's goal.

This was a shock to the Leicestershire side who had never been behind in any match and Frome kept up the pressure for the remainder of the half. The second period proved to be a siege of the Frome goal with Helen McCulloch in defence as busy as her goalkeeper sister. Although the post saved them once, Countesthorpe's deserved equaliser came with eighteen minutes left and, if anything, the pressure increased.

Again Frome were saved by the post but incredibly with ten minutes left, they regained the lead. Wakefield played a clearance to Lisa Sweeney who beat her marker and swept a pass to Katie Gomes. Gomes still had a lot to do but she checked inside and found the inside of the post and the centre of the net.

The last ten minutes produced even more excitement as Countesthorpe pressed for the equaliser which even Frome admitted they deserved but despite hitting the post yet again, they could not overcome that gallant defence.

Frome Community College: Jo McCulloch, Helen McCulloch, Kayleigh Holden, Emma Whittaker, Lisa Cusmans, Tina Wakefield, Lisa Sweeney, Stacey Anstis, Katie Clements, Kate Gomes, Ali Hudd, Becky Lockyer.

Countesthorpe College: Charlotte Ward, Stephanie Ballard, Kim Haswell, Louise Ward, Emma Saunt, Claire Malham, Laura Dickinson, Sammy Morris, Amie Chivers, Neely Simons, Lana Woolley, Leanne Stringfellow, Vicky Graham, Emma McDonald, Charlotte Christy, Hannah Troughton, Carolyn Walley.

Above left: Goalie Jo McCulloch who saved plenty of possible goals during the match.

Right: Captain Tina Wakefield receives the trophy from Geoff Lee, past chairman of the English Schools Football Association.

E.S.F.A. GERRARD UNDER 14 CUP

FINAL
Vermuyden School (Goole, Humberside)   2   v   1   Edmonton County School (Middlesex)
at Villa Park, Aston Villa FC

These two schools were the survivors of over a thousand schools who played the first round in September and after ten rounds, it was not surprising that they produced a very close final. Edmonton had early chances to take the lead but they were made to pay for failing to find the net when Vermuyden showed a more clinical touch in front of goal; Brookes-Meade parried a shot but the ball fell to Nicky Heywood who made no mistake from six yards.

Vermuyden extended their lead midway through the second half when a Jake Stannard long ball fell into the path of Lindon Theaker who scored from the edge of the box. Edmonton fought back well and skipper Alaric Williams scored from close range to set up a thrilling last fifteen minutes which Vermuyden managed to survive.

THE SMALL-SIDED COMPETITIONS
All played on a League basis between four regional winners at Lilleshall National Sports Centre

E.S.F.A. UNDER 11 INDIVIDUAL SCHOOLS' 6-A-SIDE CHAMPIONSHIP

	P	W	D	L	F	A	Pts
Farnborough Road School (Merseyside)	3	3	0	0	4	1	9
Close Junior School (Staffordshire)	3	1	1	1	3	2	4
Liberty Middle School (Surrey)	3	1	1	1	3	2	4
Montpellier Junior School (Devon)	3	0	0	3	1	5	0

E.S.F.A. UNDER 11 INTER-ASSOCIATION 7-A-SIDE CHAMPIONSHIP

	P	W	D	L	F	A	Pts
Bexley (Kent Schools' FA)	3	2	0	1	3	2	6
Oldham (Greater Manchester SFA)	3	2	0	1	3	2	6
Bristol and South Gloucestershire	3	1	0	2	3	4	3
Stoke-on-Trent (Staffordshire SFA)	3	1	0	2	2	3	3

FINAL PLAY-OFF
Bexley   1   v   0   Oldham

E.S.F.A. CAPRI SUN SMALL PRIMARY SCHOOLS SOCCER SIXES

	P	W	D	L	F	A	Pts
Corpus Christi School (Merseyside)	3	2	1	0	4	1	7
Onny Primary School (Shropshire)	3	2	0	1	4	3	6
Wisborough Green School (Sussex)	3	1	0	2	1	3	3
Fourlanesend Primary School (Cornwall)	3	0	1	2	2	4	1

E.S.F.A. WAGON WHEELS UNDER 12 INDOOR 5-A-SIDE CUPS
at JJB Soccerdome, Wigan

BOYS' FINAL
St Ignatius College (Enfield SFA)   4   v   3   Bradon Forest School (Swindon SFA)
St Ignatius won on golden goal in extra time

GIRLS' FINAL
Thomas Telford School (Telford SFA)   1   v   0   Newlands School (Middlesbrough SFA)

F.A. YOUTH CUP 2001-02

FIRST ROUND QUALIFYING

No.				Result	Att.
1	Witton Albion	v	Workington	3-2	52
2	Crook Town	v	Gretna	3-5	89
3	Guiseley	v	Chester City	0-3	52
4	Altrincham	v	Leek Town	3-2	84
5	Consett	v	Northwich Victoria	1-5	100
6	Emley	v	Chester-le-Street Town	3-2	48
7	Dunston Fed Brewery	v	Marine	5*5	156

(Marine won 7-6 on kicks from the penalty mark)

No.				Result	Att.
8	Farsley Celtic	v	Pontefract Collieries @PC	5-0	39
9	Hallam	v	Selby Town	2-0	80
10	Thackley	v	Nantwich Town	3-1	70
11	Alfreton Town	v	Warrington Town	1-2	63
12	Lancaster City	v	Kendal Town	5-3	49
13	New Mills	v	Barrow	5-1	90
14	Stocksbridge Pk Stls	v	Bottesford Town	3-0	50
15	Worksop Town	v	Atherton Collieries	2-0	91
16	Ossett Town	v	Burscough	1-5	62
17	Chadderton	v	Winsford United	2-1	60
18	Congleton Town	v	Morecambe	1-8	42
19	Scarborough	v	Glossop North End	5-0	58
20	Rugby United	v	Matlock Town	1-2	70
21	Dudley Sports	v	Eynesbury Rovers	4-1	31
22	Marconi	v	Belper Town @BT	1-0	59
23	Burton Albion	v	Malvern Town	6-1	61
24	Redditch United	v	Oadby Town	0*2	29
25	Northampton Spncr	v	Racing Club Warwick	1-0	63
26	Sutton Coldfield Tn	v	Banbury United	6-2	54
27	Telford United	v	Corby Town	4-3	55
28	Handrahan Timbers	v	Lincoln United	2-5	27
29	Bedworth United	v	Boldmere St Michaels	0-1	60
30	Hinckley United	v	Atherstone United	4-0	79
31	Hednesford Town	v	Willenhall Town	5-1	126
32	Nuneaton Borough	v	Birstall United	1-0	111
33	Gresley Rovers	v	Mickleover Sports	2-0	85
34	Paget Rangers	v	Long Buckby	19-0	74
35	Stamford	v	Boston United		

(walkover for Boston United - Stamford withdrawn)

No.				Result	Att.
36	Hucknall Town	v	Bromsgrove Rovers		

(walkover for Hucknall Town - Bromsgrove Rovers withdrawn)

No.				Result	Att.
37	Kettering Town	v	St Ives Town	3-1	57
38	Gornal Athletic	v	Alvechurch	1-3	48
39	Grantham Town	v	Chasetown	4-0	62
40	Holbeach United	v	Arnold Town	1-2	37
41	Bloxwich United	v	Holwell Sports		

(walkover for Bloxwich United - Holwell Sports withdrawn)

No.				Result	Att.
42	Newcastle Town	v	St Neots Town		

(walkover for St Neots Town - Newcastle Town withdrawn)

No.				Result	Att.
43	Aylesbury United	v	Romford	3-2	75
44	Cambridge City	v	Chelmsford City	5-1	92
45	Cogenhoe United	v	Wisbech Town	3-2	51
46	Hornchurch	v	Ware	1-3	80
47	Wingate & Finchley	v	Brentwood	3-6	70
48	Uxbridge	v	Leighton Town	3-5	63
49	Hitchin Town	v	Northwood	4-0	54
50	Clacton Town	v	Edgware Town @ET	0-5	40
51	Wealdstone	v	Hemel Hempstead Town	0-3	71
52	Hoddesdon Town	v	Purfleet @P	0*2	31
53	Ruislip Manor	v	Boreham Wood	1-0	52
54	Ilford	v	Beaconsfield SYCOB	1-0	53
55	Southall	v	Witham Town		

(walkover for Witham Town - Southall withdrawn)

No.				Result	Att.
56	Woodbridge Town	v	Ford United	2-0	51
57	Braintree Town	v	Canvey Island	0-1	91
58	Ipswich Wanderers	v	Bugbrooke St Michaels	2-1	54
59		v	Hayes		

(walkover for Hayes - Tring Town withdrawn)

No.				Result	Att.
60	Clapton	v	Barton Rovers @BR	3-0	32
61	Haringey Borough	v	Stevenage Borough	1-4	43
62	Potters Bar Town	v	Wroxham	2-1	67
63	Concord Rangers	v	Bury Town	0-6	90
64	Marlow	v	Milton Keynes City	5*4	48

No.				Result	Att.
65	Letchworth	v	Leyton	3*3	

(Leyton won 5-4 on kicks from the penalty mark)

No.				Result	Att.
66	Kempston Rovers	v	Southend Manor	3-7	41
67	Soham Town Rngrs	v	Bowers United	3*1	41
68	AFC Wallingford	v	Hullbridge Sports	1-3	65
69	Bedford Town	v	Cheshunt	3-0	64
70	Heybridge Swifts	v	Tiptree United	1-3	74
71	Gt Wakering Rovers	v	Tilbury	3-0	92
72	Newmarket Town	v	Burnham Ramblers	0-2	30
73	St Albans City	v	Great Yarmouth Town	3-1	60
74	Royston Town	v	Welwyn Garden City	5-1	24
75	Chesham United	v	Arlesey Town	2-1	65
76	Erith Town	v	Whyteleafe	2-0	56
77	Whitstable Town	v	Three Bridges	3*3	73

(Whitstable Town won 3-1 on kicks from the penalty mark)

No.				Result	Att.
78	Dulwich Hamlet	v	Chichester City United	1*0	42
79	Chipstead	v	Chessington United	3-1	42
80	Horsham	v	Camberley Town	4-3	86
81	Molesey	v	Sittingbourne	5-1	30
82	Tooting & Mitcham U	v	Burgess Hill Town	1*1	50

(Tooting & Mitcham Utd won 4-3 on kicks from the penalty mark)

No.				Result	Att.
83	Littlehampton Town	v	Walton & Hersham	1-2	43
84	Lordswood	v	Sutton United	1-2	55
85	Leatherhead	v	Hillingdon Borough	4-2	56
86	Saltdean United	v	Bedfont (26/8)	5*5	47

(Saltdean United won 4-2 on kicks from the penalty mark)

No.				Result	Att.
87	Eastbourne Town	v	Bracknell Town	3*3	30

(Eastbourne Town won 4-1 on kicks from the penalty mark)

No.				Result	Att.
88	Greenwich Borough	v	Didcot Town	1-2	29
89	Reading Town	v	Merstham	8-2	29
90	North Leigh	v	Alton Town	2-1	27
91	Leyton Pennant	v	Abingdon United	2*3	30
92	Woking	v	Dartford	7-2	101
93	Sandhurst Town	v	Gravesend & Northfleet	1-11	66
94	Westfield	v	Ashford Town (Middx)	2-3	35
95	Godalming & G'ford	v	Welling United		

(Walkover for Welling United - Godalming & Guildford withdrawn)

No.				Result	Att.
96	Eastbourne United	v	Fisher Athletic	0*1	33
97	Dover Athletic	v	Thamesmead Town	1*2	61
98	Fleet Town	v	Faversham Town		

(walkover for Fleet Town - Faversham Town removed)

No.				Result	Att.
99	Chatham Town	v	Havant & Waterlooville	0-3	19
100	Walton Casuals	v	Crowborough Athletic	1-4	43
101	Beckenham Town	v	Farnborough Town	3-2	44
102	Wokingham Town	v	Lewes	4-2	42
103	Milton United	v	Banstead Athletic @BA	3*4	57
104	Aldershot Town	v	Thame United	5*3	101
105	Kingstonian	v	Croydon Athletic	1*1	77

(Kingstonian won 8-7 on kicks from the penalty mark)

No.				Result	Att.
106	Carshalton Athletic	v	Horndean	7-0	54
107	Croydon	v	Tonbridge Angels	0-2	66
108	Yeovil Town	v	Bournemouth	5-0	137
109	Thatcham Town	v	Frome Town	3-1	24
110	Wimborne Town	v	Basingstoke Town		

(walkover for Basingstoke Town - Wimborne Town withdrawn)

No.				Result	Att.
111	Evesham United	v	Chippenham Town	1-5	92
112	Bristol Manor Farm	v	Worcester City	1-3	52
113	Street	v	Eastleigh	0-1	35
114	Cirencester Town	v	Cinderford Town	10-0	63
115	Salisbury City	v	Newport County	1*2	76
116	Brislington	v	Bath City	1-2	41
117	Forest Green Rovers	v	Bashley	2-4	93
118	AFC Newbury	v	Gloucester City	0-3	47

Byes: Bishop's Stortford, Cobham, Doncaster Rvrs, Folkestone Invicta, Histon, Horsham YMCA, Lowestoft Tn, Mangotsfield Utd, Moneyfields & Tamworth

No.Games: 109*   **Home Win:** 64   **Away Win:** 45
Home Goals: 289   **Away Goals:** 229   **Hatricks:** 23
Average Attendance: 59
Best Home Win: Paget Rangers v Long Buckby 19-0
Best Away Win: Sandhurst Town v Gravesend & Northfleet 1-11
Best Attendances: Dunston Federation Brewery v Marine 156
Yeovil Town v Bournemouth 137
* Not including walkovers

SECOND ROUND QUALIFYING

1	Witton Albion	v	Lancaster City	1-2	60
2	Thackley	v	Chadderton	2-0	82
3	Burscough	v	New Mills	7-0	48
4	Stocksbridge Pk Stls	v	Worksop Town	3-1	55
5	Doncaster Rovers	v	Emley	4*3	115
6	Warrington Town	v	Farsley Celtic	1-3	46
7	Northwich Victoria	v	Morecambe	1-5	76
8	Hallam	v	Scarborough	1-2	85
9	Altrincham	v	Gretna	3-1	32
10	Marine	v	Chester City	3*3	160

(Marine won 4-3 on kicks from the penalty mark)

11	Gresley Rovers	v	Telford United	0-2	74
12	Kettering Town	v	St Neots Town	6-1	58
13	Matlock Town	v	Lincoln United	0-3	126
14	Grantham Town	v	Burton Albion	5-4	53
15	Hinckley United	v	Hucknall Town	0-1	73
16	Dudley Sports	v	Marconi	0-1	35
17	Hednesford Town	v	Arnold Town	7-2	121
18	Nuneaton Borough	v	Sutton Coldfield Town	1-0	52
19	Alvechurch	v	Oadby Town	2*1	35
20	Tamworth	v	Northampton Spencer	2-1	36
21	Boldmere St Michaels	v	Boston United	2-4	62
22	Bloxwich United	v	Paget Rangers	2-0	33
23	Ipswich Wanderers	v	Marlow	2-1	35
24	Stevenage Borough	v	Soham Town Rangers	5-0	80
25	Aylesbury United	v	Southend Manor	2*2	37

(Southend Manor won 4-3 on kicks from the penalty mark)

26	Bedford Town	v	Canvey Island	1-3	56
27	Bishop's Stortford	v	Chesham United	3-7	62
28	Ruislip Manor	v	Woodbridge Town	4*4	51

(Woodbridge Town won 5-4 on kicks from the penalty mark)

29	Ware	v	St Albans City	4-2	44
30	Histon	v	Hayes	0-3	42
31	Great Wakering Rvrs	v	Leyton	0*2	70
32	Burnham Ramblers	v	Cogenhoe United	2-0	55
33	Cambridge City	v	Hitchin Town	4-2	51
34	Clapton	v	Hemel Hempstead Tn	4-1	81

(at Aveley FC)

35	Lowestoft Town	v	Royston Town	6-1	44
36	Brentwood	v	Edgware Town	2-5	29
37	Potters Bar Town	v	Witham Town	7-1	37
38	Bury Town	v	Leighton Town	3-4	71
39	Tiptree United	v	Hullbridge Sports	1-3	45
40	Ilford	v	Purfleet	1-3	58
41	Abingdon United	v	Thamesmead Town		

(walkover for Abingdon United - Thamesmead Town withdrawn)

42	Ashford Tn (Middx)	v	Crowborough Athletic	0-2	47
43	Erith Town	v	Havant & Waterlooville	2-3	62
44	Wokingham Town	v	North Leigh	10-0	35
45	Horsham YMCA	v	Folkestone Invicta	0-6	25
46	Saltdean United	v	Reading Town	1*1	31

(Saltdean United won 3-2 on kicks from the penalty mark)

47	Chipstead	v	Carshalton Athletic	0-4	42
48	Moneyfields	v	Woking	1-3	36
49	Aldershot Town	v	Fleet Town	3-0	109
50	Kingstonian	v	Dulwich Hamlet	1*1	89

(Kingstonian won 5-4 on kicks from the penalty mark)

51	Whitstable Town	v	Tooting & Mitcham United	0-3	70
52	Gravesend & N'fleet	v	Sutton United	1-2	114
53	Cobham	v	Tonbridge Angels	1-3	30
54	Horsham	v	Walton & Hersham	0-3	64
55	Welling United	v	Didcot Town	4-1	114
56	Fisher Athletic	v	Molesey	1-0	58
57	Banstead Athletic	v	Beckenham Town	1-2	63
58	Eastbourne Town	v	Leatherhead	1-2	40
59	Gloucester City	v	Chippenham Town	4-2	44
60	Yeovil Town	v	Bath City	7-5	133
61	Eastleigh	v	Thatcham Town	4*3	60
62	Worcester City	v	Bashley	2-8	87
63	Cirencester Town	v	Mangotsfield United	3*2	68
64	Newport County	v	Basingstoke Town	3*0	101

No.Games: 63*   **Home Win:** 31   **Away Win:** 32
Home Goals: 152   **Away Goals:** 142   **Hatricks:** 10
Average Attendance: 71
Best Home Win: Wokingham Town v North Leigh 10-0
Best Away Wins: Horsham YMCA v Folkestone Invicta 0-6
Worcester City v Bashley 2-8
Best Attendance: Marine v Chester City 160

THIRD ROUND QUALIFYING

1	Thackley	v	Lancaster City	3*1	75
2	Burscough	v	Marine	2-0	112
3	Doncaster Rovers	v	Scarborough	0-2	148
4	Morecambe	v	Altrincham	1-2	106
5	Farsley Celtic	v	Stocksbridge Pk Steels	3*2	81
6	Boston United	v	Grantham Town	1-4	167
7	Telford United	v	Alvechurch	6-2	50
8	Marconi	v	Kettering Town	3-1	46
9	Hucknall Town	v	Tamworth	2-0	63
10	Hednesford Town	v	Bloxwich United	3-0	132
11	Nuneaton Borough	v	Lincoln United	2*4	70
12	Ipswich Wanderers	v	Hayes	1-4	82
13	Leighton Town	v	Stevenage Borough	1-4	87
14	Cogenhoe United	v	Southend Manor	1*3	63
15	Cambridge City	v	Ware	2-1	89
16	Chesham United	v	Canvey Island	0-1	40
17	Edgware Town	v	Woodbridge Town	9-1	30
18	Potters Bar Town	v	Clapton	5-0	60
19	Leyton	v	Purfleet	1-2	90
20	Lowestoft Town	v	Hullbridge Sports	3-2	63
21	Abingdon United	v	Woking	0*4	65
22	Fisher Athletic	v	Crowborough Athletic	1-4	73
23	Kingstonian	v	Havant & Waterlooville	3-1	90
24	Tooting & Mitcham U	v	Carshalton Athletic	2-4	70
25	Folkestone Invicta	v	Wokingham Town	0-2	55
26	Walton & Hersham	v	Saltdean United	2*2	77

(Walton & Hersham won 5-4 on kicks from the penalty mark)

27	Welling United	v	Sutton United	1-4	120
28	Aldershot Town	v	Leatherhead	6-1	155
29	Tonbridge Angels	v	Beckenham Town	2-0	
30	Eastleigh	v	Cirencester Town	2-6	47
31	Yeovil Town	v	Bashley	3-2	144
32	Newport County	v	Gloucester City	6-2	101

No.Games: 32   **Home Win:** 17   **Away Win:** 15
Home Goals: 77   **Away Goals:** 68   **Hatricks:** 5
Average Attendance: 82
Best Home Win: Edgware Town v Woodbridge Town 9-1
Best Away Win: Eastleigh v Cirencester Town 2-6
Best Attendance: Boston United v Grantham Town 167

FIRST ROUND PROPER

1	Rushden & Diamonds	v	Stoke City	0-3	147
2	Peterborough United	v	Bury	5-3	319
3	Tranmere Rovers	v	Wigan Athletic	4-2	271
4	Huddersfield Town	v	Chesterfield	4-1	289
5	Thackley	v	Port Vale	0-2	185
6	Scarborough	v	Burscough	1*2	65
7	York City	v	Hartlepool United	0-3	169
8	Halifax Town	v	Shrewsbury Town	2-0	100
9	Macclesfield Town	v	Kidderminster Harriers	0-1	120
10	Wrexham	v	Altrincham	2-1	189
11	Grantham Town	v	Telford United	1*0	105
12	Oldham Athletic	v	Hednesford Town	4*3	302
13	Notts County	v	Lincoln United	3-1	139
14	Blackpool	v	Mansfield Town	3*2	206
15	Farsley Celtic	v	Darlington	2-0	106
16	Carlisle United	v	Hucknall Town	4-2	105
17	Hull City	v	Lincoln City	5-0	229
18	Rochdale	v	Marconi	8-0	204
19	Scunthorpe United	v	Northampton Town	1-0	178
20	Reading	v	Woking	6-0	437
21	Leyton Orient	v	Carshalton Athletic	3-0	202
22	Cardiff City	v	Aldershot Town	0*0	211

(Cardiff City won 3-0 on kicks from the penalty mark)

23	Plymouth Argyle	v	Sutton United	0-1	151
24	AFC Bournemouth	v	Queens Pk Rngrs @QPR	1-3	317
25	Yeovil Town	v	Tonbridge Angels	2-1	162
26	Torquay United	v	Cambridge United	1*1	91

(Torquay United won 4-3 on kicks from the penalty mark)

27	Potters Bar Town	v	Edgware Town	4-3	91
28	Bristol Rovers	v	Cambridge City	4-2	140
29	Crowborough Ath	v	Newport County	1-2	239
30	Swindon Town	v	Southend Manor	3-0	84
31	Brentford	v	Exeter City	4-1	204
32	Swansea City	v	Cirencester Town	1-2	106
33	Wokingham Town	v	Brighton & Hove Albion	1-4	84
34	Cheltenham Town	v	Luton Town	3-4	149
35	Southend United	v	Walton & Hersham	3-1	232
36	Bristol City	v	Lowestoft Town	2-1	84
37	Hayes	v	Colchester United	0-5	129

38	Purfleet	v	Stevenage Borough	3*3	71

(Purfleet won 3-2 on kicks from the penalty mark)

39	Canvey Island	v	Wycombe Wanderers	2-5	195
40	Kingstonian	v	Oxford United	2-0	90

No.Games: 40 **Home Win:** 27 **Away Win:** 13
Home Goals: 95 **Away Goals:** 63 **Hatricks:** 4
Average Attendance: 174
Best Home Win: Rochdale v Marconi 8-0
Best Away Win: Hayes v Colchester United 0-5
Best Attendance: Reading v Woking 437

SECOND ROUND PROPER

1	Port Vale	v	Burscough	2-1	138
2	Kidderminster Harriers	v	Scunthorpe United	2-0	76
3	Stoke City	v	Hartlepool United	0-2	137
4	Tranmere Rovers	v	Rochdale	5-0	239
5	Notts County	v	Huddersfield Town	3-2	141
6	Farsley Celtic	v	Wrexham	0-5	116
7	Peterborough United	v	Oldham Athletic	4-3	505
8	Halifax Town	v	Blackpool	3*2	150
9	Carlisle United	v	Hull City	0-2	118
10	Swindon Town	v	Grantham Town	5-0	89
11	Torquay United	v	Purfleet	2*2	117

(Torquay United won 3-2 on kicks from the penalty mark)

12	Cardiff City	v	Sutton United	1-2	153
13	Newport County	v	Brighton & Hove Albion	1-3	181
14	Queens Park Rngrs	v	Leyton Orient	3-2	403
15	Yeovil Town	v	Kingstonian	3-2	171
16	Luton Town	v	Brentford	0-2	241
17	Bristol Rovers	v	Colchester United	2-3	123
18	Wycombe Wndrs	v	Cirencester Town	3-0	311
19	Southend United	v	Reading	0-2	229
20	Potters Bar Town	v	Bristol City	0-3	164

No.Games: 20 **Home Win:** 11 **Away Win:** 9
Home Goals: 39 **Away Goals:** 38 **Hatricks:** 1
Average Attendance: 190
Best Home Wins: Tranmere Rovers v Rochdale 5-0
Swindon Town v Grantham Town 5-0
Best Away Win: Farsley Celtic v Wrexham 0-5
Best Attendance: Peterborough United v Oldham Athletic 505

THIRD ROUND PROPER

1	Crystal Palace	v	Wolverhampton Wndrs	1*1	829

(Crystal Palace won 4-2 on kicks from the penalty mark)

2	Leeds United	v	Liverpool	1*0	1045
3	Coventry City	v	Southampton	3-0	187
4	Manchester City	v	Burnley	3-0	588
5	Derby County	v	Barnsley	1-3	199
6	Ipswich Town	v	Bristol City	5-0	339
7	West Ham United	v	Everton	1-2	1188
8	Middlesbrough	v	Notts County	5-0	548
9	Tranmere Rovers	v	Sheffield Wednesday	4-1	259
10	Blackburn Rovers	v	Chelsea	4-0	777
11	Crewe Alexandra	v	Portsmouth	1-0	762
12	Brighton & Hove Alb	v	Hull City	4-0	212
13	Norwich City	v	Newcastle United	2-1	807
14	Rotherham United	v	Gillingham	1-2	181
15	Halifax Town	v	Reading	1*2	261
16	Aston Villa	v	Wimbledon	2*1	238
17	Arsenal	v	Colchester United	5-0	694
18	Sunderland	v	Nottingham Forest	2*4	355
19	Grimsby Town	v	Peterborough United	3-2	73
20	Watford	v	Stockport County	1-0	258
21	Hartlepool United	v	Brentford	2*2	304

(Hartlepool United won 5-4 on kicks from the penalty mark)

22	West Bromwich Alb	v	Millwall	1-0	230
23	Kidderminster Harr.	v	Sutton United	3-1	107
24	Bolton Wanderers	v	Bradford City	2-1	762
25	Birmingham City	v	Torquay United	3-1	166
26	Preston North End	v	Fulham	0-1	406
27	Charlton Athletic	v	Leicester City	0-1	304
28	Walsall	v	Tottenham Hotspur	1-5	1041
29	Sheffield United	v	Wycombe Wanderers	1-3	228
30	Yeovil Town	v	Swindon Town	0-2	274
31	Port Vale	v	Wrexham	1-0	116
32	Queens Park Rngrs	v	Manchester United	1-3	2330

No.Games: 32 **Home Win:** 21 **Away Win:** 11
Home Goals: 65 **Away Goals:** 39 **Hatricks:** 2
Average Attendance: 501
Best Home Wins: Ipswich Town v Bristol City 5-0
Middlesbrough v Notts County 5-0
Arsenal v Colchester United 5-0
Best Away Win: Walsall v Tottenham Hotspur 1-5
Best Attendance: Queens Park Rangers v Manchester United 2330

FOURTH ROUND PROPER

1	Everton	v	West Bromwich Albion	2-0	790
2	Port Vale	v	Fulham	0-3	331
3	Bolton Wanderers	v	Tottenham Hotspur	1-2	1518
4	Reading	v	Barnsley	0-3	502
5	Middlesbrough	v	Leeds United	1*1	978

(Leeds United won 4-3 on kicks from the penalty mark)

6	Kidderminster Harriers	v	Grimsby Town	2-1	373
7	Manchester City	v	Gillingham	7-1	483
8	Aston Villa	v	Tranmere Rovers	4*3	1169
9	Crewe Alexandra	v	Arsenal	0-1	1259
10	Brighton & Hove Alb	v	Leicester City	3-2	564
11	Wycombe Wanderers	v	Norwich City	2*2	343

(Wycombe Wanderers won 7-6 on kicks from the penalty mark)

12	Nottingham Forest	v	Watford	5-1	671
13	Ipswich Town	v	Coventry City	3-1	876
14	Blackburn Rovers	v	Swindon Town	2-1	520
15	Birmingham City	v	Manchester United	2-3	1789
16	Crystal Palace	v	Hartlepool United	1-2	259

No.Games: 16 **Home Win:** 9 **Away Win:** 7
Home Goals: 35 **Away Goals:** 27 **Hatricks:** 0
Average Attendance: 777
Best Home Win: Manchester City v Gillingham 7-1
Best Away Win: Port Vale v Fulham 0-3
Reading v Barnsley 0-3
Best Attendances: Birmingham City v Manchester United 1789
Bolton Wanderers v Tottenham Hotspur 1518

FIFTH ROUND PROPER

1	Barnsley	v	Wycombe Wanderers	0*0	494

(Barnsley won 5-4 on kicks from the penalty mark)

2	Manchester United	v	Hartlepool United	3*2	3732
3	Leeds United	v	Tottenham Hotspur	0-1	1343
4	Aston Villa	v	Brighton & Hove Albion	2-0	1820
5	Nottingham Forest	v	Kidderminster Harriers	3-0	734
6	Arsenal	v	Blackburn Rovers	0-2	963
7	Fulham	v	Ipswich Town	3*2	337
8	Everton	v	Manchester City	4-2	1080

No.Games: 8 **Home Win:** 6 **Away Win:** 2
Home Goals: 15 **Away Goals:** 9 **Hatricks:** 0
Average Attendance: 1313
Best Home Win: Nottingham Forest v Kidderminster Harriers 3-0
Best Away Win: Arsenal v Blackburn Rovers 0-2
Best Attendance: Manchester United v Hartlepool United 3,732

SIXTH ROUND PROPER

1	Tottenham Hotspur	v	Blackburn Rovers	2-0	2604
2	Everton	v	Nottingham Forest	2-1	1420
3	Fulham	v	Aston Villa	0-3	951
4	Manchester United	v	Barnsley	3*3	3538

(Barnsley won 3-1 on kicks from the penalty mark)

No.Games: 4 **Home Win:** 2 **Away Win:** 2
Home Goals: 7 **Away Goals:** 7 **Hatricks:** 0
Average Attendance: 2128
Best Home Win: Tottenham Hotspur v Blackburn Rovers 2-0
Best Away Win: Fulham v Aston Villa 0-3
Best Attendance: Manchester United v Barnsley 3538

SEMI FINAL

1st LEG

1	Aston Villa	v	Barnsley	3-1	1224
2	Everton	v	Tottenham Hotspur	2-1	3706

2nd LEG

1	Barnsley	v	Aston Villa	1-3	1753

(Aston Villa win 6-2 on aggregate)

2	Tottenham Hotspur	v	Everton	1-2	4407

(Everton win 4-2 on aggregate)

FINAL

1st LEG TUESDAY 14 MAY 2002

1	Everton	v	Aston Villa	1-4	15280

2nd LEG SATURDAY 18 MAY 2002

1	Aston Villa	v	Everton	0-1	18651

(Aston Villa win 4-2 on aggregate)

F.A. SUNDAY CUP 2001-02

FIRST ROUND
£100 TO WINNERS & £50 TO LOSERS

1	Fantail Manfast	v	Ford Motors	4-0
2	Sandon Dock	v	Orchard Park	1-3
3	Bolton Woods	v	Allerton	2-3
4	Frames	v	Britannia	

(walkover for Britannia - Frames withdrawn)

5	Prestige Brighams	v	Queens Park	3-2
6	Canon	v	A3 (Canada)	1-6
7	East Bowling Unity	v	Cramlington Ben'tine	5-0
8	Ship Inn	v	Smith & Nephew	1-2
9	Nicosia	v	Northwood	

(walkover for Nicosia - Northwood withdrawn)

10	Grosvenor Park	v	Rolls Royce Celtic	1-2
11	Standens Barn	v	Slade Celtic	2-0
12	Capel Plough	v	Bretforton Sports Vic	

(walkover for Capel Bretforton failed to fulfil tie)

13	Lodge Cottrell	v	Duke of York	0-1
14	Wyrley Club	v	Readflex Rangers	2-0
15	Holly Lane Delta	v	Greyhound Dog	0-1
16	Pilot	v	Jolly Farmers	

(walkover for Jolly Farmers - Pilot withdrawn)

17	Stile	v	Mackadown Lane	1-2
18	Trooper	v	Toll End	1-5
19	Lebeq Tavern Courage	v	Percival	1-0
20	St Josephs (Luton)	v	Rainham Sports	1-0
21	Moat	v	Old Oak	3-0
22	Wishing Well	v	Ouzavich	4-0
23	Gossoms End	v	Hammer	1-2
24	Pioneer	v	Heybridge Social	3-2
25	St Josephs (S Oxhey)	v	Theale	1*2
26	Grasshoppers	v	Kempston Fox	1*1

(Grasshoppers won 4-3 on kicks from the penalty mark)

27	Mayfair United	v	Lewsey Social	5-0
28	Poole Wanderers	v	Palmerston WMC	1-2
29	Reading Irish	v	Queensmen	3*2

SECOND ROUND
£100 TO WINNERS & £50 TO LOSERS

1	Fantail Manfast	v	Orchard Park	1-0
2	Britannia	v	East Bowling Unity	3*2
3	Allerton	v	Prestige Brighams	1-0
4	Mainstay	v	Oakenshaw	2*2

(Oakenshaw won 3-2 on kicks from the penalty mark)

5	A3 (Canada)	v	Smith & Nephew	4-3
6	Flathouse	v	Rolls Royce Celtic	

(Flathouse unable to provide venue - tie awarded RR Celtic)

7	Nicosia	v	Broseley Town	3-0
8	Lobster	v	Cheadle United	2-0
9	Hartlepool Lion Hillcarter	v	Town Green	1-0
10	Burnley Boys	v	Hessle Rangers	

(walkover for Hessle - Burnley Boys withdrawn)

11	Seymour	v	Wedgwood	4*4

(Seymour won 5-3 on kicks from the penalty mark)

12	Clubmoor Nalgo	v	Western Approaches	5-1
13	Salerno	v	Albion Sports	0-1
14	Mackadown Lane	v	St Josephs (Luton)	0-4
15	Jolly Farmers	v	Wyrley Club	1-3
16	Schofields	v	Standens Barn	5-2
17	Moat	v	Hammer	2-0
18	St Gerards	v	Duke of York	2-6
19	FC Houghton Centre	v	Axe & Compass	5-1
20	Mayfair United	v	Palmerston WMC	3-0
21	Pioneer	v	Belstone	1-3
22	Celtic SC	v	Biggleswade	5-1
23	Melton Youth OB	v	Concord Rangers	3-2
24	Hexton	v	Watford Labour	2-0
25	Azaad Sports	v	Wishing Well	1-2
26	Greyhound Dog	v	Lebeq Tavern Courage	1-3
27	Theale	v	Toll End	3-2
28	Capel Plough	v	Peacock	1*1

(Peacock won 5-4 on kicks from the penalty mark)

29	Little Paxton	v	Grasshoppers	4-2
30	Longfleet St Marys	v	Reading Irish	2-1
31	Bournemouth Electric	v	Finchampstead Ath	3-1

bye - General Panel Sports

THIRD ROUND
£200 TO WINNERS & £75 TO LOSERS

1	Britannia	v	Allerton	4*4

(Britannia won 4-3 on penalties)

2	Fantail Manfast	v	Hartlepool Lion Hillcarter	0-1
3	Hessle Rangers	v	Lobster	1*2
4	Seymour	v	Nicosia (9/12)	6*3

(tie awarded Nicosia - Seymour played ineligible player)

5	Rolls Royce Celtic	v	Oakenshaw	3-1
6	Clubmoor Nalgo	v	Wyrley Club	1*1

(Clubmoor won 4-3 on kicks from the penalty mark)

7	A3 (Canada)	v	Albion Sports	4-5
8	Mayfair United	v	St Josephs (Luton)	0-4
9	Melton Youth OB	v	Hexton	2-5
10	Moat	v	Lebeq Tavern Courage	1-2
11	Celtic SC	v	Wishing Well	2-1
12	Schofields	v	General Panel Sports	2-0
13	Peacock	v	Theale	3-4
14	Little Paxton	v	Longfleet St Marys	5-0
15	Duke of York	v	Belstone	4-0
16	FC Houghton Centre	v	Bournemouth Electric	3-1

FOURTH ROUND
£250 TO WINNERS & £100 TO LOSERS

1	Britannia	v	Schofields	6-0
2	Lobster	v	Hartlepool Lion Hillcarter	1-4

3	Nicosia	v	Albion Sports	3*3

(Albion Sports won 4-2 on kicks from the penalty mark)

4	Clubmoor Nalgo	v	Rolls Royce Celtic	2*2

(Rolls Royce won 5-4 on kicks from the penalty mark)

5	St Josephs (Luton)	v	FC Houghton Centre	1-2
6	Lebeq Tavern Courage	v	Hexton	3-1
7	Celtic SC	v	Duke of York	3-4
8	Little Paxton	v	Theale	1-0

FIFTH ROUND
£300 TO WINNERS & £125 TO LOSERS

1	Duke Of York	v	Rolls Royce Celtic	1-3
2	FC Houghton Centre	v	Little Paxton	2*3
3	Hartlepool Lion Hillcarter	v	Albion Sports	0*0

(Albion Sports won 4-3 on kicks from the penalty mark)

4	Britannia	v	Lebeq Tavern Courage	7-0

SEMI-FINALS
£400 TO WINNERS & £150 TO LOSERS

1	Rolls Royce Celtic	v	Britannia	1-2	315
2	Little Paxton	v	Albion Sports	0*0	602

(Little Paxton won 4-3 on kicks from the penalty mark)

FINAL

SUNDAY 28 APRIL 2002
£600 TO WINNERS & £400 TO LOSERS

1	Britannia	v	Little Paxton	2-0	650
	(at Aston Villa FC)				

F.A. COUNTY YOUTH CUP 2001-02

FIRST ROUND

1	Leic'rshire & Rutland	v	Staffordshire	4-2
2	Durham	v	Cumberland	5-0
3	Isle of Man	v	Cheshire	0-1
4	East Riding	v	Lincolnshire	4-1
5	Manchester	v	Lancashire	1-3
6	Essex	v	Surrey	7-1
7	Suffolk	v	Berks & Bucks	2-1
8	Hampshire	v	Norfolk	6-2
9	Hertfordshire	v	Sussex	1-5
10	Herefordshire	v	Somerset	0-4
11	Kent	v	Guernsey	3-2
12	Worcestershire	v	Bedfordshire	2-1
13	Devon	v	Jersey	0-1
14	Dorset	v	Wiltshire	2*3

SECOND ROUND

1	Liverpool	v	Northumberland	1-2
2	Leic'rshire & Rutland	v	East Riding	0*1
3	West Riding	v	Lancashire	1*3
4	Sheffield & Hallamshire	v	Birmingham	0-3
5	Westmorland	v	Durham	0-7
6	Shropshire	v	Nottinghamshire	0-3
7	North Riding	v	Cheshire	1-3
8	Sussex	v	Oxfordshire	4*4

(Oxfordshire won 4-2 on kicks from the penalty mark)

9	Suffolk	v	Gloucestershire	3-2
10	Jersey	v	Kent	2-0
11	Worcestershire	v	Somerset	2-1
12	Wiltshire	v	Army	5-0
13	London	v	Hampshire	1-3
14	Middlesex	v	Huntingdonshire	5-1
15	Essex	v	Northamptonshire	5-0
16	Cornwall	v	Cambridgeshire	3-0

THIRD ROUND

1	East Riding	v	Middlesex	1*3
2	Cheshire	v	Northumberland	3-0
3	Suffolk	v	Hampshire	6-2
4	Oxfordshire	v	Nottinghamshire	1-6
5	Worcestershire	v	Lancashire	2*3
6	Cornwall	v	Jersey	0-1
7	Durham	v	Essex	3-0
8	Wiltshire	v	Birmingham	2*3

FOURTH ROUND

1	Middlesex	v	Birmingham	1-2
2	Jersey	v	Lancashire	1-2
3	Durham	v	Suffolk	2-1
4	Cheshire	v	Nottinghamshire	1-3

SEMI FINAL

1	Nottinghamshire	v	Birmingham	0-3
2	Durham	v	Lancashire	2*1

FINAL TIE

SATURDAY 27 APRIL 2002

Birmingham	v	Durham	2-1

Att: 650
at Walsall FC

A Tribute to Boston United

Supporting Boston United must involve an emotional rollercoaster of a life in which you really don't know whether to laugh or cry.

A thrilling promotion race was won on the last day of the season, bringing the championship to York Street on goal difference ahead of their great rivals Dagenham & Redbridge.

This was a triumph for a very good squad of players inspired by the brilliant performances of Irish striker Daryl Clare. But as the players proved their quality and spirit each week, the headlines sadly featured the contentious remarks and actions of their Scottish manager Steve Evans. Consequently the neutrals were less likely to appreciate and applaud 'The Pilgrims' undoubted success.

Worse was to follow, as irregularities in the clubs' conduct brought The Football Association enquiry and a big black cloud hung over the whole issue of the magical promotion to which everyone in the town was looking forward.

Eventually the news emerged that a fine and four points docked was all the punishment received and a place in Division Three was theirs.

This was fine for the players and the supporters, but the general public had certainly lost its confidence in the club whose popularity sadly dipped.

The manager was suspended and unfortunately a great season never really received the tributes the players deserved. The club's future in Division Three will be extremely difficult to negotiate, especially in the early months of the new season.

TW

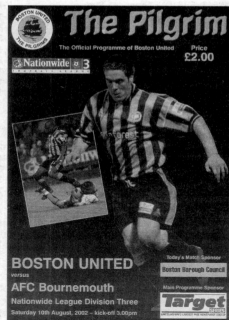

The Pilgrim

The Official Programme of Boston United

Price £2.00

Nationwide 3

BOSTON UNITED
versus
AFC Bournemouth
Nationwide League Division Three
Saturday 10th August, 2002 – kick-off 3.00pm

Today's Match Sponsor
Boston Borough Council

Main Programme Sponsor
Target SERIES

BOSTON UNITED   SEASON 2001-02

	APPEARANCES				GOALSCORERS			
	Lg	FAC	FAT	TOTAL	Lg	FAC	FAT	TOTAL
ANGEL Mark	26+8			26+8	4			4
BASTOCK Paul	41	1	1	43				
BEESLEY Darren	3+3			3+3				
BRABIN Gary	1			1				
BROWN Mick	21+5	1		22+5	3			3
CHARLERY Ken	12			12	8			8
CLARE Daryl	39+1	1	1	41+1	(7p) 24	1		25 (7p)
CLIFFORD Mark	40	1	1	42				
CONROY Nick	0+1			0+1				
COOK Jamie	11+20	1	1	13+20	4			4
COSTELLO Peter	17+8		1	18+8	1			1
ELDING Anthony	12+6		1	13+6	6			6
ELLENDER Paul	36	1	1	38	2			2
EVANS James	1			1				
GOULD James	26+6	1	1	28+6	3			3
GRAY Phil	3			3				
LODGE Andy	19+3			19+3				
MARSH Mike	7			7	1			1
McGARRY Steve	2+4			2+4				
MONINGTON Mark	25	1		26				
MURPHY Gez	4+14	1		5+14	2			2
RODWELL Jim	16			16	2			2
RUSK Simon	23+4		1	24+4	2			2
SCOTT Dion	7		1	8	1			1
TARRANT Neil	4+6			4+6	1			1
THOMPSON Neil	4			4				
TOWN David	5+18			5+18	4			4
WARBURTON Ray	5+1			5+1	1			1
WEATHERSTONE Ross	19+5	1	1	21+5	1			1
WEATHERSTONE Simon	33+1	1		34+1	12			12
OWN GOALS					2			2

BOSTON UNITED

	Date	Comp.	Opponents	Att.	Score	Goalscorers
1	18/08	Conf.	MARGATE	1909	0 - 1	
2	21/08	Conf.	Woking	1701	2 - 0	S Weatherstone 8, Clare 44
3	25/08	Conf.	Forest Green Rovers	816	3 - 0	Charlery 8 35, Cook 69
4	29/08	Conf.	STALYBRIDGE CELTIC	2015	4 - 1	S Weatherstone 6 79, Charlery 74, Clare 81[p]
5	01/09	Conf.	Northwich Victoria	1086	2 - 1	Clare 8, Charlery 56
6	05/09	Conf.	DONCASTER ROVERS	2272	2 - 2	
7	08/09	Conf.	YEOVIL TOWN	2282	4 - 0	
8	10/09	Conf.	Dover Athletic	882	2 - 3	Charlery 45, Leberl 70[og]
9	15/09	Conf.	Chester City	821	2 - 1	S Weatherstone 24, Marsh 70
10	19/09	Conf.	DAGENHAM & REDBRIDGE	2434	1 - 2	S Weatherstone 48
11	22/09	Conf.	HAYES	1709	4 - 1	Charlery 43, S Weatherstone 71, Angel 73, Town 90
12	29/09	Conf.	Farnborough Town	1175	2 - 0	
13	02/10	Conf.	Telford United	1113	2 - 2	Murphy 60, Costello 73
14	06/10	Conf.	SCARBOROUGH	1700	2 - 2	
15	10/10	Conf.	MORECAMBE	1740	2 - 1	Clare 23, Town 29
16	13/10	Conf.	Hereford United	1647	1 - 0	
17	20/10	Conf.	Barnet	1858	1 - 0	
18	03/11	Conf.	SOUTHPORT	1694	0 - 0	
19	10/11	Conf.	Stevenage Borough	2078	2 - 1	Clare 76, Town 86
20	24/11	Conf.	LEIGH RMI	1940	2 - 1	
21	01/12	Conf.	Margate	1745	1 - 1	
22	15/12	Conf.	WOKING	1949	4 - 0	Elding 53 61, Angel 69, Gould 76
23	26/12	Conf.	Nuneaton Borough	2203	1 - 1	Elding 28
24	29/12	Conf.	FOREST GREEN ROVERS	2190	6 - 1	Scott 15, Ellender 25, Gould 30, S Weatherstone 49, Cook 79, Clare 84
25	19/01	Conf.	NORTHWICH VICTORIA	1981	3 - 2	S Weatherstone 44 45, Elding 50
26	26/01	Conf.	Stalybridge Celtic	1023	1 - 2	Ellender 59
27	18/02	Conf.	HEREFORD UNITED	3013	3 - 4	Clare 6 12, Tarrant 58
28	04/03	Conf.	Dagenham & Redbridge	3805	0 - 1	
29	09/03	Conf.	DOVER ATHLETIC	2042	4 - 2	Clare 21[p] 53 84[p] 90
30	12/03	Conf.	Doncaster Rovers	4027	1 - 0	Clare 54[p]
31	16/03	Conf.	TELFORD UNITED	2265	3 - 1	Angel 28, Cook 41, Rodwell 60
32	20/03	Conf.	NUNEATON BOROUGH	4200	4 - 1	R Weatherstone 3, Brown 42, Clare 62, McKenzie 75[og]
33	23/03	Conf.	CHESTER CITY	2519	0 - 1	
34	26/03	Conf.	Yeovil Town	5061	1 - 0	Clare 4
35	29/03	Conf.	BARNET	3669	1 - 1	Rodwell 90
36	01/04	Conf.	Southport	1295	3 - 2	Clare 57 90, Teale 90[og]
37	08/04	Conf.	STEVENAGE BOROUGH	3841	0 - 0	
38	13/04	Conf.	Leigh RMI	788	2 - 1	Clare 4, Brown 42
39	16/04	Conf.	Scarborough	2228	0 - 2	
40	20/04	Conf.	FARNBOROUGH TOWN	3764	4 - 0	Rusk 2, Angel 17, Elding 58, Clare 87
41	23/04	Conf.	Morecambe	1374	0 - 0	
42	28/04	Conf.	Hayes	3249	2 - 0	S Weatherstone 4, Warburton 49
	13/08	Lincs SC 1	SCUNTHORPE UNITED	n/k	3 - 3	Lost 7-8 after pens.
	27/10	FA Cup Q4	BRIGG TOWN	1727	0 - 1	
	12/01	FA Trophy 3	Northwich Victoria	966	1 - 3	Clare 57

1	2	3	4	5	6	7	8	9	10	11	Substitutes Used
Evans	Clifford	Lodge	Ellender	Monington	Marsh	Brown	Charlery	Clare	S W'stone	Angel	Murphy 11 Town 3 R W'stone 8
Bastock	Clifford	Lodge	R W'stone	Monington	Ellender	Marsh	Charlery	Clare	S W'stone	Cook	Murphy 9 Gould 3 Town 8
Bastock	Clifford	Lodge	R W'stone	Monington	Ellender	Marsh	Charlery	Clare	S W'stone	Cook	Brown 4 Murphy 11 Gould 7
Bastock	Clifford	Lodge	R W'stone	Monington	Ellender	Marsh	Charlery	Clare	S W'stone	Cook	Brown 11 Town 8 Murphy 9
Bastock	Clifford	Lodge	R W'stone	Costello	Ellender	Marsh	Charlery	Clare	S W'stone	Cook	Brown 7 Town 9 Angel 11
Bastock	Clifford	Lodge	R W'stone	Monington	Ellender	Costello	Charlery	Clare	S W'stone	Cook	Brown 11 Murphy 3
Bastock	Clifford	Lodge	Brown	Monington	Ellender	S W'stone	Charlery	Clare	Costello	Cook	Murphy 4 Town 10 Gould 11
Bastock	Clifford	Lodge	Brown	Monington	Ellender	S W'stone	Charlery	Clare	Costello	Gould	Murphy 4 Cook 11 R W'stone 2
Bastock	Costello	Lodge	R W'stone	Monington	Ellender	Marsh	Charlery	Clare	S W'stone	Brown	Murphy 9 Town 8
Bastock	Clifford	Lodge	Costello	Monington	Ellender	Marsh	Charlery	Clare	S W'stone	Brown	Murphy 9 Town 3 Cook 7
Bastock	Clifford	Lodge	R W'stone	Monington	Brabin	Costello	Charlery	Clare	S W'stone	Brown	Town 9 Angel 11 Cook 6
Bastock	Clifford	Lodge	R W'stone	Monington	Ellender	Costello	Charlery	Clare	S W'stone	Cook	Town 9 Angel 11 Gould 3
Bastock	Clifford	Gould	R W'stone	Monington	Ellender	Costello	Murphy	Clare	S W'stone	Angel	Cook 11
Bastock	Clifford	Lodge	R W'stone	Monington	Ellender	Costello	Murphy	Clare	S W'stone	Angel	Town 8 Cook 4 Gould 3
Bastock	Clifford	Gould	R W'stone	Monington	Ellender	Town	Gray	Clare	S W'stone	Angel	Cook 11 Murphy 7 Rusk 14(Mur)
Bastock	Clifford	Gould	R W'stone	Monington	Ellender	Town	Gray	Clare	S W'stone	Angel	Cook 7 Murphy 8 Rusk 11
Bastock	Clifford	Gould	R W'stone	Monington	Ellender	Rusk	Gray	Clare	S W'stone	Angel	Murphy 8 Cook 11 Lodge 7
Bastock	Clifford	Gould	R W'stone	Scott	Rusk	Brown	Elding	Clare	S W'stone	Angel	Town 3 Cook 11
Bastock	Clifford	Gould	Elding	Scott	Thompson	Rusk	Town	Clare	S W'stone	Brown	Angel 11 Cook 8 Lodge 9
Bastock	Clifford	Gould	R W'stone	Scott	Thompson	Rusk	Town	Clare	S W'stone	Ellender	Elding 8 Angel 6 Costello 8
Bastock	Clifford	Gould	R W'stone	Scott	Ellender	Rusk	Town	Clare	S W'stone	Angel	Elding 3 Costello 7 Cook 11
Bastock	Clifford	Lodge	Rusk	Monington	Ellender	Angel	Brown	Elding	S W'stone	Gould	Town 9 Costello 10 Cook 8
Bastock	Clifford	Lodge	Gould	Monington	Ellender	Rusk	Brown	Elding	S W'stone	Angel	R W'stone 11 Clare 8
Bastock	Clifford	Scott	R W'stone	Monington	Ellender	Gould	Elding	Clare	S W'stone	Angel	Cook 4 Rusk 5 Costello 6
Bastock	Clifford	Lodge	Scott	Monington	Ellender	Beesley	Elding	Clare	S W'stone	Angel	McGarry 7 Tarrant 8 R W'stone 5
Bastock	Rusk	Lodge	R W'stone	Scott	Ellender	Beesley	Elding	McGarry	S W'stone	Angel	Gould 3 Brown 7 Tarrant 8
Bastock	Clifford	Gould	Beesley	Monington	Rodwell	McGarry	Tarrant	Clare	Angel	S W'stone	Elding 2 Rusk 5
Bastock	Clifford	Lodge	Thompson	Monington	Rodwell	Rusk	Tarrant	Clare	S W'stone	Elding	McGarry 3 Beesley 10 Angel 8
Bastock	Clifford	Gould	Thompson	Monington	Rodwell	Rusk	Tarrant	Clare	Brown	Angel	Elding 8 Town 4 Beesley 9
Bastock	Clifford	Gould	Ellender	Monington	Rodwell	Brown	Cook	Clare	Rusk	Angel	McGarry 9 Town 8
Bastock	Clifford	Gould	Ellender	Monington	Rodwell	Brown	Cook	Clare	Rusk	Angel	McGarry 9 Elding 5 Town 8
Bastock	Clifford	Gould	Ellender	R W'stone	Rodwell	Brown	Cook	Clare	Rusk	Angel	Conroy 6 Town 8 Costello 5
Bastock	Clifford	Gould	Ellender	Warburton	Rodwell	Brown	Cook	Clare	Rusk	Angel	Town 8 Tarrant 3 Costello 5
Bastock	Clifford	Gould	Ellender	Warburton	Rodwell	Brown	Costello	Clare	Rusk	Angel	Murphy 8
Bastock	Clifford	Gould	Ellender	Warburton	Rodwell	Brown	Costello	Clare	Rusk	Angel	Cook 3 Tarrant 8 Murphy 7
Bastock	Clifford	Gould	Ellender	Warburton	Rodwell	Brown	Murphy	Clare	Rusk	Angel	Cook 3 Costello 8
Bastock	Clifford	Gould	Ellender	Warburton	Rodwell	Brown	Murphy	Clare	Rusk	Angel	Cook 8 Costello 5 S W'stone 3
Bastock	Clifford	Gould	Ellender	Costello	Rodwell	Brown	Elding	Clare	S W'stone	Rusk	Cook 7 Angel 3 Town 8
Bastock	Clifford	Lodge	Ellender	Costello	Rodwell	Brown	Elding	Clare	S W'stone	Rusk	Cook 7 Angel 3 R W'stone 4
Bastock	Clifford	Gould	Ellender	Costello	Rodwell	Rusk	Elding	Clare	S W'stone	Angel	Cook 8 Tarrant 9 Beesley 5
Bastock	Clifford	Gould	Ellender	Costello	Rodwell	Rusk	Elding	Clare	S W'stone	Angel	Cook 9 Tarrant 8
Bastock	Clifford	Gould	Ellender	Costello	Rodwell	Rusk	Tarrant	Clare	S W'stone	Angel	Lodge 7 Elding 9 Warburton 8
Bastock	Clifford	Gould	R W'stone	Monington	Ellender	Brown	Murphy	Clare	S W'stone	Cook	? ? ?
Bastock	Clifford	Gould	R W'stone	Scott	Ellender	Rusk	Elding	Clare	Costello	Cook	? ? ?

THE FOOTBALL ASSOCIATION

FIXTURE LIST 2002-03

JULY 2002

06/07	Sat/Sun	UEFA Intertoto Cup 2 (1)
13/14	Sat/Sun	UEFA Intertoto Cup 2 (2)
17	Wed	UEFA Champions League 1Q (1)
20/21	Sat/Sun	UEFA Intertoto Cup 3 (1)
24	Wed	UEFA Champions League 1Q (2)
27	Sat	UEFA Intertoto Cup 3 (2)
31	Wed	UEFA Champions League 2Q (1)
		UEFA Intertoto Cup Semi Final (1)

AUGUST 2002

07	Wed	UEFA Champions League 2Q (2)
		UEFA Intertoto Cup Semi Final (2)
10	Sat	Football League Commences
11	Sun	F.A. Community Shield
		Arsenal v Liverpool at The Millennium Stadium, Cardiff - 2.00
13/14	Tue/Wed	UEFA Champions League 3Q (1)
		UEFA Intertoto Cup Final (1)
15	Thur	UEFA Cup Q (1)
17	Sat	F.A. Premier League Commences
18	Sun	Start of F.A. Women's Premier League
21	Wed	Friendly Internationals
23	Fri	UEFA Super Cup
24	Sat	F.A. Cup EP
26	Mon	Bank Holiday
27	Tue	UEFA Intertoto Cup Final (2)
27/28	Tue/Wed	UEFA Champions League 3Q (2)
29	Thur	UEFA Cup Q (2)
31	Sat	F.A. Cup P

SEPTEMBER 2002

07	Sat	UEFA 2004 Qualifying

Internationals

		F.A. Vase 1Q
		F.A. Youth Cup 1Q*
08	Sun	F.A. Women's Cup 1Q
		F.A. Women's Premier League Cup P
11	Wed	FL Worthington Cup 1
14	Sat	F.A. Cup 1Q
17/18	Tue/Wed	UEFA Champions League Match Day (1)
19	Thur	UEFA Cup (1)
21	Sat	F.A. Vase 2Q
		F.A. Youth Cup 2Q*
22	Sun	F.A. Women's Premier League Cup 1
24/25	Tue/Wed	UEFA Champions League Match Day (2)
28	Sat	F.A. Cup 2Q
29	Sun	F.A. Women's Cup 2Q

OCTOBER 2002

01/02	Tue/Wed	UEFA Champions League Match Day (3)
02	Wed	FL Worthington Cup 2
03	Thur	UEFA Cup 1 (2)
05	Sat	F.A. Trophy P
		F.A. Youth Cup 3Q*
		F.A. County Youth Cup 1*
06	Sun	F.A. Sunday Cup 1
12	Sat	Slovakia v England - UEFA 2004 Qualifying
		F.A. Cup 3Q
16	Wed	England v FYR Macedonia - UEFA 2004 Qualifying
19	Sat	F.A. Vase 1P
22/23	Wed	UEFA Champions League Match Day (4)
23	Wed	FL LDV Vans Trophy 1

26	Sat	F.A. Cup 4Q
27	Sun	F.A. Women's Cup 1P
		F.A. Youth Cup 1P*
		F.A. Women's Premier League Cup 2
29/30	Tue/Wed	UEFA Champions League Match Day (5)
31	Wed	UEFA Cup 2 (1)

NOVEMBER 2002

02	Sat	F.A. Trophy 1
03	Sun	F.A. Sunday Cup 2
06	Wed	FL Worthington Cup 3
09	Sat	F.A. Vase 2P
		F.A. Youth Cup 2P*
		F.A. County Youth Cup 2*
10	Sun	F.A. Women's Cup 2P
12/13	Tue/Wed	UEFA Champions League Match Day (6)
13	Wed	FL LDV Vans Trophy 2
14	Thur	UEFA Cup 2 (2)
16	Sat	F.A. Cup 1P
20	Wed	Friendly Internationals
24	Sun	F.A. Women's Premier League Cup 3
26/27	Tue/Wed	UEFA Champions League Match Day (7)
27	Wed	F.A. Cup 1R
28	Thur	UEFA Cup 3 (1)
30	Sat	F.A. Trophy 2

DECEMBER 2002

01	Sun	F.A. Sunday Cup 3
03	Tue	Inter-Continental Cup
04	Wed	FL Worthington Cup 4
07	Sat	F.A. Cup 2P
		F.A. Vase 3P
		F.A. Youth Cup 3P*
08	Sun	F.A. Women's Cup 3P
10/11	Tue/Wed	UEFA Champions League Match Day (8)
11	Wed	FL LDV Vans Trophy QF
12	Thu	UEFA Cup 3 (2)
14	Sat	F.A. County Youth Cup 3*

| 18 | Wed | F.A. Cup 2R |
| | | FL Worthington Cup 5 |

JANUARY 2003

04	Sat	F.A. Cup 3P
05	Sun	F.A. Women's Cup 4P
08	Wed	FL Worthington Cup SF1
11	Sat	F.A. Trophy 3
12	Sun	F.A. Sunday Cup 4
15	Wed	F.A. Cup 3R
18	Sat	F.A. Vase 4P
19	Sun	F.A. Women's Premier League Cup SF
22	Wed	FL Worthington Cup SF2
		FL LDV Vans Trophy SF
25	Sat	F.A. Cup 4P
		F.A. Youth Cup 4P*
26	Sun	F.A. Women's Cup 5P

FEBRUARY 2003

01	Sat	F.A. Trophy 4
		F.A. County Youth Cup 4*
02	Sun	F.A. Sunday Cup 5
05	Wed	F.A. Cup 4R
08	Sat	F.A. Vase 5P
09	Sun	F.A. Women's Cup 6P
12	Wed	International (Friendly)
15	Sat	F.A. Cup 5P
		F.A. Youth Cup 5P*
18/19	Tue/Wed	UEFA Champions League Match Day (9)
19	Wed	FL LDV Vans Trophy Area Final 1
20	Thur	UEFA Cup 4 (1)
22	Sat	F.A. Trophy 5
25/26	Tue/Wed	UEFA Champions League Match Day (10)
26	Wed	F.A. Cup 5R
		FL LDV Vans Trophy Area Final 2
27	Thur	UEFA Cup 4 (2)

MARCH 2003

| 01 | Sat | F.A. Vase 6P |

02	Sun	FL Worthington Cup Final
08	Sat	F.A. Cup 6P
		F.A. Youth Cup 6P*
		F.A. County Youth Cup Semi Final*
11/12	Tue/Wed	UEFA Champions League Match Day (11)
13	Thur	UEFA Cup Quarter Final (1)
15	Sat	F.A. Trophy 6
16	Sun	F.A. Sunday Cup Semi Final
		F.A. Women's Premier League Cup Final
18/19	Tue/Wed	UEFA Champions League Match Day (12)
19	Wed	F.A. Cup 6R
20	Thur	UEFA Cup Quarter Final (2)
22	Sat	F.A. Vase Semi Final (1)
29	Sat	Liechtenstein v England - UEFA 2004 Qualifying
		F.A. Vase Semi Final (2)
		F.A. Youth Cup Semi Final 1st Leg*
30	Sun	F.A. Women's Cup Semi Final

APRIL 2003

02	Wed	England v Turkey - UEFA 2004 Qualifying
05	Sat	F.A. Trophy Semi Final (1)
06	Sun	FL LDV Vans Final
08/09	Tue/Wed	UEFA Champions League Quarter Final (1)
10	Thur	UEFA Cup Semi Final (1)
12	Sat	F.A. Trophy Semi Final (2)
		F.A. Youth Cup Semi Final 2nd Leg*
13	Sun	F.A. Cup Semi Finals
22/23	Tue/Wed	UEFA Champions League Quarter Final (2)
24	Thur	UEFA Cup Semi Final (2)
26	Sat	F.A. County Youth Cup Final
27	Sun	F.A. Sunday Cup Final
30	Wed	International (Friendly)

MAY 2003

03	Sat	End of Football League
05	Mon	F.A. Women's Cup Final
06/07	Tue/Wed	UEFA Champions League Semi Final (1)

10	Sat	End of Premier League
		F.A. Vase Final
11	Sun	FL Play-off Semi (1)
13/14	Tue/Wed	UEFA Champions League Semi Final (2)
14	Wed	FL Play-off Semi (2)
16	Thur	F.A. Youth Cup Final 1 (prov)
17	Sat	F.A. Cup Final
18	Sun	F.A. Trophy Final
21	Wed	UEFA Cup Final
22	Thur	F.A. Youth Cup Final 2 (prov)
24	Sat	FL 3rd Div Play-off Final
25	Sun	FL 2nd Div Play-off Final
26	Mon	FL 1st Div Play-off Final
28	Wed	UEFA Champions League Final

JUNE 2003

11	Wed	England v Slovakia - UEFA 2004 Qualifying

* closing date of round

Other UEFA 2004 Qualifying Ties

Sat 6 Sept 2003 - FYR Macedonia v England

Wed 10 Sept 2003 - England v Liechtenstein

Sat 11 Oct 2003 - Turkey v England

Final Competition

Draw - 30 November 2003

Opening Match, Porto - 12 June 2004

End of group stage - 23 June 2004

Quarter Final 1 - 26 June 2004

Quarter Final 2 - 27 June 2004

Semi Final 1 - 30 June 2004

Semi Final 2 - 1 July 2004

Final - 4 July 2004

WOMEN'S FOOTBALL

FINAL LEAGUE TABLES
C - Champions   P - Promoted   R - Relegated

AXA FA WOMEN'S PREMIER LEAGUE 2001-02

NATIONAL DIVISION

	P	W	D	L	F	A	Pts		P	W	D	L	F	A	Pts
Arsenal (C)	18	16	1	1	60	15	49	Tranmere Rovers	18	7	3	8	31	36	24
Doncaster Belles	18	13	2	3	57	21	41	Brighton & HA	18	7	3	8	19	33	24
Charlton Athletic	18	10	1	7	40	24	31	Southampton Sts	18	5	3	10	19	34	18
Leeds United	18	7	5	6	36	37	26	Barry Town (R)	18	2	3	13	19	46	9
Everton	18	8	2	8	30	31	26	Sunderland AFC (R)	18	1	5	12	15	46	8

NORTHERN DIVISION

	P	W	D	L	F	A	Pts
Birmingham City (P)	20	16	3	1	68	21	51
Wolves	20	11	4	5	39	27	37
Oldham Curzon	20	10	6	4	39	22	36
Ilkeston Town	20	9	6	5	43	27	33
Liverpool	20	8	6	6	41	27	30
Bangor City	20	7	8	5	40	36	29
Sheff Wednesday	20	6	7	7	33	38	25
Aston Villa	20	6	6	8	42	39	24
Garswood Saints	20	4	6	10	21	47	18
Manchester City	20	4	4	12	19	45	16
Coventry City (R)	20	0	2	18	8	64	2
(North Notts withdrew)							

SOUTHERN DIVISION

	P	W	D	L	F	A	Pts
Fulham (P)	22	22	0	0	234	6	66
Bristol Rovers	22	14	2	6	72	35	44
Milwall Lionesses	22	14	1	7	55	55	43
Chelsea	22	13	2	7	59	51	41
Langford	22	12	1	9	53	46	37
Wimbledon	22	11	3	8	41	55	36
Ipswich Town	22	8	4	10	43	52	28
Barking	22	7	2	13	40	79	32
Newport County	22	6	3	13	37	60	21
Barnet	22	5	6	11	27	75	18
QPR (R)	22	3	5	14	19	60	14
Berkhamsted Tn (R)	22	1	3	18	10	116	6

PREMIER LEAGUE REVIEW

Arsenal were again champions elect, but they were challenged for part of the season by Doncaster Belles. The two promoted teams, Leeds and Brighton faired well with United particularly impressive to take a top four spot.

Birmingham were a revelation in the Northern Division and almost made it to the Premier League Cup Final after a stunning 4-3 quarter final win at Doncaster Belles, while professional Fulham walked away with the Southern Division and did so with a frightening goal difference.

FOURTH ANNUAL F.A. WOMEN'S FOOTBALL AWARDS

AXA PREMIER LEAGUE PLAYER OF THE YEAR
National Division
Marieanne Spacey (Arsenal)
Northern Division
Ann Blackham (Wolves)
Southern Division
Marianne Pettersen (Fulham)

AXA PREMIER LEAGUE TOP SCORER
National Division
Marieanne Spacey (Arsenal)
Northern Division
Katy Ward (Birmingham City)
Southern Division
Marianne Pettersen (Fulham)

SPECIAL ACHIEVEMENT AWARD
Marieanne Spacey

**NATIONWIDE INTERNATIONAL
PLAYER OF THE YEAR**
Kate Chapman (Fulham)

WALKERS YOUNG PLAYER OF THE YEAR
Fara Williams (Charlton Athletic)

MANAGER OF THE YEAR
Mark Hodgson (Leeds United)

TEAM OF THE YEAR
Birmingham City

SHE KICKS MEDIA AWARD
Lincoln City

WOMEN'S FOOTBALL

NORTHERN COMBINATION	Pld	Pts	GD
Middlesbrough (P)	22	54	+58
Blackpool Wren Rovers	22	46	+35
Newcastle	22	41	+23
Blackburn Rovers	21	41	+20
Scunthorpe United	22	36	+17
Manchester United	21	35	+12
Chester City	22	32	+14
Stockport County	22	31	+ 3
Huddersfield Town	21	21	-33
Leeds City Vixens	21	17	-64
Chester-le-Street Town (R)	21	14	-32
Bradford City (R)	21	8	-48

SOUTH EAST COMBINATION	Pld	Pts	GD
P Enfield (P)	22	53*	+51
Stowmarket	22	46	+27
Watford	22	40	+12
Norwich City Racers	22	38	+23
Chesham United	22	29	-13
Bedford Town Bells	22	24	-13
Cambridge University	22	22*	- 2
Hampton	22	21*	- 2
Gillingham	22	20	-18
Chelmsford City	22	20	-30
Whitehawk (R)	22	19*	-10
Charlton (R)	22	17*	-28

MIDLANDS COMBINATION	Pld	Pts	GD
Lincoln City (P)	22	51	+23
Parkgate	22	46	+39
Highfield Rangers	22	45	+35
Chesterfield	22	44	+14
Lichfield Dimaonds	22	30	+ 1
Shrewsbury Town	22	27	+ 3
Peterborough United	22	27	- 1
Telford United	22	26	-20
Ilkeston	22	22	-10
Stafford Rangers	22	19	-14
Derby County (R)	22	15	-53
Port Vale (R)	22	14	-23

SOUTH WEST COMBINATION	Pld	Pts	GD
Bristol City (P)	22	54	+60
Portsmouth	22	49	+47
Reading Royals	22	40	+17
Swindon Town	22	39	+28
Cardiff City	22	37	+22
Yeovil Town	22	32	+ 2
Clevedon Town SBW	22	29	- 9
Newton Abbot	22	28	- 3
Reading	22	24	-10
Plymouth Argyle	22	23	-32
Cheltenham Town (R)	22	11*	-38
Southampton WFC (R)	22	6	-80

WOMEN'S PYRAMID OF FOOTBALL

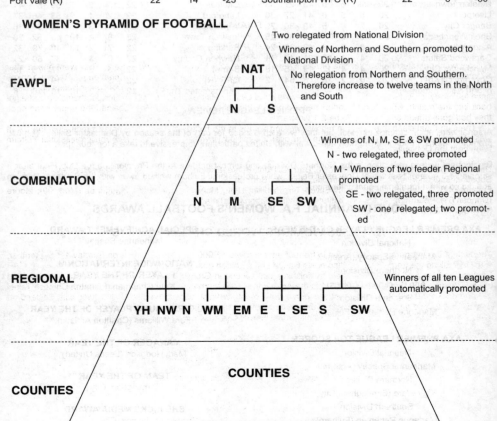

FAWPL

NAT

N   S

Two relegated from National Division

Winners of Northern and Southern promoted to National Division

No relegation from Northern and Southern. Therefore increase to twelve teams in the North and South

COMBINATION

N   M   SE   SW

Winners of N, M, SE & SW promoted

N - two relegated, three promoted

M - Winners of two feeder Regional promoted

SE - two relegated, three promoted

SW - one relegated, two promoted

REGIONAL

YH NW N   WM EM   E L SE   S   SW

Winners of all ten Leagues automatically promoted

COUNTIES

COUNTIES

AXA F.A. WOMEN'S CUP 2002

QUARTER-FINALS

Garswood Saints	0	v	4	Charlton Athletic
Doncaster Belles	2	v	1	Arsenal
Tranmere Rovers	6	v	1	Oldham Curzon
Everton	0	v	4	Fulham

SEMI-FINALS

Tranmere Rovers	1	v	3	Doncaster Belles

At Tranmere Rovers FC

Although Tranmere rarely got out of their half in the first 45, they managed to take an early lead against the run of play. A 28th minute penalty, scored by Kate Hooley, was awarded after a Belles player was judged to have handled the ball in the area. The Belles then had the chance to level when Karen Walker was brought down in the box in the 44th minute. Karen Burke's well struck penalty was saved leaving the Belles trailing as they went into the break. The equaliser eventually came in the 75th minute through Carly Hunt. Karen Walker then went on to score two and confirm the Belles a place in the AXA FA Women's Cup Final

Fulham	4	v	1	Charlton Athletic

At Woking FC

With two major cup games in eight days, Fulham had first to concentrate on their desire for a second crack at the FA Cup final. Addicks fans were in the majority but on 26 minutes Fulham gained the advantage on the pitch. Marianne Pettersen met a cross from the right wing, her powerful strike giving Pauline Cope no chance. Margunn Haugenes' corner kick brought a goal for Kristy Moore ten minutes later. Carmaine Walker won a free-kick on 42 minutes and Fara Williams powered a 25 yard effort past the wall and through the legs of the surprised Fulham keeper to put the Addicks back in the game. But Pettersen restored the difference before half-time, with Moore getting her second with a powerful volley, after the break.

FINAL

Doncaster Belles	2	v	1	Fulham

At Selhurst Park
Attendance: 10,124.

Fulham went one step better than the previous year to lift the AXA FA Cup at Selhurst Park. They went ahead after 57 minutes from a free-kick, Carly Hunt having been penalised and cautioned for a challenge. Rachel Yankey stepped up to fire the free-kick inside the post. It was soon to become a double-blow for Doncaster Belles as a clearance fell nicely for Katie Chapman, whose half-volley had Leanne Hall well beaten. Doncaster got themsleves straight back into the match, when Jody Handley headed past Astrid Johannessen. But Fulham gained the upper hand once they had gone ahead and held on to be 2-1 victors.

The Cup Final clash attracted the highest viewing figures in the history of televised women's football in the UK. It was shown live on BBC1 for the first time and over 2.5 million viewers tuned in to watch the professional Fulham team beat the Doncaster Belles.

Doncaster Belles (4-4-2): Hall, Utley, Lowe, Barr, C. Hunt; Burke, Easton, Exley, G. Hunt; Walker, Handley.
Substitutes: Gomersall, Abrahams, Garside, Howarth, Borman.
Fulham (4-3-3): Johannessen; Jerray-Silver, Terp, Phillip, Unitt; McArthur, Chapman, Haugenes (Mork 90); Moore (Duncan 61), Pettersen, Yankey. Substitutes: Smith, Gibbons, Rahman.
Referee: Mr E. M.Evans

FIFA U19S WOMEN'S WORLD CHAMPIONSHIPS

The final of the tournament was played in front of an incredible 47,000 fans in Edmonton on Sunday 1st September, with USA taking the trophy after beating hosts Canada on a golden goal after drawing 0-0.
England had reached the quarter-finals by finishing joint second in Group C, behind winners USA but were knocked out by Canada, 6-2. England had lost 5-1 to the Americans in the tournament's opening game, beaten Chinese Taipei 4-0 and drawn 0-0 with Australia. Australia won a draw of lots to finish second on paper, after tying with England on goal difference and goals scored. England then claimed one of two best third-place qualifiers.
The USA won the title with a golden goal in extra time in front of a crowd of over 42,000.

SEMI FINALS

Brazil	3p, 1	v	1, 4p	Canada
USA	4	v	1	Germany

THIRD/FOURTH PLACE PLAY OFF

Brazil	3p, 1	v	1, 4p	Germany

FINAL

USA	1	v	0	Canada (aet)

LEAGUE INDEX

Leagues are listed alphabetically below with their relevant page numbers.
Where a league entry runs to more than one page, the number indicated is that of the first page of the section.

As in previous years, sponsors' names have been omitted to ease reference.

League sponsors, however, get their deserved recognition in the appropriate sections

Capital Football League 933
Central Conference League 934
Central Midlands 409
Channel Islands 1044
Combined Counties 891
Conference 125
Devon County League 725
Dorset Combination 691
Eastern Counties League 569
Essex Senior 901
Essex & Herts Border Combination . . 932
Gloucestershire County League 729
Hampshire League 687
Hellenic League 589
Herts Senior County League 925
Isle of Man 1047
Isthmian League
          Premier 769
          Division One South 827
          Division One North 851
          Division Two 875
Kent League 613
Kent County League 625
League of Wales 1005
Leicestershire Senior League 765
Lincolnshire Football League 463
Liverpool County Combination 373
Manchester League 385
Mid Cheshire 379
Middlesex County Football League . . 928
Midland Alliance 733
Midland Combination 747
Midland League 382

Northern Alliance 451
Northern Counties East 391
Northern Premier
          Premier 271
          Division One 326
Northern League 425
North West Counties 351
Nottinghamshire Alliance 419
Reading Football League 929
Sheffield County Senior League 457
Somerset County Football League . . . 727
Southern League
          Premier 470
          Western 522
          Eastern 545
South Western Football League 715
South Midlands 909
Suburban Football League 931
Surrey County Senior League 930
Sussex County League 631
Teesside League 455
United Counties 653
Wearside League 445
Wessex League 675
West Cheshire 375
West Lancashire 383
West Midlands Regional League 755
West Riding County Amateur 461
West Yorkshire Association League . . 459
Western League 695
Wiltshire Football League 731
Womens National League 1069

Vase & Trophy CLUB INDEX

Club	Pages	League	FA
Abbey Hey FC	355-364	North West Counties 1	Manchester FA
Abingdon Town FC	875-884	Isthmian 2	Berks & Bucks FA
Abingdon United FC	593-603	Hellenic P	Berks & Bucks FA
Accrington Stanley FC	278	Northern Prem. P	Lancashire FA
AFC Newbury	678-686	Wessex 1	Berks & Bucks FA
AFC Sudbury	572-582	Eastern Counties P	Suffolk FA
AFC Totton	678-686	Wessex 1	Hampshire FA
AFC Wallingford	894-900	Combined Counties P	Berks & Bucks FA
Aldershot Town FC	776	Isthmian P	Hampshire FA
Alfreton Town FC	327	Northern Prem. 1	Derbyshire FA
Almondsbury Town FC	593-603	Hellenic P	Gloucestershire FA
Alnwick Town FC	438-443	Northern 2	Northumberland FA
Alsager Town FC	355-364	North West Counties 1	Cheshire FA
Alton Town FC	678-686	Wessex 1	Hampshire FA
Altrincham FC	280	Northern Prem. P	Cheshire FA
Alvechurch FC	749-753	Midland Combination P	Birmingham FA
Amesbury Town FC	689-690	Hampshire P	Wiltshire FA
Andover FC	678-686	Wessex 1	Hampshire FA
Anstey Nomads FC	766-67	Leicestershire Senior P	Leics. & Rutland FA
Arlesey Town FC	851	Isthmian 1N	Bedfordshire FA
Armthorpe Welfare FC	395-402	Northern Counties East P	W. Riding FA
Arnold Town FC	395-402	Northern Counties East P	Nottinghamshire FA
Arundel FC	636-645	Sussex 1	Sussex FA
Ash United FC	894-900	Combined Counties P	Surrey FA
Ashford Town (Middx) FC	827	Isthmian 1S	Middlesex FA
Ashford Town FC	546	Southern E	Kent FA
Ashington FC	438-443	Northern 2	Northumberland FA
Ashton United FC	282	Northern Prem. P	Manchester FA
Atherstone United FC	523	Southern W	Birmingham FA
Atherton Collieries FC	355-364	North West Counties 1	Lancashire FA
Atherton LR FC	355-364	North West Counties 1	Lancashire FA
Aveley FC	852	Isthmian 1N	Essex FA
Aylesbury United FC	778	Isthmian P	Berks & Bucks FA
Backwell United FC	699-707	Western P	Somerset FA
Bacup Borough FC	365-370	North West Counties 2	Lancashire FA
Bamber Bridge FC	328	Northern Prem. 1	Lancashire FA
Banbury United FC	547	Southern E	Oxfordshire FA
Banstead Athletic FC	828	Isthmian 1S	Surrey FA
Barking & East Ham United FC	853	Isthmian 1N	London FA
Barnet FC	139	Conference	Hertfordshire FA
Barnstaple Town FC	699-707	Western P	Devon FA
Barrow FC	284	Northern Prem. P	Lancashire FA
Barrow Town FC	766-67	Leicestershire Senior P	Leics. & Rutland FA
Barton Rovers FC	854	Isthmian 1N	Bedfordshire FA
Barwell FC	737-745	Midland Alliance	Leics. & Rutland FA
Bashley FC	548	Southern E	Hampshire FA

INDEX

Basildon United FC	903-907	Essex Senior P	Essex FA
Basingstoke Town FC	780	Isthmian P	Hampshire FA
BAT Sports FC	678-686	Wessex 1	Hampshire FA
Bath City FC	474	Southern P	Somerset FA
Beaconsfield SYCOB FC	911-917	Spartan South Mids. P	Berks & Bucks FA
Beckenham Town FC	616-624	Kent	Kent FA
Bedfont FC	894-900	Combined Counties P	Middlesex FA
Bedford Town FC	782	Isthmian P	Bedfordshire FA
Bedford United & Valerio FC	911-917	Spartan South Mids. P	Bedfordshire FA
Bedlington Terriers FC	429-437	Northern 1	Northumberland FA
Bedworth United FC	524	Southern W	Birmingham FA
Belper Town FC	329	Northern Prem. 1	Derbyshire FA
Bemerton Heath Harlequins FC	678-686	Wessex 1	Wiltshire FA
Berkhamsted Town FC	855	Isthmian 1N	Hertfordshire FA
Bicester Town FC	593-603	Hellenic P	Oxfordshire FA
Biddulph Victoria FC	737-745	Midland Alliance	Staffordshire FA
Bideford FC	699-707	Western P	Devon FA
Biggleswade Town FC	911-917	Spartan South Mids. P	Bedfordshire FA
Biggleswade United FC	918-924	Spartan South Mids. 1	Bedfordshire FA
Billericay Town FC	784	Isthmian P	Essex FA
Billingham Synthonia FC	429-437	Northern 1	Durham FA
Billingham Town FC	429-437	Northern 1	Durham FA
Birstall United FC	766-67	Leicestershire Senior P	Leics. & Rutland FA
Bishop Auckland FC	330	Northern Prem. 1	Durham FA
Bishop Sutton FC	699-707	Western P	Somerset FA
Bishop's Stortford FC	786	Isthmian P	Hertfordshire FA
Bitton AFC	708-713	Western 1	Gloucestershire FA
Blaby & Whetstone Athletic FC	766-67	Leicestershire Senior P	Leics. & Rutland FA
Blackfield & Langley FC	678-686	Wessex 1	Hampshire FA
Blackpool Mechanics FC	365-370	North West Counties 2	Lancashire FA
Blackstones FC	658-666	United Counties P	Lincolnshire FA
Blackwell MW FC	412-416	Central Midlands S.D.	Derbyshire FA
Blyth Spartans AFC	286	Northern Prem. P	Northumberland FA
Bognor Regis Town FC	829	Isthmian 1S	Sussex FA
Boldmere St Michaels FC	737-745	Midland Alliance	Birmingham FA
Bolehall Swifts FC	749-753	Midland Combination P	Birmingham FA
Boreham Wood FC	788	Isthmian P	Hertfordshire FA
Borrowash Victoria FC	395-402	Northern Counties East P	Derbyshire FA
Boston Town FC	658-666	United Counties P	Lincolnshire FA
Bourne Town FC	658-666	United Counties P	Lincolnshire FA
Bournemouth FC	678-686	Wessex 1	Hampshire FA
Bowers United FC	903-907	Essex Senior P	Essex FA
Brackley Town FC	593-603	Hellenic P	Northants. FA
Bracknell Town FC	830	Isthmian 1S	Berks & Bucks FA
Bradford (Park Avenue) FC	288	Northern Prem. P	W. Riding FA
Braintree Town FC	790	Isthmian P	Essex FA
Brandon United FC	429-437	Northern 1	Durham FA
Brentwood FC	903-907	Essex Senior P	Essex FA

Bridgnorth Town FC	737-745	Midland Alliance	Shropshire FA
Bridgwater Town FC	699-707	Western P	Somerset FA
Bridlington Town FC	395-402	Northern Counties East P	E. Riding FA
Bridport FC	699-707	Western P	Dorset FA
Brierley & Hagley FC	759-763	West Midlands P	Birmingham FA
Brigg Town FC	395-402	Northern Counties East P	Lincolnshire FA
Brightlingsea United FC	583-587	Eastern Counties 1	Essex FA
Brimsdown Rovers FC	918-924	Spartan South Mids. 1	London FA
Brislington FC	699-707	Western P	Somerset FA
Bristol Manor Farm FC	708-713	Western 1	Gloucestershire FA
Broadbridge Heath FC	646-651	Sussex 2	Sussex FA
Brockenhurst FC	678-686	Wessex 1	Hampshire FA
Brodsworth M.W. FC	395-402	Northern Counties East P	Sheff. & Hallams. FA
Bromley FC	831	Isthmian 1S	Kent FA
Bromsgrove Rovers FC	525	Southern W	Worcesters. FA
Bromyard Town FC	759-763	West Midlands P	Herefordshire FA
Brook House FC	911-917	Spartan South Mids. P	Middlesex FA
Broxbourne Borough V&E FC	911-917	Spartan South Mids. P	Hertfordshire FA
Buckingham Town FC	658-666	United Counties P	Berks & Bucks FA
Bugbrooke St Michaels FC	667-673	United Counties 1	Northants. FA
Burgess Hill Town FC	636-645	Sussex 1	Sussex FA
Burnham FC	549	Southern E	Berks & Bucks FA
Burnham Ramblers FC	903-907	Essex Senior P	Essex FA
Burscough FC	290	Northern Prem. P	Liverpool FA
Burton Albion FC	145	Conference	Birmingham FA
Bury Town FC	572-582	Eastern Counties P	Suffolk FA
Buxton FC	395-402	Northern Counties East P	Derbyshire FA
Calne Town FC	708-713	Western 1	Wiltshire FA
Camberley Town FC	875-884	Isthmian 2	Surrey FA
Cambridge City FC	476	Southern P	Cambridgeshire FA
Cammell Laird FC	377-378	West Cheshire 1	Cheshire FA
Canvey Island FC	792	Isthmian P	Essex FA
Carlton Town FC	412-416	Central Midlands S.D.	Nottinghamshire FA
Carshalton Athletic FC	832	Isthmian 1S	Surrey FA
Carterton Town FC	593-603	Hellenic P	Oxfordshire FA
Causeway United FC	737-745	Midland Alliance	Birmingham FA
Chadderton FC	365-370	North West Counties 2	Manchester FA
Chalfont St Peter FC	875-884	Isthmian 2	Berks & Bucks FA
Chard Town FC	708-713	Western 1	Somerset FA
Chasetown FC	737-745	Midland Alliance	Staffordshire FA
Chatham Town FC	550	Southern E	Kent FA
Cheadle Town FC	365-370	North West Counties 2	Cheshire FA
Chelmsford City FC	478	Southern P	Essex FA
Chertsey Town FC	833	Isthmian 1S	Surrey FA
Chesham United FC	794	Isthmian P	Berks & Bucks FA
Cheshunt FC	875-884	Isthmian 2	Hertfordshire FA
Chessington & Hook United FC	894-900	Combined Counties P	Surrey FA
Chessington United FC	894-900	Combined Counties P	Surrey FA

Chester City FC	151	Conference	Cheshire FA
Chester-Le-Street Town FC	429-437	Northern 1	Durham FA
Chichester City United FC	636-645	Sussex 1	Sussex FA
Chippenham Town FC	480	Southern P	Wiltshire FA
Chipping Norton Town FC	604-608	Hellenic 1W	Oxfordshire FA
Chipstead FC	894-900	Combined Counties P	Surrey FA
Chorley FC	331	Northern Prem. 1	Lancashire FA
Christchurch FC	678-686	Wessex 1	Hampshire FA
Cinderford Town FC	526	Southern W	Gloucestershire FA
Cirencester Town FC	527	Southern W	Gloucestershire FA
Cirencester Academy FC	593-603	Hellenic P	Gloucestershire FA
Clacton Town FC	572-582	Eastern Counties P	Essex FA
Clapton FC	875-884	Isthmian 2	London FA
Clevedon Town FC	528	Southern W	Somerset FA
Clevedon United FC	727-728	Somerset Senior P	Somerset FA
Clitheroe FC	355-364	North West Counties 1	Lancashire FA
Coalville Town FC	766-67	Leicestershire Senior P	Leics. & Rutland FA
Cobham FC	894-900	Combined Counties P	Surrey FA
Cockfosters FC	918-924	Spartan South Mids. 1	London FA
Cogenhoe United FC	658-666	United Counties P	Northants. FA
Colne FC	365-370	North West Counties 2	Lancashire FA
Colney Heath FC	918-924	Spartan South Mids. 1	Hertfordshire FA
Colwyn Bay FC	292	Northern Prem. P	Wales
Concord Rangers FC	903-907	Essex Senior P	Essex FA
Congleton Town FC	355-364	North West Counties 1	Cheshire FA
Consett FC	429-437	Northern 1	Durham FA
Corby Town FC	551	Southern E	Northants. FA
Corinthian Casuals FC	834	Isthmian 1S	London FA
Cornard United FC	583-587	Eastern Counties 1	Suffolk FA
Corsham Town FC	708-713	Western 1	Wiltshire FA
Cove FC	894-900	Combined Counties P	Hampshire FA
Coventry Sphinx FC	749-753	Midland Combination P	Birmingham FA
Cowes Sports FC	678-686	Wessex 1	Hampshire FA
Cradley Town FC	737-745	Midland Alliance	Birmingham FA
Crawley Town FC	482	Southern P	Sussex FA
Cray Wanderers FC	616-624	Kent	Kent FA
Crook Town FC	438-443	Northern 2	Durham FA
Crowborough Athletic FC	652	Sussex 3	Sussex FA
Croydon FC	835	Isthmian 1S	Surrey FA
Croydon Athletic FC	836	Isthmian 1S	London FA
Cullompton Rangers FC	725-726	Devon	Devon FA
Curzon Ashton FC	355-364	North West Counties 1	Manchester FA
Dagenham & Redbridge FC	157	Conference	Essex FA
Dartford FC	552	Southern E	Kent FA
Darwen FC	365-370	North West Counties 2	Lancashire FA
Daventry Town FC	658-666	United Counties P	Northants. FA
Dawlish Town FC	699-707	Western P	Devon FA
Deal Town FC	616-624	Kent	Kent FA

Deeping Rangers FC	658-666	United Counties P	Lincolnshire FA
Dereham Town FC	572-582	Eastern Counties P	Norfolk FA
Desborough Town FC	658-666	United Counties P	Northants. FA
Devizes Town FC	699-707	Western P	Wiltshire FA
Didcot Town FC	593-603	Hellenic P	Berks & Bucks FA
Diss Town FC	572-582	Eastern Counties P	Norfolk FA
Doncaster Rovers FC	163	Conference	Sheff. & Hallams. FA
Dorchester Town FC	553	Southern E	Dorset FA
Dorking FC	875-884	Isthmian 2	Surrey FA
Dover Athletic FC	484	Southern P	Kent FA
Downes Sports FC	766-67	Leicestershire Senior P	Leics. & Rutland FA
Downham Town FC	583-587	Eastern Counties 1	Norfolk FA
Downton FC	678-686	Wessex 1	Wiltshire FA
Droylsden FC	294	Northern Prem. P	Manchester FA
Dudley Town FC	759-763	West Midlands P	Birmingham FA
Dulwich Hamlet FC	837	Isthmian 1S	London FA
Dunkirk FC	412-416	Central Midlands S.D.	Nottinghamshire FA
Dunstable Town FC	911-917	Spartan South Mids. P	Bedfordshire FA
Dunston Federation Brewery FC	429-437	Northern 1	Durham FA
Durham City FC	429-437	Northern 1	Durham FA
Easington Colliery FC	438-443	Northern 2	Durham FA
East Grinstead Town FC	646-651	Sussex 2	Sussex FA
East Preston FC	636-645	Sussex 1	Sussex FA
East Thurrock United FC	856	Isthmian 1N	Essex FA
Eastbourne Borough FC	554	Southern E	Sussex FA
Eastbourne Town FC	646-651	Sussex 2	Sussex FA
Eastbourne United FC	646-651	Sussex 2	Sussex FA
Eastleigh FC	678-686	Wessex 1	Hampshire FA
Eastwood Town FC	332	Northern Prem. 1	Nottinghamshire FA
Eccleshill United FC	395-402	Northern Counties East P	W. Riding FA
Edgware Town FC	875-884	Isthmian 2	Middlesex FA
Egham Town FC	838	Isthmian 1S	Surrey FA
Elmore FC	699-707	Western P	Devon FA
Ely City FC	572-582	Eastern Counties P	Cambridgeshire FA
Enfield FC	796	Isthmian P	Middlesex FA
Enfield Town FC	903-907	Essex Senior P	Middlesex FA
Epsom & Ewell FC	839	Isthmian 1S	Surrey FA
Erith & Belvedere FC	555	Southern E	Kent FA
Erith Town FC	616-624	Kent	London FA
Esh Winning FC	429-437	Northern 1	Durham FA
Eton Manor FC	903-907	Essex Senior P	Essex FA
Evenwood Town FC	438-443	Northern 2	Durham FA
Evesham United FC	529	Southern W	Worcesters. FA
Exmouth Town FC	708-713	Western 1	Devon FA
Eynesbury Rovers FC	667-673	United Counties 1	Huntingdonshire FA
Fairford Town FC	593-603	Hellenic P	Gloucestershire FA
Fakenham Town FC	572-582	Eastern Counties P	Norfolk FA
Falmouth Town AFC	717-722	South Western	Cornwall FA

Chester City - Falmouth Town

INDEX

Fareham Town FC	678-686	Wessex 1	Hampshire FA
Farnborough Town FC	169	Conference	Hampshire FA
Farnham Town FC	894-900	Combined Counties P	Surrey FA
Farsley Celtic FC	333	Northern Prem. 1	W. Riding FA
Felixstowe & Walton United FC	583-587	Eastern Counties 1	Suffolk FA
Fernhill County Sports FC	749-753	Midland Combination P	Worcesters. FA
Fisher Athletic FC	556	Southern E	London FA
Flackwell Heath FC	875-884	Isthmian 2	Berks & Bucks FA
Fleet Town FC	557	Southern E	Hampshire FA
Fleetwood Town FC	355-364	North West Counties 1	Lancashire FA
Flixton FC	355-364	North West Counties 1	Manchester FA
Folkestone Invicta FC	486	Southern P	Kent FA
Ford Sports Daventry FC	658-666	United Counties P	Northants. FA
Ford United FC	798	Isthmian P	London FA
Forest Green Rovers FC	175	Conference	Gloucestershire FA
Formby FC		Liverpool	Liverpool FA
Friar Lane OB FC	766-67	Leicestershire Senior P	Leics. & Rutland FA
Frickley Athletic FC	296	Northern Prem. P	Sheff. & Hallams. FA
Frome Town FC	699-707	Western P	Somerset FA
Gainsborough Trinity FC	298	Northern Prem. P	Lincolnshire FA
Garforth Town FC	395-402	Northern Counties East P	W. Riding FA
Gateshead FC	300	Northern Prem. P	Durham FA
Gedling Town FC	404-408	Northern Counties East 1	Nottinghamshire FA
Glapwell FC	395-402	Northern Counties East P	Derbyshire FA
Glasshoughton Welfare FC	395-402	Northern Counties East P	W. Riding FA
Glossop North End FC	355-364	North West Counties 1	Derbyshire FA
Gloucester City FC	530	Southern W	Gloucestershire FA
Gloucester United FC	593-603	Hellenic P	Gloucestershire FA
Godalming & Guildford FC	894-900	Combined Counties P	Surrey FA
Goole AFC	395-402	Northern Counties East P	W. Riding FA
Gorleston FC	572-582	Eastern Counties P	Norfolk FA
Gornal Athletic FC	759-763	West Midlands P	Birmingham FA
Gosport Borough FC	678-686	Wessex 1	Hampshire FA
Grantham Town FC	488	Southern P	Lincolnshire FA
Gravesend & Northfleet FC	181	Conference	Kent FA
Grays Athletic FC	800	Isthmian P	Essex FA
Great Harwood Town FC	365-370	North West Counties 2	Lancashire FA
Great Wakering Rovers FC	857	Isthmian 1N	Essex FA
Great Yarmouth Town FC	572-582	Eastern Counties P	Norfolk FA
Greenacres(Hemel Hempstead) FC	911-917	Spartan South Mids. P	Hertfordshire FA
Greenwich Borough FC	616-624	Kent	Kent FA
Gresley Rovers FC	531	Southern W	Derbyshire FA531
Grosvenor Park FC	737-745	Midland Alliance	Birmingham FA
Guisborough Town FC	429-437	Northern 1	N. Riding FA
Guiseley AFC	334	Northern Prem. 1	W. Riding FA
Hadleigh United FC	583-587	Eastern Counties 1	Suffolk FA
Hailsham Town FC	636-645	Sussex 1	Sussex FA
Halesowen Harriers FC	737-745	Midland Alliance	Birmingham FA

Halesowen Town FC	490	Southern P	Birmingham FA
Halifax Town FC	187	Conference	W. Riding FA
Hall Road Rangers FC	404-408	Northern Counties East 1	E. Riding FA
Hallam FC	395-402	Northern Counties East P	Sheff. & Hallams. FA
Hallen FC	708-713	Western 1	Gloucestershire FA
Halstead Town FC	583-587	Eastern Counties 1	Essex FA
Hampton & Richmond Bor. FC	802	Isthmian P	Middlesex FA
Hamworthy United FC	693-694	Dorset Premier	Dorset FA
Handrahan Timbers FC	749-753	Midland Combination P	Birmingham FA
Hanwell Town FC	911-917	Spartan South Mids. P	Middlesex FA
Harefield United FC	911-917	Spartan South Mids. P	Middlesex FA
Haringey Borough FC	911-917	Spartan South Mids. P	London FA
Harlow Town FC	858	Isthmian 1N	Essex FA
Harpenden Town FC	918-924	Spartan South Mids. 1	Hertfordshire FA
Harrogate Railway FC	395-402	Northern Counties East P	W. Riding FA
Harrogate Town FC	302	Northern Prem. P	W. Riding FA
Harrow Borough FC	804	Isthmian P	Middlesex FA
Harrow Hill FC	604-608	Hellenic 1W	Gloucestershire FA
Hartley Wintney FC	894-900	Combined Counties P	Hampshire FA
Harwich & Parkeston FC	572-582	Eastern Counties P	Essex FA
Hassocks FC	636-645	Sussex 1	Sussex FA
Hastings United FC	492	Southern P	Sussex FA
Hatfield Main FC	404-408	Northern Counties East 1	W. Riding FA
Havant & Waterlooville FC	494	Southern P	Hampshire FA
Haverhill Rovers FC	583-587	Eastern Counties 1	Suffolk FA
Hayes FC	806	Isthmian P	Middlesex FA
Heanor Town FC	412-416	Central Midlands S.D.	Derbyshire FA
Heath Hayes FC	759-763	West Midlands P	Staffordshire FA
Hebburn Town FC	438-443	Northern 2	Durham FA
Hednesford Town FC	496	Southern P	Birmingham FA
Hemel Hempstead Town FC	859	Isthmian 1N	Hertfordshire FA
Hendon FC	808	Isthmian P	Middlesex FA
Henley Town FC	593-603	Hellenic P	Oxfordshire FA
Hereford United FC	193	Conference	Herefordshire FA
Herne Bay FC	616-624	Kent	Kent FA
Hertford Town FC	860	Isthmian 1N	Hertfordshire FA
Heybridge Swifts FC	810	Isthmian P	Essex FA
Highfield Rangers FC	766-67	Leicestershire Senior P	Leics. & Rutland FA
Highworth Town FC	593-603	Hellenic P	Wiltshire FA
Hillingdon Borough FC	911-917	Spartan South Mids. P	Middlesex FA
Hinckley United FC	498	Southern P	Leics. & Rutland FA
Histon FC	558	Southern E	Cambridgeshire FA
Hitchin Town FC	812	Isthmian P	Hertfordshire FA
Hoddesdon Town FC	911-917	Spartan South Mids. P	Hertfordshire FA
Holbeach United FC	658-666	United Counties P	Lincolnshire FA
Holker Old Boys FC	365-370	North West Counties 2	Lancashire FA
Holmer Green FC	911-917	Spartan South Mids. P	Berks & Bucks FA
Holwell Sports FC	766-67	Leicestershire Senior P	Leics. & Rutland FA

Hook Norton FC	593-603	Hellenic P	Oxfordshire FA
Horden CW FC	438-443	Northern 2	Durham FA
Hornchurch FC	861	Isthmian 1N	Essex FA
Horndean FC	689-690	Hampshire P	Hampshire FA
Horsham FC	840	Isthmian 1S	Sussex FA
Horsham YMCA FC	636-645	Sussex 1	Sussex FA
Hucknall Town FC	304	Northern Prem. P	Nottinghamshire FA
Hullbridge Sports FC	903-907	Essex Senior P	Essex FA
Hungerford Town FC	875-884	Isthmian 2	Berks & Bucks FA
Hyde United FC	306	Northern Prem. P	Cheshire FA
Hythe Town FC	616-624	Kent	Kent FA
Ibstock Welfare FC	766-67	Leicestershire Senior P	Leics. & Rutland FA
Ilford FC	903-907	Essex Senior P	Essex FA
Ilfracombe Town FC	708-713	Western 1	Devon FA
Ilkeston Town FC	500	Southern P	Derbyshire FA
Ipswich Wanderers FC	572-582	Eastern Counties P	Suffolk FA
Jarrow Roofing Boldon CA FC	429-437	Northern 1	Durham FA
Kempston Rovers FC	658-666	United Counties P	Bedfordshire FA
Kendal Town FC	335	Northern Prem. 1	Westmorland FA
Kennek Ryhope CA FC	438-443	Northern 2	Durham FA
Kettering Town FC	199	Conference	Northants. FA
Keynsham Town FC	699-707	Western P	Somerset FA
Kidsgrove Athletic FC	336	Northern Prem. 1	Staffordshire FA
Kimberley Town FC	417-418	Central Midlands P	Nottinghamshire FA
Kings Heath FC	749-753	Midland Combination P	Birmingham FA
Kings Lynn FC	559	Southern E	Norfolk FA
Kingsbury Town FC	875-884	Isthmian 2	Middlesex FA
Kingstonian FC	814	Isthmian P	Surrey FA
Kirby Muxloe FC	766-67	Leicestershire Senior P	Leics. & Rutland FA
Lancaster City FC	308	Northern Prem. P	Lancashire FA
Lancing FC	646-651	Sussex 2	Sussex FA
Langford FC	918-924	Spartan South Mids. 1	Bedfordshire FA
Launceston FC	717-722	South Western	Cornwall FA
Leamington FC	749-753	Midland Combination P	Birmingham FA
Leatherhead FC	841	Isthmian 1S	Surrey FA
Ledbury Town FC	759-763	West Midlands P	Herefordshire FA
Leek CSOB FC	365-370	North West Counties 2	Staffordshire FA
Leek Town FC	337	Northern Prem. 1	Staffordshire FA
Leigh RMI FC	205	Conference	Lancashire FA
Leighton Town FC	875-884	Isthmian 2	Bedfordshire FA
Letchworth FC	911-917	Spartan South Mids. P	Hertfordshire FA
Leverstock Green FC	918-924	Spartan South Mids. 1	Hertfordshire FA
Lewes FC	842	Isthmian 1S	Sussex FA
Leyton FC	875-884	Isthmian 2	London FA
Leyton Pennant FC	862	Isthmian 1N	Essex FA
Lincoln Moorlands FC	404-408	Northern Counties East 1	Lincolnshire FA
Lincoln United FC	338	Northern Prem. 1	Lincolnshire FA
Liskeard Athletic FC	717-722	South Western	Cornwall FA

Little Drayton Rangers FC	759-763	West Midlands P	Shropshire FA
Littlehampton Town FC	636-645	Sussex 1	Sussex FA
Liversedge FC	395-402	Northern Counties East P	W. Riding FA
London Colney FC	911-917	Spartan South Mids. P	Hertfordshire FA
Long Buckby FC	658-666	United Counties P	Northants. FA
Long Eaton United FC	404-408	Northern Counties East 1	Derbyshire FA
Lordswood FC	616-624	Kent	Kent FA
Louth United FC	404-408	Northern Counties East 1	Lincolnshire FA
Lowestoft Town FC	572-582	Eastern Counties P	Suffolk FA
Ludlow Town FC	737-745	Midland Alliance	Shropshire FA
Lye Town FC	759-763	West Midlands P	Birmingham FA
Lymington & New Milton FC	678-686	Wessex 1	Hampshire FA
Lymington Town FC	689-690	Hampshire P	Hampshire FA
Maidenhead United FC	816	Isthmian P	Berks & Bucks FA
Maidstone United FC	616-624	Kent	Kent FA
Maine Road FC	365-370	North West Counties 2	Manchester FA
Maldon Town FC	572-582	Eastern Counties P	Essex FA
Maltby Main FC	404-408	Northern Counties East 1	Sheff. & Hallams. FA
Malvern Town FC	759-763	West Midlands P	Worcesters. FA
Mangotsfield United FC	532	Southern W	Gloucestershire FA
March Town United FC	583-587	Eastern Counties 1	Cambridgeshire FA
Marconi FC	749-753	Midland Combination P	Birmingham FA
Margate FC	211	Conference	Kent FA
Marine FC	310	Northern Prem. P	Liverpool FA
Marlow FC	863	Isthmian 1N	Berks & Bucks FA
Marske United FC	429-437	Northern 1	N. Riding FA
Matlock Town FC	339	Northern Prem. 1	Derbyshire FA
Meir KA FC	749-753	Midland Combination P	Staffordshire FA
Melksham Town FC	699-707	Western P	Wiltshire FA
Merstham FC	894-900	Combined Counties P	Surrey FA
Merthyr Tydfil FC	533	Southern W	Wales
Metropolitan Police FC	834	Isthmian 1S	London FA
Mickleover Sports FC	404-408	Northern Counties East 1	Derbyshire FA
Mildenhall Town FC	572-582	Eastern Counties P	Suffolk FA
Milton Keynes City FC	911-917	Spartan South Mids. P	Berks & Bucks FA
Milton United FC	608-611	Hellenic 1E	Berks & Bucks FA
Minehead Town FC	708-713	Western 1	Somerset FA
Molesey FC	844	Isthmian 1S	Surrey FA
Moneyfields FC	678-686	Wessex 1	Hampshire FA
Moor Green FC	502	Southern P	Birmingham FA
Morecambe FC	217	Conference	Lancashire FA
Morpeth Town FC	429-437	Northern 1	Northumberland FA
Mossley AFC	355-364	North West Counties 1	Manchester FA
Murton FC	438-443	Northern 2	Durham FA
Nantwich Town FC	355-364	North West Counties 1	Cheshire FA
Needham Market FC	583-587	Eastern Counties 1	Suffolk FA
Nelson FC	365-370	North West Counties 2	Lancashire FA
Nettleham FC	412-416	Central Midlands S.D.	Lincolnshire FA

New Mills FC	387-388	Manchester P	Derbyshire FA
Newcastle Benfield Saints FC	453-454	Northern Alliance P	Northumberland FA
Newcastle Blue Star FC	429-437	Northern 1	Northumberland FA
Newcastle Town FC	355-364	North West Counties 1	Staffordshire FA
Newmarket Town FC	572-582	Eastern Counties P	Suffolk FA
Newport County FC	504	Southern P	Wales
Newport(IW) FC	560	Southern E	Hampshire FA
Newton Abbot FC	725-726	Devon	Devon FA
North Ferriby United FC	340	Northern Prem. 1	E. Riding FA
North Leigh FC	593-603	Hellenic P	Oxfordshire FA
North Shields FC	447-449	Wearside	Northumberland FA
Northallerton Town FC	438-443	Northern 2	N. Riding FA
Northampton Spencer FC	658-666	United Counties P	Northants. FA
Northwich Victoria FC	223	Conference	Cheshire FA
Northwood FC	864	Isthmian 1N	Middlesex FA
Norton & Stockton Ancients FC	438-443	Northern 2	Durham FA
Norton United FC	365-370	North West Counties 2	Staffordshire FA
Norwich United FC	572-582	Eastern Counties P	Norfolk FA
Nuneaton Borough FC	229	Conference	Birmingham FA
Nuneaton Griff FC	749-753	Midland Combination P	Birmingham FA
Oadby Town FC	737-745	Midland Alliance	Leics. & Rutland FA
Oakwood FC	646-651	Sussex 2	Sussex FA
Odd Down FC	699-707	Western P	Somerset FA
Oldbury United FC	737-745	Midland Alliance	Birmingham FA
Oldham Town FC	365-370	North West Counties 2	Manchester FA
Ossett Albion FC	395-402	Northern Counties East P	W. Riding FA
Ossett Town FC	341	Northern Prem. 1	W. Riding FA
Oxford City FC	865	Isthmian 1N	Oxfordshire FA
Pagham FC	636-645	Sussex 1	Sussex FA
Parkgate FC	404-408	Northern Counties East 1	Sheff. & Hallams. FA
Paulton Rovers FC	699-707	Western P	Somerset FA
Peacehaven & Telscombe FC	636-645	Sussex 1	Sussex FA
Pegasus Juniors FC	593-603	Hellenic P	Herefordshire FA
Pelsall Villa FC	737-745	Midland Alliance	Staffordshire FA
Penrith FC	438-443	Northern 2	Cumberland FA
Pershore Town FC	749-753	Midland Combination P	Worcesters. FA
Peterlee Newtown FC	429-437	Northern 1	Durham FA
Petersfield Town FC	689-690	Hampshire P	Hampshire FA
Pewsey Vale FC	593-603	Hellenic P	Wiltshire FA
Pickering Town FC	395-402	Northern Counties East P	N. Riding FA
Pontefract Collieries FC	404-408	Northern Counties East 1	W. Riding FA
Poole Town FC	689-690	Hampshire P	Dorset FA
Porthleven FC	717-722	South Western	Cornwall FA
Portland United FC	678-686	Wessex 1	Dorset FA
Potters Bar Town FC	911-917	Spartan South Mids. P	Hertfordshire FA
Potton United FC	667-673	United Counties 1	Bedfordshire FA
Poulton Victoria FC	377-378	West Cheshire 1	Cheshire FA
Prescot Cables FC	355-364	North West Counties 1	Liverpool FA

Prudhoe Town FC	429-437	Northern 1	Northumberland FA
Purfleet FC	818	Isthmian P	Essex FA
Quorn FC	737-745	Midland Alliance-	Leics. & Rutland FA
Racing Club Warwick FC	534	Southern W	Birmingham FA
Radcliffe Borough FC	342	Northern Prem. 1	Lancashire FA
Rainworth MW FC	421-423	Notts. Alliance	Nottinghamshire FA
Ramsbottom United FC	355-364	North West Counties 1	Lancashire FA
Ramsgate FC	616-624	Kent	Kent FA
Raunds Town FC	658-666	United Counties P	Northants. FA
Raynes Park Vale FC	894-900	Combined Counties P	Surrey FA
Reading Town FC	894-900	Combined Counties P	Berks & Bucks FA
Redditch United FC	535	Southern W	Birmingham FA
Redhill FC	636-645	Sussex 1	Surrey FA
Retford United FC	412-416	Central Midlands S.D.	Nottinghamshire FA
Ringmer FC	636-645	Sussex 1	Sussex FA
Rocester FC	536	Southern W	Staffordshire FA
Rolls Royce Leisure FC	412-416	Central Midlands S.D.	Nottinghamshire FA
Romford FC	903-907	Essex Senior P	Essex FA
Rossendale United FC	343	Northern Prem. 1	Lancashire FA
Rossington Main FC	404-408	Northern Counties East 1	Sheff. & Hallams. FA
Rothwell Corinthians FC	667-673	United Counties 1	Northants. FA
Rothwell Town FC	561	Southern E	Northants. FA
Royston Town FC	911-917	Spartan South Mids. P	Hertfordshire FA
Rugby Town FC	749-753	Midland Combination P	Birmingham FA
Rugby United FC	537	Southern W	Birmingham FA
Ruislip Manor FC	911-917	Spartan South Mids. P	Middlesex FA
Runcorn FC Halton	312	Northern Prem. P	Liverpool FA
Rushall Olympic FC	737-745	Midland Alliance	Staffordshire FA
Saffron Walden Town FC	903-907	Essex Senior P	Essex FA
Salford City FC	355-364	North West Counties 1	Manchester FA
Salisbury City FC	562	Southern E	Wiltshire FA
Saltdean United FC	646-651	Sussex 2	Sussex FA
Sandhurst Town FC	894-900	Combined Counties P	Berks & Bucks FA
Sawbridgeworth Town FC	903-907	Essex Senior P	Hertfordshire FA
Scarborough FC	235	Conference	N. Riding FA
Seaham Red Star FC	438-443	Northern 2	Durham FA
Selby Town FC	395-402	Northern Counties East P	W. Riding FA
Selsey FC	636-645	Sussex 1	Sussex FA
Shawbury United FC	759-763	West Midlands P	Shropshire FA
Sheffield FC	395-402	Northern Counties East P	Sheff. & Hallams. FA
Shepshed Dynamo FC	538	Southern W	Leics. & Rutland FA
Shepton Mallet AFC	708-713	Western 1	Somerset FA
Shifnal Town FC	737-745	Midland Alliance	Shropshire FA
Shildon FC	429-437	Northern 1	Durham FA
Shirebrook Town FC	404-408	Northern Counties East 1	Derbyshire FA
Shortwood United FC	593-603	Hellenic P	Gloucestershire FA
Shotton Comrades FC	438-443	Northern 2	Durham FA
Sidlesham FC	636-645	Sussex 1	Sussex FA

Sidley United FC	636-645	Sussex 1	Sussex FA
Sittingbourne FC	563	Southern E	Kent FA
Skelmersdale United FC	355-364	North West Counties 1	Liverpool FA
Slade Green FC	616-624	Kent	Kent FA
Slough Town FC	866	Isthmian 1N	Berks & Bucks FA
Soham Town Rangers FC	572-582	Eastern Counties P	Cambridgeshire FA
Solihull Borough FC	539	Southern W	Birmingham FA
Somersham Town FC	583-587	Eastern Counties 1	Huntingdonshire FA
South Normanton Athletic FC	412-416	Central Midlands S.D.	Derbyshire FA
South Shields FC	438-443	Northern 2	Durham FA
Southall FC	894-900	Combined Counties P	Middlesex FA
Southall Town FC	593-603	Hellenic P	Middlesex FA
Southend Manor FC	903-907	Essex Senior P	Essex FA
Southport FC	241	Conference	Lancashire FA
Southwick FC	636-645	Sussex 1	Sussex FA
Spalding United FC	564	Southern E	Lincolnshire FA
Spennymoor United FC	344	Northern Prem. 1	Durham FA
Squires Gate FC	355-364	North West Counties 1	Lancashire FA
St Albans City FC	820	Isthmian P	Hertfordshire FA
St Andrews FC	766-67	Leicestershire Senior P	Leics. & Rutland FA
St Blazey FC	717-722	South Western	Cornwall FA
St Helens Town FC	355-364	North West Counties 1	Liverpool FA
St Ives Town FC	667-673	United Counties 1	Huntingdonshire FA
St Leonards FC	565	Southern E	Sussex FA
St Margaretsbury FC	911-917	Spartan South Mids. P	Hertfordshire FA
St Neots Town FC	658-666	United Counties P	Huntingdonshire FA
Stafford Rangers FC	506	Southern P	Staffordshire FA
Stafford Town FC	737-745	Midland Alliance	Staffordshire FA
Staines Town FC	845	Isthmian 1S	Middlesex FA
Stalybridge Celtic FC	314	Northern Prem. P	Cheshire FA
Stamford AFC	566	Southern E	Lincolnshire FA
Stand Athletic FC	365-370	North West Counties 2	Lancashire FA
Stansted FC	903-907	Essex Senior P	Essex FA
Stanway Rovers FC	583-587	Eastern Counties 1	Essex FA
Staveley MW FC	404-408	Northern Counties East 1	Derbyshire FA
Stevenage Borough FC	247	Conference	Hertfordshire FA
Stewarts & Lloyds FC	658-666	United Counties P	Northants. FA
Stocksbridge Park Steels FC	345	Northern Prem. 1	Sheff. & Hallams. FA
Stone Dominoes FC	365-370	North West Counties 2	Staffordshire FA
Stotfold FC	658-666	United Counties P	Bedfordshire FA
Stourbridge FC	737-745	Midland Alliance	Birmingham FA
Stourport Swifts FC	540	Southern W	Worcesters. FA
Stowmarket Town FC	572-582	Eastern Counties P	Suffolk FA
Stratford Town FC	737-745	Midland Alliance	Birmingham FA
Street FC	708-713	Western 1	Somerset FA
Studley FC	737-745	Midland Alliance-	Birmingham FA
Sutton Coldfield Town FC	541	Southern W	Birmingham FA
Sutton Town FC	412-416	Central Midlands S.D.	Nottinghamshire FA

Sutton United FC	822	Isthmian P	Surrey FA
Swindon Supermarine FC	542	Southern W	Wiltshire FA
Tadcaster Albion FC	404-408	Northern Counties East 1	W. Riding FA
Tamworth FC	508	Southern P	Birmingham FA
Taunton Town FC	543	Southern W	Somerset FA
Team Bath FC	699-707	Western P	Somerset FA
Telford United FC	253	Conference	Shropshire FA
Thackley FC	395-402	Northern Counties East P	W. Riding FA
Thame United FC	867	Isthmian 1N	Oxfordshire FA
Thamesmead Town FC	616-624	Kent	London FA
Thatcham Town FC	678-686	Wessex 1	Berks & Bucks FA
Thetford Town FC	583-587	Eastern Counties 1	Norfolk FA
Thornaby FC	438-443	Northern 2	N. Riding FA
Three Bridges FC	636-645	Sussex 1	Sussex FA
Tilbury FC	868	Isthmian 1N	Essex FA
Tipton Town FC	759-763	West Midlands P	Birmingham FA
Tiptree United FC	572-582	Eastern Counties P	Essex FA
Tiverton Town FC	510	Southern P	Devon FA
Tividale FC	759-763	West Midlands P	Birmingham FA
Tonbridge Angels FC	567	Southern E	Kent FA
Tooting & Mitcham United FC	846	Isthmian 1S	Surrey FA
Torrington FC	708-713	Western 1	Devon FA
Tow Law Town FC	429-437	Northern 1	Durham FA
Trafford FC	346	Northern Prem. 1	Manchester FA
Tring Town FC	875-884	Isthmian 2	Hertfordshire FA
Tuffley Rovers FC	593-603	Hellenic P	Gloucestershire FA
Tunbridge Wells FC	616-624	Kent	Kent FA
Uxbridge FC	869	Isthmian 1N	Middlesex FA
Vauxhall Motors FC	316	Northern Prem. P	Cheshire FA
VCD Athletic FC	616-624	Kent	Kent FA
Viking Greenford FC	894-900	Combined Counties P	Middlesex FA
Wakefield & Emley FC	318	Northern Prem. P	Sheff. & Hallams. FA
Walton & Hersham FC	847	Isthmian 1S	Surrey FA
Walton Casuals FC	894-900	Combined Counties P	Surrey FA
Wantage Town FC	593-603	Hellenic P	Berks & Bucks FA
Warboys Town FC	583-587	Eastern Counties 1	Huntingdonshire FA
Ware FC	875-884	Isthmian 2	Hertfordshire FA
Warrington Town FC	355-364	North West Counties 1	Cheshire FA
Washington FC	429-437	Northern 1	Durham FA
Washington Nissan FC	438-443	Northern 2	Durham FA
Wealdstone FC	870	Isthmian 1N	Middlesex FA
Wednesfield FC	737-745	Midland Alliance	Birmingham FA
Welling United FC	512	Southern P	London FA
Wellington FC	759-763	West Midlands P	Herefordshire FA
Wellington Town FC	708-713	Western 1	Somerset FA
Welton Rovers FC	699-707	Western P	Somerset FA
Welwyn Garden City FC	918-924	Spartan South Mids. 1	Hertfordshire FA
Wembley FC	871	Isthmian 1N	Middlesex FA

West Allotment Celtic FC	453-454	Northern Alliance P	Northumberland FA
West Auckland Town FC	429-437	Northern 1	Durham FA
West Midlands Police FC	749-753	Midland Combination P	Birmingham FA
Westbury United FC	708-713	Western 1	Wiltshire FA
Westfield FC	894-900	Combined Counties P	Surrey FA
Westfields FC	759-763	West Midlands P	Herefordshire FA
Weston Super Mare FC	544	Southern W	Somerset FA
Weymouth FC	514	Southern P	Dorset FA
Whickham FC	438-443	Northern 2	Durham FA
Whitby Town FC	320	Northern Prem. P	N. Riding FA
Whitchurch United FC	678-686	Wessex 1	Hampshire FA
Whitehawk FC	636-645	Sussex 1	Sussex FA
Whitley Bay FC	429-437	Northern 1	Northumberland FA
Whitstable Town FC	616-624	Kent	Kent FA
Whitton United FC	583-587	Eastern Counties 1	Suffolk FA
Whyteleafe FC	848	Isthmian 1S	Surrey FA
Wick FC	636-645	Sussex 1	Sussex FA
Willand Rovers FC	708-713	Western 1	Devon FA
Willenhall Town FC	737-745	Midland Alliance	Birmingham FA
Willington FC	438-443	Northern 2	Durham FA
Wimborne Town FC	678-686	Wessex 1	Dorset FA
Winchester City FC	689-690	Hampshire P	Hampshire FA
Windsor & Eton FC	849	Isthmian 1S	Berks & Bucks FA
Wingate & Finchley FC	872	Isthmian 1N	London FA
Winsford United FC	355-364	North West Counties 1	Cheshire FA
Winterton Rangers FC	404-408	Northern Counties East 1	Lincolnshire FA
Wisbech Town FC	572-582	Eastern Counties P	Cambridgeshire FA
Witham Town FC	875-884	Isthmian 2	Essex FA
Withdean 2000 FC	894-900	Combined Counties P	Sussex FA
Witton Albion FC	347	Northern Prem. 1	Cheshire FA
Wivenhoe Town FC	873	Isthmian 1N	Essex FA
Woking FC	259	Conference	Surrey FA
Wokingham Town FC	875-884	Isthmian 2	Berks & Bucks FA
Woodbridge Town FC	572-582	Eastern Counties P	Suffolk FA
Woodford Town FC	903-907	Essex Senior P	London FA
Woodley Sports FC	355-364	North West Counties 1	Cheshire FA
Wootton Bassett Town FC	593-603	Hellenic P	Wiltshire FA
Wootton Blue Cross FC	658-666	United Counties P	Bedfordshire FA
Worcester City FC	516	Southern P	Worcesters. FA
Workington FC	348	Northern Prem. 1	Cumberland FA
Worksop Town FC	322	Northern Prem. P	Sheff. & Hallams. FA
Worsbrough Bridge MW FC	404-408	Northern Counties East 1	Sheff. & Hallams. FA
Worthing FC	850	Isthmian 1S	Sussex FA
Wroxham FC	572-582	Eastern Counties P	Norfolk FA
Yate Town FC	593-603	Hellenic P	Gloucestershire FA
Yaxley FC	658-666	United Counties P	Huntingdonshire FA
Yeading FC	874	Isthmian 1N	Middlesex FA
Yeovil Town FC	265	Conference	Somerset FA
Yorkshire Amateur FC	404-408	Northern Counties East 1	W. Riding FA

Why not reserve your non-league publications this year?

Following the closing down of Non-League Media plc I am pleased to say that we will be doing all we can to provide non-league enthusiasts with useful and enjoyable publications to back up the wonderful 'The Non-League Paper' which will continue to be available on Sundays under the guidance of a new owner.

If you would like us to send you details of any of the publications listed below, as they become available, please complete your details below and return to us:

Send to: TWP, Freepost, Taunton, Somerset TA3 6BR

The Non-League Diary (Aug. 02-Dec. 03) ☐

The Non-League Poster ☐

25in25 all editions ☐

- Combined Counties League ☐
- Eastern Counties League ☐
- Essex Senior League ☐
- Football Conference ☐
- Hellenic League ☐
- Isthmian League ☐
- Kent League ☐
- Midland Combination ☐
- Midland Football Alliance ☐
- Northern League ☐
- Northern Premier League ☐
- Northern Counties East ☐
- North West Counties ☐
- Southern League ☐
- South Western League ☐
- Spartan South Midlands League ☐
- Sussex County League ☐
- United Counties League ☐
- Wearside League ☐
- Wessex League ☐
- Western League ☐
- West Midlands League ☐
- F.A. Trophy ☐
- F.A. Vase ☐
- Representative Football ☐

Non-League Club Directory 2004 ☐

Please send me full details of availability, price and available discounts for the publications ticked above

NAME:

ADDRESS:

TEL.:   Club Supported: